I

105th Congress, 2d Session - - - - - - - - - - - - - - House Document 105–311

PART 1

APPENDICES TO THE REFERRAL TO THE UNITED STATES HOUSE OF REPRESENTATIVES PURSUANT TO TITLE 28, UNITED STATES CODE, SECTION 595(c) SUBMITTED BY THE OFFICE OF THE INDEPENDENT COUNSEL, SEPTEMBER 9, 1998

COMMUNIC[A

FROM

THE OFFICE OF THE INDEPENDENT COUNSEL, KENNETH W. STARR

TRANSMITTING

APPENDICES TO THE REFERRAL TO THE UNITED STATES HOUSE OF REPRESENTATIVES PURSUANT TO TITLE 28, UNITED STATES CODE, SECTION 595(c) SUBMITTED BY THE OFFICE OF THE INDEPENDENT COUNSEL, SEPTEMBER 9, 1998

SEPTEMBER 18, 1998.—Referred to the Committee on the Judiciary pursuant to H. Res. 525 and ordered to be printed

U.S. GOVERNMENT PRINTING OFFICE

50–892 WASHINGTON : 1998

II

ONE HUNDRED FIFTH CONGRESS

Congress of the United States

House of Representatives

COMMITTEE ON THE JUDICIARY

2138 RAYBURN HOUSE OFFICE BUILDING

WASHINGTON, DC 20515–6216

(202) 225–3951
http://www.house.gov/judiciary

THOMAS E. MOONEY, SR.
CHIEF OF STAFF – GENERAL COUNSEL

JON DUDAS
STAFF DIRECTOR – DEPUTY GENERAL COUNSEL

JULIAN EPSTEIN
MINORITY CHIEF COUNSEL
AND STAFF DIRECTOR

September 18, 1998

Foreword

Pursuant to H. Res. 525, which was adopted by the House of Representatives on September 11, 1998, by a vote of 363-63, the Committee on the Judiciary, on September 18, 1998, ordered the public printing of volumes two through seven of the Referral from Independent Counsel Kenneth Starr. The materials printed herein have been redacted by the Committee. All redactions approved by the Committee are indicated in the attached redaction report.

At this time, the Committee has elected not to release certain material filed under seal with the United States District Court for the Eastern District of Arkansas.

HENRY J. HYDE
Chairman
House Committee on the Judiciary

JOHN CONYERS, JR.
Ranking Minority Member
House Committee on the Judiciary

House Committee on the Judiciary Redaction Report	
Page or other Identification Number	**Reason for Redacted Material**
Vol. II, Tab D, Map	National Security
Vol. II, Tab G	Personal Identifying Information
Vol. II, Tab I, pp. 10-19	National Security
Vol. III, Tab 1	Deposition of William Jefferson Clinton, Jones V. Clinton Sealed Pursuant to Court Order
Vol. III, Tab 4	Deposition Exhibit 3 Jones V. Clinton Sealed Pursuant to Court Order
Vol. III, Tab 5	Deposition Exhibit 5 Jones V. Clinton Sealed Pursuant to Court Order
Vol. III, Tab 8	Deposition Exhibit 8 Jones V. Clinton Sealed Pursuant to Court Order
Vol. III, Tab 9	President Clinton's Response to Plaintiff's Third Set of Interrogatories, Jones V. Clinton Sealed Pursuant to Court Order
Vol. III, Tab 10	President Clinton's Responses to Plaintiff's First Set of Interrogatories, Jones V. Clinton Sealed Pursuant to Court Order

House Committee on the Judiciary Redaction Report	
Page or other Identification Number	**Reason for Redacted Material**
Vol. III, Tab 11	Deposition Exhibit 11 Jones V. Clinton Sealed Pursuant to Court Order
Vol. III, Tab 12	Deposition Exhibit 12 Jones V. Clinton Sealed Pursuant to Court Order
Vol. III, Tab 13	Deposition Exhibit 13 Jones V. Clinton Sealed Pursuant to Court Order
Vol. III, Tab 14	President Clinton's Supplemental Responses to Plaintiff's Second Set of Interrogatories Jones V. Clinton Sealed Pursuant to Court Order
Vol. III, Tab 15, 849-DC-634	Personal Identifying Information
Vol. IV, Tab 2, p. 111, lines 24-25- p. 112, lines 1-7	Privacy
Vol. IV, Tab 3, p. 53, lines 3-20	Privacy
Vol. IV, Tab 3, pp. 88, 95, 96, index	Privacy
Vol. IV, Tab 6, p. 1	Personal Identifying Information
Vol. IV, Tab 10, p. 4	Privacy
Vol. IV, Tab 7, p. 1	Personal Identifying Information
Vol. IV, Tab 15, p. 10, lines 18-20 (non-compressed copy, p. 9, lines 18-20)	Privacy

House Committee on the Judiciary
Redaction Report

Page or other Identification Number	Reason for Redacted Material
Vol. IV, Tab 15, p. 12, lines 3-11 (compressed copy, p. 13, lines 3-11)	Sexual Description
Vol. IV, Tab 15, p. 17, line 4-5 (compressed copy, p. 18, line 4-5)	Sexual Description
Vol. IV, Tab 15, p. 18, lines 22 ½ - 24 (compressed copy, p. 19, lines 22 ½ - 24)	Sexual Description
Vol. IV, Tab 15, p. 19, lines 3-17 (compressed copy, p. 20, lines 3-16)	Sexual Description
Vol. IV, Tab 15, p. 29, line 21-30, p. 31, line 12 (compressed copy p. 30, line 21- p. 31, line 12)	Sexual Description
Vol. IV, Tab 15, p. 46, lines 16-22 (compressed copy p. 47, lines 16-21)	Sexual Description
Vol. IV, Tab 15, p. 47, lines 8-11 (compressed copy p. 48, lines 8-11)	Sexual Description
Vol. IV, Tab 15, p. 49, lines 15-24 (compressed copy of p. 50, lines 15-24)	Sexual Description
Vol. IV, Tab 15, p. 69, index	Privacy
Vol. IV, Tab 16, pp. 1-4, 6	Privacy
Vol. IV, Tab 17, pp. 1-3	Privacy
Vol. IV, Tab 19, p. 1	Privacy
Vol. IV, Tab 19, p. 4, para. 1	Privacy
Vol. IV, Tab 19, p. 7, para. 2	Privacy
Vol. IV, Tab 20, p. 1	Privacy

House Committee on the Judiciary Redaction Report	
Page or other Identification Number	**Reason for Redacted Material**
Vol. IV, Tab 20, p. 2, para. 1	Privacy
Vol. IV, Tab 20, p. 8, para. 2	Sexual Description
Vol. IV, Tab 20, p. 9, para. 1	Sexual Description
Vol. IV, Tab 20, p. 10, para. 1	Sexual Description
Vol. IV, Tab 20, p. 14, para. 3	Sexual Description
Vol. IV, Tab 20, p. 15, para. 3	Sexual Description
Vol. IV, Tab 20, p. 16, para. 4	Sexual Description
Vol. IV, Tab 20, p. 19, para. 1	Sexual Description
Vol. IV, Tab 21, p. 1	Privacy
Vol. IV, Tab 21, p. 9, para. 2	Privacy
Vol. IV, Tab 21, p. 16, para. 7	Privacy
Vol. IV, Tab 22, p. 1	Privacy
Vol. IV, Tab 22, p. 11, para. 4	Privacy
Vol. IV, Tab 23, p. 1	Privacy
Vol. IV, Tab 24, p. 1	Privacy
Vol. IV, Tab 24, p. 3, para. 2	Privacy
Vol. IV, Tab 24, p. 10, paras. 3, 5, 6	Privacy
Vol. IV, Tab 24, p. 11	Privacy
Vol. IV, Tab 25, p. 2, para. 3	Privacy
Vol. IV, Tab 25, p. 4, para. 1	Privacy
Vol. IV, Tab 25, p. 8, para 2 (first)	Expletives
Vol. IV, Tab 25, p. 8, para. 2	Privacy

House Committee on the Judiciary Redaction Report	
Page or other Identification Number	**Reason for Redacted Material**
Vol. IV, Tab 26, p. 1	Privacy
Vol. IV, Tab 27, p. 1	Privacy
Vol. IV, Tab 27, p. 5, para. 3	Sexual Description
Vol. IV, Tab 27, p. 9, para. 2	Privacy
Vol. IV, Tab 27, p. 9, para. 3	Privacy
Vol. IV, Tab 28, p. 1	Privacy
Vol. IV, Tab 29, p. 1	Privacy
Vol. IV, Tab 29, p. 2, paras. 4-5	Privacy
Vol. IV, Tab 29, p. 4, para. 3	Privacy
Vol. IV, Tab 30, p. 1	Privacy
Vol. IV, Tab 30, p. 6, para. 5	Privacy
Vol. IV, Tab 31, p. 1	Privacy
Vol. IV, Tab 32, p. 1	Privacy
Vol. IV, Tab 33, p. 1	Privacy
Vol. IV, Tab 34, p. 1	Privacy
Vol. IV, Tab 35, p. 1	Privacy
Vol. IV, Tab 37, pp. 2, 5, 6, 8, 12, 13	Privacy
Vol. V, Tab 28, pp. 1-5	Privacy
Vol. V, Tab 31, p. 1	Privacy
Vol. VI, Tab 49, p. 1	Privacy
Vol. VI, Tab 54	Privacy
Vol. VI, Tab 55	Privacy

House Committee on the Judiciary Redaction Report	
Page or other Identification Number	**Reason for Redacted Material**
Vol. VI, Tab 59	Privacy
Vol. VI, Tab 60, p. 3	Privacy
Vol. VI, Tab 61	Privacy
Vol. VI, Tab 64	Privacy
Vol. VI, Tab 74	Privacy
Vol. VI, Tab 78, first occurrence	Privacy
Vol. VI, Tab 78, second occurrence	Sexual Description
Vol. VI, 0812-DC-2	Personal Identifying Information
Vol. VI, 0828-DC-12	Personal Identifying Information
Vol. VI, 0828-DC-13	Personal Identifying Information
Vol. VI, 0828-DC-23	Personal Identifying Information
Vol. VI, 0830-DC-7	Personal Identifying Information
Vol. VI, 0830-DC-17	Personal Identifying Information
Vol. VI, 0831-DC-8-11	Personal Identifying Information
Vol. VI, 0832-DC-4-5	Personal Identifying Information
Vol. VI, 0833-DC-980	Personal Identifying Information
Vol. VI, 0833-DC-1857	Expletive
Vol. VI, 0833-DC-2716	Personal Identifying Information
Vol. VI, 0833-DC-3207	Personal Identifying Information
Vol. VI, 0833-DC-17867, 69, 75, 86, 90, 903, 904, 908	Personal Identifying Information
Vol. VI, 0837-DC-1-4, 6-19, 21-24	Personal Identifying Information

House Committee on the Judiciary
Redaction Report

Page or other Identification Number	Reason for Redacted Material
Vol. VI, 0837-DC-25-27	Redacted Prior to Receipt
Vol. VI, 0845-DC-190	Personal Identifying Information
Vol. VI, 0849-DC-90-102	President Clinton's Responses to Plaintiffs Third Set of Interrogatories, Jones V. Clinton Sealed Pursuant to Court Order
Vol. VI, 0849-DC-121-137	Plaintiff's Witness List Jones V. Clinton Sealed Pursuant to Court Order
Vol. VI, 0849-DC-352	Transcript of Videotaped Oral Deposition U.S. V. Clinton Sealed Pursuant to Court Order
Vol. VI, 0849-DC-586	Deposition Exhibit 1 Jones V. Clinton Sealed Pursuant to Court Order
Vol. VI, 0849-DC-634	Deposition Exhibit 15 Jones V. Clinton Sealed Pursuant to Court Order
Vol. VI, 0852-DC-35, 37, 44, 45	Personal Identifying Information
Vol. VI, 0854-DC-1485	Personal Identifying Information
Vol. VI, 0856-DC-2	Personal Identifying Information
Vol. VI, 0880-DC-2	Personal Identifying Information
Vol. VI, 08902-DC-33	Personal Identifying Information
Vol. VI, 08902-DC-135	Personal Identifying Information
Vol. VI, 0916-DC-3	Personal Identifying Information

House Committee on the Judiciary
Redaction Report

Page or other Identification Number	Reason for Redacted Material
Vol. VI, 0920-DC-13	Personal Identifying Information
Vol. VI, 0920-DC-517-525	Order, Jones V. Clinton Sealed Pursuant to Court Order
Vol. VI, 0921-61-62	Clerk's Minutes, Jones V. Clinton Sealed Pursuant to Court Order
Vol. VI, 0921-DC-96-100	Plaintiff's Motion to Compel Responses to Plaintiff's Second Set of Interrogatories to Defendant Clinton Jones V. Clinton Sealed Pursuant to Court Order
Vol. VI, 0921-DC-101-119	Second Set of Interrogatories from Plaintiff to Defendant Clinton Jones V. Clinton Sealed Pursuant to Court Order
Vol. VI, 0921-DC-120-137	President Clinton's Responses to Plaintiff's Second Set of Interrogatories Jones V. Clinton Sealed Pursuant to Court Order
Vol. VI, 0921-DC-138-143	Exhibit 3, Jones V. Clinton Sealed Pursuant to Court Order
Vol. VI, 0921-DC-144-145	Exhibit 4, Jones V. Clinton Sealed Pursuant to Court Order
Vol. VI, 0921-DC-150-151	Exhibit 5, Jones V. Clinton Sealed Pursuant to Court Order

House Committee on the Judiciary
Redaction Report

Page or other Identification Number	Reason for Redacted Material
Vol. VI, 0921-DC-459-466	Order, Jones V. Clinton Sealed Pursuant to Court Order
Vol. VI, 0921-736-744	Order, Jones V. Clinton Sealed Pursuant to Court Order
Vol. VI, 0921-751-752	Clerk's Minutes, Jones V. Clinton Sealed Pursuant to Court Order
Vol. VI, 0921-DC-770-72	Clerk's Minutes, Jones V. Clinton Sealed Pursuant to Court Order
Vol. VI, 0921-DC-775-778	Motion for Protective Order Jones V. Clinton Sealed Pursuant to Court Order
Vol. VI, 0929-DC-56	Personal Identifying Information
Vol. VI, 0964-DC-862	Personal Identifying Information
Vol. VI, 0968-DC-73, 187, 236, 263, 303	Redacted Prior to Receipt
Vol. VI, 0968-DC-3506, 10, 22, 33, 46, 50, 56, 58, 69	Personal Identifying Information
Vol. VII, 1000-DC-768	Personal Identifying Information
Vol. VII, 1013-DC-95-96	Personal Identifying Information
Vol. VII, 1014-DC-22	Personal Identifying Information
Vol. VII, 1033-DC-33-35	Personal Identifying Information
Vol. VII, 1033-DC-115-16	Personal Identifying Information

House Committee on the Judiciary
Redaction Report

Page or other Identification Number	Reason for Redacted Material
Vol. VII, 1034-DC-60-63, 99, 103, 109, 111	Privacy
Vol. VII, 1037-DC-11, 17, 22, 38, 40, 42, 63, 86, 103, 107, 265, 280, 296, 318, 338, 341, 553, 583	Personal Identifying Information
Vol. VII, 1037-DC-39, 168, 318, 341	Expletives
Vol. VII, 1051-DC-3	Personal Identifying Information
Vol. VII, 1064-DC-8	Personal Identifying Information
Vol. VII, 1065-DC-6, 8	Personal Identifying Information
Vol. VII, 1078-DC-2	Personal Identifying Information
Vol. VII, 1178-DC-5, 11, 13-16, 18-21, 23	Personal Identifying Information and Certain Material Redacted Prior to Receipt
Vol. VII, 1178-DC-26	Personal Identifying Information
Vol. VII, 1205-DC-16	Personal Identifying Information
Vol. VII, 1216-DC-22-23	Personal Identifying Information
Vol. VII, 1248-DC-8, 305, 307, 311, 312-315, 319, 327-328, 381, 444	Personal Identifying Information
Vol. VII, 1362-DC-1171	National Security
Vol. VII, 1407-DC-5	Personal Identifying Information
Vol. VII, 1408-DC-5	Personal Identifying Information
Vol. VII, 1414-DC-001, 1006-1014	Order, Jones V. Clinton Sealed Pursuant to Court Order

House Committee on the Judiciary
Redaction Report

Page or other Identification Number	Reason for Redacted Material
Vol. VII, 1414-DC-1188-1192	Order, Jones V. Clinton Sealed Pursuant to Court Order
Vol. VII, 1414-DC-1327-1346	Hearing Transcript Jones V. Clinton Sealed Pursuant to Court Order
Vol. VII, 1414-DC-1534-1546	Second Set of Requests from Plaintiff to Defendant Clinton for Production of Documents Jones V. Clinton Sealed Pursuant to Court Order
Vol. VII, 1472-DC-6-20	Personal Identifying Information
Vol. VII, 1506-DC-29, 31, 50	Personal Identifying Information
Vol. VII, 1506-DC-57-58	Redacted Prior to Receipt
Vol. VII, 1506-DC-68, 70, 102, 139, 144, 192, 275, 373	Personal Identifying Information
Vol. VII, 2004-DC-83, 85, 86, 87, 88, 90, 91	Personal Identifying Information
Vol. VII, MSL-55-DC-94, 124	Privacy
Vol. VII, MSL-DC-1166	Personal Identifying Information
Vol. VII, MSL-DC-1176, 1192	Personal Identifying Information
Vol. VII, V002-DC-5	Personal Identifying Information
Vol. VII, V002-DC-6-15	President Clinton's Responses to Plaintiff's First Set of Interrogatories Jones V. Clinton Sealed Pursuant to Court Order

House Committee on the Judiciary Redaction Report	
Page or other Identification Number	**Reason for Redacted Material**
Vol. VII, V002-DC-16-32	President Clinton's Responses to Plaintiff's Second Set of Interrogatories Jones V. Clinton Sealed Pursuant to Court Order
Vol. VII, V002-DC-52-55	President Clinton's Supplemental Responses to Plaintiff's Second Set of Interrogatories Jones V. Clinton Sealed Pursuant to Court Order
Vol. VII, V002-DC-56-92	President Clinton's Responses to Plaintiff's First Set of Requests for Projection of Documents and Things, Jones V. Clinton Sealed Pursuant to Court Order
Vol. VII, V002-DC-93-116	President Clinton's Responses to Plaintiff's Second Set of Document Requests, Jones V. Clinton Sealed Pursuant to Court Order
Vol. VII, V004-DC-134-167	Personal Identifying Information
Vol. VII, V004-DC-171-172	Redacted Prior to Receipt
Vol. VII, V004-DC-183	Personal Identifying Information
Vol. VII, V005-DC-58, 60-61	Redacted Prior to Receipt
Vol. VII, V006-DC-7-9	Personal Identifying Information
Vol. VII, V006-DC-20	Personal Identifying Information
Vol. VII, V006-DC-118	Personal Identifying Information

House Committee on the Judiciary Redaction Report	
Page or other Identification Number	**Reason for Redacted Material**
Vol. VII, V006-DC-157-159, 162, 167, 180, 181, 183	Personal Identifying Information
Vol. VII, V006-DC-225	Personal Identifying Information
Vol. VII, V006-DC-391	Personal Identifying Information
Vol. VII, V006-DC-1770, 1792, 1796	Personal Identifying Information
Vol. VII, V006-DC-1813-1814	Personal Identifying Information
Vol. VII, V006-DC-2064-2071	Personal Identifying Information and Certain Material Redacted Prior to Receipt
Vol. VII, V006-DC-2095, 2130, 140, 142, 146-147, 156, 158, 214, 243	Redacted Prior to Receipt
Vol. VII, V006-DC-3719	Personal Identifying Information

CONTENTS

Volume II: Appendix

REFERRAL

TO THE

UNITED STATES HOUSE OF REPRESENTATIVES

PURSUANT TO

TITLE 28, UNITED STATES CODE, § 595(C)

APPENDIX

SUBMITTED BY

THE OFFICE OF THE INDEPENDENT COUNSEL

SEPTEMBER 9, 1998

Appendix
Table of Contents

Tab A

Statement of the OIC's Jurisdiction

UNITED STATES COURT OF APPEALS
FOR THE DISTRICT OF COLUMBIA CIRCUIT

Division for the Purpose of
Appointing Independent Counsels

United States Court of Appeals
For the District of Columbia Circuit

FILED JAN 16 1998

Special Division

In re: Madison Guaranty Savings & Loan Association

Division No. 94-1

Before: Sentelle, Presiding, Butzner and Fay, Senior Circuit Judges

UNDER SEAL

ORDER

Upon consideration of an oral application for the expansion of jurisdiction of an Independent Counsel provided to this Court on behalf of the Attorney General on January 16, 1998, it is hereby

ORDERED that the investigative and prosecutorial jurisdiction over the following matters be referred to Independent Counsel Kenneth W. Starr and to the Office of the Independent Counsel as an expansion of prosecutorial jurisdiction in lieu of the appointment of another Independent Counsel pursuant to 593(c)(1):

(1) The Independent Counsel shall continue to enjoy the full jurisdiction initially conferred upon him as a result of the August 5, 1994, order of the Special Division of the Court and all subsequent orders concerning jurisdiction. Pursuant to 28 U.S.C. § 593(c)(1), the Independent Counsel's jurisdiction shall be expanded to include the following:

(2) The Independent Counsel shall have jurisdiction and authority to investigate to the maximum extent authorized by the Independent Counsel Reauthorization Act of 1994 whether Monica Lewinsky or others suborned perjury, obstructed justice, intimidated witnesses, or otherwise violated federal law other than a Class B or C misdemeanor or infraction in dealing with witnesses, potential witnesses,

attorneys, or others concerning the civil case Jones v. Clinton.

(3) The Independent Counsel shall have jurisdiction and authority to investigate related violations of federal criminal law, other than a Class B or C misdemeanor or infraction, including any person or entity who has engaged in unlawful conspiracy or who has aided or abetted any federal offense, as necessary to resolve the matter described above.

(4) The Independent Counsel shall have jurisdiction and authority to investigate crimes, such as any violation of 28 U.S.C. § 1826, any obstruction of the due administration of justice, or any material false testimony or statement in violation of federal criminal law, arising out of his investigation of the matter described above.

(5) The Independent Counsel shall have all the powers and authority provided by the Independent Counsel Reauthorization Act of 1994.

It is further ORDERED that this document and its contents be and remain UNDER SEAL absent further Order of this Court.

This the 16th day of January, 1998.

Per Curiam
For the Court:

Marilyn Sargent
Chief Deputy Clerk

Tab B

Order Permitting Disclosure of Grand Jury Material

United States Court of Appeals
For the District of Columbia Circuit

UNITED STATES COURT OF APPEALS
FOR THE DISTRICT OF COLUMBIA CIRCUIT

FILED JUL 7 1998

Special Division

Division for the Purpose of
Appointing Independent Counsels

Ethics in Government Act of 1978, As Amended

In Re: Madison Guaranty Savings & Loan Association

Division No. 94-1

FILED UNDER SEAL

Before: SENTELLE, *Presiding Judge*, and BUTZNER and FAY, *Senior Circuit Judges*.

ORDER

Upon consideration of the "Ex Parte Motion for Approval of Disclosure of Matters Occurring Before a Grand Jury" filed by Independent Counsel Kenneth W. Starr on July 2, 1998, the Court finds that it is appropriate for the Independent Counsel to convey the materials described in that motion to the House of Representatives. Accordingly, it is

ORDERED that the motion be granted. The Court hereby authorizes the Independent Counsel to deliver to the House of Representatives materials that the Independent Counsel determines constitute information of the type described in 28 U.S.C. § 595(c). This authorization constitutes an order for purposes of Federal Rule of Criminal Procedure 6(e)(3)(C)(i) permitting disclosure of all grand jury material that the independent counsel deems necessary to comply with the requirements of § 595(c). This order may be disclosed as required in connection with the Independent Counsel's compliance with his statutory mandate.

Per Curiam

For the Court:
Mark J. Langer, Clerk

by

Marilyn R. Sargent
Chief Deputy Clerk

Tab C

Procedural Background and History of *Jones v. Clinton*

Procedural History and Background of the Jones v. Clinton Litigation

TABLE OF CONTENTS

50-892 98 - 2

CHRONOLOGY

May 1991	Alleged Hotel Incident (Governor Bill Clinton allegedly summons Paula Jones to his room at the Excelsior Hotel in Little Rock).
May 1994	Paula Jones files suit in federal district court in Arkansas.
December 1994	Judge Susan Webber Wright orders discovery to proceed, but says that she won't let the case go to trial until Bill Clinton's presidency is over.
January 1996	The U.S. Court of Appeals for the Eighth Circuit orders the case to proceed with no stay of the trial.
January 1997	The Supreme Court hears oral argument in Clinton v. Jones.
May 1997	The Supreme Court unanimously affirms the Eighth Circuit and remands the case to the district court for discovery and trial.
June 1997	Ms. Jones's lawyers serve their first set of interrogatories to the President, asking about the alleged Hotel Incident.
August 1997	Judge Wright grants President's motion to dismiss two counts of the complaint, denies the motion for the remaining two counts, and orders discovery to proceed
September 22, 1997	The President answers the first set of interrogatories, denying that he harassed Ms. Jones.
September 30, 1997	The President verifies under "penalty of perjury" that his interrogatory answers are true.
October 1, 1997	• The new Jones lawyers serve a second set of interrogatories to the President; #10-11 asks whether he had had, or had proposed having, sexual relations with any woman (other than Hillary Rodham Clinton) while he was Attorney General of Arkansas, Governor of Arkansas, or President of the United States. • Ms. Jones's lawyers also serve the President with their first set of requests for documents and things related to other women.

October 8, 1997	Ms. Jones's attorneys serve the President with their first set of requests for admissions; #51-65 ask about "sexual relations" with other women.
October 13, 1997	Ms. Jones's lawyers serve the President with a third set of interrogatories, asking him to name any person with discoverable information.
October 28, 1997	• The President's lawyers seek a protective order limiting discovery to instances of nonconsensual conduct in the AIDC (Ms. Jones's state agency) workplace and prohibiting general questions about other women. • Dolly Kyle Browning testifies at a deposition.
October 29, 1997	Ms. Jones's lawyers issue a subpoena to Jane Doe #1 commanding her to appear for a deposition on Nov. 18, bringing documents and things related to her meetings with the President.
October 30, 1997	• Judge Wright orders that discovery be confidential. • Ms. Jones's lawyers serve Jane Doe #2 with a subpoena commanding her to appear for a deposition, and serve a copy of this subpoena to the President's lawyers.
November 3, 1997	The President answers part of the second set of interrogatories under "penalty of perjury," but the President objects to and does not answer Interrogatories #10-11 (about "other women").
November 10, 1997	• The President responds to the first set of requests for admissions; he denies that he asked Ms. Jones to have sexual relations with him, but objects to and does not answer "other women" questions. • State troopers begin testifying.
November 12, 1997	• The President answers the third set of interrogatories, but fails to include Ms. Lewinsky on the list of those with discoverable information; he reserves the right to add more names. • Ms. Jones's attorneys ask Judge Wright to order the President to answer Interrogatories #10-11 from the second set of interrogatories. • Ms. Jones testifies at a deposition which continues the next day.
November 13, 1997	Jane Doe #3 receives a subpoena.

November 14, 1997	• Gennifer Flowers testifies at a deposition. • Jane Doe #7 receives a subpoena.
November 17, 1997	The President responds to the first request for documents and things, objecting to the requests insofar as they seek items related to "other women," but then asserts that he "has no documents responsive to" the request.
November 18, 1997	• Jane Doe #1 begins her deposition but immediately asserts a "privacy" privilege; Judge Wright holds a hearing but decides only that, because Jane Doe #1 is ill, the deposition will not continue that day. • Jane Doe #7 signs an affidavit claiming no pertinent knowledge, and moves to quash her deposition.
November 19, 1997	• Judge Wright denies Jane Doe #7's motion to quash her subpoena. • Judge Merhige denies Kathleen Willey's motion to quash her subpoena.
November 20, 1997	• The President's lawyers file a memorandum in support of the motions to quash filed by Jane Does #1-3. • Jane Doe #1 asks that her deposition (begun on Nov. 18) be terminated. • Ms. Jones's lawyers issue a subpoena to Jane Doe #5 (who received it Nov. 22).
November 21, 1997	• Jane Doe #2 moves to quash her subpoena. • Ms. Jones's lawyers serve the President's lawyers with an amended notice about the deposition of Jane Doe #3. • Jane Doe #7 testifies at a deposition.
November 24, 1997	Judge Wright conducts a hearing on Jane Doe #1's privacy objection to a deposition and overrules the objection.
December 2, 1997	Judge Wright denies Jane Doe #2's motion to quash.
December 3, 1997	• Jane Doe #2's second deposition begins but she refuses to answer sex-related questions. • Kathleen Willey suddenly cancels her deposition because of neck surgery.
December 4, 1997	Jane Doe #3 moves to quash her subpoena; Judge Wright denies the motion.

December 5, 1997	• Ms. Jones's lawyers serve the President's lawyers with their witness list for trial; Monica Lewinsky's name is on the list. • Ms. Jones's lawyers file an amended complaint adding the allegation that the President discriminated against Ms. Jones by granting employment benefits only to women who acceded to his requests for sex.
December 6, 1997	• The President meets with his lawyers. • The President verifies under "penalty of perjury" his supplemental responses to the second set of interrogatories (containing certain medical information about himself); he continues to fail to answer Interrogatories #10-11.
December 10, 1997	• Ms. Jones's lawyers move to compel Jane Does #1-3 to answer their deposition questions. • Jane Doe #2 files an opposition to this motion, arguing that Ms. Jones's lawyers have not established a sufficient predicate for delving into her privacy. • Danny Ferguson testifies at a deposition about the President's meetings with Jane Doe #1 and with Paula Jones.
December 11, 1997	• Judge Wright partially grants Ms. Jones's motion of Nov. 12; using a "meticulous" standard of materiality, she orders the President to answer Interrogatory #10-11 if (i) encounter was later than May 7, 1986; and (ii) either state troopers facilitated encounter, or the woman was a present or prospective government employee.
December 12, 1997	The President's lawyers file their opposition to Ms. Jones's motion (of Dec. 10) to compel the Jane Does.
December 15, 1997	• Ms. Jones's lawyers notify the President's lawyers that they will depose Jane Doe #5 on Jan. 9. • Ms. Jones's lawyers depose Onie E. "Betsey" Wright, who had been responsible for responding to "other women" accusations during the 1992 campaign.

December 16, 1997	• Ms. Jones's lawyers move to compel the President to answer the remaining questions in their first set of requests for admissions (#51-65) and their third set of interrogatories (asking for names of those with discoverable information). • Ms. Jones's lawyers serve their second request that the President produce documents and things, this time asking for those that concerned Ms. Lewinsky. • At 2:00 a.m. that night (on 12/17/97), the President calls Ms. Lewinsky and tells her that she is on the witness list.
December 18, 1997	Holding the testimony of Jane Does #1-3 "discoverable," Judge Wright grants Ms. Jones's motion to compel their testimony but requires that Ms. Jones establish a "factual predicate" and meet certain other conditions.
December 19, 1997	• Ms. Lewinsky receives a subpoena then meets with Vernon Jordan.
December 22, 1997	Vernon Jordan introduces Ms. Lewinsky to Frank Carter.
December 23, 1997	• The President serves supplemental responses to the second set of interrogatories, answering #10-11 (asking for names of women with whom he has had or proposed having "sexual relations") with "none." The President verifies "under penalty of perjury" that this answer is true and correct. • Mr. Carter meets with the President's lawyers.
December 24, 1997	Ms. Jones's lawyers move for reconsideration of Judge Wright's Dec. 18 order establishing the "factual predicate" requirement.
December 30, 1997	• The President's lawyer, Robert Bennett, concede during a hearing before Judge Wright that questions related to "sex-for-jobs" would be "fair game." • Ms. Jones's lawyers move to sanction the President's lawyers for making argumentative and suggestive objections to deposition questions.
January 2, 1998	• Jane Doe #2 testifies at a deposition. • Jane Doe #5 signs an affidavit denying any "sexual activity" with the President.
January 5, 1998	• Ms. Lewinsky meets with her attorney. • Ms. Jones's lawyers notify the President's lawyers that they plan to depose Jane Doe #5; Jane Doe #5 moves to quash, attaching her affidavit.

January 7, 1998	• Ms. Lewinsky prepares and signs an affidavit denying sexual relations with the President. • The President's lawyers file an opposition to Ms. Jones's motion for reconsideration of the Dec. 18 order.
January 8, 1998	• Judge Wright orders the President to answer the as-yet-unanswered questions from the third set of interrogatories and the first set of requests for admission (#51-65), holding that such answers were "relevant to the case." • Judge Wright denies Jane Doe #5's motion to quash.
January 9, 1998	• Judge Wright partly grants Ms. Jones's motion for reconsideration of her Dec. 18 order, allowing more questions than she has before. • Jane Doe #5 testifies at a deposition.
January 11, 1998	Kathleen Willey testifies at a deposition.
January 12, 1998	• Judge Wright holds a hearing discussing the President's deposition and what evidence she might permit at trial, but encourages the parties to settle.
January 15, 1998	• The President serves supplemental answers to the first and second sets of requests for documents and things, asserting that he has no documents or tangible things related to Ms. Lewinsky or Ms. Willy. • The President serves supplemental responses to the first set of requests for admissions, objecting to but then denying requests #51-65 (which ask him to name other women with whom he has had "sexual relations"). • The President serves supplemental responses to the third set of interrogatories, naming two other people with discoverable information (but not naming Ms. Lewinsky). • The President verifies all these supplemental answers "under penalty of perjury."
January 16, 1998	• Ms. Jones's lawyers notifies the President's lawyers that Jane Doe #3 would be deposed on Jan. 28. • Mr. Carter moves to quash Ms. Lewinsky's subpoena.
January 17, 1998	The President testified, in a videotaped deposition, that he had not had sexual relations (as defined) with Ms. Lewinsky.

January 22, 1998	• Judge Wright conducts a hearing on Ms. Lewinsky's motion to quash, then directs Ms. Lewinsky's deposition to proceed but grants a motion to reschedule.
January 27, 1998	The Office of the Independent Counsel ("OIC") moves to intervene in the Jones case.
January 29, 1998	• The OIC asks Judge Wright to postpone the deposition of Ms. Lewinsky until the completion of its criminal investigation. • After a hearing, Judge Wright decides to exclude the Lewinsky evidence altogether, because (i) waiting would frustrate timely resolution of the Jones case; and (ii) the Lewinsky evidence, though it "might be relevant to the issues in this case," is "not essential to the core issues in this case.
January 30, 1998	• Another "other woman" testifies at a deposition, denying any "sexual activity" with the President. • Ms. Jones's lawyers move to compel the President to produce as-yet-unproduced documents, arguing that his claims of privilege are meritless.
February 10, 1998	Ms. Jones's lawyers move for reconsideration of the order excluding the Lewinsky evidence.
February 17, 1998	The President's lawyers move for summary judgment. (Mr. Ferguson's lawyers do likewise on March 4.)
March 9, 1998	Judge Wright denies Ms. Jones's motion for reconsideration of her order excluding the Lewinsky evidence, stating that although "such evidence might have helped [Jones] establish . . . intent, absence of mistake, motive, and habit . . . . it simply is not essential to the core issues in this case."
April 1998	Judge Wright dismisses the Jones case on the ground that Ms. Jones has not presented sufficient evidence to put the case before a jury. Ms. Jones appeals.

BACKGROUND

A. Introduction

Paula Corbin Jones sued President Clinton (and former Arkansas State Police officer Danny Ferguson) in May 1994, seeking civil damages in relation to an incident that allegedly took place in the Excelsior Hotel in Arkansas in 1991.[1] The discovery period, however, did not begin until 1997, when the Supreme Court held unanimously that the case could go forward while President Clinton was still serving as President.

In May 1997, federal district judge Susan Webber Wright began managing the civil discovery process -- a procedure in which both sides exchange relevant information in order to prepare for the next stage of the case. The specifics of the discovery period are described in the next section.

After the close of discovery, the President and Mr. Ferguson both filed motions for summary judgment. Judge Wright granted these motions on April 1, 1998, holding that Ms. Jones had "failed to demonstrate that she has a case worthy of submitting to a jury."[2] Ms. Jones has appealed, and the case is currently pending before the United States Court of Appeals for the Eighth Circuit.

---

[1] The case is captioned Jones v. Clinton, LR-C-94-290.

[2] Jones v. Clinton, 990 F. Supp. 657, 679 (E.D. Ark. 1998).

B. Scope of Discovery

During the discovery period, the parties exchanged interrogatories, requests for admissions of fact, and requests for documents; they also took 56 depositions.[3] As with all federal civil cases, the scope of discovery was governed by the Federal Rules of Civil Procedure. These general rules were supplemented by several orders of Judge Wright. This section briefly describes these rules and orders.

1. The Types and Scope of Civil Discovery. Federal Rule of Civil Procedure 26(b)(1) provides the general standard for discoverable material:

> Parties may obtain discovery regarding any matter, not privileged, which is relevant to the subject matter involved in the pending action, whether it relates to the claim or defense of the party seeking discovery or to the claim or defense of any other party, including the existence, description, nature, custody, condition, and location of any books, documents, or other tangible things and the identity and location of persons having knowledge of any discoverable matter. The information sought need not be admissible at the trial if the information sought appears reasonably calculated to lead to the discovery of admissible evidence.[4]

Such material can be provided in response to interrogatories, requests for documents or tangible things, or testimony in depositions.

Interrogatories -- lists of written questions exchanged by the parties and answered in writing -- are governed by Federal

---

[3] A list of the 56 deponents in Jones can be found at 1292-DC-00000647 (List of Depositions).

[4] Fed. R. Civ. P. 26(b)(1) (emphases added).

Rule of Civil Procedure 33, which states that interrogatories "may relate to any matters which can be inquired into under Rule 26(b)(1)."[5] In other words, an interrogatory may ask about any information that is "relevant to the subject matter" and "reasonably calculated to lead to the discovery of admissible evidence." Ms. Jones's lawyers served the President with three sets of interrogatories, as described below.

Requests for production of documents and tangible things in the "possession, custody or control of the party upon whom the request is served"[6] are permitted pursuant to Federal Rule of Civil Procedure 34. Rule 34(a) permits discovery of matters within the scope of Rule 26(b), which allows discovery of information "reasonably calculated to lead to the discovery of admissible evidence."[7]

Requests for admissions may be served upon parties under Rule 36, to the extent they request the verification of the "truth of any matters within the scope of Rule 26(b)(1)."[8] If a party makes a admission, the matter admitted is considered conclusively established absent a court order.[9]

Depositions -- statements made under oath -- are governed by Rule 30. Although Rule 30 does not explicitly limit the

---

[5] Fed. R. Civ. P. 33(c).

[6] Fed. R. Civ. P. 34(a).

[7] Fed. R. Civ. P. 34(a), 26(b)(1).

[8] Fed. R. Civ. P. 36(a).

[9] Fed. R. Civ. P. 36(b).

permissible scope of deposition questioning, all discovery is limited by Rule 26(b)(1) and must be reasonably calculated to lead to admissible evidence.[10]

When a party receives an interrogatory, request for production of documents, or request for admissions, or is asked a question in a deposition, he must either answer truthfully or object. If the judge overrules the objection, the party must answer truthfully or be held in contempt. In addition, Rule 26(e) requires every party to supplement or correct a response to an interrogatory, production request, or request for admission if "the party learns that the response is in some material respect incomplete or incorrect and if the additional or corrective information has not otherwise been made known to the other parties during the discovery process or in writing."[11]

Special rules apply to sexual harassment cases. Principally, Federal Rule of Evidence 412 -- which was amended in 1994 "to expand the protection afforded alleged victims of sexual misconduct" -- is intended to "protect alleged victims against invasions of privacy, potential embarrassment, and unwarranted sexual stereotyping, and . . . to encourage victims to come forward when they have been sexually molested."[12] Toward that end, Rule 412(a) restricts the admissibility of "[e]vidence

---

[10] Fed. R. Civ. P. 30, 26(b)(1).

[11] Fed. R. Civ. P. 26(e)(2).

[12] Fed. R. Evid. 412, advisory committee's notes, 1994 amendments.

offered to prove that any alleged victim engaged in other sexual behavior."[13] Rule 412(a) also restricts the admissibility of "[e]vidence offered to prove any alleged victim's sexual predisposition."[14] Rule 412(b)(2) defines the exceptions to Rule 412(a)'s prohibitions:

> In a civil case, evidence offered to prove the sexual behavior or sexual predisposition of any alleged victim is admissible if it is otherwise admissible under these rules and its probative value substantially outweighs the danger of harm to any victim and of unfair prejudice to any party. Evidence of an alleged victim's reputation is admissible only if it has been placed in controversy by the alleged victim.[15]

There is no comparable rule for the accused, other than the generally applicable evidence rules.

2. The Scope of Discovery in Jones v. Clinton. Within the general framework set out by these rules, discovery in Jones was subject to the oversight of Judge Wright. Throughout the discovery period, the President, through his lawyers, repeatedly attempted to limit the amount of information Ms. Jones and her attorneys could discover about "other women" (women other than Hillary Rodham Clinton with whom the President had allegedly engaged in sexual relations).[16] Some of these "other women" who

---

13 Fed. R. Evid. 412(a)(1).

14 Fed. R. Evid. 412(a)(2).

15 Fed. R. Evid. 412(b)(2).

16 Monica Lewinsky was referred to in court papers as "Jane Doe #6." The "other women" at issue during discovery in Jones included Gennifer Flowers, Dolly Kyle Browning, and several women identified in court papers only as "Jane Does #1-7." It is common for courts to refer to persons as "Jane Doe" or "John Doe" when necessary to protect their anonymity. This memorandum

were identified, as well as Ms. Jones herself, also objected to some of the attempts to discover information about them.

The key events in this discovery dispute occurred between August 22, 1997, and January 30, 1998. In four different orders, Judge Wright decided and emphasized that information related to the President's relationships with Monica Lewinsky and other women was properly discoverable because it was "reasonably likely to lead to admissible evidence."

Out of respect for the office of the Presidency, Judge Wright applied a "meticulous standard" of materiality (higher than the normal standard) in determining the scope of the questioning she would allow for discovery directed at the President.[17] Applying this standard, the judge limited the questioning on this subject: The Jones lawyers could ask only about encounters the President may have had after May 7, 1986, that involved state or federal employees and those whose liaisons were facilitated by state troopers. Within these restrictions, however, the judge held that Ms. Jones was entitled to information regarding any individuals with whom the President had sexual relations or proposed or sought to have sexual relations.[18]

---

attempts to protect the confidentiality of the Jane Does wherever possible.

[17] 1414-DC-00000901 (Order of Dec. 11, 1997, at 5) (quoting United States v. Poindexter, 732 F. Supp. 142, 147 (D.D.C. 1990)).

[18] 1414-DC-00000899 (Order of Dec. 11, 1997, at 3).

In a later order, issued December 18, 1997, in which she directed Jane Does #1-3 to testify at depositions, the judge made clear that in determining the scope of discovery,

> the issue [at hand was] one of discovery, not admissibility of evidence at trial. Discovery, as all counsel know, by its very nature takes unforeseen twists and turns and goes down numerous paths, and whether those paths lead to the discovery of admissible evidence often simply cannot be predetermined.[19]

On December 30, 1997, at a telephone conference regarding the scope of discovery, Judge Wright explained that at trial Ms. Jones's attorneys would have to limit their evidence regarding "other women," but that some such evidence might be admissible: "I will not permit you to spend a lot of court time on this business about of [sic] other women. I do believe it is relevant and I will let you get some evidence in on that, but you're going to have to pick your evidence carefully."[20] Judge Wright further explained that, although she would "require the President's deposition to be tailored," she would not limit it to "stuff that's not embarrassing."[21] The judge recognized that certain information that was discoverable might be embarrassing and intrusive, but stated, "I can't protect the parties from embarrassment."[22]

---

[19] 1414-DC-00001012-13 (Order of Dec. 18, 1997, at 7-8).

[20] 1414-DC-00001491 (Telephone Conference 12/30/97 Tr. at 47).

[21] 1414-DC-00001493 (Telephone Conference 12/30/97 Tr. at 49).

[22] 1414-DC-00001493 (Telephone Conference 12/30/97 Tr. at 47).

Judge Wright returned to this theme at the President's January 17, 1998, deposition, where she rejected the President's counsel's attempt to place new limits on the scope of questioning. In so ruling, Judge Wright again commented: "Unfortunately, the nature of this case is such that people will be embarrassed. I have never had a sexual harassment case where there was not some embarrassment."[23]

DISCOVERY

1994 - 1997 **Prelude to discovery: the Complaint, the attempt to stay the case until after the President's Term, and the motion to dismiss**

At the time of the alleged Excelsior Hotel incident, Ms. Jones was employed by the Arkansas Industrial Development Commission ("AIDC"), a state government agency.[24] According to Ms. Jones's allegations, then-Governor Clinton made unwelcome sexual advances toward her, and she rejected the Governor's advances.[25] Ms. Jones further alleged that the advances, and subsequent lack of job advancement, had violated several laws and constitutional provisions.[26]

The four counts of the complaint alleged, respectively:

---

[23] 849-DC-00000360 (Clinton 1/17/98 Depo. at 9).

[24] Jones v. Clinton, 990 F. Supp. 657, 662-64 (E.D. Ark. 1998).

[25] Id. at 663-64.

[26] Id. at 665-66.

(1) that then-Governor Clinton, acting under color of state law, deprived [Ms. Jones] of her constitutional rights to equal protection and due process under the Fifth and Fourteenth Amendments to the United States Constitution by sexually harassing and assaulting her;

(2) that Governor Clinton and Ferguson conspired to deprive [Ms. Jones] of her rights to equal protection of the laws and of equal privileges and immunities under the laws;

(3) intentional infliction of emotional distress [by] the President, based primarily on the alleged incident at the hotel but also encompassing subsequent alleged acts; and

(4) that the President, through his press aides and attorney, defamed [Ms. Jones] by denying the allegations that underlie [her] lawsuit and by questioning her motives, and that Ferguson defamed her by making comments to the press suggesting that she willingly participated in a sexual encounter.[27]

On August 10, 1994, the President moved to dismiss Ms. Jones's complaint,[28] arguing that he was immune from suit until after he completed his service as President.[29] Judge Wright denied the President's motion and ruled that discovery in the case could proceed, but that any trial would not occur until the President left office.[30] Both parties appealed, and in January 1996, a divided panel of the United States Court of Appeals for the Eighth Circuit affirmed Judge Wright's decision

---

[27] Jones v. Clinton, 974 F. Supp. 712, 718 (E.D. Ark. 1997).

[28] Id. at 715 n.1.

[29] Jones v. Clinton, 869 F. Supp. 690, 692 (E.D. Ark. 1994).

[30] Id. at 699-700.

to order discovery, but reversed her decision to postpone any trial until after the President left office.[31]

The case then went to the Supreme Court, which heard oral argument in Jones in January 1997.[32] During oral argument, the President's attorney, Robert Bennett, warned that permitting a case like Jones to go forward could embarrass the Presidency, in part because the trial court might permit inquiry into contacts between the President and members of the opposite sex.[33] In May 1997 the Supreme Court unanimously affirmed the Eighth Circuit's decision and remanded the case to the district court so that discovery (and any further proceedings such as trial) could proceed.[34]

The President's lawyers then moved, pursuant to Rule 12(c) of the Federal Rules of Civil Procedure, for dismissal of the complaint for failure to state a claim.[35] Granting in part and denying in part, Judge Wright in August 1997 dismissed Ms. Jones's due process claim in Count I and her defamation claim against the President in Count IV. As to the other claims (the

---

[31] Jones v. Clinton, 72 F.3d 1354 (8th Cir. 1996).

[32] Clinton v. Jones, 117 S. Ct. 1636, 1636 (1997).

[33] 1414-DC-00000690-91 (Official Transcript, Proceedings before the Supreme Court of the United States, Clinton v. Jones, No. 95-1853, at 13-14 (Jan. 13, 1997)).

[34] Clinton v. Jones, 117 S. Ct. 1636, 1651 (1997).

[35] In other words, they argued that even if every factual allegation made by Ms. Jones were true, the law did not authorize the court to grant her a remedy.

intentional infliction of emotional distress, the equal protection claim, and the defamation claim against Trooper Ferguson), Judge Wright held that discovery could proceed.[36]

Sept.-Oct. 1997: Discovery begins with interrogatories

Attorneys for Ms. Jones had submitted her first set of interrogatories to the President on June 19, 1997. The six interrogatories asked the President about his alleged encounter with Paula Jones on May 8, 1991.[37] On September 22, 1997, the President served his responses to those interrogatories,[38] and on September 30, the President declared "under penalty of perjury" that these responses were "true and correct to the best of my knowledge and belief."[39]

The next day -- Wednesday, October 1, 1997 -- Ms. Jones's new law firm (Rader, Campbell, Fisher & Pyke)[40] served the President's counsel with a second set of interrogatories.[41] Interrogatory No. 10 stated:

---

36 Jones v. Clinton, 974 F. Supp. 712, 732 (E.D. Ark. 1997).

37 849-DC-00000002-10 (Plaintiff's First Set of Interrogatories to Defendant William Jefferson Clinton).

38 849-DC-00000011-17 (President Clinton's Responses to Plaintiff's First Set of Interrogatories).

39 849-DC-00000018 (Verification).

40 921-DC-00000048 (Plaintiff's Motion for Protective Order (Concerning Plaintiff's Deposition)).

41 921-DC-00000101-18 (Second Set of Interrogatories from Plaintiff to Defendant Clinton).

> Please state the name, address, and telephone number of each and every individual (other than Hillary Rodham Clinton) with whom you had sexual relations when you held any of the following positions:
> a. Attorney General of the State of Arkansas;
> b. Governor of the State of Arkansas;
> c. President of the United States.[42]

Interrogatory No. 11 stated:

> Please state the name, address, and telephone number of each and every individual (other than Hillary Rodham Clinton) with whom you proposed having sexual relations, or with whom you sought to have sexual relations, when you held any of the following positions:
> a. Attorney General of the States of Arkansas;
> b. Governor of the States of Arkansas;
> c. President of the United States.[43]

The phrase "sexual relations" was not defined.

Also on October 1, 1997, Ms. Jones's attorneys asked the President to provide certain categories of documents and tangible things -- if they were in the President's "immediate possession" or under his "custody or control"[44] -- that related to Ms. Jones, several other individuals, the President's sexual activities, the President's legal fees, and various other subjects.[45] The request defined "document" to mean "any tangible thing on which appears, or in which is stored or contained, any words, numbers,

---

[42] 921-DC-00000107 (Second Set of Interrogatories from Plaintiff to Defendant Clinton at 7).

[43] 921-DC-00000108 (Second Set of Interrogatories from Plaintiff to Defendant Clinton at 8).

[44] 1414-DC-00001510 (First Set of Requests from Plaintiff to Defendant Clinton for Production of Documents and Things at 3).

[45] 1414-DC-00001508-33 (First Set of Requests from Plaintiff to Defendant Clinton for Production of Documents and Things).

symbols, or images," as well as "any and all writings, drawings, graphs, charts, photographs, phono records, and other data compilations from which information can be obtained and translated, if necessary, through detection devices, into reasonably usable form."[46]

Early Oct. 1997: **Requests for admissions served on the President**

On Wednesday, October 8, 1997, Ms. Jones's lawyers served the President's lawyers with their first set of requests for admissions.[47] These requests asked the President to admit or deny issues related to Ms. Jones and other women. In particular, Requests #51-65 asked the President about "sexual relations" he had with "other women."[48] The requests did not define "sexual relations."

Mid-Oct. 1997: **Depositions begin; Dolly Kyle Browning subpoenaed**

On Monday, October 13, 1997, Ms. Jones's attorneys served the President's lawyers with a third set of interrogatories. The interrogatories asked the President about any person who may have discoverable information; any conversation the President may have

---

[46] 1414-DC-00001509 (First Set of Requests from Plaintiff to Defendant Clinton for Production of Documents and Things at 2).

[47] 1414-DC-00000002-23 (First Set of Requests from Plaintiff to Defendant Clinton for Admissions).

[48] 1414-DC-000000015-19 (First Set of Requests from Plaintiff to Defendant Clinton for Admissions at 14-18). These requests were filed with the District Court on October 14, 1997. 1414-DC-00000002 (First Set of Requests from Plaintiff to Defendant Clinton for Admissions at 1).

had with Mr. Ferguson; and any conversation the President had had with anyone about the alleged May 8, 1991, Excelsior Hotel incident.[49]

On Tuesday, October 14, the President's lawyers and Mr. Ferguson's lawyers deposed Lydia Cathey (Ms. Jones's sister). They asked Ms. Cathey about Ms. Jones's description of her alleged encounter with the President.[50]

On Monday, October 20, 1997, Ms. Jones's lawyers filed a deposition notice for Dolly Kyle Browning, stating that Ms. Browning's deposition would commence in Dallas, Texas on Tuesday, October 28, 1997.[51]

Two days later, on Wednesday, October 22, 1997, two investigators visited an alleged "other woman," Jane Doe #7, and asked her, in her words, "highly embarrassing, suggestive and vile questions concerning my private life."[52]

Meanwhile, one of the President's lawyers, Mitchell S. Ettinger, sent a letter dated October 23, 1997, and a draft pleading to Dolly Kyle Browning's lawyer, Dorcy Corbin. The letter described an earlier conversation in which Ms. Corbin told

---

[49] 1414-DC-00000984-92 (Third Set of Interrogatories from Plaintiff to Defendant Clinton).

[50] 1414-DC-00000543-48 (Cathey 10/14/97 Depo. at 165-70).

[51] 921-DC-00000043-46 (Plaintiff's Notice Duces Tecum of the Deposition upon Oral Examination of Dolly Kyle Browning).

[52] 920-DC-00000895 (Jane Doe #7 11/18/97 Aff. at 3). (Jane Doe #7 received a subpoena from Ms. Jones's attorneys on November 14, 1997, and testified at a deposition on November 21, 1997. See infra.)

the President's lawyer that Ms. Browning "does not possess any information relevant to the Paula Jones matter and therefore does not wish to be deposed."[53] The attachments to the letter were a draft motion to quash the subpoena and an accompanying draft of a supporting memorandum of points and authorities.[54]

Oct. 28-29, 1997: **The President's attorneys move to limit discovery of "other women"; Dolly Kyle Browning testifies; Ms. Jones's attorneys move to limit discovery of her sexual history; Jane Doe #1 subpoenaed**

On Tuesday, October 28, 1997, the President through his attorneys moved for a protective order to limit the scope of discovery regarding "other women."[55] Specifically, the President's lawyers requested that discovery be limited to non-consensual conduct occurring close in time, and in the same work place as the alleged incident with Ms. Jones.[56]

---

[53] DE-DC-00000081 (Letter from Mitchell S. Ettinger to Dorcy Corbin (Oct. 23, 1997)).

[54] DE-DC-00000082-82 (Motion for a Protective Order and Motion to Quash Subpoena Duces Tecum and Notice of Deposition); DE-DC-00000083-87 (Dolly Kyle Browning's Memorandum of Points and Authorities in Support of Motion for Protective Order and Motion to Quash).

[55] 1414-DC-00000627-30 (President Clinton's Motion for Protective Order); 1414-DC-00000631-51 (Memorandum in Support of President Clinton's Motion for a Protective Order). This motion was file-stamped on November 5. 1414-DC-00000627 (President Clinton's Motion for Protective Order at 1).

[56] 1414-DC-00000628 (President Clinton's Motion for Protective Order at 2).

Also on October 28, 1997, Dolly Kyle Browning testified at a deposition. She was questioned by Ms. Jones's attorneys about an alleged sexual relationship with President Clinton.[57]

Also on October 28, 1997, Ms. Jones's attorneys served an emergency motion asking Judge Wright to limit the President's attempted discovery of alleged "other men" (that is, men who allegedly had sexual relations with Ms. Jones), arguing that the discovery was "conducted solely to annoy and oppress Plaintiff."[58]

The next day, Wednesday, October 29, 1997, Ms. Jones's attorneys issued a subpoena to a woman anonymously identified as Jane Doe #1, requiring her to appear for a deposition on November 18, 1997.[59] The subpoena also commanded Jane Doe #1 to produce documents and other tangible things that referenced her communications and meetings with the President.[60]

---

[57] DE-DC-00000028 (Browning 10/28/97 Depo. at 29-30).

[58] 1414-DC-00000518-33 (Emergency Motion of Plaintiff under Rule 30(d)(3) and Rule 26(c) for Protection against Defendants' Bad-Faith Deposition Campaign Orchestrated and Conducted Solely to Annoy and Oppress Plaintiff and Brief Thereon). The motion was file-stamped on November 3, 1997. 1414-DC-00000518 (Emergency Motion of Plaintiff under Rule 30(d)(3) and Rule 26(c) for Protection against Defendants' Bad-Faith Deposition Campaign Orchestrated and Conducted Solely to Annoy and Oppress Plaintiff and Brief Thereon at 1)

[59] 921-DC-00000165-67 (Subpoena in a Civil Case to [Jane Doe #1]).

[60] 921-DC-00000167 (Requests for Production).

Oct. 30-Nov. 5, 1997: Jane Doe #2 subpoenaed; the President objects to "other women" interrogatories; investigators visit Jane Doe #5

On Thursday, October 30, 1997, Judge Wright entered an order that set forth restrictions and conditions on all discovery in the Jones case.[61] Also on October 30, 1997, a process server gave Jane Doe #2 a subpoena, albeit with some difficulty.[62] Ms. Jones's attorneys on this day served the President's lawyers with a copy of the subpoena given to Jane Doe #2.[63]

On Monday, November 3, 1997, the President's attorneys served Ms. Jones's attorneys with responses to her second set of interrogatories.[64] The President "declare[d] under penalty of perjury" that the responses given were "true and correct to the best of my knowledge and belief."[65] The President objected to and refused to answer several of the interrogatories, including Interrogatories #10 & 11[66] (which asked the President about his "sexual relations" he had had or proposed having with "other women.")

---

[61] Confidentiality Order on Consent of All Parties, Jones v. Clinton, No. LR-C-94-290 (Oct. 31, 1997)).

[62] The subpoena scheduled the deposition for November 7, 1997. 920-DC-00000654 (Subpoena in a Civil Case).

[63] 920-DC-00000660-64 (Plaintiff's Notice Duces Tecum of the Deposition upon Oral Examination of [Jane Doe #2]).

[64] 849-DC-00000037-53 (President Clinton's Responses To Plaintiff's Second Set of Interrogatories).

[65] 849-DC-00000052 (Verification).

[66] 849-DC-00000041-42 (President Clinton's Responses To Plaintiff's Second Set of Interrogatories at 5-6).

In Arkansas, investigators for Ms. Jones continued their work. At some point in November, "two private investigators retained by Paula Corbin Jones approached [Jane Doe #5] at [her] residence. [She] declined to speak with them, but provided the name of [her] family attorney. [She] subsequently was served with a subpoena seeking the production of documents and purporting to require [her] testimony at a deposition . . . ."[67]

On November 5, 1997, Ms. Jones's lawyers filed a motion asking that Ms. Jones's deposition -- scheduled for November 20, 1997 -- occur at a location other than the Little Rock law firm of Wright, Lindsey & Jennings, so that Ms. Jones and her lawyers could avoid a "media sideshow."[68]

Nov. 6, 1997: **The parties discuss the President's deposition**

On Thursday, November 6, 1997, Judge Wright conducted a hearing on L.D. Brown's request for a protective order and denied it. Judge Wright also denied Ms. Jones's motion for a protective order for her deposition, and then determined that the deposition of the President would occur on January 17, 1998.[69] Counsel for

---

[67] 920-DC-00000962 (Jane Doe #5 1/2/98 Aff. at 1). The date of Jane Doe #5's first subpoena was November 20, 1997. 920-DC-00000967 (Subpoena in a Civil Case). She was served with that subpoena on November 22, 1997. 920-DC-00000969 (Affidavit of Service). Her second subpoena was dated December 11, 1997, and she was served with the second subpoena on December 18, 1997. 920-DC-00000972 (Affidavit of Service).

[68] 921-DC-00000050 (Plaintiff's Motion for Protective Order (Concerning Plaintiff's Deposition) at 4).

[69] 921-DC-00000061-62 (Clerk's Minutes). According to the minutes, one of Ms. Jones's counsel "state[d] a date is needed

the parties then discussed the President's deposition, at least with respect to witnesses with "knowledge concerning events," and Judge Wright explained that Ms. Jones and her attorneys "will have names of potential witnesses in earlier discovery."[70]

Nov. 7, 1997: **Jane Doe #2 fails to appear for a deposition**

On Friday, November 7, 1997, attorneys for Ms. Jones traveled to Little Rock for the scheduled deposition of Jane Doe #2. Jane Doe #2 failed to appear.[71] (Attorneys for Ms. Jones re-noticed the deposition for November 24, 1997. The attorney for Jane Doe #2 then re-scheduled the deposition for December 5, 1997, and then filed a motion asking Judge Wright for a protective order and to quash the subpoena.)[72]

Nov. 10-12, 1997: **The President answers requests for admissions and third set of interrogatories; troopers testify; Jane Does #2-3 subpoenaed; deposition of Paula Jones begins**

On Monday, November 10, 1997, the President through his counsel responded to Ms. Jones's first set of requests for

for [President] Clinton's discovery deposition. Bennett respond[ed] that they would like it to be Saturday, January 17th." 921-DC-00000062 (Clerk's Minutes at 2).

[70] 921-DC-00000062 (Clerk's Minutes at 2).

[71] 921-DC-00000293 (Plaintiff's Memorandum in Opposition to the Motion of "Jane Doe No. 2" for Protective Order and Motion to Quash Subpoena Dues [sic] Tecum and Notice of Deposition at 1).

[72] 921-DC-00000294 (Plaintiff's Memorandum in Opposition to the Motion of "Jane Doe No. 2" for Protective Order and Motion to Quash Subpoena Dues [sic] Tecum and Notice of Deposition at 2).

admissions (served on October 8, 1997).[73] The President answered some of the questions. For example, he denied that he had asked Ms. Jones to have "sexual relations" with him.[74] The President objected to and refused to answer other questions. For example, Request for Admission #51, and the President's response, stated:

> Please admit or deny the following: While he was Governor of the State of Arkansas, Defendant Clinton had sexual relations with at least one woman (other than Hillary Rodham Clinton), and at least one member of the Arkansas State Police arranged at least one meeting between Defendant Clinton and the woman.
>
> **RESPONSE:** President Clinton objects to this Request for Admission in that it is intended solely to harass, embarrass and humiliate the President and the Office he occupies. President Clinton also objects to this Request for Admission in that it pertains to subject matter beyond the reasonable scope of discovery in this proceeding.[75]

Also on November 10, 1997, former Arkansas state trooper L.D. Brown testified at a deposition in Little Rock.[76] The next morning, Arkansas state trooper Larry Patterson testified at a deposition in Little Rock.[77] Both troopers were questioned about

---

[73] 921-DC-00000067-95 (President Clinton's Responses to Plaintiff's First Set of Requests for Admissions).

[74] 921-DC-00000081-82 (President Clinton's Responses to Plaintiff's First Set of Requests for Admissions at 15-16).

[75] 921-DC-00000083-84 (President Clinton's Responses to Plaintiff's First Set of Requests for Admissions at 17-18).

[76] 1292-DC-00000255-377 (Brown 11/10/97 Depo.).

[77] 1292-DC-00000407-585 (Perry 11/11/98 Depo.).

whether they had arranged private meetings for Governor Clinton and other women.[78]

On Wednesday, November 12, 1997, the President through his attorneys served Ms. Jones's attorneys with the President's responses to Ms. Jones's third set of interrogatories (those served on October 13).[79] In response to an interrogatory that asked the President to state the name, address, and telephone numbers of "each and every person who has, or who is likely to have, discoverable information relevant to one or more disputed facts alleged with particularity in the pleadings in this case," the President provided a list of names that did not include Ms. Lewinsky.[80] The President then stated, "I have read the foregoing responses to Plaintiff's Third Set of Interrogatories and declare under penalty of perjury that they are true and correct to the best of my knowledge and belief."[81] The President did, however, "reserve[] the right to supplement this response with additional names."[82]

Also on November 12, 1997, Ms. Jones through her counsel filed a motion (with accompanying memorandum) seeking to compel

---

78 See, e.g., 1292-DC-00000272 (Brown 11/10/97 Depo. at 17); 1292-DC-00000417 (Patterson Depo. at 10).

79 849-DC-00000090-102 (President Clinton's Responses to Plaintiff's Third Set of Interrogatories).

80 849-DC-00000090-92 (President Clinton's Responses to Plaintiff's Third Set of Interrogatories at 1-3).

81 849-DC-00000096 (Verification).

82 849-DC-00000091-92 (President Clinton's Responses to Plaintiff's Third Set of Interrogatories at 2-3).

the President to respond to those questions in her second set of interrogatories that he had refused to answer in his answer of November 3, 1997 (Interrogatories #10, 11).[83] In the motion, counsel for Ms. Jones argued that the President ought to be required to answer these two interrogatories -- the "other women" interrogatories -- and asserted that "discovery . . . is governed by very liberal standards that give Plaintiff a wide berth."[84] Counsel for Ms. Jones observed that the President "has made it clear in the past, and confirms in the Responses, that he disagrees with the Court's statements that there are at least some situations, in cases such as this, in which evidence of the defendant's extramarital sexual activity, is not only relevant and discoverable, but admissible."[85] Ms. Jones's counsel then argued that it was important for Ms. Jones to obtain this information prior to the President's deposition because Judge

---

[83] 921-DC-00000096-151 (Plaintiff's Motion to Compel Responses to Plaintiff's Second Set of Interrogatories to Defendant Clinton); 921-DC-00000152-61 (Memorandum in Support of Plaintiff's Motion to Compel Responses to Plaintiff's Second Set of Interrogatories to Defendant Clinton).

[84] 921-DC-00000155 (Memorandum in Support of Plaintiff's Motion to Compel Responses to Plaintiff's Second Set of Interrogatories to Defendant Clinton at 4).

[85] 921-DC-00000156 (Memorandum in Support of Plaintiff's Motion to Compel Responses to Plaintiff's Second Set of Interrogatories to Defendant Clinton at 5) (emphasis in original). Admissibility in this context apparently refers to evidence that would be admissible at a trial, a much narrower category of information than is available to parties during discovery in civil cases. For example, a hearsay question that would be plainly inadmissible at trial would be discoverable, because it would allow a party to learn the identity of a witness.

Wright had indicated that the President's deposition would be of limited duration because of the respect due his office.[86]

Also on November 12, 1997, Ms. Jones's counsel notified the President's counsel of a second deposition notice issued to Jane Doe #2[87] and issued a subpoena to Jane Doe #3, which she received the next day.[88]

And, still on November 12, 1997, the President's attorneys deposed Paula Jones. Ms. Jones testified about what she claimed was sexually unwelcome "disgusting" conduct by the President.[89] The President's lawyer, Robert Bennett, asked Ms. Jones about the alleged May 8, 1991, Excelsior Hotel incident.[90] The lawyer for Defendant Ferguson, Mr. Bristow, asked Ms. Jones about Ms. Jones's pre-marital sexual relations with her husband and other men.[91]

---

[86] 921-DC-00000157 (Memorandum in Support of Plaintiff's Motion to Compel Responses to Plaintiff's Second Set of Interrogatories to Defendant Clinton at 6).

[87] 920-DC-00000665-69 (Plaintiff's Amended Notice Duces Tecum of the Deposition upon Oral Examination of [Jane Doe#2]).

[88] 920-DC-00000796-800 (Subpoena in a Civil Case).

[89] 1414-DC-00000130(Jones 11/12/97 Depo. at 108).

[90] 1414-DC-00000102-20 (Jones 11/12/97 Depo. at 79-97).

[91] 1414-DC-00000196-200 (Jones 11/12/97 Depo. at 174-78).

Nov. 13-14, 1997: **Deposition of Paula Jones finishes; Jane Doe #7 served with a subpoena; deposition of Gennifer Flowers**

On Thursday, November 13, 1997, Ms. Jones completed her deposition testimony.[92] The next day, Jane Doe #7 received a subpoena directing her to appear for a deposition on November 19, 1997, and to produce documents.[93] And in Dallas, Texas, Gennifer Flowers was asked about her alleged sexual relationship with President Clinton.[94]

Nov. 17, 1997: **The President responds to plaintiff's first request for documents and things**

On November 17, 1997, the President responded to Ms. Jones's first request for documents and things (which he had received on October 1, 1997). The President's lawyers raised numerous objections to the requests. In particular, the President, through his attorneys, objected to the requests but stated that he had no documents or other things that related to other women.[95] For example, one request and the President's response state:

> **REQUEST FOR PRODUCTION NO. 30:** Please produce each and every document (including but not limited to letters, memoranda, postcards, and e-mails) sent at any time to

---

[92] 1414-DC-00000290-510 (Jones 11/13/97 Depo. at 486-87).

[93] 920-DC-00000895 (Jane Doe #7 11/18/97 Aff. at 3); 920-DC-00000898 (Affidavit Of Service).

[94] 1292-DC-00000586-645 (Flowers 11/14/97 Depo.).

[95] V002-DC-00000056-92 (President Clinton's Responses to Plaintiff's First Set of Requests for Production of Documents and Things).

Defendant Clinton by any woman (other than Hillary Rodham Clinton) with whom Defendant Clinton had sexual relations when he held any of the following positions:

a. Attorney General of the State of Arkansas;
b. Governor of the State of Arkansas;
c. President of the United States.

RESPONSE: President Clinton objects to this Request for Production as it is intended solely to harass, embarrass, and humiliate the President and the Office he occupies. President Clinton also objects to this Request for Production in that it pertains to subject matter beyond the reasonable scope of discovery in this proceeding, is overbroad, redundant and not likely to lead to the discovery of admissible evidence. Notwithstanding the above objections, and General Objection 4, President Clinton has no documents responsive to this Request.[96]

General Objection 4 states:

> President Clinton objects to the First Set of Requests for Production of Documents and Things to the extent it is designed to elicit production of materials from President Clinton's campaigns for public office, including the 1996 Presidential Election Campaign, that were created merely for the purpose of responding to the rumors, speculation and innuendo generated by the tabloid press and political opponents of the President. Notwithstanding this objection, President Clinton personally has no such documents. Nonetheless, we are inquiring of other persons or entities who may have possession, custody or control of campaign materials as to whether any such materials are responsive.[97]

Nov. 18-19, 1997: Objections of alleged "other women" Jane Doe #1 and Jane Doe #7; Jane Doe #7 ordered to testify

On Tuesday, November 18, 1997, counsel for Ms. Jones deposed Jane Doe #1, but the deposition ended after less than an hour

[96] V002-DC-00000075 (President Clinton's Responses to Plaintiff's First Set of Requests for Production of Documents and Things at 20) (emphasis added).

[97] V002-DC-00000057 (President Clinton's Responses to Plaintiff's First Set of Requests for Production of Documents and Things at 2) (emphasis added).

when Jane Doe #1 asserted a "constitutional privilege of privacy."[98] Judge Wright conducted two hearings to address this issue, but decided that the deposition would "not go on today," because Jane Doe #1 was ill.[99]

Also on November 18, 1997, Jane Doe #1 filed objections to the subpoenas she had received.[100] Jane Doe #7 signed an affidavit in which she asserted that she "simply do[es] not have any knowledge that is pertinent to the lawsuit filed by Paula Jones."[101] Her attorneys also moved to quash her subpoena and sought a protective order.[102]

The next day, Wednesday, November 19, 1997, Judge Wright conducted a brief hearing to consider Jane Doe #7's motion to quash her subpoena, denied the motion, and indicated that "it is appropriate for [the] deposition to go forward."[103] Judge Wright explained that she had to "treat [this case] as a sexual harassment case as other such cases and state[d] reasons for

---

[98] 921-DC-00000204-29 (Jane Doe #1 11/18/97 Depo.).

[99] 921-DC-00000265 (Clerk's Minutes).

[100] 921-DC-00000162-67 (Objection of Jane Doe [#1] to Subpoena Duces Tecum).

[101] 920-DC-00000896 (Jane Doe #7 11/18/97 Aff. at 4).

[102] 921-DC-00000168-75 (Motion to Quash Subpoena and for Protective Order); 921-DC-00000176-85 (Brief in Support of Motion to Quash Subpoena and for Protective Order).

[103] 921-DC-00000266 (Clerk's Minutes at 1).

allowing [the] discovery process and cannot protect them from this."[104]

Also on November 19, 1997, in Richmond, Virginia, Judge Robert R. Merhige of the United States District Court for the Eastern District of Virginia conducted a closed hearing on a motion filed by Kathleen Willey in which she sought to quash the subpoena commanding her to appear for a deposition on December 4, 1997.[105] Ms. Jones's attorneys had originally subpoenaed Ms. Willey herein for her deposition and document production on July 29, 1997, but, according to Ms. Jones's attorneys, Ms. Willey "vigorously opposed" the subpoena.[106] (On December 16, 1997, Judge Merhige then issued an order requiring Ms. Willey to testify at a deposition, which Ms. Willey eventually did on January 11, 1998.)[107]

Nov. 20, 1997: **The President supports Jane Does' motions; Jane Doe #1 moves to terminate her deposition; Jane Doe #5 subpoenaed**

On November 20, 1997, the President through his counsel filed a pleading supporting the Jane Does' motions to quash. The President's memorandum complained that "plaintiff's discovery in this matter . . . has improperly invaded the rights of privacy of

---

[104] 921-DC-00000266 (Clerk's Minutes at 1).

[105] 1414-DC-00001150-68 (Sealed Hearing 11/19/97 Tr.).

[106] DE-DC-00000204 (Plaintiff's Motion to Compel Further Deposition Testimony from Kathleen Willey at 1).

[107] DE-DC-00000215-16 (Order Regarding Kathleen Willey Deposition Date).

innocent third parties whose only connection to this matter is that they may have worked for or been a friend of President Clinton."[108] The President's memorandum charged that "plaintiff's entire discovery plan is designed to harass and cause embarrassment to the President and others, not to obtain relevant information or information that is likely to lead to the discovery of admissible evidence."[109]

Also on November 20, 1997, Jane Doe #1 filed a motion and an accompanying memorandum with Judge Wright.[110] Her motion requested that Judge Wright order her deposition "terminate[d] or eliminate[d]."[111] And, on November 20, 1997, Ms. Jones's attorneys issued a subpoena for Jane Doe #5, which she received the subpoena on November 22, 1997.[112]

Nov. 21, 1997: **Ms. Jones's lawyers file a response to Jane Doe #1's motion; Jane Doe #2 files a motion to quash; Jane Doe #7 testifies**

On November 21, 1997, Ms. Jones's counsel responded to Jane Doe #1's November 20, 1997, motion seeking to stop her

---

108 921-DC-00000186 (President Clinton's Memorandum in Support of Third Parties' Motion to Quash at 1).

109 921-DC-00000187-88 (President Clinton's Memorandum in Support of Third Parties' Motion to Quash at 2-3).

110 921-DC-00000190-92 (Motion of Jane Doe [#1] to Terminate or Limit Examination); 921-DC-00000193-200 (Brief in Support of Motion of Jane Doe [#1] to Terminate or Limit Examination).

111 921-DC-00000191 (Motion of Jane Doe [#1] to Terminate or Limit Examination at 2).

112 920-DC-00000967-68 (Subpoena in a Civil Case) 920-DC-00000969 (Affidavit of Service).

deposition.[113] In the response, Ms. Jones's counsel explained that the purpose of the deposition was "to discover additional facts establishing a pattern of improper action under color of state law. It concerns the illegal use of state resources to facilitate, and to conceal, Defendant Clinton's predatory sexual activity while he was Governor of the State of Arkansas and in command of those resources."[114] Counsel for Ms. Jones noted that Judge Wright "has already ruled that the discovery of such facts may go forward -- under the strict confidentiality provisions imposed by the Court."[115]

Also on November 21, 1997, Jane Doe #2 filed a motion and accompanying memorandum to quash the subpoena she had received.[116] Ms. Jones's attorneys served another amended deposition notice that day on Jane Doe #2, scheduling her deposition for December 5, 1997.[117]

---

[113] 921-DC-00000248-56 (Plaintiff's Memorandum in Opposition to the Motion of [Jane Doe #1] to Terminate or to Limit her Deposition and to Protect Constitutional Privilege).

[114] 921-DC-00000248-49 (Plaintiff's Memorandum in Opposition to the Motion of [Jane Doe #1] to Terminate or to Limit her Deposition and to Protect Constitutional Privilege at 1-2).

[115] 921-DC-00000249 (Plaintiff's Memorandum in Opposition to the Motion of [Jane Doe #1] to Terminate or to Limit her Deposition and to Protect Constitutional Privilege at 2).

[116] 921-DC-00000257-58 (Motion for a Protective Order and Motion to Quash Subpoena Duces Tecum and Notice of Deposition); 921-DC-00000259-63 (Brief in Support of Motion for Protective Order and Motion to Quash).

[117] 920-DC-00000670-74 (Plaintiff's Amended Notice Duces Tecum of the Deposition upon Oral Examination Of [Jane Doe #2]).

Additionally, Ms. Jones's lawyers served the President's lawyers with a notice of their intent to depose Jane Doe #3 on December 5, 1997.[118] (The depositions of both Jane Doe #2 and Jane Doe #3 occurred on December 5, 1997, but both refused to answer questions, as explained below.) Jane Doe #7 testified at a deposition for one hour, stating that the President had never acted in a "sexual manner" in her presence.[119]

Nov. 24-26, 1997: **Judge Wright orders discovery of Jane Doe #1 to proceed; Jane Doe #1 claims that her name was leaked to the media; the President argues that he has a constitutional privacy interest in not responding to interrogatories**

In Little Rock on November 24, 1997, Judge Wright considered the objection of Jane Doe #1 to her deposition. Judge Wright overruled Jane Doe #1's objection, explaining:

> [Plaintiff] is entitled to ask questions that are calculated to lead to admissible evidence; Court states areas that would be discoverable material.
>
> [Robert] Bennett [the President's lawyer] argues that he does not agree with the Court. . . .
>
> * * * *
>
> In response to Bennett's concerns, Court states that [counsel for Ms. Jones] has to lay predicate for certain questions but she can't claim privacy for address and where she works.
>
> In response to Bennett's concerns that pleadings will become public and do damage to institution of presidency, Court states questions have to be related to this cause of action and believes the Rules of

---

118 920-DC-00000806-10 (Plaintiff's Amended Notice Duces Tecum of the Deposition upon Oral Examination of [Jane Doe #3]).

119 921-DC-00000837 (Jane Doe #7 11/21/97 Depo. at 31-32).

> Evidence and rules governing sexual harassment require Court to permit the questions.[120]

Judge Wright also issued an order allowing Ms. Jones's attorneys to amend her complaint, but she indicated that the amendments would not be construed as new causes of action.[121]

The next day, Tuesday, November 25, 1997, Judge Wright conducted a brief hearing to address the President's efforts to obtain discovery of matters that related to the Paula Jones Legal Fund and the importance of keeping discovery matters under seal.[122] She then ruled that the identity of donors was protected but other legal fund information was not protected, except to the extent that attorney-client privilege applied.[123]

That same day, the President's lawyers served Ms. Jones's lawyers with the President's opposition to Ms. Jones's motion to compel the President to finish responding to her second set of interrogatories (those served on October 1, 1997).[124] The President's lawyers complained about the "obnoxious and intrusive interrogatories," and argued that the President had a

---

120 921-DC-00000268-69 (Clerk's Minutes at 1-2).

121 1414-DC-00001190 (Order of Jan. 9, 1998, at 3) (discussing the Order of Nov. 24, 1997).

122 921-DC-00000280 (Clerk's Minutes).

123 921-DC-00000270-79 (Order of Nov. 25, 1997).

124 1414-DC-00000753-80 (President Clinton's Opposition to Plaintiff's Motion to Compel Responses to Plaintiff's Second Set of Interrogatories).

"constitutionally-protected privacy interest" that protected his "intimate personal conduct."[125]

One day later, Wednesday, November 26, 1997, Jane Doe #1 filed a motion requesting sanctions in which she alleged, among other things, that someone affiliated with Ms. Jones had improperly leaked her name to the media in violation of a confidentiality order issued by Judge Wright.[126]

Dec. 1-3, 1997: **Ms. Jones's attorneys oppose Jane Doe #2's efforts to avoid a deposition; Judge Wright rules that discovery of Jane Doe #2 could proceed; Judge Wright permits the videotaping of Jane Doe #1's deposition; Jane Doe #1 testifies; Kathleen Willey's neck surgery delays her deposition**

On Monday, December 1, 1997, Ms. Jones's attorneys filed a response to Jane Doe #2's November 21, 1997, motion to quash her subpoena.[127] Ms. Jones's attorneys cited the deposition testimony of two Arkansas state troopers, L.D. Brown and Larry Patterson, and argued that this testimony provided evidence in support of Ms. Jones's claim.[128]

---

[125] 1414-DC-00000754 (President Clinton's Opposition to Plaintiff's Motion to Compel Responses to Plaintiff's Second Set of Interrogatories at 2).

[126] 921-DC-00000284-86 (Jane Doe #1's Motion to Show Cause at 4-6).

[127] 921-DC-00000293-316 (Plaintiff's Memorandum in Opposition to the Motion of "Jane Doe No. 2" for Protective Order and Motion to Quash Subpoena Duces Tecum and Notice of Deposition).

[128] 921-DC-00000294-95 (Plaintiff's Memorandum in Opposition to the Motion of "Jane Doe No. 2" for Protective Order and Motion to Quash Subpoena Duces Tecum and Notice of Deposition at 2-3).

The next day, Tuesday, December 2, 1997, counsel for the Jones parties and counsel for Jane Does #1 and #2 participated in a hearing with Judge Wright about Jane Doe #2's motion to quash and Jane Doe #1's motion objecting to a videotape deposition.[129] Judge Wright denied Jane Doe #2's motion to quash because Jane Doe #2 "might have testimony that could lead to admissible evidence."[130]

The next day, Wednesday, December 3, 1997, Judge Wright entered a protective order that allowed Ms. Jones's attorneys to videotape Jane Doe #1's deposition subject to the restrictions set forth in Judge Wright's October 30, 1997, order and additional confidentiality safeguards.[131] That same day, Ms. Jones's attorneys began questioning Jane Doe #1 at a deposition. Ms. Jones's attorneys asked Jane Doe #1 about her contacts with the President. Jane Doe #1 refused to answer sexually-related questions pursuant to instructions she received from her lawyer.[132]

Also on December 3, 1997, Ms. Jones's "counsel was en route to Richmond[, Virginia] from Dallas in order to take the deposition of Ms. Willey when [Ms. Willey's attorney] Mr. Gecker suddenly formally notified the Court and Plaintiff that Ms. Willey allegedly required 'neck surgery' that just

---

[129] 921-DC-00000329-30 (Clerk's Minutes).

[130] 921-DC-00000330 (Clerk's Minutes at 2).

[131] 921-DC-00000317 (Protective Order, Dec. 3, 1997).

[132] 1414-DC-00000840-48 (Jane Doe #1 12/3/97 Depo.).

coincidentally was precipitously scheduled for December 4, 1997."[133] On Thursday, December 4, 1997, the district court in Richmond "held an in-chambers hearing regarding the situation, signed Plaintiff's version of the Protective Order Regarding Kathleen Willey Deposition, and, after personally talking with Ms. Willey's attending physician, ordered Ms. Willey to appear for her deposition in early January."[134]

Dec. 4, 1997: **Jane Doe #3 moves to quash her subpoena**

On Thursday, December 4, 1997, Jane Doe #3 moved to quash the subpoena she had received.[135] That afternoon Judge Wright conducted a brief hearing on this motion and denied it. Judge Wright also directed the parties not to file witness lists but rather to exchange the lists with each other.[136]

Dec. 5, 1997: **Ms. Lewinsky appears on the witness list; Jane Doe #2 and Jane Doe #3 refuses to answer deposition questions**

On Friday, December 5, 1997, Ms. Jones's lawyers served the President's lawyers with their witness list. Monica Lewinsky's

---

[133] DE-DC-00000205 (Plaintiff's Motion to Compel Further Deposition Testimony from Kathleen Willey at 2).

[134] DE-DC-00000205 (Plaintiff's Motion to Compel Further Deposition Testimony from Kathleen Willey at 2).

[135] 921-DC-00000321-22 (Motion for Protective order and Motion to Quash Subpoena Duces Tecum and Notice of Deposition); 921-DC-00000323-27 (Brief in Support of Motion for Protective order and Motion to Quash Subpoena Duces Tecum and Notice of Deposition).

[136] 921-DC-00000331 (Clerk's Minutes).

name was on it.[137] Ms. Jones's attorneys also that day filed and served an amended complaint[138] (pursuant to Judge Wright's permission granted on November 24, 1997). The amended complaint repeated the allegations of Ms. Jones's original complaint and added more accusations against the President and Mr. Ferguson, including that the President had

> discriminated against Plaintiff because of her sex by systematically granting, directly and indirectly, governmental and employment benefits . . . to other women who succumbed to Defendant Clinton's . . . pattern, and practice of using State . . . resources to solicit sexual favors . . . while continually denying . . . any such . . . benefits . . . to Plaintiff because she would not accede to Defendant Clinton's repeated solicitations of sex from her.[139]

Also on Friday, December 5, 1998, Ms. Jones's attorneys attempted to depose Jane Doe #2 and Jane Doe #3. Both refused to answer questions asked by Ms. Jones's attorneys.[140]

Dec. 6-7, 1997: **The President meets with his lawyers; the President verifies supplemental interrogatory responses**

On Saturday, December 6, 1997, the President met with his personal attorneys and Deputy White House counsel Bruce Lindsey. The subject of the meeting was the Jones case in general and the

---

[137] 849-DC-00000121-37 (Plaintiff's Witness List).

[138] Plaintiff's First Amended Complaint, Jones v. Clinton, No. LR-C-94-290.

[139] Id. at 14.

[140] 921-DC-00000340 (Plaintiff's Motion to Compel Jane Doe #1, Jane Doe #2, and Jane Doe #3 to Answer Deposition Questions, and Motion to Prevent Further Obstruction of Depositions at 1); 920-DC-00000551-626 (Jane Doe #2 12/5/98 Depo.); 920-DC-00000740-95 (Jane Doe #3 12/5/98 Depo.).

witness list in particular.[141] That same day, the President verified supplemental responses (and continued objections) to Ms. Jones's second set of interrogatories, declaring "under penalty of perjury [that his responses were] . . . true and correct to the best of [his] knowledge and belief."[142] These supplemental responses (which would be served to Ms. Jones's lawyers the following Wednesday, December 10) still did not provide an answer to Interrogatories #10 & 11.

Dec. 8-10, 1997: **Ms. Jones's attorneys move to compel Jane Does; Danny Ferguson testifies**

On Monday, December 8, 1997, Ms. Jones's attorneys responded to Jane Doe #1's November 26, 1997, motion for sanctions, asserting that there was "no evidence before the Court that Plaintiff [Ms. Jones] or her counsel violated [Judge Wright's] Confidentiality Order."[143]

On Wednesday, December 10, 1997, Ms. Jones's attorneys filed a motion to compel Jane Does #1-3 to answer deposition questions.[144] Ms. Jones's attorneys asserted in their motion that the Jane Does and the defendants "are obstructing legitimate

---

141 Lindsey 3/12/98 GJ at 64-66; Lindsey 2/19/98 GJ at 9-10.

142 V002-DC-00000046-51 (President Clinton's Supplemental Responses and Objections to Plaintiff's Second Set of Interrogatories); V002-DC-00000050 (Verification).

143 921-DC-00000332 (Plaintiff's Statement in Opposition to Jane Doe #1's Motion to Show Cause at 1).

144 921-DC-00000340-440 (Plaintiff's Motion to Compel Jane Doe #1, Jane Doe #2, and Jane Doe #3 to Answer Deposition Questions, and Motion to Prevent Further Obstruction of Depositions).

discovery when they have tried and failed to obtain an order limiting the scope of the depositions."[145] Citing the Violence Against Women Act, Ms. Jones's attorneys asserted that "a defendant's sexual propensity . . . is not only to be considered discoverable under the new law, but is indeed admissible at trial -- yet Defendants continue to forestall even the discovery of facts relevant to Defendant Clinton's sexual propensities. . . . It is time for the games and stonewalling to end."[146]

Also on December 10, 1997, Jane Doe #2's attorney filed a response (and supporting memorandum) to Ms. Jones's December 10 motion to compel.[147] The response claimed that Ms. Jones's counsel had not established a sufficient predicate for "delving into Jane Doe #2's private life."[148]

---

145 921-DC-00000341 ((Plaintiff's Motion to Compel Jane Doe #1, Jane Doe #2, and Jane Doe #3 to Answer Deposition Questions, and Motion to Prevent Further Obstruction of Depositions at 2).

146 921-DC-00000351-52 (Plaintiff's Motion to Compel Jane Doe #1, Jane Doe #2, and Jane Doe #3 to Answer Deposition Questions, and Motion to Prevent Further Obstruction of Depositions at 12-13) (emphasis in original).

147 921-DC-00000441-49 (Response of Jane Doe #2 to Plaintiff's Motion to Compel Jane Doe #1, Jane Doe #2, and Jane Doe #3 to Answer Deposition Questions and Motion to Prevent Further Obstruction of Depositions); 921-DC-00000450-59 (Brief in Support of Response of Jane Doe #2 to Plaintiff's Motion to Compel Jane Doe #1, Jane Doe #2, and Jane Doe #3 to Answer Deposition Questions and Motion to Prevent Further Obstruction of Depositions).

148 921-DC-00000442 (Response of Jane Doe #2 to Plaintiff's Motion to Compel Jane Doe #1, Jane Doe #2, and Jane Doe #3 to Answer Deposition Questions and Motion to Prevent Further Obstruction of Depositions at 2); 921-DC-00000450 (Brief in Support of Response of Jane Doe #2 to Plaintiff's Motion to Compel Jane Doe #1, Jane Doe #2, and Jane Doe #3 to Answer Deposition Questions and Motion to Prevent Further Obstruction of

In Little Rock, the President's co-defendant, Danny Ferguson, testified at a deposition.[149] Mr. Ferguson was asked about alleged meetings between the Governor and certain Jane Does, as well as about the alleged incident with Paula Jones in Governor Clinton's room at the Excelsior Hotel.[150]

Dec. 11, 1997: **Judge Wright issues an order allowing "other women" discovery to proceed and establishes a "meticulous" materiality standard**

The next day, Thursday, December 11, 1997 -- the same day Ms. Lewinsky met Mr. Jordan for the second time[151] -- Judge Wright issued an order partially granting Ms. Jones's November 12, 1997, motion to compel the President to respond to her second set of interrogatories.[152] With regard to Interrogatories #10 & 11, Judge Wright ordered the President to provide answers subject to limitations:

> [T]he Court will establish a time frame that spans 5 years prior to May 8, 1991 (the date of the alleged incident that is the primary subject of this lawsuit), up to the present. Second, the Court will limit the class of individuals within this time frame to two categories, those who were state or federal employees, and those whose liaisons with Governor Clinton were

---

Depositions at 1).

[149] 1292-DC-00000937-1075 (Ferguson 12/10/97 Depo.).

[150] 1292-DC-00000937-1075 (Ferguson 12/10/97 Depo. at 16-42, 45-69, 73-76, 92-99, 102-03).

[151] V004-DC-00000171 (Akin, Gump production; visitor records).

[152] 921-DC-00000459-66 (Order of Dec. 11, 1997). The motion sought to compel responses to Ms. Jones's second set of interrogatories.

> procured, protected, concealed, and/or facilitated by State Troopers assigned to the Governor.
>
> The Court finds, therefore, that <u>the plaintiff is entitled to information regarding any individuals with whom the President had sexual relations or proposed or sought to have sexual relations and who were during the relevant time frame state or federal employees</u>. Plaintiff is also entitled to information regarding every person whom the President asked, during the relevant time frame, to arrange a private meeting between himself and any female state or federal employee which was attended by no one else and was held at any location other than his office. The Court cannot say that such information is not reasonably calculated to lead to the discovery of admissible evidence.
>
> The Court further finds that plaintiff is entitled to information regarding any individuals, whether or not state or federal employees, whose liaisons with Governor Clinton were procured, protected, concealed, and/or facilitated by State Troopers assigned to the Governor. Such information may bear on plaintiff's efforts at establishing a pattern or practice of conduct.[153]

Judge Wright added:

> [A]ny alleged relationships and/or arranged meetings with a federal employee that occurred when the President was not in a position to directly affect that individual's employment, <u>i.e.</u>, when he was still Governor and was not President-elect, would fall outside of the guidelines the Court today establishes. Likewise, any alleged relationships and/or arranged meetings with a state employee that occurred when the President was no longer in a position to directly affect that individual's state employment would also fall outside of the Court's guidelines.[154]

As to materiality of the President's testimony, Judge Wright explained:

---

[153] 921-DC-00000461 (Order of Dec. 11, 1997, at 3) (emphasis added).

[154] 921-DC-00000461 n.2 (Order of Dec. 11, 1997, at 3 n.2).

> The standard that this Court will utilize in addressing any questions regarding the necessity and scope of the President's testimony at any deposition or trial will be "if the Court is satisfied that his testimony would be material as tested by a meticulous standard, as well as being necessary in the sense of being a more logical and more persuasive source of evidence than alternatives that might be suggested."[155]

Judge Wright added that "[t]his was the standard utilized by this Court in determining the necessity of the President's videotaped testimony in United States v. Branscum, No. 96-CR-49 (E.D. Ark. June 7, 1996)."[156]

Dec. 12-15, 1997: **The President's lawyers oppose efforts to compel Jane Does #1-3 to testify; Judge Merhige orders Kathleen Willey deposition to proceed; the President tells Ms. Lewinsky that she is on the witness list; Judge Wright compels Jane Does #1-3 to testify and clarifies the necessary factual predicate; Jane Doe #5 subpoenaed**

On Friday, December 12, 1997, the President's attorneys filed a brief opposing Ms. Jones's motion to compel the testimony of Jane Does #1-3.[157] In that brief, the President's attorneys asserted that "[p]laintiff has failed to establish the appropriate predicate with each deponent before prying into her private affairs, as the Court has required. Each of these women

---

155 921-DC-00000463 (Order of Dec. 11, 1997, at 5) (quoting United States v. Poindexter, 732 F. Supp. 142, 147 (D.D.C. 1990)) (emphases added).

156 921-DC-00000463 (Order of Dec. 11, 1997, at 5). This Office prosecuted the Branscum case.

157 920-DC-00000405-26 (President Clinton's Opposition to Plaintiff's Motion to Compel Jane Doe #1, Jane Doe #2, and Jane Doe #3 to Answer Deposition Questions).

has testified on the record, under oath, that she was never sexually harassed or subjected to unwelcomed sexual advances by Governor Clinton."[158] Therefore, the President's attorneys argued, Ms. Jones's motion to compel testimony should be denied. That same day, December 12, 1997, Judge Wright issued an order permitting Ms. Jones's attorneys to videotape the deposition of Jane Doe #2.[159]

On December 15, 1997, Ms. Jones's attorneys notified the President's attorneys that they would depose Jane Doe #5 on January 9, 1998.[160] And, in New York City, Ms. Jones's attorneys deposed Onie E. "Betsey" Wright.[161] Ms. Jones's attorneys asked Ms. Wright several questions about her "other women" discussions with the President.[162]

On Tuesday, December 16, 1997, Judge Robert R. Merhige, Jr., of the United States District Court for the Eastern District of Virginia, issued an order -- the result of his November 19 hearing -- requiring Kathleen Willey to "present herself for her

---

[158] 920-DC-00000405 (President Clinton's Opposition to Plaintiff's Motion to Compel Jane Doe #1, Jane Doe #2, and Jane Doe #3 to Answer Deposition Questions at 1).

[159] 920-DC-00000721-22 (Agreed Protection Order of Dec. 12, 1997).

[160] 920-DC-00000978-82 (Plaintiff's Notice Duces Tecum of the Deposition upon Oral Examination of [Jane Doe #5]).

[161] Ms. Wright was the political supporter of President Clinton who was responsible for responding to "other women" allegations during the 1992 campaign. See Lois Romano, On the Warpath for Clinton, Wash. Post, Sept. 21, 1992, at D3.

[162] 1414-DC-00001099-102, 104-08, 112-13 (Wright 12/15/97 Depo. at 91-101, 112-26, 143-46).

previously ordered deposition."[163] In the order, Judge Merhige ordered the deposition to proceed on January 2, 1998. (As explained below, however, Ms. Willey's deposition actually occurred on January 11, 1998.)

That same day, December 16, 1997, Ms. Jones's attorneys served the President's lawyers with a motion to compel the President to answer Ms. Jones's first set of requests for admissions and her third set of interrogatories, and another motion to compel him to respond to her first set of requests for the production of documents.[164] (The first set of requests for admissions had been served on the President on October 8, 1997; he had answered in part on November 10, 1997, but had objected to Requests #51-65 (having to do with "other women"). The third set of interrogatories had been served on the President on October 13, 1997, and partially answered by him on November 12, 1997. The first set of requests for the production of documents was served on the President on October 1, 1997, and partially answered by him on November 17, 1997.)

Meanwhile, in New York City, the President's lawyers deposed two book publishers who had contacts with affiliates of Ms. Jones: Judith T. Regan, the president and publisher of Regan Books,[165] and Adrian Z. Zackheim, an employee of publisher

---

[163] DE-DC-00000215-16 (Order of Dec. 16, 1997, at 1).

[164] 1414-DC-00001237-43 (Plaintiff's Motion to Compel Production of Documents or, in the Alternative, Motion for In Camera Inspection).

[165] 1414-DC-00001224-35 (Regan 12/1/6/97 Depo.).

HarperCollins.[166] (The next day, December 17, 1998, they deposed literary agent Scott Waxman, asking him about his contacts with affiliates of Ms. Jones and about his involvement in a possible book about Ms. Jones.[167])

Also on December 16, Mitchell S. Ettinger, one of the President's lawyers, received Ms. Jones's second request for documents and items.[168] The Requests commanded the President to produce documents that concerned "Monica Lewisky [sic]" and others.[169]

According to Monica Lewinsky, that night at about 2:00 a.m., (now Wednesday, December 17, 1997), the President called and suggested the possibility that she could avoid a deposition by filing an affidavit.[170] Ms. Lewinsky testified that the President advised her that she could always say that she was delivering papers or visiting Betty Currie when she came to the White House.[171]

On Thursday, December 18, 1997, Judge Wright granted Ms. Jones's motion to compel Jane Does #1-3 to testify at

---

[166] 1414-DC-00001214-23 (Zackheim 12/16/97 Depo.).

[167] 1414-DC-00001131-49 (Waxman 12/17/97 Depo.).

[168] 1414-DC-00001534-46 (Second Set of Requests from Plaintiff to Defendant Clinton for Production of Documents and Things).

[169] 1414-DC-00001539 (Second Set of Requests from Plaintiff to Defendant Clinton for Production of Documents and Things at 6).

[170] Lewinsky 8/6/98 GJ at 123.

[171] Id. at 124.

depositions.[172] The order "clarif[ied] the factual predicate that [Ms. Jones] must . . . establish[] with each deponent prior to inquiring into alleged sexual activity."[173] This factual predicate could be established by a showing that the deponents had an existing or potential employment nexus to the President.[174] The order stated, however, that in the absence of any state employment connection, Ms. Jones's attorneys' ability to establish a nexus to state troopers did not itself permit Ms. Jones's attorneys to ask questions about any sexual activity between the President and the Jane Does.[175] Rather, Ms. Jones's attorneys could ask the Jane Does

> whether they have ever discussed with Governor or President Clinton the possibility of employment with either state or federal government or whether they have ever applied for such employment or whether he ever offered such employment. If the answer to any of these questions is in the affirmative, then counsel may continue the deposition by asking the personal and potentially embarrassing questions concerning their alleged sexual relationship with President Clinton.[176]

---

[172] 920-DC-00000517-25 (Order of Dec. 18, 1997).

[173] 920-DC-00000518 (Order of Dec. 18, 1997, at 2).

[174] 920-DC-00000520 (Order of Dec. 18, 1997, at 4). Judge Wright's December 18, 1997, Order referred only to state employment, because it considered only discovery of women the President allegedly had sexual relations with before he became President. Judge Wright's December 11, 1997, Order, however, had established that information about alleged "other women" who were federal employees since Mr. Clinton became President would also be discoverable.

[175] 920-DC-00000521 (Order of Dec. 18, 1997, at 5).

[176] 920-DC-00000522 (Order of Dec. 18, 1997, at 6).

In this same order, Judge Wright indicated that not all discoverable evidence was necessarily admissible, and that if the case went to trial, Judge Wright "anticipate[d] limiting the amount of time and number of witnesses that will be spent on issues of alleged sexual activity of both the President and the plaintiff (should such matters otherwise be deemed admissible)."[177] Judge Wright made clear, however, that "the issue [at hand was] one of discovery, not admissibility of evidence at trial. Discovery, as all counsel know, by its very nature takes unforseen twists and turns and goes down numerous paths, and whether those paths lead to the discovery of admissible evidence often simply cannot be predetermined."[178]

On this same date, December 18, 1997, Jane Doe #5 received a subpoena.[179]

Dec. 19-24, 1997: **Ms. Lewinsky subpoenaed, then meets with Vernon Jordan and Frank Carter; Mr. Carter informs the President's lawyers of his plan to file a motion to quash Ms. Lewinsky's subpoena; the President answers interrogatories #10-11**

Ms. Lewinsky was served with a subpoena duces tecum in the Jones case on Friday, December 19, 1997,[180] which required her to

---

177 920-DC-00000523 (Order of Dec. 18, 1997, at 7).

178 920-DC-00000523-24 (Order of Dec. 18, 1997, at 7-8).

179 920-DC-00000970-72 (Subpoena in a Civil Case). The subpoena was issued on December 11, 1997. 920-DC-00000970 (Subpoena in a Civil Case)

180 Lewinsky 8/6/98 GJ at 128; Harte 4/17/98 Int. at 1. The subpoena was signed and dated on Wednesday, December 17, 1997.

appear, and be deposed, on January 23, 1998. The subpoena also required Ms. Lewinsky to produce a number of items, including all gifts she had received from the President. After she received the subpoena, Ms. Lewinsky met with Vernon Jordan.[181]

On Monday, December 22, 1997, Ms. Lewinsky met Mr. Jordan at his office, and together they went to Frank Carter's office.[182] Ms. Lewinsky retained Frank Carter as her attorney to represent her in the Jones matter.[183]

The following day, Tuesday, December 23, 1997, Mr. Carter met with the President's personal attorneys. The President's attorneys informed Mr. Carter that other witnesses had filed motions to quash and offered to provide him with assistance.[184]

That same day, December 23, 1997, in obedience to Judge Wright's order of December 11, 1997, the President through his lawyers served a second set of supplemental responses to Ms. Jones's second set of interrogatories (those originally served on him on October 1, 1997) and the President verified that he had "read the . . . supplemental responses to Plaintiff's Second Set of Interrogatories and declare[d] under penalty of

921-DC-00000792-95 (Subpoena in a Civil Case).

181 Lewinsky 8/6/98 GJ at 129; V004-DC-00000172 (Akin, Gump visitor logs).

182 Lewinsky 8/6/98 GJ at 138-39.

183 Carter 6/18/98 GJ at 12, 14.

184 Carter 6/18/98 GJ at 39-42.

perjury that they are true and correct to the best of my knowledge and belief."[185]

The President's responses were limited in scope to the information required by Judge Wright in that order, in that they related only to events since May 8, 1986, and individuals who were state or federal employees, or whose liaisons with then-Governor Clinton were facilitated by State Troopers assigned to his security detail.[186]

Within these limits, however, the President answered Interrogatories #10 & 11, which asked about his actual, and proposed, sexual relations with other women. The President answered "None" to both.[187] With regard to Interrogatory #17, which asked the President to name each and every person whom he asked to arrange a private meeting with another woman at a location other than his office at any time, the President stated that he "has attended literally hundred of meetings . . . and cannot recall which, if any, meetings were attended only by himself and a federal or state female employee at a location other than his office."[188]

---

[185] 849-DC-00000066-70(President Clinton's Supplemental Responses to Plaintiff's Second Set of Interrogatories); 849-DC-00000069 (Verification).

[186] 849-DC-00000066 (President Clinton's Supplemental Responses to Plaintiff's Second Set of Interrogatories at 1).

[187] 849-DC-00000067 (President Clinton's Supplemental Responses to Plaintiff's Second Set of Interrogatories at 2).

[188] 849-DC-00000067 (President Clinton's Supplemental Responses to Plaintiff's Second Set of Interrogatories at 2).

The next day, Wednesday, December 24, 1997, Ms. Jones's attorneys filed a motion asking Judge Wright to reconsider her December 18, 1997, ruling ordering the Jane Does to testify but placing certain limits upon the scope of the questioning by requiring the Jones attorneys to establish a "factual predicate" for their questions and placing certain other restrictions on discovery.[189] The motion also complained of "dilatory, obstructionist tactics" used by lawyers for the President and Mr. Ferguson, including coaching of witnesses as to what other witnesses have said and making inappropriate "speaking objections" during depositions.[190]

Dec. 30-31, 1997: **Mr. Bennett concedes that "sex-for-jobs" is "fair game"; Ms. Jones's attorneys ask for sanctions.**

On Tuesday, December 30, 1997, Judge Wright held a hearing with counsel for all parties.[191] During the hearing, Judge Wright discussed Ms. Jones's motion December 24, 1997, motion for reconsideration of her ruling limiting the scope of the depositions of Jane Doc #1-3, but indicated that she was not yet ready to rule on the motion. Judge Wright also warned Mr. Bennett and Mr. Ferguson's lawyer (Bill Bristow) about their interrupting and disrupting depositions, and threatened to lift

---

[189] 1414-DC-00001015-62 (Plaintiff's Motion to Reconsider Court's December 18, 1997 Order).

[190] 1414-DC-00001024 (Plaintiff's Motion to Reconsider Court's December 18, 1997 Order at 10).

[191] 921-DC-00000711 (Clerk's Minutes); 1414-DC-00001445-1505 (Telephone Conference 12/30/97 Tr.).

the restrictions on "other women" discovery if their behavior did not improve.[192]

Mr. Bennett in turn warned that he was ready for a "free-for-all" consisting of 30-40 rebuttal witnesses if Ms. Jones's attorneys opposed "a ruling from the Court that the probative value of the sex life of Mr. Clinton and the sex life of Ms. Jones is far out weighed by other considerations."[193]

Mr. Bennett asserted that he would "really oppose" the efforts of Ms. Jones's attorneys attempts to "show that Bill Clinton is not a faithful husband. And I think we have to have a conference devoted to how far you're going to let them go on some of this stuff."[194] Mr. Bennett did concede, however, that questions related to sex-for-jobs would be "fair game."[195] Mr. Bennett also commented about Ms. Jones's sexual history compared to the President's sexual history: "Frankly, . . . if you unleash every deposition that's been taken to date, Paula Jones makes Bill Clinton look like a choir boy."[196]

---

[192] 1414-DC-00001450, 66 (Telephone Conference 12/30/97 Tr. at 6, 22).

[193] 1414-DC-00001473 (Telephone Conference 12/30/97 Tr. at 29).

[194] 1414-DC-00001480 (Telephone Conference 12/30/97 Tr. at 36).

[195] 1414-DC-00001494 (Telephone Conference 12/30/97 Tr. at 50).

[196] 1414-DC-00001496 (Telephone Conference 12/30/97 Tr. at 52).

Judge Wright explained that Ms. Jones's attorneys would at trial have to limit their evidence regarding "other women," but that some such evidence might be admissible: "I will not permit you to spend a lot of court time on this business about of [sic] other women. I do believe it is relevant and I will let you get some evidence in on that, but you're going to have to pick your evidence carefully."[197] Judge Wright also explained that although she had "permitted in the answers to interrogatories some pretty embarrassing questions," she would "require the President's deposition to be tailored"; nonetheless, she made clear that she would not limit it to "stuff that's not embarrassing."[198]

Also on December 30, 1997, Ms. Jones's attorneys moved to sanction the President's attorneys for leaks and for violating Rule 30(d)(1), which provides that "[a]ny objection to evidence during a deposition shall be stated concisely and in a non-argumentative and non-suggestive answer."[199] The attorneys argued that "[c]ounsel for Defendant Clinton has, during the depositions, frequently used their prerogative to object as an excuse to make arguments, 'coaching' non-party deponents and

---

[197] 1414-DC-00001491 (Telephone Conference 12/30/97 Tr. at 47) (emphasis added).

[198] 1414-DC-00001493 (Telephone Conference 12/30/97 Tr. at 49).

[199] Fed. R. Civ. P. 30(d)(1); 1414-DC-00001063-1168 (Plaintiff's Motion for a Protective Order and Sanctions Based on Violations of the Confidentiality Order and Rule 30(d)(1)).

their counsel to answer evasively and suggesting grounds for refusing to answer."[200]

Jan. 2-7, 1998: **Jane Doe #2 testifies; Jane Doe #5 signs an affidavit; Ms. Lewinsky meets with Frank Carter; Jane Doe #5 files a motion to quash her subpoena; Ms. Lewinsky signs her affidavit.**

On Friday, January 2, 1998, Jane Doe #2 testified at a deposition. Jane Doe #2 denied that she ever engaged in any "sexual activity" with the President.[201]

On the same day, Jane Doe #5 signed an affidavit in which she denied that the President made "unwelcome sexual advances toward me in the late seventies."[202] (On April 8, 1998, however, Jane Doe #5 stated to OIC investigators that this affidavit was false.[203])

On Monday, January 5, 1998, Ms. Lewinsky met with her attorney, Francis Carter, to discuss her subpoena in the Jones case.[204] That same day, Ms. Jones's attorneys served the President's attorneys with notice that the deposition of Jane Doe

---

[200] 1414-DC-00001069 (Plaintiff's Motion for a Protective Order and Sanctions Based on Violations of the Confidentiality Order and Rule 30(d)(1) at 7).

[201] 920-DC-00000629-53 (Jane Doe #2 1/2/98 Depo. at 59).

[202] 920-DC-00000962-63 (Jane Doe #5 1/2/98 Aff.).

[203] Jane Doe #5 4/8/98 Int. at 6.

[204] 902-DC-00000232 (Mr. Carter's diary); 902-DC-00000037 (Mr. Carter's bill).

#3 was scheduled for Tuesday, January 20, 1998.[205] Jane Doe #5, by her attorneys, moved for a protective order and to quash the subpoena.[206] Jane Doe #5's counsel attached to the motion an affidavit in which Jane Doe #5 attested that she did not "possess any information that could possibly be relevant to the allegations advanced by Paula Corbin Jones or which could lead to admissible evidence in her case."[207]

Ms. Lewinsky signed her affidavit the next day, Wednesday, January 7, 1998.[208] That same day, January 7, 1998, the President's attorneys served and filed an opposition to Ms. Jones's attorneys' December 24, 1997, motion to reconsider Judge Wright's December 18, 1997, order requiring a "factual predicate" in order to question the Jane Does.[209] The President's lawyers also asked Judge Wright not to limit discovery of Ms. Jones's sexual history.[210]

---

205 920-DC-00000818-822 (Plaintiff's Second Amended Notice Duces Tecum of the Deposition upon Oral Examination of [Jane Doe #3]).

206 920-DC-00000983-93 (Motion for a Protective Order and to Quash Subpoena Duces Tecum and Deposition Subpoena).

207 920-DC-00000992 (Motion for a Protective Order and to Quash Subpoena Duces Tecum and Deposition Subpoena at exhibit B).

208 849-DC-00000314-16 (Lewinsky 1/7/98 Aff.).

209 1414-DC-00001169-87 (President Clinton's Opposition to Plaintiff's Motion to Reconsider the Court's December 18, 1997 Order).

210 1414-DC-00001183-84 (President Clinton's Opposition to Plaintiff's Motion to Reconsider the Court's December 18, 1997 Order at 15-16).

Jan. 8, 1998: **Judge Wright orders the President to answer "other women" interrogatories; Judge Wright denies Jane Doe #5's motion to quash**

On Thursday, January 8, 1998 Judge Wright issued an order addressing outstanding discovery motions in the case, including the President's motion to compel Ms. Jones to answer certain interrogatories and document requests, and Ms. Jones's motion[211] to compel the President to finish answering her third set of interrogatories, and first set of requests for admissions, and to produce certain documents and things.[212] (Ms. Jones's motion of December 17 had, among other things, complained that the President had not yet answered her requests for admission -- numbered 51-65[213] -- as to whether, as Governor, he ever "had sexual relations with certain women (other than his wife) in meetings that were arranged, facilitated, concealed, and/or assisted by at least one member of the Arkansas State Police and that some of these women were or became employees of the State of Arkansas (or an agency thereof)."[214])

Judge Wright's order partially granted Ms. Jones's motion to compel, explaining:

---

211 1414-DC-0000926-32 (Plaintiff's Motion to Compel Answers to Plaintiff's First Set of Requests for Admissions and Third Set of Interrogatories to Defendant Clinton).

212 921-DC-00000736-44 (Order of Jan. 8, 1998).

213 1414-DC-0000927 (Plaintiff's Motion to Compel Answers to Plaintiff's First Set of Requests for Admissions and Third Set of Interrogatories to Defendant Clinton at 2).

214 921-DC-00000738 (Order of Jan. 8, 1998, at 3).

> The Court has already ruled that questions regarding whether the President, as Governor of Arkansas, had sexual relations with certain women (other than his wife) in meetings that were arranged, facilitated, concealed, and/or assisted by at least one member of the Arkansas State Police and whether some of these women were or became employees of the State of Arkansas (or an agency thereof) are within the scope of the issues in this case. To the extent the President denies these allegations, he can so state without any undue burden. To the extent answers to such question [sic] require something other than an outright denial, the Court finds that such answers may not necessarily be redundant to any previous answers the President has given to such questions and, further, that such answers may be relevant to the issues in this case and may lead to the discovery of admissible evidence. Accordingly, the Court finds that plaintiff's motion to compel on this point should be granted.[215]

Judge Wright also held that "the President should answer interrogatories requesting full identifying information (names, addresses, and telephone numbers) concerning every person who has discoverable information relevant to this case and of every person to whom the President has made statements concerning plaintiff's allegations."[216] Judge Wright therefore directed the President "to answer plaintiff's first set of requests for admissions and third set of interrogatories on or before January 15, 1998."[217]

---

[215] 921-DC-00000739 (Order of Jan. 8, 1998, at 4) (emphasis added).

[216] 921-DC-00000739-40 (Order of Jan. 8, 1998, at 4-5).

[217] 921-DC-00000740 (Order of Jan. 8, 1998, at 5). The court also ordered the President to respond to Ms. Jones's first set of requests for production of documents to the extent of revealing the total amount of legal fees he had so far incurred. 921-DC-00000741 (Order of Jan. 8, 1998, at 6).

This same order of January 8, 1998, also required Ms. Jones to respond to interrogatories and to produce documents to the President by January 15, 1997.[218]

Later this same day, January 8, 1998, Judge Wright conducted a hearing at which counsel from all parties participated by phone. During the hearing, Judge Wright informed all counsel about the order described in first paragraph of this subsection.[219] Judge Wright also denied Jane Doe #5's motion to quash her subpoena for a deposition.[220]

During this same hearing, Judge Wright also expressed general concern about how the depositions had proceeded. As the Clerk put it, Judge Wright "again discusse[d] with counsel [her] concern of excess objections and advantage taken by [defendants'] counsel on Court's ruling on limitations of scope of deposition; [the Court] believes it should enforce Rule 30(d)(1)."[221]

---

[218] 921-DC-00000736-38 (Order of Jan. 8, 1998, at 1-3).

[219] 921-DC-00000751-52 (Clerk's Minutes). The clerk of the court then mailed a copy of the order to all parties. 921-DC-00000743 (Mailing Certificate of Clerk)

[220] 921-DC-00000751 (Clerk's Minutes at 1).

[221] 921-DC-00000752 (Clerk's Minutes at 2). Federal Rule of Civil Procedure 30(d)(1) states:

> Any objection to evidence during a deposition shall be stated concisely and in a non-argumentative and non-suggestive manner. A party may instruct a deponent not to answer only when necessary to preserve a privilege, to enforce a limitation on evidence directed by the court, or to present a motion under paragraph (3).

Fed. R. Civ. P. 30(d)(3) governs depositions "conducted in bad faith or in such manner as unreasonably to annoy, embarrass, or oppress the deponent or party" and directs parties or deponents

Jan. 9-12, 1998: **Judge Wright modifies the required factual predicate for "other women" questions; Jane Doe #5 testifies; Kathleen Willey testifies.**

On Friday, January 9, 1998, Judge Wright issued an order granting in part and denying in part Ms. Jones's motion to reconsider the December 18, 1997 Order.[222] Judge Wright granted the part of Ms. Jones's motion regarding questioning Jane Does #1-3 about potential state employment, holding that if the Jane Does admitted whether they had ever applied for a state job, ever discussed employment with President Clinton, or had reason to believe that President Clinton knew of their interest in such employment, then Ms. Jones could ask about sexual activities with the President.[223]

Judge Wright denied the portion of Ms. Jones's attorneys' motion with regard to the "trooper nexus." (Ms. Jones's attorneys had sought reconsideration of Judge Wright's ruling that "the state trooper nexus is insufficient alone to permit the sexual activities question because the depositions, as they now read, do not support plaintiff's allegations of a pattern or practice of sexual harassment."[224]) Ms. Jones's attorneys claimed that the trooper ruling would preclude her from establishing her claim for sex discrimination. Judge Wright disagreed, and found

---

to file a motion with the district court if a part conducts such an improper deposition.

[222] 1414-DC-00001188-92 (Order of Jan. 9, 1998).

[223] 1414-DC-00001189 (Order of Jan. 9, 1998 at 2).

[224] 1414-DC-00001189 (Order of Jan. 9, 1998 at 2).

that Ms. Jones did not have a viable sex discrimination claim, only a sexual harassment claim. Judge Wright ruled that the use of troopers did not establish an adequate nexus absent an unwelcome sexual contact.[225]

Finally, Judge Wright warned the parties about improper deposition objections and witness coaching: "any objection to evidence during a deposition 'shall be stated concisely and in a non-argumentative and non-suggestive manner,' and without any coaching of the witness as to what previous discovery may or may not have disclosed."[226]

On January 9, 1998, Jane Doe #5 testified at a deposition.[227] She testified that if she previously had said that the President had sexually assaulted her, "it was untrue."[228] Jane Doe #5 also testified that an affidavit she had signed was true and correct.[229] The affidavit denied that "Mr. Clinton had made unwelcome sexual advances toward me in the late seventies."[230] On Sunday, January 11, 1998, Kathleen Willey testified at a

---

[225] 1414-DC-00001191 (Order of Jan. 9, 1998, at 4).

[226] 1414-DC-00001192 (Order of Jan. 9, 1998, at 5) (quoting Fed. R. Civ. P. 30(d)(1)).

[227] 920-DC-00000922-29 (Jane Doe #5 1/9/98 Depo.).

[228] 920-DC-00000926 (Jane Doe #5 1/9/98 Depo. at 15-16).

[229] 920-DC-00000928 (Jane Doe #5 1/9/98 Depo. at 22-23).

[230] 920-DC-00000962 (Jane Doe #5 1/2/98 Aff. at 1).

deposition in the United States District Court in Richmond, Virginia.[231]

Jan. 12, 1998: **Hearing about discovery, evidence at trial, deposition of the President; Frank Carter speaks with Ms. Jones's attorney; Judge Wright urges the parties to settle.**

On Monday, January 12, 1998 -- as Frank Carter spoke to Mr. Pyke, one of Ms. Jones's attorneys, and attempted to persuade him not to depose Ms. Lewinsky -- Judge Wright held a lengthy hearing to discuss witness issues, the President's upcoming January 17, 1998, deposition, and the evidence that the parties planned to put on at trial.[232] During the hearing, which lasted almost the entire day, Judge Wright asked the parties to discuss the proof they each planned to introduce at trial.[233]

Ms. Jones's counsel went first, and explained that there were several different categories of witnesses that they intended to call at trial. Ms. Jones's counsel told Judge Wright that some of these witnesses "relate to the pattern and practice issue, the habit evidence. And that, obviously, is focused on his harassment of other women. And there are witnesses that relate to the issue that I will generally describe as the cover-up, the suppression of evidence, the intimidation of witnesses in

---

231 DE-DC-00000217-27 (Willey 1/11/98 Depo. excerpts).

232 921-DC-00000770-72 (Clerk's Minutes); 1414-DC-00001291-1444 (Hearing 1/12/98 Tr.).

233 The hearing began at 10:25 a.m. and ended at 4:05 p.m. (with breaks throughout the day). 1414-DC-00001291-1444 (Hearing 1/12/98 Tr.).

a concerted, systematic effort to prevent our client and others like her from developing cases that they might bring."[234]

Ms. Jones's counsel then named the "other women" he planned to call at trial:

MR FISHER: They would include . . . [Jane Doe #2], Monica Lewinsky . . . .

THE COURT: Can you tell me who she is?

MR. FISHER: Yes, your Honor.

THE COURT: I never heard of her.

MR. FISHER: She's the young woman who worked in the White House for a period of time and was later transferred to a job in the Pentagon. . . . [And the other women are Jane Doe #7, Jane Doe #5] . . . Gennifer Flowers . . . [and there] are three other women who are possibilities in our thinking at this point . . . .

* * * *

THE COURT: Well, I'm going to have something to say about all of this stuff. But I'm going -- I'm letting you put on -- tell me what evidence you want to put on. Go ahead . . . .

* * * *

THE COURT: . . . . I'm literally asking the plaintiff and you to put out what evidence you've got. In other words, this is a civil case. I don't want to be -- I'm not -- I'm not going -- counting surprise, and I don't want the President's precious time to be occupied in a discovery deposition with a lot of stuff that either is a dead end street or I'm not going to let it in. . . .

* * * *

---

234 1414-DC-00001326 (Hearing 1/12/98 Tr. at 36).

> Now, I have repeatedly said that the plaintiff will not be able to put on all the evidence that she has about what -- about Mr. Clinton's sexual proclivities. I've also said that she can put on some. . . .

* * * *

> [Addressing the plaintiff] It would make me very happy if you just stuck to . . . the direct knowledge witnesses. And I know that the Rules of Evidence don't require you to do that, and in fact, the Rules of Evidence in harassment cases -- and I'm not citing any authority right now for it, but I know in harassment cases, frequently, court's [sic] permit other bad acts, other volatile acts, that kind of thing. And I'm also aware that in sexual assault cases, the Rules of Evidence promulgated by the Violence Against Women Act has certainly opened it up. So I can't say that you can't call any of the witnesses in group B [the pattern and practice issue witnesses].[235]

Judge Wright then explained why she was concerned about certain witnesses Ms. Jones's attorneys planned to call, such as a trooper with a memory of only assisting the President with visits with "nameless" women,[236] "other women" who did not have an employment nexus to the President,[237] and Jane Doe #5.[238] Judge Wright indicated that Ms. Jones's attorneys proposed to use "just too many witnesses," and told Ms. Jones's attorneys that she was planning on limiting the number of witnesses at trial.[239] For

---

235 1414-DC-00001327-33 (Hearing 1/12/98 Tr. at 37-43).

236 1414-DC-00001334 (Hearing 1/12/98 Tr. at 44).

237 1414-DC-00001335 (Hearing 1/12/98 Tr. at 45).

238 1414-DC-00001339 (Hearing 1/12/98 Tr. at 49).

239 1414-DC-00001335 (Hearing 1/12/98 Tr. at 45).

purposes of discovery, however, Judge Wright permitted Ms. Jones's attorneys to ask the President "about people whose -- you know, whose names have been given you or people whom you have, you know, a reasonable basis for asking about."[240] Judge Wright also expressed concern about leaks to "Mr. Drudge" and the "Drudge report."[241]

During the hearing, Judge Wright encouraged the parties to settle the case, and she offered to speak directly with Ms. Jones about this prospect. Judge Wright made several comments to Ms. Jones's counsel about the strength of Ms. Jones's case. Judge Wright warned Ms. Jones's lawyers that she thought "it's unlikely that a jury will find for [Ms. Jones] if this matter goes to trial."[242]

Judge Wright also cautioned that settlement might be in the President's best interests, in part because "if this thing does go to trial, some of the Jane Does will be mentioned not as Jane Doe but as someone else, and some of the people who have been his friends will be very embarrassed and tainted for life as a result of embarrassing testimony about them."[243] Judge Wright reminded the parties that "I have repeatedly said that the plaintiff will not be able to put on all the evidence that she has about what --

---

240 1414-DC-00001336 (Hearing 1/12/98 Tr. at 46).

241 1414-DC-00001299-300 (Hearing 1/12/98 Tr. at 9-10).

242 1414-DC-00001314 (Hearing 1/12/98 Tr. at 24).

243 1414-DC-00001315 (Hearing 1/12/98 Tr. at 25).

about Mr. Clinton's sexual proclivities. I've also said that she can put on some."[244]

Judge Wright discussed the President's deposition. She informed defense counsel that she was "not limiting the President's deposition" in the way that she limited the deposition of Jane Does #1-3.[245] Judge Wright also cautioned counsel about the matter and method of objections during the deposition:

> I do not want the President's deposition to read like Jane Doe 1's first deposition or Jane Doe 3's deposition or the Betsey Wright deposition.
>
> * * * *
>
> If you have an objection, you are to state your objection. And you're not going to be misleading in any way or coach the witness in any way following your objection . . . . And I don't want you, you know, holding up the Jane Doe 1, 2 and 3 depositions and pointing to some sentence in there and reading it out of context, because that's -- I've been burned on that, Mr. Ettinger. And I'm not going to have it from you anymore.
>
> * * * *
>
> I'm talking about from your side, from the defense side and the witnesses' lawyers.[246]

The hearing also involved discussion about the potential use of the President's deposition. Judge Wright asked defense

---

[244] 1414-DC-00001332 (Hearing 1/12/98 Tr. at 42).

[245] 1414-DC-00001407 (Hearing 1/12/98 Tr. at 117).

[246] 1414-DC-00001407-08 (Hearing 1/12/98 Tr. at 117-18). When Mr. Ettinger, one of the President's lawyers, objected to this characterization, Judge Wright stated that counsel for the witnesses were as culpable as other counsel for the defense, "if not more so." 1414-DC-00001408 (Hearing 1/12/98 Tr. at 118).

counsel whether the deposition would be a discovery deposition, rather than an evidence deposition:

> THE COURT: And the President's deposition, I assume is a discovery one and will not be used as an evidentiary deposition; is that correct?
>
> MR. BENNETT: Well, I don't know. I mean, that remains to be seen. I mean, what if on the date of the trial there's a world war? I mean, he --
>
> THE COURT: Let me suggest this. I want you to conduct this deposition with one thing in mind. I don't want anyone to make any strategic moves and later tell me that this is in reliance on what I'm about --
>
> MR. BENNETT: No.
>
> THE COURT: -- to say. But keep in mind that because it is possible that -- because he is the President, he might not be here.
>
> MR. BENNETT: And the Supreme Court said he didn't have to be.
>
> THE COURT: That's right. And I would never require him to be here -- that you might have to use his deposition as evidence.
>
> MR. BENNETT: That's correct.
>
> MR. FISHER: Exactly, Your Honor. We -- we intend to.[247]

---

[247] 1414-DC-00001425-26 (Hearing 1/12/98 Tr. at 135-36); <u>see also</u> Fed. R. Civ. P. 32(a)(3) (use of a deposition at a trial as substantive evidence).

Jan. 15, 1998: **<u>The President serves responses to document requests, interrogatories, and requests for admissions</u>**

On January 15, 1998, the President's attorneys served Ms. Jones's attorneys with the President's response to Ms. Jones's second set of document requests.[248] Requests #5-7 had asked the President to produce all documents and tangible things that related to "Monica Lewisky [sic]," and others.[249] In his response, the President objected to those requests, but stated that, notwithstanding his objections, he had "no documents" that would be responsive to the requests.[250]

The President's lawyers also served Ms. Jones's lawyers with the President's supplemental responses to Ms. Jones's first set of requests for admissions.[251] (Among these requests were Requests for Admissions 51-65, which had asked the President to admit or deny sexual relations with women other than Hillary Rodham Clinton and to admit or deny the use of state troopers for Governor Clinton's sexually-related encounters with "other

[248] V002-DC-00000093-116 (President Clinton's Responses to Plaintiff's Second Set of Document Requests).

[249] V002-DC-00000102-05 (President Clinton's Responses to Plaintiff's Second Set of Document Requests at 10-13)

[250] V002-DC-00000103-05 (President Clinton's Responses to Plaintiff's Second Set of Document Requests at 11-13).

[251] 849-DC-00000283-86 (President Clinton's Supplemental Responses to Plaintiff's First Set of Requests for Admissions).

women."[252]) The President objected to these requests, but then denied the suggested sexual activity.[253]

Finally, also on January 15, 1998, the President's lawyers served President Clinton's supplemental responses to Ms. Jones's third set of interrogatories and her first request for documents.[254] That same day, January 15, 1998, the President verified "under penalty of perjury" that these supplemental interrogatory responses were "true and correct to the best of my knowledge and belief."[255] The supplemental responses identified: (1) two individuals not previously identified who had discoverable information (Diane Evans of the AIDC and Linus Raines of the Excelsior Hotel); and (2) persons to whom the President had denied the May 1991 Excelsior Hotel-related allegations, including Vernon Jordan, Bruce Lindsey, George Stephanopoulos, Dee Dee Myers, and James Carville.[256] With respect to the documents sought -- namely, those concerning legal

---

[252] 849-DC-00000283-86 (President Clinton's Supplemental Responses to Plaintiff's First Set of Requests for Admissions); 849-DC-00000158-162 (First Set of Requests from Plaintiff to Defendant Clinton at 14-18).

[253] 849-DC-00000284 (President Clinton's Supplemental Response to Plaintiff's First Set of Requests for Admissions at 2).

[254] 849-DC-00000103-10 (President Clinton's Supplemental Responses to Plaintiff's Third Set of Interrogatories and Plaintiff's First Request for the Production Of Documents).

[255] 849-DC-00000109 (Verification).

[256] 849-DC-00000103-06 (President Clinton's Supplemental Responses to Plaintiff's Third Set of Interrogatories and Plaintiff's First Request for the Production Of Documents at 3-4).

fees -- the President objected to the request, but pursuant to court order revealed that his counsel had billed over $2.3 million as of January 15.[257]

Jan. 16, 1998: **President's lawyers notified of Jane Doe #3's deposition; Ms. Lewinsky moves to quash subpoena**

On Friday, January 16, 1998, Ms. Jones's attorneys served the President's lawyers with a notice scheduling Jane Doe #3's deposition for January 28, 1998.[258]

Also on Friday, January 16, 1998, Frank Carter, counsel for Ms. Lewinsky, filed a motion for a protective order and sought to quash her subpoena.[259] Mr. Carter indicated that he had spoken with Ms. Jones's counsel on January 12, 1998, and again on January 15, 1998, in an unsuccessful attempt to persuade Ms. Jones's counsel not to proceed with the Lewinsky deposition. Mr. Carter explained: "I sent [Ms. Jones's counsel] a letter emphasizing my former arguments for not going forward with the deposition and enclosing an Affidavit from Jane Doe #6 [Monica Lewinsky] about her lack of knowledge of relevant evidence for

---

[257] 849-DC-00000107 (President Clinton's Supplemental Responses to Plaintiff's Third Set of Interrogatories and Plaintiff's First Request for the Production Of Documents at 5).

[258] 920-DC-00000823-27 (Plaintiff's Third Amended Notice Duces Tecum Of The Deposition Upon Oral Examination Of [Jane Doe #3]).

[259] 1292-DC-00000657-60 (Motion of Jane Doe #6 for Protective Order and Motion to Quash); 1292-DC-00000661-86 (Memorandum in Support of Motion of Jane Doe #6 for Protective Order and Motion to Quash). The motion is file-stamped Tuesday, January 20, 1998. 850-DC-0000082 (Docket Sheet).

this case."[260] Because Ms. Jones's counsel had not acceded to this request, the motion asked Judge Wright to quash the subpoena and cancel Ms. Lewinsky's deposition because "[t]he deposition will not produce any relevant information and will be unreasonable and oppressive for Jane Doe #6."[261]

Jan. 17, 1998: **<u>The President's deposition</u>**

On Saturday, January 17, 1998, the President testified at a sworn deposition attended by Judge Wright.[262] As the deposition started, Judge Wright addressed the President's counsel's concerns regarding the scope of the President's deposition testimony. Judge Wright rejected the President's counsel's attempt to place new limits on the scope of deposition questioning. In so ruling, Judge Wright commented about the nature of the questions that the President would be asked: "Unfortunately, the nature of this case is such that people will be embarrassed."[263]

---

[260] 1292-DC-00000658-59 (Motion of Jane Doe #6 for Protective Order and Motion to Quash at 2-3).

[261] 1292-DC-00000657-58 (Motion of Jane Doe #6 for Protective Order and Motion to Quash at 1-2).

[262] 849-DC-00000351-585 (Clinton 1/17/98 Depo.).

[263] 849-DC-00000360 (Clinton 1/17/98 Depo. at 9).

Jan. 21-30, 1998: **Nathaniel Speights appears; OIC intervenes; Judge Wright excludes evidence about Ms. Lewinsky; another "other woman" testifies; discovery ends**

On Wednesday, January 21, 1998, Nate Speights entered his appearance as counsel for Monica Lewinsky, and requested that Mr. Carter withdraw as counsel.[264]

The next day, Thursday, January 22, 1998, Ms. Jones's attorneys served an opposition to Ms. Lewinsky's motion for a protective order.[265] Ms. Jones's counsel argued that "[t]he parties and the various Jane Does have briefed extensively the law governing discovery of 'other women' in this case and Plaintiff will not burden the record by repeating that briefing."[266] Ms. Jones's counsel asserted that "Plaintiff believes that many statements in [Monica Lewinsky]'s affidavit are not true and that Mr. Clinton or those acting on his behalf encouraged her to lie. Plaintiff is entitled to discovery to pursue these theories, including the deposition of [Monica Lewinsky]."[267]

---

[264] 921-DC-00000805 (Notice of Appearance for Nathaniel H. Speights).

[265] 921-DC-00000807-26 (Plaintiff's Statement in Opposition to Motion of Jane Doe #6 for Protective Order and Motion to Quash).

[266] 921-DC-00000807 (Plaintiff's Statement in Opposition to Motion of Jane Doe #6 for Protective Order and Motion to Quash at 1).

[267] 921-DC-00000807 (Plaintiff's Statement in Opposition to Motion of Jane Doe #6 for Protective Order and Motion to Quash at 1).

Later that day, Judge Wright conducted a hearing with counsel from all parties, and during part of the hearing, counsel for Monica Lewinsky. The Clerk's minutes reveal that during the hearing, Judge Wright denied Ms. Lewinsky's motion to quash. With regard to whether Ms. Lewinsky's deposition would proceed, the Clerk's minutes state:

> Court states same rule will apply as to other Jane Does with respect to deposition and questions to be asked of her. . . . Court takes up supplemental motion of whether Court should continue deposition pending resolution of criminal investigation and advises counsel it would deny and Jane Doe would have to attend deposition and tell truth and could invoke 5th if about to incriminate herself.
>
> * * * *
>
> After additional discussions, Court directs that deposition should go forth but grants motion to reschedule . . . .[268]

In connection with the permission to reschedule, on Thursday, January 22, 1998, Judge Wright issued an order that "indefinitely continued" Ms. Lewinsky's deposition.[269]

On Monday, January 26, 1998, the President's attorneys issued a subpoena to the Office of the Independent Counsel ("OIC") that requested that the OIC to produce all documents it had that related to Monica Lewinsky, Linda Tripp, and Lucianne S. Goldberg.[270]

---

[268] 921-DC-00000982 (Clerk's Minutes).

[269] 921-DC-00000827 (Order of Jan. 23, 1998).

[270] Letter from Robert S. Bennett to Kenneth W. Starr and attached subpoena, dated January 26, 1998.

The next day, Tuesday, January 27, 1998, the OIC filed a motion requesting a limited intervention in the Jones case so that the OIC could conduct its criminal investigation without interference.[271] Two days later, on Thursday, January 29, 1998, the OIC filed a motion to stay discovery in the Jones case, requesting Judge Wright to stay discovery pending resolution of the related criminal investigation.[272]

That same day, Thursday, January 29, 1998, Judge Wright held a hearing at which counsel for the parties and the OIC were present. Judge Wright issued an order later that day in which she observed that "OIC's motion comes with less than 48 hours left in the period for conducting discovery, the cutoff date being January 30, 1998." For this reason, Judge Wright stated that she was required to rule on the admissibility of the Monica Lewinsky evidence at that time. Citing Federal Rule of Evidence 403, which requires a judge to weigh the probative value of evidence against the prejudice it may cause, Judge Wright concluded:

> [Rule 403']s weighing process compels the conclusion that evidence concerning Monica Lewinsky should be excluded from the trial of this matter.
>
> The Court acknowledges that evidence concerning Monica Lewinsky might be relevant to the issues in this case. This Court would await resolution of the criminal investigation currently underway if the Lewinsky evidence were essential to the plaintiff's

---

[271] See Motion of the United States for Limited Intervention and for Modification of October 30, 1997 Protective Order.

[272] See Motion of the United States for Limited Intervention and a Stay of Discovery.

> case. The Court determines, however, that it is not essential to the core issues in this case. In fact, some of this evidence might even be inadmissable as extrinsic evidence under Rule 608(b) of the Federal Rules of Evidence. Admitting any evidence of the Lewinsky matter would frustrate the timely resolution of this case and would undoubtedly cause undue expense and delay.[273]

Judge Wright held, however, that her "ruling today does not preclude admission of any other evidence of alleged improper conduct occurring in the White House."[274]

As discovery closed, Ms. Jones's attorneys deposed another "other woman" on Friday, January 30, 1998.[275] She denied that she ever engaged in "sexual activity" with the President.[276]

Finally, Ms. Jones's attorneys filed another motion to compel discovery from the President on January 30, 1998. This last motion to compel argued that the President was withholding documents by using privilege claims.[277] The documents in question related to the 1992 Clinton presidential campaign, James Lyons, Betsey Wright, Gennifer Flowers, Jane Doe #4, "J. Palladino," and others.[278] Ms. Jones's lawyers alleged that Mr. Palladino's

---

273 Order of Jan. 29, 1998, at 2 Jones v. Clinton, No. LR-C-94-290 (emphasis in original).

274 Id.

275 920-DC-00001001-26 ("Other Woman" 1/30/98 Depo.).

276 920-DC-00001014 ("Other Woman" 1/30/98 Depo. at 76-77)

277 1414-DC-00001237-61 (Plaintiff's Motion to Compel Production of Documents or, in the Alternative, Motion for In Camera Inspection).

278 1414-DC-00001237-55 (Plaintiff's Motion to Compel Production of Documents or, in the Alternative, Motion for In

"assignment was to 'dig up dirt' on various women and to induce them not to disclose their sexual relationships with Defendant Clinton."[279]

Feb.-Apr. 1998: **Ms. Jones's lawyers fail to persuade Judge Wright to reconsider the exclusion of evidence about Ms. Lewinsky; Judge Wright grants summary judgment for the defendants**

On Tuesday, February 10, 1998, attorneys for Ms. Jones moved for reconsideration of Judge Wright's January 29, 1998, Order excluding testimony about Monica Lewinsky. Counsel for Ms. Jones argued that Judge Wright had erred in excluding the Monica Lewinsky testimony at this stage of the proceedings because, among other reasons, Rule 403 determinations should not be made before trial, Ms. Lewinsky's testimony was relevant to show a pattern and practice of behavior, and Ms. Lewinsky's testimony was relevant to demonstrate a pattern of suppressing evidence in the Jones case.[280]

A week later, on Tuesday, February 17, 1998, the President's attorneys filed a motion for summary judgment, with supporting

---

Camera Inspection).

[279] 1414-DC-00001239 (Plaintiff's Motion to Compel Production of Documents or, in the Alternative, Motion for In Camera Inspection at 3).

[280] Plaintiff's Motion for Reconsideration or, in the Alternative, for Section 1292(b) Certification of Order Excluding Evidence Concerning Monica Lewinsky, Jones v. Clinton, No. LR-C-94-290 (Feb. 10, 1998); Memorandum in Support of Plaintiff's Motion for Reconsideration or, in the Alternative, for Section 1292(b) Certification of Order Excluding Evidence Concerning Monica Lewinsky at 7-11, Jones v. Clinton, No. LR-C-94-290 (Feb. 10, 1998).

material.[281] The President's lawyers argued that "Plaintiff's purported 'other acts' evidence concerning other women . . . is irrelevant to resolution of this Motion, because plaintiff cannot establish that she herself suffered a cognizable injury pursuant to a claim for sexual harassment or outrage."[282] The President's lawyers added that "[t]hus, even if plaintiff had evidence with respect to other women that could be said to establish a 'pattern and practice' of sexual harassment -- which we vigorously contend she does not -- such evidence is not material to this summary judgment motion . . . ."[283] On Wednesday, March 4, 1998, Mr. Ferguson filed his motion for summary judgment.[284]

On Monday, March 9, 1998, Judge Wright issued an order denying Ms. Jones's motion for reconsideration of the decision to exclude the Monica Lewinsky evidence. The order provided in relevant part:

> The Court does not take the denial of plaintiff's motion for reconsideration lightly. The Court readily acknowledges that evidence of the Lewinsky matter might have been relevant to plaintiff's case and, as she argues, that such evidence might possibly have helped her establish, among other things, intent, absence of

---

[281] President Clinton's Motion for Summary Judgment, Jones v. Clinton, No. LR-C-94-290 (Feb. 17, 1998); Memorandum in Support of President Clinton's Motion for Summary Judgment, Jones v. Clinton, No. LR-C-94-290 (Feb. 17, 1998).

[282] Memorandum in Support of President Clinton's Motion for Summary Judgment at 3, Jones v. Clinton, No. LR-C-94-290 (Feb. 17, 1998).

[283] Id.

[284] Jones v. Clinton, 990 F. Supp. 657, 666 (E.D. Ark. 1998).

> mistake, motive, and habit on the part of the President. . . . Nevertheless, whatever relevance such evidence may otherwise have . . . it simply is not essential to the core issues in this case.[285]

On Friday, March 13, 1998, Ms. Jones's attorneys filed their opposition to the President's summary judgment motion. In the motion, Ms. Jones's attorneys argued that evidence of the President's treatment of other women, and his use of state troopers to facilitate relationships with other women, rendered summary judgment inappropriate and required the case to proceed to trial.[286]

On Wednesday, April 1, 1998, Judge Wright issued an order granting the defendants' motions for summary judgment and dismissed the case.[287] Judge Wright found that the Ms. Jones "failed to demonstrate that she has a case worthy of submitting to a jury."[288] The order concluded: "One final matter concerns alleged suppression of pattern and practice evidence. Whatever relevance such evidence may have to prove other elements of plaintiff's case, it does not have anything to do with the issues

---

[285] Jones v. Clinton, 993 F. Supp. 1217, 1222 (E.D. Ark. 1998) (emphases added).

[286] Plaintiff's Opposition to Defendant Clinton's Motion for Summary Judgment, Jones v. Clinton, No. LR-C-94-290 (Mar. 13, 1998).

[287] Jones v. Clinton, 990 F. Supp. 657 (E.D. Ark. 1998).

[288] Jones v. Clinton, 990 F. Supp. 657, 679 (E.D. Ark. 1998).

presented by the President's and Ferguson's motions for summary judgment."[289]

Ms. Jones appealed. The case is currently pending before the United States Court of Appeals for the Eighth Circuit.

[289] Jones v. Clinton, 990 F. Supp. 657, 678 (E.D. Ark. 1998).

Tab D

Map of the White House, West Wing

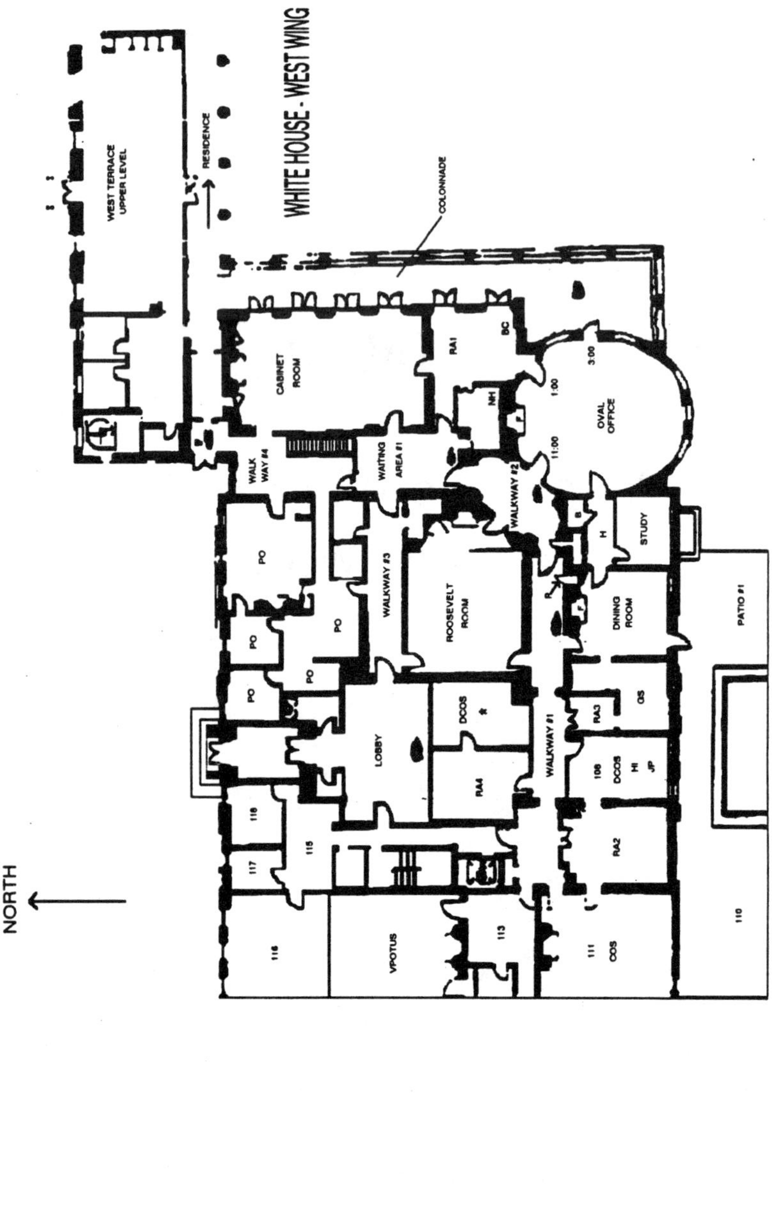
WHITE HOUSE - WEST WING
WEST TERRACE UPPER LEVEL
RESIDENCE
COLONNADE
CABINET ROOM
RA1
BC
OVAL OFFICE
3:00
1:00
11:00
NH
WALK WAY #4
WAITING AREA #1
WALKWAY #2
WALKWAY #3
ROOSEVELT ROOM
PO
PO
PO
PO
PO
H
STUDY
DINING ROOM
PATIO #1
LOBBY
DCOS
RA4
WALKWAY #1
RA3
GS
106 DCOS HI JP
RA2
118
117
115
116
VPOTUS
113
111 COS
110
NORTH

KEY TO THE WHITE HOUSE MAP

B	President's bathroom
BC	Betty Currie
DCOS	Deputy Chief of Staff
[redacted]	
F	Fireplace
GS	George Stephanopoulos
H	Hallway #1
HI	Harold Ickes
JP	John Podesta
NH	Nancy Hernreich
P	Pantry
PO	Press Office
RA1	Reception Area #1 (assistants to the President)
RA2	Reception Area #2 (assistants to Chief of Staff and Deputy Chief of Staff)
RA3	Reception Area #3 (assistants to George Stephanopoulos)
RA4	Reception Area #4 (assistants to Nancy Hernreich and others)
VPOTUS	Vice-President Al Gore
*	Erskine Bowles then Evelyn Lieberman then Sylvia Mathews
1:00	Oval Office door at 1:00 (to Reception Area#1)
3:00	Oval Office door at 3:00 (to Colonnade)
11:00	Oval Office door at 11:00 (to Walkway #3)
108	Deputy Chief of Staff (Harold Ickes then John Podesta)
111	Chief of Staff
113	Vice-President's assistants/secretaries
115	National Security Advisor and staff
116	National Security Advisor and staff
117	National Security Advisor and staff
118	National Security Advisor and staff

Tab E

Table of Monica Lewinsky White House Visits

RECORDED[1]
LEWINSKY VISITS TO THE WHITE HOUSE
6/7/96 - 12/28/97

Summary:
- **44 visits.**
- **12 visits in which record shows only the President, and no others, was present.**

No.	DATE	ENTRY TIME	EXIT TIME	REQUESTOR	VISITEE	PRESIDENT'S LOCATION	PURPOSE OF VISIT	REFERENCES
1	06/07/96 (Fri.)	12:51	13:03	Wozniak	Johnson	Oval Office (arrived at 13:05)	Deliver papers from Bacon to Johnson	V006-DC-00000007 (WAVES record) 827-DC-00000016 (Epass Entry Log) 827-DC-00000017 (Epass Exit Log) 968-DC-00000037 (President Notepad Log) Wozniak 3/5/98 Int. at 2
2	06/14/96 (Fri.)	16:51	No exit time logged	Hernreich	President Clinton	Oval Office	Attend radio address with Lewinsky family	V006-DC-00000007 (WAVES record) V006-DC-00002109 (Presidential Movement Log) V006-DC-00000534 (Radio Address Guest List)
3	06/18/96 (Tues.)	17:59	No exit time logged	Widdess	President Clinton	Oval Office Cabinet Room (arrived at 18:27) Oval Office (arrived at 19:29) Residence (arrived at 19:51)	Attend press picnic	V006-DC-00000007 (WAVES record) V006-DC-00002113 (Presidential Movement Log) V006-DC-00000473 (Press Picnic Guest List) Widdess Int. 2/19/98 at 2

[1] There is at least some record of each visit by Ms. Lewinsky to the White House during this time, but in many cases only incomplete information is available from White House personnel and the official White House logs. The information in this chart is derived solely from these logs and personnel. For a comprehensive list of all encounters between Ms. Lewinsky and President Clinton, see Tab F.

KEY:
- Requestor — The person at whose behest the visitor was cleared into the White House through the WAVES system.
- Visitee — The person whom the requestor listed as the person to be visited when requesting clearance for the Ms. Lewinsky.
- Purpose — The purpose recalled by the requestor or visitee during an interview with the OIC.
- References — The official White House logs that contain the information upon which this chart is based.
- Shaded Areas — Visits during which Ms. Lewinsky and the President were in the Oval Office area, and no one else was known to be present.

(See "Understanding the Evidence" section, Tab G, for details.)

4	08/29/96 (Thurs.)	15:06	15:47	Bobowick	Bobowick	Chicago	White House tour or radio address with Lewinsky family[2]	V006-DC-00000007 (WAVES record) 827-DC-00000017 (Epass Entry & Exit Logs) 968-DC-00000045 (Presidential Movement Logs) Bobowick 2/11/98 Int. at 3
5	08/29/96 (Thurs.)	17:15 (scheduled)	No exit time logged	Bobowick	Bobowick	Chicago	White House tour or radio address with Lewinsky family[2]	V006-DC-00000007 (WAVES record) 968-DC-00000045 (Presidential Movement Logs) Bobowick 2/11/98 Int. at 3
6	08/29/96 (Thurs.)	18:22	19:03	Raines	Raines	Chicago	No purpose recalled/known	V006-DC-00000007 (WAVES record) 827-DC-00000017 (Epass Entry & Exit Logs) 968-DC-00000045 (Presidential Movement Logs)
7	10/11/96 (Fri.)	12:49	13:49	Raines	Johnson	Oval Office (arrived at 12:40) South Grounds (arrived at 13:03)	No purpose recalled/known	V006-DC-00000007 (WAVES record) 827-DC-00000017 (Epass Entry & Exit Logs) 968-DC-00000048 (Presidential Movement Log)
8	10/24/96 (Thurs.)	07:42	10:11	Shaddix	Shaddix	Oval Office (arrived at 08:43) South Grounds (arrived at 09:00) Departed White House (at 09:05)	Visit Photo Office	V006-DC-00000007 (WAVES record) 827-DC-00000017 (Epass Entry & Exit Logs) 1234-DC-00000010 (Presidential Movement Log) Shaddix 2/24/98 Int. at 2

[2] Ms. Bobowick remembered clearing Ms. Lewinsky into the White House for a tour with her family and for a radio address with her family. She did not remember specific dates.

KEY:
- Requestor — The person at whose behest the visitor was cleared into the White House through the WAVES system.
- Visitee — The person whom the requestor listed as the person to be visited when requesting clearance for the Ms. Lewinsky.
- Purpose — The purpose recalled by the requestor or visitee during an interview with the OIC.
- References — The official White House logs that contain the information upon which this chart is based.
- Shaded Areas — Visits during which Ms. Lewinsky and the President were in the Oval Office area, and no one else was known to be present.

(See "Understanding the Evidence" section, Tab G, for details.)

9	12/17/96 (Tues.)	16:15	No exit time logged	Widdess	President Clinton	Oval Office Second Floor (arrived at 18:56)	Attend Christmas Party	V006-DC-00000007 (WAVES record) 968-DC-00000059 (Presidential Movement Log) 1222-DC-00000231 (Presidential Activity Report) V006-DC-00000505 (Christmas Party Guest List) Widdess 2/19/98 Int. at 2
10	12/17/96 (Tues.)	19:34	20:11	Raines	Raines	Second Floor	No purpose recalled/known	V006-DC-00000007 (WAVES record) 827-DC-00000017 (Epass Entry & Exit Logs) 968-DC-00000060 (Presidential Movement Log) 1222-DC-00000231 (Presidential Activity Report)
11	12/30/96 (Mon.)	13:01	13:43	Currie	Currie	Hilton Head, South Carolina	No purpose recalled/known	V006-DC-00000007 (WAVES record) 827-DC-00000017 (Epass Entry & Exit Logs) 968-DC-00000063 (Presidential Movement Log)
12	02/24/97 (Mon.)	09:38	10:32	Kessinger	Kessinger	Oval Office	Return borrowed photo	V006-DC-00000008 (WAVES record) 827-DC-00000018 (Epass Entry & Exit Logs) 968-DC-00000066 (Presidential Movement Log) Kessinger 2/24/98 Int. at 1-2
13	02/28/97 (Fri.)	17:48	19:07	Currie	Currie	Oval Office	Attend radio address	V006-DC-00000008 (WAVES record) 827-DC-00000018 (Epass Entry & Exit Logs) 968-DC-00000074 (Presidential Movement Log) V006-DC-00000536 (Radio Address Guest List)
14	03/13/97 (Thurs.)	10:01	10:15	Currie	Currie	North Carolina & Florida	No purpose recalled/known	V006-DC-00000008 (WAVES record) 827-DC-00000018 (Epass Entry & Exit Logs) 1222-DC-00000235 (Presidential Activity Report)
15	03/13/97 (Thurs.)	21:21	21:49	Raines	Raines	North Carolina & Florida	No purpose recalled/known	V006-DC-00000008 (WAVES record) 827-DC-00000018 (Epass Entry & Exit Logs) 1222-DC-00000235 (Presidential Activity Report)

KEY: Requestor — The person at whose behest the visitor was cleared into the White House through the WAVES system.
Visitee — The person whom the requestor listed as the person to be visited when requesting clearance for the Ms. Lewinsky.
Purpose — The purpose recalled by the requestor or visitee during an interview with the OIC.
References — The official White House logs that contain the information upon which this chart is based.
Shaded Areas — Visits during which Ms. Lewinsky and the President were in the Oval Office area, and no one else was known to be present.
(See "Understanding the Evidence" section, Tab G, for details.)

16	03/29/97 (Sat.)	14:03	15:16	Currie	Currie	Oval Office	No purpose recalled/known	V006-DC-00000008 (WAVES record) 827-DC-00000018 (Epass Entry & Exit Logs) V006-DC-00002130 (Presidential Movement Log)
17	04/15/97 (Tues.)	14:00 (schedule)	No exit time logged	Naplan	Naplan	New York	No purpose recalled/known	V006-DC-00000008 (WAVES record) 968-DC-00002318 (Press Schedule) Naplan 3/3/98 Int. at 2
18	04/16/97 (Wed.)	09:49	09:56	Currie	Currie	Residence	No purpose recalled/known	V006-DC-00000008 (WAVES record) 827-DC-00000018 (Epass Entry & Exit Logs) 968-DC-00000096 (Presidential Movement Log)
19	05/01/97 (Thurs.)	17:43	No exit time logged	Stott	Stott	Oval Office Residence (arrived at 18:40)	Press Office job interview	V006-DC-00000008 (WAVES record) 827-DC-00000018 (Epass Entry Log) 1234-DC-00000029 (Presidential Movement Log) Stott 2/27/98 Int. at 1
20	05/02/97 (Fri.)	19:57	20:21	Raines	Raines	Residence	No purpose recalled/known	V006-DC-00000008 (WAVES record) 827-DC-00000018 (Epass Entry & Exit Logs) 968-DC-00000112 (Presidential Movement Log)
21	05/24/97 (Sat.)	12:21	13:54	Currie	Currie	Oval Office (arrived at 11:59) Pool (arrived at 13:47) Oval Office Study (arrived at 13:50)	No purpose recalled/known	V006-DC-00000008 (WAVES record) 827-DC-00000018 (Epass Entry & Exit Logs) 1222-DC-00000242 (Presidential Activity Report)

KEY:
Requestor — The person at whose behest the visitor was cleared into the White House through the WAVES system.
Visitee — The person whom the requestor listed as the person to be visited when requesting clearance for the Ms. Lewinsky.
Purpose — The purpose recalled by the requestor or visitee during an interview with the OIC.
References — The official White House logs that contain the information upon which this chart is based.
Shaded Areas — Visits during which Ms. Lewinsky and the President were in the Oval Office area, and no one else was known to be present.
(See "Understanding the Evidence" section, Tab G, for details.)

22	05/30/97 (Fri.)	15:32	16:01	Dimel	Dimel	Oval Office	Initial NSC job interview	V006-DC-00000008 (WAVES record) 827-DC-00000018 (Epass Entry & Exit Logs) 968-DC-00000120 (Presidential Movement Log) Dimel 2/18/98 Int. at 1
23	06/11/97 (Wed.)	10:58	12:04	Dimel	Dimel	Oval Office	Follow-up NSC job interview	V006-DC-00000008 (WAVES record) 827-DC-00000018 (Epass Entry & Exit Logs) 968-DC-00000121 (Presidential Movement Log) Dimel 2/18/98 at 1
24	06/16/97 (Mon.)	14:47	16:11	Croft	Croft	Oval Office	Marsha Scott interview	V006-DC-00000008 (WAVES record) 827-DC-00000018 (Epass Entry & Exit Logs) 968-DC-00000132 (Presidential Movement Log) Scott 3/19/98 GJ at 28-29
25	06/24/97 (Tues.)	18:59	19:19	Currie	Currie	Army Navy Country Club	No purpose recalled/known	V006-DC-00000008 (WAVES record) 827-DC-00000018 (Epass Entry & Exit Log) 1234-DC-00000033 (Presidential Movement Log)
26	07/04/97 (Fri.)	08:51	No exit time logged	Currie	Currie	Oval Office South Grounds (arrived at 11:08)	No purpose recalled/known	V006-DC-00000008 (WAVES record) 827-DC-00000018 (Epass Entry Log) 1222-DC-00000249 (Presidential Activity Report)
27	07/14/97 (Mon.)	21:34	23:23	Currie	Currie	Oval Office (arrived at 21:28) Appointment Secretary's Office (arrived at 21:41) Residence (arrived at 23:25)	No purpose recalled/known	V006-DC-00000008 (WAVES record) 827-DC-00000018 (Epass Entry & Exit Logs) V006-DC-00002142 (Presidential Movement Log) 1222-DC-00000251 (Presidential Activity Report)

KEY:
- Requestor — The person at whose behest the visitor was cleared into the White House through the WAVES system.
- Visitee — The person whom the requestor listed as the person to be visited when requesting clearance for the Ms. Lewinsky.
- Purpose — The purpose recalled by the requestor or visitee during an interview with the OIC.
- References — The official White House logs that contain the information upon which this chart is based.
- Shaded Areas — Visits during which Ms. Lewinsky and the President were in the Oval Office area, and no one else was known to be present.

(See "Understanding the Evidence" section, Tab G, for details.)

28	07/16/97 (Wed.)	10:46	11:42	Scott	Scott	Oval Office	Job interview	V006-DC-00000008 (WAVES record) 827-DC-00000018 (Epass Entry & Exit Logs) 1222-DC-00000253 (Presidential Activity Report) Scott 3/19/98 Int. at 64-68
29	07/24/97 (Thurs.)	18:04	18:27	Currie	Currie	Oval Office	No purpose recalled/known	V006-DC-00000008 (WAVES record) 827-DC-00000018 (Epass Entry & Exit Logs) 968-DC-00000155 (Presidential Movement Log)
30	08/01/97 (Fri.)	10:46	11:40	Unknown	Unknown	Oval Office Rose Garden (arrived at 11:10) Oval Office (arrived at 11:17)	No purpose recalled/known	827-DC-00000002 (Epass Entry & Exit Logs) 1222-DC-00000255 (Presidential Activity Report)
31	08/01/97 (Fri.)	12:19	No exit time logged	Unknown	Unknown	Oval Office Cabinet Room (arrived at 12:28) Oval Office (arrived at 12:45) Residence (arrived at 13:16)	No purpose recalled/known	827-DC-00000002 (Epass Entry Log)1222- 1222-DC-00000255 (Presidential Activity Report)
32	08/16/97 (Sat.)	09:02	10:20	Currie	Currie	Oval Office (arrived at 09:20) Second Floor (arrived at 10:05)	No purpose recalled/known	V006-DC-00000008 (WAVES record) 827-DC-00000018 (Epass Entry & Exit Logs) V006-DC-00002146 (Presidential Movement Log)
33	09/11/97 (Thurs.)	18:59	19:06	Raines	Raines	Oval Office	No purpose recalled/known	V006-DC-00000008 (WAVES record) 827-DC-00000018 (Epass Entry & Exit Logs)

KEY: Requestor — The person at whose behest the visitor was cleared into the White House through the WAVES system.
Visitee — The person whom the requestor listed as the person to be visited when requesting clearance for the Ms. Lewinsky.
Purpose — The purpose recalled by the requestor or visitee during an interview with the OIC.
References — The official White House logs that contain the information upon which this chart is based.
Shaded Areas — Visits during which Ms. Lewinsky and the President were in the Oval Office area, and no one else was known to be present.
(See "Understanding the Evidence" section, Tab G, for details.)

50-892 98 - 5

34	09/12/97 (Fri.)	19:41	20:22	Currie	Currie	Residence	No purpose recalled/known	V006-DC-00000008 (WAVES record) 827-DC-00000018 (Epass Entry & Exit Logs) 968-DC-00000172 (Presidential Movement Log)
35	09/22/97 (Mon.)	19:11	19:25	Raines	Raines	New York	No purpose recalled/known	V006-DC-00000008 (WAVES record) 827-DC-00000018 (Epass Entry & Exit Logs) 968-DC-00000179 (Presidential Movement Log)
36	10/11/97 (Sat.)	09:37	10:54	Currie	Currie	Oval Office (arrived at 09:54)	No purpose recalled/known	V006-DC-00000008 (WAVES record) 827-DC-00000018 (Epass Entry & Exit Logs) V006-DC-00002151 (Presidential Movement Log)
37	10/29/97 (Wed.)	No entry time logged	No exit time logged	Wilson	President Clinton	White House	No purpose recalled/known	V006-DC-00000008 (WAVES record) 1234-DC-00000048 (Presidential Movement Log)
38	11/13/97 (Thurs.)	No entry time logged	No exit time logged	Wozniak	Wozniak	White House	Attend military function	V006-DC-00000008 (WAVES record) V006-DC-00002156 (Presidential Movement Log) Wozniak 3/5/98 Int. at 2
39	11/13/97 (Thurs.)	18:21	No exit time logged	Currie	Currie	Oval Office (arrived at 18:34)	No purpose recalled/known	V006-DC-00000008 (WAVES record) 827-DC-00000018 (Epass Entry Log) 968-DC-00000190 (Presidential Movement Log)
40	12/05/97 (Fri.)	No entry time logged	No exit time logged	Schwartz	President Clinton	White House	Christmas Party	V006-DC-00000009 (WAVES record) 1222-DC-00000264 (Presidential Activity Report) V006-DC-00000521 (Holiday Reception Guest List) V006-DC-00001765 (WAVES request)
41	12/06/97 (Sat.)	12:52	13:36	Currie	Currie	Oval Office Residence (arrived at 13:54)	No purpose recalled/known	V006-DC-00000009 (WAVES record) 827-DC-00000018 (Epass Entry & Exit Logs) V006-DC-00002158 (Presidential Movement Log)

KEY: Requestor — The person at whose behest the visitor was cleared into the White House through the WAVES system.
Visitee — The person whom the requestor listed as the person to be visited when requesting clearance for the Ms. Lewinsky.
Purpose — The purpose recalled by the requestor or visitee during an interview with the OIC.
References — The official White House logs that contain the information upon which this chart is based.
Shaded Areas — Visits during which Ms. Lewinsky and the President were in the Oval Office area, and no one else was known to be present.
(See "Understanding the Evidence" section, Tab G, for details.)

42	12/15/97 (Mon.)	11:31	12:39	Luzzatto	Wozniak	Oval Office	To do "some things" for Ken Bacon	V006-DC-00000009 (WAVES record) 827-DC-00000018 (Epass Entry & Exit Logs) 968-DC-00000198 (Presidential Movement Log) Wozniak 3/5/98 Int. at 2
43	"A day or two" before or after 12/15/98	No entry time logged	No exit time logged	Wozniak	Wozniak	Unknown	To do "some things" for Ken Bacon	V006-DC-00000009 (WAVES record) Wozniak 3/5/98 Int. at 2
44	12/28/97 (Sun.)	08:16	No exit time logged	Currie	Currie	Oval Office (arrived at 08:10) Residence (arrived at 09:52)	No purpose recalled/known	V006-DC-00000009 (WAVES record) 827-DC-00000018 (Epass Entry Log) V006-DC-00002159 (Presidential Movement Log)

KEY: **Requestor** The person at whose behest the visitor was cleared into the White House through the WAVES system.
Visitee The person whom the requestor listed as the person to be visited when requesting clearance for the Ms. Lewinsky.
Purpose The purpose recalled by the requestor or visitee during an interview with the OIC.
References The official White House logs that contain the information upon which this chart is based.
Shaded Areas Visits during which Ms. Lewinsky and the President were in the Oval Office area, and no one else was known to be present.
(See "Understanding the Evidence" section, Tab G, for details.)

Tab F

Table of Contacts between Monica Lewinsky and the President

INTRODUCTION TO THE CHART OF CONTACTS BETWEEN THE PRESIDENT AND MONICA LEWINSKY

The Office of the Independent Counsel ("OIC") prepared the following Chart with Monica Lewinsky's assistance. In her words, "it's a chronology that marks some of the highlights of my relationship with the President. It definitely includes the visits that I had with him and most of the gifts we exchanged. It reflects most of the phone calls that I remember."[1] Dates on which sexual contact occurred are designated in bold.

The most important source of information for this Chart was Ms. Lewinsky's recollections, which were refreshed in small part by the near-contemporaneous compiled record in her Filofax calendar.[2] To an even smaller degree, the OIC used some evidence gathered in its investigation to assist Ms. Lewinsky in refreshing her memory of events. Ms. Lewinsky reviewed several predecessor versions of the Chart over three or four days and made minor modifications before confirming its accuracy.[3]

This Chart was used as Grand Jury Exhibit ML-7 when Ms. Lewinsky testified before the grand jury on August 6, 1998.[4] When she testified, Ms. Lewinsky noted that one change should be made to the chart: The October 23, 1996, contact on page five should also reflect the fact that Ms. Lewinsky attended a

---

[1] Lewinsky 8/6/98 GJ at 27-28.

[2] Id. at 28-29.

[3] Lewinsky 8/5/98 Int. at 1.

[4] Id. at 27-28.

Democratic fundraiser on that date.[5] Ms. Lewinsky testified that she believed that the Chart was otherwise accurate, with that correction.[6] On August 26, 1998, Ms. Lewinsky again verified the accuracy of the Chart in a sworn deposition.[7]

Since Ms. Lewinsky last verified the Chart, Ms. Lewinsky has examined a substantial amount of evidence, including the transcripts and audio tapes of several of her conversations with Linda Tripp. In reviewing that evidence, Ms. Lewinsky realized that there were two minor discrepancies between the Chart and the actual sequence of events regarding when she and the President exchanged two gifts. She now recalls that the President gave her the Annie Lenox compact disc on October 11, 1997, rather than on December 6, 1997, as listed on the Chart. Similarly, she now believes she may have sent the package to the President containing sunglasses, an erotic postcard, and a note about education reform on October 16, 1997, rather than on October 21 or 22, 1997, as listed on the Chart.[8] Ms. Lewinsky has made no other revisions to the Chart.

This Chart is a counterpart to the Chart of Recorded Lewinsky Visits to the White House, at Tab E. That chart details Ms. Lewinsky's presence at the White House with documentary evidence.

---

[5] Id. at 28.

[6] Id.

[7] Lewinsky 8/26/98 Depo. at 6.

[8] Lewinsky 9/6/98 Int. at 2-3.

CONTACTS BETWEEN THE PRESIDENT AND MONICA LEWINSKY

DATE	IN - PERSON CONTACTS	PHONE CALLS	GIFTS/ NOTES ML TO WJC	GIFTS/NOTES WJC TO ML
Approx. 8/9/95 Wednesday	Departure ceremony - nonverbal connection - eye contact - green suit			
Approx. 8/10/95 Thursday	Public function - Pres. 49th B-day party - flirtation - eye contact - green suit			
Approx. 8/13 or 8/14/95 Sun. - Mon.	Departure ceremony - intro. to Pres.			
Mid to late 9/95	Photo opportunity - WW basement - Ungvari - Pres. said he knew who ML was			
Approx. 10/95	Chance meeting - West Exec. Ave. - waved at Pres.			
11/15/95 Wednesday	Pres. made several visits to Panetta's office where ML was working			
1/15/95 ednesday	Private encounter - approx. 8 p.m. - hallway by study - kissing			
11/15/95 Wednesday	Second private encounter - sometime b/t 8 and 10 p.m. - study and hallway by study - physical intimacy including oral sex			
11/17/95 Friday	Private encounter - approx. 8 p.m. - study area - pizza night - kissing			
11/17/95 Friday	Second private meeting of night - bathroom by study - phone call - pizza night - physical intimacy including oral sex			
11/20/95 Monday			Zegna tie - ML gave to Currie to give to Pres	
12/5/95 Tuesday	Brief private encounter - oval office and back study - no sexual contact			autographed photo wearing tie
12/31/95 Sunday	Private encounter - sometime b/t 12 and 1 p.m. - approx. 20 or 25 min. - hallway by study - physical intimacy including oral sex			"Davidoff" cigars

DATE	IN - PERSON CONTACTS	PHONE CALLS	GIFTS/ NOTES ML TO WJC	GIFTS/NOTES WJC TO ML
1/7/96 Sunday		conversation - first call to ML's home		
1/7/96 Sunday		conversation - ML at office		
1/7/96 Sunday	Private encounter - late afternoon - mtg. lasted approx. 45 min. - bathroom by study - physical intimacy including oral sex			
1/15 or (early a.m.) 1/16/96 Mon. or Tues.		conversation, including phone sex - approx. 12:30 a.m. - ML at home		
1/21/96 Sunday	Chance encounter then private encounter - sometime b/t 3 and 5 p.m. approx. 30 to 40 min. - hallway by study - physical intimacy including oral sex - kissing in N. Hernreich's office			
Approx. 1/28/96 ınday		caller ID on ML's office phone indicated POTUS call		
1/30/96 Tuesday		conversation - during middle of workday at ML's office		
1/30/96 Tuesday	Public function - Griffin's going away party			
2/4/96 Sunday		conversations - ML at office - multiple calls		
2/4/96 Sunday	Private encounter- study and hallway - approx. 1 ½ hr. - physical intimacy including oral sex			Signed "State of Union" address (date approx.)
2/4/96 Sunday		conversation - ML at office		
2/7 or 2/8/96 Wed. or Thurs.		conversation - ML at home		

DATE	IN - PERSON CONTACTS	PHONE CALLS	GIFTS/ NOTES ML TO WJC	GIFTS/NOTES WJC TO ML
2/8 or 2/9/96 Thurs. or Fri.		conversation, including phone sex - ML at home		
2/19/96 Monday		conversation - ML at home		
2/19/96 Monday	Private encounter - approx. 25 min. sometime b/t 12 and 2 p.m. - oval office - no sexual contact			
Approx. 2/28 or 3/5/96		conversation - approx. 20 min. - after chance meeting in hallway - ML at home		
3/10/96 Sunday	Accidental meeting - outside restroom in WH - Ungvari present			
3/25/96 Monday	Accidental meeting - pass each other in hallway - ML looked away			
3/26/96 Tuesday		conversation - approx. 11 a.m. - ML at office		
3/29/96 riday	Accidental meeting - after jog - ML hurt hand	conversation - ML at office - approx. 8 p.m. - invitation to movie		
3/31/96 Sunday		conversation - ML at office - approx. 1 p.m. - Pres. ill		
3/31/96 Sunday	Private encounter - approx. 45 min. - hallway by study - physically intimate contact		Hugo Boss tie - carried to mtg.	cigars
4/7/96 Easter Sunday		conversation - ML at home		
4/7/96 - Easter Sunday	Private encounter - sometime b/t 5 and 6 p.m.- approx. 30 min. - hallway by study and study - intervening phone call - physical intimacy including oral sex			
4/7/96 Easter Sunday		conversation - ML at home - why ML left		

DATE	IN - PERSON CONTACTS	PHONE CALLS	GIFTS/ NOTES ML TO WJC	GIFTS/NOTES WJC TO ML
4/12/96 Friday		conversation - ML at home - daytime		
4/12 or (early a.m.) 4/13/96 Fri. or Sat.		conversation - ML at home - after midnight		
4/22/96 Monday		conversation - job talk - ML at home		
Approx. 4/28/96 Sunday	Public function - AIPAC meeting			
4/29 or 4/30/96 Mon. or Tues.		message - after 6:30 a.m.		
5/2/96 Thursday		conversation, possibly including phone sex - ML at home		
5/6/96 Monday		possible phone call		
pprox. 5/8/96 Wednesday	Public function - Saxophone Club event			
5/16/96 Thursday		conversation - ML at home		
5/21/96 Tuesday	Public function - Adm. Boorda memorial service			
5/21/96 Tuesday		conversation, including phone sex - ML at home		
5/31/96 Friday		message		
6/5/96 Wednesday		conversation - ML at home - early evening		
Approx. 6/13/96 Thursday	Public function - arrival of Irish President			
6/14/96 Friday	Public function - radio address - family			

DATE	IN - PERSON CONTACTS	PHONE CALLS	GIFTS/ NOTES ML TO WJC	GIFTS/NOTES WJC TO ML
6/23/96 Sunday		conversation, possibly including phone sex - ML at home		
7/5 or (early a.m.) 7/6/96 Fri. or Sat.		conversation, including phone sex - ML at home		
7/19/96 Friday		conversation, including phone sex - 6:30 a.m. - ML at home		
7/28/96 Sunday		conversation - ML at home		
8/4/96 Sunday		conversation, including phone sex - ML at home		
Before 8/16/96			Zegna tie - also t-shirt from Bosnia - ML sent to Betty to give to the President	
8/18/96 Sunday	Public function - Pres. 50th B-day party - limited intimate contact			
/24/96 ˌaturday		conversation, including phone sex - ML at home		
9/5/96 Thursday				thank you note - hand signed addendum - "tie is really beautiful"
9/5/96 Thursday		conversation, possibly including phone sex - Pres. in Fla. - ML at home		
9/10/96 Tuesday		message		
9/30/96 Monday		conversation, possibly including phone sex		
10/22/96 Tuesday		conversation, including phone sex - ML at home		
10/23 or (early a.m.) 10/24/96 Wed. or Thurs.		conversation - ML at home		

DATE	IN - PERSON CONTACTS	PHONE CALLS	GIFTS/ NOTES ML TO WJC	GIFTS/NOTES WJC TO ML
11/6/96 Wednesday	Public function - South Lawn Rally			
12/2/96 Monday		conversation - approx. 10 - 15 min. - ML at home		
12/2/96 Monday		conversation, including phone sex - later that evening - ML at home - approx. 10:30 p.m. - Pres. fell asleep		
12/17/96 Tuesday	Public function - Christmas party			
12/18/96 Wednesday		conversation - approx. 5 min.- 10:30 p.m. - ML at home		
After Christmas 1996			Sherlock Holmes game - glow in dark frog - ML dropped off gifts with Currie	
12/30/96 Monday		message		
12/97 Sunday		conversation, including job talk and possibly phone sex - ML at home		
Sometime between 2/97 and 5/97			two books, Oy Vey and a golf book - card or letter	
2/8/97 Saturday		conversation - ML at home - mid-day - 11:30 or 12:00		
2/8/97 Saturday		conversation, including job talk and phone sex - 1:30 or 2:00 p.m. - ML at home		
2/14/97 Friday			Washington Post ad - Happy Valentine's Day	
2/28/97 Friday	Private encounter after radio address - early evening - approx. 20 to 25 min. - study and bathroom by study - physical intimacy including oral sex to completion		Golf ball and tees from Harrods - plastic pocket frog	hatpin - the book, Leaves of Grass

DATE	IN - PERSON CONTACTS	PHONE CALLS	GIFTS/ NOTES ML TO WJC	GIFTS/NOTES WJC TO ML
Between 3/3 and 3/9/97			Thank you note - Hugo Boss tie - ML sent package by Federal Express	
3/12/97 Wednesday		conversation - three minutes - ML at work		
After 3/14/97			care package after Pres. injured his leg - "Hi ya, handsome!" card, metal magnet with Pres. seal for his crutches, license plate with "BILL" for his wheelchair, knee pads with Pres. seal - ML sent package by Federal Express	
3/29/97 Saturday	Private encounter - approx. 1:30 or 2 p.m. - study - Pres. on crutches - physical intimacy including oral sex to completion and brief direct genital contact		penny medallion with the heart cut out - her personal copy of Vox - framed Valentine's Day ad [ML also replaced the cut Hugo Boss tie]	
4/26/97 Saturday		conversation - late afternoon - 20 min. - ML at home		
5/17/97 Saturday		conversations - multiple calls		
5/18/97 Sunday		conversations - multiple calls		
5/24/97 Saturday	Private encounter - "D-Day" - mid-day - hugging - dining room, study and hallway		Banana Republic long sleeve casual shirt - puzzle on golf mysteries	
6/29/97 Sunday			letter	
7/3/97 Thursday			letter - frustration re: jobs	
7/4/97 Friday Indep. Day	Private encounter - approx. 9:15 - mtg. ended b/t 10 and 11 a.m. - study and hallway - argument - kiss on neck			
7/8/97 Tuesday	Public function - Madrid - flirtation			

DATE	IN - PERSON CONTACTS	PHONE CALLS	GIFTS/ NOTES ML TO WJC	GIFTS/NOTES WJC TO ML
7/14/97 Monday	Private encounter - Hernreich's office - late evening - Pres. had conference call during middle of mtg. - ML did not participate in conference call - no sexual contact		wooden B with a frog in it from Budapest - card with a watermelon on it	
7/15/97 Tuesday		conversation - ML at home		
7/24/97 Thursday	Private encounter - oval office - approx. 10 min. - early evening - no sexual contact			b-day gifts: antique flower pin in wooden box and porcelain objet d' art handed to ML by Currie - ML picked up signed picture
8/1/97 Friday		conversation		
Week of 8/10/97 but before 8/16/97			a book, The Notebook and a card	
/16/97 aturday	Private encounter - physical intimacy including birthday kiss - study		b-day gifts: antique book on Peter the Great, apple square - ML also gave Pres. card game "Royalty" and a book, Disease and Misrepresentation	
Early 9/97				Black Dog items: t-shirts, baseball cap, mug and cotton dress - given to ML by Currie
9/30/97 Tuesday			memorandum - to "HANDSOME" re: "the New Deal"	
9/30/97 Tuesday		conversation, possibly including phone sex		
10/7/97 Tuesday			couriered package - letter - job talk	

DATE	IN - PERSON CONTACTS	PHONE CALLS	GIFTS/ NOTES ML TO WJC	GIFTS/NOTES WJC TO ML
10/9 or (early a.m.) 10/10/97 Thurs. or Fri.		conversation - long, from 2 or 2:30 a.m. until 3:30 or 4:00 a.m. - job talk - argument - ML at home		
10/11/97 Saturday	Private encounter - approx. 9:30 a.m. - study - job talk - no sexual contact			
10/16/97 Thursday			letter - job-related - "whole fat packet" of job stuff -via Federal Express	
10/21 or 10/22/97 Tues. or Wed.			Calvin Klein tie - a pair of sunglasses - a card, a postcard (erotic painting) - note re: education reform	
10/23/97 Thursday		conversation - ML at home - end b/c HRC		
10/28/97 Tuesday			unidentified couriered package	
0/30/97 hursday		conversation - ML at home - interview prep		
Approx. week before 10/31/97			Halloween gifts: card - pumpkin lapel pin - wooden letter opener with a frog on the handle - plastic pumpkin filled with candy	
11/3/97 Monday			unidentified couriered package	
11/12/97 Wednesday		conversation, possibly including phone sex - discuss re: ML visit		
11/12/97 Wednesday			unidentified couriered package	
11/13/97 Thursday			Ginko biloba and zinc lozenges - ML gave to Currie to give to Pres. per Pres. request	

DATE	IN - PERSON CONTACTS	PHONE CALLS	GIFTS/ NOTES ML TO WJC	GIFTS/NOTES WJC TO ML
11/13/97 Thursday	Private encounter in study - approx. 5 min. - evening - Zedillo visit		antique paperweight depicting the WH	
11/20/97 Thursday			courier record - letter	
11/21/97 Friday			courier record - cassette tape	
Late 11/97 Early 12/97			letter - ML give to Currie to give to Pres. - Not delivered until 12/5	
12/5/97 Friday	Public function - Christmas party			
12/6/97 Saturday		conversation - approx. 30 min. - ML at home		
12/6/97 Saturday	Private encounter - after NW Gate incident - job talk		Christmas gift: antique standing cigar holder - - Other gifts: Starbucks Santa Monica mug - tie from London - book, <u>Our Patriotic Presidents</u> - Hugs and Kisses box	Annie Lenox compact disc
12/8/97 Monday			courier record - card - peach candies	
12/17 or (early a.m.) 12/18/97 Wed. or Thurs.		conversation - b/t 2:00 a.m. and 3:00 a.m. - ML at home - witness list		
12/28/97 Sunday	Private encounter - Christmas kiss - doorway by study and bathroom by study - b/t 9 and 10 a.m.		Hand painted Easter Egg - "gummy boobs" from Urban Outfitters	large Rockettes blanket from New York - pin of the New York skyline - a "marble-like" bear's head from Vancouver - a pair of joke sunglasses - a small box of cherry chocolates - Black Dog canvas bag - Black Dog stuffed animal

DATE	IN - PERSON CONTACTS	PHONE CALLS	GIFTS/ NOTES ML TO WJC	GIFTS/NOTES WJC TO ML
./4/98 Sunday			Titanic note - book - Presidents of the United States - dropped off w/Currie	
1/5/98 Monday		conversation		

Tab G

Tables of Phone Conversations

Telephone Calls

TABLE 1

November 15, 1995

No.	Time	Call From	Call To	Length of Call
1	9:25 PM	President Clinton	Rep. Jim Chapman, [redacted]	5:00
2	9:31 PM	President Clinton	Rep. John Tanner, [redacted]	4:00

Source Documents

Call 1: 1472-DC-00000006 (Presidential call log)

Call 2: 1472-DC-00000008 (Presidential call log)

Telephone Calls

TABLE 2

November 17, 1995

No.	Time	Call From	Call To	Length of Call
1	9:53 PM	President Clinton	Rep. H.L. Callahan	21:00

Source Documents

Call 1: 1472-DC-00000015 (Presidential call log)

Telephone Calls

TABLE 3

December 31, 1995

No.	Time	Call From	Call To	Length of Call
1	12:53 PM	Secretary William Perry, White House signal 7-3107	President Clinton	5:00

Source Documents

Call 1: 1506-DC-00000029 (Presidential call log)

Telephone Calls

TABLE 4

January 7, 1996

No.	Time	Call From	Call To	Length of Call
1	4:39 PM	President Clinton	Gene Sperling, White House Admin., [redacted]	10:00

Source Documents

Call 1: 1506-DC-00000031 (Presidential call log)

Telephone Calls

TABLE 5

January 21, 1996

No.	Time	Call From	Call To	Length of Call
1	3:47 PM	Nancy Mitchell, White House Admin., [redacted]	President Clinton	1:00

Source Documents

Call 1: 1506-DC-00000050 (Presidential call log)

Telephone Calls

TABLE 6

February 4, 1996

No.	Time	Call From	Call To	Length of Call
1	4:45 PM	Rahm Emanuel, [redacted]	President Clinton	5:00

Source Documents

Call 1: 1506-DC-00000068 (Presidential call log)

Telephone Calls

TABLE 7

February 19, 1996

No.	Time	Call From	Call To	Length of Call
1	12:42 PM	Alfonso Fanjul, [redacted]	President Clinton	22:00

Source Documents

Call 1: 1472-DC-00000017 (Presidential call log)

Telephone Calls

TABLE 8

March 31, 1996

No.	Time	Call From	Call To	Length of Call
1	3:06 PM	President Clinton	Sen. Barbara Mikulski, [redacted]	1:00

Source Documents

Call 1: 1506-DC-00000139 (Presidential call log)

Telephone Calls

TABLE 9

April 7, 1996

No.	Time	Call From	Call To	Length of Call
1	5:11 PM	Richard Morris, Paris, France, [redacted]	President Clinton	9:00
2	5:30 PM	President Clinton	Evelyn Lieberman, ext. [redacted]	2:00

Source Documents

Calls 1 and 2: 1506-DC-00000144 (Presidential call log)

Telephone Calls

TABLE 10

April 9, 1996

No.	Time	Call From	Call To	Length of Call
1	2:18 PM	Monica Lewinsky's residence, [redacted]	Walter Kaye, [redacted]	19:00
2	4:37 PM	Monica Lewinsky's residence, [redacted]	Walter Kaye, [redacted]	2:00
3	5:05 PM	Monica Lewinsky's residence, [redacted]	Walter Kaye, [redacted]	7:00

Source Documents

Call 1: 1000-DC-00000768 (MCI toll records)

Calls 2 and 3: 1000-DC-00000769 (MCI toll records)

Telephone Calls

TABLE 11

April 10, 1996

No.	Time	Call From	Call To	Length of Call
1	4:56 PM	Monica Lewinsky's residence, [redacted]	Walter Kaye, [redacted]	10:00

Source Documents

Call 1: 1000-DC-00000769 (MCI toll records)

Telephone Calls

TABLE 12

April 12, 1996

No.	Time	Call From	Call To	Length of Call
1	12:38 PM	Monica Lewinsky's residence, [redacted]	Walter Kaye, [redacted]	1:00

Source Documents

Call 1: 1000-DC-00000770 (MCI toll records)

Telephone Calls

TABLE 13

April 15, 1996

No.	Time	Call From	Call To	Length of Call
1	5:18 PM	Monica Lewinsky's residence, [redacted]	Walter Kaye [redacted]	11:00

Source Documents

Call 1: 1000-DC-00000771 (MCI toll records)

Telephone Calls

TABLE 14

July 19, 1996

No.	Time	Call From	Call To	Length of Call
1	12:11 AM	President Clinton	White House Operator	1:00
2	6:40 AM	President Clinton	White House Operator	1:00

Source Documents

Calls 1 and 2: 1506-DC-00000275 (Presidential call log); 1506-DC-00000638 (Presidential diarists notes)

50-892 98 - 6

Telephone Calls

TABLE 15

March 29, 1997

No.	Time	Call From	Call To	Length of Call
1	8:37 AM	Ms. Lewinsky's cellular phone, [redacted]	Ms. Currie's office, [redacted]	1:00

Source Documents

Call 1: 1014-DC-00000022 (Cellular One toll records)

Telephone Calls

TABLE 16

July 4, 1997

No.	Time	Call From	Call To	Length of Call
1	10:22 AM	President Clinton	Bruce Lindsey's cellular phone	3:00
2	10:25 AM	President Clinton	Nancy Hernreich	11:00

Source Documents

Calls 1 and 2: 968-DC-00003546 (Presidential call log)

Telephone Calls

TABLE 17

July 14, 1997

No.	Time	Call From	Call To	Length of Call
1	10:03 PM	President Clinton	Conference call with Robert Bennett and Charles Ruff	51:00
2	10:55 PM	President Clinton	Bruce Lindey's residence, [redacted]	6:00

<u>Source Documents</u>

Calls 1 and 2: 968-DC-00003550 (Presidential call log)

Telephone Calls

TABLE 18

August 16, 1997

No.	Time	Call From	Call To	Length of Call
1	9:18 AM	President Clinton	Ms. Currie's office, ext. [redacted]	1:00

Source Documents

Call 1: 968-DC-00003558 (Presidential call log)

Telephone Calls

TABLE 19

September 3, 1997

No.	Time	Call From	Call To	Length of Call
1	2:24 PM	Ms. Lewinsky's office, [redacted]	Marsha Scott's office, [redacted]	2:25
2	4:55 PM	Ms. Lewinsky's office, [redacted]	Marsha Scott's office, [redacted]	46:58

Source Documents

Calls 1 and 2: 833-DC-00017857 (Pentagon phone records)

Telephone Calls

TABLE 20

October 6, 1997

No.	Time	Call From	Call To	Length of Call
1	3:44 PM	Ms. Lewinsky's office, [redacted]	Ms. Currie's office, [redacted]	5:53
2	4:16 PM	Ms. Lewinsky's office, [redacted]	Ms. Currie's office, [redacted]	7:00

Source Documents

Calls 1 and 2: 833-DC-00017867 (Pentagon phone records)

Telephone Calls

TABLE 21

October 11, 1997

No.	Time	Call From	Call To	Length of Call
1	10:57 AM	Vernon Jordan, [redacted]	President Clinton	9:00

Source Documents

Call 1: 968-DC-00003569 (Presidential call log)

Telephone Calls

TABLE 22

October 21, 1997

No.	Time	Call From	Call To	Length of Call
1	3:09 PM	Ms. Currie, fax number [redacted]	Fax to United Nations	N/A
2	7:01 PM	Ambassador William Richardson's office, [redacted]	Ms. Lewinsky's residence, [redacted]	5:42

Source Documents

Call 1: 828-DC-00000012 (faxed copy of Ms. Lewinsky's resume, produced by United Nations)

Call 2: 828-DC-00000004 (State Department phone records)

Telephone Calls

TABLE 24

November 4, 1997

No.	Time	Call From	Call To	Length of Call
1	3:52 PM	Mr. Jordan's office, [redacted]	Ms. Currie's office [redacted]	0:54
2	3:54 PM	Ms. Lewinsky's office, [redacted]	Mr. Jordan's office, [redacted]	3:32
3	4:09 PM	Mr. Jordan's office, [redacted]	Ms. Currie's office, [redacted]	0:42
4	4:38 PM	Mr. Jordan's office, [redacted]	Ms. Currie's office, [redacted]	1:06

Source Documents

Calls 1, 3, and 4: V004-DC-00000134 (Akin, Gump, Strauss, Hauer & Feld phone records)

Call 2: 833-DC-00017875 (Pentagon phone records)

Telephone Calls

TABLE 25

November 5, 1997

No.	Time	Call From	Call To	Length of Call
1	8:50 AM	Mr. Jordan's office, [redacted]	President Clinton	5:00
2	8:56 AM	Mr. Jordan's office, [redacted]	Ms. Hernreich's office, [redacted]	6:30
3	11:05 AM	Mr. Jordan's office, [redacted]	Ms. Hernreich's office, [redacted]	0:48
4	11:44 AM	Mr. Jordan's office, [redacted]	Ms. Hernreich's office, [redacted]	1:06
5	2:34 PM	Mr. Jordan's office, [redacted]	Ms. Hernreich's office, [redacted]	1:24
6	2:36 PM	Mr. Jordan's office, [redacted]	Ms. Currie's office, [redacted]	1:30

<u>Source Documents</u>

Call 1: 1178-DC-00000011 (Presidential call log)

Calls 2, 3, 4, 5, and 6: V004-DC-00000135 (Akin, Gump, Strauss, Hauer & Feld phone records)

Telephone Calls

TABLE 26

November 24, 1997

No.	Time	Call From	Call To	Length of Call
1	10:14 AM	Ms. Lewinsky's office, [redacted]	Mona Sutphen's office, United Nations, [redacted]	6:44

Source Documents

Call 1: 833-DC-00017908 (Pentagon phone records)

Telephone Calls

TABLE 27

November 26, 1997

No.	Time	Call From	Call To	Length of Call
1	10:32 AM	Ms. Lewinsky at Bernard Lewinsky's residence, [redacted]	Ms. Currie's office, [redacted]	1:00
2	2:53 PM	Vernon Jordan's office, [redacted]	Ms. Currie's office, [redacted]	0:30
3	3:07 PM	Ms. Currie	Ms. Lewinsky's pager; message reads: "PLEASE CALL VERNON JORDAN, BETTY CURRY."	N/A

Source Documents

Call 1: 1205-DC-00000016 (MCI toll records; times adjusted from Pacific to Eastern Standard time)

Call 2: V004-DC-00000143 (Akin, Gump, Strauss, Hauer & Feld phone records)

Call 3: 831-DC-00000011 (Pagemart; times adjusted from Pacific to Eastern Standard time)

Telephone Calls

TABLE 28

December 5, 1997

No.	Time	Call From	Call To	Length of Call
1	1:11 PM	Ms. Lewinsky's residence, [redacted]	Ms. Currie's office, [redacted]	0:10
2	1:24 PM	Ms. Lewinsky's residence, [redacted]	Ms. Currie's office, [redacted]	0:15
3	3:15 PM	Ms. Lewinsky's residence, [redacted]	Ms. Currie's office, [redacted]	2:31
4	3:43 PM	Ms. Lewinsky's residence, [redacted]	Ms. Currie's office, [redacted]	0:43
5	4:03 PM	Ms. Lewinsky's residence, [redacted]	Ms. Currie's office, [redacted]	0:04
6	4:21 PM	Ms. Lewinsky's residence, [redacted]	Ms. Currie's office, [redacted]	0:03
7	4:34 PM	Ms. Lewinsky's residence, [redacted]	Ms. Currie's office, [redacted]	0:31
8	5:41 PM	Rader, Campbell, Fisher & Pyke	Fax to Robert Bennett	N/A

Source Documents

Calls 1, 2, 3, 4, 5, 6, and 7: 1216-DC-00000022 (Bell Atlantic toll records)

Call 8: 1408-DC-00000005 (Fax confirmation sheet; produced by Rader, Campbell, Fisher & Pyke; times adjusted from Central to Eastern Standard time)

Telephone Calls

TABLE 29

December 6, 1997

No.	Time	Call From	Call To	Length of Call
1	8:41 AM	Ms. Lewinsky's residence, [redacted]	Ms. Currie's office, [redacted]	0:00
2	8:51 AM	Ms. Lewinsky's residence, [redacted]	Ms. Currie's office, [redacted]	0:17
3	9:21 AM	Ms. Lewinsky's residence, [redacted]	Ms. Currie's office, [redacted]	0:10
4	10:48 AM	Ms. Lewinsky's residence, [redacted]	Ms. Currie's office, [redacted]	0:29
5	10:57 AM	Ms. Lewinsky's residence, [redacted]	Ms. Currie's office, [redacted]	6:51
6	11:37 AM	Ms. Lewinsky's residence, [redacted]	Ms. Currie's office, [redacted]	56:23
7	12:05 PM	Betty Currie	Bruce Lindsey's pager; message reads: "Call Betty ASAP [redacted]"	N/A

Source Documents

Calls 1, 2, 3, 4, 5, and 6: 1216-DC-00000022 (Bell Atlantic toll records)
Call 7: 964-DC-00000862 (White House pager records)

Telephone Calls

TABLE 30

December 11, 1997

No.	Time	Call From	Call To	Length of Call
1	9:45 AM	Mr. Jordan's office, [redacted]	Young & Rubicam, [redacted]	0:36
2	10:18 AM	Mr. Jordan's office, [redacted]	Ms. Hernreich's office, [redacted]	1:12
3	10:39 AM	Mr. Jordan's office, [redacted]	Barbara Neysmith, American Express, [redacted]	0:54
4	10:59 AM	Mr. Jordan's office, [redacted]	Barbara Neysmith, American Express, [redacted]	3:36
5	11:12 AM	Mr. Jordan's office, [redacted]	Howard Gittis, McAndrews & Forbes, [redacted]	4:24
6	12:47 PM	Mr. Jordan's office, [redacted]	Barbara Neysmith, American Express, [redacted]	0:48
7	12:49 PM	Mr. Jordan's office [redacted]	Young & Rubicam, [redacted]	1:00
8	12:51 PM	Mr. Jordan's office, [redacted]	Howard Gittis, McAndrews & Forbes, [redacted]	1:06
9	1:06 PM	Mr. Jordan's office, [redacted]	Barbara Neysmith, American Express, [redacted]	0:30
10	1:07 PM	Mr. Jordan's office, [redacted]	Richard Halperin, McAndrews & Forbes, [redacted]	1:06
11	1:36 PM	Mr. Jordan's office, [redacted]	Marcia Lewis, Strauss Communications, [redacted]	0:36
12	1:38 PM	Mr. Jordan's office, [redacted]	Peter Strauss residence, [redacted]	0:30

Source Documents

Calls 1, 2, 3, 4, 5, 6, 7, 8, 9, 10, 11, and 12: V004-DC-00000148 (Akin, Gump, Strauss, Hauer & Feld phone records)

Telephone Calls

TABLE 31

December 19, 1997

No.	Time	Call From	Call To	Length of Call
1	1:47 PM	Ms. Lewinsky's office, [redacted]	Mr. Jordan's office, [redacted]	1:50
2	3:51 PM	Mr. Jordan's office, [redacted]	President Clinton; talked with Debra Schiff	1:00
3	4:17 PM	Mr. Jordan's office, [redacted]	White House Social Office, [redacted]	2:42
4	5:01 PM	President Clinton	Mr. Jordan's office, [redacted]	4:30 *
5	5:06 PM	Mr. Jordan's office, [redacted]	Francis Carter's office, [redacted]	1:54

Source Documents

Call 1: 833-DC-00017890 (Pentagon phone records)

Call 2: 1178-DC-00000013 (Presidential call log); V004-DC-00000151 (Akin, Gump, Strauss, Hauer & Feld phone record)

Calls 3 and 5: V004-DC-00000151 (Akin, Gump, Strauss, Hauer & Feld phone record)

Call 4: 1178-DC-00000014 (Presidential call log); V004-DC-00000151 (Akin, Gump, Strauss, Hauer & Feld phone record)

* Presidential call logs indicate that President Clinton placed a call to Mr. Jordan at 4:57 PM and that they talked from 5:01 PM to 5:08 PM. The best interpretation of the evidence suggests that the call did not end at 5:08 PM. The Presidential call logs are maintained by hand, whereas the automated Akin, Gump, Strauss, Hauer & Feld phone records reflect that the conversation actually ended at 5:05 PM.

Telephone Calls

TABLE 32

December 22, 1997

No.	Time	Call From	Call To	Length of Call
1	unknown	Francis Carter	Message for Robert Bennett	N/A
2	9:02 AM	Ms. Lewinsky's office, [redacted]	Mr. Jordan's office, [redacted]	0:23
3	2:15 PM	Ms. Lewinsky's office, [redacted]	Mr. Jordan's office, [redacted]	0:46
4	5:03 PM	Mr. Jordan's office, [redacted]	Ms. Lewinsky's office, [redacted]	0:18

Source Documents

Call 1: 902-DC-00000038 (Carter & Varrone billing statement)

Calls 2 and 3: 833-DC-00017891 (Pentagon phone records)

Call 4: V004-DC-00000151 (Akin, Gump, Strauss, Hauer & Feld phone records)

Telephone Calls

TABLE 33

December 30, 1997

No.	Time	Call From	Call To	Length of Call
1	9:27 AM	President Clinton	Mr. Jordan's residence, [redacted]	24:00
2	1:54 PM	Mr. Jordan's office, [redacted]	White House Operator, [redacted]	3:12
3	1:54 PM	Ms. Lewinsky at Strauss residence, [redacted]	Mr. Jordan's office, [redacted]	7:00
4	2:01 PM	Mr. Jordan's office, [redacted]	Mr. Carter's office, [redacted]	0:36
5	6:09 PM	Mr. Jordan's office, [redacted]	White House Counsel's office, [redacted]	1:42

Source Documents

Call 1: 1178-DC-00000015 (Presidential call log)

Calls 2, 4, and 5: V004-DC-00000154 (Akin, Gump, Strauss, Hauer & Feld phone records)

Call 3: 2004-DC-00000083 (Bell Atlantic toll records)

Telephone Calls

TABLE 34

January 5, 1998

No.	Time	Call From	Call To	Length of Call
1	11:32 AM	Ms. Lewinsky at Ms. Finerman's residence, [redacted]	Mona Sutphen's office, United Nations, [redacted]	1:00

Source Documents

Call 1: 1013-DC-00000095 (MCI toll records)

Telephone Calls

TABLE 35

January 6, 1998

No.	Time	Call from	Call to	Length of call
1	11:32 AM	Mr. Carter	Ms. Lewinsky's pager; message reads: "PLEASE CALL FRANK CARTER @ [redacted]"	N/A
2	2:08 PM	Mr. Jordan's office, [redacted]	Ms. Lewinsky's residence, [redacted]	1:48
3	3:14 PM	Mr. Carter	Ms. Lewinsky's pager; message reads: "FRANK CARTER AT [redacted] I WILL SEE YOU TOMORROW MORNING AT 10:00 IN MY OFFICE."	N/A
4	3:26 PM	Mr. Jordan's office, [redacted]	Mr. Carter, [redacted]	6:42
5	3:38 PM	Mr. Jordan's office, [redacted]	Ms. Hernreich, White House, [redacted]	2:12
6	3:48 PM	Mr. Jordan's office, [redacted]	Ms. Lewinsky's residence, [redacted]	0:24
7	3:49 PM	Mr. Jordan's office, [redacted]	Ms. Lewinsky at Ms. Finerman's residence, [redacted]	5:54
8	4:19 PM	President Clinton	Mr. Jordan's office, [redacted]	13:00
9	4:32 PM	Mr. Jordan's office, [redacted]	Mr. Carter, [redacted]	1:06
10	4:34 PM	Mr. Jordan's office, [redacted]	Mr. Carter, [redacted]	2:30
11	5:15 PM	Mr. Jordan's office, [redacted]	White House, [redacted]	4:06

Source Documents

Calls 1 and 3:	831-DC-00000010 (Pagemart; all times have been adjusted from Pacific to Eastern Standard Time)
Calls 2, 4, 5, 6, 7, 9, 10, and 11:	V004-DC-00000158 (Akin, Gump, Straus, Hauer & Feld call log)
Call 8:	1178-DC-00000016 (Presidential call log)

Telephone Calls

TABLE 36

January 7, 1998

No.	Time	Call from	Call to	Length of call
1	9:26 AM	Mr. Jordan's office, [redacted]	Mr. Carter, [redacted]	3:30
2	11:58 AM	Mr. Jordan's office, [redacted]	White House, [redacted]	11:30
3	5:46 PM	Mr. Jordan's office, [redacted]	Ms. Hernreich, White House, [redacted]	10:48
4	6:50 PM	Mr. Jordan's limousine, [redacted]	White House, [redacted]	4:00

Source Documents

Call 1: V004-DC-00000158 (Akin, Gump, Strauss, Hauer & Feld call logs)

Call 2 and 3: V004-DC-00000159 (Akin, Gump, Strauss, Hauer & Feld call logs)

Call 4: 1033-DC-00000115 (Bell Atlantic Mobile toll records)

Telephone Calls

TABLE 37

January 8, 1998

No.	Time	Call from	Call to	Length of call
1	9:21 AM	Mr. Jordan's office, [redacted]	White House Counsel's office, [redacted]	0:42
2	9:21 AM	Mr. Jordan's office, [redacted]	White House, [redacted]	0:48
3	11:50 AM	Ms. Lewinsky at Strauss residence, [redacted]	Mr. Jordan's office, [redacted]	1:00
4	3:09 PM	Ms. Lewinsky at Strauss residence, [redacted]	Mr. Jordan's office, [redacted]	1:00
5	4:48 PM	Ms. Lewinsky at Strauss residence, [redacted]	Mr. Jordan's office, [redacted]	5:00
6	4:54 PM	Mr. Jordan's office, [redacted]	Mr. Perelman, Revlon, [redacted]	1:42
7	4:56 PM	Mr. Jordan's office, [redacted]	Ms. Lewinsky at Strauss residence, [redacted]	0:54
8	6:39 PM	Mr. Jordan's limousine, [redacted]	White House Counsel's office, [redacted]	2:00
9	9:02 PM	Ms. Lewinsky at Strauss residence, [redacted]	Mr. Jordan's office, [redacted]	1:00

Source Documents

Calls 1, 2:	V004-DC-00000159 (Akin, Gump, Strauss, Hauer & Feld call logs)
Call 3:	2004-DC-00000085 (Bell Atlantic toll records)
Calls 4 and 5:	2004-DC-00000086 (Bell Atlantic toll records)
Calls 6 and 7:	V004-DC-00000160 (Akin, Gump, Strauss, Hauer & Feld call logs)
Call 8:	1033-DC-00000116 (Bell Atlantic Mobile toll records)
Call 9:	2004-DC-00000087 (Bell Atlantic toll records)

Telephone Calls

TABLE 38

January 9, 1998

No.	Time	Call from	Call to	Length of call
1	10:19 AM	Mr. Jordan's office, [redacted]	Mr. Perelman, Revlon, [redacted]	0:54
2	1:29 PM	Ms. Lewinsky at Strauss residence, [redacted]	Mr. Jordan's office, [redacted]	1:00
3	1:29 PM	Ms. Lewinsky at Strauss residence, [redacted]	Akin Gump, [redacted]	1:00
4	4:14 PM	Ms. Lewinsky at Strauss residence, [redacted]	Mr. Jordan's office, [redacted]	7:00
5	4:37 PM	Ms. Lewinsky at Strauss residence, [redacted]	Mr. Carter, [redacted]	1:00
6	5:04 PM	Ms. Lewinsky at Strauss residence, [redacted]	Mr. Jordan's office, [redacted]	1:00
7	5:05 PM	Ms. Lewinsky at Strauss residence, [redacted]	Ms. Currie's office, [redacted]	1:00
8	5:08 PM	President Clinton	Ms. Currie, White House Signal [redacted]	1:00
9	5:09 PM	Ms. Lewinsky at Strauss residence, [redacted]	Mr. Jordan's office, [redacted]	2:00
10	5:12 PM	Ms. Currie, White House Signal [redacted]	President Clinton	1:00
11	5:18 PM	Mr. Jordan's office, [redacted]	Ms. Lewinsky at Strauss residence, [redacted]	2:48
12	5:21 PM	Ms. Lewinsky at Strauss residence, [redacted]	Ms. Currie's office, [redacted]	5:00

Source Documents

Call 1: V004-DC-00000160 (Akin, Gump, Strauss, Hauer & Feld call logs)

Calls 2, 3, and 4: 2004-DC-00000087 (Bell Atlantic toll records)

Calls 5, 6, 7, 9 and 12: 2004-DC-00000088 (Bell Atlantic toll records)

Calls 8 and 10: V006-DC-00002064 (Presidential call log)

TABLE 38 continued

Call 11: V004-DC-00000161 (Akin, Gump, Strauss, Hauer & Feld call logs)

Telephone Calls

TABLE 39

January 10, 1998

No.	Time	Call from	Call to	Length of call
1	3:02 PM	Mr. Jordan's office, [redacted]	White House Counsel's office, [redacted]	0:24
2	3:02 PM	Mr. Jordan's office, [redacted]	White House, [redacted]	1:18

Source Documents

Call 1: V004-DC-00000161 (Akin, Gump, Strauss, Hauer & Feld call logs)

Call 2: V004-DC-00000162 (Akin, Gump, Strauss, Hauer & Feld call logs)

Telephone Calls

TABLE 40

January 11, 1998

No.	Time	Call from	Call to	Length of call
1	12:18 PM	Mr. Jordan's office, [redacted]	Cheryl Mills, White House Counsel's office, [redacted]	0:18

Source Documents

Call 1: V004-DC-00000162 (Akin, Gump, Strauss, Hauer & Feld call logs)

Telephone Calls

TABLE 41

January 12, 1998

No.	Time	Call from	Call to	Length of call
1	11:18 AM	Mr. Carter, Attorney	Ms. Lewinsky's pager; message reads: "PLEASE CALL FRANK CARTER AT [redacted]"	N/A
2	11:26 AM	Ms. Lewinsky at Strauss residence, [redacted]	Mr. Carter, [redacted]	5:00
3	11:50 AM	Ms. Lewinsky at Strauss residence, [redacted]	Mr. Jordan's office, [redacted]	1:00
4	3:33 PM	Mr. Jordan's office, [redacted]	White House Counsel's office, [redacted]	1:06
5	4:09 PM	Ms. Lewinsky at Strauss residence, [redacted]	Mr. Jordan's office, [redacted]	4:00
6	4:17 PM	Mr. Jordan's office, [redacted]	Ms. Lewinsky at Strauss residence, [redacted]	2:00
7	4:35 PM	Mr. Jordan's office, [redacted]	White House, [redacted]	5:06
8	5:00 PM	Ms. Lewinsky at Strauss residence, [redacted]	Ms. Currie's office, [redacted]	3:00
9	6:45 PM	Ms. Lewinsky at Strauss residence, [redacted]	Ms. Currie's office, [redacted]	1:00
10	7:48 PM	Ms. Lewinsky at Strauss residence, [redacted]	Ms. Currie's office, [redacted]	1:00

Source Documents

Call 1:	831-DC-00000010 (Pagemart)
Calls 2 and 3:	2004-DC-00000090 (Bell Atlantic toll records)
Calls 4, 6, and 7:	V004-DC-00000162 (Akin, Gump, Strauss, Hauer & Feld call logs)
Calls 5, 8, 9, and 10:	2004-DC-00000091 (Bell Atlantic toll records)

Telephone Calls

TABLE 42

January 13, 1998

No.	Time	Call from	Call to	Length of call
1	11:11 AM	Ms. Currie	Ms. Lewinsky's pager; message reads: "WILL KNOW SOMETHING THIS AFTERNOON. KAY."	N/A
2	2:20 PM	Ms. Currie	Ms. Lewinsky's pager; message reads: "PLEASE CALL ME. KAY"	N/A
3	5:10 PM	Mr. Jordan at Renaissance Vinoy, St. Petersburg, FL	Ms. Hernreich, White House, 202-[redacted]	5:17
4	9:42 PM	Mr. Jordan at Renaissance Vinoy, St. Petersburg, FL	White House, [redacted]	3:48

<u>Source Documents</u>

Calls 1 and 2: 831-DC-00000010 (Pagemart)

Calls 3 and 4: 1064-DC-00000008 (Renaissance Vinoy Resort phone records)

Telephone Calls

TABLE 43

January 14, 1998

No.	Time	Call from	Call to	Length of call
1	6:56 AM	Mr. Jordan at Renaissance Vinoy, St. Petersburg, FL	White House, [redacted]	1:47
2	9:55 AM	President Clinton	Ms. Currie, [redacted]	2:00
3	unknown	Mr. Jordan at St. Regis Hotel, New York, NY	White House, [redacted]	unknown
4	unknown	Mr. Jordan at St. Regis Hotel, New York, NY	White House, [redacted]	unknown

<u>Source Documents</u>

Call 1: 1064-DC-00000008 (Renaissance Vinoy Resort phone records)

Call 2: V006-DC-00002065 (Presidential call log)

Calls 3 and 4: 1065-DC-00000006 (St. Regis Hotel receipt)

Telephone Calls

TABLE 44

January 15, 1998

No.	Time	Call from	Call to	Length of call
1	unknown	Mr. Jordan at St. Regis Hotel, New York, NY	White House, [redacted]	unknown
2	unknown	Ms. Currie's office, [redacted]	Vernon Jordan's office; message reads:"Betty- POTUS; [redacted] KIND OF IMPORTANT"	N/A
3	10:22 AM	Mr. Carter	Ms. Lewinsky's pager; message reads: "PLEASE CALL FRANCIS CARTER @ [redacted]	N/A
4	12:31 PM	Ms. Currie	Ms. Lewinsky's pager; message reads: "PLEASE CALL KAY."	N/A
5	1:08 PM	Mr. Carter	Ms. Lewinsky's pager; message reads: "PLEASE CALL FRANK CARTER AT [redacted]	N/A
6	3:02 PM	Mr. Jordan's office, [redacted]	Ms. Hernreich, White House, [redacted]	1:30
7	3:04 PM	Mr. Jordan's office, [redacted]	White House, [redacted]	1:54
8	5:16 PM	Mr. Jordan's office, [redacted]	White House, [redacted]	2:48
9	5:22 PM	Ms. Currie	Ms. Lewinsky's pager; message reads:"PLEASE CALL KAY ASAP."	N/A
10	6:45 PM	Mr. Jordan's office, [redacted]	Ms. Currie's residence, [redacted]	0:12

Source Documents

Call 1: 1065-DC-00000006 (St. Regis Hotel receipt)

Call 2: V005-DC-00000058 (Vernon Jordan's message log)

Calls 3, 4, 5 and 9: 831-DC-00000008 (Pagemart)

Calls 6, 7, 8 and 10: V004-DC-00000164 (Akin, Gump, Strauss, Hauer & Feld call logs)

Telephone Calls

TABLE 45

January 16, 1998

No.	Time	Call from	Call to	Length of call
1	11:17 AM	Mr. Jordan's office, [redacted]	Ms. Currie, White House, [redacted]	1:24
2	9:41 PM	Mr. Jordan's residence, [redacted]	President Clinton	5:00

Source Documents

Call 1: V004-DC-00000164 (Akin, Gump, Strauss, Hauer & Feld call logs)

Call 2: 1178-DC-00000018 (Presidential call log)

Telephone Calls

TABLE 46

January 17, 1998

No.	Time	Call from	Call to	Length of call
1	5:19 PM	Mr. Jordan's mobile phone, [redacted]	White House, [redacted]	1:00
2	5:38 PM	President Clinton	Mr. Jordan's residence, [redacted]	2:00
3	7:02 PM	President Clinton	Mr. Jordan's office, [redacted]	2:00
4	7:13 PM	President Clinton	Ms. Currie's residence, [redacted]	1:00

Source Documents

Call 1: 1033-DC-00000033 (Bell Atlantic Mobile toll records)

Call 2: 1178-DC-00000019 (Presidential call log)

Call 3: 1178-DC-00000020 (Presidential call log)

Call 4: V006-DC-00002066 (Presidential call log)

50-892 98 - 7

Telephone Calls

TABLE 47

January 18, 1998

No.	Time	Call From	Call To	Length of Call
1	11:49 AM	Mr. Jordan's office, [redacted]	White House, [redacted]	1:12
2	12:50 PM	President Clinton	Mr. Jordan's residence, [redacted]	2:00
3	1:11 PM	President Clinton	Ms. Currie's residence, [redacted]	3:00
4	2:15 PM	Mr. Jordan's mobile phone, [redacted]	White House, [redacted]	4:00
5	2:55 PM	Mr. Jordan's residence, [redacted]	President Clinton "hold per PRESUS, 9:20 PM"	N/A
6	5:12 PM	Ms. Currie	Ms. Lewinsky's pager; message reads: "PLEASE CALL KAY AT HOME."	N/A
7	6:22 PM	Ms. Currie	Ms. Lewinsky's pager; message reads: "PLEASE CALL KAY AT HOME."	N/A
8	7:06 PM	Ms. Currie	Ms. Lewinsky's pager; message reads: "PLEASE CALL KAY AT HOME."	N/A
9	7:19 PM	Mr. Jordan's office [redacted]	Cheryl Mills, White House Counsel's Office, [redacted]	1:06
10	8:28 PM	Ms. Currie	Ms. Lewinsky's pager; message reads: "CALL KAY"	N/A
11	11:02 PM	President Clinton	Ms. Currie's residence, [redacted]	1:00

Source Documents

Calls 1 and 9: V004-DC-00000165 (Akin, Gump, Strauss, Hauer & Feld call logs)

Call 2: 1178-DC-00000021 (Presidential call log)

Call 3: V006-DC-00002067 (Presidential call log)

Call 4: 1033-DC-00000034 (Bell Atlantic Mobile toll records)

Call 5: 1248-DC-00000312 (Presidential call log)

Calls 6, 7, 8, and 10: 831-DC-00000008 (Pagemart)

TABLE 47 continued

Call 11: V006-DC-00002068 (Presidential call log)

Telephone Calls

TABLE 48

January 19, 1998

No.	Time	Call From	Call To	Length of Call
1	7:02 AM	Ms. Currie	Ms. Lewinsky's pager; message reads: "PLEASE CALL KAY AT HOME AT 8:00 THIS MORNING."	N/A
2	8:08 AM	Ms. Currie	Ms. Lewinsky's pager; message reads: "PLEASE CALL KAY."	N/A
3	8:33 AM	Ms. Currie	Ms. Lewinsky's pager; message reads: "PLEASE CALL KAY AT HOME."	N/A
4	8:37 AM	Ms. Currie	Ms. Lewinsky's pager; message reads: "PLEASE CALL KAY AT HOME. IT'S A SOCIAL CALL. THANK YOU"	N/A
5	8:41 AM	Ms. Currie	Ms. Lewinsky's pager; message reads: "KAY IS AT HOME. PLEASE CALL"	N/A
6	8:43 AM	Ms. Currie's residence, [redacted]	President Clinton	1:00
7	8:44 AM	Ms. Currie	Ms. Lewinsky's pager; message reads: "PLEASE CALL KATE RE: FAMILY EMERGENCY."	N/A
8	8:50 AM	President Clinton	Ms. Currie's residence, [redacted]	1:00
9	8:51 AM	Ms. Currie	Ms. Lewinsky's pager; message reads: "MSG. FROM KAY. PLEASE CALL, HAVE GOOD NEWS."	N/A
10	8:56 AM	President Clinton	Mr. Jordan's residence, [redacted]	9:00
11	10:29 AM	Mr. Jordan's office, [redacted]	White House, [redacted]	3:42
12	10:36 AM	Mr. Jordan's office, [redacted]	Ms. Lewinsky's pager; message reads: "PLEASE CALL MR. JORDAN AT [redacted]	N/A
13	10:35 AM	Mr. Jordan's office, [redacted]	Nancy Hernreich, White House, [redacted]	1:12
14	10:44 AM	Mr. Jordan's office, [redacted]	Erskine Bowles, White House, [redacted]	1:00

TABLE 48 continued

No.	Time	Call From	Call To	Length of Call
15	10:53 AM	Mr. Jordan's office, [redacted]	Frank Carter's office, [redacted]	0:36
16	10:58 AM	President Clinton	Mr. Jordan's office, [redacted]	1:00
17	11:04 AM	Mr. Jordan's office, [redacted]	Bruce Lindsey, White House, [redacted]	0:24
18	11:16 AM	Mr. Jordan	Ms. Lewinsky's pager; message reads: "PLEASE CALL MR. JORDAN AT [redacted]"	0:36
19	11:17 AM	Mr. Jordan's office, [redacted]	Bruce Lindsey, White House, [redacted]	1:36
20	12:31 PM	Mr. Jordan's mobile phone, [redacted]	White House, [redacted]	3:00
21	1:45 PM	President Clinton	Ms. Currie's residence, [redacted]	2:00
22	2:29 PM	Mr. Jordan's mobile phone, [redacted]	White House, [redacted]	2:00
23	2:46 PM	Frank Carter	Ms. Lewinsky's pager; message reads: "PLEASE CALL FRANK CARTER AT [redacted]"	N/A
24	4:51 PM	Mr. Jordan's office [redacted]	Ms. Currie's residence, [redacted]	1:42
25	4:53 PM	Mr. Jordan's office [redacted]	Frank Carter's residence, [redacted]	0:24
26	4:54 PM	Mr. Jordan's office, [redacted]	Frank Carter's office, [redacted]	4:00
27	4:58 PM	Mr. Jordan's office, [redacted]	Bruce Lindsey, White House, [redacted]	0:12
28	4:59 PM	Mr. Jordan's office, [redacted]	Cheryl Mills, White House Counsel's office, [redacted]	0:42
29	5:00 PM	Mr. Jordan's office, [redacted]	Bruce Lindsey, White House, [redacted]	0:18
30	5:00 PM	Mr. Jordan's office, [redacted]	Charles Ruff, White House Counsel, [redacted]	0:24
31	5:05 PM	Mr. Jordan's office, [redacted]	Bruce Lindsey, White House, [redacted]	0:06

TABLE 48 continued

No.	Time	Call From	Call To	Length of Call
32	5:05 PM	Mr. Jordan's office, [redacted]	Bruce Lindsey, White House, [redacted]	0:18
33	5:05 PM	Mr. Jordan's office, [redacted]	White House, [redacted]	2:12
34	5:09 PM	Mr. Jordan's office, [redacted]	Cheryl Mills, White House Counsel's office, [redacted]	1:06
35	5:14 PM	Mr. Jordan's office, [redacted]	Frank Carter's office, [redacted]	8:24
36	5:22 PM	Mr. Jordan's office, [redacted]	Bruce Lindsey, White House, [redacted]	0:06
37	5:22 PM	Mr. Jordan's office, [redacted]	Cheryl Mills, White House Counsel's office, [redacted]	0:18
38	5:55 PM	Mr. Jordan's office, [redacted]	Ms. Currie's residence, [redacted]	0:24
39	5:56 PM	President Clinton	Mr. Jordan's office, [redacted]	7:00
40	6:04 PM	Mr. Jordan's office, [redacted]	Ms. Currie's residence, [redacted]	3:00
41	6:26 PM	Mr. Jordan's office, [redacted]	Stephen Goodin, White House, [redacted]	0:42

Source Documents

Calls 1, 2, 3, 4, 5, 7, 9, 12, 18, and 23:	831-DC-00000009 (Pagemart)
Calls 6 and 8:	V006-DC-00002069 (Presidential call log)
Call 10:	1178-DC-00000023 (Presidential call log)
Calls 11, 12, 13, 14, 15, 17, 19, 24, 25, 26, 27, 28, 29, 30, 31, 32, 33, 34, 35, 36, and 37:	V004-DC-00000165 (Akin, Gump, Strauss, Hauer & Feld call log)
Call 16, 39:	1248-DC-00003319 (Presidential call log)
Calls 20 and 22:	1033-DC-00000035 (Bell Atlantic Mobile toll records)

TABLE 48 continued

Call 21:	V006-DC-00002070 (Presidential call log)
Calls 38, 40, and 41:	V004-DC-00000166 (Akin, Gump, Strauss, Hauer & Feld call log)

Telephone Calls

TABLE 49

January 20, 1998

No.	Time	Call From	Call To	Length of Call
1	unknown	Frank Carter, no phone number indicated	Mr. Jordan (as per Mr. Jordan's message log)	N/A
2	unknown	Robert Bennett, no phone number indicated	Mr. Jordan (as per Mr. Jordan's message log)	N/A
3	10:41 AM	Mr. Jordan's office, [redacted]	Robert Bennett, [redacted]	3:48
4	12:01 P.M.	Mr. Jordan's office, [redacted]	Frank Carter's office, [redacted]	2:48
5	12:04 P.M.	Mr. Jordan's office, [redacted]	Frank Carter's office, [redacted]	0:06
6	unknown	Mr. Jordan at St. Regis Hotel	Bruce Lindsey, White House, [redacted]	unknown
7	unknown	Mr. Jordan at St. Regis Hotel	Robert Bennett, [redacted]	unknown
8	unknown	Mr. Jordan at St. Regis Hotel	White House, [redacted]	unknown

Source Documents

Calls 1 and 2: V005-DC-00000060-61 (Mr. Jordan's message log)

Calls 3, 4, and 5: V004-DC-00000166 (Akin, Gump, Strauss, Hauer & Feld call log)

Calls 6, 7, and 8: 1065-DC-00000006 (St. Regis Hotel receipt)

Telephone Calls

TABLE 50

January 21, 1998

No.	Time	Call From	Call To	Length of Call
1	12:09 AM	President Clinton	Robert Bennett's residence, [redacted]	30:00
2	12:41 AM	President Clinton	Bruce Lindsey's residence, [redacted]	29:00
3	1:16 AM	President Clinton	Ms. Currie's residence, [redacted]	20:00
4	1:36 AM	Bruce Lindsey's residence, [redacted]	President Clinton	2:00
5	1:39 AM	Bruce Lindsey's residence, [redacted]	President Clinton	1:00
6	7:14 AM	President Clinton	Bruce Lindsey's residence, [redacted]	8:00
7	7:26 AM	President Clinton	David Kendall's residence, [redacted]	28:00
8	8:02 AM	President Clinton	Robert Bennett's office, [redacted]	14:00
9	8:11 AM	Mr. Jordan at Revlon, [redacted]	Akin, Gump, Strauss, Hauer & Feld main line, [redacted]	0:30
10	8:19 AM	Mr. Jordan at Revlon, [redacted]	Cheryl Mills, White House Counsel's office, [redacted]	10:06
11	8:32 AM	Mr. Jordan at Revlon, [redacted]	Akin Gump, [redacted]	0:54
12	9:12 AM	Mr. Jordan at Revlon, [redacted]	Mr. Jordan's office, [redacted]	7:26
13	2:48 PM	Mr. Jordan's office, [redacted]	Cheryl Mills, White House Counsel's office, [redacted]	5:12
14	3:59 PM	Mr. Jordan's office, [redacted]	Frank Carter's office, [redacted]	0:24
15	4:00 PM	Mr. Jordan's office, [redacted]	Cheryl Mills, White House Counsel's office, [redacted]	0:06
16	4:01 PM	Mr. Jordan's office, [redacted]	Nancy Hernreich, White House, [redacted]	1:54

TABLE 50 continued

No.	Time	Call From	Call To	Length of Call
17	7:02 PM	Mr. Jordan's office, [redacted]	Frank Carter's office, [redacted]	0:36

Source Documents

Calls 1, 2, 3, 4, and 5:	1248-DC-00000327 (Presidential call log)
Call 6, 7, and 8:	1248-DC-00000328 (Presidential call log)
Calls 9, 10, and 11:	832-DC-00000004 (McAndrews and Forbes Holding toll records)
Call 12:	832-DC-00000005 (McAndrews and Forbes Holding toll records)
Calls 13, 14, 15, 16, and 17:	V004-DC-00000167 (Akin, Gump, Strauss, Hauer & Feld)

Tab H

Litigation History

LITIGATION HISTORY

I. Introduction

This investigation has centered around the behavior and actions of the President of the United States. As a consequence, it has been necessary to seek information from the White House, a variety of government officials, and the President himself. The President and the Department of Justice have vigorously sought to prevent this Office from obtaining this information, usually through litigation.

This memorandum is a brief chronology of the history of this Office's litigation against the President and government officials in the pursuit of evidence in the Lewinsky matter. This information should allow Congress to understand some of the gaps in the evidence we are providing. For example, we have not been able to report to Congress what the President told White House lawyers about his relationship with Monica Lewinsky. This memorandum explains the reason for this omission.

More importantly, Congress may wish to conduct its own investigation of the events related in this referral. In such an event, Congress may well face the same sort of litigation obstacles that this Office has. We hope that this memorandum will assist Congress in any efforts it finds necessary to obtain information relevant to its inquiry.

We have not included any description of litigation that did not involve our Office seeking investigative materials. Similarly, we have not included any litigation against persons or institutions other than President Clinton and his agents, the White House, or the Department of Justice. Specifically, we have not included our lengthy litigation with Monica S. Lewinsky and her agents.

The following is a brief description of the relevant events in this Office's litigation. Because we have provided Congress with the actual filings, we have not attempted to describe the filings in greater detail than necessary to understand the chronology of events. We encourage interested persons to consult the particular filings when an issue is significant.

II. Executive Privilege

Date	Event
Feb. 18, 1998	● Bruce Lindsey refuses to answer many questions before the grand jury because the answers are "potentially covered" by the following privileges: • Executive Privilege (presidential communications and deliberative process); • Governmental Attorney-Client Privilege and Work-Product Doctrine; • Personal Attorney-Client Privilege and Work Product Doctrine. Mr. Lindsey refuses either to invoke any such privilege or to contact President Clinton to determine whether to do so. ● Chief Judge Johnson instructs Lindsey to decide whether he will invoke privileges or not. (The next day, she mentions that "[i]f he had come in here today still not claiming any privileges and simply telling me he wasn't going to answer the questions, he would be in D.C. Jail by now." Tr. 53)

Feb. 19, 1998	• Neil Eggleston, a private lawyer hired by White House Counsel Charles Ruff, pursuant to Attorney General Janet Reno's authorization, to represent the White House with respect to executive privilege and governmental attorney-client privilege, informs Chief Judge Johnson that the President "has informed and directed Mr. Lindsey" to invoke privileges in response to various questions (Tr. 32). The OIC orally moves to compel him to testify. Chief Judge Johnson determines that she cannot decide the issue without a more developed record and orders that questioning continue. • Before the grand jury, Mr. Lindsey invokes all the privileges listed above. Among other things, he invokes executive privilege over a lunch conversation with Vernon Jordan.
Feb. 24, 1998	• The OIC issues a subpoena for Sidney Blumenthal to testify, seeking to discover what substantive information he has about the Lewinsky matter and to determine whether anyone in the White House is obstructing justice by spreading disinformation about the OIC. Mr. Blumenthal moves to quash, citing: • Executive Privilege; • the First Amendment; and • Overbreadth. Chief Judge Johnson holds a hearing and denies motion. • Before the grand jury, Mr. Blumenthal invokes executive privilege and refuses to answer several questions, including questions about his conversations with the First Lady.
Feb. 25, 1998	Nancy Hernreich, the administrator of the President's secretarial staff, testifies before the grand jury and invokes executive privilege and attorney client-privilege in refusing to answer several questions.
Mar. 4, 1998	Mr. Eggleston sends a proposal to the OIC suggesting an agreement whereby White House attorneys would be absolutely protected while White House non-attorneys would provide "factual information" but not "strategic deliberations and communications." Chief Judge Johnson later holds that the proposal was so vague that it was not worth considering: "Not only was the White House offer ambiguous, but there is also some question as to whether it was a firm offer. Given the ambiguity of the offer, the Court declines to factor it into its decision." Mem. Op. at 13 n.6 (May 4, 1998).

Mar. 6, 1998	The OIC moves to compel Bruce Lindsey (98-095), Sidney Blumenthal (98-096), and Nancy Hernreich (98-097) to testify over their assertions of executive privilege, governmental attorney-client privilege, and personal attorney-client privilege. The OIC argues that because the questions were about the President's personal conduct, executive privilege does not apply at all.
Mar. 10, 1998	The OIC files three motions (one for each case number) to expedite the executive privilege litigation. The OIC suggests a hearing for the week of March 23.
Mar. 12, 1998	The White House, responding to the motions to expedite, states that no hearing would be possible between March 22 and April 5 because the President, Mr. Lindsey, and Cheryl Mills would be traveling to Africa. The White House states that March 19 or 20 would be acceptable.
Mar. 13, 1998	The OIC files reply memoranda in support of its motions to expedite the executive privilege litigation. The OIC asserts that the week of March 23 still would be best, but that March 20 is better than a two-week delay.
Mar. 16, 1998	Chief Judge Johnson sets the executive privilege hearing for March 20.
Mar. 17, 1998	The White House files an opposition to the OIC's motions to compel testimony. President Clinton, in his personal capacity, intervenes to argue that intermediary privilege and various other personal attorney-client privilege theories prevent any testimony by Mr. Lindsey other than "cocktail talk" (as David Kendall, private attorney for President Clinton, said in oral argument before the D.C. Circuit). The White House drops the assertions of privilege by Ms. Hernreich.
Mar. 18, 1998	The OIC files three motions (one for each case number) to unseal the executive privilege litigation.
Mar. 19, 1998	The OIC files reply memoranda in support of its motions to compel. The White House moves to authorize release of papers to the Department of Justice ("DOJ"), and also responds to the earlier unsealing motion filed by the OIC. The White House requests that the March 20 hearing be held in secret but that the transcript later be released to the press.

Mar. 20, 1998	Oral argument before Chief Judge Johnson in the executive privilege litigation.
Mar. 24, 1998	Oral argument before Chief Judge Johnson on President Clinton's personal attorney-client privilege. The OIC discovers that President Clinton has denied knowledge of specific privilege assertions to the press. The OIC sends a letter to Mr. Eggleston seeking an explanation; Mr. Eggleston replies that President Clinton had authorized the invocation of privilege generally and had delegated to White House Counsel Charles Ruff the task of determining exactly what should be privileged.
Mar. 25, 1998	Chief Judge Johnson orders OIC to provide (by April 1) a need submission sufficient to overcome the White House's assertion of executive privilege.
Mar. 27, 1998	• The DOJ moves for access to pleadings, asks for 10 days to file amicus brief, and requests access to grand jury transcripts. The DOJ mistakenly represents that the OIC supports its motion. (Two days later, the DOJ withdraws this claim). This request comes one day after Mr. Lindsey moves for access to his grand jury transcript. • President Clinton files a supplemental memorandum in support of his personal attorney-client privilege invocation.
Mar. 31, 1998	• The OIC opposes the DOJ's motion for grand jury transcripts. • Chief Judge Johnson grants the DOJ access to sealed pleadings, but denies the DOJ's motion for grand jury transcripts. Chief Judge Johnson orders that any amicus brief be filed by April 8 (later extended to April 12 because of a delay in serving the court's order). • The White House files a supplemental memorandum regarding the Lindsey privilege assertions.
Apr. 1, 1998	The OIC files an in camera need submission, showing its need for materials covered by executive privilege.
Apr. 7, 1998	The White House files a document styled "Reply to the OIC's In Camera Submission." The White House argues, inter alia, that the OIC could not have shown need because it had not brought Mr. Blumenthal back before grand jury after the White House stated that he would testify as to "factual matters."

Apr. 12, 1998	The DOJ files an amicus brief criticizing the OIC's public-private distinction and arguing (contrary to the White House's position) that non-strategic factual information is covered by executive privilege. The DOJ also asserts that a balancing test is required to assess claims of governmental attorney-client privilege.
Apr. 15, 1998	Chief Judge Johnson orders the OIC to make a need submission for information covered by governmental attorney-client privilege by April 24.
Apr. 24, 1998	The OIC submits an in camera need submission detailing its need for information covered by governmental attorney-client privilege.
Apr. 30, 1998	The White House files a document styled as a reply to the OIC's in camera need submission. Inter alia, the White House argues that the OIC could not have shown need unless it had questioned "all other available witnesses."
May 4, 1998	Chief Judge Johnson issues an order compelling Messrs. Lindsey and Blumenthal to answer all questions.
May 11, 1998	The White House moves to reconsider the district court's opinion of May 4, 1998. Inter alia, the White House argues that Chief Judge Johnson erred in determining need by reference to categories of questions and in finding no common interest between the Office of the President and President Clinton in his personal capacity. The White House also argues for additional briefing of specific questions and in camera review of all answers.
May 13, 1998	The White House files notices of appeal from the executive privilege decision, despite the pending reconsideration motion. President Clinton in his personal capacity also appeals. The White House requests a slightly expedited 29/22/7 briefing schedule.
May 14, 1998	The OIC moves to dismiss the appeals of the White House and President Clinton from the executive privilege decision, arguing that the D.C. Circuit has no jurisdiction because the motion for reconsideration is still pending.
May 18, 1998	The White House responds to the OIC's motion to dismiss its appeal, largely agreeing with the motion and labeling its notice of appeal a "protective notice of appeal."

May 19, 1998	• The OIC files an opposition to the motion to reconsider the executive privilege decision. • The OIC files a reply in support of its motion to dismiss the appeals of the White House and President Clinton for want of jurisdiction.
May 21, 1998	The D.C. Circuit holds the executive privilege appeals in abeyance pending Chief Judge Johnson's decision on the motion for reconsideration.
May 22, 1998	The White House files a reply memorandum in support of its reconsideration motion.
May 26, 1998	Chief Judge Johnson substantially denies the White House's reconsideration motion. (She modifies one footnote that contains only dicta).
May 28, 1998	The OIC files in Supreme Court a petition for a writ of certiorari before judgment in the executive privilege case.
June 1, 1998	The White House files an opposition to the OIC's petition for a writ of certiorari before judgment. The White House drops its executive privilege appeal, asserting that it had decided not to appeal the executive privilege issue before the petition for a writ of certiorari before judgment was filed. President Clinton in his personal capacity also files a brief in opposition.
June 2, 1998	The OIC files a reply brief in support of its petition for a writ of certiorari before judgment in the (now) governmental attorney-client privilege appeal.
June 4, 1998	The Supreme Court denies the OIC's petition for a writ of certiorari before judgment in the governmental attorney-client privilege case.
June 5, 1998	The D.C. Circuit sets an expedited 10/7/3 briefing schedule in the governmental attorney-client privilege appeal.
June 15, 1998	The White House files a brief appealing the governmental attorney-client privilege ruling. President Clinton also files a brief on personal attorney-client privilege issues.

June 17, 1998	The DOJ files an amicus brief in the governmental attorney-client appeal, arguing that governmental attorney-client privilege should be more protected than executive privilege and that the need standard should be higher, and urging the D.C. Circuit to remand the issue whether there is an absolute governmental attorney-client privilege in the impeachment context.
June 22, 1998	The OIC files its appellee brief in the governmental attorney-client privilege appeal.
June 25, 1998	The White House and President Clinton file reply briefs in the governmental attorney-client privilege appeal.
June 26, 1998	The OIC files a supplemental filing in the governmental attorney-client privilege appeal.
June 29, 1998	Oral argument before the D.C. Circuit in the governmental attorney-client privilege appeal.
July 27, 1998	The D.C. Circuit rules that the governmental attorney-client privilege cannot be maintained in face of a federal grand jury subpoena.
July 31, 1998	The OIC issues a grand jury subpoena to Lanny Breuer, requiring his testimony on August 4.
Aug. 3, 1998	• The White House moves to stay any testimony by Bruce Lindsey pending disposition of a (as yet unfiled) petition for a writ of certiorari, and asks for a protective order preventing testimony of Mr. Breuer. The same day, the OIC files its opposition, and the D.C. Circuit denies the motion as unripe. • The White House asks the Supreme Court to stay any testimony by Messrs. Lindsey or Breuer pending the disposition of a (as yet unfiled) petition for a writ of certiorari. The OIC files an opposition to this motion. • Mr. Breuer moves to stay his testimony pending disposition of the White House's (as yet unfiled) petition for a writ of certiorari.

Aug. 4, 1998	• The Chief Justice denies the White House's motion to stay the testimony of Messrs. Lindsey and Breuer pending disposition of the White House's (as yet unfiled) petition for a writ of certiorari. • The OIC files an opposition to Mr. Breuer's motion to stay his grand jury testimony. Chief Judge Johnson allows questioning to go forward. While testifying before grand jury, Mr. Breuer invokes executive privilege and governmental attorney-client privilege. The OIC orally moves to compel Mr. Breuer's testimony.
Aug. 5, 1998	Chief Judge Johnson orders the parties to brief the executive privilege and governmental attorney-client privilege issues in an expedited fashion.
Aug. 6, 1998	The White House submits memoranda in support of Mr. Breuer's governmental attorney-client privilege claim and in support of a stay pending disposition of a (as yet unfiled) petition for a writ of certiorari. The White House also files a pleading arguing that <u>In re Lindsey</u> <u>sub silentio</u> overruled <u>In re Sealed Case</u>, raising the need standard required to overcome a claim of executive privilege. The OIC files an <u>in camera</u> need submission and a memorandum opposing a stay.
Aug. 7, 1998	Chief Judge Johnson compels Mr. Breuer to testify over his claims of governmental attorney-client privilege, but grants a stay pending appeal.
Aug. 11, 1998	Chief Judge Johnson compels Mr. Breuer to testify over his claims of executive privilege
Aug. 17, 1998	The White House and Mr. Breuer appeal from the district court's order compelling Mr. Breuer to testify over his claims of governmental attorney-client privilege. Mr. Breuer's appeal is dismissed by the D.C. Circuit, on the OIC's motion, three days later. (In grand jury testimony, President Clinton testifies that he strongly supported dropping executive privilege in May, that he never was afraid of the information the White House attorneys have, and that his only concern was to win judicial reaffirmation of existence of executive privilege.)

Aug. 21, 1998	• The White House and Mr. Breuer appeal from the order compelling Mr. Breuer to testify over his claims of executive privilege. Mr. Breuer's appeal is dismissed by the D.C. Circuit, on the OIC's motion, 10 days later. • The White House files a petition for a writ of certiorari in the governmental attorney-client privilege case.
Aug. 25, 1998	The White House moves to hold its Breuer appeal in abeyance pending disposition of petition for a writ of certiorari. The OIC supports that motion two days later, and the D.C. Circuit grants it four days after that.

Case Numbers

98-095	District Court	Bruce Lindsey testimony
98-096	District Court	Sidney Blumenthal testimony
98-097	District Court	Nancy Hernreich testimony
98-278	District Court	Lanny Breuer testimony
98-3060	D.C. Circuit	White House appeal re: Lindsey
98-3061	D.C. Circuit	White House appeal re: Blumenthal
98-3062	D.C. Circuit	Pres. Clinton appeal re: Lindsey
98-3072	D.C. Circuit	White House appeal re: Lindsey
98-3092	D.C. Circuit	Breuer appeal re: Breuer
98-3093	D.C. Circuit	White House appeal re: Breuer
98-3098	D.C. Circuit	Breuer appeal re: Breuer
98-3099	D.C. Circuit	White House appeal re: Breuer
97-1924	Supreme Court	OIC Petition for a Writ of Certiorari before Judgment
98-316	Supreme Court	White House Petition for a Writ of Certiorari

III. Secret Service "Protective Function Privilege"

Date	**Event**
late Jan.-early Feb.	Secret Service Director Lewis Merletti speaks informally to the OIC about why the OIC should not question Secret Service personnel.
Feb. 17, 1998	Former Secret Service officer Lewis Fox testifies before the grand jury.
Feb. 24, 1998	Deputy Assistant Attorney General Gary Grindler sends a letter to Independent Counsel Starr outlining the proposed "protective function" privilege.

Mar. 13, 1998	• Mr. Grindler sends another letter to the OIC outlining the proposed privilege. • The OIC deposes Secret Service officers Gary Byrne and Brian Henderson, who assert "protective function" privilege.
Mar. 23, 1998	The OIC deposes Secret Service General Counsel John Kelleher, who asserts the "protection function" privilege and the governmental attorney-client privilege.
Mar. 29, 1998	Attorney General Reno and Independent Counsel Starr meet to discuss the proposed "protective function" privilege.
Apr. 8, 1998	Deputy Independent Counsel Robert Bittman sends a letter to Mr. Grindler asking whether the President is invoking the "protective function" privilege. The next day, Mr. Grindler states that President Clinton has not directed assertion of a "protective function" privilege.
Apr. 10, 1998	The OIC moves to compel the testimony of Secret Service personnel over claims of "protective function" privilege and governmental attorney-client privilege.
Apr. 20, 1998	The DOJ and the OIC agree that the DOJ will proffer non-privileged information to the OIC and then allow interviews.
Apr. 21, 1998	The DOJ files an opposition to the OIC's motion to compel the testimony of Secret Service personnel.
Apr. 28, 1998	The OIC files a reply memorandum in support of compelling the testimony of Secret Service personnel.
May 11, 1998	White House Counsel Charles Ruff sends a letter to the OIC stating that President Clinton does not believe it is appropriate for him to instruct the Secret Service to testify.
May 14, 1998	Hearing before Chief Judge Johnson on the "protective function" privilege.

May 22, 1998	Chief Judge Johnson rules there is no "protective function" privilege for Secret Service personnel, and orders the OIC to provide a need showing to overcome governmental attorney-client privilege as to John Kelleher. Five days later, the OIC withdraws its request that the Secret Service lawyer testify.
May 25, 1998	Four former Attorney Generals send a letter to Attorney General Reno urging her not to appeal the Secret Service decision.
May 27, 1998	Independent Counsel Starr meets with Solicitor General Seth Waxman, urging the DOJ not to appeal the Secret Service decision.
May 29, 1998	Independent Counsel Starr meets with Attorney General Reno, urging the DOJ not to appeal the Secret Service decision. Later, DOJ attorney Jonathan Schwartz suggests a compromise, and the OIC expresses interest.
May 31, 1998	In a meeting between the OIC and DOJ attorneys, the DOJ proposes a settlement that the OIC believes is far less favorable to the OIC than that suggested by Mr. Schwartz two days earlier. The OIC rejects the proposal.
June 1, 1998	The DOJ files a notice of appeal in the Secret Service case and proposes an expedited 14/14/7 briefing schedule.
June 2, 1998	The OIC files a petition for a writ of certiorari before judgment in the Secret Service appeal.
June 3, 1998	The DOJ files a brief in response to the OIC's petition for a writ of certiorari before judgment in Secret Service appeal, criticizing the petition but not urging its denial.
June 4, 1998	The Supreme Court denies the OIC's petition for a writ of certiorari before judgment in the Secret Service appeal.
June 5, 1998	The D.C. Circuit sets an expedited 7/7/3 briefing schedule in the Secret Service appeal.
June 9, 1998	Mr. Grindler asserts in a letter to Mr. Bittman that the "protective function" privilege applies to former Secret Service personnel.

June 11, 1998	Mr. Bittman sends a letter to Neil Eggleston asking him whether the White House would assert executive privilege over a particular conversation overheard by a Secret Service officer.
June 12, 1998	The DOJ files a brief appealing the Secret Service decision. Former Secret Service agents file an amicus brief in support of the DOJ's position.
June 15, 1998	In a letter to Mr. Bittman, Mr. Eggleston informs the OIC that the White House is not asserting executive privilege over the conversation overheard by a Secret Service officer.
June 19, 1998	The OIC files its appellee brief in the Secret Service appeal. Four former Attorney Generals file an amicus brief in support of the OIC's position.
June 22, 1998	The DOJ files a reply brief in the Secret Service appeal.
July 7, 1998	The D.C. Circuit holds that there is no "protective function" privilege.
July 13, 1998	The OIC subpoenas six Secret Service officers, one agent, and one former agent.
July 14, 1998	• The DOJ petitions for rehearing and suggests rehearing en banc in the Secret Service appeal. • The DOJ moves for stay pending appeal (and protective order) of the Secret Service decision.
July 15, 1998	• The OIC files an opposition to the DOJ's motion for a stay pending appeal of the Secret Service decision. Chief Judge Johnson holds an oral hearing on the motion. • The DOJ moves for a stay pending appeal of the Secret Service decision (and a protective order) in the D.C. Circuit. The OIC files an opposition to that motion. • The DOJ moves in the Supreme Court for a stay and a protective order preventing Secret Service testimony. The OIC files an opposition.

July 16, 1998	• Chief Judge Johnson declines to grant a stay pending appeal of the Secret Service decision. • After approximately one minute of testimony by a Secret Service officer, the D.C. Circuit grants an administrative stay of Secret Service testimony, to consider the stay motion. • Later that day, the D.C. Circuit denies the petition for rehearing and suggestion for rehearing en banc and vacates the stay. The D.C. Circuit issues a temporary stay until Noon the next day, to allow Supreme Court to decide whether to grant a stay. • The DOJ files a petition for a writ of certiorari in the Secret Service case.
July 17, 1998	• The OIC files a brief in opposition to the DOJ's petition for a writ of certiorari in the Secret Service case. • The DOJ files a reply brief in support of its stay motion. The Chief Justice denies the stay. • Secret Service officers testify.

Case Numbers

98-148	District Court	Secret Service Testimony
98-3069	D.C. Circuit	Secret Service Testimony
98-3085	D.C. Circuit	Protective Order
97-1942	Supreme Court	OIC Petition for a Writ of Certiorari before Judgment
98-93	Supreme Court	DOJ Petition for a Writ of Certiorari

IV. White House Documents

Date	**Event**
May 27, 1998	The OIC files a motion to compel the White House to comply with grand jury subpoenas for President Clinton's meeting records and phone logs. The White House had been redacting such documents on relevancy grounds and refusing to provide phone logs unless the OIC gave them a list of all persons in which the grand jury was interested.
June 12, 1998	The White House files an opposition to the OIC's motion to compel production of meeting records and phone logs, and tries to "reserve[] the right to assert executive privilege over the material."

June 19, 1998	The OIC files a reply memorandum in support of its motion to compel the White House to produce meeting records and phone logs.
June 26, 1998	Chief Judge Johnson orders the White House to produce meeting records and phone logs to the grand jury.

Case Number
98-202 District Court White House documents

V. Presidential Testimony

Date	Event
July 17, 1998	The OIC issues a grand jury subpoena for President Clinton's testimony on July 28.
July 22, 1998	David Kendall, President Clinton's private attorney, calls Deputy Independent Counsel Robert Bittman and asks to have until August 4 to respond to the grand jury subpoena to President Clinton.
July 23, 1998	Mr. Bittman offers Mr. Kendall an extension until July 31, conditioned on Mr. Kendall agreeing not to seek additional time.
July 24, 1998	Mr. Kendall sends a letter to Mr. Bittman stating that the President is willing to "provide testimony" to grand jury. He insists that the grand jury subpoena be withdrawn, asserting that he would explain why on July 28. Mr. Bittman responds by letter, refusing to withdraw the subpoena until, at very least, President Clinton agrees upon a firm date.
July 27, 1998	Mr. Kendall sends another letter to Mr. Bittman, stating that President would testify but only if (i) the grand jury subpoena were withdrawn; (ii) the testimony were given in the White House, with a time limit and with a description of the general subject areas of questioning; (iii) there were protection against leaks; and (iv) the testimony were no earlier than September 13. Mr. Kendall states that President Clinton cannot testify during his vacation because he would be preparing for a foreign trip. Mr. Bittman responds that any date later than August 7 would be unacceptable.

July 28, 1998	President Clinton moves to postpone any response to the grand jury subpoena until August 11. He wants until this date even to decide whether he will testify or oppose the subpoena. That afternoon, Chief Judge Johnson holds a hearing.
July 30, 1998	Having agreed to testify on August 17, President withdraws his motion for continuance. (Chief Judge Johnson had been prepared to rule earlier, but withheld her ruling to encourage a settlement.)
Aug. 17, 1998	President Clinton testifies to grand jury.

Case Number
98-267 District Court Presidential subpoena

VI. Terry Lenzner Subpoena

Date	Event
Feb. 24, 1998	Williams & Connolly and Skadden Arps file a motion to quash the grand jury subpoena issued to Terry F. Lenzner and Investigative Group International, Inc. (After hearing reports that Mr. Lenzner and IGI were researching the private lives of career prosecutors, the OIC had issued this subpoena to try to determine whether this was true and, if so, whether this was part of scheme to obstruct the OIC's investigation.) After the President's law firms claim attorney-client privilege and work product protection, Mr. Lenzner appears, provides a privilege log of documents, and refuses to reveal the general subject matter of his retention.
Mar. 9, 1998	The OIC files an opposition to the motion to quash the grand jury subpoena, arguing that the attorney-client privilege does not protect the general subject matter of retention, amount of fees, or identity of fee payer.
Mar. 16, 1998	Williams & Connolly and Skadden Arps file a reply memorandum in support of their motion to quash Lenzner subpoena.

July 29, 1998	Chief Judge Johnson issues an order on the grand jury subpoena to Terry Lenzner, ruling that Mr. Lenzner must provide all fee information to the grand jury, but that the general subject matter of his retention is protected by the attorney-client privilege.

Tab I

Evidence Reference

EVIDENCE REFERENCE

Although the Office of the Independent Counsel has gathered and verified the information presented in this Referral from a wide variety of sources, the information falls into two broad categories. First, there is the direct testimony of numerous witnesses, who were called before grand juries, deposed under oath, or questioned by agents of the Federal Bureau of Investigation. Second, information was obtained from the many documents, tapes, and physical objects which the Office has subpoenaed and collected -- including some of the many gifts exchanged by the President and Monica Lewinsky, the logs kept by the White House and the Secret Service (which record entries and exits of staff and visitors, the movements of the President, and telephone calls involving the President), and private records (such as appointment diaries, business telephone logs, and financial records).

This section discusses some of the issues and questions related to the evidence that might arise when reviewing the Referral. Part I provides an overview of the potential rules for the admissibility of evidence, drawing a comparison between the rules that would apply in a courtroom and those that may apply in Congress. Part II briefly describes the particular evidence sources upon which we rely -- focusing upon those that may be unfamiliar -- and provides the footnote citation forms for each type of source. Part III discusses the tape recorded conversations made by Linda Tripp. The first section in Part III addresses potential problems raised by the possibility that some of the tapes that were made by Linda Tripp and turned over to the OIC are duplicate, rather than original, tapes. The second section then explains in detail how the Office was able to assign dates to the particular conversations on the tapes.

I. ADMISSIBILITY

Much of the OIC's investigative time and effort was devoted to verifying information provided by the main witnesses: it pursued corroborating witnesses, telephone records, gift receipts, correspondence, movement logs, and other evidence that would support or refute the critical facts. In making the reliability of the evidence the touchstone of the investigation, the OIC nevertheless recognized that some of the information gathered and cited in the Referral might not be admissible in a judicial trial. For example, a court might not permit a jury to consider testimony by one Secret Service officer about what he heard another Secret Service officer say. If that testimony were used to prove that what the first officer said was true, then the testimony would be "hearsay," which is inadmissible at a trial under the Federal Rules of Evidence (unless an exception applies).[1]

In compiling this Referral, the OIC has thought carefully about the role of federal evidentiary rules. Whenever feasible, the OIC has sought direct and circumstantial evidence that federal courts would admit, and indeed, this Office believes that the vast majority of the salient facts are supported by this type of information. Ultimately, however, the Office chose not to limit itself to *judicially* admissible evidence for several reasons.

---

[1] See Fed. R. Evid. 801-804 (discussing hearsay rules and exceptions).

First, the Rules of Evidence sometimes exclude reliable evidence for reasons that the OIC considers inapplicable in the context of this Referral. For instance, some rules of evidence address special concerns of the jury system. The hearsay rule is one example: If the jury hears only a report of what a declarant has said, it ordinarily cannot assess the declarant's perception, memory, narration, or sincerity. This Office believes that the inclusion of hearsay information is appropriate in the context of this Referral, however, both because 28 U.S.C. § 595(c) contemplates a written referral that necessarily prevents the assessment of live witnesses, and because members of the House of Representatives may conduct their own investigation and call witnesses directly.

Second, the Congress need not adhere to the Federal Rules of Evidence when deciding whether to impeach federal officers. The House of Representatives historically has delegated the task of gathering information to a committee (usually, the Judiciary Committee), which traditionally has collected and considered evidence that would be inadmissible in federal court.[2] Similarly, although the Senate customarily has followed some

---

[2] See House Rules Manual (House Document No. 104-272) §§ 603-606 (1998) (describing House procedures for investigating prior to voting whether to impeach); Charles L. Black, Jr., Impeachment: A Handbook 7 (1974) (describing the impeachment process in the House). The committee, however, does take evidentiary concerns into account when assessing the strength of the case for impeachment. See Warren S. Grimes, Hundred-Ton-Gun Control: Preserving Impeachment as the Exclusive Removal Mechanism For Federal Judges, 38 UCLA L. Rev. 1209, 1226 (1991).

evidentiary rules in impeachment proceedings,[3] it has no fixed set of evidentiary rules.[4] The Constitution requires the Senate merely to "try" impeachments.[5] It does not specify the requirements for trial, and the federal courts will not review the procedures that the Senate decides to use.[6] In an impeachment proceeding, therefore, the Senate also is not obligated to follow the Federal Rules of Evidence,[7] and may choose to disregard or relax some rules that would apply in a trial conducted by the judiciary branch.[8]

---

[3] See Stephen B. Burbank, Alternative Career Resolution: An Essay on the Removal of Federal Judges, 76 Ky. L.J. 643, 693 (1988) (noting that the Senate has always applied some rules of evidence); 3 Asher C. Hinds, Hinds' Precedents of the House of Representatives 537-643 (1907) (describing evidentiary rules used by the Senate in 19th-century impeachment trials).

[4] The Senate has adopted a set of "Rules of Procedure and Practice in the Senate When Sitting on Impeachment Trials." Senate Manual (Senate Document 104-1) 177-185 (1998). These rules do not include rules of evidence, however. See id.; see also Michael J. Gerhardt, Rediscovering Nonjusticiability: Judicial Review of Impeachments after Nixon, 44 Duke L.J. 231, 267 (1994)(discussing the possibility of adopting rules of evidence for impeachments).

[5] See U.S. Const. art. I, § 3, cl. 6.

[6] See Nixon v. United States, 506 U.S. 224, 230 (1993) (holding that "the word 'try' in the first sentence of the Impeachment Trial Clause lacks sufficient precision to afford any judicially manageable standard of review of the Senate's actions").

[7] See Black, supra note 2, at 18; see also Hastings v. United States Senate, Impeachment Trial Committee, 716 F. Supp. 38 (D.D.C.), aff'd sub nom. Nixon v. United States Senate, 887 F.2d 332 (D.C. Cir. 1989) ("It is clear that the federal rules of evidence do not apply in impeachment trials ....").

[8] See Michael J. Broyde, Expediting Impeachment: Removing Article III Federal Judges after Criminal Conviction, 17 Harv. J.L. & Pub. Pol'y 157, 180 n.97 (1994) (noting that the Senate

Third, many of the Rules of Evidence would serve little purpose in an impeachment context. As Professor Charles L. Black, Jr., explained:

> [The] technical rules of evidence were elaborated primarily to hold *juries* within narrow limits. They have no place in the impeachment process. Both the House and the Senate ought to hear and consider *all* evidence which seems relevant, without regard to technical rules. Senators are in any case continually exposed to "hearsay" evidence; they cannot be sequestered and kept away from newspapers, like a jury. If they cannot be trusted to weigh evidence, appropriately discounting for all the factors of unreliability that have led to our keeping evidence away from juries, then they are not in any way up to the job, and "rules of evidence" will not help.[9]

The Congress therefore may decide in a particular impeachment trial to adopt only a few broad rules that exclude irrelevant evidence, but that generally admit any other reliable evidence.[10]

---

often relaxes the rules of evidence).

[9] Black, supra note 2, at 18. Other scholars have echoed this analysis. See Michael J. Gerhardt, The Constitutional Limits to Impeachment and its Alternatives, 68 Tex. L. Rev. 1, 93 (1991) ("The concerns leading to the use of special rules of evidence in state and federal courts do not apply to impeachment proceedings."); Broyde, supra note 9, at 180 n.97 (arguing that the rules of evidence "are designed to prevent confusion or manipulation of a lay jury and are not really necessary in the Senate, which includes many lawyers").

[10] Professor Stephen B. Burbank has recommended that the Senate exclude irrelevant evidence but admit relevant hearsay. See Burbank, supra note 4, at 693. He explains:

> Relevance remains the cornerstone of modern evidence law, and it is an imperative for impeachment trials as much as for any other trial. Hearsay, if by that word we intend the elaborate and largely irrational system accreted over two centuries of distrust for juries, is not a cornerstone of anything except the incomes of law professors. Trustworthiness and necessity should be the dominant considerations in the Senate's decision

II. UNDERSTANDING THE EVIDENCE

For the reader's convenience, this part briefly describe the sources of evidence upon which the Office has relied. Each description includes the abbreviated footnote form used in the rest of the Referral to refer to the particular source.

A. Direct Testimony

Testimony before the grand jury and testimony given in a deposition is given under oath, while testimony provided in interviews with the OIC is not.

1. Grand Jury Testimony.

The Grand Jury has heard the sworn testimony of many witnesses during the course of this investigation. Questions posed to witnesses before the grand jury may be asked either by members of the Independent Counsel's Office, or by members of the grand jury. Every question and answer spoken in the grand jury is recorded and then transcribed by a professional transcriber who is not affiliated with the OIC. Information gained from grand jury testimony is referred to in the footnotes with [name] [date] GJ at [#]. "GJ," of course, refers to "grand jury." The rest of the details identify the name of the witness, the date of that particular testimony, and the pages of the transcript upon which the information appears.

> whether to admit relevant evidence that is hearsay according to whatever test is accepted.

Id. at 693-94 (footnotes omitted).

2. Deposition Testimony.

A deposition is a sworn statement in which a person responds to questions from the opposing side in a civil case. Depositions are recorded and then transcribed word-for-word by an independent transcriber. Depositions are cited in the footnotes as "[name] [date] Depo. at [#]. This format provides the last name of the person who testified at the deposition, the date of the deposition, and the page number(s) of the transcript pages relied upon. Thus, for example, President Clinton's deposition of January 17, 1998, which is frequently cited in the Referral, is referred to in the footnotes as "Clinton 1/17/98 Depo. at __."

3. Interviews with FBI Agents.

During the course of the investigation, FBI agents have interviewed many witnesses and taken detailed notes of those interviews. Although interviewees do not take an oath to answer truthfully, a knowing misstatement of a material fact to an FBI agent during the course of an investigation is subject to criminal punishment.[11] An FBI interview is referred to in the footnotes as "[name] [date] Int. at [#]." This citation format provides the last name of the person interviewed, the date of the particular interview, and the page of the interview notes upon which the information in the text appears.

---

[11] 18 U.S.C. § 1001.

B. Subpoenaed Documentary and Physical Evidence

A subpoena is a legal command issued to a person or entity by the authority of a court. A subpoena may direct a person to appear and give testimony at a trial or deposition, or, as discussed in this section, may also direct that the recipient turn over documents or things to the investigating authority -- in this case, the OIC. The recipient of a subpoena must either truthfully and fully produce the material described in the subpoena, or challenge the subpoena in court. Generally, a person producing materials in response to a subpoena will then "verify" under penalty of perjury that the materials produced are truly those called for by the subpoena, and that the person does not have other responsive documents that he has not produced. Subpoenas may seek government, financial, or personal records; they may also seek tangible physical things such as clothing or tapes. The OIC has served and received responses to a large number of subpoenas during the course of this investigation. Some of the specific types of documents are described in greater detail in the next part of this section.

Information derived from subpoenas is referred to in the footnotes in the following way: ###-DC-########. The first three (or four)-digit number refers to the subpoena's place in the sequence of all subpoenas served during the course of this investigation. "DC" indicates that the subpoena was issued from the D.C. office.[12] The eight-digit number indicates the particular page or pages of the document(s) produced in response to the subpoena that are being relied upon. Because the response to one subpoena may include many different documents, all of which would share the same initial number, the OIC has at times provided a parenthetical reference after the numbered reference (which gives the type of document -- or the name of the particular document -- being referenced).

1. White House Records.

[redacted][13] [redacted]

a. White House Access Logs

[redacted]

---

[12] A few subpoena references begin with the letter "V." This indicates that they were issued from a Virginia grand jury.

[13] B. Smith, Moffit, Dougherty, and Dates 3/16/98 Int. at 1.

[redacted][14] [redacted]

(i) Epass records

[redacted][15] [redacted][16] [redacted]

[14] Dougherty 2/11/98 Int. at 2.

[15] Id.

[16] Id.

[redacted]

[redacted][17] [redacted].[18] [redacted].

(ii) **WAVES records**

[redacted][19] [redacted][20] [redacted]. [redacted]

[17] Dougherty 2/11/98 Int. at 2.

[18] Id.

[19] B. Smith et al. 3/16/98 Int. at 4.

[20] Id.

[redacted][21] [redacted][22] [redacted][23] [redacted][24] [redacted].[25]

[redacted]

---

[21] Id.

[22] B. Smith et al. 3/16/98 Int. at 2.

[23] Id.

[24] Id.

[25] Dougherty 2/11/98 Int. at 1-2.

[redacted][26] [redacted][27] [redacted][28]

b. Presidential Telephone Logs

[redacted][29] [redacted][30] [redacted][31] [redacted]

---

[26] B. Smith 3/16/98 Int. at 3.

[27] Id.

[28] Id.

[29] Nagy 2/19/98 Int. at 1.

[30] Nagy 2/19/98 Int. at 2; S. Smith 7/20/98 Depo. at 18, 24.

[31] Nagy 2/19/98 Int. at 1; S. Smith 7/20/98 Depo. at 36-37.

(i) **WHTS**

[redacted].[32] [redacted][33] [redacted][34] [redacted][35] [redacted].[36]

[redacted].[37] [redacted]

[redacted]

---

[32] Nagy 5/18/98 Depo. at 9-10.

[33] Id.

[34] Nagy 5/18/98 Depo. at 44.

[35] Nagy 2/19/98 Int. at 2.

[36] Nagy 2/19/98 Int. at 4.

[37] Nagy 5/18/98 Depo. at 69-71.

[redacted].[38] [redacted][39]

(ii) WHCA

[redacted].[40] [redacted].[41] [redacted].[42] [redacted]

[38] Nagy 5/18/98 Depo at 69.

[39] Nagy 5/18/98 Depo. at 69-70.

[40] S. Smith 7/20/98 Depo. at 19. [redacted]

[41] Id. at 20-21.

[42] Id. at 36-41.

[redacted].[43] [redacted].[44]

[redacted].[45] [redacted].[46] [redacted][47] [redacted].[48]

2. United States Secret Service Records.

[redacted]

---

[43] Id. at 38-41.

[44] Id. at 37.

[45] Id. at 47-50.

[46] Id.

[47] Id.

[48] Id.

a. Uniform Division Itineraries

[redacted].[49] [redacted].[50] [redacted]

b. POTUS Movement Logs/ First Family Locator Command Post Log

[redacted]

c. Protective Operations Activity and Personnel Reports

[redacted]

---

[49] Wilson 7/23/98 GJ at 14-15.

[50] Id.

[redacted][51] [redacted][52] [redacted][53] [redacted].[54]

d. F1 Movement Logs

[redacted][55] [redacted][56]

---

[51] Wilson 7/23/98 GJ at 19-20.

[52] Id.

[53] Id. at 62.

[54] Id. at 29-31, 40-43.

[55] [redacted]

[56] Wilson 7/23/98 GJ at 54-55.

C. Other Documentary and Physical Evidence

1. Searches.

The OIC has also obtained documentary and physical evidence through voluntary production of that evidence and through searches of certain locations, such as Ms. Lewinsky's apartment and Ms. Tripp's house. The search of Ms. Lewinsky's apartment is referred to in the footnotes as "MSL-55-DC-####." The transcript of Ms. Lewinsky's telephone answering machine tapes is referred to as "Search.001 at #.

The search of Ms. Tripp's house was directed solely toward finding the tapes she made of conversations with Ms. Lewinsky. The tapes are cited as T# at #. "T#" refers to the number of the tape on which the conversation is recorded, and "at #" refers to the transcript page on which the transcribed conversation appears. (Details of how the tapes were dated are given in Part III, below.)

2. The Dress.

In accordance with her cooperation agreement, on July 29, 1998, Ms. Lewinsky produced to the OIC a navy blue dress that she said might contain stains corroborating the sexual nature of her relationship with the President.[57] The OIC subsequently submitted the dress to the FBI lab for examination.[58] On Friday, July 31, 1998, the FBI lab orally informed the OIC that the

---

[57] See FBI form FD-597, Receipt for Property, 7/29/98.

[58] See Memorandum, FBI File No. 29D-OIC-LR-35063, Lab No. 980730002 S BO, Aug. 3, 1998.

stains on the dress tested positive for human semen, and recommended that the OIC obtain a blood sample from any known subject.[59] On August 3, 1998, in the presence of FBI and OIC personnel, the President provided a blood sample, which was turned over to the FBI for comparison.[60]

The first examination the FBI conducted was a PCR-based DNA test.[61] On August 6, 1998, the FBI notified the OIC that all the PCR markers from the test matched the DNA of President Clinton.[62] The FBI lab was able to extract enough quality DNA from the dress for additional analysis, so it began an RFLP-based DNA test.[63] During the week of August 10, the FBI lab orally informed the OIC that, based on its continuing comparison using RFLP, the lab believed its tests would show a more discriminating match between the DNA from the semen stain and the President's DNA. On the morning of August 17, 1998, the FBI formally concluded that the

---

59 See Report of Examination, FBI File No. 29D-OIC-LR-35063, Lab No. 980730002 S BO, Aug. 3, 1998.

60 See FBI Memorandum of SSA Jenifer A.L. Smith, Aug. 3, 1998.

61 PCR is the acronym for polymerase chain reaction, a less definitive DNA test that can be completed relatively quickly and requires only a small specimen of genetic material.

62 The FBI concluded that the "probability of selecting an unrelated individual [from President Clinton's population] at random" was 1 in 43,000. Report of Examination, FBI File No. 29D-OIC-LR-35063, Lab Nos. 980730002 S BO and 980803100 S BO, Aug. 6, 1998.

63 RFLP is the acronym for restriction fragment length polymorphism, an extremely definitive DNA test that requires a generous, high quality DNA specimen and usually takes additional time.

President "is the source of the DNA obtained from [Ms. Lewinsky's dress], to a reasonable degree of scientific certainty."[64]

III. CONVERSATIONS TAPED BY LINDA TRIPP.

A. Background

After receiving court-ordered immunity under 18 U.S.C. §6002, Linda Tripp produced several cassette tapes and testified before the grand jury.[65] Among other subjects, she discussed notes and tape recordings she made of several conversations between herself and Monica Lewinsky.

Ms. Lewinsky began confiding in Ms. Tripp soon after Ms. Lewinsky began working at the Pentagon. Ms. Tripp took two sets of notes during their conversations. The first notes are in a Skilcraft Steno Notebook.[66] Ms. Tripp testified she took these between May 23, 1997, and July 1997.[67] The second notes are on a series of papers. Ms. Tripp testified she took these during

---

[64] Report of Examination, FBI File No. 29D-OIC-LR-35063, Lab Nos. 980730002 S BO and 980803100 S BO, Aug. 17, 1998. The FBI concluded that the "probability of selecting an unrelated individual [from President Clinton's population] at random" was 1 in 7.87 trillion.

[65] See Tripp GJ, 6/30/98, pg. 8-14 (The Office of the Independent Counsel also promised Ms. Tripp that it would do what it could to persuade the State of Maryland from prosecuting Ms. Tripp for any violations of the state wiretapping law.).

[66] 845-DC-00000001-25.

[67] May 23, 1997, is the last date recorded in the notebook. Linda Tripp testified she wrote the book in July, see Tripp 7/7/98 GJ at 111, but did so before she knew about the contact between Ms. Lewinsky and Bruce Lindsey on July 14, 1997. Id. at 135.

several conversations, starting in September 1997.[68] Ms. Tripp indicated that Ms. Lewinsky was aware of the first note-taking but not the second.[69] Ms. Lewinsky said, though, that she never knew Ms. Tripp was taking notes.[70]

From approximately October 3, 1997, to January 15, 1998, Linda Tripp tape recorded many of her telephone conversations with Monica Lewinsky. According to Ms. Tripp, on October 3, 1997, she purchased a voice activated tape recorder with a manual pause capability from Radio Shack (model CTR107), and connected it to a telephone in the study of her home. Ms. Tripp testified that she set the system to record all conversations from the study telephone so long as there was a tape in the machine and the machine remained on. Ms. Tripp added that because of the length of the conversations and the tapes, most of the tapes contain several conversations. As Ms. Tripp further told the grand jury, because the recorder was always working unless she turned it off, she captured conversations with people other than Ms. Lewinsky.

On October 6, 1997, after making two tapes, Ms. Tripp met in

---

[68] Tripp GJ 7/16/98 at 112-13.

[69] Tripp 7/7/98 GJ at 108-109, 160; Tripp 7/16/98 GJ at 113.

[70] The dates in the notebook sometimes appear to be a day or two off. One note, for instance, refers to Sunday, March 30, 1996; Sunday actually fell on March 31. See 845-DC-00000011 (notes); Tripp GJ 7/9/98 at 17. Ms. Tripp surmised that Ms. Lewinsky was consulting a 1997 calendar for dates without realizing the discrepancy. Tripp GJ 7/9/98 at 18.

Washington, D.C. with her friend Lucianne Goldberg, Jonah Goldberg (Ms. Goldberg's son), and Michael Isikoff. After this meeting, Ms. Goldberg kept the two tapes and brought them to New York. Ms. Goldberg made copies of these tapes, and she presented the two originals and copies of them to the Office of the Independent Counsel in January 1998.

Ms. Tripp told the grand jury she continued to make recordings and keep them in a bowl on a piece of furniture. She testified that around the beginning of 1998, she gave most of the tapes to her lawyer, Kirby Behre. According to Ms. Tripp, she changed attorneys and retained Jim Moody. She stated that Mr. Moody obtained the tapes from Mr. Behre and provided them to the OIC in early January 1998.

Later, the OIC received four additional tapes from Ms. Tripp. On March 3, 1998, Ms. Tripp searched her home with the help of her new attorney, Anthony Zaccagnini, and several FBI Special Agents assigned to the OIC. During this search, Ms. Tripp and the others found three additional tapes. After previewing these tapes on the cassette player in his car, Mr. Zaccagnini presented them to the Special Agents. Ms. Tripp told the grand jury that just before March 17, 1998, she found another tape in her home and gave it to Mr. Zaccagnini. He brought it to the Office of the Independent Counsel on March 17, 1998.

The OIC provided to the FBI Audio Signal Analysis Unit in Quantico, Virginia, all of the tapes obtained from Ms. Tripp. This unit is engaged in the elaborate and time-consuming process of authenticating the tapes, but it has provided some results.

* Examination has preliminarily determined that 8 of the tapes submitted do not exhibit signs of duplication.

* Examination has preliminarily determined that 9 of the tapes submitted exhibit characteristics that are not consistent with being recorded on the Radio Shack CTR107 tape recorder Ms. Tripp says she used to record the original tapes.

* Examination has preliminarily determined that the 9 tapes inconsistent with the tape recorder Ms. Tripp says she used exhibit signs of duplication.

* Examination has preliminarily determined that 7 of the tapes that exhibit signs of duplication are consistent with the use of one tape recorder to duplicate.

* The examination has preliminarily determined that one of the tapes that exhibits signs of duplication was produced by a recorder that was stopped during the recording process.

These results raise three important issues. First, the Office of the Independent Counsel does not possess original recordings for nine of the tapes Ms. Tripp made. Two of these tapes contain inaudible recordings. Second, the OIC is not aware who made the "likely to be duplicate" tapes. Third, if Ms. Tripp duplicated any tapes herself or knew of their duplication, then she has lied under oath before the grand jury and in a deposition. The OIC continues to investigate this matter.

In light of these three issues, and to help ensure the reliability, authenticity, and accuracy of the evidence, the accompanying submission only refers to recorded conversations which meet four conditions: (1) the recorded conversation is contained on a tape that FBI examination has preliminarily determined not to exhibit signs of duplication; (2) Monica Lewinsky has listened to the recording and identified her voice and Linda Tripp's voice;[71] (3) Monica Lewinsky has identified the recording as an accurate depiction of a conversation she remembers;[72] and (4) there is independent evidence to corroborate the contents of the recorded conversation.

Even though they do not appear in the submission, the Office of Independent Counsel has provided all of the recorded conversations as raw evidence. Consequently, a fourth issue arises when assigning dates to the tapes that exhibit signs of duplication.

When a tape was filled with recorded conversations, Ms. Tripp removed the tape and stored it in the bowl. Ms. Tripp did not mark the tapes, and she did not catalog them. As a result, the only way to determine which day Ms. Tripp recorded each tape was to use the information she provided while she was debriefed,[73] combined with information from the conversations.

---

[71] Ms. Lewinsky stated with respect to these recordings that she believes the voice on the tapes is hers, based on "intonation and content."

[72] Although Ms. Lewinsky cannot attest to whether there are missing portions of the conversations, she could not recall any specific conversation that was excluded from the particular conversations on the tapes. Ms. Lewinsky noted, however, that she had many more conversations with Linda Tripp about certain subject matters than were captured on tape.

[73] Ms. Tripp appeared at the Office of the Independent Counsel on many occasions between January 1998, and July 1998. During most of her initial visits, Ms. Tripp listened to the recordings of her conversations with Ms. Lewinsky and compared them with transcripts that the Office of the Independent Counsel prepared. Ms. Tripp corrected the transcripts as necessary. Ms. Tripp told the grand jury that the tapes accurately depict her conversations with Ms. Lewinsky and that the transcripts are accurate.

For the seven tapes which contain audible conversations and which exhibit signs of duplication, the Office of the Independent Counsel cannot exclude the possibility of tampering at this time. For this reason, the Office of the Independent Counsel cannot have full confidence that the dates assigned to these tapes are accurate. The following appendix represents the opinion of the Independent Counsel regarding the date of each tape. The tapes that exhibit signs of duplication are marked to reduce the possibility of confusion.

B. Dating the Tape Recorded Conversations

The following discussion represents the opinion of the Office of the Independent Counsel regarding the date of each tape. Although they are assigned dates, the duplicates are marked to reduce the possibility of confusion.

In her later visits to the Office of the Independent Counsel, Ms. Tripp participated in debriefing sessions with investigators and attorneys. One aspect of these sessions included eliciting information about the tapes and when Ms. Tripp made them.

1. Reference Charts Summarizing The Dates of the Tapes

Conversations Listed By Date

1. Friday, October 3, 1997:
Tape 18, side A, first conversation on tape.
Transcript pages: 2-25.

2. Friday, October 3, 1997:
Tape 18, side A, second conversation on tape.
Transcript pages: 25-71.

3. Saturday, October 4, 1997:
Tape 18, side B, third conversation on tape.
Transcript pages: 71-110.

4. Sunday, October 5, 1997:
Tape 19, side A, first conversation on tape.
Transcript pages: 2-21.

5. Sunday, October 5, 1997:
Tape 19, side A, second conversation on tape.
Transcript pages: 21-34.

6. Sunday, October 5, 1997:
Tape 19, side A, third conversation on tape.
Transcript page: 34.

7. Monday, October 6, 1997:
Tape 19, side A, fourth conversation on tape.
Transcript pages: 35-41.

8. Monday, October 6, 1997:
Tape 1, Side A, first conversation on tape.
Transcript pages: 2-40.

9. Monday, October 6, 1997:
Tape 1, side A, second conversation on tape.
Transcript pages: 40-110.

10. Thursday, October 16, 1997:
Tape 2, Side A, third conversation on tape.
Transcript pages: 2-38.

11. Thursday, October 16, 1997:
Tape 13, Side A, first conversation on tape.
Transcript pages 2-30.

Conversations Listed By Tape

Note: Tapes Which Exhibit Sign of Duplication Are Printed In Italics

1. Tape 1, Side A, first conversation on tape:
Transcript pages: 2-40.
Monday, October 6, 1997

2. Tape 1, side A, second conversation on tape:
Transcript pages: 40-110.
Monday, October 6, 1997.

3. Tape 2, Side A, third conversation on tape:
Transcript pages: 2-38.
Thursday, October 16, 1997.

4. Tape 3, side A, first conversation on tape:
Transcript: pages 2-39.
Saturday, October 18, 1997.

5. Tape 5, side A, first conversation on tape:
Transcript pages: 2-16.
Thursday, November 20, 1997.

6. Tape 5, side A, third conversation on tape:
Transcript pages: 17-41.
Thursday, November 20, 1997.

7. Tape 5, side A, fourth conversation on tape:
Transcript pages: 41-47.
Thursday, November 20, 1997.

8. Tape 5, side A, fifth conversation on tape:
Transcript pages: 47-52.
Friday, November 21, 1997.

9. Tape 5, side B, sixth conversation on tape:
Transcript pages: 53-55.
Friday, November 21, 1997.

10. Tape 5, side B, seventh conversation on tape:
Transcript pages: 55-59.
Friday, November 21, 1997.

11. Tape 5, side B, eighth conversation on tape:
Transcript pages: 59-91.
Friday, November 21, 1997.

12. Friday, October 17, 1997:
Tape 13, side A. second conversation on tape.
Transcript pages: pages 30-38.

13. Saturday, October 18, 1997:
Tape 3, side A, first conversation on tape.
Transcript: pages 2-39.

14. Saturday, October 18, 1997:
Tape 8, Side A, first conversation on tape.
Transcript pages 2-34.

15. Sunday October 19, 1997:
.Tape 7, Side A, first conversation on tape.
Transcript pages: 2-51.

16. Thursday, October 23, 1997:
Tape 15, Side A, first conversation on tape.
Transcript pages: 2-30.

17. Thursday, October 23, 1997:
Tape 15, Side A, second conversation on tape.
Transcript pages: 30-73.

18. Wednesday, October 29, 1997:
Tape 11, first conversation on tape.
Transcript pages: 2-57.

19. Monday, November 3, 1997:
Tape 11, Side B, fifth conversation on tape.
Transcript pages: 58-113.

20. Saturday, November 8, 1997:
Tape 16, side B, sixth conversation on tape.
Transcript pages: 60-103.

21. Tuesday, November 11, 1997:
Tape 16, side B, ninth conversation on tape.
Transcript pages: 104-114.

22. Tuesday, November 11, 1997:
Tape 26, side A, first conversation on tape.
Transcript pages: 2-5.

23. Tuesday, November 11, 1997:
Tape 26, side A, second conversation on tape.
Transcript pages: 5-32.

24. Tuesday, November 11, 1997:
Tape 26, side A, third conversation on tape.
Transcript pages: 32-55.

12. Tape 6, side A, second conversation on tape:
Transcript pages: 2-24.
Monday, December 22, 1997.

13. Tape 6, side A, fourth conversation on tape:
Transcript pages: 24-32.
Monday, December 22, 1997.

14. Tape 6, side B, fifth conversation on tape:
Transcript pages: 33-68.
Monday, December 22, 1997.

15. Tape 7, Side A, first conversation on tape:
Transcript pages: 2-51.
Sunday October 19, 1997.

16. Tape 8, Side A, first conversation on tape:
Transcript pages 2-34.
Saturday, October 18, 1997.

17. Tape 9, side A, first conversation on tape:
Transcript pages: 2-33.
Sunday, November 16, 1997.

18. Tape 9, side A, second conversation on tape:
Transcript pages: 33-51.
Monday, November 17, 1997.

19. Tape 9, side B, third conversation on tape:
Transcript pages: 51-79.
Tuesday, November 18, 1997.

20. Tape 9, side B, fourth conversation on tape:
Transcript pages: 79-100.
Thursday, November 20, 1997

21. Tape 11, Side A, first conversation on tape:
Transcript pages: 2-57.
Wednesday, October 29, 1997

22. Tape 11, Side B, fifth conversation on tape:
Transcript pages: 58-113.
Monday, November 3, 1997.

23. Tape 13, Side A, first conversation on tape:
Transcript pages 2-30.
Thursday, October 16, 1997.

24. Tape 13, side A, second conversation on tape:
Transcript pages: pages 30-38.
Friday, October 17, 1997.

25. Thursday, November 13, 1997:
Tape 16, side A, first conversation on tape.
Transcript pages: 2-9.

26. Friday, November 14, 1997:
Tape 16, side A, second conversation on tape.
Transcript pages: 9-51.

27. Sunday, November 16, 1997:
Tape 16, side A, third conversation on tape.
Transcript pages: 52-60.

28. Sunday, November 16, 1997:
Tape 9, side A, first conversation on tape.
Transcript pages: 2-33.

29. Monday, November 17, 1997:
Tape 9, side A, second conversation on tape.
Transcript pages: 33-51.

30. Tuesday, November 18, 1997:
Tape 9, side B, third conversation on tape.
Transcript pages: 51-79.

31. Thursday, November 20, 1997:
Tape 9, side B, fourth conversation on tape.
Transcript pages: 79-100.

32. Thursday, November 20, 1997:
Tape 5, side A, first conversation on tape.
Transcript pages: 2-16.

33. Thursday, November 20, 1997:
Tape 5, side A, third conversation on tape.
Transcript pages: 17-41.

34. Thursday, November 20, 1997:
Tape 5, side A, fourth conversation on tape.
Transcript pages: 41-47.

35. Friday, November 21, 1997:
Tape 5, side A, fifth conversation on tape.
Transcript pages: 47-52.

36. Friday, November 21, 1997:
Tape 5, side A, sixth conversation on tape.
Transcript pages: 53-55.

37. Friday, November 21, 1997:
Tape 5, side A, seventh conversation on tape.
Transcript pages: 55-59.

25. Tape 15, Side A, first conversation on tape:
Transcript pages: 2-30.
Thursday, October 23, 1997.

26. Tape 15, Side A, second conversation on tape:
Transcript pages: 30-73.
Thursday, October 23, 1997.

27. Tape 16, side A, first conversation on tape:
Transcript pages: 2-9.
Thursday, November 13, 1997.

28. Tape 16, side A, second conversation on tape:
Transcript pages: 9-51.
Friday, November 14, 1997.

29. Tape 16, side B, sixth conversation on tape:
Transcript pages: 60-103.
Saturday, November 8, 1997.

30. Tape 16, side B, ninth conversation on tape.
Transcript pages: 104-114.
Tuesday, November 11, 1997:

31. Tape 16, side A, third conversation on tape:
Transcript pages: 52-60.
Sunday, November 16, 1997.

32. Tape 18, side A, first conversation on tape:
Transcript pages: 2-25.
Friday, October 3, 1997.

33. Tape 18, side A, second conversation on tape:
Transcript pages: 25-71.
Friday, October 3, 1997.

34. Tape 18, side B, third conversation on tape:
Transcript pages: 71-110.
Saturday, October 4, 1997.

35. Tape 19, side A, first conversation on tape:
Transcript pages: 2-21.
Sunday, October 5, 1997

36. Tape 19, side A, second conversation on tape:
Transcript page: 21-34.
Sunday, October 5, 1997

37. Tape 19, side A, third conversation on tape:
Transcript pages: 34.
Sunday, October 5, 1997.

38. Friday, November 21, 1997:
Tape 5, side A, eighth conversation on tape.
Transcript pages: 59-91.

39. Tuesday, December 9, 1997:
Tape 23, side A, first conversation on tape.
Transcript pages: 2-6.

40. Tuesday, December 9, 1997:
Tape 23, side A, second conversation on tape.
Transcript pages: 6-56.

41. Friday, December 12, 1997:
Tape 23, side A, fifth conversation on tape.
Transcript pages: 57-68.

42. Friday, December 12, 1997:
Tape 23, side B, sixth conversation on tape.
Transcript pages: 68-127.

43. Friday, December 12, 1997:
Tape 23, side B, eighth conversation on tape.
Transcript pages: 127-131.

44. Monday, December 22, 1997:
Tape 6, side A, second conversation on tape.
Transcript pages: 2-24.

45. Monday, December 22, 1997:
Tape 6, side A, fourth conversation on tape.
Transcript pages: 24-32.

46. Monday, December 22, 1997:
Tape 6, side B, fifth conversation on tape.
Transcript pages: 33-68.

47. Thursday, January 15, 1998:
Tape 22, side A, first conversation on tape.
Transcript pages: 2-55.

48. Thursday, January 15, 1998:
Tape 22, side A, second conversation on tape.
Transcript pages: 55-76.

38. Tape 19, side A, fourth conversation on tape:
Transcript pages: 35-41.
Monday, October 6, 1997.

39. Tape 22, side A, first conversation on tape:
Transcript pages: 2-55.
Thursday, January 15, 1998.

40. Tape 22, side A, second conversation on tape:
Transcript pages: 55-76.
Thursday, January 15, 1998.

41. Tape 23, side A, first conversation on tape:
Transcript pages: 2-6.
Tuesday, December 9, 1997.

42. Tape 23, side A, second conversation on tape:
Transcript pages: 6-56.
Tuesday, December 9, 1997.

43. Tape 23, side A, fifth conversation on tape:
Transcript pages: 57-68.
Friday, December 12, 1997.

44. Tape 23, side B, sixth conversation on tape:
Transcript pages: 68-127.
Friday, December 12, 1997.

45. Tape 23, side B, eighth conversation on tape:
Transcript pages: 127-131.
Friday, December 12, 1997

46. Tape 26, side A, first conversation on tape:
Transcript pages: 2-5.
Tuesday, November 11, 1997.

47. Tape 26, side A, second conversation on tape:
Transcript pages: 5-32.
Tuesday, November 11, 1997.

48. Tape 26, side A, third conversation on tape:
Transcript pages: 32-55.
Tuesday, November 11, 1997.

2. **How the OIC Determined the Chronology of these Undated Tapes**

Conversation # 1:
Friday, October 3, 1997
Tape 18, side A, first conversation on the tape.
Transcript pages: 2-25.

During this conversation, Ms. Tripp says it is October. See T18 at 24. Ms. Lewinsky observes that the President will be delivering a radio address on the following morning, and then traveling to Maryland and Camp David. See T18 at 20. The President's October 4, 1997, schedule shows he gave a radio address, see 968-DC-00003058, and then traveled to Prince George's County, Maryland and Camp David. See 968-DC-00003059. Ms. Lewinsky also comments the President will be at an event in Virginia on Saturday night. See page 21. The Presidential Press Schedule shows the President attended a function at the National Airport Hilton on October 4, 1997. See 968-DC-00003060.

These factors are consistent with a conversation on October 3, 1997.

Conversation # 2:
Friday, October 3, 1997
Tape 18, side A, second conversation on the tape.
Transcript pages: 25-71.

During this conversation, Ms. Tripp says it is Friday night, and Ms. Lewinsky says she is going to New York City on the next Saturday for the weekend. See T18 at 28. Ms. Lewinsky's American Express bill reveals she bought an airplane ticket from LaGuardia Airport to the Ronald Reagan National Airport on October 13, 1997. See 852-DC-00000042. Ms. Lewinsky also mentions that the

President is leaving the following Sunday, October 12, 1997. See T18 at 41. The President's schedule shows he left for a week-long trip to Latin America on October 11, 1997. See United States President, Weekly Compilations of Presidential Documents at 1608, 1609, 1652.

These factors are consistent with a conversation on Friday, October 3, 1997.

Conversation # 3:
Saturday, October 4, 1997
Tape 18, side B, third conversation on the tape.
Transcript pages: 71-110.

The conversation that immediately precedes this conversation on the tape occurred on Friday, October 3, 1997. At the end of the previous portion, Ms. Lewinsky notes that it is 10:20, that she is going to sleep, and she indicates that she is not working the next day. See T18 at 70. This conversation begins with Ms. Lewinsky describing her trip to the Potomac Mills Mall for the day. See T18 at 70-79. The placement of the conversation on the tape and the day-long trip to the mall are consistent with a weekend day.

In addition, Ms. Lewinsky says Betty Currie was in the office during the morning because of the Radio Address. See T18 at 88. The President delivered a Radio Address on Saturday October 4, 1997, at 10:06 am. Also, Betty Currie rarely works on Sunday because it is her "church day." See Currie 5/7/98 GJ at 91. Ms. Lewinsky further says she wants to buy the President a gift because he now had a hearing aid. See T18 at 80. The

President was fitted for hearing aids on October 3, 1997. See "Age Catching Up With Clinton; He's Getting Hearing Aids," Sandra Sobieraj, The Associated Press, October 3, 1997.

Ms. Lewinsky also says there are three months before the beginning of the year, and she refers to sunglasses she bought the President for his Latin America trip. See T18 at 103-4. This statement would place the tape in early October.

These factors are consistent with a conversation on October 4, 1997.

Conversation # 4:
Sunday, October 5, 1997
Tape 19, side A, first conversation on the tape.
Transcript pages: 2-21.

Ms. Lewinsky tells Ms. Tripp that CNN is leading its "Headline News" with a story about the White House releasing video tapes of the coffee receptions for Democratic supporters. See T19 at 2. At the outset of the call, Ms. Lewinsky is waiting excitedly for the next half hour news cycle so she can see the whole story. Evidently, she was concerned the White House might have a video taping system that showed her on tape.

The White House released these tapes, and the story broke on October 5, 1997. See Videotapes Released Showing Presidential Coffee Meetings, NBC Nightly News, October 5, 1997. Because of her excitement and the fact that Ms. Lewinsky followed White House news so carefully, it is likely she is describing the story that broke earlier in the day.

In addition, Ms. Tripp refers to a message she received at

work on Friday, and she says she did not call back because it was "the kind of thing that could wait until Monday." See T19 at 31. This statement is consistent with a weekend conversation. Also, Ms. Tripp and Ms. Lewinsky discuss how Ms. Lewinsky will help Ms. Tripp with parking at work the next day. See T19 at 15. This final point places this conversation on a Sunday night.

These factors are consistent with a conversation on Sunday, October 5, 1997.

Conversation # 5:
Sunday, October 5, 1997
Tape 19, side A, second conversation on the tape.
Transcript pages: 21-34.

Ms. Lewinsky discusses the sunglasses she bought for the President and how she will send them to him. See T19 at 24. Because Ms. Lewinsky bought these sunglasses on October 4, 1997, this conversation must have occurred after that day. Ms. Tripp also says Ms. Lewinsky should send the glasses by FedEx. FedEx receipts show that Ms. Lewinsky sent a Federal Express package to the White House on October 10, 1997. See 925-DC-00000003. For this reason, the conversation probably occurred before October 10, 1997.

In the conversation that immediately precedes this conversation, Ms. Lewinsky and Ms. Tripp discussed their parking plans for the next morning. Ms. Lewinsky said she would be in a meeting until approximately 8:00 am, and then she could bring Ms. Tripp into the parking lot. See T19 at 16. Ms. Tripp and Ms. Lewinsky ended this conversation by bidding each other good night and with Ms. Tripp saying she would call Ms. Lewinsky "probably eight-ish." See T19 at 34. For these reasons, the conversation that immediately precedes this conversation likely occurred on October 5, 1997.

The conversation that immediately follows this one also occurred on October 5, 1997 (see explanation of next conversation). Because this conversation comes between two October 5 conversations on T19, it most likely occurred on October 5, 1997.

These factors are consistent with a conversation on Sunday, October 5, 1997.

Conversation # 6:
Sunday, October 5, 1997
Tape 19, side A, third conversation on the tape.
Transcript page: 34.

Ms. Lewinsky and Ms. Tripp spoke during the early evening of October 5, 1997. See T19 at 2-21. After this first conversation, Ms. Tripp went to the gym to exercise and Ms. Lewinsky called back. See 19 at 21-34. Sometime after that conversation ended, Ms. Tripp received a call from her friend Kate Friederich and turned off the recorder. See T19 at 34. Ms. Tripp knows the conversation with Ms. Friederich occurred in the late evening of Sunday, October 5, 1997, because the conversation happened the day before Ms. Tripp met with Lucianne Goldberg, Jonah Goldberg, and Michael Isikoff. That meeting occurred October 6, 1997. Furthermore, in a letter to the President, Ms. Lewinsky wrote that Ms. Friederich spoke to Ms. Tripp on Sunday

50-892 98-9

night. See MSL-55-DC-0178.

These factors are consistent with a conversation on Sunday October 5, 1997.

Conversation 7:
Monday, October 6, 1997
Tape 19, side A, fourth conversation on the tape.
Transcript pages: 35-41.

The segment of conversation that immediately precedes this conversation is the interrupted discussion between Ms. Tripp and Ms. Friedrich. In this conversation, Ms. Tripp tells Ms. Lewinsky what Ms. Friederich said. During her debriefing, Ms. Tripp remembered having this conversation the morning after speaking with Ms. Friederich. One thing that sparked Ms. Tripp's memory was her statement during the conversation, "Let me get my coffee . . . I've got to wake up." T19 at 35. According to Ms. Tripp, she usually only drinks coffee in the morning.

There are further indications that this conversation occurred on October 6, 1997. In this conversation, Ms. Tripp says she has not spoken to Kate in a month. During a conversation taped on the night of October 6, 1997, Ms. Tripp and Ms. Lewinsky discussed this conversation again. See T1 at 13-23. Consequently, this conversation must have occurred before the evening of October 6, 1997.

These factors are consistent with a conversation on October 6, 1997.

Conversation # 8:
Monday, October 6, 1997
Tape 1, Side A, first conversation on the tape.
Transcript pages: 2-40.

Ms. Lewinsky tells Ms. Tripp that Ms. Currie would not get her into the White House this evening because of a dinner. See T1 at 6. The Presidential press schedule reveals the President hosted a state dinner with the President of Israel on October 6, 1997. See 968-DC-00003063.

Also, this conversation ends with a discussion about a letter that Ms. Lewinsky intends to send to the President. At the end of the conversation, Ms. Lewinsky says she will write the letter and call Ms. Tripp back in about 15-20 minutes. See T1 at 40. The next conversation, which follows immediately on the tape, begins with a discussion of the letter Ms. Lewinsky has composed. The next conversation also features Ms. Lewinsky saying it is the 6th. See T1 at 90.

In addition, Ms. Lewinsky and Ms. Tripp discuss a conversation between Ms. Tripp and her friend Kate Friederich who works at the National Security Council. See T1 at 13-36. For the reasons cited above, the conversation between Ms. Tripp and Ms. Friederich occurred on the previous night.

These factors are consistent with a conversation on Monday, October 6, 1997.

Conversation # 9:
Monday, October 6, 1997
Tape 1, side A, second conversation on the tape.
Transcript pages: 40-110.

During this conversation, Ms. Lewinsky says: "Today is the 6th." See T1 at 90. In addition, Ms. Lewinsky and Ms. Tripp are discussing a letter that Ms. Lewinsky intends to send to the

White House. There is a courier receipt which shows a delivery from Ms. Lewinsky to the White House on October 7, 1997. See 837-DC-00001.

Ms. Lewinsky also observes that Mrs. Clinton "is coming home Friday night from Panama to go to South America with him on Sunday, just so she can be here for their anniversary." See T1 at 69. The First Lady's travel schedule reveals Mrs. Clinton returned from Panama on Friday, October 10. See 968-DC-00003477. Ms. Lewinsky further refers to the fact that the President is leaving for Latin America on Sunday. See T1 at 69. The Presidential Press Schedule shows that the President left for Latin American on Sunday October 12, 1997. See 968-DC-00003076.

These factors are consistent with a conversation on Monday, October 6, 1997.

Conversation # 10:
Thursday, October 16, 1997
Tape 2, Side A, third conversation on the tape.
Transcript pages: 2-38.

Ms. Tripp says tomorrow is the 17th. See T2 at 31. Also, on page 4, Ms. Lewinsky says the President is in Latin America and will be back on Sunday morning. The Presidential Press Schedule reveals the President returned from Latin America on October 19, 1997. See 968-DC-00003141.

These factors are consistent with a conversation on October 16, 1997.

Conversation # 11:
Thursday, October 16, 1997
Tape 13, Side A, first conversation on the tape.
Transcript pages: 2-30.

This conversation ends with Ms. Tripp telling Ms. Lewinsky, "I'll talk to you tomorrow." See T13 at 30. The next conversation on the tape begins with Ms. Tripp asking Ms. Lewinsky what Ms. Lewinsky is still doing in the office on a Friday night. See T13 at 30. These factors are consistent with a Thursday conversation.

The following factors place the conversation in a more general time frame. Ms. Lewinsky says the President will get a package she has sent him on Monday. See T13 at 17. The Presidential Press Schedule shows the President returned from his Latin America trip on Sunday, October 19, 1997. See 968-DC-00003141. Ms. Lewinsky also indicates the First Lady will be in New York on Monday and then go to Chicago "for some big birthday thing." See T13 at 17. The First Lady's schedule reveals that she was in New York on October 20, 1997, that her birthday was October 26, 1997, and that she went to Chicago on October 27, 1997. See 968-DC-00003477.

All of these factors are consistent with a conversation on Thursday, October 16, 1997.

Conversation # 12:
Friday, October 17, 1997
Tape 13, side A, second conversation on the tape.
Transcript pages: pages 30-38.

At the outset of this tape, Ms. Tripp asks Ms. Lewinsky why she is working late on a Friday night. See T13 at 31. October

17, 1997, was a Friday. Also, Ms. Lewinsky tells Ms. Tripp the First Lady's birthday is the next week. See T13 at 12. The First Lady's birthday is October 26. See 968-DC-00003477.

These factors are consistent with a conversation on Friday October 17, 1997.

Conversation # 13:
Saturday, October 18, 1997
Tape 3, side A, first conversation on the tape.
Transcript: pages 2-39.

In a question regarding the President, Ms. Tripp asks: "When does he get back? Tonight, tomorrow?" Ms. Lewinsky responds: "I think early tomorrow morning." See T3 at 12. The President's schedule reveals that he returned from Latin America on the morning of October 19. See 968-DC-00003141. Later, Ms. Lewinsky once again notes that the First Lady's birthday is the next weekend, and she recites the First Lady's travel schedule including a trip to New York, a trip to Chicago, and a trip to Ireland. The First Lady's travel schedule includes a trip to New York (October 20), her birthday (October 26), and a trip to Ireland (Starting October 30). See 968-DC-00003477.

These factors are consistent with a conversation on Saturday, October 18, 1997.

Conversation # 14:
Saturday, October 18, 1997
Tape 8, Side A, first conversation on tape.
Transcript pages 2-34.

Ms. Lewinsky says she called Andy Bleiler earlier in the day. See T8 at 8. Phone records reflect four calls from Ms. Lewinsky to Mr. Bleiler on October 18 (three were one minute each and one was four minutes, the first at 7:33 p.m. and the last at 7:41 p.m.). See 810-DC-00000017. In addition, Ms. Lewinsky says she first told the President she wanted help finding a job on January 8, 1997-- ten months ago. This statement is consistent with this conversation's being in October.

These factors are consistent with a conversation on Saturday, October 18, 1997.

Conversation 15:
Sunday October 19, 1997
Tape 7, Side A, first conversation on the tape.
Transcript pages: 2-51.

Ms. Lewinsky mentions that the President returned from Latin America and could have gone to his office and seen her package. See T7 at 10. The Presidential travel schedule reveals the President returned from Latin America on the morning of Sunday, October 19. See 968-DC-00003141. Also, Ms. Lewinsky comments that a World Series game is on television. See T7 at 2. Game 2 of the 1997 World Series occurred on Sunday, October 19, 1997. See "The Schedule," The Daily News, October 19, 1997.

There are other indications that this call happened on a Sunday. First, Ms. Lewinsky suggests that the President can call her on a Sunday even if Mrs. Clinton is in the White House. See T7 at 10-11. Lewinsky also mentions that Ms. Currie usually does not come in on Sundays. See T7 at 14. Furthermore, Ms. Lewinsky refers to going to the Mall earlier that day. See T7 at 2-5. This assertion is consistent with a weekend conversation.

These factors are consistent with a conversation on Sunday,

October 19, 1997.

Conversation # 16:
Thursday, October 23, 1997
Tape 15, Side A, first conversation on tape.
Transcript pages: 2-30.

Ms. Lewinsky indicates that Ambassador Richardson called on Tuesday. See T15 at 15. Phone records reflect a call from Ambassador Richardson's line to Ms. Lewinsky on Tuesday, October 21. See 828-DC-00000004.

These factors are consistent with a conversation on Thursday, October 23, 1997.

Conversation # 17:
Thursday, October 23, 1997
Tape 15, Side A, second conversation on the tape.
Transcript pages: 30-73.

This is a continuation of the previous conversation. In the conversation that immediately precedes this conversation on the tape, Lewinsky is upset because she has not had enough contact with the President. During this previous conversation, Ms. Lewinsky says it is 8:15 and she promises to call Ms. Tripp as soon as the President calls her. See T15 at 27.

This conversation opens with Ms. Lewinsky describing the conversation she has just finished with the President. Ms. Lewinsky says it is 10:30. See T15 at 34. This timing and Ms. Lewinsky's comments are consistent with back-to-back phone calls. Also, Ms. Lewinsky says she told the President that Ambassador Richardson called her on Tuesday. See T15 at 31. Ambassador Richardson called Ms. Lewinsky on Tuesday, October 21, 1997. See 828-DC-00000004. Also, as a general matter, Ms. Lewinsky says it is October. See T15 at 65.

These factors are consistent with a conversation on Thursday, October 23, 1997.

Conversation 18:
Wednesday, October 29, 1997
Tape 11, first conversation on tape.
Transcript pages: 2-57.

This Conversation Appears On A "Likely To Be Duplicate Tape."

Ms. Lewinsky says she spoke to Bayani Nelvis on the telephone that afternoon. T11 at 2. Telephone records reflect a conversation between Mr. Nelvis and Ms. Lewinsky on this day. See 1051-DC-00000003. Ms. Lewinsky also says she last spoke to the President a week ago. See T11 at 30. At this time, Ms. Lewinsky and the President last spoke six days before--on October 23. Finally, Ms. Lewinsky says she sent the President a present. On October 28, Ms. Lewinsky sent a package to the White House via Speed Service Couriers. See 837-DC-00000004.

These factors are consistent with a conversation on Wednesday, October 29, 1997.

Conversation # 19:
Monday, November 3, 1997
Tape 11, Side B, fifth conversation on the tape.
Transcript pages: 58-113.

This Conversation Appears On A Tape That Exhibits Signs of Duplication.

Ms. Lewinsky refers to a call from the U.N. regarding a job offer. See T11 at 60-63. Phone records show a call from the U.N. to Ms. Lewinsky at 11:02 a.m. See 828-DC-00000003. Ms.

Lewinsky further says she arranged with Ms. Currie to send a package to the White House by courier. See T11 at 84. A courier receipt reflects that Ms. Lewinsky sent a package to the White House on November 3, 1997. See 837-DC-00000006. Moreover, Ms. Lewinsky remarks that the First Lady is leaving on Sunday. The First Lady's travel schedule reveals that she left for London on Sunday, November 9, 1997.

These factors are consistent with a conversation on Monday, November 3, 1997.

Conversation # 20:
Saturday, November 8, 1997
Tape 16, side B, sixth conversation on tape.
Transcript pages: 60-103.

This Conversation Appears On A Tape That Exhibits Signs of Duplication.

An answering machine recording that immediately precedes this conversation identifies the date as November 8. See T16 at 60. In addition, Ms. Lewinsky tells Ms. Tripp the First Lady is leaving the next day. See T16 at 69. Mrs. Clinton left for London on Sunday, November 9, 1997. There are two additional indications that this conversation occurred on a Saturday. First, Ms. Lewinsky says that, when she asked Ms. Currie if she could see the President "tomorrow," Ms. Currie said the President would be attending church in the morning. See T16 at 68. Second, Ms. Lewinsky says that she was told by Ms. Currie that the President taped the Radio Address on the previous day. See T16 at 65. Furthermore, because Ms. Lewinsky tells Ms. Tripp how she asked Ms. Currie for a Veterans Day meeting with the President, the conversation must have occurred before November 11. See T16 at 69.

These factors are consistent with a conversation on Monday, November 8, 1997.

Conversation # 21:
Tuesday, November 11, 1997
Tape 16, side B, ninth conversation on tape.
Transcript pages: 104-114.

This Conversation Appears On A Tape That Exhibits Signs of Duplication.

Ms. Tripp says she has a message from Norma Asnes in which Ms. Asnes invites Ms. Tripp to a play at the Arena Theatre for the next night. See T16 at 104. That event was on November 12, 1997. Also, Ms. Lewinsky describes a conversation with Ms. Currie in which she asked about the President's schedule "tonight," then "tomorrow," then Thursday, and then Friday. See T16 at 107-08. This sequence places this conversation on a Tuesday. November 11, 1997, was a Tuesday.

These factors are consistent with a conversation on Tuesday, November 11, 1997.

Conversation # 22:
Tuesday, November 11, 1997
Tape 26, side A, first conversation on tape.
Transcript pages: 2-5.

This Conversation Appears On A Tape That Exhibits Signs of Duplication.

Ms. Tripp asks Ms. Lewinsky whether she would like to attend the play with Ms. Tripp, Ms. Asnes, and others. As noted in the description of conversation 21, this production occurred on November 12, 1997. Also, in the next conversation, which is clearly a continuation of this one, Ms. Tripp says it is the 11th. See T26 at 22.

These factors are consistent with a conversation on Tuesday, November 11, 1997.

Conversation # 23:
Tuesday, November 11, 1997
Tape 26, side A, second conversation on tape.
Transcript pages: 25-32.

This Conversation Appears On A Tape That Exhibits Signs of Duplication.

Ms. Tripp says it is the 11th. See T26 at 22. This exchange is clearly a continuation of the conversation that immediately precedes it on the tape because the topic is the same, and Ms. Lewinsky hung up from the last conversation merely to get a telephone number from information. Ms. Lewinsky said she would call back immediately. See T26 at 5.

These factors are consistent with a conversation on Tuesday, November 11, 1997.

Conversation # 24:
Tuesday, November 11, 1997
Tape 26, side A, third conversation on tape.
Transcript pages: 32-55.

This Conversation Appears On A Tape That Exhibits Signs of Duplication.

Ms. Lewinsky says she wants to see the President because it is Veterans Day and he is all alone. See T26 at 35. Veterans Day is November 11. In addition, this conversation is a continuation of the previous conversation (also dated November 11) which was interrupted by call waiting. Ms. Tripp says she just got off the phone with Ms. Asnes, whom Ms. Tripp was trying to reach. See T26 at 36.

These factors are consistent with a conversation on Tuesday, November 11, 1997.

Conversation # 25:
Thursday, November 13, 1997
Tape 16, side A, first conversation on tape.
Transcript pages: 2-9.

This Conversation Appears On A Tape That Exhibits Signs of Duplication.

In this brief conversation, Ms. Lewinsky says she was in the White House earlier in the evening while President Zedillo of Mexico was there. She says she saw the President for 60 seconds. President Zedillo dined at the White House on November 13. See Baltimore Sun (Nov. 14, 1997, at 17A. WAVES records confirm Ms. Lewinsky was at the White House on this date. See 827-DC-000018, V006-DC-000008, 137-DC-000318.

These factors are consistent with a conversation on Thursday, November 13, 1997.

Conversation # 26:
Friday, November 14, 1997
Tape 16, side A, second conversation on tape.
Transcript pages: 9-51.

This Conversation Appears On A Tape That Exhibits Signs of Duplication.

On T16, this conversation immediately follows the one in which Ms. Lewinsky describes her visit earlier in the day with

President Clinton while President Zedillo was in the White House. The previous discussion ends with Ms. Lewinsky and Ms. Tripp exchanging "good night" wishes. See T16 at 9. This conversation begins with Ms. Lewinsky commenting that the President is in Las Vegas. See T16 at 9. The President's travel schedule indicates he was in Las Vegas on November 14, 1997. See 968-DC-0003257. Also, Ms. Lewinsky says she is going to New York by train. See T16 at 11. On November 14, 1997, Ms. Lewinsky sent an e-mail which indicated her plans to travel to New York by train. See V06-DC-000359.

These factors are consistent with a conversation on Friday, November 14, 1997.

Conversation # 27:
Sunday, November 16, 1997
Tape 16, side A, third conversation on tape.
Transcript pages: 52-60.

This Conversation Appears On A Tape That Exhibits Signs of Duplication.

This very brief conversation, which is the last one on T16, immediately follows a Friday, November 14, 1997, conversation. This conversation is also cut off in the middle. The first conversation on T9 is also from Sunday night, November 16, 1997. Ms. Tripp told the Office of the Independent Counsel she would record until a tape ran out and then replace it with another tape. Ms. Tripp also told the Office of the Independent Counsel that when a tape was filled up, she would not put it in the recorder again.

Ms. Lewinsky left for New York City early in the morning on November 15, 1997. Ms. Lewinsky returned the night of the 16th. In this conversation, she describes her trip. Sunday night would have been the first time she could have made such a call. Moreover, T9 contains additional discussion of the weekend in New York City, and it was also recorded on Sunday night. For all of these reasons, it is likely that Ms. Tripp began this recording of Ms. Lewinsky on Sunday night and the tape ran out. Ms. Tripp then apparently inserted T9 into the recorder and captured the remaining discussion.

These factors are consistent with a conversation on Monday, November 16, 1997.

Conversation # 28:
Sunday, November 16, 1997
Tape 9, side A, first conversation on tape.
Transcript pages: 2-33.

This Conversation Appears On A Tape That Exhibits Signs of Duplication.

Ms. Lewinsky says that she arrived in New York City "yesterday." See T9 at 3. Ms. Lewinsky was in New York City on November 15 and 16. These facts would place this conversation on Sunday night, November 16, 1997. In addition, Ms. Lewinsky describes a chance encounter with Ambassador Richardson in a restaurant in New York the day before. During this meeting, Ambassador Richardson commented on Ms. Lewinsky's pending job offer. See Richardson 4/30/98 Depo. at 115 (recalling encounter with Ms. Lewinsky on his birthday, November 15).

More generally, Ms. Lewinsky says she tried to buy Ms. Tripp a birthday present at a flea market in New York City over the weekend. See T9 at 8. Ms. Tripp's birthday is November 24. Since Ambassador Richardson offered Ms. Lewinsky a job at the UN on November 3, 1997, this conversation would have to be between these two dates. Of the three intervening weekends, Ms. Lewinsky was in New York City only once: on November 15 and 16.

These factors are consistent with a conversation on Sunday, November 16, 1997.

Conversation # 29:
Monday, November 17, 1997
Tape 9, side A, second conversation on tape.
Transcript pages: 33-51.

This Conversation Appears On A Tape That Exhibits Signs of Duplication.

Ms. Lewinsky mentions it is November. See T9 at 41. Furthermore, Ms. Lewinsky says she spotted an attractive man in New York the day before. See T9 at 43. During November 1997, Ms. Lewinsky was only in New York City on November 15 and 16. In addition, this conversation immediately follows a conversation from Sunday, November 16, 1997, on tape T9. The previous conversation ended with Ms. Tripp and Ms. Lewinsky saying good night. In the next conversation on T9, Ms. Lewinsky says it is Tuesday.

These factors are consistent with a conversation on Monday, November 17, 1997.

Conversation # 30:
Tuesday, November 18, 1997
Tape 9, side B, third conversation on tape.
Transcript pages: 51-79.

This Conversation Appears On A Tape That Exhibits Signs of Duplication.

Ms. Lewinsky says it is Tuesday. See T9 at 60. In addition, the conversation that immediately precedes this one on T9 is November 17, 1997, the Monday Ms. Lewinsky returned from New York City. Also, Ms. Lewinsky says she spoke with the President a week ago. See T9 at 60. According to an e-mail Ms. Lewinsky sent to a friend, she spoke to the President on November 12, 1997, six days earlier. See 1037-DC-0000318.

These factors are consistent with a conversation on Tuesday, November 18, 1997.

Conversation # 31:
Thursday, November 20, 1997
Tape 9, side B, fourth conversation on tape.
Transcript pages: 79-100.

This Conversation Appears On A Tape That Exhibits Signs of Duplication.

Ms. Lewinsky says her 60 second meeting with the President was one week before. See T9 at 84. Ms. Lewinsky visited with the President for 60 seconds on November 13, 1997, when President Zedillo of Mexico was at the White House. In addition, Ms. Lewinsky describes a conversation with Ms. Currie in which Ms. Lewinsky says the First Lady is leaving tomorrow. T9 at 80. The First Lady's travel schedule shows she left for Los Angeles on November 21, 1997. See 968-DC-00003478.

These factors are consistent with a conversation on Thursday, November 20, 1997.

Conversation # 32:
Thursday, November 20, 1997
Tape 5, side A, first conversation on tape.
Transcript pages: 2-16.

Conversation # 33:
Thursday, November 20, 1997
Tape 5, side A, third conversation on tape.
Transcript pages: 17-41.

Conversation # 34:
Thursday, November 20, 1997
Tape 5, side A, fourth conversation on tape.
Transcript pages: 41-47.

These 3 Conversations Appear On A Tape That Exhibits Signs of Duplication.

Conversations 32-34 (treated together here) concern an audio tape that Ms. Lewinsky is making for the President. In the first two conversations, Ms. Lewinsky plays portions of the tape for Ms. Tripp and asks for advice preparing it. In conversation 34, Ms. Lewinsky calls Ms. Tripp to thank her for her help. Consistent with Ms. Lewinsky's sending the tape the next morning, courier receipts show Ms. Lewinsky ordered a courier delivery from the Pentagon to the White House at 8:18 a.m. on November 21. See 837-DC-00000014.

Also, Ms. Lewinsky says that Ms. Currie told her the President will leave too early on Saturday to allow a 15-minute visit by Ms. Lewinsky. See T5 at 5. According to the Presidential schedule, the President left for Vancouver on

November 22. Baggage check-in occurred at 6:00 a.m. at Andrews Air Force Base, and Air Force One press pool check-in occurred at 8:30. 968-DC-00003301. This schedule is consistent with an early wake-up at the White House.

These factors are consistent with a conversation on Thursday, November 20, 1997.

Conversation # 35:
Friday, November 21, 1997
Tape 5, side A, fifth conversation on tape.
Transcript pages: 47-52.

This Conversation Appears On A Tape That Exhibits Signs of Duplication.

This conversation immediately follows a conversation from November 20, 1997, on the tape. Ms. Lewinsky ended the last conversation by saying, "I'll see you tomorrow." See T5 at 47. This conversation is clearly the next day because Ms. Lewinsky describes several phone calls she had with Ms. Currie during the day, including calls after an interview the President was taping at 6:15 p.m. See T5 at 51.

These factors are consistent with a conversation on Monday, November 21, 1997.

Conversation # 36:
Friday, November 21, 1997
Tape 5, side A, sixth conversation on tape.
Transcript pages: 53-55.

This Conversation Appears On A Tape That Exhibits Signs of Duplication.

At the end of the conversation that immediately precedes this conversation on T5, Ms. Tripp instructs Ms. Lewinsky to call

Ms. Currie and Ms. Currie her to remain at work until the President leaves. See T5 at 52. At the beginning of this conversation Ms. Lewinsky reports the results of the call. T5 at 53. These exchanges indicate this conversation was shortly after conversation 33. In addition, Ms. Currie told Ms. Lewinsky she was waiting for the President to leave the office and return to the residence. See T5 at 53. Since the President left for Denver, Seattle, and Vancouver early in the morning on November 22, see 968-DC-00003301, this conversation most likely occurred on November 21, 1997.

These factors are consistent with a conversation on Monday, November 21, 1997.

Conversation # 37:
Friday, November 21, 1997
Tape 5, side A, seventh conversation on tape.
Transcript pages: 55-59.

This Conversation Appears On A Tape That Exhibits Signs of Duplication.

This conversation is another report from Ms. Lewinsky regarding whether Ms. Currie gave Ms. Lewinsky's cassette tape to the President. Besides the context of the tapes, in the conversation that immediately follows this one, Ms. Tripp says it is the 21st. See T5 at 69.

These factors are consistent with a conversation on Monday, November 21, 1997.

Conversation # 38:
Friday, November 21, 1997
Tape 5, side A, eighth conversation on tape.
Transcript pages: 59-91.

This Conversation Appears On A Tape That Exhibits Signs of Duplication.

Ms. Tripp says it is the 21st during this conversation. See T5 at 69. Also, Lewinsky says that Monday is the 24th. See T5 at 81. November 21, 1997, was a Friday, so November 24, 1997, was a Monday. Moreover, this conversation is clearly a continuation of the earlier conversations in the evening because Ms. Lewinsky gives another report regarding Ms. Currie and the cassette tape Ms. Lewinsky sent to the President.

These factors are consistent with a conversation on Monday, November 21, 1997.

Conversation # 39:
Tuesday, December 9, 1997
Tape 23, side A, first conversation on tape.
Transcript pages: 2-6.

This Conversation Appears On A Tape That Exhibits Signs of Duplication.

Ms. Lewinsky says she delivered something to the White House on "Monday," which was "yesterday morning." See T5 at 4-5. This statement is consistent with a courier receipt which shows a delivery from Ms. Lewinsky at the Pentagon to the White House on December 8, 1997. See 837-DC-00000017. In addition, Ms. Lewinsky says she is having lunch with Vernon Jordan on Thursday. See T23 at 2. The visitor log at Mr. Jordan's law firm and his calendar reveal that Ms. Lewinsky met with Mr. Jordan on

Thursday, December 11, 1997. See V004-DC-00000171. (Akin and Gump visitor/contact log); V004-DC-00000148. (Vernon Jordan's calendar).

These factors are consistent with a conversation on Monday, December 9, 1997.

Conversation # 40:
Tuesday, December 9, 1997
Tape 23, side A, second conversation on tape.
Transcript pages: 6-56.

This Conversation Appears On A Tape That Exhibits Signs of Duplication.

Ms. Tripp says it is "Tuesday afternoon." See T23 at 19. December 9, 1997, was a Tuesday. Ms. Tripp also says, "I can't believe you got in there Saturday." See T23 at 44. Epass records reveal Ms. Lewinsky saw the President at the White House on Saturday, December 6, 1997. See 827-DC-00000018. Ms. Tripp further mentions that Ms. Lewinsky will be seeing Mr. Jordan on Thursday. The visitor log at Mr. Jordan's law firm and his calendar reveal that Ms. Lewinsky met with Mr. Jordan on Thursday December 11, 1997. See V004-DC-00000171. (Akin and Gump visitor/contact log); V004-DC-00000148. (Vernon Jordan's calendar).

Moreover, Ms. Tripp mentions Ms. Lewinsky had an item sent to the White House by courier on Monday morning. See T23 at 19. A courier receipt reveals a delivery from Ms. Lewinsky at the Pentagon to the White House on Monday, December 8, 1997. See 837-DC-17, 20.

These factors are consistent with a conversation on Monday, December 9, 1997.

Conversation # 41:
Friday, December 12, 1997
Tape 23, side A, fifth conversation on tape.
Transcript pages: 57-68.

Conversation # 42:
Friday, December 12, 1997
Tape 23, side B, sixth conversation on tape.
Transcript pages: 68-127.

Conversation # 43:
Friday, December 12, 1997
Tape 23, side B, eighth conversation on tape.
Transcript pages: 127-131.

These Conversations Appear On A Tape That Exhibits Signs of Duplication.

These three segments on tape 23 were likely two different conversations held on the same night. Because they concern the same subject matter (Ms. Tripp's meeting with her attorney regarding the subpoena she received in the Jones case), and because they wrap around two sides of the same cassette tape (conversation 39 ends side A and conversation 40 begins side B of tape 23) conversation 39 and conversation 40 are most likely the same discussion interrupted by side A of the tape's running out.

Conversation 41 is most likely a new conversation on the same night. In conversation 41, Ms. Lewinsky reads a letter she composed to the President. The letter concerns suggestions on how to settle the Jones case. See T23 at 129. Ms. Tripp and Ms. Lewinsky discussed this issue in conversation 40. See T23 at 88.

In addition, conversation 40 ends with Ms. Tripp saying she will speak to her attorney in the morning and then call Ms. Lewinsky. See T23 at 126. At the outset of conversation 41, Ms. Tripp says, "I cannot believe someone who I thought was already in bed is at the computer." This statement is consistent with a later call on the same night.

Given these circumstances, the date for all three conversations comes from conversation 40. In conversation 40, Ms. Tripp describes how she watched a movie called "A Home of Our Own" on this evening. The Family Channel broadcast this movie on December 12, 1997 at 8:00 p.m. During her debriefings, Ms. Tripp confirmed she watched the movie on the night it was broadcast on the Family channel.

These factors are consistent with a conversation on Monday, December 12, 1997.

Conversation # 44:
Monday, December 22, 1997
Tape 6, side A, second conversation on tape.
Transcript pages: 2-24.

This Conversation Appears On A Tape That Exhibits Signs of Duplication.

Ms. Lewinsky received her subpoena on December 19, 1997. See 902-DC-00000135-138. In this conversation, Ms. Tripp refers to the subpoena and the fact that it calls for a hat pin. See T6 at 3. For this reason, the conversation has to be after the 19th. Ms. Lewinsky also says she had a short meeting with Mr. Jordan on this day. Mr. Jordan's calendar reveals he met with

Ms. Lewinsky on December 22, 1997. This is the day Mr. Jordan brought Ms. Lewinsky to see Frank Carter. See V004-DC-0000072, 1034-DC-00000103. Vernon Jordan also met with Ms. Lewinsky on December 19, 1997, but that meeting was for 45 minutes. See V004-DC-00000172.

These factors are consistent with a conversation on Monday, December 22, 1997.

Conversation # 45:
Monday, December 22, 1997
Tape 6, side A, fourth conversation on tape.
Transcript pages: 24-32.

This Conversation Appears On A Tape That Exhibits Signs of Duplication.

This brief conversation is a continuation of conversation 42. At the end of conversation 42, Ms. Tripp told Ms. Lewinsky to speak with her mother about their plan to avoid the subpoena. See T6 at 23. At the beginning of this conversation, Ms. Lewinsky says her mother thinks the plan is brilliant. See T6 at 24.

These factors are consistent with a conversation on Monday, December 22, 1997.

Conversation # 46:
Monday, December 22, 1997
Tape 6, side B, fifth conversation on tape.
Transcript pages: 33-68.

This Conversation Appears On A Tape That Exhibits Signs of Duplication.

Conversation 43 is brief because the first side of the tape runs out. This conversation, which is the first conversation on side B, is clearly a continuation of the same conversation. Ms. Tripp and Ms. Lewinsky were speaking about Ms. Currie at the end of conversation 43. See T6 at 32. This conversation begins with a continuation of the same conversation about Ms. Currie. See T6 at 33.

These factors are consistent with a conversation on Monday, December 22, 1997.

Conversation # 47:
Thursday, January 15, 1998
Tape 22, side A, first conversation on tape.
Transcript pages: 2-55.

Conversation # 48:
Thursday, January 15, 1998
Tape 22, side A, second conversation on tape.
Transcript pages: 55-76.

Both of the conversations on this tape were made under the supervision of the Office of the Independent Counsel. For this reason, the OIC knows the date of the conversations independently from the contents of the tapes.

Tab J

Legal Reference

LEGAL REFERENCE

LEGAL REFERENCE

This section contains a brief summary of the statutes and legal precepts that, in the context of a criminal proceeding, would be germane to a determination of the criminality of the conduct described in the Referral. The Office of Independent Counsel recognizes that Congress, in assessing whether the information presented constitutes "substantial and credible" information that "may constitute grounds for an impeachment" need not consider the elements of analogous criminal offenses. In other words, a showing of criminality is neither necessary nor sufficient to an impeachment; Congress may impeach for conduct that is less than criminal or decline to impeach for conduct that, nonetheless, constitutes a crime.

However, as an Office which exercises the investigative and prosecutorial function of the Department of Justice, see 28 U.S.C. § 594(a), our assessment of what constitutes "substantial and credible" information that "may constitute grounds for an impeachment" is necessarily informed by our understanding of criminal law. Hence, we deem it appropriate to set forth our understanding of the law that would be applicable to the conduct described in the Referral if that conduct were to be judged in a criminal proceeding. We do not attempt to be comprehensive, but merely set forth principles of law that might reasonably be deemed applicable.

Briefly, we highlight the following legal conclusions of

general applicability:

- Perjury in connection with a pending civil proceeding may be, and has been, charged as a violation of 18 U.S.C. §§ 1621, 1623, see infra § I.C.2.b ;
- False statements made during the course of civil discovery can be material to perjury charged as a violation of 18 U.S.C. §§ 1621, 1623, see infra §§ I.C.5.c, I.C.5.d;
- The Court of Appeals for the District of Columbia Circuit has determined that Monica Lewinsky's affidavit was material to the Jones v. Clinton matter and was legally sufficient to support a charge of perjury in violation of 18 U.S.C. § 1623 and a charge of obstruction of justice in violation of 18 U.S.C. § 1503, see infra §§ I.C.5.d.ii, II.B.3;
- Feigned forgetfulness and other evasive conduct may form the basis for a charge of perjury in violation of 18 U.S.C. §§ 1621, 1623, see infra § I.E;
- Obstruction of justice in connection with a pending civil proceeding may be, and has been, charged as a violation of 18 U.S.C. § 1503, see infra §§ II.B.2, II.D.2;
- Concealment of documents and other materials called for by a subpoena may form the basis for a charge of obstruction of justice in violation of 18 U.S.C. §§ 1503, 1512, see infra §§ II.D, III;
- Seeking to influence the testimony of a potential witness may form the basis for a charge of obstruction of justice in violation of 18 U.S.C. § 1503, see infra § II.D, or a charge of witness tampering in violation of 18 U.S.C. § 1512, see infra § III.

I. Perjury -- 18 U.S.C. §§ 1621 & 1623

Two separate statutes address the crime of perjury. 18 U.S.C. § 1621[1] covers perjury "generally," while 18 U.S.C. §

---

[1] Section 1621 provides:

Whoever --

(1) having taken an oath before a competent tribunal, officer or person, in any case in which a law of the United States authorizes an oath to be administered, that he will testify, declare, depose, or

1623[2] specifically addresses false declarations before a grand jury or court.[3] The elements of perjury under § 1621 and § 1623 are virtually the same but, as discussed below, with § 1623 Congress eased some of the prosecution's burden imposed by the common law.

A. Elements of § 1621

"The essential elements of the crime of perjury as defined

---

certify truly, or that any written testimony, declaration, deposition, or certificate by him subscribed, is true, willfully and contrary to such oath states or subscribes any material matter which he does not believe to be true; or

(2) in any declaration, certificate, verification, or statement under penalty of perjury as permitted under section 1746 of title 28, United States Code, willfully subscribes as true any material matter which he does not believe to be true;

is guilty of perjury . . . .

[2] Section 1623 provides:

(a) Whoever under oath (or in any declaration, certificate, verification, or statement under penalty of perjury as permitted under section 1746 of title 28, United States Code) in any proceeding before or ancillary to any court or grand jury of the United States knowingly makes any false material declaration or makes or uses any other information, including any book, paper, document, record, recording, or other material, knowing the same to contain any false material declaration, shall be fined under this title or imprisoned not more than five years, or both.

18 U.S.C. § 1623 (1996 Supp.).

[3] Both provisions note that where 28 U.S.C. § 1746 permits the use of an unsworn declaration "under penalty of perjury" in place of an oath, then it is also a crime to make a false statement in such a declaration. <u>See</u> <u>United States v. Gomez-Vigil</u>, 929 F.2d 254, 258 (6th Cir. 1991).

in 18 U.S.C. § 1621 . . . are (1) an oath authorized by a law of the United States, (2) taken before a competent tribunal, officer or person, and (3) a false statement wilfully made as to facts material to the hearing."[4] Because perjury has a specific intent element, "[t]estimony resulting from confusion, mistake or faulty memory cannot support a perjury conviction."[5]

B. Elements of § 1623

The government's burden for establishing false declarations before a court under 18 U.S.C. § 1623 is largely the same as its burden under 18 U.S.C. § 1621.[6] The prosecution must

---

[4] United States v. Hvass, 355 U.S. 570, 574 (1958) (internal quotation marks omitted). The Model Jury Instructions for Perjury under D.C. Code § 22-2511 provide:

> [t]he essential elements of perjury, each of which the government must prove beyond a reasonable doubt, are:
> 1. That the defendant testified under oath or affirmation;
> 2. That the oath or affirmation were taken before a competent [tribunal] [officer] [person] in a case in which the law authorized that oath or affirmation;
> 3. That in his/her testimony the defendant made the statements detailed in the indictment;
> 4. That the statements were false; and
> 5. That the defendant knew or believed that the statements were false when s/he made them.

Criminal Jury Instructions for the District of Columbia (4th ed. 1993) 4.87.

[5] United States v. Dean, 55 F.3d 640, 659 (D.C. Cir. 1995), cert. denied, 116 S. Ct. 1288 (1996) (citing United States v. Dunnigan, 507 U.S. 87, 94 (1993)).

[6] Section 1623 differs from § 1621 in five minor respects. First, § 1623 applies only to false statements made during or ancillary to grand jury or court proceedings, whereas § 1621 applies also to false statements made under oath in other proceedings. Second, Congress expressly exempted § 1623 prosecutions from the two-witness rule; the government need only

50-892 98 - 10

demonstrate: "1. that the defendant testified under oath before [or in a proceeding ancillary to a court or] grand jury; 2. that the testimony so given was false in one or more respects charged; 3. that the false testimony concerned matters that were material to the [court proceedings]; and, 4. that the false testimony was knowingly given as charged."[7]

C. Essential Elements Further Defined

1. Oath

The taking of an oath before giving allegedly false testimony is an essential element of the crime of perjury.[8]

2. Civil Proceedings and Criminal Charges

---

prove beyond a reasonable doubt that the defendant make a knowing false declaration. See 18 U.S.C. § 1623(e). Third, "[i]n contrast to § 1621, the Government need not prove the falsity of [inconsistent] declarations under § 1623(c); rather, the Government [need only] prove that 'the defendant under oath has knowingly made two or more declarations, which are inconsistent to the degree that one of them is necessarily false.'" United States v. McAfee, 8 F.3d 1010, 1014 (5th Cir. 1993) (quoting 18 U.S.C. § 1623(c)). Fourth, under § 1623, retraction of a false statement is a defense to prosecution "if, at the time the admission is made, the declaration has not substantially affected the proceeding, or it has not become manifest that such falsity has been or will be exposed." 18 U.S.C. § 1623(d); see United States v. Moore, 613 F.2d 1029, 1039 (D.C. Cir.), cert. denied, 446 U.S. 954 (1980); cf. United States v. Norris, 300 U.S. 564, 573 (1937) (under [the predecessor to 18 U.S.C. § 1621] witnesses who testified falsely cannot purge themselves by later recanting). Finally, while § 1621 requires proof that a false statement was made "willfully," § 1623 requires proof that the false statement was made "knowingly."

[7] United States v. Bridges, 717 F.2d 1444, 1449 n.30 (D.C. Cir. 1983) (citations omitted), cert. denied, 465 U.S. 1036 (1984).

[8] United States v. Debrow, 346 U.S. 374, 377 (1953).

Section 1623 applies only to "proceedings before or ancillary to any court or grand jury of the United States." Courts uniformly agree that civil depositions taken pursuant to Fed. R. Civ. P. 30 are ancillary proceedings under § 1623.[9] Even though civil depositions, unlike their criminal counterparts, do not require a court order, courts faced with the issue have rejected the argument that § 1623 is thereby limited to criminal proceedings.[10]

The Department of Justice often prosecutes for perjury that occurs during the course of civil proceedings. This section details some of the recent cases[11] in which the Department has

---

[9] See, e.g., United States v. Wilkinson, 137 F.3d 214 (4th Cir. 1998) (deposition is ancillary proceeding for purposes of § 1632); United States v. McAfee, 8 F.3d 1010, 1014 (5th Cir. 1993) (affirming conviction in prosecution under § 1623(c) for inconsistent statements made in two deposition testimonies); United States v. Scott, 682 F.2d 695, 698 (8th Cir. 1982) (terms "deposition" and "ancillary proceeding" are synonymous); United States v. Krogh, 366 F. Supp. 1255-56 (D.D.C. 1973) (sworn deposition taken at Office of the United States Attorney found to be "ancillary" to Watergate grand jury proceedings). In Dunn v. United States, 442 U.S. 100, 113 (1979), the Supreme Court held that § 1623 does not encompass statements made in contexts less formal than a deposition -- implying that it does cover deposition testimony.

[10] See McAfee, 8 F.3d at 1014.

[11] Several other cases involving criminal perjury charges for actions in civil cases are described in the discussions of materiality in civil cases (Kross; Holley; Naddeo; Edmonson; Clark; Adams; Hale; Hendrickson; Allen), feigned forgetfulness as perjury (Chaplin; Moreno Morales) and obstruction of justice charges for actions in civil cases (Roberts), infra. This is, of course, a list of only some of the cases which have been reported. By definition, an unknown number of similar unreported cases may also exist.

brought criminal charges for civil perjury.[12]

- A partner at a New York law firm was charged under § 1623, convicted, and sentenced to 15 months imprisonment for declaring under oath in a civil bankruptcy proceeding that he was "unaware of any other current representation by Milbank [Tweed] of any equity security holder or institutional creditor" of Bucyrus-Erie when he was, in fact, aware that Milbank Tweed was representing certain creditors of Bucyrus-Erie in a legal dispute against Bucyrus-Erie.[13] The partner had been retained to represent Bucyrus-Erie in filing for bankruptcy, and had made the false statement during a hearing relating to Milbank Tweed's approximately $2 million in legal fees.[14]
- Another corporate defendant was charged with perjury for falsely denying -- during his civil deposition in a civil suit based on a corporate failure to satisfy an outstanding loan -- that he knew about the use of a fictitious name in the accounting books of the company. He was convicted, and his conviction was affirmed by the Fourth Circuit.[15]

---

[12] On occasion civil perjury is charged as obstruction of justice. A summary of recent instances of such charges is included in the obstruction of justice section _infra_.

[13] _See_ _United States v. Gellene_, (No. 97-Cr-221, E.D. Wisc., Dec. 9, 1997) (Indictment, Count Three).

[14] Gellene was also charged with, and convicted of, two violations of 18 U.S.C. § 152, which proscribes the making of a false declaration in relation to a bankruptcy proceeding.

[15] _See_ _United States v. Wilkinson_, 137 F.3d 214, 225 (4th Cir. 1998).

- Another defendant in a civil suit filed an affidavit (in response to plaintiff's motion for summary judgment) in which he falsely denied any knowledge of the fraudulent scheme[16] that was the subject of the suit. For filing this false affidavit, he was charged and convicted of perjury; his conviction was affirmed on appeal.[17]
- Another defendant was charged with, and convicted of, perjury under 18 U.S.C. § 1621 after he made a false declaration about his financial status (so that he would be able to prosecute an appeal from a civil judgment in forma pauperis) and repeated that declaration in a post-judgment deposition.[18] The district court, citing the civil nature of Holland's perjury, declined to apply the Sentencing Guidelines (which called for a sentence of 87 to 108 months) and instead sentenced Holland to home detention. On appeal, however, the Eleventh Circuit vacated the sentence and remanded for application of the Sentencing Guidelines. The court held that the perjury statute applies "without distinction both to perjury committed in a civil proceeding and to perjury in a criminal prosecution."[19] In so holding,

---

[16] The plaintiff had alleged that Sassanelli had fraudulently inflated construction bills and created fictitious invoices.

[17] See United States v. Sassanelli, 118 F.3d 495 (6th Cir. 1997).

[18] See United States v. Holland, 22 F.3d 1040 (11th Cir.), cert. denied, 513 U.S. 1109 (1994).

[19] Id. at 1047.

the court:

> categorically reject[ed] any suggestion, implicit or otherwise, that perjury is somehow less serious when made in a civil proceeding. Perjury, regardless of the setting, is a serious offense that results in incalculable harm to the functioning and integrity of the legal system as well as to private individuals. In the instant case, Holland's perjury inexcusably wasted valuable and scarce public resources. His actions needlessly consumed court time, forced the Federal Bureau of Investigation and the United States Attorney's Office to engage in prolonged investigations, and attempted to prevent private citizens . . . from satisfying their judgment.[20]

3. Falsity

Under both § 1621 and § 1623, the government must prove the falsity of the statement that is the basis for the perjury accusation. As discussed in detail infra, "the falsity of an 'I don't recall' answer must be proven by circumstantial evidence."[21] Furthermore, under the less burdensome § 1623(c), the government may prove that a statement is false merely by proving that the defendant made two "irreconcilably contradictory declarations."[22]

4. State of Mind

While § 1621's "wilfulness" requirement appears on its face to demand a more burdensome showing than § 1623's knowledge

---

[20] Id. at 1047-48.

[21] United States v. Chapin, 515 F.2d 1274, 1284 (D.C. Cir.), cert. denied, 423 U.S. 1015 (1975).

[22] For example, United States v. McAfee, 8 F.3d 1010 (5th Cir. 1993), affirmed the conviction of a defendant under § 1623(c) based upon two contradictory statements he gave in two civil depositions.

element, the cases make little, if anything, of the distinction.[23] Indeed, the D.C. Circuit has held that "in the perjury statute [willfully] means 'knowingly' or 'intentionally.'"[24] In order to prove that a defendant's false testimony was provided "knowingly" or "wilfully," the government must prove beyond a reasonable doubt that the defendant did not believe his testimony to be true at the time he testified.[25] Often, the government may do so merely by proving that the testimony was in fact false.[26]

5. Materiality

Under both § 1621 and § 1623, the government must prove that the misrepresentation was "material." In 1995, the Supreme Court held that whether the misrepresentation was material is a question of fact that must go to the jury.[27] The jury may be

---

[23] See United States v. Endo, 635 F.2d 321, 323 (4th Cir. 1980)("The substantive difference (whether the accused acted 'knowingly' or 'willfully') . . . has no pertinence for our purposes.").

[24] Maragon v. United States, 187 F.2d 79, 80 (D.C. Cir. 1950) (sustaining perjury conviction under D.C. Code § 22-2501), cert. denied, 341 U.S. 932 (1951).

[25] Young v. United States, 212 F.2d 236, 240 (D.C. Cir.), cert. denied, 347 U.S. 1015 (1954).

[26] See id. at 241 ("Generally, a belief as to the falsity of testimony may be inferred by the jury from proof of the falsity itself.").

[27] See United States v. Gaudin, 115 S. Ct. 2310 (1995) (in construing 18 U.S.C. § 1001 Court holds materiality is a question of fact); see also United States v. Levine, 72 F.3d 920 (D.C. Cir. 1995) (extending Gaudin to § 1621).. Prior to the Supreme Court's decision, most courts had treated materiality as a question of law for the judge to decide.

guided by the precepts explained in the following discussion.

a. General Definition

A misrepresentation or concealment is material if it "was predictably capable of affecting, i.e., had a natural tendency to affect, the official decision;"[28] or if it concerns "'a fact that would be of importance to a reasonable person in making a decision about a particular matter or transaction;'"[29] or if "a truthful answer would have aided the inquiry."[30] "[T]he effect necessary to meet the materiality test is relatively slight, and certainly not substantial."[31]

In addition, in proving that a statement was material, the government need not prove that the false statement actually was

---

[28] Kungys v. United States, 485 U.S. 759, 771 (1988). Although Kungys construes a denaturalization statute rather than § 1001 or a perjury statute, the Court indicated that "material" bears the same meaning in all three spheres. See Kungys, 485 U.S. at 769-72. Kungys also might be distinguished on the ground that it treats materiality as a question of law, see id. at 772, a doctrine that Gaudin overturned. But Gaudin did not modify the materiality standard; in fact it cites Kungys for the applicable standard. 115 S. Ct. at 2313.

[29] United States v. Winstead, 74 F.3d 1313, 1320 (D.C. Cir. 1996) (quoting and approving language in jury instructions); see also United States v. Allen, 131 F. Supp. 323, 325 (E.D. Mich. 1955) (citations omitted) ("A material matter does not necessarily mean a matter that directly affects the ultimate issue of the trial. . . . It is sufficient if the false testimony gives weight and force to or detracts from testimony as to matters that are material.").

[30] United States v. Cunningham, 723 F.2d 217, 226 (2d Cir. 1983), cert. denied, 466 U.S. 951 (1984).

[31] United States v. Moore, 613 F.2d 1029, 1038 (D.C. Cir. 1979) (distinguishing materiality from "substantial effect" standard of perjury recantation provision), cert. denied, 446 U.S. 954 (1980)

relied upon, but rather need show only that the statement was capable of influencing the outcome -- or of adding or detracting to facts that themselves could influence the outcome -- if it had been relied upon.[32] For example, the Eighth Circuit affirmed the perjury conviction of an individual whose false testimony (that he had not visited Florida during 1983) had been contradicted by the testimony of other witnesses, despite the defendant's argument that his statements before the grand jury were not material. The court found that "Moeckly's denials, regardless of the availability to the grand jury of accurate information through other witnesses, tended to obscure Moeckly's whereabouts at critical times during the conspiracies."[33]

b. Causation in Investigations

In cases involving investigations or other inquiries,[34] the

---

[32] See United States v. Dale, 991 F.2d 819, 834 n.27 (D.C. Cir.), cert. denied, 114 S. Ct. 286 (1993); United States v. Jones, 464 F.2d 1118, 1122 (8th Cir. 1972), cert. denied, 409 U.S. 1111 (1973); United States v. Hendrickson, 200 F.2d 137 (7th Cir. 1952). The causation aspect of false statements in civil actions has been infrequently addressed by the courts. When they do address it, however, courts have interpreted causation broadly. For example, when a defendant argued that his false testimony was immaterial because the topic concerning which he had testified falsely was not directly relevant to the question before the court in which he testified, the Seventh Circuit held that: "[W]here the false testimony is capable of influencing the tribunal, then the actual effect of the false testimony is not the determining factor, but its capacity to affect or influence the trial judge in his judicial action and the issue before him." Hendrickson, 200 F.2d at 139.

[33] United States v. Moeckly, 769 F.2d 453, 465 (8th Cir. 1985), cert. denied, 475 U.S. 1015 (1986).

[34] When assessing materiality, courts do not distinguish between the various contexts -- civil, administrative, or

test for materiality has been stated as "whether a truthful answer would have aided the inquiry."[35] This question seems to call for speculation as to the likelihood that a truthful answer would have changed the course of official actions, such as by provoking or re-channeling an investigation that in turn might have altered the final outcome. The Supreme Court has suggested that a fact can be material even if there was a less than 50% chance of changing the official decision: "It has never been the test of materiality that the misrepresentation or concealment would more likely than not have produced an erroneous decision, or even that it would more likely than not have triggered an investigation."[36]

Other courts agree that the government need not show such a consequence to have been likelier than not. The D.C. Circuit, for example, has held in connection with the false statements statute, 18 U.S.C. § 1001, that "[a]pplication of § 1001 does not require judges to function as amateur sleuths, inquiring whether

---

criminal -- in which an investigation can arise.

[35] United States v. Cunningham, 723 F.2d 217, 226 (2d Cir. 1983), cert. denied, 466 U.S. 951 (1984). One court in the Southern District of New York applied a similar test in a case charging false statements to prosecutors as well as courtroom perjury: "[M]ateriality is the flimsiest of obstacles to a perjury conviction. 'Materiality is . . . demonstrated if the question posed is such that a truthful answer could help the inquiry, or a false response hinder it, and these effects are weighed in terms of potentiality rather than probability.'" United States v. Guariglia, 757 F. Supp. 259, 266 (S.D.N.Y. 1991) (quoting United States v. Berardi, 629 F.2d 723, 728 (2d Cir.), cert. denied, 449 U.S. 995 (1980)).

[36] Kungys, 485 U.S. at 771.

information specifically requested and unquestionably relevant to the department's or agency's charge would really be enough to alert a reasonably clever investigator that wrongdoing was afoot."[37]

Another Circuit opinion, in a different formulation, has said that a statement is material if it would have caused investigators to make additional inquiries, even if it would not have affected the agency's ultimate decision. The court found a defendant's false answers in a security clearance application to be material because truthful responses would have prompted investigators to make further inquiries. Whether the clearance would still have been granted was irrelevant, the court said, because "[m]ateriality . . . is not concerned with whether the alleged omission would have affected the ultimate agency determination."[38] The court appeared to reason that a statement's materiality is judged by its effect on an ongoing investigation, rather than its effect on the ultimate decision. In other words, materiality exists if a statement would have had a 100 percent likelihood of affecting an investigation, even if it that effect on the investigation would in turn have had a zero percent likelihood of changing the agency outcome.[39]

---

37 United States v. Hansen, 772 F.2d 940, 950 (D.C. Cir. 1985), cert. denied, 475 U.S. 1045 (1986).

38 United States v. Dale, 782 F. Supp. 615, 625-26 (D.D.C. 1991).

39 Cf. United States v. Di Fonzo, 603 F.2d 1260, 1266 (7th Cir. 1979) (a statement is material if it influences the agency's decision to investigate or the agency's conclusion as to whether

"[W]hether a truthful answer would have aided the inquiry" depends to some degree upon the type of investigation occurring. "[I]n a grand jury setting," the D.C. Circuit has said, "the false testimony must have the natural effect or tendency to impede, influence or dissuade the grand jury from pursuing its investigation."[40] Because a grand jury investigation is usually wide-reaching, information can be material to a grand jury even if it might not be material to a more tightly focused inquiry.[41] For example, information is material if it would help investigators locate other witnesses whose testimony would be directly pertinent to the grand jury. The Second Circuit affirmed the conviction of a defendant whose false statements impeded investigation because "they covered up the fact that additional witnesses . . . should also have been interviewed."[42] Similarly, in an Prohibition-era case, a grand jury witness was

---

it has jurisdiction), cert. denied, 444 U.S. 1018 (1980); United States v. Rose, 570 F.2d 1358, 1364 (9th Cir. 1978) (false statement to a customs inspector was material because a truthful answer would have led to a more rigorous inspection).

[40] United States v. Moore, 613 F.2d 1029, 1038 (D.C. Cir. 1979), cert. denied, 446 U.S. 954 (1980) (internal quotation marks and citation omitted).

[41] See United States v. Paxson, 861 F.2d 730, 733 (D.C. Cir. 1988) (finding false statements before grand jury material and noting that "[m]any cases have recognized that hindsight is not the proper perspective for discerning the limits of a grand jury's investigative power. It must pursue its leads before it can know its final decisions."); LaRocca v. United States, 337 F.2d 39, 43 (8th Cir. 1964) ("the grand jury is imbued with broad inquisitorial powers").

[42] United States v. Gribben, 984 F.2d 47, 52 (2d Cir. 1993).

convicted for falsely denying that a particular woman had been present at a party where liquor allegedly had been served: "A false statement as to the woman tended to mislead the grand jury, and to deprive them of knowledge as to who she was, so that she might not be obtained as a witness."[43]

c. Interpretation in Civil Proceedings

Courts act similarly in deciding the materiality of false statements made in the context of civil discovery -- i.e., false affidavits, false deposition testimony, or false responses to discovery requests. As the Supreme Court has explained, in deciding whether a statement is material a court must

> determin[e] at least two subsidiary questions of purely historical fact: (a) "what statement was made?"; and (b) "what decision was the [decisionmaker] trying to make?" The ultimate question: (c) "whether the statement was material to the decision," requires applying the legal standard of materiality [as defined in Kungys] to these historical facts.[44]

The third of these issues -- application of the legal standard to the facts -- is characterized as a mixed question of law and fact which requires "delicate assessments of the inferences a 'reasonable [decision maker]' would draw from a given set of facts and the significance of those inferences to him."[45]

In deciding "what decision is being made" in the context of

---

[43] Carroll v. United States, 16 F.2d 951, 954 (2d Cir.), cert. denied, 273 U.S. 763 (1927).

[44] United States v. Gaudin, 515 U.S. 506, 512 (1995).

[45] Id. (quoting TSC Industries, Inc. v. Northway, Inc., 426 U.S. 438, 450 (1976)).

a discovery deposition, courts have generally concluded that the decision being made is not, "does this prove the case?" but rather "does this inquiry lead to potentially relevant evidence?" This is because, as when analyzing materiality in other investigative contexts, the courts look at what decision is "being made" in response to the (false) information provided in the deposition or discovery answer, rather than at the ultimate issue for decision in the case.

The definition of "materiality" in the context of a deposition or discovery response, therefore, is tied to the purposes of civil discovery. Discovery is intended to allow a party to uncover any information that "appears reasonably calculated to lead to the discovery of admissible evidence." Fed. R. Civ. P. 26(b)(1). Discoverable information need not itself be admissible -- to the contrary it encompasses many matters that are manifestly inadmissible in a civil trial. Thus, as the Second Circuit has explained, a false statement in a civil deposition is material when "a truthful answer might reasonably be calculated to lead to the discovery of evidence admissible at the trial of the underlying suit."[46] In other words, as one court has said, the broad scope of civil discovery means that the test for materiality in a civil context is "broader than that used to determine materiality during trial."[47]

---

[46] United States v. Kross, 14 F.3d 751, 754 (2d Cir.), cert. denied, 513 U.S. 828 (1994).

[47] United States v. Naddeo, 336 F. Supp. 238, 240 (N.D. Ohio 1972).

Such a broader definition of materiality in the discovery context is appropriate and even necessary. Otherwise, the oath to testify truthfully would become a contingent one. A person could knowingly tell a falsehood in the hope or expectation that if the "information elicited . . . ultimately turn[s] out not to [meet the higher standards of admissibility] at a subsequent trial,"[48] then the person would suffer no penalty for the lie.

In determining materiality in the context of civil discovery, then, some courts have treated the question categorically, so that if the question falsely answered was itself permissible under the rules of discovery, then the false answer is deemed material. For example, while convicting a defendant of perjury for his false civil deposition in a civil forfeiture case pendent to a criminal investigation, the Second Circuit reasoned that there was "no persuasive reason not to apply [to the defendant's statements] the broad standard of materiality of whether a truthful answer might reasonably be calculated to lead to the discovery of evidence admissible at trial."[49]

Other courts have engaged in a inquiry -- albeit a very limited one -- to ensure that the questions and answers at issue in the perjury charge bore some general relationship to the underlying civil litigation. For example, the chairman of a bank

---

[48] United States v. Holley, 942 F.2d 916, 925 (5th Cir. 1991), cert. denied 510 U.S. 821 (1993).

[49] Kross, 14 F. 3d at 754.

was charged with and convicted of perjury for lying in a deposition -- taken in the course of civil bankruptcy proceedings initiated by the bank -- about his actions at the bank. On appeal he argued that the materiality of his statements had to be measured against the issues specifically raised in the bank's bankruptcy filings and, thus, that the court should ask whether his false statements were about those transactions that had caused a loss to the bank. The Fifth Circuit rejected this narrow reading of materiality and found that so long as the false statements were related to the allegations of the underlying civil complaint in a general way, they would be material to the ongoing discovery.[50]

One reason that the standard is not quite settled is that the proximate relation between the false statements supporting the perjury charge, and the underlying civil case, can be quite attenuated and still satisfy the materiality requirement. For example, the plaintiffs in a civil rights lawsuit charging a police department with racial bias falsely claimed in a deposition that they had not violated the department's sick leave policy. The Ninth Circuit began with the premise of Kungys -- that a statement is material if it has a "natural tendency to influence" the decision maker -- and read this broadly to define a material false statement as "one which 'is relevant to any

---

[50] See Holley, 942 F.2d at 924-25; accord United States v. Edmondson, 410 F.2d 670, 673 (5th Cir. 1969) (false letters used at a bankruptcy creditors' meeting were material).

subsidiary issue under consideration.'"[51] Because the plaintiffs' violation of a sick leave policy was, to some degree, relevant to their underlying complaint of racial bias, the court concluded that false statements about the violation were material to the underlying civil litigation and were a sufficient basis for a perjury charge. This attenuated standard makes the difference more one of theory than of practice, and seems to have made it unnecessary for most courts to resolve the issue.[52]

Despite the attenuated nature of the materiality standard, it does sometimes operate to preclude prosecution. At least one reported case has overturned a perjury conviction based upon a civil deposition because it found that the misrepresentation was not material. In this case the defendant had been asked in a civil deposition for the source of the prior earnings figures she had provided to her employer, she had replied that it was a "Schedule C worksheet [used] in preparation for doing the income taxes,"[53] and she had been convicted of perjury because she had,

---

[51] United States v. Clark, 918 F.2d 843, 846 (9th Cir. 1990) (quoting United States v. Lococo, 450 F.2d, 1196, 1199 (9th Cir. 1971)), overruled on other grounds, United States v. Keys, 95 F.3d 874 (9th Cir. 1996).

[52] For example, in a recent case the Fourth Circuit recognized these somewhat diverging treatments of civil materiality but found it unnecessary to resolve the question in disposing of the case because the matters were material under any standard of materiality adopted. See Wilkinson, 137 F.3d at 224-25.

[53] United States v. Adams, 870 F.2d 1140, 1147 (6th Cir. 1989) (involving a sex discrimination law suit against the Equal Employment Opportunity Commission).

in fact, taken the figures from a prepared Schedule C rather than a Schedule C worksheet.[54] The Sixth Circuit overturned the conviction. While agreeing generally that the "test of whether a false declaration satisfies the materiality requirement is whether a truthful answer might have assisted or influenced the tribunal in its inquiry,"[55] and recognizing the contingent nature of the materiality inquiry, the court concluded that there was no adequate explanation for why the difference between a prepared Schedule C and a Schedule C worksheet mattered to any decisionmaker.[56]

Another method of assessing materiality considers the timing of the false statement. Under this method of analysis, the question is not whether the false statements are material to some issue at the underlying civil trial, but rather whether the statements were "at the time made, material to the proceeding in which [the] deposition was taken."[57]

Such an analysis makes clear that statements do not lose

---

[54] Id. at 1147.

[55] Id. (citing United States v. Swift, 809 F.2d 320, 324 (6th Cir. 1987)).

[56] Adams, 879 F.2d at 1147. The Court appeared to be animated in part by its concern that the perjury prosecution was vindictive retaliation for Adams' discrimination suit. Id. at 1145-46 (noting the "thinness of the [criminal] charges" and holding that "there is enough smoke here, in our view, to warrant the unusual step of letting defendants find out how this unusual prosecution came about")

[57] Holley, 942 F.2d at 923 (citing United States v. Gremillion, 464 F.2d 901, 904-05 (5th Cir.), cert. denied, 409 U.S. 1085 (1972)).

their materiality because of subsequent developments. Indeed, courts generally do not hold that settlement of a case renders a false statement immaterial; nor do they accept the argument that a decision to exclude a statement at trial (based upon the stricter standards for trial admissibility) reaches backward, to make immaterial, statements that were material during a deposition. For example, one defendant convicted of perjury in connection with a civil deposition argued on appeal that his deposition was immaterial because it had not been used at trial.[58] The Tenth Circuit rejected those arguments: "When the oath was administered to Hale and he thereafter willfully gave false testimony as to material facts in the case, all of the elements of the offense were present and the crime of perjury had been committed."[59]

The Second Circuit has made this point strongly, albeit in a criminal context.[60] A defendant's conviction under the Wagering Tax Act[61] was reversed on appeal because the underlying statutes were deemed unconstitutional violations of the Fifth Amendment privilege against self-incrimination; the United States then

---

[58] See Hale v. United States, 406 F.2d 476 (10th Cir.) (rejecting the defendant's argument that he could not be charged with perjury because he had not read or signed the deposition after it was transcribed), cert. denied, 395 U.S. 977 (1969).

[59] Id. at 480 (citing United States v. Norris, 300 U.S. 564 (1957)).

[60] See United States v. Manfredonia, 414 F.2d 760 (2nd Cir. 1969).

[61] 26 U.S.C. §§ 4401, 4411, 7203 and 7262 (1968).

charged him with perjury because he had lied in his original criminal trial when he denied accepting wagers. After his perjury conviction, the defendant argued on appeal that the lies were not "material" because his underlying wagering conviction had been vacated on constitutional grounds, effectively rendering the perjury prosecution legally "untenable." The Second Circuit rejected this argument as follows:

> In advancing this argument appellant completely ignores the purpose of the perjury statute which is to keep the process of justice free from the contamination of false testimony. It is for the wrong done the courts and the administration of justice that punishment is given, not for the effect that any particular testimony might have on the outcome of any given trial. . . .
>
> Indeed, it has long been established that an acquittal of the defendant in a trial where false testimony was given does not bar a prosecution for perjury. . . . It has likewise been held that the reversal of a conviction because of an improper indictment will not prevent a prosecution for perjury committed at the former trial. . . . In all of these cases the questioned testimony was material at the time it was given and subsequent events do not eliminate that materiality. To sustain a conviction of perjury ' * * * materiality must be established only as of the time the answers were given.'[62]

d. Legal Rulings Relating to Jones v. Clinton

This Referral concerns, in part, allegedly false statements made in connection with Jones v. Clinton No. LR-C-94-290 (E.D. Ark.), a civil rights case filed in the Eastern District of Arkansas. The materiality of some of those statements has already been the subject of court rulings, as detailed below.

---

[62] Manfredonia, 414 F.2d at 764-65 (citations and footnotes omitted) (asterisks in original).

i. Rulings by Judge Wright in Jones v. Clinton

During discovery in the Jones case, the plaintiff, Paula Jones, repeatedly sought discovery as to whether President Clinton had sexual encounters with women other than his wife during the time that he was Governor and then President.[63] The district court judge, Judge Susan Webber Wright, rejected most of the President's arguments against such discovery. Her discovery orders reflect her conclusion that the evidence about "other women" known as "Jane Does" -- including evidence related to Ms. Lewinsky -- was relevant and material to the discovery process in Jones (and potentially relevant or material to summary judgment or trial, though, as discussed above, admissibility at trial is typically not a part of a materiality inquiry).

Judge Wright twice held that Ms. Jones was entitled to the testimony of the Jane Does. First, on November 24, 1997 Judge Wright held that Ms. Jones could question the Jane Does if Ms. Jones first established a factual predicate for doing so. In the words of the Clerk's minutes:

> Plaintiff is entitled to ask questions that are calculated to lead to admissible evidence;. . . In response to [President Clinton's counsel, Robert] Bennett's concerns that pleadings will become public and do damage to institution of presidency, Court states questions have to be related to this cause of action and believes the Rules of Evidence and rules governing sexual harassment require Court to permit the

[63] Ms. Jones's attorneys intended to use evidence of any such encounters to establish that the President was engaged in a pattern and practice of sexual advances in the workplace.

questions [about sexual activity with the President].[64]

Second, on December 18, 1997 Judge Wright issued an order discussing the materiality and relevance of testimony about "other women." She indicated that it was likely that not all of the discoverable evidence would be admissible, and stated that if the case went to trial, then she "anticipate[d] limiting the amount of time and number of witnesses that will be spent on issues of alleged sexual activity of both the President and the plaintiff (should such matters be deemed admissible)."[65] Judge Wright then held, however, that the "other women" questions were proper questions to ask during discovery. As she explained, "the issue [before the Court was] one of discovery, not admissibility of evidence at trial. Discovery, as all counsel know, by its very nature takes unforseen twists and turns and goes down numerous paths, and whether those paths lead to the discovery of admissible evidence often simply cannot be predetermined."[66] For this reason, Judge Wright ordered the Jane Does to answer certain deposition questions regarding whether they had engaged in sexual activity with Mr. Clinton.

Judge Wright also several times held that the President was obliged to answer written or oral questions about whether he had engaged in sexual activity with other women. First, on December

---

[64] See 921-DC-00000268-69 (Clerk's Minutes of In-Camera Hearing, Nov. 24, 1997).

[65] 1414-DC-00001012-13 (Dec. 18 Order, at 7).

[66] 1414-DC-00001012-13 (Dec. 18 Order at 7-8).

11, 1997, Judge Wright held that "the plaintiff is entitled to information regarding any individuals with whom the President had sexual relations or proposed or sought to have sexual relations and who were during the relevant time frame state or federal employees." [67]

Second, on January 8, 1998, Judge Wright reiterated that:

> [she] ha[d] already ruled that questions regarding whether the President, as Governor of Arkansas, had sexual relations with certain women (other than his wife) in meetings that were arranged, facilitated, concealed, and/or assisted by at least one member of the Arkansas State Police and whether some of these women were or became employees of the State of Arkansas (or an agency thereof) <u>are within the scope of the issues in the case</u>. To the extent the President denies these allegations, he can so state without any undue burden. To the extent answers to the questions require something other than an outright denial, the Court finds that such answers may not necessarily be redundant to any previous answers the President has given to such questions and, further, that <u>such answers may be relevant to the issues in this case and may lead to the discovery of admissible evidence</u>.[68]

Third, at a January 12, 1998 hearing, Judge Wright ruled that Ms. Jones would be permitted to ask questions about "other women" during the President's deposition. During the same hearing, Judge Wright also required the plaintiffs to describe all the evidence they planned to introduce at trial, and then made several comments about the potential admissibility of that evidence at trial:

---

[67] 921-DC-0000461 (Dec. 11 Order, at 3) (emphasis supplied). Judge Wright did establish a limited time frame for such discovery, and also required that any women questioned have been federal or state employees during the time of their encounter with the President.

[68] 921-DC-00000734 (Jan. 8 Order, at 4)(emphasis supplied).

> [T]he Rules of Evidence in harassment cases -- and I'm not citing any authority right now for it, but I know in harassment cases, frequently, court's [sic] permit other bad acts, other volatile acts, that kind of thing. And I'm also aware that in sexual assault cases, the Rules of Evidence promulgated by the Violence Against Women Act has certainly opened it up. So I can't say that you can't call any of the witnesses in group B [the pattern and practice issue witnesses].[69]

Judge Wright concluded that for purposes of discovery and depositions, she would permit Ms. Jones's attorneys to ask the President "about people whose -- you know, whose names have been given you or people whom you have, you know, a reasonable basis for asking about."[70] This list included Monica Lewinsky.

Fourth, just before Ms. Jones' attorneys deposed President Clinton on Saturday, January 17, 1998, Judge Wright rejected the President's counsel's attempt to place limits on the scope of deposition questioning. In so ruling, she commented about the nature of the questions that President Clinton would be asked: "Unfortunately, the nature of this case is such that people will be embarrassed. I have never had a sexual harassment case where there was not some embarrassment."[71] President Clinton's counsel also attempted to stop the questioning about Ms. Lewinsky during the deposition, by citing Ms. Lewinsky's affidavit. Judge

---

[69] 1414-DC-00001327-32 (Transcript of Jan. 12, 1998 Hearing, at 37-42).

[70] 1414-DC-00001336 (Transcript of Jan. 12, 1998 Hearing, at 46).

[71] Clinton 1/17/98 Depo. at 9.

Wright refused to limit the questioning.[72]

Finally, on January 29, 1998, after the OIC moved to suspend discovery relating to Ms. Lewinsky because she was the subject of a pending criminal investigation, Judge Wright concluded that Lewinsky-related evidence might be capable of influencing the ultimate decision in the lawsuit,[73] but determined pursuant to Fed. R. Evid. 403[74] that the probative value of the evidence was outweighed by the prejudice that would result from delaying the trial to allow the evidence to be obtained without conflicting with the OIC's criminal investigation. Judge Wright's order also held that other evidence of improper conduct occurring in the White House would not be precluded by the Court's ruling.

Judge Wright amplified this holding in an Order entered March 9, 1998. She first "readily acknowledg[ed] that evidence of the Lewinsky matter might have been relevant to the plaintiff's case,"[75] but then reiterated her decision to exclude

---

[72] Id. at 53-56.

[73] Jones v. Clinton, Jan. 29 Order, at 2 ("The Court acknowledges that evidence concerning Monica Lewinsky might be relevant to the issues in this case.").

[74] Federal Rule of Evidence 403, entitled "Exclusion of Relevant Evidence on Grounds of Prejudice, Confusion, or Waste of Time" provides:

> Although relevant, evidence may be excluded if its probative value is substantially outweighed by the danger of unfair prejudice, confusion of the issues, or misleading the jury, or by considerations of undue delay, waste of time, or needless presentation of cumulative evidence.

[75] Jones v. Clinton, March 9 Order, at 9 (footnote omitted).

the evidence under Fed. R. Evid. 403 on the ground that it was not "essential to the core issues" of the case (namely, whether "plaintiff herself was the victim of quid pro quo sexual harassment.")[76]

ii. Ruling by the D.C. Circuit

The materiality of the allegedly false statements made in Jones v. Clinton has also been litigated by the OIC. Chief Judge Norma Holloway Johnson of the District Court for the District of Columbia ordered Francis Carter (Ms. Lewinsky's first lawyer) to testify as to matters relating to his representation of Ms. Lewinsky. In ordering the testimony, the court invoked the crime-fraud exception to the attorney-client privilege, based on the OIC's prima facie showing that Ms. Lewinsky had used Mr. Carter to prepare a false affidavit "for the purpose of committing perjury and obstructing justice."[77] On appeal to the United States Court of Appeals for the District of Columbia Circuit, Ms. Lewinsky argued that her affidavit related to matters later excluded from the Jones case and hence, as a matter of law, was not "material."[78] The appellate court rejected this argument:

---

[76] Id. (emphasis in original)

[77] In re Grand Jury Proceedings, slip op. at 5 (D.D.C., Misc. No. 98-68, March 31, 1998).

[78] Being immaterial, she argued, the affidavit could not form the basis for a criminal charge and thus the crime-fraud exception could not be applied to vitiate her attorney-client privilege.

Lewinsky tells us she could not have committed [the] crime: the government could not establish perjury because her denial of having had a "sexual relationship" with President Clinton was not "material" to the Arkansas proceedings within the meaning of 18 U.S.C. § 1623(a). . . . Lewinsky's proposition[] rel[ies] on the Arkansas district court's ruling on January 30 [sic], 1998, after Lewinsky had filed her affidavit, that although evidence concerning Lewinsky might be relevant, it would be excluded from the civil case under Fed. R. Evid. 403 as unduly prejudicial, "not essential to the core issues in th[e] case" and to prevent undue delay resulting from the Independent Counsel's Investigation.

A statement is "material" if it "has a natural tendency to influence, or was capable of influencing, the decision of the tribunal in making a [particular] determination." United States v. Barrett, 111 F.3d 947, 953 (D.C. Cir.), cert. denied, 118 S.Ct. 176 (1997). The "central object" of any materiality inquiry is "whether the misrepresentation or concealment was predictably capable of affecting, i.e., had a natural tendency to affect, the official decision." Kungys v. United States, 485 U.S. 759, 771 (1988). Lewinsky used the statement in her affidavit, quoted above, to support her motion to quash the subpoena issued in the discovery phase of the Arkansas litigation. District courts faced with such motions must decide whether the testimony or material sought is reasonably calculated to lead to admissible evidence and, if so, whether the need for the testimony, its probative value, the nature and importance of the litigation, and similar factors outweigh any burden enforcement of the subpoena might impose. See Fed. R. Civ. P. 26(b)(a),. 45(c)(3)(A)(iv); Linder v. Department of Defense, 133 F.3d 17, 24 (D.C. Cir. 1998); see generally 9A Charles Allan Wright & Arthur R. Miller, Federal Practice and Procedure § 2459 (2d ed. 1995). There can be no doubt that Lewinsky's statements in her affidavit were -- in the words of Kungys v. United States -- predictably capable of affecting this decision. She executed and filed her affidavit for this very purpose.[79]

[79] In re Sealed Case, slip op. at 4-6 (D.C. Cir., Nos. 98-3052, 98-3053, 98-3059, May 26, 1998) (brackets and ellipsis in original).

D. Literal Truth Defense to Perjury

Where a witness's answers are literally true -- even if they are unresponsive, misleading, or false by negative implication -- a perjury conviction cannot be maintained.[80] This is because, as the Supreme Court held in Bronston, "If a witness evades, it is the lawyer's responsibility to recognize the evasion and to bring the witness back to the mark, to flush out the whole truth with the tools of adversary examination."[81]

In Bronston, the defendant was convicted of perjury for testimony given at a bankruptcy hearing relating to a corporation of which he was the sole owner. In pertinent part, the following colloquy gave rise to the conviction:

> Q. Do you have any bank accounts in Swiss banks, Mr. Bronston?
>
> A. No, sir.
>
> Q. Have you ever?
>
> A. The company had an account there for about six months, in Zurich.

Mr. Bronston had in fact had a personal bank account in Geneva for five years, but his answers were literally truthful: he did not have a Swiss bank account at the time of the questioning and his company did have the account described. The prosecution's theory in the lower court was "that in order to mislead his questioner, petitioner answered the second question with literal

---

[80] Bronston v. United States, 409 U.S. 352, 360 (1973).

[81] Id. at 358-59.

truthfulness but unresponsively addressed his answer to the company's assets and not to his own -- thereby implying that he had no personal Swiss bank account at the relevant time."[82]

The Supreme Court, however, found it irrelevant that Bronston may have intended to mislead the questioner and reversed the perjury conviction. The Court explained that though in casual conversation one might interpret the responses to mean that there was never a personal bank account, "the statute does not make it a criminal act for a witness to willfully state any material matter that implies any material matter that he does not believe to be true."[83] Following Bronston, courts have repeatedly found literal truth a complete defense to perjury where the witness's answer was literally true but misleading or unresponsive.[84]

Bronston made clear, however, that in order for a statement

---

[82] 409 U.S. at 354.

[83] Id. at 357-58.

[84] See, e.g., United States v. Chaplin, 25 F.3d 1373, 1380 (7th Cir. 1994) (defense applies where witness denied giving $8,000 on October 23 and government only showed that transaction took place sometime in October); United States v. Earp, 812 F.2d 917, 919 (4th Cir. 1987) ("[I]n questioning [defendant], the questioner simply did not probe deep enough to recognize any potential evasion."); United States v. Tedder, 801 F.2d 1437, 1447-48 (4th Cir. 1986) (defense applicable where government failed to ask defendant if he knew of prior bank accounts held by named individual and defendant truthfully answered question posed in the present tense), cert. denied, 480 U.S. 938 (1987); cf. United States v. Rymer, No. 91-5585, 1992 WL 86528, at *3 (6th Cir. April 27, 1992) (defense not applicable to defendant's testimony that he could not recall statements he made to FBI a year earlier, as his answers were not non-responsive) (unpublished disposition).

to be considered literally true, it must be true in the context of the question. The Court analyzed a hypothetical example in which a witness, when asked how many times she entered a store on a given day, responds "five" when she actually visited the store 50 times. The district court had considered the response in this hypothetical to be literally true, but had instructed the jury that a defendant could be convicted of perjury if the answer was "'not literally false but when considered in the context in which it was given, nevertheless constitute[d] a false statement.'"[85] The Supreme Court agreed that a perjury conviction would be proper in such a case, noting that "the answer 'five times' is responsive to the hypothetical question and contains nothing to alert the questioner that he may be sidetracked."[86] The Court also expressed doubt that the answer in the hypothetical was literally true in any event, explaining: "Whether an answer is true must be determined with reference to the question it purports to answer, not in isolation. An unresponsive answer is unique in this respect because its unresponsiveness by definition prevents its truthfulness from being tested in the context of the question."[87]

In light of Bronston, a witness who gives a responsive answer that is false when viewed in the context of the question

---

[85] 409 U.S. at 354.

[86] Id. at 354 n.3.

[87] Id.

may not benefit from the literal truth defense.[88] Indeed, most courts (including the D.C. Circuit) have held that the literal truth defense does not bar perjury convictions where the defendant and the government interpret the relevant question differently. In other words, most circuits hold that Bronston's literal truth defense is inapposite where "the answer is true only if one of two asserted interpretations of the question is accepted."[89] The Bell court, for example, said:

> In Bronston, the answer was a full, explanatory sentence, the truthfulness of which could be determined without reference to the question. Here, the answer simply was "no"; the truthfulness of that answer can be determined only by first looking to the question. Bronston simply did not deal with a yes or no answer given to a question susceptible to more than one interpretation.[90]

Under these circumstances, when the defendant claims that he understood the question differently from the questioner "the

---

[88] See United States v. Schafrick, 871 F.2d 300, 303 (2d Cir. 1989) ("In Bronston, the crucial factor was that the answer Bronston gave was not responsive to the question he was asked. . . . If an answer is responsive to the question, then there is no notice to the examiner and no basis for applying Bronston."); United States v. Kehoe, 562 F.2d 65, 68-69 (1st Cir. 1977) ("An answer that is responsive and false on its face does not come within Bronston's literal truth analysis simply because the defendant can postulate unstated premises of the question that would make his answer literally true."); United States v. Crippen, 570 F.2d 535, 537 (5th Cir. 1978) ("The words used were to be understood in their common sense, not as they might be warped by sophistry or twisted"), cert. denied, 439 U.S. 1069 (1979).

[89] United States v. Bell, 623 F.2d 1132, 1136 (5th Cir. 1980). As discussed below, only the First Circuit's Glantz decision may be at odds with this line of cases.

[90] Id. at 1136.

defendant's understanding of the question is a matter for the jury to decide."[91] (The First Circuit has, however, applied the literal truth defense to "bar perjury convictions for arguably untrue answers to vague or ambiguous questions when there is insufficient evidence of how they were understood by the witness."[92])

In a Watergate-related case, for example, the defendant was convicted of falsely stating that he was not "'familiar with'" the distribution of negative campaign literature by a Nixon staffer he had hired, and that he did not recall "'express[ing] any interest . . . or giv[ing him] any directions or instructions with respect to any single or particular candidate.'"[93] The government had charged that the defendant did know of the literature distribution and that he did give specific instructions regarding a particular Senator, Senator Muskie, a

---

[91] Id. (collecting cases). Bell itself held "that [because] 'a reasonably minded jury must have a reasonable doubt as to the existence of the essential elements of the crime charged,' the conviction may not stand." Id. (quoting United States v. Reynolds, 511 F.2d 603, 606 (5th Cir. 1975)); cf. Kehoe, 562 F.2d at 69 (finding no evidence to support defendant's claim that the context of the questions was unclear); United States v. Cash, 522 F.2d 1025, 1029-30 (9th Cir. 1975) (affirming perjury conviction where jury chose to disbelieve defendant's purported understanding of question); cf. United States v. Thompson, 637 F.2d 267, 270 (5th Cir. 1981) (Bronston "does not mean . . . that question and answer must be aligned in categorical and digital order.").

[92] United States v. Glantz, 847 F.2d 1, 6 (1st Cir. 1988). Glantz might be viewed as premised on an insufficiency of the evidence analysis, however the court characterized it as a literal truth defense.

[93] See United States v. Chapin, 515 F.2d 1274, 1277 (D.C. Cir. 1975), cert. denied, 423 U.S. 1015 (1975).

potential political opponent of President Nixon. The defendant argued on appeal that because the questions were vague, his answers were truthful: he did not know whether the staffer actually passed out literature, and he never gave directions about one candidate to the exclusion of others. The D.C. Circuit rejected this argument, explaining:

> As another court stated when faced with the charge that "met with" and "regular" were too vague, "mere vagueness or ambiguity in the questions is not enough to establish a defense to perjury. Almost any question or answer can be interpreted in several ways when subjected to ingenious scrutiny after the fact." When the questions involved here are considered in the context of both the purpose of the grand jury investigation, which was known to Chapin, and the series of questions actually asked, we cannot say that the words involved could not be "subject to a reasonable and definite interpretation by the jury."[94]

The court distinguished Bronston, in which the answer was unresponsive, because there "[t]he [Supreme] Court explicitly considered only the problem posed by a declarative statement which was true no matter what the question might have meant, and did not consider the effect of any possible vagueness of the question." The court then explained that "Bronston does not deal with the situation where a defendant has given a 'yes or no' answer, the truth of which can be ascertained only in the context of the question posed."[95]

---

[94] Id. at 1279-80 (quoting United States v. Ceccerelli, 350 F. Supp. 475, 478 (W.D. Penn. 1972) and United States v. Marchisio, 344 F.2d 653, 662 (2d Cir. 1965), respectively); see also Chapin, 515 F.2d at 1280 n.3 (collecting cases in which questions challenged as ambiguous were upheld as sufficient to support an indictment or a conviction).

[95] Chapin, 515 F.2d at 1279-80.

The court was also unpersuaded by the defendant's argument that the lack of follow-up questions meant "that the prosecutors were not successfully misled by Chapin."[96] Instead, the court observed that "neither the court nor the jury must accept as conclusive the meaning the defendant, after the fact, puts on a question." The court found the jury's interpretation of the question, as evidenced by the verdict, the "only reasonable [one]."[97]

One D.C. district court has recently relied upon Chapin to reject an Iran-Contra defendant's motion to dismiss perjury counts based on his having "dissect[ed] each of the alleged perjuries to demonstrate that they are true, albeit unresponsive."[98] The court explained:

> Such stretching of the language would be unnecessary were the contested statements literally true. Nor does Bronston give a defendant latitude to insulate himself from prosecution by reinterpreting his statements in order to give them a meaning which is literally true. . . . Bronston requires the court to dismiss the indictment only when it is plain that the government cannot prove that the defendant's statement was false. In situations, as here, where there may be one or more arguable constructions of the defendant's statements under which those statements might be true, and the

---

96 Id. at 1283.

97 Id. In Chapin, the district court had charged the jury that it could not convict if any reasonable interpretation of the question rendered the answer true. The D.C. Circuit therefore did not need to decide "whether a conviction would be upheld if the government proved that the defendant was truthfully answering some possible-and-reasonable interpretation of the question but falsely answering the question as he himself interpreted it." Id. at 1280.

98 See United States v. Clarridge, 811 F. Supp. 697, 712 (D.D.C. 1992).

> other constructions that the statements were, the question is left for the jury.[99]

The difference between perjury and literal truth is well illustrated by another high-profile case, in which the D.C. Circuit affirmed a perjury count involving conflicting interpretations of questions and answers but reversed another count because the statement was literally true.[100] The defendant, a HUD official, had been convicted of four counts of perjury and four § 1001 violations for statements made during congressional hearings investigating favoritism in the administration of funding for substandard housing. A Senator had asked the defendant, in pertinent part:

> [I]t is suggested that informal solicitations and unawarded applications from the past are guarded by you, and that you personally go through the selections, excluding review by the appropriate staff experts.
>
> Furthermore, it is suggested that developers have personally come to you asking for awards. Now, as you know, the proper procedure is for the HUD Washington office to deal with housing authorities and for them to deal with developers. In some cases, the housing authorities have subsequently alerted HUD that these funds aren't even needed. How do you respond to that?[101]

In response, the defendant had explained the procedure for reviewing funding applications, including review by a panel. The statement found perjurious was that "[t]hat panel goes solely on

---

[99] Id.

[100] United States v. Dean, 55 F.3d 640, 659 (D.C. Cir. 1995), cert. denied, 516 U.S. 1184 (1996) (citing United States v. Dunnigan, 507 U.S. 87, 94 (1993)).

[101] Id. at 659.

information provided by the Assistant Secretary for Housing."[102] Challenging her perjury conviction on appeal, the defendant claimed that she had answered the question asked, to wit, whether she made funding decisions alone. The court rejected the argument, saying that "[t]he thrust of the Senator's inquiry was whether Dean played a part in any moderate rehabilitation funding decision in which Departmental regulations were not followed," and that "[i]n essence, Dean denied [the Senator's] intimations."[103] The court concluded from the government's evidence that "the jury was entitled to find that the panel did not base its decisions solely on information provided by the Assistant Secretary for Housing."[104] Thus, notwithstanding the wordiness and complexity of the question and the defendant's explanation of how she understood it, the court affirmed the conviction on this count.

Dean reversed the defendant's conviction on a separate perjury count, however. The defendant had been convicted for stating that "no moderate rehabilitation [funds] have ever gone to my home State of Maryland, simply for that reason -- that I sat on the panel [which made allocation decisions]".[105] The D.C.

---

[102] Id.

[103] Id. at 660 (emphasis added); cf. Schafrick, 871 F.2d at 304 ("The questions as well as the answers, and the answers understood as a whole, are crucial to the determination of whether [defendant]'s statements were perjury.").

[104] Dean, 55 F.3d at 660.

[105] Id. at 661.

Circuit rejected the government's claim that the statement represented the defendant's denial of ever having participated in a moderate rehabilitation funding decision for a Maryland project, because "that is not literally what she said." The court wrote:

> While Dean had participated in decisions for Maryland projects, her testimony indicated that those projects did not receive special consideration "simply" because Dean sat on the panel. Dean's statement could have been true, and, in any event, the government never proved at trial that she showed particular favoritism to Maryland projects. Although it may be, as Mark Twain said, that "[o]ften, the surest way to convey misinformation is to tell the strict truth," a statement that is literally true cannot support a perjury conviction.[106]

In addition, the prosecution provided no evidence to support the alleged falsity of the defendant's statement, and the defendant made the statement gratuitously -- it was not in response to a pending question. Thus, unlike the perjury count discussed above, the court could not view the answer in the context of the question to determine the defendant's understanding. As a result, it concluded that the conviction could not stand as it might be literally true.

E. Perjury in Cases of Feigned Forgetfulness

Perjury cases can be and have been charged when a witness feigns forgetfulness about the events in question. When this type of charge is brought, the government must prove that the witness in fact had knowledge about the events as to which he claims

---

[106] Id. at 662 (citing Bronston, 409 U.S. at 360).

memory loss.

1. Proof of Knowledge

Because proving feigned forgetfulness requires proving the state of mind of the witness, the key issue is "whether th[e] circumstantial evidence meets the test of proof beyond a reasonable doubt."[107] In rare instances, direct proof of feigned forgetfulness -- an inconsistent statement of recollection, for example -- might be available, and such proof would constitute "direct evidence that the defendant did know or recall the fact that he denied knowing or recalling under oath." [108]

Such direct proof is unlikely and courts have generally concluded that the government can also meet its burden (to prove

---

[107] Id; see also United States v. Mathern, 329 F. Supp. 536, 538 (E.D. Pa. 1971); Chapin, 515 F.2d at 1284 ("Of course . . . the falsity of an 'I don't recall' answer must be proven by circumstantial evidence."); Fotie v. United States, 137 F.2d 831, 842 (8th Cir. 1943) ("Necessarily the recollection of a witness must be shown by circumstantial evidence.").

[108] Gebhard v. United States, 422 F.2d 281, 287-88 (9th Cir. 1970); see also United States v. Forrest, 623 F.2d 1107, 1111-12 (5th Cir. 1980) (admission recounted by another witness is direct evidence of falsity), cert. denied, 449 U.S. 924 (1980); United States v. Chapin, 515 F.2d 1274, 1284 (D.C. Cir.) (implying that only possible direct evidence tending to prove falsity of claimed inability to recall would be statement of defendant), cert. denied, 423 U.S. 1015 (1975); United States v. Sweig, 441 F.2d 114, 116 (2d Cir.) (same), cert. denied, 403 U.S. 932 (1971); United States v. Beach, 296 F.2d 153, 157 (4th Cir. 1961) (direct evidence of defendant, and others, that he knew certain men, supported perjury conviction for defendant's grand jury testimony that he did not know identity of men); United States v. Bergman, 354 F.2d 931, 934 (2d Cir. 1966) (upholding conviction for false of grand jury testimony denying recollection of receipt of kickbacks and income from unlawful sources when such income was proven by extrajudicial admissions and circumstantial evidence that defendant possessed additional funds).

beyond a reasonable doubt that claimed forgetfulfulness was feigned) when it presents enough circumstantial evidence that a defendant must have remembered.[109] A broad range of circumstantial evidence can support a perjury conviction on the theory that purported inability to remember was a lie. In general, just as with any other attempt to prove a defendant's state of mind,

> [t]he jury must infer the state of a man's mind from the things he says and does. Such an inference may come from proof of the objective falsity itself, from proof of a motive to lie, and from other facts tending to show that the defendant really knew the things he claimed not to know.[110]

Thus, in order to prove the claimed forgetfulness was feigned, "the witness must testify to some overt act from which the jury may infer the accused's actual belief."[111] As the D.C. Circuit has said, in a different formulation of the same principle, "a belief as to the falsity of testimony may be inferred by the jury from proof of the falsity itself."[112]

2. Cases in Brief

The following subsection briefly reviews some representative

---

109 See Behrle v. United States, 100 F.2d 714, 716 (D.C. Cir. 1938) (prosecution may use circumstantial evidence to prove that a witness charged with perjury must have remembered facts about which he testified that "he 'remembered nothing'").

110 Sweig, 441 F.2d at 117.

111 Beach, 296 F.2d at 155 (internal quotation marks omitted).

112 Young v. United States, 212 F.2d 236, 241 (D.C. Cir.), cert. denied, 347 U.S. 1015 (1954).

reported cases involving feigned forgetfulness and perjury charges. The next subsection summarizes principles gleaned from a larger number of such cases.[113]

- A witness to a shooting, who had made a written statement to the police and testified before the grand jury, was convicted of perjury when -- after being called to testify at the trial of the men charged with the shooting -- he first denied having seen anything happen; then, when shown his signed statement, admitted his signature but said he did not know the contents; and finally, when the statement was read to him, said he did not remember whether any of the events described in it happened or not.[114] The D.C. Circuit affirmed the conviction, stating: While "[d]irect proof that [the defendant] did remember was impossible, [t]he circumstantial evidence that he must have remembered was, if believed, enough to overcome the presumption of innocence

---

[113] Claims of inability to remember past events have arisen in obstruction of justice cases as well. See, e.g., United States v. Alo, 439 F.2d 751, 754 (2d Cir. 1971) (affirming obstruction of justice conviction for professed memory loss in connection with SEC Investigation), cert. denied, 404 U.S. 850 (1971); Avionic Co. v. General Dynamics Corp., 957 F.2d 555, 557 (8th Cir. 1992) (affirming sanction for obstruction of discovery where defendant avoided having to disclose information he later claimed not to recall); United States v. Murray, 65 F.3d 1161, 1165 (4th Cir. 1995)(district court properly enhanced sentence on perjury conviction for obstruction of justice where defendant signed statement implicating another individual but testified that she could not remember making statement about other's involvement). Typically, however, feigned forgetfulness is charged as a perjury violation.

[114] See Behrle v. United States, 100 F.2d 714, 715-16 (D.C. Cir. 1938).

and leave no reasonable doubt of guilt."[115]

- Another defendant was convicted of perjury under § 1623 for testifying before a grand jury investigating a drug conspiracy that "he did not recall being in Florida during 1983."[116] But "[t]here was other grand jury testimony, however, that Moeckly had been in Florida, and had stayed with [a co-conspirator] and studied Spanish there."[117] The Eighth Circuit affirmed the conviction.
- A justice of the Michigan Supreme Court was convicted under § 1621 when he testified before a grand jury that "he had no recollection of two conversations with" a co-defendant, but then two days later (after he became aware that some of his activities had been the subject of FBI surveillance) told the grand jury that the conversations had taken place.[118] The Sixth Circuit affirmed the conviction. The court first noted that,

---

[115] Id. at 716. Citing Behrle, the Eight Circuit reversed a perjury conviction because the defendant recanted his allegedly false statement. Fotie v. United States, 137 F.2d 831, 842 (8th Cir. 1943). The defendant had claimed no recollection of ever having filed for naturalization papers or having sworn that he was born in Italy. When shown the original and duplicate of his declaration of intention to become a citizen, which was made 24 years before he made the allegedly perjurious statement, "he promptly admitted it." Id. The court distinguished the case from instances where witnesses recant statements once their perjury is exposed. Id. at 843.

[116] United States v. Moeckly, 769 F.2d 453, 459-65 (8th Cir. 1985), cert. denied, 475 U.S. 1015 (1986).

[117] Id. at 459.

[118] See United States v. Swainson, 548 F.2d 657, 662 (6th Cir.), cert. denied, 431 U.S. 937 (1977).

> [w]hen the alleged perjury relates to the state of mind of the accused, as in the present case ('I have no recollection'), proof of perjury must necessarily consist of proof of facts from which the jury could infer that the defendant must have known or remembered that which he denied knowing or remembering while under oath.[119]

The court found that in this case there was enough evidence that the jury could infer that the defendant "had wilfully failed to answer the questions concerning these conversations truthfully at his first appearance."[120]

- Another defendant had been convicted under § 1621 for 15 counts of perjury before a grand jury investigating illegal card games at a club.[121] Gebhard had been questioned (under a grant of immunity) about his role in the installation and operation of electronic devices placed in the club to enable gamblers to fleece fellow members. In pertinent part, Gebhard's "responses to the questions involved in [certain] counts of the indictment were invariably, 'I don't recall' or 'I don't know' or 'I don't remember.'"[122] The appeals court noted that "[g]iven answers of this nature, it would be difficult to find two witnesses to testify that the defendant did in fact know or believe or recall a matter

---

[119] Id. at 662.

[120] Id.

[121] See Gebhard v. United States, 422 F.2d 281, 283-88 (9th Cir. 1970).

[122] Id. at 287.

which he said he did not."[123] The court therefore concluded that circumstantial evidence could be used to prove the case for perjury: "[i]f the government can build up a strong enough set of facts to show what the truth of the matter was and what the defendant must have known, this should be enough to go to the jury."[124]

- In the Watergate-era case mentioned earlier, the defendant (Nixon's Appointment Secretary, Chapin) was convicted under § 1623 for stating "Not that I recall" in answer to a question about whether he had hired a particular aide (Donald" Segretti) to play pranks on the contenders for the Democratic nomination, or had given Segretti "any instructions with respect to any single or particular candidate."[125] The D.C. Circuit affirmed the conviction, noting that the "the falsity of an 'I don't recall' answer must be proven by circumstantial evidence," that in this case the evidence showed that Chapin had given the aide "a large number of instructions about Senator Muskie over a six-month period," and that Chapin's "obvious desire before

[123] Id. The court also suggested that a contrary admission by the defendant would constitute direct evidence of his state of mind. Id.

[124] Id. at 288.

[125] United States v. Chapin, 515 F.2d 1274, 1274-90 (D.C. Cir.), cert. denied, 423 U.S. 1015 (1975). Chapin had in 1971 hired Segretti to play "political pranks" on the contenders for the Democratic presidential nomination. The actual question in full was: "Did you ever express any interest to [Segretti], or give him any instructions with respect to any single or particular candidate?" Chapin responded, "Not that I recall."

the grand jury and the court to put himself as far as possible from the specifics of Segretti's campaign provided sufficient evidence of his motive to conveniently omit recollection of any specific instructions."[126] Even though Chapin argued on appeal that he had believed the question was asking whether he had given any instructions to "zero in" on a particular candidate to the exclusion of others, and that he had not done so, the court rejected the argument, finding that if that had been Chapin's true understanding, "he would not have responded so unequivocally as he did, 'Not that I recall' . . . but would probably have given a flat and emphatic negative," and that "[t]his was too central a matter not to be clear in his mind."[127]

- Another defendant, was convicted of perjury under § 1623 for testifying to a grand jury first that he had been in Florida during a major fire in Lynn, Massachusetts, and later that he could not remember the exact date that he had returned to Lynn.[128] At trial, the government had introduced evidence to show that Goguen had been in Lynn and that, because of the fire's magnitude, it was more than likely that when Goguen appeared before the grand jury he did remember that he had been in Lynn during the fire. The First Circuit affirmed

---

[126] Id. at 1284.

[127] Id. at 1283.

[128] See United States v. Goguen, 723 F.2d 1012, 1014-15 (1st Cir. 1983).

the conviction, noting that "while the average person may not remember where he was the day before President Kennedy was assassinated, he surely would remember if he was at the Texas Book Depository in Dallas the day before the assassination."[129]

3. Summary

A review of the case law reveals that perjury convictions for false claims of memory loss are likely where there is either strong circumstantial evidence or other factors tending to show that the witness must have remembered, such as a motive to lie (Behrle; Seltzer, Nicoletti, Ponticelli, Chapin);[130] a reason to remember (Ponticelli, Chapin); a selectively spotty memory (Nicoletti); a suddenly revived memory upon learning of the government's evidence (Swainson);[131] testimony or other evidence confirming the occurrence of an event and the likelihood that the defendant would not have forgotten it (Moeckly, Camporeale,

---

[129] Id. at 1021 n.11.

[130] Behrle v. United States, 100 F.2d 714 (D.C. Cir. 1938); United States v. Seltzer, 794 F.2d 1114 (7th Cir. 1986), cert. denied, 479 U.S. 1054 (1987); United States v. Nicoletti, 310 F.2d 359 (7th Cir. 1962), cert. denied, 372 U.S. 942 (1963); United States v. Ponticelli, 622 F.2d 985 (9th Cir.), cert. denied, 449 U.S. 1016 (1980), overruled on other grounds, United States v. Debright, 730 F.2d 1255, 1259 (9th Cir. 1984); United States v. Chapin, 515 F.2d 1274 (D.C. Cir.), cert. denied, 423 U.S. 1015 (1975)

[131] United States v. Swainson, 548 F.2d 657 (6th Cir.), cert. denied, 431 U.S. 937 (1977).

Ponticelli, Devitt, Chapin; but see Clizer);[132] or statements by the defendant contradicting the claim (Behrle, Nicoletti). Courts have also considered the chronology of a defendant's statements or inconsistent claims of forgetfulness (Behrle), or proximity in time between the testimony and the event at issue (Nicoletti, Mathern; cf. Fotie, Devitt).[133] Moreover, courts have adverted to the "enormity of the events" as an indication that purported failure to recollect was a lie (Seltzer, Moreno Morales, Ponticelli, Goguen),[134] or have highlighted the repetitiveness of some witnesses' claims of inability to remember (Gebhard).[135] The defendant's uncooperative attitude in testifying before a grand jury is also relevant (Seltzer).

F. Inconsistent Statements Under § 1623(c)

As noted above, under § 1623(c) the government may prosecute a perjury charge based solely upon inconsistent statements (if both of the statements in question were made under oath, before

---

[132] United States v. Moeckly, 769 F.2d 453 (8th Cir. 1985), cert. denied, 475 U.S. 1015 (1986); United States v. Camporeale, 515 F.2d 184 (2d Cir. 1975); United States v. Devitt, 499 F.2d 135 (7th Cir. 1974), cert. denied, 421 U.S. 975 (1975); United States v. Clizer, 464 F.2d 121 (9th Cir.), cert. denied, 409 U.S. 1086 (1972).

[133] United States v. Mathern, 329 F. Supp. 536 (E.D. Pa. 1971); Fotie v. United States, 137 F.2d 831 (8th Cir. 1943).

[134] United States v. Moreno Morales, 815 F.2d 725 (1st Cir.), cert. denied, 484 U.S. 966 (1987); United States v. Goguen, 723 F.2d 1012 (1st Cir. 1983).

[135] Gebhard v. United States, 422 F.2d 281 (9th Cir. 1970).

or ancillary to a court or grand jury).[136] The prosecution need not prove which statement is false, but need only prove beyond a

[136] Section 1623(c) of Title 18 provides:

> Any indictment or information for violation of this section alleging that, in any proceedings before or ancillary to any court or grand jury of the United States, the defendant under oath has knowingly made two or more declarations, which are inconsistent to the degree that one of them is necessarily false, need not specify which declaration is false if --
>
> (1) each declaration was material to the point in question, and
>
> (2) each declaration is made within the period of the statute of limitations for the offense charged under this section.
>
> In any prosecution under this section, the falsity of the declaration set forth in the indictment or information shall be established sufficient for conviction by proof that the defendant while under oath made irreconcilably contradictory declarations material to the point in question in any proceeding before or ancillary to any court or grand jury.

This provision is the result of a 1970 amendment to § 1623 that was intended to "provide[] specifically for the prosecution of a false declaration in the case of irreconcilable contradictory statements _without_ the necessity of specifying which of the declarations is false." H.R. Rep. No. 1549, 91st Cong., 2nd Sess., _reprinted in_ 1970 U.S.C.C.A.N. 4007 (emphasis added). Of course, both statements must be made under oath before or ancillary to a court or grand jury. _See_ _United States v. Jaramillo_, 69 F.3d 388, 390 (9th Cir. 1995) ("To take advantage of § 1623(c)'s lesser requirement of proof, the government must demonstrate, inter alia, that both contradictory declarations are within the scope of 18 U.S.C. § 1623(c)."); _cf._ _United States v. Harvey_, 657 F. Supp. 111, 113-14 (E.D. Tenn. 1987) (including as an element of crime under § 1623(c) that the statements "were made before or ancillary to a federal court or grand jury proceeding").

Section 1623(c) also provides that "[i]t shall be a defense to an indictment or information made pursuant to the first sentence of this subsection that the defendant at the time he made each declaration believed the declaration was true." 18 U.S.C. § 1623(c)(2).

reasonable doubt that the statements are irreconcilably contradictory (and material to the case).[137]

G. Perjury Trap Defense

The so-called "perjury trap defense" has been discussed by many courts, but adopted by few.[138] In theory, "[a] perjury trap is created when the government calls a witness before the grand jury for the primary purpose of obtaining testimony from him in order to prosecute him later for perjury."[139] The essence of this theory is that by using its power to compel testimony toward this end, particularly when the perjured information is neither material nor germane to the legitimate ongoing investigation of the grand jury,[140] the government violates the Due Process clause of the Fifth Amendment and that this conduct requires dismissal of the indictment.[141] Criminal defendants often argue that their indictments should be dismissed for improprieties surrounding the requirement that they give grand jury testimony.

---

[137] See United States v. Porter, 994 F.2d 470, 473 n.4 (8th Cir. 1993). Thus, in order to sustain a conviction under § 1623(c), based upon inconsistent statements the government must prove the following elements beyond a reasonable doubt: (1) a defendant, under oath; (2) made two or more declarations; (3) which were irreconcilably inconsistent; (4) each of which was material to the point in question, and (5) each of which was made within the statute of limitations.

[138] See Wheel v. Robinson, 34 F.3d 60, 67-68 (2d Cir.1994).

[139] United States v. Chen, 933 F.2d 793, 796 (9th Cir. 1991).

[140] See United States v. Crisconi, 520 F. Supp. 915, 920 (D.Del.1981).

[141] Id. at 67 (quoting Chen, 933 F.2d at 796-97).

Insofar as the doctrine exists, "any application of the 'perjury trap' doctrine" is precluded if there is a "legitimate basis" for an investigation and for the particular questions answered falsely.[142] When testimony is elicited before a grand jury that is "attempting to obtain useful information in furtherance of its investigation"[143] or "conducting a legitimate investigation into crimes which had in fact taken place within its jurisdiction,"[144] the perjury trap defense cannot succeed.

Furthermore, no perjury trap defense is available simply because the government anticipated that the defendant would commit perjury in testifying before the grand jury. Even if the government anticipates that a defendant would give false testimony, the government is entitled to hope "that [the defendant] ... might provide information about the pending investigation"[145] and to anticipate that a witness will testify truthfully once placed in the solemn atmosphere of the grand jury room. "[F]or many witnesses the grand jury room engenders an atmosphere conducive to truthtelling, for it is likely that upon

---

142 Wheel, 34 F.3d at 68; see also United States v. Regan, 103 F.3d 1072 (2nd Cir.1997), cert. denied, 117 S.Ct. 2484 (1997).

143 United States v. Devitt, 499 F.2d 135, 140 (7th Cir. 1974), cert. denied, 421 U.S. 975(1975).

144 United States v. Chevoor, 526 F.2d 178, 185 (1st Cir.1975), cert. denied, 425 U.S.(1976). See United States v. Chen, 933 F.2d 793, 797 (9th Cir. 1991); see also United States v. Brown, 49 F.3d 1162, 1168 (6th Cir. 1995).

145 United States v. Caputo, 633 F. Supp. 1479, 1487 (E.D.Pa.1986), rev'd on other grounds, 823 F.2d 754 (3d Cir. 1987).

being brought before such a body of neighbors and fellow citizens, and having been placed under a solemn oath to tell the truth, many witnesses feel obliged to do just that."[146]

II. Obstruction of Justice -- 18 U.S.C. § 1503

The obstruction of justice statute applicable to cases involving a defendant's false swearing or obstructive conduct is 18 U.S.C. § 1503.[147] Section 1503 provides:

> (a) Whoever corruptly, or by threats or force, or by any threatening letter or communication, endeavors to influence, intimidate, or impede any grand or petit juror, or officer in or of any court of the United States, or officer who may be serving at any examination or other proceeding before any United States magistrate judge or other committing magistrate,

---

[146] United States v. Washington, 431 U.S. 181, 187-88 (1977).

[147] Section 1505 of Title 18 applies to pending "department or agency" proceedings, not to pending judicial or grand jury proceedings. While "mere 'police investigation[s]'" do not constitute proceedings for purposes of the statute, "agency investigative activities are proceedings within the scope of § 1505 [where they] involve[] agencies with some adjudicative power, or with the power to enhance their investigations through the issuance of subpoenas or warrants." United States v. Kelley, 36 F.3d 1118, 1127 (D.C. Cir. 1994)(citation omitted).

In the D.C. Circuit, § 1505 applies only where the defendant influenced another person to violate the law. In United States v. Poindexter, 951 F.2d 369 (D.C. Cir. 1991), cert. denied, 506 U.S. 1021 (1992), the court applied a "transitive" reading to § 1505 and held that, "[a]s used in § 1505 . . . the term 'corruptly' is too vague to provide constitutionally adequate notice that it prohibits lying to the Congress." Id. at 379. The court thus narrowed § 1505 "to include only 'corrupting' another person by influencing him to violate his legal duty." Id. (emphasis added). The court observed, however, that the "language of § 1505 is materially different from that of § 1503." Id. at 385. The transitive Poindexter reading of § 1505 does not apply to § 1503. United States v. Russo, 104 F.3d 431, 435-47 (D.C. Cir. 1997); United States v. Watt, 911 F. Supp. 538, 545-47 (D.D.C. 1995).

> in the discharge of his duty, . . . or corruptly or by threats of force, or by any threatening letter or communication, influences, obstructs, or impedes, or endeavors to influence, obstruct, or impede, the due administration of justice, shall be punished as provided in subsection (b).[148]

The underlined "'Omnibus Clause' serves as a catchall, prohibiting persons from endeavoring to influence, obstruct, or impede the due administration of justice. The latter clause, it can be seen, is far more general in scope than the earlier clauses of the statute."[149] Put differently, the omnibus clause "prohibits acts that are similar in result, rather than manner, to the conduct described in the first part of the statute."[150]

The Court of Appeals for the District of Columbia Circuit has characterized the offense of § 1503 obstruction of justice as having three main elements: (1) the government must prove that the defendant engaged in conduct or behavior or endeavored to engage in conduct or behavior; (2) that the defendant engaged in such behavior corruptly and with specific intent; and (3) that the defendant's intent was to impede the due administration of justice.[151] In order for § 1503 to apply, there must be judicial proceedings pending at the time of the defendant's conduct, such

---

[148] 18 U.S.C. § 1503 (emphasis added).

[149] United States v. Aguilar, 515 U.S. 593, 598 (1995).

[150] United States v. Howard, 569 F.2d 1331, 1333 (5th Cir.), cert. denied, 439 U.S. 834 (1978).

[151] United States v. Bridges, 717 F.2d 1444, 1449 n.30 (D.C. Cir. 1983), cert. denied, 465 U.S. 1036 (1984); see also Pyramid Securities Ltd. v. IB Resolution Inc., 924 F.2d 1114, 1119 (D.C. Cir.), cert. denied, 502 U.S. 822 (1991).

as a grand jury investigation.[152] Finally, knowledge of the pending judicial proceedings is required.[153] Other courts have combined these elements as follows:

> [T]he elements of obstruction of justice, pursuant to the omnibus clause of section 1503, are (1) a pending judicial proceeding; (2) the defendant must have knowledge or notice of the pending proceeding; and (3) the defendant must have acted corruptly, that is with the intent to influence, obstruct, or impede that proceeding in its due administration of justice.[154]

A. Elements of § 1503 Further Defined

---

152 Pyramid Securities Ltd., 924 F.2d at 1119.

153 Aguilar, 515 U.S. at 599. It bears noting that materiality is not an element of the offense under § 1503. E.g. United States v. Rankin, 1 F.Supp.2d 445, 454 (E.D. Pa. 1998) (citing United States v. Rankin, 870 F.2d 109, 112 (3d Cir. 1989)).

154 United States v. Grubb, 11 F.3d 426, 437 (4th Cir. 1993); see also United States v. Wood, 6 F.3d 692, 695 (10th Cir. 1993); United States v. Williams, 874 F.2d 968, 977 (5th Cir. 1989). The Model Jury Instructions for "Obstructing the Due Administration of Justice" under D.C. Code § 22-722(a) are:

> 1. That the defendant acted corruptly, by means of threat or force, [obstructed or impeded] [endeavored to obstruct or impede] the due administration of justice in the ____ Court of the District of Columbia; and
>
> 2. That the defendant acted with specific intent to obstruct or impede the due administration of justice.
>
> You are instructed that the term 'corruptly' means with an improper motive. The term 'endeavor' means any effort, whether successful or not. The term 'threats' means any words or actions having a reasonable tendency to intimidate the ordinary person.

Criminal Jury Instructions for the District of Columbia (4th ed. 1993) 4.81(B). The Comment provides that pendency of formal court proceedings and a showing of knowledge are also required.

1. Pending Judicial Proceeding

A pending investigation by a grand jury is a judicial proceeding for purposes of § 1503.[155] Similarly, a civil proceeding is a pending judicial proceeding for purposes of § 1503.[156]

2. Knowledge of Pending Judicial Proceeding

"[A] defendant may be convicted under section 1503 only when he knew or had notice of [the] pending proceeding."[157] In Aguilar, the Supreme Court held that a judge's utterance of false statements to an FBI agent "who might or might not testify before a grand jury is [not] sufficient to make out a violation of the catchall provision of § 1503."[158] The Court indicated that the government must show the defendant "knew that his false statement would be provided to the grand jury"; evidence that the defendant

---

155 Wood, 6 F.3d at 696. The Third Circuit has held that a grand jury proceeding is pending once a "subpoena [has been] issued in furtherance of an actual grand jury investigation, i.e., to secure a presently contemplated presentation of evidence before [a regularly sitting] grand jury." United States v. Walasek, 527 F.2d 676, 678 (3d Cir. 1975).

156 United States v. Lundwall, 1 F.Supp.2d 249, 251 (S.D.N.Y. 1998). Section 1503 has been applied in a wide variety of civil matters. United States v. Muhammad, 120 F.3d 688 (7th Cir. 1997) (civil juror solicits bribe from litigant); United States v. London, 714 F.2d 1558 (11th Cir. 1983) (lawyer presents fraudulent civil judgment to client); Roberts v. United States, 239 F.2d 467, 470 (9th Cir. 1956) ("obstruction of justice statute is broad enough to cover attempted corruption of a prospective witness in a civil action").

157 United States v. Frankhauser, 80 F.3d 641, 650 (1st Cir. 1996).

158 515 U.S. at 600.

was aware of the proceeding is usually not sufficient.[159] "[I]f the defendant lacks knowledge that his actions are likely to affect the judicial proceeding, he lacks the requisite intent to obstruct."[160]

3. Specific Intent

The term "corruptly" in the omnibus clause connotes specific intent.[161] Courts have, however, defined the term "corruptly" in somewhat differing terms.[162] "[S]uch intent may be inferred from proof that the defendant knew that his corrupt actions would obstruct justice then actually being administered."[163]

In Haldeman, the D.C. Circuit approved a jury instruction for obstruction of justice which charged that the jury "must find, in addition to the other elements, that [the defendant] had the specific intent to obstruct, impair, or impede the due

---

159 Id. at 601.

160 Id. at 599; cf. Grubb, 11 F.3d at 437 (false statement to FBI agent supported obstruction of justice conviction where defendant "was well aware of the existence of the grand jury investigation when interviewed").

161 See United States v. Haldeman, 559 F.2d 31, 114 (D.C. Cir. 1976) (per curiam), cert. denied, 431 U.S. 933 (1977).

162 See, e.g., United States v. Partin, 552 F.2d 621, 641-42 (5th Cir.) (improper motive or with evil or wicked purpose), cert. denied, 434 U.S. 903 (1977); United States v. Rasheed, 663 F.2d 843, 852 (9th Cir. 1981) (with purpose of obstructing justice), cert. denied, 454 U.S. 1157 (1982); United States v. Barfield, 999 F.2d 1520, 1524 (11th Cir. 1993) (knowingly and intentionally undertaking act from which obstruction was reasonably foreseeable result).

163 United States v. Buffalino, 727 F.2d 50, 54 (2d Cir. 1984).

administration of justice and that his endeavor was not accidental or inadvertent."[164] The district court defined the term "corruptly" as used in § 1503 as "having an evil or improper purpose or intent."[165]

In Aguilar, the Supreme Court stated that, under the "very broad language of the catchall provision" of the omnibus clause, "[t]he action taken by the accused must be with an intent to influence judicial or grand jury proceedings; it is not enough that there be an intent to influence some ancillary proceeding, such as an investigation independent of the Court's or grand jury's authority."[166] The Court further observed that "[s]ome courts have phrased this showing as a 'nexus' requirement -- that the act must have a relationship in time, causation or logic with the judicial proceedings. . . . In other words, the endeavor must have the natural and probable effect of interfering with the due administration of justice."[167]

Even if one is acting from a seemingly benign motive, a jury may nonetheless conclude that the acts were done corruptly. For example, one court reviewed the conviction of a defendant who had altered and defaced certain corporate records relating to an

---

[164] Haldeman, 559 F.2d at 114; see also Caldwell v. United States, 218 F.2d 370, 372 (D.C. Cir. 1954) ("The only intent involved in the crime is the intent to do the forbidden act."), cert. denied, 349 U.S. 930 (1955).

[165] Haldeman, 559 F.2d at 115 n.229;.

[166] Aguilar, 515 U.S. at 599.

[167] Id. (quotations omitted).

ongoing grand jury investigation of Medicare fraud. Faudman argued that he lacked the requisite intent because he intended by his acts only to "protect his brother and the company he had spent his life building."[168] The jury rejected this defense and the court affirmed his conviction, concluding that his conduct was "corrupt" conduct covered by the omnibus clause of § 1503.[169]

B. False and Evasive Testimony as Obstruction of Justice

1. Generally

"[S]tatements . . . made directly to the grand jury itself, in the form of false testimony or false documents," may provide a basis for § 1503 liability.[170] For false statements to form the basis of obstruction, however, the government must prove the person making the statements had the intent to impede or effect of impeding the due administration of justice.[171] Likewise the D.C. Circuit recently concluded that "anyone who intentionally lies to a grand jury is on notice that he may be corruptly

---

[168] United States v. Faudman, 640 F.2d 20, 21 (6th Cir. 1981).

[169] Id. at 23.

[170] Aguilar, 515 U.S. at 600 & n.2 (collecting cases); see also United States v. Norris, 300 U.S. 564, 574 (1937) ("Perjury is an obstruction of justice; its perpetration may well affect the dearest concerns of the parties before a tribunal.").

[171] United States v. Russo, 104 F.3d 431, 435-36 (D.C. Cir. 1997); see also United States v. Perkins, 748 F.2d 1519, 1528 (11th Cir. 1984) (false statement impeding justice); United States v. Watt, 911 F. Supp. 538, 547 (D.D.C. 1995) (while the government must plead and prove that the false testimony impeded the due administration of justice, "no additional act need be alleged in the indictment").

obstructing the grand jury's investigation . . . . Whatever the outer limits of 'corruptly' in § 1503 . . . acts of perjury [are] near its center."[172] Similarly, the district court reasoned that false testimony obstructs justice because it "could cause undue delay, import unnecessary confusion into the grand jury process, and potentially lead to an erroneous indictment."[173]

Even evasive testimony which is literally true may form the basis for an obstruction charge, though this is an unusual occurrence.[174] One district court examined an indictment containing multiple perjury charges and an obstruction charge. The court dismissed a number of the perjury charges as being literally true, given a "precise grammatical reading of the challenged question and answer."[175] Notwithstanding her conclusion that certain of the perjury charges were legally insufficient, Judge Rymer concluded that a § 1503 charge based

---

[172] Russo, 104 F.3d at 436 (citations omitted); see also United States v. Watt, 911 F. Supp. 538, 547 (D.D.C. 1995)("the government may charge a defendant under the omnibus clause for making false statements before a grand jury while under oath if the making of such statements obstructs the due administration of justice"). Both Russo, 104 F.3d at 436, and Watt, 911 F. Supp. at 546-47, rejected application of Poindexter's "transitive" reading of § 1505 to § 1503, as, indeed, Poindexter itself foretold, 951 F.2d at 385.

[173] Watt, 911 F. Supp. at 547; see also United States v. Paxson, 861 F.2d 730 (D.C. Cir. 1988) (affirming conviction for making false declarations before a grand jury in violation of 18 U.S.C. §§ 1503, 1623).

[174] United States v. Spalliero, 602 F. Supp. 417 (C.D. Cal. 1984) (Rymer, J.).

[175] Id. at 422 (quoting United States v. Cook, 489 F.2d 286, 287(9th Cir. 1972)); see also Spalliero, 602 F. Supp. at 424 (literal truth in response to double negative question).

upon misleading, but true, statements should not be dismissed. Summarizing her own reservations, she wrote:

> [T]o the extent that defendant's testimony is not perjurious but rather evasive, or misleading, I think that interpreting § 1503 to obtain a result unobtainable under the perjury statute is ill-advised. . . . Although conviction under § 1503 may require proof of intention to impede justice thereby excluding the misleading or non-responsive statement, innocently made, the fear of possible prosecution for evasive or misleading testimony under § 1503 will burden every witness before a grand jury.[176]

Nonetheless, the court concluded that giving evasive answers to a grand jury could violate § 1503 and denied the motion to dismiss.[177]

2. Civil Proceedings

False statements in connection with a pending civil proceeding can also form the basis an obstruction of justice charge under § 1503. We provide two examples:

- One defendant was alleged to have given false testimony in a civil forfeiture proceeding relating to the proceeds of narcotics transactions. Thomas denied that he knew a co-defendant, one Ronald Calhoun, by the alias Robert Johnson. The Eleventh Circuit reaffirmed its view that "false testimony can provide the basis for a conviction under section 1503."[178] It emphasized, however, the need

---

[176] Id. at 426.

[177] Id. (relying on United States v. Rasheed, 663 F.2d 843, 852 (9th Cir. 1981)).

[178] United States v. Thomas, 916 F.2d 647, 652 (11th Cir. 1990) (citing United States v. Perkins, 748 F.2d 1519, 1527-28

for a "nexus between the false statements and the obstruction of the administration of justice."[179] Thus, the court concluded that it was "incumbent on the government to prove the statements had the natural and probable effect of impeding justice."[180]

- Barbara Battalino was a psychiatrist at a Veterans Administration hospital in Boise, Idaho.[181] While working at the hospital she provided psychiatric treatment to a U.S. Army veteran, Edward Arthur. On at least one occasion, on June 27, 1991, while treating Mr. Arthur, Battalino performed oral sex on him. Thereafter, Battalino and Arthur began an intimate affair. Battalino resigned when her supervisor learned of the affair.

  Later Arthur filed a complaint against Battalino and the United States alleging that Battalino's sexual conduct with him constituted medical malpractice. Battalino requested that the United States Attorney for the District of Idaho "certify" her under the Federal Tort Claims Act,

---

(11th Cir. 1984)).

179 Thomas, 916 F.2d at 652 (citing In re Michael, 326 U.S. 224, 228 (1945)).

180 Thomas, 916 F.2d at 652 (citing United States v. Fields, 835 F.2d 1571, 1573 (11th Cir. 1988); United States v. Silverman, 745 F.2d 1386, 1393 (11th Cir. 1984)). Because the district court's jury instructions did not enunciate this requirement and because the government's proof was insufficient, the court reversed Thomas's conviction. Thomas, 916 F.2d at 654.

181 United States v. Battalino, Crim. No. 98-38-S-EJC (D. Idaho April 14, 1998).

("FTCA").[182] Battalino was interviewed by attorneys for the United States and denied that she had engaged in sexual relations with Arthur in her office on June 27, 1991. Based in part on that denial, she was certified for coverage under the FTCA as to her conduct occurring on or before June 27, 1991.

Battalino appealed the United States Attorney's decision denying certification as within the scope of her employment for her conduct after June 27, 1991. At a hearing held before a United States Magistrate on July 13-14, 1995, while Arthur's civil claim remained pending, Battalino was examined as follows:

> Q. Did anything of a sexual nature take place in your office on June 27, 1991?
>
> A. No, sir.[183]

In April 1998, Battalino was charged with a single count information alleging that she had violated 18 U.S.C. § 1503 by "corruptly endeavor[ing] to influence, obstruct and impede the due administration of justice in connection with a pending proceeding before a court of the United States" by making the false and misleading statements quoted

---

[182] 28 U.S.C. § 1346 et seq. Under the FTCA, if a federal employee is sued and it is certified that the employee's allegedly tortious conduct occurred "within the scope" of the employee's federal employment, the United States is substituted as a defendant and the employee cannot be held personally liable for damages.

[183] Plea Agreement at 9-12, United States v. Battalino, Crim. No. 98-38-S-EJC (D. Idaho April 14, 1998).

1. Generally

Obstructive behavior can comprise behavior other than the false testimony of a defendant. One who proposes to a witness that the witness lie in a judicial proceeding is guilty of obstructing justice.[189] A conviction for such conduct will be sustained where the evidence shows that the conduct had a "reasonable tendency to impede the witness in the discharge of her duties."[190] The endeavor to influence the witness need not be successful to be criminal.[191]

Several cases are instructive examples of the type of fact pattern that will support a criminal obstruction charge:

- One defendant was convicted of obstructing a grand jury investigation in violation of § 1503, by attempting to influence a witness to lie to the grand jury.[192] He challenged his conviction on the ground that it was not supported by sufficient evidence. The witness, Roeske, admitted to hiding income in a bank under a fictitious name. In Tranakos's obstruction trial Roeske testified:

  Q. What did Mr. Tranakos tell you?

---

[189] United States v. Davis, 752 F.2d 963, 973 n.11 (5th Cir. 1985).

[190] United States v. Harris, 558 F.2d 366, 369 (7th Cir. 1977) (citation omitted).

[191] United States v. Barfield, 999 F.2d 1520, 1523 (11th Cir. 1993); see also Osborn v. United States, 385 U.S. 323, 332-33 (1966).

[192] United States v. Tranakos. 911 F.2d 1422 (10th Cir. 1990).

A. He said that -- he looked at me and he smiled and he said, 'Well you don't own any trusts, do you?' And then he said -- he said, 'You don't have any bank accounts in Montana, do you?' And I took that to mean that all of this flow of paper, this complexity of paper meant that the things legally were not under my control and that was the whole reason for setting up this vast matrix of trusts and that I didn't have control over these things or I didn't own the bank accounts. It was a matter of semantics as far as I understood it at the time.

. . . .

Q. What happened when you appeared before the grand jury then?

A. They . . . asked me if I had any bank accounts in Montana and I said no. Or they might have said, 'Do you know of any bank accounts in Montana?' And I said, 'No.'

. . . .

Q. You used the word 'semantics' a while ago. It was not what he said, it was the way he said it to you, the smile [you] said he had on his face?

A. Yes.[193]

The court readily concluded that this conduct constituted obstruction of justice, inasmuch as the "statute prohibits elliptical suggestions as much as it does direct commands."[194] It therefore held that a reasonable finder of fact could have concluded from this evidence that Tranakos

---

[193] Id. at 1431-32 (ellipsis and brackets in original).

[194] Id. at 1432 (citing United States v. Russell, 255 U.S. 138, 141-43 (1921); United States v. Arnold, 773 F.2d 823, 834 (7th Cir. 1985); United States v. O'Keefe, 722 F.2d 1175, 1181 (5th Cir. 1983)).

had suggested to Roeske that he testify falsely to the grand jury.

- Former Congressman Mario Biaggi appealed his conviction for (among other charges) obstructing a grand jury investigation, in violation of § 1503, by attempting to influence the testimony of a co-defendant, Meade Esposito.[195] At issue were Esposito's allegedly illegal payment of Biaggi' expenses for trips Biaggi took to St. Maarten and a Florida health spa. As the court recounted the evidence, after Biaggi became aware of a grand jury investigation, he called Esposito:

> There can be no doubt that Biaggi sought to have Esposito impede the investigation. For example, having coached Esposito to characterize the Florida spa trips as emanating simply from an old and dear friend's concern for Biaggi's health (Biaggi: "You knew I had, you knew I had some trouble with my heart?" Esposito: "When?"), Biaggi urged concealment of the St. Maarten trip:
>
> MB [Biaggi]: . . . Uh, don't mention St. Maartens [sic] . . . cause I . . .
>
> ME [Esposito]: Oh, I thought you mentioned it.
>
> MB: No, they just, I didn't mention it.
>
> ME: Okay.
>
> MB: Uh, we just mentioned the two times at the spa.
>
> ME: No problem.
>
> Returning to the matter of the spa vacations, defendants agreed:
>
> ME: This is not a gift. It's uh, it's a, uh,

---

[195] United States v. Biaggi, 853 F.2d 89 (2d Cir. 1988), cert. denied, 489 U.S. 1989).

manifestation of my love for you.

MB: You didn't give it to me because I'm a member, member of Congress.

ME: Nah. Never, no bull. No way.

MB: Have you ever done, have you ever done anything for me?

ME: Have I ever done anything for you?

MB: I, I told them, "No." We say you haven't done anything form me and I haven't done anything for you. . . .

ME: That's right.

MB: And that's the way we're gonna keep it.

On this evidence the court saw "no basis for overturning Biaggi's conviction for obstruction of justice."[196]

- While an indictment of one Robert Gulino was pending, a potential witness in that trial, Robert Perry, approached the defendant, Jeremiah Buckley and asked his assistance in making "arrangements for a job outside of the United States so that he, Perry, could not be subpoenaed in" the Gulino case.[197] Perry testified that he told Buckley he would "tell all" at the Gulino trial. Buckley found Perry a job in Mexico and Perry avoided the subpoena. On appeal, Buckley argued that he was not guilty of obstruction in violation of § 1503 because he did not improperly induce the witness to testify, but only responded to Perry's request

---

196 Id. 105 (ellipsis in original).

197 United States v. Washington Water Power Co., 793 F.2d 1079, 1084 (9th Cir. 1986).

for assistance. The court rejected the argument, applying § 1503 to this form of witness tampering.[198]

- Another defendant attempted to subtly influence a potential witness to "hold back" on his grand jury testimony. Defendant suggested to witness that a third party (and common friend) "could do a lot for him," but never explicitly asked the witness to lie.[199] The court held that this was enough to convict under the omnibus clause of § 1503. "'[T]he fact that the effort to influence was subtle or circuitous made no difference. 'If reasonable jurors could conclude, from circumstances of the conversation, that the defendant had sought, however cleverly and with whatever cloaking of purpose, to influence improperly [a witness], the offense was complete.'"[200]
- One defendant was also convicted of obstruction of justice for attempting to convince a witness to testify falsely. After trying to convince the witness that the $900,000 payment in question was, instead, a loan, O'Keefe said "[i]f you don't explain this thing right, I'm in jail."[201] The court affirmed the conviction.
- Another defendant was convicted under the omnibus clause of

---

198 Id. at 1084-85.

199 United States v. Tedesco, 635 F.2d 902, 903-04 (1st Cir. 1980), cert. denied, 452 U.S. 962 (1981).

200 Id. at 907 (citation omitted).

201 United States v. O'Keefe, 722 F.2d 1175, 1181 (5th Cir. 1983)(brackets in original).

§ 1503 for "urg[ing] or persuad[ing] a prospective witness to give false testimony."[202] Defendant approached the witness, a bank teller, and advised her that it would be "in her best interest" to forget about any large currency transactions which she may have processed for him.

Misleading conduct or false statements towards an attorney can also constituted criminal obstructive behavior if they may "materially alter" the conduct of a proceeding.[203] Two examples are instructive:

- One defendant, Barfield, worked as a DEA informant in connection with the investigation of Donald Flores.[204] After Flores was indicted, Barfield contacted Flores's attorney and provided the attorney with information regarding the factual basis for the indictment of Flores. Thereafter, in an apparent effort to assist Flores's defense, Barfield gave a sworn statement to Flores's attorney that was inconsistent with information he had originally provided. The United States indicted Barfield for obstruction of justice, alleging that his provision of inconsistent information to Flores's attorney was intended to obstruct justice by providing Flores's attorney with a basis for cross-examining

---

[202] United States v. Shannon, 836 F.2d 1125, 1128 (8th Cir.) (citing United States v. Risken, 788 F.2d 1361, 1369 (8th Cir. 1986)), cert. denied, 486 U.S. 1058 (1988).

[203] United States v. Field, 738 F.2d 1571, 1574 (11th Cir. 1988).

[204] United States v. Barfield, 999 F.2d 1520, 1523 (11th Cir. 1993).

Barfield and impeaching his testimony at Flores's trial. The Court concluded that the false statement to Flores's attorney was intended to "materially alter [the] government's treatment" of Flores, and thus constituted obstruction of justice.[205]

- Two other defendants were officers of the Border Patrol.[206] They were charged with conspiring to secure sexual favors from illegal aliens whom they had encountered. While those charges were pending, they gave documentation to their attorneys which purported to provide them with an alibi and their attorneys provided the documentation to the United States. Subsequent investigation established that the documentation was fabricated, and a superceding indictment added a charge of obstruction of justice in violation of § 1503. Defendants' challenge to the sufficiency of the evidence supporting their conviction was rejected.[207]

2. Civil Proceedings

Obstruction of justice charges may also arise in the context of civil proceedings. For example, in a recent case of some notoriety the defendants were former officials of Texaco, Inc.[208] Texaco was sued in a civil class action employment discrimination

---

[205] Id. at 1524 (citation omitted).

[206] United States v. Davila, 704 F.2d 749 (5th Cir. 1983).

[207] Id. at 752-53.

[208] United States v. Lundwall, 1 F.Supp.2d 249 (S.D.N.Y. 1998).

suit, alleging racial discrimination. The defendants were advised of the pendency of the lawsuit and the need to retain documents relevant to the lawsuit. Following a request for document production, the defendants allegedly withheld and then destroyed documents sought by plaintiff's counsel. Defendants were charged with a violation of § 1503. They moved to dismiss the indictment, arguing that the destruction of documents during civil discovery was not covered by § 1503.

The district court rejected the defendants' argument. First, the court broadly construed the term "due administration of justice":

> [T]he words 'due administration of justice' import a free and fair opportunity to every litigant in a pending cause in federal court to learn what he may learn (if not impeded or obstructed) concerning the material facts and to exercise his option as to introducing testimony or such facts. The violation of the law may consist in preventing a litigant from learning facts which he might otherwise learn, and in thus preventing him from deciding for himself whether or not to make use of such facts.[209]

The court thus recognized that § 1503 had been "repeatedly applied in a wide variety of civil matters."[210] It therefore concluded that nothing in the statute limited its application to grand jury proceedings and denied the motion to dismiss.

The court also offered these observations on the use of § 1503 in the prosecution of civil obstruction:

> Of course, there are a great many good reasons why federal prosecutors should be reluctant to bring

---

209 Id. at 252.

210 Id. at 253.

> criminal charges relating to conduct in ongoing civil litigation. Civil litigation typically involves parties protected by counsel who bring frequently exaggerated claims that, under supervision of a judicial officer, are narrowed and ultimately compromised during pretrial proceedings. Prosecutorial resources would risk quick depletion if abuses in civil proceedings -- even the most flagrant ones -- were the subject of criminal prosecutions rather than civil remedies. Thus, for numerous prudential reasons, prosecutors might avoid entering this area. But that is quite different from concluding that § 1503 precludes their doing so.
>
> . . . .
>
> This case, however, goes beyond civil discovery abuse remediable through civil sanctions. Defendants here are not charged with concealing and destroying documents they incorrectly concluded were not sought, or erroneously thought to be irrelevant or burdensome. Rather, they are charged with seeking to impair a pending court proceeding through the intentional destruction of documents sought in, and highly relevant to, that proceeding.[211]

In an earlier Ninth Circuit decision during the course of a civil case, the defendant falsely swore that a written employment agreement existed.[212] He also attempted to induce a witness to testify that she had seen a copy of the written agreement. Roberts was charged with perjury[213] and with obstruction of justice for his effort to influence a witness. He argued that a simple effort to suborn perjury was not a violation of § 1503. The court rejected that argument, holding that the "obstruction of justice statute is broad enough to cover the attempted

---

[211] Id. at 254-55. The defendants were subsequently acquitted, following trial.

[212] Roberts v. United States, 239 F.2d 467 (9th Cir. 1956).

[213] Thus, Roberts is another civil perjury case charged as a criminal violation.

corruption of a prospective witness in a civil action in Federal District Court."[214]

A seminal Fourth Circuit case also bears mention.[215] The defendants were charged under the predecessor statute of § 1503,[216] for soliciting false testimony in a civil action. The court said:

> [t]he contention that a violation of section 5339, consisting of obstructing the administration of justice in a civil litigation, between private citizens in a federal court, is not an offense against the United States, need not be discussed at any length. One of the sovereign powers of the United States is to administer justice in its courts between private citizens. Obstructing such administration is an offense against the Untied States, in that it prevents or tends to prevent the execution of one of the powers of the government.[217]

It therefore rejected the defendant's demurrer to the indictment.

III. Witness and Evidence Tampering -- 18 U.S.C. § 1512

Although witness and evidence tampering are prohibited by § 1503's general prohibition upon obstruction of justice,[218] they are also specifically prohibited by § 1512. This latter section

---

[214] Id. at 470.

[215] Wilder v. United States, 143 F. 433 (4th Cir. 1906).

[216] section 5339, Rev. Stat. (U.S. Comp. 1901).

[217] Id. at 440 (citations omitted).

[218] The House and Senate agree that actions prosecutable under § 1512 can be prosecuted under § 1503 as well. See 134 Cong. Rec. S7446-01 (June 8, 1988) (stating that the amendments are intended "merely to include in section 1512 the same protection of witnesses from non-coercive influence that was (and is) found in section 1503") (emphasis added); 134 Cong. Rec. S17360-02 (Nov. 10, 1988) (same).

provides, in part:

> (b) Whoever knowingly uses intimidation or physical force, threatens, or corruptly persuades another person, or attempts to do so, or engages in misleading conduct[219] toward another person, with intent to --
>
> (1) influence, delay, or prevent the testimony of any person in an official proceeding;
>
> (2) cause or induce any person to --
>
> (A) withhold testimony, or withhold a record document, or other object, from an official proceeding;
>
> (B) alter, destroy, mutilate or conceal an object with intent to impair the object's integrity or availability for use in an official proceeding . . .
>
> shall be fined under this title or imprisoned for not more than ten years, or both.

18 U.S.C. § 1512(b).

A. Elements

Some elements of a § 1512(b) offense vary with the nature of the conduct charged -- for example, whether the person is charged under § 1512 (b)(1) or under § 1512(b)(2), and whether the person is charged with tampering with the witness or evidence through "force," "corrupt[] persua[sion]," or "misleading conduct."

---

219 Misleading conduct is defined by the statute as:

> (A) knowingly making a false statement;
> (B) intentionally omitting information from a statement and thereby causing a portion of such statement to be misleading, or intentionally concealing a material fact, and thereby creating a false impression by such statement; . . .
> (E) knowingly using a trick, scheme, or device with intent to mislead[.]

18 U.S.C. § 1515(a)(3).

However, because the elements break down into two types -- the defendant must have acted in a certain manner, and must have done so with the specific intent to tamper with a witness[220] -- the courts have generally interpreted the common elements uniformly, without regard to the subsection under which the defendant is charged.[221]

In proving intent to influence a witness's testimony or tamper with evidence, the government need not show that the action (whether corrupt persuasion, misleading conduct, or force) was successful -- or even likely to be successful -- in altering that conduct.[222] Rather, courts have stated that in proving

---

[220] See United States v. Gabriel, 125 F.3d 89, 104 (2d Cir. 1997) ("Section 1512(b) has two elements that are germane to the offenses charged: (1) that the defendant engaged in misleading conduct or corruptly persuaded a person, and (2) that the defendant acted with an intent to influence the person's testimony at an official proceeding.").

[221] See, e.g., Gabriel, 125 F.3d at 103 (relying on case construing § 1512(a)(1)(C) to interpret § 1512(b)(1)). Compare the following: In connection with a charged violation of § 1512(b)(2)(B), the government must prove: "the defendant . . . knowingly attempted to use intimidation or to corruptly persuade the person identified in the indictment; and the defendant did so with the intent to cause or induce the person to alter, destroy, mutilate, or conceal an object or impair the object's integrity or availability for use in a federal . . . proceeding." United States v. Mullins, 22 F.3d 1365,1369 (6th Cir. 1994). Similarly, "[i]n order to prove the defendant guilty of the [§ 1512(a)(1)(C)] charge in the indictment, the government must prove each of the following elements beyond a reasonable doubt: First, that on or about the date charged, the defendant used intimidation, physical force, or threats, or attempted to do so; and second, that the defendant acted knowingly and with intent to prevent the communication to a law enforcement officer of information relating to the commission or possible commission of a federal offense." United States v. Stansfield, 101 F.3d 909, 912-13 (3d Cir. 1996).

[222] Gabriel, 125 F.3d at 103-05.

intent under § 1512, "it is the endeavor to bring about a forbidden result and not the success in actually achieving the result that is forbidden."[223] Unsuccessful or inchoate efforts to influence are also covered by the statute, therefore.[224] For example, when a defendant killed a potential witness in violation of § 1512(a), the Government could prosecute him without having to prove that the victim "was willing to cooperate or that an investigation was underway . . . or even [that the victim] had evinced an intention or desire to so cooperate."[225]

B. Pending and Civil Proceedings

Section 1503's prohibition against obstruction of justice applies only when there is a proceeding pending at the time of the offense, but there is no such limitation upon § 1512.[226]

---

223 United States v. Maggitt, 784 F.2d 590, 593 (5th Cir. 1986) (citations omitted)

224 It is an affirmative defense available to a defendant to show by a preponderance of the evidence "that the conduct [in question] consisted solely of lawful conduct and that the defendant's sole intention was to encourage, induce or cause the other person to testify truthfully." 18 U.S.C. § 1512(d). A defendant is not, of course, obliged to present such evidence. See generally United States v. Clemons, 658 F. Supp. 1116, 1123-26 (W.D. Pa. 1987).

225 United States v. Romero, 54 F.3d 56, 62 (2d Cir. 1995).

226 The Senate Report notes that the Congress intended in § 1512 to remove the requirements in § 1503 that an inquiry be "pending" and that the witness's testimony be admissible in court. See S. Rep. 97-532, 97th Cong., 2d Sess. § 4.C (1982). Specifically, the Report notes that "(d)(1) obviates the requirement that there be an official proceeding in progress or pending" and that "the scope of the offense should not be limited by concerns about the status of the victim as a person who has testified or will be able to testify in court." See also Stansfield, 101 F.3d at 913 ("The law does not require that a

Furthermore, a person may be charged under § 1512 even when the testimony or record in question is subject to a claim of privilege or otherwise not likely to be admitted at trial.[227] While conviction under § 1512 does not require "proof that the proceeding in question actually was pending . . . it [does] require[] . . . that the defendant 'fear[ed]' that such a proceeding 'had been or might be instituted' and 'corruptly persuaded persons with the intent to influence their possible testimony in such a proceeding.'"[228] In other words, there is still a requirement that the defendant intended to influence any possible future proceeding.[229]

It is also evident that § 1512 permits prosecution for

---

federal proceeding be pending at the time or even that it was about to be initiated when the intimidation, physical force or threats were made."); but see United States v. Kassouf, 144 F.3d 952 (6th Cir. 1998) (applying pending investigation limit of § 1503 to § 1512, over dissent citing other circuits to argue that no such limit applies).

The Senate Report also states that "(d)(2) makes explicit the theory that section 1512 is meant to protect the integrity of the process. It is not for the alleged violator to determine what is, or is not, legally privileged evidence or what evidence may prove to be legally inadmissible. These findings are made by the court, not someone who seeks to withhold the evidence." S. Rep. No 97-532 at § 4.C.

[227] 18 U.S.C. § 1512(e).

[228] United States v. Morrison, 98 F.3d 619 (D.C. Cir. 1996) (quoting United States v Kelley, 36 F.3d 1118, 1128 (D.C. Cir. 1994)) (some brackets in original).

[229] Cf. United States v. Aguilar, 515 U.S. 593 (1995) (reversing conviction for witness tampering under § 1503 -- which does have pending proceeding requirement -- where court found defendant had not intended to influence grand jury proceeding but had intended only to misdirect separate FBI investigation that did not count as "proceeding" under § 1503).

witness or evidence tampering in a civil matter as well as in a criminal one, because § 1512(i) provides for enhanced penalties when the conduct in question occurs in the context of criminal proceedings -- enhancements that would be unnecessary if the general statute did not apply to the civil context.

C. Intent

To sustain a tampering charge, the government must prove intent. The type of proof needed depends upon whether the tampering was performed through force, corrupt persuasion, or misleading conduct.

1. "Misleading Conduct"

Section 1512(b)(1) prohibits engaging in misleading conduct in order to influence testimony before a grand jury or other investigative body. "The most obvious example of a section 1512 violation [for misleading conduct] may be the situation where a defendant tells a potential witness a false story as if the story were true, intending that the witness believe the story and testify to it before the grand jury."[230]

Such a violation occurred when the Governor of Guam (Ricardo Bordallo), who was accepting bribes and keeping the money for his personal use, told the person paying the bribes (Johnny Carpio)

---

[230] See United States v. Rodolitz, 786 F.2d 77 (2d Cir. 1986) (dicta describing statute). An unpublished disposition extended Rodolitz by holding that "[t]he witness tampering statute is offended not only by making false statements but also by providing potential witnesses with incomplete information in an attempt to hinder a prosecution." Kliczak v. United States, 940 F.2d 660 (Table), 1991 WL 132499 (6th Cir., July. 19, 1991).

that the money was being used to help the poor. The Governor was convicted of witness tampering under § 1512, and the Ninth Circuit upheld the jury verdict, stating: "The jury could have concluded that Bordallo initially knowingly misled Carpio, intending that Carpio would offer Bordallo's explanation concerning the funds to the FBI."[231]

Analogously, several cases have held that a defendant violates § 1512 by falsifying a handwriting exemplar with the intent to mislead a handwriting expert into testifying that the exemplar did not match the handwriting on the sample.[232]

2. "Corruptly Persuades"

The term "corruptly persuades" was added to the statue in 1988, when Congress amended § 1512 in order to reach actions that reflected an intent to tamper with a witness but did not fall within the definition of "misleading conduct."[233] The difference between the two turns more upon the witness's level of knowledge and upon the defendant's degree of honesty. As explained above,

---

[231] See United States v. Bordallo, 879 F.2d 519, 525 (9th Cir.) (citing Rodolitz), amended on other grounds, 872 F.2d 334 (9th Cir. 1988).

[232] See, e.g. United States v. Yusufu, 63 F.3d 505 (7th Cir. 1995) (giving obstruction-of-justice sentence enhancement under 3C1.1 to defendant who so falsified his handwriting; citing three other cases doing same).

[233] See H.R. Rep. No. 100-169, at 13 n.27 (100th Cong., 1st Sess., 1987). The revision was necessary because some circuits had held that the 1982 version of § 1512 did not prohibit simply asking a witness to lie, reasoning that doing so was neither "misleading" nor "intimidating." See, e.g., United States v. King, 762 F.2d 232 (2d Cir. 1985); United States v. Kulczyk, 931 F.2d 542, 547 (9th Cir. 1991).

when a defendant lies to a witness hoping the witness will believe the falsehood and pass it on to investigators, this is "misleading conduct." But when a defendant simply asks a witness to lie (and the witness knows that he is being asked to lie), then the defendant is "corruptly persuading" that witness.

Several cases have recently discussed the meaning of "corruptly persuades."

- The D.C. Circuit comprehensively reviewed the interpretation of the term "corruptly persuades" in a 1991 case.[234] The defendant in that case, Morrison, had been charged with attempting to prevent a witness from testifying truthfully at trial because he had asked her to tell "anyone who asked" that he had been living with her for the past year (which he had not). Morrison argued on appeal that the term "corruptly persuades" excluded from its coverage a "simple request to testify falsely."[235] He also argued that the term

[234] See United States v. Morrison, 98 F.3d 619 (D.C. Cir. 1996).

[235] Id. at 629.

required a "transitive" reading, referring to the "manner of influencing another, not the motive for influencing another."[236] The court agreed that the term "corruptly persuades" has a transitive meaning under § 1512, but concluded that asking a person to lie did constitute corrupt persuasion because it constituted "'corrupt[ion' of] another person by influencing him to violate his legal duty."[237] The Court therefore concluded that the evidence was sufficient to support Morrison's conviction. As the Court said: "while Morrison assuredly didn't use the word 'testify' or 'trial' when he attempted to influence Holmes' behavior, the clear import of this request was that 'anyone who asked' should be deceived."[238]

- In another case, the defendant spoke to the mother of his friend Brian shortly after FBI agents had visited her.[239] He

---

[236] Id. (relying on the "transitive" reading given to the term "corruptly persuades" in the D.C. Circuit's interpretation of § 1505, see United States v. Poindexter, 951 F.2d 369, 379 (D.C. Cir. 1992)).

[237] Id.

[238] Id. at 630; see also United States v. Hernandez-Limon, 15 F.3d 1092, 1994 WL 2543 at **1, **7 (9th Cir. 1994) (unpublished) (upholding conviction of defendant who told witness: "Tell the truth, that if you didn't know anything, I knew even less," as a corrupt attempt to persuade a co-defendant to lie).

Courts have rejected challenges to the use of the phrase "corruptly" in § 1512 as unconstitutionally vague. United States v. Schott, 145 F.3d 1289, 1998 WL 384047 at *9-*10 (11th Cir. July 10, 1998)(collecting cases).

[239] See United States v. Frankhauser, 80 F.3d 641 (1st Cir. 1996).

advised her to "clean out everything that's upstairs in Brian's room, get rid of everything because the FBI will be back with a search warrant," and admonished her: "Do you want to be responsible for putting your son in jail?"[240] On appeal, the First Circuit affirmed his conviction for violating § 1512(b)(2)(B). Construing the phrase "corrupt persuasion," the court held that a defendant must "act knowingly and with intent to impair an object's availability for use in a particular official proceeding."[241]

- In another D.C. Circuit case, the court held that the jury must "be reasonably able to infer from the circumstances that [defendant], fearing that a grand jury proceeding had been or might be instituted, corruptly persuaded persons with the intent to influence their possible testimony at such a proceeding."[242]

IV. Conspiracy -- 18 U.S.C. § 371

A. Generally

Title 18 U.S.C. § 371 provides, in pertinent part, that it is a crime:

---

240 Id. at 646.

241 Id. at 651.

242 United States v. Kelley, 36 F.3d 1118, 1128 (D.C. Cir. 1994). See also United States v. Mullins, 22 F.3d 1365 (6th Cir. 1996) (finding intent proven where government showed that defendant had instructed various employees to alter their log books prior to producing them in response to a grand jury subpoena, because intent encompassed the "general intent of knowledge as well as the specific intent of purpose to obstruct").

> If two or more persons conspire . . . to commit any offense against the United States . . . and one or more of such persons do any act to effect the object of the conspiracy . . . .

The essence of the crime of conspiracy is a criminal partnership, that is, an "agreement among the conspirators to commit an offense attended by an act of one or more of the conspirators to effect the object of the conspiracy."[243] "[T]he gist of conspiracy is the agreement; that of aiding, abetting or counseling is in consciously advising or assisting another to commit particular offenses, and thus becoming a party to them; that of substantive crime, going a step beyond mere aiding, abetting, counseling to completion of the offense."[244]

Section 371 is violated when two or more persons conspire or agree to engage in conduct which is prohibited by a substantive federal statute, and one does an act in furtherance of that agreement. This includes federal statutes prohibiting obstruction of justice and false statements.[245] A single

---

[243] United States v. Falcone, 311 U.S. 205, 210 (1940).

[244] Pinkerton v. United States, 328 U.S. 640, 649 (1946) (Rutledge, J. dissenting) (emphasis added).

[245] See, e.g., United States v. Fulbright, 105 F.3d 443, 446 (9th Cir. 1997) (conspiracy to obstruct justice); United States v. Kelley, 36 F.3d 1118 (D.C. Cir. 1994) (conspiracy to obstruct justice and tamper with witnesses in violation of 18 U.S.C. §§ 1503, 1512); United States v. Ballis, 28 F.3d 1399, 1403 (5th Cir. 1994) (conspiracy to obstruct justice); United States v. Mullins, 22 F.3d 1365, 1367 (6th Cir. 1994) (same); United States v. Cure, 804 F.2d 625, 628 (11th Cir. 1986) (conspiracy to make false statements in violation of 18 U.S.C. § 1001); United States v. Jeter, 775 F.2d 670, 682-83 (6th Cir. 1985) (conspiracy to obstruct justice under 18 U.S.C. § 1503); United States v. Treadwell, 760 F.2d 327, 333 (D.C. Cir. 1985) (conspiracy to make false statements in violation of 18 U.S.C. § 1001); United States

conspiracy may involve the violation of many statutes.[246]

Because it is the criminal partnership agreement itself which is the crime, the success of the conspiracy or the attainment of its objective is immaterial. The crime is complete once the agreement is reached and a reasonably foreseeable overt act is committed in furtherance of the objective of the conspiracy by one of its members.[247] Moreover, because the agreement is a crime in and of itself, a defendant may be convicted of both the conspiracy and the substantive offense which is the object of the conspiracy.[248]

A conspirator is criminally liable not only for his or her own acts but "all of the acts of his coconspirators undertaken in furtherance of the conspiracy and reasonably foreseeable to" the defendant.[249] Thus, if a co-conspirator commits a crime that (1) furthers the object of the conspiracy that (2) the defendant could have reasonably foreseen, the defendant is criminally

---

v. Heldt, 668 F.2d 1238, 1250-51 (D.C. Cir. 1981) (describing conspiracy to obstruct justice under § 1503 and upholding conviction); United States v. Shoupe, 608 F.2d 950, 956 (3d Cir. 1979) (upholding conviction for conspiracy to obstruct justice under § 1503); United States v. Franklin, 598 F.2d 954, 955 n.1 (5th Cir. 1979) (per curiam) (conspiracy to obstruct justice).

[246] See, e.g., United States v. Richerson, 833 F.2d 1147, 1153-54 (5th Cir. 1987).

[247] See United States v. Kibby, 848 F.2d 920, 922 (8th Cir. 1988); United States v. Nicoll, 664 F.2d 1308, 1315 (5th Cir. 1982).

[248] See Pinkerton, 328 U.S. at 645-46.

[249] United States v. Doyle, 121 F.3d 1078, 1091 (7th Cir. 1997); see also United States v. Casiano, 113 F.3d 420, 427 (3d Cir. 1997).

liable as if he or she had committed the crime personally.

B. Elements of § 371

To sustain a conviction for conspiracy, the government must prove three elements: (1) that there was an agreement to commit a federal offense; (2) that the defendant knowingly and voluntarily joined the agreement; and (3) that at least one overt act was committed in furtherance of the object of the agreement.[250]

1. Existence of an Agreement

In general, a conspiracy requires an agreement or understanding to violate the law. This criminal partnership or meeting of the minds "need not be proven by direct evidence; a common purpose and plan may be inferred from a 'development and

---

[250] See United States v. Mullins, 22 F.3d 1365, 1368 (6th Cir. 1994); accord United States v. Dean, 55 F.3d 640, 647 (D.C. Cir. 1995); United States v. Treadwell, 760 F.2d 327, 333 (D.C. Cir. 1985). The model federal jury instructions denote the elements thus:

1. The conspiracy, agreement, or understanding to violate one or more federal statutes or defraud the United States was formed, reached or entered into by two or more persons;

2. At some time during the existence or life of the conspiracy, agreement, or understanding, one of its alleged members knowingly performed an overt act in order to further or advance the purpose of the agreement;

3. At some time during the existence or life of the conspiracy, agreement or understanding, the defendant knew the purpose of the agreement, and then deliberately joined the conspiracy, agreement or understanding.

Edward J. Devitt, Charles B. Blackmar & Kevin F. O'Malley, FEDERAL JURY PRACTICE AND INSTRUCTIONS § 28.03 (1990).

collocation of circumstances.'"[251] "Conspiracy can be proven circumstantially; direct evidence is not crucial. . . . Seemingly innocent acts taken individually may indicate complicity when viewed collectively and with reference to the circumstances in general."[252] "Because a conspiratorial agreement is often reached in secrecy, the existence of the agreement or common purpose may be inferred from relevant and competent circumstantial evidence."[253]

---

[251] Glasser v. United States, 315 U.S. 60, 80 (1942); United States v. Khoury, 901 F.2d 948, 962 (11th Cir. 1990).

[252] United States v. Mariani, 725 F.2d 862, 865 (2d Cir. 1984) (citations omitted).

[253] United States v. Ballard, 663 F.2d 534, 543 (5th Cir. 1981). Thus courts charge juries:

> A criminal conspiracy is an agreement or a mutual understanding knowingly made or knowingly entered into by at least two people to violate the law by some joint or common plan or course of action. A conspiracy is, in a very true sense, a partnership in crime.
>
> A conspiracy or agreement to violate the law, like any other kind of agreement or understanding, need not be formal, written, or even expressed directly in every detail.
>
> To prove the existence of a conspiracy or an illegal agreement, the government is not required to produce a written contract between the parties or even produce evidence of an express oral agreement spelling out all the details of the understanding. . . .
>
> The government must prove that the defendant and at least one other person knowingly and deliberately arrived at some type of agreement or understanding that they, and perhaps others, would (violate some law(s)) by means of some common plan or course of action. . . . It is proof of this conscious understanding and deliberate agreement by the alleged members that should be central to your consideration of the charge of conspiracy.

Devitt, Blackmar & O'Malley, FEDERAL JURY PRACTICE AND INSTRUCTIONS

For example, "coordinated actions of the co-defendants are strong circumstantial evidence of an agreement."[254] The jury "may infer the existence of a conspiracy from the presence, association, and concerted action of the defendant with others."[255] The government need merely prove that the "defendant knew the essential objective of the conspiracy;" it need not prove that the defendant knew the details or played an extensive role.[256]

A tacit or implicit understanding is sufficient to fulfill the agreement requirement; the conspirators need not formally contract with each other.[257] The existence of an implicit agreement "may be inferred from acts done with a common purpose."[258] The government may establish an implicit agreement

§ 28.04.

[254] United States v. Hernandez, 876 F.2d 774, 777 (9th Cir. 1989).

[255] United States v. Gonzales, 121 F.3d 928, 935 (5th Cir. 1997).

[256] See United States v. Suba, 132 F.3d 662, 672 (11th Cir. 1998).

[257] See United States v. Boone, 951 F.2d 1526, 1543 (9th Cir. 1991); United States v. Reifsteck, 841 F.2d 701, 704 (6th Cir. 1988) ("A tacit or mutual understanding between or among the alleged conspirators is sufficient to show a conspiratorial agreement."); United States v. Ayotte, 741 F.2d 865, 867 (6th Cir. 1984) ("Proof of some kind of formal agreement is not necessary to establish a conspiracy").

[258] Ayotte, 741 F.2d at 867; accord United States v. Alvarez, 548 F.2d 542, 544 (5th Cir. 1977).

by showing "[t]he coordinated actions of the co-defendants,"[259] or by "acts done with a common purpose."[260] A jury can conclude that the defendant was part of an implicit agreement from evidence that the conspirators "acted as a team" or by a defendant's "knowledge of the scope of the operation."[261]

For example, the Sixth Circuit found an implicit agreement to commit health insurance fraud by misrepresenting the identity of the patient even though the defendant (the patient) was unconscious and injured when the conspiracy began. The court held that the defendant "furthered the conspiracy" by responding to the name of a person with insurance, and "signed various forms." "These acts sufficiently established a tacit and mutual understanding . . . and show conspiratorial agreement."[262]

2. Membership in the Conspiracy

The prosecution must also prove a defendant's membership in a conspiracy. The evidence need not prove that the defendant knew all the details of the conspiracy or the identities of all the participants.[263] Mere presence or association, however, is

---

259 United States v. Hernandez, 876 F.2d 774, 788 (9th Cir. 1989).

260 United States v. Milligan, 17 F.3d 177, 183 (6th Cir. 1994).

261 Boone, 951 F.2d at 1543.

262 Milligan, 17 F.3d at 183.

263 See United States v. Massa, 740 F.2d 629, 636 (8th Cir. 1984); United States v. Diecidue, 603 F.2d 535, 548 (5th Cir. 1979).

not sufficient to establish membership in a conspiracy.[264]

The acts and declarations of co-conspirators are admissible to prove a defendant's membership in a conspiracy.[265] To admit a co-conspirator statement or act, the prosecution need only show by a preponderance of the evidence to the trial judge there is "evidence that there was a conspiracy involving the declarant and the nonoffering party, and that the statement was made in the course and in furtherance of the conspiracy."[266] The trial

---

[264] See United States v. Cintolo, 818 F.2d 980, 1003 (1st Cir. 1987); United States v. Mariani, 725 F.2d 862, 865 (2d Cir. 1984). Thus, the standard charge to the jury is:

> the evidence . . . must show beyond a reasonable doubt that the defendant knew the purpose or goal of the agreement or understanding and deliberately entered into the agreement intending, in some way, to accomplish the goal or purpose by this common plan or joint action.
>
> If the evidence establishes beyond a reasonable doubt that the defendant knowingly and deliberately entered into an agreement . . . the fact that the defendant did not join the agreement at its beginning, or did not know all of the details of the agreement, or did not participate in each act of the agreement, or did not play a major role in accomplishing the unlawful goal is not important to your decision regarding membership in the conspiracy.
>
> Merely associating with others and discussing common goals, mere similarity of conduct between or among such persons, merely being present at the place where a crime takes place or is discussed, or even knowing about criminal conduct does not, of itself, make someone a member of the conspiracy or a conspirator.

Devitt, Blackmar & O'Malley, FEDERAL JURY PRACTICE AND INSTRUCTIONS § 28.05.

[265] Fed. R. Evid. 801(d)(2)(E) ("A statement is not hearsay if . . . [it is] a statement by a co-conspirator of a party during the course and in furtherance of the conspiracy.").

[266] Bourjaily v. United States, 483 U.S. 171, 173-79 (1987) (citing Fed. R. Evid. 104).

court's inquiry at this stage "is not whether the proponent of the evidence wins or loses his case on the merits, but whether the evidentiary Rules have been satisfied. Thus, the evidentiary standard is unrelated to the burden of proof on the substantive issue."[267]

Once the government demonstrates that a conspiracy exists, its burden in showing that any particular defendant was a member of that conspiracy is light. The government need merely present "slight evidence . . . to implicate a defendant."[268] "[E]vidence which established beyond a reasonable doubt that a defendant is even slightly connected with the conspiracy is sufficient to convict him of knowing participation in the conspiracy."[269]

3. Overt Act

To sustain a conviction of conspiracy the government must also prove beyond a reasonable doubt that an overt act was done in furtherance of the conspiracy. The government need not prove that the defendant personally committed an overt act in furtherance of the conspiracy. The government need only prove

---

[267] Bourjaily, 483 U.S. at 175. The prosecutor need not produce evidence independent of the statements themselves to show the existence of a conspiracy for evidentiary purposes, rather any evidence, except privileged communications, may be considered by the trial court, including the very statements being offered into evidence. Id. at 177(overruling the "independent evidence" holdings of Glasser v. United States, 315 U.S. 60 (1942), and United States v. Nixon, 418 U.S. 683 (1974)).

[268] United States v. Milligan, 17 F.3d 177, 183 (6th Cir. 1994).

[269] United States v. Boone, 951 F.2d 1526, 1543 (9th Cir. 1991).

"that one of the co-conspirators did one or more overt acts in furtherance of the conspiracy."[270]

C. Withdrawal Defense

Withdrawal from the conspiracy can be a conditional or an absolute defense to the crime of conspiracy, depending on when the withdrawal occurs. If the defendant withdraws from the conspiracy before any of the co-conspirators commits an overt act in furtherance of the conspiracy, the withdrawal is an absolute defense and the defendant cannot be convicted of the conspiracy. If a single overt act has occurred, withdrawal is not an absolute

---

[270] United States v. Holloway, 128 F.3d 1254, 1257 (8th Cir. 1997). Thus the pattern jury instruction reads:

> that one of the members to the agreement knowingly performed at least one overt act and that this overt act was performed during the existence or life of the conspiracy and was done to somehow further the goal(s) of the conspiracy or agreement.
>
> The term "overt act" means some type of outward, objective action performed by one of the parties to or one of the members of the agreement or conspiracy which evidences that agreement.
>
> Although you must unanimously agree that the same overt act was committed, the government is not required to prove more than one of the overt acts charged.
>
> The overt act may, but for the alleged illegal agreement, appear totally innocent and legal.

Devitt, Blackmar & O'Malley, FEDERAL JURY PRACTICE AND INSTRUCTIONS § 28.07; see also United States v. Hermes, 847 F.2d 493, 495 (8th Cir. 1988) ("government need show that only one of the conspirators engaged in one overt act in furtherance of the conspiracy, and the act itself need not be criminal in nature").

defense to the conspiracy charge.[271]

Withdrawal after the commission of an overt act, on the other hand, is a conditional defense. Such withdrawal excuses the defendant from liability for all criminal acts committed by the co-conspirators after the date of the withdrawal.[272] The defendant remains liable, however, for all reasonably foreseeable crimes committed by co-conspirators in furtherance of the conspiracy before the date of withdrawal, as well as for the conspiracy itself.

To demonstrate withdrawal from the conspiracy, the defendant must prove (1) that he or she has taken affirmative steps, inconsistent with the objectives of the conspiracy, to disavow or to defeat the objectives of the conspiracy and (2) that he or she has made a reasonable effort to communicate those acts to the co-conspirators or that he or she has disclosed the scheme to law enforcement authorities.[273] The burden of proof of withdrawal rests on the defendant.[274] The Eleventh Circuit has characterized the defendant's burden as "substantial."[275]

Mere physical distance from the co-conspirators is

---

[271] See United States v. Sarault, 840 F.2d 1479, 1487 (9th Cir. 1988).

[272] See United States v. Lash, 937 F.2d 1077, 1083-85 (6th Cir. 1991).

[273] See United States v. Dabbs, 134 F.3d 1071, 1083 (11th Cir. 1998) (citation omitted).

[274] See United States v. Payne, 962 F.2d 1228, 1234-35 (6th Cir. 1992).

[275] Dabbs, 134 F.3d at 1083.

insufficient to demonstrate withdrawal. If, however, the defendant completely severs ties with the conspiracy, a court will find that the defendant withdrew absent evidence of continued acts in furtherance of the conspiracy or evidence that the defendant continued to receive benefits from the conspiracy.[276]

Even if the defendant takes affirmative action contrary to the objectives of the conspiracy, his or her withdrawal may be ineffective if he or she acquiesced in the conspiracy after the affirmative act. Thus, "[c]ontinued acquiescence negates withdrawal, leaving [the defendant] liable for the continuing acts in furtherance of the conspiracy by the other conspirators."[277]

V. Aiding and Abetting -- 18 U.S.C. § 2(a)

A. Generally

Title 18 U.S.C. § 2(a) governs liability for aiding and

---

[276] Id.; see United States v. Antar, 53 F.3d 568, 582-83 (3d Cir. 1995).

[277] Lash, 937 F.2d at 1084. As the model federal jury instructions put it:

> In order to withdraw from the conspiracy the defendant must take some definite, decisive, and affirmative action to disavow (himself) (herself) from the conspiracy or to defeat the goal or purpose of the conspiracy.
>
> Merely stopping activities or cooperation or merely being inactive for a period of time is not sufficient to constitute the defense of withdrawal.

Devitt, Blackmar & O'Malley, FEDERAL JURY PRACTICE AND INSTRUCTIONS § 28.11; see, e.g., United States v. Nerlinger, 862 F.2d 967, 974 (2d Cir. 1988).

abetting in the commission of a federal crime. This section provides:

> (a) Whoever commits an offense against the United States or aids, abets, counsels, commands, induces or procures its commission, is punishable as a principal.

This section is premised on the common law view that a person who does not personally commit a crime but orders or assists another in committing that crime is as guilty as if he or she had committed the crime personally. The quintessential case of aiding and abetting is the getaway driver for a bank robbery. Although the getaway driver does not personally rob the bank, his or her assistance in the crime is sufficient to warrant his or her prosecution for the crime of bank robbery itself.[278]

In an aiding and abetting case, the person who actually commits the crime is called the principal. If the jury finds, beyond a reasonable doubt, that the aider and abettor aided, abetted, counseled, commanded, induced, or procured the principal to commit a federal crime, it should find the aider and abettor guilty. The aider and abettor is then subject to the same criminal penalties as the principal would be.

---

[278] Also of potential applicability to conduct of this general nature is the misprision of felony provision, 18 U.S.C. § 4 which provides:

> Whoever, having knowledge of the actual commission of a felony cognizable by a court of the United States, conceals and does not as soon as possible make known the same to some judge or other person in civil or military authority under the United States, shall be fined under this title or imprisoned for not more than three years, or both.

Defendants have been charged with aiding and abetting the obstruction of justice on numerous occasions.[279]

In one case, the Sixth Circuit affirmed a conviction for aiding and abetting the obstruction of justice when a defendant attempted to convince a witness to tell a false story to federal investigators to keep a third person from being prosecuted for a weapons violation. This charge was affirmed despite the fact that the third person was not charged with the weapons violation.[280]

B. Elements of § 2(a)

The crime of aiding and abetting has three elements. The government must prove beyond a reasonable doubt (1) an act by a defendant that (2) contributes to the execution of a federal crime (3) committed with the intent to aid in the commission of that crime.[281]

---

[279] See, e.g., United States v. Fulbright, 105 F.3d 443 (9th Cir. 1997) (allowing the charge, although finding insufficient evidence); United States v. Morris, 1997 WL 331784, at *1 (4th Cir. June 18, 1997) (per curiam); United States v. Ballis, 28 F.3d 1399, 1403 (5th Cir. 1994); United States v. Rankin, 870 F.2d 109, 110 (3d Cir. 1989); United States v. McKnight, 799 F.2d 443, 445 (8th Cir. 1986); United States v. Franklin, 598 F.2d 954, 955 n.1 (5th Cir. 1979); Hornick v. United States, 891 F. Supp. 72, 73 (N.D.N.Y. 1995); United States v. Tota, 672 F. Supp. 716, 723-24 (S.D.N.Y. 1987); United States v. Louie, 625 F. Supp. 1327, 1331 (S.D.N.Y. 1985).

[280] See United States v. Winkelman, 1996 WL 665379 (6th Cir. Nov. 15, 1996).

[281] See United States v. Stanley, 765 F.2d 1224, 1242 (5th Cir. 1985). The model federal jury instructions denote it thus:

> In order to be found guilty of aiding and abetting the commission of the crime charged in . . . the indictment, the

1. Act

The statute itself lists several acts, all in the nature of instruction, that are sufficient to support liability.[282] Therefore, if the defendant directs the principal to commit the crime, that fact in and of itself is sufficient to satisfy the act element of aiding and abetting.

Besides instruction, the aider and abettor may simply perform some act that assists the principal in completing the crime. This occurs when the defendant "does not do all of the things which causes a crime to be complete but only a portion of the various items that are required to complete the crime."[283] The defendant must have "committed some overt act designed to facilitate the success of the criminal venture," and the act must

---

government must prove beyond a reasonable doubt that the Defendant:

One, knew that the crime charged was to be committed or was being committed,

Two, knowingly did some act for the purpose of (aiding) (commanding) (encouraging) the commission of that crime, and

Three, acted with the intention of causing the crime charged to be committed.

Edward J. Devitt, Charles B. Blackmar, Michael A. Wolff & Kevin F. O'Malley, FEDERAL JURY PRACTICE AND INSTRUCTIONS § 18.01 (1992).

[282] See 18 U.S.C. § 2(a) ("counsels, commands, induces or procures").

[283] United States v. Waller, 607 F.2d 49, 51 (3d Cir. 1979) (approving jury instructions).

"contribute[] to the execution of a crime."[284]

2. Crime Committed

The principal need not be convicted and punished for the aider and abettor to be charged. In fact, the Supreme Court has held that a conviction for aiding and abetting should be upheld even if the principal has been acquitted of that offense.[285]

Nonetheless, the jury must be convinced that the federal crime, in fact, did occur.[286] Thus, showing that the government failed to prove beyond a reasonable doubt that a completed federal crime was committed is a complete defense to aiding and abetting.

3. Intent

Central to the crime of aiding and abetting is the aider and abettor's affirmative desire to see that the federal crime actually be committed. An unknowing participant in a crime, who assists without knowledge of the principal's criminal intentions, is not guilty of aiding and abetting.

The aider and abettor must share with the principal "a community of unlawful purpose at the time the act is

---

[284] United States v. Stanley, 765 F.2d 1224, 1242 (5th Cir. 1985).

[285] See Stanfeder v. United States, 447 U.S. 10, 14-20 (1980).

[286] See United States v. Fulbright, 105 F.3d 443, 452 (9th Cir. 1997); United States v. Waller, 607 F.2d 49, 52 (3d Cir. 1979).

committed."[287] The aider and abettor must wish that the crime occur and must seek by his or her acts to make it succeed.[288]

The sharing of criminal intent need not rise to the level of an agreement that would support a conspiracy charge.[289] Similarly, the "aider and abettor need not know every last detail of the substantive offense."[290] As the Eighth Circuit has put it: "Participation is wilful if done voluntarily and intentionally, and with the specific intent to do something the law forbids, or with the specific intent to fail to do something that the law requires to be done."[291]

C. Defenses and Limitations

The government may not convict a defendant for aiding and abetting merely because the defendant was present at the scene of the crime or was known to associate with the principal.[292] As explained above, the government must show that the defendant intended for the crime to be committed and assisted in its

---

287 Johnson v. United States, 195 F.2d 673, 675 (8th Cir. 1952).

288 See United States v. Martin, 920 F.2d 345, 348 (6th Cir. 1990).

289 See Nye & Nisen v. United States, 336 U.S. 613, 618 (1949).

290 United States v. Sanborn, 563 F.2d 488, 491 (1st Cir. 1977).

291 United States v. McKnight, 799 F.3d 443, 446 (8th Cir. 1986) (approving jury instruction).

292 See United States v. Oberle, 136 F.3d 1414, 1422 (10th Cir. 1998).

commission by some act.

Aiding and abetting is a specific intent crime.[293] As a result, for example, voluntary intoxication is a defense to the crime of aiding and abetting.[294] This is true even if voluntary intoxication is not a defense to the underlying crime.[295]

VI. Use of an Intermediary -- 18 U.S.C. § 2(b)

A. Generally

Traditional aider-and-abettor liability under 18 U.S.C. § 2(a) requires that the principal and the defendant share criminal intent. Because a defendant using an innocent dupe to commit a crime is no less culpable than a defendant assisting another in the commission of a crime, Congress passed 18 U.S.C. § 2(b) to criminalize the use of an intermediary to commit a crime. This section provides:

> Whoever willfully causes an act to be done which if directly performed by him or another would be an offense against the United States, is punishable as a principal.

The quintessential case is an employer who instructs an employee to mail a fraudulent document. Even though the employer did not use the mails directly, he or she still is guilty of mail

---

293 See United States v. Sayetsitty, 107 F.3d 1405, 1412 (9th Cir. 1997); but see United States v. Roan Eagle, 867 F.2d 436, 445 (8th Cir. 1989).

294 See United States v. Hatatley, 130 F.3d 1399, 1404-05 (10th Cir. 1997).

295 See Id. at 1404 (voluntary intoxication is not a defense to voluntary manslaughter but is a defense to aiding and abetting voluntary manslaughter).

fraud.[296]

The primary burden of the government is to show that the defendant "willfully cause[d] an act to be done by another which would be illegal if he did it himself."[297] The actions of the intermediary must be such that, had the defendant done them personally, the defendant would have committed a crime.

B. Intent

Unlike traditional aider-and-abettor liability, the government need not prove that the intermediary had any criminal intent.[298] The intermediary's mental state is wholly irrelevant; the government need not prove that the intermediary was innocent either.[299] The government must prove that the defendant had the mental state that would be required for a violation of the underlying offense.[300]

---

[296] See Pereira v. United States, 347 U.S. 1 (1954).

[297] United States v. West Indies Transport, Inc., 127 F.3d 299, 307 (3d Cir. 1997).

[298] See, e.g., United States v. West Indies Transport, Inc., 127 F.3d 299, 307 (3d Cir. 1997); United States v. Walser, 3 F.3d 380, 388 (11th Cir. 1993) ("an individual is criminally culpable for causing an intermediary to commit a criminal act even though the intermediary has no criminal intent and is innocent of the substantive crime"); see also United States v. Laurins, 857 F.2d 529, 535 (9th Cir. 1988).

[299] See United States v. Rapoport, 545 F.2d 802, 806 (2d Cir. 1976).

[300] See United States v. Gabriel, 125 F.3d 89, 99, 101 (2d Cir. 1997); United States v. Trie, 1998 WL 427550 at *4- *6 (D.D.C. July 17, 1998) (holding same but noting elements of such proof would be higher in federal election law context); United States v. Curran, 20 F.3d 560, 569 (3d Cir. 1994) (same).

C. Particular Cases

Courts have allowed charges for using an intermediary to commit a perjury or false statements offense.[301]

- The Eleventh Circuit found that a defendant was guilty of perjury where he gave a witness a false document and then allowed the witness to introduce it into evidence at a trial. Even though the defendant was not under oath and the witness did not commit perjury because he was not aware that the document was false, the defendant's actions were sufficient to trigger criminal liability under § 2(b).[302]
- In another case, the Second Circuit found sufficient evidence to support a conviction where the defendant used an intermediary in filing a false report. There, the defendant knew that the intermediary was preparing the report, "knew that the portfolio reports were false and misleading," and failed to provide correct information though requested to do so by the preparer. This evidence was found sufficient to support the conviction.[303]

---

[301] See, e.g., United States v. Nolan, 136 F.3d 265 (2d Cir. 1998) (filing false reports under 18 U.S.C. § 1027); United States v. West Indies Transport, Inc., 127 F.3d 299, 307 (3d Cir. 1997) ("When a defendant uses an innocent intermediary to . . . make false statements to the government, the criminal intent of the intermediary is not an element of the crime."); United States v. Gabriel, 125 F.3d 89, 99 (2d Cir. 1997) (false statements in violation of 18 U.S.C. § 1001); United States v. Walser, 3 F.3d 380, 388 (11th Cir. 1993) (perjury).

[302] See Walser, 3 F.3d at 389.

[303] Nolan, 136 F.3d at 272.

- In a third case, a jury found a defendant guilty of making false statements in the form of false packing slips. The court found that evidence that the defendant "had some influence" over the slip preparers and "used that influence to cause [the preparers] to prepare the false slip" was sufficient to support criminal liability.[304]

VII. **Evidentiary Issues**

We briefly summarize in this section certain evidentiary principles that appear to bear on the conduct described in this Referral. It is, of course, for Congress to assess the evidence as it sees fit. These principles, however, bore upon the Office's own judgment as to the substance and credibility of the information presented.

A. **Circumstantial Evidence**

Courts distinguish "direct evidence" from "circumstantial evidence." A witness may provide direct evidence of a fact by stating the fact in testimony based on personal knowledge.[305] For example, a witness might provide direct evidence that a defendant destroyed documents by testifying that he or she saw the defendant shred them.

A witness may supply circumstantial evidence of a fact by

---

[304] See Gabriel, 125 F.3d at 100.

[305] See Black's Law Dictionary 460 (6th ed. 1990) (defining direct evidence as "testimony from a witness who actually saw, heard or touched the subject of questioning").

testifying about circumstances from which the jury may infer the fact.[306] For instance, a witness may provide circumstantial evidence that the defendant destroyed documents by testifying that the documents were intact when the defendant went to examine them, but were found shredded immediately afterward. Although the witness did not see the defendant destroy the documents, the jury may infer that the defendant shredded them based on the witness's testimony.

One Court of Appeals has explained the difference between direct evidence and circumstantial evidence as follows:

> The distinction between these two types of evidence is that with direct evidence, the jury does not have to draw inferences to decide whether the fact asserted exists, the evidence directly supports the existence or non-existence of the fact and the jury's involvement is to decide whether they believe what the witness says. With circumstantial evidence the jury must decide whether to draw the inference or connection between the evidence presented and the fact asserted.[307]

Even though the two types of evidence may be distinguished they are of equal probative weight.[308] A jury may convict a

---

[306] Black's Law Dictionary, at 243 (defining circumstantial evidence as "[t]estimony not based on actual personal knowledge or observation of the facts in controversy, but of other facts from which deductions are drawn, showing indirectly the facts sought to be proved.").

[307] United States v. Henderson, 693 F.2d 1028, 1031 (11th Cir. 1982).

[308] Thus, the standard jury instruction on the consideration of evidence reads:

> There are two types of evidence you may consider. One is direct evidence -- such as testimony of an eyewitness. The other is indirect or circumstantial evidence -- the proof of circumstances that tend to prove or disprove the existence or nonexistence of

defendant of a crime based solely on circumstantial evidence, provided that the evidence proves the defendant guilty of each of the elements of the crime beyond a reasonable doubt.[309] For example, in one case a jury convicted the defendant of obstruction of justice based solely on circumstantial evidence that he had altered documents sought by a subpoena. Although the defendant denied wrongdoing, the court stated: "A reasonable jury was entitled to believe the government's circumstantial evidence and disbelieve [the defendant]."[310]

Civil proceedings usually require proof only by a preponderance of the evidence. Because circumstantial evidence can prove guilt beyond a reasonable doubt, it naturally also can satisfy this lower standard.[311] As the Supreme Court stated in one civil case, "direct evidence of a fact is not required.

> certain other facts. The law makes no distinction between direct and circumstantial evidence, but simply requires that you find the facts from a preponderance of all the evidence, both direct and circumstantial.

Devitt, Blackmar & O'Malley, FEDERAL JURY PRACTICE AND INSTRUCTIONS § 72.03.

[309] See Holland v. United States, 348 U.S. 121, 139-140 (1954). At one time, some courts held that a jury could convict based solely on circumstantial evidence only if the evidence excluded "every reasonable hypothesis except that of guilt." Johnson v. United States, 408 F.2d 1097, 1098 (5th Cir. 1969). All of the circuits, however, now have rejected that rule. See United States v. Bell, 678 F.2d 547, 549 n.3 (5th Cir. 1982) (en banc) (listing cases), aff'd 462 U.S. 356 (1983).

[310] United States v. Brooks, 111 F.3d 365, 373 (4th Cir. 1997).

[311] See Federal Power Commission v. Florida Power & Light Co., 404 U.S. 453, 469 & n.21 (1972).

Circumstantial evidence is not only sufficient, but may also be more certain, satisfying and persuasive than direct evidence."[312]

B. Inferences from False Exculpatory Testimony

Criminal suspects often make exculpatory statements to investigators or to the courts (an alibi, for example). The courts have held that, if a jury determines that the exculpatory statement was false, it may draw an inference adverse to the suspect. In particular, the jury may consider the false statement to be circumstantial evidence that the defendant had a consciousness of guilt.[313] The jury may draw this inference because an innocent person generally does not have a reason to fabricate a description of his or her conduct.[314]

One defendant, for example, told the police that he could not have committed a robbery because he was at a different location when the robbery occurred. The prosecution later produced evidence contradicting this statement. The court of appeals held that the trial judge properly had instructed the jury that, if it found the defendant's testimony false, it could infer that the defendant was conscious of his guilt.[315]

---

312 Michalic v. Cleveland Tankers, Inc., 364 U.S. 325, 330 (1960).

313 See Government of Virgin Islands v. Testamark, 570 F.2d 1162, 1168 (3d Cir. 1978).

314 See United States v. Littlefield, 840 F.2d 143, 148 n.4 (1st Cir.), cert. denied 488 U.S. 860 (1988).

315 United States v. Ingram, 600 F.2d 260, 262 (10th Cir. 1979).

C. Willful Blindness

The term "willful blindness" refers "to a situation where the defendant tries to avoid knowing something that will incriminate."[316] The federal courts equate willful blindness with knowledge.[317] As a result, if a federal criminal statute requires a defendant to have knowledge of a fact, proof of deliberate ignorance of the fact generally will suffice to establish proof of knowledge of the fact.[318]

For example, a participant in a drug smuggling operation deliberately avoided determining that a secret compartment in an automobile contained marijuana.[319] He argued that a jury could not convict him of knowingly importing drugs into the United States because he did not actually know that the compartment contained drugs. The Ninth Circuit rejected this argument, holding that "deliberate ignorance and positive knowledge are equally culpable."[320]

---

[316] Black's Law Dictionary 1600 (6th ed. 1990).

[317] See United States v. Campbell, 977 F.2d 854, 858-59 (4th Cir. 1992), cert. denied, 507 U.S. 938 (1993); United States v. Antzoulatos, 962 F.2d 720, 724 (7th Cir.), cert. denied, 506 U.S. 919 (1992).

[318] See Leary v. United States, 395 U.S. 6, 46 n.93 (1969) (adopting Model Penal Code rule that "When knowledge of the existence of a particular fact is an element of an offense, such knowledge is established if a person is aware of a high probability of its existence, unless he actually believes that it does not exist.").

[319] United States v. Jewell, 532 F.2d 697, 698 (9th Cir.), cert. denied, 426 U.S. 951 (1976).

[320] Id. at 704.

Federal judges may instruct juries about willful blindness when the facts warrant. "A willful blindness instruction is appropriate when the defendant asserts a lack of guilty knowledge but the evidence supports an inference of deliberate ignorance."[321]

D. Testimony of a Cooperating Witness

In general, courts agree that the testimony of a witness who has been immunized or entered into a plea bargain in return for the his or her cooperation must be viewed with caution. Caution, however, does not equate to disregard and courts are equally clear that a cooperating witness's testimony is competent and forms a lawfully sufficient basis for conviction if the finder of fact determines it to be credible.[322]

---

[321] United States v. Gruenberg, 989 F.2d 971, 974 (8th Cir.) (quoting United States v. Long, 977 F.2d at 1264, 1271 (8th Cir. 1992)), cert. denied 510 U.S. 873 (1993). The court in Gruenberg approved the following jury instruction on willful blindness:

> The element of knowledge may be satisfied by inferences drawn from proof that a defendant deliberately closed his eyes to what would otherwise have been obvious to him. A finding beyond reasonable doubt of a conscious purpose to avoid enlightenment would permit an inference of knowledge. Stated another way, a defendant's knowledge of a fact may be inferred from willful blindness to the existence of the fact. It is entirely up to you as to whether you find any deliberate closing of the eyes and the inference to be drawn from any such evidence. A showing of negligence or mistake is not sufficient to support a finding of willfulness or knowledge.

989 F.2d at 974.

[322] Thus, the standard jury instruction reads:

The testimony of an immunized witness, someone who has

Giving this type of instruction is generally considered "the better practice."[323] However, this cautionary instruction is not mandatory; failure to give such an instruction is not usually considered reversible error.[324]

Indeed, notwithstanding the cautionary instructions recommended, there "is no absolute rule of law preventing convictions on the testimony of accomplices if juries believe

---

> been told either that (his) (her) crimes will go unpunished in return for testimony or that (his) (her) testimony will not be used against (him) (her) in return for that cooperation, must be examined and weighed by the jury with greater care than the testimony of someone who is appearing in court without the need for such an agreement with the government.
>
> ___________ may be considered to be an immunized witness in this case.
>
> The jury must determine whether the testimony of the immunized witness has been affected by self-interest, or by the agreement (he) (she) has with the government, or by (his own) (her own) interest in the outcome of this case, or by prejudice against the defendant.

Devitt, Blackmar, Wolff, & O'Malley, FEDERAL JURY PRACTICE AND INSTRUCTIONS § 15.03 (1992).

[323] Caminetti v. United States, 242 U.S. 470, 495 (1917) ("better practice for courts to caution juries against too much reliance upon the testimony of accomplices, and to require corroborating testimony before giving credence to such evidence").

[324] United States v. McGinnis, 783 F.2d 755, 758 (8th Cir. 1986); see also United States v. Braxton, 877 F.2d 556, 565 (7th Cir. 1989) (better practice is to instruct but failure to do so is not reversible error if corroborating evidence exists); United States v. Shriver, 838 F.2d 980, 983 (8th Cir. 1988) ("no absolute and mandatory duty is imposed upon the court to advise the jury by instruction that they should consider the testimony of an uncorroborated accomplice with caution")(internal quotations and citation omitted); but see United States v. Morgan, 555 F.2d 238, 242-43 (9th Cir. 1977) (defendant entitled to cautionary jury instruction).

them."[325] Decisions as to the credibility of a cooperating witness's testimony remain for the jury to make.[326]

In addition, courts agree that evidence of a cooperating witness's duty to testify truthfully as part of the plea agreement may be admitted into evidence.[327] Thus, evidence concerning a plea agreement and its provisions may have both a bolstering effect (because of the truthfulness requirement) and an impeaching effect (because of the promise of leniency) on the witness's credibility.[328] Hence, the entirety of the plea agreement allows the jury to accurately assess the witness's credibility.[329]

---

[325] Caminetti, 242 U.S. at 495 (citation omitted); see also United States v. Winter, 663 F.2d 1120, 1134 n.24 (1st Cir. 1981) (approving instruction that reads, in part, "[o]ne who testifies with the benefit of immunity, with a promise from the government that he will not be prosecuted, does not become an incompetent witness"), cert. denied, 460 U.S. 1011 (1983).

[326] McGinnis, 783 F.2d at 758.

[327] See, e.g. United States v. Lord, 907 F.2d 1028, 1029-31 (10th Cir. 1990) (collecting cases); cf. United States v. Sobamowo, 892 F.2d 90, 95 n.3 (D.C. Cir. 1989) (witness' testimony that he was ordered by the court to cooperate as part of plea bargain was admissible). The only dispute is whether evidence of the truthfulness requirement of a plea agreement may be admitted on direct examination of the witness, as the majority of circuits permit, or whether it may only be offered as evidence in rebuttal to a challenge to the credibility of the witness, as a minority of the circuits require. See Lord, 907 F.2d at 1029-31 (describing majority rule of First, Third, Fourth, Fifth, Sixth, Seventh, Eighth and Tenth Circuits and contrasting with minority rule of Second and Eleventh Circuits).

[328] United States v. Drews, 877 F.2d 10, 12 (8th Cir. 1989); United States v. Townsend, 796 F.2d 158, 163 (6th Cir. 1986).

[329] United States v. Mealy, 851 F.2d 890, 899 (7th Cir. 1988).

E. Testimony of the Accused

As with the testimony of a cooperating witness, courts agree that the testimony of an accused who has an interest in the resolution of the allegations made against him must also be viewed with caution. Here too, caution does not equate with disregard and the courts agree that an accused's testimony is competent and may be credited by a finder-of-fact.

Thus, while "[t]he fact that [a witness] is a defendant does not condemn him as unworthy of belief, . . . at the same time it creates an interest greater than that of any other witness, and to that extent [it] affects the question of credibility. It is therefore a matter properly to be suggested by the court to the jury."[330] Accordingly courts generally agree that, while it is not mandatory, it is "not improper for [a] district court, in instructing the jury about [a] defendant's credibility as a witness, to point out [the] defendant's vital interest in the outcome of the case."[331] Typical of such instructions is one reminding the jury of a defendants "very keen personal interest in the result of your verdict."[332]

---

[330] Reagan v. United States, 157 U.S. 301, 305 (1895).

[331] United States v. Firgurski, 545 F.2d 389, 392 (4th Cir. 1976); see also United States v. Anderson, 642 F.2d 281, 286 (9th Cir. 1981).

[332] United States v. Ylda, 643 F.2d, 348, 352 (5th Cir. 1981); see also United States v. Stout, 601 F.2d 325, 329 (7th Cir. 1979) (accused has a "vital interest in the outcome of his trial"), cert. denied, 444 U.S. 979 (1980); United States v. Vega, 589 F.2d 1147, 1154 n.6 (2d Cir. 1978) (accused's "deep

Tab K

Monica Lewinsky Immunity Agreement

Office of the Independent Counsel

1001 Pennsylvania Avenue, N.W.
Suite 490-North
Washington, DC 20004
(202) 514-8688
Fax (202) 514-8802

AGREEMENT

This is an agreement ("Agreement") between Monica S. Lewinsky and the United States, represented by the Office of the Independent Counsel ("OIC"). The terms of the Agreement are as follows:

1. Ms. Lewinsky agrees to cooperate fully with the OIC, including special agents of the Federal Bureau of Investigation ("FBI") and any other law enforcement agencies that the OIC may require. This cooperation will include the following:

A. Ms. Lewinsky will provide truthful, complete and accurate information to the OIC. She will provide, upon request, any documents, records, or other tangible evidence within her custody or control relating to the matters within the OIC's jurisdiction. She will assist the OIC in gaining access to such materials that are not within her custody and control, and she will assist in locating and gaining the cooperation of other individuals who possess relevant information. Ms. Lewinsky will not attempt to protect any person or entity through false information or omission, and she will not attempt falsely to implicate any person or entity.

B. Ms. Lewinsky will testify truthfully before grand juries in this district and elsewhere, at any trials in this district and elsewhere, and in any other executive, military, judicial or congressional proceedings. Pending a final resolution of this matter, neither Ms. Lewinsky nor her agents will make any statements about this matter to witnesses, subjects, or targets of the OIC's investigation, or their agents, or to representatives of the news media, without first obtaining the OIC's approval.

C. Ms. Lewinsky will be fully debriefed concerning her knowledge of and participation in any activities within the OIC's jurisdiction. This debriefing will be conducted by the OIC, including attorneys, law enforcement agents, and representatives of any other institutions as the OIC may require. Ms. Lewinsky will make herself available for any interviews upon reasonable request.

D. Ms. Lewinsky acknowledges that she has orally proffered information to the OIC on July 27, 1998, pursuant to a proffer agreement. Ms. Lewinsky further represents that the statements she made during that proffer session were truthful and accurate to the best of her knowledge. She agrees that during her cooperation, she will truthfully elaborate with respect to these and other subjects.

E. Ms. Lewinsky agrees that, upon the OIC's request, she will waive any evidentiary privileges she may have, except for the attorney-client privilege.

2. If Ms. Lewinsky fully complies with the terms and understandings set forth in this Agreement, the OIC: 1) will not prosecute her for any crimes committed prior to the date of this Agreement arising out of the investigations within the jurisdiction of the OIC; 2) will grant her derivative use immunity within the meaning and subject to the limitations of 18 United States Code, Section 6002, and will not use, in any criminal prosecution against Ms. Lewinsky, testimony or other information provided by her during the course of her debriefing, testimony, or other cooperation pursuant to this agreement, or any information derived directly or indirectly from such debriefing, testimony, information, or other cooperation; and 3) will not prosecute her mother, Marsha Lewis, or her father, Bernard Lewinsky, for any offenses which may have been committed by them prior to this Agreement arising out of the facts summarized above, provided that Ms. Lewis and Mr. Lewinsky cooperate with the OIC's investigation and provide complete and truthful information regarding those facts.

3. If the OIC determines that Ms. Lewinsky has intentionally given false, incomplete, or misleading information or testimony, or has otherwise violated any provision of this Agreement, the OIC may move the United States District Court for the District of Columbia which supervised the grand jury investigating this matter for a finding that Ms. Lewinsky has breached this Agreement, and, upon such a finding by the Court, Ms. Lewinsky shall be subject to prosecution for any federal criminal violation of which the OIC has knowledge, including but not limited to perjury, obstruction of justice, and making false statements to government agencies. In such a prosecution, the OIC may use information provided by Ms. Lewinsky during the course of her cooperation, and such information, including her statements, will be admissible against her in any grand jury, court, or other official proceedings.

4. Pending a final resolution of this matter, the OIC will not make any statements about this Agreement to representatives of the news media.

5. This is the entire agreement between the parties. There are no other agreements, promises or inducements.

If the foregoing terms are acceptable, please sign, and have your client sign, in the spaces indicated below.

Date: July 28, 1998

KENNETH W. STARR
Independent Counsel

I have read this entire Agreement and I have discussed it with my attorneys. I freely and voluntarily enter into this Agreement. I understand that if I violate any provisions of this Agreement, the Agreement will be null and void, and I will be subject to federal prosecution as outlined in the Agreement.

Date: July 28, 1998

Monica S. Lewinsky

Counsel for Ms. Lewinsky:

Jacob A. Stein

Plato Cacheris

Volume III:

Document Supplement, Part A

William J. Clinton Statements

REFERRAL

TO THE

UNITED STATES HOUSE OF REPRESENTATIVES

PURSUANT TO

TITLE 28, UNITED STATES CODE, § 595(C)

DOCUMENT SUPPLEMENT A

SUBMITTED BY

THE OFFICE OF THE INDEPENDENT COUNSEL

SEPTEMBER 9, 1998

Table of Contents

595(c) REPORT

DOCUMENT SUPPLEMENT A - CLINTON STATEMENTS

INDEX

Tab	Description
1.	1/17/98 Deposition of President William Jefferson Clinton in the case of *Jones v. Clinton*
2.	1/17/98 Deposition Exhibit No. 1 - Definition of Sexual Relations
3.	1/17/98 Deposition Exhibit No. 2 - Definition of Sexual Assault and Offense of Sexual Assault
4.	1/17/98 Deposition Exhibit No. 3 - 18 USCS §2244 & §2245 - Sexual Abuse
5.	1/17/98 Deposition Exhibit No. 5 - Office of the Governor Sexual Harassment Policy
6.	1/17/98 Deposition Exhibit No. 6 - Third Annual Governor's Quality Conference Agenda, Wednesday, May 8, 1991
7.	1/17/98 Deposition Exhibit No. 7 - 4/1/91 Memo from Partain to Hernrich re: Governor's Role in Quality Conference
8.	1/17/98 Deposition Exhibit No. 8 - DF Call
9.	1/17/98 Deposition Exhibit No. 9 - President Clinton's Responses to Plaintiff's Third Set of Interrogatories
10.	1/17/98 Deposition Exhibit No. 10 - President Clinton's Responses to Plaintiff's First Set of Interrogatories
11.	1/17/98 Deposition Exhibit No. 11 - Handwritten Note from Gennifer to Bill
12.	1/17/98 Deposition Exhibit No. 12 - Handwritten Note from Gennifer to Bill Stamped Received on 2/25/91
13.	1/17/98 Deposition Exhibit No. 13 - Handwritten and Typed Note of President Clinton's encounter with Dolly Kyle at their Class Reunion
14.	1/17/98 Deposition Exhibit No. 14 - President Clinton's Supplemental Responses to Plaintiff's Second Set of Interrogatories
15.	1/17/98 Deposition Exhibit No. 15 - Affidavit of Jane Doe #6 signed by Monica S. Lewinsky on 1/7/98
16.	8/17/98 Grand Jury Testimony of President William Jefferson Clinton

Tab	Description
17.	8/17/98 Grand Jury Exhibit No. WJC-1 - Statement of President Clinton
18.	8/17/98 Grand Jury Exhibit No. WJC-2 - *Jones v. Clinton* Definition of Sexual Relations
19.	8/17/98 Grand Jury Exhibit No. WJC-3 - 1/17/98 Deposition of President William Jefferson Clinton in the case of *Jones v. Clinton*
20.	8/17/98 Grand Jury Exhibit No. WJC-4 - Affidavit of Jane Doe #6 signed by Monica S. Lewinsky on 1/7/98
21.	8/17/98 Grand Jury Exhibit No. WJC-5 - Photograph of President Clinton dated 8/6/98
22.	8/17/98 Grand Jury Exhibit No. WJC-6 - Photograph of the tie worn by President Clinton dated 8/6/98

Tab 1

DEPOSITION OF
WILLIAM JEFFERSON CLINTON
JONES V. CLINTON
SEALED PURSUANT TO
COURT ORDER

Tab 2

Paula Jones v. William Jefferson Clinton and Danny Ferguson
No. LR-C-94-290 (E.D. Ark.)

DEPOSITION OF WILLIAM JEFFERSON CLINTON

Definition of Sexual Relations

For the purposes of this deposition, a person engages in "sexual relations" when the person knowingly engages in or causes -

(1) contact with the genitalia, anus, groin, breast, inner thigh, or buttocks of any person with an intent to arouse or gratify the sexual desire of any person;

(2) contact between any part of the person's body or an object and the genitals or anus of another person; or

(3) contact between the genitals or anus of the person and any part of another person's body.

"Contact" means intentional touching, either directly or through clothing.

849-DC-00000586

DEPOSITION EXHIBIT
1
Clinton 1-17-98

Tab 3

Paula Jones v. William Jefferson Clinton and Danny Ferguson
No. LR-C-94-290 (E.D. Ark.)

DEPOSITION OF WILLIAM JEFFERSON CLINTON

Definition of Sexual Assualt and Offense of Sexual Assault

For the purposes of this deposition, a person commits a "sexual assault" and commits an "offense of sexual assault" when the person commits a crime under Federal law or the law of a State that involved -

(1) any conduct proscribed by Section 2244(b) of title 18, United States Code;

(2) contact, without consent, between any part of the defendant's body or an object and the genitals or anus of another person;

(3) contact, without consent, between the genitals or anus of the defendant and any part of another person's body; or

(4) an attempt or conspiracy to engage in conduct described in paragraphs (1) and (2).

"Contact" means intentional touching, either directly or through clothing.

849-DC-00000587

DEPOSITION EXHIBIT
2
Clinton 1-17-98

Tab 4

DEPOSITION EXHIBIT 3
JONES V. CLINTON
SEALED PURSUANT TO COURT ORDER

Tab 5

DEPOSITION EXHIBIT 5
JONES V. CLINTON
SEALED PURSUANT TO COURT ORDER

Tab 6

Third Annual
Governor's Quality Conference

Excelsior Hotel
Little Rock, Arkansas

Wednesday, May 8, 1991

AGENDA

7:30	Registration
8:00	Welcome, Introduction Dave Harrington, *Executive Director, AIDC*
	Opening Remarks Bill Clinton, *Governor, State of Arkansas*
8:30	Total Systems Approach to Quality Manufacturing Lew Springer, *Former Senior Vice President with Campbell Soup Company*
10:00	*Break*
10:20	Lew Springer—continued
12:15	*Lunch*
1:15	The Improvement Process: How America's Leading Companies Improve Quality Jim Harrington, *International Quality Advisor for Ernst and Young*
2:15	*Break*
2:30	Jim Harrington—continued
3:30	Questions and Answers Dave Harrington, Moderator
4:00	Adjourn

849-DC-00000592

DEPOSITION EXHIBIT 6 Clinton 1-17-98

Tab 7

April 1, 1991

MEMORANDUM

TO: Nancy Hernrich

FROM: Jan Partain

RE: Governor's role in Quality Conference

The agenda for the Governor's Quality Conference on May 8 is enclosed, as well as the mail-outs we have done thus far.

We had planned for the Governor to kick off and to wrap up the conference; however, his presence for the entire day would be significant. The meeting is designed specifically for top managers, and they are requested not to send substitutes.

Please call me at 27327 if you have questions.

cc: Dave Harrington
Jim Blakley

849-DC-00000593

DEPOSITION
EXHIBIT
7

Third Annual Governor's Quality Conference
Wednesday, May 8, 1991
Excelsior Hotel

8:00	Introductions Dave introduces Gove: nor Governor talks about importance of Quality Management to manufacturers and thus to the state's economy, QM in state government, continued commitment to QM across the country, etc. Governor introduces speakers.	
8:30	Lew Springer	
10:00	Break	
10:30	Lew Springer	
12:00	Lunch	
1:00	Jim Harrington	
2:00	Break	
2:30	Jim Harrington	
3:30	Q & A	
3:50	Wrap-up Governor wraps-up	849-DC-00000594
4:00	Adjourn	

Tab 8

DEPOSITION EXHIBIT 8
JONES V. CLINTON
SEALED PURSUANT TO COURT ORDER

Tab 9

PRESIDENT CLINTON'S RESPONSE TO PLAINTIFF'S THIRD SET OF INTERROGATORIES JONES V. CLINTON SEALED PURSUANT TO COURT ORDER

Tab 10

PRESIDENT CLINTON'S RESPONSES TO PLAINTIFF'S FIRST SET OF INTERROGATORIES JONES V. CLINTON SEALED PURSUANT TO COURT ORDER

Tab 11

DEPOSITION EXHIBIT 11
JONES V. CLINTON
SEALED PURSUANT TO
COURT ORDER

Tab 12

DEPOSITION EXHIBIT 12
JONES V. CLINTON
SEALED PURSUANT TO
COURT ORDER

DEPOSITION EXHIBIT 13
JONES V. CLINTON
SEALED PURSUANT TO COURT ORDER

Tab 14

PRESIDENT CLINTON'S SUPPLEMENTAL RESPONSES TO PLAINTIFF'S SECOND SET OF INTERROGATORIES JONES V. CLINTON SEALED PURSUANT TO COURT ORDER

Tab 15

DEPOSITION EXHIBIT 15 Clinton 1-17-98

AFFIDAVIT OF JANE DOE # 6

1. My name is Jane Doe #6 . I am 24 years old and I currently reside at [redacted].

2. On December 19, 1997, I was served with a subpoena from the plaintiff to give a deposition and to produce documents in the lawsuit filed by Paula Corbin Jones against President William Jefferson Clinton and Danny Ferguson.

3. I can not fathom any reason that the plaintiff would seek information from me for her case.

4. I have never met Ms. Jones, nor do I have any information regarding the events she alleges occurred at the Excelsior Hotel on May 8, 1991 or any other information concerning any of the allegations in her case.

5. I worked at the White House in the summer of 1995 as a White House intern. Beginning in December, 1995, I worked in the Office of Legislative Affairs as a staff assistant for correspondence. In April, 1996, I accepted a job as assistant to the Assistant Secretary for Public Affairs at the U.S. Department of Defense. I maintained that job until December 26, 1997. I am currently unemployed but seeking a new job.

6. In the course of my employment at the White House I met President Clinton several times. I also saw the President at a number of social functions held at the White House. When I worked as an intern, he appeared at occasional functions attended by me and several other interns. The correspondence I drafted while I worked at the Office of Legislative Affairs was seen and edited by supervisors who either had the President's signature affixed by mechanism or, I believe, had the President sign the correspondence itself.

7. I have the utmost respect for the President who has always behaved appropriately in my presence.

8. I have never had a sexual relationship with the President, he did not propose that we have a sexual relationship, he did not offer me employment or other benefits in exchange for a sexual relationship, he did not deny me employment or other benefits for rejecting a sexual relationship. I do not know of any

other person who had a sexual relationship with the President, was offered employment or other benefits in exchange for a sexual relationship, or was denied employment or other benefits for rejecting a sexual relationship. The occasions that I saw the President after I left my employment at the White House in April, 1996, were official receptions, formal functions or events related to the U.S. Department of Defense, where I was working at the time. There were other people present on those occasions.

9. Since I do not possess any information that could possibly be relevant to the allegations made by Paula Jones or lead to admissible evidence in this case, I asked my attorney to provide this affidavit to plaintiff's counsel. Requiring my deposition in this matter would cause disruption to my life, especially since I am looking for employment, unwarranted attorney's fees and costs, and constitute an invasion of my right to privacy.

I declare under the penalty of perjury that the foregoing is true and correct.

Monica S. Lewinsky

MONICA S. LEWINSKY

* * * * * * * * * *

849-DC-00000635

DISTRICT OF COLUMBIA, ss:

MONICA S. LEWINSKY, being first duly sworn on oath according to law, deposes and says that she has read the foregoing AFFIDAVIT OF JANE DOE #6 by her subscribed, that the matters stated herein are true to the best of her information, knowledge and belief.

Monica S Lewinsky
MONICA S. LEWINSKY

SUBSCRIBED AND SWORN to before me this 7th day of January, 1998.

Kathleen M Grimes
NOTARY PUBLIC, D.C.
My Commission expires: My Commission Expires August 31, 1998

849-DC-00000636

Tab 16

OFFICE OF THE INDEPENDENT COUNSEL

-----------------------------x

TESTIMONY OF : Monday, August 17, 1998

WILLIAM JEFFERSON CLINTON : Washington, D. C.

-----------------------------x

Videotaped testimony of

PRESIDENT WILLIAM JEFFERSON CLINTON

before the Independent Counsel, held at The White House, Washington, D. C., beginning at 1:03 p.m., when were present on behalf of the respective parties:

FOR THE INDEPENDENT COUNSEL: KENNETH W. STARR, ESQ.
Independent Counsel

JACKIE M. BENNETT, JR., ESQ.
ROBERT J. BITTMAN, ESQ.
SOLOMON L. WISENBERG, ESQ.
Deputy Independent Counsel

MICHAEL W. EMMICK, ESQ.
MARY ANNE WIRTH, ESQ.
BERNARD JAMES APPERSON, ESQ.
Associate Independent Counsel

FOR THE PRESIDENT: DAVID E. KENDALL, ESQ.
NICOLE SELIGMAN, ESQ.
Williams & Connolly

CHARLES F. C. RUFF, ESQ.
Counsel to the President

ALSO PRESENT: JAMES P. RICKARDS, JR.
Senior Consultant, OIC

GARY E. BRESNAHAN
White House Technical Staff

Secret Service Agent

Court Reporter: Elizabeth A. Eastman

be

P R O C E E D I N G S

MR. APPERSON: Mr. Wisenberg, the grand jury is in session. There is a quorum. There are no unauthorized persons in the grand jury room and they are prepared to receive the testimony of the President.

MR. WISENBERG: Thank you, Mr. Apperson. If we could proceed with the oath, please?

WHEREUPON,

WILLIAM JEFFERSON CLINTON

having been called for examination by the Independent Counsel, and having been first duly sworn, was examined and testified as follows:

EXAMINATION BY THE INDEPENDENT COUNSEL

BY MR. WISENBERG:

Q Good afternoon, Mr. President.

A Good afternoon.

Q Could you please state your full name for the record, sir?

A William Jefferson Clinton.

Q My name is Sol Wisenberg and I'm a Deputy Independent Counsel with the Office of Independent Counsel. With me today are some other attorneys from the Office of Independent Counsel.

At the courtroom are the ladies and gentlemen of the grand jury prepared to receive your testimony as you give

be

it. Do you understand, sir?

A Yes, I do.

Q This proceeding is subject to Rule 6(e) of the Federal Rules of Criminal Procedure as modified by Judge Johnson's order. You are appearing voluntarily today as a part of an agreement worked out between your attorney, the Office of the Independent Counsel, and with the approval of Judge Johnson.

Is that correct, sir?

A That is correct.

MR. KENDALL: Mr. Wisenberg, excuse me. You referred to Judge Johnson's order. I'm not familiar with that order. Have we been served that, or not?

MR. WISENBERG: No. My understanding is that that is an order that the Judge is going to sign today. She didn't have the name of a WHCA person. And basically my understanding is that it will cover all of the attorneys here today and the technical people in the room, so that they will be authorized persons permitted to hear grand jury testimony that they otherwise wouldn't be authorize to hear.

MR. KENDALL: Thank you.

BY MR. WISENBERG:

Q The grand jury, Mr. President, has been empaneled by the United States District Court for the District of Columbia. Do you understand that, sir?

be

A I do.

Q And, among other things, is currently investigating under the authority of the Court of Appeals upon application by the Attorney General, whether Monica Lewinsky or others obstructed justice, intimidated witnesses, or committed other crimes related to the case of Jones v. Clinton.

Do you understand that, sir?

A I do.

Q And today, you will be receiving questions not only from attorneys on the OIC staff, but from some of the grand jurors, too. Do you understand that?

A Yes, sir, I do.

Q I'm going to talk briefly about your rights and responsibilities as a grand jury witness. Normally, grand jury witnesses, while not allowed to have attorneys in the grand jury room with them, can stop and consult with their attorneys. Under our arrangement today, your attorneys are here and present for consultation and you can break to consult with them as necessary, but it won't count against our total time.

Do you understand that, sir?

A I do understand that.

Q You have a privilege against self-incrimination. If a truthful answer to any question would tend to incriminate you, you can invoke the privilege and that be 5

invocation will not be used against you. Do you understand that?

A I do.

Q And if you don't invoke it, however, any answer that you do give can and will be used against you. Do you understand that, sir?

A I do.

Q Mr. President, you understand that your testimony here today is under oath?

A I do.

Q And do you understand that because you have sworn to tell the truth, the whole truth, and nothing but the truth, that if you were to lie or intentionally mislead the grand jury, you could be prosecuted for perjury and/or obstruction of justice?

A I believe that's correct.

Q Is there anything that you -- I've stated to you regarding your rights and responsibilities that you would like me to clarify or that you don't understand?

A No, sir.

Q Mr. President, I would like to read for you a portion of Federal Rule of Evidence 603, which discusses the important function the oath has in our judicial system.

It says that the purpose of the oath is one, "calculated to awaken the witness' conscience and impress the

be

witness' mind with the duty" to tell the truth.

Could you please tell the grand jury what that oath means to you for today's testimony?

A I have sworn an oath to tell the grand jury the truth, and that's what I intend to do.

Q You understand that it requires you to give the whole truth, that is, a complete answer to each question, sir?

A I will answer each question as accurately and fully as I can.

Q Now, you took the same oath to tell the truth, the whole truth, and nothing but the truth on January 17th, 1998 in a deposition in the Paula Jones litigation; is that correct, sir?

A I did take an oath then.

Q Did the oath you took on that occasion mean the same to you then as it does today?

A I believed then that I had to answer the questions truthfully, that is correct.

Q I'm sorry. I didn't hear you, sir.

A I believed that I had to answer the questions truthfully. That's correct.

Q And it meant the same to you then as it does today?

A Well, no one read me a definition then and we didn't go through this exercise then. I swore an oath to

be

tell the truth, and I believed I was bound to be truthful and I tried to be.

Q At the Paula Jones deposition, you were represented by Mr. Robert Bennett, your counsel, is that correct?

A That is correct.

Q He was authorized by you to be your representative there, your attorney, is that correct?

A That is correct.

Q Your counsel, Mr. Bennett, indicated at page 5 of the deposition, lines 10 through 12, and I'm quoting, "the President intends to give full and complete answers as Ms. Jones is entitled to have".

My question to you is, do you agree with your counsel that a plaintiff in a sexual harassment case is, to use his words, entitled to have the truth?

A I believe that I was bound to give truthful answers, yes, sir.

Q But the question is, sir, do you agree with your counsel that a plaintiff in a sexual harassment case is entitled to have the truth?

A I believe when a witness is under oath in a civil case, or otherwise under oath, the witness should do everything possible to answer the questions truthfully.

MR. WISENBERG: I'm going to turn over questioning now to Mr. Bittman of our office, Mr. President.

be

BY MR. BITTMAN:

Q Good afternoon, Mr. President.

A Good afternoon, Mr. Bittman.

Q My name is Robert Bittman. I'm an attorney with the Office of Independent Counsel.

Mr. President, we are first going to turn to some of the details of your relationship with Monica Lewinsky that follow up on your deposition that you provided in the Paula Jones case, as was referenced, on January 17th, 1998.

The questions are uncomfortable, and I apologize for that in advance. I will try to be as brief and direct as possible.

Mr. President, were you physically intimate with Monica Lewinsky?

A Mr. Bittman, I think maybe I can save the -- you and the grand jurors a lot of time if I read a statement, which I think will make it clear what the nature of my relationship with Ms. Lewinsky was and how it related to the testimony I gave, what I was trying to do in that testimony. And I think it will perhaps make it possible for you to ask even more relevant questions from your point of view.

And, with your permission, I'd like to read that statement.

Q Absolutely. Please, Mr. President.

A When I was alone with Ms. Lewinsky on certain

be

occasions in early 1996 and once in early 1997, I engaged in conduct that was wrong. These encounters did not consist of sexual intercourse. They did not constitute sexual relations as I understood that term to be defined at my January 17th, 1998 deposition. But they did involve inappropriate intimate contact.

These inappropriate encounters ended, at my insistence, in early 1997. I also had occasional telephone conversations with Ms. Lewinsky that included inappropriate sexual banter.

I regret that what began as a friendship came to include this conduct, and I take full responsibility for my actions.

While I will provide the grand jury whatever other information I can, because of privacy considerations affecting my family, myself, and others, and in an effort to preserve the dignity of the office I hold, this is all I will say about the specifics of these particular matters.

I will try to answer, to the best of my ability, other questions including questions about my relationship with Ms. Lewinsky; questions about my understanding of the term "sexual relations", as I understood it to be defined at my January 17th, 1998 deposition; and questions concerning alleged subornation of perjury, obstruction of justice, and intimidation of witnesses.

be

That, Mr. Bittman, is my statement.

Q Thank you, Mr. President. And, with that, we would like to take a break.

A Would you like to have this?

Q Yes, please. As a matter of fact, why don't we have that marked as Grand Jury Exhibit WJC-1.

(Grand Jury Exhibit WJC-1 was marked for identification.)

THE WITNESS: So, are we going to take a break?

MR. KENDALL: Yes. We will take a break. Can we have the camera off, now, please? And it's 1:14.

(Whereupon, the proceedings were recessed from 1:14 p.m. until 1:30 p.m.)

MR. KENDALL: 1:30, Bob.

MR. BITTMAN: It's 1:30 and we have the feed with the grand jury.

BY MR. BITTMAN:

Q Good afternoon again, Mr. President.

A Good afternoon, Mr. Bittman.

(Discussion off the record.)

BY MR. BITTMAN:

Q Mr. President, your statement indicates that your contacts with Ms. Lewinsky did not involve any inappropriate, intimate contact.

MR. KENDALL: Mr. Bittman, excuse me. The

be

witness --

THE WITNESS: No, sir. It indicates --

MR. KENDALL: The witness does not have --

THE WITNESS: -- that it did involve inappropriate and intimate contact.

BY MR. BITTMAN:

Q Pardon me. That it did involve inappropriate, intimate contact.

A Yes, sir, it did.

MR. KENDALL: Mr. Bittman, the witness -- the witness does not have a copy of the statement. We just have the one copy.

MR. BITTMAN: If he wishes --

MR. KENDALL: Thank you.

MR. BITTMAN: -- his statement back?

BY MR. BITTMAN:

Q Was this contact with Ms. Lewinsky, Mr. President, did it involve any sexual contact in any way, shape, or form?

A Mr. Bittman, I said in this statement I would like to stay to the terms of the statement. I think it's clear what inappropriately intimate is. I have said what it did not include. I -- it did not include sexual intercourse, and I do not believe it included conduct which falls within the definition I was given in the Jones deposition. And I would like to stay with that characterization.

be

Q Let us then move to the definition that was provided you during your deposition. We will have that marked as Grand Jury Exhibit WJC-2.

(Grand Jury Exhibit WJC-2 was marked for identification.)

BY MR. BITTMAN:

Q This is an exact copy, Mr. President, of the exhibit that was provided you during that deposition. And I'm sure you remember from the deposition that paragraph (1) of the definition remained in effect. Judge Wright ruled that that was to be the guiding definition, and that paragraphs (2) and (3) were stricken.

Do you remember that, Mr. President?

A Yes. Specifically what I remember is there were two different discussions, I think, of this. There was quite an extended one in the beginning, and everybody was entering into it. And in the end, the Judge said that she would take the first definition and strike the rest of it. That's my memory.

Q Did you -- well, at page 19 of your deposition in that case, the attorney who provided you with the definition asked you, "Would you please take whatever time you need to read this definition". And later on in the deposition, you did, of course, refer to the definition several times.

Were you, during the deposition, familiar with the

be

definition?

A Yes, sir. My -- let me just ask a question. If you are going to ask me about my deposition, could I have a copy of it? Does anybody have a copy of it?

Q Yes. We have a copy. We'll provide you with a copy.

MS. WIRTH: We will mark it as Grand Jury Exhibit WJC-3.

(Grand Jury Exhibit WJC-3 was marked for identification.)

THE WITNESS: Now, did you say that was on page 19, Mr. Bittman?

BY MR. BITTMAN:

Q It was at page 19, Mr. President, beginning at line 21, and I'll read it in full. This is from the Jones attorney. "Would you please take whatever time you need to read this definition, because when I use the term 'sexual relations', this is what I mean today."

A All right. Yes, that starts on 19. But let me say that there is a -- just for the record, my recollection was accurate. There is a long discussion here between the attorney and the Judge. It goes on until page 23. And in the end the Judge says, "I'm talking only about part one in the definition", and "Do you understand that"? And I answer, "I do."

be

The judge says part one, and then the lawyer for Ms. Jones says he's only talking about part one and asked me if I understand it. And I say, I do, and that was my understanding.

I might also note that when I was given this and began to ask questions about it, I actually circled number one. This is my circle here. I remember doing that so I could focus only on those two lines, which is what I did.

Q Did you understand the words in the first portion of the exhibit, Mr. President, that is, "For the purposes of this deposition, a person engages in 'sexual relations' when the person knowingly engages in or causes"?

Did you understand, do you understand the words there in that phrase?

A Yes. My -- I can tell you what my understanding of the definition is, if you want me to --

Q Sure.

A -- do it. My understanding of this definition is it covers contact by the person being deposed with the enumerated areas, if the contact is done with an intent to arouse or gratify. That's my understanding of the definition.

Q What did you believe the definition to include and exclude? What kinds of activities?

A I thought the definition included any activity by

be

the person being deposed, where the person was the actor and came in contact with those parts of the bodies with the purpose or intent or gratification, and excluded any other activity.

For example, kissing is not covered by that, I don't think.

Q Did you understand the definition to be limited to sexual activity?

A Yes, I understood the definition to be limited to, to physical contact with those areas of the bodies with the specific intent to arouse or gratify. That's what I understood it to be.

Q What specific acts did the definition include, as you understood the definition on January 17, 1998?

A Any contact with the areas there mentioned, sir. If you contacted, if you contacted those parts of the body with an intent to arouse or gratify, that is covered.

Q What did you understand --

A The person being deposed. If the person being deposed contacted those parts of another person's body with an intent to arouse or gratify, that was covered.

Q What did you understand the word "causes", in the first phrase? That is, "For the purposes of this deposition, a person engaged in 'sexual relations' when the person knowingly" causes contact?

be

A I don't know what that means. It doesn't make any sense to me in this context, because -- I think what I thought there was, since this was some sort of -- as I remember, they said in the previous discussion -- and I'm only remembering now, so if I make a mistake you can correct me. As I remember from the previous discussion, this was some kind of definition that had something to do with sexual harassment. So, that implies it's forcing to me, and I -- and there was never any issue of forcing in the case involving, well, any of these questions they were asking me.

They made it clear in this discussion I just reviewed that what they were referring to was intentional sexual conduct, not some sort of forcible abusive behavior.

So, I basically -- I don't think I paid any attention to it because it appeared to me that that was something that had no reference to the facts that they admitted they were asking me about.

Q So, if I can be clear, Mr. President, was it your understanding back in January that the definition, now marked as Grand Jury Exhibit 2, only included consensual sexual activity?

A No. My understanding -- let me go back and say it. My understanding -- I'll tell you what it did include. My understanding was, what I was giving to you, was that what was covered in those first two lines was any direct contact

be

by the person being deposed with those parts of another person's body, if the contact was done with an intent to arouse or gratify. That's what I believed it meant.

That's what I believed it meant then reading it. That's what I believe it means today.

Q I'm just trying to understand, Mr. President. You indicated that you put the definition in the context of a sexual harassment case.

A No, no. I think it was not in the context of sexual harassment. I just reread those four pages, which obviously the grand jury doesn't have. But there was some reference to the fact that this definition apparently bore some, had some connection to some definition in another context, and that this was being used not in that context, not necessarily in the context of sexual harassment.

So, I would think that this "causes" would be, would mean to force someone to do something. That's what I read it. That's the only point I'm trying to make.

Therefore, I did not believe that anyone had ever suggested that I had forced anyone to do anything, and that I -- and I did not do that. And so that could not have had any bearing on any questions related to Ms. Lewinsky.

Q I suppose, since you have now read portions of the transcript again, that you were reminded that you did not ask for any clarification of the terms. Is that correct? Of the

be

definition?

A No, sir. I thought it was a rather -- when I read it, I thought it was a rather strange definition. But it was the one the Judge decided on and I was bound by it. So, I took it.

Q During the deposition, you remember that Ms. Lewinsky's name came up and you were asked several questions about her. Do you remember that?

A Yes, sir, I do.

Q During those -- or before those questions actually got started, your attorney, Mr. Bennett, objected to any questions about Ms. Lewinsky, and he represented to Judge Wright, who was presiding -- that was unusual, wasn't it, that a federal judge would come and actually -- in your experience -- that a federal judge would come and preside at a deposition?

MR. KENDALL: Mr. Bittman, excuse me. Could you identify the transcript page upon which Mr. Bennett objected to all testimony about Ms. Lewinsky before it got started?

MR. BITTMAN: The objection, this quote that I'm referring to, is going to begin at page 54 of the deposition.

MR. KENDALL: That is into the testimony though, after the testimony about Ms. Lewinsky has begun, is it not?

BY MR. BITTMAN:

Q Mr. President, is it unusual for a federal judge to

be

preside over a civil deposition?

A I think it is, but this was an unusual case. I believe I know why she did it.

Q Your attorney, Mr. Bennett, objected to the questions about Ms. Lewinsky, didn't he?

A What page is that on, sir?

Q Page 54, where he questions whether the attorneys for Ms. Jones had a good faith basis to ask some of the questions that they were posing to you. His objections actually begin on page 53.

Since, as the President pointed out that the grand jurors correctly do not have a copy of the deposition, I will read the portion that I am referring to. And this begins at line 1 on page 54.

"I question the good faith of counsel, the innuendo in the question. Counsel is fully aware that Ms. Lewinsky has filed, has an affidavit which they are in possession of saying that there is absolutely no sex of any kind in any manner, shape or form, with President Clinton".

A Where is that?

Q That is on page 54, Mr. President, beginning at line 1, about midway through line 1.

A Well, actually, in the present tense that is an accurate statement. That was an, that was an accurate statement, if -- I don't -- I think what Mr. Bennett was

be

concerned about, if I -- maybe it would be helpful to you and to the grand jurors, quite apart from these comments, if I could tell you what his state of mind was, what my state of mind was, and why I think the Judge was there in the first place.

If you don't want me to do it, I won't. But I think it will help to explain a lot of this.

Q Well, we are interested, and I know from the questions that we've received from the grand jurors they are interested in knowing what was going on in your mind when you were reading Grand Jury Exhibit 2, and what you understood that definition to include.

Our question goes to whether -- and you were familiar, and what Mr. Bennett was referring to obviously is Ms. Lewinsky's affidavit. And we will have that marked, Mr. President, as Grand Jury Exhibit WJC-4.

(Grand Jury Exhibit WJC-4 was marked for identification.)

BY MR. BITTMAN:

Q And you remember that Ms. Lewinsky's affidavit said that she had had no sexual relationship with you. Do you remember that?

A I do.

Q And do you remember in the deposition that Mr. Bennett asked you about that. This is at the end of the --

be

towards the end of the deposition. And you indicated, he asked you whether the statement that Ms. Lewinsky made in her affidavit was --

A   Truthful.

Q   -- true. And you indicated that it was absolutely correct.

A   I did. And at the time that she made the statement, and indeed to the present day because, as far as I know, she was never deposed since the Judge ruled she would not be permitted to testify in a case the Judge ruled had no merit; that is, this case we're talking about.

I believe at the time that she filled out this affidavit, if she believed that the definition of sexual relationship was two people having intercourse, then this is accurate. And I believe that is the definition that most ordinary Americans would give it.

If you said Jane and Harry have a sexual relationship, and you're not talking about people being drawn into a lawsuit and being given definitions, and then a great effort to trick them in some way, but you are just talking about people in ordinary conversations, I'll bet the grand jurors, if they were talking about two people they know, and said they have a sexual relationship, they meant they were sleeping together; they meant they were having intercourse together.

be

So, I'm not at all sure that this affidavit is not true and was not true in Ms. Lewinsky's mind at the time she swore it out.

Q Did you talk with Ms. Lewinsky about what she meant to write in her affidavit?

A I didn't talk to her about her definition. I did not know what was in this affidavit before it was filled out specifically. I did not know what words were used specifically before it was filled out, or what meaning she gave to them.

But I'm just telling you that it's certainly true what she says here, that we didn't have -- there was no employment, no benefit in exchange, there was nothing having anything to do with sexual harassment. And if she defined sexual relationship in the way I think most Americans do, meaning intercourse, then she told the truth.

Q My question --

A And that depends on what was in her mind. I don't know what was in her mind. You'll have to ask her that.

Q But you indicated before that you were aware of what she intended by the term "sexual relationship".

A No, sir. I said I thought that this could be a truthful affidavit. And when I read it, since that's the way I would define it, since -- keep in mind, she was not, she was not bound by this sexual relations definition, which is

be

highly unusual; I think anybody would admit that. When she used a different term, sexual relationship, if she meant by that what most people mean by it, then that is not an untruthful statement.

Q So, your definition of sexual relationship is intercourse only, is that correct?

A No, not necessarily intercourse only. But it would include intercourse. I believe, I believe that the common understanding of the term, if you say two people are having a sexual relationship, most people believe that includes intercourse. So, if that's what Ms. Lewinsky thought, then this is a truthful affidavit. I don't know what was in her mind. But if that's what she thought, the affidavit is true.

Q What else would sexual relationship include besides intercourse?

A Well, that -- I think -- let me answer what I said before. I think most people when they use that term include sexual relationships and whatever other sexual contact is involved in a particular relationship. But they think it includes intercourse as well. And I would have thought so. Before I got into this case and heard all I've heard, and seen all I've seen, I would have thought that that's what nearly everybody thought it meant.

Q Well, I ask, Mr. President, because your attorney, using the very document, Grand Jury Exhibit 4, WJC-4,

be

represented to Judge Wright that his understanding of the meaning of that affidavit, which you've indicated you thought Ms. Lewinsky thought was, she was referring just to intercourse, he says to Judge Wright that it meant absolutely no sex of any kind in any manner, shape or form.

A Well, let me say this. I didn't have any discussion obviously at this moment with Mr. Bennett. I'm not even sure I paid much attention to what he was saying. I was thinking, I was ready to get on with my testimony here and they were having these constant discussions all through the deposition. But that statement in the present tense, at least, is not inaccurate, if that's what Mr. Bennett meant. That is, at the time that he said that, and for some time before, that would be a completely accurate statement.

Now, I don't believe that he was -- I don't know what he meant. You'd have to talk to him, because I just wasn't involved in this, and I didn't pay much attention to what was being said. I was just waiting for them to get back to me. So, I can't comment on, or be held responsible for, whatever he said about that, I don't think.

Q Well, if you -- do you agree with me that if he mislead Judge Wright in some way that you would have corrected the record and said, excuse me, Mr. Bennett, I think the Judge is getting a misimpression by what you're saying?

A Mr. Bennett was representing me. I wasn't representing him. And I wasn't even paying much attention to this conversation, which is why, when you started asking me about this, I asked to see the deposition. I was focusing on my answers to the questions. And I've told you what I believe about this deposition, which I believe to be true.

And it's obvious, and I think by your questions you have betrayed that the Jones lawyers' strategy in this case had nothing to do with uncovering or proving sexual harassment.

By the time this discovery started, they knew they had a bad case on the law and they knew what our evidence was. They knew they had a lousy case on the facts. And so their strategy, since they were being funded by my political opponents, was to have this dragnet of discovery. They wanted to cover everybody. And they convinced the Judge, because she gave them strict orders not to leak, that they should be treated like other plaintiffs in other civil cases, and how could they ever know whether there had been any sexual harassment, unless they first knew whether there had been any sex.

And so, with that broad mandate limited by time and employment in the federal or state government, they proceeded to cross the country and try to turn up whatever they could; not because they thought it would help their case. By the

be

time they did this discovery, they knew what this deal was in their case, and they knew what was going to happen. And Judge Wright subsequently threw it out. What they --

Q With all respect, Mister --

A Now, let me finish, Mr. Bennett [sic]. I mean, you brought this up. Excuse me, Mr. Bittman.

What they wanted to do, and what they did do, and what they had done by the time I showed up here, was to find any negative information they could on me, whether it was true or not; get it in a deposition; and then leak it, even though it was illegal to do so. It happened repeatedly. The Judge gave them orders.

One of the reasons she was sitting in that deposition was because she was trying to make sure that it didn't get out of hand.

But that was their strategy, and they did a good job of it, and they got away with it. I've been subject to quite a lot of illegal leaking, and they had a very determined deliberate strategy, because their real goal was to hurt me. When they knew they couldn't win the lawsuit, they thought, well, maybe we can pummel him. Maybe they thought I'd settle. Maybe they just thought they would get some political advantage out of it. But that's what was going on here.

Now, I'm trying to be honest with you, and it hurts

be

me. And I'm trying to tell you the truth about what happened between Ms. Lewinsky and me. But that does not change the fact that the real reason they were zeroing in on anybody was to try to get any person in there, no matter how uninvolved with Paula Jones, no matter how uninvolved with sexual harassment, so they could hurt me politically. That's what was going on.

Because by then, by this time, this thing had been going on a long time. They knew what our evidence was. They knew what the law was in the circuit in which we were bringing this case. And so they just thought they would take a wrecking ball to me and see if they could do some damage.

Q Judge Wright had ruled that the attorneys in the Jones case were permitted to ask you certain questions, didn't she?

A She certainly did. And they asked them and I did my best to answer them. I'm just trying to tell --

Q And was it your responsibility --

A -- you what my state of mind was.

Q -- to answer those questions truthfully, Mr. President?

A It was.

Q And was --

A But it was not my responsibility, in the face of their repeated illegal leaking, it was not my responsibility

be

to volunteer a lot of information. There are many cases in this deposition where I gave -- and keep in mind, I prepared, I treated them, frankly, with respect. I prepared very well for this deposition on the Jones matters. I prepared very well on that. I did not know that Linda Tripp had been involved in the preparation of this deposition, or that all of you --

Q Do you know that now?

A No, I don't. I just know that -- what I read in the papers about it. But I had no way of knowing that they would ask me all these detailed questions. I did the best I could to answer them.

Q Did you prepare --

A But in this deposition, Mr. Bittman, I was doing my best to be truthful. I was not trying to be particularly helpful to them, and I didn't think I had an obligation to be particularly helpful to them to further a -- when I knew that there was no evidence here of sexual harassment, and I knew what they wanted to do was to leak this, even though it was unlawful to do so. That's --

Q Did you believe, Mr. President --

A -- what I knew.

Q -- that you had an obligation to make sure that the presiding federal judge was on board and had the correct facts? Did you believe that was your obligation?

be

A Sir, I was trying to answer my testimony. I was thinking about my testimony. I don't believe I ever even focused on what Mr. Bennett said in the exact words he did until I started reading this transcript carefully for this hearing. That moment, that whole argument just passed me by. I was a witness. I was trying to focus on what I said and how I said it.

And, believe me, I knew what the purpose of the deposition was. And, sure enough, by the way, it did all leak, just like I knew it would.

Q Let me ask you, Mr. President, you indicate in your statement that you were alone with Ms. Lewinsky. Is that right?

A Yes, sir.

Q How many times were you alone with Ms. Lewinsky?

A Let me begin with the correct answer. I don't know for sure. But if you would like me to give an educated guess, I will do that, but I do not know for sure. And I will tell you what I think, based on what I remember. But I can't be held to a specific time, because I don't have records of all of it.

Q How many times do you think?

A Well, there are two different periods here. There's the period when she worked in the White House until April of '96. And then there's the period when she came back

be

to visit me from February '97 until late December '97.

Based on our records -- let's start with the records, where we have the best records and the closest in time. Based on our records, between February and December, it appears to me that at least I could have seen her approximately nine times. Although I do not believe I saw her quite that many times, at least it could have happened.

There were -- we think there were nine or 10 times when she was in, in the White House when I was in the Oval Office when I could have seen her. I do not believe I saw her that many times, but I could have.

Now, we have no records for the time when she was an employee at the White House, because we have no records of that for any of the employees at the White House, unless there was some formally scheduled meeting that was on the, on the calendar for the day.

I remember -- I'll tell you what I remember. I remember meeting her, or having my first real conversation with her during the government shutdown in November of '95, when she -- as I explained in my deposition, during the government shutdown, the -- most federal employees were actually prohibited from coming to work, even in the White House. Most people in the White House couldn't come to work. The Chief of Staff could come to work. My National Security Advisor could come to work. I could.

be

Therefore, interns were assigned to all offices. And I believe it was her last week as an intern. Anyway, she worked in the Chief of Staff's Office. One night she brought me some pizza. We had some remarks.

Now, the next time I remember seeing her alone was on a couple of occasions when she was working in the Legislative Affairs Office as a full-time employee. I remember specifically, I have a specific recollection of two times. I don't remember when they were, but I remember twice when, on Sunday afternoon, she brought papers down to me, stayed, and we were alone.

And I am frankly quite sure -- although I have no specific memory, I am quite sure there were a couple of more times, probably two times more, three times more. That's what I would say. That's what I can remember. But I do not remember when they were, or at what time of day they were, or what the facts were. But I have a general memory that would say I certainly saw her more than twice during that period between January and April of 1996, when she worked there.

Q So, if I could summarize your testimony, approximately five times you saw her before she left the White House, and approximately nine times after she left the employment of the White House?

A I know there were several times in '97. I've told you that I've looked at my calendar and I tell you what I.

be

think the outer limits are. I would think that would sound about right. There could be, in that first four-month period, there, maybe there's one or two more, maybe there's one less. I just don't know. I don't remember. I didn't keep records.

But I'm giving you what I specifically remember and then what I generally remember. I'm doing the best to be helpful to you.

Q Have you reviewed the records for December 28th, 1997, Mr. President?

A Yes, sir, I have.

Q Do you believe that Ms. Lewinsky was at the White House and saw you on December 28th, 1997?

A Yes, sir, I do.

Q And do you remember talking with Ms. Lewinsky about her subpoena that she received for the Paula Jones case on that day?

A I remember talking with Ms. Lewinsky about her testimony, or about the prospect that she might have to give testimony. And she, she talked to me about that. I remember that.

Q And you also gave her Christmas gifts, is that not correct, Mr. President?

A That is correct. They were Christmas gifts and they were going-away gifts. She was moving to New York to,

be

taking a new job, starting a new life. And I gave her some gifts.

Q And you actually requested this meeting, is that not correct?

A I don't remember that, Mr. Bittman, but it's quite possible that I invited her to come by before she left town. But usually when we met, she requested the meetings. And my recollection is, in 1997 she asked to meet with me several times when I could not meet with her and did not do so. But it's quite possible that I -- that because she had given me a Christmas gift, and because she was leaving, that I invited her to come by the White House and get a couple of gifts before she left town.

I don't remember who requested the meeting though. I'm sorry, I don't.

Q You were alone with her on December 28, 1997, is that --

A Yes, sir.

Q -- right?

A I was.

Q The gifts that you gave her were a canvas bag from The Black Dog restaurant at Martha's Vineyard, is that right?

A Well, that was just, that was just something I had in the place to, to contain the gifts. But I believe that

be

the gifts I gave her were -- I put them in that bag. That's what I had there, and I knew she liked things from The Black Dog. So, I gave her -- I think that's what I put the presents in.

I remember what the presents were. I don't remember what the bag was I gave them in.

Q Did you also give her a marble bear's head carving from Vancouver, Canada?

A I did do that. I remember that.

Q And you also gave her a Rockettes blanket; that is, the famous Rockettes from New York?

A I did do that. I had that, I had had that in my possession for a couple of years but had never used it, and she was going to New York. So, I thought it would be a nice thing to give her.

Q You gave her a box of cherry chocolates, is that right?

A I don't remember that, sir. I mean, there could have been. I, I just don't remember. I remember giving the bear and the throw. I don't remember what else. And it seems to me like there was one other thing in that bag. I didn't remember the cherry chocolates.

Q How about a pin of the New York skyline? Did you give --

A That --

Q -- her that?

A That could have been in there. I seem to remember I gave her some kind of pin.

Q What about a pair of joke sunglasses?

A I don't remember that. I'm not denying it. I just -- I'm telling you what I remember and what I don't.

Q You had given Ms. Lewinsky gifts on other occasions though, is that right, Mr. President?

A Yes, I had.

Q This, though, was -- you gave her the most gifts that you had ever given her in a single day, is that right?

A Well, that's probably true. It was sort of like a going-away present and a Christmas present as well. And she had given me a particularly nice book for Christmas, an antique book on Presidents. She knew that I collected old books and it was a very nice thing. And I just thought I ought to get up a few things and give them to her before she left.

Q You mentioned that you discussed her subpoena in the Paula Jones case. Tell us specifically, what did you discuss?

A No, sir, that's not what I said. I said, my recollection is I knew by then, of course, that she had gotten a subpoena. And I knew that she was, therefore, was slated to testify. And she mentioned to me -- and I believe it was at this meeting. She mentioned -- I remember a conversation about the possibility of her testifying. I believe it must have occurred on the 28th.

She mentioned to me that she did not want to testify. So, that's how it came up. Not in the context of, I heard you have a subpoena, let's talk about it.

She raised the issue with me in the context of her desire to avoid testifying, which I certainly understood; not only because there were some embarrassing facts about our relationship that were inappropriate, but also because a whole lot of innocent people were being traumatized and dragged through the mud by these Jones lawyers with their dragnet strategy. They --

Q So --

A And so I -- and since she didn't know Paula Jones and knew nothing about sexual harassment, and certainly had no experience with that, I, I clearly understood why she didn't want to be a part of it.

Q And you didn't want her to testify, did you? You didn't want her to disclose these embarrassing facts of this inappropriate intimate relationship that you had, is that correct?

A Well, I did not want her to have to testify and go through that. And, of course, I didn't want her to do that, of course not.

be

Q Did you want those facts, not only the fact that she would testify, but did you want the facts that she had about your embarrassing inappropriate intimate relationship to be disclosed?

A Not there, but not in any context. However, I, I never had any high confidence that they wouldn't be.

Q Did anyone, as far as you knew, know about your embarrassing inappropriate intimate relationship that you had with Ms. Lewinsky?

A At that time, I was unaware that she had told anyone else about it. But if, if I had known that, it would not have surprised me.

Q Had you told anyone?

A Absolutely not.

Q Had you tried, in fact, not to let anyone else know about this relationship?

A Well, of course.

Q What did you do?

A Well, I never said anything about it, for one thing. And I did what people do when they do the wrong thing. I tried to do it where nobody else was looking at it.

Q How many times did you do that?

A Well, if you go back to my statement, I remember there were a few times in '96, I can't say with any certainty. There was once in early '97. After she left the

be

White House, I do not believe I ever had any inappropriate contact with her in the rest of '96. There was one occasion in '97 when, regrettably, that we were together for a few minutes, I think about 20 minutes, and there was inappropriate contact. And after that, to the best of my memory and belief, it did not occur again.

Q Did you tell her in the conversation about her being subpoenaed -- she was upset about it, you acknowledge that?

A (Witness nodded indicating an affirmative response.)

Q I'm sorry, you have to respond for the record. Yes or no? Do you agree that she was upset about being subpoenaed?

A Oh, yes, sir, she was upset. She -- well, she -- we -- she didn't -- we didn't talk about a subpoena. But she was upset. She said, I don't want to testify; I know nothing about this; I certainly know nothing about sexual harassment; why do they want me to testify. And I explained to her why they were doing this, and why all these women were on these lists, people that they knew good and well had nothing to do with any sexual harassment.

I explained to her that it was a political lawsuit. They wanted to get whatever they could under oath that was damaging to me, and then they wanted to leak it in violation

be

of the Judge's orders, and turn up their nose and say, well, you can't prove we did it. Now, that was their strategy. And that they were very frustrated because everything they leaked so far was old news. So, they desperately were trying to validate this massive amount of money they'd spent by finding some new news. And --

Q You were familiar --

A -- she didn't want to be caught up in that, and I didn't blame her.

Q You were familiar, weren't you, Mr. President, that she had received a subpoena. You've already acknowledged that.

A Yes, sir, I was.

Q And Mr. Jordan informed you of that, is that right?

A No, sir. I believe -- and I believe I testified to this in my deposition. I think the first person who told me that she had been subpoenaed was Bruce Lindsey. I think the first -- and I was -- in this deposition, it's a little bit cloudy, but I was trying to remember who the first person who told me was, because the question was, again as I remember it -- could we go to that in the deposition, since you asked me that?

Q Actually, I think you're -- with all respect, I think you may be confusing when Mr. Lindsey -- well, perhaps Mr. Lindsey did tell you she was subpoenaed, I don't know.

be

But in your deposition, you were referring to Mr. Lindsey notifying you that she had been identified as a witness.

A Where is that, sir? I don't want to get -- I just want -- what page is that?

Q Well, actually --

A No, it had to be, because I saw a witness list much earlier than that.

Q Much earlier that December 28?

A Oh, sure. And it had been earlier than -- she would -- I believe Monica --

MR. KENDALL: Page 69.

THE WITNESS: I believe Monica Lewinsky's name was on a witness list earlier than she was subpoenaed.

BY MR. BITTMAN:

Q Yes.

A So, I believe when I was answering this question, at least I thought I was answering when I found out -- yes. See, there's -- on page 68, "Did anyone other than your attorneys ever tell you that Monica Lewinsky had been served with a subpoena in this case?" Then I said, "I don't think so." Then I [sic] said, "Did you ever talk" to Monica "about the possibility that she might be asked to testify in this case?"

Then I gave an answer that was nonresponsive, that really tried to finish the answer above. I said, "Bruce

be

Lindsey, I think Bruce Lindsey told me that she was, I think maybe that's the first person told me she was. I want to be as accurate as I can."

And that -- I believe that Bruce is the first person who told me that Monica had gotten a subpoena.

Q Did you, in fact, have a conversation with Mr. Jordan on the evening of December 19, 1997, in which he talked to you about Monica being in Mr. Jordan's office, having a copy of the subpoena, and being upset about being subpoenaed?

A I remembered that Mr. Jordan was in the White House on December 19th and for an event of some kind. That he came up to the Residence floor and told me that he had, that Monica had gotten a subpoena and, or that Monica was going to have to testify. And I think he told me he recommended a lawyer for her. I believe that's what happened. But it was a very brief conversation. He was there for some other reason.

Q And if Mr. Jordan testified that he had also spoken to you at around 5 p.m., and the White House phone logs reflect this, that he called you at around the time he met with Ms. Lewinsky and informed you then that she had been subpoenaed, is that consistent with your memory? Also on the 19th?

A I had a lot of phone conversations with Vernon

be

about this. I didn't keep records of them. I now have some records. My memory is not clear and my testimony on that was not clear. I just knew that I talked to Vernon at some time, but I thought that Bruce was the first person who told me.

Q But Mr. Jordan had also told you, is that right?

A Yes. I now know I had a conversation with Mr. Jordan about it where he said something to me about that.

Q And that was probably on the 19th, December 19th?

A Well, I know I saw him on the 19th. So, I'm quite sure. And if he says he talked to me on the 19th, I believe he would have better records and I certainly think he's a truthful person.

Q Getting back to your meeting with Ms. Lewinsky on December 28, you are aware that she's been subpoenaed. You are aware, are you not, Mr. President, that the subpoena called for the production of, among other things, all the gifts that you had given Ms. Lewinsky? You were aware of that on December 28th, weren't you?

A I'm not sure. And I understand this is an important question. I did have a conversation with Ms. Lewinsky at some time about gifts, the gifts I'd given her. I do not know whether it occurred on the 28th, or whether it occurred earlier. I do not know whether it occurred in person or whether it occurred on the telephone. I have searched my memory for this, because I know it's an important

be

issue.

Perhaps if you -- I can tell you what I remember about the conversation and you can see why I'm having trouble placing the date.

Q Please.

A The reason I'm not sure it happened on the 28th is that my recollection is that Ms. Lewinsky said something to me like, what if they ask me about the gifts you've given me. That's the memory I have. That's why I question whether it happened on the 28th, because she had a subpoena with her, request for production.

And I told her that if they asked her for gifts, she'd have to give them whatever she had, that that's what the law was.

And let me also tell you, Mr. Bittman, if you go back and look at my testimony here, I actually asked the Jones lawyers for help on one occasion, when they were asking me what gifts I had given her, so they could -- I was never hung up about this gift issue. Maybe it's because I have a different experience. But, you know, the President gets hundreds of gifts a year, maybe more. I have always given a lot of gifts to people, especially if they give me gifts. And this was no big deal to me. I mean, it's nice. I enjoy it. I gave dozens of personal gifts to people last Christmas. I give gifts to people all the time. Friends of

be

mine give me gifts all the time, give me ties, give me books, give me other things. So, it was just not a big deal.

And I told Ms. Lewinsky that, just -- I said, you know, if they ask you for this, you'll have to give them whatever you have. And I think, Mr. Bittman, it must have happened before then, because -- either that, or Ms. Lewinsky didn't want to tell me that she had the subpoena, because that was the language I remember her using.

Q Well, didn't she tell you, Mr. President, that the subpoena specifically called for a hat pin that you had produced, pardon me, that you had given her?

A I don't remember that. I remember -- sir, I've told you what I remember. That doesn't mean that my memory is accurate. A lot of things have happened in the last several months, and a lot of things were happening then. But my memory is she asked me a general question about gifts. And my memory is she asked me in the hypothetical. So, it's possible that I had a conversation with her before she got a subpoena. Or it's possible she didn't want to tell me that was part of the subpoena. I don't know.

But she may have been worried about this gift business. But it didn't bother me. My experience was totally different. I told her, I said, look, the way these things work is, when a person get a subpoena, you have to give them whatever you have; that's what's the rule, that's

be

what the law is.

And when I was asked about this in my deposition, even though I was not trying to be helpful particularly to these people that I thought were not well-motivated, or being honest or even lawful in their conduct vis-a-vis me, that is, the Jones legal team, I did ask them specifically to enumerate the gifts. I asked them to help me because I couldn't remember the specifics.

So, all I'm saying is, it didn't -- I wasn't troubled by this gift issue.

Q And your testimony is that Ms. Lewinsky was concerned about her turning over any gifts that you had given her, and that your recommendation to her was, absolutely, Monica, you have to produce everything that I have given you. Is that your testimony?

A My testimony is what I have said, and let me reiterate it. I don't want to agree to a characterization of it. I want to just say what it was.

My testimony is that my memory is that on some day in December, and I'm sorry I don't remember when it was, she said, well, what if they ask me about the gifts you have given me. And I said, well, if you get a request to produce those, you have to give them whatever you have.

And it just, to me, it -- I don't -- I didn't then, I don't now see this as a problem. And if she thought it was

be

a problem, I think it -- it must have been from a, really, a misapprehension of the circumstances. I certainly never encouraged her not to, to comply lawfully with a subpoena.

Q Mr. President, if your intent was, as you have earlier testified, that you didn't want anybody to know about this relationship you had with Ms. Lewinsky, why would you feel comfortable giving her gifts in the middle of discovery in the Paula Jones case?

A Well, sir, for one thing, there was no existing improper relationship at that time. I had, for nearly a year, done my best to be a friend to Ms. Lewinsky, to be a counselor to her, to give her good advice, and to help her. She had, for her part, most of the time, accepted the changed circumstances. She talked to me a lot about her life, her job ambitions, and she continued to give me gifts. And I felt that it was a right thing to do to give her gifts back.

I have always given a lot of people gifts. I have always been given gifts. I do not think there is anything improper about a man giving a woman a gift, or a woman giving a man a gift, that necessarily connotes an improper relationship. So, it didn't bother me.

I wasn't -- you know, this was December 28th. I was -- I gave her some gifts. I wasn't worried about it. I thought it was an all right thing to do.

Q What about notes and letters, cards, letters and

be

notes to Ms. Lewinsky? After this relationship, this inappropriate intimate relationship between you and Ms. Lewinsky ended, she continued to send you numerous intimate notes and cards, is that right?

A Well, they were -- some of them were, were somewhat intimate. I'd say most of them, most of the notes and cards were, were affectionate all right, but, but she had clearly accepted the fact that there could be no contact between us that was in any way inappropriate.

Now, she, she sent cards sometimes that were just funny, even a little bit off-color, but they were funny. She liked to send me cards, and I got a lot of those cards; several, anyway, I don't know a lot. I got a few.

Q She professed her love to you in these cards after the end of the relationship, didn't she?

A Well, --

Q She said she loved you?

A Sir, the truth is that most of the time, even when she was expressing her feelings for me in affectionate terms, I believed that she had accepted, understood my decision to stop this inappropriate contact. She knew from the very beginning of our relationship that I was apprehensive about it. And I think that in a way she felt a little freer to be affectionate, because she knew that nothing else was going to happen. I can't explain entirely what was in her mind.

be

But most of these messages were not what you would call over the top. They weren't things that, if you read them, you would say, oh, my goodness, these people are having some sort of sexual affair.

Q Mr. President, the question --

A But some of them were quite affectionate.

Q My question was, did she or did she not profess her love to you in those cards and letters that she sent to you after the relationship ended?

A Most of them were signed, "Love", you know, "Love, Monica." I don't know that I would consider -- I don't believe that in most of these cards and letters she professed her love, but she might well have. I -- but, you know, love can mean different things, too, Mr. Bittman. I have -- there are a lot of women with whom I have never had any inappropriate conduct who are friends of mine, who will say from time to time, I love you. And I know that they don't mean anything wrong by that.

Q Specifically, Mr. President, do you remember a card she sent you after she saw the movie Titanic, in which she said that she reminisced or dreamed about the romantic feelings that occurred in the movie, and how that reminded her of you two? Do you remember that?

A No, sir, but she could have sent it. I -- just because I don't remember it doesn't mean it wasn't there.

be

Q You're not denying that, that --
A Oh, no. I wouldn't deny that. I just don't remember it. You asked me if I remembered. I don't. She might have done it.
Q Do you ever remember telling her, Mr. President, that she should not write some of the things that she does in those cards and letters that she sends to you because it reveals, if disclosed, this relationship that you had, and that she shouldn't do it?
A I remember telling her she should be careful what she wrote, because a lot of it was clearly inappropriate and would be embarrassing if somebody else read it. I don't remember when I said that. I don't remember whether it was in '96 or when it was. I don't remember.
Q Embarrassing, in that it was revealing of the intimate relationship that you and she had, is that right?
A I do not know when I said this. So, I don't know whether we did have any sort of inappropriate relationship at the time I said that to her. I don't remember. But it's obvious that if she wrote things that she should not have written down and someone else read it, that it would be embarrassing.
Q She certainly sent you something like that after the relationship began, didn't she? And so, therefore, there was, at the time she sent it, something inappropriate going

be

on?

A Well, my recollection is that she -- that maybe because of changed circumstances in her own life in 1997, after there was no more inappropriate contact, that she sent me more things in the mail, and that there was sort of a disconnect sometimes between what she was saying and the plain facts of our relationship. And I don't know what caused that. But it may have been dissatisfaction with the rest of her life. I don't know.

You know, she had, from the time I first met her, talked to me about the rest of her personal life, and it may be that there was some reason for that. It may be that when I did the right thing and made it stick, that in a way she felt a need to cling more closely, or try to get closer to me, even though she knew nothing improper was happening or was going to happen. I don't know the answer to that.

Q After you gave her the gifts on December 28th, did you speak with your secretary, Ms. Currie, and ask her to pick up a box of gifts that were some compilation of gifts that Ms. Lewinsky would have --

A No, sir, I didn't do that.

Q -- to give to Ms. Currie?

A I did not do that.

Q When you testified in the Paula Jones case, this was only two and a half weeks after you had given her these

be

six gifts, you were asked, at page 75 in your deposition, lines 2 through 5, "Well, have you ever given any gifts to Monica Lewinsky?" And you answer, "I don't recall."

And you were correct. You pointed out that you actually asked them, for prompting, "Do you know what they were?"

A I think what I meant there was I don't recall what they were, not that I don't recall whether I had given them. And then if you see, they did give me these specifics, and I gave them quite a good explanation here. I remembered very clearly what the facts were about The Black Dog. And I said that I could have given her a hat pin and a Walt Whitman book; that I did not remember giving her a gold broach, which was true. I didn't remember it. I may have given it to her, but I didn't remember giving her one.

They didn't ask me about the, about the Christmas gifts, and I don't know why I didn't think to say anything about them. But I have to tell you again, I even invited them to have a list.

It was obvious to me by this point in the definition, in this deposition, that they had, these people had access to a lot of information from somewhere, and I presume it came from Linda Tripp. And I had no interest in not answering their questions about these gifts. I do not believe that gifts are incriminating, nor do I think they are

be

wrong. I think it was a good thing to do. I'm not, I'm still not sorry I gave Monica Lewinsky gifts.

Q Why did you assume that that information came from Linda Tripp?

A I didn't then.

Q Well, you didn't? I thought you just testified you did then?

A No, no, no. I said I now assume that because --

Q You now assume.

A -- of all of the subsequent events. I didn't know. I just knew that --

Q Let me ask you about --

A -- that somebody had access to some information and they may have known more about this than I did.

Q Let me ask you about the meeting you had with Betty Currie at the White House on Sunday, January 18 of this year, the day after your deposition. First of all, you didn't -- Mrs. Currie, your secretary of six-some years, you never allowed her, did you, to watch whatever intimate activity you did with Ms. Lewinsky, did you?

A No, sir, not to my knowledge.

Q And as far as you know, she couldn't hear anything either, is that right?

A There were a couple of times when Monica was there when I asked Betty to be places where she could hear, because

Monica was upset and I -- this was after there was -- all the inappropriate contact had been terminated.

Q No, I'm talking --

A But --

Q -- about the times that you actually had the intimate contact.

A She was -- I believe that -- well, first of all, on that one occasion in 1997, I do not know whether Betty was in the White House after the radio address in the Oval Office complex. I believe she probably was, but I'm not sure. But I'm certain that someone was there. I always -- always someone was there.

In 1996, I think most of the times that Ms. Lewinsky was there, there may not have been anybody around except maybe coming in and out, but not permanently so. I -- that's correct. I never -- I didn't try to involve Betty in that in any way.

Q Well, not only did you not try to involve her, you specifically tried to exclude her and everyone else, isn't that right?

A Well, yes. I've never -- I mean, it's almost humorous, sir. I'd, I'd, I'd have to be an exhibitionist not to have tried to exclude everyone else.

Q So, if Ms. Currie testified that you approached her on the 18th, or you spoke with her and you said, you were

be

always there when she was there, she wasn't, was she? That is, Mrs. Currie?

A She was always there in the White House, and I was concerned -- let me back up and say --

Q What about the radio address, Mr. President?

A Let me back up a second, Mr. Bittman. I knew about the radio address. I was sick after it was over and I, I was pleased at that time that it had been nearly a year since any inappropriate contact had occurred with Ms. Lewinsky. I promised myself it wasn't going to happen again. The facts are complicated about what did happen and how it happened. But, nonetheless, I'm responsible for it. On that night, she didn't.

I was more concerned about the times after that when Ms. Lewinsky was upset, and I wanted to establish at least that I had not -- because these questions were -- some of them were off the wall. Some of them were way out of line, I thought.

And what I wanted to establish was that Betty was there at all other times in the complex, and I wanted to know what Betty's memory was about what she heard, what she could hear. And what I did not know was -- I did not know that. And I was trying to figure out, and I was trying to figure out in a hurry because I knew something was up.

Q So, you wanted --

be

A After that deposition.
Q -- to check her memory for what she remembered, and that is --
A That's correct.
Q -- whether she remembered nothing, or whether she remembered an inappropriate intimate --
A Oh, no, no, no, no.
Q -- relationship?
A No. I didn't ask her about it in that way. I asked her about what the -- what I was trying to determine was whether my recollection was right and that she was always in the office complex when Monica was there, and whether she thought she could hear any conversations we had, or did she hear any.

And then I asked her specifically about a couple of times when -- once when I asked her to remain in the dining room, Betty, while I met with Monica in my study. And once when I took Monica in the, the small office Nancy Hernreich occupies right next to Betty's and talked to her there for a few minutes. That's my recollection of that.

I was trying to -- I knew, Mr. Bittman, to a reasonable certainty that I was going to be asked more questions about this. I didn't really expect you to be in the Jones case at the time. I thought what would happen is that it would break in the press, and I was trying to get the

be

facts down. I was trying to understand what the facts were.

Q If Ms. Currie testified that these were not really questions to her, that they were more like statements, is that not true?

A Well, I can't testify as to what her perception was. I can tell you this. I was trying to get information in a hurry. I was downloading what I remembered. I think Ms. Currie would also testify that I explicitly told her, once I realized that you were involved in the Jones case -- you, the Office of Independent Counsel -- and that she might have to be called as a witness, that she should just go in there and tell the truth, tell what she knew, and be perfectly truthful.

So, I was not trying to get Betty Currie to say something that was untruthful. I was trying to get as much information as quickly as I could.

Q What information were you trying to get from her when you said, I was never alone with her, right?

A I don't remember exactly what I did say with her. That's what you say I said.

Q If Ms. Currie testified to that, if she says you told her, I was never alone with her, right?

A Well, I was never alone with her --

Q Did you not say that, Mr. President?

A Mr. Bittman, just a minute. I was never alone with

be

her, right, might be a question. And what I might have meant by that is, in the Oval Office complex.

Could --

Q Well, you knew the answer to that, didn't you?

A We've been going for more than an hour. Would you mind if we took a break? I need to go to the restroom.

MR. BITTMAN: Let's take a break.

MR. KENDALL: It's 2:38.

(Whereupon, the proceedings were recessed from 2:38 p.m. until 2:48 p.m.)

MR. KENDALL: It is 2:38 -- sorry, 2:48.

BY MR. WISENBERG:

Q Mr. President, I want to, before I go into a new subject area, briefly go over something you were talking about with Mr. Bittman.

The statement of your attorney, Mr. Bennett, at the Paula Jones deposition, "Counsel is fully aware" -- it's page 54, line 5 -- "Counsel is fully aware that Ms. Lewinsky has filed, has an affidavit which they are in possession of saying that there is absolutely no sex of any kind in any manner, shape or form, with President Clinton".

That statement is made by your attorney in front of Judge Susan Webber Wright, correct?

A That's correct.

Q That statement is a completely false statement.

be

Whether or not Mr. Bennett knew of your relationship with Ms. Lewinsky, the statement that there was "no sex of any kind in any manner, shape or form, with President Clinton," was an utterly false statement. Is that correct?

A It depends on what the meaning of the word "is" is. If the -- if he -- if "is" means is and never has been, that is not -- that is one thing. If it means there is none, that was a completely true statement.

But, as I have testified, and I'd like to testify again, this is -- it is somewhat unusual for a client to be asked about his lawyer's statements, instead of the other way around. I was not paying a great deal of attention to this exchange. I was focusing on my own testimony.

And if you go back and look at the sequence of this, you will see that the Jones lawyers decided that this was going to be the Lewinsky deposition, not the Jones deposition. And, given the facts of their case, I can understand why they made that decision. But that is not how I prepared for it. That is not how I was thinking about it.

And I am not sure, Mr. Wisenberg, as I sit here today, that I sat there and followed all these interchanges between the lawyers. I'm quite sure that I didn't follow all the interchanges between the lawyers all that carefully. And I don't really believe, therefore, that I can say Mr. Bennett's testimony or statement is testimony and is

be

imputable to me. I didn't -- I don't know that I was even paying that much attention to it.

Q You told us you were very well prepared for the deposition.

A No. I said I was very well prepared to talk about Paula Jones and to talk about Kathleen Willey, because she had made a related charge. She was the only person that I think I was asked about who had anything to do with anything that would remotely approximate sexual harassment. The rest of this looked to me like it was more of a way to harass me.

Q You are the President of the United States and your attorney tells a United States District Court Judge that there is no sex of any kind, in any way, shape or form, whatsoever. And you feel no obligation to do anything about that at that deposition, Mr. President?

A I have told you, Mr. Wisenberg, I will tell you for a third time. I am not even sure that when Mr. Bennett made that statement that I was concentrating on the exact words he used.

Now, if someone had asked me on that day, are you having any kind of sexual relations with Ms. Lewinsky, that is, asked me a question in the present tense, I would have said no. And it would have been completely true.

Q Was Mr. Bennett aware of this tense-based distinction you are making now --

be

A I don't --

MR. KENDALL: I'm going to object to any questions about communications with private counsel.

MR. WISENBERG: Well, the witness has already testified, I think, that Mr. Bennett didn't know about the inappropriate relationship with Ms. Lewinsky. I guess --

THE WITNESS: Well, you'll have to ask him that, you know. He was not a sworn witness and I was not paying that close attention to what he was saying. I've told you that repeatedly. I was -- I don't -- I never even focused on that until I read it in this transcript in preparation for this testimony.

When I was in there, I didn't think about my lawyers. I was, frankly, thinking about myself and my testimony and trying to answer the questions.

BY MR. WISENBERG:

Q I just want to make sure I understand, Mr. President. Do you mean today that because you were not engaging in sexual activity with Ms. Lewinsky during the deposition that the statement of Mr. Bennett might be literally true?

A No, sir. I mean that at the time of the deposition, it had been -- that was well beyond any point of improper contact between me and Ms. Lewinsky. So that anyone generally speaking in the present tense, saying there is not an improper relationship, would be telling the truth if that person said there was not, in the present tense; the present tense encompassing many months. That's what I meant by that.

Not that I was -- I wasn't trying to give you a cute answer, that I was obviously not involved in anything improper during a deposition. I was trying to tell you that generally speaking in the present tense, if someone said that, that would be true. But I don't know what Mr. Bennett had in his mind. I don't know. I didn't pay any attention to this colloquy that went on. I was waiting for my instructions as a witness to go forward. I was worried about my own testimony.

Q I want to go back to some questions about Mr. Jordan and we are going to touch a little bit on the December 19th meeting and some others. Mr. Jordan is a long-time friend of yours, is that correct, Mr. President?

A Yes, sir. We've been friends probably 20 years, maybe more.

Q You said you consider him to be a truthful person, correct?

A I do.

Q If Mr. Jordan has told us that he visited you in the Residence on the night of the 19th, after a White House holiday dinner, to discuss Monica Lewinsky and her subpoena with you, do you have any reason to doubt it?

be

A No. I've never known him to say anything that wasn't true. And his memory of these events, I think, would be better than mine because I had a lot of other things going on.

Q We have WAVE records that will show that, but in the interest of time I'm not going to -- since you don't dispute that, I'm not going to show them right now.

And, in fact, that was the very day Monica Lewinsky was subpoenaed, wasn't it, the night that he came to see you?

A I don't have an independent memory of that, but you would probably know that. I mean, I'm sure there is a record of when she got her subpoena.

Q If Mr. Jordan has told us that he spoke with you over the phone within about an hour of Monica receiving her subpoena, and later visited you that very day, the night at the White House, to discuss it, again you'd have no reason to doubt him, is that correct?

A I've already -- I believe I've already testified about that here today, that I had lots of conversations with Vernon. I'm sure that I had lots of conversations with him that included comments about this. And if he has a specific memory of when I had some conversation on a certain day, I would be inclined to trust his memory over mine, because under the present circumstances my head's probably more cluttered than his, and my schedule is probably busier. He's

be

probably got better records.

Q And when Mr. Jordan met with you at the Residence that night, sir, he asked you if you'd been involved in a sexual relationship with Monica Lewinsky, didn't he?

A I do not remember exactly what the nature of the conversation was. I do remember that I told him that there was no sexual relationship between me and Monica Lewinsky, which was true. And that -- then all I remember for the rest is that he said he had referred her to a lawyer, and I believe it was Mr. Carter, and I don't believe I've ever met Mr. Carter. I don't think I know him.

Q Mr. President, if Mr. Jordan has told us that he had a very disturbing conversation with Ms. Lewinsky that day, then went over to visit you at the White House, and that before he asked you the question about a sexual relationship, related that disturbing conversation to you, the conversation being that Ms. Lewinsky had a fixation on you and thought that perhaps the First Lady would leave you at the end of -- that you would leave the First Lady at the end of your term and come be with Ms. Lewinsky, do you have any reason to doubt him that it was on that night that that conversation happened?

A All I can tell you, sir, is I, I certainly don't remember him saying that. Now, he could have said that because, as you know, a great many things happened in the

be

ensuing two or three days. And I could have just forgotten it. But I don't remember him ever saying that.

Q At any time?

A No, I don't remember him saying that. What I remember was that he said that Monica came to see him, that she was upset that she was going to have to testify, that he had referred her to a lawyer.

Q In fact, she was very distraught about the subpoena, according to Mr. Jordan, wasn't she?

A Well, he said she was upset about it. I don't remember -- I don't remember any, at any time when he said this, this other thing you just quoted me. I'm sorry. I just don't remember that.

Q That is something that one would be likely to remember, don't you think, Mr. President?

A I think I would, and I'd be happy to share it with you if I did. I only had one encounter with Ms. Lewinsky, I seem to remember, which was somewhat maybe reminiscent of that. But not that, if you will, obsessive, if that's the way you want to use that word.

Q Do you recall him at all telling you that he was concerned about her fascination with you, even if you don't remember the specific conversation about you leaving the First Lady?

A I recall him saying he thought that she was upset

be

with -- somewhat fixated on me, that she acknowledged that she was not having a sexual relationship with me, and that she did not want to be drug into the Jones lawsuit. That's what I recall. And I recall his getting, saying that he had recommended a lawyer to her and she had gone to see the lawyer. That's what I recall.

I don't remember the other thing you mentioned. I just -- I might well remember it if he had said it. Maybe he said it and I've forgotten it, but I don't -- I can't tell you that I remember that.

Q Mr. President, you swore under oath in the Jones case that you didn't think anyone other than your lawyers had ever told you that Monica Lewinsky had been subpoenaed. Page 68, line 22 [sic] through page 69, line 3. Here's the testimony, sir.

Question -- we've gone over it a little bit before: "Did anyone other than your attorneys ever tell you that Monica Lewinsky had been served with a subpoena in this case?" Answer, "I don't think so."

Now, this deposition was taken just three and a half weeks after, by your own testimony, Vernon Jordan made a trip at night to the White House to tell you, among other things, that Monica Lewinsky had been subpoenaed and was upset about it. Why did you give that testimony under oath in the Jones case, sir?

be

A Well, Mr. Wisenberg, I think you have to -- again, you have to put this in the context of the flow of questions, and I've already testified to this once today. I will testify to it again.

My answer to the next question, I think, is a way of finishing my answer to the question and the answer you've said here. I was trying to remember who the first person, other than Mr. Bennett -- I don't think Mr. Bennett -- who the first person told me that, who told me Paula Jones had, I mean, excuse me, Monica Lewinsky had a subpoena. And I thought that Bruce Lindsey was the first person. And that's how I was trying to remember that.

Keep in mind, sort of like today, these questions are being kind of put at me rapid-fire. But, unlike today, I hadn't had the opportunity to prepare at this level of detail. I didn't -- I was trying to keep a lot of things in my head that I had remembered with regard to the Paula Jones case and the Kathleen Willey matter, because I knew I would be asked about them. And I gave the best answers I could. Several of my answers are somewhat jumbled.

But this is an honest attempt here -- if you read both these answers, it's obvious they were both answers to that question you quoted, to remember the first person, who was not Mr. Bennett, who told me. And I don't believe Vernon was the first person who told me. I believe Bruce Lindsey

be

was.

Q Let me read the question, because I want to talk about the first person issue. The question on line 25 of page 68 is, "Did anyone other than your attorneys ever tell you that Monica Lewinsky had been served with a subpoena in this case?" Answer, "I don't think so."

You would agree with me, sir, that the question doesn't say, the question doesn't say anything about who was the first person. It just says, did anyone tell you. Isn't that correct?

A That's right. And I said Bruce Lindsey, because I was trying to struggle with who -- where I had heard this. And they were free to ask a follow-up question, and they didn't.

Q Mr. President, three and a half weeks before, Mr. Jordan had made a special trip to the White House to tell you Ms. Lewinsky had been subpoenaed; she was distraught; she had a fixation over you. And you couldn't remember that, three and a half weeks later?

A Mr. Wisenberg, if -- they had access to all this information from their conversations with Linda Tripp, if that was the basis of it. They were free to ask me more questions. They may have been trying to trick me.

Now, they knew more about the details of my relationship with Monica Lewinsky. I'm not sure everything

be

they knew was true, because I don't know. I've not heard these tapes or anything. But they knew a lot more than I did. And instead of trying to trick me, what they should have done is to ask me specific questions, and I invited them on more than one occasion to ask follow-up questions.

This is the third or fourth time that you seem to be complaining that I did not do all their work for them. That just sitting here answering these questions to the best of my memory, with limited preparation, was not enough. That I should have actually been doing all their work for them.

Now, they'd been up all night with Linda Tripp, who had betrayed her friend, Monica Lewinsky, stabbed her in the back and given them all this information. They could have helped more. If they wanted to ask me follow-up questions, they could. They didn't. I'm sorry. I did the best I could.

Q Can you tell the grand jury what is tricky about the question, "Did anyone other than your attorneys ever tell you" --

A No, there's nothing -- I'm just telling -- I have explained. I will now explain for the third time, sir. I was being asked a number of questions here. I was struggling to remember then. There were lots of things that had gone on during this time period that had nothing to do with Monica Lewinsky.

be

You know, I believed then, I believe now that Monica Lewinsky could have sworn out an honest affidavit, that under reasonable circumstances, and without the benefit of what Linda Tripp did to her, would have given her a chance not to be a witness in this case.

So, I didn't have perfect memory of all these events that have now, in the last seven months, since Ms. Lewinsky was kept for several hours by four or five of your lawyers and four or five FBI agents, as if she were a serious felon, these things have become the most important matters in the world. At the moment they were occurring, many other things were going on.

I honestly tried to remember when -- you know, if somebody asked you, has anybody ever talked to you about this, you normally think, well, where was the first time I heard that. That's all I was trying to do here. I was not trying to say not Vernon Jordan, but Bruce Lindsey. Everybody knows Vernon Jordan is a friend of mine. I probably would have talked to Vernon Jordan about the Monica Lewinsky problem if he had never been involved in it. So, I was not trying to mislead them. I was trying to answer this question with the first person who told me that.

Now, I realize that wasn't the specific question. They were free to ask follow-ups, just like you're asking follow-ups today. And I can't explain why I didn't answer

be

every question in the way you seem to think I should have, and I certainly can't explain why they didn't ask what seemed to me to be logical follow-ups, especially since they spent all that time with Linda Tripp the night before.

Q You've told us that you understand your obligation then, as it is now, is to tell the whole truth, sir. Do you recall that?

A I took the oath here.

Q If Vernon Jordan --

A You even read me a definition of the oath.

Q If Vernon Jordan has told us that you have an extraordinary memory, one of the greatest memories he's ever seen in a politician, would that be something you would care to dispute?

A No, I do have a good memory. At least, I have had a good memory in my life.

Q Do you understand that if you answered, "I don't think so", to the question, has anyone other than your attorneys told you that Monica Lewinsky has been served with a subpoena in this case, that if you answered, "I don't think so", but you really knew Vernon Jordan had been telling you all about it, you understand that that would be a false statement, presumably perjurious?

A Mr. Wisenberg, I have testified about this three times. Now, I will do it the fourth time. I am not going to

be

answer your trick questions.

I -- people don't always hear the same questions in the same way. They don't always answer them in the same way. I was so concerned about the question they asked me that the next question I was asked, I went back to the previous question, trying to give an honest answer about the first time I heard about the Lewinsky subpoena.

I -- look. I could have had no reasonable expectation that anyone would ever know that, that -- or not, excuse me, not know if this thing -- that I would talk to Vernon Jordan about nearly everything. I was not interested in -- if the implication of your question is that somehow I didn't want anybody to know I had ever talked to Vernon Jordan about this, that's just not so.

It's also -- if I could say one thing about my memory. I have been blessed and advantaged in my life with a good memory. Now, I have been shocked, and so have members of my family and friends of mine, at how many things that I have forgotten in the last six years, I think because of the pressure and the pace and the volume of events in the President's life, compounded by the pressure of your four-year inquiry, and all the other things that have happened, I'm amazed there are lots of times when I literally can't remember last week.

If you ask me, did you talk to Vernon -- when was

be

the last time you talked to Vernon Jordan, what time of day was it, when did you see him, what did you say, my answer was the last -- you know, if you answered [sic] me, when was the last time you saw a friend of yours in California, if you asked me a lot of questions like that, my memory is not what it was when I came here, because my life is so crowded.

And now that -- as I said, you have made this the most important issue in America. I mean, you have made it the most important issue in America from your point of view. At the time this was occurring, even though I was concerned about it, and I hoped she didn't have to testify, and I hoped this wouldn't come out, I felt -- I will say again -- that she could honestly fill out an affidavit that, under reasonable circumstances, would relieve her of the burden of testifying.

I am not trying to exclude the fact that I talked to Vernon here. I just -- all I can tell you is I believe this answer reflects I was trying to remember the first person who told me who was not Mr. Bennett, and I believe it was Bruce Lindsey.

Q As you yourself recalled, just recalled, Mr. President, Vernon Jordan not only discussed the subpoena with you that night, but discussed Frank Carter, the lawyer he had gotten for Ms. Lewinsky. And also Mr. Jordan discussed with you over the next few weeks, after the 19th of December, in

be

addition to the job aspects of Ms. Lewinsky's job, he discussed with you her affidavit that she was preparing in the case. Is that correct, sir?

A I believe that he did notify us, I think, when she signed her affidavit. I have a memory of that. Or it seems like he said that she had signed her affidavit.

Q If he's told us that he notified you around January 7th, when she signed her affidavit, and that you generally understood that it would deny a sexual relationship, do you have any reason to doubt that?

A No.

Q So, that's the affidavit, the lawyer, and the subpoena. And yet when you were asked, sir, at the Jones deposition about Vernon Jordan, and specifically about whether or not he had discussed the lawsuit with you, you didn't reveal that to the Court.

I want to refer you to page 72, line 16. It's where this starts. It's going to go down, it might go down somewhat.

Line 16. Question, "Has it ever been reported to you that he" -- and that's referring to Mr. Jordan. At line 12 you were asked, "You know a man named Vernon Jordan?", and you answer, "I know him well."

Going down to 16, "Has it ever been reported to you that he met with Monica Lewinsky and talked about this case?"

be

This is your answer, or a portion of it: "I knew that he met with her. I think Betty suggested that he meet with her. Anyway, he met with her. I, I thought that he talked to her about something else."

Why didn't you tell the Court, when you were under oath and sworn to tell the truth, the whole truth, and nothing but the truth, that you had been talking with Vernon Jordan about the case, about the affidavit, the lawyer, the subpoena?

A Well, that's not the question I was asked. I was not asked any question about -- I was asked, "Has it ever been reported to you that he met with Monica Lewinsky and talked about this case." I believe -- I may be wrong about this -- my impression was that at the time, I was focused on the meetings. I believe the meetings he had were meetings about her moving to New York and getting a job.

I knew at some point that she had told him that she needed some help, because she had gotten a subpoena. I'm not sure I know whether she did that in a meeting or a phone call. And I was not, I was not focused on that.

I know that, I know Vernon helped her to get a lawyer, Mr. Carter. And I, I believe that he did it after she had called him, but I'm not sure. But I knew that the main source of their meetings was about her move to New York and her getting a job.

be

Q Are you saying, sir, that you forgot when you were asked this question that Vernon Jordan had come on December 19th, just three and a half weeks before, and said that he had met that day, the day that Monica got the subpoena?

A It's quite possible -- it's a sort of a jumbled answer. It's quite possible that I had gotten mixed up between whether she had met with him or talked to him on the telephone in those three and a half weeks.

Again, I say, sir, just from the tone of your voice and the way you are asking questions here, it's obvious that this is the most important thing in the world, and that everybody was focused on all the details at the time. But that's not the way it worked. I was, I was doing my best to remember.

Now, keep in mind, I don't know if this is true, but the news reports are that Linda Tripp talked to you, then went and talked to the Jones lawyers, and, you know, that she prepared them for this. Now, maybe -- you seem to be criticizing me because they didn't ask better questions and, as if you didn't prepare them well enough to sort of set me up or something. I don't know what's going on here.

All I can tell you is I didn't remember all the details of all this. I didn't remember what -- when Vernon talked to me about Monica Lewinsky, whether she talked to him on the telephone or had a meeting. I didn't remember all

be

those details. I was focused on the fact that Monica went to meet with Vernon after Betty helped him set it up, and had subsequent meetings to talk about her move to New York.

Now, keep in mind at this time, at this time, until this date here when it's obvious that something funny's going on here and there's some sort of a gotcha game at work in this deposition, until this date, I didn't know that Ms. Lewinsky's deposition [sic] wasn't going to be sufficient for her to avoid testifying. I didn't, you know --

MR. KENDALL: Excuse me, Mr. President, I think --

THE WITNESS: So, all these details --

MR. KENDALL: -- you mean her affidavit.

BY MR. WISENBERG:

Q You mean her affidavit?

A Excuse me. I'm sorry. Her affidavit. Thank you.

So, I don't necessarily remember all the details of all these questions you're asking me, because there was a lot of other things going on, and at the time they were going on, until all this came out, this was not the most important thing in my life. This was just another thing in my life.

Q But Vernon Jordan met with you, sir, and he reported that he had met with Monica Lewinsky, and the discussion was about the lawsuit, and you didn't inform, under oath, the Court of that in your deposition?

A I gave the best answer I could, based on the best

be

memory I had at the time they asked me the question. That's the only answer I can give you, sir.

Q And before --

A And I think I may have been confused in my memory, because I've also talked to him on the phone about what he said about whether he talked to her or met with her. That's all I can tell you.

But, let me say again, I don't have the same view about this deposition -- I mean, this affidavit -- that I think you do. I felt very strongly that Ms. Lewinsky and everybody else that didn't know anything about Paula Jones and anything about sexual harassment, that she and others were themselves being harassed for political purposes, in the hope of getting damaging information that the Jones lawyers could unlawfully leak.

Now, I believed then, I believe today, that she could execute an affidavit which, under reasonable circumstances with fair-minded, non politically-oriented people, would result in her being relieved of the burden to be put through the kind of testimony that, thanks to Linda Tripp's work with you and with the Jones lawyers, she would have been put through. I don't think that's dishonest. I don't think that's illegal. I think what they were trying to do to her and all these other people, who knew nothing about sexual harassment, was outrageous, just so they could hurt me

be

politically.

So, I just don't have the same attitude about it that you do.

Q Well, you're not telling our grand jurors that because you think the case was a political case or a setup, Mr. President, that that would give you the right to commit perjury or --

A No, sir.

Q -- not to tell the full truth?

A No, sir. In the face of their, the Jones lawyers, the people that were questioning me, in the face of their illegal leaks, their constant, unrelenting illegal leaks in a lawsuit that I knew and, by the time this deposition and this discovery started, they knew was a bogus suit on the law and a bogus suit on the facts.

Q The question is --

A In the face of that, I knew that in the face of their illegal activity, I still had to behave lawfully. But I wanted to be legal without being particularly helpful. I thought that was, that was what I was trying to do. And this is the first -- you are the first persons who ever suggested to me that, that I should have been doing their lawyers' work for them, when they were perfectly free to ask follow-up questions. On one or two occasions, Mr. Bennett invited them to ask follow-up questions.

be

It now appears to me they didn't because they were afraid I would give them a truthful answer, and that there had been some communication between you and Ms. Tripp and them, and they were trying to set me up and trick me. And now you seem to be complaining that they didn't do a good enough job.

I did my best, sir, at this time. I did not know what I now know about this. A lot of other things were going on in my life. Did I want this to come out? No. Was I embarrassed about it? Yes. Did I ask her to lie about it? No. Did I believe there could be a truthful affidavit? Absolutely.

Now, that's all I know to say about this. I will continue to answer your questions as best I can.

Q You're not going back on your earlier statement that you understood you were sworn to tell the truth, the whole truth, and nothing but the truth to the folks at that deposition, are you, Mr. President?

A No, sir, but I think we might as well put this out on the table. You tried to get me to give a broader interpretation to my oath than just my obligation to tell the truth. In other words, you tried to say, even though these people are treating you in an illegal manner in illegally leaking these depositions, you should be a good lawyer for them. And if they don't have enough sense to write -- to ask

be

a question, and even if Mr. Bennett invited them to ask follow-up questions, if they didn't do it, you should have done all their work for them.

Now, so I will admit this, sir. My goal in this deposition was to be truthful, but not particularly helpful. I did not wish to do the work of the Jones lawyers. I deplored what they were doing. I deplored the innocent people they were tormenting and traumatizing. I deplored their illegal leaking. I deplored the fact that they knew, once they knew our evidence, that this was a bogus lawsuit, and that because of the funding they had from my political enemies, they were putting ahead. I deplored it.

But I was determined to walk through the mine field of this deposition without violating the law, and I believe I did.

Q You are not saying, are you, Mr. President, in terms of doing the work for the Jones folks, the Jones lawyers, that you could, you could say, as part of your not helping them, "I don't know" to a particular question, when you really knew, and that it was up to them -- even if you really knew the answer, it was up to them to do the follow-up, that you kind of had a one free "I don't know" --

A No, sir.

Q If I could finish up? I've been very patient, Mr. President, in letting you finish.

be

You didn't think you had a free shot to say, "I don't know", or "I don't recall", but when you really did know and you did recall, and it was just up to them, even if you weren't telling the truth, to do a follow-up and to catch you?

A No, sir, I'm not saying that. And if I could give you one example? That's why I felt that I had to come back to that question where I said, I don't know that, and talk about Bruce Lindsey, because I was trying, I was honestly trying to remember how I had first heard this. I wasn't hung up about talking about this.

All I'm saying is, the -- let me say something sympathetic to you. I've been pretty tough. So, let me say something sympathetic.

All of you are intelligent people. You've worked hard on this. You've worked for a long time. You've gotten all the facts. You've seen a lot of evidence that I haven't seen. And it's, it's an embarrassing and personally painful thing, the truth about my relationship with Ms. Lewinsky.

So, the natural assumption is that while all this was going on, I must have been focused on nothing but this; therefore, I must remember everything about it in the sequence and form in which it occurred. All I can tell you is, I was concerned about it. I was glad she saw a lawyer. I was glad she was doing an affidavit. But there were a lot

be

of other things going on, and I don't necessarily remember it all. And I don't know if I can convince you of that.

But I tried to be honest with you about my mindset, about this deposition. And I'm just trying to explain that I don't have the memory that you assume that I should about some of these things.

Q I want to talk to you for a bit, Mr. President, about the incident that happened at the Northwest Gate of the White House on December 5th -- sorry, December 6th, 1997. If you would give me just a moment?

That was a -- let me ask you first. In early nineteen -- in early December 1997, the Paula Jones case was pending, correct?

A Yes, sir.

Q You were represented by Mr. Bennett, of course?

A That's correct.

Q In that litigation?

A Yes, I did.

Q How --

A He was.

Q I'm sorry. Go ahead.

A No, no. Yes, he was representing me.

Q How often did you talk to him or meet with him, if you can just recall, at that time in the litigation?

A Well, we met, I would say -- I wish Mr. Ruff were

be

answering this question, instead of me. His memory would be better. We met probably, oh, for a long time we didn't meet all that often, maybe once a month. And then the closer we got to the deposition, we would meet more frequently. So, maybe by this time we were meeting more.

We also -- there was a period when we had been approached about --

MR. KENDALL: Again, the question only goes to the number of meetings and not the content of any conversations with your lawyer.

THE WITNESS: I understand. We're not talking about the content.

There was a, there was a period in which we, I think back in the summer before this, when we had met more frequently. But I would say normally once a month. Sometimes something would be happening and we'd meet more. And then, as we moved toward the deposition, we would begin to meet more.

BY MR. WISENBERG:

Q A witness list came out on December 5th of 1997, with Monica Lewinsky's name on it. Mr. President, when did you find out that Monica's name was on that witness list?

A I believe that I found out late in the afternoon on the 6th. That's what I believe. I've tried to remember with great precision, and because I thought you would ask me about

be

this day, I've tried to remember the logical question, which is whether, whether I knew it on the 6th and, if so, at what time.

I don't -- I had a meeting in the late afternoon on the 5th, on the 6th -- excuse me, on the 6th -- and I believe that's when I learned about it.

Q Now, on the morning of the 6th, Monica Lewinsky came to the Northwest Gate and found out that you were being visited by Eleanor Mondale at the time, and had an extremely angry reaction. You know that, sir, now, don't you?

A I have, I have -- I know that Monica Lewinsky came to the gate on the 6th and apparently directly called in and wanted to see me and couldn't, and was angry about it. I know that.

Q And she expressed that anger to Betty Currie over the telephone, isn't that correct, sir?

A That, Betty told me that.

Q And she then later expressed her anger to you in one of her telephone conversations with Betty Currie, is that correct?

A You mean did I talk to her on the phone?

Q Monica Lewinsky, that day, before she came in to visit in the White House?

A Mr. Wisenberg, I remember that she came in to visit that day. I remember that she was upset. I don't recall

be

whether I talked to her on the phone before she came in to visit, but I well may have. I'm not denying it that I did. I just don't recall that.

Q And Mrs. Currie and yourself were very irate that Ms. Lewinsky had overheard that you were in the Oval Office with a visitor on that day, isn't that correct, that you and Mrs. Currie were very irate about that?

A Well, I don't remember all that. What I remember is that she was very -- Monica was very upset. She got upset from time to time. And, and I was, you know, I couldn't see her. I had, I was doing, as I remember, I had some other work to do that morning and she had just sort of showed up and wanted to be let in, and wanted to come in at a certain time and she wanted everything to be that way, and we couldn't see her. Now, I did arrange to see her later that day. And I was upset about her conduct.

I'm not sure that I knew or focused on at that moment exactly the question you asked. I remember I was, I thought her conduct was inappropriate that day.

Q I want to go back and I want to take them one at a time. Number one, did you find out at some point during that day that Monica had overheard from somebody in the Secret Service that you were meeting with Ms. Mondale, and that Monica got very irate about that?

A I knew that at some point. I don't know whether I

be

found out that, that day. I knew that day, I knew that somehow she knew that among, that, that Eleanor Mondale was in to see us that day. I knew that. I don't know that I knew how she knew that on that day. I don't remember that.

Q That leads into my second question, which is, weren't you irate at the Secret Service precisely because they had revealed this information to Ms. Lewinsky on that very day, so irate that you told several people, or at least one person, that somebody should be fired over this, on that very day?

A I don't remember whether it happened on that very day. But, let me tell you that the Uniformed Secret Service, if that is in fact what happened and I will stipulate that that is, that no one should be telling anybody, not anybody, not a member of my staff, who the President is meeting with. That's an inappropriate thing to do.

So, I would think that if that, in fact, is what I heard when I heard it, I would have thought that was a bad thing. I don't know that I said that. I don't, I don't remember what I said, and I don't remember to whom I said it.

Q It would be an inappropriate thing, sir, and that leads into my next question is that why did Mrs. Currie, on your instructions, later that day tell many of the Secret Service Officers involved that it never happened, to forget about it?

be

A That what never happened?

Q The incident that you were so irate about earlier; the incident of somebody disclosing to Ms. Lewinsky that Ms. Mondale was in the Oval Office?

A I don't know the answer to that. I think maybe, you know, I don't know. I don't know the answer.

Q You don't recall that you later gave orders to the effect that we are going to pretend this never happened, or something --

A No, sir.

Q -- like that?

A No, sir. I don't recall it. First of all, I don't recall that I gave orders to fire anybody, if that was the implication of your first statement.

Q It wasn't an implication. Actually, the question was that you initially wanted somebody fired. You were so mad that you wanted somebody fired.

A I don't remember that, first of all. I remember thinking it was an inappropriate thing to do. And I, I, I remember, as I usually do when I'm mad, after awhile I wasn't so mad about it, and I'm quite aware that Ms. Lewinsky has a way of getting information out of people when she's either charming or determined. And it -- I could have just said, well, I'm not so mad about it any more.

But I don't remember the whole sequence of events

be

you're talking to me about now, except I do remember that somehow Monica found out Eleanor Mondale was there. I learned either that day or later that one of the Uniformed Division personnel had told her. I do -- I thought then it was a mistake. I think now it was a mistake. I'm not sure it's a mistake someone should be terminated over. I think that, you know, you could just tell them not to do that any more.

Q In fact, it would kind of be an overreaction, to get irate or terminate somebody for revealing to a former White House staffer who visits where the President is, don't you think, sir?

A Well, it would depend upon the facts. I think on the whole people in the Uniformed Secret Service who are working on the gate have no business telling anybody anything about the President's schedule, just as a general principal. I didn't mind anybody knowing that she was there, if that's what you're saying. I could care less about that. But I think that the schedule itself -- these uniformed people, you know, somebody shouldn't just be able to come up on the street and, because they know who the Secret Service agent is, he says who the President's with. I don't think that's proper.

Q I agree, Mr. President.

A But, on the other hand, I didn't, you know, I, I

be

wanted to know what happened. I think we found out what happened. And then they were, I think, told not to let it happen again, and I think that's the way it should have been handled. I think it was handled in the appropriate way.

Q You have no knowledge of the fact that Secret Service officers were told later in the day something to the effect of, this never happened, this event never happened? You have no knowledge of that?

A I'm not sure anybody ever told that to me. I mean, I thought you were asking -- let me just say, my interpretation of this, of your previous question was different than what you're asking now.

What I remember was being upset that this matter would be discussed that -- by anybody. It's incidental it happened to be Monica Lewinsky. And that, that whatever I said, I don't recall. But then thinking that the appropriate thing to do was to say, look, just this, this is not an appropriate thing for you to be talking about, the President's schedule, and it shouldn't happen again.

Now, the question you seem to be asking me now -- I just want to be sure I'm getting the right question -- is whether I gave instructions, in effect, to pretend that Monica Lewinsky was never at the gate. And if --

Q To the effect of pretend --

A And if that is the question you are asking me, I

be

don't believe I ever did that, sir. I certainly have no memory of doing that.

Q Or anything to that effect?

A I don't know what that means.

Q Is that your testimony?

A What does that mean, anything to that effect?

Q Well, Mr. President, you've told us that you were not going to try to help the Jones attorneys, and I think it's clear from your testimony that you were pretty literal at times. So, that's why I'm saying, I don't necessarily know the exact words. The question was, do you have any knowledge of the fact --

A Of that?

Q -- of the fact that later in the day, on Saturday, the 6th of December, 1997, Secret Service people were then, were told something to this effect: This event never happened, let's just pretend this event did not happen. Do you have knowledge of it, or not?

A No, sir. And I, I didn't instruct the Secret Service in that regard. I have no memory of saying anything to anybody in the Secret Service that would have triggered that kind of instruction.

Q Did you tell Captain Purdy, while you were standing in the doorway between the Oval Office and Betty Currie's office, did you tell Captain Purdy of the Uniformed Division,

be

I hope I can count on your discretion in this matter? At the end of the day when you all were talking about that earlier incident, did you tell him that or anything like that, sir?

A I don't remember anything I said to him in that regard. I have no recollection of that whatever.

MR. WISENBERG: Let's take a break now.

MR. KENDALL: Thank you, 3:38.

(Whereupon, the proceedings were recessed from 3:38 p.m. until 4:01 p.m.)

MR. KENDALL: It is 4:01.

BY MR. WISENBERG:

Q Mr. President, the next series of questions are from the grand jurors. And let me tell you that the grand jurors want you to be more specific about the inappropriate conduct.

The first question was, one of the grand jurors has said that you referred to what you did with Ms. Lewinsky as inappropriate contact; what do you mean by that?

A I mean just what I said. But I would like to ask the grand jury, because I think I have been quite specific and I think I've been willing to answer some specific questions that I haven't been asked yet, but I do not want to discuss something that is intensely painful to me. This has been tough enough already on me and on my family, although I take responsibility for it. I have no one to blame but myself.

be

What I meant was, and what they can infer that I meant was, that I did things that were -- when I was alone with her, that were inappropriate and wrong. But that they did not include any activity that was within the definition of sexual relations that I was given by Judge Wright in the deposition. I said that I did not do those things that were in that, within that definition, and I testified truthfully to that. And that's all I can say about it.

Now, you know, if there's any doubt on the part of the grand jurors about whether I believe some kind of activity falls within that definition or outside that definition, I'd be happy to try to answer that.

Q Well, I have a question regarding your definition then. And my question is, is oral sex performed on you within that definition as you understood it, the definition in the Jones --

A As I understood it, it was not, no.

Q The grand jurors would like to know upon what basis, what legal basis you are declining to answer more specific questions about this? I've mentioned to you that obviously you have privileges, privileges against self-incrimination. There's no general right not to answer questions.

And so one of the questions from the grand jurors is what basis, what legal basis are you declining to answer

be

these questions?

A I'm not trying to evade my legal obligations or my willingness to help the grand jury achieve their legal obligations. As I understand it, you want to examine whether you believe I told the truth in my deposition, whether I asked Ms. Lewinsky not to tell the truth, and whether I did anything else with evidence, or in any other way, amounting to an obstruction of justice or a subornation of perjury. And I'm prepared to answer all questions that the grand jury needs to draw that conclusion.

Now, respectfully, I believe the grand jurors can ask me if I believe -- just like that grand juror did -- could ask me, do you believe that this conduct falls within that definition. If it does, then you are free to conclude that my testimony is that I didn't do that. And I believe that you can achieve that without requiring me to say and do things that I don't think are necessary and that I think, frankly, go too far in trying to criminalize my private life.

Q If a person touched another person, if you touched another person on the breast, would that be, in your view, and was it within your view, when you took the deposition, within the definition of sexual relations?

A If the person being deposed --

Q Yes.

A -- in this case, me, directly touched the breast of

be

another person, with the purpose to arouse or gratify, under that definition that would be included.

Q Only directly, sir, or would it be directly or through clothing?

A Well, I would -- I think the common sense definition would be directly. That's how I would infer what it means.

Q If the person being deposed kissed the breast of another person, would that be in the definition of sexual relations as you understood it when you were under oath in the Jones case?

A Yes, that would constitute contact. I think that would. If it were direct contact, I believe it would. I -- maybe I should read it again, just to make sure.

Because this basically says if there was any direct contact with an intent to arouse or gratify, if that was the intent of the contact, then that would fall within the definition. That's correct.

Q So, touching, in your view then and now -- the person being deposed touching or kissing the breast of another person would fall within the definition?

A That's correct, sir.

Q And you testified that you didn't have sexual relations with Monica Lewinsky in the Jones deposition, under that definition, correct?

be

A That's correct, sir.

Q If the person being deposed touched the genitalia of another person, would that be -- and with the intent to arouse the sexual desire, arouse or gratify, as defined in definition (1), would that be, under your understanding then and now --

A Yes, sir.

Q -- sexual relations?

A Yes, sir.

Q Yes, it would?

A Yes, it would. If you had a direct contact with any of these places in the body, if you had direct contact with intent to arouse or gratify, that would fall within the definition.

Q So, you didn't do any of those three things --

A You --

Q -- with Monica Lewinsky?

A You are free to infer that my testimony is that I did not have sexual relations, as I understood this term to be defined.

Q Including touching her breast, kissing her breast, or touching her genitalia?

A That's correct.

Q Would you agree with me that the insertion of an object into the genitalia of another person with the desire

be

to gratify sexually would fit within the definition used in the Jones case as sexual relations?

A There's nothing here about that, is there? I don't know that I ever thought about that one way or the other.

Q The question is, under the definition as you understood it then, under the definition as you understand it now -- pardon me just a minute.

Pardon me, Mr. President.

(Pause)

Deposition Exhibit 1, question 1, under the -- in the Jones case, Definition of Sexual Relations --

MR. KENDALL: Do you have that before you, Mr. President? Excuse me.

THE WITNESS: I do, sir.

MR. KENDALL: Good.

THE WITNESS: I've got it right here. I'm looking at it.

BY MR. WISENBERG:

Q As you understood the definition then, and as you understood it now, would it include sticking an object into the genitalia of another person in order to arouse or gratify the sexual desire of any person? Would it constitute, in other words, contact with the genitalia?

A I don't know the answer to that. I suppose you could argue that since section 2, paragraph (2) was

be

eliminated, and paragraph (2) actually dealt with the object issue, that perhaps whoever wrote this didn't intend for paragraph (1) to cover an object, and basically meant direct contact.

So, if I were asked -- I've not been asked this question before. But I guess that's the way I would read it.

Q If it -- that it would not be covered? That activity would not be covered?

A That's right. If the activity you just mentioned would be covered in number (2), and number (2) were stricken, I think you can infer logically that paragraph (1) was not intended to cover it. But, as I said, I've not been asked this before. I'm just doing the best I can.

Q Well, if someone were to hold or a judge were to hold that you are incorrect and that definition (1) does include the hypo I've given to you -- because we're talking in hypos, so that you don't -- under your request here, if someone were to tell you or rule that you are wrong, that the insertion of an object into somebody else's genitalia with the intent to arouse or gratify the sexual desire of any person is within definition (1) --

MR. KENDALL: Mr. Wisenberg, excuse me. I have not objected heretofore to any question you've asked. I must tell you, I cannot understand that question. I think it's improper. And, if the witness can understand it, he may.

be

answer.

MR. WISENBERG: I'll be happy to rephrase it.

BY MR. WISENBERG:

Q If you're wrong and it's within definition (1), did you engage in sexual relations under the definition, with Monica Lewinsky?

A But, Mr. Wisenberg, I have said all along that I would say what I thought it meant, and you can infer that I didn't. This is an unusual question, but it's a slippery slope. We can -- I have tried to deal with some very delicate areas here, and, and in one case I've given you a very forthright answer about what I thought was not within here.

All I can tell you is, whatever I thought was covered, and I thought about this carefully. And let me just point out, this was uncomfortable for me. I had to acknowledge, because of this definition, that under this definition I had actually had sexual relations once with Gennifer Flowers, a person who had spread all kinds of ridiculous, dishonest, exaggerated stories about me for money. And I knew when I did that, it would be leaked. It was. And I was embarrassed. But I did it.

So, I tried to read this carefully. I can tell you what I thought it covered, and I can tell you that I do not believe I did anything that I thought was covered by this.

be

Q As I understand your testimony, Mr. President, touching somebody's breast with the intent to arouse, with the intent to arouse or gratify the sexual desire of any person is covered; kissing the breast is covered; touching the genitalia is covered; correct?

MR. KENDALL: In fairness, the witness said directly in each one of those cases.

BY MR. WISENBERG:

Q Directly, is covered, correct?

A I believe it is, yes, sir.

Q Oral sex, in your view, is not covered, correct?

A If performed on the deponent.

Q Is not covered, correct?

A That's my reading of this number (1).

Q And you are declining to answer the hypothetical about insertion of an object.

I need to inform you, Mr. President -- we'll go on, at least for now. But I need to inform you that the grand jury will consider your not answering the questions more directly in their determination of whether or not they are going to issue another subpoena.

Let me switch the topic and talk to you about John Podesta and some of the other aides you've met with and spoke to after this story became public on January 21st, 1998, the day of The Washington Post story.

be

Do you recall meeting with him around January 23rd, 1998, a Friday a.m. in your study, two days after The Washington Post story, and extremely explicitly telling him that you didn't have, engage in any kind of sex, in any way, shape or form, with Monica Lewinsky, including oral sex?

A I meet with John Podesta almost every day. I meet with a number of people. The only thing I -- what happened in the couple of days after what you did was revealed, is a blizzard to me. The only thing I recall is that I met with certain people, and a few of them I said I didn't have sex with Monica Lewinsky, or I didn't have an affair with her or something like that. I had a very careful thing I said, and I tried not to say anything else.

And it might be that John Podesta was one of them. But I do not remember this specific meeting about which you asked, or the specific comments to which you refer. And --

Q You don't remember --

A -- seven months ago, I'd have no way to remember, no.

Q You don't remember denying any kind of sex in any way, shape or form, and including oral sex, correct?

A I remember that I issued a number of denials to people that I thought needed to hear them, but I tried to be careful and to be accurate, and I do not remember what I said to John Podesta.

be

Q Surely, if you told him that, that would be a falsehood, correct?

A No, I didn't say that, sir. I didn't say that at all. That is not covered by the definition and I did not address it in my statement.

Q Well, let me ask you then. If you told him -- perhaps he thought it was covered, I don't know. But if you told him, if you denied to him sex in any way, shape or form, kind of similar to what Mr. Bennett did at the deposition, including oral sex, wouldn't that have been a falsehood?

A Now, Mr. Wisenberg, I told you in response to a grand juror's question, you asked me did I believe that oral sex performed on the person being deposed was covered by that definition, and I said no. I don't believe it's covered by the definition.

I said you are free to conclude that I did not do things that I believe were covered by the definition, and you have asked me a number of questions and I have acknowledged things that I believe are covered by the definition. Since that was not covered by the definition, I want to fall back on my statement.

Look, I'm not trying to be evasive here. I'm trying to protect my privacy, my family's privacy, and I'm trying to stick to what the deposition was about. If the deposition wasn't about this and didn't cover it, then I

be

don't believe that I should be required to go beyond my statement.

Q Mr. President, it's not our intent to embarrass you. But since we have to look, among other things, at obstruction of justice, questions of obstruction of justice and perjury, the answer to some of these delicate and unfortunate questions are absolutely required. And that is the purpose that we have to ask them for.

A It's not --

Q I'm unaware of any --

A Mr. Wisenberg, with respect, you don't need to know the answer for that, if the answer, no matter what the answer is, wouldn't constitute perjury because it wasn't sexual relations as defined by the Judge.

Q Mister --

A The only reason you need to know that is for some other reason. It couldn't have anything to do with perjury.

Q Mr. President, one of the, one of the nice things about -- one of the normal things about an investigation and a grand jury investigation is that the grand jurors and the prosecutors get to ask the questions unless they are improper, and unless there is a legal basis.

As I understand from your answers, there is no legal basis for which you decline to answer these questions. And I'll ask you again to answer the question. I'm unaware

be

of any legal basis for you not to. If you told --

MR. KENDALL: Mr. Wisenberg, could you just restate the question, please?

BY MR. WISENBERG:

Q The question is, if you told John Podesta two days after the story broke something to this effect, that you didn't have any kind of sex in any way, shape or form, including oral sex with Ms. Lewinsky, were you telling him the truth?

A And let me say again, with respect, this is an indirect way to try to get me to testify to questions that have no bearing on whether I committed perjury. You apparently agree that it has no bearing --

Q Oh, I don't --

A -- no bearing on whether I --

Q I don't agree.

A -- committed perjury.

Q Mr. President, I'm sorry, with respect, I don't agree with that. I'm not going to argue with you about it. I just am going to ask you again, in fact direct you to answer the question.

A I'm not going to answer that question, because I believe it's a question about conduct that, whatever the answer to it is, would, does not bear on the perjury because oral sex performed on the deponent under this definition is

be

not sexual relations. It is not covered by this definition.

MR. KENDALL: The witness is not declining to tell you anything he said to John Podesta.

BY MR. WISENBERG:

Q You denied the --

MR. WISENBERG: The witness is not declining to tell me anything?

BY MR. WISENBERG:

Q Did you deny oral sex in any way, shape or form, to John Podesta?

A I told you, sir, before, and I will say again, in the aftermath of this story breaking, and what was told about it, the next two days, next three days are just a blur to me. I don't remember to whom I talked, when I talked to them, or what I said.

Q So, you are not declining to answer, you just don't remember?

A I honestly don't remember, no.

Q Okay.

A I'm not saying that anybody who had a contrary memory is wrong. I do not remember.

Q Do you recall denying any sexual relationship with Monica Lewinsky to the following people: Harry Thomasson, Erskine Bowles, Harold Ickes, Mr. Podesta, Mr. Blumenthal, Mr. Jordan, Ms. Betty Currie? Do you recall denying any

be

sexual relationship with Monica Lewinsky to those individuals?

A I recall telling a number of those people that I didn't have, either I didn't have an affair with Monica Lewinsky or didn't have sex with her. And I believe, sir, that -- you'll have to ask them what they thought. But I was using those terms in the normal way people use them. You'll have to ask them what they thought I was saying.

Q If they testified that you denied sexual relations or relationship with Monica Lewinsky, or if they told us that you denied that, do you have any reason to doubt them, in the days after the story broke; do you have any reason to doubt them?

A No. The -- let me say this. It's no secret to anybody that I hoped that this relationship would never become public. It's a matter of fact that it had been many, many months since there had been anything improper about it, in terms of improper contact. I --

Q Did you deny it to them or not, Mr. President?

A Let me finish. So, what -- I did not want to mislead my friends, but I wanted to find language where I could say that. I also, frankly, did not want to turn any of them into witnesses, because I -- and, sure enough, they all became witnesses.

Q Well, you knew they might be --

be

A And so --

Q -- witnesses, didn't you?

A And so I said to them things that were true about this relationship. That I used -- in the language I used, I said, there's nothing going on between us. That was true. I said, I have not had sex with her as I defined it. That was true. And did I hope that I would never have to be here on this day giving this testimony? Of course.

But I also didn't want to do anything to complicate this matter further. So, I said things that were true. They may have been misleading, and if they were I have to take responsibility for it, and I'm sorry.

Q It may have been misleading, sir, and you knew though, after January 21st when the Post article broke and said that Judge Starr was looking into this, you knew that they might be witnesses. You knew that they might be called into a grand jury, didn't you?

A That's right. I think I was quite careful what I said after that. I may have said something to all these people to that effect, but I'll also -- whenever anybody asked me any details, I said, look, I don't want you to be a witness or I turn you into a witness or give you information that could get you in trouble. I just wouldn't talk. I, by and large, didn't talk to people about this.

Q If all of these people -- let's leave out Mrs.

be

Currie for a minute. Vernon Jordan, Sid Blumenthal, John Podesta, Harold Ickes, Erskine Bowles, Harry Thomasson, after the story broke, after Judge Starr's involvement was known on January 21st, have said that you denied a sexual relationship with them. Are you denying that?

A No.

Q And you've told us that you --

A I'm just telling you what I meant by it. I told you what I meant by it when they started this deposition.

Q You've told us now that you were being careful, but that it might have been misleading. Is that correct?

A It might have been. Since we have seen this four-year, $40-million-investigation come down to parsing the definition of sex, I think it might have been. I don't think at the time that I thought that's what this was going to be about.

In fact, if you remember the headlines at the time, even you mentioned the Post story. All the headlines were -- and all the talking, people who talked about this, including a lot who have been quite sympathetic to your operation, said, well, this is not really a story about sex, or this is a story about subornation of perjury and these talking points, and all this other stuff.

So, what I was trying to do was to give them something they could -- that would be true, even if

be

misleading in the context of this deposition, and keep them out of trouble, and let's deal -- and deal with what I thought was the almost ludicrous suggestion that I had urged someone to lie or tried to suborn perjury, in other words.

Q I want to go over some questions again. I don't think you are going to answer them, sir. And so I don't need a lengthy response, just a yes or a no. And I understand the basis upon which you are not answering them, but I need to ask them for the record.

If Monica Lewinsky says that while you were in the Oval Office area you touched her breasts, would she be lying?

A Let me say something about all this.

Q All I really need for you, Mr. President --

A I know.

Q -- is to say --

A But you --

Q -- I won't answer under the previous grounds, or to answer the question, you see, because we only have four hours, and your answers --

A I know.

Q -- have been extremely lengthy.

A I know that. I'll give you four hours and 30 seconds, if you'll let me say something general about this. I will answer to your satisfaction that I won't -- based on my statement, I will not answer. I would like 30 seconds at

be

the end to make a statement, and you can have 30 seconds more on your time, if you'll let me say this to the grand jury and to you. And I don't think it's disrespectful at all. I've had a lot of time to think about this.

But, go ahead and ask your questions.

Q The question is, if Monica Lewinsky says that while you were in the Oval Office area you touched her breasts, would she be lying?

A That is not my recollection. My recollection is that I did not have sexual relations with Ms. Lewinsky and I'm staying on my former statement about that.

Q If she said --

A My, my statement is that I did not have sexual relations as defined by that.

Q If she says that you kissed her breasts, would she be lying?

A I'm going to revert to my former statement.

Q Okay. If Monica Lewinsky says that while you were in the Oval Office area you touched her genitalia, would she be lying? And that calls for a yes, no, or reverting to your former statement.

A I will revert to my statement on that.

Q If Monica Lewinsky says that you used a cigar as a sexual aid with her in the Oval Office area, would she be lying? Yes, no, or won't answer?

be

A I will revert to my former statement.

Q If Monica Lewinsky says that you had phone sex with her, would she be lying?

A Well, that is, at least in general terms, I think, is covered by my statement. I addressed that in my statement, and that, I don't believe, is --

Q Let me define phone sex for purposes of my question. Phone sex occurs when a party to a phone conversation masturbates while the other party is talking in a sexually explicit manner. And the question is, if Monica Lewinsky says that you had phone sex with her, would she be lying?

A I think that is covered by my statement.

Q Did you, on or about January the 13th, 1998, Mr. President, ask Erskine Bowles to ask John Hilley if he would give a recommendation for Monica Lewinsky?

A In 1998?

Q Yes. On or about January 13th, 1998, did you ask Erskine Bowles, your Chief of Staff, if he would ask John Hilley to give a recommendation for Monica Lewinsky?

A At some point, sir, I believe I talked to Erskine Bowles about whether Monica Lewinsky could get a recommendation that was not negative from the Legislative Affairs Office. I believe I did.

Q I just didn't hear the very last part.

be

A I think the answer is, I think, yes. At some point I talked to Erskine Bowles about this.

Q Okay.

A I do not know what the date was. At some point I did talk to him.

Q And if Erskine Bowles has told us that he told John Podesta to carry out your wishes, and John Podesta states that it was three or four days before your deposition, which would be the 13th or the 14th, are you in a position to deny that?

A The 13th or 14th of?

Q January, as to date.

A I don't know. I don't know when the date was.

Q Okay.

A I'm not in a position to deny it. I won't deny it. I'm sure that they are both truthful men. I don't know when the date was.

Q Do you recall asking Erskine Bowles to do that?

A I recall talking to Erskine Bowles about that, and my recollection is, sir, that Ms. Lewinsky was moving to New York, wanted to get a job in the private sector; was confident she would get a good recommendation from the Defense Department; and was concerned that because she had been moved from the Legislative Affairs Office, transferred to the Defense Department, that her ability to get a job

be

might be undermined by a bad recommendation from the Legislative Affairs Office.

So, I asked Erskine if we could get her a recommendation that just was at least neutral, so that if she had a good recommendation from the Defense Department it wouldn't prevent her from getting a job in the private sector.

Q If Mr. Bowles has told us that, in fact, you told him that she already had a job and had already listed Mr. Hilley as a reference and wanted him to be available as a recommendation, would you be in -- is that inconsistent with your memory?

A A little bit, but I think -- my memory is that when you're, when you get a job like that you have to give them a resume, which says where you've worked and who your supervisor was. And I think that that's my recollection. My recollection is that -- slightly different from that.

Q And who was it that asked you to do that on Monica Lewinsky's behalf?

A I think she did. You know, she tried for months and months to get a job back in the White House, not so much in the West Wing but somewhere in the White House complex, including the Old Executive Office Building. And she talked to Marsha Scott, among others. She very much wanted to come back. And she interviewed for some jobs but never got one.

be

She was, from time to time, upset about it.

And I think what she was afraid of is that she couldn't get a -- from the minute she left the White House she was worried about this. That if she didn't come back to the White House and work for awhile and get a good job recommendation, that no matter how well she had done at the Pentagon it might hurt her future employment prospects.

Well, it became obvious that, you know, her mother had moved to New York. She wanted to go to New York. She wasn't going to get a job in the White House. So, she wanted to get a job in the private sector, and said, I hope that I won't get a letter out of the Legislative Affairs Office that will prevent my getting a job in the private sector. And that's what I talked to Erskine about.

Now, that's my entire memory of this.

Q All right. I want to go back briefly to the December 28th conversation with Ms. Lewinsky. I believe you testified to the effect that she asked you, what if they ask me about gifts you gave me. My question to you is, after that statement by her, did you ever have a conversation with Betty Currie about gifts, or picking something up from Monica Lewinsky?

A I don't believe I did, sir. No.

Q You never told her anything to this effect, that Monica has something to give you?

be

A No, sir.

Q That is to say, Betty Currie?

A No, sir, I didn't. I don't have any memory of that whatever.

Q And so you have no knowledge that, or you had no knowledge at the time, that Betty Currie went and picked up, your secretary went and picked up from Monica Lewinsky items that were called for by the Jones subpoena and hid them under her bed? You had no knowledge that anything remotely like that was going to happen?

A I did not. I did not know she had those items, I believe, until that was made public.

Q And you agree with me that that would be a very wrong thing to do, to hide evidence in a civil case, or any case? Isn't that true?

A Yes. I don't know that, that Ms. Currie knew that that's what she had at all. But --

Q I'm not saying she did. I'm just saying --

A I had -- it is, if Monica Lewinsky did that after they had been subpoenaed and she knew what she was doing, she should not have done that.

Q And if you knew, you --

A And I --

Q -- shouldn't have done it?

A Indeed, I, myself, told her, if they ask you for

be

gifts you have to give them what you have. And I don't understand if, in fact, she was worried about this, why she was so worried about it. It was no big deal.

Q I want to talk about a December 17th phone conversation you had with Monica Lewinsky at approximately 2:00 a.m. Do you recall making that conversation and telling her initially about the death of Betty's brother, but then telling her that she was on the witness list, and that it broke your heart that she was on the witness list?

A No, sir, I don't, but it would -- it, it would -- it is quite possible that that happened, because, if you remember, earlier in this meeting you asked me some questions about what I'd said to Monica about testimony and affidavits, and I was struggling to try to remember whether this happened in a meeting or a phone call.

Now, I remember I called her to tell her Betty's brother had died. I remember that. And I know it was in the middle of December, and I believe it was before Monica had been subpoenaed. So, I think it is quite possible that if I called her at that time and had not talked to her since the 6th -- and you asked me this earlier -- I believe when I saw her on the 6th, I don't think I knew she was on the witness list then, then it's quite possible I would say something like that. I don't have any memory of it, but I certainly wouldn't dispute that I might have said that.

be

Q And in that conversation, or in any conversation in which you informed her she was on the witness list, did you tell her, you know, you can always say that you were coming to see Betty or bringing me letters? Did you tell her anything like that?

A I don't remember. She was coming to see Betty. I can tell you this. I absolutely never asked her to lie.

Q Sir, every time she came to see Betty and you were in the Oval Office, she was coming to see you, too, wasn't she, or just about every time?

A I think just about every time. I don't think every time. I think there was a time or two where she came to see Betty when she didn't see me.

Q So, do you remember telling her any time, any time when you told her, or after you told her that she was on the witness list, something to this effect: You know, you can always say you were coming to see Betty, or you were bringing me letters?

A I don't remember exactly what I told her that night.

Q Did you --

A I don't remember that. I remember talking about the nature of our relationship, how she got in. But I also will tell you that I felt quite comfortable that she could have executed a truthful affidavit, which would not have

be

disclosed the embarrassing details of the relationship that we had had, which had been over for many, many months by the time this incident occurred.

Q Did you tell her anytime in December something to that effect: You know, you can always say that you were coming to see Betty or you were bringing me letters? Did you say that, or anything like that, in December '97 or January '98, to Monica Lewinsky?

A Well, that's a very broad question. I do not recall saying anything like that in connection with her testimony. I could tell you what I do remember saying, if you want to know. But I don't -- we might have talked about what to do in a non legal context at some point in the past, but I have no specific memory of that conversation.

I do remember what I said to her about the possible testimony.

Q You would agree with me, if you did say something like that to her, to urge her to say that to the Jones people, that that would be part of an effort to mislead the Jones people, no matter how evil they are and corrupt?

A I didn't say they were evil. I said what they were doing here was wrong, and it was.

Q Wouldn't that be misleading?

A Well, again, you are trying to get me to characterize something that I'm -- that I don't know if I said or not, without knowing whether the whole, whether the context is complete or not. So, I would have to know, what was the context, what were all the surrounding facts.

I can tell you this: I never asked Ms. Lewinsky to lie. The first time that she raised with me the possibility that she might be a witness or I told her -- you suggested the possibility in this December 17th timeframe -- I told her she had to get a lawyer. And I never asked her to lie.

Q Did you ever say anything like that, you can always say that you were coming to see Betty or bringing me letters? Was that part of any kind of a, anything you said to her or a cover story, before you had any idea she was going to be part of Paula Jones?

A I might well have said that.

Q Okay.

A Because I certainly didn't want this to come out, if I could help it. And I was concerned about that. I was embarrassed about it. I knew it was wrong. And, you know, of course, I didn't want it to come out. But --

Q But you are saying that you didn't say anything -- I want to make sure I understand. Did you say anything like that once you knew or thought she might be a witness in the Jones case? Did you repeat that statement, or something like it to her?

A Well, again, I don't recall, and I don't recall

be

whether I might have done something like that, for example, if somebody says, what if the reporters ask me this, that or the other thing. I can tell you this: In the context of whether she could be a witness, I have a recollection that she asked me, well, what do I do if I get called as a witness, and I said, you have to get a lawyer. And that's all I said. And I never asked her to lie.

Q Did you tell her to tell the truth?

A Well, I think the implication was she would tell the truth. I've already told you that I felt strongly that she could issue, that she could execute an affidavit that would be factually truthful, that might get her out of having to testify. Now, it obviously wouldn't if the Jones people knew this, because they knew that if they could get this and leak it, it would serve their larger purposes, even if the judge ruled that she couldn't be a witness in the case. The judge later ruled she wouldn't be a witness in the case. The judge later ruled the case had no merit.

So, I knew that. And did I hope she'd be able to get out of testifying on an affidavit? Absolutely. Did I want her to execute a false affidavit? No, I did not.

Q If Monica Lewinsky has stated that her affidavit that she didn't have a sexual relationship with you is, in fact, a lie, I take it you disagree with that?

A No. I told you before what I thought the issue was

be

there. I think the issue is how do you define sexual relationship. And there was no definition imposed on her at the time she executed the affidavit. Therefore, she was free to give it any reasonable meaning.

Q And if she says she was lying --

A And I believe --

Q -- under your common sense ordinary meaning that you talked about earlier, Mr. President, that most Americans would have, if she says sexual relationship, saying I didn't have one was a lie because I had oral sex with the President, I take it, you would disagree with that?

A Now, we're back to where we started and I have to invoke my statement. But, let me just say one thing. I've read a lot, and obviously I don't know whether any of it's accurate, about what she said, and what purports to be on those tapes.

And this thing -- and I searched my own memory. This reminds me, to some extent, of the hearings when Clarence Thomas and Anita Hill were both testifying under oath. Now, in some rational way, they could not have both been telling the truth, since they had directly different accounts of a shared set of facts. Fortunately, or maybe you think unfortunately, there was no special prosecutor to try to go after one or the other of them, to take sides and try to prove one was a liar. And so, Judge Thomas was able to go

be

on and serve on the Supreme Court.

What I learned from that, I can tell you that I was a citizen out there just listening. And when I heard both of them testify, what I believed after it was over, I believed that they both thought they were telling the truth.

This is -- you're dealing with, in some ways, the most mysterious area of human life. I'm doing the best I can to give you honest answers.

Q Mr. President --

A And that's all I can say.

Q I'm sorry.

A And, you know, those people both testified under oath. So, if there'd been a special prosecutor, they could, one of them could have gone after Anita Hill, another could have gone after Clarence Thomas. I thank God there was no such thing then, because I don't believe that it was a proper thing.

Q One of --

A And I think they both thought they were telling the truth. So, maybe Ms. Lewinsky believes she's telling the truth, and I'm glad she got her mother and herself out of trouble. I'm glad you gave her that sweeping immunity. I'm glad for the whole thing. I, I, I -- it breaks my heart that she was ever involved in this.

Q I want to go back to a question about Vernon

be

Jordan. I want to go back to late December and early January, late December of '97 and early January of '98. During this time, Mr. President, you are being sued for sexual harassment by a woman who claims, among other things, that others got benefits that she didn't because she didn't have oral sex with you. While this is happening, your powerful friend, Vernon Jordan, is helping to get Monica Lewinsky a job and a lawyer. He's helping to get a job and a lawyer for someone who had some kind of sex with you, and who has been subpoenaed in the very case, the Jones case.

Don't you see a problem with this? Didn't you see a problem with this?

A No. Would you like to know why?

Q Isn't that why -- I would. But isn't that why Vernon Jordan asked you on December 19th whether or not you had sexual relationships with Monica Lewinsky and why he asked her, because he knew it would be so highly improper to be helping her with a lawyer and a job if, in fact, she had had a relationship with you?

A I don't know. I don't believe that at all. I don't believe that at all, particularly since, even if you look at the facts here in their light most unfavorable to me, no one has suggested that there was any sexual harassment on my part. And I don't think it was wrong to be helping her. Look --

be

Q A subpoenaed witness in a case against you?
A Absolutely. Look, for one thing, I had already proved in two ways that I was not trying to influence her testimony. I didn't order her to be hired at the White House. I could have done so. I wouldn't do it. She tried for months to get in. She was angry.
Secondly, after I --
Q Wasn't she kept --
A After I terminated the improper contact with her, she wanted to come in more than she did. She got angry when she didn't get in sometimes. I knew that that might make her more likely to speak, and I still did it because I had to limit the contact.
And, thirdly, let me say, I formed an opinion really early in 1996, and again -- well, let me finish the sentence. I formed an opinion early in 1996, once I got into this unfortunate and wrong conduct, that when I stopped it, which I knew I'd have to do and which I should have done a long time before I did, that she would talk about it. Not because Monica Lewinsky is a bad person. She's basically a good girl. She's a good young woman with a good heart and a good mind. I think she is burdened by some unfortunate conditions of her, her upbringing. But she's basically a good person.
But I knew that the minute there was no longer any

be

contact, she would talk about this. She would have to. She couldn't help it. It was, it was a part of her psyche. So, I had put myself at risk, sir. I was not trying to buy her silence or get Vernon Jordan to buy her silence. I thought she was a good person. She had not been involved with me for a long time in any improper way, several months, and I wanted to help her get on with her life. It's just as simple as that.

MR. WISENBERG: It's time for a break.

MR. KENDALL: Okay. 4:49.

(Whereupon, the proceedings were recessed from 4:49 p.m. until 5:05 p.m.)

MR. KENDALL: Bob, we are at 2 hours and 55 minutes.

MR. BITTMAN: Two hours and 55 minutes, thank you.

BY MR. BITTMAN:

Q Mr. President.

A Mr. Bittman.

Q Apparently we have one hour and five minutes left, if we stick to the four-hour timeframe.

MR. KENDALL: Plus 30 seconds.

MR. BITTMAN: And 30 seconds, that's right.

THE WITNESS: You gave me my 30 seconds' soliloquy. So, I owe you 30 seconds.

be

BY MR. BITTMAN:

Q You are very generous. That actually segues very nicely into one of the grand juror's asked, pointed out actually, that you indicated at the beginning of the deposition that you would, you would answer all the grand jurors, you wanted to answer all the grand jurors' questions. And they wanted to know whether you would be willing to stay beyond the four-hour period to, in fact, answer all their questions.

A Well, let's see how we do in the next hour, and then we'll decide.

Q Okay. Let me draw your attention to early January of this year, after Christmas, before your deposition. Do you remember talking to Betty Currie about Monica, who had just called her and said that she, Monica, needed to talk to you before she signed something?

A I'm not sure that I do remember that. But, go ahead.

Q This is in early January. And then Betty Currie relayed this to you that Monica called, it's important, she needs to talk to you before she signs something. And then you do, indeed, talk to Monica that day on the telephone.

A I did talk to her that day?

Q Yes.

MR. KENDALL: Mr. President, excuse me. That's a

be

question. If you have a memory of that, you can answer.

THE WITNESS: I'm trying to remember when the last time I talked to her was. I am aware, sir, that she signed this affidavit about this time, sometime in the first week in January. I may have talked to her before she did it. I don't know. I talked to her a number of times between the time Betty's brother died and Christmas. Then I saw her on December 28. I may have talked to her, but I don't remember the specific conversation.

BY MR. BITTMAN:

Q And you would have talked about the -- she had just given you a gift actually in early January, a book on the Presidents of the United States. And you discussed this with her and she said that you said you liked it a lot.

A I did like it a lot. I told you that. My impression, my belief was that she gave me that book for Christmas. Maybe that's not right. I think she had that book delivered to me for Christmas. And then, as I remember, I went to Bosnia and for some reason she wasn't there around Christmas time.

But, anyway, maybe I didn't get it until January. My recollection was that I had gotten it right before Christmas.

Q Let me see if I can jog your memory further. Monica talked to you in that phone conversation that told you

be

that she had just met with her attorney that Mr. Jordan arranged with her, and the attorney said that if she is deposed that they were going to ask her how she got her job at the Pentagon. And Monica then asked you, what do you think I should say, how do I answer that question, how did I get the job at the Pentagon. Did you talk to Monica about that, about possibilities --

A I don't believe -- no. I don't remember her asking me that. But if she, if she had asked me that, I would have told her to tell the truth. I -- and I didn't, you know, I don't know exactly how she got her job at the Pentagon. I know Evelyn Lieberman wanted to transfer her out of the job she had, and somebody must have arranged that. But I didn't arrange it.

Q Now, that's actually not my question. My question is whether you remember talking to Monica about her being concerned that, I may have to answer some questions about how and why I was transferred to the Pentagon out of the White House, fearing that this would --

A No, I don't remember that at all.

Q -- lead to questions, or answers that would reveal your relationship?

A Oh, no, sir. I don't remember that. Maybe somebody -- maybe she did. But I only remember -- well, I don't remember that. That's all I can tell you. I don't

be

remember that.

Q Are you saying, Mr. President, that you did not then say to Ms. Lewinsky that you could always say that people in Legislative Affairs got you the job, or helped you get it?

A I have no recollection of that whatever.

Q Are you saying you didn't say it?

A No, sir. I'm telling you, I want to say I don't recall -- I don't have any memory of this as I sit here today. And I can tell you this, I never asked her to lie. I never did. And I don't have any recollection of the specific thing you are saying to me.

Now, if I could back up, there were several times when Monica Lewinsky talked to me on the telephone in 1996, in person in 1997, about her being concerned about what anybody would say about her transfer from the White House to the Pentagon. But I remember no conversation in which she was concerned about it for the reasons you just mentioned.

And all my memory is, she was worried about it because she thought it would keep her from getting a good job down the road, and she talked to me about it constantly in 1997. She thought, well, I'll never have my record clear unless I work somewhere in the White House complex where I can get a good recommendation. But in the context that you mention it, I do not recall a conversation.

be

Q Did you ever tell Ms. Lewinsky, or promise to her that you would do your best to get her back into the White House after the 1996 Presidential elections?

A What I told Ms. Lewinsky was that I would, I would do what I could to see, if she had a good record at the Pentagon, and she assured me she was doing a good job and working hard, that I would do my best to see that the fact that she had been sent away from the Legislative Affairs section did not keep her from getting a job in the White House, and that is, in fact, what I tried to do. I had a conversation with Ms. Scott about it, and I tried to do that.

But I did not tell her I would order someone to hire her, and I never did, and I wouldn't do that. It wouldn't be right.

Q When you received the book, this gift from Monica, the Presidents of the United States, this book that you liked and you talked with Monica about, did it come with a note? Do you remember the note that it came with, Mr. President?

A No, sir, I don't.

Q Do you remember that in the note she wrote that, she expressed how much she missed you and how much she cared for you, and you and she later talked about this in this telephone conversation, and you said -- and she apologized for putting such emotional, romantic things in this note, and you said, yeah, you shouldn't have written some of those

be

things, you shouldn't put those things down on paper? Did you ever say anything like that to Ms. Lewinsky?

A Oh, I believe I did say something like that to Ms. Lewinsky. I don't remember doing something as late as you suggest. I'm not saying I didn't. I have no recollection of that.

Keep in mind now, it had been quite a long time since I had had any improper contact with her. And she was, in a funny way, almost more attached to me than she had been before. In '96, she had a long relationship, she said, with a man whom she liked a lot. And I didn't know what else was going on in her private life in '97. But she talked to me occasionally about people she was going out with.

But normally her language at this point was, if affectionate, was, was not improperly affectionate, I would say. So -- but, it could have happened. I wouldn't say it didn't. I just don't remember it at this late date.

Q Let me refer back to one of the subjects we talked about at one of the earlier breaks, right before one of the earlier breaks, and that is your meeting with Mrs. Currie on January 18th. This is the Sunday after your deposition in the Paula Jones case.

You said that you spoke to her in an attempt to refresh your own recollection about the events involving Monica Lewinsky, is that right?

be

A Yes.

Q How did you making the statement, I was never alone with her, right, refresh your recollection?

A Well, first of all, let's remember the context here. I did not at that time know of your involvement in this case. I just knew that obviously someone had given them a lot of information, some of which struck me as accurate, some of which struck me as dead wrong. But it led them to write, ask me a whole serious of questions about Monica Lewinsky.

Then on Sunday morning, this Drudge report came out, which used Betty's name, and I thought that we were going to be deluged by press comments. And I was trying to refresh my memory about what the facts were.

So, when I said, we were never alone, right, I think I also asked her a number of other questions, because there were several times, as I'm sure she would acknowledge, when I either asked her to be around. I remember once in particular when I was talking with Ms. Lewinsky when I asked Betty to be in the, actually, in the next room in the dining room, and, as I testified earlier, once in her own office.

But I meant that she was always in the Oval Office complex, in that complex, while Monica was there. And I believe that this was part of a series of questions I asked her to try to quickly refresh my memory. So, I wasn't trying

be

to get her to say something that wasn't so. And, in fact, I think she would recall that I told her to just relax, go in the grand jury and tell the truth when she had been called as a witness.

Q So, when you said to Mrs. Currie that, I was never alone with her, right, you just meant that you and Ms. Lewinsky would be somewhere perhaps in the Oval Office or many times in your back study, is that correct?

A That's right. We were in the back study.

Q And then --

A Keep in mind, sir, I just want to make it -- I was talking about 1997. I was never, ever trying to get Betty Currie to claim that on the occasions when Monica Lewinsky was there when she wasn't anywhere around, that she was. I would never have done that to her, and I don't think she thought about that. I don't think she thought I was referring to that.

Q Did you put a date restriction? Did you make it clear to Mrs. Currie that you were only asking her whether you were never alone with her after 1997?

A Well, I don't recall whether I did or not, but I assumed -- if I didn't, I assumed she knew what I was talking about, because it was the point at which Ms. Lewinsky was out of the White House and had to have someone WAVE her in, in order to get in the White House. And I do not believe to

be

this day that I was -- in 1997, that she was ever there and that I ever saw her unless Betty Currie was there. I don't believe she was.

Q Do you agree with me that the statement, "I was never alone with her", is incorrect? You were alone with Monica Lewinsky, weren't you?

A Well, again, it depends on how you define alone. Yes, we were alone from time to time, even during 1997, even when there was absolutely no improper contact occurring. Yes, that is accurate.

But there were also a lot of times when, even though no one could see us, the doors were open to the halls, on both ends of the halls, people could hear. The Navy stewards could come in and out at will, if they were around. Other things could be happening. So, there were a lot of times when we were alone, but I never really thought we were.

And sometimes when we, when -- but, as far as I know, what I was trying to determine, if I might, is that Betty was always around, and I believe she was always around where I could basically call her or get her if I needed her.

Q When you said to Mrs. Currie, you could see and hear everything, that wasn't true either, was it, as far as you knew? You've already --

A My memory of that --

Q -- testified that Betty was not there.

be

A My memory of that was that, that she had the ability to hear what was going on if she came in the Oval Office from her office. And a lot of times, you know, when I was in the Oval Office, she just had the door open to her office. Then there was -- the door was never completely closed to the hall. So, I think there was -- I'm not entirely sure what I meant by that, but I could have meant that she generally would be able to hear conversations, even if she couldn't see them. And I think that's what I meant.

Now, I could have been referring not generally to every time she was there, but one, one particular time I remember when Ms. Lewinsky was there when I asked Betty -- and I'm sorry to say for reasons I don't entirely remember -- to actually stay in the dining room while I talked with Monica. I do remember one such instance.

Q Well, you've already testified that this -- you did almost everything you could to keep this relationship secret. So, would it be fair to say -- even from Mrs. Currie. She didn't know about the nature, that is, your intimate, physically intimate relationship with Ms. Lewinsky, did she?

A As far as I know, she is unaware of what happened on the, on the occasions when I saw her in 1996 when something improper happened. And she was unaware of the one time that I recall in 1997 when something happened.

I think she was quite well aware that I was

be

determined to impose the appropriate limits on the relationship when I was trying to do it. And the -- you know, anybody would hope that this wouldn't become public. Although I frankly, from 1996 on, always felt that if I severed inappropriate contact with Ms. Lewinsky, sooner or later it would get public. And I never thought it would be part of the Jones case. I never even thought about that. I never thought -- I certainly never thought it would be part of your responsibilities.

Q My question was --

A But I did believe that she would talk about it.

Q My question was more simple than that. Mrs. Currie did not know of the physically intimate nature of your relationship, did she?

A I don't believe she did, no.

Q Okay. So, you would have done -- you tried to keep that nature of the relationship from Mrs. Currie?

A Absolutely. I --

Q So, you would not have engaged in those physically intimate acts if you knew that Mrs. Currie could see or hear that, is that correct?

A That's correct. But, keep in mind, sir, I was talking about 1997. That occurred, to the -- and I believe that occurred only once in February of 1997. I stopped it. I never should have started it, and I certainly shouldn't

be

have started it back after I resolved not to in 1996. And I was referring to 1997.

And I -- what -- as I say, I do not know -- her memory and mine may be somewhat different. I do not know whether I was asking her about a particular time when Monica was upset and I asked her to stand, stay back in the dining area. Or whether I was, had reference to the fact that if she kept the door open to the Oval Office, because it was always -- the door to the hallway was always somewhat open, that she would always be able to hear something if anything went on that was, you know, too loud, or whatever.

I do not know what I meant. I'm just trying to reconcile the two statements as best I can, without being sure.

Q There was at least one event where Mrs. Currie was definitely not even in the Oval Office area, isn't that right? And I think you began to testify about that before. That was at the radio address.

A I'm not sure of that. But in that case, there was, there was certainly someone else there. I don't know --

Q Well, why would you be testing Mrs. Currie's memory about whether someone else was there?

A Well, I can say this. If I'm in the Oval Office -- my belief is that there was someone else there, somewhere in the Oval Office complex. I've looked at our -- I've looked

be

at the film. This, this night has become legendary now, you know. I've looked at the, I've looked at the film we have. I've looked at my schedules. I've seen the people that were at the radio address.

I do believe that I was alone with her from 15 to 20 minutes. I do believe that things happened then which were inappropriate. I don't remember whether Betty was there or not, but I can't imagine that, since all this happened more or less continuously in that time period, there must have been someone who was working around the radio address who stayed around somewhere. That would be my guess. I don't know. I'm sorry. I don't have records about who it would be. But I doubt very seriously if we were all alone in that Oval Office complex then.

Q Mr. President, if there is a semen stain belonging to you on a dress of Ms. Lewinsky's, how would you explain that?

A Well, Mr. Bittman, I, I don't -- first of all, when you asked me for a blood test, I gave you one promptly. You came over here and got it. That's -- we met that night and talked. So, that's a question you already know the answer to. Not if, but you know whether.

And the main thing I can tell you is that doesn't affect the opening statement I made. The opening statement I made is that I had inappropriate intimate contact. I take

be

full responsibility for it. It wasn't her fault, it was mine. I do not believe that I violated the definition of sexual relations I was given by directly touching those parts of her body with the intent to arouse or gratify. And that's all I have to say.

I think, for the rest, you know, you know what the evidence is and it doesn't affect that statement.

Q Is it possible or impossible that your semen is on a dress belonging to Ms. Lewinsky?

A I have nothing to add to my statement about it, sir. You, you know whether -- you know what the facts are. There's no point in a hypothetical.

Q Don't you know what the facts are also, Mr. President?

A I have nothing to add to my statement, sir.

Q Getting back to the conversation you had with Mrs. Currie on January 18th, you told her -- if she testified that you told her, Monica came on to me and I never touched her, you did, in fact, of course, touch Ms. Lewinsky, isn't that right, in a physically intimate way?

A Now, I've testified about that. And that's one of those questions that I believe is answered by the statement that I made.

Q What was your purpose in making these statements to Mrs. Currie, if they weren't for the purpose to try to

be

suggest to her what she should say if ever asked?

A Now, Mr. Bittman, I told you, the only thing I remember is when all this stuff blew up, I was trying to figure out what the facts were. I was trying to remember. I was trying to remember every time I had seen Ms. Lewinsky. Once this thing was in Drudge, and there was this argument about whether it was or was not going to be in Newsweek, that was a clear signal to me, because Newsweek, frankly, was -- had become almost a sponsoring media outlook for the Paula Jones case, and had a journalist who had been trying, so far fruitlessly, to find me in some sort of wrongdoing.

And so I knew this was all going to come out. I was trying -- I did not know at the time -- I will say again, I did not know that any of you were involved. I did not know that the Office of Independent Counsel was involved. And I was trying to get the facts and try to think of the best defense we could construct in the face of what I thought was going to be a media onslaught.

Once you became involved, I told Betty Currie not to worry, that, that she had been through a terrible time. She had lost her brother. She had lost her sister. Her mother was in the hospital. I said, Betty, just don't worry about me. Just relax, go in there and tell the truth. You'll be fine. Now, that's all there was in this context.

Q Did the conversations that you had with Mrs.

be

Currie, this conversation, did it refresh your recollection as to events involving Ms. Lewinsky?

A Well, as I remember, I do believe, in fairness, that, you know, she may have felt some ambivalence about how to react, because there were some times when she seemed to say yes, when I'm not sure she meant yes. There was a time -- it seems like there was one or two things where she said, well, remember this, that or the other thing, which did reflect my recollection.

So, I would say a little yes, and a little no.

Q Why was it then that two or three days later, given that The Washington Post article came out on January 21st, why would you have had another conversation with Betty Currie asking or making the exact same statements to her?

A I don't know that I did. I remember having this one time. I was, I was -- I don't know that I did.

Q If Mrs. Currie says you did, are you disputing that?

A No, sir, I'm not disputing --

MR. KENDALL: Excuse me. Is your representation that she testified that that conversation was -- when?

MR. BITTMAN: I'm not making a representation as to what Mrs. Currie said. I'm asking the President if Mrs. Currie testified two or three days later, that two or three days after the conversation with the President on January

be

18th, that he called her into the Oval Office and went over the exact same statements that the President made to her on the 18th.

BY MR. BITTMAN:

Q Is that accurate? Is that a truthful statement by Mrs. Currie, if she made it?

A I do not remember how many times I talked to Betty Currie or when. I don't. I can't possibly remember that. I do remember, when I first heard about this story breaking, trying to ascertain what the facts were, trying to ascertain what Betty's perception was. I remember that I was highly agitated, understandably, I think.

And then I remember when I knew she was going to have to testify to the grand jury, and I, I felt terrible because she had been through this loss of her sister, this horrible accident Christmas that killed her brother, and her mother was in the hospital. I was trying to do -- to make her understand that I didn't want her to, to be untruthful to the grand jury. And if her memory was different from mine, it was fine, just go in there and tell them what she thought. So, that's all I remember.

BY MR. BENNETT:

Q Mr. President, my name is Jackie Bennett. If I understand your current line of testimony, you are saying that your only interest in speaking with Ms. Currie in the

be

days after your deposition was to refresh your own recollection?

A Yes.

Q It was not to impart instructions on how she was to recall things in the future?

A No, and certainly not under oath. That -- every day, Mr. Bennett, in the White House and in every other political organization when you are subject to a barrage of press questions of any kind, you always try to make the best case you can consistent with the facts; that is, while being truthful.

But -- so, I was concerned for a day or two there about this as a press story only. I had no idea you were involved in it for a couple of days.

I think Betty Currie's testimony will be that I gave her explicit instructions or encouragement to just go in the grand jury and tell the truth. That's what I told her to do and I thought she would.

Q Mr. President, when did you learn about the Drudge Report reporting allegations of you having a sexual relationship with someone at the White House?

A I believe it was the morning of the 18th, I think.

Q What time of day, sir?

A I have no idea.

Q Early morning hours?

be

A Yeah, I think somebody called me and told me about it. Maybe Bruce, maybe someone else. I'm not sure. But I learned early on the 18th of the Drudge Report.

Q Very early morning hours, sir?

A Now, my deposition was on the 17th, is that right?

Q On Saturday, the 17th, sir.

A Yeah, I think it was when I got up Sunday morning, I think. Maybe it was late Saturday night. I don't remember.

Q Did you call Betty Currie, sir, after the Drudge Report hit the wire?

A I did.

Q Did you call her at home?

A I did. Was that the night of the 17th?

Q Night of the 17th, early morning hours of the 18th?

A Okay, yes. That's because -- yes. I worked with Prime Minister Netanyahu that night until about midnight.

MR. KENDALL: Wait.

THE WITNESS: Isn't that right?

MR. KENDALL: Excuse me. I think the question is directed -- Mr. Bennett, if you could help out by putting the day of the week, I think that would be helpful.

BY MR. BENNETT:

Q Saturday night, Sunday morning.

A Yes. I called Betty Currie as soon -- I think

be

about as soon as I could, after I finished with Prime Minister Netanyahu, and in the aftermath of that meeting planning where we were going next in the Middle East peace process.

MR. KENDALL: Can we take a two-minute break, please?

MR. BITTMAN: May I ask one other question first, Mr. Kendall?

MR. KENDALL: Certainly. I think the witness is confused on dates. That's all.

MR. BITTMAN: Okay.

THE WITNESS: That's what -- I didn't think it was the night of the 17th.

MR. KENDALL: Mr. President, I think we'll do it in a break.

THE WITNESS: Can we have a break and I could get straightened out?

MR. BITTMAN: Sure. May I ask one other quick -- this is a question I forgot to ask from the grand jurors.

THE WITNESS: I don't want to get mixed up on these dates now. Go ahead.

BY MR. BITTMAN:

Q This is -- they wanted to know whether, they want us to clarify that the President's knowledge, your knowledge, Mr. President, as to the approach to our office this morning;

be

that is, we were told that you would give a general statement about the nature of your relationship with Ms. Lewinsky, which you have done. Yet that you would -- you did not want to go in any of the details about the relationship. And that if we pressed on going into the details, that you would object to going into the details.

And the grand jurors, before they wanted, they wanted to vote on some other matters, they wanted to know whether you were aware of that? That we were told that?

MR. KENDALL: Well, Mr. Bittman, who told you that? This is, this is, this is not a fair question, when you say you were told. Who told you?

MR. BITTMAN: Who told me what, the question?

MR. KENDALL: You said, you said the grand jury was told.

MR. BITTMAN: We have kept the grand jury informed, as we normally would, of the proceedings here.

MR. KENDALL: Right. And, I'm sorry. Who, who are you representing told you or the grand jurors anything? Is that, is that our conversation?

MR. BITTMAN: Yes.

MR. STARR: Yes, our conversation.

MR. BITTMAN: Yes. That was in substance related to the grand jurors.

THE WITNESS: And what's your question to me, Mr.

be

Bittman?

BY MR. BITTMAN:

Q Whether you were aware of the facts that I just described?

A Yes, sir. Let me say this. I knew that Mr. Kendall was going to talk with Judge Starr. What we wanted to do was to be as helpful as we could to you on the question of whether you felt I was being truthful, when I said I did not have sexual relations with Ms. Lewinsky, as defined in that definition (1) in this, in my testimony.

And I thought the best way to do that, and still preserve some measure of privacy and dignity, would be to invite all of you and the grand jurors to ask, well, would you consider this, that, or the other thing covered by the definition. You asked me several questions there, and I did my best to answer whether I thought they were covered by the definition, and said if I thought they were covered, you could conclude from that that my testimony is I did not do them.

If those things, if things are not covered by the definition, and I don't believe they are covered, then I could not -- then they shouldn't be within this discussion one way or the other.

Now, I know this is somewhat unusual. But I would say to the grand jury, put yourself in my position. This is

be

not a typical grand jury testimony. I, I have to assume a report is going to Congress. There's a videotape being made of this, allegedly because only one member of the grand jury is absent. This is highly unusual. And, in addition to that, I have sustained a breathtaking number of leaks of grand jury proceedings.

And, so, I think I am right to answer all the questions about perjury, but not to say things which will be forever in the historic annals of the United States because of this unprecedented videotape and may be leaked at any time. I just think it's a mistake.

And, so, I'm doing my best to cooperate with the grand jury and still protect myself, my family, and my office.

MR. BITTMAN: Thank you.

MR. KENDALL: This will be two minutes.

(Whereupon, the proceedings were recessed from 5:37 p.m. until 5:43 p.m.)

BY MR. BENNETT:

Q Mr. President, before we broke, we were talking about the sequencing of your conversations with Betty Currie following your deposition on Saturday, January 17th. Do you recall that?

A I do.

Q All right. And you recall contacting Betty Currie,

be

calling her and instructing her on the evening of Saturday night, after your deposition, and telling her to come in the next day?

A Yes, sir, I do.

Q Sunday was normally her day off, isn't that so?

A Yes, it was.

Q And so you were making special arrangements for her to come back into the White House, isn't that so?

A Well, yes. I asked her to come back in and talk to me.

Q And it was at that time that you spoke with her, and Mr. Bittman and Mr. Wisenberg have asked you questions about what you said in that conversation, isn't that so?

A Yes, they have -- I don't know whether that's the time, but they -- I did talk to her as soon as I realized that the deposition had become more about Monica Lewinsky than Paula Jones. I asked her, you know, if she knew anything about this. I said, you know, it's obvious that this is going to be a matter of press speculation, and I was trying to go through the litany of what had happened between us, and asked some questions.

Q On fairness, it would be more than a matter of simple press speculation, isn't that so? Mr. President, there was a question about whether you had testified fully, completely, and honestly on the preceding day in your

be

deposition.

A Well, actually, Mr. Bennett, I didn't think about that then. I -- this has been a rather unprecedented development, and I wasn't even thinking about the Independent Counsel getting into this. So, at that moment, I knew nothing about it and I was more interested in what the facts were and whether Ms. Currie knew anything about it, knew anything about what Monica Lewinsky knew about it.

Q Mr. President, you've told us at least a little bit about your understanding of how the term sexual relations was used, and what you understood it to mean in the context of your deposition. Isn't that correct?

A That is correct.

Q And you've told us -- I mean, that was a lawsuit Paula Jones filed in which she alleged that you asked her to perform oral sex, isn't that so?

A That was her allegation.

Q That was her allegation. And, notwithstanding that that was her allegation, you've testified that you understood the term sexual relations, in the context of the questions you were being asked, to mean something else, at least insofar as you were the recipient rather than the performer?

A Sir, Paula Jones' lawyers pulled out that definition, not me. And Judge Susan Webber Wright ruled on it, just as she later ruled their case had no merit in the

be

first place, no legal merit, and dismissed it.

I had nothing to do with the definition. I had nothing to do with the Judge's rulings. I was simply there answering the questions they put to me, under the terms of reference they imposed.

Q Well, the grand jury would like to know, Mr. President, why it is that you think that oral sex performed on you does not fall within the definition of sexual relations as used in your deposition.

A Because that is -- if the deponent is the person who has oral sex performed on him, then the contact is with -- not with anything on that list, but with the lips of another person. It seems to be self-evident that that's what it is. And I thought it was curious.

Let me remind you, sir, I read this carefully. And I thought about it. I thought about what "contact" meant. I thought about what "intent to arouse or gratify" meant.

And I had to admit under this definition that I'd actually had sexual relations with Gennifer Flowers. Now, I would rather have taken a whipping than done that, after all the trouble I'd been through with Gennifer Flowers, and the money I knew that she had made for the story she told about this alleged 12-year affair, which we had done a great deal to disprove.

So, I didn't like any of this. But I had done my

be

best to deal with it and the -- that's what I thought. And I think that's what most people would think, reading that.

Q Would you have been prepared, if asked by the Jones lawyers, would you have been prepared to answer a question directly asked about oral sex performed on you by Monica Lewinsky?

A If the Judge had required me to answer it, of course, I would have answered it. And I would have answered it truthfully, if I --

Q By the way, do you believe that the --

A -- had been required.

Q -- Jones litigants had the same understanding of sexual relations that you claim you have?

A I don't know what their understanding was, sir. My belief is that they thought they'd get this whole thing in, and that they were going to -- what they were trying to do is do just what they did with Gennifer Flowers. They wanted to find anything they could get from me or anyone else that was negative, and then they wanted to leak it to hurt me in the press, which they did even though the Judge ordered them not to.

So, I think their --

Q Wouldn't it -- I'm sorry.

A I think their position, Mr. Bennett -- you asked the question -- their position was, we're going to cast the

be

widest net we can and get as much embarrassing stuff as we can, and then dump it out there and see if we can make him bleed. I think that's what they were trying to do.

Q Don't you think, sir, that they could have done more damage to you politically, or in whatever context, if they had understood the definition in the same way you did and asked the question directly?

A I don't know, sir. As I said, I didn't work with their lawyers in preparing this case. I knew the case was wrong. I knew what our evidence was. By the time of this deposition, they knew what their evidence was.

Their whole strategy was, well, our lawsuit's not good, but maybe we can hurt him with the discovery. And, you know, they did some. But it didn't amount to much.

And did I want, if I could, to avoid talking about Monica Lewinsky? Yes, I'd give anything in the world not to be here talking about it. I'd be giving -- I'd give anything in the world not to have to admit what I've had to admit today.

But if you look at my answer in the Flowers [sic] deposition, at least you know I tried to carefully fit all my answers within the framework there, because otherwise there was no reason in the wide world for me to do anything other than make the statements I'd made about Gennifer Flowers since 1991, that I did not have a 12-year affair with her,

be

and that these, the following accusations she made are false.

So, that's all I can tell you. I can't prove anything.

Q But you did have a great deal of anxiety in the hours and days following the end of your deposition on the 17th. Isn't that fair to say?

A Well, I had a little anxiety the next day, of course, because of the Drudge Report. And I had an anxiety after the deposition because it was more about Monica Lewinsky than it was about Paula Jones.

Q The specificity of the questions relating to Monica Lewinsky alarmed you, isn't that fair to say?

A Yes, and it bothered me, too, that I couldn't remember the answers. It bothered me that I couldn't -- as Mr. Wisenberg pointed out, it bothered me that I couldn't remember all the answers. I did the best I could. And so I wanted to know what the deal was. Sure.

Q Mr. President, to your knowledge, have you turned over, in response to the grand jury subpoenas, all gifts that Monica Lewinsky gave you?

A To my knowledge, I have, sir. As you know, on occasion, Mr. Kendall has asked for your help in identifying those gifts. And I think there were a couple that we came across in our search that were not on the list you gave us, that I remembered in the course of our search had been given to me by Monica Lewinsky and we gave them to you.

So, to the best of my knowledge, we have given you everything we have.

Q Can you explain why, on the very day that Monica Lewinsky testified in the grand jury on August 6th of this year, you wore a necktie that she had given you?

A No, sir, I don't believe I did. What necktie was it?

Q The necktie you wore on August 6th, sir.

A Well, I don't know that it was a necktie that Monica Lewinsky gave me. Can you describe it to me?

Q Well, I don't want to take time at this point, but we will provide you with photographic evidence of that, Mr. President.

A If you give me -- I don't believe that's accurate, Mr. Bennett.

Q So, let me ask the question --

A But if you give it to me, and I look at it and I remember that she gave it to me, I'll be happy to produce it. I do not believe that's right.

Q Well, if you remember that she gave it to you, why haven't you produced it to the grand jury?

A I don't remember that she gave it to me. That's why I asked you what the tie was. I have --

Q Can you --

be

A -- no earthly idea. I believe that, that I did not wear a tie she gave me on August the 6th.

Q Can you tell us why Bayani Nelvis wore a tie that Monica Lewinsky had given you on the day he appeared in the grand jury?

A I don't know that he did.

Q Have you given Bayani Nelvis any ties, sir?

A Oh, yes, a lot of ties.

Q And so if he wore the tie that you gave him, that Monica Lewinsky had given you, that would not have been by design, is that what you are telling us?

A Oh, absolutely not. Let me --

Q You are not --

A May I explain, Mr. Bennett? It won't --

Q Yes.

A -- take long. Every year, since I've been President, I've gotten quite a large number of ties, as you might imagine. I get, I have a couple of friends, one in Chicago and one in Florida who give me a lot of ties, a lot of other people who send me ties all the time, or give them to me when I see them.

So, I always have the growing number of ties in my closet. What I normally do, if someone gives me a tie as a gift, is I wear it a time or two. I may use it. But at the end of every year, and sometimes two times a year, sometimes

be

more, I go through my tie closet and I think of all the things that I won't wear a lot or that I might give away, and I give them mostly to the men who work there.

I give them to people like Glen and Nelvis, who work in the kitchen, back in the White House, or the gentlemen who are my stewards or the butlers, or the people who run the elevators. And I give a lot of ties away a year. I'll bet I -- excluding Christmas, I bet I give 30, 40, maybe more ties away a year, and then, of course, at Christmas, a lot.

So, there would be nothing unusual if, in fact, Nelvis had a tie that originally had come into my tie closet from Monica Lewinsky. It wouldn't be unusual. It wouldn't be by design. And there are several other people of whom that is also true.

Q Mr. President, I'd like to move to a different area right now. I'd like to ask you some questions about Kathleen Willey. You met Kathleen Willey during your 1992 campaign, isn't that so?

A Yes, sir, I did.

Q As a matter of fact, you first saw her at a rope line at the Richmond, Virginia airport on October 13, 1992, is that not correct?

A I don't believe that is correct.

Q When did you first meet her, sir?

be

A Well, let me ask you this. When was the debate in Richmond?

Q I believe it was October 13, 1992, sir.

A Well, I believe that I had met her -- I believe I had met her before then, because Governor Wilder, I believe that was his last year as governor -- I think that's right, 92-93. I believe that I met her in connection with her involvement with Governor Wilder.

And I have the impression -- it's kind of a vague memory, but I have the impression that I had met her once before, at least once before I came to that Richmond debate. Now, I'm not sure of that.

Q Well, at least if you had met her before --

A But I am quite sure she was at the Richmond debate and I did meet her there. I'm quite sure of that.

Q Mr. President, you've seen television footage of you standing on a rope line with Donald Beyer, Lt. Governor Donald Beyer --

A I have.

Q -- asking Mr. Beyer for the name of Kathleen Willey? You've seen that footage, haven't you?

A I don't know that I've seen it, but I am aware that it exists.

Q All right. And you can see him, you can read his lips. He's saying the name Kathleen Willey in response to a

be

question from you, isn't that so?
A That's what I've heard.
Q And, as a matter of fact, you sent Nancy Hernreich, who was present on that day, to go get her telephone number, didn't you, sir?
A I don't believe so.
Q You don't believe so?
A Well, let me say this. If that is true, then I'm quite certain that I had met her before. I would never call someone out of the blue that I saw on a rope line and send Nancy Hernreich to get her number to do it.
Q Even if you were just learning her name for the first time?
A That's correct. I'm not so sure that I didn't ask Don Beyer, if he was on the rope line with me, who she was because I thought I had seen her before or I knew I had seen her before and I didn't remember her name. Now, I do that all the time. For men --
Q Mr. President --
A -- and women.
Q I'm sorry. Do you recall that you sent Nancy Hernreich for her telephone number?
A No, I don't.
Q All right. Do you recall, having received her telephone number, calling her that night?

be

A No, sir, I don't.
Q Do you recall inviting her to meet with you at your hotel that night?
A No, sir, I do not.
Q Do you recall where you stayed in Richmond, Virginia during the debates you've told us about?
A Well, I stayed at some hotel there, I believe.
Q Actually, did you stay at the Williamsburg Inn, not in Richmond?
A Yeah, that's right. We prepared in Williamsburg. That's correct. I believe we prepared in Williamsburg and then went to Richmond for the debate, and then I think we spent the night in Richmond. And the next day, I think we had a rally before we left town. I believe that's right.
Q Do you know of any reason Kathleen Willey's telephone number would appear on your toll records from your room in Williamsburg?
A No, there --
Q If you didn't call her?
A No, I'm not denying that I called her, sir. You asked me a specific question. I won't deny that I called her. I don't know whether I did or not.
Q As a matter of fact, you called her twice that day, didn't you, sir?
A I don't recall. I may well have done it and I

be

don't know why I did it.

Q Well, does it refresh your recollection that you called her and invited her to come to your room that night, sir?

A I don't believe I did that, sir.

Q If Kathleen Willey has said that, she's mistaken or lying, is that correct, Mr. President?

A I do not believe I did that. That's correct.

Q But what is your best recollection of that conversation, those conversations?

A I don't remember talking to her. But I -- it seems to me that at some point -- this is why I believe I had met her before, too. But at some point I had some actual person-to-person conversation with her about my sore throat, or what she thought would be good for it, or something like that. I have some vague memory of that. That's it.

Q Is this the chicken soup conversation, Mr. President?

A Well, I don't know if I would -- maybe that's what she said I should have. I don't remember. But I have no recollection, sir, of asking her to come to my room. I -- and I -- I'm sorry, I don't. I can't -- I won't deny calling her. I don't know if I did call her. I don't know if she tried to call me first. I don't know anything about that. I, I just -- I met her and Doug Wilder. I remember that she

be

and her husband were active for Government Wilder, and that's about all I remember, except that I had a conversation with her around the Richmond debate. I do remember talking to her there.

Q Mr. President, let's move ahead to the episode on November 29, 1993, in which Mrs. Willey met you in your office at the Oval, the subject matter of the "60 Minutes" broadcast a few months ago. You recall that episode?

A I certainly do.

Q Mr. President, in fact, on that date you did make sexual advances on Kathleen Willey, is that not correct?

A That's false.

Q You did grab her breast, as she said?

A I did not.

Q You did place your hand on her groin area, as she said?

A No, I didn't.

Q And you placed her hand on your genitals, did you not?

A Mr. Bennett, I didn't do any of that, and the questions you're asking, I think, betray the bias of this operation that has troubled me for a long time. You know what evidence was released after the "60 Minutes" broadcast that I think pretty well shattered Kathleen Willey's credibility. You know what people down in Richmond said

be

about her. You know what she said about other people that wasn't true. I don't know if you've made all of this available to the grand jury or not.

She was not telling the truth. She asked for the appointment with me. She asked for it repeatedly.

Q Did she make a sexual advance on you, Mr. President?

A On that day, no, she did not. She was troubled.

Q On some other day?

A I wouldn't call it a sexual advance. She was always very friendly. But I never took it seriously.

Q Mr. President, you mentioned the documents that were released and information that came out from people in Richmond, et cetera, after the "60 Minutes" piece was broadcast. As a matter of fact, you were required, under the Court's rulings, to produce those documents in response to document requests by the Jones litigants, isn't that correct?

A No. I believe the Jones litigants' request for production of documents to me ran to documents that were in my personal files and in my personal possessions, and did not cover documents that were White House files. So, I don't believe we were required to produce them.

As a matter of fact, when that story first ran, sir, before "60 Minutes", back in July or so of '97, I was aware that we had some letters. I didn't -- I didn't

be

remember that she'd written us as much as she had and called as much as she had, and asked to see me as often as she had, after this alleged incident. I didn't know the volume of contact that she had which undermined the story she has told. But I knew there was some of it.

And I made a decision that I did not want to release it voluntarily after the Newsweek ran the story, because her friend Julie Steele was in the story saying she asked her -- she, Kathleen Willey -- asked her to lie. And because, frankly, her husband had committed suicide. She apparently was out of money. And I thought, who knows how anybody would react under that. So, I didn't.

But, now when "60 Minutes" came with the story and everybody blew it up, I thought we would release it. But I do not believe we were required to release White House documents to the Jones lawyers.

Q Mr. President, have you made a decision on whether to stay beyond the four hours we agreed to, to accept questions from the grand jury?

MR. KENDALL: We have made an agreement, Mr. Bennett, to give you four hours. We're going to do that. By my watch, there are about 12 minutes left.

MR. BENNETT: I guess that's no. Is that correct, Mr. Kendall?

MR. KENDALL: Yes, that's correct.

be

THE WITNESS: May I ask this question? Could I have a two-minute break?

MR. BENNETT: Sure.

THE WITNESS: I'm sorry to bother you with this. I know we're getting to the end, but I need a little break.

(Whereupon, the proceedings were recessed from 6:04 p.m. until 6:09 p.m.)

BY MR. STARR:

Q Mr. President, at various times in this investigation, officials have invoked executive privilege in response to questions that have been posed to them by the grand jury and in the grand jury. One of the grand jurors has posed the question, did you personally authorize the invocation of executive privilege?

A If the answer is authorized, I think the answer to that would be yes. But I would like the grand jury to know something.

In the cases where we raised the lawyer/client privilege, or executive privilege, or where the Secret Service raised their privilege, and when I say -- I had nothing to do with that. I did not authorize it, approve it, or anything else. That was something they asked to be free to make their decision on by themselves.

In none of those cases did I actually have any worry about what the people involved would say. The reason

be

those privileges were advanced and litigated was that I believed that there was an honest difference between Judge Starr and the Office of Independent Counsel, and Mr. Ruff, my counsel, and I about what the proper balance was in the Constitutional framework.

And I did not want to put the Presidency at risk of being weakened as an institution, without having those matters litigated. Now, we've lost some of those matters. Our people have testified and the grand jury is free to conclude whether they believe that the testimony they gave was damaging to me. But I don't, I don't imagine it was and I wasn't worried about it. It was an honest difference of Constitutional principal between Judge Starr and the Office of Independent Counsel and the White House.

Q Mr. President, a couple of very brief questions, given our time. The White House's outside counsel, Mr. Eggleston, withdrew the White House's appeal from Chief Judge Johnson's ruling that the invocation of executive privilege had to give way to the grand jury's right to the information, that ruling in connection with the testimony of Mr. Blumenthal and Mr. Lindsey.

Were you informed of that fact that the appeal had been withdrawn?

A I was informed of it and, as a matter of fact, I was consulted about it and I strongly supported it. I didn't

be

want to appeal it.

Q Okay.

A It was -- I had -- my main difference, Judge Starr, as you know with you, is, and with some of the Court decisions, is on the extent to which members of the White House Counsel's staff, like Mr. Lindsey, should be able to counsel the President on matters that may seem like they are private, like the Jones case, but inevitably intrude on the daily work of the President.

But I didn't really want to advance an executive privilege claim in this case beyond having it litigated, so that we, we had not given up on principal this matter, without having some judge rule on it. So, I made --

Q Excuse me. And you are satisfied that you now have the benefit of that ruling, is that correct?

A Well, yes. I just didn't want to, I didn't want to -- yes. And I didn't -- I made the -- I actually, I think, made the call, or at least I supported the call. I did not, I strongly felt we should not appeal your victory on the executive privilege issue.

MR. STARR: Thank you.

BY MR. WISENBERG:

Q Mr. President, among the many remaining questions of the grand jurors is one that they would like answered directly without relation to, without regard to inferences,

be

which is the following: Did Monica Lewinsky perform oral sex on you? They would like a direct answer to that, yes or no?

A Well, that's not the first time that question's been asked. But since I believe, and I think any person, reasonable person would believe that that is not covered in the definition of sexual relations I was given, I'm not going to answer, except to refer to my statement.

I had intimate contact with her that was inappropriate. I do not believe any of the contacts I had with her violated the definition I was given. Therefore, I believe I did not do anything but testify truthfully on these matters.

Q We have a couple of photos of the tie that you wore.

A Would you please give them to me?

Q Yes.

A Now, this is August 6th, is that correct?

Q 1998, the day that Monica Lewinsky appeared at the grand jury. And my question to you on that is, were you sending some kind of a signal to her by wearing --

A No, sir.

Q -- one of the ties -- let me finish, if you don't mind, sir.

A Sure. I'm sorry. My apology.

Q Were you sending some kind of a signal to her by

be

wearing a tie she had given you on the day that she appeared in front of the grand jury?

A No, sir. I don't believe she gave me this tie. And if I was sending a signal, I'm about to send a terrible signal, and maybe you ought to invite her to talk again. I don't, I don't want to make light about this. I don't believe she gave me this tie. I don't remember giving, her giving me this tie. And I had absolutely no thought of this in my mind when I wore it.

If she did, I, I, I, I don't remember it, and this is the very first I've ever heard of it.

Q Did you realize when you --

MR. WISENBERG: Can I just have for the record, what are the exhibit numbers?

MS. WIRTH: Yes. They should be WJC-5 and 6.

(Grand Jury Exhibits WJC-5 and WJC-6 were marked for identification.)

MR. WISENBERG: Mr. Bennett has some more questions.

BY MR. BENNETT:

Q Mr. President, we were talking about your responses to document requests in the Jones litigation, and I had just asked you about turning over the Kathleen Willey correspondence. Do you recall that?

be

A Yes, sir, I do.

Q And, if I understand your testimony, you did not believe that the request for documents compelled you to search for those documents in the White House?

A Mr. Bennett, I want to answer this question in a way that is completely satisfactory to you and the grand jury, without violating the lawyer/client privilege, which is still intact.

It was my understanding that in the request for production of documents, that those requests ran against and operated against my personal files. Now, I have some personal files in the White House. And, I'm sorry. In this case I'm not my own lawyer, and I don't know how the distinction is made between files which are the personal files of the President, and files which are White House files.

But I do have a very clear memory that we were duty-bound to search and turn over evidence or, excuse me, documents that were in my personal file, but not in the White House files. And I believe that the letters to which you refer, Ms. Willey's letters and Ms. Willey's phone messages, were in the White House files. And, therefore, I was instructed at least that they were, that we had fully compiled with the Jones lawyers' request, and that these documents were outside the request.

be

Q Mr. President, you're not contending that White House documents, documents stored in the fashion that these were stored, are beyond your care, custody or control, are you?

A Mr. Bennett, that may be a legal term of art that I don't have the capacity to answer. I can only tell you what I remember. I remember being told in no uncertain terms that if these were personal files of the President, we had to produce documents. If they were essentially White House files, we were not bound to do so. So, we didn't.

Q So, you are saying somebody told you that you didn't have to produce White House documents?

A That's --

MR. KENDALL: I'm going to caution the witness that this question should not invade the sphere of the attorney/client privilege, and any conversations with counsel are privileged.

THE WITNESS: Let me say, and maybe, Mr. Kendall, we need a break here. I'm not trying -- I'm trying to avoid invading the lawyer/client privilege.

I can just tell you that I did, I did the best I could to comply with this. And eventually we did make, of course, all of this public. And it was damaging to Ms. Willey and her credibility. It was terribly damaging to her. And the first time she came out with this story, I didn't do

be

it. I only did it when they went back on "60 Minutes" and they made this big deal of it.

It turned out she had tried to sell this story and make all this money. And, I must say, when I saw how many letters and phone calls and messages there were that totally undercut her account, I, myself, was surprised.

BY MR. BENNETT:

Q But you knew there were letters?

A I did, sir.

Q And the White House --

A I knew that --

Q -- is under your control, isn't it, Mr. President?

A Well, Mr. Bennett, again, I'm not trying to be -- some days I think it's under my control and some days I'm not so sure.

But, if you're asking me, as a matter of law, I don't want to discuss that because that's -- I mean, I'll be glad to discuss it, but I'm not the person who should make that decision. That decision should be made by someone who can give me appropriate advice, and I don't want to violate the lawyer/client privilege here.

Q Well, Mr. President, how are the letters from Kathleen Willey that surfaced after the "60 Minutes" episode aired any different from the correspondence and other matters, tangible items, tangible things, of Monica Lewinsky?

be

A Well, the items you asked for from Monica Lewinsky that I produced to you, you know that there was a tie, a coffee cup, a number of other things I had. Then I told you there were some things that had been in my possession that I no longer had, I believe. I don't remember if I did that. There was one book, I remember, that I left on vacation last summer.

Q The same documents that the Jones litigants had asked you for?

A Yes. But, at any rate, they were different. They were in my -- the gifts were in my personal possession, clearly.

Q In your office at the Oval?

A Well, in the books, now, the Presidential books were with my other books that belong to me personally. They were in the Oval.

Q Where do you draw the line, sir, between personal and White House? Now, you are talking about some documents that are in the Oval Office and we don't see where you are drawing the line.

A Well, Mr. Bennett, I don't think these -- I think the Lewinsky gifts were all non-documents. And you can --

MR. KENDALL: Is that the time?

THE WITNESS: Just a moment.

MR. KENDALL: Excuse me, Mr. Bennett.

be

THE WITNESS: Well, I'd like to --

MR. KENDALL: You've got thirty more seconds.

THE WITNESS: -- finish answering the question, please, because this is a legitimate question, I think.

There is somebody in the White House, Mr. Bennett, who can answer your question, and you could call them up and they could answer it, under oath, for you. There is some way of desegregating what papers are personal to the President and what papers are part of the White House official archives papers. And I don't know how the distinction is made. I just don't know.

BY MR. BENNETT:

Q Did you direct personnel, Nancy Hernreich or anyone else, to make a search for correspondence from Kathleen Willey and Monica Lewinsky when those documents were called for in the Jones litigation, sir? Did you direct that somebody on the White House staff look for those documents?

A I don't believe that I was in charge of doing that, the document search, sir. So, the strict answer to that question is that I didn't.

Q So, you sat back and relied on this legalistic distinction between your personal, which you are in control of, and the White House which, by the way, you are also in control of; is that not correct?

MR. KENDALL: I won't object to the argumentative

be

form of the question. We'll allow the witness to answer it. We're now over time, even the 30 seconds. So, this will be it.

THE WITNESS: Mr. Bennett, I haven't said this all day long, but I would like to say it now.

Most of my time and energy in the last five and a half years have been devoted to my job. Now, during that five and a half years, I have also had to contend with things no previous President has ever had to contend with: a lawsuit that was dismissed for lack of legal merit, but that cost me a fortune and was designed to embarrass me; this independent counsel inquiry, which has gone on a very long time and cost a great deal of money, and about which serious questions have been raised; and a number of other things.

And, during this whole time, I have tried as best I could to keep my mind on the job the American people gave me. I did not make the legal judgment about how the documents were decided upon that should be given to the Jones lawyers, and ones that shouldn't.

And, I might add that Ms. Willey would have been very happy that these papers were not turned over, because they damaged her credibility so much, had they not ultimately been turned over after she made, I think, the grievous error of going on "60 Minutes" and saying all those things that were not true.

be

But I did not make the decision. It was not my job. This thing is being managed by other people. I was trying to do my job.

BY MR. BENNETT:

Q Mr. President, the grand jury, I am notified, still has unanswered questions of you, and we appeal to you again to make yourself available to answer those questions.

MR. KENDALL: Mr. Bennett, our agreement was for four hours and we have not counted the break time against that, and I think that will be --

THE WITNESS: You know, Mr. Bennett, I wish I could do it. I wish the grand jurors had been allowed to come here today as we invited them to do. I wanted them down here. I wanted them to be able to see me directly. I wanted them to be able to ask these questions directly. But, we made an agreement that was different, and I think I will go ahead and stick with the terms of it.

BY MR. BENNETT:

Q The invitation was made after there was political fallout over the deposition circumstances with the satellite transmission and the taping. Isn't that so?

A I don't know about the taping, Mr. Bennett. I understood that the prospect of the grand jurors coming down here was raised fairly early. I don't know.

Q Just for the record --

be

A But, anyway, I wish they could have. I respect the grand jury. I respect the --

MR. WISENBERG: Just for the record, the invitation to the grand jury was contingent upon us not videotaping, and we had to videotape because we have an absent grand juror.

MR. KENDALL: Is that the only reason, Mr. Wisenberg, you have to videotape?

THE WITNESS: Well, yes. Do you want to answer that?

MR. BITTMAN: Thank you, Mr. President.

(Whereupon, at 6:25 p.m., the proceedings were concluded.)

* * * * *

CERTIFICATE OF COURT REPORTER - NOTARY PUBLIC

I, Elizabeth A. Eastman, the officer before whom the foregoing proceedings were taken, do hereby certify that the witness whose testimony appears in the foregoing was duly sworn by me; that the testimony of said witness was taken by me electronically and thereafter reduced to typewriting by me; that this is a true record of the testimony given by said witness; that I am neither counsel for, related to, nor employed by any of the parties to the action in which this deposition was taken; and, further, that I am not a relative or employee of any attorney or counsel employed by the parties hereto, nor financially or otherwise interested in the outcome of the action.

Elizabeth A. Eastman
NOTARY PUBLIC FOR THE
DISTRICT OF COLUMBIA

My Commission Expires:
July 31, 2000

William Jefferson Clinton, 8/17/98

Videotaped Testimony before the Grand Jury

Page 2 to Page

CONDENSED TRANSCRIPT AND CONCORDANCE
PREPARED BY:

OFFICE OF THE INDEPENDENT COUNSEL
1001 Pennsylvania Avenue, N.W.
Suite 490-North
Washington, DC 20004
Phone: 202-514-8688
FAX: 202-514-8802

Page 2

OFFICE OF THE INDEPENDENT COUNSEL

TESTIMONY OF
WILLIAM JEFFERSON CLINTON

Monday, August 17, 1998
Washington, D. C.

Videotaped testimony of
PRESIDENT WILLIAM JEFFERSON CLINTON
before the Independent Counsel, held at The White House, Washington, D. C., beginning at 1:03 p.m., when were present on behalf of the respective parties:

FOR THE INDEPENDENT COUNSEL:
KENNETH W. STARR, ESQ.
Independent Counsel
JACKIE M. BENNETT, JR., ESQ.
ROBERT J. BITTMAN, ESQ.
SOLOMON L. WISENBERG, ESQ.
Deputy Independent Counsel
MICHAEL W. EMMICK, ESQ.
MARY ANNE WIRTH, ESQ.
BERNARD JAMES APPERSON, ESQ.
Associate Independent Counsel

FOR THE PRESIDENT:
DAVID E. KENDALL, ESQ.
NICOLE SELIGMAN, ESQ.
Williams & Connolly
CHARLES F. C. RUFF, ESQ.
Counsel to the President

ALSO PRESENT:
JAMES P. RICKARDS, JR.
Senior Consultant, OIC
GARY E. BRESNAHAN
White House Technical Staff
Secret Service Agent

Court Reporter: Elizabeth A. Eastman

Page 3

PROCEEDINGS

MR. APPERSON: Mr. Wisenberg, the grand jury is in session. There is a quorum. There are no unauthorized persons in the grand jury room and they are prepared to receive the testimony of the President.
MR. WISENBERG: Thank you, Mr. Apperson. If we could proceed with the oath, please?
WHEREUPON,
WILLIAM JEFFERSON CLINTON
having been called for examination by the Independent Counsel, and having been first duly sworn, was examined and testified as follows:
EXAMINATION BY THE INDEPENDENT COUNSEL
BY MR. WISENBERG:
Q Good afternoon, Mr. President.
A Good afternoon.
Q Could you please state your full name for the record, sir?
A William Jefferson Clinton.
Q My name is Sol Wisenberg and I'm a Deputy Independent Counsel with the Office of Independent Counsel. With me today are some other attorneys from the Office of Independent Counsel.
At the courtroom are the ladies and gentlemen of the grand jury prepared to receive your testimony as you give

Page 4

it. Do you understand, sir?
A Yes, I do.
Q This proceeding is subject to Rule 6(e) of the Federal Rules of Criminal Procedure as modified by Judge Johnson's order. You are appearing voluntarily today as a part of an agreement worked out between your attorney, the Office of the Independent Counsel, and with the approval of Judge Johnson.
Is that correct, sir?
A That is correct.
MR. KENDALL: Mr. Wisenberg, excuse me. You referred to Judge Johnson's order. I'm not familiar with that order. Have we been served that, or not?
MR. WISENBERG: No. My understanding is that that is an order that the Judge is going to sign today. She didn't have the name of a WHCA person. And basically my understanding is that it will cover all of the attorneys here today and the technical people in the room, so that they will be authorized persons permitted to hear grand jury testimony that they otherwise wouldn't be authorize to hear.
MR. KENDALL: Thank you.
BY MR. WISENBERG:
Q The grand jury, Mr. President, has been empaneled by the United States District Court for the District of Columbia. Do you understand that, sir?

Page 5

A I do.
Q And, among other things, is currently investigating under the authority of the Court of Appeals upon application by the Attorney General, whether Monica Lewinsky or others obstructed justice, intimidated witnesses, or committed other crimes related to the case of Jones v. Clinton.
Do you understand that, sir?
A I do.
Q And today, you will be receiving questions not only from attorneys on the OIC staff, but from some of the grand jurors, too. Do you understand that?
A Yes, sir, I do.
Q I'm going to talk briefly about your rights and responsibilities as a grand jury witness. Normally, grand jury witnesses, while not allowed to have attorneys in the grand jury room with them, can stop and consult with their attorneys. Under our arrangement today, your attorneys are here and present for consultation and you can break to consult with them as necessary, but it won't count against our total time.
Do you understand that, sir?
A I do understand that.
Q You have a privilege against self-incrimination. If a truthful answer to any question would tend to incriminate you, you can invoke the privilege and that

Page 6

invocation will not be used against you. Do you understand that?
A I do.
Q And if you don't invoke it, however, any answer that you do give can and will be used against you. Do you understand that, sir?
A I do.
Q Mr. President, you understand that your testimony here today is under oath?
A I do.
Q And do you understand that because you have sworn to tell the truth, the whole truth, and nothing but the truth, that if you were to lie or intentionally mislead the grand jury, you could be prosecuted for perjury and/or obstruction of justice?
A I believe that's correct.
Q Is there anything that you -- I've stated to you regarding your rights and responsibilities that you would like me to clarify or that you don't understand?
A No, sir.
Q Mr. President, I would like to read for you a portion of Federal Rule of Evidence 603, which discusses the important function the oath has in our judicial system.
It says that the purpose of the oath is one, "calculated to awaken the witness' conscience and impress the

Page 7

witness' mind with the duty" to tell the truth.
Could you please tell the grand jury what that oath means to you for today's testimony?
A I have sworn an oath to tell the grand jury the truth, and that's what I intend to do.
Q You understand that it requires you to give the whole truth, that is, a complete answer to each question, sir?
A I will answer each question as accurately and fully as I can.
Q Now, you took the same oath to tell the truth, the whole truth, and nothing but the truth on January 17th, 1998 in a deposition in the Paula Jones litigation; is that correct, sir?
A I did take an oath then.
Q Did the oath you took on that occasion mean the same to you then as it does today?
A I believed then that I had to answer the questions truthfully, that is correct.
Q I'm sorry. I didn't hear you, sir.
A I believed that I had to answer the questions truthfully. That's correct.
Q And it meant the same to you then as it does today?
A Well, no one read me a definition then and we didn't go through this exercise then. I swore an oath to

Page 8

tell the truth, and I believed I was bound to be truthful and I tried to be.

Q At the Paula Jones deposition, you were represented by Mr. Robert Bennett, your counsel, is that correct?

A That is correct.

Q He was authorized by you to be your representative there, your attorney, is that correct?

A That is correct.

Q Your counsel, Mr. Bennett, indicated at page 5 of the deposition, lines 10 through 12, and I'm quoting, "the President intends to give full and complete answers as Ms. Jones is entitled to have".

My question to you is, do you agree with your counsel that a plaintiff in a sexual harassment case is, to use his words, entitled to have the truth?

A I believe that I was bound to give truthful answers, yes, sir.

Q But the question is, sir, do you agree with your counsel that a plaintiff in a sexual harassment case is entitled to have the truth?

A I believe when a witness is under oath in a civil case, or otherwise under oath, the witness should do everything possible to answer the questions truthfully.

MR. WISENBERG: I'm going to turn over questioning now to Mr. Bittman of our office, Mr. President.

Page 9

BY MR. BITTMAN:

Q Good afternoon, Mr. President.

A Good afternoon, Mr. Bittman.

Q My name is Robert Bittman. I'm an attorney with the Office of Independent Counsel.

Mr. President, we are first going to turn to some of the details of your relationship with Monica Lewinsky that follow up on your deposition that you provided in the Paula Jones case, as was referenced, on January 17th, 1998.

The questions are uncomfortable, and I apologize for that in advance. I will try to be as brief and direct as possible.

Mr. President, were you physically intimate with Monica Lewinsky?

A Mr. Bittman, I think maybe I can save the – you and the grand jurors a lot of time if I read a statement, which I think will make it clear what the nature of my relationship with Ms. Lewinsky was and how it related to the testimony I gave, what I was trying to do in that testimony. And I think it will perhaps make it possible for you to ask even more relevant questions from your point of view.

And, with your permission, I'd like to read that statement.

Q Absolutely. Please, Mr. President.

A When I was alone with Ms. Lewinsky on certain

Page 10

occasions in early 1996 and once in early 1997, I engaged in conduct that was wrong. These encounters did not consist of sexual intercourse. They did not constitute sexual relations as I understood that term to be defined at my January 17th, 1998 deposition. But they did involve inappropriate intimate contact.

These inappropriate encounters ended, at my insistence, in early 1997. I also had occasional telephone conversations with Ms. Lewinsky that included inappropriate sexual banter.

I regret that what began as a friendship came to include this conduct, and I take full responsibility for my actions.

While I will provide the grand jury whatever other information I can, because of privacy considerations affecting my family, myself, and others, and in an effort to preserve the dignity of the office I hold, this is all I will say about the specifics of these particular matters.

I will try to answer, to the best of my ability, other questions including questions about my relationship with Ms. Lewinsky; questions about my understanding of the term "sexual relations", as I understood it to be defined at my January 17th, 1998 deposition; and questions concerning alleged subornation of perjury, obstruction of justice, and intimidation of witnesses.

Page 11

That, Mr. Bittman, is my statement.

Q Thank you, Mr. President. And, with that, we would like to take a break.

A Would you like to have this?

Q Yes, please. As a matter of fact, why don't we have that marked as Grand Jury Exhibit WJC-1.

(Grand Jury Exhibit WJC-1 was marked for identification.)

THE WITNESS: So, are we going to take a break?

MR. KENDALL: Yes. We will take a break. Can we have the camera off, now, please? And it's 1:14.

(Whereupon, the proceedings were recessed from 1:14 p.m. until 1:30 p.m.)

MR. KENDALL: 1:30, Bob.

MR. BITTMAN: It's 1:30 and we have the feed with the grand jury.

BY MR. BITTMAN:

Q Good afternoon again, Mr. President.

A Good afternoon, Mr. Bittman.

(Discussion off the record.)

BY MR. BITTMAN:

Q Mr. President, your statement indicates that your contacts with Ms. Lewinsky did not involve any inappropriate, intimate contact.

MR. KENDALL: Mr. Bittman, excuse me. The

Page 12

witness –

THE WITNESS: No, sir. It indicates –

MR. KENDALL: The witness does not have –

THE WITNESS: – that it did involve inappropriate and intimate contact.

BY MR. BITTMAN:

Q Pardon me. That it did involve inappropriate, intimate contact.

A Yes, sir, it did.

MR. KENDALL: Mr. Bittman, the witness – the witness does not have a copy of the statement. We just have the one copy.

MR. BITTMAN: If he wishes –

MR. KENDALL: Thank you.

MR. BITTMAN: – his statement back?

BY MR. BITTMAN:

Q Was this contact with Ms. Lewinsky, Mr. President, did it involve any sexual contact in any way, shape, or form?

A Mr. Bittman, I said in this statement I would like to stay to the terms of the statement. I think it's clear what inappropriately intimate is. I have said what it did not include. I – it did not include sexual intercourse, and I do not believe it included conduct which falls within the definition I was given in the Jones deposition. And I would like to stay with that characterization.

Page 13

Q Let us then move to the definition that was provided you during your deposition. We will have that marked as Grand Jury Exhibit WJC-2.

(Grand Jury Exhibit WJC-2 was marked for identification.)

BY MR. BITTMAN:

Q This is an exact copy, Mr. President, of the exhibit that was provided you during that deposition. And I'm sure you remember from the deposition that paragraph (1) of the definition remained in effect. Judge Wright ruled that that was to be the guiding definition, and that paragraphs (2) and (3) were stricken.

Do you remember that, Mr. President?

A Yes. Specifically what I remember is there were two different discussions, I think, of this. There was quite an extended one in the beginning, and everybody was entering into it. And in the end, the Judge said that she would take the first definition and strike the rest of it. That's my memory.

Q Did you – well, at page 19 of your deposition in that case, the attorney who provided you with the definition asked you, "Would you please take whatever time you need to read this definition". And later on in the deposition, you did, of course, refer to the definition several times.

Were you, during the deposition, familiar with the

Page 14

definition?

A Yes, sir. My – let me just ask a question. If you are going to ask me about my deposition, could I have a copy of it? Does anybody have a copy of it?

Q Yes. We have a copy. We'll provide you with a copy.

MS. WIRTH: We will mark it as Grand Jury Exhibit WJC-3.

(Grand Jury Exhibit WJC-3 was marked for identification.)

THE WITNESS: Now, did you say that was on page 19, Mr. Bittman?

BY MR. BITTMAN:

Q It was at page 19, Mr. President, beginning at line 21, and I'll read it in full. This is from the Jones attorney. "Would you please take whatever time you need to read this definition, because when I use the term `sexual relations', this is what I mean today."

A All right. Yes, that starts on 19. But let me say that there is a – just for the record, my recollection was accurate. There is a long discussion here between the attorney and the Judge. It goes on until page 23. And in the end the Judge says, "I'm talking only about part one in the definition", and "Do you understand that"? And I answer, "I do."

Page 15

The judge says part one, and then the lawyer for Ms. Jones says he's only talking about part one and asked me if I understand it. And I say, I do, and that was my understanding.

I might also note that when I was given this and began to ask questions about it, I actually circled number one. This is my circle here. I remember doing that so I could focus only on those two lines, which is what I did.

Q Did you understand the words in the first portion of the exhibit, Mr. President, that is, "For the purposes of this deposition, a person engages in `sexual relations' when the person knowingly engages in or causes"?

Did you understand, do you understand the words there in that phrase?

A Yes. My – I can tell you what my understanding of the definition is, if you want me to –

Q Sure.

A – do it. My understanding of this definition is it covers contact by the person being deposed with the enumerated areas, if the contact is done with an intent to arouse or gratify. That's my understanding of the definition.

Q What did you believe the definition to include and exclude? What kinds of activities?

A I thought the definition included any activity by

Page 16

the person being deposed, where the person was the actor and came in contact with those parts of the bodies with the purpose or intent or gratification, and excluded any other activity.

For example, kissing is not covered by that, I don't think.

Q Did you understand the definition to be limited to sexual activity?

A Yes, I understood the definition to be limited to, to physical contact with those areas of the bodies with the specific intent to arouse or gratify. That's what I understood it to be.

Q What specific acts did the definition include, as you understood the definition on January 17, 1998?

A Any contact with the areas there mentioned, sir. If you contacted, if you contacted those parts of the body with an intent to arouse or gratify, that is covered.

Q What did you understand –

A The person being deposed. If the person being deposed contacted those parts of another person's body with an intent to arouse or gratify, that was covered.

Q What did you understand the word "causes", in the first phrase? That is, "For the purposes of this deposition, a person engaged in `sexual relations' when the person knowingly" causes contact?

Page 17

A I don't know what that means. It doesn't make any sense to me in this context, because – I think what I thought there was, since this was some sort of – as I remember, they said in the previous discussion – and I'm only remembering now, so if I make a mistake you can correct me. As I remember from the previous discussion, this was some kind of definition that had something to do with sexual harassment. So, that implies it's forcing to me, and I – and there was never any issue of forcing in the case involving, well, any of these questions they were asking me.

They made it clear in this discussion I just reviewed that what they were referring to was intentional sexual conduct, not some sort of forcible abusive behavior.

So, I basically – I don't think I paid any attention to it because it appeared to me that that was something that had no reference to the facts that they admitted they were asking me about.

Q So, if I can be clear, Mr. President, was it your understanding back in January that the definition, now marked as Grand Jury Exhibit 2, only included consensual sexual activity?

A No. My understanding – let me go back and say it. My understanding – I'll tell you what it did include. My understanding was, what I was giving to you, was that what was covered in those first two lines was any direct contact

Page 18

by the person being deposed with those parts of another person's body, if the contact was done with an intent to arouse or gratify. That's what I believed it meant.

That's what I believed it meant then reading it. That's what I believe it means today.

Q I'm just trying to understand, Mr. President. You indicated that you put the definition in the context of a sexual harassment case.

A No, no. I think it was not in the context of sexual harassment. I just reread those four pages, which obviously the grand jury doesn't have. But there was some reference to the fact that this definition apparently bore some, had some connection to some definition in another context, and that this was being used not in that context, not necessarily in the context of sexual harassment.

So, I would think that this "causes" would be, would mean to force someone to do something. That's what I read it. That's the only point I'm trying to make.

Therefore, I did not believe that anyone had ever suggested that I had forced anyone to do anything, and that I – and I did not do that. And so that could not have had any bearing on any questions related to Ms. Lewinsky.

Q I suppose, since you have now read portions of the transcript again, that you were reminded that you did not ask for any clarification of the terms. Is that correct? Of the

Page 19

definition?

A No, sir. I thought it was a rather – when I read it, I thought it was a rather strange definition. But it was the one the Judge decided on and I was bound by it. So, I took it.

Q During the deposition, you remember that Ms. Lewinsky's name came up and you were asked several questions about her. Do you remember that?

A Yes, sir, I do.

Q During those – or before those questions actually got started, your attorney, Mr. Bennett, objected to any questions about Ms. Lewinsky, and he represented to Judge Wright, who was presiding – that was unusual, wasn't it, that a federal judge would come and actually – in your experience – that a federal judge would come and preside at a deposition?

MR. KENDALL: Mr. Bittman, excuse me. Could you identify the transcript page upon which Mr. Bennett objected to all testimony about Ms. Lewinsky before it got started?

MR. BITTMAN: The objection, this quote that I'm referring to, is going to begin at page 54 of the deposition.

MR. KENDALL: That is into the testimony though, after the testimony about Ms. Lewinsky has begun, is it not?

BY MR. BITTMAN:

Q Mr. President, is it unusual for a federal judge to

Page 20

preside over a civil deposition?

A I think it is, but this was an unusual case. I believe I know why she did it.

Q Your attorney, Mr. Bennett, objected to the questions about Ms. Lewinsky, didn't he?

A What page is that on, sir?

Q Page 54, where he questions whether the attorneys for Ms. Jones had a good faith basis to ask some of the questions that they were posing to you. His objections actually begin on page 53.

Since, as the President pointed out that the grand jurors correctly do not have a copy of the deposition, I will read the portion that I am referring to. And this begins at line 1 on page 54.

"I question the good faith of counsel, the innuendo in the question. Counsel is fully aware that Ms. Lewinsky has filed, has an affidavit which they are in possession of saying that there is absolutely no sex of any kind in any manner, shape or form, with President Clinton".

A Where is that?

Q That is on page 54, Mr. President, beginning at line 1, about midway through line 1.

A Well, actually, in the present tense that is an accurate statement. That was an, that was an accurate statement, if – I don't – I think what Mr. Bennett was

Page 21

concerned about, if I – maybe it would be helpful to you and to the grand jurors, quite apart from these comments, if I could tell you what his state of mind was, what my state of mind was, and why I think the Judge was there in the first place.

If you don't want me to do it, I won't. But I think it will help to explain a lot of this.

Q Well, we are interested, and I know from the questions that we've received from the grand jurors they are interested in knowing what was going on in your mind when you were reading Grand Jury Exhibit 2, and what you understood that definition to include.

Our question goes to whether – and you were familiar, and what Mr. Bennett was referring to obviously is Ms. Lewinsky's affidavit. And we will have that marked, Mr. President, as Grand Jury Exhibit WJC-4.

(Grand Jury Exhibit WJC-4 was marked for identification.)

BY MR. BITTMAN:

Q And you remember that Ms. Lewinsky's affidavit said that she had had no sexual relationship with you. Do you remember that?

A I do.

Q And do you remember in the deposition that Mr. Bennett asked you about that. This is at the end of the –

Page 22

towards the end of the deposition. And you indicated, he asked you whether the statement that Ms. Lewinsky made in her affidavit was –

A Truthful.

Q – true. And you indicated that it was absolutely correct.

A I did. And at the time that she made the statement, and indeed to the present day because, as far as I know, she was never deposed since the Judge ruled she would not be permitted to testify in a case the Judge ruled had no merit; that is, this case we're talking about.

I believe at the time that she filled out this affidavit, if she believed that the definition of sexual relationship was two people having intercourse, then this is accurate. And I believe that is the definition that most ordinary Americans would give it.

If you said Jane and Harry have a sexual relationship, and you're not talking about people being drawn into a lawsuit and being given definitions, and then a great effort to trick them in some way, but you are just talking about people in ordinary conversations, I'll bet the grand jurors, if they were talking about two people they know, and said they have a sexual relationship, they meant they were sleeping together; they meant they were having intercourse together.

Page 23

So, I'm not at all sure that this affidavit is not true and was not true in Ms. Lewinsky's mind at the time she swore it out.

Q Did you talk with Ms. Lewinsky about what she meant to write in her affidavit?

A I didn't talk to her about her definition. I did not know what was in this affidavit before it was filled out specifically. I did not know what words were used specifically before it was filled out, or what meaning she gave to them.

But I'm just telling you that it's certainly true what she says here, that we didn't have – there was no employment, no benefit in exchange, there was nothing having anything to do with sexual harassment. And if she defined sexual relationship in the way I think most Americans do, meaning intercourse, then she told the truth.

Q My question –

A And that depends on what was in her mind. I don't know what was in her mind. You'll have to ask her that.

Q But you indicated before that you were aware of what she intended by the term "sexual relationship".

A No, sir. I said I thought that this could be a truthful affidavit. And when I read it, since that's the way I would define it, since – keep in mind, she was not, she was not bound by this sexual relations definition, which is

Page 24

highly unusual; I think anybody would admit that. When she used a different term, sexual relationship, if she meant by that what most people mean by it, then that is not an untruthful statement.

Q So, your definition of sexual relationship is intercourse only, is that correct?

A No, not necessarily intercourse only. But it would include intercourse. I believe, I believe that the common understanding of the term, if you say two people are having a sexual relationship, most people believe that includes intercourse. So, if that's what Ms. Lewinsky thought, then this is a truthful affidavit. I don't know what was in her mind. But if that's what she thought, the affidavit is true.

Q What else would sexual relationship include besides intercourse?

A Well, that – I think – let me answer what I said before. I think most people when they use that term include sexual relationships and whatever other sexual contact is involved in a particular relationship. But they think it includes intercourse as well. And I would have thought so. Before I got into this case and heard all I've heard, and seen all I've seen, I would have thought that that's what nearly everybody thought it meant.

Q Well, I ask, Mr. President, because your attorney, using the very document, Grand Jury Exhibit 4, WJC-4,

Page 25

represented to Judge Wright that his understanding of the meaning of that affidavit, which you've indicated you thought Ms. Lewinsky thought was, she was referring just to intercourse, he says to Judge Wright that it meant absolutely no sex of any kind in any manner, shape or form.

A Well, let me say this. I didn't have any discussion obviously at this moment with Mr. Bennett. I'm not even sure I paid much attention to what he was saying. I was thinking, I was ready to get on with my testimony here and they were having these constant discussions all through the deposition. But that statement in the present tense, at least, is not inaccurate, if that's what Mr. Bennett meant. That is, at the time that he said that, and for some time before, that would be a completely accurate statement.

Now, I don't believe that he was – I don't know what he meant. You'd have to talk to him, because I just wasn't involved in this, and I didn't pay much attention to what was being said. I was just waiting for them to get back to me. So, I can't comment on, or be held responsible for, whatever he said about that, I don't think.

Q Well, if you – do you agree with me that if he mislead Judge Wright in some way that you would have corrected the record and said, excuse me, Mr. Bennett, I think the Judge is getting a misimpression by what you're saying?

Page 26

A Mr. Bennett was representing me. I wasn't representing him. And I wasn't even paying much attention to this conversation, which is why, when you started asking me about this, I asked to see the deposition. I was focusing on my answers to the questions. And I've told you what I believe about this deposition, which I believe to be true.

And it's obvious, and I think by your questions you have betrayed that the Jones lawyers' strategy in this case had nothing to do with uncovering or proving sexual harassment.

By the time this discovery started, they knew they had a bad case on the law and they knew what our evidence was. They knew they had a lousy case on the facts. And so their strategy, since they were being funded by my political opponents, was to have this dragnet of discovery. They wanted to cover everybody. And they convinced the Judge, because she gave them strict orders not to leak, that they should be treated like other plaintiffs in other civil cases, and how could they ever know whether there had been any sexual harassment, unless they first knew whether there had been any sex.

And so, with that broad mandate limited by time and employment in the federal or state government, they proceeded to cross the country and try to turn up whatever they could; not because they thought it would help their case. By the

Page 27

time they did this discovery, they knew what this deal was in their case, and they knew what was going to happen. And Judge Wright subsequently threw it out. What they –

Q With all respect, Mister –

A Now, let me finish, Mr. Bennett [sic]. I mean, you brought this up. Excuse me, Mr. Bittman.

What they wanted to do, and what they did do, and what they had done by the time I showed up here, was to find any negative information they could on me, whether it was true or not; get it in a deposition; and then leak it, even though it was illegal to do so. It happened repeatedly. The Judge gave them orders.

One of the reasons she was sitting in that deposition was because she was trying to make sure that it didn't get out of hand.

But that was their strategy, and they did a good job of it, and they got away with it. I've been subject to quite a lot of illegal leaking, and they had a very determined deliberate strategy, because their real goal was to hurt me. When they knew they couldn't win the lawsuit, they thought, well, maybe we can pummel him. Maybe they thought I'd settle. Maybe they just thought they would get some political advantage out of it. But that's what was going on here.

Now, I'm trying to be honest with you, and it hurts

Page 28

me. And I'm trying to tell you the truth about what happened between Ms. Lewinsky and me. But that does not change the fact that the real reason they were zeroing in on anybody was to try to get any person in there, no matter how uninvolved with Paula Jones, no matter how uninvolved with sexual harassment, so they could hurt me politically. That's what was going on.

Because by then, by this time, this thing had been going on a long time. They knew what our evidence was. They knew what the law was in the circuit in which we were bringing this case. And so they just thought they would take a wrecking ball to me and see if they could do some damage.

Q Judge Wright had ruled that the attorneys in the Jones case were permitted to ask you certain questions, didn't she?

A She certainly did. And they asked them and I did my best to answer them. I'm just trying to tell –

Q And was it your responsibility –

A – you what my state of mind was.

Q – to answer those questions truthfully, Mr. President?

A It was.

Q And was –

A But it was not my responsibility, in the face of their repeated illegal leaking, it was not my responsibility

Page 29

to volunteer a lot of information. There are many cases in this deposition where I gave – and keep in mind, I prepared, I treated them, frankly, with respect. I prepared very well for this deposition on the Jones matters. I prepared very well on that. I did not know that Linda Tripp had been involved in the preparation of this deposition, or that all of you –

Q Do you know that now?

A No, I don't. I just know that – what I read in the papers about it. But I had no way of knowing that they would ask me all these detailed questions. I did the best I could to answer them.

Q Did you prepare –

A But in this deposition, Mr. Bittman, I was doing my best to be truthful. I was not trying to be particularly helpful to them, and I didn't think I had an obligation to be particularly helpful to them to further a – when I knew that there was no evidence here of sexual harassment, and I knew what they wanted to do was to leak this, even though it was unlawful to do so. That's –

Q Did you believe, Mr. President –

A – what I knew.

Q – that you had an obligation to make sure that the presiding federal judge was on board and had the correct facts? Did you believe that was your obligation?

Page 30

A Sir, I was trying to answer my testimony. I was thinking about my testimony. I don't believe I ever even focused on what Mr. Bennett said in the exact words he did until I started reading this transcript carefully for this hearing. That moment, that whole argument just passed me by. I was a witness. I was trying to focus on what I said and how I said it.

And, believe me, I knew what the purpose of the deposition was. And, sure enough, by the way, it did all leak, just like I knew it would.

Q Let me ask you, Mr. President, you indicate in your statement that you were alone with Ms. Lewinsky. Is that right?

A Yes, sir.

Q How many times were you alone with Ms. Lewinsky?

A Let me begin with the correct answer. I don't know for sure. But if you would like me to give an educated guess, I will do that, but I do not know for sure. And I will tell you what I think, based on what I remember. But I can't be held to a specific time, because I don't have records of all of it.

Q How many times do you think?

A Well, there are two different periods here. There's the period when she worked in the White House until April of '96. And then there's the period when she came back

Page 31

to visit me from February '97 until late December '97.

Based on our records – let's start with the records, where we have the best records and the closest in time. Based on our records, between February and December, it appears to me that at least I could have seen her approximately nine times. Although I do not believe I saw her quite that many times, at least it could have happened.

There were – we think there were nine or 10 times when she was in, in the White House when I was in the Oval Office when I could have seen her. I do not believe I saw her that many times, but I could have.

Now, we have no records for the time when she was an employee at the White House, because we have no records of that for any of the employees at the White House, unless there was some formally scheduled meeting that was on the, on the calendar for the day.

I remember – I'll tell you what I remember. I remember meeting her, or having my first real conversation with her during the government shutdown in November of '95, when she – as I explained in my deposition, during the government shutdown, the – most federal employees were actually prohibited from coming to work, even in the White House. Most people in the White House couldn't come to work. The Chief of Staff could come to work. My National Security Advisor could come to work. I could.

Page 32

Therefore, interns were assigned to all offices. And I believe it was her last week as an intern. Anyway, she worked in the Chief of Staff's Office. One night she brought me some pizza. We had some remarks.

Now, the next time I remember seeing her alone was on a couple of occasions when she was working in the Legislative Affairs Office as a full-time employee. I remember specifically, I have a specific recollection of two times. I don't remember when they were, but I remember twice when, on Sunday afternoon, she brought papers down to me, stayed, and we were alone.

And I am frankly quite sure – although I have no specific memory, I am quite sure there were a couple of more times, probably two times more, three times more. That's what I would say. That's what I can remember. But I do not remember when they were, or at what time of day they were, or what the facts were. But I have a general memory that would say I certainly saw her more than twice during that period between January and April of 1996, when she worked there.

Q So, if I could summarize your testimony, approximately five times you saw her before she left the White House, and approximately nine times after she left the employment of the White House?

A I know there were several times in '97. I've told you that I've looked at my calendar and I tell you what I

Page 33

think the outer limits are. I would think that would sound about right. There could be, in that first four-month period, there, maybe there's one or two more, maybe there's one less. I just don't know. I don't remember. I didn't keep records.

But I'm giving you what I specifically remember and then what I generally remember. I'm doing the best to be helpful to you.

Q Have you reviewed the records for December 28th, 1997, Mr. President?

A Yes, sir, I have.

Q Do you believe that Ms. Lewinsky was at the White House and saw you on December 28th, 1997?

A Yes, sir, I do.

Q And do you remember talking with Ms. Lewinsky about her subpoena that she received for the Paula Jones case on that day?

A I remember talking with Ms. Lewinsky about her testimony, or about the prospect that she might have to give testimony. And she, she talked to me about that. I remember that.

Q And you also gave her Christmas gifts, is that not correct, Mr. President?

A That is correct. They were Christmas gifts and they were going-away gifts. She was moving to New York to,

Page 34

taking a new job, starting a new life. And I gave her some gifts.

Q And you actually requested this meeting, is that not correct?

A I don't remember that, Mr. Bittman, but it's quite possible that I invited her to come by before she left town. But usually when we met, she requested the meetings. And my recollection is, in 1997 she asked to meet with me several times when I could not meet with her and did not do so. But it's quite possible that I – that because she had given me a Christmas gift, and because she was leaving, that I invited her to come by the White House and get a couple of gifts before she left town.

I don't remember who requested the meeting though. I'm sorry, I don't.

Q You were alone with her on December 28, 1997, is that –

A Yes, sir.

Q – right?

A I was.

Q The gifts that you gave her were a canvas bag from The Black Dog restaurant at Martha's Vineyard, is that right?

A Well, that was just, that was just something I had in the place to, to contain the gifts. But I believe that

Page 35

the gifts I gave her were – I put them in that bag. That's what I had there, and I knew she liked things from The Black Dog. So, I gave her – I think that's what I put the presents in.

I remember what the presents were. I don't remember what the bag was I gave them in.

Q Did you also give her a marble bear's head carving from Vancouver, Canada?

A I did do that. I remember that.

Q And you also gave her a Rockettes blanket; that is, the famous Rockettes from New York?

A I did do that. I had that, I had had that in my possession for a couple of years but had never used it, and she was going to New York. So, I thought it would be a nice thing to give her.

Q You gave her a box of cherry chocolates, is that right?

A I don't remember that, sir. I mean, there could have been. I, I just don't remember. I remember giving the bear and the throw. I don't remember what else. And it seems to me like there was one other thing in that bag. I didn't remember the cherry chocolates.

Q How about a pin of the New York skyline? Did you give –

A That –

Page 36

Q – her that?

A That could have been in there. I seem to remember I gave her some kind of pin.

Q What about a pair of joke sunglasses?

A I don't remember that. I'm not denying it. I just -- I'm telling you what I remember and what I don't.

Q You had given Ms. Lewinsky gifts on other occasions though, is that right, Mr. President?

A Yes, I had.

Q This, though, was – you gave her the most gifts that you had ever given her in a single day, is that right?

A Well, that's probably true. It was sort of like a going-away present and a Christmas present as well. And she had given me a particularly nice book for Christmas, an antique book on Presidents. She knew that I collected old books and it was a very nice thing. And I just thought I ought to get up a few things and give them to her before she left.

Q You mentioned that you discussed her subpoena in the Paula Jones case. Tell us specifically, what did you discuss?

A No, sir, that's not what I said. I said, my recollection is I knew by then, of course, that she had gotten a subpoena. And I knew that she was, therefore, was slated to testify. And she mentioned to me – and I believe

Page 37

it was at this meeting. She mentioned – I remember a conversation about the possibility of her testifying. I believe it must have occurred on the 28th.

She mentioned to me that she did not want to testify. So, that's how it came up. Not in the context of, I heard you have a subpoena, let's talk about it.

She raised the issue with me in the context of her desire to avoid testifying, which I certainly understood; not only because there were some embarrassing facts about our relationship that were inappropriate, but also because a whole lot of innocent people were being traumatized and dragged through the mud by these Jones lawyers with their dragnet strategy. They –

Q So –

A And so I – and since she didn't know Paula Jones and knew nothing about sexual harassment, and certainly had no experience with that, I, I clearly understood why she didn't want to be a part of it.

Q And you didn't want her to testify, did you? You didn't want her to disclose these embarrassing facts of this inappropriate intimate relationship that you had, is that correct?

A Well, I did not want her to have to testify and go through that. And, of course, I didn't want her to do that, of course not.

Page 38

Q Did you want those facts, not only the fact that she would testify, but did you want the facts that she had about your embarrassing inappropriate intimate relationship to be disclosed?

A Not there, but not in any context. However, I, I never had any high confidence that they wouldn't be.

Q Did anyone, as far as you knew, know about your embarrassing inappropriate intimate relationship that you had with Ms. Lewinsky?

A At that time, I was unaware that she had told anyone else about it. But if, if I had known that, it would not have surprised me.

Q Had you told anyone?

A Absolutely not.

Q Had you tried, in fact, not to let anyone else know about this relationship?

A Well, of course.

Q What did you do?

A Well, I never said anything about it, for one thing. And I did what people do when they do the wrong thing. I tried to do it where nobody else was looking at it.

Q How many times did you do that?

A Well, if you go back to my statement, I remember there were a few times in '96, I can't say with any certainty. There was once in early '97. After she left the

Page 39

White House, I do not believe I ever had any inappropriate contact with her in the rest of '96. There was one occasion in '97 when, regrettably, that we were together for a few minutes, I think about 20 minutes, and there was inappropriate contact. And after that, to the best of my memory and belief, it did not occur again.

Q Did you tall her in the conversation about her being subpoenaed – she was upset about it, you acknowledge that?

A (Witness nodded indicating an affirmative response.)

Q I'm sorry, you have to respond for the record. Yes or no? Do you agree that she was upset about being subpoenaed?

A Oh, yes, sir, she was upset. She – well, she – we – she didn't – we didn't talk about a subpoena. But she was upset. She said, I don't want to testify; I know nothing about this; I certainly know nothing about sexual harassment; why do they want me to testify. And I explained to her why they were doing this, and why all these women were on these lists, people that they knew good and well had nothing to do with any sexual harassment.

I explained to her that it was a political lawsuit. They wanted to get whatever they could under oath that was damaging to me, and then they wanted to leak it in violation

Page 40

of the Judge's orders, and turn up their nose and say, well, you can't prove we did it. Now, that was their strategy. And that they were very frustrated because everything they leaked so far was old news. So, they desperately were trying to validate this massive amount of money they'd spent by finding some new news. And –

Q You were familiar –

A – she didn't want to be caught up in that, and I didn't blame her.

Q You were familiar, weren't you, Mr. President, that she had received a subpoena. You've already acknowledged that.

A Yes, sir, I was.

Q And Mr. Jordan informed you of that, is that right?

A No, sir. I believe – and I believe I testified to this in my deposition. I think the first person who told me that she had been subpoenaed was Bruce Lindsey. I think the first – and I was – in this deposition, it's a little bit cloudy, but I was trying to remember who the first person who told me was, because the question was, again as I remember it – could we go to that in the deposition, since you asked me that?

Q Actually, I think you're – with all respect, I think you may be confusing when Mr. Lindsey – well, perhaps Mr. Lindsey did tell you she was subpoenaed, I don't know.

Page 41

But in your deposition, you were referring to Mr. Lindsey notifying you that she had been identified as a witness.

A Where is that, sir? I don't want to get – I just want – what page is that?

Q Well, actually –

A No, it had to be, because I saw a witness list much earlier than that.

Q Much earlier that December 28?

A Oh, sure. And it had been earlier than – she would – I believe Monica –

MR. KENDALL: Page 69.

THE WITNESS: I believe Monica Lewinsky's name was on a witness list earlier than she was subpoenaed.

BY MR. BITTMAN:

Q Yes.

A So, I believe when I was answering this question, at least I thought I was answering when I found out – yes. See, there's – on page 68, "Did anyone other than your attorneys ever tell you that Monica Lewinsky had been served with a subpoena in this case?" Then I said, "I don't think so." Then I [sic] said, "Did you ever talk" to Monica "about the possibility that she might be asked to testify in this case?"

Then I gave an answer that was nonresponsive, that really tried to finish the answer above. I said, "Bruce

Page 42

Lindsey, I think Bruce Lindsey told me that she was, I think maybe that's the first person told me she was. I want to be as accurate as I can."

And that – I believe that Bruce is the first person who told me that Monica had gotten a subpoena.

Q Did you, in fact, have a conversation with Mr. Jordan on the evening of December 19, 1997, in which he talked to you about Monica being in Mr. Jordan's office, having a copy of the subpoena, and being upset about being subpoenaed?

A I remembered that Mr. Jordan was in the White Hous on December 19th and for an event of some kind. That he came up to the Residence floor and told me that he had, that Monica had gotten a subpoena and, or that Monica was going to have to testify. And I think he told me he recommended a lawyer for her. I believe that's what happened. But it was a very brief conversation. He was there for some other reason.

Q And if Mr. Jordan testified that he had also spoken to you at around 5 p.m., and the White House phone logs reflect this, that he called you at around the time he met with Ms. Lewinsky and informed you then that she had been subpoenaed, is that consistent with your memory? Also on the 19th?

A I had a lot of phone conversations with Vernon

Page 43

about this. I didn't keep records of them. I now have some records. My memory is not clear and my testimony on that was not clear. I just knew that I talked to Vernon at some time, but I thought that Bruce was the first person who told me.

Q But Mr. Jordan had also told you, is that right?

A Yes. I now know I had a conversation with Mr. Jordan about it where he said something to me about that.

Q And that was probably on the 19th, December 19th?

A Well, I know I saw him on the 19th. So, I'm quite sure. And if he says he talked to me on the 19th, I believe he would have better records and I certainly think he's a truthful person.

Q Getting back to your meeting with Ms. Lewinsky on December 28, you are aware that she's been subpoenaed. You are aware, are you not, Mr. President, that the subpoena called for the production of, among other things, all the gifts that you had given Ms. Lewinsky? You were aware of that on December 28th, weren't you?

A I'm not sure. And I understand this is an important question. I did have a conversation with Ms. Lewinsky at some time about gifts, the gifts I'd given her. I do not know whether it occurred on the 28th, or whether it occurred earlier. I do not know whether it occurred in person or whether it occurred on the telephone. I have searched my memory for this, because I know it's an important

Page 44

issue.

Perhaps if you – I can tell you what I remember about the conversation and you can see why I'm having trouble placing the date.

Q Please.

A The reason I'm not sure it happened on the 28th is that my recollection is that Ms. Lewinsky said something to me like, what if they ask me about the gifts you've given me. That's the memory I have. That's why I question whether it happened on the 28th, because she had a subpoena with her, request for production.

And I told her that if they asked her for gifts, she'd have to give them whatever she had, that that's what the law was.

And let me also tell you, Mr. Bittman, if you go back and look at my testimony here, I actually asked the Jones lawyers for help on one occasion, when they were asking me what gifts I had given her, so they could – I was never hung up about this gift issue. Maybe it's because I have a different experience. But, you know, the President gets hundreds of gifts a year, maybe more. I have always given a lot of gifts to people, especially if they give me gifts. And this was no big deal to me. I mean, it's nice. I enjoy it. I gave dozens of personal gifts to people last Christmas. I give gifts to people all the time. Friends of

Page 45

mine give me gifts all the time, give me ties, give me books, give me other things. So, it was just not a big deal.

And I told Ms. Lewinsky that, just – I said, you know, if they ask you for this, you'll have to give them whatever you have. And I think, Mr. Bittman, it must have happened before then, because – either that, or Ms. Lewinsky didn't want to tell me that she had the subpoena, because that was the language I remember her using.

Q Well, didn't she tell you, Mr. President, that the subpoena specifically called for a hat pin that you had produced, pardon me, that you had given her?

A I don't remember that. I remember – sir, I've told you what I remember. That doesn't mean that my memory is accurate. A lot of things have happened in the last several months, and a lot of things were happening then. But my memory is she asked me a general question about gifts. And my memory is she asked me in the hypothetical. So, it's possible that I had a conversation with her before she got a subpoena. Or it's possible she didn't want to tell me that was part of the subpoena. I don't know.

But she may have been worried about this gift business. But it didn't bother me. My experience was totally different. I told her, I said, look, the way these things work is, when a person get a subpoena, you have to give them whatever you have; that's what's the rule, that's

Page 46

what the law is.

And when I was asked about this in my deposition, even though I was not trying to be helpful particularly to these people that I thought were not well-motivated, or being honest or even lawful in their conduct vis-a-vis me, that is, the Jones legal team, I did ask them specifically to enumerate the gifts. I asked them to help me because I couldn't remember the specifics.

So, all I'm saying is, it didn't – I wasn't troubled by this gift issue.

Q And your testimony is that Ms. Lewinsky was concerned about her turning over any gifts that you had given her, and that your recommendation to her was, absolutely, Monica, you have to produce everything that I have given you. Is that your testimony?

A My testimony is what I have said, and let me reiterate it. I don't want to agree to a characterization of it. I want to just say what it was.

My testimony is that my memory is that on some day in December, and I'm sorry I don't remember when it was, she said, well, what if they ask me about the gifts you have given me. And I said, well, if you get a request to produce those, you have to give them whatever you have.

And it just, to me, it – I don't – I didn't then, I don't now see this as a problem. And if she thought it was

Page 47

a problem, I think it – it must have been from a, really, a misapprehension of the circumstances. I certainly never encouraged her not to, to comply lawfully with a subpoena.

Q Mr. President, if your intent was, as you have earlier testified, that you didn't want anybody to know about this relationship you had with Ms. Lewinsky, why would you feel comfortable giving her gifts in the middle of discovery in the Paula Jones case?

A Well, sir, for one thing, there was no existing improper relationship at that time. I had, for nearly a year, done my best to be a friend to Ms. Lewinsky, to be a counselor to her, to give her good advice, and to help her. She had, for her part, most of the time, accepted the changed circumstances. She talked to me a lot about her life, her job ambitions, and she continued to give me gifts. And I felt that it was a right thing to do to give her gifts back.

I have always given a lot of people gifts. I have always been given gifts. I do not think there is anything improper about a man giving a woman a gift, or a woman giving a man a gift, that necessarily connotes an improper relationship. So, it didn't bother me.

I wasn't – you know, this was December 28th. I was – I gave her some gifts. I wasn't worried about it. I thought it was an all right thing to do.

Q What about notes and letters, cards, letters and

Page 48

notes to Ms. Lewinsky? After this relationship, this inappropriate intimate relationship between you and Ms. Lewinsky ended, she continued to send you numerous intimate notes and cards, is that right?

A Well, they were – some of them were, were somewhat intimate. I'd say most of them, most of the notes and cards were, were affectionate all right, but, but she had clearly accepted the fact that there could be no contact between us that was in any way inappropriate.

Now, she, she sent cards sometimes that were just funny, even a little bit off-color, but they were funny. She liked to send me cards, and I got a lot of those cards; several, anyway, I don't know a lot. I got a few.

Q She professed her love to you in these cards after the end of the relationship, didn't she?

A Well, –

Q She said she loved you?

A Sir, the truth is that most of the time, even when she was expressing her feelings for me in affectionate terms, I believed that she had accepted, understood my decision to stop this inappropriate contact. She knew from the very beginning of our relationship that I was apprehensive about it. And I think that in a way she felt a little freer to be affectionate, because she knew that nothing else was going to happen. I can't explain entirely what was in her mind.

Page 49

But most of these messages were not what you would call over the top. They weren't things that, if you read them, you would say, oh, my goodness, these people are having some sort of sexual affair.

Q Mr. President, the question –

A But some of them were quite affectionate.

Q My question was, did she or did she not profess her love to you in those cards and letters that she sent to you after the relationship ended?

A Most of them were signed, "Love", you know, "Love, Monica." I don't know that I would consider – I don't believe that in most of these cards and letters she professed her love, but she might well have. I – but, you know, love can mean different things, too, Mr. Bittman. I have – there are a lot of women with whom I have never had any inappropriate conduct who are friends of mine, who will say from time to time, I love you. And I know that they don't mean anything wrong by that.

Q Specifically, Mr. President, do you remember a card she sent you after she saw the movie Titanic, in which she said that she reminisced or dreamed about the romantic feelings that occurred in the movie, and how that reminded her of you two? Do you remember that?

A No, sir, but she could have sent it. I – just because I don't remember it doesn't mean it wasn't there.

Page 50

Q You're not denying that, that –
A Oh, no. I wouldn't deny that. I just don't remember it. You asked me if I remembered. I don't. She might have done it.
Q Do you ever remember telling her, Mr. President, that she should not write some of the things that she does in those cards and letters that she sends to you because it reveals, if disclosed, this relationship that you had, and that she shouldn't do it?
A I remember telling her she should be careful what she wrote, because a lot of it was clearly inappropriate and would be embarrassing if somebody else read it. I don't remember when I said that. I don't remember whether it was in '96 or when it was. I don't remember.
Q Embarrassing, in that it was revealing of the intimate relationship that you and she had, is that right?
A I do not know when I said this. So, I don't know whether we did have any sort of inappropriate relationship at the time I said that to her. I don't remember. But it's obvious that if she wrote things that she should not have written down and someone else read it, that it would be embarrassing.
Q She certainly sent you something like that after the relationship began, didn't she? And so, therefore, there was, at the time she sent it, something inappropriate going

Page 51

on?
A Well, my recollection is that she – that maybe because of changed circumstances in her own life in 1997, after there was no more inappropriate contact, that she sent me more things in the mail, and that there was sort of a disconnect sometimes between what she was saying and the plain facts of our relationship. And I don't know what caused that. But it may have been dissatisfaction with the rest of her life. I don't know.
You know, she had, from the time I first met her, talked to me about the rest of her personal life, and it may be that there was some reason for that. It may be that when I did the right thing and made it stick, that in a way she felt a need to cling more closely, or try to get closer to me, even though she knew nothing improper was happening or was going to happen. I don't know the answer to that.
Q After you gave her the gifts on December 28th, did you speak with your secretary, Ms. Currie, and ask her to pick up a box of gifts that were some compilation of gifts that Ms. Lewinsky would have –
A No, sir, I didn't do that.
Q – to give to Ms. Currie?
A I did not do that.
Q When you testified in the Paula Jones case, this was only two and a half weeks after you had given her these

Page 52

six gifts, you were asked, at page 75 in your deposition, lines 2 through 5, "Well, have you ever given any gifts to Monica Lewinsky?" And you answer, "I don't recall."
And you were correct. You pointed out that you actually asked them, for prompting, "Do you know what they were?"
A I think what I meant there was I don't recall what they were, not that I don't recall whether I had given them. And then if you see, they did give me these specifics, and I gave them quite a good explanation here. I remembered very clearly what the facts were about The Black Dog. And I said that I could have given her a hat pin and a Walt Whitman book; that I did not remember giving her a gold broach, which was true. I didn't remember it. I may have given it to her, but I didn't remember giving her one.
They didn't ask me about the, about the Christmas gifts, and I don't know why I didn't think to say anything about them. But I have to tell you again, I even invited them to have a list.
It was obvious to me by this point in the definition, in this deposition, that they had, these people had access to a lot of information from somewhere, and I presume it came from Linda Tripp. And I had no interest in not answering their questions about these gifts. I do not believe that gifts are incriminating, nor do I think they are

Page 53

wrong. I think it was a good thing to do. I'm not, I'm still not sorry I gave Monica Lewinsky gifts.
Q Why did you assume that that information came from Linda Tripp?
A I didn't then.
Q Well, you didn't? I thought you just testified you did then?
A No, no, no. I said I now assume that because –
Q You now assume.
A – of all of the subsequent events. I didn't know. I just knew that –
Q Let me ask you about –
A – that somebody had access to some information and they may have known more about this than I did.
Q Let me ask you about the meeting you had with Betty Currie at the White House on Sunday, January 18 of this year, the day after your deposition. First of all, you didn't – Mrs. Currie, your secretary of six-some years, you never allowed her, did you, to watch whatever intimate activity you did with Ms. Lewinsky, did you?
A No, sir, not to my knowledge.
Q And as far as you know, she couldn't hear anything either, is that right?
A There were a couple of times when Monica was there when I asked Betty to be places where she could hear, because

Page 54

Monica was upset and I – this was after there was – all the inappropriate contact had been terminated.
Q No, I'm talking –
A But –
Q – about the times that you actually had the intimate contact.
A She was – I believe that – well, first of all, on that one occasion in 1997, I do not know whether Betty was in the White House after the radio address in the Oval Office complex. I believe she probably was, but I'm not sure. But I'm certain that someone was there. I always – always someone was there.
In 1996, I think most of the times that Ms. Lewinsky was there, there may not have been anybody around except maybe coming in and out, but not permanently so. I – that's correct. I never – I didn't try to involve Betty in that in any way.
Q Well, not only did you not try to involve her, you specifically tried to exclude her and everyone else, isn't that right?
A Well, yes. I've never – I mean, it's almost humorous, sir. I'd, I'd, I'd have to be an exhibitionist not to have tried to exclude everyone else.
Q So, if Ms. Currie testified that you approached her on the 18th, or you spoke with her and you said, you were

Page 55

always there when she was there, she wasn't, was she? That is, Mrs. Currie?
A She was always there in the White House, and I was concerned – let me back up and say –
Q What about the radio address, Mr. President?
A Let me back up a second, Mr. Bittman. I knew about the radio address. I was sick after it was over and I, I was pleased at that time that it had been nearly a year since any inappropriate contact had occurred with Ms. Lewinsky. I promised myself it wasn't going to happen again. The facts are complicated about what did happen and how it happened. But, nonetheless, I'm responsible for it. On that night, she didn't.
I was more concerned about the times after that when Ms. Lewinsky was upset, and I wanted to establish at least that I had not – because these questions were – some of them were off the wall. Some of them were way out of line, I thought.
And what I wanted to establish was that Betty was there at all other times in the complex, and I wanted to know what Betty's memory was about what she heard, what she could hear. And what I did not know was – I did not know that. And I was trying to figure out, and I was trying to figure out in a hurry because I knew something was up.
Q So, you wanted –

Page 56

A After that deposition.
Q – to check her memory for what she remembered, and that is –
A That's correct.
Q – whether she remembered nothing, or whether she remembered an inappropriate intimate –
A Oh, no, no, no, no.
Q – relationship?
A No. I didn't ask her about it in that way. I asked her about what the – what I was trying to determine was whether my recollection was right and that she was always in the office complex when Monica was there, and whether she thought she could hear any conversations we had, or did she hear any.
And then I asked her specifically about a couple of times when – once when I asked her to remain in the dining room, Betty, while I met with Monica in my study. And once when I took Monica in the, the small office Nancy Hernreich occupies right next to Betty's and talked to her there for a few minutes. That's my recollection of that.
I was trying to – I knew, Mr. Bittman, to a reasonable certainty that I was going to be asked more questions about this. I didn't really expect you to be in the Jones case at the time. I thought what would happen is that it would break in the press, and I was trying to get the

Page 57

facts down. I was trying to understand what the facts were.
Q If Ms. Currie testified that these were not really questions to her, that they were more like statements, is that not true?
A Well, I can't testify as to what her perception was. I can tell you this. I was trying to get information in a hurry. I was downloading what I remembered. I think Ms. Currie would also testify that I explicitly told her, once I realized that you were involved in the Jones case – you, the Office of Independent Counsel – and that she might have to be called as a witness, that she should just go in there and tell the truth, tell what she knew, and be perfectly truthful.
So, I was not trying to get Betty Currie to say something that was untruthful. I was trying to get as much information as quickly as I could.
Q What information were you trying to get from her when you said, I was never alone with her, right?
A I don't remember exactly what I did say with her. That's what you say I said.
Q If Ms. Currie testified to that, if she says you told her, I was never alone with her, right?
A Well, I was never alone with her –
Q Did you not say that, Mr. President?
A Mr. Bittman, just a minute. I was never alone with

Page 58

her, right, might be a question. And what I might have meant by that is, in the Oval Office complex.
Could –
Q Well, you knew the answer to that, didn't you?
A We've been going for more than an hour. Would you mind if we took a break? I need to go to the restroom.
MR. BITTMAN: Let's take a break.
MR. KENDALL: It's 2:38.
(Whereupon, the proceedings were recessed from 2:38 p.m. until 2:48 p.m.)
MR. KENDALL: It is 2:38 – sorry, 2:48.
BY MR. WISENBERG:
Q Mr. President, I want to, before I go into a new subject area, briefly go over something you were talking about with Mr. Bittman.
The statement of your attorney, Mr. Bennett, at the Paula Jones deposition, "Counsel is fully aware" – it's page 54, line 5 – "Counsel is fully aware that Ms. Lewinsky has filed, has an affidavit which they are in possession of saying that there is absolutely no sex of any kind in any manner, shape or form, with President Clinton".
That statement is made by your attorney in front of Judge Susan Webber Wright, correct?
A That's correct.
Q That statement is a completely false statement.

Page 59

Whether or not Mr. Bennett knew of your relationship with Ms. Lewinsky, the statement that there was "no sex of any kind in any manner, shape or form, with President Clinton," was an utterly false statement. Is that correct?
A It depends on what the meaning of the word "is" is. If the – if he – if "is" means is and never has been, that is not – that is one thing. If it means there is none, that was a completely true statement.
But, as I have testified, and I'd like to testify again, this is – it is somewhat unusual for a client to be asked about his lawyer's statements, instead of the other way around. I was not paying a great deal of attention to this exchange. I was focusing on my own testimony.
And if you go back and look at the sequence of this, you will see that the Jones lawyers decided that this was going to be the Lewinsky deposition, not the Jones deposition. And, given the facts of their case, I can understand why they made that decision. But that is not how I prepared for it. That is not how I was thinking about it.
And I am not sure, Mr. Wisenberg, as I sit here today, that I sat there and followed all these interchanges between the lawyers. I'm quite sure that I didn't follow all the interchanges between the lawyers all that carefully. And I don't really believe, therefore, that I can say Mr. Bennett's testimony or statement is testimony and is

Page 60

imputable to me. I didn't – I don't know that I was even paying that much attention to it.
Q You told us you were very well prepared for the deposition.
A No. I said I was very well prepared to talk about Paula Jones and to talk about Kathleen Willey, because she had made a related charge. She was the only person that I think I was asked about who had anything to do with anything that would remotely approximate sexual harassment. The rest of this looked to me like it was more of a way to harass me.
Q You are the President of the United States and your attorney tells a United States District Court Judge that there is no sex of any kind, in any way, shape or form, whatsoever. And you feel no obligation to do anything about that at that deposition, Mr. President?
A I have told you, Mr. Wisenberg, I will tell you for a third time. I am not even sure that when Mr. Bennett made that statement that I was concentrating on the exact words he used.
Now, if someone had asked me on that day, are you having any kind of sexual relations with Ms. Lewinsky, that is, asked me a question in the present tense, I would have said no. And it would have been completely true.
Q Was Mr. Bennett aware of this tense-based distinction you are making now –

Page 61

A I don't –
MR. KENDALL: I'm going to object to any questions about communications with private counsel.
MR. WISENBERG: Well, the witness has already testified, I think, that Mr. Bennett didn't know about the inappropriate relationship with Ms. Lewinsky. I guess –
THE WITNESS: Well, you'll have to ask him that, you know. He was not a sworn witness and I was not paying that close attention to what he was saying. I've told you that repeatedly. I was – I don't – I never even focused on that until I read it in this transcript in preparation for this testimony.
When I was in there, I didn't think about my lawyers. I was, frankly, thinking about myself and my testimony and trying to answer the questions.
BY MR. WISENBERG:
Q I just want to make sure I understand, Mr. President. Do you mean today that because you were not engaging in sexual activity with Ms. Lewinsky during the deposition that the statement of Mr. Bennett might be literally true?
A No, sir. I mean that at the time of the deposition, it had been – that was well beyond any point of improper contact between me and Ms. Lewinsky. So that anyone generally speaking in the present tense, saying there is not

Page 62

an improper relationship, would be telling the truth if that person said there was not, in the present tense; the present tense encompassing many months. That's what I meant by that.

Not that I was – I wasn't trying to give you a cute answer, that I was obviously not involved in anything improper during a deposition. I was trying to tell you that generally speaking in the present tense, if someone said that, that would be true. But I don't know what Mr. Bennett had in his mind. I don't know. I didn't pay any attention to this colloquy that went on. I was waiting for my instructions as a witness to go forward. I was worried about my own testimony.

Q I want to go back to some questions about Mr. Jordan and we are going to touch a little bit on the December 19th meeting and some others. Mr. Jordan is a long-time friend of yours, is that correct, Mr. President?

A Yes, sir. We've been friends probably 20 years, maybe more.

Q You said you consider him to be a truthful person, correct?

A I do.

Q If Mr. Jordan has told us that he visited you in the Residence on the night of the 19th, after a White House holiday dinner, to discuss Monica Lewinsky and her subpoena with you, do you have any reason to doubt it?

Page 63

A No. I've never known him to say anything that wasn't true. And his memory of these events, I think, would be better than mine because I had a lot of other things going on.

Q We have WAVE records that will show that, but in the interest of time I'm not going to – since you don't dispute that, I'm not going to show them right now.

And, in fact, that was the very day Monica Lewinsky was subpoenaed, wasn't it, the night that he came to see you?

A I don't have an independent memory of that, but you would probably know that. I mean, I'm sure there is a record of when she got her subpoena.

Q If Mr. Jordan has told us that he spoke with you over the phone within about an hour of Monica receiving her subpoena, and later visited you that very day, the night at the White House, to discuss it, again you'd have no reason to doubt him, is that correct?

A I've already – I believe I've already testified about that here today, that I had lots of conversations with Vernon. I'm sure that I had lots of conversations with him that included comments about this. And if he has a specific memory of when I had some conversation on a certain day, I would be inclined to trust his memory over mine, because under the present circumstances my head's probably more cluttered than his, and my schedule is probably busier. He's

Page 64

probably got better records.

Q And when Mr. Jordan met with you at the Residence that night, sir, he asked you if you'd been involved in a sexual relationship with Monica Lewinsky, didn't he?

A I do not remember exactly what the nature of the conversation was. I do remember that I told him that there was no sexual relationship between me and Monica Lewinsky, which was true. And that – then all I remember for the rest is that he said he had referred her to a lawyer, and I believe it was Mr. Carter, and I don't believe I've ever met Mr. Carter. I don't think I know him.

Q Mr. President, if Mr. Jordan has told us that he had a very disturbing conversation with Ms. Lewinsky that day, then went over to visit you at the White House, and that before he asked you the question about a sexual relationship, related that disturbing conversation to you, the conversation being that Ms. Lewinsky had a fixation on you and thought that perhaps the First Lady would leave you at the end of – that you would leave the First Lady at the end of your term and come be with Ms. Lewinsky, do you have any reason to doubt him that it was on that night that that conversation happened?

A All I can tell you, sir, is I, I certainly don't remember him saying that. Now, he could have said that because, as you know, a great many things happened in the

Page 65

ensuing two or three days. And I could have just forgotten it. But I don't remember him ever saying that.

Q At any time?

A No, I don't remember him saying that. What I remember was that he said that Monica came to see him, that she was upset that she was going to have to testify, that he had referred her to a lawyer.

Q In fact, she was very distraught about the subpoena, according to Mr. Jordan, wasn't she?

A Well, he said she was upset about it. I don't remember – I don't remember any, at any time when he said this, this other thing you just quoted me. I'm sorry. I just don't remember that.

Q That is something that one would be likely to remember, don't you think, Mr. President?

A I think I would, and I'd be happy to share it with you if I did. I only had one encounter with Ms. Lewinsky, I seem to remember, which was somewhat maybe reminiscent of that. But not that, if you will, obsessive, if that's the way you want to use that word.

Q Do you recall him at all telling you that he was concerned about her fascination with you, even if you don't remember the specific conversation about you leaving the First Lady?

A I recall him saying he thought that she was upset

Page 66

with – somewhat fixated on me, that she acknowledged that she was not having a sexual relationship with me, and that she did not want to be drug into the Jones lawsuit. That's what I recall. And I recall his getting, saying that he had recommended a lawyer to her and she had gone to see the lawyer. That's what I recall.

I don't remember the other thing you mentioned. I just – I might well remember it if he had said it. Maybe he said it and I've forgotten it, but I don't – I can't tell you that I remember that.

Q Mr. President, you swore under oath in the Jones case that you didn't think anyone other than your lawyers had ever told you that Monica Lewinsky had been subpoenaed. Page 68, line 22 [sic] through page 69, line 3.. Here's the testimony, sir.

Question – we've gone over it a little bit before: "Did anyone other than your attorneys ever tell you that Monica Lewinsky had been served with a subpoena in this case?" Answer, "I don't think so."

Now, this deposition was taken just three and a half weeks after, by your own testimony, Vernon Jordan made a trip at night to the White House to tell you, among other things, that Monica Lewinsky had been subpoenaed and was upset about it. Why did you give that testimony under oath in the Jones case, sir?

Page 67

A Well, Mr. Wisenberg, I think you have to – again, you have to put this in the context of the flow of questions, and I've already testified to this once today. I will testify to it again.

My answer to the next question, I think, is a way of finishing my answer to the question and the answer you've said here. I was trying to remember who the first person, other than Mr. Bennett – I don't think Mr. Bennett – who the first person told me that, who told me Paula Jones had, I mean, excuse me, Monica Lewinsky had a subpoena. And I thought that Bruce Lindsey was the first person. And that's how I was trying to remember that.

Keep in mind, sort of like today, these questions are being kind of put at me rapid-fire. But, unlike today, I hadn't had the opportunity to prepare at this level of detail. I didn't – I was trying to keep a lot of things in my head that I had remembered with regard to the Paula Jones case and the Kathleen Willey matter, because I knew I would be asked about them. And I gave the best answers I could. Several of my answers are somewhat jumbled.

But this is an honest attempt here – if you read both these answers, it's obvious they were both answers to that question you quoted, to remember the first person, who was not Mr. Bennett, who told me. And I don't believe Vernon was the first person who told me. I believe Bruce Lindsey

Page 68

was.

Q Let me read the question, because I want to talk about the first person issue. The question on line 25 of page 68 is, "Did anyone other than your attorneys ever tell you that Monica Lewinsky had been served with a subpoena in this case?" Answer, "I don't think so."

You would agree with me, sir, that the question doesn't say, the question doesn't say anything about who was the first person. It just says, did anyone tell you. Isn't that correct?

A That's right. And I said Bruce Lindsey, because I was trying to struggle with who – where I had heard this. And they were free to ask a follow-up question, and they didn't.

Q Mr. President, three and a half weeks before, Mr. Jordan had made a special trip to the White House to tell you Ms. Lewinsky had been subpoenaed; she was distraught; she had a fixation over you. And you couldn't remember that, three and a half weeks later?

A Mr. Wisenberg, if – they had access to all this information from their conversations with Linda Tripp, if that was the basis of it. They were free to ask me more questions. They may have been trying to trick me.

Now, they knew more about the details of my relationship with Monica Lewinsky. I'm not sure everything

Page 69

they knew was true, because I don't know. I've not heard these tapes or anything. But they knew a lot more than I did. And instead of trying to trick me, what they should have done is to ask me specific questions, and I invited them on more than one occasion to ask follow-up questions.

This is the third or fourth time that you seem to be complaining that I did not do all their work for them. That just sitting here answering these questions to the best of my memory, with limited preparation, was not enough. That I should have actually been doing all their work for them.

Now, they'd been up all night with Linda Tripp, who had betrayed her friend, Monica Lewinsky, stabbed her in the back and given them all this information. They could have helped more. If they wanted to ask me follow-up questions, they could. They didn't. I'm sorry. I did the best I could.

Q Can you tell the grand jury what is tricky about the question, "Did anyone other than your attorneys ever tell you" –

A No, there's nothing – I'm just telling – I have explained. I will now explain for the third time, sir. I was being asked a number of questions here. I was struggling to remember then. There were lots of things that had gone on during this time period that had nothing to do with Monica Lewinsky.

Page 70

You know, I believed then, I believe now that Monica Lewinsky could have sworn out an honest affidavit, that under reasonable circumstances, and without the benefit of what Linda Tripp did to her, would have given her a chance not to be a witness in this case.

So, I didn't have perfect memory of all these events that have now, in the last seven months, since Ms. Lewinsky was kept for several hours by four or five of your lawyers and four or five FBI agents, as if she were a serious felon, these things have become the most important matters in the world. At the moment they were occurring, many other things were going on.

I honestly tried to remember when – you know, if somebody asked you, has anybody ever talked to you about this, you normally think, well, where was the first time I heard that. That's all I was trying to do here. I was not trying to say not Vernon Jordan, but Bruce Lindsey. Everybody knows Vernon Jordan is a friend of mine. I probably would have talked to Vernon Jordan about the Monica Lewinsky problem if he had never been involved in it. So, I was not trying to mislead them. I was trying to answer this question with the first person who told me that.

Now, I realize that wasn't the specific question. They were free to ask follow-ups, just like you're asking follow-ups today. And I can't explain why I didn't answer

Page 71

every question in the way you seem to think I should have, and I certainly can't explain why they didn't ask what seemed to me to be logical follow-ups, especially since they spent all that time with Linda Tripp the night before.

Q You've told us that you understand your obligation then, as it is now, is to tell the whole truth, sir. Do you recall that?

A I took the oath here.

Q If Vernon Jordan –

A You even read me a definition of the oath.

Q If Vernon Jordan has told us that you have an extraordinary memory, one of the greatest memories he's ever seen in a politician, would that be something you would care to dispute?

A No, I do have a good memory. At least, I have had a good memory in my life.

Q Do you understand that if you answered, "I don't think so", to the question, has anyone other than your attorneys told you that Monica Lewinsky has been served with a subpoena in this case, that if you answered, "I don't think so", but you really knew Vernon Jordan had been telling you all about it, you understand that that would be a false statement, presumably perjurious?

A Mr. Wisenberg, I have testified about this three times. Now, I will do it the fourth time. I am not going to

Page 72

answer your trick questions.

I – people don't always hear the same questions in the same way. They don't always answer them in the same way. I was so concerned about the question they asked me that the next question I was asked, I went back to the previous question, trying to give an honest answer about the first time I heard about the Lewinsky subpoena.

I – look. I could have had no reasonable expectation that anyone would ever know that, that – or not, excuse me, not know if this thing – that I would talk to Vernon Jordan about nearly everything. I was not interested in – if the implication of your question is that somehow I didn't want anybody to know I had ever talked to Vernon Jordan about this, that's just not so.

It's also – if I could say one thing about my memory. I have been blessed and advantaged in my life with a good memory. Now, I have been shocked, and so have members of my family and friends of mine, at how many things that I have forgotten in the last six years, I think because of the pressure and the pace and the volume of events in the President's life, compounded by the pressure of your four-year inquiry, and all the other things that have happened, I'm amazed there are lots of times when I literally can't remember last week.

If you ask me, did you talk to Vernon – when was

Page 73

the last time you talked to Vernon Jordan, what time of day was it, when did you see him, what did you say, my answer was the last – you know, if you answered [sic] me, when was the last time you saw a friend of yours in California, if you asked me a lot of questions like that, my memory is not what it was when I came here, because my life is so crowded.

And now that – as I said, you have made this the most important issue in America. I mean, you have made it the most important issue in America from your point of view. At the time this was occurring, even though I was concerned about it, and I hoped she didn't have to testify, and I hoped this wouldn't come out, I felt – I will say again – that she could honestly fill out an affidavit that, under reasonable circumstances, would relieve her of the burden of testifying.

I am not trying to exclude the fact that I talked to Vernon here. I just – all I can tell you is I believe this answer reflects I was trying to remember the first person who told me who was not Mr. Bennett, and I believe it was Bruce Lindsey.

Q As you yourself recalled, just recalled, Mr. President, Vernon Jordan not only discussed the subpoena with you that night, but discussed Frank Carter, the lawyer he had gotten for Ms. Lewinsky. And also Mr. Jordan discussed with you over the next few weeks, after the 19th of December, in

Page 74

addition to the job aspects of Ms. Lewinsky's job, he discussed with you her affidavit that she was preparing in the case. Is that correct, sir?

A I believe that he did notify us, I think, when she signed her affidavit. I have a memory of that. Or it seems like he said that she had signed her affidavit.

Q If he's told us that he notified you around January 7th, when she signed her affidavit, and that you generally understood that it would deny a sexual relationship, do you have any reason to doubt that?

A No.

Q So, that's the affidavit, the lawyer, and the subpoena. And yet when you were asked, sir, at the Jones deposition about Vernon Jordan, and specifically about whether or not he had discussed the lawsuit with you, you didn't reveal that to the Court.

I want to refer you to page 72, line 16. It's where this starts. It's going to go down, it might go down somewhat.

Line 16. Question, "Has it ever been reported to you that he" – and that's referring to Mr. Jordan. At line 12 you were asked, "You know a man named Vernon Jordan?", and you answer, "I know him well."

Going down to 16, "Has it ever been reported to you that he met with Monica Lewinsky and talked about this case?"

Page 75

This is your answer, or a portion of it: "I knew that he met with her. I think Betty suggested that he meet with her. Anyway, he met with her. I, I thought that he talked to her about something else."

Why didn't you tell the Court, when you were under oath and sworn to tell the truth, the whole truth, and nothing but the truth, that you had been talking with Vernon Jordan about the case, about the affidavit, the lawyer, the subpoena?

A Well, that's not the question I was asked. I was not asked any question about – I was asked, "Has it ever been reported to you that he met with Monica Lewinsky and talked about this case." I believe – I may be wrong about this – my impression was that at the time, I was focused on the meetings. I believe the meetings he had were meetings about her moving to New York and getting a job.

I knew at some point that she had told him that she needed some help, because she had gotten a subpoena. I'm not sure I know whether she did that in a meeting or a phone call. And I was not, I was not focused on that.

I know that, I know Vernon helped her to get a lawyer, Mr. Carter. And I, I believe that he did it after she had called him, but I'm not sure. But I knew that the main source of their meetings was about her move to New York and her getting a job.

Page 76

Q Are you saying, sir, that you forgot when you were asked this question that Vernon Jordan had come on December 19th, just three and a half weeks before, and said that he had met that day, the day that Monica got the subpoena?

A It's quite possible – it's a sort of a jumbled answer. It's quite possible that I had gotten mixed up between whether she had met with him or talked to him on the telephone in those three and a half weeks.

Again, I say, sir, just from the tone of your voice and the way you are asking questions here, it's obvious that this is the most important thing in the world, and that everybody was focused on all the details at the time. But that's not the way it worked. I was, I was doing my best to remember.

Now, keep in mind, I don't know if this is true, but the news reports are that Linda Tripp talked to you, then went and talked to the Jones lawyers, and, you know, that she prepared them for this. Now, maybe – you seem to be criticizing me because they didn't ask better questions and, as if you didn't prepare them well enough to sort of set me up or something. I don't know what's going on here.

All I can tell you is I didn't remember all the details of all this. I didn't remember what – when Vernon talked to me about Monica Lewinsky, whether she talked to him on the telephone or had a meeting. I didn't remember all

Page 77

those details. I was focused on the fact that Monica went to meet with Vernon after Betty helped him set it up, and had subsequent meetings to talk about her move to New York.

Now, keep in mind at this time, at this time, until this date here when it's obvious that something funny's going on here and there's some sort of a gotcha game at work in this deposition, until this date, I didn't know that Ms. Lewinsky's deposition [sic] wasn't going to be sufficient for her to avoid testifying. I didn't, you know –

MR. KENDALL: Excuse me, Mr. President, I think –

THE WITNESS: So, all these details –

MR. KENDALL: – you mean her affidavit.

BY MR. WISENBERG:

Q You mean her affidavit?

A Excuse me. I'm sorry. Her affidavit. Thank you.

So, I don't necessarily remember all the details of all these questions you're asking me, because there was a lot of other things going on, and at the time they were going on, until all this came out, this was not the most important thing in my life. This was just another thing in my life.

Q But Vernon Jordan met with you, sir, and he reported that he had met with Monica Lewinsky, and the discussion was about the lawsuit, and you didn't inform, under oath, the Court of that in your deposition?

A I gave the best answer I could, based on the best

Page 78

memory I had at the time they asked me the question. That's the only answer I can give you, sir.

Q And before –

A And I think I may have been confused in my memory, because I've also talked to him on the phone about what he said about whether he talked to her or met with her. That's all I can tell you.

But, let me say again, I don't have the same view about this deposition – I mean, this affidavit – that I think you do. I felt very strongly that Ms. Lewinsky and everybody else that didn't know anything about Paula Jones and anything about sexual harassment, that she and others were themselves being harassed for political purposes, in the hope of getting damaging information that the Jones lawyers could unlawfully leak.

Now, I believed then, I believe today, that she could execute an affidavit which, under reasonable circumstances with fair-minded, non politically-oriented people, would result in her being relieved of the burden to be put through the kind of testimony that, thanks to Linda Tripp's work with you and with the Jones lawyers, she would have been put through. I don't think that's dishonest. I don't think that's illegal. I think what they were trying to do to her and all these other people, who knew nothing about sexual harassment, was outrageous, just so they could hurt me

Page 79

politically.

So, I just don't have the same attitude about it that you do.

Q Well, you're not telling our grand jurors that because you think the case was a political case or a setup, Mr. President, that that would give you the right to commit perjury or –

A No, sir.

Q – not to tell the full truth?

A No, sir. In the face of their, the Jones lawyers, the people that were questioning me, in the face of their illegal leaks, their constant, unrelenting illegal leaks in a lawsuit that I knew and, by the time this deposition and this discovery started, they knew was a bogus suit on the law and a bogus suit on the facts.

Q The question is –

A In the face of that, I knew that in the face of their illegal activity, I still had to behave lawfully. But I wanted to be legal without being particularly helpful. I thought that was, that was what I was trying to do. And this is the first – you are the first persons who ever suggested to me that, that I should have been doing their lawyers' work for them, when they were perfectly free to ask follow-up questions. On one or two occasions, Mr. Bennett invited them to ask follow-up questions.

Page 80

It now appears to me they didn't because they were afraid I would give them a truthful answer, and that there had been some communication between you and Ms. Tripp and them, and they were trying to set me up and trick me. And now you seem to be complaining that they didn't do a good enough job.

I did my best, sir, at this time. I did not know what I now know about this. A lot of other things were going on in my life. Did I want this to come out? No. Was I embarrassed about it? Yes. Did I ask her to lie about it? No. Did I believe there could be a truthful affidavit? Absolutely.

Now, that's all I know to say about this. I will continue to answer your questions as best I can.

Q You're not going back on your earlier statement that you understood you were sworn to tell the truth, the whole truth, and nothing but the truth to the folks at that deposition, are you, Mr. President?

A No, sir, but I think we might as well put this out on the table. You tried to get me to give a broader interpretation to my oath than just my obligation to tell the truth. In other words, you tried to say, even though these people are treating you in an illegal manner in illegally leaking these depositions, you should be a good lawyer for them. And if they don't have enough sense to write – to ask

Page 81

a question, and even if Mr. Bennett invited them to ask follow-up questions, if they didn't do it, you should have done all their work for them.

Now, so I will admit this, sir. My goal in this deposition was to be truthful, but not particularly helpful. I did not wish to do the work of the Jones lawyers. I deplored what they were doing. I deplored the innocent people they were tormenting and traumatizing. I deplored their illegal leaking. I deplored the fact that they knew, once they knew our evidence, that this was a bogus lawsuit, and that because of the funding they had from my political enemies, they were putting ahead. I deplored it.

But I was determined to walk through the mine field of this deposition without violating the law, and I believe I did.

Q You are not saying, are you, Mr. President, in terms of doing the work for the Jones folks, the Jones lawyers, that you could, you could say, as part of your not helping them, "I don't know" to a particular question, when you really knew, and that it was up to them – even if you really knew the answer, it was up to them to do the follow-up, that you kind of had a one free "I don't know" –

A No, sir.

Q If I could finish up? I've been very patient, Mr. President, in letting you finish.

Page 82

You didn't think you had a free shot to say, "I don't know", or "I don't recall", but when you really did know and you did recall, and it was just up to them, even if you weren't telling the truth, to do a follow-up and to catch you?

A No, sir. I'm not saying that. And if I could give you one example? That's why I felt that I had to come back to that question where I said, I don't know that, and talk about Bruce Lindsey, because I was trying, I was honestly trying to remember how I had first heard this. I wasn't hung up about talking about this.

All I'm saying is, the – let me say something sympathetic to you. I've been pretty tough. So, let me say something sympathetic.

All of you are intelligent people. You've worked hard on this. You've worked for a long time. You've gotten all the facts. You've seen a lot of evidence that I haven't seen. And it's, it's an embarrassing and personally painful thing, the truth about my relationship with Ms. Lewinsky.

So, the natural assumption is that while all this was going on, I must have been focused on nothing but this; therefore, I must remember everything about it in the sequence and form in which it occurred. All I can tell you is, I was concerned about it. I was glad she saw a lawyer. I was glad she was doing an affidavit. But there were a lot

Page 83

of other things going on, and I don't necessarily remember it all. And I don't know if I can convince you of that.

But I tried to be honest with you about my mindset about this deposition. And I'm just trying to explain that I don't have the memory that you assume that I should about some of these things.

Q I want to talk to you for a bit, Mr. President, about the incident that happened at the Northwest Gate of the White House on December 5th – sorry, December 6th, 1997. If you would give me just a moment?

That was a – let me ask you first. In early nineteen – in early December 1997, the Paula Jones case was pending, correct?

A Yes, sir.

Q You were represented by Mr. Bennett, of course?

A That's correct.

Q In that litigation?

A Yes, I did.

Q How –

A He was.

Q I'm sorry. Go ahead.

A No, no. Yes, he was representing me.

Q How often did you talk to him or meet with him, if you can just recall, at that time in the litigation?

A Well, we met, I would say – I wish Mr. Ruff were

Page 84

answering this question, instead of me. His memory would be better. We met probably, oh, for a long time we didn't meet all that often, maybe once a month. And then the closer we got to the deposition, we would meet more frequently. So, maybe by this time we were meeting more.

We also – there was a period when we had been approached about –

MR. KENDALL: Again, the question only goes to the number of meetings and not the content of any conversations with your lawyer.

THE WITNESS: I understand. We're not talking about the content.

There was a, there was a period in which we, I think back in the summer before this, when we had met more frequently. But I would say normally once a month. Sometimes something would be happening and we'd meet more. And then, as we moved toward the deposition, we would begin to meet more.

BY MR. WISENBERG:

Q A witness list came out on December 5th of 1997, with Monica Lewinsky's name on it. Mr. President, when did you find out that Monica's name was on that witness list?

A I believe that I found out late in the afternoon on the 6th. That's what I believe. I've tried to remember with great precision, and because I thought you would ask me about

Page 85

this day, I've tried to remember the logical question, which is whether, whether I knew it on the 6th and, if so, at what time.

I don't – I had a meeting in the late afternoon on the 5th, on the 6th – excuse me, on the 6th – and I believe that's when I learned about it.

Q Now, on the morning of the 6th, Monica Lewinsky came to the Northwest Gate and found out that you were being visited by Eleanor Mondale at the time, and had an extremely angry reaction. You know that, sir, now, don't you?

A I have, I have – I know that Monica Lewinsky came to the gate on the 6th and apparently directly called in and wanted to see me and couldn't, and was angry about it. I know that.

Q And she expressed that anger to Betty Currie over the telephone, isn't that correct, sir?

A That, Betty told me that.

Q And she then later expressed her anger to you in one of her telephone conversations with Betty Currie, is that correct?

A You mean did I talk to her on the phone?

Q Monica Lewinsky, that day, before she came in to visit in the White House?

A Mr. Wisenberg, I remember that she came in to visit that day. I remember that she was upset. I don't recall

Page 86

whether I talked to her on the phone before she came in to visit, but I well may have. I'm not denying it that I did. I just don't recall that.

Q And Mrs. Currie and yourself were very irate that Ms. Lewinsky had overheard that you were in the Oval Office with a visitor on that day, isn't that correct, that you and Mrs. Currie were very irate about that?

A Well, I don't remember all that. What I remember is that she was very – Monica was very upset. She got upset from time to time. And, and I was, you know, I couldn't see her. I had, I was doing, as I remember, I had some other work to do that morning and she had just sort of showed up and wanted to be let in, and wanted to come in at a certain time and she wanted everything to be that way, and we couldn't see her. Now, I did arrange to see her later that day. And I was upset about her conduct.

I'm not sure that I knew or focused on at that moment exactly the question you asked. I remember I was, I thought her conduct was inappropriate that day.

Q I want to go back and I want to take them one at a time. Number one, did you find out at some point during that day that Monica had overheard from somebody in the Secret Service that you were meeting with Ms. Mondale, and that Monica got very irate about that?

A I knew that at some point. I don't know whether I

Page 87

found out that, that day. I knew that day, I knew that somehow she knew that among, that, that Eleanor Mondale was in to see us that day. I knew that. I don't know that I knew how she knew that on that day. I don't remember that.

Q That leads into my second question, which is, weren't you irate at the Secret Service precisely because they had revealed this information to Ms. Lewinsky on that very day, so irate that you told several people, or at least one person, that somebody should be fired over this, on that very day?

A I don't remember whether it happened on that very day. But, let me tell you that the Uniformed Secret Service, if that is in fact what happened and I will stipulate that that is, that no one should be telling anybody, not anybody, not a member of my staff, who the President is meeting with. That's an inappropriate thing to do.

So, I would think that if that, in fact, is what I heard when I heard it, I would have thought that was a bad thing. I don't know that I said that. I don't, I don't remember what I said, and I don't remember to whom I said it.

Q It would be an inappropriate thing, sir, and that leads into my next question is that why did Mrs. Currie, on your instructions, later that day tell many of the Secret Service Officers involved that it never happened, to forget about it?

Page 88

A That what never happened?

Q The incident that you were so irate about earlier; the incident of somebody disclosing to Ms. Lewinsky that Ms. Mondale was in the Oval Office?

A I don't know the answer to that. I think maybe, you know, I don't know. I don't know the answer.

Q You don't recall that you later gave orders to the effect that we are going to pretend this never happened, or something –

A No, sir.

Q – like that?

A No, sir. I don't recall it. First of all, I don't recall that I gave orders to fire anybody, if that was the implication of your first statement.

Q It wasn't an implication. Actually, the question was that you initially wanted somebody fired. You were so mad that you wanted somebody fired.

A I don't remember that, first of all. I remember thinking it was an inappropriate thing to do. And I, I, I remember, as I usually do when I'm mad, after awhile I wasn't so mad about it, and I'm quite aware that Ms. Lewinsky has a way of getting information out of people when she's either charming or determined. And it – I could have just said, well, I'm not so mad about it any more.

But I don't remember the whole sequence of events

Page 89

you're talking to me about now, except I do remember that somehow Monica found out Eleanor Mondale was there. I learned either that day or later that one of the Uniformed Division personnel had told her. I do – I thought then it was a mistake. I think now it was a mistake. I'm not sure it's a mistake someone should be terminated over. I think that, you know, you could just tell them not to do that any more.

Q In fact, it would kind of be an overreaction, to get irate or terminate somebody for revealing to a former White House staffer who visits where the President is, don't you think, sir?

A Well, it would depend upon the facts. I think on the whole people in the Uniformed Secret Service who are working on the gate have no business telling anybody anything about the President's schedule, just as a general principal. I didn't mind anybody knowing that she was there, if that's what you're saying. I could care less about that. But I think that the schedule itself – these uniformed people, you know, somebody shouldn't just be able to come up on the street and, because they know who the Secret Service agent is, he says who the President's with. I don't think that's proper.

Q I agree, Mr. President.

A But, on the other hand, I didn't, you know, I, I

Page 90

wanted to know what happened. I think we found out what happened. And then they were, I think, told not to let it happen again, and I think that's the way it should have been handled. I think it was handled in the appropriate way.

Q You have no knowledge of the fact that Secret Service officers were told later in the day something to the effect of, this never happened, this event never happened? You have no knowledge of that?

A I'm not sure anybody ever told that to me. I mean, I thought you were asking – let me just say, my interpretation of this, of your previous question was different than what you're asking now.

What I remember was being upset that this matter would be discussed that – by anybody. It's incidental it happened to be Monica Lewinsky. And that, that whatever I said, I don't recall. But then thinking that the appropriate thing to do was to say, look, just this, this is not an appropriate thing for you to be talking about, the President's schedule, and it shouldn't happen again.

Now, the question you seem to be asking me now – I just want to be sure I'm getting the right question – is whether I gave instructions, in effect, to pretend that Monica Lewinsky was never at the gate. And if –

Q To the effect of pretend –

A And if that is the question you are asking me, I

Page 91

don't believe I ever did that, sir. I certainly have no memory of doing that.

Q Or anything to that effect?

A I don't know what that means.

Q Is that your testimony?

A What does that mean, anything to that effect?

Q Well, Mr. President, you've told us that you were not going to try to help the Jones attorneys, and I think it's clear from your testimony that you were pretty literal at times. So, that's why I'm saying, I don't necessarily know the exact words. The question was, do you have any knowledge of the fact –

A Of that?

Q – of the fact that later in the day, on Saturday, the 6th of December, 1997, Secret Service people were then, were told something to this effect: This event never happened, let's just pretend this event did not happen. Do you have knowledge of it, or not?

A No, sir. And I, I didn't instruct the Secret Service in that regard. I have no memory of saying anything to anybody in the Secret Service that would have triggered that kind of instruction.

Q Did you tell Captain Purdy, while you were standing in the doorway between the Oval Office and Betty Currie's office, did you tell Captain Purdy of the Uniformed Division,

Page 92

I hope I can count on your discretion in this matter? At the end of the day when you all were talking about that earlier incident, did you tell him that or anything like that, sir?

A I don't remember anything I said to him in that regard. I have no recollection of that whatever.

MR. WISENBERG: Let's take a break now.

MR. KENDALL: Thank you, 3:38.

(Whereupon, the proceedings were recessed from 3:38 p.m. until 4:01 p.m.)

MR. KENDALL: It is 4:01.

BY MR. WISENBERG:

Q Mr. President, the next series of questions are from the grand jurors. And let me tell you that the grand jurors want you to be more specific about the inappropriate conduct.

The first question was, one of the grand jurors has said that you referred to what you did with Ms. Lewinsky as inappropriate contact; what do you mean by that?

A I mean just what I said. But I would like to ask the grand jury, because I think I have been quite specific and I think I've been willing to answer some specific questions that I haven't been asked yet, but I do not want to discuss something that is intensely painful to me. This has been tough enough already on me and on my family, although I take responsibility for it.I have no one to blame but myself.

Page 93

What I meant was, and what they can infer that I meant was, that I did things that were -- when I was alone with her, that were inappropriate and wrong. But that they did not include any activity that was within the definition of sexual relations that I was given by Judge Wright in the deposition. I said that I did not do those things that were in that, within that definition, and I testified truthfully to that. And that's all I can say about it.

Now, you know, if there's any doubt on the part of the grand jurors about whether I believe some kind of activity falls within that definition or outside that definition, I'd be happy to try to answer that.

Q Well, I have a question regarding your definition then. And my question is, is oral sex performed on you within that definition as you understood it, the definition in the Jones –

A As I understood it, it was not, no.

Q The grand jurors would like to know upon what basis, what legal basis you are declining to answer more specific questions about this? I've mentioned to you that obviously you have privileges, privileges against self-incrimination. There's no general right not to answer questions.

And so one of the questions from the grand jurors is what basis, what legal basis are you declining to answer

Page 94

these questions?

A I'm not trying to evade my legal obligations or my willingness to help the grand jury achieve their legal obligations. As I understand it, you want to examine whether you believe I told the truth in my deposition, whether I asked Ms. Lewinsky not to tell the truth, and whether I did anything else with evidence, or in any other way, amounting to an obstruction of justice or a subornation of perjury. And I'm prepared to answer all questions that the grand jury needs to draw that conclusion.

Now, respectfully, I believe the grand jurors can ask me if I believe – just like that grand juror did – could ask me, do you believe that this conduct falls within that definition. If it does, then you are free to conclude that my testimony is that I didn't do that. And I believe that you can achieve that without requiring me to say and do things that I don't think are necessary and that I think, frankly, go too far in trying to criminalize my private life.

Q If a person touched another person, if you touched another person on the breast, would that be, in your view, and was it within your view, when you took the deposition, within the definition of sexual relations?

A If the person being deposed –

Q Yes.

A – in this case, me, directly touched the breast of

Page 95

another person, with the purpose to arouse or gratify, under that definition that would be included.

Q Only directly, sir, or would it be directly or through clothing?

A Well, I would – I think the common sense definition would be directly. That's how I would infer what it means.

Q If the person being deposed kissed the breast of another person, would that be in the definition of sexual relations as you understood it when you were under oath in the Jones case?

A Yes, that would constitute contact. I think that would. If it were direct contact, I believe it would. I – maybe I should read it again, just to make sure.

Because this basically says if there was any direct contact with an intent to arouse or gratify, if that was the intent of the contact, then that would fall within the definition. That's correct.

Q So, touching, in your view then and now – the person being deposed touching or kissing the breast of another person would fall within the definition?

A That's correct, sir.

Q And you testified that you didn't have sexual relations with Monica Lewinsky in the Jones deposition, under that definition, correct?

Page 96

A That's correct, sir.

Q If the person being deposed touched the genitalia of another person, would that be – and with the intent to arouse the sexual desire, arouse or gratify, as defined in definition (1), would that be, under your understanding then and now –

A Yes, sir.

Q -- sexual relations?

A Yes, sir.

Q Yes, it would?

A Yes, it would. If you had a direct contact with any of these places in the body, if you had direct contact with intent to arouse or gratify, that would fall within the definition.

Q So, you didn't do any of those three things –

A You –

Q -- with Monica Lewinsky?

A You are free to infer that my testimony is that I did not have sexual relations, as I understood this term to be defined.

Q Including touching her breast, kissing her breast, or touching her genitalia?

A That's correct.

Q Would you agree with me that the insertion of an object into the genitalia of another person with the desire

Page 97

to gratify sexually would fit within the definition used in the Jones case as sexual relations?

A There's nothing here about that, is there? I don't know that I ever thought about that one way or the other.

Q The question is, under the definition as you understood it then, under the definition as you understand it now – pardon me just a minute.

Pardon me, Mr. President.

(Pause)

Deposition Exhibit 1, question 1, under the – in the Jones case, Definition of Sexual Relations –

MR. KENDALL: Do you have that before you, Mr. President? Excuse me.

THE WITNESS: I do, sir.

MR. KENDALL: Good.

THE WITNESS: I've got it right here. I'm looking at it.

BY MR. WISENBERG:

Q As you understood the definition then, and as you understood it now, would it include sticking an object into the genitalia of another person in order to arouse or gratify the sexual desire of any person? Would it constitute, in other words, contact with the genitalia?

A I don't know the answer to that. I suppose you could argue that since section 2, paragraph (2) was

Page 98

eliminated, and paragraph (2) actually dealt with the object issue, that perhaps whoever wrote this didn't intend for paragraph (1) to cover an object, and basically meant direct contact.

So, if I were asked – I've not been asked this question before. But I guess that's the way I would read it.

Q If it – that it would not be covered? That activity would not be covered?

A That's right. If the activity you just mentioned would be covered in number (2), and number (2) were stricken, I think you can infer logically that paragraph (1) was not intended to cover it. But, as I said, I've not been asked this before. I'm just doing the best I can.

Q Well, if someone were to hold or a judge were to hold that you are incorrect and that definition (1) does include the hypo I've given to you – because we're talking in hypos, so that you don't – under your request here, if someone were to tell you or rule that you are wrong, that the insertion of an object into somebody else's genitalia with the intent to arouse or gratify the sexual desire of any person is within definition (1) –

MR. KENDALL: Mr. Wisenberg, excuse me. I have not objected heretofore to any question you've asked. I must tell you, I cannot understand that question. I think it's improper. And, if the witness can understand it, he may

Page 99

answer.

MR. WISENBERG: I'll be happy to rephrase it.

BY MR. WISENBERG:

Q If you're wrong and it's within definition (1), did you engage in sexual relations under the definition, with Monica Lewinsky?

A But, Mr. Wisenberg, I have said all along that I would say what I thought it meant, and you can infer that I didn't. This is an unusual question, but it's a slippery slope. We can – I have tried to deal with some very delicate areas here, and, and in one case I've given you a very forthright answer about what I thought was not within here.

All I can tell you is, whatever I thought was covered, and I thought about this carefully. And let me just point out, this was uncomfortable for me. I had to acknowledge, because of this definition, that under this definition I had actually had sexual relations once with Gennifer Flowers, a person who had spread all kinds of ridiculous, dishonest, exaggerated stories about me for money. And I knew when I did that, it would be leaked. It was. And I was embarrassed. But I did it.

So, I tried to read this carefully. I can tell you what I thought it covered, and I can tell you that I do not believe I did anything that I thought was covered by this.

Page 100

Q As I understand your testimony, Mr. President, touching somebody's breast with the intent to arouse, with the intent to arouse or gratify the sexual desire of any person is covered; kissing the breast is covered; touching the genitalia is covered; correct?

MR. KENDALL: In fairness, the witness said directly in each one of those cases.

BY MR. WISENBERG:

Q Directly, is covered, correct?

A I believe it is, yes, sir.

Q Oral sex, in your view, is not covered, correct?

A If performed on the deponent.

Q Is not covered, correct?

A That's my reading of this number (1).

Q And you are declining to answer the hypothetical about insertion of an object.

I need to inform you, Mr. President – we'll go on, at least for now. But I need to inform you that the grand jury will consider your not answering the questions more directly in their determination of whether or not they are going to issue another subpoena.

Let me switch the topic and talk to you about John Podesta and some of the other aides you've met with and spoke to after this story became public on January 21st, 1998, the day of The Washington Post story.

Page 101

Do you recall meeting with him around January 23rd, 1998, a Friday a.m. in your study, two days after The Washington Post story, and extremely explicitly telling him that you didn't have, engage in any kind of sex, in any way, shape or form, with Monica Lewinsky, including oral sex?

A I meet with John Podesta almost every day. I meet with a number of people. The only thing I – what happened in the couple of days after what you did was revealed, is a blizzard to me. The only thing I recall is that I met with certain people, and a few of them I said I didn't have sex with Monica Lewinsky, or I didn't have an affair with her or something like that. I had a very careful thing I said, and I tried not to say anything else.

And it might be that John Podesta was one of them. But I do not remember this specific meeting about which you asked, or the specific comments to which you refer. And –

Q You don't remember –

A – seven months ago, I'd have no way to remember, no.

Q You don't remember denying any kind of sex in any way, shape or form, and including oral sex, correct?

A I remember that I issued a number of denials to people that I thought needed to hear them, but I tried to be careful and to be accurate, and I do not remember what I said to John Podesta.

Page 102

Q Surely, if you told him that, that would be a falsehood, correct?

A No, I didn't say that, sir. I didn't say that at all. That is not covered by the definition and I did not address it in my statement.

Q Well, let me ask you then. If you told him – perhaps he thought it was covered, I don't know. But if you told him, if you denied to him sex in any way, shape or form, kind of similar to what Mr. Bennett did at the deposition, including oral sex, wouldn't that have been a falsehood?

A Now, Mr. Wisenberg, I told you in response to a grand juror's question, you asked me did I believe that oral sex performed on the person being deposed was covered by that definition, and I said no. I don't believe it's covered by the definition.

I said you are free to conclude that I did not do things that I believe were covered by the definition, and you have asked me a number of questions and I have acknowledged things that I believe are covered by the definition. Since that was not covered by the definition, I want to fall back on my statement.

Look, I'm not trying to be evasive here. I'm trying to protect my privacy, my family's privacy, and I'm trying to stick to what the deposition was about. If the deposition wasn't about this and didn't cover it, then I

Page 103

don't believe that I should be required to go beyond my statement.

Q Mr. President, it's not our intent to embarrass you. But since we have to look, among other things, at obstruction of justice, questions of obstruction of justice and perjury, the answer to some of these delicate and unfortunate questions are absolutely required. And that is the purpose that we have to ask them for.

A It's not –

Q I'm unaware of any –

A Mr. Wisenberg, with respect, you don't need to know the answer for that, if the answer, no matter what the answer is, wouldn't constitute perjury because it wasn't sexual relations as defined by the Judge.

Q Mister –

A The only reason you need to know that is for some other reason. It couldn't have anything to do with perjury.

Q Mr. President, one of the, one of the nice things about – one of the normal things about an investigation and a grand jury investigation is that the grand jurors and the prosecutors get to ask the questions unless they are improper, and unless there is a legal basis.

As I understand from your answers, there is no legal basis for which you decline to answer these questions. And I'll ask you again to answer the question. I'm unaware

Page 104

of any legal basis for you not to. If you told –

MR. KENDALL: Mr. Wisenberg, could you just restate the question, please?

BY MR. WISENBERG:

Q The question is, if you told John Podesta two days after the story broke something to this effect, that you didn't have any kind of sex in any way, shape or form, including oral sex with Ms. Lewinsky, were you telling him the truth?

A And let me say again, with respect, this is an indirect way to try to get me to testify to questions that have no bearing on whether I committed perjury. You apparently agree that it has no bearing –

Q Oh, I don't –

A – no bearing on whether I –

Q I don't agree.

A – committed perjury.

Q Mr. President, I'm sorry, with respect, I don't agree with that. I'm not going to argue with you about it. I just am going to ask you again, in fact direct you to answer the question.

A I'm not going to answer that question, because I believe it's a question about conduct that, whatever the answer to it is, would, does not bear on the perjury because oral sex performed on the deponent under this definition is

Page 105

not sexual relations. It is not covered by this definition.

MR. KENDALL: The witness is not declining to tell you anything he said to John Podesta.

BY MR. WISENBERG:

Q You denied the –

MR. WISENBERG: The witness is not declining to tell me anything?

BY MR. WISENBERG:

Q Did you deny oral sex in any way, shape or form, to John Podesta?

A I told you, sir, before, and I will say again, in the aftermath of this story breaking, and what was told about it, the next two days, next three days are just a blur to me. I don't remember to whom I talked, when I talked to them, or what I said.

Q So, you are not declining to answer, you just don't remember?

A I honestly don't remember, no.

Q Okay.

A I'm not saying that anybody who had a contrary memory is wrong. I do not remember.

Q Do you recall denying any sexual relationship with Monica Lewinsky to the following people: Harry Thomasson, Erskine Bowles, Harold Ickes, Mr. Podesta, Mr. Blumenthal, Mr. Jordan, Ms. Betty Currie? Do you recall denying any

Page 106

sexual relationship with Monica Lewinsky to those individuals?

A I recall telling a number of those people that I didn't have, either I didn't have an affair with Monica Lewinsky or didn't have sex with her. And I believe, sir, that – you'll have to ask them what they thought. But I was using those terms in the normal way people use them. You'll have to ask them what they thought I was saying.

Q If they testified that you denied sexual relations or relationship with Monica Lewinsky, or if they told us that you denied that, do you have any reason to doubt them, in the days after the story broke; do you have any reason to doubt them?

A No. The – let me say this. It's no secret to anybody that I hoped that this relationship would never become public. It's a matter of fact that it had been many, many months since there had been anything improper about it, in terms of improper contact. I –

Q Did you deny it to them or not, Mr. President?

A Let me finish. So, what – I did not want to mislead my friends, but I wanted to find language where I could say that. I also, frankly, did not want to turn any of them into witnesses, because I – and, sure enough, they all became witnesses.

Q Well, you knew they might be –

Page 107

A And so –

Q – witnesses, didn't you?

A And so I said to them things that were true about this relationship. That I used – in the language I used, I said, there's nothing going on between us. That was true. I said, I have not had sex with her as I defined it. That was true. And did I hope that I would never have to be here on this day giving this testimony? Of course.

But I also didn't want to do anything to complicate this matter further. So, I said things that were true. They may have been misleading, and if they were I have to take responsibility for it, and I'm sorry.

Q It may have been misleading, sir, and you knew though, after January 21st when the Post article broke and said that Judge Starr was looking into this, you knew that they might be witnesses. You knew that they might be called into a grand jury, didn't you?

A That's right. I think I was quite careful what I said after that. I may have said something to all these people to that effect, but I'll also – whenever anybody asked me any details, I said, look, I don't want you to be a witness or I turn you into a witness or give you information that could get you in trouble. I just wouldn't talk. I, by and large, didn't talk to people about this.

Q If all of these people – let's leave out Mrs.

Page 108

Currie for a minute. Vernon Jordan, Sid Blumenthal, John Podesta, Harold Ickes, Erskine Bowles, Harry Thomasson, after the story broke, after Judge Starr's involvement was known on January 21st, have said that you denied a sexual relationship with them. Are you denying that?

A No.

Q And you've told us that you –

A I'm just telling you what I meant by it. I told you what I meant by it when they started this deposition.

Q You've told us now that you were being careful, but that it might have been misleading. Is that correct?

A It might have been. Since we have seen this four-year, $40-million-investigation come down to parsing the definition of sex, I think it might have been. I don't think at the time that I thought that's what this was going to be about.

In fact, if you remember the headlines at the time, even you mentioned the Post story. All the headlines were – and all the talking, people who talked about this, including a lot who have been quite sympathetic to your operation, said, well, this is not really a story about sex, or this is a story about subornation of perjury and these talking points, and all this other stuff.

So, what I was trying to do was to give them something they could – that would be true, even if

Page 109

misleading in the context of this deposition, and keep them out of trouble, and let's deal – and deal with what I thought was the almost ludicrous suggestion that I had urged someone to lie or tried to suborn perjury, in other words.

Q I want to go over some questions again. I don't think you are going to answer them, sir. And so I don't need a lengthy response, just a yes or a no. And I understand the basis upon which you are not answering them, but I need to ask them for the record.

If Monica Lewinsky says that while you were in the Oval Office area you touched her breasts, would she be lying?

A Let me say something about all this.

Q All I really need for you, Mr. President –

A I know.

Q – is to say –

A But you –

Q – I won't answer under the previous grounds, or to answer the question, you see, because we only have four hours, and your answers –

A I know.

Q – have been extremely lengthy.

A I know that. I'll give you four hours and 30 seconds, if you'll let me say something general about this. I will answer to your satisfaction that I won't – based on my statement, I will not answer. I would like 30 seconds at

Page 110

the end to make a statement, and you can have 30 seconds more on your time, if you'll let me say this to the grand jury and to you. And I don't think it's disrespectful at all. I've had a lot of time to think about this.

But, go ahead and ask your questions.

Q The question is, if Monica Lewinsky says that while you were in the Oval Office area you touched her breasts, would she be lying?

A That is not my recollection. My recollection is that I did not have sexual relations with Ms. Lewinsky and I'm staying on my former statement about that.

Q If she said –

A My, my statement is that I did not have sexual relations as defined by that.

Q If she says that you kissed her breasts, would she be lying?

A I'm going to revert to my former statement.

Q Okay. If Monica Lewinsky says that while you were in the Oval Office area you touched her genitalia, would she be lying? And that calls for a yes, no, or reverting to your former statement.

A I will revert to my statement on that.

Q If Monica Lewinsky says that you used a cigar as a sexual aid with her in the Oval Office area, would she be lying? Yes, no, or won't answer?

Page 111

A I will revert to my former statement.

Q If Monica Lewinsky says that you had phone sex with her, would she be lying?

A Well, that is, at least in general terms, I think, is covered by my statement. I addressed that in my statement, and that, I don't believe, is –

Q Let me define phone sex for purposes of my question. Phone sex occurs when a party to a phone conversation masturbates while the other party is talking in a sexually explicit manner. And the question is, if Monica Lewinsky says that you had phone sex with her, would she be lying?

A I think that is covered by my statement.

Q Did you, on or about January the 13th, 1998, Mr. President, ask Erskine Bowles to ask John Hilley if he would give a recommendation for Monica Lewinsky?

A In 1998?

Q Yes. On or about January 13th, 1998, did you ask Erskine Bowles, your Chief of Staff, if he would ask John Hilley to give a recommendation for Monica Lewinsky?

A At some point, sir, I believe I talked to Erskine Bowles about whether Monica Lewinsky could get a recommendation that was not negative from the Legislative Affairs Office. I believe I did.

Q I just didn't hear the very last part.

Page 112

A I think the answer is, I think, yes. At some point I talked to Erskine Bowles about this.

Q Okay.

A I do not know what the date was. At some point I did talk to him.

Q And if Erskine Bowles has told us that he told John Podesta to carry out your wishes, and John Podesta states that it was three or four days before your deposition, which would be the 13th or the 14th, are you in a position to deny that?

A The 13th or 14th of?

Q January, as to date.

A I don't know. I don't know when the date was.

Q Okay.

A I'm not in a position to deny it. I won't deny it. I'm sure that they are both truthful men. I don't know when the date was.

Q Do you recall asking Erskine Bowles to do that?

A I recall talking to Erskine Bowles about that, and my recollection is, sir, that Ms. Lewinsky was moving to New York, wanted to get a job in the private sector; was confident she would get a good recommendation from the Defense Department; and was concerned that because she had been moved from the Legislative Affairs Office, transferred to the Defense Department, that her ability to get a job

Page 113

might be undermined by a bad recommendation from the Legislative Affairs Office.

So, I asked Erskine if we could get her a recommendation that just was at least neutral, so that if she had a good recommendation from the Defense Department it wouldn't prevent her from getting a job in the private sector.

Q If Mr. Bowles has told us that, in fact, you told him that she already had a job and had already listed Mr. Hilley as a reference and wanted him to be available as a recommendation, would you be in – is that inconsistent with your memory?

A A little bit, but I think – my memory is that when you're, when you get a job like that you have to give them a resume, which says where you've worked and who your supervisor was. And I think that that's my recollection. My recollection is that – slightly different from that.

Q And who was it that asked you to do that on Monica Lewinsky's behalf?

A I think she did. You know, she tried for months and months to get a job back in the White House, not so much in the West Wing but somewhere in the White House complex, including the Old Executive Office Building. And she talked to Marsha Scott, among others. She very much wanted to come back. And she interviewed for some jobs but never got one.

Page 114

She was, from time to time, upset about it.

And I think what she was afraid of is that she couldn't get a – from the minute she left the White House she was worried about this. That if she didn't come back to the White House and work for awhile and get a good job recommendation, that no matter how well she had done at the Pentagon it might hurt her future employment prospects.

Well, it became obvious that, you know, her mother had moved to New York. She wanted to go to New York. She wasn't going to get a job in the White House. So, she wanted to get a job in the private sector, and said, I hope that I won't get a letter out of the Legislative Affairs Office that will prevent my getting a job in the private sector. And that's what I talked to Erskine about.

Now, that's my entire memory of this.

Q All right. I want to go back briefly to the December 28th conversation with Ms. Lewinsky. I believe you testified to the effect that she asked you, what if they ask me about gifts you gave me. My question to you is, after that statement by her, did you ever have a conversation with Betty Currie about gifts, or picking something up from Monica Lewinsky?

A I don't believe I did, sir. No.

Q You never told her anything to this effect, that Monica has something to give you?

Page 115

A No, sir.

Q That is to say, Betty Currie?

A No, sir, I didn't. I don't have any memory of that whatever.

Q And so you have no knowledge that, or you had no knowledge at the time, that Betty Currie went and picked up, your secretary went and picked up from Monica Lewinsky items that were called for by the Jones subpoena and hid them under her bed? You had no knowledge that anything remotely like that was going to happen?

A I did not. I did not know she had those items, I believe, until that was made public.

Q And you agree with me that that would be a very wrong thing to do, to hide evidence in a civil case, or any case? Isn't that true?

A Yes. I don't know that, that Ms. Currie knew that that's what she had at all. But –

Q I'm not saying she did. I'm just saying –

A I had – it is, if Monica Lewinsky did that after they had been subpoenaed and she knew what she was doing, she should not have done that.

Q And if you knew, you –

A And I –

Q – shouldn't have done it?

A Indeed, I, myself, told her, if they ask you for

Page 116

gifts you have to give them what you have. And I don't understand if, in fact, she was worried about this, why she was so worried about it. It was no big deal.

Q I want to talk about a December 17th phone conversation you had with Monica Lewinsky at approximately 2:00 a.m. Do you recall making that conversation and telling her initially about the death of Betty's brother, but then telling her that she was on the witness list, and that it broke your heart that she was on the witness list?

A No, sir, I don't, but it would – it, it would – it is quite possible that that happened, because, if you remember, earlier in this meeting you asked me some questions about what I'd said to Monica about testimony and affidavits, and I was struggling to try to remember whether this happened in a meeting or a phone call.

Now, I remember I called her to tell her Betty's brother had died. I remember that. And I know it was in the middle of December, and I believe it was before Monica had been subpoenaed. So, I think it is quite possible that if I called her at that time and had not talked to her since the 6th – and you asked me this earlier – I believe when I saw her on the 6th, I don't think I knew she was on the witness list then, then it's quite possible I would say something like that. I don't have any memory of it, but I certainly wouldn't dispute that I might have said that.

Page 117

Q And in that conversation, or in any conversation in which you informed her she was on the witness list, did you tell her, you know, you can always say that you were coming to see Betty or bringing me letters? Did you tell her anything like that?

A I don't remember. She was coming to see Betty. I can tell you this. I absolutely never asked her to lie.

Q Sir, every time she came to see Betty and you were in the Oval Office, she was coming to see you, too, wasn't she, or just about every time?

A I think just about every time. I don't think every time. I think there was a time or two where she came to see Betty when she didn't see me.

Q So, do you remember telling her any time, any time when you told her, or after you told her that she was on the witness list, something to this effect: You know, you can always say you were coming to see Betty, or you were bringing me letters?

A I don't remember exactly what I told her that night.

Q Did you –

A I don't remember that. I remember talking about the nature of our relationship, how she got in. But I also will tell you that I felt quite comfortable that she could have executed a truthful affidavit, which would not have

Page 118

disclosed the embarrassing details of the relationship that we had had, which had been over for many, many months by the time this incident occurred.

Q Did you tell her anytime in December something to that effect: You know, you can always say that you were coming to see Betty or you were bringing me letters? Did you say that, or anything like that, in December '97 or January '98, to Monica Lewinsky?

A Well, that's a very broad question. I do not recall saying anything like that in connection with her testimony. I could tell you what I do remember saying, if you want to know. But I don't – we might have talked about what to do in a non legal context at some point in the past, but I have no specific memory of that conversation.

I do remember what I said to her about the possible testimony.

Q You would agree with me, if you did say something like that to her, to urge her to say that to the Jones people, that that would be part of an effort to mislead the Jones people, no matter how evil they are and corrupt?

A I didn't say they were evil. I said what they were doing here was wrong, and it was.

Q Wouldn't that be misleading?

A Well, again, you are trying to get me to characterize something that I'm – that I don't know if I

Page 119

said or not, without knowing whether the whole, whether the context is complete or not. So, I would have to know, what was the context, what were all the surrounding facts.

I can tell you this: I never asked Ms. Lewinsky to lie. The first time that she raised with me the possibility that she might be a witness or I told her – you suggested the possibility in this December 17th timeframe – I told her she had to get a lawyer. And I never asked her to lie.

Q Did you ever say anything like that, you can always say that you were coming to see Betty or bringing me letters? Was that part of any kind of a, anything you said to her or a cover story, before you had any idea she was going to be part of Paula Jones?

A I might well have said that.

Q Okay.

A Because I certainly didn't want this to come out, if I could help it. And I was concerned about that. I was embarrassed about it. I knew it was wrong. And, you know, of course, I didn't want it to come out. But –

Q But you are saying that you didn't say anything – I want to make sure I understand. Did you say anything like that once you knew or thought she might be a witness in the Jones case? Did you repeat that statement, or something like it to her?

A Well, again, I don't recall, and I don't recall

Page 120

whether I might have done something like that, for example, if somebody says, what if the reporters ask me this, that or the other thing. I can tell you this: In the context of whether she could be a witness, I have a recollection that she asked me, well, what do I do if I get called as a witness, and I said, you have to get a lawyer. And that's all I said. And I never asked her to lie.

Q Did you tell her to tell the truth?

A Well, I think the implication was she would tell the truth. I've already told you that I felt strongly that she could issue, that she could execute an affidavit that would be factually truthful, that might get her out of having to testify. Now, it obviously wouldn't if the Jones people knew this, because they knew that if they could get this and leak it, it would serve their larger purposes, even if the judge ruled that she couldn't be a witness in the case. The judge later ruled she wouldn't be a witness in the case. The judge later ruled the case had no merit.

So, I knew that. And did I hope she'd be able to get out of testifying on an affidavit? Absolutely. Did I want her to execute a false affidavit? No, I did not.

Q If Monica Lewinsky has stated that her affidavit that she didn't have a sexual relationship with you is, in fact, a lie, I take it you disagree with that?

A No. I told you before what I thought the issue was

Page 121

there. I think the issue is how do you define sexual relationship. And there was no definition imposed on her at the time she executed the affidavit. Therefore, she was free to give it any reasonable meaning.

Q And if she says she was lying –

A And I believe –

Q – under your common sense ordinary meaning that you talked about earlier, Mr. President, that most Americans would have, if she says sexual relationship, saying I didn't have one was a lie because I had oral sex with the President, I take it, you would disagree with that?

A Now, we're back to where we started and I have to invoke my statement. But, let me just say one thing. I've read a lot, and obviously I don't know whether any of it's accurate, about what she said, and what purports to be on those tapes.

And this thing – and I searched my own memory. This reminds me, to some extent, of the hearings when Clarence Thomas and Anita Hill were both testifying under oath. Now, in some rational way, they could not have both been telling the truth, since they had directly different accounts of a shared set of facts. Fortunately, or maybe you think unfortunately, there was no special prosecutor to try to go after one or the other of them, to take sides and try to prove one was a liar. And so, Judge Thomas was able to go

Page 122

on and serve on the Supreme Court.

What I learned from that, I can tell you that I was a citizen out there just listening. And when I heard both of them testify, what I believed after it was over, I believed that they both thought they were telling the truth.

This is – you're dealing with, in some ways, the most mysterious area of human life. I'm doing the best I can to give you honest answers.

Q Mr. President –

A And that's all I can say.

Q I'm sorry.

A And, you know, those people both testified under oath. So, if there'd been a special prosecutor, they could, one of them could have gone after Anita Hill, another could have gone after Clarence Thomas. I thank God there was no such thing then, because I don't believe that it was a proper thing.

Q One of –

A And I think they both thought they were telling the truth. So, maybe Ms. Lewinsky believes she's telling the truth, and I'm glad she got her mother and herself out of trouble. I'm glad you gave her that sweeping immunity. I'm glad for the whole thing. I, I, I – it breaks my heart that she was ever involved in this.

Q I want to go back to a question about Vernon

Page 123

Jordan. I want to go back to late December and early January, late December of '97 and early January of '98. During this time, Mr. President, you are being sued for sexual harassment by a woman who claims, among other things, that others got benefits that she didn't because she didn't have oral sex with you. While this is happening, your powerful friend, Vernon Jordan, is helping to get Monica Lewinsky a job and a lawyer. He's helping to get a job and a lawyer for someone who had some kind of sex with you, and who has been subpoenaed in the very case, the Jones case.

Don't you see a problem with this? Didn't you see a problem with this?

A No. Would you like to know why?

Q Isn't that why – I would. But isn't that why Vernon Jordan asked you on December 19th whether or not you had sexual relationships with Monica Lewinsky and why he asked her, because he knew it would be so highly improper to be helping her with a lawyer and a job if, in fact, she had had a relationship with you?

A I don't know. I don't believe that at all. I don't believe that at all, particularly since, even if you look at the facts here in their light most unfavorable to me, no one has suggested that there was any sexual harassment on my part. And I don't think it was wrong to be helping her. Look –

Page 124

Q A subpoenaed witness in a case against you?

A Absolutely. Look, for one thing, I had already proved in two ways that I was not trying to influence her testimony. I didn't order her to be hired at the White House. I could have done so. I wouldn't do it. She tried for months to get in. She was angry.

Secondly, after I –

Q Wasn't she kept –

A After I terminated the improper contact with her, she wanted to come in more than she did. She got angry when she didn't get in sometimes. I knew that that might make her more likely to speak, and I still did it because I had to limit the contact.

And, thirdly, let me say, I formed an opinion really early in 1996, and again – well, let me finish the sentence. I formed an opinion early in 1996, once I got into this unfortunate and wrong conduct, that when I stopped it, which I knew I'd have to do and which I should have done a long time before I did, that she would talk about it. Not because Monica Lewinsky is a bad person. She's basically a good girl. She's a good young woman with a good heart and a good mind. I think she is burdened by some unfortunate conditions of her, her upbringing. But she's basically a good person.

But I knew that the minute there was no longer any

Page 125

contact, she would talk about this. She would have to. She couldn't help it. It was, it was a part of her psyche. So, I had put myself at risk, sir. I was not trying to buy her silence or get Vernon Jordan to buy her silence. I thought she was a good person. She had not been involved with me for a long time in any improper way, several months, and I wanted to help her get on with her life. It's just as simple as that.

MR. WISENBERG: It's time for a break.

MR. KENDALL: Okay. 4:49.

(Whereupon, the proceedings were recessed from 4:49 p.m. until 5:05 p.m.)

MR. KENDALL: Bob, we are at 2 hours and 55 minutes.

MR. BITTMAN: Two hours and 55 minutes, thank you.

BY MR. BITTMAN:

Q Mr. President.

A Mr. Bittman.

Q Apparently we have one hour and five minutes left, if we stick to the four-hour timeframe.

MR. KENDALL: Plus 30 seconds.

MR. BITTMAN: And 30 seconds, that's right.

THE WITNESS: You gave me my 30 seconds' soliloquy. So, I owe you 30 seconds.

Page 126

BY MR. BITTMAN:

Q You are very generous. That actually segues very nicely into one of the grand juror's asked, pointed out actually, that you indicated at the beginning of the deposition that you would, you would answer all the grand jurors, you wanted to answer all the grand jurors' questions. And they wanted to know whether you would be willing to stay beyond the four-hour period to, in fact, answer all their questions.

A Well, let's see how we do in the next hour, and then we'll decide.

Q Okay. Let me draw your attention to early January of this year, after Christmas, before your deposition. Do you remember talking to Betty Currie about Monica, who had just called her and said that she, Monica, needed to talk to you before she signed something?

A I'm not sure that I do remember that. But, go ahead.

Q This is in early January. And then Betty Currie relayed this to you that Monica called, it's important, she needs to talk to you before she signs something. And then you do, indeed, talk to Monica that day on the telephone.

A I did talk to her that day?

Q Yes.

MR. KENDALL: Mr. President, excuse me. That's a

Page 127

question. If you have a memory of that, you can answer.

THE WITNESS: I'm trying to remember when the last time I talked to her was. I am aware, sir, that she signed this affidavit about this time, sometime in the first week in January. I may have talked to her before she did it. I don't know. I talked to her a number of times between the time Betty's brother died and Christmas. Then I saw her on December 28. I may have talked to her, but I don't remember the specific conversation.

BY MR. BITTMAN:

Q And you would have talked about the – she had just given you a gift actually in early January, a book on the Presidents of the United States. And you discussed this with her and she said that you said you liked it a lot.

A I did like it a lot. I told you that. My impression, my belief was that she gave me that book for Christmas. Maybe that's not right. I think she had that book delivered to me for Christmas. And then, as I remember, I went to Bosnia and for some reason she wasn't there around Christmas time.

But, anyway, maybe I didn't get it until January. My recollection was that I had gotten it right before Christmas.

Q Let me see if I can jog your memory further. Monica talked to you in that phone conversation that told you

Page 128

that she had just met with her attorney that Mr. Jordan arranged with her, and the attorney said that if she is deposed that they were going to ask her how she got her job at the Pentagon. And Monica then asked you, what do you think I should say, how do I answer that question, how did I get the job at the Pentagon. Did you talk to Monica about that, about possibilities –

A I don't believe – no. I don't remember her asking me that. But if she, if she had asked me that, I would have told her to tell the truth. I – and I didn't, you know, I don't know exactly how she got her job at the Pentagon. I know Evelyn Lieberman wanted to transfer her out of the job she had, and somebody must have arranged that. But I didn't arrange it.

Q Now, that's actually not my question. My question is whether you remember talking to Monica about her being concerned that, I may have to answer some questions about how and why I was transferred to the Pentagon out of the White House, fearing that this would –

A No, I don't remember that at all.

Q – lead to questions, or answers that would reveal your relationship?

A Oh, no, sir. I don't remember that. Maybe somebody – maybe she did. But I only remember – well, I don't remember that. That's all I can tell you. I don't

Page 129

remember that.

Q Are you saying, Mr. President, that you did not then say to Ms. Lewinsky that you could always say that people in Legislative Affairs got you the job, or helped you get it?

A I have no recollection of that whatever.

Q Are you saying you didn't say it?

A No, sir. I'm telling you, I want to say I don't recall – I don't have any memory of this as I sit here today. And I can tell you this, I never asked her to lie. I never did. And I don't have any recollection of the specific thing you are saying to me.

Now, if I could back up, there were several times when Monica Lewinsky talked to me on the telephone in 1996, in person in 1997, about her being concerned about what anybody would say about her transfer from the White House to the Pentagon. But I remember no conversation in which she was concerned about it for the reasons you just mentioned.

And all my memory is, she was worried about it because she thought it would keep her from getting a good job down the road, and she talked to me about it constantly in 1997. She thought, well, I'll never have my record clear unless I work somewhere in the White House complex where I can get a good recommendation. But in the context that you mention it, I do not recall a conversation.

Page 130

Q Did you ever tell Ms. Lewinsky, or promise to her that you would do your best to get her back into the White House after the 1996 Presidential elections?

A What I told Ms. Lewinsky was that I would, I would do what I could to see, if she had a good record at the Pentagon, and she assured me she was doing a good job and working hard, that I would do my best to see that the fact that she had been sent away from the Legislative Affairs section did not keep her from getting a job in the White House, and that is, in fact, what I tried to do. I had a conversation with Ms. Scott about it, and I tried to do that.

But I did not tell her I would order someone to hire her, and I never did, and I wouldn't do that. It wouldn't be right.

Q When you received the book, this gift from Monica, the Presidents of the United States, this book that you liked and you talked with Monica about, did it come with a note? Do you remember the note that it came with, Mr. President?

A No, sir, I don't.

Q Do you remember that in the note she wrote that, she expressed how much she missed you and how much she cared for you, and you and she later talked about this in this telephone conversation, and you said – and she apologized for putting such emotional, romantic things in this note, and you said, yeah, you shouldn't have written some of those

Page 131

things, you shouldn't put those things down on paper? Did you ever say anything like that to Ms. Lewinsky?

A Oh, I believe I did say something like that to Ms. Lewinsky. I don't remember doing something as late as you suggest. I'm not saying I didn't. I have no recollection of that.

Keep in mind now, it had been quite a long time since I had had any improper contact with her. And she was, in a funny way, almost more attached to me than she had been before. In '96, she had a long relationship, she said, with a man whom she liked a lot. And I didn't know what else was going on in her private life in '97. But she talked to me occasionally about people she was going out with.

But normally her language at this point was, if affectionate, was, was not improperly affectionate, I would say. So – but, it could have happened. I wouldn't say it didn't. I just don't remember it at this late date.

Q Let me refer back to one of the subjects we talked about at one of the earlier breaks, right before one of the earlier breaks, and that is your meeting with Mrs. Currie on January 18th. This is the Sunday after your deposition in the Paula Jones case.

You said that you spoke to her in an attempt to refresh your own recollection about the events involving Monica Lewinsky, is that right?

Page 132

A Yes.

Q How did you making the statement, I was never alone with her, right, refresh your recollection?

A Well, first of all, let's remember the context here. I did not at that time know of your involvement in this case. I just knew that obviously someone had given them a lot of information, some of which struck me as accurate, some of which struck me as dead wrong. But it led them to write, ask me a whole serious of questions about Monica Lewinsky.

Then on Sunday morning, this Drudge report came out, which used Betty's name, and I thought that we were going to be deluged by press comments. And I was trying to refresh my memory about what the facts were.

So, when I said, we were never alone, right, I think I also asked her a number of other questions, because there were several times, as I'm sure she would acknowledge, when I either asked her to be around. I remember once in particular when I was talking with Ms. Lewinsky when I asked Betty to be in the, actually, in the next room in the dining room, and, as I testified earlier, once in her own office.

But I meant that she was always in the Oval Office complex, in that complex, while Monica was there. And I believe that this was part of a series of questions I asked her to try to quickly refresh my memory. So, I wasn't trying

Page 133

to get her to say something that wasn't so. And, in fact, I think she would recall that I told her to just relax, go in the grand jury and tell the truth when she had been called as a witness.

Q So, when you said to Mrs. Currie that, I was never alone with her, right, you just meant that you and Ms. Lewinsky would be somewhere perhaps in the Oval Office or many times in your back study, is that correct?

A That's right. We were in the back study.

Q And then –

A Keep in mind, sir, I just want to make it – I was talking about 1997. I was never, ever trying to get Betty Currie to claim that on the occasions when Monica Lewinsky was there when she wasn't anywhere around, that she was. I would never have done that to her, and I don't think she thought about that. I don't think she thought I was referring to that.

Q Did you put a date restriction? Did you make it clear to Mrs. Currie that you were only asking her whether you were never alone with her after 1997?

A Well, I don't recall whether I did or not, but I assumed – if I didn't, I assumed she knew what I was talking about, because it was the point at which Ms. Lewinsky was out of the White House and had to have someone WAVE her in, in order to get in the White House. And I do not believe to

Page 134

this day that I was – in 1997, that she was ever there and that I ever saw her unless Betty Currie was there. I don't believe she was.

Q Do you agree with me that the statement, "I was never alone with her", is incorrect? You were alone with Monica Lewinsky, weren't you?

A Well, again, it depends on how you define alone. Yes, we were alone from time to time, even during 1997, even when there was absolutely no improper contact occurring. Yes, that is accurate.

But there were also a lot of times when, even though no one could see us, the doors were open to the halls, on both ends of the halls, people could hear. The Navy stewards could come in and out at will, if they were around. Other things could be happening. So, there were a lot of times when we were alone, but I never really thought we were.

And sometimes when we, when – but, as far as I know, what I was trying to determine, if I might, is that Betty was always around, and I believe she was always around where I could basically call her or get her if I needed her.

Q When you said to Mrs. Currie, you could see and hear everything, that wasn't true either, was it, as far as you knew? You've already –

A My memory of that –

Q – testified that Betty was not there.

Page 135

A My memory of that was that, that she had the ability to hear what was going on if she came in the Oval Office from her office. And a lot of times, you know, when I was in the Oval Office, she just had the door open to her office. Then there was – the door was never completely closed to the hall. So, I think there was – I'm not entirely sure what I meant by that, but I could have meant that she generally would be able to hear conversations, even if she couldn't see them. And I think that's what I meant.

Now, I could have been referring not generally to every time she was there, but one, one particular time I remember when Ms. Lewinsky was there when I asked Betty – and I'm sorry to say for reasons I don't entirely remember – to actually stay in the dining room while I talked with Monica. I do remember one such instance.

Q Well, you've already testified that this – you did almost everything you could to keep this relationship secret. So, would it be fair to say – even from Mrs. Currie. She didn't know about the nature, that is, your intimate, physically intimate relationship with Ms. Lewinsky, did she?

A As far as I know, she is unaware of what happened on the, on the occasions when I saw her in 1996 when something improper happened. And she was unaware of the one time that I recall in 1997 when something happened.

I think she was quite well aware that I was

Page 136

determined to impose the appropriate limits on the relationship when I was trying to do it. And the – you know, anybody would hope that this wouldn't become public. Although I frankly, from 1996 on, always felt that if I severed inappropriate contact with Ms. Lewinsky, sooner or later it would get public. And I never thought it would be part of the Jones case. I never even thought about that. I never thought – I certainly never thought it would be part of your responsibilities.

Q My question was –

A But I did believe that she would talk about it.

Q My question was more simple than that. Mrs. Currie did not know of the physically intimate nature of your relationship, did she?

A I don't believe she did, no.

Q Okay. So, you would have done – you tried to keep that nature of the relationship from Mrs. Currie?

A Absolutely. I –

Q So, you would not have engaged in those physically intimate acts if you knew that Mrs. Currie could see or hear that, is that correct?

A That's correct. But, keep in mind, sir, I was talking about 1997. That occurred, to the – and I believe that occurred only once in February of 1997. I stopped it. I never should have started it, and I certainly shouldn't

Page 137

have started it back after I resolved not to in 1996. And I was referring to 1997.

And I – what – as I say, I do not know – her memory and mine may be somewhat different. I do not know whether I was asking her about a particular time when Monica was upset and I asked her to stand, stay back in the dining area. Or whether I was, had reference to the fact that if she kept the door open to the Oval Office, because it was always – the door to the hallway was always somewhat open, that she would always be able to hear something if anything went on that was, you know, too loud, or whatever.

I do not know what I meant. I'm just trying to reconcile the two statements as best I can, without being sure.

Q There was at least one event where Mrs. Currie was definitely not even in the Oval Office area, isn't that right? And I think you began to testify about that before. That was at the radio address.

A I'm not sure of that. But in that case, there was, there was certainly someone else there. I don't know –

Q Well, why would you be testing Mrs. Currie's memory about whether someone else was there?

A Well, I can say this. If I'm in the Oval Office – my belief is that there was someone else there, somewhere in the Oval Office complex. I've looked at our – I've looked

Page 138

at the film. This, this night has become legendary now, you know. I've looked at the, I've looked at the film we have. I've looked at my schedules. I've seen the people that were at the radio address.

I do believe that I was alone with her from 15 to 20 minutes. I do believe that things happened then which were inappropriate. I don't remember whether Betty was there or not, but I can't imagine that, since all this happened more or less continuously in that time period, there must have been someone who was working around the radio address who stayed around somewhere. That would be my guess. I don't know. I'm sorry. I don't have records about who it would be. But I doubt very seriously if we were all alone in that Oval Office complex then.

Q Mr. President, if there is a semen stain belonging to you on a dress of Ms. Lewinsky's, how would you explain that?

A Well, Mr. Bittman, I, I don't – first of all, when you asked me for a blood test, I gave you one promptly. You came over here and got it. That's – we met that night and talked. So, that's a question you already know the answer to. Not if, but you know whether.

And the main thing I can tell you is that doesn't affect the opening statement I made. The opening statement I made is that I had inappropriate intimate contact. I take

Page 139

full responsibility for it. It wasn't her fault, it was mine. I do not believe that I violated the definition of sexual relations I was given by directly touching those parts of her body with the intent to arouse or gratify. And that's all I have to say.

I think, for the rest, you know, you know what the evidence is and it doesn't affect that statement.

Q Is it possible or impossible that your semen is on a dress belonging to Ms. Lewinsky?

A I have nothing to add to my statement about it, sir. You, you know whether – you know what the facts are. There's no point in a hypothetical.

Q Don't you know what the facts are also, Mr. President?

A I have nothing to add to my statement, sir.

Q Getting back to the conversation you had with Mrs. Currie on January 18th, you told her – if she testified that you told her, Monica came on to me and I never touched her, you did, in fact, of course, touch Ms. Lewinsky, isn't that right, in a physically intimate way?

A Now, I've testified about that. And that's one of those questions that I believe is answered by the statement that I made.

Q What was your purpose in making these statements t Mrs. Currie, if they weren't for the purpose to try to

Page 140

suggest to her what she should say if ever asked?

A Now, Mr. Bittman, I told you, the only thing I remember is when all this stuff blew up, I was trying to figure out what the facts were. I was trying to remember. I was trying to remember every time I had seen Ms. Lewinsky. Once this thing was in Drudge, and there was this argument about whether it was or was not going to be in Newsweek, that was a clear signal to me, because Newsweek, frankly, was – had become almost a sponsoring media outlook for the Paula Jones case, and had a journalist who had been trying, so far fruitlessly, to find me in some sort of wrongdoing.

And so I knew this was all going to come out. I was trying – I did not know at the time – I will say again, I did not know that any of you were involved. I did not know that the Office of Independent Counsel was involved. And I was trying to get the facts and try to think of the best defense we could construct in the face of what I thought was going to be a media onslaught.

Once you became involved, I told Betty Currie not to worry, that, that she had been through a terrible time. She had lost her brother. She had lost her sister. Her mother was in the hospital. I said, Betty, just don't worry about me. Just relax, go in there and tell the truth. You'll be fine. Now, that's all there was in this context.

Q Did the conversations that you had with Mrs.

Page 141

Currie, this conversation, did it refresh your recollection as to events involving Ms. Lewinsky?

A Well, as I remember, I do believe, in fairness, that, you know, she may have felt some ambivalence about how to react, because there were some times when she seemed to say yes, when I'm not sure she meant yes. There was a time – it seems like there was one or two things where she said, well, remember this, that or the other thing, which did reflect my recollection.

So, I would say a little yes, and a little no.

Q Why was it then that two or three days later, given that The Washington Post article came out on January 21st, why would you have had another conversation with Betty Currie asking or making the exact same statements to her?

A I don't know that I did. I remember having this one time. I was, I was – I don't know that I did.

Q If Mrs. Currie says you did, are you disputing that?

A No, sir, I'm not disputing –

MR. KENDALL: Excuse me. Is your representation that she testified that that conversation was – when?

MR. BITTMAN: I'm not making a representation as to what Mrs. Currie said. I'm asking the President if Mrs. Currie testified two or three days later, that two or three days after the conversation with the President on January

Page 142

18th, that he called her into the Oval Office and went over the exact same statements that the President made to her on the 18th.

BY MR. BITTMAN:

Q Is that accurate? Is that a truthful statement by Mrs. Currie, if she made it?

A I do not remember how many times I talked to Betty Currie or when. I don't. I can't possibly remember that. I do remember, when I first heard about this story breaking, trying to ascertain what the facts were, trying to ascertain what Betty's perception was. I remember that I was highly agitated, understandably, I think.

And then I remember when I knew she was going to have to testify to the grand jury, and I, I felt terrible because she had been through this loss of her sister, this horrible accident Christmas that killed her brother, and her mother was in the hospital. I was trying to do – to make her understand that I didn't want her to, to be untruthful to the grand jury. And if her memory was different from mine, it was fine, just go in there and tell them what she thought. So, that's all I remember.

BY MR. BENNETT:

Q Mr. President, my name is Jackie Bennett. If I understand your current line of testimony, you are saying that your only interest in speaking with Ms. Currie in the

Page 143

days after your deposition was to refresh your own recollection?

A Yes.

Q It was not to impart instructions on how she was to recall things in the future?

A No, and certainly not under oath. That – every day, Mr. Bennett, in the White House and in every other political organization when you are subject to a barrage of press questions of any kind, you always try to make the best case you can consistent with the facts; that is, while being truthful.

But – so, I was concerned for a day or two there about this as a press story only. I had no idea you were involved in it for a couple of days.

I think Betty Currie's testimony will be that I gave her explicit instructions or encouragement to just go in the grand jury and tell the truth. That's what I told her to do and I thought she would.

Q Mr. President, when did you learn about the Drudge Report reporting allegations of you having a sexual relationship with someone at the White House?

A I believe it was the morning of the 18th, I think.

Q What time of day, sir?

A I have no idea.

Q Early morning hours?

Page 144

A Yeah, I think somebody called me and told me about it. Maybe Bruce, maybe someone else. I'm not sure. But I learned early on the 18th of the Drudge Report.

Q Very early morning hours, sir?

A Now, my deposition was on the 17th, is that right?

Q On Saturday, the 17th, sir.

A Yeah, I think it was when I got up Sunday morning, I think. Maybe it was late Saturday night. I don't remember.

Q Did you call Betty Currie, sir, after the Drudge Report hit the wire?

A I did.

Q Did you call her at home?

A I did. Was that the night of the 17th?

Q Night of the 17th, early morning hours of the 18th?

A Okay, yes. That's because – yes. I worked with Prime Minister Netanyahu that night until about midnight.

MR. KENDALL: Wait.

THE WITNESS: Isn't that right?

MR. KENDALL: Excuse me. I think the question is directed – Mr. Bennett, if you could help out by putting the day of the week, I think that would be helpful.

BY MR. BENNETT:

Q Saturday night, Sunday morning.

A Yes. I called Betty Currie as soon – I think

Page 145

about as soon as I could, after I finished with Prime Minister Netanyahu, and in the aftermath of that meeting planning where we were going next in the Middle East peace process.

MR. KENDALL: Can we take a two-minute break, please?

MR. BITTMAN: May I ask one other question first, Mr. Kendall?

MR. KENDALL: Certainly. I think the witness is confused on dates. That's all.

MR. BITTMAN: Okay.

THE WITNESS: That's what – I didn't think it was the night of the 17th.

MR. KENDALL: Mr. President, I think we'll do it in a break.

THE WITNESS: Can we have a break and I could get straightened out?

MR. BITTMAN: Sure. May I ask one other quick – this is a question I forgot to ask from the grand jurors.

THE WITNESS: I don't want to get mixed up on these dates now. Go ahead.

BY MR. BITTMAN:

Q This is – they wanted to know whether, they want us to clarify that the President's knowledge, your knowledge, Mr. President, as to the approach to our office this morning;

Page 146

that is, we were told that you would give a general statement about the nature of your relationship with Ms. Lewinsky, which you have done. Yet that you would -- you did not want to go in any of the details about the relationship. And that if we pressed on going into the details, that you would object to going into the details.
And the grand jurors, before they wanted, they wanted to vote on some other matters, they wanted to know whether you were aware of that? That we were told that?
MR. KENDALL: Well, Mr. Bittman, who told you that? This is, this is, this is not a fair question, when you say you were told. Who told you?
MR. BITTMAN: Who told me what, the question?
MR. KENDALL: You said, you said the grand jury was told.
MR. BITTMAN: We have kept the grand jury informed, as we normally would, of the proceedings here.
MR. KENDALL: Right. And, I'm sorry. Who, who are you representing told you or the grand jurors anything? Is that, is that our conversation?
MR. BITTMAN: Yes.
MR. STARR: Yes, our conversation.
MR. BITTMAN: Yes. That was in substance related to the grand jurors.
THE WITNESS: And what's your question to me, Mr.

Page 147

Bittman?
BY MR. BITTMAN:
Q Whether you were aware of the facts that I just described?
A Yes, sir. Let me say this. I knew that Mr. Kendall was going to talk with Judge Starr. What we wanted to do was to be as helpful as we could to you on the question of whether you felt I was being truthful, when I said I did not have sexual relations with Ms. Lewinsky, as defined in that definition (1) in this, in my testimony.
And I thought the best way to do that, and still preserve some measure of privacy and dignity, would be to invite all of you and the grand jurors to ask, well, would you consider this, that, or the other thing covered by the definition. You asked me several questions there, and I did my best to answer whether I thought they were covered by the definition, and said if I thought they were covered, you could conclude from that that my testimony is I did not do them.
If those things, if things are not covered by the definition, and I don't believe they are covered, then I could not -- then they shouldn't be within this discussion one way or the other.
Now, I know this is somewhat unusual. But I would say to the grand jury, put yourself in my position. This is

Page 148

not a typical grand jury testimony. I, I have to assume a report is going to Congress. There's a videotape being made of this, allegedly because only one member of the grand jury is absent. This is highly unusual. And, in addition to that, I have sustained a breathtaking number of leaks of grand jury proceedings.
And, so, I think I am right to answer all the questions about perjury, but not to say things which will be forever in the historic annals of the United States because of this unprecedented videotape and may be leaked at any time. I just think it's a mistake.
And, so, I'm doing my best to cooperate with the grand jury and still protect myself, my family, and my office.
MR. BITTMAN: Thank you.
MR. KENDALL: This will be two minutes.
(Whereupon, the proceedings were recessed from 5:37 p.m. until 5:43 p.m.)
BY MR. BENNETT:
Q Mr. President, before we broke, we were talking about the sequencing of your conversations with Betty Currie following your deposition on Saturday, January 17th. Do you recall that?
A I do.
Q All right. And you recall contacting Betty Currie,

Page 149

calling her and instructing her on the evening of Saturday night, after your deposition, and telling her to come in the next day?
A Yes, sir, I do.
Q Sunday was normally her day off, isn't that so?
A Yes, it was.
Q And so you were making special arrangements for he to come back into the White House, isn't that so?
A Well, yes. I asked her to come back in and talk to me.
Q And it was at that time that you spoke with her, and Mr. Bittman and Mr. Wisenberg have asked you questions about what you said in that conversation, isn't that so?
A Yes, they have -- I don't know whether that's the time, but they -- I did talk to her as soon as I realized that the deposition had become more about Monica Lewinsky than Paula Jones. I asked her, you know, if she knew anything about this. I said, you know, it's obvious that this is going to be a matter of press speculation, and I was trying to go through the litany of what had happened between us, and asked some questions.
Q On fairness, it would be more than a matter of simple press speculation, isn't that so? Mr. President, there was a question about whether you had testified fully, completely, and honestly on the preceding day in your

Page 150

deposition.
A Well, actually, Mr. Bennett, I didn't think about that then. I -- this has been a rather unprecedented development, and I wasn't even thinking about the Independent Counsel getting into this. So, at that moment, I knew nothing about it and I was more interested in what the facts were and whether Ms. Currie knew anything about it, knew anything about what Monica Lewinsky knew about it.
Q Mr. President, you've told us at least a little bit about your understanding of how the term sexual relations was used, and what you understood it to mean in the context of your deposition. Isn't that correct?
A That is correct.
Q And you've told us -- I mean, that was a lawsuit Paula Jones filed in which she alleged that you asked her to perform oral sex, isn't that so?
A That was her allegation.
Q That was her allegation. And, notwithstanding that that was her allegation, you've testified that you understood the term sexual relations, in the context of the questions you were being asked, to mean something else, at least insofar as you were the recipient rather than the performer?
A Sir, Paula Jones' lawyers pulled out that definition, not me. And Judge Susan Webber Wright ruled on it, just as she later ruled their case had no merit in the

Page 151

first place, no legal merit, and dismissed it.
I had nothing to do with the definition. I had nothing to do with the Judge's rulings. I was simply there answering the questions they put to me, under the terms of reference they imposed.
Q Well, the grand jury would like to know, Mr. President, why it is that you think that oral sex performed on you does not fall within the definition of sexual relations as used in your deposition.
A Because that is -- if the deponent is the person who has oral sex performed on him, then the contact is with -- not with anything on that list, but with the lips of another person. It seems to be self-evident that that's what it is. And I thought it was curious.
Let me remind you, sir, I read this carefully. And I thought about it. I thought about what "contact" meant. I thought about what "intent to arouse or gratify" meant.
And I had to admit under this definition that I'd actually had sexual relations with Gennifer Flowers. Now, I would rather have taken a whipping than done that, after all the trouble I'd been through with Gennifer Flowers, and the money I knew that she had made for the story she told about this alleged 12-year affair, which we had done a great deal to disprove.
So, I didn't like any of this. But I had done my

Page 152

best to deal with it and the – that's what I thought. And I think that's what most people would think, reading that.

Q Would you have been prepared, if asked by the Jones lawyers, would you have been prepared to answer a question directly asked about oral sex performed on you by Monica Lewinsky?

A If the Judge had required me to answer it, of course, I would have answered it. And I would have answered it truthfully, if I –

Q By the way, do you believe that the –

A – had been required.

Q – Jones litigants had the same understanding of sexual relations that you claim you have?

A I don't know what their understanding was, sir. My belief is that they thought they'd get this whole thing in, and that they were going to – what they were trying to do is do just what they did with Gennifer Flowers. They wanted to find anything they could get from me or anyone else that was negative, and then they wanted to leak it to hurt me in the press, which they did even though the Judge ordered them not to.

So, I think their –

Q Wouldn't it – I'm sorry.

A I think their position, Mr. Bennett – you asked the question – their position was, we're going to cast the

Page 153

widest net we can and get as much embarrassing stuff as we can, and then dump it out there and see if we can make him bleed. I think that's what they were trying to do.

Q Don't you think, sir, that they could have done more damage to you politically, or in whatever context, if they had understood the definition in the same way you did and asked the question directly?

A I don't know, sir. As I said, I didn't work with their lawyers in preparing this case. I knew the case was wrong. I knew what our evidence was. By the time of this deposition, they knew what their evidence was.

Their whole strategy was, well, our lawsuit's not good, but maybe we can hurt him with the discovery. And, you know, they did some. But it didn't amount to much.

And did I want, if I could, to avoid talking about Monica Lewinsky? Yes, I'd give anything in the world not to be here talking about it. I'd be giving – I'd give anything in the world not to have to admit what I've had to admit today.

But if you look at my answer in the Flowers [sic] deposition, at least you know I tried to carefully fit all my answers within the framework there, because otherwise there was no reason in the wide world for me to do anything other than make the statements I'd made about Gennifer Flowers since 1991, that I did not have a 12-year affair with her,

Page 154

and that these, the following accusations she made are false.

So, that's all I can tell you. I can't prove anything.

Q But you did have a great deal of anxiety in the hours and days following the end of your deposition on the 17th. Isn't that fair to say?

A Well, I had a little anxiety the next day, of course, because of the Drudge Report. And I had an anxiety after the deposition because it was more about Monica Lewinsky than it was about Paula Jones.

Q The specificity of the questions relating to Monica Lewinsky alarmed you, isn't that fair to say?

A Yes, and it bothered me, too, that I couldn't remember the answers. It bothered me that I couldn't – as Mr. Wisenberg pointed out, it bothered me that I couldn't remember all the answers. I did the best I could. And so I wanted to know what the deal was. Sure.

Q Mr. President, to your knowledge, have you turned over, in response to the grand jury subpoenas, all gifts that Monica Lewinsky gave you?

A To my knowledge, I have, sir. As you know, on occasion, Mr. Kendall has asked for your help in identifying those gifts. And I think there were a couple that we came across in our search that were not on the list you gave us, that I remembered in the course of our search had been given

Page 155

to me by Monica Lewinsky and we gave them to you.

So, to the best of my knowledge, we have given you everything we have.

Q Can you explain why, on the very day that Monica Lewinsky testified in the grand jury on August 6th of this year, you wore a necktie that she had given you?

A No, sir, I don't believe I did. What necktie was it?

Q The necktie you wore on August 6th, sir.

A Well, I don't know that it was a necktie that Monica Lewinsky gave me. Can you describe it to me?

Q Well, I don't want to take time at this point, but we will provide you with photographic evidence of that, Mr. President.

A If you give me – I don't believe that's accurate, Mr. Bennett.

Q So, let me ask the question –

A But if you give it to me, and I look at it and I remember that she gave it to me, I'll be happy to produce it. I do not believe that's right.

Q Well, if you remember that she gave it to you, why haven't you produced it to the grand jury?

A I don't remember that she gave it to me. That's why I asked you what the tie was. I have –

Q Can you –

Page 156

A – no earthly idea. I believe that, that I did not wear a tie she gave me on August the 6th.

Q Can you tell us why Bayani Nelvis wore a tie that Monica Lewinsky had given you on the day he appeared in the grand jury?

A I don't know that he did.

Q Have you given Bayani Nelvis any ties, sir?

A Oh, yes, a lot of ties.

Q And so if he wore the tie that you gave him, that Monica Lewinsky had given you, that would not have been by design, is that what you are telling us?

A Oh, absolutely not. Let me –

Q You are not –

A May I explain, Mr. Bennett? It won't –

Q Yes.

A – take long. Every year, since I've been President, I've gotten quite a large number of ties, as you might imagine. I get, I have a couple of friends, one in Chicago and one in Florida who give me a lot of ties, a lot of other people who send me ties all the time, or give them to me when I see them.

So, I always have the growing number of ties in my closet. What I normally do, if someone gives me a tie as a gift, is I wear it a time or two. I may use it. But at the end of every year, and sometimes two times a year, sometimes

Page 157

more, I go through my tie closet and I think of all the things that I won't wear a lot or that I might give away, and I give them mostly to the men who work there.

I give them to people like Glen and Nelvis, who work in the kitchen, back in the White House, or the gentlemen who are my stewards or the butlers, or the people who run the elevators. And I give a lot of ties away a year. I'll bet I – excluding Christmas, I bet I give 30, 40, maybe more ties away a year, and then, of course, at Christmas, a lot.

So, there would be nothing unusual if, in fact, Nelvis had a tie that originally had come into my tie closet from Monica Lewinsky. It wouldn't be unusual. It wouldn't be by design. And there are several other people of whom that is also true.

Q Mr. President, I'd like to move to a different area right now. I'd like to ask you some questions about Kathleen Willey. You met Kathleen Willey during your 1992 campaign, isn't that so?

A Yes, sir, I did.

Q As a matter of fact, you first saw her at a rope line at the Richmond, Virginia airport on October 13, 1992, is that not correct?

A I don't believe that is correct.

Q When did you first meet her, sir?

Page 158

A Well, let me ask you this. When was the debate in Richmond?

Q I believe it was October 13, 1992, sir.

A Well, I believe that I had met her – I believe I had met her before then, because Governor Wilder, I believe that was his last year as governor – I think that's right, 92-93. I believe that I met her in connection with her involvement with Governor Wilder.

And I have the impression – it's kind of a vague memory, but I have the impression that I had met her once before, at least once before I came to that Richmond debate. Now, I'm not sure of that.

Q Well, at least if you had met her before –

A But I am quite sure she was at the Richmond debate and I did meet her there. I'm quite sure of that.

Q Mr. President, you've seen television footage of you standing on a rope line with Donald Beyer, Lt. Governor Donald Beyer –

A I have.

Q – asking Mr. Beyer for the name of Kathleen Willey? You've seen that footage, haven't you?

A I don't know that I've seen it, but I am aware that it exists.

Q All right. And you can see him, you can read his lips. He's saying the name Kathleen Willey in response to a

Page 159

question from you, isn't that so?

A That's what I've heard.

Q And, as a matter of fact, you sent Nancy Hemreich, who was present on that day, to go get her telephone number, didn't you, sir?

A I don't believe so.

Q You don't believe so?

A Well, let me say this. If that is true, then I'm quite certain that I had met her before. I would never call someone out of the blue that I saw on a rope line and send Nancy Hemreich to get her number to do it.

Q Even if you were just learning her name for the first time?

A That's correct. I'm not so sure that I didn't ask Don Beyer, if he was on the rope line with me, who she was because I thought I had seen her before or I knew I had seen her before and I didn't remember her name. Now, I do that all the time. For men –

Q Mr. President –

A – and women.

Q I'm sorry. Do you recall that you sent Nancy Hemreich for her telephone number?

A No, I don't.

Q All right. Do you recall, having received her telephone number, calling her that night?

Page 160

A No, sir, I don't.

Q Do you recall inviting her to meet with you at your hotel that night?

A No, sir, I do not.

Q Do you recall where you stayed in Richmond, Virginia during the debates you've told us about?

A Well, I stayed at some hotel there, I believe.

Q Actually, did you stay at the Williamsburg Inn, not in Richmond?

A Yeah, that's right. We prepared in Williamsburg. That's correct. I believe we prepared in Williamsburg and then went to Richmond for the debate, and then I think we spent the night in Richmond. And the next day, I think we had a rally before we left town. I believe that's right.

Q Do you know of any reason Kathleen Willey's telephone number would appear on your toll records from your room in Williamsburg?

A No, there –

Q If you didn't call her?

A No, I'm not denying that I called her, sir. You asked me a specific question. I won't deny that I called her. I don't know whether I did or not.

Q As a matter of fact, you called her twice that day, didn't you, sir?

A I don't recall. I may well have done it and I

Page 161

don't know why I did it.

Q Well, does it refresh your recollection that you called her and invited her to come to your room that night, sir?

A I don't believe I did that, sir.

Q If Kathleen Willey has said that, she's mistaken or lying, is that correct, Mr. President?

A I do not believe I did that. That's correct.

Q But what is your best recollection of that conversation, those conversations?

A I don't remember talking to her. But I – it seems to me that at some point – this is why I believe I had met her before, too. But at some point I had some actual person-to-person conversation with her about my sore throat, or what she thought would be good for it, or something like that. I have some vague memory of that. That's it.

Q Is this the chicken soup conversation, Mr. President?

A Well, I don't know if I would – maybe that's what she said I should have. I don't remember. But I have no recollection, sir, of asking her to come to my room. I – and I – I'm sorry, I don't. I can't – I won't deny calling her. I don't know if I did call her. I don't know if she tried to call me first. I don't know anything about that. I, I just – I met her and Doug Wilder. I remember that she

Page 162

and her husband were active for Government Wilder, and that's about all I remember, except that I had a conversation with her around the Richmond debate. I do remember talking to her there.

Q Mr. President, let's move ahead to the episode on November 29, 1993, in which Mrs. Willey met you in your office at the Oval, the subject matter of the "60 Minutes" broadcast a few months ago. You recall that episode?

A I certainly do.

Q Mr. President, in fact, on that date you did make sexual advances on Kathleen Willey, is that not correct?

A That's false.

Q You did grab her breast, as she said?

A I did not.

Q You did place your hand on her groin area, as she said?

A No, I didn't.

Q And you placed her hand on your genitals, did you not?

A Mr. Bennett, I didn't do any of that, and the questions you're asking, I think, betray the bias of this operation that has troubled me for a long time. You know what evidence was released after the "60 Minutes" broadcast that I think pretty well shattered Kathleen Willey's credibility. You know what people down in Richmond said

Page 163

about her. You know what she said about other people that wasn't true. I don't know if you've made all of this available to the grand jury or not.

She was not telling the truth. She asked for the appointment with me. She asked for it repeatedly.

Q Did she make a sexual advance on you, Mr. President?

A On that day, no, she did not. She was troubled.

Q On some other day?

A I wouldn't call it a sexual advance. She was always very friendly. But I never took it seriously.

Q Mr. President, you mentioned the documents that were released and information that came out from people in Richmond, et cetera, after the "60 Minutes" piece was broadcast. As a matter of fact, you were required, under the Court's rulings, to produce those documents in response to document requests by the Jones litigants, isn't that correct?

A No. I believe the Jones litigants' request for production of documents to me ran to documents that were in my personal files and in my personal possessions, and did not cover documents that were White House files. So, I don't believe we were required to produce them.

As a matter of fact, when that story first ran, sir, before "60 Minutes", back in July or so of '97, I was aware that we had some letters. I didn't – I didn't

Page 164

remember that she'd written us as much as she had and called as much as she had, and asked to see me as often as she had, after this alleged incident. I didn't know the volume of contact that she had which undermined the story she has told. But I knew there was some of it.

And I made a decision that I did not want to release it voluntarily after the Newsweek ran the story, because her friend Julie Steele was in the story saying she asked her – she, Kathleen Willey – asked her to lie. And because, frankly, her husband had committed suicide. She apparently was out of money. And I thought, who knows how anybody would react under that. So, I didn't.

But, now when "60 Minutes" came with the story and everybody blew it up, I thought we would release it. But I do not believe we were required to release White House documents to the Jones lawyers.

Q Mr. President, have you made a decision on whether to stay beyond the four hours we agreed to, to accept questions from the grand jury?

MR. KENDALL: We have made an agreement, Mr. Bennett, to give you four hours. We're going to do that. By my watch, there are about 12 minutes left.

MR. BENNETT: I guess that's no. Is that correct, Mr. Kendall?

MR. KENDALL: Yes, that's correct.

Page 165

THE WITNESS: May I ask this question? Could I have a two-minute break?

MR. BENNETT: Sure.

THE WITNESS: I'm sorry to bother you with this. I know we're getting to the end, but I need a little break.

(Whereupon, the proceedings were recessed from 6:04 p.m. until 6:09 p.m.)

BY MR. STARR:

Q Mr. President, at various times in this investigation, officials have invoked executive privilege in response to questions that have been posed to them by the grand jury and in the grand jury. One of the grand jurors has posed the question, did you personally authorize the invocation of executive privilege?

A If the answer is authorized, I think the answer to that would be yes. But I would like the grand jury to know something.

In the cases where we raised the lawyer/client privilege, or executive privilege, or where the Secret Service raised their privilege, and when I say – I had nothing to do with that. I did not authorize it, approve it, or anything else. That was something they asked to be free to make their decision on by themselves.

In none of those cases did I actually have any worry about what the people involved would say. The reason

Page 166

those privileges were advanced and litigated was that I believed that there was an honest difference between Judge Starr and the Office of Independent Counsel, and Mr. Ruff, my counsel, and I about what the proper balance was in the Constitutional framework.

And I did not want to put the Presidency at risk of being weakened as an institution, without having those matters litigated. Now, we've lost some of those matters. Our people have testified and the grand jury is free to conclude whether they believe that the testimony they gave was damaging to me. But I don't, I don't imagine it was and I wasn't worried about it. It was an honest difference of Constitutional principal between Judge Starr and the Office of Independent Counsel and the White House.

Q Mr. President, a couple of very brief questions, given our time. The White House's outside counsel, Mr. Eggleston, withdrew the White House's appeal from Chief Judge Johnson's ruling that the invocation of executive privilege had to give way to the grand jury's right to the information, that ruling in connection with the testimony of Mr. Blumenthal and Mr. Lindsey.

Were you informed of that fact that the appeal had been withdrawn?

A I was informed of it and, as a matter of fact, I was consulted about it and I strongly supported it. I didn't

Page 167

want to appeal it.

Q Okay.

A It was – I had – my main difference, Judge Starr, as you know with you, is, and with some of the Court decisions, is on the extent to which members of the White House Counsel's staff, like Mr. Lindsey, should be able to counsel the President on matters that may seem like they are private, like the Jones case, but inevitably intrude on the daily work of the President.

But I didn't really want to advance an executive privilege claim in this case beyond having it litigated, so that we, we had not given up on principal this matter, without having some judge rule on it. So, I made –

Q Excuse me. And you are satisfied that you now have the benefit of that ruling, is that correct?

A Well, yes. I just didn't want to, I didn't want to – yes. And I didn't – I made the – I actually, I think, made the call, or at least I supported the call. I did not, I strongly felt we should not appeal your victory on the executive privilege issue.

MR. STARR: Thank you.

BY MR. WISENBERG:

Q Mr. President, among the many remaining questions of the grand jurors is one that they would like answered directly without relation to, without regard to inferences,

Page 168

which is the following: Did Monica Lewinsky perform oral sex on you? They would like a direct answer to that, yes or no?

A Well, that's not the first time that question's been asked. But since I believe, and I think any person, reasonable person would believe that that is not covered in the definition of sexual relations I was given, I'm not going to answer, except to refer to my statement.

I had intimate contact with her that was inappropriate. I do not believe any of the contacts I had with her violated the definition I was given. Therefore, I believe I did not do anything but testify truthfully on these matters.

Q We have a couple of photos of the tie that you wore.

A Would you please give them to me?

Q Yes.

A Now, this is August 6th, is that correct?

Q 1998, the day that Monica Lewinsky appeared at the grand jury. And my question to you on that is, were you sending some kind of a signal to her by wearing –

A No, sir.

Q – one of the ties – let me finish, if you don't mind, sir.

A Sure. I'm sorry. My apology.

Q Were you sending some kind of a signal to her by

Page 169

wearing a tie she had given you on the day that she appeared in front of the grand jury?

A No, sir. I don't believe she gave me this tie. And if I was sending a signal, I'm about to send a terrible signal, and maybe you ought to invite her to talk again. I don't, I don't want to make light about this. I don't believe she gave me this tie. I don't remember giving, her giving me this tie. And I had absolutely no thought of this in my mind when I wore it.

If she did, I, I, I, I don't remember it, and this is the very first I've ever heard of it.

Q Did you realize when you –

MR. WISENBERG: Can I just have for the record, what are the exhibit numbers?

MS. WIRTH: Yes. They should be WJC-5 and 6.

(Grand Jury Exhibits WJC-5 and WJC-6 were marked for identification.)

MR. WISENBERG: Mr. Bennett has some more questions.

BY MR. BENNETT:

Q Mr. President, we were talking about your responses to document requests in the Jones litigation, and I had just asked you about turning over the Kathleen Willey correspondence. Do you recall that?

Page 170

A Yes, sir, I do.
Q And, if I understand your testimony, you did not believe that the request for documents compelled you to search for those documents in the White House?
A Mr. Bennett, I want to answer this question in a way that is completely satisfactory to you and the grand jury, without violating the lawyer/client privilege, which is still intact.
It was my understanding that in the request for production of documents, that those requests ran against and operated against my personal files. Now, I have some personal files in the White House. And, I'm sorry. In this case I'm not my own lawyer, and I don't know how the distinction is made between files which are the personal files of the President, and files which are White House files.
But I do have a very clear memory that we were duty-bound to search and turn over evidence or, excuse me, documents that were in my personal file, but not in the White House files. And I believe that the letters to which you refer, Ms. Willey's letters and Ms. Willey's phone messages, were in the White House files. And, therefore, I was instructed at least that they were, that we had fully compiled with the Jones lawyers' request, and that these documents were outside the request.

Page 171

Q Mr. President, you're not contending that White House documents, documents stored in the fashion that these were stored, are beyond your care, custody or control, are you?
A Mr. Bennett, that may be a legal term of art that I don't have the capacity to answer. I can only tell you what I remember. I remember being told in no uncertain terms that if these were personal files of the President, we had to produce documents. If they were essentially White House files, we were not bound to do so. So, we didn't.
Q So, you are saying somebody told you that you didn't have to produce White House documents?
A That's –
MR. KENDALL: I'm going to caution the witness that this question should not invade the sphere of the attorney/client privilege, and any conversations with counsel are privileged.
THE WITNESS: Let me say, and maybe, Mr. Kendall, we need a break here. I'm not trying – I'm trying to avoid invading the lawyer/client privilege.
I can just tell you that I did, I did the best I could to comply with this. And eventually we did make, of course, all of this public. And it was damaging to Ms. Willey and her credibility. It was terribly damaging to her. And the first time she came out with this story, I didn't do

Page 172

it. I only did it when they went back on "60 Minutes" and they made this big deal of it.
It turned out she had tried to sell this story and make all this money. And, I must say, when I saw how many letters and phone calls and messages there were that totally undercut her account, I, myself, was surprised.
BY MR. BENNETT:
Q But you knew there were letters?
A I did, sir.
Q And the White House –
A I knew that –
Q – is under your control, isn't it, Mr. President?
A Well, Mr. Bennett, again, I'm not trying to be – some days I think it's under my control and some days I'm not so sure.
But, if you're asking me, as a matter of law, I don't want to discuss that because that's – I mean, I'll be glad to discuss it, but I'm not the person who should make that decision. That decision should be made by someone who can give me appropriate advice, and I don't want to violate the lawyer/client privilege here.
Q Well, Mr. President, how are the letters from Kathleen Willey that surfaced after the "60 Minutes" episode aired any different from the correspondence and other matters, tangible items, tangible things, of Monica Lewinsky?

Page 173

A Well, the items you asked for from Monica Lewinsky that I produced to you, you know that there was a tie, a coffee cup, a number of other things I had. Then I told you there were some things that had been in my possession that I no longer had, I believe. I don't remember if I did that. There was one book, I remember, that I left on vacation last summer.
Q The same documents that the Jones litigants had asked you for?
A Yes. But, at any rate, they were different. They were in my – the gifts were in my personal possession, clearly.
Q In your office at the Oval?
A Well, in the books, now, the Presidential books were with my other books that belong to me personally. They were in the Oval.
Q Where do you draw the line, sir, between personal and White House? Now, you are talking about some documents that are in the Oval Office and we don't see where you are drawing the line.
A Well, Mr. Bennett, I don't think these – I think the Lewinsky gifts were all non-documents. And you can –
MR. KENDALL: Is that the time?
THE WITNESS: Just a moment.
MR. KENDALL: Excuse me, Mr. Bennett.

Page 174

THE WITNESS: Well, I'd like to –
MR. KENDALL: You've got thirty more seconds.
THE WITNESS: – finish answering the question, please, because this is a legitimate question, I think.
There is somebody in the White House, Mr. Bennett, who can answer your question, and you could call them up and they could answer it, under oath, for you. There is some way of desegregating what papers are personal to the President and what papers are part of the White House official archives papers. And I don't know how the distinction is made. I just don't know.
BY MR. BENNETT:
Q Did you direct personnel, Nancy Hemreich or anyone else, to make a search for correspondence from Kathleen Willey and Monica Lewinsky when those documents were called for in the Jones litigation, sir? Did you direct that somebody on the White House staff look for those documents?
A I don't believe that I was in charge of doing that, the document search, sir. So, the strict answer to that question is that I didn't.
Q So, you sat back and relied on this legalistic distinction between your personal, which you are in control of, and the White House which, by the way, you are also in control of; is that not correct?
MR. KENDALL: I won't object to the argumentative

Page 175

form of the question. We'll allow the witness to answer it. We're now over time, even the 30 seconds. So, this will be it.
THE WITNESS: Mr. Bennett, I haven't said this all day long, but I would like to say it now.
Most of my time and energy in the last five and a half years have been devoted to my job. Now, during that five and a half years, I have also had to contend with things no previous President has ever had to contend with: a lawsuit that was dismissed for lack of legal merit, but that cost me a fortune and was designed to embarrass me; this independent counsel inquiry, which has gone on a very long time and cost a great deal of money, and about which serious questions have been raised; and a number of other things.
And, during this whole time, I have tried as best I could to keep my mind on the job the American people gave me. I did not make the legal judgment about how the documents were decided upon that should be given to the Jones lawyers, and ones that shouldn't.
And, I might add that Ms. Willey would have been very happy that these papers were not turned over, because they damaged her credibility so much, had they not ultimately been turned over after she made, I think, the grievous error of going on "60 Minutes" and saying all those things that were not true.

Page 176

But I did not make the decision. It was not my job. This thing is being managed by other people. I was trying to do my job.

BY MR. BENNETT:

Q Mr. President, the grand jury, I am notified, still has unanswered questions of you, and we appeal to you again to make yourself available to answer those questions.

MR. KENDALL: Mr. Bennett, our agreement was for four hours and we have not counted the break time against that, and I think that will be –

THE WITNESS: You know, Mr. Bennett, I wish I could do it. I wish the grand jurors had been allowed to come here today as we invited them to do. I wanted them down here. I wanted them to be able to see me directly. I wanted them to be able to ask these questions directly. But, we made an agreement that was different, and I think I will go ahead and stick with the terms of it.

BY MR. BENNETT:

Q The invitation was made after there was political fallout over the deposition circumstances with the satellite transmission and the taping. Isn't that so?

A I don't know about the taping, Mr. Bennett. I understood that the prospect of the grand jurors coming down here was raised fairly early. I don't know.

Q Just for the record –

Page 0

A But, anyway, I wish they could have. I respect the grand jury. I respect the –

MR. WISENBERG: Just for the record, the invitation to the grand jury was contingent upon us not videotaping, and we had to videotape because we have an absent grand juror.

MR. KENDALL: Is that the only reason, Mr. Wisenberg, you have to videotape?

THE WITNESS: Well, yes. Do you want to answer that?

MR. BITTMAN: Thank you, Mr. President.

(Whereupon, at 6:25 p.m., the proceedings were concluded.)

* * * * *

CERTIFICATE OF COURT REPORTER - NOTARY PUBLIC

I, Elizabeth A. Eastman, the officer before whom the foregoing proceedings were taken, do hereby certify that the witness whose testimony appears in the foregoing was duly sworn by me; that the testimony of said witness was taken by me electronically and thereafter reduced to typewriting by me; that this is a true record of the testimony given by said witness; that I am neither counsel for, related to, nor employed by any of the parties to the action in which this deposition was taken; and, further, that I am not a relative or employee of any attorney or counsel employed by the parties hereto, nor financially or otherwise interested in the outcome of the action.

Concordance Report

Unique Words: **2,140**

Total Occurrences: **11,523**

Total Words In File: **39,820**

Single File Concordance

Case Sensitive

Cover Pages = **1**

Includes **ALL** Text Occurrences

Dates **ON**

Includes Pure Numbers

Possesive Forms **ON**

-- DATES --

-- B --

- - G - -

- - H - -

Tab 17

STATEMENT

When I was alone with Ms. Lewinsky on certain occasions in early 1996 and once in early 1997, I engaged in conduct that was wrong. These encounters did not consist of sexual intercourse; they did not constitute "sexual relations" as I understood that term to be defined at my January 17, 1998, deposition; but they did involve inappropriate intimate contact. These inappropriate encounters ended, at my insistence, in early 1997. I also had occasional telephone conversations with Ms. Lewinsky that included inappropriate sexual banter.

I regret that what began as a friendship came to include this conduct. I take full responsibility for my actions.

While I will provide the grand jury whatever other information I can, because of privacy considerations affecting my family, myself, and others, and in an effort to preserve the dignity of the Office I hold, this is all I will say about the specifics of these particular matters. I will try to answer to the best of my ability other questions, including questions about my relationship with Ms. Lewinsky, questions about my understanding of the term "sexual relations" as I understood that term to be defined at my January 17, 1998, deposition, and questions concerning alleged subornation of perjury, obstruction of justice, and intimidation of witnesses.

[redacted]

Tab 18

Paula Jones v. William Jefferson Clinton and Danny Ferguson
No. LR-C-94-290 (E.D. Ark.)

DEPOSITION OF WILLIAM JEFFERSON CLINTON

Definition of Sexual Relations

For the purposes of this deposition, a person engages in "sexual relations" when the person knowingly engages in or causes -

(1) contact with the genitalia, anus, groin, breast, inner thigh, or buttocks of any person with an intent to arouse or gratify the sexual desire of any person;

(2) contact between any part of the person's body or an object and the genitals or anus of another person; or

(3) contact between the genitals or anus of the person and any part of another person's body.

"Contact" means intentional touching, either directly or through clothing.

849-DC-00000586

[redacted]

DEPOSITION EXHIBIT
1
Clinton 1-17-98

Tab 19

1/17/98 Deposition of
President William Jefferson Clinton
in the case of *Jones v. Clinton*

See Tab 1

50-892 98 - 23

Tab 20

DEPOSITION EXHIBIT
15
Clinton 1-17-98

AFFIDAVIT OF JANE DOE # 6

1. My name is Jane Doe #6 . I am 24 years old and I currently reside at 700 New Hampshire Avenue, N.W., Washington, D.C. 20037.

2. On December 19, 1997, I was served with a subpoena from the plaintiff to give a deposition and to produce documents in the lawsuit filed by Paula Corbin Jones against President William Jefferson Clinton and Danny Ferguson.

3. I can not fathom any reason that the plaintiff would seek information from me for her case.

4. I have never met Ms. Jones, nor do I have any information regarding the events she alleges occurred at the Excelsior Hotel on May 8, 1991 or any other information concerning any of the allegations in her case.

5. I worked at the White House in the summer of 1995 as a White House intern. Beginning in December, 1995, I worked in the Office of Legislative Affairs as a staff assistant for correspondence. In April, 1996, I accepted a job as assistant to the Assistant Secretary for Public Affairs at the U.S. Department of Defense. I maintained that job until December 26, 1997. I am currently unemployed but seeking a new job.

6. In the course of my employment at the White House I met President Clinton several times. I also saw the President at a number of social functions held at the White House. When I worked as an intern, he appeared at occasional functions attended by me and several other interns. The correspondence I drafted while I worked at the Office of Legislative Affairs was seen and edited by supervisors who either had the President's signature affixed by mechanism or, I believe, had the President sign the correspondence itself.

7. I have the utmost respect for the President who has always behaved appropriately in my presence.

8. I have never had a sexual relationship with the President, he did not propose that we have a sexual relationship, he did not offer me employment or other benefits in exchange for a sexual relationship, he did not deny me employment or other benefits for rejecting a sexual relationship. I do not know of any

[redacted]

other person who had a sexual relationship with the President, was offered employment or other benefits in exchange for a sexual relationship, or was denied employment or other benefits for rejecting a sexual relationship. The occasions that I saw the President after I left my employment at the White House in April, 1996, were official receptions, formal functions or events related to the U.S. Department of Defense, where I was working at the time. There were other people present on those occasions.

9. Since I do not possess any information that could possibly be relevant to the allegations made by Paula Jones or lead to admissible evidence in this case, I asked my attorney to provide this affidavit to plaintiff's counsel. Requiring my deposition in this matter would cause disruption to my life, especially since I am looking for employment, unwarranted attorney's fees and costs, and constitute an invasion of my right to privacy.

I declare under the penalty of perjury that the foregoing is true and correct.

Monica S. Lewinsky

MONICA S. LEWINSKY

*

*

*

*

*

*

*

*

*

*

849-DC-00000635

DISTRICT OF COLUMBIA, ss:

MONICA S. LEWINSKY, being first duly sworn on oath according to law, deposes and says that she has read the foregoing AFFIDAVIT OF JANE DOE # 6 by her subscribed, that the matters stated herein are true to the best of her information, knowledge and belief.

Monica S Lewinsky
MONICA S. LEWINSKY

SUBSCRIBED AND SWORN to before me this 7th day of January, 1998.

Kathleen M. Grimes
NOTARY PUBLIC, D.C.
My Commission expires: My Commission Expires August 31, 1998

849-DC-00000636

Tab 21

August 6, 1998

Tab 22

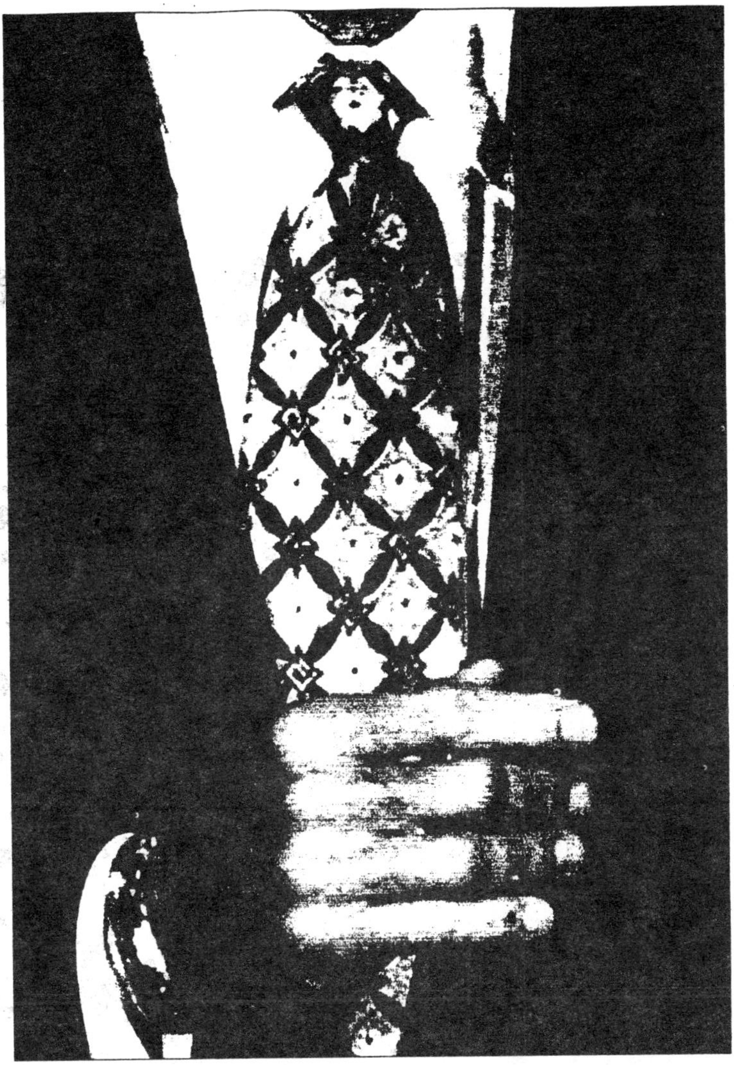

August 6, 1998

Volume IV:

Document Supplement, Part B

Monica S. Lewinsky Statements

REFERRAL

TO THE

UNITED STATES HOUSE OF REPRESENTATIVES

PURSUANT TO

TITLE 28, UNITED STATES CODE, § 595(C)

DOCUMENT SUPPLEMENT B

SUBMITTED BY

THE OFFICE OF THE INDEPENDENT COUNSEL

SEPTEMBER 9, 1998

Table of Contents

595(c) REPORT

DOCUMENT SUPPLEMENT B - LEWINSKY STATEMENTS

INDEX

TAB	DESCRIPTION
1.	2/1/98 Handwritten Proffer of Monica Lewinsky
2.	8/6/98 Grand Jury Testimony of Monica S. Lewinsky
3.	8/20/98 Grand Jury Testimony of Monica S. Lewinsky
4.	Grand Jury Exhibit ML-1 - 2/1/98 Handwritten Proffer of Monica Lewinsky
5.	Grand Jury Exhibit ML-2 - 7/28/98 Agreement between the United States and Monica Lewinsky
6.	Grand Jury Exhibit ML-3 - Draft Jane Doe Affidavit
7.	Grand Jury Exhibit ML-4 - Affidavit of Jane Doe #6 signed by Monica S. Lewinsky on 1/7/98
8.	Grand Jury Exhibit ML-5 - points to make in affidavit
9.	Grand Jury Exhibit ML-6 - Definition of Sexual Relations
10.	Grand Jury Exhibit ML-7 - Chart of Contacts between the President and Monica Lewinsky
11.	Grand Jury Exhibit ML-8 - Photograph of Clinton Family taken 6/24/98
12.	Grand Jury Exhibit ML-9 - Photograph of President Clinton taken 7/6/98
13.	Grand Jury Exhibit ML-10 - Photograph of President Clinton taken 7/9/98
14.	Grand Jury Exhibit ML-11 - Photocopy of video tape dated 8/6/98 entitled "WJC Rose Garden Speech - Gun Control TIE"
15.	8/26/98 OIC Deposition of Monica Lewinsky
16.	1/16/98 OIC-302 of Monica Lewinsky
17.	5/28/98 OIC-302 of Monica Lewinsky
18.	7/27/98 OIC-302 of Monica Lewinsky
19.	7/29/98 OIC-302 of Monica Lewinsky
20.	7/30/98 OIC-302 of Monica Lewinsky

TAB	DESCRIPTION
21.	7/31/98 OIC-302 of Monica Lewinsky
22.	8/1/98 OIC-302 of Monica Lewinsky
23.	8/2/98 OIC-302 of Monica Lewinsky
24.	8/3/98 OIC-302 of Monica Lewinsky
25.	8/4/98 OIC-302 of Monica Lewinsky
26.	8/5/98 OIC-302 of Monica Lewinsky
27.	8/11/98 OIC-302 of Monica Lewinsky
28.	8/13/98 OIC-302 of Monica Lewinsky
29.	8/19/98 OIC-302 of Monica Lewinsky
30.	8/24/98 OIC-302 of Monica Lewinsky
31.	8/26/98 OIC-302 of Monica Lewinsky
32.	9/3 - 9/6/98 OIC-302 of Monica Lewinsky
33.	9/3/98 OIC-302 of Monica Lewinsky
34.	9/5/98 OIC-302 of Monica Lewinsky
35.	9/6/98 OIC-302 of Monica Lewinsky
36.	Tape Transcript of Search.001 (Lewinsky's Apartment)
37.	Lewinsky Apt. - Tape 002 - Search Warrant

Tab 1

(—1— (2/1/98

1. Ms. Lewinsky had an intimate and emotional relationship with President Clinton beginning in 1995. At various times between 1995 and 1997, Ms. Lewinsky and the President had physically intimate contact. This included oral sex, but excluded intercourse.

2. When asked what should be said if anyone questioned Ms. Lewinsky about her being with the President, he said she should say she was bringing him letters (when she worked in Legislative Affairs) or visiting Betty Currie (after she left the WH). There is truth to both of these statements.

3. After Ms. Lewinsky was informed she was being transferred to the Pentagon, Mr. Clinton told her that a) he promised to bring her back to the WH after the election and (in a subsequent conversation), b) Evelyn Lieberman spearheaded the transfer because she felt the President paid to much attention to me and vice versa. Ms. Lieberman told the Pres. that she didn't care who worked there after the election, but they needed to be careful until then.

After the election, Ms. Lewinsky asked the Pres. to bring her back to the WH. In the following

months, Mr. Clinton told Ms. Lewinsky that Bob Nash was handling it and then Marsha Scott became the contact person. Ms. L met with Ms. Scott twice. In the second meeting, Ms. Scott told Ms. L she would detail her from the Pentagon to her (Ms. Scott's) office, so people could see Ms. L's good work and stop referring to her as "The Stalker." Ms. Scott told Ms. L they had to be careful and protect the Pres. Ms. Scott later rescinded her offer to detail Ms. Lewinsky to her office.

Ms. Betty Currie asked Mr. John Podesta to take over placing me in the WH. Three weeks after that, Ms. Linda Tripp informed Ms. L that a friend of Ms. Tripp's in the NSC, Kate, had heard rumors about Ms. L; Ms. L would never work at the WH with a blue pass; and suggested to Ms. Tripp that Ms. L leave Washington, DC.

Following this conversation, Ms. Lewinsky requested of the Pres. that he ask Vernon Jordan to help secure her a non-government position in NY. He agreed to ask Mr. Jordan.

In an effort to help Ms. L, Ms. Currie asked Mr. Podesta to assist, as well. Ms. L believes that

-3-

the Pres. ~~asked~~ spoke with Mr. Erskine Bowles regarding Ms. L's employment in NY. Mr. Podesta arranged for Ms. L to interview with Amb. Richardson who later offered Ms. L a position in communications/Public Affairs at the USUN.

In the beginning of November 1997, Ms. L met with Mr. Jordan. He asked Ms. L why she was there to see him. Ms. L explained to him (in more detail) that she and the Pres. were friends and people got the wrong idea, resulting in Ms. L's banishment to the Pentagon. Ms. L said she was seeking Mr. Jordan's help to begin a new life; he agreed to help.

Ms. L met again with Mr. Jordan in the beginning of December '97, at which time he provided Ms. L with a list of three people to contact and suggested language to use in her letters to them. At some point, Mr. Jordan remarked something about Ms. L being a friend of the Pres. of the United States. Ms. L responded that she never really saw him as "the President"; she spoke to him like a normal man and even got angry with him like a normal man. Mr. Jordan asked what Ms. L got angry about. Ms. L replied that the Pres. doesn't see or call her enough. Mr. Jordan said

Ms. L should take her frustrations out on ~~the~~ him-- not the President.

The following week Ms. L had two interviews in NY in response to ~~as a result of~~ her letters.

4. After Ms. Lewinsky was informed, by the Pres., that she was identified as a possible witness in the Jones case, the Pres. and Ms. L discussed what she should do. The Pres. told her he was not sure she would be subpoenaed, but in the event that she was, she should contact Ms. Currie. When asked what to do if she was subpoenaed, the Pres. suggested she could sign an affidavit to try to satisfy their inquiry and not be deposed. In general, Ms. L should say she visited the WH to see Ms. Currie and, on occasion when working at the WH, she brought him letters when no one else was around. Neither of those statements untrue. To the best of Ms. L's memory, she does not believe they discussed the content of any deposition that Ms. L might be involved in at a later date.

5. After receiving a subpoena two days later, Ms. L contacted Mr. Jordan (because Ms. Currie's brother had been killed in a car accident). Mr. Jordan told Ms. L to come see him ~~that~~ at 5pm because he couldn't understand Ms. L ~~through her tears~~ on the phone, through her tears. Upon Ms. L's request, Mr. Jordan arranged an appointment for her with an attorney, Mr. Frank Carter.

Ms. L expressed ~~any~~ anxiety with respect to her subpoena requesting the production of any gifts from the Pres., specifically citing hat pins which the Pres. had in fact given her. Mr. Jordan allayed her concerns by telling her it was standard language. Mr. Jordan asked Ms. Lewinsky two questions: Did you have sex with the Pres. and/or did he ask you for sex? ~~[illegible]~~ Ms. L responded to both questions with "no."

Possibly later in that meeting but more probably the next meeting, Ms. L ~~was~~ tried to make it clear to Mr. Jordan that she, in fact, did have a physically intimate relationship with the Pres. ~~On more than one occasion, Ms. L expressed concern about signing an affidavit~~

Ms. L made it clear she intended to deny the sexual relationship with the Pres.

On the day Mr. Jordan drove Ms. L to Mr. Carter's office, she showed Mr. Jordan the items she was producing in response to the subpoena. Ms. L believes she made it clear this was not everything she had that could respond to the subpoena, but she thought it was enough to satisfy. ~~and still~~ ~~[illegible]~~. Mr. Jordan made no comment about whether or not ~~[illegible]~~ what Ms. L brought was right or wrong. Mr. J drove Ms. L to Mr. Carter's office; introduced them; and left.

6. The Pres., through Ms. Currie, invited Ms. L to come see him to get her Christmas presents. They played with Buddy, he gave her the presents, they ~~spoke~~ talked casually and spoke for a few minutes about the case. Ms. L asked him how he thought the ~~Pa~~ attorneys for Paula Jones found out about her. He thought it was probably "that woman from the summer... with Kathleen Willey" (Linda Tripp) who lead them to Ms. L or possibly the uniformed agents. He shared Ms. L's concern about the hat pin. He asked Ms. L if she had told anyone that he had given it to her and she replied, "no."

-7-

Ms. L then asked if she should put away (outside her home) the gifts he had given her or, maybe, give them to someone else. [Ms. Currie called Ms. L later that afternoon as said that the Pres. had told her Ms. L wanted her to hold onto something for her. Ms. L boxed up most of the gifts she had received and gave them to Ms. Currie. It is unknown if Ms. Currie knew the contents of the box.]

Ms. L told the Pres. she was planning to sign an affidavit. When Ms. L and the Pres. discussed when Ms. L was moving to NY, the Pres. thought it might be possible that they would not seek her deposition if she was in NY.

7. Ms. Lewinsky called Mr. Jordan several times concerning her employment in NY. When she called one day especially concerned about the case, Mr. Jordan suggested they meet for breakfast.

At breakfast, Ms. L expressed concern about Ms. Tripp saying she (Ms. L) had trusted her before, but was now suspicious of her.

MAC

Ms. L said Ms. Tripp may have seen notes when she was in Ms. L's home. Mr. Jordan asked if the notes were from the Pres. Ms. L said that they were notes to the Pres. Mr. Jordan suggested to Ms. L she check to make sure they are not there (something to that effect). Ms. L interpreted that to mean she should get rid of whatever is there.

~~On the~~
In the car on the way to his office, Ms. L asked Mr. Jordan if he thought the Pres. would always be married to Mrs. Clinton. Mr. Jordan replied that he thought they would always be married, as they should be. ~~[illegible]~~ ~~as~~ Ms. L expressed disappointment and then Mr. Jordan said, "well, maybe you two will have an affair when he's out of office." Ms. L replied that she and the Pres. had alread had an affair minus having sex -- but it included everything else. Ms. L believes they did not get into any more detail

After Ms. L received the draft of the affidavit, she called Mr. Jordan to ask that he look it over before she sign it. He instructed her to drop off a copy at his office. They spoke later by phone about the affidavit agreeing to make some changes.

That evening, Ms. L placed a phone call to Ms. Currie asking her to tell the Pres. that she wanted to speak with him before she signed something the next day. He returned Ms. L's call a few hours later. Ms. L told him Mr. Carter had asked her some sample questions that might be asked of her in the deposition and she didn't know how to answer them. Furthermore, she was concerned that if the answers involved naming people in the WH who didn't like her they would try to screw her over. Ms. L asked him how she should respond to the question, "How did you get your job at the Pentagon?" He replied "The people in Legislative Affairs helped you." This is, in fact, part of the truth -- but not the whole truth. The Pres. told Ms. L not to worry about the affidavit as he had seen 15 others.

9. Ms.L started to become wary of Ms.Tripp in the beginning of Dec. 1997, when Ms.Tripp told Ms.L she had received a subpoena in the Jones case and if asked about Ms.L or others, she would divulge all she knew.

10. Ms.L had a physically intimate relationship with the President. Neither the Pres. nor Mr. Jordan (or anyone on their behalf) asked or encouraged ~~me~~ Ms.L to lie. ~~I~~ Ms.L was comfortable signing the affidavit with regard to the "sexual relationship" because she could justify to herself that ~~they~~ she and the Pres. did not have sexual intercourse.

11. At some point in the relationship between Ms.L and the President, the President told Ms.L to deny a relationship, if ever asked about it. He also said something to the effect of if ~~two~~ the two people who are involved say it didn't happen -- it didn't happen. ~~[illegible]~~ Ms.L knows this was said some time prior to the subpoena in the Paula Jones case.

12. Item #2 above also occurred prior to the subpoena in the Paula Jones case.

Tab 2

UNITED STATES DISTRICT COURT
FOR THE DISTRICT OF COLUMBIA

- - - - - - - - - - - - - - - - - - x
:
IN RE: :
:
GRAND JURY PROCEEDINGS :
:
:
- - - - - - - - - - - - - - - - - - x

Grand Jury Room No. 3
United States District Court
for the District of Columbia
3rd & Constitution, N.W.
Washington, D.C. 20001

Thursday, August 6, 1998

The testimony of MONICA S. LEWINSKY was taken in the presence of a full quorum of Grand Jury 97-2, impaneled on September 19, 1997, commencing at 9:34 a.m., before:

SOLOMON WISENBERG
Deputy Independent Counsel
MICHAEL EMMICK
KARIN IMMERGUT
MARY ANNE WIRTH
Associate Independent Counsel
Office of Independent Counsel
1001 Pennsylvania Avenue, N.W.
Suite 490 North
Washington, D.C. 20004

C O N T E N T S

P R O C E E D I N G S

Whereupon,

MONICA S. LEWINSKY

was called as a witness and, after having been first duly sworn by the Foreperson of the Grand Jury, was examined and testified as follows:

EXAMINATION

BY MR. EMMICK:

Q Good morning.

A Good morning.

Q Ms. Lewinsky, this is the grand jury appearance that you'll be making or at least the first of the grand jury appearances, if there will be any more. What we routinely do with witnesses before the grand jury is that we begin the appearance by discussing your rights and your obligations and so that's what we'll do right now.

A Okay.

Q What I'd like to say first is that you have a Fifth Amendment right. That Fifth Amendment right is the right to refuse to answer any questions that may tend to incriminate you. Do you understand that right?

A Yes, I do.

Q Now, ordinarily, you could refuse to answer questions that would tend to incriminate you. As I understand it, here you have entered into an agreement with the government that provides you with immunity, in exchange for which you will be cooperating with the government. Is that right?

A Correct.

MR. EMMICK: What I would like to do is show you a copy of what has been marked as Exhibit ML-2.

(Grand Jury Exhibit No. ML-2 was marked for identification.)

BY MR. EMMICK:

Q Do you recognize this?

A Yes, I do.

Q On the third page of that document, there is a signature line that says Monica Lewinsky. Is that your signature?

A Yes, it is.

Q All right. You also have a right to counsel. What that means is that although your attorney cannot be in the grand jury room here with you, your attorney can be outside the grand jury room and available to answer whatever questions you might have. Do you understand that right?

A Yes, I do.

Q Do you have an attorney?

A Yes, I do.

Q Who would that be?

A Several.

Q All right.

A Jake Stein, Plato Cacheris -- do you want me to name all of them who are here or just the lead?

Q All right. Those are the lead counsel?

A Those are the lead counsel.

Q All right. And are they outside?

A Yes, they are.

Q You understand that if you need to speak with them, all you need to say is "I'd like to speak with my attorneys about something for just a minute"?

A Yes.

Q All right. In addition to those two rights that you have, you also have an obligation and that obligation is to tell the truth. That obligation is imposed on you because you have taken an oath and that is the oath to tell the truth. Do you understand that?

A Yes, I do.

Q Do you understand that if you were to intentionally say something that's false, in common parlance, if you were to lie, that would constitute perjury and perjury is a felony and it's punishable by up to five years in prison? Do you understand that?

A Yes.

Q Do you understand as well that because of the agreement that you have signed if you were to lie, if you were to intentionally lie, that would mean that the agreement that you have that gives you immunity could be voided and you could be prosecuted? Do you understand that?

A Mm-hmm.

Q All right. And that in simple parlance, what that means, is that you can retain immunity, but only if you do not lie. Do you understand that?

A Yes.

Q Okay. What I'd like to do is simply discuss with you briefly or clarify with you the fact that we have had interviews with you since the time when you signed this agreement. Is that right?

A Yes.

Q All right. We've had interviews with you, I believe, every day since the signing of the agreement.

A Correct.

Q Several hours a day?

A Yes.

Q Is that right? All right. I also wanted to ask you a question having to do with your mental state right now. How are you feeling?

A Nervous.

Q Okay. I wanted also to ask you, are you taking any medication at this time?

A Yes, I am.

Q What I'd like to ask about that is simply is that having any effect on your ability to recall or to communicate that in some way will hinder your ability to answer questions?

A I don't believe so, but it affects my short-term memory just a little bit.

Q Okay. That's fine. Understand, if you will, that your role today is simply to answer questions that we pose to you.

We have spoken with you for a number of hours, a number of days, and we're going to be asking you to talk about essentially three years of conduct. We are not going to be asking you to recount every detail of the last three years of your life and we are not going to be asking you to recount everything that you've told us over the last ten days or so. You'll just be answering questions and we understand that you have other details that you could provide on other occasions.

A Yes.

MR. EMMICK: All right. What I'd like to do next is to let you know what our approach is going to be today.

What we're going to do is we're going to start off talking about your internship at the White House and then we're going to ask you questions having to do with your relationship with the President.

Because we think that that will proceed more comfortably if those questions are asked by Ms. Immergut, I'm going to turn the questioning over to her and at some point, then, we'll collaborate in asking further follow-up questions. So without further ado --

BY MS. IMMERGUT:

Q Ms. Lewinsky, when did you start working at the White House?

A My internship began July of 1995.

Q And when you say "internship," could you just very briefly describe what it is you were doing and where you were working?

A Sure. I was interning for Mr. Panetta, who was Chief of Staff at that time, and I worked in his correspondence office preparing his correspondence, drafting some of the language.

Q Was there ever a time -- or I guess --- after beginning your internship, how long did you serve as an intern in the White House?

A About four, four and a half months. Four and a half months.

Q And was there ever a time that you then assumed a staff position that was not an intern position?

A Yes.

Q And when would that have been?

A In November of 1995.

Q When did you first notice the President of the United States?

A Our first encounter, I guess non-verbal encounter, was August 9, 1995.

Q And could you describe what that encounter was?

A Yes. It was a departure ceremony on the South Lawn and, as he was going by on the rope line shaking hands, we made eye contact and it was more intense eye contact than I had experienced before with him.

Q Okay. And did you have any further such contact sort of later, after that initial time?

A Yes. The next day the President -- I guess the staff had a birthday party for the President on the South Lawn and the interns were invited to that later in the day. And at that party, there was sort of a more intense flirtation that went on at a distance.

Q Okay. Did you feel that he was flirting with you as well? Or how would you describe the behavior that you both exhibited?

A It was intense eye contact and when he went by the rope line to shake hands, it was -- I mean, he -- he's a charismatic person and so -- just when he shook my hand and -- there was an intense connection.

Q Okay. And could you sort of just summarize the

early relationship that you had with the President before any first sexual contact?

A I think it was intense flirting.

Q Okay. Did you have conversations with him?

A Brief conversations that I think in passing -- if I saw him or -- at a departure ceremony, "Have a nice trip." I introduced myself at one point.

Q Okay. And how did you manage to run into him or even see him? Was that a common occurrence or how would that be accomplished?

A Before the relationship began, it was mainly at departure ceremonies, I think there were a few, and then on one occasion my best friend was in town and she was getting a tour of the West Wing and I was waiting for her in the basement lobby and met him that way. There were several other people there.

Q Okay. Was there ever a time that your relationship became more of a romantic and sexual relationship?

A Yes.

Q And when did that occur?

A On November 15, 1995.

Q Okay. And although as I've told you, I'm not going to go into a lot of specific dates, this is one that I wanted you to explain sort of how it came about.

A It was during the furlough. I was up in

Mr. Panetta's West Wing office answering phones. The President came down several times during the day.

There was the continued flirtation and around 8:00 in the evening or so I was in the hallway going to the restroom, passing Mr. Stephanopoulos' office, and he was in the hall and invited me into Mr. Stephanopoulos' office and then from there invited me back into his study.

Q Okay. And what happened there?

A We talked briefly and sort of acknowledged that there had been a chemistry that was there before and that we were both attracted to each other and then he asked me if he could kiss me.

Q And what did you say?

A Yes.

Q And did you kiss on that occasion?

A Yes.

Q And where in the -- you mentioned you went back to the study area.

A Mm-hmm.

Q Where exactly did the kiss occur?

A Right outside his bathroom, in the hallway, inside -- adjacent to the study, to the office.

Q Okay. And how did you end that -- was there anything more than a romantic kiss on that sort of first encounter?

A No.

Q Okay. Did you have any later encounter with him on that same date?

A Yes, I did.

Q Okay. Could you describe how that occurred?

A The President came down to Mr. Panetta's office, I think it might have been around 10 p.m., and told me that if I wanted to meet him back in Mr. Stephanopoulos' office in five minutes, that that would be fine. And I agreed. And I met him back there. We went back to his office again, in the back study area.

Q Okay. And what happened in the back study area?

A We talked and we were more physically intimate.

Q Okay. And on that occasion, did you perform oral sex on the President?

A Yes.

Q With respect to physical intimacy, other than oral sex, was there other physical intimacy performed?

A Yes. Everything up until oral sex.

MS. IMMERGUT: Okay. And just for the grand jury purposes, I have marked as an exhibit ML-6 and I'll just read it the grand jury and place it before you.

(Grand Jury Exhibit No. ML-6 was marked for identification.)

MS. IMMERGUT: It states "Definition of Sexual

Relations. For the purposes of this grand jury session, a person engages in 'sexual relations' when the person knowingly engages or causes contact with the genitalia, anus, groin, breast, inner thigh, or buttocks of any person with an intent to arouse or gratify the sexual desire of any person. Contact means intentional touching, either directly or through clothing."

BY MS. IMMERGUT:

Q Ms. Lewinsky, do you understand that definition?

A Yes, I do.

MS. IMMERGUT: And I do have copies to pass out to the grand jury.

BY MS. IMMERGUT:

Q When you described that you had other physical intimacy during your contact with the President on November 15, 1995, did that include sexual relations within the definition that I've just read to you?

A Yes, it does.

Q In that -- again, that second contact with him on November 15, 1995, where exactly did the sexual contact that you've described occur?

A In the same hallway, by the back study, and then also in his back office.

Q Okay. And the back office, would that be the study area?

A Yes.

Q Okay. Did you have any further sexual encounters with him after that first time on the 15th?

A Yes.

Q When was the next time?

A On the 17th of November.

Q And could you explain how that contact occurred?

A We were again working late because it was during the furlough and Jennifer Palmieri and I, who was Mr. Panetta's assistant, had ordered pizza along with Ms. Currie and Ms. Hernreich.

And when the pizza came, I went down to let them know that the pizza was there and it as at that point when I walked into Ms. Currie's office that the President was standing there with some other people discussing something.

And they all came back down to the office and Mr. -- I think it was Mr. Toiv, somebody accidently knocked pizza on my jacket, so I went to go use the restroom to wash it off and as I was coming out of the restroom, the President was standing in Ms. Currie's doorway and said, "You can come out this way."

So we went back into his back study area, actually, I think, in the bathroom or in the hallway right near the bathroom, and we were intimate.

Q Okay. And at that point, what sort of intimacy was it?

A I believe it was just kissing at that point.

Q Okay. And how did that encounter end?

A I said I needed to back and he said, "Well, why don't you bring me some pizza?" So I asked him if he wanted vegetable or meat.

Q Okay. And, actually, where did the kissing occur that time?

A It was -- I think it was in the bathroom or it was right outside the bathroom, in the hallway adjacent to the bathroom.

Q Okay. So did you go back and get him some pizza?

A Yes, I did.

BY MR. WISENBERG:

Q Pardon me. Sorry to interrupt. That's the bathroom adjacent to the hallway that leads from the Oval Office to the dining room. Is that correct?

A Correct.

MR. WISENBERG: Sorry for interrupting.

BY MS. IMMERGUT:

Q Did you go back and get pizza?

A Yes, I did.

Q And did you ever return to the President with the pizza?

A Yes, I did.

Q Could you describe what happened when you returned?

A Yes. I went back to Ms. Currie's office and told her the President had asked me to bring him some pizza.

She opened the door and said, "Sir, the girl's here with the pizza." He told me to come in. Ms. Currie went back into her office and then we went into the back study area again.

Q Okay. And what happened in the back study area?

A We were in the -- well, we talked and then we were physically intimate again.

Q Okay. And was there oral sex performed on that occasion?

A Yes.

Q Okay. And that would be you performing oral sex on him?

A Mm-hmm.

Q Okay. And, again -- and I have to sort of tell you, you can't answer "Mm-hmm" --

A Oh, sorry.

Q Just yes or no, just for the record. With respect to the physical intimacy again, does that fall -- when you say "physical intimacy," do you mean sexual relations within the definition?

A Yes, I do.

Q Now, without going into sort of a lot of details of specific dates, I wanted to ask you some general questions about the relationship and to make clear, although we've already -- Mr. Emmick already asked you whether or not you've met with us on several occasions, is it fair to say you've given us many, many details about each of the specific dates involved in the relationship?

A Yes.

Q Did the relationship with the President develop into or also have a non-sexual component to it?

A Yes, it did.

Q Could you describe sort of that aspect of the relationship for the grand jury?

A We enjoyed talking to each other and being with each other. We were very affectionate.

Q What sorts of things would you talk about?

A We would tell jokes. We would talk about our childhoods. Talk about current events. I was always giving him my stupid ideas about what I thought should be done in the administration or different views on things. I think back on it and he always made me smile when I was with him. It was a lot of -- he was sunshine.

Q And did he make you feel like he enjoyed your being there and talking to you about things?

A Yes.

Q Were there times that you visited him in the Oval Office where there was no sexual contact at all?
A Yes.
Q Was there sort of affectionate contact during some of those times?
A Very. Yes.
Q Okay. And how would you describe sort of affectionate but non-sexual contact?
A A lot of hugging, holding hands sometimes. He always used to push the hair out of my face.
Q Okay. Could you describe generally how those meetings were set up or how those encounters were actually set up as a general matter?
A After the first few incidents that sort of happened during the furlough, they were set up -- when I was working in Legislative Affairs, usually the President would call my office on a weekend.
He had told me earlier on that he was usually around on the weekends and that it was okay to come see him on the weekends. So he would call and we would arrange either to bump into each other in the hall or that I would bring papers to the office.
Do you want me to do after?
Q Okay. Then what happened after?
A Once I left the White House, Ms. Currie arranged

the visits.

Q Okay. And how would she arrange those, typically?

A I don't understand. I'm sorry.

Q When you say Ms. Currie would arrange them, how would it come about that they would be set up?

A Usually either through my talking to the President prior to and then him talking to Ms. Currie or me bugging Ms. Currie to ask the President.

Q Okay. All right. Did the relationship after the events you've described of November 15th and 17th, did it continue also to have a sexual component?

A Yes, it did.

Q After the two incidents that you've described, did you have further sexual contact with him?

A Yes.

Q And I'm going to ask you just some general questions about that. The grand jurors heard that there's a chart and we'll sort of go through a chart afterwards in less detail. Approximately how many times do you recall performing oral sex on the President?

A I think about nine.

Q Did he ever perform oral sex on you?

A No. We had discussed it and there were times when it almost happened, but mother nature was in the way.

Q Okay. How many times did he ejaculate when you

performed oral sex?

A In my presence?

Q In your presence.

A Twice.

Q Okay. And do you recall the dates of those times?

A Mm-hmm. February 28, 1997 and March -- I think it's the 29th, 1997.

Q Did you engage, other than oral sex, in other physical intimacy that would fall within the definition of sexual relations that we've read to you?

A Yes.

Q Were you alone with the President when you had these sexual encounters with him?

A Yes.

Q It seems like an obvious question, but I have to ask it. Did the President ever have telephone calls while you were actually engaging with oral sex with him?

A Twice.

Q And when those telephone calls occurred, did he ever talk on the phone while you were performing oral sex?

A Yes.

Q Do you have any recollection about when those occurred?

A I believe one was November 15, 1995, in my second visit with him, and I know April 7, 1996.

Q Okay. Did you ever have sexual intercourse with the President?

A No.

Q Was there ever a time when your genitals actually touched each other?

A Grazed each other, yes.

Q And do you remember when that occurred?

A Yes. February 28, 1997. Oh, no. I'm sorry. March 29th, not February 28th. Sorry.

Q Okay. And could you explain why you didn't have sexual intercourse with him?

A He didn't want to. The President said that he -- that at his age, that there was too much of a consequence in doing that and that when I got to be his age I would understand. But I wasn't happy with that.

Q Okay. I want to move away from that now.

A Okay.

Q And ask you whether or not you've ever spoken to the President on the telephone.

A Yes.

Q And can you estimate approximately how many times since the beginning of your relationship with him that you've spoken to him on the phone?

A Over 50, probably.

Q And has he initiated any of those calls?

A Yes.

Q Do you have any sort of idea how many times he's called you?

A Most of those phone calls were calls that he placed to me directly.

Q Okay. Did he ever leave any messages for you at your home?

A Yes.

Q And you remember about how many times he left messages?

A I think about four.

Q Did you save any of those messages?

A Yes, I did.

Q And have you provided any cassette tape of those messages to the OIC?

A Yes, I have.

Q Do you remember any particular messages that he left you?

A I remember them all.

Q Okay. Why don't you just tell the grand jury what they say.

A They're pretty innocuous. Sometimes -- or one time, it was, you know, "Sorry I missed you." One time, it was just "Hello." And then one time he called really late at night when I was not at home and it was whispered kind of loudly, you know, "Come on. It's me." Something like that. It was always nice to hear his voice.

Q Okay. Did he ever tell you how he felt about leaving messages on your home machine?

A Yes.

Q What did he tell you about that?

A I believe it was the beginning of 1996, at some point, he just remarked that he didn't like to do that, he just -- I think felt it was a little unsafe.

Q Okay. Did he ever call you late at night?

A Yes.

Q Can you tell us a little bit about that? Did that happen on many occasions?

A Yes. He's a night owl, so it would be customary for him to call sometimes 2:00 in the morning, 2:30 in the morning.

Q Okay. What sorts of things did you discuss with him generally of a non-sexual nature on your telephone calls with him?

A Similar to what we discussed in person, just how we were doing. A lot of discussions about my job, when I was trying to come back to the White House and then once I decided to move to New York. We told jokes. We talked about everything under the sun.

Q Okay. Was there ever a time that you began to

engage in phone sex on the telephone?

A Mm-hmm. Yes.

Q And do you remember when that started to occur?

A In the beginning of 1996.

Q Okay. Did he participate in that?

A Yes.

Q Okay. And about how many times did you have phone sex with him, if you know?

A Oh, maybe 10, 15. I'm not really -- I'm not really sure.

Q Okay. We can look at the chart after to refresh your recollection, but that sounds sort of ballpark?

A I think so.

Q More than 10, about? In your view?

A Yes, I think so.

Q Did the President ever tell you that he wanted to end the sexual relationship with you?

A Yes.

Q And did he tell you that more than once?

A Yes.

Q Could you tell us when he told you that?

A February -- it was Presidents Day of 1996. I think that's February 19th. And also on May 24, 1996 -- no, 1997. I'm sorry.

Q And just for the grand jury's information, on the

chart that we're going to show them in a little bit, how do you list -- do you have a term that you refer to the May 24, 1997 meeting with him?

A D-day.

Q And what does that stand for?

A Dump day.

Q And on those two occasions, what did he tell you about wanting to end the relationship? Just generally.

A Both were, I think, motivated sort of by guilt and just not wanting to -- more I think on the 24th of May in '97, just really wanting to do the right thing in God's eyes and do the right thing for his family and he just -- he didn't feel right about it.

Q Did you engage in sexual contact with him after those times?

A Yes. Kissing.

Q Okay. After the -- well, after the February 19, 1996 time?

A Yes. Yes.

Q And what about after the May 24, 1997 time?

A Just kissing.

Q Did your relationship involve giving gifts to each other?

A Mm-hmm. Yes. I'm sorry.

Q And did you give any gifts to him?

A Yes.

Q Do you have any sort of ballpark figure of how many gifts you've given to him since you've known him?

A About 30.

Q And what about him to you? Do you have any estimate of how many gifts he gave you?

A I think about 18.

Q Did you ever write him any notes or letters or cards?

A Yes.

Q And what sort of cards or letters or notes would you write to him?

A It varied on the occasion. It could be a funny card that I saw or a Halloween card. If I was angry, it could be an angry letter. If I was missing him, it was a missing him letter.

Q Okay. So were some of them -- is it fair to say some of them were romantic in nature?

A Yes.

Q And when they were angry, what would you be angry about in your letters or cards?

A Either job-related issues or him not paying enough attention to me.

Q Okay. Did he write you any letters or notes?

A No.

Q Did he ever say why he wasn't writing you any letters or notes?

A No.

MS. IMMERGUT: I'd now like to show you what I had previously marked as Exhibit 7, I believe. Perhaps somebody has the other original version.

(Grand Jury Exhibit No. ML-7 was marked for identification.)

BY MS. IMMERGUT:

Q I'm going to place this before you and ask if you recognize that chart.

A Yes, I do.

Q And have you seen that chart before?

A Yes, I have.

Q Did you assist the Office of Independent Counsel in preparing that chart?

A Yes.

Q Did you provide all of the information that's listed on that chart?

A Yes.

Q Could you describe for the grand jury just generally what is described by that chart?

A I think it's a chronology that marks some of the highlights of my relationship with the President. It definitely includes the visits that I had with him and most of the gifts that we exchanged. It reflects most of the phone calls that I remember.

Q And to the best of your knowledge, is the chart accurate?

A Yes.

Q Have you noticed anything that you would add or delete from the chart since you've reviewed it?

A Yes. On page --

MS. IMMERGUT: Do the grand jurors have the chart?

MR. EMMICK: They do. Yes.

THE WITNESS: On page 5, the last entry in the chart, on 10/23, I attended a Democratic fundraiser that you guys have all probably seen on T.V. lately.

BY MS. IMMERGUT:

Q Okay. Anything else that you've noticed?

A No.

Q Okay. Otherwise, would you say that the chart is a -- pretty accurate rendition or description of your memory of all of the events?

A Yes.

Q How is it that you remember all the events in such detail over really sort of what is a few years?

A I've always been a date-oriented person and I had a -- probably a habit of circling dates in my Filofax when I either talked to the President or saw him.

Q And did you provide those Filofax sheets to the Office of Independent Counsel?
A Yes.
Q And did that assist you in remembering the dates?
A Yes, it did.
Q And were these encounters important to you?
A Very.
Q And, again, on that chart there are various categories. In the visit category -- or descriptions in the visit category area that are described as physical intimacy. And with respect to all of those, do they fall within the definition of sexual relations that I've presented as Exhibit 6 to the grand jury?
A Yes.
Q So anywhere physical intimacy is listed on the chart, it falls within that definition. Is that correct?
A Right. I think the only thing that might be missing is kissing.
Q Okay. And kissing is separately described on the chart, is it not?
A No, not necessarily.
Q Okay.
A I mean, because the physical intimacy -- wherever there's physical intimacy, there was always -- there was always kissing.

7/98D

Q Okay. But where there's physical intimacy, there was also then more than kissing.

A Correct.

Q Okay. So physical intimacy is never on the chart to describe only kissing.

A Correct.

Q Okay. There's one particular date also that I wanted to cover with you which is February 28, 1997.

A Okay.

Q Because at that time, as the chart demonstrates, you haven't really seen the President since April of the year before. Could you describe what the circumstances were leading up to your visit with him on February 28, 1997?

A The President had told me in December that he had a Christmas present for me and I ended up not getting it until the end of February. Ms. Currie called me at work during that week to -- or I guess it was that day, I'm sorry, that Friday, to invite me to a radio address that evening.

I went to the radio address and when I went to take my picture with the President, he said to go see Betty because he had something to give me after. So I waited a little while for him and then Betty and the President and I went into the back office.

Q Okay. And why did Betty come in the back office with you?

A I later found out that -- I believe it was Stephen Goodin who said to Ms. Currie and the President that the President couldn't be alone with me, so Ms. Currie came back into the back office with us.

Q And then what?

A And then left.

Q Okay. She left? And do you know where she went?

A I came to learn later, I believe she was in the pantry. In the back pantry.

Q Okay. And how did you learn that later?

A I think that Mr. Nelvis told me. Or Ms. Currie told me.

Q Okay. What happened when she went to the back pantry? Did you remain with the President?

A Yes, I did.

Q And could you describe what you and the President did?

A Mm-hmm. He gave me my hat pin and the book "Leaves of Grass" and I was pestering him to kiss me and so we moved -- that was in the back study and then we moved over to the back hallway by the bathroom and we were physically intimate.

Q Okay. And did you perform oral sex on that occasion?

A Yes.

Q And how did you -- do you remember what dress you were wearing on that occasion?

A Yes.

Q What dress was it?

A The navy blue dress from The Gap.

Q And after that incident, did you ever tell Linda Tripp that there might be the President's semen on that dress?

A Yes, I did.

Q And why did you tell her that? Or did you believe that that could be true?

A I thought it was possible.

Q Were you positive it was true?

A No.

Q Back to the incident with the President, how did you leave it with him on that occasion? Sort of once you finished the visit, what happened?

A Betty came back into the back study and then I think Ms. Currie walked me out.

Q Okay. How much about your relationship with the President did you tell Linda Tripp?

A A lot. Most everything.

Q Okay. And did you tell her about the sexual encounters that you had with him?

A Yes.

Q Did you also tell her about the emotional encounters and the gifts?

A Yes.

Q Were you truthful about the relationship when you told Linda Tripp about it?

A Most of the time, but sometimes -- there were occasions when I wasn't truthful.

Q Were you truthful about the sexual parts of the relationship with her?

A Yes.

Q And what about the emotional component, when you would tell her -- and why don't I say before December of 1997, were you truthful about the emotional components of the relationship?

A Yes.

Q I'm actually done with my questioning on that. Do you want to break now or continue to different subjects?

A A five-minute break? Could I --

THE FOREPERSON: We can take a ten-minute break.

MS. IMMERGUT: Okay. A ten-minute break.

MR. EMMICK: A ten-minute break.

MS. IMMERGUT: Would that be all right?

THE WITNESS: Okay.

MR. EMMICK: That's fine.

(Witness excused. Witness recalled.)

MS. IMMERGUT: Madam Foreperson, are there any unauthorized persons present?

THE FOREPERSON: No, there are none.

MS. IMMERGUT: Do we have a quorum?

THE FOREPERSON: Yes, we do.

Ms. Lewinsky, I would like to remind you that you are still under oath.

THE WITNESS: Thank you.

BY MS. IMMERGUT:

Q Ms. Lewinsky, the grand jurors had a few follow-up questions --

A Sure.

Q -- for you that I wanted to ask you before we move on to other topics. You mentioned that on the occasions where you had sexual contact with that were described, sexual contact with the President, that it occurred in the hallway, as you described, or sometimes in the back study.

A Mm-hmm.

Q Why did --

A JUROR: Pardon me.

BY MS. IMMERGUT:

Q Oh, excuse me. Why did you choose the hallway?

A Because I believe it was -- it was really more the President choosing the hallway, I think, and it was -- there weren't any windows there. It was the most secluded of all the places in the back office. Well, that's not true. The bathroom is the most secluded, I guess, because you can close the door.

Q And did you sometimes have sexual encounters in the bathroom?

A Mm-hmm.

Q And then next to the bathroom, would you say that the hallway is --

A Right.

Q -- off the study is the next most --

A He has a bad back and so I think a lot of times we ended up just sort of standing there and talking there because he could close the door to the bathroom and lean up against the bathroom and then he was -- I guess it made his back feel better and also made him a little shorter. So --

Q Did the President ever tell you he was concerned about being seen?

A I'm sure that came up in conversation.

BY MR. EMMICK:

Q Did he ever indicate to you looking outside that he might be concerned, for example?

A Yes, yes.

BY MS. IMMERGUT:

Q Can you describe that?

A Sure. I think the one that comes to mind was

actually December 28th of last year when I was getting my Christmas kiss. And he was kissing me in the doorway between the back study, or the office, and the hallway, and I sort of opened my eyes and he was looking out the window with his eyes wide open while he was kissing me and then I got mad because it wasn't very romantic. And then so then he said, "Well, I was just looking to see to make sure no one was out there."

Q Can you generalize about the locations where you had your sexual encounters with the President?

A I'd say they mainly took place in that hallway, but there were occasions on which we were intimate in the office and then also in the bathroom.

Q Okay. And when you say the office, do you mean the back study?

A Right.

Q So not the Oval Office?

A No, no, we were never physically intimate in the Oval Office.

Q Okay. Did you notice whether doors were closed when you were physically intimate with him in the back study or hallway?

A No, he always -- well, I'm not sure about the door going in the dining room but I know that the door leading from the back hallway to the -- into the Oval Office was always kept ajar so that he could hear if someone was coming.

BY MR. WISENBERG:

Q How ajar? How much ajar?

A Maybe this much (indicating).

BY MR. EMMICK:

Q You're indicating six to eight inches, something like that?

A I'm not very good with that.

Q A foot or less, something like that?

A A foot or less. I guess that's -- I would assume that's --

Q Enough so that one could hear more easily what was going on in the next room?

A Mm-hmm. Right, or if someone came in to holler for him.

BY MS. IMMERGUT:

Q Now directing your attention back to February 28th, -- 1997, the day that you wore the blue cocktail dress --

A It's not a cocktail dress.

Q Okay, I'm sorry.

A No, that's okay. I'm a little defensive about this subject. I'm sorry.

Q How would you describe the dress?

A It's a dress from the Gap. It's a work dress. It's a casual dress.

Q With respect to that dress --

A Right, I'm sorry.

Q -- you mentioned that you believe that there could be semen on it. Could you describe what you did with the President that led you to believe that?

A We were in the bathroom and -- can I close my eyes so I don't have to --

Q Well, you have to speak up. That's the only --

A Okay. We were in the bathroom and I was performing oral sex. I'm sorry, this is embarrassing. And usually he doesn't want to -- he didn't want to come to completion.

Q Ejaculate?

A Yes. And this has sort of been a subject that we had talked about many times before and he was always saying it had issues to do with trust and not knowing me well enough at first and then not feeling right about things, and not that he said this but I took away from that to sort of mean that maybe in his mind if he didn't come then maybe it wasn't -- he didn't need to feel guilty about that, that maybe with it not coming to completion that that was easier for him to rationalize.

And it was on this occasion that since we hadn't been alone together since April 7th of '96 that after we had engaged in oral sex for a while and he stopped me as he normally did, I said to him, you know -- this is so embarrassing, I'm sorry. I said to him, you know, I really -- I want to make you come. I mean, this is --

Q Okay. Why don't you just describe the position that you were in once he had tried to stop you. What did you do that led you to believe there might get semen on your dress?

A I told him that I really cared about him and he told me that he didn't want to get addicted to me and he didn't want me to get addicted to him, and we embraced at that point and that's -- I mean, it was -- it's just a little tiny spot down here and a little tiny spot up here and --

Q Okay. And to get -- when you're pointing down here, you mean sort of your right lower hip area?

A Well, one of my -- I don't know if it was my right or left, but lower hip area.

Q Okay. And the chest area would be the second place that you thought you might have gotten some?

A Mm-hmm.

Q And is that from when you -- when you did actually continue to perform oral sex on him later?

A I believe so.

Q Did you ever see something that you thought was semen on the dress that led you to conclude that?

A The next time I went to wear the dress.

Q So at the time you didn't notice anything on the

dress?

A I don't believe so.

Q Okay. What happened then the next time you wore the dress that led you to conclude that?

A Well, I also -- can I say here? I also -- I think I wore the dress out to dinner that night, so which is why I'm not sure that that's what it is.

Q Okay.

A So it could be spinach dip or something. I don't know. I'm sorry, could you repeat the question?

Q Sure. When was the -- when was it that you at least began to believe that maybe there was semen on the dress?

A I really don't remember when it was the next time I went to wear the dress, but I gained weight so I couldn't wear the dress and it didn't fit. And I'm not a very organized person. I don't clean my clothes until I'm going to wear them again.

Q Did you notice there was something on the dress?

A Yes. And at that point I noticed it and I kind of thought, oh, this is dirty, it needs to get cleaned. And then I remembered that I had worn it the last time I saw the President, and I believe it was at that point that I thought to myself, oh, no. And it was -- it --

Q So at that point, you weren't positive what it was.

And why did you tell Linda that you thought there was semen on the dress?

A I think it just sort of came up in conversation somehow and then -- as kind of this funny, gross thing. And then the next time she was at my house I still couldn't fit into the dress and believe that I said to her, oh, look, you want to see this? You know, this is what I was talking about.

And but I just want to say because I know everybody here reads the newspapers and listens to TV that I didn't keep this dress as a souvenir. I was going to wear it on Thanksgiving and my cousins, who I always try to look skinny for because they are all skinny -- and I know it sounds stupid. And when I told Linda I was thinking about wearing the dress, she discouraged me. She brought me one of her jackets from her thinner closet. And so it wasn't a souvenir. I was going to clean it. I was going to wear it again.

Q Different topic. Where was Nel when you were -- or do you have any idea where Nel was when you were in the hallway or the study with the President?

A On which --

Q On any of the occasions. I mean, would Nel be around generally?

A There were some occasions that -- very few

occasions, I think, that Nel was there -- was at the White House. And I don't know where he would have necessarily -- I think he was in the pantry on the 28th of February.

Q Do you know where he was on any of the other occasions? And, again, where you had sexual contact with the President.

A I don't think so.

Q Did you ever use hand towels in the bathroom to wipe your lipstick?

A Hand towels, no.

Q What about tissues?

A I believe I used a tissue sometimes to wipe off my lipstick.

MR. WISENBERG: Karen, can I ask something really quick?

MS. IMMERGUT: Sure.

BY MR. WISENBERG:

Q How about, do you think Nel would have been around on renaissance -- right before the departure for renaissance weekend?

A New Year's Eve '95?

Q Yeah.

A Yes, he was.

Q Also, did you ever show -- did -- I don't -- it's my bad. Did you ever show the dress to Linda Tripp?

A Yes.

MR. EMMICK:

Q You mentioned that the President called you on a number of occasions. Some of those occasions included phone sex. Did he indicate where he was when he was placing those calls?

A Not always, but sometimes.

Q And where did he say he was when he did say where he was?

A At home.

Q Meaning the White House residence?

A Yes.

Q Where else might he have placed calls from?

A There were, I think, two times that he placed calls from the campaign term, from Florida I think.

Q Do you know whether he sometimes placed calls from the Oval Office or other places?

A Yes, yes.

Q How do you know that?

A Sometimes he would mention it and say he was in the office. I know one time I said -- I knew he was in the office and I asked him if he was in the back or could he go in the back.

Q Did he not only call you, what, at your home but also call you at your office?

A When I was working at the White House, yes.

Q But not while you were working at the Pentagon?

A He never directly called me when I was working at the Pentagon.

Q When you say didn't directly call, what do you mean?

A I mean he -- there were, I think, maybe two occasions when I was working at the Pentagon when Betty placed a call for him, and when that didn't occur he picked up the phone and dialed the phone number himself.

Q When he placed calls to you when you were at Leg Affairs, or Legislative Affairs, excuse me, was there anything that indicated on your caller ID?

A Yes. When he called from the Oval Office, the phones have a caller ID up at the top, and when he calls from the Oval Office it says POTUS and when he calls from the residence it has an asterisk.

Q And did you ever discuss with him the fact that you had POTUS on your ID?

A Yeah.

Q Tell us about that.

A I think one time when he called and I picked up the phone I said something that indicated to him that I knew who it was. And he said, "Well, how did you know it was me?" And I told him, "Well, don't you know that it lights up POTUS when you call from the Oval Office?" And he said, "No, I didn't know that." So I thought that was funny.

Q When you --

A And he made an effort one time to call me from the residence on a line and called and said, "Did it show up a phone number instead of -- " So it had. He seemed proud of himself.

Q All right. You had mentioned earlier that on, I think it was February 28th, Steve Goodin spoke with Betty and the President about being -- about him being alone with you.

A Mm-hmm.

Q Could you give us a little more detail about what you saw and what you later learned and where you later learned it so that we can figure out what you know from personal knowledge?

A Okay. What I saw was Steve Goodin and Ms. Currie going into the Oval Office. I think --

Q Where are you at this time?

A Oh, I'm sorry. I was in Ms. Currie's office and I was waiting with Ms. Currie. And I believe Stephen was there at some point and he might have gone into the Oval Office first and then called Ms. Currie in a few minutes after or maybe the President called her in after. And they spoke sort of --

A JUROR: (Coughing.)

THE WITNESS: Do you want some water? Oh, okay. So --

BY MR. EMMICK:

Q Was there anyone else in the Oval Office, as far as you know?

A It's possible I think I might have seen Rahm Emanuel in there at some point, but I'm not really sure that he was included in this conversation.

Q So they go into the Oval Office, and what do you next see or hear?

A I believe Betty came out to get me. I was really nervous because I hadn't been alone with the President since the elections so I was focused -- I was kind of internal, focused on being nervous.

Q Betty came out to get you and what did the two of you do?

A The three of us went into the back office.

Q You had mentioned earlier that you later came to learn that there was a discussion between them, between them, about you and the President and whether you should be alone. Tell us when you learned that approximately and what you learned.

A I think I learned it, I believe, maybe shortly after -- not on that day, maybe within the next few weeks, I guess -- that Stephen had said to the President or maybe had said to Betty, you know, she can't be alone with him. So, and I don't recall if I learned that from Ms. Currie or from Nel.

BY MR. WISENBERG:

Q But it -- was it when, based on what you were told, it was a conversation between -- it was a conversation in which Goodin, Ms. Currie and the President were there?

A Correct.

BY MR. EMMICK:

Q Let's focus a little bit about the Presidential aides. You mentioned Steve Goodin. Where are the aides at the time you are having your encounters, if we can call them that, with the President?

A Most of the time they weren't -- they weren't there. They weren't at the White House.

Q And how was that arranged?

A When I was working in Legislative Affairs, I don't think -- I don't know if it was ever verbally spoken but it was understood between the President and myself that most of the -- most people weren't in on the weekends so there was -- it would be safer to do that then.

And then after I left the White House, that was sort of always a concern that Betty and I had just because she knew and I knew that a lot of people there didn't like me.

Q So is it fair to say then that the Presidential aides, whether they be Steve Goodin or Andrew Friendly or whoever it might be, were not around at the time?

A Correct. They may have been but --

Q Mm-hmm. I wonder if you could expand a little bit on the nature of your relationship with Betty and then the nature of your relationship with Nel, and specifically what we mean to ask is to what extent were these relationships genuine relationships and to what extent were they, in part, based on an interest in cultivating their friendship because of your relationship with the President?

A I think that they -- both of them started out probably at the latter of what you said, as maybe a function of making my relationship with the President easier, or for me, I guess, getting information, but that they both came to have a very genuine component to them. I still care very deeply about Betty.

Q When you talk about getting information, could you expand on what you mean by that?

A I think sometimes if it was from Ms. Currie finding out what the President's schedule was, when he might be around, what might be a good time to come by or maybe for her to talk to him to let him know something.

With Nel, Nel and I developed a friendship that started during the furlough and I thought he was a really nice guy and didn't get treated correctly or properly, I guess. And the kind of information, he sort of just would give me information about the President. I mean, I don't think that was the only -- that wasn't the only component of the friendship, but that was a component of it.

Q You have discussed how Betty helped arrange for you to come visit the President, especially in 1997, I think it would be fair to say.

A Yes.

Q When those arrangements were made, who initiated the arrangements? How did they start off? Did you ask? Did the President ask? Did Betty ask?

A I'd say most of the time it was probably me asking -- either asking the President directly or asking him through Betty or through sending a note of some sort. And there were occasions that he initiated, so it would come through Betty.

Q All right. Let me ask you the following question. You have described the ways that Betty helped let you in --

A Mm-hmm.

Q -- facilitate the relationship, if you will. Do you think Betty Currie knew about your relationship with the President?

A I don't know. It's possible she could have gleaned that from witnessing that the -- you know, that the President was having a relationship that caused -- with a 25 year-old woman or, at the time, younger -- you know, that made me emotional. But I really can't answer that question.

Q She saw you under circumstances where she realized you and the President had an emotional tie.

A I believe so. I'm not really -- I'm not really comfortable sort of answering questions about what -- you know, what Betty knew because --

Q Well, then let me focus more on what Betty was in a position to see.

A Okay.

Q Was Betty in a position to see that you and the President visited frequently and had a strong emotional attachment?

A I believe so, yes.

Q Did you ever expressly tell Betty about the relationship?

A What aspect of the relationship?

Q Well, let me separate it out for you.

A Okay.

Q Did you ever expressly tell Betty about the emotional aspect of the relationship?

A I believe I characterized that to her.

Q Did you ever expressly tell Betty about the sexual aspect of the relationship?

A No, I don't believe so.

Q Let me ask the question, why not?

A Because it's not appropriate. I mean, I think -- I don't think people necessarily talk about these things. I mean, there is a difference between a relationship that you have with someone who is sort of involved in a situation, and then the kind of relationship you have with a friend whom you talk to. I think with -- a little bit with Betty's age and it wasn't clear to me that the -- you know, the President didn't tell her so, if he didn't tell her, why should I tell her.

Q Let me ask similar questions about Nel. Do you think Nel knew?

A Nel knew --

Q About the emotional aspect of the relationship?

A Yes, I think so.

Q Is that based on what you told him or what you think he must have seen, or both?

A I think probably based more on what I told him.

Q Do you think Nel knew about the sexual aspect of the relationship?

A We never directly discussed it, so I don't know if -- I don't know how to answer that.

Q Did he ever say things to you that made you think that he must know about the sexual aspect of the relationship?

A Not that I remember.

Q You mentioned earlier, perhaps an obvious thing, that you were alone with the President on the times that you had sexual contact with the President.

A Yes.

Q Were there also times when you were alone with the President that you did not have sexual contact with the President?

A Mm-hmm, yes.

Q Can you give us sort of a general description about how those encounters occurred and where they occurred?

A Okay. There were numerous that ranged from the beginning of our relationship till the end of our relationship.

Q Were some of them brief? Were some of them substantial in length?

A Mm-hmm, yes.

Q Where within the White House would those have occurred?

A One occurred in the Oval Office and then the others occurred -- oh, that's not true. Two occurred in the Oval Office and the others were in the back study area.

I should also just -- maybe I could just add right now that every -- that every time I had a visit with the

President when I was working there -- not after, but when I was working there -- we usually would -- we'd start in the back and we'd talk and that was where we were physically intimate, and we'd usually end up, kind of the pillow talk of it, I guess, was sitting in the Oval Office talking. So there's --

BY MR. WISENBERG:

Q And, again, when you say when you started in the back, that could either be the hallway or the back?

A Correct, yes.

BY MR. EMMICK:

Q I would like to ask you some questions about any steps you took to try to keep your relationship with the President secret.

A A lot.

Q All right. Well, why don't we just ask the question open-endedly and we'll follow up.

A Okay. I'm sure, as everyone can imagine, that this is a kind of relationship that you keep quiet, and we both wanted to be careful being in the White House. Whenever I would visit him during -- when -- during my tenure at the White House, we always -- unless it was sort of a chance meeting on a weekend and then we ended up back in the office, we would usually plan that I would either bring papers, or one time we had actually accidentally bumped into each other in the hall and went from that way, so then we planned to do that again because that seemed to work well. But we always -- there was always some sort of a cover.

Q When you say that you planned to bring papers, did you ever discuss with the President the fact that you would try to use that as a cover?

A Yes.

Q Okay. What did the two of you say in those conversations?

A I don't remember exactly. I mean, in general, it might have been something like me saying, well, maybe once I got there kind of saying, "Oh, gee, here are your letters," wink, wink, wink, and him saying, "Okay, that's good," or --

Q And as part of this concealment, if you will, did you carry around papers when you went to the visit the President while you worked at Legislative Affairs?

A Yes, I did.

Q Did you ever actually bring him papers to sign as part of business?

A No.

Q Did you actually bring him papers at all?

A Yes.

Q All right. And tell us a little about that.

A It varied. Sometimes it was just actual copies of letters. One time I wrote a really stupid poem. Sometimes I put gifts in the folder which I brought.

Q And even on those occasions, was there a legitimate business purpose to that?

A No.

Q Did you have any discussions with the President about what you would say about your frequent visits with him after you had left Legislative Affairs?

A Yes.

Q Yes. What was that about?

A I think we -- we discussed that -- you know, the backwards route of it was that Betty always needed to be the one to clear me in so that, you know, I could always say I was coming to see Betty.

Q And is there some truth in the notion that you were coming to see Betty?

A Coming to see Betty, I don't know. Did I -- I saw Betty on every time that I was there.

Q What was your purpose though in going --

A My purpose was -- most of the time my purpose was to see the President, but there were some times when I did just go see Betty but the President wasn't in the office.

Q When the President was in the office, was your purpose in going there to see the President?

A Yes.

Q What about the writing of things down on paper?

Was there any discussion between you and the President about the risks of writing things down and whether you should write things down?

A Yes.

Q All right. Tell us about that.

A There were on some occasions when I sent him cards or notes that I wrote things that he deemed too personal to put on paper just in case something ever happened, if it got lost getting there or someone else opened it. So there were several times when he remarked to me, you know, you shouldn't put that on paper.

Q We'll have occasion to get into some details about that in a bit. I don't know how to ask this question more delicately, so I'll just ask you. Did you take any steps to try to be careful with how loud you might be in sexual matters?

A Yes.

Q All right. Can you tell us, as discreetly as you can and as -- about that?

A I think we were both aware of the volume and sometimes I'd use my hand -- I bit my hand -- so that I wouldn't make any noise.

Q All right, that's fine. Let me ask another question. Did you try to take -- are you okay?

A Yeah, this is just embarrassing.

Q Did you try to take different routes in and out of the Oval Office area as part of your way of concealing the relationship?

A Yes, I did.

Q Could you tell us about that?

A I made an effort on my own to go out a different door than the door that I came in so that if there was a guard that was on duty in the front of the Oval Office he might see me going in but a different guard would see me leave, so no one would know exactly how long I had been in there.

Q Did you try to do that most of the time, all of the time?

A I'd say 90 percent of the time. I mean, I can't really recall a time that I didn't do that, but it's possible. That was the pattern.

Q Were there some people that you tried to specifically avoid when you were visiting with the President?

A Yes.

Q All right. Who were they, please?

A Pretty much everybody but Betty.

Q Okay. What about, for example, Nancy Hernreich?

A Yes.

Q All right. And how would you take steps to avoid Nancy Hernreich?

A Generally, coming in on the weekend. This is after I left?

Q Yes.

A Okay. After I left the White House it was coming in on the weekend or sometimes we -- I tried to see him but I don't think it actually ever occurred on Tuesday nights because Ms. Hernreich has yoga, I think -- I believe.

BY MR. WISENBERG:

Q Who told you that she had yoga?

A Ms. Currie.

BY MR. EMMICK:

Q Any discussion with the President about trying to make sure that there are fewer people around when you were to visit?

A When I worked in Legislative Affairs, I think that was sort of the understanding that the weekend was the -- there weren't a lot of people around. And there were times when I think that the President might have said, oh, there are too many people here because there was some big issue or some big event happening maybe.

Q Were there any occasions when you tried to make arrangements to see the President but for some reason or another Betty was not in a position to let you in?

A Sure, I think so.

Q Any occasions when you had actually planned to

visit and then for some reason or another she wasn't there, that you remember?

A No, not that I remember.

Q What about throwing away notes that you had written to the President? Was there any discussion of throwing out the notes or any notations that you would write on the notes to remind him to throw them out?

A Yes, I think that I may have had a discussion with the President about him throwing things away, I think, or making sure that they're not there. I know one specific occasion in one of the notes that I sent him I made a joke that really was reminding him not to -- to make sure he threw the -- make sure he threw it away.

Q I've asked you a number of questions having to do with how you tried to keep the relationship secret. Let me ask, did you tell some people about the relationship?

A Unfortunately, yes.

Q All right. Could you tell us some of the people that you've told about the relationship?

A Linda Tripp, Catherine Davis, Neysa Erbland, Dale Young, Ashley Raines, and my mom and my aunt. Everybody knew a different amount of -- had a different amount of information.

Q Natalie Ungvari?

A Oh, Natalie Ungvari, yes.

Q Did you tell any of your -- any counselors or therapists of any kind about your relationship?

A Yes, I did.

Q All right. Would you tell us who they would be?

A Dr. Irene Kassorla, and I believe it's Dr. Kathy Estep.

Q When you talked about your relationship with the President with these people, did you lie about your relationship?

A No. I may have not told them every detail, but I don't believe I ever lied. Oh, about the -- oh, wait, do you mean the doctors or was that in general?

Q I meant in general.

A Well, there were -- about my relationships -- I'm sorry, could you be more specific?

Q Sure. You listed a number of people that you had told about your relationship with the President.

A Right.

Q I'm just trying to figure out if you told the truth to those people when you described the relationship.

A Yes. There were some occasions when I wasn't truthful about certain things, but not having to do with, I think, the general relationship. Does that make sense?

Q Expand on that just a little. I'm just not sure.

A Well, I think with Linda Tripp, I mean there were

times that I was not truthful with her. I mean, I didn't know if that's what you were encompassing by saying relationship or not.

Q Let's put Linda Tripp aside for a bit because I think I know what you have in mind.

A Right.

Q Put Linda Tripp aside for a bit. Were you truthful with the others about your description of the relationship?

A Yes.

Q And since you mentioned Linda Tripp, were there occasions toward the end of, I guess it would be December or January, when you said some things to Linda Tripp that were not true?

A Yes.

Q All right. We'll have a chance to get to that in a bit.

A Okay.

Q What I would like to turn to next is the -- is April of 1996 and your transfer from the White House to the Department of Defense. When were you first told about the fact that you were being terminated from Legislative Affairs?

A On the 5th -- I think it was the 5th of April, Friday.

Q Did you later have a telephone conversation with the President about your being terminated?

A Yes, I did.

Q When was that?

A On the 7th, on Easter.

Q Easter Sunday, April 7th of 1996?

A Correct.

Q Would you tell us first what your reaction was when you were told that you were going to be terminated from Legislative Affairs?

A My initial reaction was that I was never going to see the President again. I mean, my relationship with him would be over.

Q You did not want to go to the Pentagon?

A No.

Q When you spoke with the President on April 7th, did you call him or did he call you?

A He called me.

Q Would you tell us how that telephone conversation proceeded and then we'll talk about the meeting.

A Okay. I had asked him how -- if he was doing okay with Ron Brown's death, and then after we talked about that for a little bit I told him that my last day was Monday. And he was -- he seemed really upset and sort of asked me to tell him what had happened. So I did and I was crying and I asked him if I could come see him, and he said that that was fine.

Q Did you go over to the White House?

A Yes, I did.

Q About what time of day, if you remember?

A I think it was around 6:00 p.m.

Q Who let you in?

A I had a pass at the time.

Q How long did you visit with the President that day?

A Maybe a half an hour. I'm not very good with the time estimates.

Q You've already had occasion to talk a little bit about the sexual aspect of your encounter with the President at that time and the phone call that you -- that came in in the midst. I'm not going to ask you about that. What I am going to ask you about instead was your discussions with the President about the termination and about what the future would hold for you.

A He told me that he thought that my being transferred had something to do with him and that he was upset. He said, "Why do they have to take you away from me? I trust you." And then he told me -- he looked at me and he said, "I promise you if I win in November I'll bring you back like that."

Q How were things left at the end of that meeting?

A I sort of ran out.

Q Right. I guess what I mean by that -- I'm sorry, I didn't mean to be that specific.

A Okay.

Q At the end of the meeting, were you going to go to the Pentagon?

A Well, he was going to see what he could do.

Q I see. All right.

A He said he'd try to see. He said he was going to ask -- try to find out what had happened. And I told him that I was going to be meeting with Ms. Hernreich the next day and he sort of said, "Let me see what I can do."

Q Did you later have a telephone call with the President where you discussed what he had learned?

A Yes.

Q When was that?

A The following Friday.

Q That would have been then April 12th?

A Yes, I think so.

Q Did he call you or did you call him?

A He called me.

Q Where were you?

A I was at home.

Q How long was the telephone conversation?

A Maybe about 20 minutes.

Q Tell us what the two of you talked about.

A He told me that he had asked Nancy and Marsha Scott to find out why I had been transferred, and that what he had come to learn was that Evelyn Lieberman had sort of spearheaded the transfer, and that she thought he was paying too much attention to me and I was paying too much attention to him and that she didn't necessarily care what happened after the election but everyone needed to be careful before the election.

Q Did he offer any of his views about what you should do with respect to this Pentagon job?

A He told me that I should try it out and if I didn't like it that he would get me a job on the campaign.

Q What was your reaction to that?

A I think I was disappointed. I didn't want to go to the Pentagon and I didn't really see what the difference on the campaign was going to be -- why I couldn't work -- if I could work at the campaign why I couldn't work at the White House. So --

Q Did you start working at the Pentagon?

A Yes.

Q What position did you hold when you worked at the Pentagon?

A Confidential Assistant to Ken Bacon, who is the Pentagon spokesman.

Q Let's talk generally, if you will, about what sort of contact you had with the President during the rest of 1996. Did you see him in person?

65

A Yes, I did.

Q Okay. Did you see him in person very often?

A No. I wasn't alone with him so when I saw him it was in some sort of event or group setting.

Q Did you continue to have telephone contact with him?

A Yes.

Q And those telephone contacts are set out in the chart that we've put together --

A Mm-hmm.

Q -- with your assistance?

A I guess. Yes. I'm sorry.

Q Let's then just turn to the first part of 1997. The election is over. Did you talk with the President about getting you back to the White House?

A Yes.

Q All right. Would you tell us about that?

A I believe the first time I might have mentioned it to him was in January of '97 in a phone conversation, and he told me that he would talk to Bob Nash, who is the head of White House or Presidential Personnel, I think it is, about bringing me back. In the next phone call he said he had spoken to Bob Nash and then -- do you want me to go as far as --

Q Just a bit more detail so that we can get a sense

of what efforts you thought were being taken and whether you came to be disappointed with those efforts.

A Very disappointed. He -- my understanding at first was that the ball had sort of been passed to Bob Nash to bring me -- to find a position for me to come back to the White House. I then came to learn maybe in March or so that the ball had been passed from Bob Nash to Marsha Scott. And then Marsha Scott was supposed to help me find a position at the White House, which didn't work out, then she was going to detail me to her office in the White House and then she later rescinded that offer.

Keep going?

Q Were you frustrated with all that?

A Very frustrated.

Q And did you communicate your frustration to the President?

A Yes, I did.

Q Tell us about how you communicated your frustration to the President.

A There were various occasions, different things that happened. Sometimes it was in our phone conversations, sometimes it was in a letter, sometimes it was in person.

Q Let me direct your attention to July 3rd of 1997. Did you cause some sort of a communication to be made to the President on that day?

A Yes.

Q Tell us about that.

A I had been trying to get in touch with him maybe since the latter part of June to discuss some of my meetings with Marsha Scott that had not gone as I had hoped they would and -- excuse me -- the President wasn't responding to me and wasn't returning my calls and wasn't responding to my notes. And I got very upset so I sat down that morning actually and scribbled out a long letter to him that talked about my frustrations and that he had promised to bring me back; if he wasn't going to bring me back that I -- you know, then could be help me find a job -- at that point I said in New York at the United Nations, and that I sort of dangled in front of him to remind him that if I wasn't coming back to the White House I was going to need to explain to my parents exactly why that wasn't happening.

Q And what was your purpose in sending a letter of that kind to the President?

A I think it was sort of had a few purposes, in that towards the end of the letter I softened up again and was back to my mushy self, but the purpose was -- one of the purposes, I think, was to kind of remind him that I had left the White House like a good girl in April of '96. A lot of other people might have made a really big stink and said that they weren't going to lose their job and they didn't want to do that and would have talked about what kind of relationship they had with the President so they didn't lose their job, and that I had been patient and had waited and that all of this had gone on. So I was frustrated.

Q Did you -- how did you get this letter to the President?

A I gave it to Ms. Currie.

Q Did you meet with the President on the 3rd of July?

A Mm-hmm. Yes, I'm sorry.

Q Did you meet with the President on the 4th of July?

A Yes, I did.

Q Would you tell us how that was arranged?

A I spoke with Ms. Currie later that afternoon on the 3rd and she told me to come to the White House at 9 o'clock the next morning.

Q You showed up at the White House?

A (Nodding.)

Q What I would like to do with respect to this meeting is just ask you to give a very general description of the meeting, whether it was emotional.

A It was very emotional.

Q I don't want to focus on the emotional aspect of that meeting. What I want to do is focus on the end of the meeting.

A Okay.

Q And whether or not you said anything to the President about Kathleen Willey.

A Yes, I did.

Q Can you tell us what happened in that conversation?

A Can I jump back a little to how I got the information or do you want me to just stick to what I told him?

Q Sure, why don't you. Okay, jump back to how you got the information and then we'll plug it in.

A Just so everyone understands. I believe it was in February or March of that year when I was friends with Linda, she had frantically come to me telling me that this reporter whom I had never heard of before that day, Michael Isikoff, had shown up in her office to question her about Kathleen Willey, who was this woman that you all know now but who was this woman who had -- that Linda had worked with in the White House and that I guess this woman had told Michael Isikoff that the President had sexually harassed her and that Linda would corroborate that fact.

And Linda was -- she had said to me that she was nervous and she responded that no -- I think she had sort of tried to lead Michael Isikoff away from the fact that it had been sexual harassment but, at the same time, had sort of confirmed to Michael Isikoff that something might have happened there.

I'm sorry, I'm going too long.

Q It's all right.

A Throughout the next couple months I had encouraged Linda to get in touch with someone at the White House to let them know that this was out here. Being a political appointee, I thought that was something that should be done.

Q Who at the White House did you encourage her to contact?

A Well, she said she would feel comfortable either getting in contact with Nancy Hernreich or Bruce Lindsey from her experiences at the White House. And I don't really remember how it came to be Bruce Lindsey but that -- I don't remember who encouraged what. She contacted Bruce, or she told me she contacted Bruce Lindsey and that Mr. Lindsey did not return her phone call or answer her page.

Q So jumping forward to July --

A Right.

Q -- what were you trying to convey to the President and what did you say to him?

A Just let me add that I think right -- at some point before July 4th, soon before July 4th, Michael Isikoff had again contacted Linda and so the story was sort of bubbling again. And I was concerned that the President had no idea this was going on and that this woman was going to be another Paula Jones and he didn't really need that.

A So --

Q This is another grand juror who has just walked in.

A Okay.

Q So that you know.

A Thanks. So I wanted to inform the President about what he should sort of be aware of. And at the end of our meeting -- it had been a really emotional meeting -- I told him that I wanted to talk to him about something serious and that while I didn't want to be the one to talk about this with him, I thought it was important he know.

And I told him that a woman whom I was friendly with at the Pentagon had been approached by Michael Isikoff and sort of informed her that Kathleen Willey was claiming -- I know I didn't use the term sexually harassed because I would have felt uncomfortable saying that to the President, so I think I said something or another that indicated what Kathleen Willey was claiming, and that this woman had known Kathleen Willey when she worked at the White House and she -- I think I may have indicated that she had -- did not corroborate Kathleen Willey's story.

Q Did you identify Ms. Tripp by name?

A No, I did not.

Q Did the President ask who it was you were referring to?

A No, he did not.

Q Continue. I think you were --

A At that point -- I don't know if it was at that point in the conversation, then the President informed me that Kathleen Willey had actually called Nancy Hernreich during the week earlier and had said -- excuse me, sorry -- and had said that this reporter was chasing after her trying to find out her relationship with the President.

And so to me, what that meant was that when -- I thought that meant that when Kathleen found out Linda wasn't going to corroborate her story that she was trying to cover her tracks with the White House so that they wouldn't then find out or think that she was trying to encourage Michael Isikoff.

So I thought everything was over with and I later told that to Linda.

Q Why did you want to say anything to the President at all about that? What did you think the President might do to respond?

A I thought he -- I thought maybe, you know, my understanding from Linda was that Kathleen had been trying to get a job, and I could certainly understand the frustrations of being told someone is going to help you get a job and then you don't. And I thought at that point -- I didn't know too many details about what was going on. I don't think she was in the Paula Jones case and I thought, well, gee, maybe if you know someone who needs -- who would want to hire her you can make this go away for -- that's how I thought of it. Then I thought maybe there was something he could do to fix it or someone else could do to fix it, or just be aware of it.

Q He might get her a job, for example?

A He might. I mean, I think that was one of the things that crossed my mind.

Q At that time, did the President ask you whether you had disclosed anything about your relationship to anyone else?

A Not at that time.

Q Did he at some other time?

A Yes, he did.

Q When was that?

A I think there might have been several times throughout the relationship, but he specifically asked me about Linda Tripp on July 14th.

Q All right. Then we'll get to that in just a moment.

A Okay.

Q At the beginning of the meeting with the President on July 4th, you had sent him a letter in which you said that you were considering telling your parents. Did he ever say anything to you about, you know, you shouldn't be threatening the President or something like that?

A Yes. Our meeting started out with a fight, so he sat down and we sat down and he lectured me and, you know, "First of all, it's illegal to threaten the President of the United States and, second of all -- " I mean, it was just -- and then I started crying so --

Q All right, fine. After the meeting on July 4th concluded, did you leave the country?

A Yes.

Q All right. Where did you go?

A I think a few days after that. I went to Madrid.

Q When did you return, as best you can remember?

A On the 14th of July.

Q All right. Then let's turn our attention to the 14th of July. You got back from overseas. Did you get a call from Betty?

A Yes, I did.

Q Tell us about that.

A She called around -- I think it might have been around 7:30 -- I was already in bed because of jet lag and everything -- and told me that she thought the President either wanted to talk to me or see me later, and that I believe he was out golfing at the time, and that she'd call me back later to let me know what was going to happen. And she did. She called back maybe around 8:30 or so, 8:30, 9 o'clock, and asked me to come over to the White House. So I did.

Q When you got to the White House, did you see the President?

A Yes, I did.

Q Could you tell us how that meeting went?

A It was an unusual meeting, I mean, first because we -- he met me in Betty's office and we went into Nancy Hernreich's office, which is adjacent to Ms. Currie's office, and sat on the sofa and talked. It was very distant and very cold. And he asked me if the -- I don't remember the sequence of things necessarily, but at one point he asked me if the woman that I had mentioned on July 4th was Linda Tripp. And I hesitated and then answered yes, and he talked about that there was some issue with -- this had to do with Kathleen Willey and that, as he called it, that there was something on the sludge report, that there had been some information.

And what his main concern seemed to be was that Kathleen Willey had called Nancy again that week and was upset because Michael Isikoff had told her that he knew she had called the White House saying he was pursuing her and her story. Is that clear?

A JUROR: No.

THE WITNESS: Okay. Kathleen had called Nancy, and

the President had told me that Kathleen had called Nancy. This was on July 4th. And then that following week when I was in Madrid, I believe -- I know I was in Madrid, I think it was that following week -- Kathleen called Nancy again. And Kathleen was upset because Michael Isikoff had told Kathleen that he knew that she had called Nancy the previous week.

Does that make a little more sense?

A JUROR: Yes, thank you.

THE WITNESS: So what the President's concern was that the only people who knew that Kathleen had called Nancy originally were Nancy, Bruce Lindsey, the President and myself, and Kathleen. So he was concerned and had asked me if I had told Linda the information he had shared with me, and I had said yes, I did because I thought that meant it was over, that Kathleen was trying to backtrack.

So that alarmed me because, obviously, someone had told Michael Isikoff. And he was concerned about Linda, and I reassured him. He asked me if I trusted her, and I said yes. And he -- we had talked about -- oh, I had -- I'm sorry, I'm sorry. On July 4th I had mentioned that -- to the President that this woman had tried to contact Bruce Lindsey and that Bruce Lindsey didn't return her phone call.

So on July 14th, the President asked me if I thought Linda would call Bruce Lindsey again, and I told him that she is a really proud woman and that she was really offended that he didn't call her back and it was -- so I didn't think she would. And he asked me if I would just try to see if she would call, and so I said I would try.

BY MR. EMMICK:

Q Did he ask you whether you had told anything to Linda about your relationship with the President?

A Yes, he did.

Q All right. Tell us about that.

A He asked me just that, and I said no.

Q Where was this conversation taking place with the President?

A In Nancy Hernreich's office.

Q Did there come a time when he left to take a conference call?

A Yes, he did.

Q All right. Did you know who the conference call -- was with?

A That's a little murky for me. I believe it might have been with his attorneys, but I don't remember how I know that. So it's possible it was with his attorneys.

BY MR. WISENBERG:

Q How would you know it? I mean, how would you know it?

A I don't know. That's just what sounds -- that's

what came to my mind when I was recalling the event. And I don't recall how I knew that so I don't know if maybe that's just how I'm recalling it or that I knew it and I don't remember who told me.

Q Was there anybody there to tell you he was talking to his attorneys other than him that day?

A It could have been Betty. I sat with Betty when -- in her office when he was on the conference call in the Oval Office or in the back. I don't know where he was, actually.

BY MR. EMMICK:

Q Other than the President asking you to get a hold of Linda and have Linda call Bruce Lindsey, how were things left at the end of the meeting?

A He asked me to let Betty know the following day without getting into details with her, even mentioning names with her, if I had, you know, kind of mission accomplished sort of thing with Linda.

Q And did you?

A Yes, I got in touch with Betty the next day and I told her that I needed to talk to the President having to do with what he had asked me.

Q And did you follow up with that?

A Yes, he called me that evening.

Q Okay. And what did the two of you talk about?

A We discussed the -- I guess that I had tried to

talk to Linda and that she didn't seem very receptive to trying to get in touch with Bruce Lindsey again, but that I would continue to try. And I think I just gave him some more -- I think I gave him maybe the background information about what I knew when Linda worked there and gave him, I think, a fuller version of whatever it was I knew about this situation.

MR. EMMICK: I'm prepared to move on. Is this an appropriate time for another break?

THE FOREPERSON: Most appropriate.

MR. EMMICK: Okay. Good timing.

THE WITNESS: Me, too. Too much water.

MS. IMMERGUT: Ten minutes?

MR. EMMICK: Let's just take ten minutes.

THE FOREPERSON: Ten minutes, please.

(Witness excused. Witness recalled.)

THE WITNESS: So where are we?

MR. EMMICK: In fact, I'll even walk up and show you where we are, but first we have to clarify that there are no unauthorized persons present and we have a quorum.

THE FOREPERSON: That's correct.

And I need to remind you that you're still under oath.

THE WITNESS: Thanks.

MR. EMMICK: Just to make some reference here, we

are here at the end of July, but there are some questions. I'm going to circle back to April 7th.

THE WITNESS: Okay.

MR. EMMICK: We're going to ask some more detail on April 7th and we're going to talk a little bit about a call that you had from the President in -- I think it is April of '97 about some conversations that --

THE WITNESS: Okay.

MR. EMMICK: A call in that time period.

THE WITNESS: Okay.

MR. EMMICK: There were also some -- let's call them sort of a laundry list of follow-up questions.

THE WITNESS: Okay.

MR. EMMICK: So we'll focus there and a little bit on the 14th and a little bit on that phone call.

THE WITNESS: I thought I -- I also might just say that if, as happened before, if I'm saying something and I'm not clear, I'm not understanding, just let me know, because I do that a lot.

BY MR. EMMICK:

Q All right. Let's start off with some questions. First, let's focus on July 14th because the President wanted you to have Linda contact Lindsey. Why wouldn't Lindsey just contact Linda? Was there any discussion of that? Why did it have to go one way rather than the other way?

A I don't believe there was a discussion about it. I have my own thoughts on it, but there wasn't a discussion about it.

Q What were your own thoughts on it?

A That it would just -- I -- I think I sort of thought that it would probably be more proper -- not in a chain of command, necessarily, but -- it just seemed more appropriate for Linda to call Bruce Lindsey.

Q Did it look -- do you think it would have looked inappropriate for Lindsey to contact Tripp?

A I think it would have been awkward because I think -- how would -- you know, how would Bruce Lindsey have known to call -- you know, to call Linda at that point? If -- you know, the President thought at that point that -- you know, that Linda didn't know anything, so if Linda didn't know anything, then how -- wouldn't it be odd for Bruce Lindsey to just call her back out of the blue?

Q Okay.

A I mean, that was sort of how I thought of it.

Q But in either event, there wasn't any actual discussion about the strategy behind who would have to call whom?

A Not that I remember. No.

BY MR. WISENBERG:

Q Well, did you say to him anything like, "Hey, she

tried to call him before."

A Right.

Q "She isn't going to call him this time." I mean, anything like that?

A Yes. I think I had mentioned that before. I mean, that might have been -- you know, I think was sort of -- he was saying, "Well, just try to see."

BY MR. EMMICK:

Q Let me approach the question in just a little bit different way. When you talked to Linda and tried to convince Linda to talk to Bruce Lindsey, what did you say to her to try to convince her to talk to her? Do you understand what I mean?

A Right. Well, I didn't tell Linda that -- and this was unusual, I didn't tell Linda that I had seen the President on the 14th of July because I was somewhat wary of her, having learned that someone had told Michael Isikoff, and I knew it wasn't me, so sort of assuming that Linda had talked to Michael Isikoff and not really knowing where she was coming from on this, so I just kept encouraging her to call Bruce Lindsey again, that this was heating up more and you really should call Bruce Lindsey.

Q All right. Let me go to another question. You made a reference earlier to the fact that you felt that Nel hadn't been treated well or hadn't been treated respectfully.

Could you tell us what you meant by that?

A People in the White House -- I mean, Nel is stationed in the pantry, which is right -- I mean, which is even a part of the Oval Office area and he's always there and he takes very good care of the President and people just walk right past him, they don't say hi to him, a lot of people don't acknowledge him.

And they just -- you know, they kind of come to him when they need something, but aren't -- and I just -- I don't think people should be treated like that. I mean, I think anybody who -- and especially everyone who is working at the White House and who works -- I've always categorized people as people who are there to serve the President and people who are there to serve themselves through the President and I think Nel has a lot of loyalty to the President.

Q Would it be fair to say that it's no so much that they were affirmatively mistreating him, but they were treating him as a non-person almost? Or is that --

A I think that's a mistreatment.

Q Yes. That's a mistreatment. Okay. That's a fair characterization.

A In my opinion.

Q We had talked earlier about certain people that you wanted to avoid in order to help keep the relationship secret and you talked about Nancy Hernreich as being one of those people. Can you tell us what other people you wanted to sort of avoid in that same vein?

A Stephen Goodin. Let's see. I guess it's different from when I was at the White House to after. When I was there, Evelyn Lieberman, Harold Ickes, anybody who knew who I was, certainly. And after I left, I think it was mainly anybody who knew me from before. So --

Q All right.

A Does that -- does that answer it?

Q If that's the answer, then that's the best we can do.

A Okay.

Q We talked earlier about February 28th and about Steve Goodin going into the Oval Office with Betty and what you learned about that conversation they had.

A Mm-hmm.

Q The question is this: why would Steve Goodin, who is after all just a presidential aide, why would he be in a position to be able to tell the President, "You can't be with Monica Lewinsky alone"?

A I don't know. And that was a question that I -- that I posed -- I don't think I posed it as a question, but I sort of made a comment, you know, who is -- and then -- I don't remember if it was to Betty or to Nel, you know, why would -- you know, how inappropriate that was.

Q Right.

A And maybe Stephen made the comment to Betty. Maybe just Betty. I -- I -- I -- you know, I wasn't in the room, so I don't know what the course of the conversation was. Maybe Stephen said it to Betty and Betty told the President that Stephen had said that to Betty. So I'm not sure, but I thought it was inappropriate, too.

MR. EMMICK: Any other follow-up on that?

A JUROR: I think a point be is that did he feel that he had the authority do so because someone else was encouraging him to monitor that sort of activity, such as Evelyn Lieberman, for example?

THE WITNESS: That's a good thought. I don't know. I don't have any knowledge of that. I never thought of that.

BY MR. EMMICK:

Q You mentioned that during 1997 especially you frequently complained to the President that although he said he could bring you back (snapping finger) like that, it wasn't happening. How did the President respond when you complained about these things?

A You know, I mean, it was the -- "Bob Nash is handling it," "Marsha's going to handle it" and "We just sort of need to be careful." You know, and, "Oh, I'll -- " he would always sort of -- what's the word I'm looking for?

Kind of validate what I was feeling by telling me something that I don't necessarily know is true. "Oh, I'll talk to her," "I'll -- you know, I'll see blah, blah, blah," and it was just "I'll do," "I'll do," "I'll do." And didn't, didn't, didn't.

Q All right. You mentioned that in that July 3rd letter that you sent to the President through Betty you made a reference to the fact that you might have to explain things to your parents. What did you mean by that?

A If I was going to pick up and move from Washington -- first of all, I had told my -- well, my mom knew, you know, that I was having some sort of a relationship with the President. My dad had no idea. And I had told my dad that was I -- you know, I was told I could probably come back to the White House after the election, as Tim Keating had told me. And the President.

So I had sort of told him that course and I would have needed to explain to them why I was going to pick up and move to New York without -- what the point would be.

Q Were you meaning to threaten the President that you were going to tell, for example, your father about the sexual relationship with the President?

A Yes and no. I don't think I -- I know that I never would have done that. I think it was more -- the way I felt was, you know, you should remember that I sort of -- I've been a good girl up until now.

I mean, I kind of have -- that I think I tended to -- I know that I thought he tended to forget what I had gone through already and that -- and so that this wasn't an issue of, well, you know, "We can do this in a little while, this is maybe changing your job while you're in the White House," you know, if I had wanted to maybe do something different, it was a lot more significant. And I felt that he was giving me the runaround a bit, too.

Q Is it fair to say that it was in part an implied threat?

A Yes, but I think -- but I think if you want to look at it that way, it was a threat to him as a man and not a threat to him as president. Does that -- I mean --

Q What do you mean?

A Well, I think when I hear you say, you know, "Was that an implied threat" that that letter being sent to any man who is having an illicit relationship with someone would be a threat, and so it was irrelevant, the fact that he was president.

Q I see.

A So just because we had talked earlier about it and then that was what had upset me, when the President said, "It's illegal to threaten the President of the United States."

Q Right.

A And I just thought, you know, "I don't deal with you like the President, I deal with you as a person."

MR. EMMICK: All right.

MR. WISENBERG: Can I ask something about that?

MR. EMMICK: Yes.

BY MR. WISENBERG:

Q But you had said your mother by that time knew there was some of kind of a relationship.

A Right. He didn't know that, though.

Q But you hadn't told -- he didn't know that.

A I never told him that. No.

BY MR. EMMICK:

Q A question about lipstick and tissues.

A Okay.

Q You mentioned that a couple of times you used tissues to wipe lipstick off. Do you remember where you threw those tissues away and did it occur to you that somebody might see those tissues later and therefore might think of it as somehow evidencing the relationship?

A No, really the only -- the one time that I specifically remember doing that was on January 7th of '96. And -- no, I don't think that -- I mean, I had light lipstick on so I don't -- I think if it had been a darker colored lipstick that maybe I would have been concerned, I might have thought about that, but that didn't cross my mind. I don't think people go through the trash.

Q Right.

A I hope not.

Q Do you recall where you threw the tissue away on that occasion?

A It was in the bathroom. I think there's a wastebasket right next to the sink.

Q All right. A question going back to the '96 period, because you had mentioned that on February 19th of '96 the President told you essentially we should break up, we shouldn't have any more of a sexual relationship, yet five or six weeks later, there was a continuation of the sexual relationship. How does that happen? How does it get broken off and then rekindled?

A Well, there continued to sort of be this flirtation that was -- when we'd see each other. And then one night, I don't -- I think it was maybe in the end of -- the end of February or maybe some time in March when he had -- I had seen him in the hall when I was leaving to go from work, and this was the night he was coming back from the Israeli embassy from something, and we didn't make any contact or anything because he was with Evelyn Lieberman. And I went home.

About 45 minutes later, he called me and had told

me he had gone back to his office and had called my office because he wanted me to come over and visit with him, but I was home now, you know, and then he had gone back upstairs.

So that had sort of implied to me that he was interested in starting up again and then when I saw him on the 31st of March -- when he kissed me, that pretty much --

Q Just, basically, people got back together.

A Yeah. There was never a discussion of, "Okay, now we're going to resume our relationship again." I didn't want to -- why bring up the memory of the guilt? So --

Q Okay. Then what I'd like to do next is turn our attention back to April 7th, which is the Easter Sunday, and we're going to ask some more detailed questions about that period. First, when you got to the White House, did you see a Secret Service agent and did the two of you talk?

A Yes.

Q All right. Tell us who it was and what the two of you said to one another.

A It was John Muskett, I believe. And I had brought some papers with me from home and so I believe I said something, "Oh, the President asked me to bring these to him." And John Muskett said, "Oh, I'd better check with Evelyn Lieberman." And I don't remember exactly what the rest of the exchange was, but I talked him out of doing that and then I just went in.

Q Were you nervous when he said, "I've got to talk to Evelyn Lieberman"?

A Oh, yeah. Yes. Also, it alarmed me that she was there. I didn't really expect her to be there on a Sunday evening.

Q You mentioned that a telephone call came in while you were with the President. Did you later come to believe you knew who that call was from?

A I made a speculation about who that call was from. I have no knowledge nor had no knowledge about who was on the phone call.

Q Let's take this a step at a time, then.

A Okay.

Q First, what do you remember about the content of the call and then what was the reason that you drew whatever conclusion you did later?

A The content was political in nature and I drew, you -- know, the possibility that it was Dick Morris just based on -- that it was campaign stuff. And I think that how it even came up that it could possibly be Dick Morris was in a joking way with Linda on the phone.

So I don't believe that I ever -- I don't think I would have ever categorically stated that it was Dick Morris on the phone, because I didn't know that.

Q All right. About how long after April 7th did you

draw the conclusion or develop the suspicion perhaps that it was Dick Morris?

A I don't remember.

Q Okay. All right. At some point, did you hear a voice that you believed to be Harold Ickes' voice?

A Yes.

Q Okay. Tell us how that happened.

A The President and I were in -- I believe it was the back study or the study and -- or we might have been in the hallway, I don't really remember, but I -- Harold Ickes has a very distinct voice and so he -- I heard him holler "Mr. President," and the President looked at me and I looked at him and he jetted out into the Oval Office and I panicked and didn't know that -- I thought that maybe because Harold was so close with the President that they might just wander back there and the President would assume that I knew to leave. So I went out the back way.

Q When you say you went out the back way --

A Through the dining room.

Q Where did you go?

A I went through the dining room exit, to the left, past the Chief of Staff's office, to the right, down the stairs.

Q Were you in a hurry?

A Yes.

Q All right. At some point afterwards, did you get a call from the President?

A Yes.

Q All right. And what happened in that phone call?

A He asked me why I left, so I told him that I didn't know if he was going to be coming back and so he -- he was a little upset with me that I left.

MR. EMMICK: All right. Before we move off that particular call, are there any follow-up questions that you have? Yes?

MR. WISENBERG: Yes. Yes. And I'll try to be delicate. I'm not known for delicacy.

THE WITNESS: I can see that everyone seems to agree with that.

BY MR. WISENBERG:

Q First of all, Ms. Lewinsky, when you went out the dining room, did you go out through Nel's pantry door or through the main dining room door?

A I would have gone out the dining room door.

Q Okay. I want to make sure that I get the sequence right, because this is partly based on stuff we discussed Monday in New York and you correct me if I get anything wrong.

A Okay.

Q We'll do it that way. As I understand it, there

7/98D

is a -- you're back with the President that day and let me ask first if you recall, the more intimate sexual moments that day, were they in the hallway or the back study?

A Both.

Q Okay. Now, as I understand it, you're with the President. It's an intimate moment. A call comes in.

A Correct.

Q All right. And the President leaves.

A Mm-hmm.

Q You put your top back on. Your top had been off and you put your top back on.

A Mm-hmm.

Q And at some point he comes back. Is that correct?

A Mm-hmm.

Q Okay. And what I'm trying to do is distinguish between the Ickes event and the call, if there is a distinction in your mind. In other words --

A Yes.

Q The call is something different, as far as you know, from the Ickes event.

A Correct.

Q Okay. The President comes back and it's at some point later that you hear the voice of Harold Ickes.

A I'm sorry --

Q The President comes back from the phone call that

he takes --

A No. The -- someone came in to tell the President he had a phone call, so someone came in, hollered something, not Mr. Ickes.

Q Okay.

A The President went out, came back in and I think then they sent the phone call in.

Q All right. He took that in --

A He took the phone call in the back study.

Q Okay.

A Then we were -- and I think we had been in the hallway -- I know we had been in the hallway prior to that.

Q Okay.

A And he came back in and then the phone rang and he took the phone call in the back study.

Q Okay.

A Then it was much later in that same day that he heard the "Mr. President" voice.

Q Of Ickes.

A Right. And I'm going to -- I think that we were in the back study at that point because that's why he jetted so quickly, not wanting Harold, I think, to walk back there. That was --

Q Okay. Now, the voice you heard saying to the President that he had a call --

A Mm-hmm.
Q You never saw the President attached to that voice.
A No. And it wasn't a voice that was familiar to me.
Q Okay. And you never saw Ickes. Is that correct? When you later heard his voice, you didn't see him. You're just familiar with his voice.
A Correct.
Q As far as you know, did Ickes see you when you headed out the back way?
A He couldn't have.
Q Okay. Why do you say that?
A Because he was in the office.
Q Okay. And you said that Ickes was much later. I mean, much later within the whole time you were there with the President that day?
A Right. Correct.
Q Okay. I mean, not like several hours later.
A No. No.
Q Okay.
A Just much later within my visit.
MR. WISENBERG: Okay. Thank you.
BY MR. EMMICK:
Q What I'd like to do is turn our attention to a call that you got from the President some time, I believe, in April, but correct me if I'm wrong, where he asked you

something about whether you had told your mother --

A Yes.

Q -- about the relationship. Let's first talk about -- can you place this in time as best you can?

A It was April. And this came about because -- I guess Marsha Scott, I think, had relayed some information to the President about her conversations, I think possibly with Walter Kaye, who is a friend of my family's, and that from that conversation, I think Marsha either directly said to the President or the President wondered from something Marsha said, if I had told my mom -- well, it must have been the President assuming from something that Marsha said.

The President asked me if I had told my mom or had my mom told -- and where that went was had my mom told Walter Kaye. And I said no.

Q What you're describing, is it all based on what the President said in this phone call?

A I don't understand.

Q Yes. You said that at some point it was based on the fact that Walter had spoken to Marsha Scott and I'm trying to figure out if you're learning that from a different source or if it's all from the President.

A No, I was learning that from the phone call with the President.

Q All right. How long was the phone call?

A You know, I'm thinking just now, I don't know if that was in April. It could have been in May.

MR. EMMICK: Okay.

A JUROR: Of 1997?

THE WITNESS: Yes. Sorry. Okay. I don't know if the month time is important or not.

BY MR. EMMICK:

Q In April or May, you have this discussion.

A Right.

Q The President asks you if you've told your mother about the relationship.

A Right.

Q What do you respond?

A "No. Of course not."

MR. EMMICK: Okay.

MR. WISENBERG: Mike?

MR. EMMICK: Yes?

MR. WISENBERG: Can I butt in?

MR. EMMICK: Yes.

BY MR. WISENBERG:

Q Do you know independently what, if any, conversation there was -- that is, whether -- did you later learn that Walter had said something to Marsha or that somebody had said something to Walter?

A In a way, that's too broad of a question because

I think Walter Kaye kind of comes in and out -- if you look at this whole few years, he comes in and out of this in a few ways, so -- did I learn independently that Walter had had a discussion with Marsha? No. Is that what you were asking me?

Q Well, that's one. How about with anybody else? I guess did you hear anything that struck you as this is kind of consistent with what the President had told me in that conversation or this fits together now? Walter had a conversation with somebody and could have actually talked to Marsha Scott and then that got relayed to the President.

A I don't think I'm following you 100 percent. I'm sorry.

Q Okay. Well, I'm not always very articulate. I'll just --

A It --

Q Do you recall -- let me be more specific. Are you aware of your aunt ever having made a comment to Walter Kaye?

A I'm aware of Walter Kaye having made a comment to my aunt.

Q Okay. And what was that?

A He remarked something to my aunt that he had heard from people that the reason I had left the White House or had been moved from the White House was because I had had this relationship with the President.

Q Do you know what your aunt responded to Walter Kaye?

A My understanding was she got up and walked out. She was having lunch with him.

BY MR. EMMICK:

Q After you had this telephone call with the President where he asked you whether you had told your mom, was the next time that you saw the President May 24th, I think, which you refer to as dump day?

A Yes. Either way, it would have been, whether it was in April or May.

Q Right. Because you didn't see him in April --

A Right.

Q -- and you only saw him once in May.

A Right. Correct.

Q All right. And you had -- that's fine. All right. What I'd like to turn our attention to next is as we're working down our outline here, we're finished up with the July 3rd, 4th and 4th period. I take it that you remained frustrated with the President's efforts to try to get you back to the White House.

A Mm-hmm. I mean, it always -- and I did make this clear to him, that it was always more important to me to have him in my life than to -- than to get the job, but the job was something that was important to me.

Q Did there come a time in about October when you gave up, more or less, on your efforts to get back to the White House and you turned your attention more to New York City?

A Yes.

Q All right. Tell us how that happened.

A Linda Tripp called me at work on October 6th and told me that her friend Kate in the NSC had heard from -- had heard rumors about me and that I would never work in the White House again and, if I did, I wouldn't have a blue pass and that her advice to me was "get out of town." So that meant to me that I wasn't going to be coming back to the White House and I was very upset by that.

Also, she, Linda, told me that Kate had said, "You know, they create jobs at the White House, you know, six days a week." And that Stephen Goodin's girlfriend had just gotten a job, so with these examples of how there had been all these other people receiving jobs that I could have done and I didn't get it.

Q Did you communicate your additional frustration and disappointment to the President?

A Yes, I did.

Q Tell us how and when.

A I believe I sent him a short note telling him that I really needed to talk to him in person having to do with this subject matter and he and I had an argument in a conversation on the 9th of October.

Q And was that a telephone conversation?

A Yes, it was.

Q Did he call you or did you call him?

A He called me.

Q About what time, if you can remember?

A I think it was around 2:30, 3:00 in the morning.

Q Was it a long phone call?

A Yes. Yes. 2:00, 2:30 maybe.

Q Is it fair to characterize the phone call as involving an argument?

A Yes. And then we made up.

Q And then you made up.

A It was half argument, half making up.

Q Did the name Vernon Jordan come up in the course of that discussion?

A It's possible.

Q What do you have in mind about the first time that Vernon Jordan's name would have come up in conversations with the President?

A It was either in that phone call or on October 11th.

Q And tell us what was said about Vernon Jordan, whether it was in the phone call or on the 11th.

A I don't remember. I know that I had discussed with Linda and either I had had the thought or she had suggested that Vernon Jordan would be a good person who is a close friend of the President and who has a lot of contacts in New York, so that that might be someone who might be able to help me secure a position in New York, if I didn't want to go to the U.N.

Q And what was the President's response?

A "I think that was a good idea."

Q At some point, did you send the President something like a list of jobs or interests that you might have in New York?

A Yes. He asked me to prepare that on the 11th of October.

Q At some point, did you have an initial meeting with Vernon Jordan?

A Yes, I did.

Q Can you tell us when that was, as best you can recall?

A The beginning of November of last year.

Q How was that meeting arranged?

A Through conversations with the President and with Betty.

Q Without getting into a lot of detail about what happened there during the first meeting with Vernon Jordan, what did you think were your job prospects after that? Did it look like things were going to happen?

A Yes.

Q All right. And what happened with respect to the job situation from that meeting with Vernon Jordan until, say, Thanksgiving?

A Nothing, really.

Q Okay. Then let's turn our attention to the month of December. We'll have to relate back a little bit to November in order to complete things, but on December 5th, did you return to Washington from overseas?

A I did. You know -- the question you just asked me before about until Thanksgiving, I did have a conversation with him before Thanksgiving, I think it was the day before.

Q Okay.

A So --

Q Then why don't you complete that, then.

A Okay. I had spoken to Betty about -- about not being -- being able to get in touch with Mr. Jordan because he was in and out of town and then wasn't necessarily returning my call. He's a busy man. And so Betty arranged for me to speak with him again and I spoke with him when I was in Los Angeles before -- right before Thanksgiving.

Q Okay. Let's just go back, if we might, to that early November meeting with Mr. Jordan.

A Okay.

Q Did he say anything indicating to you that he had spoken with the President recently about you?

A Yes. I believe he mentioned he'd had a conversation with the President.

Q And what did he say about that or what did he say that indicated he may have spoken with the President?

A I believe he mentioned that in the course of the conversation and as I was leaving, he remarked to me that I came highly recommended.

Q Okay. Let's turn our attention to December 5th, then.

A Okay.

Q Having in mind that you had had a meeting with Vernon Jordan and a discussion and were trying to get a hold of him, when you got back from overseas, sort of what was the status of the Vernon Jordan job effort?

A When I had spoken with Mr. Jordan right before Thanksgiving, he had asked me to call him the next week, either, I think, Thursday or Friday. And because I was out of town, I called him on Friday when I got back, and it was my understanding from his secretary he had gone out of town that day, so we had missed each other.

Q All right. Did you try to arrange a meeting with President Clinton?

A Yes.

Q Tell us what you did to try to arrange meeting with President Clinton.

A I sent a note to Betty much earlier in the week that I asked her to pass along to him which in that letter requested of him that I could come have a visit that Saturday.

Q Did you follow up that note with a call to Ms. Currie?

A Yes.

Q When was that call, if you remember?

A December 5th.

Q Okay. And what happened during the call?

A Well, there were several calls, actually. And so at first, it was -- the first few, she still hadn't given him the note.

So then finally she gave him the note, just, I think, right after the radio address or right before his radio address, and then she told me that he was meeting with his lawyers all day Saturday, but that she was coming in in the morning to give a tour and she would check and see with him then, you know, if maybe I could come by, but that the prospects didn't look good.

Q Was she focused on Saturday because you had asked whether Saturday would be a good time?

A Mm-hmm. Yes. I'm sorry. Maybe he was going out of town on Sunday. I'm not sure why I would have focused on Saturday versus Sunday.

Q In any event, what she said was he was busy with meetings with lawyers, something like that?

A Yes.

Q All right. Did you go to a Christmas party that night?

A Yes, I did.

Q Did you see the President?

A Yes, I did.

Q Let's turn our attention to December 6th.

A Okay.

Q Are you doing okay?

A Yes.

Q All right. December 6th. Let me ask as a background question, had you previously purchased for the President a Christmas present?

A Yes.

Q All right. What was that Christmas present?

A It was a sterling silver antique standing cigar holder.

Q You had been unable to arrange an actual visit with the President to give him that present in person. What did you do instead?

A I had some other gifts for him as well that I had gotten on my trips and --

Q Tell us what those other gifts were, if you remember.

A A tie. A mug from Starbucks in Santa Monica. A little box that's called hugs and kisses and it's Xs and Os inside, it's really -- it's just a cute little chatchki. An antique book from the flea market in New York that was on Theodore Roosevelt. And -- I think that's it.

Q Okay. What did you try to do on the 6th in order to give those gifts to the President?

A Well, I had wanted to give them to him, if I was going to have a planned visit with him, and then through the -- just some course of events, I got upset and I decided that I was really tired of everything that was going on and I just -- it was clear to me that he was ignoring me and I just didn't want to deal with this anymore.

So I decided -- I had purchased these presents for him and I'm very -- I spend a lot of time and am very particular about the presents I give to people, so I didn't want to give them to someone else and I wanted him to have them, so I packaged them up with a note that I was going to drop off to Betty.

Q And where did you go?

A I went to the southwest gate.

Q What happened at the southwest gate?

A I paged Betty or I think I might have called her. I know I called her and she wasn't at her desk, so I paged her to let her know I was there. And then Marsha Scott drove up, so I ran away to the northwest gate because I didn't want Marsha to see me. Continue from there?

Q Yes. Did you have any trouble getting in at the northwest gate? What happened?

A Well, I wasn't trying to get in. I -- so --

Q What were you trying to do?

A I was trying to wait for Betty. So I called Betty from the northwest gate and she wasn't at her desk and then I saw someone go into the -- it was under construction at the time, so it was a different little hut than normal, and I saw someone who went in who I thought was John Podesta, so I thought I would -- since I knew that Betty had talked to John Podesta about me, I thought I would ask him, you know, maybe I would ask her -- I would give the gifts -- I would feel comfortable probably giving the gifts to John Podesta to give to Betty, just knowing that he knew I had a relationship with her.

So when I went in to ask this person who I thought was John Podesta -- it turned out to be Lanny -- I think Lanny Davis, and so then one of the guards said, "Oh, are you here to see Betty Currie?"

And I said, "No. I'm not here to see her, I'm trying to get her. She doesn't know I'm coming."

And then they told me she was giving a tour and that Eleanor -- do you want me to go into this detail?

Q Sure.

A Okay. That Eleanor Mondale had come recently and that she was giving a tour to Eleanor Mondale. Then I sort of -- wanting to know if the President was in the office, asked the guards, "Oh, well, is the President in the office? Because if he is, she's probably too busy to come out and get these gifts."

And they said, "Yes, he was."

Q What was you reaction to that?

A Not good.

Q Okay.

A Very upset. Hysterical.

Q Where did you go and what did you do?

A I turned around and walked out and I was livid. I had -- well -- are the grand jurors aware of the rumors about Eleanor Mondale that had been out? I mean, because it doesn't make sense if --

BY MS. IMMERGUT:

Q Well, why don't you say why you were upset.

A [redacted]

[redacted]

BY MR. WISENBERG:

Q A question. Pardon me for interrupting. I just wanted to -- you said you were upset. Did you show your upsetness to any of the guards?

A No.

MR. WISENBERG: Thank you.

BY MR. EMMICK:

Q Did you contact Betty?

A Yes, I did.

Q Where did you contact her from?

A I called her from the pay phone at the Corcoran Gallery.

Q Did you have a fight with her?

A I think so.

Q Okay. You say you think so --

A I'm trying to remember if I -- if I actually got her on the phone, which I think I did. I'm pretty sure I did.

Q All right. Did you eventually come to talk to the President on the telephone?

A Through a much more circuitous route, yes, I did.

Q All right. And where were you at that time?

A I was at home.

Q All right. And about what time of day was it?

A Maybe around noon or so.

Q How did the two of you come to be speaking on the phone? Who placed the calls?

A Well, I believe maybe I had called Betty or maybe Betty called me, one of the two, but she put him on the phone.

Q All right. And what happened in the conversation with the President?

A Well, we had a fight. And he was very angry with me.

Q Why was he angry with you?

A Because I had gotten so upset and I had made a stink to Betty and I had -- you know -- I -- what I came to learn, I think, is that as a result of me being upset with Betty and mentioning that I knew Eleanor Mondale was there, Betty called the guards at the northwest gate and so it had just caused a whole big commotion.

And he was just angry at me and he told me it was none of my business what -- you know, what he was doing and that -- you know, that -- that he had never been treated as poorly by anyone else as I treated him and that he spent more time with me than anyone else in the world, aside from his family, friends and staff, which I don't know exactly which category that put me in, but --

Q Okay. Was it a long phone call with the President?

A Maybe half an hour, 45 minutes.

Q Eventually, were arrangements made for you to visit him at the White House?

A Mm-hmm.

Q Are you doing okay?

A Yeah. Yes.

Q Were you surprised that he would let you come to the White House?

A Yeah, I was -- yes, I was a little bit surprised.

Q Why?

A Because none of the other times that we had really fought on the phone did it end up resulting in a visit that day.

Q All right. What about the fact that he was supposedly meeting with his lawyers all day? Did he say anything about that?

A He had in the fight. When we were fighting, he said -- you know, he was angry because he said, "I have one day to meet with my lawyers and, you know, I've got you messing things up and being upset and blah, blah, blah." So --

Q Did you go and did you meet with the President?

A Yes, I did.

Q Did Betty wave you in?

A Yes.

Q Can you describe for us in general terms how that meeting went? Did you give him the gifts, for example?

A I did. It was -- it was a really nice visit.

Q Okay. What do you mean by a "nice visit"?

A It was just sweet. He liked his Christmas presents and we were very affectionate and it just -- it was just nice to be with him.

Q Did you discuss the job search?

A I believe so.

Q At the time, how did you think the job search was going?

A Not very well. With respect to Mr. Jordan.

Q Right. And did you communicate that to the President?

A Yes.

Q Can you give us a little more detail? What would you have said to one another?

A I think I said that I -- that I was supposed to get in touch with Mr. Jordan the previous week and that things didn't work out and that nothing had really happened yet.

Q Did the President say what he was going to do?

A I think he said he would -- you know, this was sort of typical of him, to sort of say, "Oh, I'll talk to him. I'll get on it."

Q Okay. Did he say anything to you about whether he had a Christmas present for you?

A Yes, he did.

Q What did he say?

A He told me that on the phone, actually.

Q All right. What did he say about that?

A Well, I said to him, "Well, how do you have a Christmas present? I haven't read that you've gone Christmas shopping yet." And he said that he had bought it in Vancouver.

Q Okay. Did he say at any time on the 6th anything about a witness list or your being on a witness list?

A No.

Q How were things left when you left him on the 6th?

A That he would bring me -- oh, our meeting ended up -- or was cut short by the fact that he had to have a meeting with Mr. Bowles, so he told me that he'd give me my Christmas present another time and that he wouldn't jerk me around and abandon me.

You know, that -- because I think I remarked to

him, "Well, at the rate we go, I won't get it 'til Christmas of '98." So --

MR. EMMICK: I have no more questions about this date and I look at the time and it looks like it's 12:30.

THE FOREPERSON: Sol, I think, went to check on something.

MR. EMMICK: Oh, all right.

THE FOREPERSON: Did you check on something for lunch?

MR. WISENBERG: I have checked. It is here. It's been here.

MR. EMMICK: Okay. All right. Well, if this would be a good time to take a break for lunch --

THE FOREPERSON: It's fine with me.

MR. EMMICK: Okay. Let's take an hour-long break for lunch.

THE FOREPERSON: Hour-long.

MR. EMMICK: Okay.

THE WITNESS: Okay.

THE FOREPERSON: Okay.

MR. EMMICK: Thank you.

(Whereupon, at 12:34 p.m., a luncheon recess was taken.)

* * * * *

A F T E R N O O N   S E S S I O N

Whereupon, (1:38 p.m.)

MONICA S. LEWINSKY

was recalled as a witness and, after having been previously duly sworn by the Foreperson of the Grand Jury, was examined and testified further as follows:

EXAMINATION (RESUMED)

THE WITNESS: Time for a nap?

MR. EMMICK: Madam Foreperson, do we have a quorum?

THE FOREPERSON: Yes, we do.

MR. EMMICK: Are there any unauthorized persons present?

THE FOREPERSON: There are none.

Monica, I'd like to remind you that you are still under oath.

THE WITNESS: Okay. Thanks.

BY MR. EMMICK:

Q Ms. Lewinsky, we just got through speaking about the December 6th meeting that you had with the President. What I'd like to do is turn our attention next to the date of December 11th.

A Mm-hmm.

Q Did you have a meeting with Vernon Jordan on that day?

A Yes, I did.

Q Would you tell us when that meeting was?
A Around lunchtime.
Q And how was that meeting arranged?
A By his secretary.
Q What was the purpose of the meeting?
A For him to -- I learned after we had the meeting, for him to give me some contact names and some suggestion of what to do with these contact names.
Q When you say --
A For a job.
Q When you say "contact names," these are names of potential employers?
A Yes.
Q What else did the two of you talk about?
A We talked about my -- the fact that my mom's fiance at the time knew Mr. Jordan. We talked about the President.
What else did we talk about? I think that's it.
Q All right. Did he at some point make a comment to you about your being a friend of the President?
A Yes, he did.
Q Would you tell us how the conversation transpired from that point?
A I don't remember how we got to this point, but at some point, Mr. Jordan said something to me, "Well, you're a friend of the President of the United States."

And I remarked that I didn't -- I didn't really look at him as the President, that I saw him more as a man and reacted to him more as a man and got angry at him like a man and just a regular person.

And Mr. Jordan asked me what I got angry at the President about, so I told him when he doesn't call me enough or see me enough.

We were sort of bantering back and forth about that and then he told me that I shouldn't get angry at the President because he's got a lot of -- it sounds so stupid -- obviously, he has a lot of other more important things and difficult things to deal with than someone getting upset with him. And he suggested that if I was upset that I should call and take my frustrations out on Mr. Jordan instead of the President.

I mean, I think I should just say that it was all -- this was all sort of in a light tone.

Q Is this a meeting during which the subject of your possibly being in love cropped up?

A Oh, yes. So after we had the conversation I was just talking about with Mr. Jordan, he said to me, "Well, you know what your problem is?"

And I said, "What?"

He said, "Don't deny it." And he said, "You're in love, that's what your problem is."

So I think I just -- probably blushed or giggled, something like that.

Q How did the meeting end? What were you going to do and what was he going to do?

A I was planning to send the letters that he had suggested I write to the list of people and he suggested that I cc him and keep in touch with him, keep him apprised of what was happening with my job search.

Q And did you send out those letters?

A Yes, I did.

Q And make arrangements for some interviews?

A Yes, I did.

Q What I want to do next, then, is direct your attention to a few days later, several days later, a week later, I guess. Did you come to have a telephone conversation with the President on December 17th?

A Yes.

Q Would you tell us how that telephone call was -- how that conversation took place?

A Okay. The phone rang unexpectedly at about maybe 2:00 or 2:30 and --

BY MS. IMMERGUT:

Q In the morning?

A Right. In the morning. And it was the President and he called and said he had two things to tell me and then he had to call me right back. So he called me right back.

BY MR. EMMICK:

Q Did he explain why he had to call and then call back?

A I don't know. He just was very brief with me and then he said, "I'll call you right back." And he hung up and called back about a minute later.

Q Before you get to the actual things that he says next, you mentioned that you unexpectedly go the call. Why were you surprised by the call?

A Normally, the President wouldn't call me when Mrs. Clinton was in town, so -- and I usually was aware when she was out of town, so I that I would sort of be expecting or hoping that he would call. And the call came as a surprise to me.

Q He called you back?

A Right.

Q Then what happened?

A And he told me that he had two things to tell me. The first was that Betty's brother had been killed in a car accident and that -- so I reacted that and we talked about that being -- that this was the same brother who had been beaten up just a few months ago and she had lost her sister and her mom was ill. We talked about Betty for a little bit.

And then he told me he had some more bad news, that he had seen the witness list for the Paula Jones case and my name was on it.

Q Did you get an impression from him about when he had found out your name was on the witness list?

A Yes. I mean, the impression I got based on the entire conversation was that he found out recently.

Q When he told you that, what did he say about having seen your name on the witness list?

A He told me it broke his heart.

Q Tell us how the conversation went from there.

A I was -- I'm sure, as you can imagine, I was upset and shocked. He told me that it didn't necessarily mean that I would be subpoenaed, but that that was a possibility, and if I were to be subpoenaed, that I should contact Betty and let Betty know that I had received the subpoena.

I believe that I probably asked him, you know, what should I do in the course of that and he suggested, he said, "Well, maybe you can sign an affidavit."

At some point in the conversation, and I don't know if it was before or after the subject of the affidavit came up, he sort of said, "You know, you can always say you were coming to see Betty or that you were bringing me letters." Which I understood was really a reminder of things that we had discussed before.

Q So when you say things you had discussed, sort of ruses that you had developed.

A Right. I mean, this was -- this was something that -- that was instantly familiar to me.

Q Right.

A And I knew exactly what he meant.

Q Had you talked with him earlier about these false explanations about what you were doing visiting him on several occasions?

A Several occasions throughout the entire relationship. Yes. It was the pattern of the relationship, to sort of conceal it.

Q When he said that you might sign an affidavit, what did you understand it to mean at that time?

A I thought that signing an affidavit could range from anywhere -- the point of it would be to deter or to prevent me from being deposed and so that that could range from anywhere between maybe just somehow mentioning, you know, innocuous things or going as far as maybe having to deny any kind of a relationship.

Q At some point, did you talk with him about possibly settling the Paula Jones case?

A Yes. I had -- I had had a thought and then had a conversation with Linda about this and just a way that he could settle the case and I suggested it to him.

Q And what was that way? Not in a lot of detail, but --

A The gist of it is, I thought that first Mrs. Clinton should do something publicly, maybe on a T.V. show or something, and talk about how difficult the case had been for her and on her daughter and that she just wished that he would settle it and it would go away. And then the President should unannounced and unexpectedly go into the briefing room, make a brief statement that he -- in an effort to put this behind him, you know, against his attorneys' advice, he was going to pay Ms. Jones whatever it was, however much she wanted, and so that this case would be over with.

Q Did the two of you talk about how much the settlement amount would be or might be?

A Yes. I believe at some point I had mentioned that I had recently read the -- I think she had lowered her -- the amount that she wanted to $500,000 or something lower and he said, "I thought it was a million or two million dollars."

And I thought that was very strange, that he wouldn't know she had -- you know, that her lawyers -- or his lawyers had not told him that she had lowered her request for money. Or I don't know how you say that legally, whatever it is that she did.

Q Right. Demand, probably.

A The demand was lower.
Q Right.
A We also talked in this conversation about he mentioned that -- he said he'd try and see if Betty could come in on the weekend to give me my Christmas presents and I told him that was out of the question, to -- you know, let Betty be.
Q Because her brother had just been killed, right?
A Right.
Q All right. About how long was the entire phone call? Or I guess technically it would be the second phone call.
A Maybe a half an hour. Maybe I could just say since you asked me earlier that it was him suggesting that I would contact Betty if I were subpoenaed that led me to believe he didn't think I would be subpoenaed that soon because he knew Betty was going to be out, you know, he assumed obviously that Betty would be out for the week or two weeks with the unexpected loss of her brother.
Q Right.
A So that was what led me to believe he had just found out.
Q After the call was ended, did you call anyone else?
A Yes. About a half an hour later, I called Linda.
Q What did the two of you talk about?

A My conversation with the President.
Q Right. It seems self-evident, but --
A I know. I'm sorry.
Q That's all right. What did you tell Linda?
A Well, if I could just jump back --
Q Yes.
A I mean, I had -- Linda had told me some time in -- I think the second week of December that she had been subpoenaed in the Paula Jones case and that she intended to rat on me, so up until this point, I had been trying to convince her not to tell, that it's not anybody's business.

So when I -- part of my telling her that the President had called; that I, too, may be pulled into this case was just sort of -- maybe assure her that if that happened, there would be someone else denying it, it wouldn't be just Linda out there alone saying "I don't know anything about any kind of relationship between the President and Monica."
Q Kind of a unified front or something like that?
A Exactly.
Q All right. How was the conversation left with Linda?
A I think that we'd talk about it the next day.
Q Did you get subpoenaed?
A Yes, I did.

Q When did you get subpoenaed?
A On Friday, the 19th of December.
Q Can you tell us about when you believe you were subpoenaed?
A I believe it was around 3:00, 4:00 in the afternoon. I think closer to 3:00, 3:30.
Q Okay. Where were you served?
A At the Pentagon.
Q Could you tell us how it happened? Did someone call you?
A Yes. I received a call in my office from the gentleman who was to deliver the subpoena to me. He informed me he had a subpoena for me. I made a stink to him, asking him why I was being subpoenaed and I had no idea what was going on.
When he gave me the subpoena, he suggested I call Ms. Jones' attorneys, which I made a comment to him that that's not something I would do.
Q When you actually did get served, what was your real reaction inside?
A I burst into tears. It was -- it was very scary. I mean, it just -- sort of my worst nightmare, or I had thought until that point, was being subpoenaed in this case. So I was pretty upset.
Q You couldn't call Betty because Betty was --

A Right.

Q -- in mourning herself. Who did you call?

A I called Mr. Jordan.

Q From what phone did you call Mr. Jordan?

A From a pay phone.

Q Close to where you were served, the nearest pay phone around?

A No, I think it was the pay phone which is down the hall from my office, which is kind of halfway between where I was served and my office.

Q And why did you use a pay phone?

A Because I was crying and I -- I mean, I -- my office, the way my office is set up is my desk was in the same room with four or five other people, so I couldn't very well have any kind of a private discussion.

Q What did you tell Mr. Jordan?

A Well, I don't remember what I told him. I was crying and he didn't seem to understand me, so he just -- he just told me to come to his office around 5:00.

BY MS. IMMERGUT:

Q Did you tell him you'd been subpoenaed?

A I probably did. I just -- I mean, I don't -- I don't remember, I just remember being on the phone crying and him saying, "I can't understand you. I can't understand you."

Q You got off the phone. What did you do next? Did you finally go to Vernon Jordan's office?

A Yes. I tried to compose myself and I went into the office. I told Mr. -- I believe I told Mr. Bacon or some other people in the office that I had an emergency and I needed to leave. I went home, sort of put myself together, and went to Mr. Jordan's office.

Q When you got to Mr. Jordan's office, did you have to wait outside for a bit?

A Yes.

Q In like a reception area?

A I waited in the lobby, like I always did.

Q About how long did you wait in the lobby?

A I don't really remember.

Q At some point, I take it, you did actually meet with Mr. Jordan?

A Yes.

Q How did the conversation with Mr. Jordan progress?

A First, I came in and I explained to him clearly that I had been subpoenaed and that I was upset and shortly after, I think maybe I said I didn't know what I was supposed to do, I didn't have an attorney, I think I was rambling.

Shortly after I had arrived at Mr. Jordan's office, he received a phone call and I stepped out of the office.

Q Did he ask you to step out of the office?

A I think I may have offered. That was sort of par for the course. And I waited for him while he was on the phone outside his office and when I came back in, he placed a call to -- I don't know if it was right after I came back in, but at some point, when I came back in, he placed a call to Mr. Frank Carter.

Q Now, when you stepped out, he took one call and then you stepped back in, did he tell you who he'd been on the phone with?

A No.

Q All right. He places a call to Frank Carter. Do you know whether he talked to Frank Carter in person or do you know whether he just left a message or do you recall?

A I don't really recall.

Q When --

A Oh, he said something about -- well, I know he referred to Mr. Carter as Mr. Carter, so I don't know if he was talking -- I don't really remember if he was talking to Mr. Carter or he was talking to someone else, but it scared me because I thought for Mr. Jordan to be referring to someone else as Mr. something, that -- I sort of thought he must be a big deal.

Q All right. When you went to the meeting with Mr. Jordan, did you bring the subpoena with you?

A Yes, I did.

Q Did you show it to Mr. Jordan?

A I believe so.

Q What most troubled you about the language of the subpoena and what the subpoena had called for you to produce?

A The thing that alarmed me was that it asked for a hat pin.

Q Okay. And why did that alarm you?

A Because I thought that was a very specific gift and in this list of gifts, everything else seemed to be somewhat generic and then it had hat pin, which screamed out at me because that was the first gift that the President had given me and it had some significance.

Q When you showed Mr. Jordan the subpoena, did he make any remark about any of the things that were called for?

A Yes. When I mentioned to him, I think, about the hat pin, he said, "Oh, don't worry about it. This is a vanilla subpoena, this is a standard subpoena," something like that. Generic subpoena, maybe.

Q Did you know what he meant, a vanilla or standard subpoena that asks for hat pins?

A Well, what I understood that to mean was that -- that what he was trying to say is there was nothing out of the ordinary about this subpoena.

Q I see. I guess what I'm trying to get at is do you

think he was trying to imply that all subpoenas ask for that or that all subpoenas in the Paula Jones case asked for that or all subpoenas -- what was he -- from your point of view, what was he trying to convey?

A I think what he -- I think what he was trying to convey was stop worrying, that this is not something out of the -- you know, out of the realm of possibility of what might be in a subpoena.

Q All right. Were you reassured by that?

A A little. I -- I sort of felt that he wasn't -- I mean, he didn't really understand what I was saying.

Q All right. Did you have any discussion with him about letting the President know that you'd been subpoenaed?

A Yes. I asked Mr. Jordan to inform the President.

Q How did you ask? How often? How vigorously?

A I -- I mean, I asked him to -- to please make sure that he told the President. He said he was going to see the President that night, so --

Q All right. Did the subject of a possible sexual relationship between you and the President come up in the conversation?

A Yes, it did.

Q Tell us how it came up.

A Mr. Jordan said to me that there -- "There are

two important questions" or "There are two important -- " I think, "Two important questions that are related to the case: Did you have sex with the President, you know, or did he ask?" And I said no to both of those.

Q What did you interpret him to be asking when he asked you those questions?

A Well, I thought he -- I guess -- can I step back for a minute?

Q Sure. Up until a point that we'll get to, which is December 31st, I sort of -- mainly, I think, from my discussions with Linda, I was under the impression that -- that Mr. Jordan kind of knew with a wink and a nod that I was having a relationship with the President, that it was never -- he and I never discussed it, but I thought it might be possible.

I'm, you know, a young woman, sort of coming to see him, the President's mentioned me. But I also was sort of under this influence of Linda saying to me, "Of course he knows. Of course he knows. Of course he knows."

So when he asked me those questions, I thought he was asking me, saying essentially "What are you going to say?" not necessarily asking me directly what -- you know, "What are the answers to these questions?" More "What are you going to reply in regard to the case?"

Q Now, was your interpretation of his questions based

entirely on your assumption about what he knew? Or was it based in part on how he asked the questions?

A I think it was based more in part on my assumptions of what he knew.

Q Was there anything unusual or suggestive about how he asked the questions?

A No.

Q And how did you answer the questions?

A No and no.

Q Okay. Did you try to make it clear to him at all that there was more to the story than just no and no?

A Not at that point.

Q At that time, did you make arrangements to meet with the attorney who you would get, Mr. Frank Carter?

A Yes. After Mr. Jordan made the arrangements with Mr. Carter, he told me to be at his office at -- I think 11:00 or 10:30 on Monday.

Q All right. How did the meeting with Mr. Jordan end? Was there any reference to a hug?

A Oh, yes. I'm sorry.

Q That's okay.

A When I was leaving, I asked him if he would give the President a hug for me. I bugged him again about making sure he told the President. And so he said, "I don't hug men." I said, "Well, okay."

Q All right.
A But --
Q All right. Did you call Linda Tripp afterwards?
A Yes, I did.
Q What was the purpose of your call?
A In a -- to let her know that I had been subpoenaed.
Q Tell us how that conversation went.
A It probably would be impossible for anyone who didn't -- who has listened to that tape to follow. I was beyond paranoid.

I had no idea how I had gotten onto the witness list and then, of course, been subpoenaed and I was thinking at that point that maybe my phone was tapped or someone had read my e-mails or something. But in thinking that my phone might be tapped, I sort of tried to explain to this to Linda that I had been subpoenaed in a veiled fashion.
Q How did you do that? What do you mean?
A I used different cover stories. I think like it was a movie or it was a book, trying to discuss things. I think I said something -- "I received the flowers," trying to intimate that I had received the subpoena. So --
Q Eventually, did you drop the sort of disguised way of talking and just talk about the subpoena, or do you recall?
A I don't believe I did. I don't really remember,

though.

Q How were things left with Linda?

A She was having a party the next day, so we made plans that -- or I suggested that I come early and we could discuss this and that I would help her set up for her dumb party. I'm sorry.

Q Her dumb party? All right. Well, we'll skip the dumb party for now.

A I'm sorry.

MR. EMMICK: That's all right.

MR. WISENBERG: I have a quick question.

MR. EMMICK: Okay. A dumb party question?

MR. WISENBERG: Not about the dumb party.

MR. EMMICK: All right.

BY MR. WISENBERG:

Q When you were doing the flowers bit, the book bit, how was she -- you're trying to speak in code to her, how was she responding?

A I don't really remember. I just sort of remember her not understanding and me being frustrated. "Hello? Understand. We just talked about this."

A JUROR: Excuse me. May I ask a question?

MR. EMMICK: Sure. Absolutely. Yes.

A JUROR: Did you ever find out how the Paula Jones lawyers knew about the hat pin, et cetera?

THE WITNESS: I -- from what I've read in the press, yes.

A JUROR: But just from any other source? Did you ever suspect maybe Linda or --

THE WITNESS: I had -- I came to start to suspect her, but not in any way that -- that it really has turned out to be. Not to that degree.

A JUROR: Thank you.

BY MR. EMMICK:

Q Let's turn our attention, then, to December 22nd, which is the day that you met with Frank Carter and I think you had said that you were going to meet with Vernon earlier.

A Mm-hmm.

Q Tell us about that. The Vernon part.

A Okay. With all the details?

Q Well, first, when were you supposed to meet with Vernon and then did you place another call to him?

A Right. I -- I -- I asked -- I called on the morning of the 22nd to see if I could come to see Mr. Jordan earlier. And I was -- I was a little concerned. I thought maybe he didn't really understand or -- fully understand what it was that was happening here with me being subpoenaed and what this really meant. So I came to see Mr. Jordan earlier and I also wanted to find out if he had in fact told the President that I had been subpoenaed.

Q Right.

A Which I found out he did. So I -- so I told Mr. Jordan that -- I said I was concerned that maybe -- that someone had listened in on phone calls and Mr. Jordan said, "Well, you know, so what? The President's allowed to call people."

And I said, "Well, we've had phone sex."

And so Mr. Jordan said, "Well, what's phone sex?"

And so I said, "Well, you know what phone sex is."

And he said, "No, I don't. I'm just an old man. I don't know what phone sex is."

And it was kind of this -- discussion that way.

Q Did you discuss the hat pin?

A We didn't discuss the hat pin, but I brought -- I had put together sort of an assortment of things that I was planning to hand over to Mr. Carter as being in response to the subpoena, sort of things that I would -- considered gifts, being the Christmas cards that I had received from the White House, I had a copy of the President's book, "Hope and History," which he had signed to me which had a very innocuous sort of inscription. And I think brought some innocuous pictures with me. So I showed those to Mr. Jordan.

Q What did you say about those items?

A I know that -- I think I was a little more specific in my proffer about what -- I mean, what I remember saying now was that -- you know, that I sort of showed him that this is what I was going to respond to for the subpoena.

Q Well, did you bring everything that could have responded to the subpoena that day?

A No. No.

Q Did you try to convey to Mr. Jordan the fact that it wasn't everything?

A I think I might have.

Q And do you remember how you would have conveyed it? Would it have been very expressly or would it have been more impliedly?

A More impliedly.

BY MS. IMMERGUT:

Q Did you tell Mr. Jordan that the President had indeed given you a hat pin?

A I did, but I had told him that on Friday and that was what prompted the sort of "this is a vanilla response."

MR. EMMICK: Let me show you the written proffer --

THE WITNESS: Okay.

MR. EMMICK: -- and see if that helps you recall or if you know whether or not when you wrote it it's accurate.

What we're looking at is the top of page 6 -- everyone else has a copy.

THE WITNESS: Okay. There's some spelling mistakes.

MR. EMMICK: Why don't I just read out loud. This paragraph starts, "On the day Mr. Jordan drove Ms. Lewinsky to Mr. Carter's office, she showed Mr. Jordan the items she was producing in response to the subpoena. Ms. Lewinsky believes she made it clear this was not everything she had that could respond to the subpoena, but she thought it was enough to satisfy. Mr. Jordan made no comment about whether or not what Ms. Lewinsky brought was right or wrong. Mr. Jordan drove Ms. Lewinsky to Mr. Carter's office, introduced them and left."

BY MR. EMMICK:

Q Now, having read that to you, does that refresh your recollection about what was said to him?

A I think I would have implied it.

Q Yes.

A That this wasn't everything. I -- I don't really remember if I specifically said -- and from reading this, it doesn't make me think I necessarily specifically said, "This isn't everything, but it's enough to satisfy," but I could have said that.

Q At the time you wrote this, were you trying to be completely truthful and accurate?

A I was trying to be completely -- yes, I was completely truthful and accurate. I'm just also while I'm reading this now, it doesn't necessarily indicate to me that -- that what I'm saying here is sort of a direct quote of what I said.

Q Do you remember what Mr. Jordan's reaction was? There it's written that he didn't indicate whether he thought it was right or wrong, but more generally, how did he react when you tried to convey to him that this may not be everything?

A There were often times when I was with Mr. Jordan that he would have no reaction at all. He would kind of do this "Mmmph" thing.

Q I'm not sure how the court reporter is going to get that. Is that a grunt?

A And so -- I remember feeling in general with Mr. Jordan and this subject matter, just not knowing. Do you understand what I'm trying to say? Is this clear? And not really ever getting much of a reaction from him.

Q Did you take from his lack of reaction that he did understand or was it still ambiguous in your mind?

A I think sometimes I thought he understood and sometimes I thought it was ambiguous.

Q Okay. Did the subject of phone sex come up again in your conversation with Mr. Jordan?

A Aside from what I mentioned before?

Q Yes. Did you explain to him what phone sex was at some point?

A I think it -- at -- I don't think I said it. He might have said -- know, is it -- uh -- this is embarrassing. Hmm. I think he -- it's hard. I think he -- uh -- might have given some suggestion as to what he thought phone sex was and I agreed. Is that --

Q That's fine.

A -- fair?

Q That's fine.

A By this time, had you expected the President to call you?

A Mm-hmm. Yes.

MR. EMMICK: I'm sorry?

A JUROR: Before you go on, can you ask her what does that mean?

MR. EMMICK: What does phone sex --

A JUROR: No, what did he say?

MR. EMMICK: I think the grand juror is asking for more detail.

THE WITNESS: If I remember correctly, I believe that he said -- or maybe I said something like -- you know, "He's taking care of business on one end and I'm taking care of business on another." Does that --

BY MR. WISENBERG:

Q Do you remember which one of you said it?

A When I'm saying that now, I think I said it,

because that sounds more familiar to me.

Does that answer your question?

A JUROR: (Nods affirmatively.)

BY MR. EMMICK:

Q Did you expect the President to call you?

A Yes, I did.

Q Is that why you were bugging or asking Vernon so much about whether he had told the President?

A I don't know. Maybe.

Q All right.

A I think I just wanted to make sure the President knew.

BY MS. IMMERGUT:

Q That you had been subpoenaed.

A Right. Because I was supposed to call -- you know, in the event that I was subpoenaed, I was supposed to have called Betty and -- so --

BY MR. EMMICK:

Q I'm going to ask a question that will suggest what assumptions you were making about what Vernon knew or didn't. Why would you feel comfortable talking with Vernon Jordan about phone sex?

A I wasn't comfortable talking to Vernon Jordan about phone sex.

Q Okay.

A I was scared.

MR. EMMICK: Okay.

MR. WISENBERG: Questions?

MR. EMMICK: Yes?

BY MR. WISENBERG:

Q Did you say on the 22nd that you showed to Vernon Jordan the gifts you bringing to Frank Carter?

A Yes.

Q Okay. Was a hat pin among the things you showed to Vernon Jordan?

A No.

Q But you had indicated to him on the 19th that the President had given you a hat pin.

A Yes.

MR. WISENBERG: Thank you.

BY MR. EMMICK:

Q At some point, you went to Frank Carters's.

A Mm-hmm. Yes.

Q Tell us what happened when you got to Frank Carter's.

A We arrived at Mr. Carter's office and Mr. Jordan and I sat down on the sofa. Mr. Carter came out. Mr. Jordan introduced us and left.

Q In your discussions with Mr. Carter, what was the major point that you were trying to make? What was the big thing you were trying to convey to Mr. Carter?

A That there was absolutely no reason why I should have been subpoenaed in this case.

Q Okay. And --

A And that I certainly did not have a relationship with the President.

Q You said that to him.

A I don't think I said those words, but that was what I was trying to convey and certainly when asked those questions, that's what I answered.

Q Did you discuss with him how you could get out of the deposition?

A Yes.

Q Tell us what you talked about. Maybe that would be the easier way to go.

A Okay. I told Mr. Carter I really didn't want to be dragged into this, I didn't -- I thought Paula Jones' claim was bunk and I didn't want to be associated with the case. I believe I suggested maybe that I could -- maybe I asked him if I could sign an affidavit or is that something to do.

He said that the first step -- to hold off on that and that the first step is he would try to talk to the attorneys for Paula Jones and find out what it is, why they're subpoenaing me and where it is that they're going with this and that maybe one option might be is he could arrange for them to interview me, just kind of do a brief interview, versus a deposition.

Q Did you discuss with him the subpoena insofar as it requested items? Did you, for example, go through and talk about what items were called for?

A Yes, we did. Yes. And I said no to everything until we got to the gifts and then I sort of turned over what it was that I had brought with me that I thought responded to the gifts. And that was it.

Q Was there any mention made by either of you of Bob Bennett?

A Yes.

Q Tell us what was said.

A I requested of Mr. Carter that he get in touch with Mr. Bennett and just to be in touch with him and to let him know that I had been subpoenaed in this case and I didn't know why.

Q Why did you request that Mr. Carter contact Mr. Bennett?

A Because I thought in the -- how do I explain this? Sort of in the story or role, the story that I was giving to Mr. Carter and being a low level political appointee and, in general, even if I hadn't been a low level political appointee, I thought it was probably appropriate to align myself with the President's side, being that that's whose

side I was on and there was no question in my mind.
Q Is another way of saying that you were trying to send a message to the President or to Mr. Bennett?
A Not to the President. He knew. I mean, the President knew, you know? So --
Q So it was more a message to Mr. Bennett?
A I just -- to me, that seemed -- I mean, I think -- you have to look at this from the point of view that I was a political appointee. And so --
Q What does that imply for you?
A For me, that means that the reason you're in this job is you work for this administration and that you're politically aligned with this administration and everything you do is in the best interests of the administration and, ultimately, the President. And that's where your goal and your focus should be.
Q How were things left? What was he going to do and what were you going to next?
A Mr. Carter was going to get in touch with the attorneys for Paula Jones and get in touch with Mr. Bennett. And he was going to send me a retainer letter. And we'd be in touch.
Q Let me then ask you the following. You had earlier indicated that the President said that he had a Christmas present for you.

A Mm-hmm. Yes.
Q Did you ever make contact with Betty Currie in order to make arrangements to pick up the present?
A Yes.
Q Tell us about that.
A I called Betty after Christmas to see how she was doing and find out how her holiday was and to ask her -- or to let her know that the President had mentioned to me that he had a Christmas present for me and, you know, to touch base with him to see if he -- what he wanted to do, if he wanted to get together.

So she called me back and told me to come to the White House at 8:30 in the morning on Sunday, the 28th of December.
Q Did you?
A Yes, I did.
Q All right. Betty waved you in?
A Yes.
Q At about what time was it, if you can remember?
A 8:30.
Q When you got there, what happened?
A I think the President was already there. He was just coming to the Oval Office and Betty and the President and I were in the Oval Office and this was the first time I got to meet Buddy.

So we played with Buddy in the office and he was running around the carpet. And I had brought a small Christmas present for Buddy. And so the three of us were just talking and goofing off. And then the President and I went into the back study and he gave me my Christmas presents.

Q How long were you in the back study with the President?

A Maybe about 45 minutes to an hour.

Q What was the Christmas present or presents that he got for you?

A Everything was packaged in a big Black Dog -- or big canvass bag from the Black Dog store in Martha's Vineyard. And he got me a marble bear's head carving, sort of -- you know, a little sculpture, I guess, maybe.

Q Was that the item from Vancouver?

A Yes. Then he got me a big Rockettes blanket from Christmas of '95 or '96, I think. He got me a Black Dog stuffed animal that had a little Black Dog T-shirt on it.

He got me a small little box of chocolates, cherry chocolates, and then he got me some sunglasses that were a joke because I had -- I had teased him for a long time about the different sunglasses that he was wearing in public.

And so then I bought him a normal pair of sunglasses, and so we had just sort of had -- this was a long

7/98D

running joke with us, so he bought me these really funny looking sunglasses and we both were putting them on and joking around goofing off.

So -- I'm trying to think what else. Can I look at the list?

MR. EMMICK: Sure. Feel free.

THE WITNESS: Oh. He got me a pin that had the -- most of my Christmas presents were sort of New York themed, so he got me a pin that had the New York skyline on it. I think that's it. Well, it's a lot, so -- not just that's it.

BY MR. EMMICK:

Q Now, you had mentioned earlier that you were concerned about the fact that the subpoena covered this hat pin.

A Mm-hmm.

Q Did you discuss that concern with President Clinton?

A Yes. We -- we really spent maybe about five -- no more than ten minutes talking about the Paula Jones case on this day and -- do you want me to talk about the hat pin or that period of time?

Q The whole period of time, I suppose.

A I brought up the subject of the case because I was concerned about how I had been brought into the case and been put on the witness list. So I asked him how he thought I got put on the witness list and he told me he thought that maybe it was that woman from the summer with Kathleen Willey, which I knew to be Linda Tripp, or maybe -- he said maybe some of the uniformed -- maybe the uniformed officers.

We talked about that. I mentioned that I had been concerned about the hat pin being on the subpoena and he said that that had sort of concerned him also and asked me if I had told anyone that he had given me this hat pin and I said no.

Q That was false.

A Correct. Yes. When in fact I had told people about the hat pin.

Q Right.

A Let's see. And then at some point I said to him, "Well, you know, should I -- maybe I should put the gifts away outside my house somewhere or give them to someone, maybe Betty." And he sort of said -- I think he responded, "I don't know" or "Let me think about that." And left that topic.

Q When you said "the gifts," what did you mean by "the gifts"?

A I meant all the gifts that he had given me.

Q All right. Do you think that you're the one who came up with Betty's name?

A I'm not 100 percent sure, but when I received the

call from Betty, I wasn't surprised that it was Betty calling, so that's what leads me to believe that I might have suggested it.

Q Okay. Did you discuss with the President the fact that you were planning to sign an affidavit?

A I might have mentioned it, but I don't think -- we really didn't spend very much time on this subject.

Q All right. So you walked in without many gifts, you were going to walk out with a bag of gifts.

A Mm-hmm.

Q Okay. Did it strike you as unusual that when you had a subpoena calling for you to produce gifts the President is giving you a bag of gifts?

A At the time, it didn't strike me as unusual.

Q Okay. And why is that?

A I never thought about it. I mean, I was -- I was -- I had struggled for a long time before the 28th -- or I should just say -- I guess a few days before the 28th, that if I was going to see the President, if I should tell him or not that Linda knew. And I decided not to.

And so I -- I thought this might be the last time I saw him before I went to New York and I wanted it to be a really nice visit, so I was -- I -- having decided not to tell him about Linda, I kind of didn't even want to go too far there in getting mired down in the discussion of the case.

Q All right. When you left the White House, did anything unusual happen with respect to your E-pass?

A Yes. Well, I had a visitor's pass.

Q Visitor's E-pass, I guess.

A Is that what --

Q A visitor's pass?

A Visitor's -- I don't know. I know it is a visitor's pass. Betty escorted me out and I realized that I left the pass in the office, so Betty told me that she would call down to the guard station and let them know that I was fine and I had just left the pass somewhere.

Q Do you remember what gate you used when you left the White House?

A I believe it was the southwest gate.

Q Did you hear from Betty later that day?

A Yes, I did.

Q Were you surprised to hear from her?

A No. I mean, I wasn't surprised that I was hearing from Betty. I think I was a little surprised to sort of get the nature of this phone call when the President could have just said right then and there, "Well, yeah, I think, you know, why don't you give them to Betty, that's a good idea." But I wasn't terribly surprised. No.

Q What did she say?

A She said, "I understand you have something to give

me." Or, "The President said you have something to give me." Along those lines.

Q How long after you had left the White House did Betty call you?

A Several hours.

Q When she said something along the lines of "I understand you have something for me," or "The President says you have something for me," what did you understand her to mean?

A The gifts.

Q Okay.

A Kind of -- what I was reminded of then a little bit was jumping all the way back to the July 14th incident where I was supposed to call Betty the next day but not really get into details with her, that this was maybe along those same lines.

Q That actually anticipates my next question.

A Oh.

Q Did you feel any need to explain to her what was going to happen?

A No.

Q What arrangements did you make for transfer of the something?

A I think we discussed some things and Betty mentioned she was on the way to the hospital to visit her mom and she'd swing by and, you know, pick up whatever it was I was supposed to give her.

Q Now, at the time you had that conversation, were you already packing up the gifts at all?

A No.

Q When was she going to come by, then? That day?

A Yes.

Q What did you do after the phone call ended?

A I put all the gifts that he had given me on my bed and I got a big box from The Gap and went through each item and decided if I needed to give it to them or not.

Q Can you explain what you mean by that?

A It sort of was a difficult -- I -- I wasn't sure if I was going to get this box back, so I didn't want to give everything in the event that I didn't get the box back for some reason.

And I kept out some innocuous things and I kept out the -- really the most -- the most sentimental gift he had given me was the book, the "Leaves of Grass" book, so -- and it was just -- it's beautiful and it meant a lot to me, so I kept that out.

Q What other -- it sounds to me like you had one category of more sentimental gifts that you kept out of the box.

A Mm-hmm.

Q And kept for yourself. What other items were in that category, other than the "Leaves of Grass"?

A Not necessarily sentimental ones, but just -- I think I kept out the marble bear head, the bag, the canvass bag, the blanket, the sunglasses, the chocolates. And I think that's it. Oh, wait. And I might have kept out some of the Martha's Vineyard stuff that I had gotten in the fall.

Q Those were items that you've recently turned over to our office.

A Yes.

Q Which items did you put into the box? If you remember.

A The hat pin, the pin that I had received that day for Christmas, a pin that he had given me for my birthday, a picture that he had signed for me for my birthday that I had framed, a picture he had signed for me of him wearing the first tie I gave him.

Q Any other Black Dog items?

A I think there was a Black Dog hat that I put in there. And I'm not -- I'm not really sure what else was in there. Oh, I also put the copies that I had left of the Valentine's Day ad that I had put in the paper for him.

Q The Romeo and Juliet quote?

A Mm-hmm.

Q All right. Did Betty come by?

A Yes, she did. I met her outside.
Q How did you know when she was going to come by? Was there a prearranged time she was going to come by or did she call you from --
A I think she called me on her way out.
Q You met her outside, you had the box with you?
A Mm-hmm. I had taped it up and I wrote "Please do not throw away" on it.
Q Were you concerned that she might throw it away?
A Mm-hmm. Yes. Sorry.
Q Okay. Let me just ask you some questions. Did you ever discuss with her the contents of the box?
A I don't believe so.
Q Did she ever ask about the contents of the box?
A No.
Q Did she ever say anything indicating that she knew from a prior discussion the contents of the box?
A Not -- no, not that I remember.
Q Sounds like it was a short conversation.
A We talked about her mom a bit and Christmas. I think maybe I had elaborated on what I got for Christmas from him.
Q Now, you could have just thrown these items out, rather than putting them in a box. Why didn't you just throw them out?

A Because I -- they meant a lot to me.

Q Okay. You could have given the items to someone else, a friend of yours, Ashley Raines, or to your mother or just hidden them somewhere. Why didn't you do that?

A I think -- I've come to sort of see this now. I don't know that I necessarily saw it then, but I feel now a little bit that me turning over some of these things was a little bit of an assurance to the President or reassurance that, you know, that everything was okay.

Q In your mind, then, were you giving these items not just to Betty, but really to the President as well, in a manner of speaking?

A I think that was even more directly what I thought it was. Not that they were going to be in his possession, but that he would understand whatever it was I gave to Betty and that that might make him feel a little bit better.

Q Did Betty say where she was going to put the box of gifts?

A I think she said she was going to keep them in a closet. Or, you know, she'd keep the box in a closet.

Q Right.

A You asked me -- never mind.

Q The gifts. Right. I understood. I understood. All right. What I'd like to do now is ask a few questions --

MR. WISENBERG: Mike?

MR. EMMICK: Yes?

MR. WISENBERG: Before you leave that topic, I have a few on that. Do you mind?

MR. EMMICK: No. Not at all.

BY MR. WISENBERG:

Q You've said here today, Ms. Lewinsky, and I think you told us earlier in some of your sessions with us, that you were -- the non-innocuous items were going to go to Frank Carter and --

MR. EMMICK: You mean the innocuous items.

MR. WISENBERG: What did I say?

MR. EMMICK: The not innocuous items.

MR. WISENBERG: Boy. Thank you. I stand corrected.

BY MR. WISENBERG:

Q The innocuous items were going to go to Frank Carter, the non-innocuous items were not, but that one of the reasons, one of the criterion for stuff that didn't even go in the Betty Currie box that you would keep would be sentimental value.

A Mm-hmm.

Q Is that -- have I described that accurately?

A Sort of.

Q Okay. How not sort of?

A I didn't really give any gifts to Mr. Carter. Nothing that I turned over to Mr. Carter was a gift from the President. And I think the way you described the dividing of the actual gifts was sort of innocuous, you know, not innocuous -- sentimental value, I think that was more accurate.

Q Well, as between the gifts you put in the box and the gifts you kept?

A Mm-hmm.

Q All right. How would you describe today the difference between the two? I just want to make sure I understand, between the ones you kept and the ones you put in the Betty box.

A You know, I don't have a perfect memory of what the criteria was at the time. I know I kept the book out because that was the most sentimental thing to me.

And I believe that the things I put in the box were -- also in the box was a dress he gave me from Martha's Vineyard, so the things that went into the box were, I think, more along the lines of some of the things that really complied with the subpoena, that were maybe specifically named, although I think books might have been specifically named in the subpoena, but I kept the "Leaves of Grass."

Q They complied with the subpoena, but they're going to Betty Currie.

A Correct.

Q Now, my question is, and I've asked you this before, but I want to ask you in front of the grand jury, since you were basically trying to keep some sentimental things but you told us that the hat pin was sentimental to you, why is the hat pin going into the Betty box?

A Because the hat pin was the alarm of the subpoena, so -- I -- I -- to me, it seemed logical that putting the hat pin in the box -- I mean, it was what had been named in the subpoena.

MR. EMMICK: All right. Should we take a break?

THE FOREPERSON: Yes, we should.

THE WITNESS: Oh, thank goodness.

MR. EMMICK: Okay. All right. Ten minutes.

THE WITNESS: Okay.

THE FOREPERSON: Ten minutes.

(Witness excused. Witness recalled.)

MR. EMMICK: All right. Do we have a quorum?

THE FOREPERSON: Yes, we do.

MR. EMMICK: Any unauthorized persons present?

THE FOREPERSON: None at all.

THE WITNESS: Let me guess. You're going to remind me I'm still under oath.

THE FOREPERSON: There you go.

THE WITNESS: Fast learner.

BY MR. EMMICK:

Q Ms. Lewinsky, this is what we're going to do. We're going to go over some questions that we'd like to ask and then we're going to turn our attention to the December 31st meeting, the breakfast meeting with Vernon Jordan.

A Okay.

Q Let's go to questions first. One question is Betty comes by and gets this box of gifts. Is there any other way Betty would have known to call and pick up this box of gifts except for the President asking her to?

A The only thing I can think of is if he had asked someone else to ask Betty.

Q Do you have any reason to think that happened?

A No, but, I mean, I wasn't there, so I don't know -- I don't know what he said, how -- maybe he left her a note. I mean, I don't know. So --

Q Another way of asking it is did you tell someone else about this and they might have asked Betty?

A No.

BY MR. WISENBERG:

Q Did you think it as a coincidence that she called you?

A No.

BY MR. EMMICK:

Q Let me ask you a couple of questions about the

December 20th dumb party.

A Okay.

Q Okay? First, why is it a dumb party.

A Oh. Really? You want me to answer that?

Q Yes.

A Well, because it was Linda Tripp's party and -- well, that should be enough, but just that I got there and I got stuck having to do all this stuff and I had really wanted to talk to her about the predicament we were in and -- I now look back on it and just -- she had spent all this money on food and a month before she had had no money for the bus and was trying to sell her clothes and somehow she had $500 to spend on food and had money to spend on presents underneath her tree and it was just dumb.

Q Let's focus on the discussions you had with Linda at the dumb party or before the dumb party about the situation.

A I really didn't sort of get into, I think, a full discussion with her until after -- well, until I was leaving and I asked her to walk me out to my car.

Q Let's talk first then about the efforts you made to talk with her about the subpoena in the house. Did you try to?

A Probably. It was -- I got there maybe -- the -- I think the party was supposed to start around 7:30 and I got there at 5:00 and she had made no food, had done nothing. I mean, she just had this fridge stuffed with food.

So I was trying to help prepare all this stuff. There was a lot more work to do than I thought there would be and then her daughter had this obsession with vacuuming that night, so there were just a lot of people and I don't really remember trying to get a chance.

I may have tried to or sort of said "I need to talk to you," kind of a thing, but I don't recall having any discussions with her before the party.

Q Okay. And then you mentioned that you were able to talk to her a little bit outside, I think you said?

A Mm-hmm.

Q Tell us about that.

A The main -- the main feeling I had had at that point, once I had received my subpoena was that -- that now she didn't need to worry about denying that she knew anything about this relationship, because I was going to deny it under oath as well.

And so sort of just -- I figured that conversation would kind of just be mapping out what our next steps would be. But it ended up being much shorter and I -- she looked at the subpoena -- excuse me -- sorry -- and I think she -- she kept talking about how weird, "Isn't the hat pin strange? Isn't it strange that they're asking about the hat pin?"

And we talked about that. And I think that -- I -- I was -- I was -- I don't think that I was left with the feeling that she was going to continue on this path of insisting she would rat on me. So -- is that clear? I'm sorry -- no? Okay.

When I left that night, I felt a little more -- I think I felt a little more reassured that she and I would be saying the same thing in the Paula Jones case. Is that -- okay. But I wasn't 100 percent sure and I think that we left it that we'd have some more discussions about this.

Q Okay. One of the things we wanted to get back to was the whole situation on the 28th where there's a subpoena that calls for you to turn over gifts and the President is giving you gifts.

A Mm-hmm.

Q What do you think the President is thinking when he is giving you gifts when there's a subpoena covering the gifts? I mean, does he think in any way, shape or form that you're going to be turning these gifts over?

A You know, I can't answer what he was thinking, but to me, it was -- there was never a question in my mind and I -- from everything he said to me, I never questioned him, that we were ever going to do anything but keep this private, so that meant deny it and that meant do -- take whatever appropriate steps needed to be taken, you know, for that to happen, meaning that if I had turned over every gift he had given me -- first of all, the point of the affidavit and the point of everything was to try to avoid a deposition, so where I'd have to sort of -- you know, I wouldn't have to lie as much as I would necessarily in an affidavit, how I saw it.

So by turning over all these gifts, it would at least prompt them to want to question me about what kind of friendship I had with the President and they would want to speculate and they'd leak it and my name would be trashed and he would be in trouble. So --

Q So your impression, then, was in the same way that the two of you were going to deny the relationship, you would also deny or conceal the gifts that were personal that passed between you.

A And the phone call -- I mean, I think that it was everything. I think it was kind of -- at least for me, I don't know what he did, for me, this had to be thought through. You know, I had to anticipate everything that might happen and make sure -- you know --

Q You did what was necessary.

A Exactly.

BY MS. IMMERGUT:

Q Although, Ms. Lewinsky, I think what is sort of -- it seems a little odd and, I guess, really the grand jurors wanted your impression of it, was on the same day that you're discussing basically getting the gifts to Betty to conceal them, he's giving you a new set of gifts.

A You know, I have come recently to look at that as sort of a strange situation, I think, in the course of the past few weeks, but at the time, I was -- you know, I was in love with him, I was elated to get these presents and -- at the same time that I was so scared about the Paula Jones thing, I was happy to be with him and -- I -- I didn't think about that.

He had -- he had hesitated very briefly right before I left that day in kind of packaging -- he packaged all my stuff back up and I just sort of -- you know, remember him kind of hesitating and thinking to myself -- I don't think he said anything that indicated this to me, but I thought to myself, "I wonder if he's thinking he shouldn't give these to me to take out." But he did.

Q And he had already told you he had some gifts for you for Christmas.

A Correct.

BY MR. EMMICK:

Q You mentioned earlier when I asked who was on the list in your mind of people who should be avoided like Nancy Hernreich or Steve Goodin, you mentioned Mr. Ickes.

A Mm-hmm.

Q That name came up. Why was Mr. Ickes on the avoid list?

A He -- well, he -- he's just strange. And he -- I'm sorry. He would -- you know, you could be the only person in the hall and you would pass Mr. Ickes in the hall and he would just glare at you. You know.

And I'd say, "Hello," you know, as you would imagine you're supposed to do and he'd just glare at you and walk past you. And I thought that was strange. Call me weird.

Q Okay. And that's the reason that you mentioned him on the list of people to avoid?

A And I think just -- his name is sort of in my mind for having to do with things that we're discussing today and what's been in the press of it, but it really was most every senior person in the White House, I mean, except for Betty who knew who I was that would concern me.

Q Right.

A I mean, I had -- you know, I had had a lot of interaction with these people during the furlough, so --

Q Let me ask you a question about Tim Keating. Did Tim Keating tell you or imply to you that you could come back after the election?

A He told me that I could probably come back after the election.

Q Okay. Do you remember when he said that to you?
A Yes. On --
Q Go ahead.
A I'm sorry. On the day that he informed me of the transfer.
Q So that would have been the 5th of April? Does that sound right? Friday, the 5th of April?
A Correct. It was Good Friday, I remember.
Q Did he say anything about any problem of an appearance of impropriety during that conversation with you? Something like there might be an appearance before but it doesn't matter after the election, anything like that?
A No. No. No.
Q That subject didn't come up at all?
A Not with Mr. Keating.
Q You mentioned that when -- oh, I'm sorry. Go ahead. Sure.
A JUROR: I'm sorry. What would have prompted him to make a comment like that, that you could come back after the election?
THE WITNESS: I was crying and I just kept telling him, I -- you know, I didn't really want to leave and why did I have to leave and wasn't there -- you know, weren't there other openings rather than me having to go to the Pentagon because he had --

7/98D

Do you want me to get into a little bit about what was said there?

MR. EMMICK: If it will help answer the question, sure.

A JUROR: Yes. Please.

THE WITNESS: Okay. There had been problems with my supervisor, Jocelyn Jolley, and so when I was called in to Tim's office, I had thought he was -- he had just spoken with Jocelyn and I thought he was going to tell me they had fired Jocelyn and instead he told me that they were -- that for reasons having to do with some of the workload not -- things with the letters from the Office of Management and Budget, that they had to blow up -- quote-unquote, blow up the correspondence office and they were eliminating my position.

My transfer had nothing to do with my work, I shouldn't see this as a negative thing. He told me I was too sexy to be working in the East Wing and that this job at the Pentagon where I'd be writing press releases was a sexier job.

And I was crying and --

BY MR. EMMICK:

Q What do you think he meant by "too sexy"?

A I think he meant that -- he -- I think he was trying to -- you know, trying to conceal the fact that -- you know, that I now know, the real reason I was being transferred. And so I think he was trying to not maybe anger me. And thought that somehow by -- maybe he thought I'd think that was a complement.

A JUROR: Did you think he was patronizing you?

THE WITNESS: A little bit. Yeah. That's a good way to put it. I -- I just -- I just remember thinking that I was -- I was never going to see the President again and that all of a sudden that this -- you know, the end of this -- this relationship.

And I kept -- I've always sort of -- I'm the kind of person that always thinks that I can fix everything and so it was kind of this -- feeling of wait, this train's going too fast and I can't stop it and that it had already passed and -- and -- so when Tim said that, I think he sort of said that -- I don't think he meant to say that. I think that was probably more than he was supposed to say.

A JUROR: Thank you.

BY MR. EMMICK:

Q Going back again to the 17th of December when the President called you and let you know about the witness list, you said he used the phrase, "It broke my heart to see you on the witness list." What was your reaction when he said that?

A I believed him. I think I also --

Q You thought he was being sincere?

A JUROR: Can I ask another follow-up question?

MR. EMMICK: Sure.

A JUROR: Because you had nothing to do with formulating this witness list, why do you think it breaks his heart, that your name was on there? Because you're innocent of having formulated this list. Do you have -- or in your opinion, what is it that hurt him?

THE WITNESS: I think it was the idea that -- that -- this was going to -- that this was going to be a bad thing for me. I mean, if you imagine what's happened now hadn't happened and let's just say the Paula Jones thing had gone ahead and I had somehow been dragged into that, just being associate with it and it being difficult and maybe he -- maybe it was going to seriously alter any kind of friendship or relationship that we had, you know?

BY MR. EMMICK:

Q I want to ask a question about computer e-mails or files. Did you arrange for the deletion of files or e-mails that might have related to you and the President?

A Did I arrange?

Q Or did you delete them. Sorry.

A Yes, I did.

Q Okay. Did you ask Linda Tripp if she would delete e-mails relating to the President?

A Yes.

Q Did you speak with someone at the Department of

Defense in order to learn something about those deletions or to make sure that they would be more longstanding?

A Not about deletions.

Q Okay. Well, what was it that you spoke with him about?

A I asked him -- I asked Floyd, I think it is, if -- if -- sort of how easily someone could break into the computers. And I couldn't imagine how I had come to this witness -- come to be on this witness list, so one of the things I thought was maybe someone had broken into my computer and was reading my e-mails. And he told me that that was really difficult.

And then I asked him about -- then with the thought in mind of getting rid of the e-mails, I asked him what the sort of saving procedure was with the e-mails. I know at the White House, they back them up and put them in the archive forever and he told me that at the Pentagon, they sort of stay on the server for four weeks and then they're dumped into e-mail heaven or something.

Q All right. Did you ever ask Catherine Allday Davis to delete e-mails that you had sent relating to the President?

A No.

Q At any time, did you create anything like a spreadsheet that contained on it information relating to your relationship with the President?

A Yes.

Q Okay. Tell us about that.

A Linda and I had been talking and she had been talking about she's really good at coming up with patterns of things or -- I think that was the word she used.

And so she was wanting to see -- you know, I think in an effort to aid her in trying to figure out what the pattern of my relationship with the President was, I made a stupid spreadsheet on Microsoft Excel that just had the -- the numbered days of the month and the months and determined on what day was there a phone call or did I see him or see him at an event or something like that. So --

Q Is that something that you ultimately printed out and showed to her?

A Yes.

Q I take it that was on the DOD computer?

A Yes.

Q Were the entries that you made, would they have revealed that you were talking about Clinton?

A No.

Q Okay. Did you ever have an extra copy of that -- let's call it a spreadsheet?

A No.

Q Did you save the file of the spreadsheet?

A No. I don't believe so.

Q All right. Going back also to the night of the 17th, December 17th, just so that we can get clear on the date of that, it was at 2:30 in the morning. Is it literally on the 17th or is it --

A Nineteen -- eighteen -- it is literally the morning, 2:30 in the morning of the 17th. So, yes.

Q Okay. Good. When the President gave you the Vancouver bear on the 28th, did he say anything about what it means?

A Mm-hmm.

Q What did he say?

A I think he -- I believe he said that the bear is the -- maybe Indian symbol for strength, just -- you know, and to be strong like a bear.

Q And did you interpret that as be strong in your decision to continue to conceal the relationship?

A No.

MR. EMMICK: All right. Any follow-up on that?

MS. WIRTH: Can I ask one question?

MR. EMMICK: Sure.

BY MS. WIRTH:

Q Did he say something like "This is when you need to be strong," or "This is for when you need to be strong"? Beyond saying that it was a symbol of strength?

A I think he -- he held it and he said, you know, "You can hold onto this when you need to be strong."

MS. WIRTH: Thank you.

BY MR. EMMICK:

Q What I'd like to do is ask you about a passage from the proffer and I'm looking at page 5.

A Okay.

Q And you'll see at the bottom, and I'll read the passage, this is relating to the meeting on the 19th, just after you've gotten the subpoena, meeting with Vernon Jordan, and what the passage says is "Possibly later in that meeting, but more probably the next meeting," I assume that's a reference to the 22nd?

A Correct.

Q "Ms. Lewinsky tried to make it clear to Mr. Jordan that she in fact did have a physically intimate relationship with the President." And then let's go to the next page. It says, "Ms. Lewinsky made it clear she intended to deny the sexual relationship with the President."

So I guess what I want to talk about is the portion of the passage on page 5.

A Mm-hmm.

Q Tell us how you tried to make it clear to Mr. Jordan that you had a physically intimate relationship with the President.

A I think by mentioning the phone sex.

Q I see. All right. Any other way that you tried to make it clear to him?

A Not that I remember.

Q All right. And then is it your recollection now that it was on the 22nd that you were trying to make this clear to Mr. Jordan?

A Yes.

Q As opposed to the 19th?

A Yes.

MR. EMMICK: Any other follow-up on that?

BY MS. IMMERGUT:

Q Ms. Lewinsky, how did you make it clear to him that you intended to deny the relationship with the President on the 23rd? Excuse me. The 22nd.

A This is, I think, as I mentioned to you guys before, this is -- I don't have a memory of this. I know when I wrote this I was telling the truth, so I'm sure I did do this, but I don't remember.

MR. WISENBERG: Ms. Lewinsky --

Mike, do you mind if I ask some questions?

MR. EMMICK: Go right ahead.

BY MR. WISENBERG:

Q I think, you can correct me if I'm wrong, you've done it previously today, so I'm sure you will again if I am,

7/98D

you told us when we first met with you in the proffer meeting that you couldn't specifically remember that item. Is that correct?

A Yes.

Q And I think you said you couldn't specifically remember any more of the item that Mike just read to you on the bottom of the previous page about the physically intimate relationship.

A Right.

Q But that you had no doubt that it's true. Is that correct?

A I was being truthful in my proffer. Yes.

Q And the proffer, written proffer, is accurate. Is that correct?

A Yes.

Q But -- and I think you also said you feel some -- I don't know if this is the reason you don't remember it, but you have expressed to us that you feel some guilt about Vernon Jordan. Is that correct?

A Mm-hmm.

Q That's a yes?

A Yes.

Q Okay. Can you tell us why that is?

A He was the only person who did what he said he was going to do for me and -- in getting me the job. And when I met with Linda on the 13th, when she was wearing a wire, and even in subsequent or previous conversations and subsequent conversations, I attributed things to Mr. Jordan that weren't true because I knew that it had leverage with Linda and that a lot of those things that I said got him into a lot of trouble and I just -- he's a good person and --

Q Is one example of -- and then I'll leave this topic, is one example of one of the things you told Linda that isn't true, "I told Vernon Jordan no job, no affidavit"? Something along those lines?

A Yes. Because Linda made me promise her that on the 9th.

Q Okay. Of January?

A Of January.

MR. WISENBERG: Okay.

THE FOREPERSON: Do you need a minute?

THE WITNESS: I'm okay. Thanks.

A JUROR: I'm a little confused. When you said that you said certain things because you know Linda had the mike, right?

THE WITNESS: Oh, I didn't know Linda had the mike. I now know that she was wearing a wire.

A JUROR: Okay. But so why would you say these things about Mr. Jordan that were not true? What was the reason?

THE WITNESS: Because -- I had -- from some of my conversation with Linda, I started to think that she was a little bit jealous that Mr. Jordan was helping me get a job in New York and that I was leaving the Pentagon and that -- she had remarked one time that -- that, you know, Mr. Jordan who is the most powerful, you know, man in this city got me my attorney and she -- she thinks that she only had -- you know, this dinky attorney or something like that.

And I was -- I was so desperate for her to -- I was -- for her to not reveal anything about this relationship that I used anything and anybody that I could think of as leverage with her. I -- her, the President, my mom, everybody. I mean, not her, but Mr. Jordan, the President, my mom. Anybody that I thought would have any kind of influence on her, I used.

Does that answer your question?

A JUROR: Well, it doesn't. I guess what I'm trying to figure out, okay, is what was that going to accomplish? Was that going to make her -- what?

THE WITNESS: Well, specifically, with the statement about I won't sign the affidavit until I get the job, is that I had a conversation with Linda, which we'll probably get to --

MR. EMMICK: I hope.

THE WITNESS: Oh. On January 9th and in that

conversation, she had told me she had changed her mind, she was going to be vague on the truth about Kathleen Willey and then she told me -- at that point, I had told her I hadn't signed an affidavit when I had and I told I didn't have a job yet and I knew I was probably going to be getting a job that day.

And she said, "Monica, promise me you won't sign the affidavit until you get the job. Tell Vernon you won't sign the affidavit until you get the job because if you sign the affidavit before you get the job, they're never going to give you the job."

And I didn't want her to think that I had gone ahead and done anything without her and that I was leaving her in the dark. I wanted her to feel that -- sort of Linda and myself against everyone else because I felt like I needed to hold her hand through this in order to try to get her to do what I wanted, essentially.

BY MR. EMMICK:

Q We can get into that in more detail when we talk about the 13th.

A Okay.

Q Why don't we do the following. I wanted to ask some -- rather than just jumping into the 31st which is a Vernon Jordan meeting, why don't we ask some questions about which of your gifts to the President you have ever seen in the White House itself, either in the dining room or the study or the Oval Office generally.

A Does that include gifts that I gave him that I've seen him wear?

Q All right. Well, let's just start with the things that you've seen in the area itself.

A Okay. Okay. I -- can I go through -- just go through the list?

Q Sure.

A That would probably be easier. On page 6, I've seen the two little books.

Q Two little books?

A The "Oy Vey" book, which is jokes and the little golf book.

Q Do you remember when you saw those books?

A Yes. On -- I think it was November 13th.

Q Zadilla day?

A Zadilla day.

Q All right.

A I saw a copy of the Washington Post ad that I had given him in a book on his desk.

Q You gave him a smallish copy of the --

A I gave him an actual copy that I cut out from one of the papers and I glued it into a little cardboard thing.

Q And where did you see it on his desk.

A It was inside a book.

Q And the book was on the desk in the study?

A Yes.

MS. WIRTH: Mike, could I ask a question?

BY MS. WIRTH:

Q Did you see the ad in a particular book?

A Yes.

Q Which one?

A "Vox."

Q Okay. And was that on the desk in the study?

A Yes.

Q And was "Oy Vey" on the desk in the study?

A Yes.

Q What about the little golf book?

A I think it was. I -- I -- I'm not 100 percent sure it was a golf book, I'm 99.9 percent sure.

Q And about how many books does the President have on his desk in the study?

A He has maybe about 15 or 20 little books that are on his desk and he has more books over there and more books on the bookshelf.

MS. WIRTH: Thank you.

BY MR. EMMICK:

Q How about the opener?

A Right. The -- right. The wooden frog letter

opener that I gave him. I'm just trying to go through this way, so --

Q All right. Go ahead.

A I saw the -- well, I lent him the book "Disease and Misrepresentation."

Q And did you see it in the Oval Office somewhere?

A No, I saw it in the back study.

Q The back study? And that would have been on page 8, I believe?

A Right. And then the letter opener that I was mentioning a moment ago was on page 9. I saw the antique paperweight.

Q Okay. Where is it that you saw the opener?

A It was on top of -- I think it's a cigar box on his desk in the back office. I saw the antique --

BY MS. IMMERGUT:

Q When did you see that, Monica?

A Zadilla day. I saw the antique paperweight on his -- he has a collection of antique political memorabilia in the dining room on top of sort of a chest sort of thing, and I saw that there on -- I think on December 6th or December 28th.

BY MR. EMMICK:

Q Okay. Do you remember which?

A No. I saw the standing cigar holder, I think, it

was on his Oval Office desk. Or it might have been in the back. I think it was on the Oval Office desk. On the 28th of December. And that's it.

Q All right. Let's turn our attention to the 31st of December. You had indicated earlier that at some point you started to get more and more concerned about Linda Tripp and whether she was going to rat on you, I think was the way you put it. What did you do with respect to Vernon Jordan in that concern?

A Since Linda had stopped returning my calls around the 24th of December, by the end of December, I realized I'd kind of better come up with some sort of strategy as to how -- if Linda Tripp comes out and says all these things where this is coming from and try to prepare the President.

And since I couldn't find it within myself to bring it up to him directly, I called Mr. Jordan and told him that I needed to talk to him, I had some concerns about something.

Q When did you call him?

A I think it was the 30th of December.

Q Did you speak with him directly?

A I think I might have spoken with his -- with his secretary.

Q Do you remember her name?

A Gail. There was another one, too, but I've forgot

her name. And I met Mr. Jordan for breakfast on -- no, not Sunday but December 31st, the morning of the 31st, at the Park Hyatt Hotel.

And in the course of the conversation I told him that I had had this friend, Linda Tripp, who was sort of involved in the Paula Jones case with, I think, the Kathleen Willey stuff. I don't know if I went into that much detail, but I did tell him her name.

And I said that she was my friend, that I didn't really trust her -- I used to trust her, but I didn't trust her any more and I was a little bit concerned because she had spent the night at my home a few times and I thought -- I told Mr. Jordan, I said, well, maybe she's heard some -- you know -- I mean, maybe she saw some notes lying around.

And Mr. Jordan said, "Notes from the President to you?" And I said, "No, notes from me to the President." And he said, "Go home and make sure they're not there."

Q What did you understand him to mean when he said, "Go home and make sure they're not there"?

A I thought that meant that -- to go home and search around and if there are any copies of notes or anything that I sent or drafts, to throw them away.

Q Did you have any further discussions with Mr. Jordan about Mr. Clinton and the Clinton's marital status?

A Yes. After breakfast, in the car, I asked Mr. Jordan if he thought the President would always be married to the First Lady and he said, "Yes, as he should be." And gave me a quote from the Bible. And a few -- maybe a minute or so later, he said, "Well, maybe you two will have an affair when he's out of office."

And at that point, I was shocked because I thought Mr. Jordan had known that we had already had this affair and I think I alluded to this earlier today when I saying until the 31st I didn't know, and I said, "Well, we already had an affair. We just -- you know, we didn't have sex or did everything but sex," or something like that. And he just kind of went -- one of those "Mmmph." You know --

Q A grunt?

A And didn't really respond to me. So I took that as my cue to drop the subject. But -- so --

MR. EMMICK: All right.

BY MR. WISENBERG:

Q What did you eat for breakfast at the Hyatt?

A I had an -- I had an egg white omelet.

BY MR. EMMICK:

Q What did he have?

A I think he had cereal with yogurt.

BY MR. WISENBERG:

Q Do you remember who paid?

A Mr. Jordan. He's a gentleman.

Q Do you remember how he paid?

A No.

Q Has anyone from the Office of Independent Counsel or the FBI shown you any paperwork of any kind with reference to that breakfast?

A No.

MR. WISENBERG: Thank you.

BY MR. EMMICK:

Q Let's turn back to the topic of gifts.

A Okay.

Q Did you give a gift to the President in early January?

A Yes, I did. Well, I guess -- I gave it to Ms. Currie for the President.

Q What was the gift?

A It was an antique book on the various presidents with sketchings. A history book.

Q Where did you buy the book?

A At an antique bookstore in Georgetown.

Q Was there anything along with the book?

A A note.

Q Okay. What kind of a note?

A An embarrassing mushy note.

Q Okay. Did you attach the note to the book in some

way?

A I don't really -- I might have put it inside the book or I may have put it outside. I wrapped the book.

Q And how did you try to get this book to the President?

A I called Betty over the weekend and asked her if I could drop it off so I didn't have to waste money on a courier.

Q And when you say "the weekend," are you talking about that first weekend in January?

A Yes.

Q Do you remember if it was Saturday, the 3rd, or Sunday, the 4th?

A I believe it was Sunday the 4th.

Q You called Betty and what again did you say to Betty?

A I don't -- I think I said something -- you know, "I have something for him, could I drop it off to you so I don't have to waste money on a courier."

Q Okay. And what did you do?

A So she said that was fine. So I went over to her home and --

Q Had you been to her home before?

A Yes.

Q Had you ever dropped anything off at her home for

the President before?

A No.

Q What did you do when you got her home?

A Well, she was sitting on the porch, so we sat on the porch and I gave her the package and we talked for a little while.

Q Did you talk at all about the gift that was for the President?

A We might have. I might have mentioned it. Probably did. I'm not --

Q Was there any discussion about the fact that the President was himself under subpoena and was going to be deposed in a couple of weeks?

A No.

Q Were you concerned about giving him a book, a gift, under those circumstances?

A No.

Q Okay. Did you ever talk to the President and learn whether he got the book and the note?

A Yes, I did.

Q All right. When did you talk with him and learn about that?

A On the 5th of January. I think it was the 5th of January. You know -- can I just --

Q Sure. Take a look.

A Yes. It was the 5th of January.

Q And that would have been Monday?

A Correct.

Q Why don't we try to proceed through Monday because Monday started with a meeting with you and Frank Carter and then there was the phone call afterwards, so let's go first to the meeting with Frank Carter.

A Okay.

Q Feel free.

A I met with Mr. Carter to go over in more detail where we stood at that point with the Paula Jones case and he went over -- he went over what was going to happen if an affidavit wasn't going to satisfy the Paula Jones attorneys and I did have to get deposed and what the room looks like, what -- you know -- everything that happens in a deposition and he threw out a bunch of different questions.

You know, they'll probably ask you who your first grade teacher was and they'll ask you -- you know, some things and then some of the questions that concerned me were questions like "How did you get your job at the Pentagon?" And how did -- you know, and he said, "They'll ask things like did you find out about the opening on a bulletin board or did someone tell you about it? Who recommended you for the job? How did everything get facilitated for the transfer?"

7/98D

And that alarmed me because I didn't really know how to necessarily answer that. I didn't express that to Mr. Carter, but --

Q Well, when you say you didn't know how to answer it, what do you mean, you didn't know how to answer it?

A Well, I was concerned that if I said in -- you know, if possibly that was going to come up in the affidavit which hadn't bee written yet or in a deposition, if I had said -- mentioned certain people that had been involved in helping me secure the position over at the Pentagon or forcing me to go there, really, that because these people didn't like me, if they were ever questioned by the Paula Jones attorneys, that they might say something contrary to what I said just because -- to get me in trouble because they didn't like me.

So I was concerned that -- I wanted to -- I wanted to have some sort of feeling of protection, that -- you know, that I wouldn't be screwed over by these people.

Q Were you concerned that they were going to say nasty things about you or were you concerned that they were going to say things that might ultimately lead to the revealing of the relationship in some way?

A No, I was just concerned that they would purposefully say something different from whatever I said just because they had the opportunity to screw me.

I mean -- not -- never mind.

Q Okay.

A To cause trouble for me. How's that?

Q Did you discuss with Mr. Carter the affidavit that you were considering?

A Yes.

Q What did you talk about?

A I think he -- he said he would work on a draft and he'd get a draft of the affidavit to me.

Q Okay. At the time, did you want anyone else to review that affidavit before you ultimately signed it?

A At first, I didn't think about it, but then I did. I decided I wanted Mr. Jordan to look at it.

Q All right. Why did you want Mr. Jordan to look at it?

A I think I felt that -- that he being the President's best friend and having a -- a clearer understanding of my relationship with the President than Mr. Carter did, that I just would feel that it sort of had been blessed.

MR. EMMICK: Okay.

BY MS. IMMERGUT:

Q And would that be blessed by the President as well?

A Yes, I that's what I -- I mean, I -- I think I felt that -- excuse me. That, you know, if Mr. Jordan thought something was okay, that I'm sure the President would think it was fine.

MS. IMMERGUT: Okay.

BY MR. EMMICK:

Q Did you discuss the subpoena and the items that might be responsive to the subpoena anymore? I think you had talked about it earlier.

A You know, there's been a little bit of confusion for me when I gave Mr. Carter those items, so it's possible.

Q All right. You mentioned that Mr. Carter asked you some hard questions about like how you got your job. Did you want to talk with anybody about that afterwards?

A Yes. I placed a call to Ms. Currie and asked her to let the President know I needed to speak to him and it was important.

Q Did you say anything to Ms. Currie about signing something?

A I think I might have sort of said, just, you know, hoping that she might pass that along, I think.

BY MS. IMMERGUT:

Q Do you remember saying that you wanted to or needed to speak to the President before you signed something?

A I think so.

BY MR. EMMICK:

Q All right. Did you explain to her what you meant

when you said that?
A No.
Q Okay.
A I'm pretty sure I did say that to Ms. Currie.
Q Did you finally get in contact or did you at some time shortly thereafter get in contact with Mr. Clinton?
A Yes.
Q How did that happen?
A Ms. Currie called me back a few hours later and then she put the President on.
Q Before we talk about what the President and you talked about, as background, I guess, were you upset or in a mood that day from a photograph you had seen?
A Oh, you really want to embarrass me, don't you?
Q Well, I just want to get the mood right.
A I had been peeved by the photo and the footage that was in the media from the President and First Lady being romantic on their holiday vacation. So I felt a little bit like -- I -- I was just annoyed.
I was jealous and it just seemed sort of something he had never -- an aspect of their relationship that he had never really revealed to me and it made me feel bad.
So I was -- I don't know if anyone here has ever done this, where you -- you're annoyed with someone so you kind of want to pick a fight with them and you want to be a

little bit hostile so that -- you know, you just rub them the wrong way.

Q Okay.

A So that was how I was feeling.

Q That's how you exhibited the annoyance or anger or whatever.

A Mm-hmm.

Q Okay. Tell us about your conversation with the President.

A Because of those feelings, I was a little bit curt with him and so I told him that I had had this meeting with Mr. Carter and that I was concerned, you know, from the questions he asked me that if, you know, if I at some point had to kind of -- under oath, answer these questions and in the course of answering a question I mentioned people at the White House who didn't like me, that somehow I would end up getting -- they'd get me in trouble.

And so he -- so when I told him the questions about my job at the Pentagon, he said, "Well, you could always say that the people in Legislative Affairs got it for you or helped you get it."

And there was a lot of truth to that. I mean, it was a generality, but that was -- I said, "Well, that's a good idea. Okay."

Q Was there any discussion of the book?

A Yes. I had asked him if he had gotten the book that I sent with Betty and he said he did, he really liked it, and then -- I had written him this -- this note that I had sort of -- wrote -- I think it was Saturday night when I got home from the movies and I had seen the Titanic that weekend and it just was -- just brought up a lot of feelings and thoughts for me that I put on -- that I put on paper.

And so I sort of said something about, "Oh, well, I shouldn't have written some of those things in the note." Because I was angry about seeing the picture with them romantic, it made me feel really stupid for having sent this letter.

And he said, "Yeah, you shouldn't have written some of those things." Kind of along the ways he had said before, about not writing particular things on paper, you know, putting things to paper. So --

Q About how long was your telephone call with the President?

A Maybe 15 minutes.

MR. EMMICK: Anything else on that?

THE WITNESS: I see you trying not to laugh.

MR. EMMICK: What about break-wise? Where are we? Is this a good time for a break or do we want to keep going?

THE FOREPERSON: Yes. Yes.

MR. EMMICK: All right.

THE FOREPERSON: I would say only five minutes.

MR. EMMICK: All right. Five minutes it is.

THE FOREPERSON: A five-minute break. I'm sorry, guys. Okay.

(Witness excused. Witness recalled.)

MR. EMMICK: Madam Foreperson, do we have a quorum?

THE FOREPERSON: Yes, we do.

MR. EMMICK: Are there any unauthorized persons present?

THE FOREPERSON: There are none.

Monica, it's my responsibility --

THE WITNESS: I know.

THE FOREPERSON: -- to remind you you're still under oath.

THE WITNESS: Okay. Thank you.

BY MR. EMMICK:

Q We just finished talking about January 5th. Why don't we turn to January 6th. On January 6th, did you pick up a copy of the draft affidavit from Frank Carter?

A Yes, I did.

Q You had mentioned earlier that you wanted Vernon Jordan to look at it. Did you contact him?

A Yes, I did.

Q Did you speak with him personally or did you speak with someone on his staff?

A I don't really remember.

Q And did you try to get a copy of the draft affidavit to Mr. Jordan?

A Yes. I dropped off a Xerox copy in his office.

Q In his office?

A In the lobby of his -- of Akin Gump.

Q Did you make any arrangements to contact him in order to talk about the draft affidavit?

A I believe -- I think I remember Gail saying he was in a meeting and something about 4:00, that he was going to be out and he would call me at 4:00.

Q Did you talk with him on the 6th about the draft affidavit?

A Yes, I did.

Q All right. Tell us what the two of you talked about.

A I had had some concerns from looking at the draft affidavit and addressed those concerns with him and he agreed.

Q What were the nature of the concerns, if you remember?

A I think that the general concern was that Mr. Carter had inserted some information about me having possibly been alone with the President for a few minutes, bringing him a letter in Legislative Affairs.

Q Would it help you if I showed you a copy of the draft with some of your handwriting on it?

A Oh. Yes.

MR. EMMICK: I'm placing before the witness what is marked as Grand Jury Exhibit ML-3.

(Grand Jury Exhibit No. ML-3 was marked for identification.)

BY MR. EMMICK:

Q Can you tell us what this is?

A Sure. Do the grand jurors have a copy of this?

Q They do.

A Okay. This is a draft of my affidavit that Mr. Carter drew up based on his conversations with me.

Q And the handwriting on it? Whose is that?

A That's my handwriting.

Q There's also some underlining and some scratch-outs.

A Mm-hmm.

Q Did you do all of that?

A Yes.

Q Can you remember looking at that now what the two of you talked about?

A I think that -- I think that it was -- I think the two main things were this last sentence in paragraph 6 and the -- the concern was, for me at least, was not wanting to give the Paula Jones attorneys any thought about why they might need to want to talk to me. So if I had mentioned that I had been in there alone, it would kind of make them think, oh, well, what happened and did he proposition or blah, blah, blah.

And then the second thing was in the -- towards the end of paragraph 8 on page 2, the idea of with crowds of other people, I think to me was too far from the fake truth?

Q Okay.

A Does that -- is that clear? Sort of -- that that seemed to be too out of the realm of possibility, so --

Q Too implausible?

A Exactly. Thank you. So I believe that, you know, that this statement, "There were other people present on all of these occasions," was something that I discussed with Mr. Jordan.

Q Did he agree with the suggestions or thoughts that you had on those two passages?

A Yes, I believe so.

Q Was there any discussion with Mr. Jordan about the portion of paragraph 8 saying that there was no sexual relationship?

A No.

Q At any time, did Mr. Jordan say that he didn't want to speak to you about the affidavit?

A No.

Q How long was your conversation with Mr. Jordan?

A I don't remember. Not long. We may have also talked about job stuff, too. But --

Q All right, then. Let's turn our attention to the next day, which is the 7th. That's the day when you finalized and signed the affidavit. Is that right?

A Yes.

Q And you notarized it under penalty of perjury.

A Yes.

MR. EMMICK: I believe you have -- this is the final version and it is Grand Jury Exhibit ML-4.

(Grand Jury Exhibit No. ML-4 was marked for identification.)

BY MR. EMMICK:

Q I'm placing that before you.

A Okay.

Q And it says "Affidavit of Jane Doe No. 6" at the top and it has your signature, right?

A Mm-hmm.

Q When you spoke with Frank Carter that morning in order to finalize the affidavit, do you remember what changes were made?

A When I spoke with him before I arrived at his office or in his office?

Q Either time.

A I believe that I sort of dictated to him the changes -- I think that's possible or I gave them to him in person, I don't really remember. Mr. Carter had prepared three different versions of the affidavit for the significant portion related to this case, I guess, they were all denying sexual relations, all three of them. And we discussed various things about it and eventually decided on this affidavit.

Q All right. Let me ask you a straightforward question. Paragraph 8 at the start says, "I have never had a sexual relationship with the President." Is that true?

A No.

Q All right. The next logical follow-up is, and maybe it's self-evident, but why were you willing to say something that was false under penalty of perjury?

A I don't think that it's anybody's business.

Q Okay. Let me turn the page for you. At the end of paragraph 8, the statement, "The occasions that I saw the President after I left my employment at the White House in April 1996 were official receptions, formal functions or events related to the U.S. Department of Defense, where I was working at the time. There were other people present on those occasions." That's not correct either, is it?

A No, it's misleading.

Q Okay. In what respect?
A For me, at the time, I said -- well, it doesn't say the only occasions, but it's misleading in that one reading it would assume that the only occasions on which I saw the President were those listed.
Q Right.
A But I did some justifying in signing the affidavit, so --
Q Justifying -- does the word "rationalizing" apply as well?
A Rationalize, yes.
Q All right. All right. On the 7th, after you signed the affidavit, did you keep a copy of the affidavit?
A Yes, I did.
Q Where did you go later on the 7th?
A To New York.
Q Did you take a copy of the affidavit with you?
A Yes.
Q Why?
A If I remember correctly, I was in a rush and I kind of wanted to have it, if I wanted to look it over again or --
Q Why were you going to New York?
A A job interview.
Q Did you have a job interview?
A Yes, I did.

Q Was that the next day?
A Yes.
Q All right. Let's turn our attention to the job interview on the morning of the 8th. Now, was that with McAndrews & Forbes?
A Yes. This is my -- I had -- I mean, just to remind everyone, I had had some job interviews on the 18th of December up in New York at McAndrews & Forbes and Burson-Marsteller. I also took a test on the 30th, I think, of December at Burson-Marsteller and this is now another interview at McAndrews & Forbes on the 8th.
Q Do you remember who you interviewed with that morning?
A Jamie Dernan.
Q How did the interview go?
A Very poorly.
Q Okay. Tell us why it went poorly. What do you mean?
A I think it started off on the wrong foot because I was in a waiting room downstairs and I had thought they would let me know when he was available and I'd go to his office and instead he just walked in unannounced and the interview started, so I was -- I didn't have my wits together at the moment. And I was -- I just was sort of flustered from that moment on. I think everyone can relate to having a bad

interview. Maybe.

Q How long was the interview?

A Maybe 20 minutes.

Q Was that the only interview that morning?

A Yes.

Q What was your reaction afterwards?

A I was upset. I felt horrible. I might have even cried. I was embarrassed. I thought that I had sort of embarrassed Mr. Jordan, I think, in such a bad interview.

Q After having a bad interview like that, did you expect an offer?

A No, I didn't think so. My first interview with McAndrews & Forbes had been really, really good, so I wasn't sure exactly what was going to happen, but I didn't think it was --

Q Not a good sign.

A Correct.

Q What did you do after you had that bad interview?

A At some point, I called Mr. Jordan to just let him know that it had gone poorly.

Q Do you remember whether you placed one call or several calls to try to get a hold of him?

A I'm sure I placed several. It was -- he's difficult to get a hold of.

Q Did you eventually talk to him on the 8th?

A Yes, I did.
Q What did you tell him?
A I told him that it hadn't worked out and that I was asking his advice on whether I should contact Burson-Marsteller or not and that I was concerned that the McAndrews & Forbes hadn't gone well.
Q At the time you were talking to him, were you still upset about the interview?
A I don't really remember. I'm sure I was. It was kind of a depressing thing all day.
Q And did he say what he was going to do because the interview had not gone well?
A Yes.
Q What did he say?
A He said he'd call the chairman. I thought he was kidding.
Q Okay. And did he call you back some time shortly thereafter?
A Yes, he did.
Q About how long after he called -- excuse me. About how long after he said he was going to call the chairman did he call you back? If you remember.
A I don't remember. I don't think it was very long after, but --
Q What did he say when he called back?

A That not to worry -- you know, I don't remember the exact words that he used. The gist of the conversation was that, you know, the were going to call me and everything was going to be okay.

Q Did he say that he had gotten a hold of the chairman or did he mention that at all or --

A I don't remember.

Q Did Revlon or McAndrews & Forbes personnel get a hold of you later after Mr. Jordan called?

A Yes. They called to set up an interview for me with someone directly at Revlon for the next day.

Q Do you remember about when it was that you were called later on the 8th?

A I think it was some time early evening.

Q Early evening?

A Or evening.

Q Were you surprised by the call?

A From having heard from Mr. Jordan, not 100 percent.

Q All right. They set up an interview for the next day?

A Yes.

Q Did you have an interview the next day?

A Yes.

Q Who did you interview with?

A Ellen Seidman.

Q And what was the tone of that interview?
A It went very well. It was --
Q Better than with Jamie Dernan?
A Yes.
Q All right.
A It was a very good interview.
Q Did you interview with others at Revlon as well?
A Yes.
Q Do you remember about how many interviews there were?
A Two others, aside from Ms. Seidman's.
Q And you mentioned that the interviews went well. After the interviews, did you give a call to Vernon to let him know how things were going?
A I think so.
Q Later that day, did you have another call from Revlon?
A From Revlon?
Q Mm-hmm.
A Yes, I did.
Q Tell us about that.
A They sort of informally offered me a position and I informally accepted it.
Q Do you remember who it was you were speaking with at the time?

7/98D

A I believe it was Ellen Seidman.

Q Okay. You made a reference earlier in this grand jury appearance to a conversation you had with Linda Tripp on the 9th.

A Yes.

Q We're now on the 9th and I can tell you would like to talk about this conversation. Tell us about your conversation with Linda Tripp on the 9th. Let's start with when it happened.

A Well, I was returning Linda's call from earlier in the week and I think I made a couple of attempts to get a hold of her at her office and when I did get in touch with her, I told her I was on a pay phone because I was concerned about the phones.

And I just -- I -- I didn't -- I was very distrustful of her at this point, especially when I first got on the phone with her. I didn't really know why we were going to be in touch at this point, from what had happened the few weeks before.

So she started out the conversation, I think, asking me, you know, what was going on with my job stuff and everything and I told her I didn't have a job yet and that I hadn't heard from Betty, the President, or Mr. Jordan since December and I didn't know what was going on and so we were discussing that. And that was not true, obviously.

And then she told me that she had gone up to New York over Christmas to be with -- I think Norma Asness is her name, and that while she was in New York during the holidays she was shopping with Ms. Asness and this other woman on Madison Avenue buying shoes and that this woman had told Linda she was really savvy and Linda should move to New York and get a PR job in New York. Which I thought was a little strange, since I was in the process of moving to New York for a PR job.

That was just one of the indications that made me think she was a little bit jealous of the help I was getting, that I was talking about earlier.

So when we started to discuss the case, she told me that -- that because of this experience she had had in New York, she decided that maybe it would be best for her to be really vague on the truth about Kathleen Willey. You know, she really didn't know anything, she didn't really remember much, and that -- you know, led me to -- and I believe she may have even said directly that she wasn't going to tell about me or that I was -- you know, my understanding of that was that she wasn't even going to mention me and that I was safe.

Q Did this come as a surprise to you?

A Yes, it did.

Q In what way?

A Because she had -- I mean, she had stopped returning my phone calls, we had left everything in a very bad note a few weeks prior to that. So --

In the course of this conversation, when we talked about my job, she said, "Well, Monica -- " Oh. Oh. She asked me what I was going to do in the case and I told her that I was planning on signing an affidavit. Even though I had already signed the affidavit, I didn't want Linda to think that I would have gone ahead and done such a bold thing without her approval.

So she made -- that's when, as I mentioned earlier, she made me promise her that I wouldn't sign the affidavit until I got the job. She also went into this whole long story about her friend --

Am I getting into too much detail?

MR. EMMICK: Close.

JURORS: No. No.

MR. EMMICK: Okay.

THE WITNESS: Okay. All right. She told me about her -- this friend, I don't remember her name, but she's this -- she's an Indian woman who Linda goes to the gym with and that this Indian woman had gone to a psychic and the psychic had essentially said that one of her friends was in imminent danger having to do with the words she would speak.

So that that led Linda to believe, you know, along with this event in New York that she should -- you know, she's kind of going to go the good route -- well, what I considered the good route in the Paula Jones case. And it was really based on this conversation that I had with her and this sort of change that I agreed to meet with Linda on the 13th of January.

BY MR. EMMICK:

Q Then let's go to the 13th of January. Let me first cover some of the job-related items. On the 13th, did you get a formal offer from Revlon?

A Yes, I did.

Q And did you accept that offer?

A Yes, I did.

Q How was the matter left about references or recommendations?

A Well, she -- I can't remember her name, something with a J, I think. The woman in human resources with whom I was dealing about the job offer said, you know, I needed to send her some references, so this had been in -- oh. So I called Betty to ask her to remind the President or to check out for me what Mr. Hilley would say to -- I'm not saying this clearly. I'm sorry.

Q That's all right.

A One of the people that I needed to get a reference

from was John Hilley, who was the head of Legislative Affairs and had been my boss when I was there the latter half of my tenure at the White House. I was concerned that if I put him down as a reference, he might not say flattering things about me.

So I asked -- I had mentioned this to the President on October 11th and he said he'd, you know, make sure everything was okay, so I wanted to -- so I checked with Betty to ask her to kind of find out what was happening, what the status of that was. So --

Q Did you get a message later from Betty on that subject?

A Yes, I did.

Q Okay. What was that message?

A She had me page her and then later I came to find out from her that afternoon that it had been -- I think Mr. Podesta took care of it and that everything would be fine with Mr. Hilley.

Q Now, when the two of you were paging each other on this day, the name Kay was used rather than either Betty or Monica. Where did that name come from?

A This has sort of become a kind of strange area for me. I had not -- and I do not specifically remember discussing with Betty the fact that I had been subpoenaed in the Paula Jones case and anything surrounding that, but sort of I now know from -- from sort of things that I've been reminded of or shown that I must have. And one of them that indicates that to me is this notion that she -- I -- she and I had started -- I suggested that we use sort of the code name Kay in her paging me and in me paging her. And --

Q And where does the name Kay come from?

A Because Betty and I, our first encounter and our first connection was through Walter Kaye.

Q Now, had you and Betty had earlier conversations about the fact that her message indicator, I guess it would be her beeper or her pager?

A Her pager.

Q Her pager.

A Her text message pager.

Q Her text message pager on some occasion might have indicated Monica?

A Yes. There had been -- I think there had been at least one time when Betty's pager had been sitting on her desk when she was in with the President or had stepped away and someone else had picked up her pager when it went off and there was a message from me.

And so from -- you know, Betty kind of covered it, I think, by saying -- or she did actually have another friend named Monica or something or another, but it was -- you know -- Rebecca Cameron was the person who picked up the pager and so it was sort of a -- not a good thing to happen.

Q Why use any fake names, Kay or any other name? What's the reason you've got to use fake names at this time?

A I was beyond paranoid. I mean, I -- and obviously in denial. I think the -- I could not understand how I had been dragged into the Paula Jones case and so I was very wary of everything.

Q What did Betty say, if you can remember, when you suggested that you refer to one another as Kay?

A Okay.

Q Okay. Did she ask why or --

A I don't remember having this conversation with her.

Q All right. Were you also using names to refer to others? For example, the name Mary?

A Yes.

Q Who did Mary refer to?

A Linda.

Q And why were you using the name Mary to refer to Linda?

A Because that's what she chose.

Q And why were you using any name other than Linda to refer to Linda?

A Because Linda and Betty were the two people who paged me that were involved -- you know, somehow fell into this circle of the Paula Jones story. Is that -- it's not clear. I'm sorry. Okay.

Q When you were speaking with Linda about the President, did you sometimes refer to the President as "her" rather than "him"?

A Linda? No. I don't believe so.

BY MS. IMMERGUT:

Q So that was Betty?

A Yes.

BY MR. EMMICK:

Q Okay. And why did you use "her" to refer to the President?

A I believe that that was only in pages to her and it was just -- you know, I knew that the WAVES -- from having worked at the White House, I knew that people had access to the WAVES pages, let alone that someone types them, so it just was another measure of caution that I used throughout.

Q All right.

A I don't think I ever referred to the President on Betty's pages.

Q When we were talking earlier about your clarifying whether John Hilley would give you a recommendation, you indicated that you had a page from Betty. Does it refresh your recollection about what the page said if I were to read the following?

We have a page indicating that it says, "Will know something soon, Kay." Does that remind you about any pages that you got from Betty?

A Yes, I think I mentioned earlier that she paged me and then I talked to her later that day and found out about John Hilley.

Q All right. Did you -- at some point, did you send to Revlon a letter giving them the two recommendations, one of which was John Hilley?

A Yes.

Q Do you remember when that was?

A I believe I faxed it on the 14th of January.

Q So that would be the next day.

A Correct.

BY MR. WISENBERG:

Q Pardon me. Were they recommendations or references? Just as a technical matter, in other words, were they names or were they actual letters of recommendation?

A Oh. They were references, then.

BY MR. EMMICK:

Q All right. Let's go back to the 13th for just a moment because you met with Linda Tripp that day, I think you said, on the 9th you had --

A I also met with Mr. Jordan.

Q Okay. All right. Okay. Well, let's go back to Mr. Jordan, then.

A Well, I -- I mean, I was just thinking about the day. I'm sorry.

Q No, that's fine. That's fine.

A Just I stopped in to see him for five minutes, to thank him for getting me the job, and I gave him a tie and a pocket square.

MR. EMMICK: Okay.

BY MS. IMMERGUT:

Q Did you ever provide Mr. Jordan with a signed copy of the affidavit?

A I did not provide him with a copy. No.

Q Do you know whether or not he ever received a copy?

A I believe I showed him a copy. I don't know that he received a copy.

BY MR. EMMICK:

Q On this same meeting on the 13th?

A I -- I -- you know, I have to say I know I brought the copy with me to show him and I may have said, you know, "Do you want to see it?" And I think he may have not even -- I think he may have said, you know, "I don't need to see it." Or -- I --

BY MS. IMMERGUT:

Q So you don't specifically recall handing it over to

him or even showing it to him specifically.

A No.

Q But you brought it for him to --

A I did bring it.

MS. IMMERGUT: Correct.

BY MR. EMMICK:

Q All right. So that's the Vernon Jordan part of the 13th.

A Right.

Q What about the meeting with Linda Tripp?

A It was long. I was -- I was very nervous. I was wary of her. I actually thought she might have a tape recorder with her and had looked in her bag when she had gone up to the restroom. I told her a whole bunch of lies that day.

Q What were you trying to accomplish in meeting with her?

A I was trying to -- I was trying to make Linda continue to feel comfortable that she and I were sort of on the -- that we were on the same side, we were on the right side.

We -- and that -- when I had agreed to meet with her, I thought we were going to go over kind of her strategy for what she was going to do in the case and then once we got together, she kind of started wavering about what she wanted to do and then -- so I just was using everything I knew to try to convince her that -- that this is the right thing to do.

Q I think you mentioned earlier that you told her lies.

A Yes.

Q What lies do you have in mind?

A I mean, I think -- throughout that month of December, after I knew she was subpoenaed, there were various things that I think I said that were untrue, but I specifically remember from this meeting the thing that I had -- what I said to Linda was, "Oh, you know, I told -- I told Mr. Jordan that I wasn't going to sign the affidavit until I got the job." Obviously, which wasn't true.

I told her I didn't yet have a job. That wasn't true. I told her I hadn't signed the affidavit. That wasn't true. I told her that some time over the holidays I had freaked out and my mom took me to Georgetown Hospital and they put me on Paxil. That wasn't true.

I think I told her that -- you know, at various times the President and Mr. Jordan had told me I had to lie. That wasn't true. That's just a small example. Probably some more things about my mom. Linda had an obsession with my mom, so she was a good leverage.

Q Let's turn our attention back to the 14th, then.

On the 14th, the next day?

A Okay.

Q Right.

A Okay.

Q There's three pieces of paper that have come to be referred to as the talking points.

A Yes.

MR. EMMICK: I think we have them marked as Grand Jury Exhibit ML-5.

(Grand Jury Exhibit No. ML-5 was marked for identification.)

BY MR. EMMICK:

Q I'll place them in front of you.

A Okay.

Q And they are three pages. I wonder if you would tell us how those came to be written and on what computer and the like.

A Okay. First of all, they're out of order.

Q Okay.

A So the last page was actually the first page.

Q All right. Well, let's clarify. What is now the first page says "Points to make in affidavit." And the second page says, "The first few paragraphs" at the top. And the third page says, "You're not sure you've been clear." The third page should be the first page?

A Yes.
Q All right. Let's go to first the mechanics of how these got generated.
A Mm-hmm.
Q Were those printed from your printer?
A Yes.
Q Were they typed on your computer?
A Yes.
Q Was anyone present with you when they were typed?
A No.
Q When were they typed?
A On the 14th.
Q Did you talk with anyone in an effort to get assistance editing or writing or getting approval for what is in the talking points?
A No.
Q How did the -- where did you get the ideas that are reflected in the talking points?
A They were based on conversations I've had with Linda from the moment Kathleen Willey and Michael Isikoff ever entered into the picture until the conversations I had with her the morning of the 14th on the phone.
Q Tell me what you mean by that.
A At various times, especially early on, around March or so when -- when Kathleen Willey first came up, Linda

talked about how -- you know, that -- that -- what Kathleen was saying to Michael Isikoff was not true. And so, you know, we had had -- I remember having this discussion with her where we were saying, well, if -- you know, if she's lying to Michael Isikoff, how do you know she didn't lie to you?

Linda said, "Yeah, that's a good point. Maybe she did." You know?

And I said, "Yeah, sure. She could have, you know, smeared her own lipstick and untucked her own blouse."

And Linda said, "Yeah, it's true."

That was very early on and throughout my discussions with Linda, especially when she was saying -- saying things about how to be vague on the Kathleen Willey issue in the Paula Jones case, we had these sorts of discussions.

Q What did you do with the talking points? How did you relay them to Linda Tripp?

A I took a copy of them to her.

Q And how were the arrangements made to give her that copy?

A She had told me she was going to go see her attorney, Kirby, that afternoon and was going to talk to him about signing an affidavit, which is why this was all generated. And so I offered to drive her there so that we could just talk on the way because we -- we had had some time to talk that morning, but not as much as I wanted.

Q Who was driving? You were driving?

A Yes.

Q And Linda has the talking points in her hands?

A I handed them to her in the parking lot of the Pentagon.

Q Did she read them?

A Yes, she did.

Q What was she saying or doing as she was reading them?

A She was going through it and she was sort of reading and going, "Yeah. Mm-hmm. Uh-huh. Well, that's true. Oh, good point."

I think she may have said, "Oh, these are -- this is really -- that's true." You know. "Did you write this?" Sort of a thing.

Q Okay. What did you think would happen after you dropped the talking points off to Linda and then you dropped Linda off? How were things left, I guess is another way to ask that question.

A I believe that it was in the car ride home that she said -- made some comment to me about -- that, well, she -- she feels okay -- and this might have been on the 13th when she said this, she feels okay about, you know, kind of not telling the truth or being vague on the truth when she talks to me, but then when she doesn't talk to me, she -- her mind starts to wander to different things, so I just remember feeling -- oh, like I had to hold her hand through everything and I constantly had to talk to her. So I may have said, "I'll call you tonight" or something like that.

Q Have you ever talked to Bruce Lindsey?

A No. I may have said hello to him in the hall, but I -- but -- just in passing.

Q Did you ever talk with the President about the talking points?

A No.

Q Did you ever talk with anyone at Bob Bennett's firm about the talking points?

A No.

Q Did you ever talk with anyone associated with the White House in any way about the talking points?

A No. And that would include Mr. Jordan.

Q Okay. Let's turn our attention, then, to the next day, which is January 15th. Did Betty call you that day about a call she had received from Mike Isikoff?

A Yes.

Q Okay. Tell us about that telephone call.

A I had learned earlier from my attorney that the Paula Jones people had -- had -- well, I guess my attorney

7/98D

had asked me something about if I had ever received any courier packages from the White House and I hadn't, but I told him I did -- I did send things to Betty and he said, oh, well, he had heard -- I think through -- maybe through Bennett's people -- Mr. Bennett's firm, the attorneys, I'm sorry, I don't mean to be so informal, that there was some issue with these courier -- with a courier service.

So I called the courier service and was able to find out that the records could be subpoenaed and then I spoke with Betty later that day and she told me that -- that Michael Isikoff had called her or had called for her intern and Betty had answered the phone and in the course of that he had asked her about the courier, my sending things to her through a courier.

And that she sort of said she didn't really remember or know what he was talking about and that he'd get back to her. Or she'd get back to him. I'm sorry.

Q And then she called you and related this to you?

A Yes. Yes.

Q What was your reaction to that?

A I was very shocked and very -- feeling very strange, that somehow this was closing in more and I -- I didn't know how they could have gotten this information about the courier because there was -- the first person that I thought of that knew about the courier was Linda and the only other person I thought of was this gentleman in my office who was a Clinton hater, Mark Huffman. So I thought that maybe -- I thought, well, maybe he had been the one who had sort of turned me, trying to cause trouble.

Q All right. What did you and Betty talk about doing in response to the Isikoff calls?

A The President was out of town that day and so I think she said she was going to try to get in touch with the President and I believe that Betty and I may have discussed that, you know, they were -- the courier packages were always sent to her and that some of the things were for her, you know.

Q Did Vernon Jordan come up?

A Yes. I know later -- and I don't know if maybe she mentioned to me earlier in the day that she wanted to try to get in touch with Mr. Jordan, but I do know that -- that later in the evening Betty called me and asked me if I could give her a ride to Mr. Jordan's office because Bob, her husband, had the car that day and it was raining. So --

Q So you drove her to Vernon Jordan's.

A Yes.

Q Describe what happened when you drop her off.

A Well, actually, I parked the car and I decided to wait for her downstairs in the restaurant. I think it's The Front Page. And she went up to Mr. Jordan's office and was there maybe 15, 20 minutes. I'm not very good with time.

Q Why didn't she just take a taxi there? It's a three, four dollar taxi ride up there.

A I don't know.

Q Okay. How long did you wait?

THE WITNESS: You know, I need to use the restroom.

MR. EMMICK: Okay.

THE WITNESS: I'm sorry.

MR. EMMICK: The witness needs a break.

THE FOREPERSON: Yes.

MR. EMMICK: Okay. Thank you.

THE WITNESS: Two minutes.

MR. EMMICK: That's all right.

(Witness excused. Witness recalled.)

MR. WISENBERG: Let the record reflect the witness has reentered the grand jury room.

Madam Foreperson, do we have a quorum?

THE FOREPERSON: Yes.

MR. WISENBERG: Any unauthorized persons present?

THE FOREPERSON: None.

MR. WISENBERG: Anything you want to say?

THE FOREPERSON: Monica Lewinsky, I just wanted to let you know that you are still under oath.

THE WITNESS: Really?

THE FOREPERSON: Mm-hmm. Yes, I mean.

BY MR. WISENBERG:

Q I have, I hope, just one or two questions about your proffer.

A Okay.

Q Your written proffer. Can you grab a hold of that?

A Sure.

Q And what are we calling that? That is ML-1.

A Okay.

(Grand Jury Exhibit No. ML-1 was marked for identification.)

BY MR. WISENBERG:

Q If you'll take a look at page 4, paragraph 4, that has to do with the President's call to you.

A Yes?

Q At two a.m. on the 17th of December telling you, among other things, that you're on the witness list, correct?

A Correct.

Q Going to the middle portion, starting with "When asked." "When asked what to do if she was subpoenaed, the President suggested she could sign an affidavit and try to satisfy their inquiry and not be deposed."

A Mm-hmm.

Q The next sentence says, "In general, Ms. L. should say she visited the White House to see Ms. Currie and, on occasion, when working at the White House, she brought him letters when no one else was around."

Have I read that correctly? Have I read that sentence correctly?

A Yes.

Q Okay. And I think you have earlier described that as a -- maybe not in these exact words, but you saw it as a continuation on his part of the pre-established pattern of things he had said in the past. Is that correct?

A Yes.

Q All right. And would you agree with me that that is -- that if you said that to the Jones people or to anybody else that that is misleading in a sense because it doesn't tell the whole story of what you were doing when you visited the President.

A Yes.

Q Take a look at -- then I would like you to take a look at page 10, I think it's page 10, it's paragraph 10, whatever page it is.

A Okay.

Q Mine's cut off. It's the last -- I think it's the last page.

A Right.

Q I'll read it. "Ms. L. had a physically intimate relationship with the President. Neither the President nor Mr. Jordan or anyone on their behalf asked or encouraged

Ms. L. to lie." I would like you for us to reconcile if you can that statement in your proffer with statements like the ones in paragraph 4 where you talk about specific things the President said or did that were kind of continuations of this pattern.

A Sure. Gosh. I think to me that if -- if the President had not said the Betty and letters cover, let's just say, if we refer to that, which I'm talking about in paragraph 4, page 4, I would have known to use that.

So to me, encouraging or asking me to lie would have -- you know, if the President had said, "Now, listen. You better not say anything about this relationship, you better not tell them the truth, you better not -- "

For me, the best way to explain how I feel what happened was, you know, no one asked or encouraged me to lie, but no one discouraged me either.

Q Okay. So you said what you would have done if the President hadn't said that, but he did say that, what you mentioned in paragraph 4, correct?

A Right.

Q And I guess -- and you had a conversation with him about what to do gifts that you both knew were under subpoena, then you get the call from Betty. Those things happened. When we discussed this on Monday in the proffer session, I think you said something to the effect of or that in paragraph 10 you were being pretty literal. Is that accurate? When you say that no one encouraged you -- told you or encouraged you to lie?

A Yes and no. I mean, I think I also said that Monday that it wasn't as if the President called me and said, "You know, Monica, you're on the witness list, this is going to be really hard for us, we're going to have to tell the truth and be humiliated in front of the entire world about what we've done," which I would have fought him on probably. That was different.

And by him not calling me and saying that, you know, I knew what that meant. So I -- I don't see any -- I don't see any disconnect between paragraph 10 and paragraph 4 on the page. Does that answer your question?

BY MS. IMMERGUT:

Q Did you understand all along that he would deny the relationship also?

A Mm-hmm. Yes.

Q And when you say you understood what it meant when he didn't say, "Oh, you know, you must tell the truth," what did you understand that to mean?

A That -- that -- as we had on every other occasion and every other instance of this relationship, we would deny it.

MR. WISENBERG: That's all I have on that. And

probably not anything else. Maybe.

MS. IMMERGUT: I had a couple of quick questions.

THE WITNESS: Sure.

BY MS. IMMERGUT:

Q Back for just a moment to January 15th with the visit when you took Betty to Vernon Jordan after she had been called by Michael Isikoff.

A Mm-hmm.

Q Did you ever tell Ms. Currie that you had been called by Michael Isikoff?

A No.

Q Had you ever been called by Michael Isikoff before January 15th?

A No. I'm trying to remember now -- I know that I had seen the Newsweek thing light up on my caller ID, but I don't remember if that was around that time or if that was later, once the scandal started.

Q Do you recall any calls from Michael Isikoff that you would have told Betty about, calling about gifts from the President?

A No. Absolutely not.

Q You mentioned, obviously, that you've given the President several gifts. Have you given him any ties?

A Yes.

Q How many ties have you given him, just

approximately?

A Six.

Q Have you had any conversations with the President about wearing your ties?

A Almost all of our conversations included something about my ties.

Q Could you just briefly describe what things that you've said to him and he to you about wearing the ties?

A I used to bug him about wearing one of my ties because then I knew I was close to his heart.

Q And did he ever say anything about -- after he had one of your ties or to alert you when he had worn any of your ties?

A Yes, there were several occasions.

Q And what kind of thing would he say to you?

A "Did you see I wore your tie the other day?"

Q So was he aware based on things you had told him that you would be looking out for when he would wear ties on various occasions?

A Yes.

MS. IMMERGUT: I'd like to show you now what's marked as Grand Jury Exhibits ML-8, 9 and 10.

(Grand Jury Exhibits No. ML-8, ML-9 and ML-10 were marked for identification.)

MS. IMMERGUT: And, unfortunately, I don't have copies yet for the grand jury because we got them at the last --

MR. WISENBERG: I'll pass them around afterwards.

MS. IMMERGUT: Okay. And I'll spread them out for you here.

THE WITNESS: Okay.

BY MS. IMMERGUT:

Q Directing your attention first to ML-8, it's a photograph of the President, obviously. Do you recognize the tie that he's wearing in that photograph?

A Yes, I do.

Q Had you actually seen that on television on June 24, 1998?

A Yes, I did.

Q Do you recall what that's in relation to or what event is being depicted on that photograph?

A He was leaving for China.

Q And now directing your attention to Exhibit 9, do you know what that's a photograph of?

A I don't know where it's from, but it's the President wearing my tie.

Q And this one states it's Monday, July 6, 1998. Do you remember watching any of the media on that date?

A Yes, I do.

Q And do you remember seeing him wearing your tie on that date?

A Yes, I do.

Q Do you remember what event was taking place on that date that he was wearing your tie?

A I don't, but I just saw it says "Medicare costs," so --

Q Okay. And then finally, ML-10. Do you recognize what that's a photograph of?

A Yes.

Q And what is that?

A The President wearing the same tie.

Q And do you know what date that is?

A Date? It was a few days after, he wore the tie when he came back from China, so it's July 9th.

Q Okay. And what -- I guess -- did you reach any conclusions from the fact that he was wearing your tie on those days?

A I -- I -- I think -- the first time he wore the tie, I thought maybe it was a coincidence, but I didn't really think so. And then when he wore it when he came back from China on the 6th, I thought maybe it was a reminder of July 4th, because that had been the first workday after July 4th and we had had a really intense, emotional meeting July 4th of '97. And then when he wore it a few days later,

I thought he's trying to say something. I mean, the President doesn't wear the same tie twice in one week, so -- I didn't know what it meant, but it was some sort of a reminder to me.

MS. IMMERGUT: Okay. Nothing further on that.

BY MR. WISENBERG:

Q This is well after the scandal broke, is that correct?

A Yes.

BY MS. IMMERGUT:

Q This is this summer, right?

A Correct.

BY MR. WISENBERG:

Q You've told us something about seeing a picture of Nelvis, Bayani Nelvis, I think coming to the grand jury.

A Yes.

Q Can you tell us -- and you noticed something about some neckwear he was wearing?

A I think it was on Nel's maybe third appearance or his last appearance. He was wearing the first tie that I ever gave to the President.

Q Did you know that the President had ever given that tie to Mr. Nelvis?

A No.

Q And what is -- can you recall the last time the

President had ever worn that tie?

A No. I didn't see him every day, so -- I mean, I know he -- I know some of the times he wore that tie, but I don't know the last time he wore the tie.

Q Okay. Is there any question in your mind that the President knew that both these ties, the one that we're putting around pictures of and the one that Nel wore to the grand jury, were ties you had given him?

A Not in my mind, but I can't -- I can't answer that.

MR. WISENBERG: Okay.

MR. EMMICK: There's a question? Yes?

A JUROR: Did you know the President after a while gave his ties to the people who worked for him? Did you know that?

THE WITNESS: Yes, I did know that.

MR. WISENBERG: Pardon me just a minute.

(Pause.)

MR. WISENBERG: I'm going to ask the witness to be excused very briefly and we'll possibly call you back in a couple of minutes.

(The witness was excused.)

(Whereupon, at 4:45 p.m., the taking of testimony in the presence of a full quorum of the Grand Jury was concluded.)

* * * * *

CERTIFICATE OF REPORTER

I, Amy K. Rose, the reporter for the United States Attorney's Office, do hereby certify that the witness whose testimony appears in the foregoing pages was first duly sworn by the foreperson or the deputy foreperson of the grand jury when there was a full quorum of the grand jury present; that the testimony of said witness was taken by me and, thereafter, reduced to typewritten form; and that the transcript is a true record of the testimony given by said witness.

Amy K. Rose
Amy K. Rose
Official Reporter

Emily Townsend
Transcriber

Diversified Reporting Services, Inc.
1025 VERMONT AVENUE, N.W. SUITE 1250
WASHINGTON, D.C. 20005
(202) 296-2929

5/98D

THE FOLLOWING IS A COMPRESSED VERSION OF THE PRECEDING DOCUMENT

UNITED STATES DISTRICT COURT
FOR THE DISTRICT OF COLUMBIA

- - - - - - - - - - - - - - - - x

IN RE:

GRAND JURY PROCEEDINGS

- - - - - - - - - - - - - - - - x

Grand Jury Room No. 3
United States District Court
for the District of Columbia
3rd & Constitution, N.W.
Washington, D.C. 20001

Thursday, August 6, 1998

The testimony of MONICA S. LEWINSKY was taken in the presence of a full quorum of Grand Jury 97-2, impaneled on September 19, 1997, commencing at 9:34 a.m., before:

SOLOMON WISENBERG
Deputy Independent Counsel
MICHAEL EMMICK
KARIN IMMERGUT
MARY ANNE WIRTH
Associate Independent Counsel
Office of Independent Counsel
1001 Pennsylvania Avenue, N.W.
Suite 490 North
Washington, D.C. 20004

C O N T E N T S

PROCEEDINGS

Whereupon,

MONICA S. LEWINSKY

was called as a witness and, after having been first duly sworn by the Foreperson of the Grand Jury, was examined and testified as follows:

EXAMINATION

BY MR. EMMICK:

Q Good morning.
A Good morning.
Q Ms. Lewinsky, this is the grand jury appearance that you'll be making or at least the first of the grand jury appearances, if there will be any more. What we routinely do with witnesses before the grand jury is that we begin the appearance by discussing your rights and your obligations and so that's what we'll do right now.
A Okay.
Q What I'd like to say first is that you have a Fifth Amendment right. That Fifth Amendment right is the right to refuse to answer any questions that may tend to incriminate you. Do you understand that right?
A Yes, I do.
Q Now, ordinarily, you could refuse to answer questions that would tend to incriminate you. As I understand it, here you have entered into an agreement

with the government that provides you with immunity, in exchange for which you will be cooperating with the government. Is that right?
A Correct.
MR. EMMICK: What I would like to do is show you a copy of what has been marked as Exhibit ML-2.

(Grand Jury Exhibit No. ML-2 was marked for identification.)

BY MR. EMMICK:

Q Do you recognize this?
A Yes, I do.
Q On the third page of that document, there is a signature line that says Monica Lewinsky. Is that your signature?
A Yes, it is.
Q All right. You also have a right to counsel. What that means is that although your attorney cannot be in the grand jury room here with you, your attorney can be outside the grand jury room and available to answer whatever questions you might have. Do you understand that right?
A Yes, I do.
Q Do you have an attorney?
A Yes, I do.
Q Who would that be?
A Several.

Page 5

Q All right.
A Jake Stein, Plato Cacheris -- do you want me to name all of them who are here or just the lead?
Q All right. Those are the lead counsel?
A Those are the lead counsel.
Q All right. And are they outside?
A Yes, they are.
Q You understand that if you need to speak with them, all you need to say is "I'd like to speak with my attorneys about something for just a minute"?
A Yes.
Q All right. In addition to those two rights that you have, you also have an obligation and that obligation is to tell the truth. That obligation is imposed on you because you have taken an oath and that is the oath to tell the truth. Do you understand that?
A Yes, I do.
Q Do you understand that if you were to intentionally say something that's false, in common parlance, if you were to lie, that would constitute perjury and perjury is a felony and it's punishable by up to five years in prison? Do you understand that?
A Yes.
Q Do you understand as well that because of the agreement that you have signed if you were to lie, if you

Page 6

were to intentionally lie, that would mean that the agreement that you have that gives you immunity could be voided and you could be prosecuted? Do you understand that?
A Mm-hmm.
Q All right. And that in simple parlance, what that means, is that you can retain immunity, but only if you do not lie. Do you understand that?
A Yes.
Q Okay. What I'd like to do is simply discuss with you briefly or clarify with you the fact that we have had interviews with you since the time when you signed this agreement. Is that right?
A Yes.
Q All right. We've had interviews with you, I believe, every day since the signing of the agreement.
A Correct.
Q Several hours a day?
A Yes.
Q Is that right? All right. I also wanted to ask you a question having to do with your mental state right now. How are you feeling?
A Nervous.
Q Okay. I wanted also to ask you, are you taking any medication at this time?
A Yes, I am.

Page 7

Q What I'd like to ask about that is simply is that having any effect on your ability to recall or to communicate that in some way will hinder your ability to answer questions?
A I don't believe so, but it affects my short-term memory just a little bit.
Q Okay. That's fine. Understand, if you will, that your role today is simply to answer questions that we pose to you.
We have spoken with you for a number of hours, a number of days, and we're going to be asking you to talk about essentially three years of conduct. We are not going to be asking you to recount every detail of the last three years of your life and we are not going to be asking you to recount everything that you've told us over the last ten days or so. You'll just be answering questions and we understand that you have other details that you could provide on other occasions.
A Yes.
MR. EMMICK: All right. What I'd like to do next is to let you know what our approach is going to be today.
What we're going to do is we're going to start off talking about your internship at the White House and then we're going to ask you questions having to do with your relationship with the President.

Page 8

Because we think that that will proceed more comfortably if those questions are asked by Ms. Immergut, I'm going to turn the questioning over to her and at some point, then, we'll collaborate in asking further follow-up questions. So without further ado --
BY MS. IMMERGUT:
Q Ms. Lewinsky, when did you start working at the White House?
A My internship began July of 1995.
Q And when you say "internship," could you just very briefly describe what it is you were doing and where you were working?
A Sure. I was interning for Mr. Panetta, who was Chief of Staff at that time, and I worked in his correspondence office preparing his correspondence, drafting some of the language.
Q Was there ever a time -- or I guess -- after beginning your internship, how long did you serve as an intern in the White House?
A About four, four and a half months. Four and a half months.
Q And was there ever a time that you then assumed a staff position that was not an intern position?
A Yes.
Q And when would that have been?

Page 9

A In November of 1995.
Q When did you first notice the President of the United States?
A Our first encounter, I guess non-verbal encounter, was August 9, 1995.
Q And could you describe what that encounter was?
A Yes. It was a departure ceremony on the South Lawn and, as he was going by on the rope line shaking hands, we made eye contact and it was more intense eye contact than I had experienced before with him.
Q Okay. And did you have any further such contact sort of later, after that initial time?
A Yes. The next day the President -- I guess the staff had a birthday party for the President on the South Lawn and the interns were invited to that later in the day. And at that party, there was sort of a more intense flirtation that went on at a distance.
Q Okay. Did you feel that he was flirting with you as well? Or how would you describe the behavior that you both exhibited?
A It was intense eye contact and when he went by the rope line to shake hands, it was -- I mean, he -- he's a charismatic person and so -- just when he shook my hand and -- there was an intense connection.
Q Okay. And could you sort of just summarize the

Page 10

early relationship that you had with the President before any first sexual contact?
A I think it was intense flirting.
Q Okay. Did you have conversations with him?
A Brief conversations that I think in passing -- if I saw him or -- at a departure ceremony, "Have a nice trip." I introduced myself at one point.
Q Okay. And how did you manage to run into him or even see him? Was that a common occurrence or how would that be accomplished?
A Before the relationship began, it was mainly at departure ceremonies, I think there were a few, and then on one occasion my best friend was in town and she was getting a tour of the West Wing and I was waiting for her in the basement lobby and met him that way. There were several other people there.
Q Okay. Was there ever a time that your relationship became more of a romantic and sexual relationship?
A Yes.
Q And when did that occur?
A On November 15, 1995.
Q Okay. And although as I've told you, I'm not going to go into a lot of specific dates, this is one that I wanted you to explain sort of how it came about.
A It was during the furlough. I was up in

Page 11

Mr. Panetta's West Wing office answering phones. The President came down several times during the day.
There was the continued flirtation and around 8:00 in the evening or so I was in the hallway going to the restroom, passing Mr. Stephanopoulos' office, and he was in the hall and invited me into Mr. Stephanopoulos' office and then from there invited me back into his study.
Q Okay. And what happened there?
A We talked briefly and sort of acknowledged that there had been a chemistry that was there before and that we were both attracted to each other and then he asked me if he could kiss me.
Q And what did you say?
A Yes.
Q And did you kiss on that occasion?
A Yes.
Q And where in the -- you mentioned you went back to the study area.
A Mm-hmm.
Q Where exactly did the kiss occur?
A Right outside his bathroom, in the hallway, inside -- adjacent to the study, to the office.
Q Okay. And how did you end that -- was there anything more than a romantic kiss on that sort of first encounter?

Page 12

A No.
Q Okay. Did you have any later encounter with him on that same date?
A Yes, I did.
Q Okay. Could you describe how that occurred?
A The President came down to Mr. Panetta's office, I think it might have been around 10 p.m., and told me that if I wanted to meet him back in Mr. Stephanopoulos' office in five minutes, that that would be fine. And I agreed. And I met him back there. We went back to his office again, in the back study area.
Q Okay. And what happened in the back study area?
A We talked and we were more physically intimate.
Q Okay. And on that occasion, did you perform oral sex on the President?
A Yes.
Q With respect to physical intimacy, other than oral sex, was there other physical intimacy performed?
A Yes. Everything up until oral sex.
MS. IMMERGUT: Okay. And just for the grand jury purposes, I have marked as an exhibit ML-6 and I'll just read it the grand jury and place it before you.
(Grand Jury Exhibit No. ML-6 was marked for identification.)
MS. IMMERGUT: It states "Definition of Sexual

Page 13

Relations. For the purposes of this grand jury session, a person engages in 'sexual relations' when the person knowingly engages or causes contact with the genitalia, anus, groin, breast, inner thigh, or buttocks of any person with an intent to arouse or gratify the sexual desire of any person. Contact means intentional touching, either directly or through clothing."

BY MS. IMMERGUT:

Q Ms. Lewinsky, do you understand that definition?

A Yes, I do.

MS. IMMERGUT: And I do have copies to pass out to the grand jury.

BY MS. IMMERGUT:

Q When you described that you had other physical intimacy during your contact with the President on November 15, 1995, did that include sexual relations within the definition that I've just read to you?

A Yes, it does.

Q In that -- again, that second contact with him on November 15, 1995, where exactly did the sexual contact that you've described occur?

A In the same hallway, by the back study, and then also in his back office.

Q Okay. And the back office, would that be the study area?

Page 14

A Yes.

Q Okay. Did you have any further sexual encounters with him after that first time on the 15th?

A Yes.

Q When was the next time?

A On the 17th of November.

Q And could you explain how that contact occurred?

A We were again working late because it was during the furlough and Jennifer Palmieri and I, who was Mr. Panetta's assistant, had ordered pizza along with Ms. Currie and Ms. Hernreich.

And when the pizza came, I went down to let them know that the pizza was there and it as at that point when I walked into Ms. Currie's office that the President was standing there with some other people discussing something.

And they all came back down to the office and Mr. -- I think it was Mr. Toiv, somebody accidently knocked pizza on my jacket, so I went to go use the restroom to wash it off and as I was coming out of the restroom, the President was standing in Ms. Currie's doorway and said, "You can come out this way."

So we went back into his back study area, actually, I think, in the bathroom or in the hallway right near the bathroom, and we were intimate.

Page 15

Q Okay. And at that point, what sort of intimacy was it?

A I believe it was just kissing at that point.

Q Okay. And how did that encounter end?

A I said I needed to back and he said, "Well, why don't you bring me some pizza?" So I asked him if he wanted vegetable or meat.

Q Okay. And, actually, where did the kissing occur that time?

A It was -- I think it was in the bathroom or it was right outside the bathroom, in the hallway adjacent to the bathroom.

Q Okay. So did you go back and get him some pizza?

A Yes, I did.

BY MR. WISENBERG:

Q Pardon me. Sorry to interrupt. That's the bathroom adjacent to the hallway that leads from the Oval Office to the dining room. Is that correct?

A Correct.

MR. WISENBERG: Sorry for interrupting.

BY MS. IMMERGUT:

Q Did you go back and get pizza?

A Yes, I did.

Q And did you ever return to the President with the pizza?

Page 16

A Yes, I did.

Q Could you describe what happened when you returned?

A Yes. I went back to Ms. Currie's office and told her the President had asked me to bring him some pizza.

She opened the door and said, "Sir, the girl's here with the pizza." He told me to come in. Ms. Currie went back into her office and then we went into the back study area again.

Q Okay. And what happened in the back study area?

A We were in the -- well, we talked and then we were physically intimate again.

Q Okay. And was there oral sex performed on that occasion?

A Yes.

Q Okay. And that would be you performing oral sex on him?

A Mm-hmm.

Q Okay. And, again -- and I have to sort of tell you, you can't answer "Mm-hmm" --

A Oh, sorry.

Q Just yes or no, just for the record. With respect to the physical intimacy again, does that fall -- when you say "physical intimacy," do you mean sexual relations within the definition?

A Yes, I do.

Page 17

Q Now, without going into sort of a lot of details of specific dates, I wanted to ask you some general questions about the relationship and to make clear, although we've already – Mr. Emmick already asked you whether or not you've met with us on several occasions, is it fair to say you've given us many, many details about each of the specific dates involved in the relationship?
A Yes.
Q Did the relationship with the President develop into or also have a non-sexual component to it?
A Yes, it did.
Q Could you describe sort of that aspect of the relationship for the grand jury?
A We enjoyed talking to each other and being with each other. We were very affectionate.
Q What sorts of things would you talk about?
A We would tell jokes. We would talk about our childhoods. Talk about current events. I was always giving him my stupid ideas about what I thought should be done in the administration or different views on things. I think back on it and he always made me smile when I was with him. It was a lot of – he was sunshine.
Q And did he make you feel like he enjoyed your being there and talking to you about things?
A Yes.

Page 18

Q Were there times that you visited him in the Oval Office where there was no sexual contact at all?
A Yes.
Q Was there sort of affectionate contact during some of those times?
A Very. Yes.
Q Okay. And how would you describe sort of affectionate but non-sexual contact?
A A lot of hugging, holding hands sometimes. He always used to push the hair out of my face.
Q Okay. Could you describe generally how those meetings were set up or how those encounters were actually set up as a general matter?
A After the first few incidents that sort of happened during the furlough, they were set up -- when I was working in Legislative Affairs, usually the President would call my office on a weekend.
He had told me earlier on that he was usually around on the weekends and that it was okay to come see him on the weekends. So he would call and we would arrange either to bump into each other in the hall or that I would bring papers to the office.
Do you want me to do after?
Q Okay. Then what happened after?
A Once I left the White House, Ms. Currie arranged

Page 19

the visits.
Q Okay. And how would she arrange those, typically?
A I don't understand. I'm sorry.
Q When you say Ms. Currie would arrange them, how would it come about that they would be set up?
A Usually either through my talking to the President prior to and then him talking to Ms. Currie or me bugging Ms. Currie to ask the President.
Q Okay. All right. Did the relationship after the events you've described of November 15th and 17th, did it continue also to have a sexual component?
A Yes, it did.
Q After the two incidents that you've described, did you have further sexual contact with him?
A Yes.
Q And I'm going to ask you just some general questions about that. The grand jurors heard that there's a chart and we'll sort of go through a chart afterwards in less detail. Approximately how many times do you recall performing oral sex on the President?
A I think about nine.
Q Did he ever perform oral sex on you?
A No. We had discussed it and there were times when it almost happened, but mother nature was in the way.
Q Okay. How many times did he ejaculate when you

Page 20

performed oral sex?
A In my presence?
Q In your presence.
A Twice.
Q Okay. And do you recall the dates of those times?
A Mm-hmm. February 28, 1997 and March -- I think it's the 29th, 1997.
Q Did you engage, other than oral sex, in other physical intimacy that would fall within the definition of sexual relations that we've read to you?
A Yes.
Q Were you alone with the President when you had these sexual encounters with him?
A Yes.
Q It seems like an obvious question, but I have to ask it. Did the President ever have telephone calls while you were actually engaging with oral sex with him?
A Twice.
Q And when those telephone calls occurred, did he ever talk on the phone while you were performing oral sex?
A Yes.
Q Do you have any recollection about when those occurred?
A I believe one was November 15, 1995, in my second visit with him, and I know April 7, 1996.

Page 21

Q Okay. Did you ever have sexual intercourse with the President?
A No.
Q Was there ever a time when your genitals actually touched each other?
A Grazed each other, yes.
Q And do you remember when that occurred?
A Yes. February 28, 1997. Oh, no. I'm sorry. March 29th, not February 28th. Sorry.
Q Okay. And could you explain why you didn't have sexual intercourse with him?
A He didn't want to. The President said that he -- that at his age, that there was too much of a consequence in doing that and that when I got to be his age I would understand. But I wasn't happy with that.
Q Okay. I want to move away from that now.
A Okay.
Q And ask you whether or not you've ever spoken to the President on the telephone.
A Yes.
Q And can you estimate approximately how many times since the beginning of your relationship with him that you've spoken to him on the phone?
A Over 50, probably.
Q And has he initiated any of those calls?

Page 22

A Yes.
Q Do you have any sort of idea how many times he's called you?
A Most of those phone calls were calls that he placed to me directly.
Q Okay. Did he ever leave any messages for you at your home?
A Yes.
Q And you remember about how many times he left messages?
A I think about four.
Q Did you save any of those messages?
A Yes, I did.
Q And have you provided any cassette tape of those messages to the OIC?
A Yes, I have.
Q Do you remember any particular messages that he left you?
A I remember them all.
Q Okay. Why don't you just tell the grand jury what they say.
A They're pretty innocuous. Sometimes -- or one time, it was, you know, "Sorry I missed you." One time, it was just "Hello." And then one time he called really late at night when I was not at home and it was whispered kind of

Page 23

loudly, you know, "Come on. It's me." Something like that. It was always nice to hear his voice.
Q Okay. Did he ever tell you how he felt about leaving messages on your home machine?
A Yes.
Q What did he tell you about that?
A I believe it was the beginning of 1996, at some point, he just remarked that he didn't like to do that, he just -- I think felt it was a little unsafe.
Q Okay. Did he ever call you late at night?
A Yes.
Q Can you tell us a little bit about that? Did that happen on many occasions?
A Yes. He's a night owl, so it would be customary for him to call sometimes 2:00 in the morning, 2:30 in the morning.
Q Okay. What sorts of things did you discuss with him generally of a non-sexual nature on your telephone calls with him?
A Similar to what we discussed in person, just how we were doing. A lot of discussions about my job, when I was trying to come back to the White House and then once I decided to move to New York. We told jokes. We talked about everything under the sun.
Q Okay. Was there ever a time that you began to

Page 24

engage in phone sex on the telephone?
A Mm-hmm. Yes.
Q And do you remember when that started to occur?
A In the beginning of 1996.
Q Okay. Did he participate in that?
A Yes.
Q Okay. And about how many times did you have phone sex with him, if you know?
A Oh, maybe 10, 15. I'm not really -- I'm not really sure.
Q Okay. We can look at the chart after to refresh your recollection, but that sounds sort of ballpark?
A I think so.
Q More than 10, about? In your view?
A Yes, I think so.
Q Did the President ever tell you that he wanted to end the sexual relationship with you?
A Yes.
Q And did he tell you that more than once?
A Yes.
Q Could you tell us when he told you that?
A February -- it was Presidents Day of 1996. I think that's February 19th. And also on May 24, 1996 -- no, 1997. I'm sorry.
Q And just for the grand jury's information, on the

Page 25

chart that we're going to show them in a little bit, how do you list -- do you have a term that you refer to the May 24, 1997 meeting with him?
A D-day.
Q And what does that stand for?
A Dump day.
Q And on those two occasions, what did he tell you about wanting to end the relationship? Just generally.
A Both were, I think, motivated sort of by guilt and just not wanting to -- more I think on the 24th of May in '97, just really wanting to do the right thing in God's eyes and do the right thing for his family and he just -- he didn't feel right about it.
Q Did you engage in sexual contact with him after those times?
A Yes. Kissing.
Q Okay. After the -- well, after the February 19, 1996 time?
A Yes. Yes.
Q And what about after the May 24, 1997 time?
A Just kissing.
Q Did your relationship involve giving gifts to each other?
A Mm-hmm. Yes. I'm sorry.
Q And did you give any gifts to him?

Page 26

A Yes.
Q Do you have any sort of ballpark figure of how many gifts you've given to him since you've known him?
A About 30.
Q And what about him to you? Do you have any estimate of how many gifts he gave you?
A I think about 18.
Q Did you ever write him any notes or letters or cards?
A Yes.
Q And what sort of cards or letters or notes would you write to him?
A It varied on the occasion. It could be a funny card that I saw or a Halloween card. If I was angry, it could be an angry letter. If I was missing him, it was a missing him letter.
Q Okay. So were some of them -- is it fair to say some of them were romantic in nature?
A Yes.
Q And when they were angry, what would you be angry about in your letters or cards?
A Either job-related issues or him not paying enough attention to me.
Q Okay. Did he write you any letters or notes?
A No.

Page 27

Q Did he ever say why he wasn't writing you any letters or notes?
A No.
MS. IMMERGUT: I'd now like to show you what I had previously marked as Exhibit 7, I believe. Perhaps somebody has the other original version.
(Grand Jury Exhibit No. ML-7 was marked for identification.)
BY MS. IMMERGUT:
Q I'm going to place this before you and ask if you recognize that chart.
A Yes, I do.
Q And have you seen that chart before?
A Yes, I have.
Q Did you assist the Office of Independent Counsel in preparing that chart?
A Yes.
Q Did you provide all of the information that's listed on that chart?
A Yes.
Q Could you describe for the grand jury just generally what is described by that chart?
A I think it's a chronology that marks some of the highlights of my relationship with the President. It definitely includes the visits that I had with him and

Page 28

most of the gifts that we exchanged. It reflects most of the phone calls that I remember.
Q And to the best of your knowledge, is the chart accurate?
A Yes.
Q Have you noticed anything that you would add or delete from the chart since you've reviewed it?
A Yes. On page --
MS. IMMERGUT: Do the grand jurors have the chart?
MR. EMMICK: They do. Yes.
THE WITNESS: On page 5, the last entry in the chart, on 10/23, I attended a Democratic fundraiser that you guys have all probably seen on T.V. lately.
BY MS. IMMERGUT:
Q Okay. Anything else that you've noticed?
A No.
Q Okay. Otherwise, would you say that the chart is a pretty accurate rendition or description of your memory of all of the events?
A Yes.
Q How is it that you remember all the events in such detail over really sort of what is a few years?
A I've always been a date-oriented person and I had a -- probably a habit of circling dates in my Filofax when I either talked to the President or saw him.

Page 29

Q And did you provide those Filofax sheets to the Office of Independent Counsel?
A Yes.
Q And did that assist you in remembering the dates?
A Yes, it did.
Q And were these encounters important to you?
A Very.
Q And, again, on that chart there are various categories. In the visit category -- or descriptions in the visit category area that are described as physical intimacy. And with respect to all of those, do they fall within the definition of sexual relations that I've presented as Exhibit 6 to the grand jury?
A Yes.
Q So anywhere physical intimacy is listed on the chart, it falls within that definition. Is that correct?
A Right. I think the only thing that might be missing is kissing.
Q Okay. And kissing is separately described on the chart, is it not?
A No, not necessarily.
Q Okay.
A I mean, because the physical intimacy -- wherever there's physical intimacy, there was always -- there was always kissing.

Page 30

Q Okay. But where there's physical intimacy, there was also then more than kissing.
A Correct.
Q Okay. So physical intimacy is never on the chart to describe only kissing.
A Correct.
Q Okay. There's one particular date also that I wanted to cover with you which is February 28, 1997.
A Okay.
Q Because at that time, as the chart demonstrates, you haven't really seen the President since April of the year before. Could you describe what the circumstances were leading up to your visit with him on February 28, 1997?
A The President had told me in December that he had a Christmas present for me and I ended up not getting it until the end of February. Ms. Currie called me at work during that week to -- or I guess it was that day, I'm sorry, that Friday, to invite me to a radio address that evening.
I went to the radio address and when I went to take my picture with the President, he said to go see Betty because he had something to give me after. So I waited a little while for him and then Betty and the President and I went into the back office.
Q Okay. And why did Betty come in the back office with you?

Page 31

A I later found out that -- I believe it was Stephen Goodin who said to Ms. Currie and the President that the President couldn't be alone with me, so Ms. Currie came back into the back office with us.
Q And then what?
A And then left.
Q Okay. She left? And do you know where she went?
A I came to learn later, I believe she was in the pantry. In the back pantry.
Q Okay. And how did you learn that later?
A I think that Mr. Nelvis told me. Or Ms. Currie told me.
Q Okay. What happened when she went to the back pantry? Did you remain with the President?
A Yes, I did.
Q And could you describe what you and the President did?
A Mm-hmm. He gave me my hat pin and the book "Leaves of Grass" and I was pestering him to kiss me and so we moved -- that was in the back study and then we moved over to the back hallway by the bathroom and we were physically intimate.
Q Okay. And did you perform oral sex on that occasion?
A Yes.

Page 32

Q And how did you -- do you remember what dress you were wearing on that occasion?
A Yes.
Q What dress was it?
A The navy blue dress from The Gap.
Q And after that incident, did you ever tell Linda Tripp that there might be the President's semen on that dress?
A Yes, I did.
Q And why did you tell her that? Or did you believe that that could be true?
A I thought it was possible.
Q Were you positive it was true?
A No.
Q Back to the incident with the President, how did you leave it with him on that occasion? Sort of once you finished the visit, what happened?
A Betty came back into the back study and then I think Ms. Currie walked me out.
Q Okay. How much about your relationship with the President did you tell Linda Tripp?
A A lot. Most everything.
Q Okay. And did you tell her about the sexual encounters that you had with him?
A Yes.

Page 33

Q Did you also tell her about the emotional encounters and the gifts?
A Yes.
Q Were you truthful about the relationship when you told Linda Tripp about it?
A Most of the time, but sometimes -- there were occasions when I wasn't truthful.
Q Were you truthful about the sexual parts of the relationship with her?
A Yes.
Q And what about the emotional component, when you would tell her -- and why don't I say before December of 1997, were you truthful about the emotional components of the relationship?
A Yes.
Q I'm actually done with my questioning on that. Do you want to break now or continue to different subjects?
A A five-minute break? Could I --
THE FOREPERSON: We can take a ten-minute break.
MS. IMMERGUT: Okay. A ten-minute break.
MR. EMMICK: A ten-minute break.
MS. IMMERGUT: Would that be all right?
THE WITNESS: Okay.
MR. EMMICK: That's fine.
(Witness excused. Witness recalled.)

Page 34

MS. IMMERGUT: Madam Foreperson, are there any unauthorized persons present?
THE FOREPERSON: No, there are none.
MS. IMMERGUT: Do we have a quorum?
THE FOREPERSON: Yes, we do.
Ms. Lewinsky, I would like to remind you that you are still under oath.
THE WITNESS: Thank you.
BY MS. IMMERGUT:
Q Ms. Lewinsky, the grand jurors had a few follow-up questions --
A Sure.
Q -- for you that I wanted to ask you before we move on to other topics. You mentioned that on the occasions where you had sexual contact with that were described, sexual contact with the President, that it occurred in the hallway, as you described, or sometimes in the back study.
A Mm-hmm.
Q Why did --
A JUROR: Pardon me.
BY MS. IMMERGUT:
Q Oh, excuse me. Why did you choose the hallway?
A Because I believe it was -- it was really more the President choosing the hallway, I think, and it was -- there weren't any windows there. It was the most secluded of all

Page 35

the places in the back office. Well, that's not true. The bathroom is the most secluded, I guess, because you can close the door.
Q And did you sometimes have sexual encounters in the bathroom?
A Mm-hmm.
Q And then next to the bathroom, would you say that the hallway is --
A Right.
Q -- off the study is the next most --
A He has a bad back and so I think a lot of times we ended up just sort of standing there and talking there because he could close the door to the bathroom and lean up against the bathroom and then he was -- I guess it made his back feel better and also made him a little shorter. So --
Q Did the President ever tell you he was concerned about being seen?
A I'm sure that came up in conversation.
BY MR. EMMICK:
Q Did he ever indicate to you looking outside that he might be concerned, for example?
A Yes, yes.
BY MS. IMMERGUT:
Q Can you describe that?
A Sure. I think the one that comes to mind was

Page 36

actually December 28th of last year when I was getting my Christmas kiss. And he was kissing me in the doorway between the back study, or the office, and the hallway, and I sort of opened my eyes and he was looking out the window with his eyes wide open while he was kissing me and then I got mad because it wasn't very romantic. And then so then he said, "Well, I was just looking to see to make sure no one was out there."
Q Can you generalize about the locations where you had your sexual encounters with the President?
A I'd say they mainly took place in that hallway, but there were occasions on which we were intimate in the office and then also in the bathroom.
Q Okay. And when you say the office, do you mean the back study?
A Right.
Q So not the Oval Office?
A No, no, we were never physically intimate in the Oval Office.
Q Okay. Did you notice whether doors were closed when you were physically intimate with him in the back study or hallway?
A No, he always -- well, I'm not sure about the door going in the dining room but I know that the door leading from the back hallway to the -- into the Oval Office was

Page 37

always kept ajar so that he could hear if someone was coming.

BY MR. WISENBERG:

Q How ajar? How much ajar?

A Maybe this much (indicating).

BY MR. EMMICK:

Q You're indicating six to eight inches, something like that?

A I'm not very good with that.

Q A foot or less, something like that?

A A foot or less. I guess that's -- I would assume that's --

Q Enough so that one could hear more easily what was going on in the next room?

A Mm-hmm. Right, or if someone came in to holler for him.

BY MS. IMMERGUT:

Q Now directing your attention back to February 28th, 1997, the day that you wore the blue cocktail dress --

A It's not a cocktail dress.

Q Okay, I'm sorry.

A No, that's okay. I'm a little defensive about this subject. I'm sorry.

Q How would you describe the dress?

A It's a dress from the Gap. It's a work dress. It's a casual dress.

Page 38

Q With respect to that dress --

A Right, I'm sorry.

Q -- you mentioned that you believe that there could be semen on it. Could you describe what you did with the President that led you to believe that?

A We were in the bathroom and -- can I close my eyes so I don't have to --

Q Well, you have to speak up. That's the only --

A Okay. We were in the bathroom and I was performing oral sex. I'm sorry, this is embarrassing. And usually he doesn't want to -- he didn't want to come to completion.

Q Ejaculate?

A Yes. And this has sort of been a subject that we had talked about many times before and he was always saying it had issues to do with trust and not knowing me well enough at first and then not feeling right about things, and not that he said this but I took away from that to sort of mean that maybe in his mind if he didn't come then maybe it wasn't -- he didn't need to feel guilty about that, that maybe with it not coming to completion that that was easier for him to rationalize.

And it was on this occasion that since we hadn't been alone together since April 7th of '96 that after we had engaged in oral sex for a while and he stopped me as he normally did, I said to him, you know -- this is so

Page 39

embarrassing, I'm sorry. I said to him, you know, I really -- I want to make you come. I mean, this is --

Q Okay. Why don't you just describe the position that you were in once he had tried to stop you. What did you do that led you to believe there might get semen on your dress?

A I told him that I really cared about him and he told me that he didn't want to get addicted to me and he didn't want me to get addicted to him, and we embraced at that point and that's -- I mean, it was -- it's just a little tiny spot down here and a little tiny spot up here and --

Q Okay. And to get -- when you're pointing down here, you mean sort of your right lower hip area?

A Well, one of my -- I don't know if it was my right or left, but lower hip area.

Q Okay. And the chest area would be the second place that you thought you might have gotten some?

A Mm-hmm.

Q And is that from when you -- when you did actually continue to perform oral sex on him later?

A I believe so.

Q Did you ever see something that you thought was semen on the dress that led you to conclude that?

A The next time I went to wear the dress.

Q So at the time you didn't notice anything on the

Page 40

dress?

A I don't believe so.

Q Okay. What happened then the next time you wore the dress that led you to conclude that?

A Well, I also -- can I say here? I also -- I think I wore the dress out to dinner that night, so which is why I'm not sure that that's what it is.

Q Okay.

A So it could be spinach dip or something. I don't know. I'm sorry, could you repeat the question?

Q Sure. When was the -- when was it that you at least began to believe that maybe there was semen on the dress?

A I really don't remember when it was the next time I went to wear the dress, but I gained weight so I couldn't wear the dress and it didn't fit. And I'm not a very organized person. I don't clean my clothes until I'm going to wear them again.

Q Did you notice there was something on the dress?

A Yes. And at that point I noticed it and I kind of thought, oh, this is dirty, it needs to get cleaned. And then I remembered that I had worn it the last time I saw the President, and I believe it was at that point that I thought to myself, oh, no. And it was -- it --

Q So at that point, you weren't positive what it was.

Page 41

And why did you tell Linda that you thought there was semen on the dress?

A I think it just sort of came up in conversation somehow and then -- as kind of this funny, gross thing. And then the next time she was at my house I still couldn't fit into the dress and believe that I said to her, oh, look, you want to see this? You know, this is what I was talking about.

And but I just want to say because I know everybody here reads the newspapers and listens to TV that I didn't keep this dress as a souvenir. I was going to wear it on Thanksgiving and my cousins, who I always try to look skinny for because they are all skinny -- and I know it sounds stupid. And when I told Linda I was thinking about wearing the dress, she discouraged me. She brought me one of her jackets from her thinner closet. And so it wasn't a souvenir. I was going to clean it. I was going to wear it again.

Q Different topic. Where was Nel when you were -- or do you have any idea where Nel was when you were in the hallway or the study with the President?

A On which --

Q On any of the occasions. I mean, would Nel be around generally?

A There were some occasions that -- very few

Page 42

occasions, I think, that Nel was there -- was at the White House. And I don't know where he would have necessarily -- I think he was in the pantry on the 28th of February.

Q Do you know where he was on any of the other occasions? And, again, where you had sexual contact with the President.

A I don't think so.

Q Did you ever use hand towels in the bathroom to wipe your lipstick?

A Hand towels, no.

Q What about tissues?

A I believe I used a tissue sometimes to wipe off my lipstick.

MR. WISENBERG: Karen, can I ask something really quick?

MS. IMMERGUT: Sure.

BY MR. WISENBERG:

Q How about, do you think Nel would have been around on renaissance -- right before the departure for renaissance weekend?

A New Year's Eve '95?

Q Yeah.

A Yes, he was.

Q Also, did you ever show -- did -- I don't -- it's my bad. Did you ever show the dress to Linda Tripp?

Page 43

A Yes.

MR. EMMICK:

Q You mentioned that the President called you on a number of occasions. Some of those occasions included phone sex. Did he indicate where he was when he was placing those calls?

A Not always, but sometimes.

Q And where did he say he was when he did say where he was?

A At home.

Q Meaning the White House residence?

A Yes.

Q Where else might he have placed calls from?

A There were, I think, two times that he placed calls from the campaign term, from Florida I think.

Q Do you know whether he sometimes placed calls from the Oval Office or other places?

A Yes, yes.

Q How do you know that?

A Sometimes he would mention it and say he was in the office. I know one time I said -- I knew he was in the office and I asked him if he was in the back or could he go in the back.

Q Did he not only call you, what, at your home but also call you at your office?

Page 44

A When I was working at the White House, yes.

Q But not while you were working at the Pentagon?

A He never directly called me when I was working at the Pentagon.

Q When you say didn't directly call, what do you mean?

A I mean he -- there were, I think, maybe two occasions when I was working at the Pentagon when Betty placed a call for him, and when that didn't occur he picked up the phone and dialed the phone number himself.

Q When he placed calls to you when you were at Leg Affairs, or Legislative Affairs, excuse me, was there anything that indicated on your caller ID?

A Yes. When he called from the Oval Office, the phones have a caller ID up at the top, and when he calls from the Oval Office it says POTUS and when he calls from the residence it has an asterisk.

Q And did you ever discuss with him the fact that you had POTUS on your ID?

A Yeah.

Q Tell us about that.

A I think one time when he called and I picked up the phone I said something that indicated to him that I knew who it was. And he said, "Well, how did you know it was me?" And I told him, "Well, don't you know that it lights up POTUS

Page 45

when you call from the Oval Office?" And he said, "No. I didn't know that." So I thought that was funny.

Q When you --

A And he made an effort one time to call me from the residence on a line and called and said, "Did it show up a phone number instead of -- " So it had. He seemed proud of himself.

Q All right. You had mentioned earlier that on, I think it was February 28th, Steve Goodin spoke with Betty and the President about being -- about him being alone with you.

A Mm-hmm.

Q Could you give us a little more detail about what you saw and what you later learned and where you later learned it so that we can figure out what you know from personal knowledge?

A Okay. What I saw was Steve Goodin and Ms. Currie going into the Oval Office. I think --

Q Where are you at this time?

A Oh, I'm sorry. I was in Ms. Currie's office and I was waiting with Ms. Currie. And I believe Stephen was there at some point and he might have gone into the Oval Office first and then called Ms. Currie in a few minutes after or maybe the President called her in after. And they spoke sort of --

A JUROR: (Coughing.)

Page 46

THE WITNESS: Do you want some water? Oh, okay. So --

BY MR. EMMICK:

Q Was there anyone else in the Oval Office, as far as you know?

A It's possible I think I might have seen Rahm Emanuel in there at some point, but I'm not really sure that he was included in this conversation.

Q So they go into the Oval Office, and what do you next see or hear?

A I believe Betty came out to get me. I was really nervous because I hadn't been alone with the President since the elections so I was focused -- I was kind of internal, focused on being nervous.

Q Betty came out to get you and what did the two of you do?

A The three of us went into the back office.

Q You had mentioned earlier that you later came to learn that there was a discussion between them, between them, about you and the President and whether you should be alone. Tell us when you learned that approximately and what you learned.

A I think I learned it, I believe, maybe shortly after -- not on that day, maybe within the next few weeks, I guess -- that Stephen had said to the President or maybe had

Page 47

said to Betty, you know, she can't be alone with him. So, and I don't recall if I learned that from Ms. Currie or from Nel.

BY MR. WISENBERG:

Q But it -- was it when, based on what you were told, it was a conversation between -- it was a conversation in which Goodin, Ms. Currie and the President were there?

A Correct.

BY MR. EMMICK:

Q Let's focus a little bit about the Presidential aides. You mentioned Steve Goodin. Where are the aides at the time you are having your encounters, if we can call them that, with the President?

A Most of the time they weren't -- they weren't there. They weren't at the White House.

Q And how was that arranged?

A When I was working in Legislative Affairs, I don't think -- I don't know if it was ever verbally spoken but it was understood between the President and myself that most of the -- most people weren't in on the weekends so there was -- it would be safer to do that then.

And then after I left the White House, that was sort of always a concern that Betty and I had just because she knew and I knew that a lot of people there didn't like me.

Page 48

Q So is it fair to say then that the Presidential aides, whether they be Steve Goodin or Andrew Friendly or whoever it might be, were not around at the time?

A Correct. They may have been but --

Q Mm-hmm. I wonder if you could expand a little bit on the nature of your relationship with Betty and then the nature of your relationship with Nel, and specifically what we mean to ask is to what extent were these relationships genuine relationships and to what extent were they, in part, based on an interest in cultivating their friendship because of your relationship with the President?

A I think that they -- both of them started out probably at the latter of what you said, as maybe a function of making my relationship with the President easier, or for me, I guess, getting information, but that they both came to have a very genuine component to them. I still care very deeply about Betty.

Q When you talk about getting information, could you expand on what you mean by that?

A I think sometimes if it was from Ms. Currie finding out what the President's schedule was, when he might be around, what might be a good time to come by or maybe for her to talk to him to let him know something.

With Nel, Nel and I developed a friendship that started during the furlough and I thought he was a really

Page 49

nice guy and didn't get treated correctly or properly, I guess. And the kind of information, he sort of just would give me information about the President. I mean, I don't think that was the only -- that wasn't the only component of the friendship, but that was a component of it.

Q You have discussed how Betty helped arrange for you to come visit the President, especially in 1997, I think it would be fair to say.

A Yes.

Q When those arrangements were made, who initiated the arrangements? How did they start off? Did you ask? Did the President ask? Did Betty ask?

A I'd say most of the time it was probably me asking -- either asking the President directly or asking him through Betty or through sending a note of some sort. And there were occasions that he initiated, so it would come through Betty.

Q All right. Let me ask you the following question. You have described the ways that Betty helped let you in --

A Mm-hmm.

Q -- facilitate the relationship, if you will. Do you think Betty Currie knew about your relationship with the President?

A I don't know. It's possible she could have gleaned that from witnessing that the -- you know, that the President

Page 50

was having a relationship that caused -- with a 25 year-old woman or, at the time, younger -- you know, that made me emotional. But I really can't answer that question.

Q She saw you under circumstances where she realized you and the President had an emotional tie.

A I believe so. I'm not really -- I'm not really comfortable sort of answering questions about what -- you know, what Betty knew because --

Q Well, then let me focus more on what Betty was in a position to see.

A Okay.

Q Was Betty in a position to see that you and the President visited frequently and had a strong emotional attachment?

A I believe so, yes.

Q Did you ever expressly tell Betty about the relationship?

A What aspect of the relationship?

Q Well, let me separate it out for you.

A Okay.

Q Did you ever expressly tell Betty about the emotional aspect of the relationship?

A I believe I characterized that to her.

Q Did you ever expressly tell Betty about the sexual aspect of the relationship?

Page 51

A No, I don't believe so.

Q Let me ask the question, why not?

A Because it's not appropriate. I mean, I think -- I don't think people necessarily talk about these things. I mean, there is a difference between a relationship that you have with someone who is sort of involved in a situation, and then the kind of relationship you have with a friend whom you talk to. I think with -- a little bit with Betty's age and it wasn't clear to me that the -- you know, the President didn't tell her so, if he didn't tell her, why should I tell her.

Q Let me ask similar questions about Nel. Do you think Nel knew?

A Nel knew --

Q About the emotional aspect of the relationship?

A Yes, I think so.

Q Is that based on what you told him or what you think he must have seen, or both?

A I think probably based more on what I told him.

Q Do you think Nel knew about the sexual aspect of the relationship?

A We never directly discussed it, so I don't know if -- I don't know how to answer that.

Q Did he ever say things to you that made you think that he must know about the sexual aspect of the

Page 52

relationship?

A Not that I remember.

Q You mentioned earlier, perhaps an obvious thing, that you were alone with the President on the times that you had sexual contact with the President.

A Yes.

Q Were there also times when you were alone with the President that you did not have sexual contact with the President?

A Mm-hmm, yes.

Q Can you give us sort of a general description about how those encounters occurred and where they occurred?

A Okay. There were numerous that ranged from the beginning of our relationship till the end of our relationship.

Q Were some of them brief? Were some of them substantial in length?

A Mm-hmm, yes.

Q Where within the White House would those have occurred?

A One occurred in the Oval Office and then the others occurred -- oh, that's not true. Two occurred in the Oval Office and the others were in the back study area.

I should also just -- maybe I could just add right now that every -- that every time I had a visit with the

Page 53

President when I was working there -- not after, but when I was working there -- we usually would -- we'd start in the back and we'd talk and that was where we were physically intimate, and we'd usually end up, kind of the pillow talk of it, I guess, was sitting in the Oval Office talking. So there's --

BY MR. WISENBERG:

Q And, again, when you say when you started in the back, that could either be the hallway or the back?

A Correct, yes.

BY MR. EMMICK:

Q I would like to ask you some questions about any steps you took to try to keep your relationship with the President secret.

A A lot.

Q All right. Well, why don't we just ask the question open-endedly and we'll follow up.

A Okay. I'm sure, as everyone can imagine, that this is a kind of relationship that you keep quiet, and we both wanted to be careful being in the White House. Whenever I would visit him during -- when -- during my tenure at the White House, we always -- unless it was sort of a chance meeting on a weekend and then we ended up back in the office, we would usually plan that I would either bring papers, or one time we had actually accidentally bumped into each other

Page 54

in the hall and went from that way, so then we planned to do that again because that seemed to work well. But we always -- there was always some sort of a cover.

Q When you say that you planned to bring papers, did you ever discuss with the President the fact that you would try to use that as a cover?

A Yes.

Q Okay. What did the two of you say in those conversations?

A I don't remember exactly. I mean, in general, it might have been something like me saying, well, maybe once I got there kind of saying, "Oh, gee, here are your letters," wink, wink, wink, and him saying, "Okay, that's good," or --

Q And as part of this concealment, if you will, did you carry around papers when you went to the visit the President while you worked at Legislative Affairs?

A Yes, I did.

Q Did you ever actually bring him papers to sign as part of business?

A No.

Q Did you actually bring him papers at all?

A Yes.

Q All right. And tell us a little about that.

A It varied. Sometimes it was just actual copies of letters. One time I wrote a really stupid poem. Sometimes I

Page 55

put gifts in the folder which I brought.

Q And even on those occasions, was there a legitimate business purpose to that?

A No.

Q Did you have any discussions with the President about what you would say about your frequent visits with him after you had left Legislative Affairs?

A Yes.

Q Yes. What was that about?

A I think we -- we discussed that -- you know, the backwards route of it was that Betty always needed to be the one to clear me in so that, you know, I could always say I was coming to see Betty.

Q And is there some truth in the notion that you were coming to see Betty?

A Coming to see Betty, I don't know. Did I -- I saw Betty on every time that I was there.

Q What was your purpose though in going --

A My purpose was -- most of the time my purpose was to see the President, but there were some times when I did just go see Betty but the President wasn't in the office.

Q When the President was in the office, was your purpose in going there to see the President?

A Yes.

Q What about the writing of things down on paper?

Page 56

Was there any discussion between you and the President about the risks of writing things down and whether you should write things down?

A Yes.

Q All right. Tell us about that.

A There were on some occasions when I sent him cards or notes that I wrote things that he deemed too personal to put on paper just in case something ever happened, if it got lost getting there or someone else opened it. So there were several times when he remarked to me, you know, you shouldn't put that on paper.

Q We'll have occasion to get into some details about that in a bit. I don't know how to ask this question more delicately, so I'll just ask you. Did you take any steps to try to be careful with how loud you might be in sexual matters?

A Yes.

Q All right. Can you tell us, as discreetly as you can and as -- about that?

A I think we were both aware of the volume and sometimes I'd use my hand -- I bit my hand -- so that I wouldn't make any noise.

Q All right, that's fine. Let me ask another question. Did you try to take -- are you okay?

A Yeah, this is just embarrassing.

Page 57

Q Did you try to take different routes in and out of the Oval Office area as part of your way of concealing the relationship?
A Yes, I did.
Q Could you tell us about that?
A I made an effort on my own to go out a different door than the door that I came in so that if there was a guard that was on duty in the front of the Oval Office he might see me going in but a different guard would see me leave, so no one would know exactly how long I had been in there.
Q Did you try to do that most of the time, all of the time?
A I'd say 90 percent of the time. I mean, I can't really recall a time that I didn't do that, but it's possible. That was the pattern.
Q Were there some people that you tried to specifically avoid when you were visiting with the President?
A Yes.
Q All right. Who were they, please?
A Pretty much everybody but Betty.
Q Okay. What about, for example, Nancy Hernreich?
A Yes.
Q All right. And how would you take steps to avoid Nancy Hernreich?

Page 58

A Generally, coming in on the weekend. This is after I left?
Q Yes.
A Okay. After I left the White House it was coming in on the weekend or sometimes we -- I tried to see him but I don't think it actually ever occurred on Tuesday nights because Ms. Hernreich has yoga, I think -- I believe.
BY MR. WISENBERG:
Q Who told you that she had yoga?
A Ms. Currie.
BY MR. EMMICK:
Q Any discussion with the President about trying to make sure that there are fewer people around when you were to visit?
A When I worked in Legislative Affairs, I think that was sort of the understanding that the weekend was the -- there weren't a lot of people around. And there were times when I think that the President might have said, oh, there are too many people here because there was some big issue or some big event happening maybe.
Q Were there any occasions when you tried to make arrangements to see the President but for some reason or another Betty was not in a position to let you in?
A Sure, I think so.
Q Any occasions when you had actually planned to

Page 59

visit and then for some reason or another she wasn't there, that you remember?
A No, not that I remember.
Q What about throwing away notes that you had written to the President? Was there any discussion of throwing out the notes or any notations that you would write on the notes to remind him to throw them out?
A Yes, I think that I may have had a discussion with the President about him throwing things away, I think, or making sure that they're not there. I know one specific occasion in one of the notes that I sent him I made a joke that really was reminding him not to -- to make sure he threw the -- make sure he threw it away.
Q I've asked you a number of questions having to do with how you tried to keep the relationship secret. Let me ask, did you tell some people about the relationship?
A Unfortunately, yes.
Q All right. Could you tell us some of the people that you've told about the relationship?
A Linda Tripp, Catherine Davis, Neysa Erbland, Dale Young, Ashley Raines, and my mom and my aunt. Everybody knew a different amount of -- had a different amount of information.
Q Natalie Ungvari?
A Oh, Natalie Ungvari, yes.

Page 60

Q Did you tell any of your -- any counselors or therapists of any kind about your relationship?
A Yes, I did.
Q All right. Would you tell us who they would be?
A Dr. Irene Kassorla, and I believe it's Dr. Kathy Estep.
Q When you talked about your relationship with the President with these people, did you lie about your relationship?
A No. I may have not told them every detail, but I don't believe I ever lied. Oh, about the -- oh, wait, do you mean the doctors or was that in general?
Q I meant in general.
A Well, there were -- about my relationships -- I'm sorry, could you be more specific?
Q Sure. You listed a number of people that you had told about your relationship with the President.
A Right.
Q I'm just trying to figure out if you told the truth to those people when you described the relationship.
A Yes. There were some occasions when I wasn't truthful about certain things, but not having to do with, I think, the general relationship. Does that make sense?
Q Expand on that just a little. I'm just not sure.
A Well, I think with Linda Tripp, I mean there were

Page 61

times that I was not truthful with her. I mean, I didn't know if that's what you were encompassing by saying relationship or not.

Q Let's put Linda Tripp aside for a bit because I think I know what you have in mind.

A Right.

Q Put Linda Tripp aside for a bit. Were you truthful with the others about your description of the relationship?

A Yes.

Q And since you mentioned Linda Tripp, were there occasions toward the end of, I guess it would be December or January, when you said some things to Linda Tripp that were not true?

A Yes.

Q All right. We'll have a chance to get to that in a bit.

A Okay.

Q What I would like to turn to next is the -- is April of 1996 and your transfer from the White House to the Department of Defense. When were you first told about the fact that you were being terminated from Legislative Affairs?

A On the 5th -- I think it was the 5th of April, Friday.

Q Did you later have a telephone conversation with the President about your being terminated?

Page 62

A Yes. I did.

Q When was that?

A On the 7th, on Easter.

Q Easter Sunday, April 7th of 1996?

A Correct.

Q Would you tell us first what your reaction was when you were told that you were going to be terminated from Legislative Affairs?

A My initial reaction was that I was never going to see the President again. I mean, my relationship with him would be over.

Q You did not want to go to the Pentagon?

A No.

Q When you spoke with the President on April 7th, did you call him or did he call you?

A He called me.

Q Would you tell us how that telephone conversation proceeded and then we'll talk about the meeting.

A Okay. I had asked him how -- if he was doing okay with Ron Brown's death, and then after we talked about that for a little bit I told him that my last day was Monday. And he was -- he seemed really upset and sort of asked me to tell him what had happened. So I did and I was crying and I asked him if I could come see him, and he said that that was fine.

Q Did you go over to the White House?

Page 63

A Yes. I did.

Q About what time of day, if you remember?

A I think it was around 6:00 p.m.

Q Who let you in?

A I had a pass at the time.

Q How long did you visit with the President that day?

A Maybe a half an hour. I'm not very good with the time estimates.

Q You've already had occasion to talk a little bit about the sexual aspect of your encounter with the President at that time and the phone call that you -- that came in in the midst. I'm not going to ask you about that. What I am going to ask you about instead was your discussions with the President about the termination and about what the future would hold for you.

A He told me that he thought that my being transferred had something to do with him and that he was upset. He said, "Why do they have to take you away from me? I trust you." And then he told me -- he looked at me and he said, "I promise you if I win in November I'll bring you back like that."

Q How were things left at the end of that meeting?

A I sort of ran out.

Q Right. I guess what I mean by that -- I'm sorry, I didn't mean to be that specific.

Page 64

A Okay.

Q At the end of the meeting, were you going to go to the Pentagon?

A Well, he was going to see what he could do.

Q I see. All right.

A He said he'd try to see. He said he was going to ask -- try to find out what had happened. And I told him that I was going to be meeting with Ms. Hernreich the next day and he sort of said, "Let me see what I can do."

Q Did you later have a telephone call with the President where you discussed what he had learned?

A Yes.

Q When was that?

A The following Friday.

Q That would have been then April 12th?

A Yes, I think so.

Q Did he call you or did you call him?

A. He called me.

Q Where were you?

A I was at home.

Q How long was the telephone conversation?

A Maybe about 20 minutes.

Q Tell us what the two of you talked about.

A He told me that he had asked Nancy and Marsha Scott to find out why I had been transferred, and that what he had

Page 65

come to learn was that Evelyn Lieberman had sort of spearheaded the transfer, and that she thought he was paying too much attention to me and I was paying too much attention to him and that she didn't necessarily care what happened after the election but everyone needed to be careful before the election.
Q Did he offer any of his views about what you should do with respect to this Pentagon job?
A He told me that I should try it out and if I didn't like it that he would get me a job on the campaign.
Q What was your reaction to that?
A I think I was disappointed. I didn't want to go to the Pentagon and I didn't really see what the difference on the campaign was going to be -- why I couldn't work -- if I could work at the campaign why I couldn't work at the White House. So --
Q Did you start working at the Pentagon?
A Yes.
Q What position did you hold when you worked at the Pentagon?
A Confidential Assistant to Ken Bacon, who is the Pentagon spokesman.
Q Let's talk generally, if you will, about what sort of contact you had with the President during the rest of 1996. Did you see him in person?

Page 66

A Yes, I did.
Q Okay. Did you see him in person very often?
A No. I wasn't alone with him so when I saw him it was in some sort of event or group setting.
Q Did you continue to have telephone contact with him?
A Yes.
Q And those telephone contacts are set out in the chart that we've put together --
A Mm-hmm.
Q -- with your assistance?
A I guess. Yes. I'm sorry.
Q Let's then just turn to the first part of 1997. The election is over. Did you talk with the President about getting you back to the White House?
A Yes.
Q All right. Would you tell us about that?
A I believe the first time I might have mentioned it to him was in January of '97 in a phone conversation, and he told me that he would talk to Bob Nash, who is the head of White House or Presidential Personnel, I think it is, about bringing me back. In the next phone call he said he had spoken to Bob Nash and then -- do you want me to go as far as --
Q Just a bit more detail so that we can get a sense

Page 67

of what efforts you thought were being taken and whether you came to be disappointed with those efforts.
A Very disappointed. He -- my understanding at first was that the ball had sort of been passed to Bob Nash to bring me -- to find a position for me to come back to the White House. I then came to learn maybe in March or so that the ball had been passed from Bob Nash to Marsha Scott. And then Marsha Scott was supposed to help me find a position at the White House, which didn't work out, then she was going to detail me to her office in the White House and then she later rescinded that offer.
Keep going?
Q Were you frustrated with all that?
A Very frustrated.
Q And did you communicate your frustration to the President?
A Yes, I did.
Q Tell us about how you communicated your frustration to the President.
A There were various occasions, different things that happened. Sometimes it was in our phone conversations, sometimes it was in a letter, sometimes it was in person.
Q Let me direct your attention to July 3rd of 1997. Did you cause some sort of a communication to be made to the President on that day?

Page 68

A Yes.
Q Tell us about that.
A I had been trying to get in touch with him maybe since the latter part of June to discuss some of my meetings with Marsha Scott that had not gone as I had hoped they would and -- excuse me -- the President wasn't responding to me and wasn't returning my calls and wasn't responding to my notes. And I got very upset so I sat down that morning actually and scribbled out a long letter to him that talked about my frustrations and that he had promised to bring me back; if he wasn't going to bring me back that I -- you know, then could be help me find a job -- at that point I said in New York at the United Nations, and that I sort of dangled in front of him to remind him that if I wasn't coming back to the White House I was going to need to explain to my parents exactly why that wasn't happening.
Q And what was your purpose in sending a letter of that kind to the President?
A I think it was sort of had a few purposes, in that towards the end of the letter I softened up again and was back to my mushy self, but the purpose was -- one of the purposes, I think, was to kind of remind him that I had left the White House like a good girl in April of '96. A lot of other people might have made a really big stink and said that they weren't going to lose their job and they didn't want to

Page 73

Q Continue. I think you were --

A At that point -- I don't know if it was at that point in the conversation, then the President informed me that Kathleen Willey had actually called Nancy Hernreich during the week earlier and had said -- excuse me, sorry -- and had said that this reporter was chasing after her trying to find out her relationship with the President.

And so to me, what that meant was that when -- I thought that meant that when Kathleen found out Linda wasn't going to corroborate her story that she was trying to cover her tracks with the White House so that they wouldn't then find out or think that she was trying to encourage Michael Isikoff.

So I thought everything was over with and I later told that to Linda.

Q Why did you want to say anything to the President at all about that? What did you think the President might do to respond?

A I thought he -- I thought maybe, you know, my understanding from Linda was that Kathleen had been trying to get a job, and I could certainly understand the frustrations of being told someone is going to help you get a job and then you don't. And I thought at that point -- I didn't know too many details about what was going on. I don't think she was in the Paula Jones case and I thought, well, gee, maybe if

Page 74

you know someone who needs -- who would want to hire her you can make this go away for -- that's how I thought of it. Then I thought maybe there was something he could do to fix it or someone else could do to fix it, or just be aware of it.

Q He might get her a job, for example?

A He might. I mean, I think that was one of the things that crossed my mind.

Q At that time, did the President ask you whether you had disclosed anything about your relationship to anyone else?

A Not at that time.

Q Did he at some other time?

A Yes, he did.

Q When was that?

A I think there might have been several times throughout the relationship, but he specifically asked me about Linda Tripp on July 14th.

Q All right. Then we'll get to that in just a moment.

A Okay.

Q At the beginning of the meeting with the President on July 4th, you had sent him a letter in which you said that you were considering telling your parents. Did he ever say anything to you about, you know, you shouldn't be threatening

Page 75

the President or something like that?

A Yes. Our meeting started out with a fight, so he sat down and we sat down and he lectured me and, you know, "First of all, it's illegal to threaten the President of the United States and, second of all -- " I mean, it was just -- and then I started crying so --

Q All right, fine. After the meeting on July 4th concluded, did you leave the country?

A Yes.

Q All right. Where did you go?

A I think a few days after that. I went to Madrid.

Q When did you return, as best you can remember?

A On the 14th of July.

Q All right. Then let's turn our attention to the 14th of July. You got back from overseas. Did you get a call from Betty?

A Yes, I did.

Q Tell us about that.

A She called around -- I think it might have been around 7:30 -- I was already in bed because of jet lag and everything -- and told me that she thought the President either wanted to talk to me or see me later, and that I believe he was out golfing at the time, and that she'd call me back later to let me know what was going to happen. And she did. She called back maybe around 8:30 or so, 8:30, 9

Page 76

o'clock, and asked me to come over to the White House. So I did.

Q When you got to the White House, did you see the President?

A Yes, I did.

Q Could you tell us how that meeting went?

A It was an unusual meeting, I mean, first because we -- he met me in Betty's office and we went into Nancy Hernreich's office, which is adjacent to Ms. Currie's office, and sat on the sofa and talked. It was very distant and very cold. And he asked me if the -- I don't remember the sequence of things necessarily, but at one point he asked me if the woman that I had mentioned on July 4th was Linda Tripp. And I hesitated and then answered yes, and he talked about that there was some issue with -- this had to do with Kathleen Willey and that, as he called it, that there was something on the sludge report, that there had been some information.

And what his main concern seemed to be was that Kathleen Willey had called Nancy again that week and was upset because Michael Isikoff had told her that he knew she had called the White House saying he was pursuing her and her story. Is that clear?

A JUROR: No.

THE WITNESS: Okay. Kathleen had called Nancy, and

Page 77

the President had told me that Kathleen had called Nancy. This was on July 4th. And then that following week when I was in Madrid, I believe -- I know I was in Madrid, I think it was that following week -- Kathleen called Nancy again. And Kathleen was upset because Michael Isikoff had told Kathleen that he knew that she had called Nancy the previous week.

Does that make a little more sense?

A JUROR: Yes, thank you.

THE WITNESS: So what the President's concern was that the only people who knew that Kathleen had called Nancy originally were Nancy, Bruce Lindsey, the President and myself, and Kathleen. So he was concerned and had asked me if I had told Linda the information he had shared with me, and I had said yes, I did because I thought that meant it was over, that Kathleen was trying to backtrack.

So that alarmed me because, obviously, someone had told Michael Isikoff. And he was concerned about Linda, and I reassured him. He asked me if I trusted her, and I said yes. And he -- we had talked about -- oh, I had -- I'm sorry, I'm sorry. On July 4th I had mentioned that -- to the President that this woman had tried to contact Bruce Lindsey and that Bruce Lindsey didn't return her phone call.

So on July 14th, the President asked me if I thought Linda would call Bruce Lindsey again, and I told him

Page 78

that she is a really proud woman and that she was really offended that he didn't call her back and it was -- so I didn't think she would. And he asked me if I would just try to see if she would call, and so I said I would try.

BY MR. EMMICK:

Q Did he ask you whether you had told anything to Linda about your relationship with the President?

A Yes, he did.

Q All right. Tell us about that.

A He asked me just that, and I said no.

Q Where was this conversation taking place with the President?

A In Nancy Hernreich's office.

Q Did there come a time when he left to take a conference call?

A Yes, he did.

Q All right. Did you know who the conference call was with?

A That's a little murky for me. I believe it might have been with his attorneys, but I don't remember how I know that. So it's possible it was with his attorneys.

BY MR. WISENBERG:

Q How would you know it? I mean, how would you know it?

A I don't know. That's just what sounds -- that's

Page 79

what came to my mind when I was recalling the event. And I don't recall how I knew that so I don't know if maybe that's just how I'm recalling it or that I knew it and I don't remember who told me.

Q Was there anybody there to tell you he was talking to his attorneys other than him that day?

A It could have been Betty. I sat with Betty when -- in her office when he was on the conference call in the Oval Office or in the back. I don't know where he was, actually.

BY MR. EMMICK:

Q Other than the President asking you to get a hold of Linda and have Linda call Bruce Lindsey, how were things left at the end of the meeting?

A He asked me to let Betty know the following day without getting into details with her, even mentioning names with her, if I had, you know, kind of mission accomplished sort of thing with Linda.

Q And did you?

A Yes, I got in touch with Betty the next day and I told her that I needed to talk to the President having to do with what he had asked me.

Q And did you follow up with that?

A Yes, he called me that evening.

Q Okay. And what did the two of you talk about?

A We discussed the -- I guess that I had tried to

Page 80

talk to Linda and that she didn't seem very receptive to trying to get in touch with Bruce Lindsey again, but that I would continue to try. And I think I just gave him some more -- I think I gave him maybe the background information about what I knew when Linda worked there and gave him, I think, a fuller version of whatever it was I knew about this situation.

MR. EMMICK: I'm prepared to move on. Is this an appropriate time for another break?

THE FOREPERSON: Most appropriate.

MR. EMMICK: Okay. Good timing.

THE WITNESS: Me, too. Too much water.

MS. IMMERGUT: Ten minutes?

MR. EMMICK: Let's just take ten minutes.

THE FOREPERSON: Ten minutes, please.

(Witness excused. Witness recalled.)

THE WITNESS: So where are we?

MR. EMMICK: In fact, I'll even walk up and show you where we are, but first we have to clarify that there are no unauthorized persons present and we have a quorum.

THE FOREPERSON: That's correct.

And I need to remind you that you're still under oath.

THE WITNESS: Thanks.

MR. EMMICK: Just to make some reference here, we

Page 81

are here at the end of July, but there are some questions. I'm going to circle back to April 7th.

THE WITNESS: Okay.

MR. EMMICK: We're going to ask some more detail on April 7th and we're going to talk a little bit about a call that you had from the President in -- I think it is April of '97 about some conversations that --

THE WITNESS: Okay.

MR. EMMICK: A call in that time period.

THE WITNESS: Okay.

MR. EMMICK: There were also some -- let's call them sort of a laundry list of follow-up questions.

THE WITNESS: Okay.

MR. EMMICK: So we'll focus there and a little bit on the 14th and a little bit on that phone call.

THE WITNESS: I thought I -- I also might just say that if, as happened before, if I'm saying something and I'm not clear, I'm not understanding, just let me know, because I do that a lot.

BY MR. EMMICK:

Q All right. Let's start off with some questions. First, let's focus on July 14th because the President wanted you to have Linda contact Lindsey. Why wouldn't Lindsey just contact Linda? Was there any discussion of that? Why did it have to go one way rather than the other way?

Page 82

A I don't believe there was a discussion about it. I have my own thoughts on it, but there wasn't a discussion about it.

Q What were your own thoughts on it?

A That it would just -- I -- I think I sort of thought that it would probably be more proper -- not in a chain of command, necessarily, but -- it just seemed more appropriate for Linda to call Bruce Lindsey.

Q Did it look -- do you think it would have looked inappropriate for Lindsey to contact Tripp?

A I think it would have been awkward because I think -- how would -- you know, how would Bruce Lindsey have known to call -- you know, to call Linda at that point? If -- you know, the President thought at that point that -- you know, that Linda didn't know anything, so if Linda didn't know anything, then how -- wouldn't it be odd for Bruce Lindsey to just call her back out of the blue?

Q Okay.

A I mean, that was sort of how I thought of it.

Q But in either event, there wasn't any actual discussion about the strategy behind who would have to call whom?

A Not that I remember. No.

BY MR. WISENBERG:

Q Well, did you say to him anything like, "Hey, she tried to call him before."

A Right.

Q "She isn't going to call him this time." I mean, anything like that?

A Yes. I think I had mentioned that before. I mean, that might have been -- you know, I think was sort of -- he was saying, "Well, just try to see."

BY MR. EMMICK:

Q Let me approach the question in just a little bit different way. When you talked to Linda and tried to convince Linda to talk to Bruce Lindsey, what did you say to her to try to convince her to talk to her? Do you understand what I mean?

A Right. Well, I didn't tell Linda that -- and this was unusual, I didn't tell Linda that I had seen the President on the 14th of July because I was somewhat wary of her, having learned that someone had told Michael Isikoff, and I knew it wasn't me, so sort of assuming that Linda had talked to Michael Isikoff and not really knowing where she was coming from on this, so I just kept encouraging her to call Bruce Lindsey again, that this was heating up more and you really should call Bruce Lindsey.

Q All right. Let me go to another question. You made a reference earlier to the fact that you felt that Nel hadn't been treated well or hadn't been treated respectfully.

Page 84

Could you tell us what you meant by that?

A People in the White House -- I mean, Nel is stationed in the pantry, which is right -- I mean, which is even a part of the Oval Office area and he's always there and he takes very good care of the President and people just walk right past him, they don't say hi to him, a lot of people don't acknowledge him.

And they just -- you know, they kind of come to him when they need something, but aren't -- and I just -- I don't think people should be treated like that. I mean, I think anybody who -- and especially everyone who is working at the White House and who works -- I've always categorized people as people who are there to serve the President and people who are there to serve themselves through the President and I think Nel has a lot of loyalty to the President.

Q Would it be fair to say that it's no so much that they were affirmatively mistreating him, but they were treating him as a non-person almost? Or is that --

A I think that's a mistreatment.

Q Yes. That's a mistreatment. Okay. That's a fair characterization.

A In my opinion.

Q We had talked earlier about certain people that you wanted to avoid in order to help keep the relationship secret

Page 85

and you talked about Nancy Hernreich as being one of those people. Can you tell us what other people you wanted to sort of avoid in that same vein?

A Stephen Goodin. Let's see. I guess it's different from when I was at the White House to after. When I was there, Evelyn Lieberman, Harold Ickes, anybody who knew who I was, certainly. And after I left, I think it was mainly anybody who knew me from before. So --

Q All right.

A Does that -- does that answer it?

Q If that's the answer, then that's the best we can do.

A Okay.

Q We talked earlier about February 28th and about Steve Goodin going into the Oval Office with Betty and what you learned about that conversation they had.

A Mm-hmm.

Q The question is this: why would Steve Goodin, who is after all just a presidential aide, why would he be in a position to be able to tell the President, "You can't be with Monica Lewinsky alone"?

A I don't know. And that was a question that I -- that I posed -- I don't think I posed it as a question, but I sort of made a comment, you know, who is -- and then -- I don't remember if it was to Betty or to Nel, you know, why

Page 86

would -- you know, how inappropriate that was.

Q Right.

A And maybe Stephen made the comment to Betty. Maybe just Betty. I -- I -- I -- you know, I wasn't in the room, so I don't know what the course of the conversation was. Maybe Stephen said it to Betty and Betty told the President that Stephen had said that to Betty. So I'm not sure, but I thought it was inappropriate, too.

MR. EMMICK: Any other follow-up on that?

A JUROR: I think a point be is that did he feel that he had the authority do so because someone else was encouraging him to monitor that sort of activity, such as Evelyn Lieberman, for example?

THE WITNESS: That's a good thought. I don't know. I don't have any knowledge of that. I never thought of that.

BY MR. EMMICK:

Q You mentioned that during 1997 especially you frequently complained to the President that although he said he could bring you back (snapping finger) like that, it wasn't happening. How did the President respond when you complained about these things?

A You know, I mean, it was the -- "Bob Nash is handling it," "Marsha's going to handle it" and "We just sort of need to be careful." You know, and, "Oh, I'll -- " he would always sort of -- what's the word I'm looking for?

Page 87

Kind of validate what I was feeling by telling me something that I don't necessarily know is true. "Oh, I'll talk to her," "I'll -- you know, I'll see blah, blah, blah." and it was just "I'll do," "I'll do," "I'll do." And didn't, didn't, didn't.

Q All right. You mentioned that in that July 3rd letter that you sent to the President through Betty you made a reference to the fact that you might have to explain things to your parents. What did you mean by that?

A If I was going to pick up and move from Washington -- first of all, I had told my -- well, my mom knew, you know, that I was having some sort of a relationship with the President. My dad had no idea. And I had told my dad that was I -- you know, I was told I could probably come back to the White House after the election, as Tim Keating had told me. And the President.

So I had sort of told him that course and I would have needed to explain to them why I was going to pick up and move to New York without -- what the point would be.

Q Were you meaning to threaten the President that you were going to tell, for example, your father about the sexual relationship with the President?

A Yes and no. I don't think I -- I know that I never would have done that. I think it was more -- the way I felt was, you know, you should remember that I sort of -- I've

Page 88

been a good girl up until now.

I mean, I kind of have -- that I think I tended to -- I know that I thought he tended to forget what I had gone through already and that -- and so that this wasn't an issue of, well, you know, "We can do this in a little while, this is maybe changing your job while you're in the White House," you know, if I had wanted to maybe do something different, it was a lot more significant. And I felt that he was giving me the runaround a bit, too.

Q Is it fair to say that it was in part an implied threat?

A Yes, but I think -- but I think if you want to look at it that way, it was a threat to him as a man and not a threat to him as president. Does that -- I mean --

Q What do you mean?

A Well, I think when I hear you say, you know, "Was that an implied threat" that that letter being sent to any man who is having an illicit relationship with someone would be a threat, and so it was irrelevant, the fact that he was president.

Q I see.

A So just because we had talked earlier about it and then that was what had upset me, when the President said, "It's illegal to threaten the President of the United States."

Page 89

Q Right.
A And I just thought, you know, "I don't deal with you like the President, I deal with you as a person."
MR. EMMICK: All right.
MR. WISENBERG: Can I ask something about that?
MR. EMMICK: Yes.
BY MR. WISENBERG:
Q But you had said your mother by that time knew there was some of kind of a relationship.
A Right. He didn't know that, though.
Q But you hadn't told -- he didn't know that.
A I never told him that. No.
BY MR. EMMICK:
Q A question about lipstick and tissues.
A Okay.
Q You mentioned that a couple of times you used tissues to wipe lipstick off. Do you remember where you threw those tissues away and did it occur to you that somebody might see those tissues later and therefore might think of it as somehow evidencing the relationship?
A No, really the only -- the one time that I specifically remember doing that was on January 7th of '96. And -- no, I don't think that -- I mean, I had light lipstick on so I don't -- I think if it had been a darker colored lipstick that maybe I would have been concerned, I might have

Page 90

thought about that, but that didn't cross my mind. I don't think people go through the trash.
Q Right.
A I hope not.
Q Do you recall where you threw the tissue away on that occasion?
A It was in the bathroom. I think there's a wastebasket right next to the sink.
Q All right. A question going back to the '96 period, because you had mentioned that on February 19th of '96 the President told you essentially we should break up, we shouldn't have any more of a sexual relationship, yet five or six weeks later, there was a continuation of the sexual relationship. How does that happen? How does it get broken off and then rekindled?
A Well, there continued to sort of be this flirtation that was -- when we'd see each other. And then one night, I don't -- I think it was maybe in the end of -- the end of February or maybe some time in March when he had -- I had seen him in the hall when I was leaving to go from work, and this was the night he was coming back from the Israeli embassy from something, and we didn't make any contact or anything because he was with Evelyn Lieberman. And I went home.
About 45 minutes later, he called me and had told

Page 91

me he had gone back to his office and had called my office because he wanted me to come over and visit with him, but I was home now, you know, and then he had gone back upstairs.
So that had sort of implied to me that he was interested in starting up again and then when I saw him on the 31st of March -- when he kissed me, that pretty much --
Q Just, basically, people got back together.
A Yeah. There was never a discussion of, "Okay, now we're going to resume our relationship again." I didn't want to -- why bring up the memory of the guilt? So --
Q Okay. Then what I'd like to do next is turn our attention back to April 7th, which is the Easter Sunday, and we're going to ask some more detailed questions about that period. First, when you got to the White House, did you see a Secret Service agent and did the two of you talk?
A Yes.
Q All right. Tell us who it was and what the two of you said to one another.
A It was John Muskett, I believe. And I had brought some papers with me from home and so I believe I said something, "Oh, the President asked me to bring these to him." And John Muskett said, "Oh, I'd better check with Evelyn Lieberman." And I don't remember exactly what the rest of the exchange was, but I talked him out of doing that and then I just went in.

Page 92

Q Were you nervous when he said, "I've got to talk to Evelyn Lieberman"?
A Oh, yeah. Yes. Also, it alarmed me that she was there. I didn't really expect her to be there on a Sunday evening.
Q You mentioned that a telephone call came in while you were with the President. Did you later come to believe you knew who that call was from?
A I made a speculation about who that call was from. I have no knowledge nor had no knowledge about who was on the phone call.
Q Let's take this a step at a time, then.
A Okay.
Q First, what do you remember about the content of the call and then what was the reason that you drew whatever conclusion you did later?
A The content was political in nature and I drew, you know, the possibility that it was Dick Morris just based on -- that it was campaign stuff. And I think that how it even came up that it could possibly be Dick Morris was in a joking way with Linda on the phone.
So I don't believe that I ever -- I don't think I would have ever categorically stated that it was Dick Morris on the phone, because I didn't know that.
Q All right. About how long after April 7th did you

Page 93

draw the conclusion or develop the suspicion perhaps that it was Dick Morris?
A I don't remember.
Q Okay. All right. At some point, did you hear a voice that you believed to be Harold Ickes' voice?
A Yes.
Q Okay. Tell us how that happened.
A The President and I were in -- I believe it was the back study or the study and -- or we might have been in the hallway, I don't really remember, but I -- Harold Ickes has a very distinct voice and so he -- I heard him holler "Mr. President," and the President looked at me and I looked at him and he jetted out into the Oval Office and I panicked and didn't know that -- I thought that maybe because Harold was so close with the President that they might just wander back there and the President would assume that I knew to leave. So I went out the back way.
Q When you say you went out the back way --
A Through the dining room.
Q Where did you go?
A I went through the dining room exit, to the left, past the Chief of Staff's office, to the right, down the stairs.
Q Were you in a hurry?
A Yes.

Page 94

Q All right. At some point afterwards, did you get a call from the President?
A Yes.
Q All right. And what happened in that phone call?
A He asked me why I left, so I told him that I didn't know if he was going to be coming back and so he -- he was a little upset with me that I left.
MR. EMMICK: All right. Before we move off that particular call, are there any follow-up questions that you have? Yes?
MR. WISENBERG: Yes. Yes. And I'll try to be delicate. I'm not known for delicacy.
THE WITNESS: I can see that everyone seems to agree with that.
BY MR. WISENBERG:
Q First of all, Ms. Lewinsky, when you went out the dining room, did you go out through Nel's pantry door or through the main dining room door?
A I would have gone out the dining room door.
Q Okay. I want to make sure that I get the sequence right, because this is partly based on stuff we discussed Monday in New York and you correct me if I get anything wrong.
A Okay.
Q We'll do it that way. As I understand it, there

Page 95

is a -- you're back with the President that day and let me ask first if you recall, the more intimate sexual moments that day, were they in the hallway or the back study?
A Both.
Q Okay. Now, as I understand it, you're with the President. It's an intimate moment. A call comes in.
A Correct.
Q All right. And the President leaves.
A Mm-hmm.
Q You put your top back on. Your top had been off and you put your top back on.
A Mm-hmm.
Q And at some point he comes back. Is that correct?
A Mm-hmm.
Q Okay. And what I'm trying to do is distinguish between the Ickes event and the call, if there is a distinction in your mind. In other words --
A Yes.
Q The call is something different, as far as you know, from the Ickes event.
A Correct.
Q Okay. The President comes back and it's at some point later that you hear the voice of Harold Ickes.
A I'm sorry --
Q The President comes back from the phone call th

Page 96

he takes --
A No. The -- someone came in to tell the President he had a phone call, so someone came in, hollered something, not Mr. Ickes.
Q Okay.
A The President went out, came back in and I think then they sent the phone call in.
Q All right. He took that in --
A He took the phone call in the back study.
Q Okay.
A Then we were -- and I think we had been in the hallway -- I know we had been in the hallway prior to that.
Q Okay.
A And he came back in and then the phone rang and he took the phone call in the back study.
Q Okay.
A Then it was much later in that same day that he heard the "Mr. President" voice.
Q Of Ickes.
A Right. And I'm going to -- I think that we were in the back study at that point because that's why he jetted so quickly, not wanting Harold, I think, to walk back there. That was --
Q Okay. Now, the voice you heard saying to the President that he had a call --

Page 97

A Mm-hmm.
Q You never saw the President attached to that voice.
A No. And it wasn't a voice that was familiar to me.
Q Okay. And you never saw Ickes. Is that correct? When you later heard his voice, you didn't see him. You're just familiar with his voice.
A Correct.
Q As far as you know, did Ickes see you when you headed out the back way?
A He couldn't have.
Q Okay. Why do you say that?
A Because he was in the office.
Q Okay. And you said that Ickes was much later. I mean, much later within the whole time you were there with the President that day?
A Right. Correct.
Q Okay. I mean, not like several hours later.
A No. No.
Q Okay.
A Just much later within my visit.
MR. WISENBERG: Okay. Thank you.
BY MR. EMMICK:
Q What I'd like to do is turn our attention to a call that you got from the President some time, I believe, in April, but correct me if I'm wrong, where he asked you

Page 98

something about whether you had told your mother --
A Yes.
Q -- about the relationship. Let's first talk about -- can you place this in time as best you can?
A It was April. And this came about because -- I guess Marsha Scott, I think, had relayed some information to the President about her conversations, I think possibly with Walter Kaye, who is a friend of my family's, and that from that conversation, I think Marsha either directly said to the President or the President wondered from something Marsha said, if I had told my mom -- well, it must have been the President assuming from something that Marsha said.
The President asked me if I had told my mom or had my mom told -- and where that went was had my mom told Walter Kaye. And I said no.
Q What you're describing, is it all based on what the President said in this phone call?
A I don't understand.
Q Yes. You said that at some point it was based on the fact that Walter had spoken to Marsha Scott and I'm trying to figure out if you're learning that from a different source or if it's all from the President.
A No, I was learning that from the phone call with the President.
Q All right. How long was the phone call?

Page 99

A You know, I'm thinking just now, I don't know if that was in April. It could have been in May.
MR. EMMICK: Okay.
A JUROR: Of 1997?
THE WITNESS: Yes. Sorry. Okay. I don't know if the month time is important or not.
BY MR. EMMICK:
Q In April or May, you have this discussion.
A Right.
Q The President asks you if you've told your mother about the relationship.
A Right.
Q What do you respond?
A "No. Of course not."
MR. EMMICK: Okay.
MR. WISENBERG: Mike?
MR. EMMICK: Yes?
MR. WISENBERG: Can I butt in?
MR. EMMICK: Yes.
BY MR. WISENBERG:
Q Do you know independently what, if any, conversation there was -- that is, whether -- did you later learn that Walter had said something to Marsha or that somebody had said something to Walter?
A In a way, that's too broad of a question because

Page 100

I think Walter Kaye kind of comes in and out -- if you look at this whole few years, he comes in and out of this in a few ways, so -- did I learn independently that Walter had had a discussion with Marsha? No. Is that what you were asking me?
Q Well, that's one. How about with anybody else? I guess did you hear anything that struck you as this is kind of consistent with what the President had told me in that conversation or this fits together now? Walter had a conversation with somebody and could have actually talked to Marsha Scott and then that got relayed to the President.
A I don't think I'm following you 100 percent. I'm sorry.
Q Okay. Well, I'm not always very articulate. I'll just --
A It --
Q Do you recall -- let me be more specific. Are you aware of your aunt ever having made a comment to Walter Kaye?
A I'm aware of Walter Kaye having made a comment to my aunt.
Q Okay. And what was that?
A He remarked something to my aunt that he had heard from people that the reason I had left the White House or had been moved from the White House was because I had had this relationship with the President.

Page 101

Q Do you know what your aunt responded to Walter Kaye?

A My understanding was she got up and walked out. She was having lunch with him.

BY MR. EMMICK:

Q After you had this telephone call with the President where he asked you whether you had told your mom, was the next time that you saw the President May 24th, I think, which you refer to as dump day?

A Yes. Either way, it would have been, whether it was in April or May.

Q Right. Because you didn't see him in April --

A Right.

Q -- and you only saw him once in May.

A Right. Correct.

Q All right. And you had -- that's fine. All right. What I'd like to turn our attention to next is as we're working down our outline here, we're finished up with the July 3rd, 4th and 4th period. I take it that you remained frustrated with the President's efforts to try to get you back to the White House.

A Mm-hmm. I mean, it always -- and I did make this clear to him, that it was always more important to me to have him in my life than to -- than to get the job, but the job was something that was important to me.

Page 102

Q Did there come a time in about October when you gave up, more or less, on your efforts to get back to the White House and you turned your attention more to New York City?

A Yes.

Q All right. Tell us how that happened.

A Linda Tripp called me at work on October 6th and told me that her friend Kate in the NSC had heard from -- had heard rumors about me and that I would never work in the White House again and, if I did, I wouldn't have a blue pass and that her advice to me was "get out of town." So that meant to me that I wasn't going to be coming back to the White House and I was very upset by that.

Also, she, Linda, told me that Kate had said, "You know, they create jobs at the White House, you know, six days a week." And that Stephen Goodin's girlfriend had just gotten a job, so with these examples of how there had been all these other people receiving jobs that I could have done and I didn't get it.

Q Did you communicate your additional frustration and disappointment to the President?

A Yes, I did.

Q Tell us how and when.

A I believe I sent him a short note telling him that I really needed to talk to him in person having to do with

Page 103

this subject matter and he and I had an argument in a conversation on the 9th of October.

Q And was that a telephone conversation?

A Yes, it was.

Q Did he call you or did you call him?

A He called me.

Q About what time, if you can remember?

A I think it was around 2:30, 3:00 in the morning.

Q Was it a long phone call?

A Yes. Yes. 2:00, 2:30 maybe.

Q Is it fair to characterize the phone call as involving an argument?

A Yes. And then we made up.

Q And then you made up.

A It was half argument, half making up.

Q Did the name Vernon Jordan come up in the course of that discussion?

A It's possible.

Q What do you have in mind about the first time that Vernon Jordan's name would have come up in conversations with the President?

A It was either in that phone call or on October 11th.

Q And tell us what was said about Vernon Jordan, whether it was in the phone call or on the 11th.

Page 104

A I don't remember. I know that I had discussed with Linda and either I had had the thought or she had suggested that Vernon Jordan would be a good person who is a close friend of the President and who has a lot of contacts in New York, so that that might be someone who might be able to help me secure a position in New York, if I didn't want to go to the U.N.

Q And what was the President's response?

A "I think that was a good idea."

Q At some point, did you send the President something like a list of jobs or interests that you might have in New York?

A Yes. He asked me to prepare that on the 11th of October.

Q At some point, did you have an initial meeting with Vernon Jordan?

A Yes, I did.

Q Can you tell us when that was, as best you can recall?

A The beginning of November of last year.

Q How was that meeting arranged?

A Through conversations with the President and with Betty.

Q Without getting into a lot of detail about what happened there during the first meeting with Vernon Jordan,

Page 105

what did you think were your job prospects after that? Did it look like things were going to happen?
A Yes.
Q All right. And what happened with respect to the job situation from that meeting with Vernon Jordan until, say, Thanksgiving?
A Nothing, really.
Q Okay. Then let's turn our attention to the month of December. We'll have to relate back a little bit to November in order to complete things, but on December 5th, did you return to Washington from overseas?
A I did. You know -- the question you just asked me before about until Thanksgiving, I did have a conversation with him before Thanksgiving, I think it was the day before.
Q Okay.
A So --
Q Then why don't you complete that, then.
A Okay. I had spoken to Betty about -- about not being -- being able to get in touch with Mr. Jordan because he was in and out of town and then wasn't necessarily returning my call. He's a busy man. And so Betty arranged for me to speak with him again and I spoke with him when I was in Los Angeles before -- right before Thanksgiving.
Q Okay. Let's just go back, if we might, to that early November meeting with Mr. Jordan.

Page 106

A Okay.
Q Did he say anything indicating to you that he had spoken with the President recently about you?
A Yes. I believe he mentioned he'd had a conversation with the President.
Q And what did he say about that or what did he say that indicated he may have spoken with the President?
A I believe he mentioned that in the course of the conversation and as I was leaving, he remarked to me that I came highly recommended.
Q Okay. Let's turn our attention to December 5th, then.
A Okay.
Q Having in mind that you had had a meeting with Vernon Jordan and a discussion and were trying to get a hold of him, when you got back from overseas, sort of what was the status of the Vernon Jordan job effort?
A When I had spoken with Mr. Jordan right before Thanksgiving, he had asked me to call him the next week, either, I think, Thursday or Friday. And because I was out of town, I called him on Friday when I got back, and it was my understanding from his secretary he had gone out of town that day, so we had missed each other.
Q All right. Did you try to arrange a meeting with President Clinton?

Page 107

A Yes.
Q Tell us what you did to try to arrange meeting with President Clinton.
A I sent a note to Betty much earlier in the week that I asked her to pass along to him which in that letter requested of him that I could come have a visit that Saturday.
Q Did you follow up that note with a call to Ms. Currie?
A Yes.
Q When was that call, if you remember?
A December 5th.
Q Okay. And what happened during the call?
A Well, there were several calls, actually. And so at first, it was -- the first few, she still hadn't given him the note.
So then finally she gave him the note, just, I think, right after the radio address or right before his radio address, and then she told me that he was meeting with his lawyers all day Saturday, but that she was coming in in the morning to give a tour and she would check and see with him then, you know, if maybe I could come by, but that the prospects didn't look good.
Q Was she focused on Saturday because you had asked whether Saturday would be a good time?

Page 108

A Mm-hmm. Yes. I'm sorry. Maybe he was going out of town on Sunday. I'm not sure why I would have focused on Saturday versus Sunday.
Q In any event, what she said was he was busy with meetings with lawyers, something like that?
A Yes.
Q All right. Did you go to a Christmas party that night?
A Yes, I did.
Q Did you see the President?
A Yes, I did.
Q Let's turn our attention to December 6th.
A Okay.
Q Are you doing okay?
A Yes.
Q All right. December 6th. Let me ask as a background question, had you previously purchased for the President a Christmas present?
A Yes.
Q All right. What was that Christmas present?
A It was a sterling silver antique standing cigar holder.
Q You had been unable to arrange an actual visit with the President to give him that present in person. What did you do instead?

Page 109

A I had some other gifts for him as well that I had gotten on my trips and --
Q Tell us what those other gifts were, if you remember.
A A tie. A mug from Starbucks in Santa Monica. A little box that's called hugs and kisses and it's Xs and Os inside, it's really -- it's just a cute little chatchki. An antique book from the flea market in New York that was on Theodore Roosevelt. And -- I think that's it.
Q Okay. What did you try to do on the 6th in order to give those gifts to the President?
A Well, I had wanted to give them to him, if I was going to have a planned visit with him, and then through the -- just some course of events, I got upset and I decided that I was really tired of everything that was going on and I just -- it was clear to me that he was ignoring me and I just didn't want to deal with this anymore.
So I decided -- I had purchased these presents for him and I'm very -- I spend a lot of time and am very particular about the presents I give to people, so I didn't want to give them to someone else and I wanted him to have them, so I packaged them up with a note that I was going to drop off to Betty.
Q And where did you go?
A I went to the southwest gate.

Page 110

Q What happened at the southwest gate?
A I paged Betty or I think I might have called her. I know I called her and she wasn't at her desk, so I paged her to let her know I was there. And then Marsha Scott drove up, so I ran away to the northwest gate because I didn't want Marsha to see me. Continue from there?
Q Yes. Did you have any trouble getting in at the northwest gate? What happened?
A Well, I wasn't trying to get in. I -- so --
Q What were you trying to do?
A I was trying to wait for Betty. So I called Betty from the northwest gate and she wasn't at her desk and then I saw someone go into the -- it was under construction at the time, so it was a different little hut than normal, and I saw someone who went in who I thought was John Podesta, so I thought I would -- since I knew that Betty had talked to John Podesta about me, I thought I would ask him, you know, maybe I would ask her -- I would give the gifts -- I would feel comfortable probably giving the gifts to John Podesta to give to Betty, just knowing that he knew I had a relationship with her.
So when I went in to ask this person who I thought was John Podesta -- it turned out to be Lanny -- I think Lanny Davis, and so then one of the guards said, "Oh, are you here to see Betty Currie?"

Page 111

And I said, "No. I'm not here to see her, I'm trying to get her. She doesn't know I'm coming."
And then they told me she was giving a tour and that Eleanor -- do you want me to go into this detail?
Q Sure.
A Okay. That Eleanor Mondale had come recently and that she was giving a tour to Eleanor Mondale. Then I sort of -- wanting to know if the President was in the office, asked the guards, "Oh, well, is the President in the office? Because if he is, she's probably too busy to come out and get these gifts."
And they said, "Yes, he was."
Q What was you reaction to that?
A Not good.
Q Okay.
A Very upset. Hysterical.
Q Where did you go and what did you do?
A I turned around and walked out and I was livid. I had -- well -- are the grand jurors aware of the rumors about Eleanor Mondale that had been out? I mean, because it doesn't make sense if --
BY MS. IMMERGUT:
Q Well, why don't you say why you were upset.
A [redacted]

Page 112

[redacted]
BY MR. WISENBERG:
Q A question. Pardon me for interrupting. I just wanted to -- you said you were upset. Did you show your upsetness to any of the guards?
A No.
MR. WISENBERG: Thank you.
BY MR. EMMICK:
Q Did you contact Betty?
A Yes, I did.
Q Where did you contact her from?
A I called her from the pay phone at the Corcoran Gallery.
Q Did you have a fight with her?
A I think so.
Q Okay. You say you think so --
A I'm trying to remember if I -- if I actually got her on the phone, which I think I did. I'm pretty sure I did.

Page 113

Q All right. Did you eventually come to talk to the President on the telephone?
A Through a much more circuitous route, yes, I did.
Q All right. And where were you at that time?
A I was at home.
Q All right. And about what time of day was it?
A Maybe around noon or so.
Q How did the two of you come to be speaking on the phone? Who placed the calls?
A Well, I believe maybe I had called Betty or maybe Betty called me, one of the two, but she put him on the phone.
Q All right. And what happened in the conversation with the President?
A Well, we had a fight. And he was very angry with me.
Q Why was he angry with you?
A Because I had gotten so upset and I had made a stink to Betty and I had -- you know -- I -- what I came to learn, I think, is that as a result of me being upset with Betty and mentioning that I knew Eleanor Mondale was there, Betty called the guards at the northwest gate and so it had just caused a whole big commotion.
And he was just angry at me and he told me it was none of my business what -- you know, what he was doing and

Page 114

that -- you know, that -- that he had never been treated as poorly by anyone else as I treated him and that he spent more time with me than anyone else in the world, aside from his family, friends and staff, which I don't know exactly which category that put me in, but --
Q Okay. Was it a long phone call with the President?
A Maybe half an hour, 45 minutes.
Q Eventually, were arrangements made for you to visit him at the White House?
A Mm-hmm.
Q Are you doing okay?
A Yeah. Yes.
Q Were you surprised that he would let you come to the White House?
A Yeah, I was -- yes, I was a little bit surprised.
Q Why?
A Because none of the other times that we had really fought on the phone did it end up resulting in a visit that day.
Q All right. What about the fact that he was supposedly meeting with his lawyers all day? Did he say anything about that?
A He had in the fight. When we were fighting, he said -- you know, he was angry because he said, "I have one day to meet with my lawyers and, you know, I've got you

Page 115

messing things up and being upset and blah, blah, blah."
So --
Q Did you go and did you meet with the President?
A Yes, I did.
Q Did Betty wave you in?
A Yes.
Q Can you describe for us in general terms how that meeting went? Did you give him the gifts, for example?
A I did. It was -- it was a really nice visit.
Q Okay. What do you mean by a "nice visit"?
A It was just sweet. He liked his Christmas presents and we were very affectionate and it just -- it was just nice to be with him.
Q Did you discuss the job search?
A I believe so.
Q At the time, how did you think the job search was going?
A Not very well. With respect to Mr. Jordan.
Q Right. And did you communicate that to the President?
A Yes.
Q Can you give us a little more detail? What would you have said to one another?
A I think I said that I -- that I was supposed to get in touch with Mr. Jordan the previous week and that things

Page 116

didn't work out and that nothing had really happened yet.
Q Did the President say what he was going to do?
A I think he said he would -- you know, this was sort of typical of him, to sort of say, "Oh, I'll talk to him. I'll get on it."
Q Okay. Did he say anything to you about whether he had a Christmas present for you?
A Yes, he did.
Q What did he say?
A He told me that on the phone, actually.
Q All right. What did he say about that?
A Well, I said to him, "Well, how do you have a Christmas present? I haven't read that you've gone Christmas shopping yet." And he said that he had bought it in Vancouver.
Q Okay. Did he say at any time on the 6th anything about a witness list or your being on a witness list?
A No.
Q How were things left when you left him on the 6th?
A That he would bring me -- oh, our meeting ended up -- or was cut short by the fact that he had to have a meeting with Mr. Bowles, so he told me that he'd give me my Christmas present another time and that he wouldn't jerk me around and abandon me.
You know, that -- because I think I remarked to

Page 117

him, "Well, at the rate we go, I won't get it 'til Christmas of '98." So --
MR. EMMICK: I have no more questions about this date and I look at the time and it looks like it's 12:30.
THE FOREPERSON: Sol, I think, went to check on something.
MR. EMMICK: Oh, all right.
THE FOREPERSON: Did you check on something for lunch?
MR. WISENBERG: I have checked. It is here. It's been here.
MR. EMMICK: Okay. All right. Well, if this would be a good time to take a break for lunch --
THE FOREPERSON: It's fine with me.
MR. EMMICK: Okay. Let's take an hour-long break for lunch.
THE FOREPERSON: Hour-long.
MR. EMMICK: Okay.
THE WITNESS: Okay.
THE FOREPERSON: Okay.
MR. EMMICK: Thank you.
(Whereupon, at 12:34 p.m., a luncheon recess was taken.)

* * * * *

Page 118

AFTERNOON SESSION

Whereupon, (1:38 p.m.)

MONICA S. LEWINSKY

was recalled as a witness and, after having been previously duly sworn by the Foreperson of the Grand Jury, was examined and testified further as follows:

EXAMINATION (RESUMED)

THE WITNESS: Time for a nap?
MR. EMMICK: Madam Foreperson, do we have a quorum?
THE FOREPERSON: Yes, we do.
MR. EMMICK: Are there any unauthorized persons present?
THE FOREPERSON: There are none.
Monica, I'd like to remind you that you are still under oath.
THE WITNESS: Okay. Thanks.
BY MR. EMMICK:
Q Ms. Lewinsky, we just got through speaking about the December 6th meeting that you had with the President. What I'd like to do is turn our attention next to the date of December 11th.
A Mm-hmm.
Q Did you have a meeting with Vernon Jordan on that day?
A Yes, I did.

Page 119

Q Would you tell us when that meeting was?
A Around lunchtime.
Q And how was that meeting arranged?
A By his secretary.
Q What was the purpose of the meeting?
A For him to -- I learned after we had the meeting, for him to give me some contact names and some suggestion of what to do with these contact names.
Q When you say --
A For a job.
Q When you say "contact names," these are names of potential employers?
A Yes.
Q What else did the two of you talk about?
A We talked about my -- the fact that my mom's fiance at the time knew Mr. Jordan. We talked about the President.
What else did we talk about? I think that's it.
Q All right. Did he at some point make a comment to you about your being a friend of the President?
A Yes, he did.
Q Would you tell us how the conversation transpired from that point?
A I don't remember how we got to this point, but at some point, Mr. Jordan said something to me, "Well, you're a friend of the President of the United States."

Page 120

And I remarked that I didn't -- I didn't really look at him as the President, that I saw him more as a man and reacted to him more as a man and got angry at him like a man and just a regular person.
And Mr. Jordan asked me what I got angry at the President about, so I told him when he doesn't call me enough or see me enough.
We were sort of bantering back and forth about that and then he told me that I shouldn't get angry at the President because he's got a lot of -- it sounds so stupid -- obviously, he has a lot of other more important things and difficult things to deal with than someone getting upset with him. And he suggested that if I was upset that I should call and take my frustrations out on Mr. Jordan instead of the President.
I mean, I think I should just say that it was all -- this was all sort of in a light tone.
Q Is this a meeting during which the subject of your possibly being in love cropped up?
A Oh, yes. So after we had the conversation I was just talking about with Mr. Jordan, he said to me, "Well, you know what your problem is?"
And I said, "What?"
He said, "Don't deny it." And he said, "You're in love, that's what your problem is."

Page 121

So I think I just -- probably blushed or giggled, something like that.

Q How did the meeting end? What were you going to do and what was he going to do?

A I was planning to send the letters that he had suggested I write to the list of people and he suggested that I cc him and keep in touch with him, keep him apprised of what was happening with my job search.

Q And did you send out those letters?

A Yes, I did.

Q And make arrangements for some interviews?

A Yes, I did.

Q What I want to do next, then, is direct your attention to a few days later, several days later, a week later, I guess. Did you come to have a telephone conversation with the President on December 17th?

A Yes.

Q Would you tell us how that telephone call was -- how that conversation took place?

A Okay. The phone rang unexpectedly at about maybe 2:00 or 2:30 and --

BY MS. IMMERGUT:

Q In the morning?

A Right. In the morning. And it was the President and he called and said he had two things to tell me and then

Page 122

he had to call me right back. So he called me right back.

BY MR. EMMICK:

Q Did he explain why he had to call and then call back?

A I don't know. He just was very brief with me and then he said, "I'll call you right back." And he hung up and called back about a minute later.

Q Before you get to the actual things that he says next, you mentioned that you unexpectedly go the call. Why were you surprised by the call?

A Normally, the President wouldn't call me when Mrs. Clinton was in town, so -- and I usually was aware when she was out of town, so I that I would sort of be expecting or hoping that he would call. And the call came as a surprise to me.

Q He called you back?

A Right.

Q Then what happened?

A And he told me that he had two things to tell me. The first was that Betty's brother had been killed in a car accident and that -- so I reacted that and we talked about that being -- that this was the same brother who had been beaten up just a few months ago and she had lost her sister and her mom was ill. We talked about Betty for a little bit.

Page 123

And then he told me he had some more bad news, that he had seen the witness list for the Paula Jones case and my name was on it.

Q Did you get an impression from him about when he had found out your name was on the witness list?

A Yes. I mean, the impression I got based on the entire conversation was that he found out recently.

Q When he told you that, what did he say about having seen your name on the witness list?

A He told me it broke his heart.

Q Tell us how the conversation went from there.

A I was -- I'm sure, as you can imagine, I was upset and shocked. He told me that it didn't necessarily mean that I would be subpoenaed, but that that was a possibility, and if I were to be subpoenaed, that I should contact Betty and let Betty know that I had received the subpoena.

I believe that I probably asked him, you know, what should I do in the course of that and he suggested, he said, "Well, maybe you can sign an affidavit."

At some point in the conversation, and I don't know if it was before or after the subject of the affidavit came up, he sort of said, "You know, you can always say you were coming to see Betty or that you were bringing me letters." Which I understood was really a reminder of things that we had discussed before.

Page 124

Q So when you say things you had discussed, sort of ruses that you had developed.

A Right. I mean, this was -- this was something that -- that was instantly familiar to me.

Q Right.

A And I knew exactly what he meant.

Q Had you talked with him earlier about these false explanations about what you were doing visiting him on several occasions?

A Several occasions throughout the entire relationship. Yes. It was the pattern of the relationship, to sort of conceal it.

Q When he said that you might sign an affidavit, what did you understand it to mean at that time?

A I thought that signing an affidavit could range from anywhere -- the point of it would be to deter or to prevent me from being deposed and so that that could range from anywhere between maybe just somehow mentioning, you know, innocuous things or going as far as maybe having to deny any kind of a relationship.

Q At some point, did you talk with him about possibly settling the Paula Jones case?

A Yes. I had -- I had had a thought and then had a conversation with Linda about this and just a way that he could settle the case and I suggested it to him.

Page 125

Q And what was that way? Not in a lot of detail, but --

A The gist of it is, I thought that first Mrs. Clinton should do something publicly, maybe on a T.V. show or something, and talk about how difficult the case had been for her and on her daughter and that she just wished that he would settle it and it would go away. And then the President should unannounced and unexpectedly go into the briefing room, make a brief statement that he -- in an effort to put this behind him, you know, against his attorneys' advice, he was going to pay Ms. Jones whatever it was, however much she wanted, and so that this case would be over with.

Q Did the two of you talk about how much the settlement amount would be or might be?

A Yes. I believe at some point I had mentioned that I had recently read the -- I think she had lowered her -- the amount that she wanted to $500,000 or something lower and he said, "I thought it was a million or two million dollars."

And I thought that was very strange, that he wouldn't know she had -- you know, that her lawyers -- or his lawyers had not told him that she had lowered her request for money. Or I don't know how you say that legally, whatever it is that she did.

Q Right. Demand, probably.

Page 126

A The demand was lower.

Q Right.

A We also talked in this conversation about he mentioned that -- he said he'd try and see if Betty could come in on the weekend to give me my Christmas presents and I told him that was out of the question, to -- you know, let Betty be.

Q Because her brother had just been killed, right?

A Right.

Q All right. About how long was the entire phone call? Or I guess technically it would be the second phone call.

A Maybe a half an hour. Maybe I could just say since you asked me earlier that it was him suggesting that I would contact Betty if I were subpoenaed that led me to believe he didn't think I would be subpoenaed that soon because he knew Betty was going to be out, you know, he assumed obviously that Betty would be out for the week or two weeks with the unexpected loss of her brother.

Q Right.

A So that was what led me to believe he had just found out.

Q After the call was ended, did you call anyone else?

A Yes. About a half an hour later, I called Linda.

Q What did the two of you talk about?

Page 127

A My conversation with the President.

Q Right. It seems self-evident, but --

A I know. I'm sorry.

Q That's all right. What did you tell Linda?

A Well, if I could just jump back --

Q Yes.

A I mean, I had -- Linda had told me some time in -- I think the second week of December that she had been subpoenaed in the Paula Jones case and that she intended to rat on me, so up until this point, I had been trying to convince her not to tell, that it's not anybody's business.

So when I -- part of my telling her that the President had called; that I, too, may be pulled into this case was just sort of -- maybe assure her that if that happened, there would be someone else denying it, it wouldn't be just Linda out there alone saying "I don't know anything about any kind of relationship between the President and Monica."

Q Kind of a unified front or something like that?

A Exactly.

Q All right. How was the conversation left with Linda?

A I think that we'd talk about it the next day.

Q Did you get subpoenaed?

A Yes, I did.

Page 128

Q When did you get subpoenaed?

A On Friday, the 19th of December.

Q Can you tell us about when you believe you were subpoenaed?

A I believe it was around 3:00, 4:00 in the afternoon. I think closer to 3:00, 3:30.

Q Okay. Where were you served?

A At the Pentagon.

Q Could you tell us how it happened? Did someone call you?

A Yes. I received a call in my office from the gentleman who was to deliver the subpoena to me. He informed me he had a subpoena for me. I made a stink to him, asking him why I was being subpoenaed and I had no idea what was going on.

When he gave me the subpoena, he suggested I call Ms. Jones' attorneys, which I made a comment to him that that's not something I would do.

Q When you actually did get served, what was your real reaction inside?

A I burst into tears. It was -- it was very scary. I mean, it just -- sort of my worst nightmare, or I had thought until that point, was being subpoenaed in this case. So I was pretty upset.

Q You couldn't call Betty because Betty was --

Page 129

A Right.
Q -- in mourning herself. Who did you call?
A I called Mr. Jordan.
Q From what phone did you call Mr. Jordan?
A From a pay phone.
Q Close to where you were served, the nearest pay phone around?
A No, I think it was the pay phone which is down the hall from my office, which is kind of halfway between where I was served and my office.
Q And why did you use a pay phone?
A Because I was crying and I -- I mean, I -- my office, the way my office is set up is my desk was in the same room with four or five other people, so I couldn't very well have any kind of a private discussion.
Q What did you tell Mr. Jordan?
A Well, I don't remember what I told him. I was crying and he didn't seem to understand me, so he just -- he just told me to come to his office around 5:00.
BY MS. IMMERGUT:
Q Did you tell him you'd been subpoenaed?
A I probably did. I just -- I mean, I don't -- I don't remember, I just remember being on the phone crying and him saying, "I can't understand you. I can't understand you."

Page 130

Q You got off the phone. What did you do next? Did you finally go to Vernon Jordan's office?
A Yes. I tried to compose myself and I went into the office. I told Mr. -- I believe I told Mr. Bacon or some other people in the office that I had an emergency and I needed to leave. I went home, sort of put myself together, and went to Mr. Jordan's office.
Q When you got to Mr. Jordan's office, did you have to wait outside for a bit?
A Yes.
Q In like a reception area?
A I waited in the lobby, like I always did.
Q About how long did you wait in the lobby?
A I don't really remember.
Q At some point, I take it, you did actually meet with Mr. Jordan?
A Yes.
Q How did the conversation with Mr. Jordan progress?
A First, I came in and I explained to him clearly that I had been subpoenaed and that I was upset and shortly after, I think maybe I said I didn't know what I was supposed to do, I didn't have an attorney, I think I was rambling.
Shortly after I had arrived at Mr. Jordan's office, he received a phone call and I stepped out of the office.
Q Did he ask you to step out of the office?

Page 131

A I think I may have offered. That was sort of par for the course. And I waited for him while he was on the phone outside his office and when I came back in, he placed a call to -- I don't know if it was right after I came back in, but at some point, when I came back in, he placed a call to Mr. Frank Carter.
Q Now, when you stepped out, he took one call and then you stepped back in, did he tell you who he'd been on the phone with?
A No.
Q All right. He places a call to Frank Carter. Do you know whether he talked to Frank Carter in person or do you know whether he just left a message or do you recall?
A I don't really recall.
Q When --
A Oh, he said something about -- well, I know he referred to Mr. Carter as Mr. Carter, so I don't know if he was talking -- I don't really remember if he was talking to Mr. Carter or he was talking to someone else, but it scared me because I thought for Mr. Jordan to be referring to someone else as Mr. something, that -- I sort of thought he must be a big deal.
Q All right. When you went to the meeting with Mr. Jordan, did you bring the subpoena with you?

Page 132

A Yes, I did.
Q Did you show it to Mr. Jordan?
A I believe so.
Q What most troubled you about the language of the subpoena and what the subpoena had called for you to produce?
A The thing that alarmed me was that it asked for a hat pin.
Q Okay. And why did that alarm you?
A Because I thought that was a very specific gift and in this list of gifts, everything else seemed to be somewhat generic and then it had hat pin, which screamed out at me because that was the first gift that the President had given me and it had some significance.
Q When you showed Mr. Jordan the subpoena, did he make any remark about any of the things that were called for?
A Yes. When I mentioned to him, I think, about the hat pin, he said, "Oh, don't worry about it. This is a vanilla subpoena, this is a standard subpoena," something like that. Generic subpoena, maybe.
Q Did you know what he meant, a vanilla or standard subpoena that asks for hat pins?
A Well, what I understood that to mean was that -- that what he was trying to say is there was nothing out of the ordinary about this subpoena.
Q I see. I guess what I'm trying to get at is do you

Page 133

think he was trying to imply that all subpoenas ask for that or that all subpoenas in the Paula Jones case asked for that or all subpoenas -- what was he -- from your point of view, what was he trying to convey?

A I think what he -- I think what he was trying to convey was stop worrying, that this is not something out of the -- you know, out of the realm of possibility of what might be in a subpoena.

Q All right. Were you reassured by that?

A A little. I -- I sort of felt that he wasn't -- I mean, he didn't really understand what I was saying.

Q All right. Did you have any discussion with him about letting the President know that you'd been subpoenaed?

A Yes. I asked Mr. Jordan to inform the President.

Q How did you ask? How often? How vigorously?

A I -- I mean, I asked him to -- to please make sure that he told the President. He said he was going to see the President that night, so --

Q All right. Did the subject of a possible sexual relationship between you and the President come up in the conversation?

A Yes, it did.

Q Tell us how it came up.

A Mr. Jordan said to me that there -- "There are

Page 134

two important questions" or "There are two important -- " I think, "Two important questions that are related to the case: Did you have sex with the President, you know, or did he ask?" And I said no to both of those.

Q What did you interpret him to be asking when he asked you those questions?

A Well, I thought he -- I guess -- can I step back for a minute?

Q Sure. Up until a point that we'll get to, which is December 31st, I sort of -- mainly, I think, from my discussions with Linda, I was under the impression that -- that Mr. Jordan kind of knew with a wink and a nod that I was having a relationship with the President, that it was never -- he and I never discussed it, but I thought it might be possible.

I'm, you know, a young woman, sort of coming to see him, the President's mentioned me. But I also was sort of under this influence of Linda saying to me, "Of course he knows. Of course he knows. Of course he knows."

So when he asked me those questions, I thought he was asking me, saying essentially "What are you going to say?" not necessarily asking me directly what -- you know, "What are the answers to these questions?" More "What are you going to reply in regard to the case?"

Q Now, was your interpretation of his questions based

Page 135

entirely on your assumption about what he knew? Or was it based in part on how he asked the questions?

A I think it was based more in part on my assumptions of what he knew.

Q Was there anything unusual or suggestive about how he asked the questions?

A No.

Q And how did you answer the questions?

A No and no.

Q Okay. Did you try to make it clear to him at all that there was more to the story than just no and no?

A Not at that point.

Q At that time, did you make arrangements to meet with the attorney who you would get, Mr. Frank Carter?

A Yes. After Mr. Jordan made the arrangements with Mr. Carter, he told me to be at his office at -- I think 11:00 or 10:30 on Monday.

Q All right. How did the meeting with Mr. Jordan end? Was there any reference to a hug?

A Oh, yes. I'm sorry.

Q That's okay.

A When I was leaving, I asked him if he would give the President a hug for me. I bugged him again about making sure he told the President. And so he said, "I don't hug men." I said, "Well, okay."

Page 136

Q All right.

A But --

Q All right. Did you call Linda Tripp afterwards?

A Yes, I did.

Q What was the purpose of your call?

A In a -- to let her know that I had been subpoenaed.

Q Tell us how that conversation went.

A It probably would be impossible for anyone who didn't -- who has listened to that tape to follow. I was beyond paranoid.

I had no idea how I had gotten onto the witness list and then, of course, been subpoenaed and I was thinking at that point that maybe my phone was tapped or someone had read my e-mails or something. But in thinking that my phone might be tapped, I sort of tried to explain to this to Linda that I had been subpoenaed in a veiled fashion.

Q How did you do that? What do you mean?

A I used different cover stories. I think like it was a movie or it was a book, trying to discuss things. I think I said something -- "I received the flowers," trying to intimate that I had received the subpoena. So --

Q Eventually, did you drop the sort of disguised way of talking and just talk about the subpoena, or do you recall?

A I don't believe I did. I don't really remember,

Page 137

though.

Q How were things left with Linda?

A She was having a party the next day, so we made plans that -- or I suggested that I come early and we could discuss this and that I would help her set up for her dumb party. I'm sorry.

Q Her dumb party? All right. Well, we'll skip the dumb party for now.

A I'm sorry.

MR. EMMICK: That's all right.

MR. WISENBERG: I have a quick question.

MR. EMMICK: Okay. A dumb party question?

MR. WISENBERG: Not about the dumb party.

MR. EMMICK: All right.

BY MR. WISENBERG:

Q When you were doing the flowers bit, the book bit, how was she -- you're trying to speak in code to her, how was she responding?

A I don't really remember. I just sort of remember her not understanding and me being frustrated. "Hello? Understand. We just talked about this."

A JUROR: Excuse me. May I ask a question?

MR. EMMICK: Sure. Absolutely. Yes.

A JUROR: Did you ever find out how the Paula Jones lawyers knew about the hat pin, et cetera?

Page 138

THE WITNESS: I -- from what I've read in the press, yes.

A JUROR: But just from any other source? Did you ever suspect maybe Linda or --

THE WITNESS: I had -- I came to start to suspect her, but not in any way that -- that it really has turned out to be. Not to that degree.

A JUROR: Thank you.

BY MR. EMMICK:

Q Let's turn our attention, then, to December 22nd, which is the day that you met with Frank Carter and I think you had said that you were going to meet with Vernon earlier.

A Mm-hmm.

Q Tell us about that. The Vernon part.

A Okay. With all the details?

Q Well, first, when were you supposed to meet with Vernon and then did you place another call to him?

A Right. I -- I -- I asked -- I called on the morning of the 22nd to see if I could come to see Mr. Jordan earlier. And I was -- I was a little concerned. I thought maybe he didn't really understand or -- fully understand what it was that was happening here with me being subpoenaed and what this really meant. So I came to see Mr. Jordan earlier and I also wanted to find out if he had in fact told the President that I had been subpoenaed.

Page 139

Q Right.

A Which I found out he did. So I -- so I told Mr. Jordan that -- I said I was concerned that maybe -- that someone had listened in on phone calls and Mr. Jordan said, "Well, you know, so what? The President's allowed to call people."

And I said, "Well, we've had phone sex."

And so Mr. Jordan said, "Well, what's phone sex?"

And so I said, "Well, you know what phone sex is."

And he said, "No, I don't. I'm just an old man. I don't know what phone sex is."

And it was kind of this -- discussion that way.

Q Did you discuss the hat pin?

A We didn't discuss the hat pin, but I brought -- I had put together sort of an assortment of things that I was planning to hand over to Mr. Carter as being in response to the subpoena, sort of things that I would -- considered gifts, being the Christmas cards that I had received from the White House, I had a copy of the President's book, "Hope and History," which he had signed to me which had a very innocuous sort of inscription. And I think brought some innocuous pictures with me. So I showed those to Mr. Jordan.

Q What did you say about those items?

A I know that -- I think I was a little more specific in my proffer about what -- I mean, what I remember saying

Page 140

now was that -- you know, that I sort of showed him that this is what I was going to respond to for the subpoena.

Q Well, did you bring everything that could have responded to the subpoena that day?

A No. No.

Q Did you try to convey to Mr. Jordan the fact that it wasn't everything?

A I think I might have.

Q And do you remember how you would have conveyed it? Would it have been very expressly or would it have been more impliedly?

A More impliedly.

BY MS. IMMERGUT:

Q Did you tell Mr. Jordan that the President had indeed given you a hat pin?

A I did, but I had told him that on Friday and that was what prompted the sort of "this is a vanilla response."

MR. EMMICK: Let me show you the written proffer --

THE WITNESS: Okay.

MR. EMMICK: -- and see if that helps you recall or if you know whether or not when you wrote it it's accurate.

What we're looking at is the top of page 6 -- everyone else has a copy.

THE WITNESS: Okay. There's some spelling mistakes.

Page 141

MR. EMMICK: Why don't I just read out loud. This paragraph starts, "On the day Mr. Jordan drove Ms. Lewinsky to Mr. Carter's office, she showed Mr. Jordan the items she was producing in response to the subpoena. Ms. Lewinsky believes she made it clear this was not everything she had that could respond to the subpoena, but she thought it was enough to satisfy. Mr. Jordan made no comment about whether or not what Ms. Lewinsky brought was right or wrong. Mr. Jordan drove Ms. Lewinsky to Mr. Carter's office, introduced them and left."

BY MR. EMMICK:

Q Now, having read that to you, does that refresh your recollection about what was said to him?

A I think I would have implied it.

Q Yes.

A That this wasn't everything. I -- I don't really remember if I specifically said -- and from reading this, it doesn't make me think I necessarily specifically said, "This isn't everything, but it's enough to satisfy," but I could have said that.

Q At the time you wrote this, were you trying to be completely truthful and accurate?

A I was trying to be completely -- yes, I was completely truthful and accurate. I'm just also while I'm reading this now, it doesn't necessarily indicate to me

Page 142

that -- that what I'm saying here is sort of a direct quote of what I said.

Q Do you remember what Mr. Jordan's reaction was? There it's written that he didn't indicate whether he thought it was right or wrong, but more generally, how did he react when you tried to convey to him that this may not be everything?

A There were often times when I was with Mr. Jordan that he would have no reaction at all. He would kind of do this "Mmmph" thing.

Q I'm not sure how the court reporter is going to get that. Is that a grunt?

A And so -- I remember feeling in general with Mr. Jordan and this subject matter, just not knowing. Do you understand what I'm trying to say? Is this clear? And not really ever getting much of a reaction from him.

Q Did you take from his lack of reaction that he did understand or was it still ambiguous in your mind?

A I think sometimes I thought he understood and sometimes I thought it was ambiguous.

Q Okay. Did the subject of phone sex come up again in your conversation with Mr. Jordan?

A Aside from what I mentioned before?

Q Yes. Did you explain to him what phone sex was at some point?

Page 143

A I think it -- at -- I don't think I said it. He might have said -- know, is it -- uh -- this is embarrassing Hmm. I think he -- it's hard. I think he -- uh -- might have given some suggestion as to what he thought phone sex was and I agreed. Is that --

Q That's fine.

A -- fair?

Q That's fine.

A By this time, had you expected the President to call you?

A Mm-hmm. Yes.

MR. EMMICK: I'm sorry?

A JUROR: Before you go on, can you ask her what does that mean?

MR. EMMICK: What does phone sex --

A JUROR: No, what did he say?

MR. EMMICK: I think the grand juror is asking for more detail.

THE WITNESS: If I remember correctly, I believe that he said -- or maybe I said something like -- you know, "He's taking care of business on one end and I'm taking care of business on another." Does that --

BY MR. WISENBERG:

Q Do you remember which one of you said it?

A When I'm saying that now, I think I said it,

Page 144

because that sounds more familiar to me.

Does that answer your question?

A JUROR: (Nods affirmatively.)

BY MR. EMMICK:

Q Did you expect the President to call you?

A Yes, I did.

Q Is that why you were bugging or asking Vernon so much about whether he had told the President?

A I don't know. Maybe.

Q All right.

A I think I just wanted to make sure the President knew.

BY MS. IMMERGUT:

Q That you had been subpoenaed.

A Right. Because I was supposed to call -- you know, in the event that I was subpoenaed, I was supposed to have called Betty and -- so --

BY MR. EMMICK:

Q I'm going to ask a question that will suggest what assumptions you were making about what Vernon knew or didn't. Why would you feel comfortable talking with Vernon Jordan about phone sex?

A I wasn't comfortable talking to Vernon Jordan about phone sex.

Q Okay.

Page 145

A I was scared.

MR. EMMICK: Okay.

MR. WISENBERG: Questions?

MR. EMMICK: Yes?

BY MR. WISENBERG:

Q Did you say on the 22nd that you showed to Vernon Jordan the gifts you bringing to Frank Carter?

A Yes.

Q Okay. Was a hat pin among the things you showed to Vernon Jordan?

A No.

Q But you had indicated to him on the 19th that the President had given you a hat pin.

A Yes.

MR. WISENBERG: Thank you.

BY MR. EMMICK:

Q At some point, you went to Frank Carters's.

A Mm-hmm. Yes.

Q Tell us what happened when you got to Frank Carter's.

A We arrived at Mr. Carter's office and Mr. Jordan and I sat down on the sofa. Mr. Carter came out. Mr. Jordan introduced us and left.

Q In your discussions with Mr. Carter, what was the major point that you were trying to make? What was the big

Page 146

thing you were trying to convey to Mr. Carter?

A That there was absolutely no reason why I should have been subpoenaed in this case.

Q Okay. And --

A And that I certainly did not have a relationship with the President.

Q You said that to him.

A I don't think I said those words, but that was what I was trying to convey and certainly when asked those questions, that's what I answered.

Q Did you discuss with him how you could get out of the deposition?

A Yes.

Q Tell us what you talked about. Maybe that would be the easier way to go.

A Okay. I told Mr. Carter I really didn't want to be dragged into this, I didn't -- I thought Paula Jones' claim was bunk and I didn't want to be associated with the case. I believe I suggested maybe that I could -- maybe I asked him if I could sign an affidavit or is that something to do.

He said that the first step -- to hold off on that and that the first step is he would try to talk to the attorneys for Paula Jones and find out what it is, why they're subpoenaing me and where it is that they're going with this and that maybe one option might be is he could

Page 147

arrange for them to interview me, just kind of do a brief interview, versus a deposition.

Q Did you discuss with him the subpoena insofar as it requested items? Did you, for example, go through and talk about what items were called for?

A Yes, we did. Yes. And I said no to everything until we got to the gifts and then I sort of turned over what it was that I had brought with me that I thought responded to the gifts. And that was it.

Q Was there any mention made by either of you of Bob Bennett?

A Yes.

Q Tell us what was said.

A I requested of Mr. Carter that he get in touch with Mr. Bennett and just to be in touch with him and to let him know that I had been subpoenaed in this case and I didn't know why.

Q Why did you request that Mr. Carter contact Mr. Bennett?

A Because I thought in the -- how do I explain this? Sort of in the story or role, the story that I was giving to Mr. Carter and being a low level political appointee and, in general, even if I hadn't been a low level political appointee, I thought it was probably appropriate to align myself with the President's side, being that that's whose

Page 148

side I was on and there was no question in my mind.

Q Is another way of saying that you were trying to send a message to the President or to Mr. Bennett?

A Not to the President. He knew. I mean, the President knew, you know? So --

Q So it was more a message to Mr. Bennett?

A I just -- to me, that seemed -- I mean, I think -- you have to look at this from the point of view that I was a political appointee. And so --

Q What does that imply for you?

A For me, that means that the reason you're in this job is you work for this administration and that you're politically aligned with this administration and everything you do is in the best interests of the administration and, ultimately, the President. And that's where your goal and your focus should be.

Q How were things left? What was he going to do and what were you going to next?

A Mr. Carter was going to get in touch with the attorneys for Paula Jones and get in touch with Mr. Bennett. And he was going to send me a retainer letter. And we'd be in touch.

Q Let me then ask you the following. You had earlier indicated that the President said that he had a Christmas present for you.

Page 149

A Mm-hmm. Yes.
Q Did you ever make contact with Betty Currie in order to make arrangements to pick up the present?
A Yes.
Q Tell us about that.
A I called Betty after Christmas to see how she was doing and find out how her holiday was and to ask her -- or to let her know that the President had mentioned to me that he had a Christmas present for me and, you know, to touch base with him to see if he -- what he wanted to do, if he wanted to get together.
So she called me back and told me to come to the White House at 8:30 in the morning on Sunday, the 28th of December.
Q Did you?
A Yes, I did.
Q All right. Betty waved you in?
A Yes.
Q At about what time was it, if you can remember?
A 8:30.
Q When you got there, what happened?
A I think the President was already there. He was just coming to the Oval Office and Betty and the President and I were in the Oval Office and this was the first time I got to meet Buddy.

Page 150

So we played with Buddy in the office and he was running around the carpet. And I had brought a small Christmas present for Buddy. And so the three of us were just talking and goofing off. And then the President and I went into the back study and he gave me my Christmas presents.
Q How long were you in the back study with the President?
A Maybe about 45 minutes to an hour.
Q What was the Christmas present or presents that he got for you?
A Everything was packaged in a big Black Dog -- or big canvass bag from the Black Dog store in Martha's Vineyard. And he got me a marble bear's head carving, sort of -- you know, a little sculpture, I guess, maybe.
Q Was that the item from Vancouver?
A Yes. Then he got me a big Rockettes blanket from Christmas of '95 or '96, I think. He got me a Black Dog stuffed animal that had a little Black Dog T-shirt on it.
He got me a small little box of chocolates, cherry chocolates, and then he got me some sunglasses that were a joke because I had -- I had teased him for a long time about the different sunglasses that he was wearing in public.
And so then I bought him a normal pair of sunglasses, and so we had just sort of had -- this was a long

Page 151

running joke with us, so he bought me these really funny looking sunglasses and we both were putting them on and joking around goofing off.
So -- I'm trying to think what else. Can I look at the list?
MR. EMMICK: Sure. Feel free.
THE WITNESS: Oh. He got me a pin that had the -- most of my Christmas presents were sort of New York themed, so he got me a pin that had the New York skyline on it. I think that's it. Well, it's a lot, so -- not just that's it.
BY MR. EMMICK:
Q Now, you had mentioned earlier that you were concerned about the fact that the subpoena covered this hat pin.
A Mm-hmm.
Q Did you discuss that concern with President Clinton?
A Yes. We -- we really spent maybe about five -- no more than ten minutes talking about the Paula Jones case on this day and -- do you want me to talk about the hat pin or that period of time?
Q The whole period of time, I suppose.
A I brought up the subject of the case because I was concerned about how I had been brought into the case and been put on the witness list. So I asked him how he thought I got

Page 152

put on the witness list and he told me he thought that maybe it was that woman from the summer with Kathleen Willey, which I knew to be Linda Tripp, or maybe -- he said maybe some of the uniformed -- maybe the uniformed officers.
We talked about that. I mentioned that I had been concerned about the hat pin being on the subpoena and he said that that had sort of concerned him also and asked me if I had told anyone that he had given me this hat pin and I said no.
Q That was false.
A Correct. Yes. When in fact I had told people about the hat pin.
Q Right.
A Let's see. And then at some point I said to him, "Well, you know, should I -- maybe I should put the gifts away outside my house somewhere or give them to someone, maybe Betty." And he sort of said -- I think he responded, "I don't know" or "Let me think about that." And left that topic.
Q When you said "the gifts," what did you mean by "the gifts"?
A I meant all the gifts that he had given me.
Q All right. Do you think that you're the one who came up with Betty's name?
A I'm not 100 percent sure, but when I received the

Page 153

call from Betty, I wasn't surprised that it was Betty calling, so that's what leads me to believe that I might have suggested it.

Q Okay. Did you discuss with the President the fact that you were planning to sign an affidavit?

A I might have mentioned it, but I don't think -- we really didn't spend very much time on this subject.

Q All right. So you walked in without many gifts, you were going to walk out with a bag of gifts.

A Mm-hmm.

Q Okay. Did it strike you as unusual that when you had a subpoena calling for you to produce gifts the President is giving you a bag of gifts?

A At the time, it didn't strike me as unusual.

Q Okay. And why is that?

A I never thought about it. I mean, I was -- I was -- I had struggled for a long time before the 28th -- or I should just say -- I guess a few days before the 28th, that if I was going to see the President, if I should tell him or not that Linda knew. And I decided not to.

And so I -- I thought this might be the last time I saw him before I went to New York and I wanted it to be a really nice visit, so I was -- I -- having decided not to tell him about Linda, I kind of didn't even want to go too far there in getting mired down in the discussion of the case.

Page 154

Q All right. When you left the White House, did anything unusual happen with respect to your E-pass?

A Yes. Well, I had a visitor's pass.

Q Visitor's E-pass, I guess.

A Is that what --

Q A visitor's pass?

A Visitor's -- I don't know. I know it is a visitor's pass. Betty escorted me out and I realized that I left the pass in the office, so Betty told me that she would call down to the guard station and let them know that I was fine and I had just left the pass somewhere.

Q Do you remember what gate you used when you left the White House?

A I believe it was the southwest gate.

Q Did you hear from Betty later that day?

A Yes, I did.

Q Were you surprised to hear from her?

A No. I mean, I wasn't surprised that I was hearing from Betty. I think I was a little surprised to sort of get the nature of this phone call when the President could have just said right then and there, "Well, yeah, I think, you know, why don't you give them to Betty, that's a good idea." But I wasn't terribly surprised. No.

Q What did she say?

A She said, "I understand you have something to give me." Or, "The President said you have something to give me." Along those lines.

Page 155

Q How long after you had left the White House did Betty call you?

A Several hours.

Q When she said something along the lines of "I understand you have something for me," or "The President says you have something for me," what did you understand her to mean?

A The gifts.

Q Okay.

A Kind of -- what I was reminded of then a little bit was jumping all the way back to the July 14th incident where I was supposed to call Betty the next day but not really get into details with her, that this was maybe along those same lines.

Q That actually anticipates my next question.

A Oh.

Q Did you feel any need to explain to her what was going to happen?

A No.

Q What arrangements did you make for transfer of the something?

A I think we discussed some things and Betty mentioned she was on the way to the hospital to visit her mom and she'd swing by and, you know, pick up whatever it was I was supposed to give her.

Page 156

Q Now, at the time you had that conversation, were you already packing up the gifts at all?

A No.

Q When was she going to come by, then? That day?

A Yes.

Q What did you do after the phone call ended?

A I put all the gifts that he had given me on my bed and I got a big box from The Gap and went through each item and decided if I needed to give it to them or not.

Q Can you explain what you mean by that?

A It sort of was a difficult -- I -- I wasn't sure if I was going to get this box back, so I didn't want to give everything in the event that I didn't get the box back for some reason.

And I kept out some innocuous things and I kept out the -- really the most -- the most sentimental gift he had given me was the book, the "Leaves of Grass" book, so -- and it was just -- it's beautiful and it meant a lot to me, so I kept that out.

Q What other -- it sounds to me like you had one category of more sentimental gifts that you kept out of the box.

A Mm-hmm.

Page 157

Q And kept for yourself. What other items were in that category, other than the "Leaves of Grass"?
A Not necessarily sentimental ones, but just -- I think I kept out the marble bear head, the bag, the canvass bag, the blanket, the sunglasses, the chocolates. And I think that's it. Oh, wait. And I might have kept out some of the Martha's Vineyard stuff that I had gotten in the fall.
Q Those were items that you've recently turned over to our office.
A Yes.
Q Which items did you put into the box? If you remember.
A The hat pin, the pin that I had received that day for Christmas, a pin that he had given me for my birthday, a picture that he had signed for me for my birthday that I had framed, a picture he had signed for me of him wearing the first tie I gave him.
Q Any other Black Dog items?
A I think there was a Black Dog hat that I put in there. And I'm not -- I'm not really sure what else was in there. Oh, I also put the copies that I had left of the Valentine's Day ad that I had put in the paper for him.
Q The Romeo and Juliet quote?
A Mm-hmm.
Q All right. Did Betty come by?

Page 158

A Yes, she did. I met her outside.
Q How did you know when she was going to come by? Was there a prearranged time she was going to come by or did she call you from --
A I think she called me on her way out.
Q You met her outside, you had the box with you?
A Mm-hmm. I had taped it up and I wrote "Please do not throw away" on it.
Q Were you concerned that she might throw it away?
A Mm-hmm. Yes. Sorry.
Q Okay. Let me just ask you some questions. Did you ever discuss with her the contents of the box?
A I don't believe so.
Q Did she ever ask about the contents of the box?
A No.
Q Did she ever say anything indicating that she knew from a prior discussion the contents of the box?
A Not -- no, not that I remember.
Q Sounds like it was a short conversation.
A We talked about her mom a bit and Christmas. I think maybe I had elaborated on what I got for Christmas from him.
Q Now, you could have just thrown these items out, rather than putting them in a box. Why didn't you just throw them out?

Page 159

A Because I -- they meant a lot to me.
Q Okay. You could have given the items to someone else, a friend of yours, Ashley Raines, or to your mother or just hidden them somewhere. Why didn't you do that?
A I think -- I've come to sort of see this now. I don't know that I necessarily saw it then, but I feel now a little bit that me turning over some of these things was a little bit of an assurance to the President or reassurance that, you know, that everything was okay.
Q In your mind, then, were you giving these items not just to Betty, but really to the President as well, in a manner of speaking?
A I think that was even more directly what I thought it was. Not that they were going to be in his possession, but that he would understand whatever it was I gave to Betty and that that might make him feel a little bit better.
Q Did Betty say where she was going to put the box of gifts?
A I think she said she was going to keep them in a closet. Or, you know, she'd keep the box in a closet.
Q Right.
A You asked me -- never mind.
Q The gifts. Right. I understood. I understood. All right. What I'd like to do now is ask a few questions --

Page 160

MR. WISENBERG: Mike?
MR. EMMICK: Yes?
MR. WISENBERG: Before you leave that topic, I have a few on that. Do you mind?
MR. EMMICK: No. Not at all.
BY MR. WISENBERG:
Q You've said here today, Ms. Lewinsky, and I think you told us earlier in some of your sessions with us, that you were -- the non-innocuous items were going to go to Frank Carter and --
MR. EMMICK: You mean the innocuous items.
MR. WISENBERG: What did I say?
MR. EMMICK: The not innocuous items.
MR. WISENBERG: Boy. Thank you. I stand corrected.
BY MR. WISENBERG:
Q The innocuous items were going to go to Frank Carter, the non-innocuous items were not, but that one of the reasons, one of the criterion for stuff that didn't even go in the Betty Currie box that you would keep would be sentimental value.
A Mm-hmm.
Q Is that -- have I described that accurately?
A Sort of.
Q Okay. How not sort of?

Page 161

A I didn't really give any gifts to Mr. Carter. Nothing that I turned over to Mr. Carter was a gift from the President. And I think the way you described the dividing of the actual gifts was sort of innocuous, you know, not innocuous -- sentimental value, I think that was more accurate.
Q Well, as between the gifts you put in the box and the gifts you kept?
A Mm-hmm.
Q All right. How would you describe today the difference between the two? I just want to make sure I understand, between the ones you kept and the ones you put in the Betty box.
A You know, I don't have a perfect memory of what the criteria was at the time. I know I kept the book out because that was the most sentimental thing to me.
And I believe that the things I put in the box were -- also in the box was a dress he gave me from Martha's Vineyard, so the things that went into the box were, I think, more along the lines of some of the things that really complied with the subpoena, that were maybe specifically named, although I think books might have been specifically named in the subpoena, but I kept the "Leaves of Grass."
Q They complied with the subpoena, but they're going to Betty Currie.

Page 162

A Correct.
Q Now, my question is, and I've asked you this before, but I want to ask you in front of the grand jury, since you were basically trying to keep some sentimental things but you told us that the hat pin was sentimental to you, why is the hat pin going into the Betty box?
A Because the hat pin was the alarm of the subpoena, so -- I -- I -- to me, it seemed logical that putting the hat pin in the box -- I mean, it was what had been named in the subpoena.
MR. EMMICK: All right. Should we take a break?
THE FOREPERSON: Yes, we should.
THE WITNESS: Oh, thank goodness.
MR. EMMICK: Okay. All right. Ten minutes.
THE WITNESS: Okay.
THE FOREPERSON: Ten minutes.
(Witness excused. Witness recalled.)
MR. EMMICK: All right. Do we have a quorum?
THE FOREPERSON: Yes, we do.
MR. EMMICK: Any unauthorized persons present?
THE FOREPERSON: None at all.
THE WITNESS: Let me guess. You're going to remind me I'm still under oath.
THE FOREPERSON: There you go.
THE WITNESS: Fast learner.

Page 163

BY MR. EMMICK:
Q Ms. Lewinsky, this is what we're going to do. We're going to go over some questions that we'd like to ask and then we're going to turn our attention to the December 31st meeting, the breakfast meeting with Vernon Jordan.
A Okay.
Q Let's go to questions first. One question is Betty comes by and gets this box of gifts. Is there any other way Betty would have known to call and pick up this box of gifts except for the President asking her to?
A The only thing I can think of is if he had asked someone else to ask Betty.
Q Do you have any reason to think that happened?
A No, but, I mean, I wasn't there, so I don't know -- I don't know what he said, how -- maybe he left her a note. I mean, I don't know. So --
Q Another way of asking it is did you tell someone else about this and they might have asked Betty?
A No.
BY MR. WISENBERG:
Q Did you think it as a coincidence that she called you?
A No.
BY MR. EMMICK:
Q Let me ask you a couple of questions about the

Page 164

December 20th dumb party.
A Okay.
Q Okay? First, why is it a dumb party.
A Oh. Really? You want me to answer that?
Q Yes.
A Well, because it was Linda Tripp's party and -- well, that should be enough, but just that I got there and I got stuck having to do all this stuff and I had really wanted to talk to her about the predicament we were in and -- I now look back on it and just -- she had spent all this money on food and a month before she had had no money for the bus and was trying to sell her clothes and somehow she had $500 to spend on food and had money to spend on presents underneath her tree and it was just dumb.
Q Let's focus on the discussions you had with Linda at the dumb party or before the dumb party about the situation.
A I really didn't sort of get into, I think, a full discussion with her until after -- well, until I was leaving and I asked her to walk me out to my car.
Q Let's talk first then about the efforts you made to talk with her about the subpoena in the house. Did you try to?
A Probably. It was -- I got there maybe -- the -- I think the party was supposed to start around 7:30 and I got

Page 165

there at 5:00 and she had made no food, had done nothing. I mean, she just had this fridge stuffed with food.

So I was trying to help prepare all this stuff. There was a lot more work to do than I thought there would be and then her daughter had this obsession with vacuuming that night, so there were just a lot of people and I don't really remember trying to get a chance.

I may have tried to or sort of said "I need to talk to you," kind of a thing, but I don't recall having any discussions with her before the party.

Q Okay. And then you mentioned that you were able to talk to her a little bit outside, I think you said?

A Mm-hmm.

Q Tell us about that.

A The main -- the main feeling I had had at that point, once I had received my subpoena was that -- that now she didn't need to worry about denying that she knew anything about this relationship, because I was going to deny it under oath as well.

And so sort of just -- I figured that conversation would kind of just be mapping out what our next steps would be. But it ended up being much shorter and I -- she looked at the subpoena -- excuse me -- sorry -- and I think she -- she kept talking about how weird, "Isn't the hat pin strange? Isn't it strange that they're asking about the hat pin?"

Page 166

And we talked about that. And I think that -- I -- I was -- I was -- I don't think that I was left with the feeling that she was going to continue on this path of insisting she would rat on me. So -- is that clear? I'm sorry -- no? Okay.

When I left that night, I felt a little more -- I think I felt a little more reassured that she and I would be saying the same thing in the Paula Jones case. Is that -- okay. But I wasn't 100 percent sure and I think that we left it that we'd have some more discussions about this.

Q Okay. One of the things we wanted to get back to was the whole situation on the 28th where there's a subpoena that calls for you to turn over gifts and the President is giving you gifts.

A Mm-hmm.

Q What do you think the President is thinking when he is giving you gifts when there's a subpoena covering the gifts? I mean, does he think in any way, shape or form that you're going to be turning these gifts over?

A You know, I can't answer what he was thinking, but to me, it was -- there was never a question in my mind and I -- from everything he said to me, I never questioned him, that we were ever going to do anything but keep this private, so that meant deny it and that meant do -- take whatever appropriate steps needed to be taken, you know, for that

Page 167

to happen, meaning that if I had turned over every gift he had given me -- first of all, the point of the affidavit and the point of everything was to try to avoid a deposition, so where I'd have to sort of -- you know, I wouldn't have to lie as much as I would necessarily in an affidavit, how I saw it.

So by turning over all these gifts, it would at least prompt them to want to question me about what kind of friendship I had with the President and they would want to speculate and they'd leak it and my name would be trashed and he would be in trouble. So --

Q So your impression, then, was in the same way that the two of you were going to deny the relationship, you would also deny or conceal the gifts that were personal that passed between you.

A And the phone call -- I mean, I think that it was everything. I think it was kind of -- at least for me, I don't know what he did, for me, this had to be thought through. You know, I had to anticipate everything that might happen and make sure -- you know --

Q You did what was necessary.

A Exactly.

BY MS. IMMERGUT:

Q Although, Ms. Lewinsky, I think what is sort of -- it seems a little odd and, I guess, really the grand jurors

Page 168

wanted your impression of it, was on the same day that you're discussing basically getting the gifts to Betty to conceal them, he's giving you a new set of gifts.

A You know, I have come recently to look at that as sort of a strange situation, I think, in the course of the past few weeks, but at the time, I was -- you know, I was in love with him, I was elated to get these presents and -- at the same time that I was so scared about the Paula Jones thing, I was happy to be with him and -- I -- I didn't think about that.

He had -- he had hesitated very briefly right before I left that day in kind of packaging -- he packaged all my stuff back up and I just sort of -- you know, remember him kind of hesitating and thinking to myself -- I don't think he said anything that indicated this to me, but I thought to myself, "I wonder if he's thinking he shouldn't give these to me to take out." But he did.

Q And he had already told you he had some gifts for you for Christmas.

A Correct.

BY MR. EMMICK:

Q You mentioned earlier when I asked who was on the list in your mind of people who should be avoided like Nancy Hernreich or Steve Goodin, you mentioned Mr. Ickes.

A Mm-hmm.

Page 169

Q That name came up. Why was Mr. Ickes on the avoid list?

A He -- well, he -- he's just strange. And he -- I'm sorry. He would -- you know, you could be the only person in the hall and you would pass Mr. Ickes in the hall and he would just glare at you. You know.

And I'd say, "Hello," you know, as you would imagine you're supposed to do and he'd just glare at you and walk past you. And I thought that was strange. Call me weird.

Q Okay. And that's the reason that you mentioned him on the list of people to avoid?

A And I think just -- his name is sort of in my mind for having to do with things that we're discussing today and what's been in the press of it, but it really was most every senior person in the White House, I mean, except for Betty who knew who I was that would concern me.

Q Right.

A I mean, I had -- you know, I had had a lot of interaction with these people during the furlough, so --

Q Let me ask you a question about Tim Keating. Did Tim Keating tell you or imply to you that you could come back after the election?

A He told me that I could probably come back after the election.

Page 170

Q Okay. Do you remember when he said that to you?

A Yes. On --

Q Go ahead.

A I'm sorry. On the day that he informed me of the transfer.

Q So that would have been the 5th of April? Does that sound right? Friday, the 5th of April?

A Correct. It was Good Friday, I remember.

Q Did he say anything about any problem of an appearance of impropriety during that conversation with you? Something like there might be an appearance before but it doesn't matter after the election, anything like that?

A No. No. No.

Q That subject didn't come up at all?

A Not with Mr. Keating.

Q You mentioned that when -- oh, I'm sorry. Go ahead. Sure.

A JUROR: I'm sorry. What would have prompted him to make a comment like that, that you could come back after the election?

THE WITNESS: I was crying and I just kept telling him, I -- you know, I didn't really want to leave and why did I have to leave and wasn't there -- you know, weren't there other openings rather than me having to go to the Pentagon because he had --

Page 171

Do you want me to get into a little bit about what was said there?

MR. EMMICK: If it will help answer the question, sure.

A JUROR: Yes. Please.

THE WITNESS: Okay. There had been problems with my supervisor, Jocelyn Jolley, and so when I was called in to Tim's office, I had thought he was -- he had just spoken with Jocelyn and I thought he was going to tell me they had fired Jocelyn and instead he told me that they were -- that for reasons having to do with some of the workload not -- things with the letters from the Office of Management and Budget, that they had to blow up -- quote-unquote, blow up the correspondence office and they were eliminating my position.

My transfer had nothing to do with my work, I shouldn't see this as a negative thing. He told me I was too sexy to be working in the East Wing and that this job at the Pentagon where I'd be writing press releases was a sexier job.

And I was crying and --

BY MR. EMMICK:

Q What do you think he meant by "too sexy"?

A I think he meant that -- he -- I think he was trying to -- you know, trying to conceal the fact that -- you know, that I now know, the real reason I was being

Page 172

transferred. And so I think he was trying to not maybe anger me. And thought that somehow by -- maybe he thought I'd think that was a complement.

A JUROR: Did you think he was patronizing you?

THE WITNESS: A little bit. Yeah. That's a good way to put it. I -- I just -- I just remember thinking that I was -- I was never going to see the President again and that all of a sudden that this -- you know, the end of this -- this relationship.

And I kept -- I've always sort of -- I'm the kind of person that always thinks that I can fix everything and so it was kind of this -- feeling of wait, this train's going too fast and I can't stop it and that it had already passed and -- and -- so when Tim said that, I think he sort of said that -- I don't think he meant to say that. I think that was probably more than he was supposed to say.

A JUROR: Thank you.

BY MR. EMMICK:

Q Going back again to the 17th of December when the President called you and let you know about the witness list, you said he used the phrase, "It broke my heart to see you on the witness list." What was your reaction when he said that?

A I believed him. I think I also --

Q You thought he was being sincere?

A JUROR: Can I ask another follow-up question?

Page 173

MR. EMMICK: Sure.
A JUROR: Because you had nothing to do with formulating this witness list, why do you think it breaks his heart, that your name was on there? Because you're innocent of having formulated this list. Do you have -- or in your opinion, what is it that hurt him?
THE WITNESS: I think it was the idea that -- that -- this was going to -- that this was going to be a bad thing for me. I mean, if you imagine what's happened now hadn't happened and let's just say the Paula Jones thing had gone ahead and I had somehow been dragged into that, just being associate with it and it being difficult and maybe he -- maybe it was going to seriously alter any kind of friendship or relationship that we had, you know?
BY MR. EMMICK:
Q I want to ask a question about computer e-mails or files. Did you arrange for the deletion of files or e-mails that might have related to you and the President?
A Did I arrange?
Q Or did you delete them. Sorry.
A Yes, I did.
Q Okay. Did you ask Linda Tripp if she would delete e-mails relating to the President?
A Yes.
Q Did you speak with someone at the Department of

Page 174

Defense in order to learn something about those deletions or to make sure that they would be more longstanding?
A Not about deletions.
Q Okay. Well, what was it that you spoke with him about?
A I asked him -- I asked Floyd, I think it is, if -- if -- sort of how easily someone could break into the computers. And I couldn't imagine how I had come to this witness -- come to be on this witness list, so one of the things I thought was maybe someone had broken into my computer and was reading my e-mails. And he told me that that was really difficult.
And then I asked him about -- then with the thought in mind of getting rid of the e-mails, I asked him what the sort of saving procedure was with the e-mails. I know at the White House, they back them up and put them in the archive forever and he told me that at the Pentagon, they sort of stay on the server for four weeks and then they're dumped into e-mail heaven or something.
Q All right. Did you ever ask Catherine Allday Davis to delete e-mails that you had sent relating to the President?
A No.
Q At any time, did you create anything like a spreadsheet that contained on it information relating to your

Page 175

relationship with the President?
A Yes.
Q Okay. Tell us about that.
A Linda and I had been talking and she had been talking about she's really good at coming up with patterns of things or -- I think that was the word she used.
And so she was wanting to see -- you know, I think in an effort to aid her in trying to figure out what the pattern of my relationship with the President was, I made a stupid spreadsheet on Microsoft Excel that just had the -- the numbered days of the month and the months and determined on what day was there a phone call or did I see him or see him at an event or something like that. So --
Q Is that something that you ultimately printed out and showed to her?
A Yes.
Q I take it that was on the DOD computer?
A Yes.
Q Were the entries that you made, would they have revealed that you were talking about Clinton?
A No.
Q Okay. Did you ever have an extra copy of that -- let's call it a spreadsheet?
A No.
Q Did you save the file of the spreadsheet?

Page 176

A No. I don't believe so.
Q All right. Going back also to the night of the 17th, December 17th, just so that we can get clear on the date of that, it was at 2:30 in the morning. Is it literally on the 17th or is it --
A Nineteen -- eighteen -- it is literally the morning, 2:30 in the morning of the 17th. So, yes.
Q Okay. Good. When the President gave you the Vancouver bear on the 28th, did he say anything about what it means?
A Mm-hmm.
Q What did he say?
A I think he -- I believe he said that the bear is the -- maybe Indian symbol for strength, just -- you know, and to be strong like a bear.
Q And did you interpret that as be strong in your decision to continue to conceal the relationship?
A No.
MR. EMMICK: All right. Any follow-up on that?
MS. WIRTH: Can I ask one question?
MR. EMMICK: Sure.
BY MS. WIRTH:
Q Did he say something like "This is when you need to be strong," or "This is for when you need to be strong"? Beyond saying that it was a symbol of strength?

Page 177

A I think he -- he held it and he said, you know, "You can hold onto this when you need to be strong."

MS. WIRTH: Thank you.

BY MR. EMMICK:

Q What I'd like to do is ask you about a passage from the proffer and I'm looking at page 5.

A Okay.

Q And you'll see at the bottom, and I'll read the passage, this is relating to the meeting on the 19th, just after you've gotten the subpoena, meeting with Vernon Jordan, and what the passage says is "Possibly later in that meeting, but more probably the next meeting," I assume that's a reference to the 22nd?

A Correct.

Q "Ms. Lewinsky tried to make it clear to Mr. Jordan that she in fact did have a physically intimate relationship with the President." And then let's go to the next page. It says, "Ms. Lewinsky made it clear she intended to deny the sexual relationship with the President."

So I guess what I want to talk about is the portion of the passage on page 5.

A Mm-hmm.

Q Tell us how you tried to make it clear to Mr. Jordan that you had a physically intimate relationship with the President.

Page 178

A I think by mentioning the phone sex.

Q I see. All right. Any other way that you tried to make it clear to him?

A Not that I remember.

Q All right. And then is it your recollection now that it was on the 22nd that you were trying to make this clear to Mr. Jordan?

A Yes.

Q As opposed to the 19th?

A Yes.

MR. EMMICK: Any other follow-up on that?

BY MS. IMMERGUT:

Q Ms. Lewinsky, how did you make it clear to him that you intended to deny the relationship with the President on the 23rd? Excuse me. The 22nd.

A This is, I think, as I mentioned to you guys before, this is -- I don't have a memory of this. I know when I wrote this I was telling the truth, so I'm sure I did do this, but I don't remember.

MR. WISENBERG: Ms. Lewinsky -- Mike, do you mind if I ask some questions?

MR. EMMICK: Go right ahead.

BY MR. WISENBERG:

Q I think, you can correct me if I'm wrong, you've done it previously today, so I'm sure you will again if I am,

Page 179

you told us when we first met with you in the proffer meeting that you couldn't specifically remember that item. Is that correct?

A Yes.

Q And I think you said you couldn't specifically remember any more of the item that Mike just read to you on the bottom of the previous page about the physically intimate relationship.

A Right.

Q But that you had no doubt that it's true. Is that correct?

A I was being truthful in my proffer. Yes.

Q And the proffer, written proffer, is accurate. Is that correct?

A Yes.

Q But -- and I think you also said you feel some -- I don't know if this is the reason you don't remember it, but you have expressed to us that you feel some guilt about Vernon Jordan. Is that correct?

A Mm-hmm.

Q That's a yes?

A Yes.

Q Okay. Can you tell us why that is?

A He was the only person who did what he said he was going to do for me and -- in getting me the job. And when I

Page 180

met with Linda on the 13th, when she was wearing a wire, and even in subsequent or previous conversations and subsequent conversations, I attributed things to Mr. Jordan that weren't true because I knew that it had leverage with Linda and that a lot of those things that I said got him into a lot of trouble and I just -- he's a good person and --

Q Is one example of -- and then I'll leave this topic, is one example of one of the things you told Linda that isn't true, "I told Vernon Jordan no job, no affidavit"? Something along those lines?

A Yes. Because Linda made me promise her that on the 9th.

Q Okay. Of January?

A Of January.

MR. WISENBERG: Okay.

THE FOREPERSON: Do you need a minute?

THE WITNESS: I'm okay. Thanks.

A JUROR: I'm a little confused. When you said that you said certain things because you know Linda had the mike, right?

THE WITNESS: Oh, I didn't know Linda had the mike. I now know that she was wearing a wire.

A JUROR: Okay. But so why would you say these things about Mr. Jordan that were not true? What was the reason?

Page 181

THE WITNESS: Because -- I had -- from some of my conversation with Linda, I started to think that she was a little bit jealous that Mr. Jordan was helping me get a job in New York and that I was leaving the Pentagon and that -- she had remarked one time that -- that, you know, Mr. Jordan who is the most powerful, you know, man in this city got me my attorney and she -- she thinks that she only had -- you know, this dinky attorney or something like that.

And I was -- I was so desperate for her to -- I was -- for her to not reveal anything about this relationship that I used anything and anybody that I could think of as leverage with her. I -- her, the President, my mom, everybody. I mean, not her, but Mr. Jordan, the President, my mom. Anybody that I thought would have any kind of influence on her, I used.

Does that answer your question?

A JUROR: Well, it doesn't. I guess what I'm trying to figure out, okay, is what was that going to accomplish? Was that going to make her -- what?

THE WITNESS: Well, specifically, with the statement about I won't sign the affidavit until I get the job, is that I had a conversation with Linda, which we'll probably get to --

MR. EMMICK: I hope.

THE WITNESS: Oh. On January 9th and in that

Page 182

conversation, she had told me she had changed her mind, she was going to be vague on the truth about Kathleen Willey and then she told me -- at that point, I had told her I hadn't signed an affidavit when I had and I told I didn't have a job yet and I knew I was probably going to be getting a job that day.

And she said, "Monica, promise me you won't sign the affidavit until you get the job. Tell Vernon you won't sign the affidavit until you get the job because if you sign the affidavit before you get the job, they're never going to give you the job."

And I didn't want her to think that I had gone ahead and done anything without her and that I was leaving her in the dark. I wanted her to feel that -- sort of Linda and myself against everyone else because I felt like I needed to hold her hand through this in order to try to get her to do what I wanted, essentially.

BY MR. EMMICK:

Q We can get into that in more detail when we talk about the 13th.

A Okay.

Q Why don't we do the following. I wanted to ask some -- rather than just jumping into the 31st which is a Vernon Jordan meeting, why don't we ask some questions about which of your gifts to the President you have ever seen in

Page 183

the White House itself, either in the dining room or the study or the Oval Office generally.

A Does that include gifts that I gave him that I've seen him wear?

Q All right. Well, let's just start with the things that you've seen in the area itself.

A Okay. Okay. I -- can I go through -- just go through the list?

Q Sure.

A That would probably be easier. On page 6, I've seen the two little books.

Q Two little books?

A The "Oy Vey" book, which is jokes and the little golf book.

Q Do you remember when you saw those books?

A Yes. On -- I think it was November 13th.

Q Zadilla day?

A Zadilla day.

Q All right.

A I saw a copy of the Washington Post ad that I had given him in a book on his desk.

Q You gave him a smallish copy of the --

A I gave him an actual copy that I cut out from one of the papers and I glued it into a little cardboard thing.

Q And where did you see it on his desk.

Page 184

A It was inside a book.

Q And the book was on the desk in the study?

A Yes.

MS. WIRTH: Mike, could I ask a question?

BY MS. WIRTH:

Q Did you see the ad in a particular book?

A Yes.

Q Which one?

A "Vox."

Q Okay. And was that on the desk in the study?

A Yes.

Q And was "Oy Vey" on the desk in the study?

A Yes.

Q What about the little golf book?

A I think it was. I -- I -- I'm not 100 percent sure it was a golf book, I'm 99.9 percent sure.

Q And about how many books does the President have on his desk in the study?

A He has maybe about 15 or 20 little books that are on his desk and he has more books over there and more books on the bookshelf.

MS. WIRTH: Thank you.

BY MR. EMMICK:

Q How about the opener?

A Right. The -- right. The wooden frog letter

Page 185

opener that I gave him. I'm just trying to go through this way, so --
Q All right. Go ahead.
A I saw the -- well, I lent him the book "Disease and Misrepresentation."
Q And did you see it in the Oval Office somewhere?
A No, I saw it in the back study.
Q The back study? And that would have been on page 8, I believe?
A Right. And then the letter opener that I was mentioning a moment ago was on page 9. I saw the antique paperweight.
Q Okay. Where is it that you saw the opener?
A It was on top of -- I think it's a cigar box on his desk in the back office. I saw the antique --
BY MS. IMMERGUT:
Q When did you see that, Monica?
A Zadilla day. I saw the antique paperweight on his -- he has a collection of antique political memorabilia in the dining room on top of sort of a chest sort of thing, and I saw that there on -- I think on December 6th or December 28th.
BY MR. EMMICK:
Q Okay. Do you remember which?
A No. I saw the standing cigar holder, I think, it

Page 186

was on his Oval Office desk. Or it might have been in the back. I think it was on the Oval Office desk. On the 28th of December. And that's it.
Q All right. Let's turn our attention to the 31st of December. You had indicated earlier that at some point you started to get more and more concerned about Linda Tripp and whether she was going to rat on you, I think was the way you put it. What did you do with respect to Vernon Jordan in that concern?
A Since Linda had stopped returning my calls around the 24th of December, by the end of December, I realized I'd kind of better come up with some sort of strategy as to how -- if Linda Tripp comes out and says all these things where this is coming from and try to prepare the President.
And since I couldn't find it within myself to bring it up to him directly, I called Mr. Jordan and told him that I needed to talk to him, I had some concerns about something.
Q When did you call him?
A I think it was the 30th of December.
Q Did you speak with him directly?
A I think I might have spoken with his -- with his secretary.
Q Do you remember her name?
A Gail. There was another one, too, but I've forgot

Page 187

her name. And I met Mr. Jordan for breakfast on -- no, not Sunday but December 31st, the morning of the 31st, at the Park Hyatt Hotel.
And in the course of the conversation I told him that I had had this friend, Linda Tripp, who was sort of involved in the Paula Jones case with, I think, the Kathleen Willey stuff. I don't know if I went into that much detail, but I did tell him her name.
And I said that she was my friend, that I didn't really trust her -- I used to trust her, but I didn't trust her any more and I was a little bit concerned because she had spent the night at my home a few times and I thought -- I told Mr. Jordan, I said, well, maybe she's heard some -- you know -- I mean, maybe she saw some notes lying around.
And Mr. Jordan said, "Notes from the President to you?" And I said, "No, notes from me to the President." And he said, "Go home and make sure they're not there."
Q What did you understand him to mean when he said, "Go home and make sure they're not there"?
A I thought that meant that -- to go home and search around and if there are any copies of notes or anything that I sent or drafts, to throw them away.
Q Did you have any further discussions with Mr. Jordan about Mr. Clinton and the Clinton's marital status?

Page 188

A Yes. After breakfast, in the car, I asked Mr. Jordan if he thought the President would always be married to the First Lady and he said, "Yes, as he should be." And gave me a quote from the Bible. And a few -- maybe a minute or so later, he said, "Well, maybe you two will have an affair when he's out of office."
And at that point, I was shocked because I thought Mr. Jordan had known that we had already had this affair and I think I alluded to this earlier today when I saying until the 31st I didn't know, and I said, "Well, we already had an affair. We just -- you know, we didn't have sex or did everything but sex," or something like that. And he just kind of went -- one of those "Mmmph." You know --
Q A grunt?
A And didn't really respond to me. So I took that as my cue to drop the subject. But -- so --
MR. EMMICK: All right.
BY MR. WISENBERG:
Q What did you eat for breakfast at the Hyatt?
A I had an -- I had an egg white omelet.
BY MR. EMMICK:
Q What did he have?
A I think he had cereal with yogurt.
BY MR. WISENBERG:
Q Do you remember who paid?

Page 189

A Mr. Jordan. He's a gentleman.
Q Do you remember how he paid?
A No.
Q Has anyone from the Office of Independent Counsel or the FBI shown you any paperwork of any kind with reference to that breakfast?
A No.
MR. WISENBERG: Thank you.
BY MR. EMMICK:
Q Let's turn back to the topic of gifts.
A Okay
Q Did you give a gift to the President in early January?
A Yes, I did. Well, I guess -- I gave it to Ms. Currie for the President.
Q What was the gift?
A It was an antique book on the various presidents with sketchings. A history book.
Q Where did you buy the book?
A At an antique bookstore in Georgetown.
Q Was there anything along with the book?
A A note.
Q Okay. What kind of a note?
A An embarrassing mushy note.
Q Okay. Did you attach the note to the book in some

Page 190

way?
A I don't really -- I might have put it inside the book or I may have put it outside. I wrapped the book.
Q And how did you try to get this book to the President?
A I called Betty over the weekend and asked her if I could drop it off so I didn't have to waste money on a courier.
Q And when you say "the weekend," are you talking about that first weekend in January?
A Yes.
Q Do you remember if it was Saturday, the 3rd, or Sunday, the 4th?
A I believe it was Sunday the 4th.
Q You called Betty and what again did you say to Betty?
A I don't -- I think I said something -- you know, "I have something for him, could I drop it off to you so I don't have to waste money on a courier."
Q Okay. And what did you do?
A So she said that was fine. So I went over to her home and --
Q Had you been to her home before?
A Yes.
Q Had you ever dropped anything off at her home for

Page 191

the President before?
A No.
Q What did you do when you got her home?
A Well, she was sitting on the porch, so we sat on the porch and I gave her the package and we talked for a little while.
Q Did you talk at all about the gift that was for the President?
A We might have. I might have mentioned it. Probably did. I'm not --
Q Was there any discussion about the fact that the President was himself under subpoena and was going to be deposed in a couple of weeks?
A No.
Q Were you concerned about giving him a book, a gift, under those circumstances?
A No.
Q Okay. Did you ever talk to the President and learn whether he got the book and the note?
A Yes, I did.
Q All right. When did you talk with him and learn about that?
A On the 5th of January. I think it was the 5th of January. You know -- can I just --
Q Sure. Take a look.

Page 192

A Yes. It was the 5th of January.
Q And that would have been Monday?
A Correct.
Q Why don't we try to proceed through Monday because Monday started with a meeting with you and Frank Carter and then there was the phone call afterwards, so let's go first to the meeting with Frank Carter.
A Okay.
Q Feel free.
A I met with Mr. Carter to go over in more detail where we stood at that point with the Paula Jones case and he went over -- he went over what was going to happen if an affidavit wasn't going to satisfy the Paula Jones attorneys and I did have to get deposed and what the room looks like, what -- you know -- everything that happens in a deposition and he threw out a bunch of different questions.
You know, they'll probably ask you who your first grade teacher was and they'll ask you -- you know, some things and then some of the questions that concerned me were questions like "How did you get your job at the Pentagon?" And how did -- you know, and he said, "They'll ask things like did you find out about the opening on a bulletin board or did someone tell you about it? Who recommended you for the job? How did everything get facilitated for the transfer?"

Page 193

And that alarmed me because I didn't really know how to necessarily answer that. I didn't express that to Mr. Carter, but --

Q Well, when you say you didn't know how to answer it, what do you mean, you didn't know how to answer it?

A Well, I was concerned that if I said in -- you know, if possibly that was going to come up in the affidavit which hadn't bee written yet or in a deposition, if I had said -- mentioned certain people that had been involved in helping me secure the position over at the Pentagon or forcing me to go there, really, that because these people didn't like me, if they were ever questioned by the Paula Jones attorneys, that they might say something contrary to what I said just because -- to get me in trouble because they didn't like me.

So I was concerned that -- I wanted to -- I wanted to have some sort of feeling of protection, that -- you know, that I wouldn't be screwed over by these people.

Q Were you concerned that they were going to say nasty things about you or were you concerned that they were going to say things that might ultimately lead to the revealing of the relationship in some way?

A No, I was just concerned that they would purposefully say something different from whatever I said just because they had the opportunity to screw me.

Page 194

I mean -- not -- never mind.

Q Okay.

A To cause trouble for me. How's that?

Q Did you discuss with Mr. Carter the affidavit that you were considering?

A Yes.

Q What did you talk about?

A I think he -- he said he would work on a draft and he'd get a draft of the affidavit to me.

Q Okay. At the time, did you want anyone else to review that affidavit before you ultimately signed it?

A At first, I didn't think about it, but then I did. I decided I wanted Mr. Jordan to look at it.

Q All right. Why did you want Mr. Jordan to look at it?

A I think I felt that -- that he being the President's best friend and having a -- a clearer understanding of my relationship with the President than Mr. Carter did, that I just would feel that it sort of had been blessed.

MR. EMMICK: Okay.

BY MS. IMMERGUT:

Q And would that be blessed by the President as well?

A Yes, I that's what I -- I mean, I -- I think I felt that -- excuse me. That, you know, if Mr. Jordan thought

Page 195

something was okay, that I'm sure the President would think it was fine.

MS. IMMERGUT: Okay.

BY MR. EMMICK:

Q Did you discuss the subpoena and the items that might be responsive to the subpoena anymore? I think you had talked about it earlier.

A You know, there's been a little bit of confusion for me when I gave Mr. Carter those items, so it's possible.

Q All right. You mentioned that Mr. Carter asked you some hard questions about like how you got your job. Did you want to talk with anybody about that afterwards?

A Yes. I placed a call to Ms. Currie and asked her to let the President know I needed to speak to him and it was important.

Q Did you say anything to Ms. Currie about signing something?

A I think I might have sort of said, just, you know, hoping that she might pass that along, I think.

BY MS. IMMERGUT:

Q Do you remember saying that you wanted to or needed to speak to the President before you signed something?

A I think so.

BY MR. EMMICK:

Q All right. Did you explain to her what you meant

Page 196

when you said that?

A No.

Q Okay.

A I'm pretty sure I did say that to Ms. Currie.

Q Did you finally get in contact or did you at some time shortly thereafter get in contact with Mr. Clinton?

A Yes.

Q How did that happen?

A Ms. Currie called me back a few hours later and then she put the President on.

Q Before we talk about what the President and you talked about, as background, I guess, were you upset or in a mood that day from a photograph you had seen?

A Oh, you really want to embarrass me, don't you?

Q Well, I just want to get the mood right.

A I had been peeved by the photo and the footage that was in the media from the President and First Lady being romantic on their holiday vacation. So I felt a little bit like -- I -- I was just annoyed.

I was jealous and it just seemed sort of something he had never -- an aspect of their relationship that he had never really revealed to me and it made me feel bad.

So I was -- I don't know if anyone here has ever done this, where you -- you're annoyed with someone so you kind of want to pick a fight with them and you want to be a

Page 197

little bit hostile so that -- you know, you just rub them the wrong way.
Q Okay.
A So that was how I was feeling.
Q That's how you exhibited the annoyance or anger or whatever.
A Mm-hmm.
Q Okay. Tell us about your conversation with the President.
A Because of those feelings, I was a little bit curt with him and so I told him that I had had this meeting with Mr. Carter and that I was concerned, you know, from the questions he asked me that if, you know, if I at some point had to kind of -- under oath, answer these questions and in the course of answering a question I mentioned people at the White House who didn't like me, that somehow I would end up getting -- they'd get me in trouble.
And so he -- so when I told him the questions about my job at the Pentagon, he said, "Well, you could always say that the people in Legislative Affairs got it for you or helped you get it."
And there was a lot of truth to that. I mean, it was a generality, but that was -- I said, "Well, that's a good idea. Okay."
Q Was there any discussion of the book?

Page 198

A Yes. I had asked him if he had gotten the book that I sent with Betty and he said he did, he really liked it, and then -- I had written him this -- this note that I had sort of -- wrote -- I think it was Saturday night when I got home from the movies and I had seen the Titanic that weekend and it just was -- just brought up a lot of feelings and thoughts for me that I put on -- that I put on paper.
And so I sort of said something about, "Oh, well, I shouldn't have written some of those things in the note." Because I was angry about seeing the picture with them romantic, it made me feel really stupid for having sent this letter.
And he said, "Yeah, you shouldn't have written some of those things." Kind of along the ways he had said before, about not writing particular things on paper, you know, putting things to paper. So --
Q About how long was your telephone call with the President?
A Maybe 15 minutes.
MR. EMMICK: Anything else on that?
THE WITNESS: I see you trying not to laugh.
MR. EMMICK: What about break-wise? Where are we? Is this a good time for a break or do we want to keep going?
THE FOREPERSON: Yes. Yes.
MR. EMMICK: All right.

Page 199

THE FOREPERSON: I would say only five minutes.
MR. EMMICK: All right. Five minutes it is.
THE FOREPERSON: A five-minute break. I'm sorry, guys. Okay.
(Witness excused. Witness recalled.)
MR. EMMICK: Madam Foreperson, do we have a quorum?
THE FOREPERSON: Yes, we do.
MR. EMMICK: Are there any unauthorized persons present?
THE FOREPERSON: There are none.
Monica, it's my responsibility --
THE WITNESS: I know.
THE FOREPERSON: -- to remind you you're still under oath.
THE WITNESS: Okay. Thank you.
BY MR. EMMICK:
Q We just finished talking about January 5th. Why don't we turn to January 6th. On January 6th, did you pick up a copy of the draft affidavit from Frank Carter?
A Yes, I did.
Q You had mentioned earlier that you wanted Vernon Jordan to look at it. Did you contact him?
A Yes, I did.
Q Did you speak with him personally or did you speak with someone on his staff?

Page 200

A I don't really remember.
Q And did you try to get a copy of the draft affidavit to Mr. Jordan?
A Yes. I dropped off a Xerox copy in his office.
Q In his office?
A In the lobby of his -- of Akin Gump.
Q Did you make any arrangements to contact him in order to talk about the draft affidavit?
A I believe -- I think I remember Gail saying he was in a meeting and something about 4:00, that he was going to be out and he would call me at 4:00.
Q Did you talk with him on the 6th about the draft affidavit?
A Yes, I did.
Q All right. Tell us what the two of you talked about.
A I had had some concerns from looking at the draft affidavit and addressed those concerns with him and he agreed.
Q What were the nature of the concerns, if you remember?
A I think that the general concern was that Mr. Carter had inserted some information about me having possibly been alone with the President for a few minutes, bringing him a letter in Legislative Affairs.

Page 201

Q Would it help you if I showed you a copy of the draft with some of your handwriting on it?
A Oh. Yes.
MR. EMMICK: I'm placing before the witness what is marked as Grand Jury Exhibit ML-3.
(Grand Jury Exhibit No. ML-3 was marked for identification.)
BY MR. EMMICK:
Q Can you tell us what this is?
A Sure. Do the grand jurors have a copy of this?
Q They do.
A Okay. This is a draft of my affidavit that Mr. Carter drew up based on his conversations with me.
Q And the handwriting on it? Whose is that?
A That's my handwriting.
Q There's also some underlining and some scratch-outs.
A Mm-hmm.
Q Did you do all of that?
A Yes.
Q Can you remember looking at that now what the two of you talked about?
A I think that -- I think that it was -- I think the two main things were this last sentence in paragraph 6 and the -- the concern was, for me at least, was not wanting to

Page 202

give the Paula Jones attorneys any thought about why they might need to want to talk to me. So if I had mentioned that I had been in there alone, it would kind of make them think, oh, well, what happened and did he proposition or blah, blah, blah.
And then the second thing was in the -- towards the end of paragraph 8 on page 2, the idea of with crowds of other people, I think to me was too far from the fake truth?
Q Okay.
A Does that -- is that clear? Sort of -- that that seemed to be too out of the realm of possibility, so --
Q Too implausible?
A Exactly. Thank you. So I believe that, you know, that this statement, "There were other people present on all of these occasions," was something that I discussed with Mr. Jordan.
Q Did he agree with the suggestions or thoughts that you had on those two passages?
A Yes, I believe so.
Q Was there any discussion with Mr. Jordan about the portion of paragraph 8 saying that there was no sexual relationship?
A No.
Q At any time, did Mr. Jordan say that he didn't want to speak to you about the affidavit?

Page 203

A No.
Q How long was your conversation with Mr. Jordan?
A I don't remember. Not long. We may have also talked about job stuff, too. But --
Q All right, then. Let's turn our attention to the next day, which is the 7th. That's the day when you finalized and signed the affidavit. Is that right?
A Yes.
Q And you notarized it under penalty of perjury.
A Yes.
MR. EMMICK: I believe you have -- this is the final version and it is Grand Jury Exhibit ML-4.
(Grand Jury Exhibit No. ML-4 was marked for identification.)
BY MR. EMMICK:
Q I'm placing that before you.
A Okay.
Q And it says "Affidavit of Jane Doe No. 6" at the top and it has your signature, right?
A Mm-hmm.
Q When you spoke with Frank Carter that morning in order to finalize the affidavit, do you remember what changes were made?
A When I spoke with him before I arrived at his office or in his office?

Page 204

Q Either time.
A I believe that I sort of dictated to him the changes -- I think that's possible or I gave them to him in person, I don't really remember. Mr. Carter had prepared three different versions of the affidavit for the significant portion related to this case, I guess, they were all denying sexual relations, all three of them. And we discussed various things about it and eventually decided on this affidavit.
Q All right. Let me ask you a straightforward question. Paragraph 8 at the start says, "I have never had a sexual relationship with the President." Is that true?
A No.
Q All right. The next logical follow-up is, and maybe it's self-evident, but why were you willing to say something that was false under penalty of perjury?
A I don't think that it's anybody's business.
Q Okay. Let me turn the page for you. At the end of paragraph 8, the statement, "The occasions that I saw the President after I left my employment at the White House in April 1996 were official receptions, formal functions or events related to the U.S. Department of Defense, where I was working at the time. There were other people present on those occasions." That's not correct either, is it?
A No, it's misleading.

Page 205

Q Okay. In what respect?
A For me, at the time, I said -- well, it doesn't say the only occasions, but it's misleading in that one reading it would assume that the only occasions on which I saw the President were those listed.
Q Right.
A But I did some justifying in signing the affidavit, so --
Q Justifying -- does the word "rationalizing" apply as well?
A Rationalize, yes.
Q All right. All right. On the 7th, after you signed the affidavit, did you keep a copy of the affidavit?
A Yes, I did.
Q Where did you go later on the 7th?
A To New York.
Q Did you take a copy of the affidavit with you?
A Yes.
Q Why?
A If I remember correctly, I was in a rush and I kind of wanted to have it, if I wanted to look it over again or --
Q Why were you going to New York?
A A job interview.
Q Did you have a job interview?
A Yes, I did.

Page 206

Q Was that the next day?
A Yes.
Q All right. Let's turn our attention to the job interview on the morning of the 8th. Now, was that with McAndrews & Forbes?
A Yes. This is my -- I had -- I mean, just to remind everyone, I had had some job interviews on the 18th of December up in New York at McAndrews & Forbes and Burson-Marsteller. I also took a test on the 30th, I think, of December at Burson-Marsteller and this is now another interview at McAndrews & Forbes on the 8th.
Q Do you remember who you interviewed with that morning?
A Jamie Dernan.
Q How did the interview go?
A Very poorly.
Q Okay. Tell us why it went poorly. What do you mean?
A I think it started off on the wrong foot because I was in a waiting room downstairs and I had thought they would let me know when he was available and I'd go to his office and instead he just walked in unannounced and the interview started, so I was -- I didn't have my wits together at the moment. And I was -- I just was sort of flustered from that moment on. I think everyone can relate to having a bad

Page 207

interview. Maybe.
Q How long was the interview?
A Maybe 20 minutes.
Q Was that the only interview that morning?
A Yes.
Q What was your reaction afterwards?
A I was upset. I felt horrible. I might have even cried. I was embarrassed. I thought that I had sort of embarrassed Mr. Jordan, I think, in such a bad interview.
Q After having a bad interview like that, did you expect an offer?
A No, I didn't think so. My first interview with McAndrews & Forbes had been really, really good, so I wasn't sure exactly what was going to happen, but I didn't think it was --
Q Not a good sign.
A Correct.
Q What did you do after you had that bad interview?
A At some point, I called Mr. Jordan to just let him know that it had gone poorly.
Q Do you remember whether you placed one call or several calls to try to get a hold of him?
A I'm sure I placed several. It was -- he's difficult to get a hold of.
Q Did you eventually talk to him on the 8th?

Page 208

A Yes, I did.
Q What did you tell him?
A I told him that it hadn't worked out and that I was asking his advice on whether I should contact Burson-Marsteller or not and that I was concerned that the McAndrews & Forbes hadn't gone well.
Q At the time you were talking to him, were you still upset about the interview?
A I don't really remember. I'm sure I was. It was kind of a depressing thing all day.
Q And did he say what he was going to do because the interview had not gone well?
A Yes.
Q What did he say?
A He said he'd call the chairman. I thought he was kidding.
Q Okay. And did he call you back some time shortly thereafter?
A Yes, he did.
Q About how long after he called -- excuse me. About how long after he said he was going to call the chairman did he call you back? If you remember.
A I don't remember. I don't think it was very long after, but --
Q What did he say when he called back?

Page 209

A That not to worry -- you know, I don't remember the exact words that he used. The gist of the conversation was that, you know, the were going to call me and everything was going to be okay.
Q Did he say that he had gotten a hold of the chairman or did he mention that at all or --
A I don't remember.
Q Did Revlon or McAndrews & Forbes personnel get a hold of you later after Mr. Jordan called?
A Yes. They called to set up an interview for me with someone directly at Revlon for the next day.
Q Do you remember about when it was that you were called later on the 8th?
A I think it was some time early evening.
Q Early evening?
A Or evening.
Q Were you surprised by the call?
A From having heard from Mr. Jordan, not 100 percent.
Q All right. They set up an interview for the next day?
A Yes.
Q Did you have an interview the next day?
A Yes.
Q Who did you interview with?
A Ellen Seidman.

Page 210

Q And what was the tone of that interview?
A It went very well. It was --
Q Better than with Jamie Dernan?
A Yes.
Q All right.
A It was a very good interview.
Q Did you interview with others at Revlon as well?
A Yes.
Q Do you remember about how many interviews there were?
A Two others, aside from Ms. Seidman's.
Q And you mentioned that the interviews went well. After the interviews, did you give a call to Vernon to let him know how things were going?
A I think so.
Q Later that day, did you have another call from Revlon?
A From Revlon?
Q Mm-hmm.
A Yes, I did.
Q Tell us about that.
A They sort of informally offered me a position and I informally accepted it.
Q Do you remember who it was you were speaking with at the time?

Page 211

A I believe it was Ellen Seidman.
Q Okay. You made a reference earlier in this grand jury appearance to a conversation you had with Linda Tripp on the 9th.
A Yes.
Q We're now on the 9th and I can tell you would like to talk about this conversation. Tell us about your conversation with Linda Tripp on the 9th. Let's start with when it happened.
A Well, I was returning Linda's call from earlier in the week and I think I made a couple of attempts to get a hold of her at her office and when I did get in touch with her, I told her I was on a pay phone because I was concerned about the phones.
And I just -- I -- I didn't -- I was very distrustful of her at this point, especially when I first got on the phone with her. I didn't really know why we were going to be in touch at this point, from what had happened the few weeks before.
So she started out the conversation, I think, asking me, you know, what was going on with my job stuff and everything and I told her I didn't have a job yet and that I hadn't heard from Betty, the President, or Mr. Jordan since December and I didn't know what was going on and so we were discussing that. And that was not true, obviously.

Page 212

And then she told me that she had gone up to New York over Christmas to be with -- I think Norma Asness is her name, and that while she was in New York during the holidays she was shopping with Ms. Asness and this other woman on Madison Avenue buying shoes and that this woman had told Linda she was really savvy and Linda should move to New York and get a PR job in New York. Which I thought was a little strange, since I was in the process of moving to New York for a PR job.
That was just one of the indications that made me think she was a little bit jealous of the help I was getting, that I was talking about earlier.
So when we started to discuss the case, she told me that -- that because of this experience she had had in New York, she decided that maybe it would be best for her to be really vague on the truth about Kathleen Willey. You know, she really didn't know anything, she didn't really remember much, and that -- you know, led me to -- and I believe she may have even said directly that she wasn't going to tell about me or that I was -- you know, my understanding of that was that she wasn't even going to mention me and that I was safe.
Q Did this come as a surprise to you?
A Yes, it did.
Q In what way?

Page 213

A Because she had -- I mean, she had stopped returning my phone calls, we had left everything in a very bad note a few weeks prior to that. So --

In the course of this conversation, when we talked about my job, she said, "Well, Monica -- " Oh. Oh. She asked me what I was going to do in the case and I told her that I was planning on signing an affidavit. Even though I had already signed the affidavit, I didn't want Linda to think that I would have gone ahead and done such a bold thing without her approval.

So she made -- that's when, as I mentioned earlier, she made me promise her that I wouldn't sign the affidavit until I got the job. She also went into this whole long story about her friend --

Am I getting into too much detail?

MR. EMMICK: Close.

JURORS: No. No.

MR. EMMICK: Okay.

THE WITNESS: Okay. All right. She told me about her -- this friend, I don't remember her name, but she's this -- she's an Indian woman who Linda goes to the gym with and that this Indian woman had gone to a psychic and the psychic had essentially said that one of her friends was in imminent danger having to do with the words she would speak.

Page 214

So that that led Linda to believe, you know, along with this event in New York that she should -- you know, she's kind of going to go the good route -- well, what I considered the good route in the Paula Jones case. And it was really based on this conversation that I had with her and this sort of change that I agreed to meet with Linda on the 13th of January.

BY MR. EMMICK:

Q Then let's go to the 13th of January. Let me first cover some of the job-related items. On the 13th, did you get a formal offer from Revlon?

A Yes, I did.

Q And did you accept that offer?

A Yes, I did.

Q How was the matter left about references or recommendations?

A Well, she -- I can't remember her name, something with a J, I think. The woman in human resources with whom I was dealing about the job offer said, you know, I needed to send her some references, so this had been in -- oh. So I called Betty to ask her to remind the President or to check out for me what Mr. Hilley would say to -- I'm not saying this clearly. I'm sorry.

Q That's all right.

A One of the people that I needed to get a reference

Page 215

from was John Hilley, who was the head of Legislative Affairs and had been my boss when I was there the latter half of my tenure at the White House. I was concerned that if I put him down as a reference, he might not say flattering things about me.

So I asked -- I had mentioned this to the President on October 11th and he said he'd, you know, make sure everything was okay, so I wanted to -- so I checked with Betty to ask her to kind of find out what was happening, what the status of that was. So --

Q Did you get a message later from Betty on that subject?

A Yes, I did.

Q Okay. What was that message?

A She had me page her and then later I came to find out from her that afternoon that it had been -- I think Mr. Podesta took care of it and that everything would be fine with Mr. Hilley.

Q Now, when the two of you were paging each other on this day, the name Kay was used rather than either Betty or Monica. Where did that name come from?

A This has sort of become a kind of strange area for me. I had not -- and I do not specifically remember discussing with Betty the fact that I had been subpoenaed in the Paula Jones case and anything surrounding that, but sort

Page 216

of I now know from -- from sort of things that I've been reminded of or shown that I must have. And one of them that indicates that to me is this notion that she -- I -- she and I had started -- I suggested that we use sort of the code name Kay in her paging me and in me paging her. And --

Q And where does the name Kay come from?

A Because Betty and I, our first encounter and our first connection was through Walter Kaye.

Q Now, had you and Betty had earlier conversations about the fact that her message indicator, I guess it would be her beeper or her pager?

A Her pager.

Q Her pager.

A Her text message pager.

Q Her text message pager on some occasion might have indicated Monica?

A Yes. There had been -- I think there had been at least one time when Betty's pager had been sitting on her desk when she was in with the President or had stepped away and someone else had picked up her pager when it went off and there was a message from me.

And so from -- you know, Betty kind of covered it, I think, by saying -- or she did actually have another friend named Monica or something or another, but it was -- you know -- Rebecca Cameron was the person who picked up the

Page 217

pager and so it was sort of a -- not a good thing to happen.
Q Why use any fake names, Kay or any other name? What's the reason you've got to use fake names at this time?
A I was beyond paranoid. I mean, I -- and obviously in denial. I think the -- I could not understand how I had been dragged into the Paula Jones case and so I was very wary of everything.
Q What did Betty say, if you can remember, when you suggested that you refer to one another as Kay?
A Okay.
Q Okay. Did she ask why or --
A I don't remember having this conversation with her.
Q All right. Were you also using names to refer to others? For example, the name Mary?
A Yes.
Q Who did Mary refer to?
A Linda.
Q And why were you using the name Mary to refer to Linda?
A Because that's what she chose.
Q And why were you using any name other than Linda to refer to Linda?
A Because Linda and Betty were the two people who paged me that were involved -- you know, somehow fell into this circle of the Paula Jones story. Is that -- it's not

Page 218

clear. I'm sorry. Okay.
Q When you were speaking with Linda about the President, did you sometimes refer to the President as "her" rather than "him"?
A Linda? No. I don't believe so.
BY MS. IMMERGUT:
Q So that was Betty?
A Yes.
BY MR. EMMICK:
Q Okay. And why did you use "her" to refer to the President?
A I believe that that was only in pages to her and it was just -- you know, I knew that the WAVES -- from having worked at the White House, I knew that people had access to the WAVES pages, let alone that someone types them, so it just was another measure of caution that I used throughout.
Q All right.
A I don't think I ever referred to the President on Betty's pages.
Q When we were talking earlier about your clarifying whether John Hilley would give you a recommendation, you indicated that you had a page from Betty. Does it refresh your recollection about what the page said if I were to read the following?

Page 219

We have a page indicating that it says, "Will know something soon, Kay." Does that remind you about any pages that you got from Betty?
A Yes. I think I mentioned earlier that she paged me and then I talked to her later that day and found out about John Hilley.
Q All right. Did you -- at some point, did you send to Revlon a letter giving them the two recommendations, one of which was John Hilley?
A Yes.
Q Do you remember when that was?
A I believe I faxed it on the 14th of January.
Q So that would be the next day.
A Correct.
BY MR. WISENBERG:
Q Pardon me. Were they recommendations or references? Just as a technical matter, in other words, were they names or were they actual letters of recommendation?
A Oh. They were references, then.
BY MR. EMMICK:
Q All right. Let's go back to the 13th for just a moment because you met with Linda Tripp that day, I think you said, on the 9th you had --
A I also met with Mr. Jordan.

Page 220

Q Okay. All right. Okay. Well, let's go back to Mr. Jordan, then.
A Well, I -- I mean, I was just thinking about the day. I'm sorry.
Q No, that's fine. That's fine.
A Just I stopped in to see him for five minutes, to thank him for getting me the job, and I gave him a tie and a pocket square.
MR. EMMICK: Okay.
BY MS. IMMERGUT:
Q Did you ever provide Mr. Jordan with a signed copy of the affidavit?
A I did not provide him with a copy. No.
Q Do you know whether or not he ever received a copy?
A I believe I showed him a copy. I don't know that he received a copy.
BY MR. EMMICK:
Q On this same meeting on the 13th?
A I -- I -- you know, I have to say I know I brought the copy with me to show him and I may have said, you know, "Do you want to see it?" And I think he may have not even -- I think he may have said, you know, "I don't need to see it." Or -- I --
BY MS. IMMERGUT:
Q So you don't specifically recall handing it over to

Page 221

him or even showing it to him specifically.
A No.
Q But you brought it for him to --
A I did bring it.
MS. IMMERGUT: Correct.
BY MR. EMMICK:
Q All right. So that's the Vernon Jordan part of the 13th.
A Right.
Q What about the meeting with Linda Tripp?
A It was long. I was -- I was very nervous. I was wary of her. I actually thought she might have a tape recorder with her and had looked in her bag when she had gone up to the restroom. I told her a whole bunch of lies that day.
Q What were you trying to accomplish in meeting with her?
A I was trying to -- I was trying to make Linda continue to feel comfortable that she and I were sort of on the -- that we were on the same side, we were on the right side.
We -- and that -- when I had agreed to meet with her, I thought we were going to go over kind of her strategy for what she was going to do in the case and then once we got together, she kind of started wavering about what she wanted

Page 222

to do and then -- so I just was using everything I knew to try to convince her that -- that this is the right thing to do.
Q I think you mentioned earlier that you told her lies.
A Yes.
Q What lies do you have in mind?
A I mean, I think -- throughout that month of December, after I knew she was subpoenaed, there were various things that I think I said that were untrue, but I specifically remember from this meeting the thing that I had -- what I said to Linda was, "Oh, you know, I told -- I told Mr. Jordan that I wasn't going to sign the affidavit until I got the job." Obviously, which wasn't true.
I told her I didn't yet have a job. That wasn't true. I told her I hadn't signed the affidavit. That wasn't true. I told her that some time over the holidays I had freaked out and my mom took me to Georgetown Hospital and they put me on Paxil. That wasn't true.
I think I told her that -- you know, at various times the President and Mr. Jordan had told me I had to lie. That wasn't true. That's just a small example. Probably some more things about my mom. Linda had an obsession with my mom, so she was a good leverage.
Q Let's turn our attention back to the 14th, then.

Page 223

On the 14th, the next day?
A Okay.
Q Right.
A Okay.
Q There's three pieces of paper that have come to be referred to as the talking points.
A Yes.
MR. EMMICK: I think we have them marked as Grand Jury Exhibit ML-5.
(Grand Jury Exhibit No. ML-5 was marked for identification.)
BY MR. EMMICK:
Q I'll place them in front of you.
A Okay.
Q And they are three pages. I wonder if you would tell us how those came to be written and on what computer and the like.
A Okay. First of all, they're out of order.
Q Okay.
A So the last page was actually the first page.
Q All right. Well, let's clarify. What is now the first page says "Points to make in affidavit." And the second page says, "The first few paragraphs" at the top. And the third page says, "You're not sure you've been clear." The third page should be the first page?

Page 224

A Yes.
Q All right. Let's go to first the mechanics of how these got generated.
A Mm-hmm.
Q Were those printed from your printer?
A Yes.
Q Were they typed on your computer?
A Yes.
Q Was anyone present with you when they were typed?
A No.
Q When were they typed?
A On the 14th.
Q Did you talk with anyone in an effort to get assistance editing or writing or getting approval for what is in the talking points?
A No.
Q How did the -- where did you get the ideas that are reflected in the talking points?
A They were based on conversations I've had with Linda from the moment Kathleen Willey and Michael Isikoff ever entered into the picture until the conversations I had with her the morning of the 14th on the phone.
Q Tell me what you mean by that.
A At various times, especially early on, around March or so when -- when Kathleen Willey first came up, Linda

Page 225

talked about how -- you know, that -- that -- what Kathleen was saying to Michael Isikoff was not true. And so, you know, we had had -- I remember having this discussion with her where we were saying, well, if -- you know, if she's lying to Michael Isikoff, how do you know she didn't lie to you?

Linda said, "Yeah, that's a good point. Maybe she did." You know?

And I said, "Yeah, sure. She could have, you know, smeared her own lipstick and untucked her own blouse."

And Linda said, "Yeah, it's true."

That was very early on and throughout my discussions with Linda, especially when she was saying -- saying things about how to be vague on the Kathleen Willey issue in the Paula Jones case, we had these sorts of discussions.

Q What did you do with the talking points? How did you relay them to Linda Tripp?

A I took a copy of them to her.

Q And how were the arrangements made to give her that copy?

A She had told me she was going to go see her attorney, Kirby, that afternoon and was going to talk to him about signing an affidavit, which is why this was all generated. And so I offered to drive her there so that we

Page 226

could just talk on the way because we -- we had had some time to talk that morning, but not as much as I wanted.

Q Who was driving? You were driving?

A Yes.

Q And Linda has the talking points in her hands?

A I handed them to her in the parking lot of the Pentagon.

Q Did she read them?

A Yes, she did.

Q What was she saying or doing as she was reading them?

A She was going through it and she was sort of reading and going, "Yeah. Mm-hmm. Uh-huh. Well, that's true. Oh, good point."

I think she may have said, "Oh, these are -- this is really -- that's true." You know. "Did you write this?" Sort of a thing.

Q Okay. What did you think would happen after you dropped the talking points off to Linda and then you dropped Linda off? How were things left, I guess is another way to ask that question.

A I believe that it was in the car ride home that she said -- made some comment to me about -- that, well, she -- she feels okay -- and this might have been on the 13th when she said this, she feels okay about, you know, kind of not

Page 227

telling the truth or being vague on the truth when she talks to me, but then when she doesn't talk to me, she -- her mind starts to wander to different things, so I just remember feeling -- oh, like I had to hold her hand through everything and I constantly had to talk to her. So I may have said, "I'll call you tonight" or something like that.

Q Have you ever talked to Bruce Lindsey?

A No. I may have said hello to him in the hall, but I -- but -- just in passing.

Q Did you ever talk with the President about the talking points?

A No.

Q Did you ever talk with anyone at Bob Bennett's firm about the talking points?

A No.

Q Did you ever talk with anyone associated with the White House in any way about the talking points?

A No. And that would include Mr. Jordan.

Q Okay. Let's turn our attention, then, to the next day, which is January 15th. Did Betty call you that day about a call she had received from Mike Isikoff?

A Yes.

Q Okay. Tell us about that telephone call.

A I had learned earlier from my attorney that the Paula Jones people had -- had -- well, I guess my attorney

Page 228

had asked me something about if I had ever received any courier packages from the White House and I hadn't, but I told him I did -- I did send things to Betty and he said, oh, well, he had heard -- I think through -- maybe through Bennett's people -- Mr. Bennett's firm, the attorneys, I'm sorry, I don't mean to be so informal, that there was some issue with these courier -- with a courier service.

So I called the courier service and was able to find out that the records could be subpoenaed and then I spoke with Betty later that day and she told me that -- that Michael Isikoff had called her or had called for her intern and Betty had answered the phone and in the course of that he had asked her about the courier, my sending things to her through a courier.

And that she sort of said she didn't really remember or know what he was talking about and that he'd get back to her. Or she'd get back to him. I'm sorry.

Q And then she called you and related this to you?

A Yes. Yes.

Q What was your reaction to that?

A I was very shocked and very -- feeling very strange, that somehow this was closing in more and I -- I didn't know how they could have gotten this information about the courier because there was -- the first person that I thought of that knew about the courier was Linda and the only

Page 229

other person I thought of was this gentleman in my office who was a Clinton hater, Mark Huffman. So I thought that maybe -- I thought, well, maybe he had been the one who had sort of turned me, trying to cause trouble.

Q All right. What did you and Betty talk about doing in response to the Isikoff calls?

A The President was out of town that day and so I think she said she was going to try to get in touch with the President and I believe that Betty and I may have discussed that, you know, they were -- the courier packages were always sent to her and that some of the things were for her, you know.

Q Did Vernon Jordan come up?

A Yes. I know later -- and I don't know if maybe she mentioned to me earlier in the day that she wanted to try to get in touch with Mr. Jordan, but I do know that -- that later in the evening Betty called me and asked me if I could give her a ride to Mr. Jordan's office because Bob, her husband, had the car that day and it was raining. So --

Q So you drove her to Vernon Jordan's.

A Yes.

Q Describe what happened when you drop her off.

A Well, actually, I parked the car and I decided to wait for her downstairs in the restaurant. I think it's The Front Page. And she went up to Mr. Jordan's office and was

Page 230

there maybe 15, 20 minutes. I'm not very good with time.

Q Why didn't she just take a taxi there? It's a three, four dollar taxi ride up there.

A I don't know.

Q Okay. How long did you wait?

THE WITNESS: You know, I need to use the restroom.

MR. EMMICK: Okay.

THE WITNESS: I'm sorry.

MR. EMMICK: The witness needs a break.

THE FOREPERSON: Yes.

MR. EMMICK: Okay. Thank you.

THE WITNESS: Two minutes.

MR. EMMICK: That's all right.

(Witness excused. Witness recalled.)

MR. WISENBERG: Let the record reflect the witness has reentered the grand jury room.

Madam Foreperson, do we have a quorum?

THE FOREPERSON: Yes.

MR. WISENBERG: Any unauthorized persons present?

THE FOREPERSON: None.

MR. WISENBERG: Anything you want to say?

THE FOREPERSON: Monica Lewinsky, I just wanted to let you know that you are still under oath.

THE WITNESS: Really?

THE FOREPERSON: Mm-hmm. Yes, I mean.

Page 231

BY MR. WISENBERG:

Q I have, I hope, just one or two questions about your proffer.

A Okay.

Q Your written proffer. Can you grab a hold of that?

A Sure.

Q And what are we calling that? That is ML-1.

A Okay.

(Grand Jury Exhibit No. ML-1 was marked for identification.)

BY MR. WISENBERG:

Q If you'll take a look at page 4, paragraph 4, that has to do with the President's call to you.

A Yes?

Q At two a.m. on the 17th of December telling you, among other things, that you're on the witness list, correct?

A Correct.

Q Going to the middle portion, starting with "When asked." "When asked what to do if she was subpoenaed, the President suggested she could sign an affidavit and try to satisfy their inquiry and not be deposed."

A Mm-hmm.

Q The next sentence says, "In general, Ms. L. should say she visited the White House to see Ms. Currie and, on occasion, when working at the White House, she brought him

Page 232

letters when no one else was around."

Have I read that correctly? Have I read that sentence correctly?

A Yes.

Q Okay. And I think you have earlier described that as a -- maybe not in these exact words, but you saw it as a continuation on his part of the pre-established pattern of things he had said in the past. Is that correct?

A Yes.

Q All right. And would you agree with me that that is -- that if you said that to the Jones people or to anybody else that that is misleading in a sense because it doesn't tell the whole story of what you were doing when you visited the President.

A Yes.

Q Take a look at -- then I would like you to take a look at page 10, I think it's page 10, it's paragraph 10, whatever page it is.

A Okay.

Q Mine's cut off. It's the last -- I think it's the last page.

A Right.

Q I'll read it. "Ms. L. had a physically intimate relationship with the President. Neither the President nor Mr. Jordan or anyone on their behalf asked or encouraged

Page 233

Ms. L. to lie." I would like you for us to reconcile if you can that statement in your proffer with statements like the ones in paragraph 4 where you talk about specific things the President said or did that were kind of continuations of this pattern.

A Sure. Gosh. I think to me that if -- if the President had not said the Betty and letters cover, let's just say, if we refer to that, which I'm talking about in paragraph 4, page 4, I would have known to use that.

So to me, encouraging or asking me to lie would have -- you know, if the President had said, "Now, listen. You better not say anything about this relationship, you better not tell them the truth, you better not -- "

For me, the best way to explain how I feel what happened was, you know, no one asked or encouraged me to lie, but no one discouraged me either.

Q Okay. So you said what you would have done if the President hadn't said that, but he did say that, what you mentioned in paragraph 4, correct?

A Right.

Q And I guess -- and you had a conversation with him about what to do gifts that you both knew were under subpoena, then you get the call from Betty. Those things happened. When we discussed this on Monday in the proffer session, I think you said something to the effect of or that

Page 234

in paragraph 10 you were being pretty literal. Is that accurate? When you say that no one encouraged you -- told you or encouraged you to lie?

A Yes and no. I mean, I think I also said that Monday that it wasn't as if the President called me and said, "You know, Monica, you're on the witness list, this is going to be really hard for us, we're going to have to tell the truth and be humiliated in front of the entire world about what we've done," which I would have fought him on probably. That was different.

And by him not calling me and saying that, you know, I knew what that meant. So I -- I don't see any -- I don't see any disconnect between paragraph 10 and paragraph 4 on the page. Does that answer your question?

BY MS. IMMERGUT:

Q Did you understand all along that he would deny the relationship also?

A Mm-hmm. Yes.

Q And when you say you understood what it meant when he didn't say, "Oh, you know, you must tell the truth," what did you understand that to mean?

A That -- that -- as we had on every other occasion and every other instance of this relationship, we would deny it.

MR. WISENBERG: That's all I have on that. And

Page 235

probably not anything else. Maybe.

MS. IMMERGUT: I had a couple of quick questions

THE WITNESS: Sure.

BY MS. IMMERGUT:

Q Back for just a moment to January 15th with the visit when you took Betty to Vernon Jordan after she had been called by Michael Isikoff.

A Mm-hmm.

Q Did you ever tell Ms. Currie that you had been called by Michael Isikoff?

A No.

Q Had you ever been called by Michael Isikoff before January 15th?

A No. I'm trying to remember now -- I know that I had seen the Newsweek thing light up on my caller ID, but I don't remember if that was around that time or if that was later, once the scandal started.

Q Do you recall any calls from Michael Isikoff that you would have told Betty about, calling about gifts from the President?

A No. Absolutely not.

Q You mentioned, obviously, that you've given the President several gifts. Have you given him any ties?

A Yes.

Q How many ties have you given him, just

Page 236

approximately?

A Six.

Q Have you had any conversations with the President about wearing your ties?

A Almost all of our conversations included something about my ties.

Q Could you just briefly describe what things that you've said to him and he to you about wearing the ties?

A I used to bug him about wearing one of my ties because then I knew I was close to his heart.

Q And did he ever say anything about -- after he had one of your ties or to alert you when he had worn any of your ties?

A Yes, there were several occasions.

Q And what kind of thing would he say to you?

A "Did you see I wore your tie the other day?"

Q So was he aware based on things you had told him that you would be looking out for when he would wear ties on various occasions?

A Yes.

MS. IMMERGUT: I'd like to show you now what's marked as Grand Jury Exhibits ML-8, 9 and 10.

(Grand Jury Exhibits No. ML-8, ML-9 and ML-10 were marked for identification.)

Page 237

MS. IMMERGUT: And, unfortunately, I don't have copies yet for the grand jury because we got them at the last --
MR. WISENBERG: I'll pass them around afterwards.
MS. IMMERGUT: Okay. And I'll spread them out for you here.
THE WITNESS: Okay.
BY MS. IMMERGUT:
Q Directing your attention first to ML-8, it's a photograph of the President, obviously. Do you recognize the tie that he's wearing in that photograph?
A Yes, I do.
Q Had you actually seen that on television on June 24, 1998?
A Yes, I did.
Q Do you recall what that's in relation to or what event is being depicted on that photograph?
A He was leaving for China.
Q And now directing your attention to Exhibit 9, do you know what that's a photograph of?
A I don't know where it's from, but it's the President wearing my tie.
Q And this one states it's Monday, July 6, 1998. Do you remember watching any of the media on that date?
A Yes, I do.

Page 238

Q And do you remember seeing him wearing your tie on that date?
A Yes, I do.
Q Do you remember what event was taking place on that date that he was wearing your tie?
A I don't, but I just saw it says "Medicare costs," so --
Q Okay. And then finally, ML-10. Do you recognize what that's a photograph of?
A Yes.
Q And what is that?
A The President wearing the same tie.
Q And do you know what date that is?
A Date? It was a few days after, he wore the tie when he came back from China, so it's July 9th.
Q Okay. And what -- I guess -- did you reach any conclusions from the fact that he was wearing your tie on those days?
A I -- I -- I think -- the first time he wore the tie, I thought maybe it was a coincidence, but I didn't really think so. And then when he wore it when he came back from China on the 6th, I thought maybe it was a reminder of July 4th, because that had been the first workday after July 4th and we had had a really intense, emotional meeting July 4th of '97. And then when he wore it a few days later,

Page 239

I thought he's trying to say something. I mean, the President doesn't wear the same tie twice in one week, so -- I didn't know what it meant, but it was some sort of a reminder to me.
MS. IMMERGUT: Okay. Nothing further on that.
BY MR. WISENBERG:
Q This is well after the scandal broke, is that correct?
A Yes.
BY MS. IMMERGUT:
Q This is this summer, right?
A Correct.
BY MR. WISENBERG:
Q You've told us something about seeing a picture of Nelvis, Bayani Nelvis, I think coming to the grand jury.
A Yes.
Q Can you tell us -- and you noticed something about some neckwear he was wearing?
A I think it was on Nel's maybe third appearance or his last appearance. He was wearing the first tie that I ever gave to the President.
Q Did you know that the President had ever given that tie to Mr. Nelvis?
A No.
Q And what is -- can you recall the last time the

Page 240

President had ever worn that tie?
A No. I didn't see him every day, so -- I mean, I know he -- I know some of the times he wore that tie, but I don't know the last time he wore the tie.
Q Okay. Is there any question in your mind that the President knew that both these ties, the one that we're putting around pictures of and the one that Nel wore to the grand jury, were ties you had given him?
A Not in my mind, but I can't -- I can't answer that.
MR. WISENBERG: Okay.
MR. EMMICK: There's a question? Yes?
A JUROR: Did you know the President after a while gave his ties to the people who worked for him? Did you know that?
THE WITNESS: Yes, I did know that.
MR. WISENBERG: Pardon me just a minute.
(Pause.)
MR. WISENBERG: I'm going to ask the witness to be excused very briefly and we'll possibly call you back in a couple of minutes.
(The witness was excused.)
(Whereupon, at 4:45 p.m., the taking of testimony in the presence of a full quorum of the Grand Jury was concluded.)
* * * * *

-C-

-E-

-I-

-J-

-K-

-L-

-M-

-N-

-S-

-X-

-Y-

-Z-

Tab 3

UNITED STATES DISTRICT COURT
FOR THE DISTRICT OF COLUMBIA

- - - - - - - - - - - - - - - - - - x
IN RE: :
GRAND JURY PROCEEDINGS :
- - - - - - - - - - - - - - - - - - x

Grand Jury Room No. 2
United States District Court
for the District of Columbia
3rd & Constitution, N.W.
Washington, D.C. 20001

Thursday, August 20, 1998

The testimony of MONICA S. LEWINSKY was taken in the presence of a full quorum of Grand Jury 97-2, impaneled on September 19, 1997, commencing at 9:51 a.m., before:

MICHAEL EMMICK
KARIN IMMERGUT
Associate Independent Counsel
Office of Independent Counsel
1001 Pennsylvania Avenue, N.W.
Suite 490 North
Washington, D.C. 20004

8/98D

P R O C E E D I N G S

Whereupon,

MONICA S. LEWINSKY

was called as a witness and, after having been first duly sworn by the Foreperson of the Grand Jury, was examined and testified as follows:

EXAMINATION

BY MR. EMMICK:

Q Good morning, Ms. Lewinsky.

A Good morning.

Q As we did with your earlier grand jury testimony, my job is to advise you of your rights and obligations here at the beginning.

First off, you have a right under the Fifth Amendment to refuse to answer any questions that may tend to incriminate you. In this case, that right is qualified by the fact that you've signed an agreement to provide truthful testimony in connection with our investigation. Do you understand that?

A Yes, I do.

Q In addition, you have the right to have counsel present outside the grand jury to answer any questions that you may have. Do you have counsel outside?

A Yes, I do.

Q Who is that?

A Preston Burton.

Q And you understand that if you'd like to speak to your counsel, all you have to do is say "Could I take a break and speak with my counsel?"

A Yes.

Q All right. You also in addition to those two rights, you have an obligation and that obligation is to tell the truth. That obligation is imposed on you because you have been put under oath and also because in connection with your agreement you're required to tell the truth. Do you understand that?

A Yes, I do.

MR. EMMICK: What I have placed in front of you is what is marked as ML-7. This is a chart that you have earlier testified about of contacts between yourself and the President.

As I indicated to you informally beforehand, this grand jury session today is for you to answer questions from the grand jurors.

And so without any further ado, I will ask the grand jurors if they have any questions of Ms. Lewinsky.

A JUROR: I think I'm going to start out.

MR. EMMICK: Okay.

A JUROR: Ms. Lewinsky, in your testimony when you were with us on the 6th, you mentioned some of the steps that you took to maintain secrecy regarding your relationship: that you would bring papers or he'd have papers or either you would accidentally bump into each other in the hallway; you always used Betty as the excuse for you to be waved in; and on many occasions you would go in one door and out of the other door.

THE WITNESS: Yes.

A JUROR: Are there any other methods you used that I've missed? That you used to maintain your secrecy?

THE WITNESS: Hmm. I need to think about that for a minute.

A JUROR: And the second part to that question is were these ways to maintain your secrecy your idea or were they recommended to you by anyone?

THE WITNESS: I can answer the second part first.

A JUROR: Okay.

THE WITNESS: If that's okay.

A JUROR: That's fine.

THE WITNESS: Some of them were my idea. Some of them were things that I had discussed with the President. I think it was a mutual understanding between us that obviously we'd both try to be careful.

A JUROR: Do you recall at all specifically which ones he may have recommended to you as an idea on maintaining the secrecy?

THE WITNESS: Yes and no. The issue of Betty being the cover story for when I came to the White House, it became my understanding I think most clearly from the fact that I couldn't come to see him after the election until -- unless Betty was there to clear me in and that one time when I asked him why, he said because if someone comes to see him, there's a list circulated among the staff members and then everyone would be questioning why I was there to see him. So --

MR. EMMICK: Let me try to ask some follow-ups in response to your question.

BY MR. EMMICK:

Q Were there ever any discussions between you and the President about what should be done with letters that you -- letters or notes that you had sent to him? That is to say, for example, did you ever write on the bottom of any letters what to do with those letters?

A It was my understanding that obviously he would throw them away or, if he decided to keep them, which I didn't think he did, he would put them somewhere safe.

I think what you're referring to is on the bottom once of a sort of joke memo that I sent to him I in a joking manner reminded him to throw the letter away, that it wasn't -- you know, that was a joke. So --

Q What about whether on your caller ID on your telephone the word POTUS would appear and whether anything

8/98D

was done in order to make sure that POTUS did not appear on your telephone?

A My caller ID at work, it would -- when the President called from the Oval Office, it would say POTUS and when he'd call from the residence, it was an asterisk. And I told him that. I didn't know if he knew that it said POTUS when he called from the office, and I assumed he didn't, because otherwise that would be sort of silly.

So I informed him of that and then one time he called me from the residence and he -- he called on a hard line -- I don't know. I shouldn't say "hard line" because I know that has some different terminology to it, but he called on a line that had a phone number attached to it and so when he called, he said, "Oh, did it ring up, you know, phone number? It didn't say my name, did it?"

And so it was -- that was something that I was concerned about.

Q Did he ever express to you a reluctance to leave messages on your telephone voice message system?

A At home?

Q Yes.

A Yes.

Q All right. Tell us about that.

A One time in a conversation he just said he didn't like to leave messages.

Q Okay. What about the times that you would visit him? Were those times selected in a way so that there weren't people around or that certain people weren't around?

A Yes.

Q Okay. Would you tell us about that?

A There were obviously people at the White House who didn't like me and wouldn't -- wouldn't be understanding of why I was coming to see the President or accepting of that and so there was always sort of an effort made that either on the weekends -- when I was working in the White House he told me that it was usually quiet on the weekends and I knew that to be true. And after I left the White House it was always when there weren't going to be a lot of people around.

Q And what about particular individual people? Would there be particular individual people who would be -- staffers in the oval area that you would try to avoid in order to help conceal the relationship?

A Yes. Nancy Hernreich, Stephen Goodin, Evelyn Lieberman. Pretty much anybody on the first floor of the West Wing.

A JUROR: How did all these people come to not like you so much? What were you doing? Were you breaking the rules of the White House? What were you doing to draw their attention to not liking you so much? Before the relationship.

From the time you got there all the way up to the time -- what I'm saying is what did you do to deserve for them not to like you?

THE WITNESS: Before the relationship started?

A JUROR: Yes. What did you do from --

THE WITNESS: I don't think there was anything I did before the relationship started that -- the relationship started in November of '95. I had only been at the White House as an intern in the Old Executive Office Building for -- for a few months, so most of my tenure at the White House I was having a relationship with the President.

I think that -- the President seemed to pay attention to me and I paid attention to him and I think people were wary of his weaknesses, maybe, and thought -- in my opinion, I mean, this is -- I think that people -- they didn't want to look at him and think that he could be responsible for anything, so it had to all be my fault, that I was -- I was stalking him or I was making advances towards him. You know, as they've said, I wore inappropriate clothes, which is absolutely not true. I'm not really sure.

A JUROR: But you do admit a lot of the places that you weren't supposed to be you were always found. You do admit that there were things that you were doing, too, in order to see him that they were feeling that was going against the rules of the White House?

THE WITNESS: Uh --

A JUROR: You know, places that you were that you weren't supposed to be and hallways that you weren't supposed to be, you were seen in those places?

THE WITNESS: Yes and no. There really weren't any of these staffers who saw me in the places that I wasn't supposed to be. And that was part of the effort to conceal the relationship. So -- does that make sense?

I mean, when I was in the Oval Office with the President, no one else knew except for the Secret Service, no one else knew that I went in there. So for them to know -- for them to be disliking me for that reason, I don't think that they were really -- I don't know if they were aware of that or not.

I did make an effort, I think, to try to -- to have interactions with the President and I -- and I think that -- that was probably disturbing to them. I know that if the President was in the hall and he was talking to people and I passed by he'd -- he'd stop talking and say hi to me. I'm not really sure.

A JUROR: Just a follow-up to that.

THE WITNESS: Sure.

A JUROR: If they didn't see you, well, how did they know?

THE WITNESS: I don't know what they knew. I -- you know, I -- I'm not sure -- I --

A JUROR: Because if you said you made an effort to hide yourself, you know, so you wouldn't see them, the Secret Service are the ones that saw you --

THE WITNESS: Mm-hmm.

A JUROR: Okay. So, I mean, how would they -- how did they know that you were there, you know, to want to keep you away from being there?

THE WITNESS: I don't know. Maybe -- I -- I mean, I've heard reported in the newspapers and on TV that the Secret Service, someone said something to Evelyn Lieberman and I had had an -- I don't know if I went over this the last time I was here, I had had a real negative interaction with Nancy Hernreich early on in my tenure at the White House and so --

I think there was also -- I'm a friendly person and -- and I didn't know it was a crime in Washington for people -- for you to want people to like you and so I was friendly. And I guess I wasn't supposed to be.

A JUROR: So that interaction that you had with Evelyn Lieberman was when she was telling you what?

THE WITNESS: She stopped me in the hall and she asked me where I worked, in which office I worked, and I told her Legislative Affairs in the East Wing.

And she said, "You're always trafficking up this area." You know, "You're not supposed to be here. Interns aren't allowed to go past the Oval Office."

And she -- she really startled me and I walked away and I went down to the bathroom and I was crying because -- I mean, when -- you know, when an older woman sort of chastises you like that, it's upsetting.

And then I thought about what she said and I realized that, well, I wasn't an intern any more. I was working there. And I kind of believe in clear communication, so I went back to Evelyn Lieberman, to Ms. Lieberman, and I -- I said, "You know, I just wanted to clarify with you that I work here, I'm not an intern. So, you know, I am allowed to go past the Oval Office." I don't think I said that, but I had a blue pass.

And she looked at me and said, "They hired you?" And I was startled and then she said, "Oh, well, I think I mistook you for someone else or some other girl with dark hair who keeps trafficking up the area." And ever since then -- and that was maybe in December or January of '95 or '96. So --

A JUROR: Ms. Lewinsky, were you ever reprimanded or chastised by your immediate supervisor in Legislative Affairs for trafficking up the area or being where you weren't supposed to be or being away from your desk too much?

Anything like that?

THE WITNESS: Being away from my desk had been mentioned to me, but trafficking up the area and being where I'm not supposed to be, no.

I -- the -- I had a view of -- and this is sort of my view with work is that you get a lot more done and people are a lot more willing to help you when you have a personal interaction with them. And so the person who held the job before me would fax the drafts of his letters to the staff secretary's office and then at some point during the day when someone got the draft they would make the changes and then fax it back.

And I found it to be much more effective to take things over to the staff secretary's office and interact with the person -- I can't remember her name -- Helen -- to interact with Helen and have Helen edit the letters right then and there and then I could go back and to me it was a faster process.

So there was also -- you know, I also wanted to try to see the President. So, I mean, I did make efforts to try to see him in the hall or something like that because --

A JUROR: So the route to the staff person's office was a route that you could still veer off and see the President?

THE WITNESS: No. It -- it wasn't necessarily in front of the Oval Office or anything. There were -- we also had -- let me see if I can explain this. I'm sure you guys know by now that the West Wing is three stories. There's the basement, the first floor and the second floor. Legislative Affairs has an office on the second floor of the West Wing.

There are two ways to get to that office -- or three ways, I guess. There's the West Wing, you can cut across the West Wing lobby, which is where people coming to visit someone in the White House sit. There's going the back way, which you pass the Oval Office, but the door's always closed when the President's in there. And then you can go all the way down the stairs and all the way around and then all the way up two flights of stairs.

When I first started working there, it didn't seem appropriate to walk through the West -- to me, it didn't seem appropriate to walk through the West Wing lobby with papers when there were people who were visitors coming to sit and wait. I just -- I didn't think that was appropriate during the business time.

So I went the other way, behind -- which went past the Oval Office, not knowing that -- I guess you're not supposed to do that. It seemed silly. The door's closed and it's locked. And there wasn't this intention to see the

President that way.

So -- am I -- did I answer your question?

A JUROR: Yes.

THE WITNESS: Okay. I'm sorry.

MR. EMMICK: You know, one thing I might do is circle back to try to pick up some more concealment methods.

A JUROR: Okay.

MR. EMMICK: Because you asked the question are there any other methods.

A JUROR: Yes.

MR. EMMICK: And I can ask a few more questions that might direct us in that area.

THE WITNESS: Okay.

BY MR. EMMICK:

Q For example, you have indicated earlier that it was Betty Currie who waved you in all the times during 1997 that you saw the President. Did you ever talk with the President about whether he could wave you in instead or whether it would be a good idea for him to wave you in personally?

A Yes. I think that that's what I mentioned earlier.

Q Oh, okay.

A That he and I had discussed it and he said he couldn't do that because then it would be on a list.

Q Okay. What about -- you had mentioned that you took a different route into the Oval Office than you would take out of the Oval Office. In addition, did you ever take routes to get to the Oval Office that seemed calculated to avoid certain Secret Service or White House personnel?

A Not Secret Service, but I -- I liked or I preferred to sort of meet up with him and then we'd walk in together. And I preferred to go in through the Rose Garden because then I wasn't going -- I wasn't risking the possibility of running into someone in the hall right outside the Oval Office. So --

Q What about the routes that Betty would walk you in from the gates?

A Oh. When -- there were certain Secret Service officers who were friendly with Debi Schiff who Betty wanted to try to avoid because I guess they chatted with Debi Schiff a lot and there's a whole long story with Debi Schiff, so --

Q And would that be another way that you would help conceal your meetings with the President?

A Yes.

A JUROR: Just to back up for a minute. When you would meet the President and go in through the Rose Garden or meet the President before going into the Oval Office, did you discuss that with him ever about sort of what -- that that would be a way that would sort of be more concealing or --

THE WITNESS: We only did that, I think, twice. And the first time, it really was an accident. And so then the next time that we did that, I said -- you know, before -- he would call me in my office before I would come see him and we'd figure out what we were going to do.

And I think I -- I know I suggested to him, I said, "I really like that because then it's just easier, it seems." And also, I -- for me personally, I didn't -- I didn't always want to be the one that was being seen going in. Does that make sense?

So that I wasn't always bringing in the papers and it was me going to him, that in this instance if someone saw it, being the Secret Service, he invited me. So -- for me, that just made me feel better.

BY MR. EMMICK:

Q All right. I have a number of other questions about these alternative methods of concealment. Let me ask you this. I think you've testified earlier that most of the sexual contact that you had with the President tended to occur in the hallway, rather than in the study, although sometimes it was in the study itself.

Did that have anything to do with whether or not it would be easier to see you in the study as opposed to the hallway?

A I think so, but I don't specifically -- I don't

specifically remember discussing that with the President, but there were circumstances that that sort of was obvious to me.

Q And would that include the fact that windows in the study tended to be uncurtained?

A Just that, windows. Yes.

Q Right. Yes, there were windows there.

A Yes.

Q And so you might be seen there.

A Yes.

MR. EMMICK: All right.

BY MS. IMMERGUT:

Q In that regard, you also mentioned that you would move from the oval area or that sometimes you'd start in the Oval Office and then you'd move towards the hallway. Did the President ever initiate that move?

A I think we both did. I mean, it just depended on the day. It wasn't --

Q Was it understood that you wouldn't actually have a sexual encounter in the Oval Office?

A I'm sure it was understood. I -- I -- I wouldn't have done that. I mean -- so -- I'm sure he wouldn't have done that.

BY MR. EMMICK:

Q Are there windows all around the Oval Office?

A There are windows all around and it just -- I know this may sound silly, but it wouldn't be appropriate. You know.

Q What about any discussions with the President about not acknowledging one another at parties or photographs, for example?

A He called me in my office the day of Pat Griffin's going away party and had asked me if I was going to go. I said yes and he said, "Well, maybe we can get together after that."

And I told him I didn't think that was a good idea, that people were going to be watching. I was paranoid anyway and -- so I said, "I think it's a good idea if we just sort of ignore each other at the party and don't really say anything." And that's what we did.

Q And what about with respect to a photograph that was taken at the party and whether --

A I mean, we didn't discuss this. I didn't know there was going to be a picture taken. But I made an effort to stand on the -- I was the last person sort of on the outside of this picture so that -- I didn't want anyone to think that I was trying to get close to the President, I was trying to -- whatever it was.

Q So in that case, that would be a concealment effort, but not one that the President and you had collaborated on.

A No.

Q All right. What about an occasion when the President suggested that the two you might attend a movie and sort of bump into each other outside the movie? Tell us about that discussion.

A He told me he was going to watch a movie with some friends of his and that if I wanted to I could bump into him in the hall outside and then he'd invite me into the movie.

And I asked him if -- I think he said there were some friends and maybe some of his staff or I asked him if some of his staff was going to be there.

And he said yes and I don't remember who he said was going to be there, but I said I didn't think that was a good idea.

Q And why would you have to make prior arrangements for you to bump into each other rather than having sort of a -- you know, walk down the hall together to the movie?

A Well, I --

Q I know it's kind of obvious.

A For obvious reasons, I guess, because it wouldn't be appropriate. It -- people would -- people would wonder what was going on.

Q Right. Right. Okay. What about the fact that you made -- that you sent gifts and notes through Betty rather than directly to the President?

Was that something that was done in order to make it less obvious that the notes were actually to the President?

A Well, yes and no. You really -- if you send something directly to the President, if you send a gift to the President, if I sent something right now, well, I don't know, right now, but before this, it -- it -- it goes to the gift unit.

Q Right.

A And so I knew that Betty was the way -- I think that that's -- Walter Kaye would, you know, go through Betty, I think. And that's --

Q So it's yes and no, is the answer to that.

A You can't -- I mean, you can't send a courier thing to the President, you know, a courier to President Clinton, so --

A JUROR: I have a question to follow up on that. When you would send gifts and notes and what have you to Betty, as you had testified, sometimes you'd have a funny card in there, sometimes it would be something sentimental.

Did you ever give Betty license to read any of them because you thought, "Hey, take a look at this, tell me what you think," any of the cards or notes or anything?

THE WITNESS: I don't think so. Maybe I told her about a funny card or something. Not that I really remember. I don't -- I think especially if it were something that was ultra-sensitive, I don't -- you know, I don't --

A JUROR: Yes. That would probably be sealed.

THE WITNESS: Exactly.

A JUROR: But for any of the other little --

THE WITNESS: Might have been the jokes. Sometimes I would put together jokes I got on the Internet or e-mail jokes that I put together for him because, you know, everyone needs to laugh, so -- I think maybe -- maybe there was a time that I said, "Oh, you should look at these jokes, they're really funny."

A JUROR: Okay.

MR. EMMICK: Other questions? Yes, ma'am?

A JUROR: Ms. Lewinsky, did you ever discuss with the President whether you should delete documents from your hard drive, either at the office or at home?

THE WITNESS: No.

A JUROR: Nothing like that?

THE WITNESS: No.

A JUROR: Did you ever discuss with the President whether you should deny the relationship if you were asked about it?

THE WITNESS: I think I always offered that.

I think I've always --

A JUROR: In discussions with the President?

THE WITNESS: In discussions -- I told him I would always -- I would always deny it, I would always protect him.

A JUROR: And what did he say when you said that? What kind of response did you receive?

THE WITNESS: I said that often. I -- in my head, I'm seeing him smile and I'm hearing him saying "That's good," or -- something affirmative. You know. Not -- not -- "Don't deny it."

A JUROR: Thank you.

THE WITNESS: Sure.

BY MS. IMMERGUT:

Q Ms. Lewinsky, with respect to the weekend visits, did the President ever initiate that idea or say anything about it's good if you come on the weekends?

A Yes. The -- I don't remember if it was the Wednesday or the Friday when the relationship first started, he said to me at some point, you know, "You can come see me on the weekends. I'm usually around on the weekends." So --

Q And did you understand what that meant?

A Yes. To me, it meant there aren't as many people around on the weekends, so --

A JUROR: Ms. Lewinsky, when you -- now, this is a

8/98D

different kind of subject. When you first made the determination that you were moving to New York and you wanted to explore the possibilities of a job in private industry, can you recall how you first got the recommendation about Vernon Jordan's assistance in this endeavor?

THE WITNESS: I can't. I know that it was -- what I don't remember was if it was my idea or Linda's idea. And I know that that came up in discussions with her, I believe, before I discussed it with the President. I know that I suggested to the President or I -- I didn't suggest, I asked the President if Mr. Jordan might be able to assist me.

A JUROR: To go back from the job search to what we were talking about before, I seem to recall, and I may be mistaken, when you were here before you said something about Tim Keating when you were fired, said something to you like maybe you can come back after the election.

THE WITNESS: Mm-hmm.

A JUROR: And I wanted to just hear sort of a fuller explanation about that. Was it your understanding at the time that Tim Keating was sort of -- that he understood and was telling you that you were fired because of an appearance problem around the time of the election?

THE WITNESS: Not at all.

A JUROR: No?

THE WITNESS: No.

A JUROR: The other question I have, and I apologize, it's a little bit sensitive, but did you and the President in sort of discussing cover stories and, you know, how -- you know, your desire to protect him from sort of what's going on now, did you ever talk about sort of -- you know, that you weren't really having sex?

I mean, you said that he made this comment to you about not having -- you know, that certain actions have consequences at his age.

THE WITNESS: Yes.

A JUROR: Was there ever sort of an understanding that, well, oral sex isn't really sex? Or did you talk about that?

THE WITNESS: We didn't talk about it. Something that I thought on my own was one of the reasons that it -- at first that he didn't want to -- that he wouldn't let everything come to completion in terms of oral sex was I thought that that sort of had to do with maybe that was his way of being able to feel okay about it, his way of being able to justify it or rationalize it that, well --

A JUROR: But you never discussed that.

THE WITNESS: No.

MR. EMMICK: Yes, ma'am?

A JUROR: Ms. Lewinsky, getting back to -- I think you have a copy there of contacts between the President and

Monica?

THE WITNESS: Yes.

A JUROR: After you left the White House, it seems as if you attended a number of public functions where you came in contact with him.

Was that by chance? Was that something you wanted to do? Was it a way to see him? Was it something that he suggested?

Could you just tell us a little about that?

THE WITNESS: Sure. No. Those were all ways for me to get a chance to see him. I'm an insecure person and so I think -- and I was insecure about the relationship at times and thought that he would come to forget me easily and if I hadn't heard from him -- especially after I left the White House, it was -- it was very difficult for me and I always liked to see him and it -- and usually when I'd see him, it would kind of prompt him to call me. So I made an effort. I would go early and stand in the front so I could see him, blah, blah, blah.

BY MR. EMMICK:

Q Let me ask a follow-up question to that because I think it may have been in about October of '96 when you had a telephone conversation with him just prior to you going to Billy Shaddock to get a photograph.

A Right.

Q During the conversation before, did you and the President have any discussion about your dropping by and seeing him at a public departure?

A Yes.

Q All right. Would you tell us about that?

A Let's see. I spoke with him -- I think it was October 22nd, and then I saw him at an event October 23rd and he called that night and I had mentioned to him on -- I think it was a Tuesday, the first phone conversation, that I was going to be at the White House on Thursday.

And when he called me Wednesday night, he said -- I was upset with him and so then he said, you know, "Don't be mad. Don't be mad." You know. "Are you coming tomorrow?"

And I said yes.

So he said, "Well, why don't you stop by Betty's office, stop by to see Betty and then maybe you can come see me for a few minutes before I leave." So --

Q Okay. All right. The reason I was asking that as a follow-up is that's sort of a prearranged semi-public occasion for the two of you to see each other.

A Right. I don't -- I don't know necessarily that I was going to go to the departure.

Q I see.

A But that was maybe kind of a cover story.

Q I understand.

A Or I'm not -- I know he had a departure and I know that I was going to see him for a few minutes before the departure because I thought -- I remember thinking that I might get to kiss him, so --

MR. EMMICK: All right.

A JUROR: Now to follow up on your follow-up of my question --

MR. EMMICK: Yes.

A JUROR: Did you get to see him that day?

THE WITNESS: No, I didn't.

A JUROR: Okay. Could you tell us a little about that?

THE WITNESS: Sure. I -- the short of it is that I didn't end up seeing him because Evelyn Lieberman was hanging around and left with him that day.

A JUROR: She was someplace where she didn't belong.

THE WITNESS: Right. So Betty had -- I was waiting in the West Wing lobby with Billy, actually, after we had gone to look at the photos and Betty finally came out and it was really just as he was walking to the helicopter and she took me to see it, but she said that -- and it was at that point when she sort of confirmed for me that Evelyn didn't like me. So -- that --

A JUROR: The contacts with the President, on page 5, for the 18th of August --

THE WITNESS: I'm sorry, I can't hear you.

MR. EMMICK: Page 5.

A JUROR: Okay. Page 5, 18th of August, it says "Public function, President's 50th birthday party, limited intimate contact."

A JUROR: I couldn't hear her.

MR. EMMICK: Okay. Let me repeat it. There is a reference on page 5 to August 18th of '96, a Sunday, "Public function, President's 50th birthday party, limited intimate contact."

Your question about that was?

THE WITNESS: What does that mean?

MR. EMMICK: What does that mean?

THE WITNESS: It's stupid. There was a cocktail reception for his -- he had this big 50th birthday party at Radio City Music Hall and there was a cocktail reception and at the -- when he came to do the rope line and he -- after he greeted me and talked to me, he was talking to a whole bunch of people in and around my area and I had -- can I stand up and show you?

MR. EMMICK: Sure. Sure.

THE WITNESS: Okay. If this is the rope line and here are all the people and the President's standing here, as he started to talk to other people, I had my back to him and I just kind of put -- put my hand behind me and touched him. This -- so --

BY MS. IMMERGUT:

Q Touched him in the crotch area?

A Yes.

A JUROR: I didn't hear that.

MS. IMMERGUT: Touched him in the crotch area.

A JUROR: Oh.

MS. IMMERGUT: And the response was yes.

A JUROR: Okay.

A JUROR: Did anybody see you?

THE WITNESS: What? No. What's the question?

A JUROR: Did anybody see you?

THE WITNESS: No.

A JUROR: But there were people around.

THE WITNESS: There were, but it was -- he was talking -- everybody was enamored with him. I'm sure everybody saw from Monday that -- and he was talking to different people and he -- he was always very close to me when -- whenever he'd do these rope lines and would sort of make a point of talking to me around -- you know, with other -- while other people were there and he'd usually hold my hand -- you know, sort of shaking hands and just -- would continue to just touch me somewhere. I mean, not -- not intimately, not --

BY MR. EMMICK:

Q Right. Just to set the scene, are there a lot of people kind of bunched together at the time?

A Oh, they're -- they're -- I mean, if we -- if everybody in the room came and stood in this one small corner, that's -- I mean, that's how crowded it was. So it was -- and my back was to him and he was -- he was holding onto my -- I think he was holding onto one of my arms or something, I had a sleeveless dress on. So --

Q So it sounds to me like -- it's almost a situation where there are so many people that you can't really see that kind of --

A Exactly. And it wasn't -- it wasn't a -- it was -- maybe sort of a grazing over of that area, but it wasn't -- it wasn't how you might imagine it if someone described this, from a scene from a movie, it wasn't like that, but it was -- you know. I don't even know if he remembers, so --

MR. EMMICK: Okay.

A JUROR: So on this paper we have here with sexual relations, would that qualify as -- what, contact? Sexual contact? Because if I remember -- where's my paper --

THE WITNESS: Let me look at the definition.

MR. EMMICK: Sure.

A JUROR: Yes. Contact with -- number 1 --

MR. EMMICK: Just to clarify, the witness is looking at Grand Jury Exhibit ML-6.

THE WITNESS: I'm not really sure, because I don't think it was to necessarily gratify him or arouse him.

A JUROR: What was it for?

THE WITNESS: It was just -- I thought it was funny and it was sort of a -- I don't know how to explain it.

A JUROR: Contact.

BY MR. EMMICK:

Q Would it be better described as perhaps affectionate or playful?

A Playful, I think. It was just -- playful, not something I'd ever thought I'd have to discuss publicly.

A JUROR: While we're on this, I wanted to like finish it up, but I had a couple of questions with regards to the definition.

THE WITNESS: Sure.

A JUROR: Because I want to be sure in my own mind. At the bottom it says -- it says "Contact means intentional touching, either directly or through clothing."

THE WITNESS: Mm-hmm.

A JUROR: Out of all of the times you had intimate contact, were there times when the President would touch you either on the breasts or in the genital area directly to the skin or was it always through clothing?

THE WITNESS: Directly to the skin. Both.

MR. EMMICK: Yes, ma'am?

A JUROR: I have some questions about the 50th birthday. That's when you gave the President the yellow tie. Is that when you gave the President the yellow tie?

THE WITNESS: Not on that date.

A JUROR: But just before that.

THE WITNESS: But before that. Correct.

A JUROR: When it shows on the chart here, it says "Some time before August 16, 1996."

THE WITNESS: Correct.

A JUROR: And that tie is the same tie that at the end of your appearance here we saw some evidence that the President has worn a number of times this summer.

THE WITNESS: Yes.

A JUROR: There's been some press accounts about that tie, last night and today.

THE WITNESS: Sure.

A JUROR: My question to you is have you authorized your attorneys or any other spokesperson through you to discuss that evidence?

THE WITNESS: Gosh. I don't think I've necessarily given a direct authorization.

A JUROR: Do you know that they have?

THE WITNESS: Do I know if they -- I -- I don't

know if they necessarily directly have. I know there have been questions about it. I shouldn't say I know, I'm sure there have been questions about it, but there have been a lot of instances since the beginning of this thing that there's been information that's come out from places where I hadn't expected it and that includes my own -- the people on my team. So I can't -- I don't know.

A JUROR: So you don't know whether that information is coming from people that you have discussed it with?

THE WITNESS: I think that there -- there probably might have been -- I really -- I -- I wouldn't be surprised to find out that there was confirmation or some of that information came from there.

So -- but I know that also -- I'm sure it was somewhat limited because with my agreement, we're not allowed to talk to the press. We're not supposed to. So -- without prior approval.

BY MR. EMMICK:

Q So I guess there's -- let me just rephrase it. It sounds like you wouldn't be surprised by it, but do you have any direct knowledge that it occurred?

A I know that there have been calls about this tie and I know that -- that I don't think that we've been 100 percent silent about that. So -- I don't -- I mean -- I know that we didn't cause this story to come out or I don't believe that we did. So --

A JUROR: Ms. Lewinsky, it says on the chart that you received a thank you note saying that the tie is really beautiful.

THE WITNESS: Mm-hmm.

A JUROR: And that was in the President's handwriting?

THE WITNESS: It's a typed letter and then he hand signed the letter and then "The tie is really beautiful" is handwritten.

A JUROR: Did you ever discuss the tie with him in person or was it just a note?

THE WITNESS: No, we discussed it a lot on the phone.

A JUROR: And did he like the tie?

THE WITNESS: Mm-hmm.

A JUROR: Thank you.

THE WITNESS: He called me the first day he wore it. The first time he wore it.

A JUROR: All right. Thank you.

A JUROR: I have another question.

THE WITNESS: Sure.

A JUROR: On the day you were here testifying, there was a report on the TV --

THE WITNESS: Right.

A JUROR: The President in the Rose Garden wearing that tie. Did you see that?

THE WITNESS: That evening I did.

A JUROR: When you saw him with the tie, what did that say to you?

THE WITNESS: I understand you had to do what you had to do. That's what it meant to me. I had looked -- because I had seen him wear this tie prior -- a few other occasions since January, I had looked the day before my testimony because I thought he's just the kind of person that's going to wear this tie to tug on my emotional strings one last time before I go into the grand jury and say this under oath. And he didn't.

And him wearing it the day I came to testify sort of having to know that I wasn't going to see it until the end of the day, to me was just kind of -- you know, hey, you had to do what you had to do. But --

MR. EMMICK: Yes, ma'am?

A JUROR: Ms. Lewinsky, not to make a big issue about the tie, but is this tie something -- one of the ties that perhaps the President really liked, is a favorite tie?

THE WITNESS: I think so because he wore it during the campaign. He wore it once -- sometimes even twice a week. So I think he liked it a lot.

A JUROR: Do you think that he would remember that it's from you? I mean, you know, I don't know, but do you think he would?

THE WITNESS: Ties were a big issue with us and I used to bug him all the time on the phone, "Well, when are you going to wear one of my ties?" You know. Or he'd say, "Did you see -- " On one occasion, I remember specifically he said, "Did you see I wore your tie the other day?"

There's a pretty big correlation between the times when he would wear one of my ties and we either spoke the night before or that night.

And I used to say to him that "I like it when you wear my ties because then I know I'm close to your heart." So -- literally and figuratively.

A JUROR: So you think he would know, then, that that was your tie.

THE WITNESS: He should know.

A JUROR: Which brings to mind when the first appearance by Nel, when he came testify --

THE WITNESS: Yes.

A JUROR: Can you tell me what your thoughts were when you saw the pictures of Nelvis wearing the first tie that you gave the President?

THE WITNESS: Yes. Actually, you know what? I think my cup's leaking. I'm sorry.

A JUROR: Do we have another cup up there?

THE WITNESS: Am I allowed to know people's names in here?

MR. EMMICK: The answer to that is no.

THE WITNESS: Oh --

MR. EMMICK: I know it seems --

THE WITNESS: It's so awkward.

MR. EMMICK: It does seem awkward, but I think it's better if --

THE WITNESS: Okay.

MR. EMMICK: -- the record not have any identifications.

THE WITNESS: Okay.

MR. EMMICK: We didn't intentionally get you a dribble glass.

THE WITNESS: Oh, sure. At least it's water and not grape juice.

I had two very different thoughts. My first thought was "You jerk. You're trying to show me how little you care about me and how little this meant to you by giving it -- to show me that you gave it to someone else, it meant so little to you now."

And my second thought was that it was sort of some sort of message of some sorts. I don't know what. Because I could see the President kind of saying to Nel, you know, "Oh, why don't you -- " I could even see him spilling something on Nel on purpose and -- that morning and then sort of saying, "Oh, here, just wear this tie," or something like that. I mean, that's -- it's -- he's funny that way. But I thought there was some sort of deliberateness to it.

I don't know that Nel knew that, that that was the tie I gave the President but -- I don't think it was a coincidence.

MR. EMMICK: Yes, ma'am?

A JUROR: Could one of your thoughts perhaps have been that maybe he just gave him a batch of ties to Nelvis? And maybe he didn't remember?

THE WITNESS: No.

A JUROR: You really think he would have remembered that first tie?

THE WITNESS: I know he did. I mean, we -- we -- that was -- I don't know if you all know this or not, but I worked in a men's necktie store when I was in college for four years and so that was my thing, that was part -- you know, my spending money, a lot of it came from working. And so I love ties.

And I -- I mean, I can pick out -- you know, different designers and stuff. And so that was a big thing for me. And then -- and I liked to give him ties and I liked to see him wearing them.

A JUROR: Do you know how much impact Nel had on what the President wore each day?

THE WITNESS: None. To my understanding. Nel was. My understanding is that Nel's strictly in the -- while he would go to the residence on occasions, that he was usually in the oval area.

MR. EMMICK: There's a question waiting for a bit here. Yes.

A JUROR: Ms. Lewinsky, was it the President's nature to give his ties away?

THE WITNESS: Yes. I knew that -- I knew that he had given Nel ties, his ties in the past. But ties were such a big issue between the President and me that I really couldn't have imagined that he didn't -- that he didn't know.

A JUROR: Other people other than Nel as well, in terms of giving his ties away?

THE WITNESS: I don't know.

A JUROR: Okay. You just --

THE WITNESS: I'm not aware of anyone else, but that doesn't mean there aren't.

A JUROR: Okay.

THE WITNESS: Right.

A JUROR: But you did know about that.

THE WITNESS: Yes.

A JUROR: Do you happen to know whether the

President had a valet to assist him in his dressing?

THE WITNESS: Assist him in his dressing, I don't know. I know that there's a valet.

A JUROR: Or like prepare -- Mr. President, this suit goes with this tie, kind of thing?

THE WITNESS: I don't know that necessarily, but I have seen -- I had seen evidence enough that he could wear my ties when he wanted to. You know. That if he wanted to, he could go pick it out, so I don't know what his getting dressed routine is.

A JUROR: Okay. Thank you.

A JUROR: Okay. I have a question that's a bit on the delicate side.

THE WITNESS: Okay.

A JUROR: But this is just something that I need to know.

THE WITNESS: Sure.

A JUROR: Did you and the President ever engage in sexual relations using cigars?

THE WITNESS: Yes.

A JUROR: Okay.

A JUROR: Okay. I'd like to change the subject now.

THE WITNESS: Thank you. Just once. Just once.

A JUROR: When you last testified, you told us that

photographs that you saw of the President and First Lady when they were away that were romantic in nature upset you.

When you had an opportunity to speak with the President about those photographs or any film that was taken during these romantic moments, what did he say? Why they were -- because I'm just curious as to whether or not they were staged because of the legal things that were going on with the President at that time.

THE WITNESS: Right. I don't believe we discussed them. I know that that upset me and sort of put me in a bit of a contentious mood when I spoke with him on the 5th. I think it was the 5th of January of this year. And I may have said something in passing about them, but we didn't have a discussion about the pictures.

A JUROR: Okay. I was just wondering if there were --

THE WITNESS: Sure. No. I wondered, too.

A JUROR: Did you think any conversations to him about his wife were inappropriate?

THE WITNESS: I don't know if inappropriate is the right word. I tried not to. I -- there were very few discussions and I tended to say things like, "Well, when you're alone," you know, "Call me when you're alone," kind of a thing or, you know, that was how we discussed sort of Mrs. Clinton maybe not being there, was, "Well, I'll be alone on this day. Shall I -- " I think we were careful -- or I was careful, I know I was.

MR. EMMICK: Yes, ma'am?

A JUROR: Ms. Lewinsky, I wondered if you ever had any trouble with the Secret Service in trying to be near the President.

THE WITNESS: No. The only time that I remember was when I went to see him on the last time in '96, I guess it was April 7th, Easter. And when John Muskett was outside and he said he was going to check with Evelyn if I could go in and then I don't remember exactly how it happened, but I sort of -- I don't remember the exact discussion, but it ended up he ended up not talking to Evelyn and I went in. So --

A JUROR: I have a question about Linda Tripp.

THE WITNESS: Ugh. Sorry.

A JUROR: In your conversations with Ms. Tripp, was her opinion always that she must be truthful or was there a time where your impression was that she was going to provide you with cooperation as far as keeping the secrecy?

THE WITNESS: There are two areas of that, I guess. Linda always told me she would always protect me and she would never tell anybody and keep my secret, up until the Paula Jones case came about.

And I had never had any reason to think that she would ever need to discuss this under oath because I was certainly always going to deny it and I couldn't even imagine a situation where that would really come up.

But there was a point in the period prior to my learning about her being subpoenaed in the Paula Jones case, most specifically, January 9th, when she led me to believe that she was not going to tell about my relationship and that she was going to be vague on the truth about Kathleen Willey and was just not going to really remember anything else and that was why I agreed to meet with her on Tuesday the 13th.

A JUROR: In your conversations with her as you were making your move to move to New York and what have you, did you ever get the sense that she was fishing for offers of benefits or the protection of her job? You know, or where she was hoping that nothing would affect her job or if there was something in it for her?

THE WITNESS: Yes and no. When you asked me the question, the first thing that comes to my mind was it may not be directly related to that.

When the Kathleen Willey incident had come out in Newsweek, there was a period after it, Bob Bennett had referred to -- or had made that comment about Linda Tripp and she made some off-comment about if she loses her job she's going to write a tell-all book.

And so I sort of -- that was an instance where I felt I needed to assure her that that wasn't going to happen, she wasn't going to lose her job, and that -- I certainly tried to make assurances. I mean, I -- I promised -- I would have promised her the moon if I could deliver it.

And then also -- then when I spoke with her on the 9th, she talked about that she had spent some time in New York during Christmas and that she -- that someone had suggested to her that she get a job doing public relations in New York.

And that seemed a little bit strange to me, in that that was exactly what I was in the process of doing, and that maybe that was what she thought, that somehow then -- you know, I think I told her, oh, I'd try to help her come to New York and try to help her that way, but I don't know that -- that I ever said anything directly about who would help her.

A JUROR: Okay. Thank you.

BY MR. EMMICK:

Q I'd like to ask a clarifying follow-up because I wasn't sure I understood all of the sort of ins and outs, if you will, of when Linda was going to maintain the secret and when she was going to reveal it. It sounded like prior to the time when Linda got a Paula Jones subpoena, your understanding was she was doing to keep the secret.

A Correct.

Q And then after she got the Paula Jones subpoena, then she told you that she was going to disclose things and tell the truth. Is that right?

A Yes. Yes.

Q Okay. And then in this conversation on January 9th, she indicated some willingness to consider keeping the secret a bit longer.

A No, considered that she was going to do that.

Q That she was going to. All right. That's what I wanted to clarify.

A Sure.

MR. EMMICK: Thank you.

A JUROR: When you said that in your conversations with Linda Tripp you kind of had to exaggerate some things about the President to her, you exaggerated on some of the things you said to her about the President --

THE WITNESS: I'm not sure about that. I -- I don't know if exaggerate is the right -- is maybe the word I would choose.

A JUROR: Okay.

THE WITNESS: But go on. I'm sorry.

A JUROR: Well, no, I just used that word.

THE WITNESS: Okay.

A JUROR: Exaggerate. You didn't use it, but I couldn't think of the exact words you used.

THE WITNESS: Sure.

A JUROR: But were you -- why do you think that you had to not tell her some things that din actually happen, true things, in talking to her?

THE WITNESS: That really came about in relation to the Paula Jones case. I think that I was -- there were some occasions, one in particular that I remember, when I didn't disclose a contact that I had with the President -- I'm sorry, here -- I'll scoot over -- contact that I had with the President to her for some reasons, but after the Paula Jones case, I was scared to death. I mean, I was panicked that she was going to tell.

So, I mean, I -- I -- you know, along the lines of, you know, some of the things I said about Mr. Jordan, I said, you know, "Oh, the President told me I have to lie," I don't even remember everything I said, but I know that there were certainly lies at that point, not even exaggerations.

MR. EMMICK: Actually, I was going to ask that clarifying follow-up to that.

THE FOREPERSON: And then after that, we have to take a break.

MR. EMMICK: And then we'll take a break.

BY MR. EMMICK:

Q The clarifying follow-up was that I had understood that during that January period when you were talking to

Linda Tripp you were lying to her on occasion, but I wasn't clear whether those lies related to times that you had been with the President or whether they related to other things generally. Do you understand what my question is?

A No.

Q What were the nature of the lies that you were telling to Linda Tripp during that January period?

A Oh, gosh. They went from -- I guess a non-disclosure of my meeting with him on the 28th, nor my phone call with him on the 5th of January, to -- ranging to things that he said I had to do or told me to do.

I haven't -- I haven't seen transcripts of those days, thank goodness, but I just know that I was -- I was scared to death. And I thought any influence that anybody would have, my mother, Mr. Jordan, the President, anybody, would -- I used.

MR. EMMICK: All right.

THE FOREPERSON: It's break time.

MR. EMMICK: Break time.

THE FOREPERSON: It's break time. It's break time.

A JUROR: I have a follow-up to that as well.

THE FOREPERSON: Okay. So we're going to take ten minutes.

THE WITNESS: Okay.

THE FOREPERSON: And we'll come back.

A JUROR: I hope I remember my question.

THE WITNESS: Can you guys call me Monica?

Are they allowed to call me Monica instead of Ms. Lewinsky? I was just --

THE FOREPERSON: If you say so.

THE WITNESS: Okay.

MR. EMMICK: Sure.

THE WITNESS: I'm just 25. Please.

A JUROR: But you'll always be Ms. Lewinsky, whether you're 25 or 28 or --

THE WITNESS: Not if I get married.

(Witness excused. Witness recalled.)

THE FOREPERSON: Monica, I'd like to remind that you are still under oath.

THE WITNESS: Thank you.

MR. EMMICK: We have a quorum and there are no unauthorized persons present. Is that right?

THE FOREPERSON: You are absolutely correct.

MR. EMMICK: Lucky this time.

THE WITNESS: Thank you.

MR. EMMICK: Did you want to ask some follow-up questions?

MS. IMMERGUT: Yes.

BY MS. IMMERGUT:

Q Ms. Lewinsky, there are two things I wanted to

clarify. First, with respect to the tie disclosure issue --

A Yes.

Q -- you were asked about before, I believe you mentioned something to the effect that there have been things that have come out of your team that you were surprised about before. Are you referring to your current legal team?

A No. My first legal team.

Q Okay. And that's Mr. Ginsberg?

A Yes.

Q Okay. You're not aware of any unauthorized disclosures from your current camp?

A No. Nor have I authorized any disclosures.

Q Okay. So you didn't authorize a disclosure about the tie.

A No.

Q With respect to -- to switch gears -- to what we were speaking about right before the break about the things that you said to Linda Tripp at the very end, particularly on January 13, 1998, I believe --

A Yes.

Q You mentioned that an example of things that you were not truthful about was, for example, the fact you had seen the President on December 28th and that you had spoken to him on January 5th. Is that correct?

A Right. Yes. And I didn't disclose that to her.

Q Right. You did not disclose that to her.
A Quite to the contrary.
Q Okay. In fact, you told her that you hadn't seen or spoken to the President for two months.
A Or since the 17th of December.
Q Okay.
A Exactly.
Q You mentioned that there was -- you also said things about what the President had said to you to Ms. Tripp that were not true on January 13th. Do you remember any specific things that you said that the President had told you that in fact were not true?
A No. I don't remember any specifics, I just wanted to leave open the possibility. Does that clarify it?
MR. EMMICK: On the right here?
A JUROR: Monica, why did you keep that black dress?
A JUROR: Blue.
A JUROR: Blue dress.
A JUROR: Did you have a reason to keep it?
THE WITNESS: Pardon?
A JUROR: The blue dress.
A JUROR: The blue dress.
THE WITNESS: No. I didn't have a reason. The -- reason -- the dress -- I didn't realize -- if I remember

correctly, I didn't really realize that there was anything on it until I went to go wear it again and I had gained too much weight that I couldn't fit into it.

And it seemed sort of funny and I -- it may sound silly, I have a lot of clothes. I don't clean all my clothes right after I wear them, I usually don't clean them until I know I'm going to wear them again. And then I was going to wear it for Thanksgiving because I had lost weight and I had -- I had shown the dress to Linda at that point and had just sort of said to her, "Well, isn't this -- " You know, "Isn't this stupid?" Or, you know, "Look at this, isn't this gross?" Or whatever. I don't really remember exactly what I said.

And she told me that I should put it in a safe deposit box because it could be evidence one day.

And I said that was ludicrous because I would never -- I would never disclose that I had a relationship with the President, I would never need it.

And then when Thanksgiving time came around and I told her that I was going to wear it for Thanksgiving, she told me I looked fat in the dress, I shouldn't wear it. She brought me a jacket from her closet as to try to persuade me not to wear the dress.

So I ended up not wearing it and then I was going to clean it. I took it with me up to New York and was going to clean it up there and then this broke, so --

A JUROR: Okay. Your relationship with the President, did your mother at any time try to discourage the relationship?

THE WITNESS: Oh, yes.

A JUROR: Well, what kept it going? I mean, what kept it -- you keeping it active or whatever?

THE WITNESS: I fell in love.

A JUROR: I beg your pardon? I couldn't hear you.

THE WITNESS: I fell in love.

A JUROR: When you look at it now, was it love or a sexual obsession?

THE WITNESS: More love with a little bit of obsession. But definitely love.

A JUROR: Did you think that the President was in love with you also?

THE WITNESS: There was an occasion when I left the White House and I was pretty stunned at how I felt because I did think that.

A JUROR: You did?

BY MR. EMMICK:

Q Do you remember the date?

A It was July 4, 1997.

A JUROR: Were you aware that he was having problems in his marriage? Did this ever spill over in the times that you were together? Did you get a feeling that something was not right, that --

THE WITNESS: [redacted]

A JUROR: [redacted]

THE WITNESS: [redacted]

A JUROR: [redacted]

THE WITNESS: [redacted]

A JUROR: [redacted]

THE WITNESS: [redacted]

A JUROR: [redacted]

MR. EMMICK: I thought there was a question in the front here.

A JUROR: And today, Monica, do you still love the President?

THE WITNESS: Before Monday, I would have said yes.

A JUROR: So then it is no?

THE WITNESS: I don't know how I feel right now.

MR. EMMICK: A question in the front?

A JUROR: I guess I would like to know what happened Monday to make you just by Thursday change your mind so completely.

THE WITNESS: I don't think it's so much changed my mind. I think -- it's -- it was very painful for me to watch his speech on Monday night. I -- it's -- it's hard for me to feel that he has characterized this relationship as a service contract and that that was never something that I ever thought it was. And --

A JUROR: I'm sorry, you lost me already.

THE WITNESS: I'm sorry. I'm sorry. It's -- from my understanding about what he testified to on Monday, not -- just from the press accounts, is that this was a -- that this was a service contract, that all I did was perform oral sex on him and that that's all that this relationship was. And it was a lot more than that to me and I thought it was a lot more than that.

And I think I felt -- I was hurt that -- that he didn't even -- sort of acknowledge me in his remarks. And even also -- I mean, that has to do with directly with me, but I thought he should have acknowledged all the other people that have gone through a lot of pain for seven months.

I feel very responsible for a lot of what's happened, you know, in the seven months, but I tried -- I tried very hard to do what I could to not -- to not hurt him. I'm still not answering your question.

A JUROR: Well, let's -- you said the relationship was more than oral sex. I mean, it wasn't like you went out on dates or anything like that like normal people, so what more was it?

THE WITNESS: Oh, we spent hours on the phone talking. It was emotional.

A JUROR: Phone sex?

THE WITNESS: Not always. On a few occasions. I mean, we were talking. I mean, interacting. I mean, talking about what we were thinking and feeling and doing and laughing.

We were very affectionate, even when -- after he broke the relationship off in May, I mean, when I'd go to visit with him, we'd -- you know, we'd hug each other a lot. You know, he always used to like to stroke my hair. He -- we'd hold hands. We'd smile a lot. We discussed a variety -- you know, a wide range of things.

So, I mean, it was -- there was a real component of a relationship to it and I just -- I thought he had a beautiful soul. I just thought he was just this incredible person and when I looked at him I saw a little boy and -- I don't know what the truth is any more.

And that's, I think, what I took away on Monday, was that I didn't know what the truth was. And so how could I know the truth of my love for someone if it was based on him being an actor.

A JUROR: I'd like to ask you about Bayani Nelvis.

THE WITNESS: Okay.

A JUROR: How much about your relationship with the President did Bayani Nelvis know?

THE WITNESS: I think he knew that -- that we were friends and that I would come to see the President and I gave him things. I don't know -- I don't remember ever getting into any specific details. Might he have thought that from -- you know, from how much I kind of liked the President? I'm not sure.

But -- and I don't mean this in a racist way, you know, Nel's from another country and so his English is -- while his English is good, it's not perfect, not that anyone's is perfect, so I think that sometimes there was a little bit of a language barrier there, too, so I think he -- you know, Nel was just a -- is a really nice guy. He's a sweet guy and he -- he's very loyal to the President.

A JUROR: Did you ever tell him at any time that you loved the President?

THE WITNESS: I don't think so, but I might have,

but I don't think so.

A JUROR: Okay.

MR. EMMICK: Yes? A question?

A JUROR: You just mentioned real components, the relationship was -- like a real component, you mentioned things like truth. But sometimes I go back and forth not understanding because you yourself were living a lot of secrets, a lot of lies, a lot of paranoia, but yet you wanted truth, a real component?

I'm not understanding these two different things because one time you're sentimental but then again you do just the opposite of what you say you're thinking.

Did you ever think that nothing real could come of this relationship?

THE WITNESS: Did I ever thing nothing real --

A JUROR: Anything real, that anything real could -- and truthful and honest could have come from this relationship?

THE WITNESS: Yes.

A JUROR: With this married man?

THE WITNESS: I did.

A JUROR: But I have a question for you about that.

THE WITNESS: Mm-hmm.

A JUROR: It's been reported in the papers that you had a relationship before similar to this, where a lot of hurt and pain came out of this, you know, a lot of hurt and pain toward a family.

And then you turn around and you do it again. You're young, you're vibrant, I can't figure out why you keep going after things that aren't free, that aren't obtainable.

THE WITNESS: Well, there's sort of two parts to that and just to clarify, the -- the way Andy and Kate Bleiler portrayed everything on TV and through their lawyer was pretty inaccurate, so I don't know how much of that is part of your question.

A JUROR: The only part I know is that he was a married man with a wife and a family.

THE WITNESS: That's true.

A JUROR: Like I know about the President.

THE WITNESS: Mm-hmm.

A JUROR: He was a married man and it wasn't no secret of that fact. But yet you want to talk about truth, a real component, honesty. It all seems so -- like a fantasy. That's why I asked you earlier about obsession.

THE WITNESS: That's a hard question to answer because obviously there's -- there's work that I need to do on myself. There are obviously issues that -- that -- you know, a single young woman doesn't have an affair with a married man because she's normal, quote-unquote. But I think most people have issues and that's just how mine manifested themselves.

It's something I need to work on and I don't think it's right, it's not right to have an affair with a married man. I never expected to fall in love with the President. I was surprised that I did.

And I didn't -- my intention had really been to come to Washington and start over and I didn't want to have another affair with a married man because it was really painful. It was horrible. And I feel even worse about it now.

A JUROR: Monica, I'd like to change the topic, if I can.

THE WITNESS: Did I answer --

A JUROR: Yes.

THE WITNESS: Okay.

A JUROR: And I also -- I want to let you know that we're not here to judge you in any way, I think many of us feel that way.

THE WITNESS: I appreciate that. But I understand that every -- you know, this is -- this is a topic that -- there are a lot of people think it's wrong and I think it's wrong, too. I understand that.

A JUROR: I had to ask that you question because I've had to ask other questions and it wouldn't have been right for me not to ask you the question --

THE WITNESS: Sure.

A JUROR: -- that I've had to ask --

THE WITNESS: I think it's fair and I think you should -- I think it's a fair question. It's a hard one to answer. No one likes to have their weaknesses splayed out for the entire world, you know, but I understand that. And I'd rather you understand where I'm coming from, you know, and you'd probably have to know me better and know my whole journey to how I got here from birth to now to really understand it. I don't even understand it. But -- I understand. I respect your having to ask that question and I appreciate what you're saying, whatever your name is.

A JUROR: We're here only to assess the credibility of your testimony.

THE WITNESS: Sure. But I -- I can see how that would be a factor.

A JUROR: I wanted to go back to the issue of ties. It's my understanding that you testified earlier this morning that your agreement, your immunity agreement, with the Office of the Independent Counsel includes an understanding that you -- that you and your legal team need prior approval to disseminate information to the press.

THE WITNESS: Mm-hmm.

A JUROR: And in looking over Exhibit ML-2, I don't see that provision. Can you look at that?

THE WITNESS: Is that my agreement?

A JUROR: Yes.

THE WITNESS: Sure.

MR. EMMICK: Sure.

THE WITNESS: I know that portion of it very well.

A JUROR: I may be missing something.

THE WITNESS: There have been many times I've wanted to defend myself and the lies that have been spewed out.

MR. EMMICK: I think the reference is to part 1B.

A JUROR: Okay.

MR. EMMICK: Where it says "Will not make any statements -- " "Neither Ms. Lewinsky nor her agents will make any statements about this matter to witnesses, subjects, or targets of the OIC's investigation or their agents or to representatives of the news media without first obtaining the OIC's approval."

A JUROR: Okay. Thank you.

THE WITNESS: Sure.

MR. EMMICK: Other questions? Yes, ma'am?

A JUROR: I'd also like to return for a minute -- if you have that package out -- to something that was discussed this morning, earlier this morning, and that refers to your proffer. Do you have a copy of the proffer? The proffer?

MR. EMMICK: We do. Sure.

THE WITNESS: Okay.

MR. EMMICK: I'm placing Exhibit ML-1 before the witness.

THE WITNESS: Thank you.

A JUROR: Monica, if you could look at paragraph 11, I'm not sure what page it is, but it's paragraph 11.

THE WITNESS: Okay. Yes. Okay.

A JUROR: As I understood our discussion this morning, you said that you offered to deny the relationship and the President didn't discourage you, but said something like "That's good."

As I read your proffer here, it says "The President told Ms. L to deny a relationship if ever asked." And that seems to me slightly different.

THE WITNESS: I forgot this. So that's true.

A JUROR: Is this proffer statement correct, that he did tell you to deny a relationship?

THE WITNESS: Yes. I don't -- I don't -- when I answered the question earlier, that was what first came to my mind. But, I mean, I know that this is true.

I just at that point -- and I -- really reading it, I know it's true because I was truthful in my proffer, but sitting here right now, I can't remember exactly when it was, but it was something that was certainly discussed between us.

A JUROR: And what about the next sentence also? Something to the effect that if two people who are involved say it didn't happen, it didn't happen. Do you recall him saying that to you?

THE WITNESS: Sitting here today, very vaguely. I can hear -- I have a weird -- I'll explain to you guys that I have a weird sense of -- for me, my saying I remember something, if I can see it in my mind's eye or I can hear him saying it to me, then I feel pretty comfortable saying that that's pretty accurate, that I remember that. And I can hear his voice saying that to me, I just can't place it.

A JUROR: Is it --

THE WITNESS: And this was -- I mean, this was early -- this was all throughout our relationship. I mean, it was -- obviously not something that we discussed too often, I think, because it was -- it's a somewhat unpleasant thought of having to deny it, having it even come to that point, but --

A JUROR: Is it possible that you also had these discussions after you learned that you were a witness in the Paula Jones case?

THE WITNESS: I don't believe so. No.

A JUROR: Can you exclude that possibility?

THE WITNESS: I pretty much can. I really don't remember it. I mean, it would be very surprising to me to be confronted with something that would show me different, but I -- it was 2:30 in the -- I mean, the conversation I'm thinking of mainly would have been December 17th, which was --

A JUROR: The telephone call.

THE WITNESS: Right. And it was -- you know, 2:00, 2:30 in the morning. I remember the gist of it and I -- I really don't think so.

A JUROR: Thank you.

A JUROR: I have some questions about the Paula Jones lawsuit. Going back to the period before you even had any idea that you might be a witness in that, did you follow the Paula Jones lawsuit fairly closely?

THE WITNESS: I followed it. I don't know "fairly closely," but -- I think it maybe depended more on was there something in the paper and that happened to be a day that I sat and read all the papers because I had nothing to do.

I did follow it, but I wasn't -- I didn't follow it as much as I follow this case. I mean, in terms of -- no, but I mean, I'm just saying as a gauge, you know.

A JUROR: So you were holding down a full-time job and everything at that time, but you did read the papers --

THE WITNESS: I did read the papers every day and it was -- sure, I followed it. I didn't know the ins and outs of it, but I followed it.

A JUROR: Did you -- in that period again, even before anyone knew that you would be a witness, did you discuss that with the President? Was he aware that you followed it? Was that something --

THE WITNESS: No. Really, the time that I remember we discussed it was on the 17th.

A JUROR: December 17th?

THE WITNESS: And when I told him my sort of stupid idea for how he should settle it. So that was -- but, no. He wasn't -- we didn't -- I -- and I think in general just to give you guys a flavor, because there have been different subjects that have come up, when we spent time together, I know I certainly made an effort -- unless I was angry with him about something, that there were topics that I wanted to stay away from and the time that I spent with him was precious to me. So things that were unpleasant I didn't bring up unless I had to.

A JUROR: Exactly what date again did you get your subpoena to be a witness?

THE WITNESS: The 19th of December.

A JUROR: The 19th? Okay. Now, when -- and if you could retell for me the conversation you had with the President about the gifts.

THE WITNESS: Okay. It was December 28th and I was there to get my Christmas gifts from him. Excuse me. I'm sorry. And we spent maybe about five minutes or so, not very long, talking about the case. And I said to him, "Well, do you think -- "

What I mentioned -- I said to him that it had really alarmed me about the hat pin being in the subpoena and I think he said something like, "Oh," you know, "that sort of bothered me, too. That bothered me," you know, "That bothers me." Something like that.

And at one point, I said, "Well, do you think I should -- " I don't think I said "get rid of," I said, "But do you think I should put away or maybe give to Betty or give to someone the gifts?"

And he -- I don't remember his response. I think it was something like, "I don't know," or "Hmm" or -- there really was no response.

I know that I didn't leave the White House with any notion of what I should do with them, that I should do anything different than that they were sitting in my house. And then later I got the call from Betty.

A JUROR: Now, did you bring up Betty's name or did the President bring up Betty's name?

THE WITNESS: I think I brought it up. The President wouldn't have brought up Betty's name because he really didn't -- he didn't really discuss it, so either I brought up Betty's name, which I think is probably what

8/98D

happened, because I remember not being too, too shocked when Betty called.

Somewhat surprised, I guess, that he hadn't said -- you know, it would have seemed easier to sort of have said something maybe then, but I wasn't too surprised when she called.

A JUROR: Thank you.

MR. EMMICK: I think there was a question in the front. Did you have a question?

MS. IMMERGUT: Did you have a question?

A JUROR: Yes. Back to the contacts?

THE WITNESS: Yes.

A JUROR: On page 7, on the 29th of March --

THE WITNESS: On the -- sorry, what date?

A JUROR: The 29th of March. Sunday.

MR. EMMICK: Then 29th of March.

THE WITNESS: Okay.

A JUROR: "Private encounter, approximately 1:30 or 2:00 p.m., study. President on crutches. Physical intimacy including oral sex to completion and brief direct genital contact." Brief direct genital contact, could you just elaborate on that a bit?

THE WITNESS: Uh --

A JUROR: I understand --

THE WITNESS: Oh, my gosh. This is so

embarrassing.

A JUROR: You could close your eyes and talk.

A JUROR: We won't look at you.

THE WITNESS: Can I hide under the table? Uh -- I had -- I had wanted -- I tried to -- I placed his genital next to mine and had hoped that if he -- oh -- this is just too embarrassing. I don't --

A JUROR: Did you think it would lead to intercourse?

THE WITNESS: Not on that day.

A JUROR: Was that sort of the reason for doing the gesture --

THE WITNESS: Yes.

A JUROR: -- or trying to -- moving his closer to yours?

THE WITNESS: Then I -- not that we would have intercourse that day, but that that might make him want to.

A JUROR: Okay. Were you wearing clothes at the time or underwear at the time?

THE WITNESS: No.

A JUROR: And was he? Or his were pulled down?

THE WITNESS: Correct.

A JUROR: So was there direct skin-to-skin contact between your genitals and his?

THE WITNESS: I think very briefly. It was --

he -- he's really tall and he couldn't really bend because of his knee, so it was --

A JUROR: It was more of a grazing?

THE WITNESS: Yes.

A JUROR: About how many encounters did you have in the study? If you can recall.

MR. EMMICK: What do you mean by "encounters"?

A JUROR: Sexual encounters. I'm sorry.

THE WITNESS: Do you include kissing or not?

A JUROR: No kissing. According to the definition.

THE WITNESS: Okay. Two.

A JUROR: Okay. Thank you.

BY MS. IMMERGUT:

Q And why don't you give us the dates of those.

A The -- well, let me look. The 29th of March and the 28th of February. There might have been -- I mean, in terms of the clothes and stuff, there might have been playful touches here and there, but not -- nothing that I would have considered sexual encounters.

Q And that's not listed as an intimate encounter?

A No. No, it's not. No, it's not.

Q And just to clarify again, are those the two times that the President actually came to completion during the oral sex?

A Yes.

BY MR. EMMICK:

Q And I'm actually obliged to ask one follow up that I don't think will be too bad, but directing your attention to August 16th, did you attempt to touch the President on that day?

A Yes.

Q And did you actually touch him? In his groin area?

A Over his clothes.

Q Over his clothes. And did he say that's not -- "We can't do that"?

A Yes.

MR. EMMICK: Okay.

A JUROR: Did you feel any rejection the times that he wouldn't go all the way with you?

THE WITNESS: Yes.

A JUROR: Monica, I had one question to go back to the gifts. You had said that the President had called you initially to come get your Christmas gift, you had gone there, you had a talk, et cetera, and there was no -- you expressed concern, the President really didn't say anything. How much later in the afternoon did you get a call from Betty? It was that same day, is that correct?

THE WITNESS: Yes, that's correct. Let me just clarify real quickly that I had made the arrangements to go there on Sunday through Betty, just that you had said he called me.

A JUROR: So you had initiated the contact on that day?

THE WITNESS: He had -- he had told me on the 17th that he -- you know, he still had these Christmas gifts for me and then -- just shortly after Christmas and I called Betty and said, you know, "He said he had something for me," something like that, you know. And then she arranged it. So I just wanted to clarify.

A JUROR: And then how much of a time gap --

THE WITNESS: A few hours, maybe.

A JUROR: A few hours?

THE WITNESS: Maybe -- I think it was around 2:00 p.m. or so, around 2:00 in the afternoon, and I had gone there at 8:30 in the morning and left -- I'd say maybe four or five hours time span.

A JUROR: So what exactly happened? You went home and you packaged these gifts? Or had you already had them packaged?

THE WITNESS: No. I went home and I -- I think I went to New York that evening, possibly, so I was getting ready to go to New York, I think, or something.

But when Betty called, then she said, you know, "I understand you have something to give me." It was very vague. And I understood -- I mean, to me, that meant from this conversation that we had had that I should sort of -- you know, give some of the gifts.

So I put them all out on my bed and -- it's sort of been difficult to kind of explain why I put some things in and why I didn't put others in.

The things that seemed to be directly called for in the subpoena, I put in a box: the hat pin, the dress from Martha's Vineyard, some of the pictures and things, the ad to him from Valentine's Day. Not that that was directly called for, but some of the more intimate -- I guess personal things, except that I kept the "Leaves of Grass" book because that just -- I was worried, I didn't know if I would get the gifts back or not, ever, and so I -- that just -- that meant the most to me of anything he gave me.

A JUROR: And I believe your testimony last time was that you did not believe that Betty knew the contents of the package?

THE WITNESS: I don't believe so.

A JUROR: She just came and picked them up and that was it?

THE WITNESS: We chit-chatted for a little bit. She was on the way to see her mom in the hospital, so I got her a small plant to just take to her mom and --

BY MS. IMMERGUT:

Q Did she seem at all confused when you handed over

the box?

A No.

Q Did she ask you what was in it?

A No. Not that I remember. I don't believe so.

MS. IMMERGUT: Thank you.

A JUROR: And just to back up for a second on your conversation with the President that you already discussed a little bit where you said you were concerned about the subpoena and some of the items that it called for such as the hat pin which indeed the President had given you, you testified previously, I believe, that the President said he was concerned about that also when he saw the hat pin. Is that correct?

THE WITNESS: I don't know that he saw -- I don't know that he saw the hat pin on the -- I don't know that he saw the subpoena, so -- I know that the hat pin was a concern to him.

A JUROR: Okay. Do you remember what he said in response when you said you were concerned about the things called for in the subpoena?

THE WITNESS: I think he said something like "That concerned me, too."

A JUROR: Okay.

THE WITNESS: So I don't know if he saw it or someone -- you know, I don't know he learned that.

A JUROR: Okay. But he appeared to have some prior knowledge of --

THE WITNESS: I think so. I think so.

A JUROR: I have another question about that conversation on the 28th. You had already discussed with him earlier the subpoena and the fact that all of your gifts from him were under subpoena and then --

THE WITNESS: We hadn't discussed that. I wasn't -- I hadn't -- the 28th was the first time that I saw him or spoke to him since I had been subpoenaed. When he called me on the 17th, I wasn't yet subpoenaed.

A JUROR: Okay. Okay. So that conversation took place on the 28th?

THE WITNESS: Correct. The only conversation about gifts and the subpoena, really -- yes.

A JUROR: And on that same day, he gave you Christmas gifts.

THE WITNESS: Yes.

A JUROR: What was your thinking at that time about that? Did that concern you or --

THE WITNESS: No.

A JUROR: No?

THE WITNESS: I was --

A JUROR: Did you -- what did you plan to do with those gifts? Did it cross your mind that some -- that you should maybe give some of them to your attorney as responsive to the subpoena or --

THE WITNESS: No.

A JUROR: No?

MR. EMMICK: I have a quick clarifying question because you said that the only conversation you had with him about gifts after the subpoena was on the 28th. You also had a conversation with him on the 5th that related to the later gift of the book, if I remember it right.

THE WITNESS: Right. I meant my gifts that he gave to me.

MR. EMMICK: Right. Right. Right. I just wanted to clarify that.

THE WITNESS: Okay. Sure.

MR. EMMICK: Other questions?

A JUROR: Going back to your conversation with Linda Tripp --

MR. EMMICK: Which one?

THE WITNESS: Yes. Which tape are you referring to?

A JUROR: No, I'm just going to be general.

MR. EMMICK: Okay.

A JUROR: If you had to put it like percentage-wise, what you told her as being truthful and not truthful, what percentage will be not truthful?

THE WITNESS: I would say before the subpoena, before I found out she had been subpoenaed, so for argument's sake maybe saying before December of '97, I'd say 95 percent accurate. There were some things that I didn't tell her, but I usually pretty much told her everything.

A JUROR: You started talking to her when? In '95 or '96?

THE WITNESS: I first told her -- when I first told her about the relationship or when I started talking to her as a person?

A JUROR: The relationship.

THE WITNESS: The relationship, I told her in November of '96. After the election.

A JUROR: Okay. So from November '96 to December '97 --

THE WITNESS: Pretty truthful.

A JUROR: And then after '97?

THE WITNESS: Oh --

BY MR. EMMICK:

Q Could I ask just one clarifying matter about that answer? Because you had said that it was 95 percent accurate and then you also said because sometimes I didn't tell her everything. And I just want to make sure we're being clear on whether you're talking about being complete or being accurate.

In other words, are you not telling her things or are you saying things to her that are inaccurate, sort of in that 5 percent, if you will?

A Well, I don't remember the exact situations or the times that I didn't tell her something, if she had asked me about it, I would have been inaccurate about what I said.

Q All right. I see.

A So --

Q So there's kind of a blending of those two concepts.

A Correct.

BY MS. IMMERGUT:

Q And, again, to clarify, did you ever lie about your sexual relationship with the President?

A No.

MR. EMMICK: I'm sorry. I interrupted. I didn't mean to.

A JUROR: So after '97, then --

THE WITNESS: After December '97, I don't even know how to -- how to put a percentage to that.

A JUROR: Any truth at all after '97?

THE WITNESS: Yes. There were some truths in December of '97. There certainly were some true statements, but there were a lot of untrue statements. Probably the untrue statements stick out in my mind more because they caused so much trouble.

A JUROR: Which ones stick out in your mind as having been untruthful?

THE WITNESS: Stuff about my mom. Just -- a lot of different things about my mom. That I had -- that I told Mr. Jordan I wouldn't sign the affidavit until I got a job. That was definitely a lie, based on something Linda had made me promise her on January 9th. Some of the other things --

A JUROR: Did you tell Linda Tripp at any time that you had heard or understood that people don't go to jail for perjury in a civil case?

THE WITNESS: Yes, I believe -- I think I said that.

A JUROR: Did anybody tell you that?

THE WITNESS: Well, hmm.

A JUROR: Do you want to talk to -- I know there's -- is there an attorney issue there?

THE WITNESS: There's an attorney issue.

A JUROR: I see.

MR. EMMICK: Do you want to take a break and talk about the attorney issue? Because I think that may be a way to figure out if we can answer that question any more fully.

THE WITNESS: Do you want me to go talk to my attorney?

MR. EMMICK: Well, I just think it might be -- I think your attorney would like it if he were to talk to you.

THE WITNESS: Okay.

MR. EMMICK: That's the way to answer it.

THE WITNESS: Okay. So just to be clear, you're --

A JUROR: Well, maybe I can help. Just -- if I could confine it to did anyone other than your attorney ever suggest to you that perjury in a civil case would not be prosecuted?

THE WITNESS: Uh --

MS. IMMERGUT: If you need to talk to your attorney, go ahead.

A JUROR: I just thought -- did anyone other than your attorney tell you that?

THE WITNESS: No.

MR. EMMICK: I think it still would be advisable to have a more complete answer, to at least let them talk.

THE WITNESS: Okay.

MR. EMMICK: Yes.

THE WITNESS: Excuse me.

(The witness was excused to confer with counsel.)

MR. EMMICK: Do we have a quorum?

THE FOREPERSON: Yes, we do.

MR. EMMICK: And are there any unauthorized persons present?

THE FOREPERSON: Not a one.

MR. EMMICK: All right.

THE WITNESS: And I'm still under oath.

THE FOREPERSON: Yes, you are.

BY MS. IMMERGUT:

Q And just to clarify a couple of things that were right before the break, when you sort of asserted a privilege or had some questions about whether there was a privilege, I did want to ask you just to clarify that with respect to the statement about your lawyer having -- or somebody telling you whether or not you can be charged with perjury in a civil case, just to be clear, did Mr. Jordan ever tell you that?

A No.

Q Did Mr. Carter ever tell you that?

A No.

Q And otherwise, I think the question was was it another attorney and I believe that you would like to assert the attorney-client privilege.

A JUROR: No, I think I excluded attorneys from my question.

THE WITNESS: Okay. You know, can I just address -- I think sort of the -- one of the questions that you had asked me before and I just -- about --

A JUROR: Myself?

THE WITNESS: Yes. That you had asked me about the

relationship and being untruthful and things like that. And I just -- this is something that's sort of been on my mind since this whole thing started.

I have never -- I don't -- I certainly believe I have ever told a lie to hurt anybody, that I sort of -- some of the ways in which I grew up, it was -- there were secrets and inherent in a secret is a lie and so I just -- you know, I -- I just thought I'd tell you that.

A JUROR: Okay.

MR. EMMICK: Other questions?

A JUROR: Ms. Lewinsky, we're going to try, because we feel that we have been jumping around and you've done a very good job of sort of jumping from topic to topic, we're going to try to bunch our questions together around a few topics and our forelady is going to try to play traffic cop, so --

A JUROR: A little bit. No, you go ahead. This is your record. But I'll play traffic cop just a little.

A JUROR: Ms. Lewinsky, before you go into that, I just remember you saying something with Linda Tripp, you know, what was not the truth, okay? And I just remembered, was one of the things that you told her, that you gave your mother the blue dress, one of the untruths or was that true?

THE WITNESS: I don't know if I ever told Linda I gave my mom the blue dress. One of the things I did say was that I gave everything to my mom, so that probably included that and that was not true. I didn't give the evidence to my mom. My mom never hid the dress. She didn't know it was in New York.

A JUROR: Okay.

THE WITNESS: So she didn't know anything about it.

A JUROR: I've got one of those questions that goes along with what she just said.

A JUROR: Okay. Fine. That's the idea. The topic.

A JUROR: How much did your mom really know?

THE WITNESS: She knew -- she knew that I was having a relationship with the President. She knew that -- she knew that I was certainly emotional about it and that it made me miserable a lot and that sometimes I was elated and sometimes I was miserable, but I didn't -- you know, I -- I might have said something to her like, "We fooled around," but I -- not -- she didn't know as much as I led Linda to believe she knew. Is that --

A JUROR: Yes.

THE WITNESS: Okay.

A JUROR: Okay. Any other Linda Tripp questions?

A JUROR: Yes, there's one.

A JUROR: Did you ever suggest to Linda Tripp that she delete e-mails or anything like that from her computer?

THE WITNESS: Yes, I did.

A JUROR: And did you tell her that you had done the same thing?

THE WITNESS: Yes, I believe so.

A JUROR: And did anyone ever suggest to you or tell you that you should do that?

THE WITNESS: No.

A JUROR: Did you tell Linda Tripp that anyone had suggested that to you?

THE WITNESS: I don't think so.

A JUROR: Okay. Thank you.

A JUROR: Any others?

A JUROR: In that end of the year timeframe, did you ever tell Linda Tripp that you felt physically at risk?

THE WITNESS: I think so. I think I told her something about -- that -- that -- I said something about Mary Jo what's-her-name.

A JUROR: Kopechne.

THE WITNESS: Kopechne. And so -- I really didn't feel threatened, but I was trying to use anything I could to try to convince her not to tell. So that I thought that if she thought I was threatened and that was part of the reason, then she would maybe do the same.

A JUROR: So you did not at any time feel that your personal security was at risk from the White House or anyone in the White House?

THE WITNESS: No. I think that maybe there -- there -- maybe once or twice it had crossed my mind in some bizarre way because everybody's heard about the different -- you know, sure, there's the Marilyn Monroe theory. And so it -- but it was not -- it was not any factor of -- that related to my actions.

A JUROR: So any discussion that you had about the whole topic with Linda Tripp would fall into what you were describing before as a little bit of fabrication?

THE WITNESS: Yes. Yes.

BY MR. EMMICK:

Q If I could ask a follow-up on that, did your mother ever express any concerns about your safety?

A I think she might have, but it was sort of the -- I think it was more general. It might have been a more general sense.

A JUROR: Are there any other questions about personal safety?

A JUROR: Are we still on December? December, January?

A JUROR: Yes.

A JUROR: I have one follow-up question if this is

an appropriate time about the gifts. And, again, if you have your proffer there?

THE WITNESS: Yes.

A JUROR: At the top of page 7, where you say in your proffer that when Ms. Currie called later that afternoon she said, at least I think you mean that she said that the President had told her Ms. L wanted her to hold on to something for her. Do you remember Betty Currie saying that the President had told her to call?

THE WITNESS: Right now, I don't. I don't remember, but when I wrote this, I was being truthful.

The other thing, and this is something that I was thinking about this morning in relation to the proffer, that I had written this proffer obviously being truthful, but I think that when I wrote this, it was my understanding that this was to bring me to the step of getting an immunity agreement, and so I think that sometimes to -- that I didn't know this was going to become sort of this staple document, I think, for everything, and so there are things that can be misinterpreted from in here, even from me re-reading it, the conditions -- some of the conditions maybe under which I wrote it.

So I just thought I should sort of say that, that where -- I mean, I know -- I certainly was not untruthful or trying to be misleading in this. I didn't think it was going to be -- this was my understanding of a written thing that I would -- that I would attest to under oath and that it wouldn't be number 7, read this, is this -- do you --

BY MR. EMMICK:

Q So it may not be written with legal precision?

A Exactly.

Q But there's no intentional falsehoods in it?

A No.

Q You were trying to be truthful throughout?

A Exactly.

A JUROR: And my purpose in raising it really is to just see whether this might jog your recollection at all as to something you might have recalled back in February that you don't recall today.

THE WITNESS: It doesn't.

A JUROR: It does not?

THE WITNESS: It's possible, but -- I -- I -- it's not my -- you know --

A JUROR: Okay.

THE WITNESS: -- my memory right now.

A JUROR: Any other questions on that subject?

A JUROR: If we don't have any other questions, I guess the other thing that we wanted to ask you a little bit about is when you were first approached by Mr. Emmick and his colleagues at the OIC.

Can you tell us a little bit about how that happened? That's not a happy topic, either, I apologize.

MR. EMMICK: Maybe if I could ask, what areas do you want to get into? Because there's -- you know -- many hours of activity --

A JUROR: Well, one specific -- okay. One specific question that people have is when did you first learn that Linda Tripp had been taping your phone conversations?

THE WITNESS: I believe that I didn't learn the extent to which she had taped my conversations, until I read it in the press.

I learned that day that she had worn a wire at the lunch and that I -- and that there had been other people, I think, in the restaurant that had been listening in and -- so I knew -- she had -- she had said that -- that -- when I was first apprehended, she was -- she had said that they had done the same thing to her and she tried to hug me and she told me this was the best thing for me to do and -- oh.

MR. EMMICK: Any other specific questions about that day? I just -- this was a long day. There were a lot of things that --

A JUROR: We want to know about that day.

A JUROR: That day.

A JUROR: The first question.

A JUROR: Yes.

A JUROR: We really want to know about that day.
MR. EMMICK: All right.
THE WITNESS: Linda was supposed to go see this new attorney that she had claimed she had gotten and was going to try to sign an affidavit so she paged me in the morning, I called her back and she told me she wanted to meet me before she went to see the attorney. So we planned to meet at the Ritz Carlton in the food court at -- I think it was quarter to one.
She was late. I saw her come down the escalator. And as I -- as I walked toward her, she kind of motioned behind her and Agent [redacted] and Agent [redacted] presented themselves to me and --
A JUROR: Do you want to take a minute?
THE WITNESS: And flashed their badges at me. They told me that I was under some kind of investigation, something had to do with the Paula Jones case, that they -- that they wanted to talk to me and give me a chance, I think, to cooperate, maybe.
I -- to help myself. I told them I wasn't speaking to them without my attorney.
They told me that that was fine, but I should know I won't be given as much information and won't be able to help myself as much with my attorney there. So I agreed to go. I was so scared.

(The witness begins crying.)

A JUROR: So, Monica, did you go to a room with them at that time?

THE WITNESS: Yes.

A JUROR: And at that time, did you talk to anybody or what did you do? Did you want to call your mother?

THE WITNESS: Can Karen do the questioning now? This is -- can I ask you to step out?

MR. EMMICK: Sure. Okay. All right.

MS. IMMERGUT: I guess, Monica, if Mike could just stay -- do you mind if Mike is in here?

THE WITNESS: (Nods affirmatively.)

MS. IMMERGUT: Okay. Would you rather --

THE WITNESS: (Nods affirmatively.)

MR. EMMICK: Okay. That's fine.

BY MS. IMMERGUT:

Q Okay. Did you go to a room with them at the hotel?

A Yes.

Q And what did you do then? Did you ever tell them that you wanted to call your mother?

A I told them I wanted to talk to my attorney.

Q Okay. So what happened?

A And they told me -- Mike came out and introduced himself to me and told me that -- that Janet Reno had sanctioned Ken Starr to investigate my actions in the Paula

Jones case, that they -- that they knew that I had signed a false affidavit, they had me on tape saying I had committed perjury, that they were going to -- that I could go to jail for 27 years, they were going to charge me with perjury and obstruction of justice and subornation of perjury and witness tampering and something else.

Q And you're saying "they," at that point, who was talking to you about that stuff?

A Mike Emmick and the two FBI guys. And I made Linda stay in the room. And I just -- I felt so bad.

Q Now, when you say you felt bad, because you felt responsible somehow for pulling the President into something?

A Yes.

Q And is that something that still weighs heavily on you, that you feel responsible?

A Yes.

Q And is it -- do you feel responsible because you told Linda about your relationship?

A Yes.

Q I guess later just to sort of finish up, I guess, with the facts of that day, was there a time then that you were -- you just waited with the prosecutors until your mother came down?

A No.

Q Okay.

A I mean, there was, but they -- they told me they wanted me to cooperate. I asked them what cooperating meant, it entailed, and they told me that -- they had -- first they had told me before about that -- that they had had me on tape saying things from the lunch that I had had with Linda at the Ritz Carlton the other day and they -- then they told me that I -- that I'd have to agree to be debriefed and that I'd have to place calls or wear a wire to see -- to call Betty and Mr. Jordan and possibly the President. And --

Q And did you tell them you didn't want to do that?

A Yes. I -- I -- I remember going through my mind, I thought, well, what if -- you know, what if I did that and I messed up, if I on purpose -- you know, I envisioned myself in Mr. Jordan's office and sort of trying to motion to him that something had gone wrong. They said that they would be watching to see if it had been an intentional mistake.

Then I wanted to call my mom and they kept telling me that they didn't -- that I couldn't tell anybody about this, they didn't want anyone to find out and that they didn't want -- that was the reason I couldn't call Mr. Carter, was because they were afraid that he might tell the person who took me to Mr. Carter.

They told me that I could call this number and get another criminal attorney, but I didn't want that and I didn't trust them. Then I just cried for a long time.

A JUROR: All while you were crying, did they keep asking you questions? What were they doing?

THE WITNESS: No, they just sat there and then -- they just sort of sat there.

A JUROR: How many hours did this go on?

THE WITNESS: Maybe around two hours or so. And then they were -- they kept saying there was this time constraint, there was a time constraint, I had to make a decision.

And then Bruce Udolf came in at some point and then -- then Jackie Bennett came in and there were a whole bunch of other people and the room was crowded and he was saying to me, you know, you have to make a decision. I had wanted to call my mom, they weren't going to let me call my attorney, so I just -- I wanted to call my mom and they --

Then Jackie Bennett said, "You're 24, you're smart, you're old enough, you don't need to call your mommy."

And then I said, "Well, I'm letting you know that I'm leaning towards not cooperating," you know.

And they had told me before that I could leave whenever I wanted, but it wasn't -- you know, I didn't -- I didn't really know -- I didn't know what that meant. I mean, I thought if I left then that they were just going to arrest me.

And so then they told me that I should know that they were planning to prosecute my mom for the things that I had said that she had done.

(The witness begins crying.)

MS. IMMERGUT: Do you want to take a break, Monica?

THE WITNESS: Yes.

(Witness excused. Witness recalled.)

THE FOREPERSON: Okay. We have a quorum. There are no unauthorized people and Monica is already aware that she is still under oath.

MS. IMMERGUT: We just have a couple more questions and then I think we'll break for lunch.

THE WITNESS: Okay.

A JUROR: Monica, I have a question. A minute ago you explained that the reason why you couldn't call Mr. Carter was that something might be disclosed. Is that right?

THE WITNESS: It was -- they sort of said that -- you know, I -- I -- I could call Frank Carter, but that they may not -- I think it was that -- you know, the first time or the second time?

A JUROR: Any time.

THE WITNESS: Well, the first time when I asked, that I said I wasn't going to talk to them without my lawyer, they told me that if my lawyer was there, they wouldn't give me as much information and I couldn't help myself as much, so that --

A JUROR: Did they ever tell you that you could not call Mr. Carter?

THE WITNESS: No. What they told me was that if I called Mr. Carter, I wouldn't necessarily still be offered an immunity agreement.

A JUROR: And did you feel threatened by that?

THE WITNESS: Yes.

A JUROR: And you said they offered you a chance to call another attorney?

THE WITNESS: Yes.

A JUROR: And did you take them up on that offer?

THE WITNESS: No.

A JUROR: Why not?

THE WITNESS: Because I didn't trust them.

A JUROR: I see. And at some point in this meeting, did you -- you did obtain an attorney? Mr. Ginsberg?

THE WITNESS: Well, like at 11:00 that night.

A JUROR: So it was seven hours or eight hours or more later?

THE WITNESS: They -- they finally let me call my mom, so I went to call my mom and then -- and I saw Linda again. She had been shopping or something like that. But I called my mom and then Mike had said that she could call him, so they called her or she called him or something like that and then they agreed to let her come down.

So she took the train and then -- and then he just sort of -- I shut down and I kind of -- you know, I thought maybe I should try and make these people like me, so I tried to be nice and I told jokes and I asked if we could walk around the mall because I couldn't sit in that room any more. And I just --

BY MS. IMMERGUT:

Q So did they let you do that?

A Mm-hmm. So Mike and Agent [redacted] took me and we walked around the mall and we ate dinner and then we went back to the room and I read Psalm 21 about a million times. And my mom's train had been -- there were problems with her train and then finally she got there and they told me they were going to want to talk to my mom alone for a little bit, but I got to talk to her.

And I was -- I didn't -- I didn't want to cooperate. I mean, I didn't -- I just kept thinking to myself, well -- well, I'll just say I made it all up, I'll just -- I'll just -- I -- I couldn't imagine -- I couldn't imagine doing this to the President. And I felt so wrong and guilty for having told Linda and that she had done all this.

But -- so then they took my mom into another room for a really long time and she had -- then when she came back, they called my dad. And then we finally -- and then I talked to my dad and then -- then -- Ginsberg came on the scene. And he --

A JUROR: So if I understand it, you first met the agents, Agents [redacted] and [redacted], at around 1:00 and it wasn't until about 11 p.m. that you had an opportunity to talk to a lawyer?

THE WITNESS: Yes.

BY MS. IMMERGUT:

Q Although you were allowed to -- the thing with Frank Carter was that they were afraid he would tell Vernon Jordan? Is that what they expressed to you?

A Right. And I had -- I had -- I think that someone said that Frank wasn't even -- Frank was a civil attorney and so that he really couldn't help me anyway, so I asked him if at least I could call and ask him for a recommendation for a criminal attorney and they didn't think that was a good idea.

And then I said, well, what about -- if I want to get in touch with Mr. Carter later, if I decide that's what I want to do, you know, and he's not there, because it's Friday and it was a holiday weekend, so then Agent Fallon went in the other room to find out if he had a service or something or another, a pager, I don't know --

Q Some way for you to reach him later?

A Mm-hmm.

A JUROR: Sounds as though they were actively discouraging you from talking to an attorney.

THE WITNESS: Yes.

A JUROR: Is that a fair characterization?

THE WITNESS: Yes.

BY MS. IMMERGUT:

Q Well, from Frank Carter.

A From Frank Carter, who was my only attorney at that point.

MS. IMMERGUT: Right. Right.

THE WITNESS: So I could have called any other attorney but --

A JUROR: You didn't have another attorney.

THE WITNESS: I didn't have another attorney and this was my attorney for this case, so -- I mean, this was --

A JUROR: And this is the attorney who had helped you with the affidavit.

THE WITNESS: Yes. And that -- the affidavit -- well, the affidavit wasn't even filed yet. It was Fed Ex'd out on that day. So --

A JUROR: Monica, when you called your mother, how much were you able to tell her over the phone? Very little or --

THE WITNESS: I was hysterical. She didn't understand what I was saying, but I told her that -- that the

8/98D

FBI had me and there was something with the Paula Jones case and Linda and then she -- she -- I said that -- that the guy said you could call her -- you can call him and so she just told me to calm down and I was screaming that, you know, "They want me to cooperate and I don't want to cooperate, don't make me cooperate, don't make me do this," and she -- she said it was okay, don't worry, don't worry, and then she talked to Mike Emmick and they let her come down. So, I mean, she -- I don't know.

A JUROR: Did you feel better after you talked to your mother?

THE WITNESS: Oh, yeah.

A JUROR: Gained that support?

THE WITNESS: Yeah.

A JUROR: Okay.

THE WITNESS: Yeah. I mean --

A JUROR: And what were you thinking about Linda at this time?

THE WITNESS: Linda? Did you say --

A JUROR: Mm-hmm. Did you know exactly what had happened? That you had been --

THE WITNESS: No. I was under the impression that -- what I was thinking at that point was that they had -- that they had listened in on our conversation on the phone and that then they came to her and said she was in trouble for something and that then she let them listen in on this lunch conversation because she had said "They did the same thing to me. They did the same thing to me." So I didn't understand what she meant by that.

And then she said, "This is the best thing for you," as if I was left to believe that she had -- this was somehow something she had done and that she was trying to help me.

And I thought, "Why did she tell them? Why didn't she just say it was nonsense, it wasn't true? Why did she tell them that I had had this relationship with him?" And so -- you know -- and they had pictures of me at lunch with her. So --

A JUROR: The pictures were the taped lunch?

THE WITNESS: Yes. The wire lunch.

A JUROR: The wired lunch.

THE WITNESS: Yes. So that -- because they -- because I had said on one of the tapes that -- you know, if there was a tape of me -- I had -- I had -- I didn't know how the Paula Jones people had gotten my name and I thought maybe they had tapped my phone or maybe they had broken into my computer and read my e-mails.

I didn't know how I had gotten involved in this case and so I had said to Linda, "Well, if they have me on tape, I'll just say it's not me. I'll just say it's not me.

I'll deny it. I'll deny everything."

A JUROR: So they took pictures.

THE WITNESS: Right. So they said, "We have you on tape saying that you'd deny it and we have pictures to prove that you were there." So --

A JUROR: During this time in the hotel with them, did you feel threatened?

THE WITNESS: Yes.

A JUROR: Did you feel that they had set a trap?

THE WITNESS: I -- I -- I did and I had -- I didn't understand -- I didn't understand why they -- why they had to trap me into coming there, why they had to trick me into coming there. I mean, this had all been a set-up and that why -- I mean, that was just so frightening. It was so incredibly frightening.

And they told me, you know, over and over again I was free to leave whenever I wanted, but -- I -- I didn't -- I didn't know that there's a grand jury and indicted and then you go to jail. I mean, and a trial and everything. I didn't understand that.

And so I didn't -- you know, then there was something that, well, if I partially cooperate, they'll talk to the judge, some -- you know, we're prepared to indict you or something like that for all these things. And I just didn't --

BY MS. IMMERGUT:

Q So you didn't know what would happen if you left.

A No. And then it wasn't until my mom was there that Mike Emmick cleared it up and said to my mom, "Well, it's not that we'll arrest you tonight when you leave the hotel." You know. Because I didn't -- I didn't know.

Q And you didn't end up cooperating that evening.

A No, I didn't. Because -- well --

A JUROR: Excuse me. When you said they trapped you, you went there on the invitation of Linda for lunch or something?

THE WITNESS: Yes.

A JUROR: So, I mean, how did -- I mean, in your mind, how did you get to the fact that they were the one? Wasn't it just Linda?

THE WITNESS: No, because they were with Linda. When I met Linda in the food court at Pentagon City, the two agents were with her.

A JUROR: Oh, okay.

THE WITNESS: Yeah. And that's where -- so it was right -- have you ever been to Pentagon City mall?

A JUROR: Mm-hmm.

THE WITNESS: So it was right down in the food court, you know the escalator to come down is over here?

A JUROR: Mm-hmm.

THE WITNESS: So -- see, they were with her when she met me right -- right in the middle.

A JUROR: Okay.

THE WITNESS: And that's where -- and then --

(Pause.)

A JUROR: I think that's all the questions on that topic. There is one other question.

Going back to Monday night and the President's speech, what did you want or expect to hear from the President?

THE WITNESS: I think what I wanted and expected were two different things. I had -- I had been hurt when he referred to me as "that woman" in January, but I was also glad. I was glad that he made that statement and I felt that was the best thing for him to do, was to deny this. And -- but I had been hurt. I mean, it showed me how angry he was with me and I understood that.

And his -- the people who work for him have trashed me, they claim they haven't said anything about me, they have smeared me and they called me stupid, they said I couldn't write, they said I was a stalker, they said I wore inappropriate clothes, I mean, you all know.

I mean, you've heard them in here, you've read the papers, you've seen on TV, and yet -- and then when it came out about the talking points, then somehow no one ever asked the question, well, how could -- if she was so stupid and she couldn't write, how is it possible that she wrote the talking points? So then it was, well, someone must have helped her with that. Oh, it's okay, though, it wasn't someone in the White House.

So I just -- my family had been maligned because of a lot of their tactics and I felt that -- I had wanted him to say that I was a nice, decent person and that he was sorry this had happened because I -- I tried to do as much as I could to protect him.

I mean, I didn't -- I didn't -- I didn't allow him to be put on tape that night and I didn't -- and I -- I felt that I waited, you know, and I would have gone to trial had -- had -- in my mind, had there never been a point where the Office of the Independent Counsel and myself could come to - they could come to accept the truth I had to say, that that was the truth I had to give, and I'm only 24 and so I felt that I -- this has been hard for me and this has been hard on my family and I just wanted him to take back -- by saying something nice, he would have taken back every disgusting, horrible thing that anyone has said about me from that White House. And that was what I wanted.

What I expected him to do was to just acknowledge in his -- either in his apology -- you know, that first of all I think he should have straight out apologized and I think that he could have acknowledged that -- you know, apologized to me, I think, to the other people who were involved in this and to my family.

My -- my dad didn't know anything about the relationship and when he went on his -- the few interviews he did, he was telling the truth when he said he didn't know. But out of respect for the President and the presidency, he didn't say -- he could have easily said if this is true; X, Y and Z about the President, and I think that because my family didn't start a huge uproar about how wrong or improper or inappropriate it was for a 50-year-old man to be having a relationship with a young woman, we afforded him that, that was one less headache that he had to deal with, and I think he could have acknowledged that. That was what I expected. Does that --

A JUROR: Monica, none of us in this room are perfect. We all fall and we fall several times a day. The only difference between my age and when I was your age is now I get up faster. If I make a mistake and fall, I get up and brush myself off. I used to stay there a while after a mistake. That's all I have to say.

THE WITNESS: Thank you.

MS. IMMERGUT: Let me just check with Mike.

THE FOREPERSON: We do want to share something with her.

MS. IMMERGUT: Okay. So do you want to -- why don't we hold off for just a second and let me check with Mr. Emmick.

THE FOREPERSON: Okay.

(Pause.)

MS. IMMERGUT: We don't have any further questions.

A JUROR: Could I ask one?

Monica, is there anything that you would like to add to your prior testimony, either today or the last time you were here, or anything that you think needs to be amplified on or clarified? I just want to give you the fullest opportunity.

THE WITNESS: I would. I think because of the public nature of how this investigation has been and what the charges aired, that I would just like to say that no one ever asked me to lie and I was never promised a job for my silence.

And that I'm sorry. I'm really sorry for everything that's happened. (The witness begins to cry.) And I hate Linda Tripp.

A JUROR: Can I just say -- I mean, I think I should seize this opportunity now, that we've all fallen short. We sin every day. I don't care whether it's murder, whether it's affairs or whatever. And we get over that. You ask forgiveness and you go on.

There's some that are going to say that they don't forgive you, but he whose sin -- you know -- that's how I feel about that. So to let you know from here, you have my forgiveness. Because we all fall short.

A JUROR: And that's what I was trying to say.

A JUROR: That's what it's about.

THE WITNESS: Thank you.

A JUROR: And I also want to say that even though right now you feel a lot of hate for Linda Tripp, but you need to move on and leave her where she is because whatever goes around comes around.

A JUROR: It comes around.

A JUROR: It does.

A JUROR: And she is definitely going to have to give an account for what she did, so you need to just go past her and don't keep her because that's going to keep you out.

A JUROR: That's right.

A JUROR: And going to keep you from moving on.

A JUROR: Allowing you to move on.

BY MS. IMMERGUT:

Q And just to clarify, and I know we've discussed this before, despite your feelings about Linda Tripp, have you lied to this grand jury about anything with regard to Linda Tripp because you don't like her?

A I don't think that was necessary. No. It wouldn't

have been necessary to lie. I think she's done enough on her own, so --

Q You would not do that just because of your feelings about her.

A No.

THE FOREPERSON: Basically what we wanted to leave with, because this will probably be your last visit to us, I hope, I hope I'm not going to have to do this any more and I hope you won't have to come here any more, but we wanted to offer you a bouquet of good wishes that includes luck, success, happiness and blessings.

THE WITNESS: Thank you. (The witness begins to cry.) I appreciate all of your understanding for this situation and your -- your ability to open your heart and your mind and -- and your soul. I appreciate that.

THE FOREPERSON: So if there's nothing else?

MR. EMMICK: Nothing else.

THE FOREPERSON: We'd like to excuse you and thank you very much for your testimony.

THE WITNESS: Thank you.

(The witness was excused.)

(Whereupon, at 12:54 p.m., the taking of testimony in the presence of a full quorum of the Grand Jury was concluded.)

* * * * *

CERTIFICATE OF REPORTER

I, Amy K. Rose, the reporter for the United States Attorney's Office, do hereby certify that the witness whose testimony appears in the foregoing pages was first duly sworn by the foreperson or the deputy foreperson of the grand jury when there was a full quorum of the grand jury present; that the testimony of said witness was taken by me and, thereafter, reduced to typewritten form; and that the transcript is a true record of the testimony given by said witness.

Amy K. Rose
Official Reporter

Transcriber

Diversified Reporting Services, Inc.
1025 VERMONT AVENUE, N.W. SUITE 1250
WASHINGTON, D.C. 20005
(202) 296-2929

THE FOLLOWING IS A COMPRESSED VERSION OF THE PRECEDING DOCUMENT

UNITED STATES DISTRICT COURT
FOR THE DISTRICT OF COLUMBIA

IN RE:

GRAND JURY PROCEEDINGS

Grand Jury Room No. 2
United States District Court
for the District of Columbia
3rd & Constitution, N.W.
Washington, D.C. 20001

Thursday, August 20, 1998

The testimony of MONICA S. LEWINSKY was taken in the presence of a full quorum of Grand Jury 97-2, impaneled on September 19, 1997, commencing at 9:51 a.m., before:

MICHAEL EMMICK
KARIN IMMERGUT
Associate Independent Counsel
Office of Independent Counsel
1001 Pennsylvania Avenue, N.W.
Suite 490 North
Washington, D.C. 20004

Page 2

PROCEEDINGS

Whereupon,

MONICA S. LEWINSKY

was called as a witness and, after having been first duly sworn by the Foreperson of the Grand Jury, was examined and testified as follows:

EXAMINATION

BY MR. EMMICK:

Q Good morning, Ms. Lewinsky.

A Good morning.

Q As we did with your earlier grand jury testimony, my job is to advise you of your rights and obligations here at the beginning.

First off, you have a right under the Fifth Amendment to refuse to answer any questions that may tend to incriminate you. In this case, that right is qualified by the fact that you've signed an agreement to provide truthful testimony in connection with our investigation. Do you understand that?

A Yes, I do.

Q In addition, you have the right to have counsel present outside the grand jury to answer any questions that you may have. Do you have counsel outside?

A Yes, I do.

Q Who is that?

Page 3

A Preston Burton.

Q And you understand that if you'd like to speak to your counsel, all you have to do is say "Could I take a break and speak with my counsel?"

A Yes.

Q All right. You also in addition to those two rights, you have an obligation and that obligation is to tell the truth. That obligation is imposed on you because you have been put under oath and also because in connection with your agreement you're required to tell the truth. Do you understand that?

A Yes, I do.

MR. EMMICK: What I have placed in front of you is what is marked as ML-7. This is a chart that you have earlier testified about of contacts between yourself and the President.

As I indicated to you informally beforehand, this grand jury session today is for you to answer questions from the grand jurors.

And so without any further ado, I will ask the grand jurors if they have any questions of Ms. Lewinsky.

A JUROR: I think I'm going to start out.

MR. EMMICK: Okay.

A JUROR: Ms. Lewinsky, in your testimony when you were with us on the 6th, you mentioned some of the steps that

Page 4

you took to maintain secrecy regarding your relationship: that you would bring papers or he'd have papers or either you would accidentally bump into each other in the hallway; you always used Betty as the excuse for you to be waved in; and on many occasions you would go in one door and out of the other door.

THE WITNESS: Yes.

A JUROR: Are there any other methods you used that I've missed? That you used to maintain your secrecy?

THE WITNESS: Hmm. I need to think about that for a minute.

A JUROR: And the second part to that question is were these ways to maintain your secrecy your idea or were they recommended to you by anyone?

THE WITNESS: I can answer the second part first.

A JUROR: Okay.

THE WITNESS: If that's okay.

A JUROR: That's fine.

THE WITNESS: Some of them were my idea. Some of them were things that I had discussed with the President. I think it was a mutual understanding between us that obviously we'd both try to be careful.

A JUROR: Do you recall at all specifically which ones he may have recommended to you as an idea on maintaining the secrecy?

Page 5

THE WITNESS: Yes and no. The issue of Betty being the cover story for when I came to the White House, it became my understanding I think most clearly from the fact that I couldn't come to see him after the election until -- unless Betty was there to clear me in and that one time when I asked him why, he said because if someone comes to see him, there's a list circulated among the staff members and then everyone would be questioning why I was there to see him. So --

MR. EMMICK: Let me try to ask some follow-ups in response to your question.

BY MR. EMMICK:

Q Were there ever any discussions between you and the President about what should be done with letters that you -- letters or notes that you had sent to him? That is to say, for example, did you ever write on the bottom of any letters what to do with those letters?

A It was my understanding that obviously he would throw them away or, if he decided to keep them, which I didn't think he did, he would put them somewhere safe.

I think what you're referring to is on the bottom once of a sort of joke memo that I sent to him I in a joking manner reminded him to throw the letter away, that it wasn't -- you know, that was a joke. So --

Q What about whether on your caller ID on your telephone the word POTUS would appear and whether anything

Page 6

was done in order to make sure that POTUS did not appear on your telephone?

A My caller ID at work, it would -- when the President called from the Oval Office, it would say POTUS and when he'd call from the residence, it was an asterisk. And I told him that. I didn't know if he knew that it said POTUS when he called from the office, and I assumed he didn't, because otherwise that would be sort of silly.

So I informed him of that and then one time he called me from the residence and he -- he called on a hard line -- I don't know. I shouldn't say "hard line" because I know that has some different terminology to it, but he called on a line that had a phone number attached to it and so when he called, he said, "Oh, did it ring up, you know, phone number? It didn't say my name, did it?"

And so it was -- that was something that I was concerned about.

Q Did he ever express to you a reluctance to leave messages on your telephone voice message system?

A At home?

Q Yes.

A Yes.

Q All right. Tell us about that.

A One time in a conversation he just said he didn't like to leave messages.

Page 7

Q Okay. What about the times that you would visit him? Were those times selected in a way so that there weren't people around or that certain people weren't around?

A Yes.

Q Okay. Would you tell us about that?

A There were obviously people at the White House who didn't like me and wouldn't -- wouldn't be understanding of why I was coming to see the President or accepting of that and so there was always sort of an effort made that either on the weekends -- when I was working in the White House he told me that it was usually quiet on the weekends and I knew that to be true. And after I left the White House it was always when there weren't going to be a lot of people around.

Q And what about particular individual people? Would there be particular individual people who would be -- staffers in the oval area that you would try to avoid in order to help conceal the relationship?

A Yes. Nancy Hernreich, Stephen Goodin, Evelyn Lieberman. Pretty much anybody on the first floor of the West Wing.

A JUROR: How did all these people come to not like you so much? What were you doing? Were you breaking the rules of the White House? What were you doing to draw their attention to not liking you so much? Before the relationship.

Page 8

From the time you got there all the way up to the time -- what I'm saying is what did you do to deserve for them not to like you?

THE WITNESS: Before the relationship started?

A JUROR: Yes. What did you do from --

THE WITNESS: I don't think there was anything I did before the relationship started that -- the relationship started in November of '95. I had only been at the White House as an intern in the Old Executive Office Building for -- for a few months, so most of my tenure at the White House I was having a relationship with the President.

I think that -- the President seemed to pay attention to me and I paid attention to him and I think people were wary of his weaknesses, maybe, and thought -- in my opinion, I mean, this is -- I think that people -- they didn't want to look at him and think that he could be responsible for anything, so it had to all be my fault, that I was -- I was stalking him or I was making advances towards him. You know, as they've said, I wore inappropriate clothes, which is absolutely not true. I'm not really sure.

A JUROR: But you do admit a lot of the places that you weren't supposed to be you were always found. You do admit that there were things that you were doing, too, in order to see him that they were feeling that was going

Page 9

against the rules of the White House?

THE WITNESS: Uh –

A JUROR: You know, places that you were that you weren't supposed to be and hallways that you weren't supposed to be, you were seen in those places?

THE WITNESS: Yes and no. There really weren't any of these staffers who saw me in the places that I wasn't supposed to be. And that was part of the effort to conceal the relationship. So – does that make sense?

I mean, when I was in the Oval Office with the President, no one else knew except for the Secret Service, no one else knew that I went in there. So for them to know – for them to be disliking me for that reason, I don't think that they were really – I don't know if they were aware of that or not.

I did make an effort, I think, to try to – to have interactions with the President and I – and I think that – that was probably disturbing to them. I know that if the President was in the hall and he was talking to people and I passed by he'd – he'd stop talking and say hi to me. I'm not really sure.

A JUROR: Just a follow-up to that.

THE WITNESS: Sure.

A JUROR: If they didn't see you, well, how did they know?

Page 10

THE WITNESS: I don't know what they knew. I – you know, I – I'm not sure – I –

A JUROR: Because if you said you made an effort to hide yourself, you know, so you wouldn't see them, the Secret Service are the ones that saw you –

THE WITNESS: Mm-hmm.

A JUROR: Okay. So, I mean, how would they – how did they know that you were there, you know, to want to keep you away from being there?

THE WITNESS: I don't know. Maybe – I – I mean, I've heard reported in the newspapers and on TV that the Secret Service, someone said something to Evelyn Lieberman and I had had an – I don't know if I went over this the last time I was here, I had had a real negative interaction with Nancy Hernreich early on in my tenure at the White House and so –

I think there was also – I'm a friendly person and – and I didn't know it was a crime in Washington for people – for you to want people to like you and so I was friendly. And I guess I wasn't supposed to be.

A JUROR: So that interaction that you had with Evelyn Lieberman was when she was telling you what?

THE WITNESS: She stopped me in the hall and she asked me where I worked, in which office I worked, and I told her Legislative Affairs in the East Wing.

Page 11

And she said, "You're always trafficking up this area." You know, "You're not supposed to be here. Interns aren't allowed to go past the Oval Office."

And she – she really startled me and I walked away and I went down to the bathroom and I was crying because – I mean, when – you know, when an older woman sort of chastises you like that, it's upsetting.

And then I thought about what she said and I realized that, well, I wasn't an intern any more. I was working there. And I kind of believe in clear communication, so I went back to Evelyn Lieberman, to Ms. Lieberman, and I – I said, "You know, I just wanted to clarify with you that I work here, I'm not an intern. So, you know, I am allowed to go past the Oval Office." I don't think I said that, but I had a blue pass.

And she looked at me and said, "They hired you?" And I was startled and then she said, "Oh, well, I think I mistook you for someone else or some other girl with dark hair who keeps trafficking up the area." And ever since then – and that was maybe in December or January of '95 or '96. So –

A JUROR: Ms. Lewinsky, were you ever reprimanded or chastised by your immediate supervisor in Legislative Affairs for trafficking up the area or being where you weren't supposed to be or being away from your desk too much? Anything like that?

Page 12

THE WITNESS: Being away from my desk had been mentioned to me, but trafficking up the area and being where I'm not supposed to be, no.

I – the – I had a view of – and this is sort of my view with work is that you get a lot more done and people are a lot more willing to help you when you have a personal interaction with them. And so the person who held the job before me would fax the drafts of his letters to the staff secretary's office and then at some point during the day when someone got the draft they would make the changes and then fax it back.

And I found it to be much more effective to take things over to the staff secretary's office and interact with the person – I can't remember her name – Helen – to interact with Helen and have Helen edit the letters right then and there and then I could go back and to me it was a faster process.

So there was also – you know, I also wanted to try to see the President. So, I mean, I did make efforts to try to see him in the hall or something like that because –

A JUROR: So the route to the staff person's office was a route that you could still veer off and see the President?

Page 13

THE WITNESS: No. It – it wasn't necessarily in front of the Oval Office or anything. There were – we also had – let me see if I can explain this. I'm sure you guys know by now that the West Wing is three stories. There's the basement, the first floor and the second floor. Legislative Affairs has an office on the second floor of the West Wing.

There are two ways to get to that office – or three ways, I guess. There's the West Wing, you can cut across the West Wing lobby, which is where people coming to visit someone in the White House sit. There's going the back way, which you pass the Oval Office, but the door's always closed when the President's in there. And then you can go all the way down the stairs and all the way around and then all the way up two flights of stairs.

When I first started working there, it didn't seem appropriate to walk through the West – to me, it didn't seem appropriate to walk through the West Wing lobby with papers when there were people who were visitors coming to sit and wait. I just – I didn't think that was appropriate during the business time.

So I went the other way, behind – which went past the Oval Office, not knowing that – I guess you're not supposed to do that. It seemed silly. The door's closed and it's locked. And there wasn't this intention to see the

Page 14

President that way.

So – am I – did I answer your question?

A JUROR: Yes.

THE WITNESS: Okay. I'm sorry.

MR. EMMICK: You know, one thing I might do is circle back to try to pick up some more concealment methods.

A JUROR: Okay.

MR. EMMICK: Because you asked the question are there any other methods.

A JUROR: Yes.

MR. EMMICK: And I can ask a few more questions that might direct us in that area.

THE WITNESS: Okay.

BY MR. EMMICK:

Q For example, you have indicated earlier that it was Betty Currie who waved you in all the times during 1997 that you saw the President. Did you ever talk with the President about whether he could wave you in instead or whether it would be a good idea for him to wave you in personally?

A Yes. I think that that's what I mentioned earlier.

Q Oh, okay.

A That he and I had discussed it and he said he couldn't do that because then it would be on a list.

Q Okay. What about – you had mentioned that you took a different route into the Oval Office than you would

Page 15

take out of the Oval Office. In addition, did you ever take routes to get to the Oval Office that seemed calculated to avoid certain Secret Service or White House personnel?

A Not Secret Service, but I – I liked or I preferred to sort of meet up with him and then we'd walk in together. And I preferred to go in through the Rose Garden because then I wasn't going – I wasn't risking the possibility of running into someone in the hall right outside the Oval Office. So –

Q What about the routes that Betty would walk you in from the gates?

A Oh. When – there were certain Secret Service officers who were friendly with Debi Schiff who Betty wanted to try to avoid because I guess they chatted with Debi Schiff a lot and there's a whole long story with Debi Schiff, so –

Q And would that be another way that you would help conceal your meetings with the President?

A Yes.

A JUROR: Just to back up for a minute. When you would meet the President and go in through the Rose Garden or meet the President before going into the Oval Office, did you discuss that with him ever about sort of what – that that would be a way that would sort of be more concealing or –

Page 16

THE WITNESS: We only did that, I think, twice. And the first time, it really was an accident. And so then the next time that we did that, I said – you know, before – he would call me in my office before I would come see him and we'd figure out what we were going to do.

And I think I – I know I suggested to him, I said, "I really like that because then it's just easier, it seems." And also, I – for me personally, I didn't – I didn't always want to be the one that was being seen going in. Does that make sense?

So that I wasn't always bringing in the papers and it was me going to him, that in this instance if someone saw it, being the Secret Service, he invited me. So – for me, that just made me feel better.

BY MR. EMMICK:

Q All right. I have a number of other questions about these alternative methods of concealment. Let me ask you this. I think you've testified earlier that most of the sexual contact that you had with the President tended to occur in the hallway, rather than in the study, although sometimes it was in the study itself.

Did that have anything to do with whether or not it would be easier to see you in the study as opposed to the hallway?

A I think so, but I don't specifically – I don't

Page 17

specifically remember discussing that with the President, but there were circumstances that that sort of was obvious to me.

Q And would that include the fact that windows in the study tended to be uncurtained?

A Just that, windows. Yes.

Q Right. Yes, there were windows there.

A Yes.

Q And so you might be seen there.

A Yes.

MR. EMMICK: All right.

BY MS. IMMERGUT:

Q In that regard, you also mentioned that you would move from the oval area or that sometimes you'd start in the Oval Office and then you'd move towards the hallway. Did the President ever initiate that move?

A I think we both did. I mean, it just depended on the day. It wasn't --

Q Was it understood that you wouldn't actually have a sexual encounter in the Oval Office?

A I'm sure it was understood. I -- I -- I wouldn't have done that. I mean -- so -- I'm sure he wouldn't have done that.

BY MR. EMMICK:

Q Are there windows all around the Oval Office?

Page 18

A There are windows all around and it just -- I know this may sound silly, but it wouldn't be appropriate. You know.

Q What about any discussions with the President about not acknowledging one another at parties or photographs, for example?

A He called me in my office the day of Pat Griffin's going away party and had asked me if I was going to go. I said yes and he said, "Well, maybe we can get together after that."

And I told him I didn't think that was a good idea, that people were going to be watching. I was paranoid anyway and -- so I said, "I think it's a good idea if we just sort of ignore each other at the party and don't really say anything." And that's what we did.

Q And what about with respect to a photograph that was taken at the party and whether --

A I mean, we didn't discuss this. I didn't know there was going to be a picture taken. But I made an effort to stand on the -- I was the last person sort of on the outside of this picture so that -- I didn't want anyone to think that I was trying to get close to the President, I was trying to -- whatever it was.

Q So in that case, that would be a concealment effort, but not one that the President and you had

Page 19

collaborated on.

A No.

Q All right. What about an occasion when the President suggested that the two you might attend a movie and sort of bump into each other outside the movie? Tell us about that discussion.

A He told me he was going to watch a movie with some friends of his and that if I wanted to I could bump into him in the hall outside and then he'd invite me into the movie.

And I asked him if -- I think he said there were some friends and maybe some of his staff or I asked him if some of his staff was going to be there.

And he said yes and I don't remember who he said was going to be there, but I said I didn't think that was a good idea.

Q And why would you have to make prior arrangements for you to bump into each other rather than having sort of a -- you know, walk down the hall together to the movie?

A Well, I --

Q I know it's kind of obvious.

A For obvious reasons, I guess, because it wouldn't be appropriate. It -- people would -- people would wonder what was going on.

Q Right. Right. Okay. What about the fact that you made -- that you sent gifts and notes through Betty rather

Page 20

than directly to the President?

Was that something that was done in order to make it less obvious that the notes were actually to the President?

A Well, yes and no. You really -- if you send something directly to the President, if you send a gift to the President, if I sent something right now, well, I don't know, right now, but before this, it -- it -- it goes to the gift unit.

Q Right.

A And so I knew that Betty was the way -- I think that that's -- Walter Kaye would, you know, go through Betty, I think. And that's --

Q So it's yes and no, is the answer to that.

A You can't -- I mean, you can't send a courier thing to the President, you know, a courier to President Clinton, so --

A JUROR: I have a question to follow up on that. When you would send gifts and notes and what have you to Betty, as you had testified, sometimes you'd have a funny card in there, sometimes it would be something sentimental.

Did you ever give Betty license to read any of them because you thought, "Hey, take a look at this, tell me what you think," any of the cards or notes or anything?

Page 21

THE WITNESS: I don't think so. Maybe I told her about a funny card or something. Not that I really remember. I don't -- I think especially if it were something that was ultra-sensitive, I don't -- you know, I don't --

A JUROR: Yes. That would probably be sealed.

THE WITNESS: Exactly.

A JUROR: But for any of the other little --

THE WITNESS: Might have been the jokes. Sometimes I would put together jokes I got on the Internet or e-mail jokes that I put together for him because, you know, everyone needs to laugh, so -- I think maybe -- maybe there was a time that I said, "Oh, you should look at these jokes, they're really funny."

A JUROR: Okay.

MR. EMMICK: Other questions? Yes, ma'am?

A JUROR: Ms. Lewinsky, did you ever discuss with the President whether you should delete documents from your hard drive, either at the office or at home?

THE WITNESS: No.

A JUROR: Nothing like that?

THE WITNESS: No.

A JUROR: Did you ever discuss with the President whether you should deny the relationship if you were asked about it?

THE WITNESS: I think I always offered that.

Page 22

I think I've always --

A JUROR: In discussions with the President?

THE WITNESS: In discussions -- I told him I would always -- I would always deny it, I would always protect him.

A JUROR: And what did he say when you said that? What kind of response did you receive?

THE WITNESS: I said that often. I -- in my head, I'm seeing him smile and I'm hearing him saying "That's good," or -- something affirmative. You know. Not -- not -- "Don't deny it."

A JUROR: Thank you.

THE WITNESS: Sure.

BY MS. IMMERGUT:

Q Ms. Lewinsky, with respect to the weekend visits, did the President ever initiate that idea or say anything about it's good if you come on the weekends?

A Yes. The -- I don't remember if it was the Wednesday or the Friday when the relationship first started, he said to me at some point, you know, "You can come see me on the weekends. I'm usually around on the weekends." So --

Q And did you understand what that meant?

A Yes. To me, it meant there aren't as many people around on the weekends, so --

A JUROR: Ms. Lewinsky, when you -- now, this is a

Page 23

different kind of subject. When you first made the determination that you were moving to New York and you wanted to explore the possibilities of a job in private industry, can you recall how you first got the recommendation about Vernon Jordan's assistance in this endeavor?

THE WITNESS: I can't. I know that it was -- what I don't remember was if it was my idea or Linda's idea. And I know that that came up in discussions with her, I believe, before I discussed it with the President. I know that I suggested to the President or I -- I didn't suggest, I asked the President if Mr. Jordan might be able to assist me.

A JUROR: To go back from the job search to what we were talking about before, I seem to recall, and I may be mistaken, when you were here before you said something about Tim Keating when you were fired, said something to you like maybe you can come back after the election.

THE WITNESS: Mm-hmm.

A JUROR: And I wanted to just hear sort of a fuller explanation about that. Was it your understanding at the time that Tim Keating was sort of -- that he understood and was telling you that you were fired because of an appearance problem around the time of the election?

THE WITNESS: Not at all.

A JUROR: No?

THE WITNESS: No.

Page 24

A JUROR: The other question I have, and I apologize, it's a little bit sensitive, but did you and the President in sort of discussing cover stories and, you know, how -- you know, your desire to protect him from sort of what's going on now, did you ever talk about sort of -- you know, that you weren't really having sex?

I mean, you said that he made this comment to you about not having -- you know, that certain actions have consequences at his age.

THE WITNESS: Yes.

A JUROR: Was there ever sort of an understanding that, well, oral sex isn't really sex? Or did you talk about that?

THE WITNESS: We didn't talk about it. Something that I thought on my own was one of the reasons that it -- at first that he didn't want to -- that he wouldn't let everything come to completion in terms of oral sex was I thought that that sort of had to do with maybe that was his way of being able to feel okay about it, his way of being able to justify it or rationalize it that, well --

A JUROR: But you never discussed that.

THE WITNESS: No.

MR. EMMICK: Yes, ma'am?

A JUROR: Ms. Lewinsky, getting back to -- I think you have a copy there of contacts between the President and

Page 25

Monica?

THE WITNESS: Yes.

A JUROR: After you left the White House, it seems as if you attended a number of public functions where you came in contact with him.

Was that by chance? Was that something you wanted to do? Was it a way to see him? Was it something that he suggested?

Could you just tell us a little about that?

THE WITNESS: Sure. No. Those were all ways for me to get a chance to see him. I'm an insecure person and so I think – and I was insecure about the relationship at times and thought that he would come to forget me easily and if I hadn't heard from him – especially after I left the White House, it was – it was very difficult for me and I always liked to see him and it – and usually when I'd see him, it would kind of prompt him to call me. So I made an effort. I would go early and stand in the front so I could see him, blah, blah, blah.

BY MR. EMMICK:

Q Let me ask a follow-up question to that because I think it may have been in about October of '96 when you had a telephone conversation with him just prior to you going to Billy Shaddock to get a photograph.

A Right.

Page 26

Q During the conversation before, did you and the President have any discussion about your dropping by and seeing him at a public departure?

A Yes.

Q All right. Would you tell us about that?

A Let's see. I spoke with him – I think it was October 22nd, and then I saw him at an event October 23rd and he called that night and I had mentioned to him on – I think it was a Tuesday, the first phone conversation, that I was going to be at the White House on Thursday.

And when he called me Wednesday night, he said – I was upset with him and so then he said, you know, "Don't be mad. Don't be mad." You know. "Are you coming tomorrow?"

And I said yes.

So he said, "Well, why don't you stop by Betty's office, stop by to see Betty and then maybe you can come see me for a few minutes before I leave." So –

Q Okay. All right. The reason I was asking that as a follow-up is that's sort of a prearranged semi-public occasion for the two of you to see each other.

A Right. I don't – I don't know necessarily that I was going to go to the departure.

Q I see.

A But that was maybe kind of a cover story.

Page 27

Q I understand.

A Or I'm not – I know he had a departure and I know that I was going to see him for a few minutes before the departure because I thought – I remember thinking that I might get to kiss him, so –

MR. EMMICK: All right.

A JUROR: Now to follow up on your follow-up of my question –

MR. EMMICK: Yes.

A JUROR: Did you get to see him that day?

THE WITNESS: No, I didn't.

A JUROR: Okay. Could you tell us a little about that?

THE WITNESS: Sure. I – the short of it is that I didn't end up seeing him because Evelyn Lieberman was hanging around and left with him that day.

A JUROR: She was someplace where she didn't belong.

THE WITNESS: Right. So Betty had – I was waiting in the West Wing lobby with Billy, actually, after we had gone to look at the photos and Betty finally came out and it was really just as he was walking to the helicopter and she took me to see it, but she said that – and it was at that point when she sort of confirmed for me that Evelyn didn't like me. So – that –

Page 28

A JUROR: The contacts with the President, on page 5, for the 18th of August –

THE WITNESS: I'm sorry, I can't hear you.

MR. EMMICK: Page 5.

A JUROR: Okay. Page 5, 18th of August, it says "Public function, President's 50th birthday party, limited intimate contact."

A JUROR: I couldn't hear her.

MR. EMMICK: Okay. Let me repeat it. There is a reference on page 5 to August 18th of '96, a Sunday, "Public function, President's 50th birthday party, limited intimate contact."

Your question about that was?

THE WITNESS: What does that mean?

MR. EMMICK: What does that mean?

THE WITNESS: It's stupid. There was a cocktail reception for his -- he had this big 50th birthday party at Radio City Music Hall and there was a cocktail reception and at the – when he came to do the rope line and he – after he greeted me and talked to me, he was talking to a whole bunch of people in and around my area and I had – can I stand up and show you?

MR. EMMICK: Sure. Sure.

THE WITNESS: Okay. If this is the rope line and here are all the people and the President's standing here, as

Page 29

he started to talk to other people, I had my back to him and I just kind of put -- put my hand behind me and touched him. This -- so --

BY MS. IMMERGUT:

Q Touched him in the crotch area?

A Yes.

A JUROR: I didn't hear that.

MS. IMMERGUT: Touched him in the crotch area.

A JUROR: Oh.

MS. IMMERGUT: And the response was yes.

A JUROR: Okay.

A JUROR: Did anybody see you?

THE WITNESS: What? No. What's the question?

A JUROR: Did anybody see you?

THE WITNESS: No.

A JUROR: But there were people around.

THE WITNESS: There were, but it was -- he was talking -- everybody was enamored with him. I'm sure everybody saw from Monday that -- and he was talking to different people and he -- he was always very close to me when -- whenever he'd do these rope lines and would sort of make a point of talking to me around -- you know, with other -- while other people were there and he'd usually hold my hand -- you know, sort of shaking hands and just -- would continue to just touch me somewhere. I mean, not -- not

Page 30

intimately, not --

BY MR. EMMICK:

Q Right. Just to set the scene, are there a lot of people kind of bunched together at the time?

A Oh, they're -- they're -- I mean, if we -- if everybody in the room came and stood in this one small corner, that's -- I mean, that's how crowded it was. So it was -- and my back was to him and he was -- he was holding onto my -- I think he was holding onto one of my arms or something, I had a sleeveless dress on. So --

Q So it sounds to me like -- it's almost a situation where there are so many people that you can't really see that kind of --

A Exactly. And it wasn't -- it wasn't a -- it was -- maybe sort of a grazing over of that area, but it wasn't -- it wasn't how you might imagine it if someone described this, from a scene from a movie, it wasn't like that, but it was -- you know. I don't even know if he remembers, so --

MR. EMMICK: Okay.

A JUROR: So on this paper we have here with sexual relations, would that qualify as -- what, contact? Sexual contact? Because if I remember -- where's my paper --

THE WITNESS: Let me look at the definition.

MR. EMMICK: Sure.

A JUROR: Yes. Contact with -- number 1 --

Page 31

MR. EMMICK: Just to clarify, the witness is looking at Grand Jury Exhibit ML-6.

THE WITNESS: I'm not really sure, because I don' think it was to necessarily gratify him or arouse him.

A JUROR: What was it for?

THE WITNESS: It was just -- I thought it was funny and it was sort of a -- I don't know how to explain it.

A JUROR: Contact.

BY MR. EMMICK:

Q Would it be better described as perhaps affectionate or playful?

A Playful, I think. It was just -- playful, not something I'd ever thought I'd have to discuss publicly.

A JUROR: While we're on this, I wanted to like finish it up, but I had a couple of questions with regards to the definition.

THE WITNESS: Sure.

A JUROR: Because I want to be sure in my own mind. At the bottom it says -- it says "Contact means intentional touching, either directly or through clothing."

THE WITNESS: Mm-hmm.

A JUROR: Out of all of the times you had intimate contact, were there times when the President would touch you either on the breasts or in the genital area directly to the skin or was it always through clothing?

Page 32

THE WITNESS: Directly to the skin. Both.

MR. EMMICK: Yes, ma'am?

A JUROR: I have some questions about the 50th birthday. That's when you gave the President the yellow tie. Is that when you gave the President the yellow tie?

THE WITNESS: Not on that date.

A JUROR: But just before that.

THE WITNESS: But before that. Correct.

A JUROR: When it shows on the chart here, it says "Some time before August 16, 1996."

THE WITNESS: Correct.

A JUROR: And that tie is the same tie that at the end of your appearance here we saw some evidence that the President has worn a number of times this summer.

THE WITNESS: Yes.

A JUROR: There's been some press accounts about that tie, last night and today.

THE WITNESS: Sure.

A JUROR: My question to you is have you authorized your attorneys or any other spokesperson through you to discuss that evidence?

THE WITNESS: Gosh. I don't think I've necessaril, given a direct authorization.

A JUROR: Do you know that they have?

THE WITNESS: Do I know if they -- I -- I don't

Page 33

know if they necessarily directly have. I know there have been questions about it. I shouldn't say I know, I'm sure there have been questions about it, but there have been a lot of instances since the beginning of this thing that there's been information that's come out from places where I hadn't expected it and that includes my own -- the people on my team. So I can't -- I don't know.

A JUROR: So you don't know whether that information is coming from people that you have discussed it with?

THE WITNESS: I think that there -- there probably might have been -- I really -- I -- I wouldn't be surprised to find out that there was confirmation or some of that information came from there.

So -- but I know that also -- I'm sure it was somewhat limited because with my agreement, we're not allowed to talk to the press. We're not supposed to. So -- without prior approval.

BY MR. EMMICK:

Q So I guess there's -- let me just rephrase it. It sounds like you wouldn't be surprised by it, but do you have any direct knowledge that it occurred?

A I know that there have been calls about this tie and I know that -- that I don't think that we've been 100 percent silent about that. So -- I don't -- I mean -- I know

Page 34

that we didn't cause this story to come out or I don't believe that we did. So --

A JUROR: Ms. Lewinsky, it says on the chart that you received a thank you note saying that the tie is really beautiful.

THE WITNESS: Mm-hmm.

A JUROR: And that was in the President's handwriting?

THE WITNESS: It's a typed letter and then he hand signed the letter and then "The tie is really beautiful" is handwritten.

A JUROR: Did you ever discuss the tie with him in person or was it just a note?

THE WITNESS: No, we discussed it a lot on the phone.

A JUROR: And did he like the tie?

THE WITNESS: Mm-hmm.

A JUROR: Thank you.

THE WITNESS: He called me the first day he wore it. The first time he wore it.

A JUROR: All right. Thank you.

A JUROR: I have another question.

THE WITNESS: Sure.

A JUROR: On the day you were here testifying, there was a report on the TV --

Page 35

THE WITNESS: Right.

A JUROR: The President in the Rose Garden wearing that tie. Did you see that?

THE WITNESS: That evening I did.

A JUROR: When you saw him with the tie, what did that say to you?

THE WITNESS: I understand you had to do what you had to do. That's what it meant to me. I had looked -- because I had seen him wear this tie prior -- a few other occasions since January, I had looked the day before my testimony because I thought he's just the kind of person that's going to wear this tie to tug on my emotional strings one last time before I go into the grand jury and say this under oath. And he didn't.

And him wearing it the day I came to testify sort of having to know that I wasn't going to see it until the end of the day, to me was just kind of -- you know, hey, you had to do what you had to do. But --

MR. EMMICK: Yes, ma'am?

A JUROR: Ms. Lewinsky, not to make a big issue about the tie, but is this tie something -- one of the ties that perhaps the President really liked, is a favorite tie?

THE WITNESS: I think so because he wore it during the campaign. He wore it once -- sometimes even twice a week. So I think he liked it a lot.

Page 36

A JUROR: Do you think that he would remember that it's from you? I mean, you know, I don't know, but do you think he would?

THE WITNESS: Ties were a big issue with us and I used to bug him all the time on the phone, "Well, when are you going to wear one of my ties?" You know. Or he'd say, "Did you see -- " On one occasion, I remember specifically he said, "Did you see I wore your tie the other day?"

There's a pretty big correlation between the times when he would wear one of my ties and we either spoke the night before or that night.

And I used to say to him that "I like it when you wear my ties because then I know I'm close to your heart." So -- literally and figuratively.

A JUROR: So you think he would know, then, that that was your tie.

THE WITNESS: He should know.

A JUROR: Which brings to mind when the first appearance by Nel, when he came testify --

THE WITNESS: Yes.

A JUROR: Can you tell me what your thoughts were when you saw the pictures of Nelvis wearing the first tie that you gave the President?

THE WITNESS: Yes. Actually, you know what? I think my cup's leaking. I'm sorry.

A JUROR: Do we have another cup up there?

THE WITNESS: Am I allowed to know people's names in here?

MR. EMMICK: The answer to that is no.

THE WITNESS: Oh –

MR. EMMICK: I know it seems –

THE WITNESS: It's so awkward.

MR. EMMICK: It does seem awkward, but I think it's better if –

THE WITNESS: Okay.

MR. EMMICK: – the record not have any identifications.

THE WITNESS: Okay.

MR. EMMICK: We didn't intentionally get you a dribble glass.

THE WITNESS: Oh, sure. At least it's water and not grape juice.

I had two very different thoughts. My first thought was "You jerk. You're trying to show me how little you care about me and how little this meant to you by giving it – to show me that you gave it to someone else, it meant so little to you now."

And my second thought was that it was sort of some sort of message of some sorts. I don't know what. Because I could see the President kind of saying to Nel, you know, "Oh,

why don't you – " I could even see him spilling something on Nel on purpose and – that morning and then sort of saying, "Oh, here, just wear this tie," or something like that. I mean, that's – it's – he's funny that way. But I thought there was some sort of deliberateness to it.

I don't know that Nel knew that, that that was the tie I gave the President but – I don't think it was a coincidence.

MR. EMMICK: Yes, ma'am?

A JUROR: Could one of your thoughts perhaps have been that maybe he just gave him a batch of ties to Nelvis? And maybe he didn't remember?

THE WITNESS: No.

A JUROR: You really think he would have remembered that first tie?

THE WITNESS: I know he did. I mean, we – we – that was – I don't know if you all know this or not, but I worked in a men's necktie store when I was in college for four years and so that was my thing, that was part – you know, my spending money, a lot of it came from working. And so I love ties.

And I – I mean, I can pick out – you know, different designers and stuff. And so that was a big thing for me. And then – and I liked to give him ties and I liked to see him wearing them.

A JUROR: Do you know how much impact Nel had on what the President wore each day?

THE WITNESS: None. To my understanding. Nel was. My understanding is that Nel's strictly in the – while he would go to the residence on occasions, that he was usually in the oval area.

MR. EMMICK: There's a question waiting for a bit here. Yes.

A JUROR: Ms. Lewinsky, was it the President's nature to give his ties away?

THE WITNESS: Yes. I knew that – I knew that he had given Nel ties, his ties in the past. But ties were such a big issue between the President and me that I really couldn't have imagined that he didn't – that he didn't know.

A JUROR: Other people other than Nel as well, in terms of giving his ties away?

THE WITNESS: I don't know.

A JUROR: Okay. You just –

THE WITNESS: I'm not aware of anyone else, but that doesn't mean there aren't.

A JUROR: Okay.

THE WITNESS: Right.

A JUROR: But you did know about that.

THE WITNESS: Yes.

A JUROR: Do you happen to know whether the

President had a valet to assist him in his dressing?

THE WITNESS: Assist him in his dressing, I don't know. I know that there's a valet.

A JUROR: Or like prepare – Mr. President, this suit goes with this tie, kind of thing?

THE WITNESS: I don't know that necessarily, but I have seen – I had seen evidence enough that he could wear my ties when he wanted to. You know. That if he wanted to, he could go pick it out, so I don't know what his getting dressed routine is.

A JUROR: Okay. Thank you.

A JUROR: Okay. I have a question that's a bit on the delicate side.

THE WITNESS: Okay.

A JUROR: But this is just something that I need to know.

THE WITNESS: Sure.

A JUROR: Did you and the President ever engage in sexual relations using cigars?

THE WITNESS: Yes.

A JUROR: Okay.

A JUROR: Okay. I'd like to change the subject now.

THE WITNESS: Thank you. Just once. Just once.

A JUROR: When you last testified, you told us that

Page 41

photographs that you saw of the President and First Lady when they were away that were romantic in nature upset you.

When you had an opportunity to speak with the President about those photographs or any film that was taken during these romantic moments, what did he say? Why they were -- because I'm just curious as to whether or not they were staged because of the legal things that were going on with the President at that time.

THE WITNESS: Right. I don't believe we discussed them. I know that that upset me and sort of put me in a bit of a contentious mood when I spoke with him on the 5th. I think it was the 5th of January of this year. And I may have said something in passing about them, but we didn't have a discussion about the pictures.

A JUROR: Okay. I was just wondering if there were --

THE WITNESS: Sure. No. I wondered, too.

A JUROR: Did you think any conversations to him about his wife were inappropriate?

THE WITNESS: I don't know if inappropriate is the right word. I tried not to. I -- there were very few discussions and I tended to say things like, "Well, when you're alone," you know, "Call me when you're alone," kind of a thing or, you know, that was how we discussed sort of Mrs. Clinton maybe not being there, was, "Well, I'll be alone

Page 42

on this day. Shall I -- " I think we were careful -- or I was careful, I know I was.

MR. EMMICK: Yes, ma'am?

A JUROR: Ms. Lewinsky, I wondered if you ever had any trouble with the Secret Service in trying to be near the President.

THE WITNESS: No. The only time that I remember was when I went to see him on the last time in '96, I guess it was April 7th, Easter. And when John Muskett was outside and he said he was going to check with Evelyn if I could go in and then I don't remember exactly how it happened, but I sort of -- I don't remember the exact discussion, but it ended up he ended up not talking to Evelyn and I went in. So --

A JUROR: I have a question about Linda Tripp.

THE WITNESS: Ugh. Sorry.

A JUROR: In your conversations with Ms. Tripp, was her opinion always that she must be truthful or was there a time where your impression was that she was going to provide you with cooperation as far as keeping the secrecy?

THE WITNESS: There are two areas of that, I guess. Linda always told me she would always protect me and she would never tell anybody and keep my secret, up until the Paula Jones case came about.

Page 43

And I had never had any reason to think that she would ever need to discuss this under oath because I was certainly always going to deny it and I couldn't even imagine a situation where that would really come up.

But there was a point in the period prior to my learning about her being subpoenaed in the Paula Jones case, most specifically, January 9th, when she led me to believe that she was not going to tell about my relationship and that she was going to be vague on the truth about Kathleen Willey and was just not going to really remember anything else and that was why I agreed to meet with her on Tuesday the 13th.

A JUROR: In your conversations with her as you were making your move to move to New York and what have you, did you ever get the sense that she was fishing for offers of benefits or the protection of her job? You know, or where she was hoping that nothing would affect her job or if there was something in it for her?

THE WITNESS: Yes and no. When you asked me the question, the first thing that comes to my mind was it may not be directly related to that.

When the Kathleen Willey incident had come out in Newsweek, there was a period after it, Bob Bennett had referred to -- or had made that comment about Linda Tripp and she made some off-comment about if she loses her job she's going to write a tell-all book.

Page 44

And so I sort of -- that was an instance where I felt I needed to assure her that that wasn't going to happen, she wasn't going to lose her job, and that -- I certainly tried to make assurances. I mean, I -- I promised -- I would have promised her the moon if I could deliver it.

And then also -- then when I spoke with her on the 9th, she talked about that she had spent some time in New York during Christmas and that she -- that someone had suggested to her that she get a job doing public relations in New York.

And that seemed a little bit strange to me, in that that was exactly what I was in the process of doing, and that maybe that was what she thought, that somehow then -- you know, I think I told her, oh, I'd try to help her come to New York and try to help her that way, but I don't know that -- that I ever said anything directly about who would help her.

A JUROR: Okay. Thank you.

BY MR. EMMICK:

Q I'd like to ask a clarifying follow-up because I wasn't sure I understood all of the sort of ins and outs, if you will, of when Linda was going to maintain the secret and when she was going to reveal it. It sounded like prior to the time when Linda got a Paula Jones subpoena, your understanding was she was doing to keep the secret.

A Correct.

Page 45

Q And then after she got the Paula Jones subpoena, then she told you that she was going to disclose things and tell the truth. Is that right?

A Yes. Yes.

Q Okay. And then in this conversation on January 9th, she indicated some willingness to consider keeping the secret a bit longer.

A No, considered that she was going to do that.

Q That she was going to. All right. That's what I wanted to clarify.

A Sure.

MR. EMMICK: Thank you.

A JUROR: When you said that in your conversations with Linda Tripp you kind of had to exaggerate some things about the President to her, you exaggerated on some of the things you said to her about the President --

THE WITNESS: I'm not sure about that. I -- I don't know if exaggerate is the right -- is maybe the word I would choose.

A JUROR: Okay.

THE WITNESS: But go on. I'm sorry.

A JUROR: Well, no, I just used that word.

THE WITNESS: Okay.

A JUROR: Exaggerate. You didn't use it, but I couldn't think of the exact words you used.

Page 46

THE WITNESS: Sure.

A JUROR: But were you -- why do you think that you had to not tell her some things that din actually happen, true things, in talking to her?

THE WITNESS: That really came about in relation to the Paula Jones case. I think that I was -- there were some occasions, one in particular that I remember, when I didn't disclose a contact that I had with the President -- I'm sorry, here -- I'll scoot over -- contact that I had with the President to her for some reasons, but after the Paula Jones case, I was scared to death. I mean, I was panicked that she was going to tell.

So, I mean, I -- I -- you know, along the lines of, you know, some of the things I said about Mr. Jordan, I said, you know, "Oh, the President told me I have to lie," I don't even remember everything I said, but I know that there were certainly lies at that point, not even exaggerations.

MR. EMMICK: Actually, I was going to ask that clarifying follow-up to that.

THE FOREPERSON: And then after that, we have to take a break.

MR. EMMICK: And then we'll take a break.

BY MR. EMMICK:

Q The clarifying follow-up was that I had understood that during that January period when you were talking to

Page 47

Linda Tripp you were lying to her on occasion, but I wasn't clear whether those lies related to times that you had been with the President or whether they related to other things generally. Do you understand what my question is?

A No.

Q What were the nature of the lies that you were telling to Linda Tripp during that January period?

A Oh, gosh. They went from -- I guess a non-disclosure of my meeting with him on the 28th, nor my phone call with him on the 5th of January, to -- ranging to things that he said I had to do or told me to do.

I haven't -- I haven't seen transcripts of those days, thank goodness, but I just know that I was -- I was scared to death. And I thought any influence that anybody would have, my mother, Mr. Jordan, the President, anybody, would -- I used.

MR. EMMICK: All right.

THE FOREPERSON: It's break time.

MR. EMMICK: Break time.

THE FOREPERSON: It's break time. It's break time.

A JUROR: I have a follow-up to that as well.

THE FOREPERSON: Okay. So we're going to take ten minutes.

THE WITNESS: Okay.

THE FOREPERSON: And we'll come back.

Page 48

A JUROR: I hope I remember my question.

THE WITNESS: Can you guys call me Monica? Are they allowed to call me Monica instead of Ms. Lewinsky? I was just --

THE FOREPERSON: If you say so.

THE WITNESS: Okay.

MR. EMMICK: Sure.

THE WITNESS: I'm just 25. Please.

A JUROR: But you'll always be Ms. Lewinsky, whether you're 25 or 28 or --

THE WITNESS: Not if I get married.

(Witness excused. Witness recalled.)

THE FOREPERSON: Monica, I'd like to remind that you are still under oath.

THE WITNESS: Thank you.

MR. EMMICK: We have a quorum and there are no unauthorized persons present. Is that right?

THE FOREPERSON: You are absolutely correct.

MR. EMMICK: Lucky this time.

THE WITNESS: Thank you.

MR. EMMICK: Did you want to ask some follow-up questions?

MS. IMMERGUT: Yes.

BY MS. IMMERGUT:

Q Ms. Lewinsky, there are two things I wanted to

Page 49

clarify. First, with respect to the tie disclosure issue --
A Yes.
Q -- you were asked about before, I believe you mentioned something to the effect that there have been things that have come out of your team that you were surprised about before. Are you referring to your current legal team?
A No. My first legal team.
Q Okay. And that's Mr. Ginsberg?
A Yes.
Q Okay. You're not aware of any unauthorized disclosures from your current camp?
A No. Nor have I authorized any disclosures.
Q Okay. So you didn't authorize a disclosure about the tie.
A No.
Q With respect to -- to switch gears -- to what we were speaking about right before the break about the things that you said to Linda Tripp at the very end, particularly on January 13, 1998, I believe --
A Yes.
Q You mentioned that an example of things that you were not truthful about was, for example, the fact you had seen the President on December 28th and that you had spoken to him on January 5th. Is that correct?
A Right. Yes. And I didn't disclose that to her.

Page 50

Q Right. You did not disclose that to her.
A Quite to the contrary.
Q Okay. In fact, you told her that you hadn't seen or spoken to the President for two months.
A Or since the 17th of December.
Q Okay.
A Exactly.
Q You mentioned that there was -- you also said things about what the President had said to you to Ms. Tripp that were not true on January 13th. Do you remember any specific things that you said that the President had told you that in fact were not true?
A No. I don't remember any specifics, I just wanted to leave open the possibility. Does that clarify it?
MR. EMMICK: On the right here?
A JUROR: Monica, why did you keep that black dress?
A JUROR: Blue.
A JUROR: Blue dress.
A JUROR: Did you have a reason to keep it?
THE WITNESS: Pardon?
A JUROR: The blue dress.
A JUROR: The blue dress.
THE WITNESS: No. I didn't have a reason. The -- reason -- the dress -- I didn't realize -- if I remember

Page 51

correctly, I didn't really realize that there was anything on it until I went to go wear it again and I had gained too much weight that I couldn't fit into it.
And it seemed sort of funny and I -- it may sound silly, I have a lot of clothes. I don't clean all my clothes right after I wear them, I usually don't clean them until I know I'm going to wear them again. And then I was going to wear it for Thanksgiving because I had lost weight and I had -- I had shown the dress to Linda at that point and had just sort of said to her, "Well, isn't this -- " You know, "Isn't this stupid?" Or, you know, "Look at this, isn't this gross?" Or whatever. I don't really remember exactly what I said.
And she told me that I should put it in a safe deposit box because it could be evidence one day.
And I said that was ludicrous because I would never -- I would never disclose that I had a relationship with the President, I would never need it.
And then when Thanksgiving time came around and I told her that I was going to wear it for Thanksgiving, she told me I looked fat in the dress, I shouldn't wear it. She brought me a jacket from her closet as to try to persuade me not to wear the dress.
So I ended up not wearing it and then I was going to clean it. I took it with me up to New York and was going

Page 52

to clean it up there and then this broke, so --
A JUROR: Okay. Your relationship with the President, did your mother at any time try to discourage the relationship?
THE WITNESS: Oh, yes.
A JUROR: Well, what kept it going? I mean, what kept it -- you keeping it active or whatever?
THE WITNESS: I fell in love.
A JUROR: I beg your pardon? I couldn't hear you.
THE WITNESS: I fell in love.
A JUROR: When you look at it now, was it love or a sexual obsession?
THE WITNESS: More love with a little bit of obsession. But definitely love.
A JUROR: Did you think that the President was in love with you also?
THE WITNESS: There was an occasion when I left the White House and I was pretty stunned at how I felt because I did think that.
A JUROR: You did?
BY MR. EMMICK:
Q Do you remember the date?
A It was July 4, 1997.
A JUROR: Were you aware that he was having problems in his marriage? Did this ever spill over in the

Page 53

times that you were together? Did you get a feeling that something was not right, that --

THE WITNESS: [redacted]

A JUROR: [redacted]

THE WITNESS: [redacted]

A JUROR: [redacted]

THE WITNESS: [redacted].

A JUROR: [redacted]

THE WITNESS: [redacted]

A JUROR: [redacted]

MR. EMMICK: I thought there was a question in the front here.

A JUROR: And today, Monica, do you still love the President?

THE WITNESS: Before Monday, I would have said yes.

Page 54

A JUROR: So then it is no?

THE WITNESS: I don't know how I feel right now.

MR. EMMICK: A question in the front?

A JUROR: I guess I would like to know what happened Monday to make you just by Thursday change your mind so completely.

THE WITNESS: I don't think it's so much changed my mind. I think -- it's -- it was very painful for me to watch his speech on Monday night. I -- it's -- it's hard for me to feel that he has characterized this relationship as a service contract and that that was never something that I ever thought it was. And --

A JUROR: I'm sorry, you lost me already.

THE WITNESS: I'm sorry. I'm sorry. It's -- from my understanding about what he testified to on Monday, not -- just from the press accounts, is that this was a -- that this was a service contract, that all I did was perform oral sex on him and that that's all that this relationship was. And it was a lot more than that to me and I thought it was a lot more than that.

And I think I felt -- I was hurt that -- that he didn't even -- sort of acknowledge me in his remarks. And even also -- I mean, that has to do with directly with me, but I thought he should have acknowledged all the other people that have gone through a lot of pain for seven months.

Page 55

I feel very responsible for a lot of what's happened, you know, in the seven months, but I tried -- I tried very hard to do what I could to not -- to not hurt him. I'm still not answering your question.

A JUROR: Well, let's -- you said the relationship was more than oral sex. I mean, it wasn't like you went out on dates or anything like that like normal people, so what more was it?

THE WITNESS: Oh, we spent hours on the phone talking. It was emotional.

A JUROR: Phone sex?

THE WITNESS: Not always. On a few occasions. I mean, we were talking. I mean, interacting. I mean, talking about what we were thinking and feeling and doing and laughing.

We were very affectionate, even when -- after he broke the relationship off in May, I mean, when I'd go to visit with him, we'd -- you know, we'd hug each other a lot. You know, he always used to like to stroke my hair. He -- we'd hold hands. We'd smile a lot. We discussed a variety -- you know, a wide range of things.

So, I mean, it was -- there was a real component of a relationship to it and I just -- I thought he had a beautiful soul. I just thought he was just this incredible person and when I looked at him I saw a little boy and -- I

Page 56

don't know what the truth is any more.

And that's, I think, what I took away on Monday, was that I didn't know what the truth was. And so how could I know the truth of my love for someone if it was based on him being an actor.

A JUROR: I'd like to ask you about Bayani Nelvis.

THE WITNESS: Okay.

A JUROR: How much about your relationship with the President did Bayani Nelvis know?

THE WITNESS: I think he knew that -- that we were friends and that I would come to see the President and I gave him things. I don't know -- I don't remember ever getting into any specific details. Might he have thought that from -- you know, from how much I kind of liked the President? I'm not sure.

But -- and I don't mean this in a racist way, you know, Nel's from another country and so his English is -- while his English is good, it's not perfect, not that anyone's is perfect, so I think that sometimes there was a little bit of a language barrier there, too, so I think he -- you know, Nel was just a -- is a really nice guy. He's a sweet guy and he -- he's very loyal to the President.

A JUROR: Did you ever tell him at any time that you loved the President?

THE WITNESS: I don't think so, but I might have,

Page 57

but I don't think so.

A JUROR: Okay.

MR. EMMICK: Yes? A question?

A JUROR: You just mentioned real components, the relationship was -- like a real component, you mentioned things like truth. But sometimes I go back and forth not understanding because you yourself were living a lot of secrets, a lot of lies, a lot of paranoia, but yet you wanted truth, a real component?

I'm not understanding these two different things because one time you're sentimental but then again you do just the opposite of what you say you're thinking.

Did you ever think that nothing real could come of this relationship? .

THE WITNESS: Did I ever thing nothing real --

A JUROR: Anything real, that anything real could -- and truthful and honest could have come from this relationship?

THE WITNESS: Yes.

A JUROR: With this married man?

THE WITNESS: I did.

A JUROR: But I have a question for you about that.

THE WITNESS: Mm-hmm.

A JUROR: It's been reported in the papers that you had a relationship before similar to this, where a lot of

Page 58

hurt and pain came out of this, you know, a lot of hurt and pain toward a family.

And then you turn around and you do it again. You're young, you're vibrant, I can't figure out why you keep going after things that aren't free, that aren't obtainable.

THE WITNESS: Well, there's sort of two parts to that and just to clarify, the -- the way Andy and Kate Bleiler portrayed everything on TV and through their lawyer was pretty inaccurate, so I don't know how much of that is part of your question.

A JUROR: The only part I know is that he was a married man with a wife and a family.

THE WITNESS: That's true.

A JUROR: Like I know about the President.

THE WITNESS: Mm-hmm.

A JUROR: He was a married man and it wasn't no secret of that fact. But yet you want to talk about truth, a real component, honesty. It all seems so -- like a fantasy. That's why I asked you earlier about obsession.

THE WITNESS: That's a hard question to answer because obviously there's -- there's work that I need to do on myself. There are obviously issues that -- that -- you know, a single young woman doesn't have an affair with a married man because she's normal, quote-unquote. But I think most people have issues and that's just how mine manifested

Page 59

themselves.

It's something I need to work on and I don't think it's right, it's not right to have an affair with a married man. I never expected to fall in love with the President. I was surprised that I did.

And I didn't -- my intention had really been to come to Washington and start over and I didn't want to have another affair with a married man because it was really painful. It was horrible. And I feel even worse about it now.

A JUROR: Monica, I'd like to change the topic, if I can.

THE WITNESS: Did I answer --

A JUROR: Yes.

THE WITNESS: Okay.

A JUROR: And I also -- I want to let you know that we're not here to judge you in any way, I think many of us feel that way.

THE WITNESS: I appreciate that. But I understand that every -- you know, this is -- this is a topic that -- there are a lot of people think it's wrong and I think it's wrong, too. I understand that.

A JUROR: I had to ask that you question because I've had to ask other questions and it wouldn't have been right for me not to ask you the question --

Page 60

THE WITNESS: Sure.

A JUROR: -- that I've had to ask --

THE WITNESS: I think it's fair and I think you should -- I think it's a fair question. It's a hard one to answer. No one likes to have their weaknesses splayed out for the entire world, you know, but I understand that. And I'd rather you understand where I'm coming from, you know, and you'd probably have to know me better and know my whole journey to how I got here from birth to now to really understand it. I don't even understand it. But -- I understand. I respect your having to ask that question and I appreciate what you're saying, whatever your name is.

A JUROR: We're here only to assess the credibility of your testimony.

THE WITNESS: Sure. But I -- I can see how that would be a factor.

A JUROR: I wanted to go back to the issue of ties. It's my understanding that you testified earlier this morning that your agreement, your immunity agreement, with the Office of the Independent Counsel includes an understanding that you -- that you and your legal team need prior approval to disseminate information to the press.

THE WITNESS: Mm-hmm.

A JUROR: And in looking over Exhibit ML-2, I don't see that provision. Can you look at that?

Page 61

THE WITNESS: Is that my agreement?
A JUROR: Yes.
THE WITNESS: Sure.
MR. EMMICK: Sure.
THE WITNESS: I know that portion of it very well.
A JUROR: I may be missing something.
THE WITNESS: There have been many times I've wanted to defend myself and the lies that have been spewed out.
MR. EMMICK: I think the reference is to part 1B.
A JUROR: Okay.
MR. EMMICK: Where it says "Will not make any statements -- " "Neither Ms. Lewinsky nor her agents will make any statements about this matter to witnesses, subjects, or targets of the OIC's investigation or their agents or to representatives of the news media without first obtaining the OIC's approval."
A JUROR: Okay. Thank you.
THE WITNESS: Sure.
MR. EMMICK: Other questions? Yes, ma'am?
A JUROR: I'd also like to return for a minute -- if you have that package out -- to something that was discussed this morning, earlier this morning, and that refers to your proffer. Do you have a copy of the proffer? The proffer?

Page 62

MR. EMMICK: We do. Sure.
THE WITNESS: Okay.
MR. EMMICK: I'm placing Exhibit ML-1 before the witness.
THE WITNESS: Thank you.
A JUROR: Monica, if you could look at paragraph 11, I'm not sure what page it is, but it's paragraph 11.
THE WITNESS: Okay. Yes. Okay.
A JUROR: As I understood our discussion this morning, you said that you offered to deny the relationship and the President didn't discourage you, but said something like "That's good."
As I read your proffer here, it says "The President told Ms. L to deny a relationship if ever asked." And that seems to me slightly different.
THE WITNESS: I forgot this. So that's true.
A JUROR: Is this proffer statement correct, that he did tell you to deny a relationship?
THE WITNESS: Yes. I don't -- I don't -- when I answered the question earlier, that was what first came to my mind. But, I mean, I know that this is true.
I just at that point -- and I -- really reading it, I know it's true because I was truthful in my proffer, but sitting here right now, I can't remember exactly when it was, but it was something that was certainly discussed between us.

Page 63

A JUROR: And what about the next sentence also? Something to the effect that if two people who are involved say it didn't happen, it didn't happen. Do you recall him saying that to you?
THE WITNESS: Sitting here today, very vaguely. I can hear -- I have a weird -- I'll explain to you guys that I have a weird sense of -- for me, my saying I remember something, if I can see it in my mind's eye or I can hear him saying it to me, then I feel pretty comfortable saying that that's pretty accurate, that I remember that. And I can hear his voice saying that to me, I just can't place it.
A JUROR: Is it --
THE WITNESS: And this was -- I mean, this was early -- this was all throughout our relationship. I mean, it was -- obviously not something that we discussed too often, I think, because it was -- it's a somewhat unpleasant thought of having to deny it, having it even come to that point, but --
A JUROR: Is it possible that you also had these discussions after you learned that you were a witness in the Paula Jones case?
THE WITNESS: I don't believe so. No.
A JUROR: Can you exclude that possibility?
THE WITNESS: I pretty much can. I really don't remember it. I mean, it would be very surprising to me to be

Page 64

confronted with something that would show me different, but I -- it was 2:30 in the -- I mean, the conversation I'm thinking of mainly would have been December 17th, which was --
A JUROR: The telephone call.
THE WITNESS: Right. And it was -- you know, 2:00, 2:30 in the morning. I remember the gist of it and I -- I really don't think so.
A JUROR: Thank you.
A JUROR: I have some questions about the Paula Jones lawsuit. Going back to the period before you even had any idea that you might be a witness in that, did you follow the Paula Jones lawsuit fairly closely?
THE WITNESS: I followed it. I don't know "fairly closely," but -- I think it maybe depended more on was there something in the paper and that happened to be a day that I sat and read all the papers because I had nothing to do.
I did follow it, but I wasn't -- I didn't follow it as much as I follow this case. I mean, in terms of -- no, but I mean, I'm just saying as a gauge, you know.
A JUROR: So you were holding down a full-time job and everything at that time, but you did read the papers --
THE WITNESS: I did read the papers every day and it was -- sure, I followed it. I didn't know the ins and outs of it, but I followed it.

Page 65

A JUROR: Did you -- in that period again, even before anyone knew that you would be a witness, did you discuss that with the President? Was he aware that you followed it? Was that something --

THE WITNESS: No. Really, the time that I remember we discussed it was on the 17th.

A JUROR: December 17th?

THE WITNESS: And when I told him my sort of stupid idea for how he should settle it. So that was -- but, no. He wasn't -- we didn't -- I -- and I think in general just to give you guys a flavor, because there have been different subjects that have come up, when we spent time together, I know I certainly made an effort -- unless I was angry with him about something, that there were topics that I wanted to stay away from and the time that I spent with him was precious to me. So things that were unpleasant I didn't bring up unless I had to.

A JUROR: Exactly what date again did you get your subpoena to be a witness?

THE WITNESS: The 19th of December.

A JUROR: The 19th? Okay. Now, when -- and if you could retell for me the conversation you had with the President about the gifts.

THE WITNESS: Okay. It was December 28th and I was there to get my Christmas gifts from him. Excuse me. I'm

Page 66

sorry. And we spent maybe about five minutes or so, not very long, talking about the case. And I said to him, "Well, do you think -- "

What I mentioned -- I said to him that it had really alarmed me about the hat pin being in the subpoena and I think he said something like, "Oh," you know, "that sort of bothered me, too. That bothered me," you know, "That bothers me." Something like that.

And at one point, I said, "Well, do you think I should -- " I don't think I said "get rid of," I said, "But do you think I should put away or maybe give to Betty or give to someone the gifts?"

And he -- I don't remember his response. I think it was something like, "I don't know," or "Hmm" or -- there really was no response.

I know that I didn't leave the White House with any notion of what I should do with them, that I should do anything different than that they were sitting in my house. And then later I got the call from Betty.

A JUROR: Now, did you bring up Betty's name or did the President bring up Betty's name?

THE WITNESS: I think I brought it up. The President wouldn't have brought up Betty's name because he really didn't -- he didn't really discuss it, so either I brought up Betty's name, which I think is probably what

Page 67

happened, because I remember not being too, too shocked when Betty called.

Somewhat surprised, I guess, that he hadn't said -- you know, it would have seemed easier to sort of have said something maybe then, but I wasn't too surprised when she called.

A JUROR: Thank you.

MR. EMMICK: I think there was a question in the front. Did you have a question?

MS. IMMERGUT: Did you have a question?

A JUROR: Yes. Back to the contacts?

THE WITNESS: Yes.

A JUROR: On page 7, on the 29th of March --

THE WITNESS: On the -- sorry, what date?

A JUROR: The 29th of March. Sunday.

MR. EMMICK: Then 29th of March.

THE WITNESS: Okay.

A JUROR: "Private encounter, approximately 1:30 or 2:00 p.m., study. President on crutches. Physical intimacy including oral sex to completion and brief direct genital contact." Brief direct genital contact, could you just elaborate on that a bit?

THE WITNESS: Uh --

A JUROR: I understand --

THE WITNESS: Oh, my gosh. This is so

Page 68

embarrassing.

A JUROR: You could close your eyes and talk.

A JUROR: We won't look at you.

THE WITNESS: Can I hide under the table? Uh -- I had -- I had wanted -- I tried to -- I placed his genital next to mine and had hoped that if he -- oh -- this is just too embarrassing. I don't --

A JUROR: Did you think it would lead to intercourse?

THE WITNESS: Not on that day.

A JUROR: Was that sort of the reason for doing the gesture --

THE WITNESS: Yes.

A JUROR: -- or trying to -- moving his closer to yours?

THE WITNESS: Then I -- not that we would have intercourse that day, but that that might make him want to.

A JUROR: Okay. Were you wearing clothes at the time or underwear at the time?

THE WITNESS: No.

A JUROR: And was he? Or his were pulled down?

THE WITNESS: Correct.

A JUROR: So was there direct skin-to-skin contact between your genitals and his?

THE WITNESS: I think very briefly. It was --

Page 69

he — he's really tall and he couldn't really bend because of his knee, so it was —
A JUROR: It was more of a grazing?
THE WITNESS: Yes.
A JUROR: About how many encounters did you have in the study? If you can recall.
MR. EMMICK: What do you mean by "encounters"?
A JUROR: Sexual encounters. I'm sorry.
THE WITNESS: Do you include kissing or not?
A JUROR: No kissing. According to the definition.
THE WITNESS: Okay. Two.
A JUROR: Okay. Thank you.
BY MS. IMMERGUT:
Q And why don't you give us the dates of those.
A The — well, let me look. The 29th of March and the 28th of February. There might have been — I mean, in terms of the clothes and stuff, there might have been playful touches here and there, but not — nothing that I would have considered sexual encounters.
Q And that's not listed as an intimate encounter?
A No. No, it's not. No, it's not.
Q And just to clarify again, are those the two times that the President actually came to completion during the oral sex?
A Yes.

Page 70

BY MR. EMMICK:
Q And I'm actually obliged to ask one follow up that I don't think will be too bad, but directing your attention to August 16th, did you attempt to touch the President on that day?
A Yes.
Q And did you actually touch him? In his groin area?
A Over his clothes.
Q Over his clothes. And did he say that's not — "We can't do that"?
A Yes.
MR. EMMICK: Okay.
A JUROR: Did you feel any rejection the times that he wouldn't go all the way with you?
THE WITNESS: Yes.
A JUROR: Monica, I had one question to go back to the gifts. You had said that the President had called you initially to come get your Christmas gift, you had gone there, you had a talk, et cetera, and there was no -- you expressed concern, the President really didn't say anything. How much later in the afternoon did you get a call from Betty? It was that same day, is that correct?
THE WITNESS: Yes, that's correct. Let me just clarify real quickly that I had made the arrangements to go there on Sunday through Betty, just that you had said he

Page 71

called me.
A JUROR: So you had initiated the contact on that day?
THE WITNESS: He had — he had told me on the 17th that he — you know, he still had these Christmas gifts for me and then — just shortly after Christmas and I called Betty and said, you know, "He said he had something for me," something like that, you know. And then she arranged it. So I just wanted to clarify.
A JUROR: And then how much of a time gap —
THE WITNESS: A few hours, maybe.
A JUROR: A few hours?
THE WITNESS: Maybe — I think it was around 2:00 p.m. or so, around 2:00 in the afternoon, and I had gone there at 8:30 in the morning and left — I'd say maybe four or five hours time span.
A JUROR: So what exactly happened? You went home and you packaged these gifts? Or had you already had them packaged?
THE WITNESS: No. I went home and I — I think I went to New York that evening, possibly, so I was getting ready to go to New York, I think, or something.
But when Betty called, then she said, you know, "I understand you have something to give me." It was very vague. And I understood — I mean, to me, that meant from

Page 72

this conversation that we had had that I should sort of — you know, give some of the gifts.
So I put them all out on my bed and — it's sort of been difficult to kind of explain why I put some things in and why I didn't put others in.
The things that seemed to be directly called for in the subpoena, I put in a box: the hat pin, the dress from Martha's Vineyard, some of the pictures and things, the ad to him from Valentine's Day. Not that that was directly called for, but some of the more intimate — I guess personal things, except that I kept the "Leaves of Grass" book because that just — I was worried, I didn't know if I would get the gifts back or not, ever, and so I — that just — that meant the most to me of anything he gave me.
A JUROR: And I believe your testimony last time was that you did not believe that Betty knew the contents of the package?
THE WITNESS: I don't believe so.
A JUROR: She just came and picked them up and that was it?
THE WITNESS: We chit-chatted for a little bit. She was on the way to see her mom in the hospital, so I got her a small plant to just take to her mom and —
BY MS. IMMERGUT:
Q Did she seem at all confused when you handed over

Page 73

the box?

A No.

Q Did she ask you what was in it?

A No. Not that I remember. I don't believe so.

MS. IMMERGUT: Thank you.

A JUROR: And just to back up for a second on your conversation with the President that you already discussed a little bit where you said you were concerned about the subpoena and some of the items that it called for such as the hat pin which indeed the President had given you, you testified previously, I believe, that the President said he was concerned about that also when he saw the hat pin. Is that correct?

THE WITNESS: I don't know that he saw -- I don't know that he saw the hat pin on the -- I don't know that he saw the subpoena, so -- I know that the hat pin was a concern to him.

A JUROR: Okay. Do you remember what he said in response when you said you were concerned about the things called for in the subpoena?

THE WITNESS: I think he said something like "That concerned me, too."

A JUROR: Okay.

THE WITNESS: So I don't know if he saw it or someone -- you know, I don't know he learned that.

Page 74

A JUROR: Okay. But he appeared to have some prior knowledge of --

THE WITNESS: I think so. I think so.

A JUROR: I have another question about that conversation on the 28th. You had already discussed with him earlier the subpoena and the fact that all of your gifts from him were under subpoena and then --

THE WITNESS: We hadn't discussed that. I wasn't -- I hadn't -- the 28th was the first time that I saw him or spoke to him since I had been subpoenaed. When he called me on the 17th, I wasn't yet subpoenaed.

A JUROR: Okay. Okay. So that conversation took place on the 28th?

THE WITNESS: Correct. The only conversation about gifts and the subpoena, really -- yes.

A JUROR: And on that same day, he gave you Christmas gifts.

THE WITNESS: Yes.

A JUROR: What was your thinking at that time about that? Did that concern you or --

THE WITNESS: No.

A JUROR: No?

THE WITNESS: I was --

A JUROR: Did you -- what did you plan to do with those gifts? Did it cross your mind that some -- that you

Page 75

should maybe give some of them to your attorney as responsive to the subpoena or --

THE WITNESS: No.

A JUROR: No?

MR. EMMICK: I have a quick clarifying question because you said that the only conversation you had with him about gifts after the subpoena was on the 28th. You also had a conversation with him on the 5th that related to the later gift of the book, if I remember it right.

THE WITNESS: Right. I meant my gifts that he gave to me.

MR. EMMICK: Right. Right. Right. I just wanted to clarify that.

THE WITNESS: Okay. Sure.

MR. EMMICK: Other questions?

A JUROR: Going back to your conversation with Linda Tripp --

MR. EMMICK: Which one?

THE WITNESS: Yes. Which tape are you referring to?

A JUROR: No, I'm just going to be general.

MR. EMMICK: Okay.

A JUROR: If you had to put it like percentage-wise, what you told her as being truthful and not truthful, what percentage will be not truthful?

Page 76

THE WITNESS: I would say before the subpoena, before I found out she had been subpoenaed, so for argument's sake maybe saying before December of '97, I'd say 95 percent accurate. There were some things that I didn't tell her, but I usually pretty much told her everything.

A JUROR: You started talking to her when? In '95 or '96?

THE WITNESS: I first told her -- when I first told her about the relationship or when I started talking to her as a person?

A JUROR: The relationship.

THE WITNESS: The relationship, I told her in November of '96. After the election.

A JUROR: Okay. So from November '96 to December '97 --

THE WITNESS: Pretty truthful.

A JUROR: And then after '97?

THE WITNESS: Oh --

BY MR. EMMICK:

Q Could I ask just one clarifying matter about that answer? Because you had said that it was 95 percent accurate and then you also said because sometimes I didn't tell her everything. And I just want to make sure we're being clear on whether you're talking about being complete or being accurate.

Page 77

In other words, are you not telling her things or are you saying things to her that are inaccurate, sort of in that 5 percent, if you will?

A Well, I don't remember the exact situations or the times that I didn't tell her something, if she had asked me about it, I would have been inaccurate about what I said.

Q All right. I see.

A So –

Q So there's kind of a blending of those two concepts.

A Correct.

BY MS. IMMERGUT:

Q And, again, to clarify, did you ever lie about your sexual relationship with the President?

A No.

MR. EMMICK: I'm sorry. I interrupted. I didn't mean to.

A JUROR: So after '97, then –

THE WITNESS: After December '97, I don't even know how to – how to put a percentage to that.

A JUROR: Any truth at all after '97?

THE WITNESS: Yes. There were some truths in December of '97. There certainly were some true statements, but there were a lot of untrue statements. Probably the untrue statements stick out in my mind more because they

Page 78

caused so much trouble.

A JUROR: Which ones stick out in your mind as having been untruthful?

THE WITNESS: Stuff about my mom. Just – a lot of different things about my mom. That I had – that I told Mr. Jordan I wouldn't sign the affidavit until I got a job. That was definitely a lie, based on something Linda had made me promise her on January 9th. Some of the other things –

A JUROR: Did you tell Linda Tripp at any time that you had heard or understood that people don't go to jail for perjury in a civil case?

THE WITNESS: Yes, I believe – I think I said that.

A JUROR: Did anybody tell you that?

THE WITNESS: Well, hmm.

A JUROR: Do you want to talk to – I know there's – is there an attorney issue there?

THE WITNESS: There's an attorney issue.

A JUROR: I see.

MR. EMMICK: Do you want to take a break and talk about the attorney issue? Because I think that may be a way to figure out if we can answer that question any more fully.

THE WITNESS: Do you want me to go talk to my attorney?

Page 79

MR. EMMICK: Well, I just think it might be – I think your attorney would like it if he were to talk to you.

THE WITNESS: Okay.

MR. EMMICK: That's the way to answer it.

THE WITNESS: Okay. So just to be clear, you're –

A JUROR: Well, maybe I can help. Just – if I could confine it to did anyone other than your attorney ever suggest to you that perjury in a civil case would not be prosecuted?

THE WITNESS: Uh –

MS. IMMERGUT: If you need to talk to your attorney, go ahead.

A JUROR: I just thought – did anyone other than your attorney tell you that?

THE WITNESS: No.

MR. EMMICK: I think it still would be advisable to have a more complete answer, to at least let them talk.

THE WITNESS: Okay.

MR. EMMICK: Yes.

THE WITNESS: Excuse me.

(The witness was excused to confer with counsel.)

MR. EMMICK: Do we have a quorum?

THE FOREPERSON: Yes, we do.

MR. EMMICK: And are there any unauthorized persons present?

Page 80

THE FOREPERSON: Not a one.

MR. EMMICK: All right.

THE WITNESS: And I'm still under oath.

THE FOREPERSON: Yes, you are.

BY MS. IMMERGUT:

Q And just to clarify a couple of things that were right before the break, when you sort of asserted a privilege or had some questions about whether there was a privilege, I did want to ask you just to clarify that with respect to the statement about your lawyer having – or somebody telling you whether or not you can be charged with perjury in a civil case, just to be clear, did Mr. Jordan ever tell you that?

A No.

Q Did Mr. Carter ever tell you that?

A No.

Q And otherwise, I think the question was was it another attorney and I believe that you would like to assert the attorney-client privilege.

A JUROR: No, I think I excluded attorneys from my question.

THE WITNESS: Okay. You know, can I just address – I think sort of the – one of the questions that you had asked me before and I just – about –

A JUROR: Myself?

THE WITNESS: Yes. That you had asked me about the

Page 81

relationship and being untruthful and things like that. And I just -- this is something that's sort of been on my mind since this whole thing started.

I have never -- I don't -- I certainly believe I have ever told a lie to hurt anybody, that I sort of -- some of the ways in which I grew up, it was -- there were secrets and inherent in a secret is a lie and so I just -- you know, I -- I just thought I'd tell you that.

A JUROR: Okay.

MR. EMMICK: Other questions?

A JUROR: Ms. Lewinsky, we're going to try, because we feel that we have been jumping around and you've done a very good job of sort of jumping from topic to topic, we're going to try to bunch our questions together around a few topics and our forelady is going to try to play traffic cop, so --

A JUROR: A little bit. No, you go ahead. This is your record. But I'll play traffic cop just a little.

A JUROR: Ms. Lewinsky, before you go into that, I just remember you saying something with Linda Tripp, you know, what was not the truth, okay? And I just remembered, was one of the things that you told her, that you gave your mother the blue dress, one of the untruths or was that true?

THE WITNESS: I don't know if I ever told Linda I gave my mom the blue dress. One of the things I did say was

Page 82

that I gave everything to my mom, so that probably included that and that was not true. I didn't give the evidence to my mom. My mom never hid the dress. She didn't know it was in New York.

A JUROR: Okay.

THE WITNESS: So she didn't know anything about it.

A JUROR: I've got one of those questions that goes along with what she just said.

A JUROR: Okay. Fine. That's the idea. The topic.

A JUROR: How much did your mom really know?

THE WITNESS: She knew -- she knew that I was having a relationship with the President. She knew that -- she knew that I was certainly emotional about it and that it made me miserable a lot and that sometimes I was elated and sometimes I was miserable, but I didn't -- you know, I -- I might have said something to her like, "We fooled around," but I -- not -- she didn't know as much as I led Linda to believe she knew. Is that --

A JUROR: Yes.

THE WITNESS: Okay.

A JUROR: Okay. Any other Linda Tripp questions?

A JUROR: Yes, there's one.

A JUROR: Did you ever suggest to Linda Tripp that she delete e-mails or anything like that from her

Page 83

computer?

THE WITNESS: Yes, I did.

A JUROR: And did you tell her that you had done the same thing?

THE WITNESS: Yes, I believe so.

A JUROR: And did anyone ever suggest to you or tell you that you should do that?

THE WITNESS: No.

A JUROR: Did you tell Linda Tripp that anyone had suggested that to you?

THE WITNESS: I don't think so.

A JUROR: Okay. Thank you.

A JUROR: Any others?

A JUROR: In that end of the year timeframe, did you ever tell Linda Tripp that you felt physically at risk?

THE WITNESS: I think so. I think I told her something about -- that -- that -- I said something about Mary Jo what's-her-name.

A JUROR: Kopechne.

THE WITNESS: Kopechne. And so -- I really didn't feel threatened, but I was trying to use anything I could to try to convince her not to tell. So that I thought that if she thought I was threatened and that was part of the reason, then she would maybe do the same.

Page 84

A JUROR: So you did not at any time feel that your personal security was at risk from the White House or anyone in the White House?

THE WITNESS: No. I think that maybe there -- there -- maybe once or twice it had crossed my mind in some bizarre way because everybody's heard about the different -- you know, sure, there's the Marilyn Monroe theory. And so it -- but it was not -- it was not any factor of -- that related to my actions.

A JUROR: So any discussion that you had about the whole topic with Linda Tripp would fall into what you were describing before as a little bit of fabrication?

THE WITNESS: Yes. Yes.

BY MR. EMMICK:

Q If I could ask a follow-up on that, did your mother ever express any concerns about your safety?

A I think she might have, but it was sort of the -- I think it was more general. It might have been a more general sense.

A JUROR: Are there any other questions about personal safety?

A JUROR: Are we still on December? December, January?

A JUROR: Yes.

A JUROR: I have one follow-up question if this is

Page 85

an appropriate time about the gifts. And, again, if you have your proffer there?

THE WITNESS: Yes.

A JUROR: At the top of page 7, where you say in your proffer that when Ms. Currie called later that afternoon she said, at least I think you mean that she said that the President had told her Ms. L wanted her to hold on to something for her. Do you remember Betty Currie saying that the President had told her to call?

THE WITNESS: Right now, I don't. I don't remember, but when I wrote this, I was being truthful.

The other thing, and this is something that I was thinking about this morning in relation to the proffer, that I had written this proffer obviously being truthful, but I think that when I wrote this, it was my understanding that this was to bring me to the step of getting an immunity agreement, and so I think that sometimes to -- that I didn't know this was going to become sort of this staple document, I think, for everything, and so there are things that can be misinterpreted from in here, even from me re-reading it, the conditions -- some of the conditions maybe under which I wrote it.

So I just thought I should sort of say that, that where -- I mean, I know -- I certainly was not untruthful or trying to be misleading in this. I didn't think it was going

Page 86

to be -- this was my understanding of a written thing that I would -- that I would attest to under oath and that it wouldn't be number 7, read this, is this -- do you --

BY MR. EMMICK:

Q So it may not be written with legal precision?

A Exactly.

Q But there's no intentional falsehoods in it?

A No.

Q You were trying to be truthful throughout?

A Exactly.

A JUROR: And my purpose in raising it really is to just see whether this might jog your recollection at all as to something you might have recalled back in February that you don't recall today.

THE WITNESS: It doesn't.

A JUROR: It does not?

THE WITNESS: It's possible, but -- I -- I -- it's not my -- you know --

A JUROR: Okay.

THE WITNESS: -- my memory right now.

A JUROR: Any other questions on that subject?

A JUROR: If we don't have any other questions, I guess the other thing that we wanted to ask you a little bit about is when you were first approached by Mr. Emmick and his colleagues at the OIC.

Page 87

Can you tell us a little bit about how that happened? That's not a happy topic, either, I apologize.

MR. EMMICK: Maybe if I could ask, what areas d you want to get into? Because there's -- you know -- many hours of activity --

A JUROR: Well, one specific -- okay. One specific question that people have is when did you first learn that Linda Tripp had been taping your phone conversations?

THE WITNESS: I believe that I didn't learn the extent to which she had taped my conversations, until I read it in the press.

I learned that day that she had worn a wire at the lunch and that I -- and that there had been other people, I think, in the restaurant that had been listening in and -- so I knew -- she had -- she had said that -- that -- when I was first apprehended, she was -- she had said that they had done the same thing to her and she tried to hug me and she told me this was the best thing for me to do and -- oh.

MR. EMMICK: Any other specific questions about that day? I just -- this was a long day. There were a lot of things that --

A JUROR: We want to know about that day.

A JUROR: That day.

A JUROR: The first question.

A JUROR: Yes.

Page 88

A JUROR: We really want to know about that day.

MR. EMMICK: All right.

THE WITNESS: Linda was supposed to go see this new attorney that she had claimed she had gotten and was going to try to sign an affidavit so she paged me in the morning, I called her back and she told me she wanted to meet me before she went to see the attorney. So we planned to meet at the Ritz Carlton in the food court at -- I think it was quarter to one.

She was late. I saw her come down the escalator. And as I -- as I walked toward her, she kind of motioned behind her and Agent [redacted] and Agent [redacted] presented themselves to me and --

A JUROR: Do you want to take a minute?

THE WITNESS: And flashed their badges at me. They told me that I was under some kind of investigation, something had to do with the Paula Jones case, that they -- that they wanted to talk to me and give me a chance, I think, to cooperate, maybe.

I -- to help myself. I told them I wasn't speaking to them without my attorney.

They told me that that was fine, but I should know I won't be given as much information and won't be able to help myself as much with my attorney there. So I agreed to go. I was so scared.

Page 89

(The witness begins crying.)
A JUROR: So, Monica, did you go to a room with them at that time?
THE WITNESS: Yes.
A JUROR: And at that time, did you talk to anybody or what did you do? Did you want to call your mother?
THE WITNESS: Can Karen do the questioning now? This is -- can I ask you to step out?
MR. EMMICK: Sure. Okay. All right.
MS. IMMERGUT: I guess, Monica, if Mike could just stay -- do you mind if Mike is in here?
THE WITNESS: (Nods affirmatively.)
MS. IMMERGUT: Okay. Would you rather --
THE WITNESS: (Nods affirmatively.)
MR. EMMICK: Okay. That's fine.
BY MS. IMMERGUT:
Q Okay. Did you go to a room with them at the hotel?
A Yes.
Q And what did you do then? Did you ever tell them that you wanted to call your mother?
A I told them I wanted to talk to my attorney.
Q Okay. So what happened?
A And they told me -- Mike came out and introduced himself to me and told me that -- that Janet Reno had sanctioned Ken Starr to investigate my actions in the Paula

Page 90

Jones case, that they -- that they knew that I had signed a false affidavit, they had me on tape saying I had committed perjury, that they were going to -- that I could go to jail for 27 years, they were going to charge me with perjury and obstruction of justice and subornation of perjury and witness tampering and something else.
Q And you're saying "they," at that point, who was talking to you about that stuff?
A Mike Emmick and the two FBI guys. And I made Linda stay in the room. And I just -- I felt so bad.
Q Now, when you say you felt bad, because you felt responsible somehow for pulling the President into something?
A Yes.
Q And is that something that still weighs heavily on you, that you feel responsible?
A Yes.
Q And is it -- do you feel responsible because you told Linda about your relationship?
A Yes.
Q I guess later just to sort of finish up, I guess, with the facts of that day, was there a time then that you were -- you just waited with the prosecutors until your mother came down?
A No.
Q Okay.

Page 91

A I mean, there was, but they -- they told me they wanted me to cooperate. I asked them what cooperating meant, it entailed, and they told me that -- they had -- first they had told me before about that -- that they had had me on tape saying things from the lunch that I had had with Linda at the Ritz Carlton the other day and they -- then they told me that I -- that I'd have to agree to be debriefed and that I'd have to place calls or wear a wire to see -- to call Betty and Mr. Jordan and possibly the President. And --
Q And did you tell them you didn't want to do that?
A Yes. I -- I -- I remember going through my mind, I thought, well, what if -- you know, what if I did that and I messed up, if I on purpose -- you know, I envisioned myself in Mr. Jordan's office and sort of trying to motion to him that something had gone wrong. They said that they would be watching to see if it had been an intentional mistake.
Then I wanted to call my mom and they kept telling me that they didn't -- that I couldn't tell anybody about this, they didn't want anyone to find out and that they didn't want -- that was the reason I couldn't call Mr. Carter, was because they were afraid that he might tell the person who took me to Mr. Carter.
They told me that I could call this number and get another criminal attorney, but I didn't want that and I didn't trust them. Then I just cried for a long time.

Page 92

A JUROR: All while you were crying, did they keep asking you questions? What were they doing?
THE WITNESS: No, they just sat there and then -- they just sort of sat there.
A JUROR: How many hours did this go on?
THE WITNESS: Maybe around two hours or so. And then they were -- they kept saying there was this time constraint, there was a time constraint, I had to make a decision.
And then Bruce Udolf came in at some point and then -- then Jackie Bennett came in and there were a whole bunch of other people and the room was crowded and he was saying to me, you know, you have to make a decision. I had wanted to call my mom, they weren't going to let me call my attorney, so I just -- I wanted to call my mom and they --
Then Jackie Bennett said, "You're 24, you're smart, you're old enough, you don't need to call your mommy."
And then I said, "Well, I'm letting you know that I'm leaning towards not cooperating," you know.
And they had told me before that I could leave whenever I wanted, but it wasn't -- you know, I didn't -- I didn't really know -- I didn't know what that meant. I mean, I thought if I left then that they were just going to arrest me.

Page 93

And so then they told me that I should know that they were planning to prosecute my mom for the things that I had said that she had done.

(The witness begins crying.)

MS. IMMERGUT: Do you want to take a break, Monica?

THE WITNESS: Yes.

(Witness excused. Witness recalled.)

THE FOREPERSON: Okay. We have a quorum. There are no unauthorized people and Monica is already aware that she is still under oath.

MS. IMMERGUT: We just have a couple more questions and then I think we'll break for lunch.

THE WITNESS: Okay.

A JUROR: Monica, I have a question. A minute ago you explained that the reason why you couldn't call Mr. Carter was that something might be disclosed. Is that right?

THE WITNESS: It was -- they sort of said that -- you know, I -- I -- I could call Frank Carter, but that they may not -- I think it was that -- you know, the first time or the second time?

A JUROR: Any time.

THE WITNESS: Well, the first time when I asked, that I said I wasn't going to talk to them without my lawyer, they told me that if my lawyer was there, they wouldn't give me as much information and I couldn't help myself as much, so

Page 94

that --

A JUROR: Did they ever tell you that you could not call Mr. Carter?

THE WITNESS: No. What they told me was that if I called Mr. Carter, I wouldn't necessarily still be offered an immunity agreement.

A JUROR: And did you feel threatened by that?

THE WITNESS: Yes.

A JUROR: And you said they offered you a chance to call another attorney?

THE WITNESS: Yes.

A JUROR: And did you take them up on that offer?

THE WITNESS: No.

A JUROR: Why not?

THE WITNESS: Because I didn't trust them.

A JUROR: I see. And at some point in this meeting, did you -- you did obtain an attorney? Mr. Ginsberg?

THE WITNESS: Well, like at 11:00 that night.

A JUROR: So it was seven hours or eight hours or more later?

THE WITNESS: They -- they finally let me call my mom, so I went to call my mom and then -- and I saw Linda again. She had been shopping or something like that. But I called my mom and then Mike had said that she could call him,

Page 95

so they called her or she called him or something like that and then they agreed to let her come down.

So she took the train and then -- and then he just sort of -- I shut down and I kind of -- you know, I thought maybe I should try and make these people like me, so I tried to be nice and I told jokes and I asked if we could walk around the mall because I couldn't sit in that room any more. And I just --

BY MS. IMMERGUT:

Q So did they let you do that?

A Mm-hmm. So Mike and Agent [redacted] took me and we walked around the mall and we ate dinner and then we went back to the room and I read Psalm 21 about a million times. And my mom's train had been -- there were problems with her train and then finally she got there and they told me they were going to want to talk to my mom alone for a little bit, but I got to talk to her.

And I was -- I didn't -- I didn't want to cooperate. I mean, I didn't -- I just kept thinking to myself, well -- well, I'll just say I made it all up, I'll just -- I'll just -- I -- I couldn't imagine -- I couldn't imagine doing this to the President. And I felt so wrong and guilty for having told Linda and that she had done all this.

But -- so then they took my mom into another room for a really long time and she had -- then when she came

Page 96

back, they called my dad. And then we finally -- and then I talked to my dad and then -- then -- Ginsberg came on the scene. And he --

A JUROR: So if I understand it, you first met the agents, Agents [redacted] and [redacted] at around 1:00 and it wasn't until about 11 p.m. that you had an opportunity to talk to a lawyer?

THE WITNESS: Yes.

BY MS. IMMERGUT:

Q Although you were allowed to -- the thing with Frank Carter was that they were afraid he would tell Vernon Jordan? Is that what they expressed to you?

A Right. And I had -- I had -- I think that someone said that Frank wasn't even -- Frank was a civil attorney and so that he really couldn't help me anyway, so I asked him if at least I could call and ask him for a recommendation for a criminal attorney and they didn't think that was a good idea.

And then I said, well, what about -- if I want to get in touch with Mr. Carter later, if I decide that's what I want to do, you know, and he's not there, because it's Friday and it was a holiday weekend, so then Agent Fallon went in the other room to find out if he had a service or something or another, a pager, I don't know --

Q Some way for you to reach him later?

A Mm-hmm.

Page 97

A JUROR: Sounds as though they were actively discouraging you from talking to an attorney.
THE WITNESS: Yes.
A JUROR: Is that a fair characterization?
THE WITNESS: Yes.
BY MS. IMMERGUT:
Q Well, from Frank Carter.
A From Frank Carter, who was my only attorney at that point.
MS. IMMERGUT: Right. Right.
THE WITNESS: So I could have called any other attorney but –
A JUROR: You didn't have another attorney.
THE WITNESS: I didn't have another attorney and this was my attorney for this case, so – I mean, this was –
A JUROR: And this is the attorney who had helped you with the affidavit.
THE WITNESS: Yes. And that – the affidavit – well, the affidavit wasn't even filed yet. It was Fed Ex'd out on that day. So –
A JUROR: Monica, when you called your mother, how much were you able to tell her over the phone? Very little or –
THE WITNESS: I was hysterical. She didn't understand what I was saying, but I told her that – that the

Page 98

FBI had me and there was something with the Paula Jones case and Linda and then she – she – I said that – that the guy said you could call her – you can call him and so she just told me to calm down and I was screaming that, you know, "They want me to cooperate and I don't want to cooperate, don't make me cooperate, don't make me do this," and she – she said it was okay, don't worry, don't worry, and then she talked to Mike Emmick and they let her come down. So, I mean, she – I don't know.
A JUROR: Did you feel better after you talked to your mother?
THE WITNESS: Oh, yeah.
A JUROR: Gained that support?
THE WITNESS: Yeah.
A JUROR: Okay.
THE WITNESS: Yeah. I mean –
A JUROR: And what were you thinking about Linda at this time?
THE WITNESS: Linda? Did you say –
A JUROR: Mm-hmm. Did you know exactly what had happened? That you had been –
THE WITNESS: No. I was under the impression that – what I was thinking at that point was that they had – that they had listened in on our conversation on the phone and that then they came to her and said she was in

Page 99

trouble for something and that then she let them listen in on this lunch conversation because she had said "They did the same thing to me. They did the same thing to me." So I didn't understand what she meant by that.
And then she said, "This is the best thing for you," as if I was left to believe that she had – this was somehow something she had done and that she was trying to help me.
And I thought, "Why did she tell them? Why didn't she just say it was nonsense, it wasn't true? Why did she tell them that I had had this relationship with him?" And so – you know – and they had pictures of me at lunch with her. So –
A JUROR: The pictures were the taped lunch?
THE WITNESS: Yes. The wire lunch.
A JUROR: The wired lunch.
THE WITNESS: Yes. So that – because they – because I had said on one of the tapes that – you know, if there was a tape of me – I had – I had – I didn't know how the Paula Jones people had gotten my name and I thought maybe they had tapped my phone or maybe they had broken into my computer and read my e-mails.
I didn't know how I had gotten involved in this case and so I had said to Linda, "Well, if they have me on tape, I'll just say it's not me. I'll just say it's not me.

Page 100

I'll deny it. I'll deny everything."
A JUROR: So they took pictures.
THE WITNESS: Right. So they said, "We have you on tape saying that you'd deny it and we have pictures to prove that you were there." So –
A JUROR: During this time in the hotel with them, did you feel threatened?
THE WITNESS: Yes.
A JUROR: Did you feel that they had set a trap?
THE WITNESS: I – I – I did and I had – I didn't understand – I didn't understand why they – why they had to trap me into coming there, why they had to trick me into coming there. I mean, this had all been a set-up and that why – I mean, that was just so frightening. It was so incredibly frightening.
And they told me, you know, over and over again I was free to leave whenever I wanted, but – I – I didn't – I didn't know that there's a grand jury and indicted and then you go to jail. I mean, and a trial and everything. I didn't understand that.
And so I didn't – you know, then there was something that, well, if I partially cooperate, they'll talk to the judge, some – you know, we're prepared to indict you or something like that for all these things. And I just didn't –

Page 101

BY MS. IMMERGUT:
Q So you didn't know what would happen if you left.
A No. And then it wasn't until my mom was there that Mike Emmick cleared it up and said to my mom, "Well, it's not that we'll arrest you tonight when you leave the hotel." You know. Because I didn't -- I didn't know.
Q And you didn't end up cooperating that evening.
A No, I didn't. Because -- well --
A JUROR: Excuse me. When you said they trapped you, you went there on the invitation of Linda for lunch or something?
THE WITNESS: Yes.
A JUROR: So, I mean, how did -- I mean, in your mind, how did you get to the fact that they were the one? Wasn't it just Linda?
THE WITNESS: No, because they were with Linda. When I met Linda in the food court at Pentagon City, the two agents were with her.
A JUROR: Oh, okay.
THE WITNESS: Yeah. And that's where -- so it was right -- have you ever been to Pentagon City mall?
A JUROR: Mm-hmm.
THE WITNESS: So it was right down in the food court, you know the escalator to come down is over here?
A JUROR: Mm-hmm.

Page 102

THE WITNESS: So -- see, they were with her when she met me right -- right in the middle.
A JUROR: Okay.
THE WITNESS: And that's where -- and then --
(Pause.)
A JUROR: I think that's all the questions on that topic. There is one other question.
Going back to Monday night and the President's speech, what did you want or expect to hear from the President?
THE WITNESS: I think what I wanted and expected were two different things. I had -- I had been hurt when he referred to me as "that woman" in January, but I was also glad. I was glad that he made that statement and I felt that was the best thing for him to do, was to deny this. And -- but I had been hurt. I mean, it showed me how angry he was with me and I understood that.
And his -- the people who work for him have trashed me, they claim they haven't said anything about me, they have smeared me and they called me stupid, they said I couldn't write, they said I was a stalker, they said I wore inappropriate clothes, I mean, you all know.
I mean, you've heard them in here, you've read the papers, you've seen on TV, and yet -- and then when it came out about the talking points, then somehow no one ever asked

Page 103

the question, well, how could -- if she was so stupid and she couldn't write, how is it possible that she wrote the talking points? So then it was, well, someone must have helped her with that. Oh, it's okay, though, it wasn't someone in the White House.
So I just -- my family had been maligned because of a lot of their tactics and I felt that -- I had wanted him to say that I was a nice, decent person and that he was sorry this had happened because I -- I tried to do as much as I could to protect him.
I mean, I didn't -- I didn't -- I didn't allow him to be put on tape that night and I didn't -- and I -- I felt that I waited, you know, and I would have gone to trial had -- had -- in my mind, had there never been a point where the Office of the Independent Counsel and myself could come to - they could come to accept the truth I had to say, that that was the truth I had to give, and I'm only 24 and so I felt that I -- this has been hard for me and this has been hard on my family and I just wanted him to take back -- by saying something nice, he would have taken back every disgusting, horrible thing that anyone has said about me from that White House. And that was what I wanted.
What I expected him to do was to just acknowledge in his -- either in his apology -- you know, that first of all I think he should have straight out apologized and I

Page 104

think that he could have acknowledged that -- you know, apologized to me, I think, to the other people who were involved in this and to my family.
My -- my dad didn't know anything about the relationship and when he went on his -- the few interviews he did, he was telling the truth when he said he didn't know. But out of respect for the President and the presidency, he didn't say -- he could have easily said if this is true; X, Y and Z about the President, and I think that because my family didn't start a huge uproar about how wrong or improper or inappropriate it was for a 50-year-old man to be having a relationship with a young woman, we afforded him that, that was one less headache that he had to deal with, and I think he could have acknowledged that. That was what I expected. Does that --
A JUROR: Monica, none of us in this room are perfect. We all fall and we fall several times a day. The only difference between my age and when I was your age is now I get up faster. If I make a mistake and fall, I get up and brush myself off. I used to stay there a while after a mistake. That's all I have to say.
THE WITNESS: Thank you.
MS. IMMERGUT: Let me just check with Mike.
THE FOREPERSON: We do want to share something with her.

Page 105

MS. IMMERGUT: Okay. So do you want to – why don't we hold off for just a second and let me check with Mr. Emmick.

THE FOREPERSON: Okay.

(Pause.)

MS. IMMERGUT: We don't have any further questions.

A JUROR: Could I ask one?

Monica, is there anything that you would like to add to your prior testimony, either today or the last time you were here, or anything that you think needs to be amplified on or clarified? I just want to give you the fullest opportunity.

THE WITNESS: I would. I think because of the public nature of how this investigation has been and what the charges aired, that I would just like to say that no one ever asked me to lie and I was never promised a job for my silence.

And that I'm sorry. I'm really sorry for everything that's happened. (The witness begins to cry.) And I hate Linda Tripp.

A JUROR: Can I just say – I mean, I think I should seize this opportunity now, that we've all fallen short. We sin every day. I don't care whether it's murder, whether it's affairs or whatever. And we get over that. You ask forgiveness and you go on.

Page 106

There's some that are going to say that they don't forgive you, but he whose sin – you knew – that's how I feel about that. So to let you know from here, you have my forgiveness. Because we all fall short.

A JUROR: And that's what I was trying to say.

A JUROR: That's what it's about.

THE WITNESS: Thank you.

A JUROR: And I also want to say that even though right now you feel a lot of hate for Linda Tripp, but you need to move on and leave her where she is because whatever goes around comes around.

A JUROR: It comes around.

A JUROR: It does.

A JUROR: And she is definitely going to have to give an account for what she did, so you need to just go past her and don't keep her because that's going to keep you out.

A JUROR: That's right.

A JUROR: And going to keep you from moving on.

A JUROR: Allowing you to move on.

BY MS. IMMERGUT:

Q And just to clarify, and I know we've discussed this before, despite your feelings about Linda Tripp, have you lied to this grand jury about anything with regard to Linda Tripp because you don't like her?

A I don't think that was necessary. No. It wouldn't

Page 107

have been necessary to lie. I think she's done enough on her own, so –

Q You would not do that just because of your feelings about her.

A No.

THE FOREPERSON: Basically what we wanted to leave with, because this will probably be your last visit to us, I hope, I hope I'm not going to have to do this any more and I hope you won't have to come here any more, but we wanted to offer you a bouquet of good wishes that includes luck, success, happiness and blessings.

THE WITNESS: Thank you. (The witness begins to cry.) I appreciate all of your understanding for this situation and your – your ability to open your heart and your mind and – and your soul. I appreciate that.

THE FOREPERSON: So if there's nothing else?

MR. EMMICK: Nothing else.

THE FOREPERSON: We'd like to excuse you and thank you very much for your testimony.

THE WITNESS: Thank you.

(The witness was excused.)

(Whereupon, at 12:54 p.m., the taking of testimony in the presence of a full quorum of the Grand Jury was concluded.)

* * * * *

-E-

-F-

-G-

-H-

Tab 4

GOVERNMENT EXHIBIT ML-1

(—1— (2/1/98

1. Ms. Lewinsky had an intimate and emotional relationship with President Clinton beginning in 1995. At various times between 1995 and 1997, Ms. Lewinsky and the President had physically intimate contact. This included oral sex, but excluded intercourse.

2. When asked what should be said if anyone questioned Ms. Lewinsky about her being with the President, he said she should say she was bringing him letters (when she worked in Legislative Affairs) or visiting Betty Currie (after she left the WH). There is truth to both of these statements.

3. After Ms. Lewinsky was informed she was being transferred to the Pentagon, Mr. Clinton told her that a) he promised to bring her back to the WH after the election and (in a subsequent conversation) b) Evelyn Lieberman spearheaded the transfer because she felt the President paid to much attention to me and vice versa. Ms. Lieberman told the Pres. that she didn't care who worked there after the election, but they needed to be careful until then.

After the election, Ms. Lewinsky asked the Pres. to bring her back to the WH. In the following

months, Mr. Clinton told Ms. Lewinsky that Bob Nash was handling it and then Marsha Scott became the contact person. Ms. L met with Ms. Scott twice. In the second meeting, Ms. Scott told Ms. L she would detail her from the Pentagon to her (Ms. Scott's) office, so people could see Ms. L's good work and stop referring to her as "The Stalker." Ms. Scott told Ms. L they had to be careful and protect the Pres. Ms. Scott later rescinded her offer to detail Ms. Lewinsky to her office.

Ms. Betty Currie asked Mr. John Podesta to take over placing me in the WH. Three weeks after that, Ms. Linda Tripp informed Ms. L that a friend of Ms. Tripp's in the NSC, Kate, had heard rumors about Ms. L; Ms. L would never work at the WH with a blue pass; and suggested to Ms. Tripp that Ms. L leave Washington, DC.

Following this conversation, Ms. Lewinsky requested of the Pres. that he ask Vernon Jordan to help secure her a non-government position in NY. He agreed to ask Mr. Jordan.

In an effort to help Ms. L, Ms. Currie asked Mr. Podesta to assist, as well. Ms. L believes that

-3-

the Pres. ~~asked~~ spoke with Mr. Erskine Bowles regarding Ms. L's employment in NY. Mr. Podesta arranged for Ms. L to interview with Amb. Richardson who later offered Ms. L a position in Communications/Public Affairs at the USUN.

In the beginning of November 1997, Ms. L met with Mr. Jordan. He asked Ms. L why she was there to see him. Ms. L explained to him (in more detail) that she and the Pres. were friends and people got the wrong idea, resulting in Ms. L's "banishment" to the Pentagon. Ms. L said she was seeking Mr. Jordan's help to begin a new life; he agreed to help.

Ms. L met again with Mr. Jordan in the beginning of December '97, at which time he provided Ms. L with a list of three people to contact and suggested language to use in her letters to them. At some point, Mr. Jordan remarked something about Ms. L being a friend of the Pres. of the United States. Ms. L responded that she never really saw him as "the President"; she spoke to him like a normal man and even got angry with him like a normal man. Mr. Jordan asked what Ms. L got angry about. Ms. L replied that the Pres. doesn't see or call her enough. Mr. Jordan said

Ms. L should take her frustrations out on ~~the~~ him -- not the President.

The following week Ms. L had two interviews in NY ~~as a result of~~ in response to her letters.

4. After Ms. Lewinsky was informed, by the Pres., that she was identified as a possible witness in the Jones case, the Pres. and Ms. L discussed what she should do. The Pres. told her ~~t~~ he was not sure she would be subpoenaed, but in the event that she was, she should contact Ms. Currie. When asked what to do if she was subpoenaed, the Pres. suggested she could sign an affidavit to try to satisfy their inquiry and not be deposed. In general, Ms. L should say she visited the WH to see ~~B~~ Ms. Currie and, on occasion when working at the WH, she brought him letters when no one else was around. Neither of those statements untrue. To the best of Ms. L's memory, she does not believe they discussed the content of any deposition that Ms. L might be involved in at a later date.

-5-

5. After receiving a subpoena two days later, Ms. L contacted Mr. Jordan (because Ms. Currie's brother had been killed in a car accident). Mr. Jordan told Ms. L to come see him at 5pm because he couldn't understand Ms. L on the phone, through her tears. Upon Ms. L's request, Mr. Jordan arranged an appointment for her with an attorney, Mr. Frank Carter.

Ms. L expressed anxiety with respect to her subpoena requesting the production of any gifts from the Pres., specifically citing hat pins which the Pres. had in fact given her. Mr. Jordan allayed her concerns by telling her it was standard language. Mr. Jordan asked Ms. Lewinsky two questions: Did you have sex with the Pres. and/or did he ask you for sex? Ms. L responded to both questions with "no."

Possibly later in that meeting but more probably the next meeting, Ms. L tried to make it clear to Mr. Jordan that she, in fact, did have a physically intimate relationship with the Pres.

Ms. L made it clear she intended to deny the sexual relationship with the Pres.

On the day Mr. Jordan drove Ms. L to Mr. Carter's office, she showed Mr. Jordan the items she was producing in response to the subpoena. Ms. L believes she made it clear this was not everything she had that could respond to the subpoena, but she thought it was enough to satisfy. ~~and still~~ ~~[illegible]~~. Mr. Jordan made no comment about whether or not ~~was~~ what Ms. L brought was right or wrong. Mr. J drove Ms. L to Mr. Carter's office; introduced them; and left.

6. The Pres., through Ms. Currie, invited Ms. L to come see him to get her Christmas presents. They played with Buddy, he gave her the presents, they ~~spoke~~ talked casually and spoke for a few minutes about the case. Ms. L asked him how he thought the ~~Pa~~ attorneys for Paula Jones found out about her. He thought it was probably "that woman from the summer... with Kathleen Willey" (Linda Tripp) who lead them to Ms. L or possibly the uniformed agents. He shared Ms. L's concern about the hat pin. He asked Ms. L if she had told anyone that he had given it to her and she replied, "no."

-7-

Ms. L then asked if she should put away (outside her home) the gifts he had given her or, maybe, give them to someone else. ~~Betty~~ [Ms. Currie called Ms. L later that afternoon as said that the Pres. had told her ~~he~~ Ms. L wanted her to hold onto something for her. ~~He~~ Ms. L boxed up most of the gifts she had received and gave them to Ms. Currie. It is unknown if Ms. Currie knew the contents of the box.]

Ms. L told the Pres. she was planning to sign an affidavit. When Ms. L and the Pres. discussed when Ms. L was moving to NY, the Pres. thought it might be possible that they would not seek her deposition if she was in NY.

7. Ms. Lewinsky called Mr. Jordan several times concerning her employment in NY. When she called one day especially concerned about the case, Mr. Jordan suggested they meet for breakfast.

At breakfast, Ms. L expressed concern about Ms. Tripp saying she (Ms. L) had trusted her before, but was now suspicious of her.

Ms. L said Ms. Tripp may have seen notes when she was in Ms. L's home. Mr. Jordan asked if the notes were from the Pres. Ms. L said that they were notes to the Pres. Mr. Jordan suggested to Ms. L she check to make sure they are not there (something to that effect). Ms. L interpreted that to mean she should get rid of whatever is there.

~~On the~~

In the car on the way to his office, Ms. L asked Mr. Jordan if he thought the Pres. would always be married to Mrs. Clinton. Mr. Jordan replied that he thought they would always be married, as they should be. ~~as~~ Ms. L expressed disappointment and then Mr. Jordan said, "well, maybe you two will have an affair when he's out of office." Ms. L replied that she and the Pres. had alread had an affair minus having sex, -- but it included everything else. Ms. L believes they did not get into any more detail

-9-

After Ms. L received the draft of the affidavit, she called Mr. Jordan to ask that he look it over before she sign it. He instructed her to drop off a copy at his office. They spoke later by phone about the affidavit agreeing to make some changes.

That evening, Ms. L placed a phone call to Ms. Currie asking her to tell the Pres. that she wanted to speak with him before she signed something the next day. He returned Ms. L's call a few hours later. Ms. L told him Mr. Carter had asked her some sample questions that might be asked of her in the deposition and she didn't know how to answer them. Furthermore, she was concerned that if the answers involved naming people in the WH who didn't like her they would try to screw her over. Ms. L asked him how she should respond to the question, "How did you get your job at the Pentagon?" He replied "The people in Legislative Affairs helped you." This is, in fact, part of the truth -- but not the whole truth. The Pres. told Ms. L not to worry about the affidavit as he had seen 15 others.

9. Ms. L started to become wary of Ms. Tripp in the beginning of Dec. 1997, when Ms. Tripp told Ms. L she had received a subpoena in the Jones case and if asked about Ms. L or others, she would divulge all she knew.

10. Ms. L had a physically intimate relationship with the President. Neither the Pres. nor Mr. Jordan (or anyone on their behalf) asked or encouraged ~~me~~ Ms. L to lie. ~~I~~ Ms. L was comfortable signing the affidavit with regard to the "sexual relationship" because she could justify to herself that ~~they~~ she and the Pres. did not have sexual intercourse.

11. At some point in the relationship between Ms. L and the President, the President told Ms. L to deny a relationship, if ever asked about it. He also said something to the effect of if ~~two~~ the two people who are involved say it didn't happen -- it didn't happen. ~~[illegible]~~ Ms. L knows this was said some time prior to the subpoena in the Paula Jones case.

12. Item #2 above also occurred prior to the subpoena in the Paula Jones case.

Tab 5

Office of the Independent Counsel

1001 Pennsylvania Avenue, N.W.
Suite 490-North
Washington, DC 20004
(202) 514-8688
Fax (202) 514-8802

GOVERNMENT EXHIBIT ML-2

AGREEMENT

This is an agreement ("Agreement") between Monica S. Lewinsky and the United States, represented by the Office of the Independent Counsel ("OIC"). The terms of the Agreement are as follows:

1. Ms. Lewinsky agrees to cooperate fully with the OIC, including special agents of the Federal Bureau of Investigation ("FBI") and any other law enforcement agencies that the OIC may require. This cooperation will include the following:

A. Ms. Lewinsky will provide truthful, complete and accurate information to the OIC. She will provide, upon request, any documents, records, or other tangible evidence within her custody or control relating to the matters within the OIC's jurisdiction. She will assist the OIC in gaining access to such materials that are not within her custody and control, and she will assist in locating and gaining the cooperation of other individuals who possess relevant information. Ms. Lewinsky will not attempt to protect any person or entity through false information or omission, and she will not attempt falsely to implicate any person or entity.

B. Ms. Lewinsky will testify truthfully before grand juries in this district and elsewhere, at any trials in this district and elsewhere, and in any other executive, military, judicial or congressional proceedings. Pending a final resolution of this matter, neither Ms. Lewinsky nor her agents will make any statements about this matter to witnesses, subjects, or targets of the OIC's investigation, or their agents, or to representatives of the news media, without first obtaining the OIC's approval.

C. Ms. Lewinsky will be fully debriefed concerning her knowledge of and participation in any activities within the OIC's jurisdiction. This debriefing will be conducted by the OIC, including attorneys, law enforcement agents, and representatives of any other institutions as the OIC may require. Ms. Lewinsky will make herself available for any interviews upon reasonable request.

D. Ms. Lewinsky acknowledges that she has orally proffered information to the OIC on July 27, 1998, pursuant to a proffer agreement. Ms. Lewinsky further represents that the statements she made during that proffer session were truthful and accurate to the best of her knowledge. She agrees that during her cooperation. she will truthfully elaborate with respect to these and other subjects.

E. Ms. Lewinsky agrees that, upon the OIC's request. she will waive any evidentiary privileges she may have, except for the attorney-client privilege.

2. If Ms. Lewinsky fully complies with the terms and understandings set forth in this Agreement, the OIC: 1) will not prosecute her for any crimes committed prior to the date of this Agreement arising out of the investigations within the jurisdiction of the OIC: 2) will grant her derivative use immunity within the meaning and subject to the limitations of 18 United States Code, Section 6002, and will not use, in any criminal prosecution against Ms. Lewinsky, testimony or other information provided by her during the course of her debriefing, testimony, or other cooperation pursuant to this agreement, or any information derived directly or indirectly from such debriefing, testimony, information, or other cooperation; and 3) will not prosecute her mother, Marsha Lewis, or her father, Bernard Lewinsky, for any offenses which may have been committed by them prior to this Agreement arising out of the facts summarized above, provided that Ms. Lewis and Mr. Lewinsky cooperate with the OIC's investigation and provide complete and truthful information regarding those facts.

3. If the OIC determines that Ms. Lewinsky has intentionally given false, incomplete, or misleading information or testimony, or has otherwise violated any provision of this Agreement, the OIC may move the United States District Court for the District of Columbia which supervised the grand jury investigating this matter for a finding that Ms. Lewinsky has breached this Agreement, and, upon such a finding by the Court, Ms. Lewinsky shall be subject to prosecution for any federal criminal violation of which the OIC has knowledge, including but not limited to perjury, obstruction of justice, and making false statements to government agencies. In such a prosecution, the OIC may use information provided by Ms. Lewinsky during the course of her cooperation, and such information, including her statements, will be admissible against her in any grand jury, court, or other official proceedings.

4. Pending a final resolution of this matter, the OIC will not make any statements about this Agreement to representatives of the news media.

5. This is the entire agreement between the parties. There are no other agreements, promises or inducements.

If the foregoing terms are acceptable, please sign, and have your client sign, in the spaces indicated below.

Date: July 28, 1998

KENNETH W. STARR
Independent Counsel

I have read this entire Agreement and I have discussed it with my attorneys. I freely and voluntarily enter into this Agreement. I understand that if I violate any provisions of this Agreement, the Agreement will be null and void, and I will be subject to federal prosecution as outlined in the Agreement.

Date: July 28, 1998

Monica S. Lewinsky

Counsel for Ms. Lewinsky:

Jacob A. Stein

Plato Cacheris

Tab 6

GOVERNMENT EXHIBIT ML-3

DRAFT

AFFIDAVIT OF JANE DOE #

1. My name is Jane Doe # . I am 24 year old and I currently reside at [redacted].

2. On December 19, 1997, I was served with a subpoena from the plaintiff to give a deposition and to produce documents in the lawsuit filed by Paula Corbin Jones against President William Jefferson Clinton and Danny Ferguson.

3. I can not fathom any reason that the plaintiff would seek information from me for her case.

4. I have never met Ms. Jones, nor do I have any information regarding the events she alleges occurred at the Excelsior Hotel on May 8, 1991 or any other information concerning any of the allegations in her case.

5. I worked at the White House in the summer of 1995 as a White House intern. Beginning in December, 1995, I worked in the Office of Legislative Affairs as a staff assistant for correspondence. In April, 1996, I accepted a job as correspondence assistant to the Assistant Secretary for Public Affairs at the U.S. Department of Defense. I maintained that job until December 2[illegible], 1997. I am currently unemployed but seeking a new job.

…aving just …ed from …egon * …is & Clark * College in Portland OR.

6. In the course of my employment at the White House, I met President Clinton on several occasions. I do not recall ever being alone with the President, although it is possible that while working in the White House Office of Legislative Affairs I may have presented him with a letter for his signature while no one else was present. This would have lasted only a matter of minutes. ~~and would not have been a "private" meeting, that is not behind~~ closed doors. ?

7. I have the utmost respect for the President who has always behaved appropriately in my presence.

8. I have never had a sexual relationship with the President, he did not propose that we have a sexual relationship, he did not offer me employment or other benefits in exchange for a sexual relationship, he did not deny me employment or other benefits for rejecting a sexual relationship. I do not know of any other person who had a sexual relationship with the President, was offered employment or other benefits in exchange for a sexual

DRAFT

relationship, or was denied employment or other benefits for rejecting a sexual relationship. The occasions that I saw the President, with crowds of other people, after I left my employment at the White House in April, 1996 related to official receptions, formal functions or events related to the U.S. Department of Defense, where I was working at the time. There were other people present on all of these occasions.

9. Since I do not possess any information that could possibly be relevant to the allegations made by Paula Jones or lead to admissible evidence in this case, I asked my attorney to provide this affidavit to plaintiff's counsel. Requiring my deposition in this matter would cause unwarranted attorney's fees and costs, disruption to my life, especially since I am looking for employment, and constitute an invasion of my right to privacy.

I declare under the penalty of perjury that the foregoing is true and correct.

MONICA S. LEWINSKY

*

*

*

*

*

*

*

*

*

*

*

DRAFT

DISTRICT OF COLUMBIA, ss:

MONICA S. LEWINSKY, being first duly sworn on oath according to law, deposes and says that she has read the foregoing AFFIDAVIT OF JANE DOE # by her subscribed, that the matters stated herein are true to the best of her information, knowledge and belief.

____
MONICA S. LEWINSKY

SUBSCRIBED AND SWORN to before me this __________ day of __________________, 1998.

____
NOTARY PUBLIC, D.C.
My Commission expires:______________

Tab 7

GOVERNMENT EXHIBIT ML-4

AFFIDAVIT OF JANE DOE # 6

1. My name is Jane Doe #6. I am 24 years old and I currently reside at [redacted]

2. On December 19, 1997, I was served with a subpoena from the plaintiff to give a deposition and to produce documents in the lawsuit filed by Paula Corbin Jones against President William Jefferson Clinton and Danny Ferguson.

3. I can not fathom any reason that the plaintiff would seek information from me for her case.

4. I have never met Ms. Jones, nor do I have any information regarding the events she alleges occurred at the Excelsior Hotel on May 8, 1991 or any other information concerning any of the allegations in her case.

5. I worked at the White House in the summer of 1995 as a White House intern. Beginning in December, 1995, I worked in the Office of Legislative Affairs as a staff assistant for correspondence. In April, 1996, I accepted a job as assistant to the Assistant Secretary for Public Affairs at the U.S. Department of Defense. I maintained that job until December 26, 1997. I am currently unemployed but seeking a new job.

6. In the course of my employment at the White House I met President Clinton several times. I also saw the President at a number of social functions held at the White House. When I worked as an intern, he appeared at occasional functions attended by me and several other interns. The correspondence I drafted while I worked at the Office of Legislative Affairs was seen and edited by supervisors who either had the President's signature affixed by mechanism or, I believe, had the President sign the correspondence itself.

7. I have the utmost respect for the President who has always behaved appropriately in my presence.

8. I have never had a sexual relationship with the President, he did not propose that we have a sexual relationship, he did not offer me employment or other benefits in exchange for a sexual relationship, he did not deny me employment or other benefits for rejecting a sexual relationship. I do not know of any

other person who had a sexual relationship with the President, was offered employment or other benefits in exchange for a sexual relationship, or was denied employment or other benefits for rejecting a sexual relationship. The occasions that I saw the President after I left my employment at the White House in April, 1996, were official receptions, formal functions or events related to the U.S. Department of Defense, where I was working at the time. There were other people present on those occasions.

9. Since I do not possess any information that could possibly be relevant to the allegations made by Paula Jones or lead to admissible evidence in this case, I asked my attorney to provide this affidavit to plaintiff's counsel. Requiring my deposition in this matter would cause disruption to my life, especially since I am looking for employment, unwarranted attorney's fees and costs, and constitute an invasion of my right to privacy.

I declare under the penalty of perjury that the foregoing is true and correct.

Monica S. Lewinsky

MONICA S. LEWINSKY

* * * * * * * * * *

849-DC-00000635

DISTRICT OF COLUMBIA, ss:

MONICA S. LEWINSKY, being first duly sworn on oath according to law, deposes and says that she has read the foregoing AFFIDAVIT OF JANE DOE # 6 by her subscribed, that the matters stated herein are true to the best of her information, knowledge and belief.

Monica S Lewinsky
MONICA S. LEWINSKY

SUBSCRIBED AND SWORN to before me this 7th day of January, 1998.

Kathleen M. Grimes
NOTARY PUBLIC, D.C.
My Commission expires: My Commission Expires August 31, 1998

849-DC-00000636

Tab 8

GOVERNMENT EXHIBIT ML-5

points to make in affidavit

Your first few paragraphs should be about yourself -- what you do now, what you did at the White House and for how many years you were there as a career person and as a political appointee.

You and Kathleen were friends. *At around the time of her husband's death* (the President has claimed it was after her husband died. Do you really want to contradict him?), she came to you after she allegedly came out of the oval and looked (however she looked), you don't recall her exact words, but she claimed at the time (whatever she claimed) and was very happy.

You did not see her go in or see her come out.

Talk about when you became out of touch with her and maybe why.

The next you heard of her was when a Newsweek reporter (I wouldn't name him specifically) showed up in your office saying she was naming you as a someone who would corroborate that she was sexually harassed. You spoke with her that evening, etc. and she relayed to you a sequence of events that was very dissimilar from what you remembered happening. As a result of your conversation with her and subsequent reports that showed she had tried to enlist the help of someone else in her lie that the President sexually harassed her, you now do not believe that what she claimed happened really happened. You now find it completely plausible that she herself smeared her lipstick, untucked her blouse, etc.

You never saw her go into the oval office, or come out of the oval office.

You have never observed the President behaving inappropriately with anybody.

The first few paragraphs should be about me-- what I do now, what I did at the White House and for how many years I was there as a career person and as a political appointee.

Kathleen and I were friends. At around the time of her husband's death, she came to me after she allegedly came out of the oval and looked ______, I don't recall her exact words, but she claimed at the time _______ and was very happy.

I did not see her go in or see her come out.

Talk about when I became out of touch with her and maybe why.

The next time I heard of her was when a Newsweek reporter showed up in my office saying she was naming me as a someone who would corroborate that she was sexually harassed by the President. I spoke with her that evening, etc. and she relayed to me a sequence of events that was very dissimilar from what I remembered happening. As a result of my conversation with her and subsequent reports that showed she had tried to enlist the help of someone else in her lie that the President sexually harassed her, I now do not believe that what she claimed happened really happened. I now find it completely plausible that she herself smeared her lipstick, untucked her blouse, etc.

I never saw her go into the oval office, or come out of the oval office.

I have never observed the President behave inappropriately with anybody.

You are not sure you've been clear about whose side you're on. (Kirby has been saying you should look neutral; better for credibility but you aren't neutral. Neutral makes you look like you're on the other team since you are a political appointee)

It's important to you that they think you're a team player, after all, you are a political appointee. You believe that they think you're on the other side because you wouldn't meet with them.

You want to meet with Bennett. You are upset about the comment he made, but you'll take the high road and do what's in your best interest.

December 18th, you were in a better position to attend an all day or half-day deposition, but now you are into JCOC mode. Your livelihood is dependent on the success of this program. Therefore, you want to provide an affidavit laying out all of the facts in lieu of a deposition.

You want Bennett's people to see your affidavit before it's signed.

Your deposition should include enough information to satisfy their questioning.

By the way, remember how I said there was someone else that I knew about. Well, she turned out to be this huge liar. I found out she left the WH because she was stalking the P or something like that. Well, at least that gets me out of another scandal I know about.

Tab 9

Definition of Sexual Relations

For the purposes of this grand jury session, a person engages in "sexual relations" when the person knowingly engages in or causes --

contact with the genitalia, anus, groin, breast, inner thigh, or buttocks of any person with an intent to arouse or gratify the sexual desire of any person;

* * * *

"Contact" means intentional touching, either directly or through clothing.

[redacted]

Tab 10

CONTACTS BETWEEN THE PRESIDENT AND MONICA LEWINSKY

DATE	IN - PERSON CONTACTS	PHONE CALLS	GIFTS/ NOTES ML TO WJC	GIFTS/NOTES WJC TO ML
Approx. 8/9/95 Wednesday	Departure ceremony - nonverbal connection - eye contact - green suit			
Approx. 8/10/95 Thursday	Public function - Pres. 49th B-day party - flirtation - eye contact - green suit			
Approx. 8/13 or 8/14/95 Sun. - Mon.	Departure ceremony - intro. to Pres.			
Mid to late 9/95	Photo opportunity - WW basement - Ungvari - Pres. said he knew who ML was			
Approx. 10/95	Chance meeting - West Exec. Ave. - waved at Pres.			
11/15/95 Wednesday	Pres. made several visits to Panetta's office where ML was working			
'1/15/95 ednesday	Private encounter - approx. 8 p.m. - hallway by study - kissing			
11/15/95 Wednesday	Second private encounter - sometime b/t 8 and 10 p.m. - study and hallway by study - physical intimacy including oral sex			
11/17/95 Friday	Private encounter - approx. 8 p.m. - study area - pizza night - kissing			
11/17/95 Friday	Second private meeting of night - bathroom by study - phone call - pizza night - physical intimacy including oral sex			
11/20/95 Monday			Zegna tie - ML gave to Currie to give to Pres	
12/5/95 Tuesday	Brief private encounter - oval office and back study - no sexual contact			autographed photo wearing tie
12/31/95 Sunday	Private encounter - sometime b/t 12 and 1 p.m. - approx. 20 or 25 min. - hallway by study - physical intimacy including oral sex			"Davidoff" cigars

[redacted]

DATE	IN - PERSON CONTACTS	PHONE CALLS	GIFTS/ NOTES ML TO WJC	GIFTS/NOTES WJC TO ML
1/7/96 Sunday		conversation - first call to ML's home		
1/7/96 Sunday		conversation - ML at office		
1/7/96 Sunday	Private encounter - late afternoon - mtg. lasted approx. 45 min. - bathroom by study - physical intimacy including oral sex			
1/15 or (early a.m.) 1/16/96 Mon. or Tues.		conversation, including phone sex - approx. 12:30 a.m. - ML at home		
1/21/96 Sunday	Chance encounter then private encounter - sometime b/t 3 and 5 p.m. approx. 30 to 40 min. - hallway by study - physical intimacy including oral sex - kissing in N. Hernreich's office			
Approx. 1/28/96 unday		caller ID on ML's office phone indicated POTUS call		
1/30/96 Tuesday		conversation - during middle of workday at ML's office		
1/30/96 Tuesday	Public function - Griffin's going away party			
2/4/96 Sunday		conversations - ML at office - multiple calls		
2/4/96 Sunday	Private encounter- study and hallway - approx. 1 ½ hr. - physical intimacy including oral sex			Signed "State of Union" address (date approx.)
2/4/96 Sunday		conversation - ML at office		
2/7 or 2/8/96 Wed. or Thurs.		conversation - ML at home		

DATE	IN - PERSON CONTACTS	PHONE CALLS	GIFTS/ NOTES ML TO WJC	GIFTS/NOTES WJC TO ML
2/8 or 2/9/96 Thurs. or Fri.		conversation, including phone sex - ML at home		
2/19/96 Monday		conversation - ML at home		
2/19/96 Monday	Private encounter - approx. 25 min. sometime b/t 12 and 2 p.m. - oval office - no sexual contact			
Approx. 2/28 or 3/5/96		conversation - approx. 20 min. - after chance meeting in hallway - ML at home		
3/10/96 Sunday	Accidental meeting - outside restroom in WH - Ungvari present			
3/25/96 Monday	Accidental meeting - pass each other in hallway - ML looked away			
3/26/96 Tuesday		conversation - approx. 11 a.m. - ML at office		
/29/96 riday	Accidental meeting - after jog - ML hurt hand	conversation - ML at office - approx. 8 p.m. - invitation to movie		
3/31/96 Sunday		conversation - ML at office - approx. 1 p.m. - Pres. ill		
3/31/96 Sunday	Private encounter - approx. 45 min. - hallway by study - physically intimate contact		Hugo Boss tie - carried to mtg.	cigars
4/7/96 Easter Sunday		conversation - ML at home		
4/7/96 - Easter Sunday	Private encounter - sometime b/t 5 and 6 p.m.- approx. 30 min. - hallway by study and study - intervening phone call - physical intimacy including oral sex			
4/7/96 Easter Sunday		conversation - ML at home - why ML left		

DATE	IN - PERSON CONTACTS	PHONE CALLS	GIFTS/ NOTES ML TO WJC	GIFTS/NOTES WJC TO ML
4/12/96 Friday		conversation - ML at home - daytime		
4/12 or (early a.m.) 4/13/96 Fri. or Sat.		conversation - ML at home - after midnight		
4/22/96 Monday		conversation - job talk - ML at home		
Approx. 4/28/96 Sunday	Public function - AIPAC meeting			
4/29 or 4/30/96 Mon. or Tues.		message - after 6:30 a.m.		
5/2/96 Thursday		conversation, possibly including phone sex - ML at home		
5/6/96 Monday		possible phone call		
..pprox. 5/8/96 Wednesday	Public function - Saxophone Club event			
5/16/96 Thursday		conversation - ML at home		
5/21/96 Tuesday	Public function - [redacted] memorial service			
5/21/96 Tuesday		conversation, including phone sex - ML at home		
5/31/96 Friday		message		
6/5/96 Wednesday		conversation - ML at home - early evening		
Approx. 6/13/96 Thursday	Public function - arrival of Irish President			
6/14/96 Friday	Public function - radio address - family			

DATE	IN - PERSON CONTACTS	PHONE CALLS	GIFTS/ NOTES ML TO WJC	GIFTS/NOTES WJC TO ML
6/23/96 Sunday		conversation, possibly including phone sex - ML at home		
7/5 or (early a.m.) 7/6/96 Fri. or Sat.		conversation, including phone sex - ML at home		
7/19/96 Friday		conversation, including phone sex - 6:30 a.m. - ML at home		
7/28/96 Sunday		conversation - ML at home		
8/4/96 Sunday		conversation, including phone sex - ML at home		
Before 8/16/96			Zegna tie - also t-shirt from Bosnia - ML sent to Betty to give to the President	
8/18/96 Sunday	Public function - Pres. 50th B-day party - limited intimate contact			
8/24/96 Saturday		conversation, including phone sex - ML at home		
9/5/96 Thursday				thank you note - hand signed addendum - "tie is really beautiful"
9/5/96 Thursday		conversation, possibly including phone sex - Pres. in Fla. - ML at home		
9/10/96 Tuesday		message		
9/30/96 Monday		conversation, possibly including phone sex		
10/22/96 Tuesday		conversation, including phone sex - ML at home		
10/23 or (early a.m.) 10/24/96 Wed. or Thurs.		conversation - ML at home		

DATE	IN - PERSON CONTACTS	PHONE CALLS	GIFTS/ NOTES ML TO WJC	GIFTS/NOTES WJC TO ML
11/6/96 Wednesday	Public function - South Lawn Rally			
12/2/96 Monday		conversation - approx. 10 - 15 min. - ML at home		
12/2/96 Monday		conversation, including phone sex - later that evening - ML at home - approx. 10:30 p.m. - Pres. fell asleep		
12/17/96 Tuesday	Public function - Christmas party			
12/18/96 Wednesday		conversation - approx. 5 min.- 10:30 p.m. - ML at home		
After Christmas 1996			Sherlock Holmes game - glow in dark frog - ML dropped off gifts with Currie	
12/30/96 Monday		message		
..12/97 Sunday		conversation, including job talk and possibly phone sex - ML at home		
Sometime between 2/97 and 5/97			two books, Oy Vey and a golf book - card or letter	
2/8/97 Saturday		conversation - ML at home - mid-day - 11:30 or 12:00		
2/8/97 Saturday		conversation, including job talk and phone sex - 1:30 or 2:00 p.m. - ML at home		
2/14/97 Friday			Washington Post ad - Happy Valentine's Day	
2/28/97 Friday	Private encounter after radio address - early evening - approx. 20 to 25 min. - study and bathroom by study - physical intimacy including oral sex to completion		Golf ball and tees from Harrods - plastic pocket frog	hatpin - the book, Leaves of Grass

DATE	IN - PERSON CONTACTS	PHONE CALLS	GIFTS/ NOTES ML TO WJC	GIFTS/NOTES WJC TO ML
Between 3/3 and 3/9/97			Thank you note - Hugo Boss tie - ML sent package by Federal Express	
3/12/97 Wednesday		conversation - three minutes - ML at work		
After 3/14/97			care package after Pres. injured his leg - "Hi ya, handsome!" card, metal magnet with Pres. seal for his crutches, license plate with "BILL" for his wheelchair, knee pads with Pres. seal - ML sent package by Federal Express	
3/29/97 Saturday	Private encounter - approx. 1:30 or 2 p.m. - study - Pres. on crutches - physical intimacy including oral sex to completion and brief direct genital contact		penny medallion with the heart cut out - her personal copy of <u>Vox</u> - framed Valentine's Day ad [ML also replaced the cut Hugo Boss tie]	
'26/97 aturday		conversation - late afternoon - 20 min. - ML at home		
5/17/97 Saturday		conversations - multiple calls		
5/18/97 Sunday		conversations - multiple calls		
5/24/97 Saturday	Private encounter - "D-Day" - mid-day - hugging - dining room, study and hallway		Banana Republic long sleeve casual shirt - puzzle on golf mysteries	
6/29/97 Sunday			letter	
7/3/97 Thursday			letter - frustration re: jobs	
7/4/97 Friday Indep. Day	Private encounter - approx. 9:15 - mtg. ended b/t 10 and 11 a.m. - study and hallway - argument - kiss on neck			
7/8/97 Tuesday	Public function - Madrid - flirtation			

DATE	IN - PERSON CONTACTS	PHONE CALLS	GIFTS/ NOTES ML TO WJC	GIFTS/NOTES WJC TO ML
7/14/97 Monday	Private encounter - Hernreich's office - late evening - Pres. had conference call during middle of mtg. - ML did not participate in conference call - no sexual contact		wooden B with a frog in it from Budapest - card with a watermelon on it	
7/15/97 Tuesday		conversation - ML at home		
7/24/97 Thursday	Private encounter - oval office - approx. 10 min. - early evening - no sexual contact			b-day gifts: antique flower pin in wooden box and porcelain objet d' art handed to ML by Currie - ML picked up signed picture
8/1/97 Friday		conversation		
Week of 8/10/97 but before 8/16/97			a book, <u>The Notebook</u> and a card	
8/16/97 Saturday	Private encounter - physical intimacy including birthday kiss - study		b-day gifts: antique book on Peter the Great, apple square - ML also gave Pres. card game "Royalty" and a book, <u>Disease and Misrepresentation</u>	
Early 9/97				Black Dog items: t-shirts, baseball cap, mug and cotton dress - given to ML by Currie
9/30/97 Tuesday			memorandum - to "HANDSOME" re: "the New Deal"	
9/30/97 Tuesday		conversation, possibly including phone sex		
10/7/97 Tuesday			couriered package - letter - job talk	

DATE	IN - PERSON CONTACTS	PHONE CALLS	GIFTS/ NOTES ML TO WJC	GIFTS/NOTES WJC TO ML
10/9 or (early a.m.) 10/10/97 Thurs. or Fri.		conversation - long, from 2 or 2:30 a.m. until 3:30 or 4:00 a.m. - job talk - argument - ML at home		
10/11/97 Saturday	Private encounter - approx. 9:30 a.m. - study - job talk - no sexual contact			
10/16/97 Thursday			letter - job-related - "whole fat packet" of job stuff -via Federal Express	
10/21 or 10/22/97 Tues. or Wed.			Calvin Klein tie - a pair of sunglasses - a card, a postcard (erotic painting) - note re: education reform	
10/23/97 Thursday		conversation - ML at home - end b/c HRC		
10/28/97 Tuesday			unidentified couriered package	
0/30/97 Thursday		conversation - ML at home - interview prep		
Approx. week before 10/31/97			Halloween gifts: card - pumpkin lapel pin - wooden letter opener with a frog on the handle - plastic pumpkin filled with candy	
11/3/97 Monday			unidentified couriered package	
11/12/97 Wednesday		conversation, possibly including phone sex - discuss re: ML visit		
11/12/97 Wednesday			unidentified couriered package	
11/13/97 Thursday			Ginko biloba and zinc lozenges - ML gave to Currie to give to Pres. per Pres. request	

DATE	IN - PERSON CONTACTS	PHONE CALLS	GIFTS/ NOTES ML TO WJC	GIFTS/NOTES WJC TO ML
11/13/97 Thursday	Private encounter in study - approx. 5 min. - evening - Zedillo visit		antique paperweight depicting the WH	
11/20/97 Thursday			courier record - letter	
11/21/97 Friday			courier record - cassette tape	
Late 11/97 Early 12/97			letter - ML give to Currie to give to Pres. - Not delivered until 12/5	
12/5/97 Friday	Public function - Christmas party			
12/6/97 Saturday		conversation - approx. 30 min. - ML at home		
12/6/97 Saturday	Private encounter - after NW Gate incident - job talk		Christmas gift: antique standing cigar holder - - Other gifts: Starbucks Santa Monica mug - tie from London - book, Our Patriotic Presidents - Hugs and Kisses box	Annie Lenox compact disc
12/8/97 Monday			courier record - card - peach candies	
12/17 or (early a.m.) 12/18/97 Wed. or Thurs.		conversation - b/t 2:00 a.m. and 3:00 a.m. - ML at home - witness list		
12/28/97 Sunday	Private encounter - Christmas kiss - doorway by study and bathroom by study - b/t 9 and 10 a.m.		Hand painted Easter Egg - "gummy boobs" from Urban Outfitters	large Rockettes blanket from New York - pin of the New York skyline - a "marble-like" bear's head from Vancouver - a pair of joke sunglasses - a small box of cherry chocolates - Black Dog canvas bag - Black Dog stuffed animal

DATE	IN - PERSON CONTACTS	PHONE CALLS	GIFTS/ NOTES ML TO WJC	GIFTS/NOTES WJC TO ML
1/4/98 Sunday			Titanic note - book - Presidents of the United States - dropped off w/Currie	
1/5/98 Monday		conversation		

50-892 98 - 41

Tab 11

CLINTON CHINA - Microsoft Internet Explorer

Back Forward Stop Refresh Home Search Favorites History Channels Fullscreen Mail

CLINTON CHINA

Info Lightbox Download

President Clinton, first lady Hillary Rodham Clinton and daughter Chelsea wave from Air Force One at Andr
Base, Md., Wednesday, June 24, 1998, as they begin a ten-day journey to China. Clinton insists his visit to C
week will advance America's interests but he has faced a rough sendoff from some in Congress. This is the fi

GOVERNMENT EXHIBIT ML-8

Tab 12

MEDICARE COST - Microsoft Internet Explorer

Stop Refresh Home Search Favorites History Channels Fullscreen Mail

MEDICARE COST

Info Lightbox Download

President Clinton makes a point during a White House Rose Garden ceremony Monday, July 6, 1998 where
campaign to make people more aware of Medicare aid and simplify enrollment for payments. A consumer gr
shows low-income and disabled Americans are not taking advantage of new assistance in paying Medicare p

Start | AP Preserver - Microsoft In... | 7.5.98.doc - WordPad | MEDICARE COST - M...

GOVERNMENT EXHIBIT ML-9

Tab 13

CLINTON ATLANTA - Microsoft Internet Explorer

Stop Refresh Home Search Favorites History Channels Fullscreen Mail

President Clinton is flanked by Georgia senatorial candidate Michael Coles as he speaks during a fund raiser Thursday, July 9, 1998 in Atlanta. Coles, who challenged House Speaker Newt Gingrich in 1996, is running Republican Sen. Paul Coverdell. (AP Photo/Joe Marquette)

Location	ATLANTA, Georgia United States
Creation Date	07/09/1998 00:00:00

Start | AP Preserver - Microsoft In... | CLINTON ATLANTA -...

GOVERNMENT EXHIBIT ML-10

Tab 14

GRAND JURY
EXHIBIT
ML11
maxell
VIDEO CASSETTE
August 6, 1998
WJC Rose Garden
speech - Gun Control
TIE
VHS

Tab 15

OFFICE OF THE INDEPENDENT COUNSEL

```
-------------------------x
                         :
  DEPOSITION OF          :     Wednesday, August 26, 1998
                         :
  MONICA S. LEWINSKY     :     Washington, D. C.
                         :
-------------------------x
```

Deposition of

MONICA S. LEWINSKY

before the Independent Counsel, held in the Conference Room of the Office of the Independent Counsel, Suite 490-North, 1001 Pennsylvania Avenue, N. W., Washington, D. C. 20004, beginning at 12:35 p.m., when were present:

For the Independent Counsel:

KARIN IMMERGUT, ESQUIRE
Associate Independent Counsel

MARY ANNE WIRTH, ESQUIRE
Associate Independent Counsel

Court Reporter: Elizabeth A. Eastman

be

P R O C E E D I N G S

MS. IMMERGUT: We are on the record. Ms. Lewinsky, could you please state and spell your full name for the record?

MS. LEWINSKY: Monica Samille Lewinsky, M-O-N-I-C-A S-A-M-I-L-L-E, L-E-W-I-N-S-K-Y.

MS. IMMERGUT: For the record, I am Karin Immergut from the Office of Independent Counsel. Seated with me is Mary Anne Wirth, also from the Office of the Independent Counsel.

WHEREUPON,

MONICA S. LEWINSKY

having been called for examination by the Office of the Independent Counsel, and having been first duly sworn by the notary, was examined and testified as follows:

EXAMINATION BY COUNSEL FOR THE INDEPENDENT COUNSEL

BY MS. IMMERGUT:

Q Before we begin the deposition, I do want to advise you of certain rights that you have in connection with this deposition. You have already, I know, testified twice before the grand jury, and essentially the same rights do apply.

First, you have a right to have an attorney present outside of the room. Do you have an attorney present?

A Yes, I do.

Q Who is that attorney?

be

A Plato Cacheris.

Q You have the right to consult with Mr. Cacheris any time during the testimony, and I simply ask that you just request a break when you need to consult with him. Do you understand that you have that right?

A Yes, I do.

Q You also generally as a witness in a deposition, or before a grand jury, have a Fifth Amendment right not to incriminate yourself. Obviously, that now is modified pursuant to the agreement that you have with the Office of the Independent Counsel.

Do you understand that?

A Yes.

Q Have you seen the agreement that you have, giving you immunity for your cooperation in this case?

A Yes, I have.

Q That also is a grand jury exhibit in this case, is it not?

A Yes, it is.

Q Do you have any questions about what your rights are not to incriminate yourself as part of that agreement?

A No, I don't.

Q In addition, as always, you are required to tell the truth during this procedure and are subject to the penalties of perjury if you do not tell the complete truth.

be

Do you understand that?

A Yes, I do.

Q Any other questions that you have before we proceed?

A No.

Q First I just want to ask you a general question. I know you have testified in two other proceedings about various aspects of your relationship with the President. Can you characterize whether or not your relationship was one that started with sex and then evolved into a friendship, or the other way around?

A It started with a physical attraction, which led to a sexual relationship, and then the emotional and friendship aspects of that relationship developed after the beginning of our sexual relationship.

Q I would like to place before you what I will mark as Deposition exhibit No. 1.

(Deposition Exhibit No. 1 was marked for identification.)

BY MS. IMMERGUT:

Q This is also a chart that was previously marked as Grand Jury Exhibit ML #7. You can see the Xerox copy of that sticker on this exhibit, and I will place that before you, and ask if you recognize what that exhibit is?

A Yes, I do.

be

5

Q What do you recognize it to be?

A A chart that I helped develop with the Office of Independent Counsel to describe and enumerate the -- my relationship with the President, the contacts between the President and myself.

Q As you've testified before, did you provide the information that is on this chart?

A Yes, I did.

Q And is it accurate to the best of your recollection of the events?

A Yes, it is.

Q What I would like to do is go through the events that are written in bold, which deal with the private encounters you had with the President that involved, for the most part, some sort of physical intimacy that we have listed as physical intimacy, including oral sex. I did want to get into some more detail about each incident.

Basically, with respect to each incident, I would like you to describe the circumstances leading up to the actual visit, who initiated it, how it was set up, and then I would like to ask you some details about the sexual encounters themselves that occurred during each of those visits.

So, why don't we start with the very first one, which is the second encounter that you had on November 15th,

be

1995 that you've already testified some about. If you can, could you just tell us how that visit was set up, and then what occurred during the visit?

A The President came back to Mr. Panetta's office and I was the only person in the office at the time, and believe it was maybe around, I think, 10 p.m. or so, and asked me, or told me that if I wanted to meet him back in Mr. Stephanopoulos' office in about 5-10 minutes, that I could. And I told him I was interested to do that.

Q At that time, did you understand what it was he wanted to meet with you about?

A I had an idea. I, I, I had assumed that since we had been intimate in our previous encounter that evening, that we would again be intimate.

Q And just to clarify for the record, the intimacy that you had earlier that night was just kissing, is that correct?

A Yes.

Q So, did you, in fact, go meet with the President?

A Yes, I did.

Q And could you describe where you went to meet him?

A I met him back in Mr. Stephanopoulos' office and he invited me into the back study again, and we were in the hallway. And we were -- I don't remember exactly how it started. But I know that we were talking a bit and kissing.

be

I remember -- I know that he -- I believe I unbuttoned my jacket and he touched my, my breasts with my bra on, and then either -- I don't remember if I unhooked my bra or he lifted my bra up, but he -- this is embarrassing.

Q Then touched your breasts with his hands?

A Yes, he did.

Q Did he touch your breasts with his mouth?

A Yes, he did.

Q Did he touch your genital area at all that day?

A Yes. We moved -- I believe he took a phone call in his office, and so we moved from the hallway into the back office, and the lights were off. And at that point, he, he put his hand down my pants and stimulated me manually in the genital area.

Q And did he bring you to orgasm?

A Yes, he did.

Q Back to the touching of your breasts for a minute, was that then through clothing or actually directly onto your skin?

A He touched my breasts through clothing, being my bra, and then also without my bra on.

Q On that occasion, did you perform oral sex on the President?

A Yes.

Q Who actually initiated your performing oral sex?

be

A I did.
Q Was the President wearing pants?
A Yes, he was.
Q Who unzipped his pants?
A I believe I went to go unbutton his pants and I had trouble. So, he did that. So, but --
Q So, you started it?
A If I remember correctly.
Q And he helped complete opening his pants?
A Yes.
Q Did the President at that time do anything to stop you from doing that?
A No. I think he asked me if I was sure I wanted to do that.
Q Did you have any other discussion with him while the sexual encounter was occurring, about the sex or what you were doing?
A No. Actually, I don't think he asked me if I were sure I wanted to do that, because he was on the telephone. So -- I'm sorry.
Could you repeat what you just asked me?
Q Did the President have any discussion with you about sex, or you with him, while the sexual encounter was occurring?
A Not at this time. He was on the telephone for the

second half when we were in the office.

Q So, he was on the telephone while you were performing oral sex?

A He was on the telephone while he was --

Q Touching you?

A Touching me, and was also on the telephone when I was performing oral sex.

Q For any part of this sexual encounter, was he then off the telephone?

A Yes, I believe towards the end of my performing oral sex.

Q Did he say anything about the oral sex or anything about the sex at all when he got off the phone, that you can remember?

A He stopped me before he came, and I told him that I wanted to, to complete that. And he said that, that he needed to wait until he trusted me more. And then I think he [redacted]

Q [redacted]

A Yes.

Q Did he ejaculate in your presence that time at all?

A No.

Q How did you depart from the office, or how did you end that visit?

be

A I believe we spoke for awhile and I know at some point in that conversation I -- oh, that might have been Friday. Hmm. I really don't remember how it ended.

Q Can you estimate at all how long the sexual part of your encounter with him lasted?

A Maybe 20 minutes?

Q How long --

A I'm not a very good estimator of times.

Q How long did the entire encounter last, if you can recall?

A The second one of that evening?

Q Yes.

A Maybe half an hour or 40 minutes?

Q So, the entire encounter did not involve simply the sexual part of it?

A No, it didn't.

Q Did you have talking beforehand or was most of the talking afterwards?

A It was before and after.

Q If I can direct your attention again back to Deposition Exhibit No. 1, the chart, the next date where you do have two encounters with the President is November 17th, 1995. Although you've described it somewhat for the grand jury, if you could now just describe in detail -- again, I'll direct your attention to that second contact where there was

be

physical intimacy, including oral sex listed -- how that contact came about and what occurred during the contact?

A Yes. I had brought the President pizza, as he had asked. And when I brought it into him at the Oval Office, then he took me into the, to the back office and said that I could leave through that way. I believe we were talking for a little bit and he then, he got a phone call and he took the phone call in his bathroom.

Oh, it might have been before the phone call that -- I don't, I don't remember who, who unbuttoned my jacket or anything like that. But we were kissing and he was fondling my breasts with his hands and with his mouth.

Q Was that through clothing or not through clothing?

A It was both.

Q Okay. So, was there a point that your bra is removed?

A Yes.

Q But you don't remember who actually removed it?

A No. I think, I think he -- rather than necessarily removing my bra, sometimes he would just expose my breasts.

Q By lifting the bra over your breasts?

A Yes, or sometimes lifting my breasts out of the bra. Oh, God.

Q So, on that occasion though, you do recall that he touched you not just through your bra, but also directly on

be

the skin?

A Yes.

Q [redacted]

A [redacted]

Q [redacted]

A [redacted]

Q Was there any discussion about sex while you were in this encounter with him?

A I don't remember the specifics of it, but I know there was another discussion, I think, about him not letting me make him come, and then I had to get back to -- I'm sorry.

Could you repeat the question?

Q Was there any discussion during the November 17th encounter about sex during the encounter?

A I don't know exactly what you mean. I mean, do you mean either about --

Q Talking --

A I mean, saying things, or --

Q Well, either about what he wanted or what you wanted, or anything like that, in terms of sex?

be

A No. I mean, I think that there were always things being said, but not necessarily in a conversational form. Does that make sense?

Q Okay. And when you say there were always things being said, do you mean kind of chatting while you were having sex, or things that felt good? I don't mean that. I mean, --

A Okay.

Q -- trying either implicitly giving you direction about what he wanted, or why he wouldn't ejaculate, anything like that?

A I believe that why he wouldn't ejaculate was, was discussed again.

Q Okay. You mentioned that the President unzipped his pants. Did you understand that to be a signal of what he wanted in terms of sex?

A Yes.

Q Did he ever say anything while that was happening about what he wanted or no?

A No. He was on the telephone.

Q Okay. And that was on the second time also?

A Yes.

Q Was he on the telephone the whole time that you performed oral sex on him on the 17th of November?

A I don't remember.

be

Q Do you remember how you finished that meeting up with him that day, how you left?

A Yes. I know I needed to get back to my office, and he -- I think I told him that he should come down and have pizza with us, he should bring his pizza down, and that everyone was down there. And at some point I believe in that meeting he told me that, or he reiterated because he might have said it on the 15th as well, that I could come see him on the weekends when, when there weren't a lot of people around.

Q With respect again to the ejaculation, that he wouldn't actually ejaculate during oral sex, were you aware, or did he ejaculate anywhere in your presence on that occasion?

A No.

Q The next date listed on the chart is December 31st, 1995, a Sunday. Could you describe how that meeting was set up and what occurred when you got to the meeting?

A Yes. I had been having a conversation with Nel and had just told him that I smoked my first cigar the night before in honor of my brother's birthday. And Nel asked me if I wanted -- or offered that he could get me one of the President's cigars from his sort of stash of cigars. I said, that would be great.

And we went through the Roosevelt Room to the

entrance into the back study which -- the door that leads into the dining room. And just as we approached the door, the door swung open and the President was standing right there, and he had something he was going to take to Mr. Panetta. So, he asked, he asked Nel to take this -- I think it was a picture actually -- a picture down to Mr. Panetta, and he invited me in.

So, I went into the office and he asked me what I was doing there. And -- well, first he told me he had been looking for me. And then he told me -- he asked me what I was doing there, and I told him that Nel was going to get me a cigar. So, he said that he would give me a cigar. So, he did give me a cigar.

And then we were talking for a little bit and I had -- do you want me to just be --

Q If you could do a narrative, that's fine.

A Well, he had -- I had thought that he had forgotten my name before, because I had seen him in the hall a few times and he kept calling me "Kiddo". So, so, I sort of reiterated my -- I said my name again to him. You know, I said, you know, it's Monica Lewinsky, President Kiddo, you know. And he said, I know your name.

And he told me that he had tried to call me and that -- he said, but you're not in the book; I even spelled your last name right. So, it was, it was really funny. It

be

was cute.

And then we were, we were kissing and he lifted my sweater and exposed my breasts and was fondling them with his hands and with his mouth. And then I believe I was fondling him over his pants in his genital area, and I think again I tried to unbutton his pants and I couldn't. So, he did it.

Q And again, just to be clear, when you mentioned he raised your sweater and fondled your breasts, were your breasts outside of your bra at that time?

A Yes.

Q [redacted]

A [redacted]

Q [redacted]

A [redacted]

Q [redacted]

A [redacted]

Q Did you have any discussion with him again about why he wasn't ejaculating, anything like that?

A Yes, I think so. It might have been at that time -- the two excuses he always used were, one, that he didn't know me well enough or he didn't trust me yet. So that it sort of seemed to be some bizarre issue for him.

Q On that occasion, did he ever ejaculate in your.

be

presence, even though not -- at any time later?

A After he told me to stop and then, and then wished me Happy New Year and kissed me goodbye, he went into the [redacted]

Q Okay. Do you know how long that sexual encounter, or the sexual aspect of that encounter lasted, not including the other discussion with him?

A Maybe 10 minutes. Not, not very long. We would always spend quite a bit of time kissing. So.

Q And kissing and talking and just --

A Uh-huh.

Q -- being affectionate?

A Yes.

Q The next one is on page 2, and that would be January 7th of '96. Could you describe how that meeting was set up and what happened when you got there?

A Yes. The President called me -- this is the first time he called me at home -- that afternoon, and it was the first day of the blizzard. And I asked him what he was doing and he said he was going to be going into the office soon. I said, oh, do you want some company. And he said, oh, that would be great. So, he said he was going into the office in about 45 minutes, and I told him that I should probably be in my office around that time, and he said he would call me in

be

my office. I gave him my office number.

Then once I was in my office, he called me and we made an arrangement that I would pass -- he would have the door to his office open, and I would pass by the office with some papers and then he would, he would sort of stop me and invite me in. So, that was exactly what happened.

I passed by and that was actually when I saw Lew Fox who was on duty outside the Oval Office, and stopped and spoke with Lew for a few minutes, and then the President came out and said, oh, hey, Monica, you know, what are you doing here, come on in, sort of.

And so we spoke for about 10 minutes in the office. We sat on the sofas. Then we went into the back study and we were intimate in the bathroom.

Q And when you say you were intimate in the bathroom, what did you do?

A We kissed and he, he fondled my breasts and exposed -- or I think pulled them out of my bra and fondled them with his hands and with his mouth, and --

Q Did he touch your genitals on that occasion?

A No. He wanted to and was talking about performing oral sex on me, [redacted]

Q [redacted]

A [redacted]

Q Okay. On that date, did you gratify him in some

be

way other than performing oral sex?

A Yes.

Q [redacted]

A [redacted]

Q [redacted]

A [redacted]

Q [redacted]

A [redacted]

Q [redacted]

A [redacted]

Q [redacted]

A [redacted]

Q [redacted]

A [redacted]

Q Did you have any discussion about sex during the encounter that you had with him?

A No.

Q How long was your encounter with him?

A Hmm. Maybe about half an hour? I, I'm -- it's really hard for me to estimate the time.

Q And that would be the sexual aspect of it though that --

be

A Correct.

Q -- we're talking about. Did he ejaculate at any point in your presence after you performed oral sex on him?

A That day?

Q Yes.

A No.

MS. IMMERGUT: Did you have a question?

BY MS. WIRTH:

Q I have a question, actually going back to November 15th, if you don't mind.

A Okay.

Q When you were talking about the President having contact with your genitals, you said, I think, that he put his hands in your pants. When he touched your genitals, was that through your underwear or directly?

A I didn't have my underwear on at that point.

Q Okay. So, it was directly then?

A Yes.

Q Okay.

BY MS. IMMERGUT:

Q The next encounter listed is January 21st of '96, also on page 2 of the exhibit. Could you describe how that encounter occurred and what happened during the encounter?

A Yes. I was -- actually, I'm looking at this right now and I think it might have been a Saturday -- no, it was a

be

Sunday. I'm sorry. Never mind. I think it might have been a Saturday, but it, it says here Sunday. I just noticed that.

I was -- I had been in my office doing work, and I was leaving, leaving for the day. And as I was walking through the Residence hall to go through the West Wing to the Old Executive Office Building, I heard his voice behind me. And either he called my name or I just heard his voice and turned around, and he had just come off of the elevator and, I guess, was going back to his office.

So, we were, we were -- we stopped, and we spoke as we continued to walk through the outdoor corridor by the Rose Garden. And when we got to the point where he turns left to then go into the Oval Office, he told me that I could go out this way with him, that I could leave through the, that I could leave through the Oval Office. So, we walked down the pathway together and then went into the Oval Office from there.

Q And could you describe your encounter once you got into the Oval Office?

A Yes. We had, we had already had phone sex for the first time the week prior, and I was feeling a little bit insecure about whether he had liked it or didn't like it, and I just -- I felt in general that I didn't know -- from having spoken to him on the phone, you know, prior to having phone

be

sex and from having had these encounters with him, I didn't know if this was sort of developing into some kind of a longer term relationship than what I thought it initially might have been, that maybe he had some regular girlfriend who was furloughed or something during the furlough.

And at that point, I, you know, I said to him, you know, I asked him why he doesn't ask me any questions about myself, and doesn't he, you know, is this just about sex, you know, because if it is, then I just want to know that; or do you have some interest in trying to get to know me as a person. And so he kind of laughed at the manner in which I was asking him and talking to him.

And we, we went into the back study and he was, he was waiting for a friend of his to come to the office, and he was talking about that he has a lot of -- that he doesn't get a lot of time to himself and he really cherishes the private times that he has with his friends, and he cherishes the time that he had with me, which seemed a little bit odd to me at that time.

But he, he was upset that day about the first soldier in Bosnia had been -- I believe it was that day -- that it was the first soldier in Bosnia had been killed just recently, and he was very upset and moved. And so I was trying to comfort him.

Q When you say you thought it was odd that he said he

be

cherished the time with you, why was that, why did you think it was odd at that point?

A Because I didn't feel, I didn't feel like he really knew me. We had spent time talking, but it didn't seem -- and, you know, he had asked some questions and I offered a lot of information about myself. But he didn't seem to ask probing questions, when you're trying to get to know someone. So, it seemed a little bit odd to me that he would sort of cherish this time, when he, you know, when I felt like he didn't really even know me yet.

Q And at that point, sex was sort of the more dominant part of the relationship?

A Yes.

Q Rather than as it became --

A There was always a lot of joking that went on between us. And so we, you know, I mean, it was fun. When we were together, it was fun. We would laugh and it would -- we were very compatible sexually. And I've always felt that he was sort of my sexual soulmate, and that I just felt very connected to him when it came to those kinds of things.

Q So, on the January 21st date --

A Right.

Q -- how did it turn into your conversation and then go into actually having a sexual encounter?

A I was in the middle of saying something and he just

be

started kissing me. And, so, it was funny. It was, it was very funny.

Q And what room were you physically in at that time?

A We were in the hallway. And we were kissing and -- oh, I had -- because I was leaving, I was having a bad hair day, and this was actually the first time that I had the infamous beret on. And so I just said something to him about feeling stupid. Here I was standing here in this dumb hat, and he said that it wasn't a dumb hat, that I looked cute and he liked it.

And so then he was kissing me, or we were kissing each other, I guess, and I think again he, he fondled my breasts with his hands and his mouth.

Q Through clothing or not through clothing?

A I think it was always through clothing, and then eventually it, it would be direct contact. So, it wouldn't just be this immediate jump to being, you know, to contact. It was -- there was sort of foreplay to the foreplay, if that makes sense.

Q Do you remember whether he removed any of your clothing on that occasion?

A I think he -- I remember him lifting my top. So -- and he, he sort of exposing my breasts.

Q Did he stimulate your genitals on that occasion?

A No.

be

Q Did you perform oral sex on him or any kind of sex on him?

A Yes, I did.

Q Could you describe how that came about?

A Yes. He unzipped his pants and sort of exposed himself and that -- and then I performed oral sex.

Q Let me ask, on all of these occasions when you've described just the pants unzipping and exposing, is it fair to say that he still kept his pants on?

A Yes.

Q It was just the zipper that --

A Yes.

Q -- was undone?

A Right. And actually at one point during this encounter, I think someone came into the, to the Oval Office and he, you know, zipped up real quickly and went out and came back in, and I -- this is probably too much information. I just -- sorry.

Q And what happened?

A I just remember laughing because he had walked out there and he was visibly aroused, and I just thought it was funny. I mean, it wouldn't, it wouldn't necessarily be visible to anyone who just walked in because they wouldn't be looking at that, but it was just funny to me. So.

And then his -- then someone -- I think at that

be

point someone came in to let him know that his friend had arrived. And so he asked me which way I wanted to leave, and I said I was going to go, I was going to leave through Betty's office. And we went into -- we went from the back study through the Oval into Betty's office area, and he took me into Nancy Hernreich's office and kissed me goodbye.

And then I went to go leave from, from Betty's office, from the door into the hallway, to the West Wing hallway, but it was locked. So, I went back in to tell him. He was still in Nancy's office. I went back into Nancy's office to tell him the door was locked, and he was manually stimulating himself.

Q Did he cause himself to ejaculate at that point, or did you see that?

A No.

Q But that was in Nancy Hernreich's office?

A Yes.

Q And what did you do when you saw that?

A I smiled.

Q Okay.

A And I think we kissed again.

Q On that occasion, you mentioned that he did not touch your genitals at all. Was there any discussion about that?

A No.

be

Q Then did you leave from Nancy Hernreich's office eventually?

A I think I left through the -- I left through the door in Betty's office that goes out into the Rose Garden.

Q On this particular entry on January 21st, it lists that the entire encounter was approximately 30 to 40 minutes. Do you recall what portion of that would have been the sexual encounter part of it, versus just talking?

A Maybe 15 minutes?

Q You just can't really estimate?

A Exactly.

Q Let's go now to February 4th of 1996, the next bold date where there was a private encounter. Could you describe how that encounter came about and what happened?

A Yes. I was in my office on Sunday and the President called me in the office and -- from the Residence, and told me that he was going to be going into the office later. And I think I asked him if I could come see him. And he said that would be fine, and then that he -- oh, I think he was, he said he was going to go into the office in an hour and a half or so.

So, then he called me -- it was actually maybe two or three hours later, because I remember I thought he forgot, maybe he had forgotten to call me and that -- so. And when he called from the Residence to say he was on his way, I told

be

him that -- I asked him if we could sort of bump into the hallway, bump into each other in the hallway on purpose this time, because when it happened accidentally, that seemed to work really well and I felt more comfortable doing that. So, that's what we did. We both said, okay, I'm going to leave now.

And indeed we bumped into each other in the hall and went through the Rose Garden into the Oval Office. And I think we went right into the back office. The -- when we got there.

Q When you say the back office, you mean the study?

A Yes. And -- let's see.

You know, I need to take a break.

Q Okay. Let's take a break.

(Whereupon, the deposition was recessed from 1:10 p.m. until 1:15 p.m.)

BY MS. IMMERGUT:

Q Ms. Lewinsky, you are still under oath.

A Yes.

Q We are still on February 4th, 1996. You've described going into the office and starting to kiss the President. What happened then?

A We were in the back office and we were kissing, and I was -- I had a dress on that buttoned all the way, all the way up and down.

be

Q To the neck?

A Correct. It was long and down to the, to my ankles, or whatever. And he unbuttoned my dress and he unhooked my bra, and sort of took the dress off of my shoulders and took the bra off of my, off of my -- I'm not explaining this right. So that he moved the bra so that my bra was kind of hanging on one shoulder and so was off. And he just was, he was looking at me and touching me and telling me how beautiful I was.

Q And did he touch your breasts with his hands?

A Yes.

Q Did he also touch them with his mouth?

A Yes.

Q And at that point, that is directly on your skin, is that right?

A Yes.

Q Did he touch your genitals?

A Yes, he did.

Q Did he bring you to orgasm on that date?

A Yes, he did.

Q [redacted]

A [redacted]

Q [redacted]

be

[redacted]

A [redacted]

Q [redacted]

A [redacted]

Q [redacted]

A [redacted]

Q And again, just with respect to bringing you to an orgasm, did he touch you directly on your skin on your genitals, or was it through underwear?

A First it was through underwear and then it was directly touching my genitals.

Q Did he take your underwear off, or did you take your underwear off?

A Hmm.

Q Or did they stay on?

A I think that -- I believe that he touched me first with my underwear on, and then placed his hand under my underwear. And I think at some point I, I removed them.

Q Okay. Did you also perform oral sex on him at that

be

time?

A Yes, I did.

Q How did it come about? Was that something that you decided to do, or did the President either, through his actions or words, indicate to you that he wanted that?

A I don't really remember. I mean, it was a mutual -- I think in all of these instances, it wasn't, you know -- I know sometimes it's sort of hard to answer these questions as more directed. But it was -- I mean, it was the course of being intimate. I mean, it was the course of having this kind of a relationship, that you -- sometimes he initiated it, sometimes I initiated it. It wasn't, you know, it wasn't -- it didn't necessarily go through my mind, okay, now it's time to perform oral sex.

I mean, it was, it was the passion of the moment. That was, I mean, just sort of in the course of things that happened, you know. I always felt that we sort of just, we both really went to a, to a whole other place together sexually.

Q Is it fair to say you were both trying to please each other by doing different things?

A Yes. Yes.

Q Is it also fair to say that you were not the sole aggressor in this sexual --

A That's very fair to say.

be

Q -- encounter?

A I was not.

Q Again, I'm just asking you every time in case you remember, do you remember how long the sexual aspect of that encounter lasted?

A I really, I really don't.

Q Okay. I just note, to direct your attention that the time that you provided us previously is approximately one and a half hours for the whole visit.

A Right. We spent a long time in the Oval Office talking after, maybe 45 minutes to an hour just talking.

Q And that --

A I think he was maybe heeding my, my advice from, from the 21st, about trying to get to know me, and so he did.

Q And is it fair to say that's sort of when the friendship really starts to develop, around that time period?

A It does. That certainly helped. I think he, he was just very sweet, and he -- when I got up to leave, he kissed my arm and told me he'd call me, and then I said, yeah, well, what's my phone number. And so he recited both my home number and my office number off the top of his head. So, I told him, you know, that he got an A.

And he called me in my office later that afternoon to tell me how much he enjoyed talking to me. So -- and then again called Wednesday night to tell me again how much he had

be

enjoyed talking to me.

So, it -- I think that certainly was a turning point in the relationship, where it kind of went from a -- obviously there's, there's some personal and intimate aspects of a sexual relationship that develop just in talking or laughing or getting to the point where you, where you kiss someone on every encounter. But for me, I think that spending the time talking to him was certainly when I, when I got to know him as a person and started to realize that he wasn't necessarily the person I thought he was at that point.

Q Let's move on to the next date, which is March 31st, 1996, the next encounter where there is physically intimate contact. Why don't you tell us how that date was set up and what happened?

A I had spoken -- well, just to back up real quickly. The President had ended things on the, I think it was the 19th of February. But then he had called me later -- I think it was late February or early March at some point -- indicating to me he wanted to sort of see me again, possibly for some intimate moments.

And it wasn't until the 31st of March that we really were together again physically. But he had called, I think two times, two times prior during that work week, leading up to the 31st. And it was on the Friday night which is, looking at the chart, which was the 29th, that I, I asked

be

him if I could see him on Sunday. And he said, he'd, you know, he'd see what he could do.

And then on Sunday, he called me in my office and -- let's see. I believe -- oh, I believe that I brought him papers that day. That I think I asked him to tell the guard outside that he was expecting some papers, expecting someone from Leg Affairs. And then when I got to the door, I told them that I was supposed to bring papers to the President.

Q And that was part of a ruse to --

A Yes.

Q -- get in to see him?

A Exactly.

Q Just to back up for a second, you mentioned that you had had some phone calls with him between February 19th, '96 when he tried to cut off the relationship --

A Yes.

Q -- or the sexual part of the relationship --

A Correct.

Q -- and the 31st, in which he had suggested that he wanted to perhaps renew the intimacy. What led you to believe that?

A I saw him on my way out one evening. It was late. And he was on his way home from, I think it was the Israeli Embassy and Evelyn Lieberman was with him. So, I certainly made a point of not having any eye contact or anything with

be

him. And he called me later that evening and said he had, he had -- after he left and went upstairs, he went back to his office and had called me in my office, hoping that I could come have a visit with him, but I had already gone home.

And so then I offered, I said, well, I could come back. And he said, no, I'm upstairs already. So.

Q Back now to March 31st --

A Yes.

Q -- of '96. So, what happens then? How actually is that then finally set up?

A He had called me in my office and then I brought papers there, or fake papers.

Q Do you then go into the Oval Office?

A Yes, I do.

Q And what happens?

A We went into the back study and we were in the, the hallway area. And it had sort of become actually a ritual sort of at this point, that we always kind of started out our meetings, that he was leaning against the closed door of the bathroom and I would rub his back, because he has a bad back. So, I used to always rub his back, and sometimes he'd rub my back. But I usually concentrated on his lower back because it was always bothering him.

And, you know, and then I'd usually move around and sort of just lovingly touch his chest and --

be

Q Was there any removal of clothing?

A Yes, there was. We kissed and, and he had not been feeling well, I guess, the past couple of days. So, really, most of -- he focused on me pretty exclusively, I guess, in a sexual manner on me that day, and kissed me, and kissed my breasts, and he, he fondled my genitals with his hands.

Q Through clothing or not through clothing?

A Not through clothing.

Q Did you have your underwear removed? Or how did your clothes get off?

A (No response.)

Q Or were they simply pulled out of the way?

A I think I -- I think that they were just sort of -- oh.

Q Pulled out of the way?

A Yeah.

Q Okay. So, he touched you. And with your breasts, was that through clothing, through your brassiere, or did he move your breasts out of the way of the brassiere?

A It was, it was both. I mean, it was always both. He -- there was never a time when he just touched my breasts through --

Q The bra?

A -- the bra, right.

Q [redacted]

be

[redacted]

A Yes.

Q Whose idea was that?

A On -- when I met with him on January 7th, after we had been intimate and we were talking in the Oval Office, he was chewing on a cigar. And then he had the cigar in his hand and he was kind of looking at the cigar in a, sort of a naughty way. And so I, I looked at the cigar and I looked at him and I said, we can do that, too, some time.

And I don't, I don't really remember how it got started, but.

Q Was it part of the sexual encounter that he did that?

A Yes, it was.

Q Did you understand it to be arousing?

A It was.

Q Okay. What happened to the cigar afterwards?

A [redacted]

Q How did you leave that encounter? So, you didn't perform oral sex on him at all that time?

A No.

Q How --

A Actually, looking also -- I should mention that, looking at the chart, that I didn't bring papers that day. I brought this tie to him in a folder. So, sometimes I brought

be

papers and this day it was I had a tie, and there probably were some papers in the folder as well.

Q And that's the Hugo Boss tie that's listed under the gift category for that date?

A Correct.

Q The next encounter is April 7th, 1996. Could you describe how that encounter was set up?

A The President had called me at home sort of in the early evening, and this was -- it was Easter Sunday and it was the first, it was the Sunday after I had found out I was to be transferred to the Pentagon. And he called -- it also had been the week that Ron Brown had passed away.

So, I asked him how he was doing and we talked about that for a little bit. And then I told him that Monday was my last day, and that I had been transferred. And I was crying and he wanted to know what happened, and I asked him if I could come see him. And he said, that's fine, but just tell me what happened first. So, I explained to him what had happened, and then he told me to come on over. So, I did.

And this is when I had this little encounter trying to get into the office with John Muskett, just that he said -- I brought papers with me from home in a folder. And so John had said something about wanting to check with Evelyn if it was okay for me to go in. And I don't remember exactly what ended up happening, but I managed to get him to not ask

be

Evelyn and I got in.

And the President and I were in the back office. He was actually on the phone when I came in. And then when he got off the phone, we went into the back office and we talked again about what had happened, in terms of my transfer.

And that was when he, he looked me in the eye and he promised me -- well, first he said that he couldn't believe that they were taking me away from him because he trusted me so much, and he was convinced that it had something to do with him, why I was being transferred. And then he looked me in the eye and he said, I promise you, if I win in November, I'll have you back like that [snapping fingers].

Q Did he say anything like, if you do a good job at the Pentagon he'll bring you back?

A No.

Q So, what else happened at that meeting?

A I, I don't remember how it exactly came about, but I know that, that, I remember kissing him and we were physically intimate.

Q In terms of the physical intimacy that day, did the President touch your genitals on that date?

A I don't think so.

Q What about your breasts?

be

A Yes.

Q With his mouth or with his hands, or both?

A With both.

Q And again, I'm assuming, unless you correct me now, that it's both through clothing and directly on the skin?

A Yes.

Q With respect to oral sex, do you just remember how that occurred, whether his pants came off, whether somebody unzipped them?

A I think he unzipped them and -- because it was sort of this running joke that I could never unbutton his pants, that I just had trouble with it. So, I was -- you know, there were times that I tried and we'd laugh and then he'd, he'd do it.

But we were -- I, I performed oral sex in the, in the back office.

Q And at that time, did he ejaculate?

A No, he did not.

Q Was there any discussion with him about the ejaculation at that time that you can remember?

A No.

Q On that date, I think you've already testified that there was a phone call during your sexual encounter with him, is that right?

A Yes, there was.

be

Q Did you perform oral sex while he was on the telephone?

A Yes. It was, it was -- I think I'll just say, because for -- there are a lot of people that could interpret that as being sort of a, that being done in a servicing sort of manner, and it was more done in kind of an exciting sort of -- I don't want to say erotic, but in a way that there was kind of this titillating like a secret, in a sense, in the same way sometimes that an affair is, that, you know, when you are doing this and obviously there is kind of the irony that the person on the other line has no idea what's going on.

So, I just wanted to clarify that.

Q Okay. Although on that occasion, I believe you previously mentioned that that was the first time that you felt a little funny about it?

A I, I did. I did. I, I, I, I was, I was pretty emotionally devastated at that point, and the prospect of going to the Pentagon was very upsetting to me. And there were moments when I felt a little uncomfortable, and moments when I didn't.

Q Although you mentioned that there were other times that he was on the phone, that you didn't think sort of anything bad about it --

A Right.

be

Q -- and on this occasion, you felt more like --
A I just --
Q -- you were servicing --
A Exactly.
Q -- on some level. And did you tell Linda Tripp about that, do you remember?
A Probably.
Q How did that encounter end, if you remember? And actually you've already testified a little bit about this. So, just if you could quickly summarize how you finished the encounter and what happened?
A We were in the back office and I heard Mr. Ickes call, say, Mr. President, from the Oval Office. And we both were startled and looked at each other, and he jetted into the Oval and I --
Q Were you performing oral sex at the time?
A I think so, but I'm not a hundred percent sure. And so then I, I left.
Q On that occasion also, when the President went to get the phone call, had you started performing oral sex on him before he went to take the phone call?
A Yes, I believe that we were -- I think that that was it. I know that we were, we were intimate in the hallway, and then it was a phone call that prompted us to go into the office. And that when we were in the office, that,

be

that he, he removed, he sort of removed his pants.

Q How did you know that you were supposed to kind of accompany him to take the phone call? Did he --

A I don't remember.

Q -- invite you to come in, in any way, or gesture for you to come along?

A I don't really remember.

Q So, you think you actually didn't begin the oral sex until he was on the phone already?

A It's --

Q Or is it not that clear?

A It's not that clear.

Q But you remember him unzipping his pants at some point?

A At some point, yes.

Q Before the oral sex?

A Yes.

Q Okay.

A I hope so.

Q At that point, and I didn't really ask you this for the other encounters, but in terms of putting your stuff back on or collecting yourself, is there any sort of general way that that happened? Did the President help you, or how did you get dressed again?

A Well, neither of us ever really took -- completely

be

took off any piece of our clothing, I think specifically because of the possibility of encounters, like what happened that day. But there had, earlier in that day on the 7th, when I -- not earlier in the day, but earlier in the encounter with the President -- when he had been kissing my breasts, someone had come in, I think to tell him he had the phone call, or something like that.

Or someone had come in at some point and he stepped out of the office, and I had put my bra and my sweater back on. And he came in and sort of made a remark about me having done that. And --

Q Do you remember the remark?

A I think he smirked and he sort of said, you know, damn, you put your top back on, or something like that. Or, why did you do that, something like that. But he was smirking and joking with me.

But then when he went into the Oval, when Mr. Ickes came in, I put myself together and hurried out the back way through the dining room.

Q The next encounter. There's luckily a big gap there. The next one is February 28th. How was this encounter set up, and then what happened?

A Betty called me at work to tell me, or to invite me to the radio address for that evening. And so I went.

Q Did she say anything about that you would see the

be

President on that date, or --

A Yes. I mean, she, she had indicated to me the President wanted me to come to this radio address. So that -- and I knew that he had -- we had spoken earlier that month and the month before, and the month before that, and I knew he had a Christmas gift for me which he had yet to give me. So, it sort of seemed, it was understandable.

I went to the radio address. And then -- it was a very small group, maybe 10 people, six, 10 people. It was quite small. And after -- or when I went to go take my picture with him, he told me to go see Betty or go wait with Betty because he had something to give me. So, I went into Betty's office and was waiting there with her. There were some other people there, staff members. And I think I've gone through the whole --

Q And you've actually testified in some detail about this before.

A Right.

Q So, actually, why don't we just go to the sexual encounter --

A Okay.

Q -- and how the actual sexual part started?

A Once we were alone in the back office, he started to say something to me and I was pestering him to kiss me, because I hadn't -- we hadn't been alone in almost a year and

-- well, I guess not a year, but it had been a long time since we had been alone. And so he, you know, he jokingly told me to, you know, just wait a sec, he wanted to give me my presents.

So, he gave me my hatpin and he sort of hurriedly put the Leaves Of Grass in my purse and he said, here, just take this with me. And then I said, what is it. I took the book out and so we, we were looking at it, and I was just, I thought it was pretty incredible. It was just a beautiful, beautiful book, and it meant a lot to me.

And then we went back over by the bathroom in the hallway, and we kissed. We were kissing and he unbuttoned my dress and fondled my breasts with my bra on, and then took them out of my bra and was kissing them and touching them with his hands and with his mouth.

[redacted]

And I continued to perform oral sex and then he pushed me away, kind of as he always did before he came, and then I stood up and I said, you know, I really, I care about you so much; I really, I don't understand why you won't let me, you know, make you come; it's important to me; I mean, it just doesn't feel complete, it doesn't seem right.

And so he -- we hugged. And, you know, he said he didn't want to get addicted to me, and he didn't want me to get addicted to him. And we were just sort of looking at each other and then, you know, he sort of, he looked at me, he said, okay. And so then I finished.

Q [redacted]

A [redacted]

Q [redacted]

A [redacted]

Q Did he touch your genitals at all during that occasion, do you remember?

A I think through my tights, but not direct genital.

Q How did the meeting then end, or the encounter?

A We, well, we kissed after --

Q The ejaculation?

A Yes. And then I think Betty knocked on the door. So, I think -- no, no, no, no, no, that's not right, because I fixed my lipstick. So, I think we sort of -- I think he said, oh, you've got to put yourself back together again. And so then I went and I got my lipstick and I put my lipstick back on, and then Betty knocked on the door.

Q The dress that you were wearing on this occasion, is that the blue dress from the Gap?

be

A Unfortunately, yes.

Q And I think we've already gone into detail about the dress on that. The next encounter is March 29th, 1997. Would you tell us how that encounter was set up?

A It was, it was set up through my conversations with Betty.

Q Did you contact Betty?

A Yes. I contacted Betty and Betty -- my understanding was Betty spoke with the President, and then Betty got in touch with me and told me to come that afternoon. I did. I was waiting for the President in the back study and then he hobbled in because he was on crutches. And we were, we were in the back office. Actually, it was sort of an overcast day. It had been raining earlier. So, it was just sort of dark and overcast.

And we were, he was -- I think he had put his crutches down and he was kind of leaning on me. So, I was holding him, you know, I mean, sort of romantically but at the same time literally holding him. And --

Q This is in the back study?

A Uh-huh, yes. And I was -- this was another one of those occasions when I was babbling on about something, and he just kissed me, kind of to shut me up, I think. And so we were kissing and then we sort of -- we turned around and he was leaning against -- he has a little, it's like a little table that I think has this stereo. I don't know if the stereo was always there. I know it was there later. But he was leaning against this little table a little bit just, I think, kind of for support.

And he unbuttoned my blouse and just sort of touched me over, over my bra. And I don't think he took, I don't think he exposed my breasts that day. And we were, we were just kissing a lot.

And then he -- oh, he went to go put his hand down my pants, and then I unzipped them because it was easier. And I didn't have any panties on. And so he manually stimulated me.

Q Did he bring you to orgasm?

A Yes, four times.

Q [redacted]

A [redacted]

Q [redacted]

A [redacted]

Q [redacted]

A [redacted]

Q [redacted]

A [redacted]

Q How did you end the contact with him on that

be

occasion?

A End the sexual contact? Or --

Q The sexual contact?

A He -- oh, well, this was also the day that before, before I performed oral sex on him, I wanted him to touch my genitals with his genitals. And so we sort of had tried to do that, but because he's really tall and he couldn't bend because of his knee, it didn't really work.

Q And I think you've previously testified your genitals grazed each other --

A Exactly.

Q -- on that occasion?

A I mean, just barely.

Q And when they grazed each other, neither of you had clothes covering your genitals, is that right?

A Correct.

Q How did you end the encounter completely that time, in terms of ending the meeting?

A Oh, we moved into the dining room and we were talking for a long time. I had brought some presents for him. So, we talked for awhile. And then Betty came back and the three of us were talking.

Q Let's move on to the next one, which is August 16th, 1997.

A I -- this was sort of his, his birthday, his

birthday encounter. And so after -- I had set up in his back office, I had brought an apple square and put a candle and had put his birthday presents out. And after he came back in and I sang happy birthday and he got his presents, I asked him if we could, if we could share a birthday kiss in honor of our birthdays, because mine had been just a few weeks before. So, he said that that was okay and we could kind of bend the rules that day.

And so we, we, we kissed. And then I was touching him in his genital area through his shorts, and then I, I went to, to --

Q Perform oral sex?

A Yes, and he wouldn't let me.

Q Did he touch you on your genitals on that date?

A No.

Q Any other physical contact that is referred to as physical intimacy on that date?

A Not that I remember.

Q How did you end that encounter with him? Any discussion about sex during that encounter, or not having sex?

A No, just he got upset when I, you know, when he stopped me and he said, I'm trying to not do this and I'm trying to be good. And he, he got visibly upset. And so I, I hugged him and I told him I was sorry and not to be upset,

be

and I was a little shocked, actually. I didn't -- he just seemed to get so emotionally upset about it. It seemed a little bit strange to me.

Q And he hadn't done that before?

A He had been emotionally visibly upset with me before, but not --

Q With regard to --

A Correct.

Q -- stopping you from having sex with him?

A Exactly.

Q Or having sexual contact with him? Is that correct?

A Yes.

Q And is that, other than any brief kiss, the last physically intimate contact that you've had with him?

A Well, our Christmas kiss was -- I mean, it was passionate. So.

Q Okay. It was --

A I don't call it a brief kiss.

Q That was a physically intimate kiss. Any other contact that would fall within the sexual relations definition --

A No.

Q -- that we've previously seen?

A I think we, you know, we would, we would joke with

be

each other sexually. And so sometimes, you know, I might hit him on the butt, or he might hit me on the butt, but it wasn't -- not under the definition.

Q So, it wouldn't be a real intent to arouse, or not the physical touching that is described --

A No.

Q -- in the definition?

A No.

Q All right. Let's move on to another topic.

A Yea.

Q Thank you for your patience. I know that those are not easy questions to get to.

A It's just hard thinking my dad might see this.

Q Why don't we move to another emotional topic, July 4th, just briefly. Is now a good time to --

A Sure.

Q -- talk about that? Why don't you tell us -- I know that you've brought up in your grand jury testimony that July 4th of 1997 was an emotional day for you in connection with your relationship with the President.

A Yes.

Q Could you just briefly tell us what you meant by that and just a little bit about your meeting with him on that date?

A Our meeting had started out in, as a, in a fight.

be

We -- and early on in this fight, I started crying, and then he -- we were in the back office and he came over and was hugging me and told me not to cry, to stop crying, and was very -- he was very sweet, and was very gentle.

And then we -- I -- there was a gardener outside. So, when I noticed the gardener, I pointed it out and we moved to the, into the hallway by the bathroom. And much of the discussion that day was he spent a lot of time talking to me, you know, about the kind of person he thought I was, and -- I'm a little bit modest. So, it's sort of -- it's hard for me to get into all the things he said. But, there just --

Q Did he say wonderful things about you?

A He did.

Q Like what kinds of things?

A Just that he thought I was smart and beautiful, and that -- you know, but that a lot of it, it centered around my needing to learn to, to sort of squelch a bit of the fire in my belly. And that, you know, he said that people like us who, you know, have a tendency to get really angry and that there are a lot of other people that, that, that don't understand that and don't know how to handle that.

And he just -- he spent a lot of time talking to me. He was very, very -- he was the most affectionate with me he'd ever been. There wasn't a second when he wouldn't be touching me, whether it was holding my hand or stroking my arm or, you know, he'd kiss my neck at one point. It was just -- or he'd, you know, put his hands, he was running his hands through my hair and touching my face. And my bra strap kept falling down my shoulder. So, he kept pushing my bra strap up.

It was just very -- it was intense. It was just really emotionally intense.

And at one point, we, we had been talking about -- I made some remarks to him about his relationship with Mrs. Clinton. And he, he remarked a little bit later than that that he wished he had more time for me. And so I said, well, maybe you will have more time in three years. And I was actually sort of thinking just when he wasn't President, he was going to have more time on his hands. And he said, well, I don't know, I might be alone in three years.

And then I said something about, you know, us sort of being together. I think I kind of said, oh, I think we'd be a good team, or something like that. And he, you know, he jokingly said, well, what are we going to do when I'm 75 and I have to pee 25 times a day. And I, you know, I told him that we'd deal with that. And it was -- there was just this incredible connection.

And I, I left that day sort of emotionally stunned, because I felt -- I was shocked. But I thought, I mean, he

be

was -- I just knew he was in love with me, and from the way he acted that day, and that's not, it's not something that I would, that I would think easily. It's not a conclusion that I would come to easily at all. And it just -- with the kind of person I am.

And I knew I was in love with him, you know, a year before, and I thought he cared about me. But just the way he looked at me and touched me, and the things he said, it just -- it was so obvious to me. And it was shocking. So, it was a bizarre day.

Q Anything else about the 4th?

A Not that I don't think I've gone over before.

Q Okay. We'll switch to a completely different topic. You previously testified that on December 17th --

A You know, I need a --

Q Do you want a break?

A I'd like just a break.

Q Sure, absolutely.

(Whereupon, the deposition was recessed from 1:57 p.m. until 2:07 p.m.)

BY MS. IMMERGUT:

Q Ms. Lewinsky, you are still under oath.

A Yes.

Q We are going to cover some other areas, hopefully quickly. You previously testified that on December 17th,

be

during your phone call with the President -- and that's in 1997 --

A Yes.

Q -- when you were discussing various things, including that your name had appeared on the witness list, that the President told you that if you were ever subpoenaed that you should contact Betty?

A That's correct.

Q Did he ever tell you at that time that you should get a lawyer?

A I don't believe so. No.

Q When you say "I don't believe so", are you quite certain of that?

A I'm, I'm 99.9 percent certain.

Q What would you have done if he had told you that you should get a lawyer?

A I would have started to think about how I was going to get a lawyer and who I should get, and I didn't do that. So, that's what leads me to believe that he didn't say that.

Q Okay. Were you ever under the impression from anything that the President said that you should turn over all the gifts that he had given you to the Paula Jones attorneys?

A No.

Q Did you ever talk to the President about turning

be

gifts over to the Jones lawyers before you were ever subpoenaed?

A No.

Q Did you actually ever talk to him about the fact that gifts could be subpoenaed prior to them actually being subpoenaed?

A No.

Q So, is it fair to say that the only time you talked about the gifts from the President, in connection with the subpoena, was on December 28th?

A That's correct.

Q Directing your attention to January 5th of 1998, when you had a telephone call with the President, you previously testified that you had some discussion about a book that you had purchased for him?

A Correct.

Q That was the book that you gave to Betty Currie on approximately January 4th to give to the President? Is that right?

A Yes.

Q What was the name of that book again? It was the book on the Presidents.

A It was a book about the Presidents of the United States.

Q Do you remember when you purchased that book?

A I believe it was that weekend, the weekend prior to the 5th.

Q Did you ever talk to him, during your meeting of December 28th, 1997, about the fact that you were going to give him that book?

A No.

Q How do you know that you didn't?

A Because I hadn't purchased the book yet.

Q Had you even thought about purchasing that particular book?

A No. It was bought on the spur of the moment.

Q Do you remember where you bought it?

A At a little bookstore in Georgetown, an antique book store.

Q I'm going to switch topics again. Do you believe that if you hadn't had a sexual relationship with the President that you would have kept your job at the White House?

A Yes.

Q Do you believe that your difficulty or inability to return to employment at the White House was because of your sexual relationship with him?

A Yes. Or the issues that, or the problems that people perceived that really were based in truth because I had a relationship with the President. But, however, some of

be

the people who worked there chose to, to see some of my behavior. Does that make sense?

Q What do you mean by that?

A I think that -- I've always felt that some of the, some of the staffers there, particularly Evelyn Lieberman and those who worked with her to move me out of the White House, instead -- looked at my behavior only, instead of looking at the President's behavior, and instead of necessarily thinking that I had a relationship with the President, were just looking at it thinking I was trying to have a relationship with the President when I already was having a relationship with him. They turned a blind eye to his actions.

Q During 1997, did you feel that the President owed you something with respect to a job?

A I did, because he, he had promised me on April 7th of '96 that he would bring me back when, if he won in November. And I had -- when he first told me that, I had had some hope and I didn't, I didn't even know if I was going to hear from him again after I left. And then when he continued to call me frequently during the campaign period, it led me to believe he would bring me back.

And then after we had a -- it was after a period when he didn't call me and I wasn't sure about things, what was happening -- I'm sorry. I'm not being clear.

Because he had sort of led me to believe that he

be

was going to bring me back and was constantly reassuring that, I, I believe that he did owe that to me. Versus him having said, I'm really sorry -- let's just say in April of '96 -- I'm really sorry that this happened, there's not, you know, there's nothing I can do, and left it at that. Then I wouldn't have felt that he owed me anything.

Q What about the fact that you had gone quietly and not revealed your relationship? Did that have anything to do with your feeling that you were entitled to something?

A It did later on. I, I would have gone quietly anyway, because that -- it was never, ever, ever my intention for this relationship to ever become public. And -- but I had felt that after having left quietly, after having been sort of maybe strung along throughout the campaign and then even way into 1997, that I had felt -- and him promising me that he'd bring me back and constantly enumerating the different steps he was trying to take to do that -- that, yes, I did feel at that point he, he certainly owed me.

Q Is that part of your letter of July 3rd to the President in 1997, where you described it previously as threatening to disclose the relationship, at least to your parents, was that part of your feeling that --

A It was never really a, a, maybe a -- it was never really a threat, because I never really was going to do that. While I had disclosed a portion of the relationship to my

be

mom, I never had any intention of telling my dad. There's no way of that.

And what I really was trying to do was trying to, in a circuitous manner, remind him that I had been a good girl, and that I hadn't, you know, disclosed this information, and that really, you know, he'd promised me he was going to do something. And I had told my parents, I had told my dad that I was coming back after the election.

Q I'd like to focus now just very briefly on your dealings with Ambassador Richardson with regard to the U.N. job.

A Yes.

Q How many times did Ambassador Richardson call you directly, do you remember?

A Do you mean someone from his -- he never directly picked up the phone and dialed my phone number.

Q Let me ask a different question.

A Okay.

Q How many times did you speak to him personally?

A I believe twice.

Q And when I say personally, on the telephone?

A Yes.

Q How do you know that you actually spoke with him on those occasions?

A Well, the first time I spoke with him I remember,

be

because I was shocked and I was, I was very nervous. And --

Q Because the Ambassador was on the phone?

A Exactly. And the second, the second time I actually hadn't really remembered, I wasn't sure. And then through documentation I was shown, it, it led me to believe that I had, in fact, spoken to him on the phone.

Q But you are positive at least one time you did, in fact, speak to him personally?

A Yes.

Q Do you remember which occasion that was, or when that occurred?

A Yes, it was sometime in October.

Q Was that the October 23rd call? Does that sound right?

A Yes.

Q And that's prior to your actual interview with him?

A Correct.

Q I'd like to just ask you very briefly about your conversation with the President the night before your interview with Ambassador Richardson for the U.N. job. Could you describe who initiated that call and what the substance of the call was?

A I had -- well, I had requested through Betty that the President call me, because I was really nervous about my interview and meeting with Ambassador Richardson. I just, I didn't, I didn't want to make anyone look bad. I didn't want to sound like a fool, or -- so, the President called me and we talked about some of the different issues at the U.N., and he gave me some suggestions of things I could say. But I think he may have also done that the previous week, too.

Q Do you remember him giving you sort of a job pep talk on --

A Yes.

Q --the 30th?

A Yes.

Q Why would you describe it as a pep talk?

A Because I was nervous. So, he, he was trying to kind of build my confidence and reassure me, you know, reassure me that I was an intelligent person, and that I had a lot to offer and that they would be happy to have me there.

Q At some point, did you tell the President that you got an offer from the U.N.?

A I believe so.

Q Did you tell Betty also that you had gotten an offer?

A Yes.

Q Do you remember any details about talking to Betty about it, or how you let her know?

A I, I remember calling Betty after the interview and telling her that it had gone much better than I had expected

be

it would, and that I was really, that I was, that I was somewhat more interested after having met the Ambassador than I was prior to the interview. And other than that, I don't really.

Q What about details about your conversation with the President telling him that you had gotten the job?

A I vaguely remember it being in context, I think, of sort of trying to press him on getting in touch with Mr. Jordan.

Q In terms of getting other jobs --

A Exactly.

Q -- you let him know this?

A Exactly.

Q That you had an offer from the U.N.?

A Right.

Q Do you remember when you got the U.N. offer?

A No.

Q Was it sometime, in relation to your interview with the Ambassador --

A It was sooner, rather than later.

Q So, sometime within a matter of a week or --

A I believe so.

Q -- some weeks?

A Somewhere within a couple, within the next two weeks or so.

be

Q And did they tell you that they would leave the job open until a certain time, for you to make the decision if you wanted it?

A Not at the point when I got the offer. I, I -- and actually I think, thinking now I'm a little bit more clearer that I did speak with the Ambassador, that he was the one who, who extended the offer to me, because I remember being nervous and not knowing what to say to him, because I didn't really want the job. And so I sort of just "yessed" him along and thanked him profusely, and told him I was excited about it.

And then I later spoke, I believe, with Mona Sutphen, and sort of relayed to her that I was interested in also trying to feel out the private sector. So, and I believe it was at that point that she said, well, let's keep in touch. We can -- this position, I think, had been open for awhile. So.

Q Did she give you any timeframe at all about how long they would wait for you to make a decision?

A It was -- I think we talked about talking maybe in a few weeks, and then at some point we said, let's get in touch around the first of January. And I was under the impression that, you know, I believed that they would hold the position open for me, but that it didn't necessarily --

Q It's not a guarantee?

A Exactly.

Q But they weren't rushing you to make an immediate decision?

A No.

Q So, you understand you basically had some leeway until January 1998 to make a decision?

A Correct.

Q January 16th, 1998, Ritz Carlton night. I really have just one question about it, which was, was there a time that you, in fact, during the course of the evening, that you, in fact, did leave the prosecutors and agents by yourself?

A Yes, when I was given, finally given permission to go call my mom. I wasn't comfortable using the phone in the room.

Q So, you went out by yourself to --

A Yes, I did.

Q Where did you go make a phone call?

A To Nordstrom's.

Q And --

A It was just one phone call, to my mother. And there was also a time -- I think one of the prosecutors came with me, I think it was Stephen Bin --

Q Binhak?

A -- I think, came downstairs with me. I used -- I

needed to return a phone call from a page. And then when I was with Mr. Emmick and Agent [redacted] they let me go to the bathroom in Macy's by myself.

Q Were you in Macy's for some time by yourself?

A Well, it, it took awhile to find a bathroom. It was kind of far away. So.

Q So, they didn't follow you into the bathroom?

A They didn't follow me in. But then when I came back, Agent [redacted] had gone looking for me. So.

Q And just with respect to the phone call to call your mother, no one accompanied you for that, is that right?

A No.

Q And finally --

A I just, I do want to state that I did -- because I know this sort of goes to this issue of being, you know, kind of told, oh, you're free to leave whenever you want, that I didn't really -- I didn't feel at any point that I could leave whenever I wanted, that I could -- that I was afraid that if I had left the Mall, I would be arrested and put in jail. So, that was my impression.

Q One last question from me. Do you, for any reason now, want to hurt the President?

A No. I'm, I'm upset with him right now, but I, no, that's the last thing in the world I want to do.

MS. IMMERGUT: That's all I have.

be

MS. WIRTH: I just have one question.

BY MS. WIRTH:

Q From your grand jury testimony last week, on August 20th, 1998, you were talking about your understanding of the President's testimony. I'm just going to read a portion of your testimony to you and ask you a question about that. This is in response to a question from a juror.

You said, "I'm sorry. I'm sorry. It's -- from my understanding about what he testified to on Monday, not -- just from the press accounts, is that this was a -- that this was a service contract, that all I did was perform oral sex on him and that that's all that this relationship was. And it was a lot more than that to me and I thought it was a lot more than that."

And the answer continues a little bit more after that.

The question I have for you is that when you mentioned your understanding of what the President testified to on the previous Monday, from what did you derive your understanding of what the President's testimony was?

A From the press accounts I had read.

Q Okay. No one from this office divulged to you anything that the President said during his testimony, did they?

A Absolutely not.

be

MR. WIRTH: Thank you.

MS. IMMERGUT: Nothing further. Do you have any questions?

THE WITNESS: No.

(Whereupon, at 2:24 p.m., the proceedings were concluded.)

* * * * *

CERTIFICATE OF COURT REPORTER - NOTARY PUBLIC

I, Elizabeth A. Eastman, the officer before whom the foregoing deposition was taken, do hereby certify that the witness whose testimony appears in the foregoing deposition was duly sworn by me; that the testimony of said witness was taken by me electronically and thereafter reduced to typewriting by me; that said deposition is a true record of the testimony given by said witness; that I am neither counsel for, related to, nor employed by any of the parties to the action in which this deposition was taken; and, further, that I am not a relative or employee of any attorney or counsel employed by the parties hereto, nor financially or otherwise interested in the outcome of the action.

Elizabeth A. Eastman

NOTARY PUBLIC FOR THE
DISTRICT OF COLUMBIA

My Commission Expires:
July 31, 2000

THE FOLLOWING IS A COMPRESSED VERSION OF THE PRECEDING DOCUMENT

Monica Lewinsky - 8/26/98

OIC Deposition

Page 2 to Page

CONDENSED TRANSCRIPT AND CONCORDANCE
PREPARED BY:

OFFICE OF THE INDEPENDENT COUNSEL
1001 Pennsylvania Avenue, N.W.
Suite 490-North
Washington, DC 20004
Phone: 202-514-8688
FAX: 202-514-8802

Page 2

OFFICE OF THE INDEPENDENT COUNSEL

-------------------------x

DEPOSITION OF : Wednesday, August 26, 1998

MONICA S. LEWINSKY : Washington, D. C.

-------------------------x

Deposition of MONICA S. LEWINSKY before the Independent Counsel, held in the Conference Room of the Office of the Independent Counsel, Suite 490-North, 1001 Pennsylvania Avenue, N. W., Washington, D. C. 20004, beginning at 12:35 p.m., when were present:

For the Independent Counsel:

KARIN IMMERGUT, ESQUIRE
Associate Independent Counsel
MARY ANNE WIRTH, ESQUIRE
Associate Independent Counsel

Court Reporter: Elizabeth A. Eastman

Page 3

PROCEEDINGS

MS. IMMERGUT: We are on the record. Ms. Lewinsky, could you please state and spell your full name for the record?
MS. LEWINSKY: Monica Samille Lewinsky, M-O-N-I-C-A S-A-M-I-L-L-E, L-E-W-I-N-S-K-Y.
MS. IMMERGUT: For the record, I am Karin Immergut from the Office of Independent Counsel. Seated with me is Mary Anne Wirth, also from the Office of the Independent Counsel.
WHEREUPON,
MONICA S. LEWINSKY
having been called for examination by the Office of the Independent Counsel, and having been first duly sworn by the notary, was examined and testified as follows:
EXAMINATION BY COUNSEL FOR THE INDEPENDENT COUNSEL
BY MS. IMMERGUT:
Q Before we begin the deposition, I do want to advise you of certain rights that you have in connection with this deposition. You have already, I know, testified twice before the grand jury, and essentially the same rights do apply.
First, you have a right to have an attorney present outside of the room. Do you have an attorney present?
A Yes, I do.
Q Who is that attorney?

Page 4

A Plato Cacheris.
Q You have the right to consult with Mr. Cacheris any time during the testimony, and I simply ask that you just request a break when you need to consult with him. Do you understand that you have that right?
A Yes, I do.
Q You also generally as a witness in a deposition, or before a grand jury, have a Fifth Amendment right not to incriminate yourself. Obviously, that now is modified pursuant to the agreement that you have with the Office of the Independent Counsel.
Do you understand that?
A Yes.
Q Have you seen the agreement that you have, giving you immunity for your cooperation in this case?
A Yes, I have.
Q That also is a grand jury exhibit in this case, is it not?
A Yes, it is.
Q Do you have any questions about what your rights are not to incriminate yourself as part of that agreement?
A No, I don't.
Q In addition, as always, you are required to tell the truth during this procedure and are subject to the penalties of perjury if you do not tell the complete truth.

Page 5

Do you understand that?
A Yes, I do.
Q Any other questions that you have before we proceed?
A No.
Q First I just want to ask you a general question. I know you have testified in two other proceedings about various aspects of your relationship with the President. Can you characterize whether or not your relationship was one that started with sex and then evolved into a friendship, or the other way around?
A It started with a physical attraction, which led to a sexual relationship, and then the emotional and friendship aspects of that relationship developed after the beginning of our sexual relationship.
Q I would like to place before you what I will mark as Deposition exhibit No. 1.
(Deposition Exhibit No. 1 was marked for identification.)
BY MS. IMMERGUT:
Q This is also a chart that was previously marked as Grand Jury Exhibit ML #7. You can see the Xerox copy of that sticker on this exhibit, and I will place that before you, and ask if you recognize what that exhibit is?
A Yes, I do.

Page 6

Q What do you recognize it to be?
A A chart that I helped develop with the Office of Independent Counsel to describe and enumerate the -- my relationship with the President, the contacts between the President and myself.
Q As you've testified before, did you provide the information that is on this chart?
A Yes, I did.
Q And is it accurate to the best of your recollection of the events?
A Yes, it is.
Q What I would like to do is go through the events that are written in bold, which deal with the private encounters you had with the President that involved, for the most part, some sort of physical intimacy that we have listed as physical intimacy, including oral sex. I did want to get into some more detail about each incident.
Basically, with respect to each incident, I would like you to describe the circumstances leading up to the actual visit, who initiated it, how it was set up, and then I would like to ask you some details about the sexual encounters themselves that occurred during each of those visits.
So, why don't we start with the very first one, which is the second encounter that you had on November 15th,

Page 7

1995 that you've already testified some about. If you can, could you just tell us how that visit was set up, and then what occurred during the visit?
A The President came back to Mr. Panetta's office and I was the only person in the office at the time, and believe it was maybe around, I think, 10 p.m. or so, and asked me, or told me that if I wanted to meet him back in Mr. Stephanopoulos' office in about 5-10 minutes, that I could. And I told him I was interested to do that.
Q At that time, did you understand what it was he wanted to meet with you about?
A I had an idea. I, I, I had assumed that since we had been intimate in our previous encounter that evening, that we would again be intimate.
Q And just to clarify for the record, the intimacy that you had earlier that night was just kissing, is that correct?
A Yes.
Q So, did you, in fact, go meet with the President?
A Yes, I did.
Q And could you describe where you went to meet him?
A I met him back in Mr. Stephanopoulos' office and he invited me into the back study again, and we were in the hallway. And we were -- I don't remember exactly how it started. But I know that we were talking a bit and kissing.

Page 8

I remember -- I know that he -- I believe I unbuttoned my jacket and he touched my, my breasts with my bra on, and then either -- I don't remember if I unhooked my bra or he lifted my bra up, but he -- this is embarrassing.
Q Then touched your breasts with his hands?
A Yes, he did.
Q Did he touch your breasts with his mouth?
A Yes, he did.
Q Did he touch your genital area at all that day?
A Yes. We moved -- I believe he took a phone call in his office, and so we moved from the hallway into the back office, and the lights were off. And at that point, he, he put his hand down my pants and stimulated me manually in the genital area.
Q And did he bring you to orgasm?
A Yes, he did.
Q Back to the touching of your breasts for a minute, was that then through clothing or actually directly onto your skin?
A He touched my breasts through clothing, being my bra, and then also without my bra on.
Q On that occasion, did you perform oral sex on the President?
A Yes.
Q Who actually initiated your performing oral sex?

Page 9

A I did.
Q Was the President wearing pants?
A Yes, he was.
Q Who unzipped his pants?
A I believe I went to go unbutton his pants and I had trouble. So, he did that. So, but --
Q So, you started it?
A If I remember correctly.
Q And he helped complete opening his pants?
A Yes.
Q Did the President at that time do anything to stop you from doing that?
A No. I think he asked me if I was sure I wanted to do that.
Q Did you have any other discussion with him while the sexual encounter was occurring, about the sex or what you were doing?
A No. Actually, I don't think he asked me if I were sure I wanted to do that, because he was on the telephone. So -- I'm sorry.
Could you repeat what you just asked me?
Q Did the President have any discussion with you about sex, or you with him, while the sexual encounter was occurring?
A Not at this time. He was on the telephone for the

Page 10

second half when we were in the office.
Q So, he was on the telephone while you were performing oral sex?
A He was on the telephone while he was --
Q Touching you?
A Touching me, and was also on the telephone when I was performing oral sex.
Q For any part of this sexual encounter, was he then off the telephone?
A Yes, I believe towards the end of my performing oral sex.
Q Did he say anything about the oral sex or anything about the sex at all when he got off the phone, that you can remember?
A He stopped me before he came, and I told him that I wanted to, to complete that. And he said that, that he needed to wait until he trusted me more. And then I think he [redacted]
Q [redacted]
A Yes.
Q Did he ejaculate in your presence that time at all?
A No.
Q How did you depart from the office, or how did you end that visit?

Page 11

A I believe we spoke for awhile and I know at some point in that conversation I -- oh, that might have been Friday. Hmm. I really don't remember how it ended.
Q Can you estimate at all how long the sexual part of your encounter with him lasted?
A Maybe 20 minutes?
Q How long --
A I'm not a very good estimator of times.
Q How long did the entire encounter last, if you can recall?
A The second one of that evening?
Q Yes.
A Maybe half an hour or 40 minutes?
Q So, the entire encounter did not involve simply the sexual part of it?
A No, it didn't.
Q Did you have talking beforehand or was most of the talking afterwards?
A It was before and after.
Q If I can direct your attention again back to Deposition Exhibit No. 1, the chart, the next date where you do have two encounters with the President is November 17th, 1995. Although you've described it somewhat for the grand jury, if you could now just describe in detail -- again, I'll direct your attention to that second contact where there was

Page 12

physical intimacy, including oral sex listed -- how that contact came about and what occurred during the contact?
A Yes. I had brought the President pizza, as he had asked. And when I brought it into him at the Oval Office, then he took me into the, to the back office and said that I could leave through that way. I believe we were talking for a little bit and he then, he got a phone call and he took the phone call in his bathroom.
Oh, it might have been before the phone call that -- I don't, I don't remember who, who unbuttoned my jacket or anything like that. But we were kissing and he was fondling my breasts with his hands and with his mouth.
Q Was that through clothing or not through clothing?
A It was both.
Q Okay. So, was there a point that your bra is removed?
A Yes.
Q But you don't remember who actually removed it?
A No. I think, I think he -- rather than necessarily removing my bra, sometimes he would just expose my breasts.
Q By lifting the bra over your breasts?
A Yes, or sometimes lifting my breasts out of the bra. Oh, God.
Q So, on that occasion though, you do recall that he touched you not just through your bra, but also directly on

Page 13

the skin?
A Yes.
Q [redacted]
A [redacted]
Q [redacted]
A [redacted]
Q Was there any discussion about sex while you were in this encounter with him?
A I don't remember the specifics of it, but I know there was another discussion, I think, about him not letting me make him come, and then I had to get back to -- I'm sorry.
Could you repeat the question?
Q Was there any discussion during the November 17th encounter about sex during the encounter?
A I don't know exactly what you mean. I mean, do you mean either about --
Q Talking --
A I mean, saying things, or --
Q Well, either about what he wanted or what you wanted, or anything like that, in terms of sex?

Page 14

A No. I mean, I think that there were always things being said, but not necessarily in a conversational form. Does that make sense?
Q Okay. And when you say there were always things being said, do you mean kind of chatting while you were having sex, or things that felt good? I don't mean that. I mean –
A Okay.
Q – trying either implicitly giving you direction about what he wanted, or why he wouldn't ejaculate, anything like that?
A I believe that why he wouldn't ejaculate was, was discussed again.
Q Okay. You mentioned that the President unzipped his pants. Did you understand that to be a signal of what he wanted in terms of sex?
A Yes.
Q Did he ever say anything while that was happening about what he wanted or no?
A No. He was on the telephone.
Q Okay. And that was on the second time also?
A Yes.
Q Was he on the telephone the whole time that you performed oral sex on him on the 17th of November?
A I don't remember.

Page 15

Q Do you remember how you finished that meeting up with him that day, how you left?
A Yes. I know I needed to get back to my office, and he – I think I told him that he should come down and have pizza with us, he should bring his pizza down, and that everyone was down there. And at some point I believe in that meeting he told me that, or he reiterated because he might have said it on the 15th as well, that I could come see him on the weekends when, when there weren't a lot of people around.
Q With respect again to the ejaculation, that he wouldn't actually ejaculate during oral sex, were you aware, or did he ejaculate anywhere in your presence on that occasion?
A No.
Q The next date listed on the chart is December 31st, 1995, a Sunday. Could you describe how that meeting was set up and what occurred when you got to the meeting?
A Yes. I had been having a conversation with Nel and had just told him that I smoked my first cigar the night before in honor of my brother's birthday. And Nel asked me if I wanted – or offered that he could get me one of the President's cigars from his sort of stash of cigars. I said, that would be great.
And we went through the Roosevelt Room to the

Page 16

entrance into the back study which – the door that leads into the dining room. And just as we approached the door, the door swung open and the President was standing right there, and he had something he was going to take to Mr. Panetta. So, he asked, he asked Nel to take this – I think it was a picture actually – a picture down to Mr. Panetta, and he invited me in.
So, I went into the office and he asked me what I was doing there. And – well, first he told me he had been looking for me. And then he told me – he asked me what I was doing there, and I told him that Nel was going to get me a cigar. So, he said that he would give me a cigar. So, he did give me a cigar.
And then we were talking for a little bit and I had – do you want me to just be –
Q If you could do a narrative, that's fine.
A Well, he had – I had thought that he had forgotten my name before, because I had seen him in the hall a few times and he kept calling me "Kiddo". So, so, I sort of reiterated my – I said my name again to him. You know, I said, you know, it's Monica Lewinsky, President Kiddo, you know. And he said, I know your name.
And he told me that he had tried to call me and that – he said, but you're not in the book; I even spelled your last name right. So, it was, it was really funny. It

Page 17

was cute.
And then we were, we were kissing and he lifted my sweater and exposed my breasts and was fondling them with his hands and with his mouth. And then I believe I was fondling him over his pants in his genital area, and I think again I tried to unbutton his pants and I couldn't. So, he did it.
Q And again, just to be clear, when you mentioned he raised your sweater and fondled your breasts, were your breasts outside of your bra at that time?
A Yes.
Q [redacted]
A [redacted]
Q [redacted]
A [redacted]
Q [redacted]
A [redacted]
Q Did you have any discussion with him again about why he wasn't ejaculating, anything like that?
A Yes, I think so. It might have been at that time – the two excuses he always used were, one, that he didn't know me well enough or he didn't trust me yet. So that it sort of seemed to be some bizarre issue for him.
Q On that occasion, did he ever ejaculate in your

Page 18

presence, even though not – at any time later?
A After he told me to stop and then, and then wished me Happy New Year and kissed me goodbye, he went into the [redacted]
Q Okay. Do you know how long that sexual encounter, or the sexual aspect of that encounter lasted, not including the other discussion with him?
A Maybe 10 minutes. Not, not very long. We would always spend quite a bit of time kissing. So.
Q And kissing and talking and just –
A Uh-huh.
Q – being affectionate?
A Yes.
Q The next one is on page 2, and that would be January 7th of '96. Could you describe how that meeting was set up and what happened when you got there?
A Yes. The President called me – this is the first time he called me at home – that afternoon, and it was the first day of the blizzard. And I asked him what he was doing and he said he was going to be going into the office soon. I said, oh, do you want some company. And he said, oh, that would be great. So, he said he was going into the office in about 45 minutes, and I told him that I should probably be in my office around that time, and he said he would call me in

Page 19

my office. I gave him my office number.
Then once I was in my office, he called me and we made an arrangement that I would pass – he would have the door to his office open, and I would pass by the office with some papers and then he would, he would sort of stop me and invite me in. So, that was exactly what happened.
I passed by and that was actually when I saw Lew Fox who was on duty outside the Oval Office, and stopped and spoke with Lew for a few minutes, and then the President came out and said, oh, hey, Monica, you know, what are you doing here, come on in, sort of.
And so we spoke for about 10 minutes in the office. We sat on the sofas. Then we went into the back study and we were intimate in the bathroom.
Q And when you say you were intimate in the bathroom what did you do?
A We kissed and he, he fondled my breasts and expose – or I think pulled them out of my bra and fondled them with his hands and with his mouth, and –
Q Did he touch your genitals on that occasion?
A No. He wanted to and was talking about performing oral sex on me, [redacted]
Q [redacted]
A [redacted]
Q Okay. On that date, did you gratify him in some

Page 20

way other than performing oral sex?
A Yes.
Q [redacted]
A [redacted]
Q [redacted]
A [redacted]
Q [redacted]
A [redacted]
Q [redacted]
A [redacted]
Q [redacted]
A [redacted]
Q [redacted]
A [redacted]
Q Did you have any discussion about sex during the encounter that you had with him?
A No.
Q How long was your encounter with him?
A Hmm. Maybe about half an hour? I, I'm – it's really hard for me to estimate the time.
Q And that would be the sexual aspect of it though that –

Page 21

A Correct.
Q – we're talking about. Did he ejaculate at any point in your presence after you performed oral sex on him?
A That day?
Q Yes.
A No.
MS. IMMERGUT: Did you have a question?
BY MS. WIRTH:
Q I have a question, actually going back to November 15th, if you don't mind.
A Okay.
Q When you were talking about the President having contact with your genitals, you said, I think, that he put his hands in your pants. When he touched your genitals, was that through your underwear or directly?
A I didn't have my underwear on at that point.
Q Okay. So, it was directly then?
A Yes.
Q Okay.
BY MS. IMMERGUT:
Q The next encounter listed is January 21st of '96, also on page 2 of the exhibit. Could you describe how that encounter occurred and what happened during the encounter?
A Yes. I was – actually, I'm looking at this right now and I think it might have been a Saturday – no, it was a

Page 22

Sunday. I'm sorry. Never mind. I think it might have been a Saturday, but it, it says here Sunday. I just noticed that.
I was – I had been in my office doing work, and I was leaving, leaving for the day. And as I was walking through the Residence hall to go through the West Wing to the Old Executive Office Building, I heard his voice behind me. And either he called my name or I just heard his voice and turned around, and he had just come off of the elevator and, I guess, was going back to his office.
So, we were, we were – we stopped, and we spoke as we continued to walk through the outdoor corridor by the Rose Garden. And when we got to the point where he turns left to then go into the Oval Office, he told me that I could go out this way with him, that I could leave through the, that I could leave through the Oval Office. So, we walked down the pathway together and then went into the Oval Office from there.
Q And could you describe your encounter once you got into the Oval Office?
A Yes. We had, we had already had phone sex for the first time the week prior, and I was feeling a little bit insecure about whether he had liked it or didn't like it, and I just – I felt in general that I didn't know – from having spoken to him on the phone, you know, prior to having phone

Page 23

sex and from having had these encounters with him, I didn't know if this was sort of developing into some kind of a longer term relationship than what I thought it initially might have been, that maybe he had some regular girlfriend who was furloughed or something during the furlough.
And at that point, I, you know, I said to him, you know, I asked him why he doesn't ask me any questions about myself, and doesn't he, you know, is this just about sex, you know, because if it is, then I just want to know that; or do you have some interest in trying to get to know me as a person. And so he kind of laughed at the manner in which I was asking him and talking to him.
And we, we went into the back study and he was, he was waiting for a friend of his to come to the office, and he was talking about that he has a lot of – that he doesn't get a lot of time to himself and he really cherishes the private times that he has with his friends, and he cherishes the time that he had with me, which seemed a little bit odd to me at that time.
But he, he was upset that day about the first soldier in Bosnia had been – I believe it was that day – that it was the first soldier in Bosnia had been killed just recently, and he was very upset and moved. And so I was trying to comfort him.
Q When you say you thought it was odd that he said he

Page 24

cherished the time with you, why was that, why did you think it was odd at that point?
A Because I didn't feel, I didn't feel like he really knew me. We had spent time talking, but it didn't seem – and, you know, he had asked some questions and I offered a lot of information about myself. But he didn't seem to ask probing questions, when you're trying to get to know someone. So, it seemed a little bit odd to me that he would sort of cherish this time, when he, you know, when I felt like he didn't really even know me yet.
Q And at that point, sex was sort of the more dominant part of the relationship?
A Yes.
Q Rather than as it became –
A There was always a lot of joking that went on between us. And so we, you know, I mean, it was fun. When we were together, it was fun. We would laugh and it would – we were very compatible sexually. And I've always felt that he was sort of my sexual soulmate, and that I just felt very connected to him when it came to those kinds of things.
Q So, on the January 21st date –
A Right.
Q – how did it turn into your conversation and then go into actually having a sexual encounter?
A I was in the middle of saying something and he just

Page 25

started kissing me. And, so, it was funny. It was, it was very funny.
Q And what room were you physically in at that time?
A We were in the hallway. And we were kissing and – oh, I had – because I was leaving, I was having a bad hair day, and this was actually the first time that I had the infamous beret on. And so I just said something to him about feeling stupid. Here I was standing here in this dumb hat, and he said that it wasn't a dumb hat, that I looked cute and he liked it.
And so then he was kissing me, or we were kissing each other, I guess, and I think again he, he fondled my breasts with his hands and his mouth.
Q Through clothing or not through clothing?
A I think it was always through clothing, and then eventually it, it would be direct contact. So, it wouldn't just be this immediate jump to being, you know, to contact. It was – there was sort of foreplay to the foreplay, if that makes sense.
Q Do you remember whether he removed any of your clothing on that occasion?
A I think he – I remember him lifting my top. So – and he, he sort of exposing my breasts.
Q Did he stimulate your genitals on that occasion?
A No.

Page 26

Q Did you perform oral sex on him or any kind of sex on him?
A Yes, I did.
Q Could you describe how that came about?
A Yes. He unzipped his pants and sort of exposed himself and that -- and then I performed oral sex.
Q Let me ask, on all of these occasions when you've described just the pants unzipping and exposing, is it fair to say that he still kept his pants on?
A Yes.
Q It was just the zipper that --
A Yes.
Q -- was undone?
A Right. And actually at one point during this encounter, I think someone came into the, to the Oval Office and he, you know, zipped up real quickly and went out and came back in, and I -- this is probably too much information. I just -- sorry.
Q And what happened?
A I just remember laughing because he had walked out there and he was visibly aroused, and I just thought it was funny. I mean, it wouldn't, it wouldn't necessarily be visible to anyone who just walked in because they wouldn't be looking at that, but it was just funny to me. So.
And then his -- then someone -- I think at that

Page 27

point someone came in to let him know that his friend had arrived. And so he asked me which way I wanted to leave, and I said I was going to go, I was going to leave through Betty's office. And we went into -- we went from the back study through the Oval into Betty's office area, and he took me into Nancy Hemreich's office and kissed me goodbye.
And then I went to go leave from, from Betty's office, from the door into the hallway, to the West Wing hallway, but it was locked. So, I went back in to tell him. He was still in Nancy's office. I went back into Nancy's office to tell him the door was locked, and he was manually stimulating himself.
Q Did he cause himself to ejaculate at that point, or did you see that?
A No.
Q But that was in Nancy Hemreich's office?
A Yes.
Q And what did you do when you saw that?
A I smiled.
Q Okay.
A And I think we kissed again.
Q On that occasion, you mentioned that he did not touch your genitals at all. Was there any discussion about that?
A No.

Page 28

Q Then did you leave from Nancy Hemreich's office eventually?
A I think I left through the -- I left through the door in Betty's office that goes out into the Rose Garden.
Q On this particular entry on January 21st, it lists that the entire encounter was approximately 30 to 40 minutes. Do you recall what portion of that would have been the sexual encounter part of it, versus just talking?
A Maybe 15 minutes?
Q You just can't really estimate?
A Exactly.
Q Let's go now to February 4th of 1996, the next bold date where there was a private encounter. Could you describe how that encounter came about and what happened?
A Yes. I was in my office on Sunday and the President called me in the office and -- from the Residence, and told me that he was going to be going into the office later. And I think I asked him if I could come see him. And he said that would be fine, and then that he -- oh, I think he was, he said he was going to go into the office in an hour and a half or so.
So, then he called me -- it was actually maybe two or three hours later, because I remember I thought he forgot, maybe he had forgotten to call me and that -- so. And when he called from the Residence to say he was on his way, I told

Page 29

him that -- I asked him if we could sort of bump into the hallway, bump into each other in the hallway on purpose this time, because when it happened accidentally, that seemed to work really well and I felt more comfortable doing that. So, that's what we did. We both said, okay, I'm going to leave now.
And indeed we bumped into each other in the hall and went through the Rose Garden into the Oval Office. And I think we went right into the back office. The -- when we got there.
Q When you say the back office, you mean the study?
A Yes. And -- let's see.
You know, I need to take a break.
Q Okay. Let's take a break.
(Whereupon, the deposition was recessed from 1:10 p.m. until 1:15 p.m.)
BY MS. IMMERGUT:
Q Ms. Lewinsky, you are still under oath.
A Yes.
Q We are still on February 4th, 1996. You've described going into the office and starting to kiss the President. What happened then?
A We were in the back office and we were kissing, and I was -- I had a dress on that buttoned all the way, all the way up and down.

Page 30

Q To the neck?
A Correct. It was long and down to the, to my ankles, or whatever. And he unbuttoned my dress and he unhooked my bra, and sort of took the dress off of my shoulders and took the bra off of my, off of my -- I'm not explaining this right. So that he moved the bra so that my bra was kind of hanging on one shoulder and so was off. And he just was, he was looking at me and touching me and telling me how beautiful I was.
Q And did he touch your breasts with his hands?
A Yes.
Q Did he also touch them with his mouth?
A Yes.
Q And at that point, that is directly on your skin, is that right?
A Yes.
Q Did he touch your genitals?
A Yes, he did.
Q Did he bring you to orgasm on that date?
A Yes, he did.
Q [redacted]
A [redacted]
Q [redacted]

Page 31

[redacted]
A [redacted]
Q [redacted]
A [redacted]
Q [redacted]
A [redacted]
Q And again, just with respect to bringing you to an orgasm, did he touch you directly on your skin on your genitals, or was it through underwear?
A First it was through underwear and then it was directly touching my genitals.
Q Did he take your underwear off, or did you take your underwear off?
A Hmm.
Q Or did they stay on?
A I think that -- I believe that he touched me first with my underwear on, and then placed his hand under my underwear. And I think at some point I, I removed them.
Q Okay. Did you also perform oral sex on him at that

Page 32

time?
A Yes, I did.
Q How did it come about? Was that something that you decided to do, or did the President either, through his actions or words, indicate to you that he wanted that?
A I don't really remember. I mean, it was a mutual – I think in all of these instances, it wasn't, you know – I know sometimes it's sort of hard to answer these questions as more directed. But it was – I mean, it was the course of being intimate. I mean, it was the course of having this kind of a relationship, that you – sometimes he initiated it, sometimes I initiated it. It wasn't, you know, it wasn't – it didn't necessarily go through my mind, okay, now it's time to perform oral sex.
I mean, it was, it was the passion of the moment. That was, I mean, just sort of in the course of things that happened, you know. I always felt that we sort of just, we both really went to a, to a whole other place together sexually.
Q Is it fair to say you were both trying to please each other by doing different things?
A Yes. Yes.
Q Is it also fair to say that you were not the sole aggressor in this sexual –
A That's very fair to say.

Page 33

Q – encounter?
A I was not.
Q Again, I'm just asking you every time in case you remember, do you remember how long the sexual aspect of that encounter lasted?
A I really, I really don't.
Q Okay. I just note, to direct your attention that the time that you provided us previously is approximately one and a half hours for the whole visit.
A Right. We spent a long time in the Oval Office talking after, maybe 45 minutes to an hour just talking.
Q And that –
A I think he was maybe heeding my, my advice from, from the 21st, about trying to get to know me, and so he did.
Q And is it fair to say that's sort of when the friendship really starts to develop, around that time period?
A It does. That certainly helped. I think he, he was just very sweet, and he – when I got up to leave, he kissed my arm and told me he'd call me, and then I said, yeah, well, what's my phone number. And so he recited both my home number and my office number off the top of his head. So, I told him, you know, that he got an A.
And he called me in my office later that afternoon to tell me how much he enjoyed talking to me. So – and then again called Wednesday night to tell me again how much he had

Page 34

enjoyed talking to me.
So, it – I think that certainly was a turning point in the relationship, where it kind of went from a – obviously there's, there's some personal and intimate aspects of a sexual relationship that develop just in talking or laughing or getting to the point where you, where you kiss someone on every encounter. But for me, I think that spending the time talking to him was certainly when I, when I got to know him as a person and started to realize that he wasn't necessarily the person I thought he was at that point.
Q Let's move on to the next date, which is March 31st, 1996, the next encounter where there is physically intimate contact. Why don't you tell us how that date was set up and what happened?
A I had spoken – well, just to back up real quickly. The President had ended things on the, I think it was the 19th of February. But then he had called me later – I think it was late February or early March at some point – indicating to me he wanted to sort of see me again, possibly for some intimate moments.
And it wasn't until the 31st of March that we really were together again physically. But he had called, I think two times, two times prior during that work week, leading up to the 31st. And it was on the Friday night which is, looking at the chart, which was the 29th, that I, I asked

Page 35

him if I could see him on Sunday. And he said, he'd, you know, he'd see what he could do.
And then on Sunday, he called me in my office and – let's see. I believe – oh, I believe that I brought him papers that day. That I think I asked him to tell the guard outside that he was expecting some papers, expecting someone from Leg Affairs. And then when I got to the door, I told them that I was supposed to bring papers to the President.
Q And that was part of a ruse to –
A Yes.
Q – get in to see him?
A Exactly.
Q Just to back up for a second, you mentioned that you had had some phone calls with him between February 19th, '96 when he tried to cut off the relationship –
A Yes.
Q – or the sexual part of the relationship –
A Correct.
Q – and the 31st, in which he had suggested that he wanted to perhaps renew the intimacy. What led you to believe that?
A I saw him on my way out one evening. It was late. And he was on his way home from, I think it was the Israeli Embassy and Evelyn Lieberman was with him. So, I certainly made a point of not having any eye contact or anything with

Page 36

him. And he called me later that evening and said he had, he had – after he left and went upstairs, he went back to his office and had called me in my office, hoping that I could come have a visit with him, but I had already gone home.
And so then I offered, I said, well, I could come back. And he said, no, I'm upstairs already. So.
Q Back now to March 31st –
A Yes.
Q – of '96. So, what happens then? How actually is that then finally set up?
A He had called me in my office and then I brought papers there, or fake papers.
Q Do you then go into the Oval Office?
A Yes, I do.
Q And what happens?
A We went into the back study and we were in the, the hallway area. And it had sort of become actually a ritual sort of at this point, that we always kind of started out our meetings, that he was leaning against the closed door of the bathroom and I would rub his back, because he has a bad back. So, I used to always rub his back, and sometimes he'd rub my back. But I usually concentrated on his lower back because it was always bothering him.
And, you know, and then I'd usually move around and sort of just lovingly touch his chest and –

Page 37

Q Was there any removal of clothing?
A Yes, there was. We kissed and, and he had not been feeling well, I guess, the past couple of days. So, really, most of – he focused on me pretty exclusively, I guess, in a sexual manner on me that day, and kissed me, and kissed my breasts, and he, he fondled my genitals with his hands.
Q Through clothing or not through clothing?
A Not through clothing.
Q Did you have your underwear removed? Or how did your clothes get off?
A (No response.)
Q Or were they simply pulled out of the way?
A I think I – I think that they were just sort of – oh.
Q Pulled out of the way?
A Yeah.
Q Okay. So, he touched you. And with your breasts, was that through clothing, through your brassiere, or did he move your breasts out of the way of the brassiere?
A It was, it was both. I mean, it was always both. He – there was never a time when he just touched my breasts through –
Q The bra?
A – the bra, right.
Q On that occasion, did the President ever insert a

Page 38

cigar into your vagina?

A Yes.

Q Whose idea was that?

A On – when I met with him on January 7th, after we had been intimate and we were talking in the Oval Office, he was chewing on a cigar. And then he had the cigar in his hand and he was kind of looking at the cigar in a, sort of a naughty way. And so I, I looked at the cigar and I looked at him and I said, we can do that, too, some time.

And I don't, I don't really remember how it got started, but.

Q Was it part of the sexual encounter that he did that?

A Yes, it was.

Q Did you understand it to be arousing?

A It was.

Q Okay. What happened to the cigar afterwards?

A He put it in his mouth and he said it tasted good.

Q How did you leave that encounter? So, you didn't perform oral sex on him at all that time?

A No.

Q How –

A Actually, looking also – I should mention that, looking at the chart, that I didn't bring papers that day. I brought this tie to him in a folder. So, sometimes I brought

Page 39

papers and this day it was I had a tie, and there probably were some papers in the folder as well.

Q And that's the Hugo Boss tie that's listed under the gift category for that date?

A Correct.

Q The next encounter is April 7th, 1996. Could you describe how that encounter was set up?

A The President had called me at home sort of in the early evening, and this was – it was Easter Sunday and it was the first, it was the Sunday after I had found out I was to be transferred to the Pentagon. And he called – it also had been the week that Ron Brown had passed away.

So, I asked him how he was doing and we talked about that for a little bit. And then I told him that Monday was my last day, and that I had been transferred. And I was crying and he wanted to know what happened, and I asked him if I could come see him. And he said, that's fine, but just tell me what happened first. So, I explained to him what had happened, and then he told me to come on over. So, I did.

And this is when I had this little encounter trying to get into the office with John Muskett, just that he said – I brought papers with me from home in a folder. And so John had said something about wanting to check with Evelyn if it was okay for me to go in. And I don't remember exactly what ended up happening, but I managed to get him to not ask

Page 40

Evelyn and I got in.

And the President and I were in the back office. He was actually on the phone when I came in. And then when he got off the phone, we went into the back office and we talked again about what had happened, in terms of my transfer.

And that was when he, he looked me in the eye and he promised me – well, first he said that he couldn't believe that they were taking me away from him because he trusted me so much, and he was convinced that it had something to do with him, why I was being transferred. And then he looked me in the eye and he said, I promise you, if I win in November, I'll have you back like that [snapping fingers].

Q Did he say anything like, if you do a good job at the Pentagon he'll bring you back?

A No.

Q So, what else happened at that meeting?

A I, I don't remember how it exactly came about, but I know that, that, I remember kissing him and we were physically intimate.

Q In terms of the physical intimacy that day, did the President touch your genitals on that date?

A I don't think so.

Q What about your breasts?

Page 41

A Yes.

Q With his mouth or with his hands, or both?

A With both.

Q And again, I'm assuming, unless you correct me now, that it's both through clothing and directly on the skin?

A Yes.

Q With respect to oral sex, do you just remember how that occurred, whether his pants came off, whether somebody unzipped them?

A I think he unzipped them and – because it was sort of this running joke that I could never unbutton his pants, that I just had trouble with it. So, I was – you know, there were times that I tried and we'd laugh and then he'd, he'd do it.

But we were – I, I performed oral sex in the, in the back office.

Q And at that time, did he ejaculate?

A No, he did not.

Q Was there any discussion with him about the ejaculation at that time that you can remember?

A No.

Q On that date, I think you've already testified that there was a phone call during your sexual encounter with him, is that right?

A Yes, there was.

Page 42

Q Did you perform oral sex while he was on the telephone?

A Yes. It was, it was – I think I'll just say, because for – there are a lot of people that could interpret that as being sort of a, that being done in a servicing sort of manner, and it was more done in kind of an exciting sort of – I don't want to say erotic, but in a way that there was kind of this titillating like a secret, in a sense, in the same way sometimes that an affair is, that, you know, when you are doing this and obviously there is kind of the irony that the person on the other line has no idea what's going on.

So, I just wanted to clarify that.

Q Okay. Although on that occasion, I believe you previously mentioned that that was the first time that you felt a little funny about it?

A I, I did. I did. I, I, I, I was, I was pretty emotionally devastated at that point, and the prospect of going to the Pentagon was very upsetting to me. And there were moments when I felt a little uncomfortable, and moments when I didn't.

Q Although you mentioned that there were other times that he was on the phone, that you didn't think sort of anything bad about it –

A Right.

Page 43

Q – and on this occasion, you felt more like –

A I just –

Q – you were servicing –

A Exactly.

Q – on some level. And did you tell Linda Tripp about that, do you remember?

A Probably.

Q How did that encounter end, if you remember? And actually you've already testified a little bit about this. So, just if you could quickly summarize how you finished the encounter and what happened?

A We were in the back office and I heard Mr. Ickes call, say, Mr. President, from the Oval Office. And we both were startled and looked at each other, and he jetted into the Oval and I –

Q Were you performing oral sex at the time?

A I think so, but I'm not a hundred percent sure. And so then I, I left.

Q On that occasion also, when the President went to get the phone call, had you started performing oral sex on him before he went to take the phone call?

A Yes, I believe that we were – I think that that was it. I know that we were, we were intimate in the hallway, and then it was a phone call that prompted us to go into the office. And that when we were in the office, that,

Page 44

that he, he removed, he sort of removed his pants.
Q How did you know that you were supposed to kind of accompany him to take the phone call? Did he –
A I don't remember.
Q – invite you to come in, in any way, or gesture for you to come along?
A I don't really remember.
Q So, you think you actually didn't begin the oral sex until he was on the phone already?
A It's –
Q Or is it not that clear?
A It's not that clear.
Q But you remember him unzipping his pants at some point?
A At some point, yes.
Q Before the oral sex?
A Yes.
Q Okay.
A I hope so.
Q At that point, and I didn't really ask you this for the other encounters, but in terms of putting your stuff back on or collecting yourself, is there any sort of general way that that happened? Did the President help you, or how did you get dressed again?
A Well, neither of us ever really took – completely

Page 45

took off any piece of our clothing, I think specifically because of the possibility of encounters, like what happened that day. But there had, earlier in that day on the 7th, when I -- not earlier in the day, but earlier in the encounter with the President – when he had been kissing my breasts, someone had come in, I think to tell him he had the phone call, or something like that.
Or someone had come in at some point and he stepped out of the office, and I had put my bra and my sweater back on. And he came in and sort of made a remark about me having done that. And –
Q Do you remember the remark?
A I think he smirked and he sort of said, you know, damn, you put your top back on, or something like that. Or, why did you do that, something like that. But he was smirking and joking with me.
But then when he went into the Oval, when Mr. Ickes came in, I put myself together and hurried out the back way through the dining room.
Q The next encounter. There's luckily a big gap there. The next one is February 28th. How was this encounter set up, and then what happened?
A Betty called me at work to tell me, or to invite me to the radio address for that evening. And so I went.
Q Did she say anything about that you would see the

Page 46

President on that date, or –
A Yes. I mean, she, she had indicated to me the President wanted me to come to this radio address. So that – and I knew that he had – we had spoken earlier that month and the month before, and the month before that, and I knew he had a Christmas gift for me which he had yet to give me. So, it sort of seemed, it was understandable.
I went to the radio address. And then – it was a very small group, maybe 10 people, six, 10 people. It was quite small. And after – or when I went to go take my picture with him, he told me to go see Betty or go wait with Betty because he had something to give me. So, I went into Betty's office and was waiting there with her. There were some other people there, staff members. And I think I've gone through the whole –
Q And you've actually testified in some detail about this before.
A Right.
Q So, actually, why don't we just go to the sexual encounter –
A Okay.
Q – and how the actual sexual part started?
A Once we were alone in the back office, he started to say something to me and I was pestering him to kiss me, because I hadn't – we hadn't been alone in almost a year and

Page 47

– well, I guess not a year, but it had been a long time since we had been alone. And so he, you know, he jokingly told me to, you know, just wait a sec, he wanted to give me my presents.
So, he gave me my hatpin and he sort of hurriedly put the Leaves Of Grass in my purse and he said, here, just take this with me. And then I said, what is it. I took the book out and so we, we were looking at it, and I was just, I thought it was pretty incredible. It was just a beautiful, beautiful book, and it meant a lot to me.
And then we went back over by the bathroom in the hallway, and we kissed. We were kissing and he unbuttoned my dress and fondled my breasts with my bra on, and then took them out of my bra and was kissing them and touching them with his hands and with his mouth.
[redacted]
And I continued to perform oral sex and then he pushed me away, kind of as he always did before he came, and then I stood up and I said, you know, I really, I care about you so much; I really, I don't understand why you won't let

Page 48

me, you know, make you come; it's important to me; I mean, it just doesn't feel complete, it doesn't seem right.
And so he – we hugged. And, you know, he said he didn't want to get addicted to me, and he didn't want me to get addicted to him. And we were just sort of looking at each other and then, you know, he sort of, he looked at me, he said, okay. And so then I finished.
Q [redacted]
A [redacted]
Q [redacted]
A [redacted]
Q Did he touch your genitals at all during that occasion, do you remember?
A I think through my tights, but not direct genital.
Q How did the meeting then end, or the encounter?
A We, well, we kissed after –
Q The ejaculation?
A Yes. And then I think Betty knocked on the door. So, I think – no, no, no, no, no, that's not right, because I fixed my lipstick. So, I think we sort of – I think he said, oh, you've got to put yourself back together again. And so then I went and I got my lipstick and I put my lipstick back on, and then Betty knocked on the door.
Q The dress that you were wearing on this occasion, is that the blue dress from the Gap?

Page 49

A Unfortunately, yes.
Q And I think we've already gone into detail about the dress on that. The next encounter is March 29th, 1997. Would you tell us how that encounter was set up?
A It was, it was set up through my conversations with Betty.
Q Did you contact Betty?
A Yes. I contacted Betty and Betty – my understanding was Betty spoke with the President, and then Betty got in touch with me and told me to come that afternoon. I did. I was waiting for the President in the back study and then he hobbled in because he was on crutches. And we were, we were in the back office. Actually, it was sort of an overcast day. It had been raining earlier. So, it was just sort of dark and overcast.
And we were, he was – I think he had put his crutches down and he was kind of leaning on me. So, I was holding him, you know, I mean, sort of romantically but at the same time literally holding him. And –
Q This is in the back study?
A Uh-huh, yes. And I was – this was another one of those occasions when I was babbling on about something, and he just kissed me, kind of to shut me up, I think. And so we were kissing and then we sort of – we turned around and he was leaning against – he has a little, it's like a little

Page 50

table that I think has this stereo. I don't know if the stereo was always there. I know it was there later. But he was leaning against this little table a little bit just, I think, kind of for support.

And he unbuttoned my blouse and just sort of touched me over, over my bra. And I don't think he took, I don't think he exposed my breasts that day. And we were, we were just kissing a lot.

And then he – oh, he went to go put his hand down my pants, and then I unzipped them because it was easier. And I didn't have any panties on. And so he manually stimulated me.

Q Did he bring you to orgasm?
A Yes, four times.
Q [redacted]
A [redacted]
Q [redacted]
A [redacted]
Q [redacted]
A [redacted]
Q [redacted]
A [redacted]
Q How did you end the contact with him on that

Page 51

occasion?
A End the sexual contact? Or –
Q The sexual contact?
A He – oh, well, this was also the day that before, before I performed oral sex on him, I wanted him to touch my genitals with his genitals. And so we sort of had tried to do that, but because he's really tall and he couldn't bend because of his knee, it didn't really work.
Q And I think you've previously testified your genitals grazed each other –
A Exactly.
Q – on that occasion?
A I mean, just barely.
Q And when they grazed each other, neither of you had clothes covering your genitals, is that right?
A Correct.
Q How did you end the encounter completely that time, in terms of ending the meeting?
A Oh, we moved into the dining room and we were talking for a long time. I had brought some presents for him. So, we talked for awhile. And then Betty came back and the three of us were talking.
Q Let's move on to the next one, which is August 16th, 1997.
A I – this was sort of his, his birthday, his

Page 52

birthday encounter. And so after – I had set up in his back office, I had brought an apple square and put a candle and had put his birthday presents out. And after he came back in and I sang happy birthday and he got his presents, I asked him if we could, if we could share a birthday kiss in honor of our birthdays, because mine had been just a few weeks before. So, he said that that was okay and we could kind of bend the rules that day.

And so we, we, we kissed. And then I was touching him in his genital area through his shorts, and then I, I went to, to –
Q Perform oral sex?
A Yes, and he wouldn't let me.
Q Did he touch you on your genitals on that date?
A No.
Q Any other physical contact that is referred to as physical intimacy on that date?
A Not that I remember.
Q How did you end that encounter with him? Any discussion about sex during that encounter, or not having sex?
A No, just he got upset when I, you know, when he stopped me and he said, I'm trying to not do this and I'm trying to be good. And he, he got visibly upset. And so I, I hugged him and I told him I was sorry and not to be upset,

Page 53

and I was a little shocked, actually. I didn't – he just seemed to get so emotionally upset about it. It seemed a little bit strange to me.
Q And he hadn't done that before?
A He had been emotionally visibly upset with me before, but not –
Q With regard to –
A Correct.
Q – stopping you from having sex with him?
A Exactly.
Q Or having sexual contact with him? Is that correct?
A Yes.
Q And is that, other than any brief kiss, the last physically intimate contact that you've had with him?
A Well, our Christmas kiss was – I mean, it was passionate. So.
Q Okay. It was –
A I don't call it a brief kiss.
Q That was a physically intimate kiss. Any other contact that would fall within the sexual relations definition –
A No.
Q – that we've previously seen?
A I think we, you know, we would, we would joke with

Page 54

each other sexually. And so sometimes, you know, I might hit him on the butt, or he might hit me on the butt, but it wasn't – not under the definition.
Q So, it wouldn't be a real intent to arouse, or not the physical touching that is described –
A No.
Q – in the definition?
A No.
Q All right. Let's move on to another topic.
A Yea.
Q Thank you for your patience. I know that those are not easy questions to get to.
A It's just hard thinking my dad might see this.
Q Why don't we move to another emotional topic, July 4th, just briefly. Is now a good time to –
A Sure.
Q – talk about that? Why don't you tell us – I know that you've brought up in your grand jury testimony that July 4th of 1997 was an emotional day for you in connection with your relationship with the President.
A Yes.
Q Could you just briefly tell us what you meant by that and just a little bit about your meeting with him on that date?
A Our meeting had started out in, as a, in a fight.

Page 55

We – and early on in this fight, I started crying, and then he – we were in the back office and he came over and was hugging me and told me not to cry, to stop crying, and was very – he was very sweet, and was very gentle.

And then we – I – there was a gardener outside. So, when I noticed the gardener, I pointed it out and we moved to the, into the hallway by the bathroom. And much of the discussion that day was he spent a lot of time talking to me, you know, about the kind of person he thought I was, and – I'm a little bit modest. So, it's sort of – it's hard for me to get into all the things he said. But, there just –
Q Did he say wonderful things about you?
A He did.
Q Like what kinds of things?
A Just that he thought I was smart and beautiful, and that – you know, but that a lot of it, it centered around my needing to learn to, to sort of squelch a bit of the fire in my belly. And that, you know, he said that people like us who, you know, have a tendency to get really angry and that there are a lot of other people that, that, that don't understand that and don't know how to handle that.

And he just – he spent a lot of time talking to me. He was very, very – he was the most affectionate with me he'd ever been. There wasn't a second when he wouldn't be

Page 56

touching me, whether it was holding my hand or stroking my arm or, you know, he'd kiss my neck at one point. It was just – or he'd, you know, put his hands, he was running his hands through my hair and touching my face. And my bra strap kept falling down my shoulder. So, he kept pushing my bra strap up.

It was just very – it was intense. It was just really emotionally intense.

And at one point, we, we had been talking about – I made some remarks to him about his relationship with Mrs. Clinton. And he, he remarked a little bit later than that that he wished he had more time for me. And so I said, well, maybe you will have more time in three years. And I was actually sort of thinking just when he wasn't President, he was going to have more time on his hands. And he said, well, I don't know, I might be alone in three years.

And then I said something about, you know, us sort of being together. I think I kind of said, oh, I think we'd be a good team, or something like that. And he, you know, he jokingly said, well, what are we going to do when I'm 75 and I have to pee 25 times a day. And I, you know, I told him that we'd deal with that. And it was – there was just this incredible connection.

And I, I left that day sort of emotionally stunned, because I felt – I was shocked. But I thought, I mean, he

Page 57

was – I just knew he was in love with me, and from the way he acted that day, and that's not, it's not something that I would, that I would think easily. It's not a conclusion that I would come to easily at all. And it just – with the kind of person I am.

And I knew I was in love with him, you know, a year before, and I thought he cared about me. But just the way he looked at me and touched me, and the things he said, it just – it was so obvious to me. And it was shocking. So, it was a bizarre day.

Q Anything else about the 4th?
A Not that I don't think I've gone over before.
Q Okay. We'll switch to a completely different topic. You previously testified that on December 17th –
A You know, I need a –
Q Do you want a break?
A I'd like just a break.
Q Sure, absolutely.
(Whereupon, the deposition was recessed from 1:57 p.m. until 2:07 p.m.)
BY MS. IMMERGUT:
Q Ms. Lewinsky, you are still under oath.
A Yes.
Q We are going to cover some other areas, hopefully quickly. You previously testified that on December 17th,

Page 58

during your phone call with the President – and that's in 1997 –
A Yes.
Q – when you were discussing various things, including that your name had appeared on the witness list, that the President told you that if you were ever subpoenaed that you should contact Betty?
A That's correct.
Q Did he ever tell you at that time that you should get a lawyer?
A I don't believe so. No.
Q When you say "I don't believe so", are you quite certain of that?
A I'm, I'm 99.9 percent certain.
Q What would you have done if he had told you that you should get a lawyer?
A I would have started to think about how I was going to get a lawyer and who I should get, and I didn't do that. So, that's what leads me to believe that he didn't say that.
Q Okay. Were you ever under the impression from anything that the President said that you should turn over all the gifts that he had given you to the Paula Jones attorneys?
A No.
Q Did you ever talk to the President about turning

Page 59

gifts over to the Jones lawyers before you were ever subpoenaed?
A No.
Q Did you actually ever talk to him about the fact that gifts could be subpoenaed prior to them actually being subpoenaed?
A No.
Q So, is it fair to say that the only time you talked about the gifts from the President, in connection with the subpoena, was on December 28th?
A That's correct.
Q Directing your attention to January 5th of 1998, when you had a telephone call with the President, you previously testified that you had some discussion about a book that you had purchased for him?
A Correct.
Q That was the book that you gave to Betty Currie on approximately January 4th to give to the President? Is that right?
A Yes.
Q What was the name of that book again? It was the book on the Presidents.
A It was a book about the Presidents of the United States.
Q Do you remember when you purchased that book?

Page 60

A I believe it was that weekend, the weekend prior to the 5th.
Q Did you ever talk to him, during your meeting of December 28th, 1997, about the fact that you were going to give him that book?
A No.
Q How do you know that you didn't?
A Because I hadn't purchased the book yet.
Q Had you even thought about purchasing that particular book?
A No. It was bought on the spur of the moment.
Q Do you remember where you bought it?
A At a little bookstore in Georgetown, an antique book store.
Q I'm going to switch topics again. Do you believe that if you hadn't had a sexual relationship with the President that you would have kept your job at the White House?
A Yes.
Q Do you believe that your difficulty or inability to return to employment at the White House was because of your sexual relationship with him?
A Yes. Or the issues that, or the problems that people perceived that really were based in truth because I had a relationship with the President. But, however, some of

Page 61

the people who worked there chose to, to see some of my behavior. Does that make sense?
Q What do you mean by that?
A I think that – I've always felt that some of the, some of the staffers there, particularly Evelyn Lieberman and those who worked with her to move me out of the White House, instead – looked at my behavior only, instead of looking at the President's behavior, and instead of necessarily thinking that I had a relationship with the President, were just looking at it thinking I was trying to have a relationship with the President when I already was having a relationship with him. They turned a blind eye to his actions.
Q During 1997, did you feel that the President owed you something with respect to a job?
A I did, because he, he had promised me on April 7th of '96 that he would bring me back when, if he won in November. And I had – when he first told me that, I had had some hope and I didn't, I didn't even know if I was going to hear from him again after I left. And then when he continued to call me frequently during the campaign period, it led me to believe he would bring me back.

And then after we had a – it was after a period when he didn't call me and I wasn't sure about things, what was happening – I'm sorry. I'm not being clear.

Because he had sort of led me to believe that he

Page 62

was going to bring me back and was constantly reassuring that, I, I believe that he did owe that to me. Versus him having said, I'm really sorry – let's just say in April of '96 – I'm really sorry that this happened, there's not, you know, there's nothing I can do, and left it at that. Then I wouldn't have felt that he owed me anything.
Q What about the fact that you had gone quietly and not revealed your relationship? Did that have anything to do with your feeling that you were entitled to something?
A It did later on. I, I would have gone quietly anyway, because that – it was never, ever, ever my intention for this relationship to ever become public. And – but I had felt that after having left quietly, after having been sort of maybe strung along throughout the campaign and then even way into 1997, that I had felt – and him promising me that he'd bring me back and constantly enumerating the different steps he was trying to take to do that – that, yes, I did feel at that point he, he certainly owed me.
Q Is that part of your letter of July 3rd to the President in 1997, where you described it previously as threatening to disclose the relationship, at least to your parents, was that part of your feeling that –
A It was never really a, a, maybe a – it was never really a threat, because I never really was going to do that. While I had disclosed a portion of the relationship to my

Page 63

mom, I never had any intention of telling my dad. There's no way of that.
And what I really was trying to do was trying to, in a circuitous manner, remind him that I had been a good girl, and that I hadn't, you know, disclosed this information, and that really, you know, he'd promised me he was going to do something. And I had told my parents, I had told my dad that I was coming back after the election.
Q I'd like to focus now just very briefly on your dealings with Ambassador Richardson with regard to the U.N. job.
A Yes.
Q How many times did Ambassador Richardson call you directly, do you remember?
A Do you mean someone from his – he never directly picked up the phone and dialed my phone number.
Q Let me ask a different question.
A Okay.
Q How many times did you speak to him personally?
A I believe twice.
Q And when I say personally, on the telephone?
A Yes.
Q How do you know that you actually spoke with him on those occasions?
A Well, the first time I spoke with him I remember,

Page 64

because I was shocked and I was, I was very nervous. And –
Q Because the Ambassador was on the phone?
A Exactly. And the second, the second time I actually hadn't really remembered, I wasn't sure. And then through documentation I was shown, it, it led me to believe that I had, in fact, spoken to him on the phone.
Q But you are positive at least one time you did, in fact, speak to him personally?
A Yes.
Q Do you remember which occasion that was, or when that occurred?
A Yes, it was sometime in October.
Q Was that the October 23rd call? Does that sound right?
A Yes.
Q And that's prior to your actual interview with him?
A Correct.
Q I'd like to just ask you very briefly about your conversation with the President the night before your interview with Ambassador Richardson for the U.N. job. Could you describe who initiated that call and what the substance of the call was?
A I had – well, I had requested through Betty that the President call me, because I was really nervous about my interview and meeting with Ambassador Richardson. I just, I

Page 65

didn't, I didn't want to make anyone look bad. I didn't want to sound like a fool, or – so, the President called me and we talked about some of the different issues at the U.N., and he gave me some suggestions of things I could say. But I think he may have also done that the previous week, too.
Q Do you remember him giving you sort of a job pep talk on –
A Yes.
Q –the 30th?
A Yes.
Q Why would you describe it as a pep talk?
A Because I was nervous. So, he, he was trying to kind of build my confidence and reassure me, you know, reassure me that I was an intelligent person, and that I had a lot to offer and that they would be happy to have me there.
Q At some point, did you tell the President that you got an offer from the U.N.?
A I believe so.
Q Did you tell Betty also that you had gotten an offer?
A Yes.
Q Do you remember any details about talking to Betty about it, or how you let her know?
A I, I remember calling Betty after the interview and telling her that it had gone much better than I had expected

Page 66

it would, and that I was really, that I was, that I was somewhat more interested after having met the Ambassador than I was prior to the interview. And other than that, I don't really.
Q What about details about your conversation with the President telling him that you had gotten the job?
A I vaguely remember it being in context, I think, of sort of trying to press him on getting in touch with Mr. Jordan.
Q In terms of getting other jobs –
A Exactly.
Q – you let him know this?
A Exactly.
Q That you had an offer from the U.N.?
A Right.
Q Do you remember when you got the U.N. offer?
A No.
Q Was it sometime, in relation to your interview with the Ambassador –
A It was sooner, rather than later.
Q So, sometime within a matter of a week or –
A I believe so.
Q – some weeks?
A Somewhere within a couple, within the next two weeks or so.

Page 67

Q And did they tell you that they would leave the job open until a certain time, for you to make the decision if you wanted it?
A Not at the point when I got the offer. I, I – and actually I think, thinking now I'm a little bit more clearer that I did speak with the Ambassador, that he was the one who, who extended the offer to me, because I remember being nervous and not knowing what to say to him, because I didn't really want the job. And so I sort of just "yessed" him along and thanked him profusely, and told him I was excited about it.
And then I later spoke, I believe, with Mona Sutphen, and sort of relayed to her that I was interested in also trying to feel out the private sector. So, and I believe it was at that point that she said, well, let's keep in touch. We can – this position, I think, had been open for awhile. So.
Q Did she give you any timeframe at all about how long they would wait for you to make a decision?
A It was – I think we talked about talking maybe in a few weeks, and then at some point we said, let's get in touch around the first of January. And I was under the impression that, you know, I believed that they would hold the position open for me, but that it didn't necessarily –
Q It's not a guarantee?

Page 68

A Exactly.
Q But they weren't rushing you to make an immediate decision?
A No.
Q So, you understand you basically had some leeway until January 1998 to make a decision?
A Correct.
Q January 16th, 1998, Ritz Carlton night. I really have just one question about it, which was, was there a time that you, in fact, during the course of the evening, that you, in fact, did leave the prosecutors and agents by yourself?
A Yes, when I was given, finally given permission to go call my mom. I wasn't comfortable using the phone in the room.
Q So, you went out by yourself to –
A Yes, I did.
Q Where did you go make a phone call?
A To Nordstrom's.
Q And –
A It was just one phone call, to my mother. And there was also a time – I think one of the prosecutors came with me, I think it was Stephen Bin –
Q Binhak?
A – I think, came downstairs with me. I used – I

Page 69

needed to return a phone call from a page. And then when I was with Mr. Emmick and Agent [redacted] they let me go to the bathroom in Macy's by myself.
Q Were you in Macy's for some time by yourself?
A Well, it, it took awhile to find a bathroom. It was kind of far away. So.
Q So, they didn't follow you into the bathroom?
A They didn't follow me in. But then when I came back, Agent [redacted] had gone looking for me. So.
Q And just with respect to the phone call to call your mother, no one accompanied you for that, is that right?
A No.
Q And finally –
A I just, I do want to state that I did – because I know this sort of goes to this issue of being, you know, kind of told, oh, you're free to leave whenever you want, that I didn't really – I didn't feel at any point that I could leave whenever I wanted, that I could – that I was afraid that if I had left the Mall, I would be arrested and put in jail. So, that was my impression.
Q One last question from me. Do you, for any reason now, want to hurt the President?
A No. I'm, I'm upset with him right now, but I, no, that's the last thing in the world I want to do.
MS. IMMERGUT: That's all I have.

Page 70

MS. WIRTH: I just have one question.
BY MS. WIRTH:
Q From your grand jury testimony last week, on August 20th, 1998, you were talking about your understanding of the President's testimony. I'm just going to read a portion of your testimony to you and ask you a question about that. This is in response to a question from a juror.
You said, "I'm sorry. I'm sorry. It's – from my understanding about what he testified to on Monday, not – just from the press accounts, is that this was a – that this was a service contract, that all I did was perform oral sex on him and that that's all that this relationship was. And it was a lot more than that to me and I thought it was a lot more than that."
And the answer continues a little bit more after that.
The question I have for you is that when you mentioned your understanding of what the President testified to on the previous Monday, from what did you derive your understanding of what the President's testimony was?
A From the press accounts I had read.
Q Okay. No one from this office divulged to you anything that the President said during his testimony, did they?
A Absolutely not.

Page 0

MR. WIRTH: Thank you.
MS. IMMERGUT: Nothing further. Do you have any questions?
THE WITNESS: No.
(Whereupon, at 2:24 p.m., the proceedings were concluded.)
* * * *

CERTIFICATE OF COURT REPORTER - NOTARY PUBLIC

I, Elizabeth A. Eastman, the officer before whom the foregoing deposition was taken, do hereby certify that the witness whose testimony appears in the foregoing deposition was duly sworn by me; that the testimony of said witness was taken by me electronically and thereafter reduced to typewriting by me; that said deposition is a true record of the testimony given by said witness; that I am neither counsel for, related to, nor employed by any of the parties to the action in which this deposition was taken; and, further, that I am not a relative or employee of any attorney or counsel employed by the parties hereto, nor financially or otherwise interested in the outcome of the action.

NOTARY PUBLIC FOR THE
DISTRICT OF COLUMBIA
My Commission Expires:
July 31, 2000

Concordance Report

Unique Words: **1,103**

Total Occurrences: **3,687**

Total Words In File: **14,847**

Single File Concordance

Case Sensitive

Cover Pages = **1**

Includes **ALL** Text Occurrences

Dates **ON**

Includes Pure Numbers

Possesive Forms **ON**

-- D --

-- E --

-- F --

Tab 16

OIC-302 (Rev. 8-19-94)

- 1 -

OFFICE OF THE INDEPENDENT COUNSEL

Date of transcription 1/23/98

On January 16, 1998, SSA [redacted] and SA [redacted]. approached MONICA LEWINSKY in the food court area of the Pentagon City, Mall Arlington, Virginia. SSA [redacted] immediately identified himself and SA [redacted] as agents of the Federal Bureau of Investigation (FBI), detailed to the Office of the Independent Counsel (OIC) for "Whitewater" and requested her presence in a room of the Ritz Carlton Hotel to discuss her status as a person suspected of committing a federal crime. LEWINSKY was advised OIC attorneys were waiting in the room, and that the agents and the attorneys wished to discuss her culpability in criminal activity related to the PAULA JONES civil lawsuit. LEWINSKY was advised she was not under arrest and the agents would not force her to accompany them to the hotel room. LEWINSKY told SSA [redacted] he could speak to her attorney. SSA [redacted] advised the offer to discuss her legal status was not being offered to her attorney, but to LEWINSKY alone. SSA [redacted] explained to LEWINSKY she was being offered an opportunity to meet with the OIC attorneys and agents and hear them explain why they felt she was in trouble without being required to make any statement. SSA [redacted] further explained LEWINSKY would then have an opportunity to ask clarifying questions of the attorneys and be better informed as to whether she wanted legal counsel before making any statements, or whether she thought it better to cooperate with the OIC. LEWINSKY voluntarily accompanied the agents to room number 1012 of the Ritz Carlton hotel, under the conditions set forth above.

Also present in room 1016, the adjoining room, were Associate Independent Counsel (AIC) BRUCE UDOLF, AIC MICHAEL EMMICK, AIC STEVEN D. BINHAK, Deputy Independent Counsel JACKIE M. BENNETT, JR., AIC STEPHEN BATES and Contract Investigator COY A. COPELAND, all members of the Office of the Independent Counsel staff. At various times during the day, OIC attorneys entered and departed room 1012. Their movement is not recorded herein. The chronology of the meeting, with all times approximate, is as follows:

1:05 p.m. Room	LEWINSKY arrived in Room 1012. AIC EMMICK entered 1012 and began talking to LEWINSKY.
1:10 p.m.	LEWINSKY given bottled water.

Investigation on 1/16/98 at Pentagon City, VA File # 29D-OIC-LR-35063

by SA [redacted] SSA [redacted]
SA [redacted] Date dictated 1/23/98

al

OIC-302a (Rev. 8-19-94)

29D-LR-35063

Continuation of OIC-302 of Log of meeting at Pentagon City, On 1/16/98, Page 2

1:33 p.m.	SSA [redacted] began reading LEWINSKY her rights as found on the form FD-395, "Interrogation; Advice of Rights." SSA [redacted] was unable to finish reading the FD-395.
1:40 p.m.	LEWINSKY was offered a towel.
1:47 p.m.	LEWINKSY was offered water.
2:02 p.m.	The air conditioning in room 1012 was turned on at LEWINSKY's request.
2:13 p.m.	LEWINKSY was offered water. LEWINSKY said, "if I don't cooperate, I can talk to whomever I want".
2:15 p.m.	SA [redacted] arrived in room 1012.
2:29 p.m.	LEWINSKY stated, "if I leave now, you will charge me now."
2:30 p.m.	LEWINSKY said, "I don't know much about the law."
2:33 p.m.	LEWINSKY asked and was allowed to go to the restroom.
2:36 p.m.	LEWINSKY requested and was given her second bottle of water. LEWINSKY said she is not diabetic and no medication was necessary.
2:50 p.m.	LEWINSKY suggested she take a taxi to her attorney's office. LEWINSKY advised she understands our risks.
3:10 p.m.	LEWINSKY asked if she could be escorted to New York to see her mother, MARCIA LEWIS.
3:20 p.m.	LEWINSKY called her mother, MARCIA LEWIS, in New York.
3:36 p.m.	LEWINSKY requested and was allowed to go to the restroom.

29D-LR-35063

3:45 p.m.	LEWINSKY departed room 1012 unescorted.
3:54 p.m.	LEWINSKY called room 1012 and advised that she was in the lobby, using a pay phone. LEWINSKY advised she changed phones she was using because some people came too close to the phone she had been using. LEWINSKY advised she called to let the Agents know, in case she was being watched.
4:08 p.m.	LEWINSKY voluntarily returned to room 1012. LEWINSKY offered and accepted coffee.
4:12 p.m.	LEWINSKY called MARCIA LEWIS. LEWIS requested to speak with an OIC attorney. AIC EMMICK and SA [redacted] got on the phone and identified themselves to LEWIS. LEWIS advised she would travel to Washington, DC via AMTRAK Metroliner.
4:20 p.m.	LEWINSKY left room 1012 with AIC BINHAK and SA [redacted] to use a pay phone in the lobby of the Ritz Carlton Hotel.
4:31 p.m.	LEWINSKY, AIC BINHAK and SA [redacted] returned to room 1012.
5:00 p.m.	LEWINSKY called her answering machine to retrieve messages.
5:21 p.m.	LEWINSKY requested and received aspirin.
5:40 p.m.	LEWINSKY, AIC EMMICK and SA [redacted] departed room 1012, en route to the Pentagon City Mall. LEWINSKY, AIC EMMICK and SA [redacted] walked in the mall.
6:03 p.m.	LEWINKSY requested and was permitted to visit the restroom on the third level of the MACY's department store in the mall.
6:30 p.m.	LEWINSKY, AIC EMMICK and SA [redacted] dined at MOZZARELLA'S American Grill, within the Pentagon City Mall. LEWINSKY paid for her portion of the dinner.

OIC-302a (Rev. 8-19-94)

29D-LR-35063

Continuation of OIC-302 of Log of meeting at Pentagon City , On 1/16/98 , Page 4

7:35 p.m. LEWINSKY, AIC EMMICK and SA [redacted] returned to room 1012.

8:00 p.m. LEWINSKY payed $2 to SA [redacted] for the cost of her coffee.

8:19 p.m. MARCIA LEWIS telephoned room 1012, and advised she was on the "163 Northeast Direct", and was experiencing travel delays.

9:05 p.m. LEWINSKY, SSA [redacted], and SA [redacted] departed room 1012 and LEWINSKY withdrew money from the automatic teller machine on the first floor at the Pentagon City Mall.

9:30 p.m. Coffee was ordered and brought to room 1012 by room service.

10:16 p.m. MARCIA LEWIS arrived and all members of the OIC staff left LEWIS and LEWINSKY alone.

10:20 p.m. A meeting was held in room 1018 between LEWIS, AIC EMMICK, SSA [redacted] and SA [redacted].

LEWIS advised that this was an emotional experience for LEWINSKY. LEWIS advised LEWINKSY was younger than her chronological age. LEWIS asked if tapes were admissible in court. LEWIS advised she wanted to protect LEWINSKY. LEWIS asked how she would know LEWINSKY would not be charged if she cooperated. LEWIS asked about LEWINSKY's safety if LEWINSKY cooperated. LEWIS advised that LEWINSKY talked about suicide six years ago. After LEWINSKY's parents divorced, LEWINSKY saw a therapist, but she is not currently seeing one. LEWIS advised she alone could not take responsibility for convincing LEWINSKY to cooperate with the OIC.

11:02 p.m. LEWIS requested and was permitted a trip to the restroom.

11:06 p.m. LEWIS telephonically contacted BERNARD LEWINSKY, her ex-husband, at [redacted]

11:20 p.m. BERNARD LEWINSKY telephoned room 1018.

OIC-302a (Rev. 8-19-94)

29D-LR-35063

Continuation of OIC-302 of Log of meeting at Pentagon City , On 1/16/98 , Page 5

11:22 p.m. AIC EMMICK talked to BERNARD LEWINSKY. Cooperation, an interview, telephone calls, body wires and testimony were mentioned. AIC EMMICK advised BERNARD LEWINSKY that MONICA LEWINSKY was free to leave anytime she wished.

11:30 p.m. MONICA LEWINSKY entered room 1018.

11:32 p.m. MARCIA LEWIS got back on the phone with BERNARD LEWINSKY. BERNARD LEWINSKY advised he would go to a pay phone and would call back.

11:35 p.m. BERNARD LEWINSKY telephoned room 1014. BERNARD LEWINSKY advised AIC EMMICK that MONICA LEWINSKY was represented by counsel.

11:36 p.m. MONICA LEWINSKY talked to BERNARD LEWINSKY on the telephone.

11:37 p.m. AIC EMMICK spoke with BERNARD LEWINSKY. AIC EMMICK asked MONICA LEWINKSY if she had an attorney and LEWINSKY advised it was GINSBURG.

AIC EMMICK advised MONICA LEWINSKY she did not have to accept an attorney she did not select.

MONICA LEWINSKY asked if there was still a chance she would go to jail if she cooperated. MONICA LEWINSKY suggested she may have not told the truth in previous conversations. MONICA LEWINSKY asked, "what if I partially cooperate?"

MARCIA LEWIS asked what would happen if MONICA LEWINSKY gave everything but did not tape anything. MONICA LEWINSKY asked if the PAULA JONES case went away would "this" go away and was advised by AIC EMMICK "no."

MONICA LEWINSKY asked how the OIC would resolve the chance that MONICA LEWINSKY said something to LINDA TRIP that was not true.

MARCIA LEWIS advised that she appreciated the OIC

OIC-302a (Rev. 8-19-94)

29D-LR-35063

Continuation of OIC-302 of Log of meeting at Pentagon City, On 1/16/98, Page 6

members waiting until she arrived to proceed. MONICA LEWINSKY advised she appreciated having her mother present.

11:55 p.m.	BILL GINSBURG telephoned room 1018 and spoke to AIC EMMICK, who advised GINSBURG he was uncomfortable with the relationship between GINSBURG and MONICA LEWINSKY. MONICA LEWINSKY advised she was not 100% sure it was the right thing to do because GINSBURG was a medical lawyer.
11:59 p.m.	MONICA LEWINSKY advised she was represented by GINSBURG.
12:08 a.m.	GINSBURG was advised by AIC EMMICK that MONICA LEWINSKY always had the right to leave at any time.
12:17 a.m.	MONICA LEWINSKY spoke with GINSBURG, outside the presence of the OIC staff.
12:23 a.m.	AIC EMMICK ended the phone call with GINSBURG and advised MONICA LEWINSKY and MARCIA LEWIS they were free to leave.
12:30 a.m.	MARCIA LEWIS and MONICA LEWINSKY thanked the Agents and the staff of the OIC for being so kind and considerate.
12:45 a.m.	SA [redacted] and SA [redacted] escorted MARCIA LEWIS and MONICA LEWINSKY to LEWINSKY's vehicle, which was parked in the parking garage adjacent to the Pentagon City Mall.

Tab 17

OIC-302 (Rev. 8-19-94)

- 1 -

OFFICE OF THE INDEPENDENT COUNSEL

Date of transcription 5/29/98

On May 28, 1998, at approximately 8:30 a.m., MONICA S. LEWINSKY (hereinafter referred to as LEWINSKY) arrived at the Federal Building, 11000 Wilshire Boulevard, Los Angeles, California, for purposes of providing her fingerprints and handwriting exemplars to the Federal Bureau of Investigation, as agreed upon by Deputy Independent Counsel (DIC) ROBERT BITTMAN of the Office of the Independent Counsel (OIC) and WILLIAM GINSBURG, LEWINSKY's attorney. Present were GINSBURG, TODD C. THEODORA, an associate with the law firm of GINSBURG, STEPHAN, ORINGHER & RICHMAN, representing LEWINSKY, BERNARD LEWINSKY, MONICA LEWINSKY's father, Associate Independent Counsel (AIC) EDWARD J.PAGE and writer.

LEWINSKY and her party were escorted from their car to the Federal Building in Los Angeles by Special Agents of the Los Angeles office of the FBI and by officers of the Federal Protective Service.

[redacted] After being processed for fingerprints by the FBI's [redacted], LEWINSKY and her party were accompanied to the 17th floor office of Los Angeles FBI [redacted] for the purpose of LEWINSKY providing handwriting exemplars.

The pens used for this examination were as follows: one Bic, round stic, medium, black ink pen; one paper mate pen with black ink; and one paper mate, gel writer, with black ink. At various times during the examination, LEWINSKY was asked to use one of the three different pens. LEWINSKY's attorneys interrupted the examination on numerous occasions so LEWINSKY could consult privately with her attorneys.

MONICA LEWINSKY was first asked to write the alphabet in its entirety, with three different pens, on an 8 1/2" x 11" sheet of paper (unless specified otherwise, each sheet of paper used was 8 1/2" x 11") attached to a pad. On the same sheet of paper, LEWINSKY was asked to write the number one thru ten, three times, using a different pen each time.

LEWINSKY was then asked to perform the same task, this time using a sheet of paper resting only on the desk where she

Investigation on 05/28/98 at Los Angeles, CA File # 29D-OIC-LR-35063

by SA [redacted] Date dictated 5/29/98

Dunleavy

OIC-302a (Rev. 8-19-94)

29D-OIC-LR-35063

Continuation of OIC-302 of Fingerprint and Handwriting Exemplars of Lewinsky . On 05/28/98 . Page 2

was sitting.

LEWINSKY was then asked to print her name three times on a sheet of paper attached to a pad, each time using a different pen. LEWINSKY was then asked to sign her name on a sheet of paper attached to a pad, each time using a different pen. LEWINSKY was then asked to perform the same task, with the sheet of paper used resting directly on the desk.

LEWINSKY was then asked to sign her name to a photocopy of a blank check. At that time, GINSBURG objected and advised his client not to sign the form. GINSBURG advised that the OIC would need to get a Court Order before his client would sign anything that resembled a check. GINSBURG advised that he had no idea what the OIC had in the way of evidence and he was not going to create an exhibit. GINSBURG asked if he could use the telephone to call his co-counsel. GINSBURG advised he would use his AT&T card when calling. GINSBURG was permitted to use the telephone in [redacted] office.

After much discussion and delay, the meeting resumed and GINSBURG was asked if a compromise could be worked out where LEWINSKY would sign the documents and GINSBURG, THEODORA and SA [redacted] would initial the front so as to limit any question about the source of the document.

At this time, LEWINSKY asked GINSBURG to have BERNARD LEWINSKY leave because if he stayed, "[the OIC] would subpoena him." Several minutes later, BERNARD LEWINSKY departed, citing the need to see patients.

The meeting resumed several minutes later. GINSBURG replied that he had just received a letter from Deputy Independent Counsel (DIC) ROBERT BITTMAN wherein BITTMAN advised that LEWINSKY had no immunity and anything she did or said could be used against her. GINSBURG advised by allowing his client to write the checks, he would be allowing the OIC to violate her 5th Amendment rights. In addition, BITTMAN's letter stated that SA [redacted] and AIC PAGE had no authority to work out any compromise on behalf of the OIC. GINSBURG continued that in fact, BITTMAN had no authority to work out any deals on behalf of the OIC and the only person who did so would be KEN STARR.

GINSBURG advised he would accept only compromises signed by STARR and GINSBURG would accept them as long as GINSBURG was permitted to get handwriting exemplars from STARR. GINSBURG continued that the only compromise he would accept would

OIC-302a (Rev. 8-19-94)

29D-OIC-LR-35063

Continuation of OIC-302 of Fingerprint and Handwriting Exemplars of Lewinsky . On 05/28/98 . Page 3

be from STARR and the OIC should send STARR to Los Angeles to work out the compromise. While refusing to explain his reasoning, GINSBURG paused and explained to AIC PAGE that none of this was personal and, in fact, PAGE and GINSBURG could go out and have a few beers together. However, GINSBURG continued, BITTMAN had drawn a "razor-fine line" in his letter and GINSBURG was going to draw a similarly fine line in representing his client.

AIC PAGE asked GINSBURG if he would permit LEWINSKY to sign checks if PAGE showed GINSBURG a case which held that the request by the OIC was permitted to obtain the exemplars in this manner on the blank check forms. GINSBURG advised he would. PAGE showed GINSBURG such a case, but GINSBURG refused to permit LEWINSKY to fill out the checks.

AIC PAGE asked GINSBURG if GINSBURG understood that the OIC could use LEWINSKY's refusal to provide the requested handwriting exemplars against her at a trial or a proceeding. GINSBURG stated he was aware of that fact.

At approximately 9:30 a.m., GINSBURG was asked if LEWINSKY had consumed any medication during the morning. GINSBURG replied that, to his knowledge, LEWINSKY had not. Upon hearing this, LEWINSKY indicated to GINSBURG that she needed to speak with him, and PAGE and [redacted] departed the room. After a break, GINSBURG advised that LEWINSKY had taken "no narcotic, benzodiazepine, or other medication which in [GINSBURG]'s opinion would affect [LEWINSKY]'s coordination or alertness." GINSBURG refused to advise what medication LEWINSKY had taken.

The handwriting examination continued until approximately 10:06 a.m., when LEWINSKY took a break to visit the restroom.

The examination resumed approximately fifteen minutes later. LEWINSKY was asked to write various words and phrases. After LEWINSKY was asked to write "I have only read excerpts from <u>Leaves of Grass</u> before," GINSBURG requested SA [redacted] and AIC PAGE to leave the room. Upon resuming the examination, GINSBURG advised that there were several exemplars which appeared to be from the same letter, so GINSBURG would permit no more exemplars from that letter.

LEWINSKY was then asked to write "The Pres., through Ms. Currie." GINSBURG objected and advised that the "proffer was off limits." LEWINSKY was asked to write certain words and

OIC-302a (Rev. 8-19-94)

29D-OIC-LR-35063

Continuation of OIC-302 of Fingerprint and Handwriting Exemplars of Lewinsky , On 05/28/98 , Page 4

phrases and to sign her name on 5" x 7" note paper. Some of the samples taken were done so with the paper attached to the pad and some were taken with the paper resting directly on the desk.

The examination continued and GINSBURG agreed, although he objected earlier, to allow LEWINSKY to sign her name to strips of paper that, though not photocopies of or the same size as checks, more closely resembled a check than an 8 1/2" by 11" piece of paper. GINSBURG would not permit LEWINSKY to write amounts or dates on the pages that were close in size to a check.

At approximately 11:00 a.m., the examination ended, at which time GINSBURG was served grand jury subpoena number D-1319 for LEWINSKY's appearance on June 4, 1998 in Washington, DC to provide handwriting exemplars. GINSBURG advised he thought that a handwriting examination was just completed. GINSBURG was advised that all requested exemplars were not provided, therefore, LEWINSKY would have to come to Washington, DC to do so.

GINSBURG, LEWINSKY and THEODORA were escorted to their car by Special Agents of the FBI's Los Angeles Office and officers of the Federal Protective Service.

Tab 18

OIC-302 (Rev. 8-19-94)

OFFICE OF THE INDEPENDENT COUNSEL

Date of transcription 07/28/98

MONICA S.LEWINSKY was interviewed in Apartment 33B, 300 East 56th Street, New York, New York. Representatives of the Office of Independent Counsel (OIC) included ROBERT J. BITTMAN, Deputy Independent Counsel (DIC), SOLOMON L. WISENBERG, DIC, MARY ANNE WIRTH, Associate Independent Counsel (AIC), and Professor SAM DASH, Consultant. Attorneys present for LEWINSKY included PLATO CACHERIS, Law Offices of PLATO CACHERIS, 1100 Connecticut Avenue NW, Washington, D.C. 20036, telephone 202-775-8700; SYDNEY HOFFMAN of the CACHERIS Law Office; and JACOB STEIN, Law Offices of STEIN, MITCHELL, & MEZINES, 1100 Connecticut Avenue NW, Washington, D.C. 20036, telephone 202-737-7777.

After each of the participants identified themselves, a proffer agreement was executed by LEWINSKY. The agreement had previously been signed on July 24, 1998 by STEIN, CACHERIS, and KENNETH W. STARR, Independent Counsel. A copy of the agreement is attached and marked "Attachment A". LEWINSKY stated that she wished to answer all questions truthfully and completely. LEWINSKY then provided the following information:

LEWINSKY is a 25 year old female with a Bachelor of Science degree in Psychology from Lewis & Clark College in Portland, Oregon. LEWINSKY has been taking two prescription anti-depressants since early February 1995. This medication, at times, causes some memory to be suppressed and this usually expresses itself as the inability to think of certain words during conversation. The drugs are Effexor and Serzone. LEWINSKY stated that she wished to proceed with the above caveat.

LEWINSKY first met the President of the United States, WILLIAM J. CLINTON, in July 1995, soon after beginning her job as an intern in LEON PANETTA's Office in the White House. The occasion was the departure of the President from the South Lawn of the White House. LEWINSKY had obtained her job through a friend of her mother's, WALTER KAYE, and through JAY FOOTLIK, who formerly worked there.

LEWINSKY began her personal relationship with the President on November 15, 1995. This was during the furlough of federal employees when LEWINSKY was in the unique position of having been hired as a paid employee in Legislative Affairs, but

Investigation on 07/27/98 at NEW YORK, NEW YORK File # 29D OIC LR 35063

by CI [redacted] Date dictated 07/28/98

OIC-302a (Rev. 8-19-94)

29D OIC LR 35063

Continuation of OIC-302 of MONICA LEWINSKY , On 07/27/98 , Page 2

before her paper work had been processed. LEWINSKY, who was still an intern working for LEON PANETTA in the West Wing of the White House, saw the President when he came to the West Wing to see PANETTA and HAROLD ICKES. LEWINSKY and the President had flirted previously and they made eye contact on this visit. Later that day there was a cake party for JENNIFER PALMIERI, which the President and LEWINSKY attended. Later the same day, LEWINSKY was walking past the office of GEORGE STEPHANOPOLOUS and noticed that the President was inside the office and a U.S. Secret Service (USSS) Agent was outside. The President motioned for LEWINSKY to come in. LEWINSKY felt that this was her big chance and she advised the President that she "had a crush on him." The President then invited LEWINSKY to the back study behind the Oval Office, where he kissed her.

The relationship then blossomed and eventually included 14 sexual encounters. Sexual encounters included one or more of the following: kissing, hugging, touching, and oral sex on the person of the President, but not intercourse. On one occasion there was unclothed genital contact. Although LEWINSKY and the President had talked about the President performing oral sex on LEWINSKY, this never occurred because many times their encounters occurred during her menstrual cycles. The relationship included about 50 telephone calls, with the majority of them being between 10:00 p.m. and 6:00 a.m. About 15 of these calls were sexually explicit telephone calls, which LEWINSKY refers to as "phone sex" with the President. The President made most of the calls from his residence, but called LEWINSKY from out of town several times, including a call from Florida at the beginning of September 1996, when he was on the campaign trail.

At least seven of the sexual acts occurred in the hallway between the Oval Office and the private study of the President. The President usually left the door between the Oval Office and the Back Office slightly ajar so there would be no suspicion of improper activity and to hear if anyone was trying to contact him. LEWINSKY explained that the Back Office includes the private study, the hallway, the dining room, and the bathroom. The President liked to stand with his back against the door frame to ease his back muscles. When the President wanted to spend time with LEWINSKY, he would call her and either arrange to meet her in the hall, or LEWINSKY would carry some papers into the Oval Office. There were about nine or ten sexual contacts prior to Easter 1996, and about four after LEWINSKY was transferred to the Pentagon. About four of the sexual events occurred on workdays between 9:00 a.m. and 5:00 p.m., with the remainder on weekends. LEWINSKY recounted a few of the sexual

OIC-302a (Rev. 8-19-94)

29D OIC LR 35063

Continuation of OIC-302 of MONICA LEWINSKY, On 07/27/98, Page 3

contacts as follows:

A. On February 27 or 28 when the President gave LEWINSKY a hatpin and a book. This included kissing, touching, and oral sex to completion.

B. On March 29 or 30 after the knee surgery. This consisted of kissing, touching, oral sex to completion and brief genital contact without clothing but not intercourse.

C. On August 16, 1997, a birthday kiss.

D. On December 28, 1997, a Christmas kiss.

BETTY CURRIE, the President's Secretary, may have seen the President and LEWINSKY hugging on occasion and possibly a kiss on the forehead. During a visit to the private study on July 4th, LEWINSKY was at times crying and fighting with the President, and hugging him, when she saw a gardener, name unknown, who was working outside a window of the back study. The President and LEWINSKY then moved out of sight into the hallway where intimate things sometimes occurred during their relationship. LEWINSKY is unsure whether the gardener observed any arguing or hugging between the President and LEWINSKY. LEWINSKY is unaware of anyone else who could have observed any sexual activity. The President was suspicious of the USSS uniformed people and of LINDA TRIPP. In April 1997, the President asked, during a telephone call to LEWINSKY, whether LEWINSKY had told her mother about their sexual relationship. This was after MARSHA SCOTT had a conversation with WALTER KAYE. LEWINSKY denied that she had. However, this was untrue, inasmuch as LEWINSKY had told her mother of the emotional details of her involvement with the President, and told her that LEWINSKY and the President had "fooled around". On Monday, July 14, 1997, the President asked LEWINSKY if LEWINSKY had told LINDA TRIPP about their relationship. LEWINSKY replied "no." On December 28, 1997, the President asked LEWINSKY if she had revealed the hat pin to anyone and LEWINSKY denied that she had. The President did not believe LEWINSKY.

BAYANI NELVIS knew that LEWINSKY had been alone with the President on December 31, 1995, between 12:00 p.m. and 1:00 p.m., because LEWINSKY had a conversation with NELVIS in the pantry/kitchen area. LEWINSKY and NELVIS were discussing the smoking of cigars. NELVIS offered to get LEWINSKY one of the President's cigars and they entered the pantry door so that

NELVIS could get one. At that point, the President came in from the Oval Office to get something for PANETTA and saw LEWINSKY. NELVIS then obtained the item for PANETTA and left LEWINSKY and the President alone in the back rooms. This resulted in LEWINSKY performing oral sex with the President.

NELVIS advised LEWINSKY on one other occasion that a uniformed officer had asked NELVIS the identity of LEWINSKY, after the officer had observed her go into the Oval Office. NELVIS told the officer that LEWINSKY was the daughter of one of the Cabinet Secretaries.

BETTY CURRIE facilitated LEWINSKY's visits with the President so that EVELYN LIEBERMAN, STEPHEN GOODIN, and NANCY HERNREICH, who did not like LEWINSKY, would not find out. CURRIE advised that HERNREICH would be gone on Monday or Tuesday evenings to attend yoga classes and that LIEBERMAN and GOODIN were gone on weekends.

On Good Friday of 1996, LEWINSKY was advised that she was being transferred out of the White House to the Pentagon.

The President called LEWINSKY on Easter Sunday 1996, about 5:00 p.m. or 6:00 p.m., and asked about the RON BROWN incident. LEWINSKY cried about being transferred out and the President asked her to visit him. LEWINSKY carried some papers to the Oval Office and Officer JOHN MUSKETT was there. MUSKETT said he would ask LIEBERMAN if LEWINSKY could see the President, but LEWINSKY skirted the issue by saying that she would only be there for a minute to drop off the papers. The President was sitting at his desk in the Oval Office talking on the telephone, presumably to Mrs. CLINTON, as the President ended the call by saying,"I love you." The President and LEWINSKY went into the back office and the President tried to soothe LEWINSKY by saying, "I promise you if I win in November I'll get you back and you can do what you want." The President said that LIEBERMAN had spearheaded LEWINSKY's transfer because LEWINSKY was paying too much attention to the President and they could not have this prior to the election. LEWINSKY soon began performing oral sex on the President, then the President took a telephone call from a political person, whom LEWINSKY later speculated to be DICK MORRIS. The telephone may have rung in the back office, or the President may have been interrupted by someone from the Oval Office to take the call. LEWINSKY felt cheap performing oral sex while the President was on the telephone. At some later date, after reading about DICK MORRIS in the newspaper, LEWINSKY wondered whether DICK MORRIS was doing the same thing with a

OIC-302a (Rev. 8-19-94)

29D OIC LR 35063

Continuation of OIC-302 of MONICA LEWINSKY , On 07/27/98 , Page 5

prostitute. The President completed the call and hung up. The oral sex was discontinued when the President answered, "Just a minute" as a result of HAROLD ICKES calling out, "Mr. President" from the door of the Oval Office. LEWINSKY had her top off. The President left the room and LEWINSKY departed through the back door after putting her top back on.

After the President won the election, LEWINSKY renewed her efforts to get back to the White House. The President advised LEWINSKY that he would talk to BOB NASH and told her at other times that both MARSHA SCOTT and NASH were working on it. LEWINSKY had given her resume to the President in March 1997. LEWINSKY applied for a job in the White House Press Office and LINDA TRIPP arranged an NSC (National Security Council) interview. LEWINSKY advised MARSHA SCOTT of her applications, but she did not get either job. When LEWINSKY told the President that she had applied for these jobs, the President retorted that he needed to know in advance so that he could do something.

By October 1997, LEWINSKY told the President that she had made up her mind to leave the Pentagon job and move to New York. LEWINSKY mentioned a job at the United Nations (UN). The President said that he would help, and he apparently spoke to JOHN PODESTA, who spoke to BILL RICHARDSON on a trip to Mexico. Ambassador RICHARDSON called LEWINSKY and set up an interview at the Watergate Hotel. Subsequently, RICHARDSON called LEWINSKY at the Pentagon and offered her the job at the UN. LEWINSKY, who had changed her mind about working at the UN, but did not know how to back out, called one of RICHARDSON's assistants and advised that she was more interested in working in the private sector.

LINDA TRIPP suggested to LEWINSKY that the President should be asked to ask VERNON JORDAN for assistance. In early October 1997, while talking to the President on the telephone from 2:30 a.m. to 4:00 a.m., LEWINSKY asked the President to call JORDAN and the President did. This long conversation included an argument about why the President was not bringing LEWINSKY back to the White House.

LEWINSKY was a willing participant in all of the sexual encounters. LEWINSKY and the President had discussed a number of times that they would never tell anyone about their sexual activities. However, in violation of this agreement, LEWINSKY did provide different levels of detail about the sexual relationship to the following persons: ANDY BLEILER, NATALIE UNGVARI, NEYSA ERBLAND, ASHLEY RAINES, CATHRYN ALDAY DAVIS, LINDA

OIC-302a (Rev. 8-19-94)

29D OIC LR 35063

Continuation of OIC-302 of MONICA LEWINSKY, On 07/27/98, Page 6

TRIPP, DALE YOUNG, Dr. CATHY ESTEP, and Dr. IRENE KASSORLA. LEWINSKY did not tell KATHY BLEILER, and did not tell DENNIS LYTTON of Los Angeles, who is unknown to her.

No sexual incidents occurred from May 1996 or earlier until after the election.

In May 1997, the President said that he did not feel right about his sexual relationship with LEWINSKY and that he just wanted to be friends. LEWINSKY referred to this as "dump day."

The President, at one time or another, made comments to LEWINSKY such as, "You are bright, attractive, and make me feel young;" he liked talking to her; "people like us" (meaning, we are the same), LEWINSKY was "emotive and full of fire"; LEWINSKY was "full of piss and vinegar;" he wished to spend more time with LEWINSKY; he might "have time in three years;" and "What if I'm 75 and have to go to the bathroom fifteen times a day?". The President sometimes called LEWINSKY "sweetie" or "baby." LEWINSKY occasionally called the President "handsome."

On December 17, 1997, during a telephone conversation between 2:00 a.m. and 3:00 a.m., the President advised LEWINSKY that she was on the PAULA JONES witness list. This was the first indication LEWINSKY had that she was to be subpoenaed. LEWINSKY believes that the President had just found out, but if the President found out about the potential witnesses on December 5th or 6th he never gave any indication of this to LEWINSKY. During this call the President advised that LEWINSKY might sign an affidavit to avoid being deposed in the JONES case; that LEWINSKY could say that she was coming to the White House to visit BETTY CURRIE; or that LEWINSKY was carrying papers to the President; and that LEWINSKY should contact BETTY CURRIE if subpoenaed. The President also advised that BETTY CURRIE's brother had been killed, and that the President had a Christmas present for LEWINSKY.

On December 19, 1997, LEWINSKY was served with a subpoena in the PAULA JONES lawsuit, between 4:00 p.m. and 4:30 p.m., at the Pentagon where LEWINSKY was then working. This was very upsetting to LEWINSKY, who then called VERNON JORDAN from a payphone in the Pentagon. JORDAN had been helping LEWINSKY seek employment in New York for the previous month and a half. LEWINSKY went to see JORDAN at his office that afternoon, showed JORDAN the subpoena, and pointed out that it included the production of a hat pin that the President had given LEWINSKY.

OIC-302a (Rev. 8-19-94)

29D OIC LR 35063

Continuation of OIC-302 of MONICA LEWINSKY, On 07/27/98, Page 7

LEWINSKY asked JORDAN about getting an attorney. JORDAN received a telephone call and asked LEWINSKY to leave the room. After about ten minutes JORDAN came back, but did not identify the caller. JORDAN called an attorney named FRANK CARTER and set up an appointment for LEWINSKY at 10:30 a.m. on the following Monday. JORDAN said there were only two important questions: 1. Did you have sex with the President? 2. Did the President ask you for sex? JORDAN said that he would see the President that evening and would tell him about LEWINSKY's subpoena. In a subsequent meeting, JORDAN assured LEWINSKY that he had advised the President of the subpoena.

LEWINSKY did not visit the President at the White House between December 6th and December 28th, 1997.

On December 28, 1997, LEWINSKY visited the President at the White House. The visit was arranged by BETTY CURRIE. When LEWINSKY arrived she talked to BETTY and played with BUDDY on the carpet with some "people bones" for about ten minutes while the President was on the telephone. The President and LEWINSKY then went into the back study and spent from 45 minutes to an hour together. The President gave LEWINSKY her Christmas gifts at this time. There was no sex on this occasion, but there may have been a kiss and a hug, as the President said that Christmas kisses were an exception to his earlier statement that there would be no more sexual contact between them. LEWINSKY expressed her concern about the gifts that the President had given LEWINSKY and specifically the hat pin that had been subpoenaed by PAULA JONES. The President seemed to know what the JONES subpoena called for in advance and did not seem surprised about the hat pin. The President asked LEWINSKY if she had told anyone about the hat pin and LEWINSKY denied that she had, but may have said that she gave some of the gifts to FRANK CARTER. LEWINSKY was concerned because this was a personal item. LEWINSKY mentioned that DEBBIE SCHIFF may have given her name to the lawyers for PAULA JONES. The President opined that it may have been "that woman from the summer that was involved in the KATHLEEN WILLEY thing." LEWINSKY asked the President if she should give the gifts to someone and the President replied, "I don't know." LEWINSKY and the President discussed her move to New York and the President said that if LEWINSKY was in New York the JONES lawyers might not call; that the sooner LEWINSKY moved the better; and that maybe the lawyers would ignore her. Sometime prior to December 28th the President had suggested that LEWINSKY submit an affidavit in lieu of testifying.

Several hours after leaving the White House LEWINSKY

received a telephone call at her apartment from BETTY CURRIE who made the statement, "You have some things to give me?" This call was not a coincidence, but a result of LEWINSKY's earlier conversation with the President. The call may have been on CURRIE's cell phone. LEWINSKY put a GAP box on her bed and placed in it a number of gifts that she had received from the President, except for some innocuous items that would not appear too personal if found in her apartment. The reason for getting some of the gifts out of the apartment was because LEWINSKY suspected that the lawyers for JONES would break into her apartment. LEWINSKY also suspected that the JONES people might tap her telephone. Besides keeping the innocuous gift items, LEWINSKY also kept some of the sentimental items from the President such as the following: a canvas bag from the BLACK DOG store, maybe some BLACK DOG T-shirts, a lithographic book, a big Rockette blanket, a pair of sunglasses, and a wooden box that had contained an earlier present. LEWINSKY kept the sentimental items because she was afraid that she would not get them back. Pursuant to the agreement that LEWINSKY and CURRIE had made during the earlier telephone call, LEWINSKY met CURRIE on 28th street outside LEWINSKY's apartment at about 2:00 p.m. and gave CURRIE the box of gifts. The box contained a hat pin, some BLACK DOG items, a broach, two signed photographs of The President, and a signed State of the Union address. However, there was no discussion of the contents. LEWINSKY had written "do not throw away" on the box. CURRIE was on her way to visit a relative in the hospital when she stopped by. CURRIE was to keep the box in a closet in CURRIE's home.

In addition to the December 19, 1997 meeting with VERNON JORDAN, LEWINSKY had met JORDAN on several previous occasions. LEWINSKY may have met with JORDAN in late November or the first week in December 1997. LEWINSKY initially met JORDAN in early November 1997, when she spent about 20 minutes in his office. The purpose of this meeting was to ask JORDAN's assistance in obtaining a job in New York. LEWINSKY knew that JORDAN and the President were good friends and JORDAN knew that LEWINSKY and the President were friends. JORDAN indicated that he had spoken with the President and LEWINSKY interpreted this to mean that the President had asked JORDAN for assistance in getting LEWINSKY a job. JORDAN said, "You've come highly recommended." LEWINSKY understood that this meant that the President had spoken to JORDAN. LEWINSKY was somewhat intimidated during this meeting. JORDAN said that he would make some telephone calls on LEWINSKY's behalf before he left Washington for the holidays.

On December 11, 1997, LEWINSKY had lunch with JORDAN at the AKIN, GUMP office, at which time JORDAN recommended that LEWINSKY write letters with certain language to three companies. JORDAN provided the language. LEWINSKY typed the letters and sent copies to JORDAN. During the meeting JORDAN indicated that he knew LEWINSKY's mother's fiance, PETER STRAUS.

At one of the December meetings, JORDAN said to LEWINSKY that LEWINSKY was a friend of the President but, "Your problem is that you're in love--don't deny it." LEWINSKY just laughed in reply. At another of the December meetings with JORDAN, they had breakfast at the HYATT first.

On December 22, 1997, LEWINSKY met with JORDAN for about 15 minutes in his office. LEWINSKY showed JORDAN the gifts that she was taking to CARTER's office. LEWINSKY believes that JORDAN knew that she was not turning over all of the gifts to CARTER. JORDAN did not tell LEWINSKY to hold back any of the items. LEWINSKY told JORDAN that she had phone sex with the President and JORDAN replied that it was alright if the President talked to people. JORDAN asked what phone sex was, but LEWINSKY did not explain. JORDAN grunted and nodded a lot during his meetings with LEWINSKY and this sometimes made it difficult to fully understand him. LEWINSKY and JORDAN had a wink and nod understanding that LEWINSKY was having sex with the President. LEWINSKY does not recall whether JORDAN explained the difference between civil and criminal perjury.

On December 22, 1997 LEWINSKY was driven to FRANK CARTER's office by VERNON JORDAN, where she discussed the JONES subpoena with CARTER. The President had previously suggested an affidavit to avoid testifying and LEWINSKY talked to CARTER about it. The President assumed that the affidavit would be to deny something, although she did not discuss specifics with the President. The pattern was to conceal and deny and there was no reason for the President to think that anything had changed. LEWINSKY had always told the President that she would protect him.

At some point in January 1996, CARTER paged LEWINSKY and advised her that the JONES lawyers had subpoenaed the courier records for the gifts that LEWINSKY sent to the White House. LEWINSKY called for the President but he was out of town. LEWINSKY suggested to BETTY CURRIE that the gifts were for CURRIE and in some cases this would be true. The same night, LEWINSKY asked LINDA TRIPP if ISIKOFF had called her, since ISIKOFF had called LEWINSKY earlier. There had been no earlier contacts by

OIC-302a (Rev. 8-19-94)

29D OIC LR 35063

Continuation of OIC-302 of MONICA LEWINSKY, On 07/27/98, Page 10

ISIKOFF with BETTY CURRIE.

On January 7, 1998, LEWINSKY signed the JONES affidavit which CARTER had prepared. LEWINSKY took the following gifts to CARTER's office: "The Hope and History" book, all Christmas cards, two signed photos, including the LEWINSKY family photo, and signed letters. There was no agreement with the President, JORDAN, or anyone else that LEWINSKY had to sign the JONES affidavit before getting a job in New York. LEWINSKY never demanded a job from JORDAN in return for a favorable affidavit. Neither the President nor JORDAN ever told LEWINSKY that she had to lie. However, LEWINSKY repeated that there had always been an understanding with the President that they would both deny a sexual relationship.

In January 1998, LEWINSKY met with JORDAN, shortly after she signed the JONES affidavit on January 7, 1998. LEWINSKY gave JORDAN a tie and pocket square, and thanked him for his assistance in getting her a job in New York. JORDAN had helped LEWINSKY get the interviews in New York with MCANDREWS AND FORBES, BURSTON MARSTELLER, and REVLON. JORDAN began helping LEWINSKY after she requested his assistance in a meeting at JORDAN's office in early November 1997. JORDAN helped LEWINSKY because LEWINSKY was a friend of the President. JORDAN was the only one in recent times who had delivered what he promised.

When LEWINSKY was subpoenaed on December 19, 1997, she telephonically discussed it in a cryptic manner with LINDA TRIPP, who had already been subpoenaed. LEWINSKY was concerned that TRIPP would testify about LEWINSKY's sexual relationship with the President, inasmuch as LEWINSKY had advised TRIPP of many details in confidence on different occasions. During previous discussions, TRIPP advised LEWINSKY that she would reveal what LEWINSKY had told her if TRIPP had to testify. LEWINSKY and TRIPP had talked about TRIPP's testimony several times.

At some point LEWINSKY typed on her home computer the talking points about how TRIPP should testify. The contents and ideas for the talking points were a summary of things that LEWINSKY and TRIPP had discussed off and on since March 1997. There was no lawyer involved in preparing the talking points, nor did LEWINSKY receive any instructions from the President, JORDAN, CARTER, or anyone from the White House. LEWINSKY gave the talking points to TRIPP at the Pentagon. TRIPP read the points and made positive statements about them by saying, "That's true," and "This is good." TRIPP had indicated that TRIPP wanted to file an affidavit to avoid testifying in the JONES matter.

OIC-302a (Rev. 8-19-94)

29D OIC LR 35063

Continuation of OIC-302 of MONICA LEWINSKY, On 07/27/98, Page 11

LEWINSKY did not always tell TRIPP the truth, i.e. LEWINSKY promised that she would not sign the JONES affidavit until she had the New York job lined up. However, when this promise was made to TRIPP the affidavit had already been signed.

LEWINSKY was not aware that TRIPP was taping her telephone calls, but did suspect that TRIPP may have been recording her during their conversation at the RITZ CARLTON HOTEL on January 13, 1998.

LEWINSKY gave a copy of the affidavit to JORDAN. JORDAN made changes to the first draft of the affidavit, but did not retain a copy. These were minor changes proposed by LEWINSKY and agreed to by JORDAN. CARTER prepared three or four drafts of the affidavit until LEWINSKY and CARTER agreed upon one. Minor changes were made. JORDAN never told LEWINSKY to file the affidavit but did discuss her concerns when LEWINSKY called him.

LEWINSKY prepared a written proffer in her own handwriting at the end of January, 1998. Attached is a copy of the proffer marked "Attachment B". The writing took from six to ten hours and was completed in one sitting. LEWINSKY asked her attorneys, BILL GINSBERG and NATE SPEIGHTS, a few questions. The attorneys were in the hallway outside of the conference room at the COSMOS CLUB when she drafted the proffer. LEWINSKY was not on medication. The proffer is generally accurate and LEWINSKY would disavow nothing in it. NATE SPEIGHTS has a copy of the first draft, which is not significantly different from the second draft. LEWINSKY made the following comments concerning specific statements in the proffer:

A. At the end of paragraph two on page two of the proffer LEWINSKY's recollection is that the words "leave Washington, DC" should read "get out of town."

B. In paragraph marked four on page four the following statement appears "In general, Ms. L should say she visited the WH to see Ms. CURRIE and, on occasion when working at the WH, she brought him letters when no one else was around." LEWINSKY commented that these statements were not untrue, but were misleading in that some facts were omitted from this statement. This was the cover story that the President had suggested that she use.

OIC-302a (Rev. 8-19-94)

29D OIC LR 35063

Continuation of OIC-302 of MONICA LEWINSKY , On 07/27/98 , Page 12

C. At the bottom of page five the wording of the two lines scratched out is "on more than one occasion Ms. L was concerned about signing an affidavit." LEWINSKY's memory is unclear on this point, but LEWINSKY may or may not have said this to JORDAN.

D. In regard to the bottom paragraph on page five, LEWINSKY said that she cannot now remember whether she told JORDAN about her sexual relationship with the President.

E. In regard to the first sentence on page six, "Ms. L made it clear she intended to deny the sexual relationship with the Pres.", LEWINSKY now is not sure of that statement.

F. In paragraph two of page eight the proffer states "Ms. L replied that she and the Pres. had already had an affair minus having sex,--but it included everything else." LEWINSKY said that this statement meant that she never had intercourse with The President.

G. In regard to paragraph ten on page ten, LEWINSKY discussed signing the affidavit denying a sexual relationship with the President. LEWINSKY said that she had never even thought about giving an affidavit wherein she would admit to having sex with the President. Based on the pattern of LEWINSKY's relationship with the President it was assumed that LEWINSKY would not admit any sexual activity. Neither the President nor anyone ever directed LEWINSKY to say anything or to lie, but neither did the President nor anyone else ever tell LEWINSKY not to lie. No one ever used the term "deny, deny" to her.

LEWINSKY now has some guilt about getting JORDAN into trouble. LEWINSKY likes JORDAN. LEWINSKY said that her memory when she wrote the proffer in January would have been better than it is today.

LEWINSKY gave the following gifts to the President:

1. A poem written by LEWINSKY on behalf of the White House interns and presented to the President by KARIN ABRAMSON.

OIC-302a (Rev. 8-19-94)

29D OIC LR 35063

Continuation of OIC-302 of MONICA LEWINSKY, On 07/27/98, Page 13

2. In November, 1995 a tie delivered to the President by BETTY CURRIE and worn in the Oval Office the day that MADELINE ALBRIGHT was appointed Secretary of State.

3. End of March, 1996 on the day RON BROWN was killed, a tie from BLOOMINGDALE'S.

4. August, 1996 a tie worn by the President in September, 1996 while signing the Defense Bill. LEWINSKY has a signed photo.

5. Fall, 1997 a CALVIN KLEIN tie worn on California trip.

6. March, 1997 a tie worn to a Governor's race rally in Virginia.

7. December 6, 1997 a tie from London.

8. Antique book on PETER THE GREAT from 1802.

9. LEWINSKY's personal copy of "Vox" (no inscription). LEWINSKY replaced her copy of the book at KRAMER BOOKS. Observed in back study of the President on November 13, 1997.

10. A copy of "The Note Book" by NICHOLAS SPARKS.

11. A copy of "Oy Vey," a book of Jewish jokes. Observed in back study of the President on November 13, 1997.

12. A book on golf.

13. An old school book entitled "Disease and Mispresentation" which was about race relations.

14. A BANANA REPUBLIC casual shirt.

15. A wooden letter opener with a frog on the handle. Observed in back study of the President.

16. A plastic pocket frog.

17. A puzzle on golf mysteries.

OIC-302a (Rev. 8-19-94)

29D OIC LR 35063

Continuation of OIC-302 of MONICA LEWINSKY, On 07/27/98, Page 14

18. A card game.

19. A copy of "SHERLOCK HOLMES".

20. An antique standing cigar holder on December 28, 1997.

21. A tie on December 28, 1997.

22. A HARROD's mug on December 28, 1997.

23. A hugs and kisses box on December 28, 1997.

24. A penny medallion with a heart cut out.

25. An antique paperweight with a painting of the White House on November 13th, the day HERNREICH testified. Purchased at flea market at 6th and 7th. President ZEDILLO of Mexico at White House. In political collection in cabinet in back dining room.

26. A STARBUCKS mug from Santa Monica. NELVIS observed the President using the mug.

27. A book about THEODORE ROOSEVELT.

28. A pair of sunglasses in Fall, worn by the President in Africa, photo in U.S. News in January, 1998.

29. A pumpkin pin that the President wore in his lapel on Halloween.

30. A care package in March, 1996 when the President injured his leg.

LEWINSKY received the following gifts from the President, some of which have been previously mentioned:

1. A lithograph on February 27 or 28, 1997 (placed in her purse unwrapped)

2. A hatpin on February 27 or 28, 1997 (placed in purse unwrapped).
3. A large BLACK DOG canvas bag from Martha's

OIC-302a (Rev. 8-19-94)

29D OIC LR 35063

Continuation of OIC-302 of MONICA LEWINSKY , On 07/27/98 , Page 15

Vineyard.

4. A large Rockettes blanket from New York.

5. An ugly but sweet pin of the New York skyline.

6. A small box of cherry chocolates.

7. A pair of joke sunglasses.

8. A stuffed animal from BLACK DOG.

9. A marble bear's head from Vancouver.

10. A London pin wrapped in a Casual Corner box.

11. A Shamrock pin.

12. A compact disk of ANNIE LENNOX.

13. Some "Davidoff" cigars.

On December 6, 1997, LEWINSKY spent about 20 or 25 minutes with the President and had gotten into a big fight with him. LEWINSKY had found out that ELEANOR MONDALE was in with the President while she waited at the northwest gate. LEWINSKY had earlier sent a note to the President that she needed to talk with him. Part of LEWINSKY's anger was caused by BETTY CURRIE, who had told LEWINSKY that the President was meeting with lawyers. LEWINSKY left the northwest gate in a very agitated state and called CURRIE from the Corcoran Gallery. LEWINSKY was very "pissed off" and called CURRIE again from her apartment. CURRIE may have paged her before this call. LEWINSKY called the White House again and talked to the President about MONDALE. During the White House argument LEWINSKY went ballistic and the President said that he never had anyone talk to him like LEWINSKY. LEWINSKY also told the President that things were not moving fast enough with VERNON JORDAN. This meant that she had not found a job in New York yet.

LEWINSKY's affidavit in the JONES case was not accurate in the following respects:

A. That LEWINSKY never had a sexual relationship with the President.

B. That LEWINSKY never was alone with the President

after she left the White House.

C. That LEWINSKY only saw the President at public functions.

LEWINSKY said that she had heard rumors from The Hill that CHRIS WALKER may have set her up with TIM KEATING. The word was that she was too sexy to work in the White House. JODIE TORKELSON had wanted to fire LEWINSKY. MARSHA SCOTT said that LEWINSKY was called "the Stalker" at the White House.

In regard to the deposition of the President in the JONES case, LEWINSKY said that she had always assumed that the President would deny any sexual relationships, but the President never said it to LEWINSKY. LEWINSKY asked the President if the ten other women on the witness list were from the White House and the President said that they were all women from the old days in Arkansas.

Tab 19

OIC-302 (Rev. 8-19-94)

- 1 -

OFFICE OF THE INDEPENDENT COUNSEL

Date of transcription 07/30/98

MONICA S. LEWINSKY was interviewed under the terms of an immunity agreement, a copy of which is attached hereto, in room 616 of the Watergate Hotel, 2650 Virginia Avenue, Northwest, Washington, D.C. Present for the interview were Associate Independent Counsel (AIC) MICHAEL EMMICK, AIC KARIN IMMERGUT, AIC JULIE MYERS, and LEWINSKY's attorney, PRESTON BURTON. Present for portions of the interview was Deputy Independent Counsel (DIC) ROBERT BITTMAN. After being apprised of the official identities of the interviewers, LEWINSKY provided the following information, beginning at approximately 4:35 p.m.

LEWINSKY was shown a copy of two pages from her day-timer calendars from 1996 and 1997. The original, which is a two-sided document, was provided by LEWINSKY to the Office of the Independent Counsel (OIC) earlier in the day. Those two pages contained all the calendar dates in 1996 and 1997. LEWINSKY advised she made notations in the calendar within a week or two of the event, but not as they happened. LEWINSKY advised the notations were made on the calendar prior to the "scandal" becoming news. LEWINSKY advised there were some dates when an event took place that she did not circle for one reason or another.

LEWINSKY explained that the dates circled on the calendar represent days LEWINSKY either saw President WILLIAM JEFFERSON CLINTON or days he called LEWINSKY. LEWINSKY explained that if CLINTON called her at 2 a.m., she may have circled the day before he actually called, because she associated that time of night with the previous day. LEWINSKY advised she may have a similar document from 1995, but she doubts it since her relationship with CLINTON began in late 1995.

The small, handwritten numbers to the side of the calendar for 1997 represent the number of weeks since LEWINSKY last had physical sex with CLINTON. LEWINSKY explained that from April 7, 1996 until February 28, 1997, she had no physical sex with CLINTON. LEWINSKY distinguished physical sex from phone sex. LEWINSKY explained she and CLINTON engaged in phone sex during this period.

LEWINSKY advised she separately kept track of the days

Investigation on 07/29/98 at Washington, DC File # 29D-OIC-LR-35063

by CI [redacted]
SA [redacted] Date dictated 07/30/98

OIC-302a (Rev. 8-19-94)

29D-OIC-LR-35063

Continuation of OIC-302 of MONICA S. LEWINSKY , On 07/29/98 , Page 2

prior to the 1996 election and the days since she worked at the White House, but the small numbers on the 1997 day-timer calendar represented days since her last physical sexual contact with CLINTON.

LEWINSKY advised that the other set of numbers below the months represented the number of times LEWINSKY saw CLINTON in a particular month. LEWINSKY advised that LINDA TRIPP suggested LEWINSKY document her contacts with CLINTON because it helped TRIPP understand LEWINSKY's situation.

LEWINSKY advised that she includes kissing when she uses the term "sexual contact." For the purposes of this interview, LEWINSKY differentiated between the kissing and the other sexual contact, without going into the details of the sexual contact.

[For the purposes of this FD-302, unless otherwise noted, physical sexual contact means more than kissing.]

LEWINSKY advised that on January 7, 1996, CLINTON called LEWINSKY for the first time at home and at her office. LEWINSKY added that on January 7, 1996, she had physical sexual contact with CLINTON. On January 15, 1996, CLINTON called LEWINSKY at her office and at her home. LEWINSKY advised on January 21, 1996 she received a phone call from CLINTON and later had physical sexual contact with him. On January 28, 1996, LEWINSKY was in San Francisco, California. When she returned to her office at the White House, she checked her caller identification feature and saw that CLINTON had called her from the Oval Office.

[LEWINSKY advised that calls from CLINTON when he was in the Oval Office would show up on the caller identification feature as "POTUS." Calls from the White House residence were indicated by a "*."]

On January 30, 1996, there was a going away party for PAT GRIFFIN. LEWINSKY advised this was the first time CLINTON called LEWINSKY at her office during working hours. CLINTON asked LEWINSKY to come see him after the party, but LEWINSKY told him she did not think that would be a good idea. LEWINSKY advised she and CLINTON agreed they would not speak to each other at the party so that others did not get any "wrong" ideas. LEWINSKY explained that in a photograph taken at the going away party, she stood as far away from CLINTON as possible for the same reason. LEWINSKY advised she and CLINTON did not get together on this date.

On February 4, 1996, CLINTON and LEWINSKY engaged in physical sexual contact. On February 7 or 8, 1996, while signing the Telecommunications Bill, CLINTON wore one of the ties LEWINSKY had given him for the first time. LEWINSKY advised CLINTON called her that evening and they engaged in phone sex.

On February 19, 1996, LEWINSKY advised CLINTON broke off their relationship for the first time. LEWINSKY advised she saw CLINTON in person and he said he was feeling guilty about continuing their relationship, so he wanted to break it off.

On March 26, 1996, CLINTON called LEWINSKY in her office at the White House from the White House Residence. LEWINSKY advised CLINTON called from the Residence for the first time, to her knowledge. CLINTON asked LEWINSKY if the caller identification showed anything and she told him it was a star.

On March 29, 1996, CLINTON called LEWINSKY at her office in the White House.

On March 31, 1996, CLINTON and LEWINSKY engaged in physical sexual contact.

On April 7, 1996, CLINTON and LEWINSKY engaged in physical sexual contact. On April 12, 1996, CLINTON called LEWINSKY twice, once during the day and once at night. LEWINSKY advised that during one of these telephone calls, CLINTON told LEWINSKY he would have her back at the White House after the election.

On April 22, 1996, CLINTON called LEWINSKY, but they did not engage in phone sex. LEWINSKY advised she was upset because she hated her job. On April 29, 1996, CLINTON called LEWINSKY at approximately 3 a.m. LEWINSKY advised this call may have actually taken place on April 30th. LEWINSKY advised this was the first time CLINTON left a message on LEWINSKY's answering machine. LEWINSKY recalled that on the message, CLINTON said "aw shucks."

On May 2, 1996, LEWINSKY attended a Saxophone Club event and saw CLINTON. LEWINSKY explained she was very upset because CLINTON had promised to call her that weekend, but did not. CLINTON called LEWINSKY that evening and said he could tell LEWINSKY was upset. CLINTON apologized for not calling LEWINSKY and said that he was sick that weekend. CLINTON also said that if LEWINSKY did not like her job at the Pentagon, he would try to get LEWINSKY a job on the campaign.

LEWINSKY advised CLINTON may have called her on May 6, 1996. LEWINSKY advised that on May 16, 1996, the night Admiral BOORDA committed suicide, CLINTON called LEWINSKY. LEWINSKY tried to initiate phone sex, but CLINTON was not in the mood. The next week, on the day of [redacted] funeral, CLINTON came to the Pentagon. Later that night, CLINTON called LEWINSKY and they engaged in phone sex. LEWINSKY advised she thinks the date of the funeral was May 21, 1996.

LEWINSKY advised that, because of a pattern that had developed, LEWINSKY would expect CLINTON to call her when HILLARY RODHAM CLINTON was out of town.

On May 31, 1996, LEWINSKY was out of town and CLINTON left a message on her home telephone answering machine. LEWINSKY thinks CLINTON may have been calling about LEWINSKY coming to a radio address. On June 5, 1996, CLINTON called LEWINSKY in the early evening, inquiring about LEWINSKY and her family attending a radio address, as had been discussed on previous occasions. CLINTON told LEWINSKY he would say something to BETTY CURRIE about arranging the attendance of LEWINSKY's family at the radio address.

The following morning, CURRIE called LEWINSKY and said there was no radio address that week, but a tour would be arranged for LEWINSKY's family.

On June 13, 1996, LEWINSKY and her family attended the arrival ceremony of the President of Ireland, which was held at Ft. Myer, Virginia. CLINTON made a comment about LEWINSKY's hat. On June 14, 1996, LEWINSKY attended a radio address with her family.

On June 23, 1996, CLINTON called LEWINSKY and the two engaged in phone sex. On July 5, 1996, CLINTON called LEWINSKY and the two engaged in phone sex. On July 19, 1996, CLINTON called LEWINSKY at 6:30 a.m. and the two engaged in phone sex. CLINTON exclaimed "good morning!" to the best of LEWINSKY's knowledge after having an orgasm.

LEWINSKY then went down a list of other dates where there was either physical and/or phone contact with CLINTON. LEWINSKY distinguished those contacts that include sex and those that did not. LEWINSKY advised that all telephone calls included

OIC-302a (Rev. 8-19-94)

29D-OIC-LR-35063

some conversation that was not of a sexual nature. The remaining dates in 1996 where LEWINSKY had contact with CLINTON were as follows:

July 28	phone call
August 4	phone sex
August 24	phone call
September 5	phone call, maybe phone sex
September 10	Clinton left a message on LEWINSKY's answering machine.
September 30	phone call
October 22	phone sex
October 23	phone call; earlier that evening, LEWINSKY saw CLINTON at an event related to the Senate.

LEWINSKY advised that there was no contact between her and CLINTON between October 23, 1996 and December 2, 1996.

December 2	phone sex
December 17	LEWINSKY saw CLINTON at some sort of official function.
December 18	phone call
December 30	CLINTON left a message on LEWINSKY's answering machine.

<u>1997</u>

January 12	phone call
February 8	phone sex
February 28	physical contact, including more than just kissing.
March 12	CLINTON calls LEWINSKY for approximately three minutes at work.
March 29	physical contact including more than just kissing.
April 26	phone call; LEWINSKY does not think the two engaged in phone sex.
May 17	phone call
May 18	phone call
May 24	LEWINSKY visits and CLINTON breaks up with her. LEWINSKY describes this day as "D-Day."
July 4	physical contact; CLINTON kissed LEWINSKY on the neck.
July 8	LEWINSKY was in Madrid, Spain at the same time CLINTON was. LEWINSKY saw CLINTON at the Ambassador's house. LEWINSKY and CLINTON make eye contact at the embassy.

OIC-302a (Rev. 8-19-94)

29D-OIC-LR-35063

Continuation of OIC-302 of MONICA S. LEWINSKY , On 07/29/98 , Page 6

1997 (Continued):

July 14	LEWINSKY visits CLINTON at the White House. No sexual contact.
July 15	phone call
July 24	LEWINSKY visits, but no sexual contact
August 1	phone call
August 16	LEWINSKY and CLINTON kissed.
September 30	phone call, maybe phone sex
October 9	very long phone call, no sex
October 11	visit; no sexual contact
October 23	phone call
October 30	phone call
November 12	phone call, maybe phone sex
November 13	very brief visit with CLINTON. Mexican President ZEDILLO at the White House.
December 5	LEWINSKY saw CLINTON at an official function.
December 6	LEWINSKY visited with CLINTON.
December 28	In person visit, only kissed.

KATHLEEN WILLEY

Prior to MICHAEL ISIKOFF interviewing LINDA TRIPP in the spring of 1997, TRIPP mentioned KATHLEEN WILLEY's story to LEWINSKY. LEWINSKY advised TRIPP did not mention WILLEY by name at first. LEWINSKY advised TRIPP's story seemed to change over time. TRIPP may have told LEWINSKY about WILLEY's name prior to ISIKOFF interviewing TRIPP. TRIPP told LEWINSKY about ISIKOFF's visit to TRIPP at TRIPP's office.

TRIPP told LEWINSKY that WILLEY was certainly not sexually harassed. TRIPP told LEWINSKY about the ISIKOFF visit the same day of the visit or the next one. At that point, TRIPP said that WILLEY called TRIPP that night.

LEWINSKY urged TRIPP to let someone in the White House know about the ISIKOFF visit. TRIPP said that she would only be comfortable speaking with NANCY HERNREICH or BRUCE LINDSEY. TRIPP said that, during the Whitewater hearings, she was told by her attorney not to talk to LINDSEY. LEWINSKY urged TRIPP to page LINDSEY. TRIPP advised that LINDSEY did not return the pages or telephone messages. LEWINSKY advised that she thinks TRIPP's ego was deflated and she seemed insulted.

In early summer, ISIKOFF contacted TRIPP again. ISIKOFF called TRIPP to ask her to go on the record with her version of the WILLEY matter. LEWINSKY advised she considered saying something to CLINTON about TRIPP on May 24, 1997, but decided not to. On July 4, 1997, LEWINSKY mentioned to CLINTON that she had a friend who knew something about WILLEY.

LEWINSKY explained that July 4, 1997 was her most emotional visit with CLINTON. LEWINSKY advised the visit lasted more than one hour. The majority of the visit was spent with LEWINSKY and CLINTON being emotionally intimate. Looking back, LEWINSKY is not sure if CLINTON was sincere during this visit. LEWINSKY questions a lot of things since the "scandal" broke. LEWINSKY does not think CLINTON was acting on July 4th, because if he was, he would be the greatest actor in the world. LEWINSKY does not think CLINTON would have fought with her at the beginning of the visit if he was acting. The fight was about a letter LEWINSKY had sent CLINTON the day before, indicating she would tell her parents about their relationship if CLINTON did not help her with a job.

At the end of the visit, LEWINSKY asked CLINTON if he knew KATHLEEN WILLEY. CLINTON advised he did. LEWINSKY said she had a friend at the Pentagon who had talked to ISIKOFF, who was looking into allegations that CLINTON had sexually harassed a woman who once worked at the White House. CLINTON advised the story was ludicrous. [redacted] CLINTON seemed surprised about LEWINSKY's friend at the Pentagon.

CLINTON said that WILLEY called HERNREICH earlier that week and was asking about ISIKOFF and WILLEY wanted to know how to get out of it. LEWINSKY told CLINTON that WILLEY may have been covering her tracks. LEWINSKY did not use TRIPP's name. LEWINSKY advised she brought this subject up because she thought CLINTON should know about it. LEWINSKY thought maybe CLINTON could get WILLEY a job to make her happy.

LEWINSKY told CLINTON that her friend once worked at the White House. CLINTON did not ask for TRIPP's name. LEWINSKY was not offended by the WILLEY story because she did not believe it. LEWINSKY said her friend had tried to get in touch with BRUCE LINDSEY, but he did not return her pages to him.

LEWINSKY advised that WILLEY may have sent CLINTON a "mixed signal." LEWINSKY does not believe the PAULA JONES story either. LEWINSKY advised CLINTON and JONES may have had a consensual relationship. LEWINSKY advised she did not get jealous of CLINTON's relationships with other women, so long as they pre-dated her relationship with CLINTON.

LEWINSKY explained how the July 4, 1997 meeting was arranged. LEWINSKY was "pissed" that CLINTON had not responded to her issues related to her job. When LEWINSKY met with MARSHA SCOTT and SCOTT did not know who LEWINSKY was, LEWINSKY was annoyed. LEWINSKY was very frustrated so she sent CLINTON a note.

LEWINSKY advised she wrote the letter on July 3 and delivered it to CURRIE the same day. LEWINSKY advised that the letter had a cold tone. For instance, the letter began "Dear Sir." LEWINSKY advised she did not think the letter was threatening, but when she saw CLINTON on July 4, he indicated he felt it was. CLINTON asked LEWINSKY if she knew that it was against the law to threaten the President of the United States.

LEWINSKY advised that the first time she mentioned the possibility of moving to New York was in this July 3rd letter to CLINTON. LEWINSKY advised she gave the letter to CURRIE at the Northwest gate. LEWINSKY advised the letter was handwritten and mentioned LEWINSKY's mother. LEWINSKY advised TRIPP had no input as to the contents of this letter. LEWINSKY advised that at the end of this letter, she expressed more emotions and even mentioned that she would give CLINTON one more chance.

LEWINSKY advised this letter was the meanest one she had ever sent to CLINTON. LEWINSKY advised the purpose of the letter was to show CLINTON how lucky he was that she was the way she was and that some people in her position, who had had an affair with him, would have played "hard ball" with him. LEWINSKY advised the letter was approximately two to three lined pages.

LEWINSKY advised that on most occasions she handwrote her notes, but she did type some. LEWINSKY advised that she sometimes prepared rough drafts of letters she eventually sent to CLINTON. LEWINSKY advised she often times bought two cards and used one to prepare a draft so that, in the event she made a mistake, she would have a duplicate card available to send.

CURRIE called LEWINSKY on the evening of July 3rd. LEWINSKY asked if CURRIE had given the package to CLINTON. CURRIE said she had and told LEWINSKY to be at the White House at 9 a.m. on July 4th.

LEWINSKY advised that CLINTON said he read the first line of the letter because CURRIE looked upset when she delivered it. CLINTON told LEWINSKY he threw the letter away after reading

OIC-302a (Rev. 8-19-94)

29D-OIC-LR-35063

Continuation of OIC-302 of MONICA S. LEWINSKY, On 07/29/98, Page 9

the first line. LEWINSKY thinks CLINTON read the whole letter. LEWINSKY believes CLINTON is the type of person who would lie about reading the letter. LEWINSKY believes CURRIE is not the type to read it.

LEWINSKY does not believe that CURRIE opened the letters LEWINSKY sent to CLINTON through CURRIE. LEWINSKY advised she typically would send things to CLINTON through CURRIE. LEWINSKY would place the item intended for CLINTON in an envelope marked either "BC" or "Mr. P." LEWINSKY said she would send that item in a larger envelope, which was addressed to CURRIE. LEWINSKY usually sent some sort of gift or card to CURRIE in the larger envelope.

When LEWINSKY first arrived at the Oval Office on July 4th at 9 a.m., LEWINSKY told CLINTON someone was outside the Oval Office, so he suggested they move to the study. While in the study, she saw a White House gardener standing outside. LEWINSKY advised the gardener was standing sideways, so she is not sure if he saw LEWINSKY.

LEWINSKY advised she then left for Madrid soon after July 4. While in Madrid, LEWINSKY went to the United States embassy or the ambassador's house for an official function. LEWINSKY saw CLINTON when she first entered the function. CLINTON was standing in a hall speaking with some of his aides, including MIKE McCURRY. When CLINTON saw LEWINSKY, they made eye contact and all the people CLINTON was speaking with turned and saw LEWINSKY.

LEWINSKY believes this is the only time she was in the same room with BRUCE LINDSEY.

On July 14, 1997, LEWINSKY returned from Bulgaria, the last leg of her European trip. LEWINSKY was awakened at 7:30 p.m. by a telephone call from CURRIE. CURRIE advised that CLINTON was out golfing, but he wanted to see or call LEWINSKY later. LEWINSKY thinks CLINTON assumed she was back from Europe because he was. LEWINSKY advised she travelled with Secretary of Defense WILLIAM COHEN's group, but does not think CLINTON kept track of those types of details.

At approximately 8:30 p.m., CURRIE called LEWINSKY again and asked if LEWINSKY could come to the White House at approximately 9:30 p.m. so CLINTON could see LEWINSKY. CURRIE cleared LEWINSKY into the White House and the two spoke for a few minutes.

CLINTON then came out of the Oval Office and took LEWINSKY into NANCY HERNREICH's office. LEWINSKY advised CLINTON was very cold and distant at this meeting. CLINTON sat on a chair in HERNREICH's office while LEWINSKY sat on a sofa.

CLINTON asked LEWINSKY if the woman she mentioned on July 4th was LINDA TRIPP. LEWINSKY responded that it was. CLINTON said that there was a paper called the "Sludge Report" that mentioned KATHLEEN WILLEY. CLINTON asked LEWINSKY if LEWINSKY had told TRIPP that WILLEY had called HERNREICH.

LEWINSKY advised that at this point, she was not sure how to answer. LEWINSKY advised she had to watch her lie because she was not sure what CLINTON's reaction would be to the truth. LEWINSKY advised that the problem was that WILLEY called HERNREICH and was upset that ISIKOFF knew about WILLEY's previous call to HERNREICH. CLINTON said the only people who knew about WILLEY's first call to HERNREICH were WILLEY, HERNREICH, CLINTON and LEWINSKY. LEWINSKY told CLINTON she (LEWINSKY) must have told TRIPP.

LEWINSKY did not want to think that TRIPP told ISIKOFF about the WILLEY telephone call. LEWINSKY told CLINTON that TRIPP was a big supporter of his and that she had big pictures of CLINTON in her office. CLINTON asked LEWINSKY if she trusted TRIPP. LEWINSKY said she did. CLINTON also asked LEWINSKY if LEWINSKY confided in TRIPP about CLINTON's relationship with LEWINSKY. LEWINSKY said she had not.

CLINTON told LEWINSKY to tell TRIPP to try to get in touch with LINDSEY again. LEWINSKY would not characterize CLINTON as "emphatic" in this request. LEWINSKY advised the interviewers if LINDSEY made the initial contact with TRIPP, there might be records reflecting that contact. CLINTON told LEWINSKY to call CURRIE the next day to see whether or not LEWINSKY was successful in getting TRIPP to contact LINDSEY. LEWINSKY did not consider TRIPP's knowledge about the WILLEY incident to be that significant because TRIPP had no first hand knowledge about what occured between CLINTON and WILLEY. LEWINSKY advised that CLINTON left her in HERNREICH's office so he could take a conference call with his attorneys. CLINTON returned from his conference call. LEWINSKY advised she spent approximately twenty-five minutes total with CLINTON during this visit. LEWINSKY advised she did not leave the White House until approximately 11:30 p.m. LEWINSKY and CLINTON spent approximately 25 minutes together on this occasion.

OIC-302a (Rev. 8-19-94)

29D-OIC-LR-35063

Continuation of OIC-302 of MONICA S. LEWINSKY , On 07/29/98 , Page 11

LEWINSKY thought it was safe for TRIPP to call LINDSEY. LEWINSKY felt it would look more sinister for LINDSEY to call TRIPP. LEWINSKY was under the impression that WILLEY was not part of the PAULA JONES suit.

LEWINSKY felt bad that she had told TRIPP about the WILLEY call. LEWINSKY felt responsible and felt she wanted to please the President so she was willing to contact TRIPP. CLINTON did not mention TRIPP getting in touch with BOB BENNETT during this call.

The following day, on July 15th, LEWINSKY tried to get information from TRIPP, including the names of the different people at the White House whom TRIPP had spoken to. LEWINSKY knew TRIPP spoke to an IRENE Last Name Unknown (LNU) and a KATE LNU, both of whom worked at the White House. LEWINSKY telephoned CURRIE later that day to let CURRIE know that LEWINSKY had information for CLINTON.

CLINTON called LEWINSKY later that night. LEWINSKY advised CLINTON was in a "shitty" mood. LEWINSKY went through the information she had for CLINTON regarding WILLEY and TRIPP. LEWINSKY advised she and CLINTON did not speak for long as CLINTON was in a bad mood.

LEWINSKY advised that at some point which LEWINSKY believes was after July 24th, she convinced TRIPP to call LINDSEY. In a Thursday evening telephone conversation, TRIPP told LEWINSKY that TRIPP was ready to meet with BOB BENNETT, as suggested to TRIPP by BRUCE LINDSEY. TRIPP said she made the arrangements for noon the following day. TRIPP told LEWINSKY she was nervous.

TRIPP was concerned that her hair did not look right, so she tried to make an appointment at ILEO. This not being successful, TRIPP made one at a salon named "3300 M Street." LEWINSKY paid for TRIPP's haircut. TRIPP was afraid BENNETT was going to say something mean to her, so she moved the appointment with BENNETT back to 3:30 p.m.

TRIPP told LEWINSKY that, before seeing BENNETT, TRIPP thought she should see TRIPP's attorney, KIRBY BEHRE. TRIPP advised that BEHRE forbade her to see BENNETT, so she did not.

LEWINSKY thinks she called CURRIE to tell her about TRIPP, but LEWINSKY did not contact CLINTON directly.

29D-OIC-LR-35063

LEWINSKY advised that she thought TRIPP was naive to talk to ISIKOFF and that it could be bad for her career. LEWINSKY thought LINDSEY would curb what TRIPP said to ISIKOFF, after LINDSEY spoke to TRIPP. LEWINSKY advised that when TRIPP first mentioned ISIKOFF, TRIPP was upset. TRIPP was friendly with WILLEY and even helped her draft letters to the President. TRIPP said there was always a possibility WILLEY made her story up. LEWINSKY thought TRIPP was on the "right" team.

When the Newsweek article was released, TRIPP was on vacation. LEWINSKY advised that the quote from TRIPP in the Newsweek article was more than TRIPP had told LEWINSKY.

After the Newsweek article that included BENNETT "slamming" TRIPP, TRIPP said she would write a "tell-all" book if she was fired. LEWINSKY said it was silly. LEWINSKY did not think BENNETT's comments were too bad. LEWINSKY advised TRIPP "scared the shit" out of LEWINSKY when TRIPP mentioned writing a book.

Prior to August 11th, LEWINSKY anonymously called BEHRE and said that TRIPP had been misquoted. LEWINSKY asked if BEHRE was going to release a statement on TRIPP's behalf, responding to the BENNETT quote. LEWINSKY suggested BEHRE call the White House. LEWINSKY thought this would help TRIPP keep her job.

On August 14th, the Washington Times had an article about BEHRE's statement on TRIPP's behalf. Throughout 1997, TRIPP mentioned being deposed in the JONES case. TRIPP said that BEHRE said she would not have to be deposed.

Sometime after August of 1997, TRIPP mentioned something about her attorney being in touch with JONES's attorneys. LEWINSKY advised she does not have a vivid memory, but TRIPP would bring up the JONES case from time to time.

LEWINSKY spoke about her friendship with TRIPP to NEYSA ERBLAND and KATHRYN ALLDAY DAVIS. LEWINSKY's mother did not know much about LEWINSKY's relationship with TRIPP. LEWINSKY tried to stay away from the WILLEY/JONES issue when speaking with CLINTON.

LEWINSKY advised that she did not have much contact with TRIPP in mid- to late November since LEWINSKY and TRIPP were fighting and LEWINSKY had been out of the country during part of this time.

Sometime in the second or third week of December, TRIPP

OIC-302a (Rev. 8-19-94)

29D-OIC-LR-35063

mentioned that she was subpoenaed in the JONES case. TRIPP did not mention when she received the subpoena. This was the first time TRIPP said she would "rat" on LEWINSKY. From this point on, LEWINSKY became more circumspect when dealing with TRIPP.

LEWINSKY advised that, during a conversation with TRIPP in December, TRIPP said that one of the reasons for TRIPP telling the truth about LEWINSKY was that BEHRE would know TRIPP was lying. LEWINSKY asked TRIPP how BEHRE would know she was lying. TRIPP advised that she had written the whole story about LEWINSKY and WILLEY and given it to BEHRE in a sealed envelope, and told BEHRE not to read it unless something happened to TRIPP. LEWINSKY advised LEWINSKY went "ape shit" when she heard this.

LEWINSKY advised she tried to protect TRIPP from getting deposed to protect LEWINSKY, which, in turn, protected CLINTON.

TRIPP's deposition was scheduled for December 18th, but was postponed because WILLEY was having back surgery.

LEWINSKY advised that CLINTON told LEWINSKY she was on the JONES witness list in a telephone conversation on December 17th. LEWINSKY advised she was in New York the previous day for job interviews. LEWINSKY was subpoenaed on December 19, 1997.

"TALKING POINTS"

LEWINSKY advised that, in late December 1997, she was trying to figure things out regarding TRIPP's deposition. LEWINSKY did not return TRIPP's calls. On January 1, 1998, LEWINSKY left a message on TRIPP's answering machine. LEWINSKY advised she was at an impasse as to what to do. LEWINSKY was shocked that TRIPP would reveal LEWINSKY.

LEWINSKY advised it made no sense to her for anyone to make the leap from PAULA JONES to LEWINSKY. LEWINSKY thinks TRIPP was jealous about LEWINSKY's job opportunities in New York. TRIPP wanted LEWINSKY to get a good job, but she was also jealous of LEWINSKY.

LEWINSKY advised that the main reason she looked for a job in New York was because TRIPP said that "KATE at NSC" said LEWINSKY would never get a job in the White House, and if she did, she certainly would not have a blue pass. LEWINSKY advised she separately told CLINTON and KEN BACON she wanted to move to New York because of her mother moving there. LEWINSKY advised

OIC-302a (Rev. 8-19-94)

29D-OIC-LR-35063

Continuation of OIC-302 of MONICA S. LEWINSKY , On 07/29/98 , Page 14

that "KATE at NSC" told TRIPP that jobs were created at the White House six days a week. LEWINSKY mentioned STEVEN GOODIN's girlfriend got a job at the White House. LEWINSKY advised TRIPP told LEWINSKY this in an October 6, 1997 telephone call.

On January 9, 1998, LEWINSKY called TRIPP from New York. LEWINSKY was wary of TRIPP, so she said she was calling from a pay phone, but she was actually calling from her mother's apartment. TRIPP said that NORMA ASNES said TRIPP should get a job in public relations in New York. TRIPP told LEWINSKY that TRIPP's Indian friend goes to a psychic and asked the psychic about her friends. The psychic said a friend of her's, whom TRIPP interpreted to be TRIPP, was in imminent danger about what she would say.

During this conversation, TRIPP asked LEWINSKY if LEWINSKY had spoken to CURRIE, JORDAN or CLINTON. LEWINSKY told TRIPP she had not spoken with them from mid-December forward. LEWINSKY told TRIPP she did not care about not speaking with them. TRIPP asked what LEWINSKY was going to do about her deposition. LEWINSKY mentioned her affidavit. TRIPP told LEWINSKY to get a job before LEWINSKY signed it. LEWINSKY did not let TRIPP know that she had already signed the affidavit.

LEWINSKY explained that TRIPP did not like LEWINSKY to exhibit independence. LEWINSKY advised that on November 22, 1997, LEWINSKY wanted to phone CURRIE to apologize, but TRIPP did not want her to. TRIPP and LEWINSKY got into fight over this issue.

LEWINSKY did not want TRIPP to know about all the help LEWINSKY got from VERNON JORDAN. On January 13th or 14th, LEWINSKY called TRIPP at work. During this conversation, TRIPP said that BEHRE did not want TRIPP to sign an affidavit and would not let her commit perjury. LEWINSKY told TRIPP to call ASNES, who could recommend a good "Democratic" attorney.

LEWINSKY told TRIPP that the purpose of the affidavit was to avoid being deposed. LEWINSKY advised that one does this by giving a portion of the whole story, so the attorneys do not think you have anything of relevance to their case. LEWINSKY advised she and TRIPP went through the different things to say in an affidavit. LEWINSKY went through the WILLEY story with TRIPP, including who saw it, that the story could be false, and that WILLEY could have smeared her own lipstick and untucked her own blouse.

OIC-302a (Rev. 8-19-94)

29D-OIC-LR-35063

Continuation of OIC-302 of MONICA S. LEWINSKY, On 07/29/98, Page 15

LEWINSKY agreed to meet TRIPP on January 13, 1998, because she felt TRIPP had changed her mind about disclosing LEWINSKY's relationship.

On January 14, 1998, LEWINSKY was supposed to take TRIPP to see BEHRE, but the plans changed and LEWINSKY drove TRIPP to TRIPP's car, which was parked at a Metro station. Prior to meeting TRIPP, LEWINSKY sat down at her computer on January 14th and typed out the "Talking Points" in one sitting. LEWINSKY typed the "Talking Points" the same day she gave them to TRIPP.

LEWINSKY advised page one of the "Talking Points" begins with "you are not sure...." LEWINSKY advised these were to be TRIPP's talking points for her meeting with BEHRE. The last part of page one was in reference to TRIPP providing BEHRE a written account of the WILLEY and LEWINSKY matters.

Page two of the "Talking Points" was written out because LEWINSKY thought she would only have a few minutes with TRIPP, so she wanted to have an outline of points for TRIPP to make in an affidavit.

LEWINSKY advised the "Talking Points" were a combination of things TRIPP said to LEWINSKY and TRIPP's public statements. Page two of the "Talking Points" was based on what was in LEWINSKY's affidavit.

Page three of the "Talking Points" was what TRIPP could give to BEHRE for BEHRE to draft an affidavit. LEWINSKY advised she printed the "Talking Points" on her printer in her apartment. LEWINSKY advised she did not save the "Talking Points." LEWINSKY advised she did not save them on her computer for a reason. LEWINSKY was trying to be circumspect about JONES related matters at that point. LEWINSKY thought the JONES' attorneys had tapped her phones. LEWINSKY thought at one point that DEBBIE SCHIFF had given JONES' attorneys LEWINSKY's name so SCHIFF would not have to testify.

LEWINSKY advised the goal of an affidavit is to be as benign as possible, so as to avoid being deposed.

LEWINSKY advised that, looking back, one can see how TRIPP's various public statements about the WILLEY incident are used throughout the "Talking Points." LEWINSKY advised she did not refer to TRIPP's public statements to draft the "Talking Points."

OIC-302a (Rev. 8-19-94)

29D-OIC-LR-35063

LEWINSKY advised that TRIPP read the "Talking Points" when LEWINSKY gave them to her. TRIPP was thankful to LEWINSKY for them. LEWINSKY advised the "Talking Points" were not a collaborative effort with TRIPP. LEWINSKY typed them up on her own, with no assistance from anyone.

EVIDENCE

LEWINSKY was shown a copy of the Federal Bureau of Investigation's (FBI's) inventory of items taken from her apartment during a consensual search on January 22, 1998. LEWINSKY advised that a note found in her apartment referring to LEWINSKY going to the White House was written on October 11, 1997. LEWINSKY explained to her aunt that LEWINSKY was to meet LEWINSKY's brother in New York, and LEWINSKY would be taking a plane there after going to the White House in the morning.

TIPPER GORE's book has a photograph of CLINTON wearing a tie LEWINSKY gave him. LEWINSKY's father may have purchased the book for her.

LEWINSKY has never been on Air Force One.

The "Saxophone Club" is an offshoot of the Democratic National Committee. LEWINSKY advised that people who donate less than $200 can belong. LEWINSKY was a member.

LEWINSKY advised she attended a cocktail party which was held in New York prior to CLINTON's fiftieth birthday celebration. LEWINSKY purchased a $250 ticket, but when LEWINSKY got to the door, she did not have a reservation. LEWINSKY got assistance from JENNIFER SCULLY, whom LEWINSKY met through WALTER KAYE. LEWINSKY, who was wearing a red dress, saw CLINTON on the rope line and he hugged her and said he liked her dress.

CLINTON gave LEWINSKY the "BLACK DOG" coffee mug.

CLINTON gave LEWINSKY an ANNIE LENNOX compact disc.

LEWINSKY bought the book "Presidential Sex" because of her relationship with CLINTON.

LEWINSKY sent a letter to CLINTON, similar to the one referencing the "New Deal" found in her apartment on January 22, 1998.

The American Express bill of WILLIAM ARBAUGH was sent

OIC-302a (Rev. 8-19-94)

29D-OIC-LR-35063

Continuation of OIC-302 of MONICA S. LEWINSKY, On 07/29/98, Page 17

to LEWINSKY by mistake.

The $10,000 credit card payment LEWINSKY's mother made had nothing to do with LEWINSKY.

LEWINSKY had a spiral notebook in which she documented the early part of her relationship with CLINTON. LEWINSKY advised the notebook was there on January 22, 1998, but not taken during the search. LEWINSKY saw the notebook after the search, but is not sure where it is now.

The notebook is not dated. The first ten pages relate to her relationship with CLINTON. LEWINSKY advised she did not keep a diary.

The blue dress LEWINSKY presented to the OIC was the same one she wore during her "Birthday" picture with CLINTON. LEWINSKY also wore the dress on February 28, 1997, the first time her sexual contact with CLINTON resulted in him ejaculating in her presence. After engaging in sexual contact with CLINTON, LEWINSKY went to MCCORMICK & SCHMICK'S restaurant and then took the dress off when she got home.

The next time LEWINSKY went to wear the dress, she noticed some faint tiny dots, which could be stains of CLINTON's semen, which could have gotten on the dress while LEWINSKY and CLINTON were hugging. LEWINSKY thought it was funny, so she put it back in the closet.

LEWINSKY showed the dress to TRIPP, who advised LEWINSKY to place the dress in a zip-lock bag and put it in a safe deposit box. LEWINSKY did not save the dress as a "trophy." LEWINSKY said she planned to get the dress cleaned before she wore it again.

That Thanksgiving, LEWINSKY told TRIPP she was going to wear the dress. TRIPP told her not to. TRIPP said LEWINSKY looked fat in the dress.

Sometime after LEWINSKY was subpoenaed on December 19th, she moved the dress to her mother's apartment in New York, with the audio cassette tapes containing CLINTON's answering machine messages to LEWINSKY.

CLINTON gave LEWINSKY the "Vancouver bear" on December 28, 1997. CLINTON told LEWINSKY the bear represented strength, and LEWINSKY would have to be strong. LEWINSKY associated that

OIC-302a (Rev. 8-19-94)

29D-OIC-LR-35063

Continuation of OIC-302 of MONICA S. LEWINSKY, On 07/29/98, Page 18

comment with her July 4th conversation with CLINTON. LEWINSKY advised there was never a question she was going to deny her relationship with CLINTON, so she did not associate the bear with that.

The interview ended at 7:41 p.m.

Tab 20

OIC-302 (Rev. 8-19-94)

OFFICE OF THE INDEPENDENT COUNSEL

Date of transcription 08/02/98

MONICA S. LEWINSKY was interviewed pursuant to an immunity agreement between the Office of the Independent Counsel (OIC), LEWINSKY, and her attorneys. Present for the interview were Associate Independent Counsel (AIC) MICHAEL EMMICK, AIC KARIN IMMERGUT, AIC MARY ANNE WIRTH, and AIC JULIE MYERS. Representing LEWINSKY were attorneys SYDNEY HOFFMAN and PRESTON BURTON of the law offices of PLATO CACHERIS. AIC WIRTH was not present for the late morning and early afternoon portions of the interview. The interview was conducted in Room 616 of the WATERGATE HOTEL, commencing at 9:40 a.m. and ending at 6:15 p.m. LEWINSKY, a white female, born July 23, 1973, provided the following information:

After the scandal broke and the "talking points" were discussed in the media, LEWINSKY realized that the quotes made by LINDA TRIPP in the Newsweek article on August 11, 1997, and in the article in the Washington Times on August 14, 1997, included concepts that LEWINSKY and TRIPP had discussed. These concepts helped influence the contents of the talking points, which were written by LEWINSKY. LEWINSKY recognized that the above mentioned public statements by LINDA TRIPP closely resembled the talking points. These ideas of TRIPP, that were publicly espoused, pointed to the likelihood that KATHLEEN WILLEY's story was more untrue than factual. TRIPP made varying statements in these articles.

During the meeting between LEWINSKY and the President on December 28, 1997, the President said something to the effect of, "That woman from the summer got you into this." By this, LEWINSKY understood that the President meant LINDA TRIPP, who had been quoted in the above articles. On this occasion, a member of the U.S. Secret Service (USSS) could have observed the President hugging LEWINSKY through the glass, but LEWINSKY is not sure.

LEWINSKY has not heard any of the tapes that TRIPP made of their conversations.

LEWINSKY provided a copy of a two-sided set of calendars for the years 1993, 1994 and 1995 entitled, "1994 Diary, FiloFax." Certain dates are circled on each calendar. On the 1995 portion of the calendar, LEWINSKY circled the dates

Investigation on 07/30/98 at WASHINGTON, D.C. File # 29D OIC LR 35063

by SA [redacted]
CI [redacted] Date dictated 08/02/98

29D OIC LR 35063

relating to encounters with ANDY BLEILER.

LEWINSKY said that in March 1998, the [redacted] matter had arisen, and since she was very sensitive about it, LEWINSKY did not wish to discuss [redacted] at this time.

LEWINSKY had created a matrix by spreadsheet in the Fall of 1997 on the Excel program of her computer at the Pentagon, at the request of LINDA TRIPP. This was created on her work computer when her boss, KEN BACON, was out of town. The matrix consisted of the dates of events, telephone calls, and personal meetings with the President. No names or identifying data were typed on the matrix. LEWINSKY made one, or possibly two copies, but did not save the matrix on her computer. LEWINSKY showed or read one copy to TRIPP and believes that she destroyed any other copy. LEWINSKY had first begun confiding in TRIPP in November 1996, at which time TRIPP urged LEWINSKY to go back to the White House to work. TRIPP advised LEWINSKY that she was the kind of woman the President would like and an affair with the President would be a neat thing to tell her grandkids. TRIPP kept hounding LEWINSKY until LEWINSKY finally said, "Look, I've already had an affair with him and it's over."

The President called LEWINSKY between 12:00 p.m. and 2:00 p.m. on January 7, 1996, which was during the snowstorm. He asked LEWINSKY to go to her office in the White House, where he again called her. While chatting, LEWINSKY asked if the President wanted some company, and the President replied that he did. Plans were made that LEWINSKY would go to the Oval Office and the door would be left open.

Upon arriving between 3:00 p.m. and 5:00 p.m., LEWINSKY, who was carrying some papers, saw uniformed USSS Officer LEWIS FOX standing in front of the Oval Office. FOX was probably standing with a USSS plain clothes agent. FOX was not there when LEWINSKY departed. At some point LEWINSKY gave a box of LADY GODIVA chocolates to FOX.

An unidentified USSS plain clothes agent, who usually worked on Sunday afternoons, was present on two different occasions when LEWINSKY was with the President. LEWINSKY met the President by the elevators once and was escorted to the Oval Office. On another occasion the plain clothes agent was present when the President was joking about LEWINSKY's footwear that she had worn because of the snow. The President said, "Chelsea has some like that." This plain clothes agent, whose name LEWINSKY did not know, was a tall, hefty, attractive, white male with

OIC-302a (Rev. 8-19-94)

29D OIC LR 35063

Continuation of OIC-302 of MONICA S. LEWINSKY, On 07/30/98, Page 3

light hair. One of these occasions was either January 21, 1996 or February 4, 1996.

A USSS officer named SANDY observed LEWINSKY with the President on December 31, 1995, when they were discussing cigars. SANDY was standing to the left of LEWINSKY, facing the door in the hallway. This was a visit with the President lasting about 20 or 25 minutes. LEWINSKY may have sent a birthday card to SANDY on a later date. SANDY was not further identified.

LEWINSKY was never refused entrance into the President's movie theater by a USSS officer. BAYANI NELVIS had once asked LEWINSKY if she had ever watched a movie with the President, and LEWINSKY responded that she had not, and as a matter of fact had never been in the theater.

On February 19, 1996, LEWINSKY went to the Oval Office without actually being invited; however, this was after talking to the President on the telephone. At this time there was a very tall, thin, plain clothes agent, with a mustache and an olive complexion, on duty. This plain clothes agent let LEWINSKY into the Oval Office between 12:00 p.m. and 2:00 p.m. This was the only time that LEWINSKY ever went to the Oval Office without the President expecting her.

The only time that LEWINSKY ever waited in the ROOSEVELT room was on July 24, 1997, and that was because BETTY CURRIE had her wait there. There were two ladies rooms in the West Wing, one being near LEON PANETTA's office and one past the Oval Office. LEWINSKY used the one near the Oval Office during the furlough. Subsequently, an E-mail came out from ANNE CATALINI that the employees of Legislative Affairs could not go by the Oval Office. There were three ways to go to the other remote offices of Legislative Affairs; one was down the stairs; one was through the West Wing lobby; and the third was past the Oval Office. EVELYN LIEBERMAN advised LEWINSKY to go through the lobby and not by the Oval Office.

Although LEWINSKY does recall a USSS plain clothes agent named GARY, Last Name Unknown(LNU), she does not recall that he ever asked LEWINSKY to leave the pantry or any other location. GARY may have said something like, "What are you up to?," but he never asked her to leave.

LEWINSKY knew a USSS plain clothes supervisor named BRYANT, who was friendly toward her, but LEWINSKY never discussed her relationship with the President with BRYANT. BRYANT could have escorted LEWINSKY to parties, but she has no memory of this.

LEWINSKY saw a USSS plain clothes agent named LOU MERLETTI several times, but had more of an acquaintance than a friendship with him. MERLETTI gave LEWINSKY his business card. LEWINSKY teased MERLETTI about being in so many photos with the President and sometimes joked with him in the hallways. LEWINSKY saw MERLETTI at the "Nutcracker" in December, 1996. MERLETTI was very friendly with LEWINSKY and she sent him a letter once. MERLETTI never saw LEWINSKY with the President to her knowledge. LEWINSKY also sent a gift to MERLETTI after she left the White House.

LEWINSKY has only a vague recollection of USSS plain clothes agent LARRY COCKELL, possibly having seen him on December 28, 1997.

On December 6, 1997, LEWINSKY went to the southwest gate and paged BETTY CURRIE to get in. While waiting, MARSHA SCOTT pulled up in her car, causing LEWINSKY to go to the northwest gate, which was under construction. When LEWINSKY arrived there, she called CURRIE, but there was no answer on CURRIE's phone. Two uniformed USSS officers, names unknown, were on duty. LEWINSKY had Christmas gifts for CURRIE and the President. Since CURRIE's telephone was not answered, LEWINSKY asked the guards to find out where CURRIE was and whether the President was in his office. One of the guards told LEWINSKY that CURRIE was giving a tour to ELEANOR MONDALE and confirmed that the President was in the Oval Office.

While at the northwest gate, LEWINSKY mistook LANNIE DAVIS for JOHN PODESTA, and after this misidentification was clarified, DAVIS was advised that LEWINSKY was waiting for BETTY CURRIE. CURRIE had told LEWINSKY earlier in the day that the President would be meeting with his lawyers on December 6th and that the President probably would not be able to meet with LEWINSKY. After finding out about MONDALE, LEWINSKY did not feel that CURRIE was truthful with her that day. LEWINSKY left the gate crying and very angry.

LEWINSKY called CURRIE from the CORCORAN GALLERY and confronted her about MONDALE visiting. CURRIE became angry also and apparently shouted at the guards for divulging that MONDALE was visiting the President. LEWINSKY assumed this, because CURRIE told LEWINSKY that LEWINSKY had gotten the guards in trouble. Later, when LEWINSKY talked to the President about this, the President asked LEWINSKY, "Do you think I'm stupid enough to go running with someone I'm messing around with?" The President also said that it was none of LEWINSKY's business what MONDALE was doing there; and that LEWINSKY should not be angry with CURRIE. LEWINSKY does not recall a discussion with the President about the guards at the northwest gate.

Later in the day, LEWINSKY bought an airline ticket and traveled to New York.

AIC WIRTH departed at this time and Deputy Independent Counsel (DIC) WISENBERG arrived.

LEWINSKY said that she had seen SARAH FARNSWORTH at the Watergate Apartments recently, but that she did not speak to FARNSWORTH, as they did not like each other.

LEWINSKY stated that she did not wish to discuss the description of anyone's genitalia, but that she disagrees with the description given by PAULA JONES.

LEWINSKY had her first sexual contact with the President on November 15, 1995. After earlier seeing the President at JENNIFER PALMIERI's party, LEWINSKY was walking to the ladies room near the Oval Office about 8:00 p.m. Upon passing the office of GEORGE STEPHANOPOLOUS, LEWINSKY saw a USSS plain clothes agent outside the door and the President inside the office. The President motioned her into STEPHANOPOLOUS's office. There had been flirtation and eye contact between the President and LEWINSKY on other occasions. LEWINSKY wore G-string panties to the earlier party and pulled her jacket up so that the President could see them at the party. No one else observed this.

LEWINSKY, after entering STEPHANOPOLOUS's office, told the President that she had a crush on him. The President asked if LEWINSKY would like to see his back office and she responded affirmatively. Upon arriving there, the President and LEWINSKY began hugging and the President asked if he could kiss LEWINSKY. With her consent the President kissed her with open mouth in a very romantic way. LEWINSKY gave the President a piece of paper with her name and telephone number on it. The President asked if LEWINSKY wanted to meet him back in his office in about ten minutes and LEWINSKY agreed. LEWINSKY returned to PANETTA's outer office, where she had been working. MARTHA FOLEY may have been working and FOLEY may have given LEWINSKY a ride home that night.

LEWINSKY recalled that she was wearing navy blue pants

OIC-302a (Rev. 8-19-94)

29D OIC LR 35063

and a dark navy jacket that night. Sometime after 8:00 p.m., and before 10:00 p.m., LEWINSKY returned to the Oval Office and the President took her to the hallway by the back study behind the Oval Office. The lights were off. The President began kissing LEWINSKY and she unbuttoned her jacket. The President pulled her bra up (he only unhooked her bra once in subsequent sexual contacts) and put his hand down into her pants. The President received a telephone call from a Congressman or Senator. While talking on the telephone, the President kept his hand in LEWINSKY's pants to stimulate her, thereby causing her to have an orgasm or two. LEWINSKY then performed oral sex on the President, but he told LEWINSKY to stop before he reached completion. The President said that it was too soon for him to do that, inasmuch as he did not know or trust LEWINSKY well enough. The President tugged on her pink intern pass and said that "this" was going to be a problem.

The President did not know that LEWINSKY had already accepted a paying position that would entitle her to an employee pass. LEWINSKY told the President that she had had an affair with a married man before and that she knew the rules. By this statement LEWINSKY was trying to make the President feel more comfortable. She was sending a signal that she could keep quiet and lie if necessary. LEWINSKY was on "cloud nine." No further plans were made at that time and the President went upstairs to have dinner with Mrs. CLINTON. LEWINSKY speculated that the President's regular girlfriend had been furloughed.

On this or some other occasion the President said that he did not want to get addicted to having sex with LEWINSKY or he would want her all of the time. LEWINSKY and the President had incredible chemistry and were sexually compatible.

On Friday November 17, 1995 pizza was ordered. LEWINSKY picked up the pizza and delivered it to PANETTA's office. LEWINSKY went to CURRIE'S office to announce that the pizza had arrived. GENE SPERLING, GEORGE STEPHANOPOLOUS, and perhaps others were there. LEWINSKY returned to her office. A short time later, the President, CURRIE, and HERNREICH came to PANETTA's outer office. BARRY TOIV bumped into LEWINSKY and got pizza on her outfit. LEWINSKY went to the restroom to clean it off.

The President was standing outside of CURRIE's office when LEWINSKY came out of the restroom. The President invited LEWINSKY over to the Oval Office and they went to the rear study. The door to the Oval Office was left ajar. LEWINSKY asked the

OIC-302a (Rev. 8-19-94)

29D OIC LR 35063

Continuation of OIC-302 of MONICA S. LEWINSKY , On 07/30/98 , Page 7

President if he remembered her name. LEWINSKY advised the President that she had gotten a permanent job in Legislative Affairs. This would allow her to get a blue pass. The President was pleased. The President and LEWINSKY were talking about Jewish things near the bathroom when the President said, "Shut up and kiss me." LEWINSKY said that she had better get back to work before people began to wonder where she was. The President asked LEWINSKY to bring him some pizza. LEWINSKY returned to PANETTA's office.

LEWINSKY returned to BETTY CURRIE's office after a little while and BETTY announced, "Girl here with the pizza." BETTY sent LEWINSKY into the Oval Office. The President took the pizza and the two of them went to the bathroom area off the Oval Office.

The President was wearing a light blue shirt and a red tie. The President loosened his tie. They began kissing and the President attempted to unbutton LEWINSKY's jacket. He could not, so she did it. The President kissed LEWINSKY's breasts. When LEWINSKY unbuttoned the President's blue shirt, the President sucked in his stomach, and LEWINSKY kissed his chest. LEWINSKY assured the President that she thought his physical shape was cute.

At some point, BETTY CURRIE came near the Oval Office door and said, "Sir, phone call." The President took the call in the bathroom from a Congressman, who the President called by some "funny," unrecalled nickname. While the President was on the telephone, LEWINSKY performed oral sex on him. The President did not ask LEWINSKY to quit during the phone call, but did not ejaculate. The President never told LEWINSKY that there was no sex between them if he did not ejaculate, but she believed that not reaching completion somehow made the President feel less guilty.

The President said, "I'm usually around on weekends when no one else is around, and you can come and see me." The President complimented LEWINSKY's smile, prettiness, and energy. The President did not tell LEWINSKY how to get access to the Oval Office.

LEWINSKY returned to her office, and a short time later the President returned with his pizza and ate it in front of everyone. The President's tie was back up and he was wearing a distinct cologne.

29D OIC LR 35063

On December 5, 1995, which was the day of the congressional Christmas Ball, the President signed the photograph of himself wearing the tie that LEWINSKY had given to him. He asked LEWINSKY if she wanted a diet Coke. LEWINSKY usually carried one out of the office for cover.

On December 31, 1995, at about noon, LEWINSKY was in the dining room talking to BAYANI NELVIS, a White House steward, about LEWINSKY recently having smoked her first cigar. NELVIS offered to get LEWINSKY a Presidential cigar and they headed to the President's back study. The President met NELVIS and LEWINSKY in the back hallway and said that he needed to get something to LEON PANETTA. The President gave the item to NELVIS to take to PANETTA. The President said that he had been looking for LEWINSKY, to which LEWINSKY replied that she had given him her number. LEWINSKY thought it was obvious that the President had forgotten her name because he saw LEWINSKY one time in the hallway and said, "Hey kiddo." The President asked why LEWINSKY was there in the back office and LEWINSKY replied that NELVIS was going to get her a Presidential cigar. The President said that he would give LEWINSKY a cigar and they went back into the study. They hugged and kissed. LEWINSKY rubbed his back. The President lifted her top and kissed her chest. LEWINSKY performed oral sex on the President, but he stopped her before completion. LEWINSKY went to leave. The President apparently thought that LEWINSKY had already left and went into the bathroom, where LEWINSKY could hear water running. LEWINSKY was putting her lipstick back on and getting herself together when she observed the President in the bathroom, [redacted]

The President was leaving for the Renaissance weekend in a helicopter soon thereafter.

LEWINSKY believes that KATHLEEN WILLEY is not telling the truth, because the President would not have let her leave without getting herself together.

On January 7, 1996, the President called LEWINSKY for the first time at her apartment. It was the first day of a blizzard. LEWINSKY was surprised when she answered the phone and realized that she was speaking to the President. The President asked LEWINSKY if she was going to the office. LEWINSKY asked the President if he wanted some company and the President replied that he did. The President said he was going to the office in about 45 minutes and LEWINSKY said she would be there in about an hour. LEWINSKY went to her office and the President called her

OIC-302a (Rev. 8-19-94)

29D OIC LR 35063

Continuation of OIC-302 of MONICA S. LEWINSKY, On 07/30/98, Page 9

there. LEWINSKY went to the Oval Office and they sat on the sofa and talked. After about ten minutes they went to the bathroom area in the back office. The President had wanted to perform oral sex on LEWINSKY, but she did not want him to because she was having her menstrual period. The President and LEWINSKY had foreplay, but the President stayed above her waist. LEWINSKY performed oral sex on the President, but he did not reach completion. The President and LEWINSKY usually kept their clothing on so that they could recover quickly if interrupted. They went to the Oval Office, where the President sat at his desk and LEWINSKY sat on the sofa. They both knew what the coverup would be to conceal their relationship. They talked and joked around for about 15 minutes before LEWINSKY left. LEWINSKY told the President that he could call her; could listen while she did the talking; and could engage in phone sex. The President said "I'll be around on weekends."

On January 16, 1996, at about 12:30 a.m., the President called LEWINSKY, after having been in Atlanta for MARTIN LUTHER KING day. The President said, "You said that I could call and listen." They had phone sex, with LEWINSKY doing all of the talking. LEWINSKY spoke all of the words. [redacted] The President ended the call by saying that maybe he would call LEWINSKY tomorrow. The President did not call, which made LEWINSKY feel insecure. LEWINSKY was worried that the President did not like the way she performed phone sex. In thinking about their relationship, LEWINSKY observed that initially she was volunteering all of the information about their personal lives and that the President did not provide any details unless LEWINSKY asked. The President sometimes told personal things, but usually spoke about general things. LEWINSKY wanted to know whether they were going to fall in love or whether it would just be a sexual relationship.

On Sunday, January 21, 1996, which was the first day that a soldier had been killed in Bosnia, LEWINSKY saw the President in the hallway near the elevator. The President was accompanied by a USSS plain clothes agent. While talking in the Oval Office, the President said it was very sad to have someone die as a result of one of his Executive Orders. LEWINSKY was feeling like she had been taken for granted. LEWINSKY wound up in the rear hallway with the President. LEWINSKY was having a "bad hair day" and was wearing her beret. This was the first time that the President had seen her with the beret and told LEWINSKY that she was cute in her hat. LEWINSKY dropped her coat on the floor. The President was wearing olive pants and a green sweater

29D OIC LR 35063

Continuation of OIC-302 of MONICA S. LEWINSKY , On 07/30/98 , Page 10

that did not match. As they were heading to the back hallway, LEWINSKY stopped the President and asked him if he was interested in anything more than sex. The President replied that he "cherished his time" with LEWINSKY and that she was a "gift" to him. LEWINSKY treated the President as a regular person and did not stand on ceremony when LEWINSKY was with him. The President said he liked that. They kissed and the President kissed her chest. LEWINSKY performed oral sex on the President in the hallway and possibly in the bathroom. The BLAIRs from Arkansas were in town visiting with the President. LEWINSKY went out to BETTY CURRIE's office with the President and he kissed her goodbye in NANCY HERNREICH's office. LEWINSKY started to leave through the other door, found it locked, and turned around to exit through the door of HERNREICH's office where they had entered. LEWINSKY passed the President, [redacted] The President grinned and kissed LEWINSKY goodbye again. LEWINSKY departed through BETTY CURRIE's office and the garden door. LEWINSKY purposely departed by a different door than the one that she had entered, so that the USSS staff would not know when LEWINSKY came and left. The BLAIRs were going out with the CLINTONs to see the VERMEER exhibit.

LEWINSKY spent the weekend ending January 28th in San Francisco. Upon LEWINSKY's return she saw on her caller identification feature that the President had called her office phone while she was in California. On Tuesday, January 30, 1996, the President called LEWINSKY on her office telephone. The display reflected "POTUS." The President said he had seen LEWINSKY getting yogurt and she looked really pretty. The President suggested that they get together after the party for PAT GRIFFIN. LEWINSKY responded that they should ignore each other at the party so that people would not get suspicious. The President asked if he could meet LEWINSKY later and LEWINSKY declined, because they had to be careful. EVELYN LIEBERMAN had already taken notice of LEWINSKY.

On Saturday, February 4, 1996, the President called LEWINSKY and they agreed that she would carry some papers and meet in the hallway. This occurred and they went to the back office. LEWINSKY was wearing a black dress with little flowers and combat boots. The President commented on the combat boots. The President unbuttoned LEWINSKY's dress and it hung down. The President pulled up LEWINSKY's bra. The President lifted LEWINSKY's dress up. At that point, LEWINSKY stated that she could not continue with the details while male staff members were present. After a short consultation with her attorney, LEWINSKY continued that she had performed oral sex on the President, but that it was not reciprocal oral sex. The President commented on LEWINSKY's state of arousal. When they were finished in the hallway, after about 45 minutes, the President and LEWINSKY went to the Oval Office, where they talked for another 45 minutes. LEWINSKY characterized the talking as "pillow talk." Upon leaving, the President told LEWINSKY to complete her tasks in another part of the West Wing before returning to her office, so that LEWINSKY would not draw attention by going directly from the Oval Office to her office.

On February 7, 1996, a party was held for STEVE FRISCHETTI. That night the President called LEWINSKY at home. Mrs. CLINTON was out of town. The President signed the telecommunications bill while wearing one of LEWINSKY's ties that day.

On Thursday, February 8, 1996, the President called LEWINSKY and at some point during the conversation they engaged in phone sex. On this occasion both the President and LEWINSKY participated verbally in a portion of the phone sex. LEWINSKY said that most of the time she initiated phone sex, but sometimes the President did. During this call, or in a previous call, the President told LEWINSKY that she reminded him of a character, but LEWINSKY could not recall any further description, other than the character had something to do with London.

On Sunday, February 19, 1996, the President called LEWINSKY from his office. The President sounded weird and LEWINSKY did not know what to make of it. LEWINSKY went to the Oval Office uninvited and observed the tall, thin, Hispanic plain clothes agent that she had described earlier in the interview. LEWINSKY advised that this was the only time she went to the Oval Office uninvited. LEWINSKY had previously told the President about ANDY BLEILER in Portland. The President said, "I don't want to be like that schmuck in Oregon." The President would only hug LEWINSKY that day, and he explained that he did not feel right about their sexual relationship; that he felt guilty; that LEWINSKY could still come by and visit; but that they would only be friends and not fool around.

LEWINSKY advised that during this visit with the President, he received a telephone call from a person whose last name began with an "F". This person and his brother had a sugar growing business in Florida. The President took some notes, hung up, and told LEWINSKY that he had to cut their meeting short so that he could talk to this gentleman. The President said that he was going to sign some legislation that was going to have a detrimental effect on the sugar business, and when he does something that is going to "screw" someone, he likes to tell them first.

On a day at the end of February or early March 1996, the President left a message on LEWINSKY's caller identification feature which indicated that "POTUS" had called. This predicated a discussion about the discovery of their relationship. It was decided that a different telephone would be used by the President when calling LEWINSKY's office, so that the readout would not give them away. This day can be established as the day that a bombing occurred and lives were lost in Israel. The President went to the Israeli Embassy to express his regrets. LEWINSKY observed the President and EVELYN LIEBERMAN in the hallway. The President called LEWINSKY at home at about 10:00 p.m. from upstairs in the residence. The President and LEWINSKY talked for about 20 minutes. LEWINSKY offered to visit, but the President declined, advising that CHELSEA CLINTON was sick.

On Friday, March 29, 1996, the President called LEWINSKY in her office. LEWINSKY had cut her hand and bruised herself. The President observed the wounds when LEWINSKY was passing the Map Room in the hallway that evening. The President was wearing the first tie LEWINSKY had given him. The President spoke to LEWINSKY and said that he was sorry that she had hurt her hand. This occurred in the presence of HAROLD ICKES and BRUCE LINDSEY. During the telephone call, the President offered to invite LEWINSKY to a movie that night if LEWINSKY would hang around in the hall just before the movie started so they could pretend to accidentally run into each other. LEWINSKY declined because staff members such as HERNREICH and STEPHANOPOLOUS would be present in the movie and might question her presence. LEWINSKY did not want people to think that she was hanging around uninvited. JENNIE CRUZANO had previously passed BAYANI NELVIS in the hallway and asked NELVIS why NELVIS was talking to LEWINSKY. LEWINSKY had also heard that EVELYN LIEBERMAN was suspicious of her. LEWINSKY concluded the call by asking whether she could see the President on Sunday.

On Sunday, March 31, 1996, LEWINSKY brought some papers to the Oval Office and entered with a USSS plain clothes agent who poked his head in the back hallway. LEWINSKY and the agent heard the toilet flush and were a bit embarrassed. The President was ill. The President was wearing blue jeans and a T-shirt. After the plain clothes agent departed, the President and LEWINSKY fooled around. They touched and kissed in the hallway.

They talked about cigars while the President was chewing on one and then the President looked at LEWINSKY sheepishly and she understood what the President was thinking. LEWINSKY allowed the President to insert the cigar into her vagina. The President placed the cigar into his mouth after withdrawing it from LEWINSKY and said, "It tastes good." The President did not smoke the cigar because smoking is forbidden in the White House. There was no oral sex on this visit. LEWINSKY had brought the President a blue HUGO BOSS tie, concealed among the papers that she carried into the Oval Office. LEWINSKY asked the President if he would wear the tie the following Wednesday for the Office of Legislative Affairs' photograph. The President did wear the tie, but the photograph was not taken due to the death of RON BROWN. This visit was in the late afternoon and lasted from 30 to 45 minutes. LEWINSKY exited via the Rose Garden.

On Easter Sunday, April 7, 1996, LEWINSKY visited the President to discuss her transfer to the Pentagon. This was a result of the President calling LEWINSKY between 5:00 p.m. and 6:00 p.m. During this call LEWINSKY cried and told the President that she had been fired. When LEWINSKY arrived uniformed USSS officer JOHN MUSKETT was there, but LEWINSKY did not recall a plain clothes agent. When LEWINSKY advised MUSKETT that she had some papers for the President, MUSKETT said that he would check with LIEBERMAN about the visit. LEWINSKY quickly said that the President had asked for the papers and that she would only be a minute. LIEBERMAN was not advised to LEWINSKY's knowledge. LEWINSKY went into the back hallway with the President and he said, "I'm sorry they're taking you away--I trust you." The President said, "After the election I'll have you back like this" and snapped his fingers.

LEWINSKY had started performing oral sex on the President when someone from the Oval Office advised the President that he had a telephone call. The President went out to the Oval Office and then took the telephone call in the back office. LEWINSKY put her bra back on at this point. The call was apparently from DICK MORRIS, although LEWINSKY did not know it then. The call concerned campaign strategy. The President wanted LEWINSKY to continue the oral sex while he was on the phone with MORRIS. LEWINSKY complied, but felt cheap doing this. HAROLD ICKES came to the door of the Oval Office and called, "Mr. President," at which time the President bolted out of the back study. LEWINSKY departed the back way and not through the Oval Office. The President called LEWINSKY later and asked why LEWINSKY had left. LEWINSKY replied that ICKES might have walked in. The President asked LEWINSKY to come back the next day to

29D OIC LR 35063

see NANCY HERNREICH about getting a job in the White House.

LEWINSKY advised that the phone sex calls continued after she left her White House job. The President usually called from his residence, or from out of town, and almost always awakened LEWINSKY during the early morning hours. Generally, the President preferred that LEWINSKY do most of the talking during phone sex.

On May 16, 1996, the President called LEWINSKY, but did not want to participate in phone sex. The President felt very badly about Admiral BOORDA committing suicide.

On July 5, 1996, the President called for phone sex when LEWINSKY came back from Bosnia. [redacted] while LEWINSKY was still talking about her trip and not talking in a sexually explicit manner. LEWINSKY asked, "Aren't you going to wait for me?"

On July 19, 1996, the President telephoned LEWINSKY at 6:30 a.m. and had phone sex. Near the end of the call the President said "good morning" in such a way that LEWINSKY was convinced that he had climaxed. The President then said something like, "What a way to start a day."

On September 5, 1996, the President called from out of town and LEWINSKY tried to convince him that they should have sex. The President said that he could not have intercourse with LEWINSKY and that there were consequences when you became older. This resulted in a fight on the telephone and the President asked if he should stop calling LEWINSKY. LEWINSKY responded that he should not.

On September 10, 1996, the President called from out of town and left a message on LEWINSKY's recorder, inasmuch as she was not home.

On October 21, 1996, the President called and they had phone sex.

On October 22, 1996, the President called and he and LEWINSKY had phone sex. The President seemed to take more control, as he talked more during the sexual portion of the call. The President liked it when LEWINSKY lead the sex talk from the start and began with such questions as, "Where are you?" and "What are you wearing?" Sometimes the President initiated the phone sex and sometimes LEWINSKY did.

On December 2, 1996, the President called LEWINSKY about 10:30 p.m., but after a short time the President hung up to take another call. The President called back a few minutes later and they began having phone sex. The President fell asleep during the call. LEWINSKY had to awaken him. LEWINSKY thought that this was "sweet" that the President would call her when he was so tired.

On February 8, 1997, the President called LEWINSKY and they had phone sex. The President said he wanted LEWINSKY to come by and pick up her hatpin. However, it was snowing that day and the President remarked that he felt bad asking BETTY CURRIE to come in (to facilitate a LEWINSKY visit). LEWINSKY and the President had phone sex.

On February 28, 1997, BETTY CURRIE called LEWINSKY at work at approximately 4:00 p.m. to invite LEWINSKY to the President's radio address. LEWINSKY hurried home to change into a new dress. LEWINSKY attended and took a photograph with the President after the address. STEVE GOODIN, RAHM EMMANUEL, and an unrecalled person were in the Oval Office. CURRIE later related that GOODIN had told her privately that she could not let the President and LEWINSKY be alone. LEWINSKY was nervous about the other visitors seeing her at the address. After the address, LEWINSKY walked to the back office with CURRIE and the President and CURRIE excused herself by going to the dining room and saying, "I'll be right back." The President and LEWINSKY went to the study, where he kissed LEWINSKY, unbuttoned her dress, pulled off her bra, and kissed her on the chest. Someone came into the Oval Office, causing the President and LEWINSKY to go into the bathroom, where the President "undid" his pants [redacted] LEWINSKY then performed oral sex on the President, but he tried to stop her before completion. They had a discussion about the President not ejaculating. [redacted] They continued the oral sex until the President ejaculated and then they hugged.

LEWINSKY returned to the dining room area and CURRIE, who had been talking to BAYANI NELVIS, walked her out. CURRIE was supposed to have acted as a chaperone after GOODIN counseled her. On this visit LEWINSKY was wearing the dress that she later noticed to be stained. LEWINSKY believes the dress may have been

29D OIC LR 35063

Continuation of OIC-302 of MONICA S. LEWINSKY, On 07/30/98, Page 16

stained by the President's semen that day after he ejaculated, but she is not sure. The President gave LEWINSKY a hat pin and a book that day.

On Wednesday, March 12, 1997, the President called LEWINSKY at work and asked LEWINSKY to visit him the next day.

On March 13, 1997, the visit was canceled because the President's schedule was too hectic.

On March 14, 1997, the President called LEWINSKY about the HUGO BOSS tie that LEWINSKY had bought in Georgetown. The President stated that the tie had a big cut in it and that he asked if LEWINSKY could exchange it. LEWINSKY picked up the tie, and after looking at the damage, was of the opinion that it had been deliberately cut. KATHRYN DAVIS's sister, KELLY DAVIS, was in town that day. KELLY DAVIS knows nothing of the relationship between LEWINSKY and the President.

On March 29, 1997, the President's brother, ROGER CLINTON, was in town. A meeting was set up between the President and LEWINSKY. LEWINSKY was supposed to bring back the HUGO BOSS tie that day. LEWINSKY went to the White House and waited in the back study. The President hobbled into the room on crutches as a result of injuring his knee in Florida several weeks earlier. This was one of the few days that the President and LEWINSKY fooled around the entire time in the study. The President was uncomfortable and could not bend over. The President unbuttoned LEWINSKY's blouse, but she did not remove the blouse. [redacted] The President spent a lot of time concentrating on LEWINSKY. LEWINSKY had four to six orgasms that day. A ray of sunshine was shining directly on LEWINSKY's face while she performed oral sex to completion on the President. The President remarked about LEWINSKY's beauty. The President spent a lot of time talking with LEWINSKY that day.

The President said that he believed that an unnamed foreign Embassy was listening in on the President's official telephones so they would have to be careful in their phone conversations. The President came up with the ruse that if LEWINSKY was ever questioned to just say that they were friends, and they were just doing it to give people a run for their money. After their private meeting the President and LEWINSKY went into

OIC-302a (Rev. 8-19-94)

29D OIC LR 35063

Continuation of OIC-302 of MONICA S. LEWINSKY, On 07/30/98, Page 17

BETTY CURRIE's office, where they sang "Try A Little Tenderness." CURRIE then walked LEWINSKY to the door. This was the last real sexual contact that LEWINSKY had with the President, other than kissing, hugging, and brief fondling.

On July 4, 1997, the President kissed LEWINSKY on the neck.

On August 16, 1997, LEWINSKY was with the President near the bathroom in the back office and he gave LEWINSKY an open mouth kiss. It was the President's birthday.

On October 10, 1997 the President called in the early morning hours, but got into a big fight with LEWINSKY. There was no phone sex. This was the longest telephone call from the President.

On November 12, 1997, the President was visited by some friend from Arkansas who had a terminal illness. That night, or early the next morning, the President called LEWINSKY and they had phone sex.

On December 28, 1997, LEWINSKY visited the President in the back office. While standing near the doorway to the study, the President gave LEWINSKY an open mouth Christmas kiss. During the kiss the President was looking out the window to make sure they were not being observed.

LEWINSKY and the President touched tongues while kissing on the day of ZEDILLO's visit. As an example of flirtation between LEWINSKY and the President, during the celebration of the President's 49th birthday, the President's elbow had grazed the breast of LEWINSKY. On the occasion of the President's 50th birthday, LEWINSKY was wearing a strapless dress and was in front of a rope line where the President was greeting guests. As the President reached over LEWINSKY to make contact with a well wisher, LEWINSKY reached back and touched the President's crotch. No one else was in a position to observe this.

LEWINSKY sent a few raunchy greeting cards and possibly a few raunchy notes/letters to the President. Although the President liked them, he cautioned her to be careful putting things in writing. LEWINSKY assumes that the President tore the cards and letters up and flushed them down the toilet.

Sometimes when the President and LEWINSKY were fooling

29D OIC LR 35063

around, LEWINSKY would wipe off her lipstick before kissing the President. LEWINSKY did not dress inappropriately while working at the White House, but did wear some low-cut clothing while working at the Pentagon.

LEWINSKY dressed well when seeing the President, but did not wear the same outfit every time. LEWINSKY wore her "lucky" green suit twice and the flower dress twice. The President wore boxer shorts on one occasion, blue briefs on another, and grey shorts when the President hurt his leg. During LEWINSKY's later visits in the back study, the President usually sat in his rocking chair and LEWINSKY sat on the floor below the rocking chair and in between his legs. This arrangement was very intimate and allowed them to touch each other.

LEWINSKY said that she did not make up the sexual activities detailed above, nor did she embellish them. Most of these incidents can be verified through her "personal diary," LINDA TRIPP. LEWINSKY confided in TRIPP on almost a daily basis for a long time, but she never suggested that TRIPP keep records or charts of her activities with the President. In February, 1997, TRIPP asked LEWINSKY to go back over the activities so that TRIPP could figure out a pattern to the sexual encounters. TRIPP was a strategist, and wanted to know if the President only called when he was upset. [redacted] SCOTT told LEWINSKY that SCOTT would detail LEWINSKY back over to the White House; however, this never happened.

In July, August, or September 1997, LEWINSKY invited BETTY CURRIE to have a drink with her at the HAY ADAMS bar to discuss LEWINSKY's job situation. However, CURRIE and LEWINSKY had coffee, not alcoholic drinks. LEWINSKY had set up the meeting to discuss her job situation. During the conversation, which lasted less than an hour, LEWINSKY reminded CURRIE that REBECCA CAMERON was still dragging her feet in giving LEWINSKY the photograph taken at the President's radio address; that MARSHA SCOTT really had not taken any action to get LEWINSKY back to the White House; and that the President did not seem to be helping either. LEWINSKY's approach was, "Hey, I've been a good girl, I went to the Pentagon, and why won't the President bring me back?" LEWINSKY opined that there was a "turf war" between some of the women at the White House. CURRIE explained that the President

OIC-302a (Rev. 8-19-94)

29D OIC LR 35063

Continuation of OIC-302 of MONICA S. LEWINSKY , On 07/30/98 , Page 19

had trouble getting people jobs, because that was done at a lower level and that she would talk to MARSHA SCOTT. CURRIE drove her car to the hotel on this occasion.

In discussing BETTY CURRIE, LEWINSKY remarked that CURRIE sometimes acted naive about what was going on, even though CURRIE had observed LEWINSKY show a lot of emotion about the President. LEWINSKY was very angry with CURRIE on December 6, 1997, when LEWINSKY called her from a pay phone. [redacted] CURRIE had previously told LEWINSKY that the President would be busy all day with his lawyers. LEWINSKY periodically talked to CURRIE about their mutual friend, WALTER KAYE, who knew that the President was fond of LEWINSKY. CURRIE never complained about coming in on weekends to facilitate LEWINSKY's visits to the President. LEWINSKY cultivated CURRIE as a friend, because CURRIE was in a good position to help LEWINSKY. LEWINSKY did not tell CURRIE of her exact relationship with the President, and she and the President attempted to be discreet in front of CURRIE.

On March 29, 1997, CURRIE called from her home to clear LEWINSKY at the White House gate and called from the hospital on October 11, 1997 to do the same. Sometimes, CURRIE conducted private tours on weekends for the President. LEWINSKY knew of no one else at her level that had the degree of access to the President that LEWINSKY did. On "dump day," May 24, 1997, LEWINSKY called CURRIE and advised that LEWINSKY was waiting to see the President. CURRIE said that she had to check Mrs. CLINTON's schedule and said Mrs. CLINTON was going to use the pool that day. This was the only time that LEWINSKY actually knew that CURRIE had factored in the whereabouts of Mrs. CLINTON with LEWINSKY's visits to the President. Mrs. CLINTON never saw LEWINSKY in the Oval Office.

Fourteen photographs of gifts and momentos were displayed to LEWINSKY, who made the following remarks:

1. Ticket to August Ball.

2. Book entitled, "Our Patriotic President," given to the President by LEWINSKY on December 6, 1997. Purchased at New York flea market for $40.00.

3. Antique book entitled "Presidents of the United States of America;" given to the President by dropping off at BETTY CURRIE's home on a weekend in early January 1998, which was the day the President and the First Lady were photographed

dancing on the beach in Florida, purchased for $40.00 at Georgetown bookstore off M Street next to the Christian Scientist book store sometime after December 28, 1997. LEWINSKY included a mushy note in the book. The President acknowledged receipt of the book and note and remarked that LEWINSKY should not have written the note because it was not good to have those things in writing. LEWINSKY's note made reference to the movie "Titanic," which she had seen that weekend.

4. Silver cigar holder purchased at flea market in New York in October/November 1997, for $180.00 in cash. Handed to President in his rocking chair on December 6, 1997, and he said, "It is beautiful." Seen by LINDA TRIPP at work and brother MICHAEL in apartment. LEWINSKY tried to buy DAVIDOFF cigars for holder but unsuccessful. LEWINSKY observed on President's desk in Oval Office on December 28, 1997.

5. STARBUCKS Santa Monica coffee cup purchased at the Los Angeles International Airport and given to President on December 6, 1997; President remarked, "I like big mugs" and LEWINSKY responded, "No, you like big jugs."

6. Gold and blue tie designed by Feraud and purchased in London for 25 pounds in early December, 1997. Presented to President on December 6, 1997.

7. A pin depicting the New York skyline given to LEWINSKY by the President on December 28, 1997.

8. Flower pin for birthday gift handed to LEWINSKY by BETTY CURRIE on behalf of the President in July 1997; may have been CURRIE's personal pin commandeered as last minute gift.

9. Hat pin purchased by the President in Albuquerque on February 28, 1997; LEWINSKY loved it and wore it with her straw hat; told NEYSA about the gift.

10. Green dress from the BLACK DOG shop given to LEWINSKY by the President; LEWINSKY considered it an important personal gift.

11. White T-shirt from BLACK DOG presented by President.

12. Green T-shirt from BLACK DOG presented by President.

13. Ball cap from BLACK DOG presented by President.

14. State Of The Union invitation signed by President and presented to LEWINSKY in 1996.

15. State Of The Union invitation in envelope (duplicate).

Photographs displayed are further described by the following Bates Stamp number:

1. MSL-DC-00000474
2. V002-DC-00000003
3. V002-DC-00000471
4. V000-DC-00000474
5. V002-DC-00000473
6. V002-DC-00000472
7. 824-DC-00000018
8. 824-DC-00000019
9. 824-DC-00000019
10. 824-DC-00000006
11. 824-DC-00000008
12. 824-DC-00000007
13. 824-DC-00000009
14. 824-DC-00000003
15. 824-DC-00000004

LEWINSKY added that she noticed that BAYANI NELVIS wore the first tie that she had given to the President to one of his grand jury appearances.

The interview was terminated at 6:15 p.m.

Tab 21

OIC-302 (Rev. 8-19-94)

- 1 -

OFFICE OF THE INDEPENDENT COUNSEL

Date of transcription 07/31/98

MONICA S. LEWINSKY was interviewed under the terms of an immunity agreement between the Office of the Independent Counsel (OIC) and her. Present for the interview were Associate Independent Counsel (AIC) MICHAEL EMMICK, AIC KARIN IMMERGUT, AIC MARY ANNE WIRTH, and AIC CRAIG LERNER. Representing LEWINSKY were attorney PRESTON BURTON and law clerk MATTHEW UMHOFER. Present for parts of the interview was Deputy Independent Counsel (DIC) ROBERT J. BITTMAN. The interview, conducted in Room 616 of the Watergate Hotel, commenced at approximately 10:08 a.m. LEWINSKY provided the following information:

LEWINSKY was shown a photograph of President WILLIAM JEFFERSON CLINTON on the next to last page of the April 13, 1998 issue of THE WEEKLY STANDARD. LEWINSKY advised she purchased and gave CLINTON the sunglasses CLINTON is wearing in the photograph.

December 5, 1997

LEWINSKY advised that on December 5, 1997, she was mad at CLINTON because he would not see her the following day. On November 30, 1997, the Sunday night before leaving for BRUSSELS, LEWINSKY mailed BETTY CURRIE a letter to give to CLINTON. LEWINSKY advised she wrote CLINTON to tell him LEWINSKY needed to see him. LEWINSKY advised she called CURRIE from Europe to see if CLINTON would be available to meet LEWINSKY anytime soon. LEWINSKY advised CURRIE later said CURRIE did not give the letter to CLINTON until December 5, 1997 at 6 p.m.

LEWINSKY advised she attended a Christmas party at the White House the evening of December 5, 1997. LEWINSKY saw CLINTON at the party, which LEWINSKY attended with BOB TYRER, the Chief of Staff to Secretary of Defense WILLIAM COHEN. LEWINSKY advised she saw CLINTON in the greeting line and, before she shook hands with him, she noticed he saw her and began fixing his hair.

LEWINSKY advised she engaged in small talk with CLINTON. LEWINSKY told HILLARY RODHAM CLINTON that she was friends with WALTER KAYE.

Investigation on 07/31/98 at Washington, DC File # 29D-OIC-LR-35063

by CI [redacted] SA [redacted] Date dictated 07/31/98

OIC-302a (Rev. 8-19-94)

29D-OIC-LR-35063

Continuation of OIC-302 of MONICA S. LEWINSKY , On 07/31/98 , Page 2

DRAFT LETTERS

LEWINSKY provided 12 pages of documents she had in her apartment which related to CLINTON.

LEWINSKY advised that on the evening of December 5, 1997, she typed, on her home computer, a letter to CLINTON she planned to give CURRIE the following day when LEWINSKY delivered CURRIE and CLINTON's Christmas presents. LEWINSKY advised she often printed out drafts of letters so she could proofread them. LEWINSKY provided copies of drafts of the letter, but she ended up seeing CLINTON the next day, so she did not give him the letter.

LEWINSKY advised the purpose of this letter was to make CLINTON feel guilty. LEWINSKY advised that when she was in England the first week of December 1997, she telephoned CURRIE once or twice. LEWINSKY advised she stayed at the GROSVENOR HOUSE and billed her telephone calls to her AMERICAN EXPRESS CARD.

LEWINSKY provided a draft of a two page letter, dated June 26, 1997, to CURRIE in which LEWINSKY provided suggestions for transcription jobs for CURRIE's mother. LEWINSKY eventually sent CURRIE a version of this letter.

LEWINSKY provided two other drafts of letters she eventually sent CLINTON. One is a November 12, 1997 letter to CLINTON in which LEWINSKY expressed her frustration at not being with CLINTON. The second letter was written sometime after LEWINSKY's November 13, 1997 visit to the White House that coincided with Mexican President ZEDILLO's visit, which LEWINSKY refers to simply as "ZEDILLO day."

LEWINSKY provided a copy of a bookmark/penny, a duplicate of which she had given CLINTON on March 29, 1997. LEWINSKY advised she purchased two of the items, gave one to CLINTON and saved one. LEWINSKY advised NATE SPEIGHTS has the other original of this item.

LEWINSKY provided another draft of a letter she wrote after her "ZEDILLO visit."

LEWINSKY provided a copy of a November 6, 1997 letter to VERNON JORDAN. LEWINSKY advised she sent a similar letter to JORDAN on November 6, 1997. LEWINSKY sent the letter to JORDAN via courier, because JORDAN was going out of town the next day. LEWINSKY advised she had taken her resume to JORDAN the previous

OIC-302a (Rev. 8-19-94)

29D-OIC-LR-35063

Continuation of OIC-302 of MONICA S. LEWINSKY , On 07/31/98 , Page 3

day when she met with him.

LEWINSKY provided a copy of a list she sent to CLINTON after her meeting with him on October 11, 1997. LEWINSKY advised CLINTON told her to prepare a list of jobs she would be interested in.

LEWINSKY provided a copy of a draft letter related to her career opportunities. LEWINSKY advised the handwriting on the draft is hers, but she cannot remember specifically what she was referring to. LEWINSKY advised she reviewed the letter with LINDA TRIPP.

LEWINSKY advised she was focused on public relations firms when she dealt with VERNON JORDAN.

FOLLOW-UP TO PREVIOUS DAY'S INTERVIEW

LEWINSKY advised she did not recall CURRIE ever being in the Oval Office bathroom while LEWINSKY and CLINTON engaged in oral sex. LEWINSKY does recall one instance when CURRIE was in the Executive dining room while LEWINSKY and CLINTON engaged in oral sex in the Oval Office hall and bathroom. CLINTON advised LEWINSKY to keep quiet during this encounter.

LEWINSKY advised that she recalls another occasion CLINTON made a comment to her about being quiet while they engaged in sexual activities.

LEWINSKY advised she recalled that on March 29, 1997, CLINTON put his hand over LEWINSKY's mouth so as to keep her quiet during one of their sexual encounters.

LEWINSKY recalls one occasion in which she had to bite her own hand during sexual activities to keep from making any noise.

LEWINSKY advised CURRIE would always knock and announce herself prior to opening the doors in the Oval Office complex. LEWINSKY advised she and CLINTON were generally not concerned about being overheard during their sexual encounters. LEWINSKY advised they were more concerned with being seen in the Oval Office because of the windows there.

LEWINSKY advised the Oval Office study has windows, but no one is usually stationed there. LEWINSKY is aware of peepholes that allow someone to look into the Oval Office from

OIC-302a (Rev. 8-19-94)

29D-OIC-LR-35063

Continuation of OIC-302 of MONICA S. LEWINSKY, On 07/31/98, Page 4

various points around the Oval Office. LEWINSKY does not recall discussing the peepholes with CLINTON or CURRIE.

CLINTON sometimes expressed concern about people looking into the Oval Office and the study. LEWINSKY recalls that when CLINTON gave her her Christmas kiss on December 28, 1997, he had his eyes wide open, looking out the window.

LEWINSKY advised she most often visited CLINTON during the day. LEWINSKY advised the hallway outside the Oval study was more comfortable because it had no windows. LEWINSKY advised that during the "ZEDILLO visit," CLINTON turned the lights to the study out while she was in there.

LEWINSKY advised that she thinks HILLARY CLINTON called when LEWINSKY was with the President on November 15, 1995. LEWINSKY advised she thinks CURRIE hollered back to CLINTON that HILLARY CLINTON was on the phone.

LEWINSKY advised most of her sexual encounters with CLINTON occurred in the hallway outside the Oval Office study, except for the second visit on November 15, 1995 and the visits on March 29, 1997 and April 7, 1996. LEWINSKY and CLINTON occasionally engaged in sexual activity in the bathroom near the study.

LEWINSKY advised she felt as if she was alone with CLINTON when the two were engaged in intimate contact, but they both were still conscious of the possibility of having to disengage on a moment's notice, so they did not disrobe entirely.

LEWINSKY advised she was never concerned about video cameras around the Oval Office, until the news about the fund-raising videos, which occurred in the Fall of 1996. LEWINSKY spoke to LINDA TRIPP about the video tapes, but later learned the videos were not secretly recorded so LEWINSKY's concerns were allayed.

LEWINSKY advised she was concerned about records of telephone calls CLINTON made to LEWINSKY. LEWINSKY's concern was sparked when she read news of the White House turning over phone records to the campaign fund-raising investigators. LEWINSKY expressed concern to CURRIE, who told LEWINSKY not to worry since CLINTON used a different phone when he called LEWINSKY. LEWINSKY may have expressed her concern to CLINTON, but she does not recall and she has no recollection of his response.

OIC-302a (Rev. 8-19-94)

29D-OIC-LR-35063

Continuation of OIC-302 of MONICA S. LEWINSKY, On 07/31/98, Page 5

LEWINSKY advised she recalls one late October 1997 telephone call from CLINTON where CLINTON had to end the call because HILLARY CLINTON had returned home.

LEWINSKY does not recall either of her two telephone calls with CLINTON, when CLINTON was on the road, ending abruptly. LEWINSKY does not recall hearing a clicking sound when she spoke with CLINTON on the telephone.

LEWINSKY advised she was discreet about her sexual relationship with CLINTON when dealing with CURRIE. CURRIE was "in the loop" when it came to keeping LEWINSKY's relationship with CLINTON discreet.

LEWINSKY assumes RAHM EMMANUAL was present in the Oval Office on February 28, 1997, and is sure STEVE GOODIN was there. LEWINSKY was told by CURRIE that GOODIN said LEWINSKY could not be alone with CLINTON. LEWINSKY assumes CLINTON was in the Oval Office with GOODIN and CURRIE when GOODIN told CURRIE this. LEWINSKY advised that when she eventually went into the Oval Office with CURRIE shortly thereafter, CLINTON did not seem surprised to see CURRIE with LEWINSKY.

LEWINSKY advised a lot of people tried to protect CLINTON by putting reins on his life, but CURRIE does what CLINTON wants done. LEWINSKY advised CURRIE was more like family to CLINTON than a subordinate. LEWINSKY advised CURRIE had a special relationship with CLINTON. LEWINSKY advised CLINTON found it comforting to have CURRIE in the Oval Office area.

LEWINSKY did not seduce CLINTON, nor did she stalk him. LEWINSKY advised their relationship was mutual, particularly with regard to initiating intimate contact.

LEWINSKY advised that, in her December 17, 1997 telephone conversation with CLINTON, CLINTON advised that if anyone asked LEWINSKY about her visits to the White House after her transfer to the Pentagon, LEWINSKY could always say she was visiting CURRIE. LEWINSKY advised this was not the first time CLINTON mentioned this scenario.

LEWINSKY advised this scenario was familiar to her, but it was not brought up on a regular basis. LEWINSKY advised that until December 17, 1997, no one had ever asked LEWINSKY about her visits to the Oval Office. LEWINSKY advised that when she visited the White House after her transfer to the Pentagon, the primary purpose of the visit was to see CLINTON, but she did see

OIC-302a (Rev. 8-19-94)

29D-OIC-LR-35063

Continuation of OIC-302 of MONICA S. LEWINSKY , On 07/31/98 , Page 6

CURRIE, as well.

LEWINSKY advised that CURRIE sometimes drove LEWINSKY out of the White House complex after one of LEWINSKY's visits. On December 28, 1997, LEWINSKY left her visitor's pass in the Oval Office, so CURRIE had to call down to the gate to allow LEWINSKY to leave.

"MEANIES"

LEWINSKY proceeded to provide a description of some of the White House employees who did not like LEWINSKY. LEWINSKY described these people as "meanies."

LEWINSKY's first encounter with EVELYN LIEBERMAN was shortly after LEWINSKY started her job in the Office of Legislative Affairs (OLA). LEWINSKY was taking papers to the West Wing when LIEBERMAN stopped her and asked where she worked. LIEBERMAN also said that LEWINSKY was always trafficking in the West Wing area. LIEBERMAN told LEWINSKY interns were not allowed in front of the Oval Office.

LEWINSKY went to the bathroom and cried and then went to LIEBERMAN's office to clarify that she was no longer an intern and had been hired as a staffer. LIEBERMAN responded derisively by saying "they hired you?" LIEBERMAN then said that she must have mistaken LEWINSKY for someone else. From that moment on, LEWINSKY was wary of LIEBERMAN. LEWINSKY advised she thinks LIEBERMAN was furloughed during the government shutdown, as LEWINSKY does not recall seeing her during that time.

LEWINSKY did not mention her encounter with LIEBERMAN to CLINTON. LEWINSKY believes her encounter with LIEBERMAN occurred in December of 1995 as LEWINSKY did not interact with CLINTON that much during December of 1995.

LEWINSKY advised that she was never reprimanded for dressing inappropriately while employed at the White House. LEWINSKY attributes those stories to a "White House smear campaign."

LEWINSKY cannot recall any other direct encounters with LIEBERMAN. LEWINSKY advised that she had a near encounter on April 7, 1996, because United States Secret Service Uniformed Officer JOHN MUSKETT asked LEWINSKY if he should check with LIEBERMAN to see if he should allow LEWINSKY into the Oval Office. LEWINSKY told MUSKETT that this would not be necessary,

OIC-302a (Rev. 8-19-94)

29D-OIC-LR-35063

Continuation of OIC-302 of MONICA S. LEWINSKY, On 07/31/98, Page 7

since she was just dropping off papers.

CLINTON told LEWINSKY that LIEBERMAN had LEWINSKY transferred to the Pentagon because 1996 was an election year. LEWINSKY advised a lot of people at the White House were wary of LIEBERMAN. LEWINSKY was especially wary of LIEBERMAN because LEWINSKY was having a relationship with CLINTON.

CLINTON telephoned LEWINSKY from Florida on October 22, 1996.

LEWINSKY advised that CURRIE was wary of LIEBERMAN, as well. LEWINSKY advised that on either October 23 or October 24, 1996, LEWINSKY saw and spoke to CLINTON at a fund-raiser for Senate Democrats. That evening, CLINTON called LEWINSKY. During the conversation, LEWINSKY said that she was going to see White House photographer BILLIE SHADDIX at the White House the following day. CLINTON told LEWINSKY to stop by the West Wing.

LEWINSKY told CLINTON to have CURRIE come down to the photo office to escort LEWINSKY to the West Wing. LEWINSKY was unable to see CLINTON and his departure ceremony that day because CURRIE said that LIEBERMAN was in the area and CURRIE had to wait until LIEBERMAN was gone before bringing LEWINSKY to the Oval Office area. CURRIE told LEWINSKY that LIEBERMAN did not like LEWINSKY.

LEWINSKY advised that her mother, MARCIA LEWIS, and step-father, PETER STRAUSS, saw LIEBERMAN at a VOICE OF AMERICA event. LIEBERMAN told MARCIA LEWIS that LEWINSKY was transferred from the White HOUSE due to political expediency. LIEBERMAN added that LEWINSKY was cursed because she was beautiful.

LEWINSKY advised that SUSAN BROPHY and others in the Office of Legislative Affairs called LEWINSKY a "stalker."

LEWINSKY did not express her frustrations with CLINTON that LEWINSKY ended up having to make most of the arrangements to meet with CLINTON.

LEWINSKY advised that STEVE GOODIN initially treated LEWINSKY kindly. LEWINSKY recalled one time when LEWINSKY and JAY FOOTLIK went to the Oval Office so LEWINSKY could deliver a tie to CLINTON. LEWINSKY and FOOTLIK bumped into GOODIN outside BETTY CURRIE's office and the three sang a parody of the song "You don't bring me flowers."

OIC-302a (Rev. 8-19-94)

29D-OIC-LR-35063

Continuation of OIC-302 of MONICA S. LEWINSKY , On 07/31/98 , Page 8

LEWINSKY recalled that on MARTIN LUTHER KING DAY, 1996, PAT GRIFFIN asked LEWINSKY to call LEON PANETTA, who was traveling with the President. LEWINSKY called GOODIN, who half-jokingly said to LEWINSKY that he only spoke to "principals." Others present laughed at LEWINSKY's expense.

LEWINSKY advised that on May 24, 1997, LEWINSKY was with CLINTON in the study. LEWINSKY had left her LOUIS VUITTON purse on the dining room table in the Executive Dining room. CLINTON had to leave the study at one point and LEWINSKY heard him speaking to GOODIN.

LEWINSKY advised that she was "paranoid" about what people were thinking about her. LEWINSKY advised CLINTON paid a lot of attention to her, sometimes in front of others. LEWINSKY felt that people in the White House did not want to acknowledge that the President might actually like LEWINSKY.

LEWINSKY advised that initially she felt HERNREICH was friendly with her. LEWINSKY saw HERNREICH on April 7, 1996 when LEWINSKY was transferred. HERNREICH told LEWINSKY to come in and see her on April 8, 1996. HERNREICH was very kind to her and consoled her. HERNREICH told LEWINSKY she would see what she could do for LEWINSKY.

After LEWINSKY was transferred, CURRIE specifically mentioned to LEWINSKY when HERNREICH was not around. CURRIE's concern with whether or not HERNREICH was around indicated to LEWINSKY that HERNREICH may have disliked LEWINSKY.

LEWINSKY advised that in early 1997, during telephone conversations on January 12 and February 8, CLINTON told her that BOB NASH was in charge of finding her a job at the White House. LEWINSKY later learned that NASH, head of Presidential Personnel, was in charge of finding jobs outside the White House. LEWINSKY then learned the "ball was passed" to MARSHA SCOTT by the end of April of 1997.

LEWINSKY advised that she spoke to SCOTT's assistant, but got the impression that SCOTT was not aware of who she was and SCOTT never returned the call. LEWINSKY then sent a nasty note to CLINTON, referencing her dealings with SCOTT. LEWINSKY thinks she either sent by courier or hand-delivered the note to CURRIE to give to CLINTON.

Several weeks later, SCOTT called LEWINSKY and said that SCOTT had been out due to back surgery and did not have a

OIC-302a (Rev. 8-19-94)

29D-OIC-LR-35063

Continuation of OIC-302 of MONICA S. LEWINSKY, On 07/31/98, Page 9

chance to call LEWINSKY. LEWINSKY thinks SCOTT either read LEWINSKY's note to CLINTON, or CLINTON conveyed the contents of it to her. SCOTT arranged an appointment for LEWINSKY to meet with her.

LEWINSKY does not recall the length of the meeting, but she does recall SCOTT asking SCOTT's assistant to leave the office during the meeting. LEWINSKY described SCOTT's tone as pleasant. LEWINSKY advised SCOTT had a picture of SCOTT and CLINTON on the wall in her office. In the photograph, CLINTON is wearing a tie LEWINSKY had given him.

SCOTT asked a lot of questions during the meeting, some of which LEWINSKY felt were intrusive. SCOTT said that JODIE TORKELSON and EVELYN LIEBERMAN did not like LEWINSKY. LEWINSKY felt an unspoken tension with SCOTT, as LEWINSKY was a current lover of CLINTON's, [redacted]

LEWINSKY advised she had two meetings with SCOTT, and is not sure about at which meeting certain things were said. At one meeting, SCOTT indicated she would "detail" LEWINSKY at the White House. In a "detail," the employee works at the White House, but is paid by another agency, like the Defense Department. LEWINSKY advised "detailees" work at the White House for a limited time, prior to going back to their agency or finding a permanent position at the White House.

LEWINSKY advised that LIZ BAILEY told LEWINSKY that SCOTT lost her "detail" post and would be unable to find a position for LEWINSKY. SCOTT told LEWINSKY the reason she was unable to find LEWINSKY a position was because KEN BACON and CLIFF BERNATH at the Pentagon said they did not want to "lose" LEWINSKY.

LEWINSKY got into an argument with SCOTT as SCOTT told LEWINSKY that she would have to wait until December, after certain people left the White House, including LIEBERMAN, before returning to the White House. LEWINSKY said that was not fair and SCOTT said life was not fair. SCOTT said it was not fair that she had incurred $400,000 in attorney's fees simply for working at the White House.

Looking back at the situation, LEWINSKY thinks SCOTT may have been trying to protect CLINTON because of LEWINSKY's association with the KATHLEEN WILLEY/LINDA TRIPP matter.

OIC-302a (Rev. 8-19-94)

29D-OIC-LR-35063

Continuation of OIC-302 of MONICA S. LEWINSKY , On 07/31/98 , Page 10

JOBS

Between September 12 and 26, 1997, CURRIE advised she was going to talk to JOHN PODESTA. On October 7, 1997, LEWINSKY talked to LINDA TRIPP, who had stayed home from work. TRIPP told LEWINSKY that TRIPP's friend, KATE, who worked at the NATIONAL SECURITY COUNCIL, said she had heard that LEWINSKY would not get back at the White House, and if she did, LEWINSKY would not get a job requiring a blue, West Wing pass. TRIPP said that KATE's advice was for LEWINSKY to "get out of town."

This conversation with TRIPP made LEWINSKY so angry she left work early that day. LEWINSKY advised she then decided to move to New York. LEWINSKY advised she had previously considered the idea of moving to New York, but the call from TRIPP was the "straw that broke the camel's back." KATE's comments confirmed LEWINSKY's hunch that she was never going to be brought back to the White House.

LEWINSKY advised that moving to New York was a possibility beginning in July of 1997. LEWINSKY advised a job at the United Nations seemed logical at the time because it was a government agency.

LEWINSKY had been suspicious of not getting a job back at the White House. LEWINSKY advised that, in an October 11, 1997 telephone conversation with CLINTON, she mentioned to him her frustration of not getting a job at the White House. CLINTON said the problem was that lower-level people knew more about the specific job openings than he did.

LEWINSKY advised that on October 9 or 10, 1997, CLINTON called her between 2:00 and 2:30 in the morning. LEWINSKY advised she was asleep when CLINTON called. The call lasted for approximately one and one half hours. LEWINSKY and CLINTON had their biggest fight ever in this telephone conversation. LEWINSKY said both she and CLINTON yelled a lot during the call.

CLINTON said that if he had known how difficult it would be to bring LEWINSKY back to the White House, he would have never let her be transferred in the first place. CLINTON said he was obsessed with her career and wanted to help her. CLINTON said his life was empty except for work. During the fight, CLINTON also said that, if he had known what type of person LEWINSKY was, he would have never become involved with her in the first place. LEWINSKY advised she was very hurt by this comment and started crying.

LEWINSKY advised that CLINTON was in the White House Residence when he made the telephone call to her. LEWINSKY advised that her caller identification feature indicated "unavailable" when CLINTON called her from the Residence. LEWINSKY advised she did not go into detail about what TRIPP said KATE had said. LEWINSKY advised she was vague with CLINTON when discussing why she wanted to move to New York.

LEWINSKY told CLINTON she had to be out of her apartment by the end of October. LEWINSKY advised that the discussion of her job situation was part of her relationship with CLINTON. CLINTON said he would get working on a job in New York for LEWINSKY.

LEWINSKY advised she stayed home from work on October 10, 1997 and had lunch with TRIPP at the CALIFORNIA PIZZA KITCHEN on Connecticut Avenue. LEWINSKY talked about her early morning telephone conversation with CLINTON. LEWINSKY advised she was emotionally exhausted as a result of the content of the phone conversation with CLINTON the night before. LEWINSKY was also disappointed she would not be going back to work at the White House.

The following morning, October 11, 1997, at approximately 8:30 a.m., CURRIE called LEWINSKY from the hospital and said CLINTON wanted to see LEWINSKY at approximately 9:00 a.m., at the White House. CURRIE told LEWINSKY that CLINTON had paged CURRIE to tell her to get in touch with LEWINSKY.

LEWINSKY advised it was CLINTON's wedding anniversary that day, and CLINTON had tasked CURRIE with finding a HALCYON box for HILLARY CLINTON. The White House Garden tours were taking place that day and CURRIE had two friends there on the tour. LEWINSKY chatted with CURRIE's friends as she waited for CLINTON. CLINTON was on the telephone with CAPRICIA MARSHALL, who had attended the wedding of LAURA HARTIGAN in Chicago.

LEWINSKY advised that she saw ANNE McCOY coming toward the Oval Office, so LEWINSKY darted to the back room of the Oval complex to avoid McCOY.

LEWINSKY met alone with CLINTON in the Dining Room. LEWINSKY gave CLINTON a list of jobs in New York she was interested in. LEWINSKY advised she mentioned First Name Unknown (FNU) KAPLAN from CNN. LEWINSKY may have also mentioned VERNON JORDAN during this conversation. LEWINSKY thinks she may have mentioned JORDAN in the previous telephone conversation in which

OIC-302a (Rev. 8-19-94)

29D-OIC-LR-35063

Continuation of OIC-302 of MONICA S. LEWINSKY , On 07/31/98 , Page 12

she and CLINTON had a fight. CLINTON was receptive to the idea of JORDAN helping LEWINSKY.

LEWINSKY mentioned JORDAN because TRIPP had said JORDAN was CLINTON's best friend and JORDAN was on the board of directors of many companies. LEWINSKY looked JORDAN up on the Internet and also saw a lot of references to him in stories about CLINTON's trip to Martha's Vineyard.

LEWINSKY advised she did not want a job in the government.

LEWINSKY advised that, at some point, she knew JOHN PODESTA had a role in LEWINSKY getting a job offer at the United Nations. CLINTON said that he did or would talk to PODESTA.

In mid-October, CLINTON was in Latin America and LEWINSKY worked on her letter to CLINTON regarding jobs. LEWINSKY bought a book at BARNES & NOBLE regarding jobs in New York.

LEWINSKY advised she sent her letter, her GS rating, the section of the PLUM Book regarding other Confidential Assistants at the Pentagon being GS-11's, (while LEWINSKY was a GS-9) to CLINTON on October 16, 1997. LEWINSKY believes she mentioned a salary of approximately $60,000.

On October 21, 1997, Ambassador WILLIAM RICHARDSON telephoned LEWINSKY at home. RICHARDSON said he understood from JOHN PODESTA that LEWINSKY was interested in working at the United Nations.

On October 23, 1997, LEWINSKY spoke with CLINTON on the telephone. During the conversation, LEWINSKY and CLINTON spoke about the sunglasses LEWINSKY recently sent CLINTON. (LEWINSKY also sent CLINTON a CALVIN KLEIN tie, the fifth tie she had given him.) During this conversation, LEWINSKY mentioned RICHARDSON's call to her. LEWINSKY tried to steer CLINTON to think of a job other than the United Nations, but CLINTON said he just wanted LEWINSKY to have options.

[LEWINSKY does not recall when she regularly started using the courier service to deliver things to CLINTON. Mid-March of 1997 was the first time LEWINSKY used the service, but she may have not used it regularly until the fall of 1997. TRIPP had said the FEDERAL EXPRESS system was unsafe. LEWINSKY advised that on March 1, 1997, she sent CLINTON a get-well package, which

OIC-302a (Rev. 8-19-94)

29D-OIC-LR-35063

Continuation of OIC-302 of MONICA S. LEWINSKY , On 07/31/98 , Page 13

included a magnet of the Seal of the President of the United States for CLINTON's metal crutches; a little license plate that said "BILL" for CLINTON's wheel-chair; and knee-pads with the seal of the President of the United States stitched on them (by LEWINSKY). LEWINSKY purchased the knee-pads at a sporting goods store on the third floor of the Pentagon City mall.]

[LEWINSKY advised her mode of delivering items to the White House depended on the sensitivity of the items. LEWINSKY advised the most secure mode was to give the item directly to CURRIE. LEWINSKY advised the cost of the delivery also played a role in her choosing a specific method. LEWINSKY advised the courier service was the most expensive of the delivery methods. LEWINSKY advised she dropped things off at the New Executive Office Building (NEOB) approximately 3 times and handed the items directly to CURRIE at one of the White House gates approximately five times. LEWINSKY advised she thought of using the Department of Defense courier to the White House, but could not do it.]

LEWINSKY did not feel it was odd for CLINTON to be helping her find a job because she "had a relationship with him."

Sometime before October 30, 1997, LEWINSKY asked CURRIE to tell CLINTON to call LEWINSKY. In the early evening, around 8 p.m., on October 30th, CLINTON called LEWINSKY at home. LEWINSKY said she was anxious about meeting RICHARDSON. CLINTON told LEWINSKY to call CURRIE after the interview to let CLINTON know how the interview went.

LEWINSKY had given CURRIE CLINTON's Halloween presents, including a lapel pin, sometime during the week before Halloween. LEWINSKY advised she saw a photograph of CLINTON wearing the pin and she read that CLINTON mentioned the pin in a speech.

On October 31, 1997, LEWINSKY met with RICHARDSON at the Watergate Hotel. MONA SUTPHEN, RICHARDSON's assistant, met LEWINSKY in the lobby and escorted LEWINSKY to RICHARDSON's room. LEWINSKY advised the setting was very casual as RICHARDSON was eating breakfast when LEWINSKY arrived. RICHARDSON asked LEWINSKY if CURRIE was her mother.

LEWINSKY mentioned working on the United States Consulate to the United Nations' web-site and suggested implementing town hall meetings, similar to the ones the Department of Defense used. LEWINSKY advised the meeting lasted approximately one-half hour.

OIC-302a (Rev. 8-19-94)

29D-OIC-LR-35063

Continuation of OIC-302 of MONICA S. LEWINSKY , On 07/31/98 , Page 14

LEWINSKY did not think the interview was perfunctory or "cake." LEWINSKY advised that REBECCA LNU and SUTPHEN were there, and at times it may have just been RICHARDSON and REBECCA Last Name Unknown (LNU) with LEWINSKY, as SUTPHEN came in and left intermittently.

LEWINSKY does not recall PODESTA's name coming up during the interview.

After LEWINSKY's interview, LEWINSKY's mother and aunt went to the United Nations in New York. LEWINSKY advised some of the reasons LEWINSKY did not want to work at the United Nations were because LEWINSKY's mother mentioned her concern that a lot of Arabs worked at the United Nations and because the United Nations was somewhat isolated from the business district in New York.

The interview with RICHARDSON ended with LEWINSKY being told that RICHARDSON or his staff would be in touch with her. LEWINSKY spoke to CURRIE after the interview and LEWINSKY was a lot more optimistic about her job opportunities than she was before the interview. CLINTON was out of town at the time.

On November 3, 1997, or later, LEWINSKY received a telephone call from RICHARDSON and was offered a job at the United Nations.

<u>VERNON JORDAN</u>

On either October 23 or 30, 1997, LEWINSKY and CLINTON discussed VERNON JORDAN helping LEWINSKY in her job search.

On November 3 or 4, 1997, CURRIE called LEWINSKY and told her to call JORDAN's secretary GAYLE LNU. CURRIE told LEWINSKY to say she was CURRIE's friend. LEWINSKY advised that CURRIE had called JORDAN to arrange the meeting, so that gave LEWINSKY some indication that CLINTON was involved.

In the late morning of November 5, 1997, LEWINSKY had an appointment to see JORDAN. LEWINSKY was nervous as she waited in the lobby for twenty minutes before meeting with JORDAN. LEWINSKY brought the same package she had sent CLINTON earlier, sans the cover sheet and the GS scale.

LEWINSKY sat in JORDAN's office before he came in. JORDAN made LEWINSKY feel nervous. JORDAN was not very effusive in this meeting. The meeting lasted approximately twenty minutes. After introducing each other, JORDAN asked LEWINSKY why she was there. LEWINSKY told JORDAN she was hoping to move to New York. JORDAN asked her why she wanted to leave Washington, D.C. LEWINSKY said that she wanted to get a fresh start.

LEWINSKY mentioned her employment at the White House. JORDAN inquired as to why he never saw LEWINSKY during one of his visits to the White House. LEWINSKY gave JORDAN the "vanilla" story about why she left employment at the White House. LEWINSKY said that LIEBERMAN did not like her. JORDAN said LIEBERMAN disliked him as well. JORDAN said he had spoken to CLINTON about LEWINSKY.

LEWINSKY and JORDAN went over her list of possible employers. LEWINSKY felt awkward in the meeting as JORDAN did not respond to her often. JORDAN mentioned one his daughters worked at one of the companies on LEWINSKY's list. At the end of the meeting, JORDAN said he and LEWINSKY were "in business."

JORDAN said that LEWINSKY came "highly recommended." LEWINSKY is not sure if JORDAN meant that CLINTON said nice things about her, or if he meant CLINTON had mentioned his relationship with LEWINSKY. In their November 12, 1997 telephone conversation, CLINTON said he had spoken to JORDAN.

JORDAN was going out of town the day after LEWINSKY met with him. LEWINSKY called CURRIE and left a couple of messages with JORDAN's secretary, but JORDAN did not return LEWINSKY's call. LEWINSKY called CURRIE to see what she should do, since she had not heard from JORDAN in almost two weeks.

On November 26, 1997, CURRIE paged LEWINSKY while LEWINSKY was in Los Angeles. LEWINSKY called CURRIE from a pay phone at the WILSHIRE COURTYARD MARRIOTT. LEWINSKY was told to call JORDAN and she did. JORDAN told LEWINSKY he was leaving for China and he told LEWINSKY to call him around the first week of December. JORDAN told LEWINSKY he was working on her job search.

LEWINSKY was anxious as she had given notice at the Pentagon that she was going to leave, though she did not give a specific date.

On December 8, 1997, LEWINSKY sent, by courier, a package to JORDAN, which included a note, a hat and some chocolate, to remind him she still existed.

During LEWINSKY's December 6, 1997 meeting with CLINTON, she thinks he said he would contact JORDAN. LEWINSKY

OIC-302a (Rev. 8-19-94)

29D-OIC-LR-35063

Continuation of OIC-302 of MONICA S. LEWINSKY , On 07/31/98 , Page 16

advised CLINTON was the type of person who would say he was going to do something and not really mean it.

LEWINSKY advised that she had breakfast with VERNON JORDAN on December 31, 1997 at the HYATT. LEWINSKY advised JORDAN paid for the breakfast; LEWINSKY had an egg-white omelette, and JORDAN had cereal or yogurt.

CLINTON's Testimony

LEWINSKY is surprised CLINTON has agreed to testify before the Grand Jury. LEWINSKY thinks CLINTON is walking into a "perjury trap." LEWINSKY advised that, with the existence of the dress being leaked, CLINTON may do a "mea culpa." LEWINSKY advised she guessed what CLINTON would say about her when he testified in the JONES case, and she was correct. LEWINSKY advised, though they did not discuss the issue in specific relation to the JONES matter, she and CLINTON had discussed what to say when asked about LEWINSKY's visits to the White House.

LEWINSKY advised she still has feelings towards CLINTON and she finds it hard to provide the OIC questions that may end up hurting CLINTON.

LEWINSKY would ask CLINTON why he wore the same tie twice in once week. (LEWINSKY advised she gave CLINTON the tie.)

LEWINSKY would ask CLINTON why he would give NELVIS the first tie LEWINSKY gave CLINTON. NELVIS then wore it to one of his grand jury appearances. LEWINSKY would ask CLINTON if he was trying to send LEWINSKY a message.

LEWINSKY does not think CLINTON is concerned about BRUCE LINDSEY testifying, as she is unaware of LINDSEY's knowledge of her relationship with CLINTON.

[redacted] CLINTON advised he made a concerted effort not to have sex with other women. CLINTON seemed to feel guilty about cheating on his wife.

When CLINTON was in Mexico, he became ill. When he returned, he asked LEWINSKY if she could tell he was sick.

OIC-302a (Rev. 8-19-94)

29D-OIC-LR-35063

Continuation of OIC-302 of MONICA S. LEWINSKY , On 07/31/98 , Page 17

During their second telephone conversation of December 2, 1996, CLINTON told LEWINSKY about a jazz musician who had been killed on a boat. CLINTON seemed shocked about the musician's death.

LEWINSKY advised, if she were questioning CLINTON, she would show CLINTON pictures of items she had given him which he had not turned over, to refresh his memory.

LEWINSKY advised she never met CLINTON outside the White House for a private meeting.

The interview ended at approximately 4:40 p.m.

Tab 22

OIC-302 (Rev. 8-19-94)

OFFICE OF THE INDEPENDENT COUNSEL

Date of transcription 08/05/98

MONICA S. LEWINSKY was interviewed pursuant to an immunity agreement between the Office of the Independent Counsel (OIC), LEWINSKY, and her attorneys. Present for the interview were Associate Independent Counsel (AIC) MICHAEL EMMICK, AIC KARIN IMMERGUT, AIC MARY ANNE WIRTH, AIC CRAIG LERNER, and Deputy Independent Counsel SOLOMON WISENBERG. Representing LEWINSKY were attorneys PRESTON BURTON of the law offices of PLATO CACHERIS, and ROBERT BREDHOFF of STEIN, MITCHELL & MEZINES. The interview was conducted at the Watergate Hotel in Washington, D.C. beginning at 10:06 a.m. LEWINSKY provided the following information:

LEWINSKY began taking a new prescription medication this morning, which consisted of 10 milligrams of Prozac. LEWINSKY is still taking Serzone; other prescriptions have been discontinued.

When LEWINSKY learned that the President would testify in the PAULA JONES case, she assumed that the President would deny their relationship. There was no explicit agreement that the President would testify in a specific way, but there had been a pattern of denial in their relationship.

Calendars for December 1997 and January 1998 were shown to LEWINSKY. She briefly reviewed and confirmed a number of events occurring during those months. However, LEWINSKY did not remember speaking to BAYANI NELVIS on January 15, 1998.

On her second visit to the White House on December 6, 1997, LEWINSKY was supposed to meet BETTY CURRIE in the basement of the West Wing of the White House, per CURRIE's instructions. LEWINSKY saw MARSHA SCOTT walk by and left the basement to avoid SCOTT. LEWINSKY had earlier avoided SCOTT at the southwest gate. LEWINSKY called CURRIE and then met CURRIE in the West Wing lobby. CURRIE usually directed LEWINSKY away from United States Secret Service (USSS) uniformed guards who were friendly to DEBBIE SCHIFF. CURRIE told LEWINSKY not to come to the northwest gate as, "Those guys are mad at you." CURRIE was referring to the incident earlier in the day. LEWINSKY waited in the President's back study, which she entered through the dining room. The President said that it was very difficult for him to

Investigation on 08/01/98 at WASHINGTON, D. C. File # 29D OIC LR 35063

by SA [redacted]
CI [redacted] Date dictated 08/05/98

see LEWINSKY that day because "of all of this shit going on" and that he only had one day to see the lawyers about the JONES case. LEWINSKY was surprised that she got into the White House and had thought that she would only be able to talk to the President on the telephone that day. The President said that he had a gift from Vancouver for LEWINSKY. The President then received a call from ERSKINE BOWLES, apparently made an appointment to see BOWLES, and told LEWINSKY to come back another day to get her gift. The President said, "Don't worry, you'll get your gift." The President did not discuss the JONES witness list with LEWINSKY. The President said that he would talk to VERNON JORDAN on LEWINSKY's behalf about jobs. The President also said, "I promise, I won't abandon you." Nothing the President said left LEWINSKY with the impression that their relationship was any different than it was before. The visit lasted about 20 or 25 minutes. CURRIE helped LEWINSKY exit out the back way before BOWLES arrived.

On the evening of December 6, 1997, LEWINSKY went to New York and stayed with her mother. She told her about the Christmas Party on Friday, that LEWINSKY had been very upset on Saturday, and that she had gotten in to see the President on Saturday.

On December 7, 1997, LEWINSKY returned to Washington by airplane. Enroute, LEWINSKY wrote the "whipped cream" card, which she sent in the next day or so. The card said something to the effect of, "Nothing would make me happier than to see you, except to see you naked with a winning lottery ticket in one hand and a can of whipped cream in the other."

On December 8, 1997, LEWINSKY sent a package to VERNON JORDAN containing a white "NATO" ballcap, some chocolate, a note, and possibly a copy of her resume. LEWINSKY did this as a friendly reminder to JORDAN to keep helping her.

Sometime during this week GAIL from JORDAN's office called LEWINSKY to set up a meeting.

LEWINSKY does not recall whether she called BETTY CURRIE to ascertain whether the card for the President had arrived, nor does she recall whether she called LINDA TRIPP that day.

In regard to BAYANI NELVIS, LEWINSKY described him as a nice person, but not everyone at the White House treated him right. NELVIS is very loyal to the President. LEWINSKY first

OIC-302a (Rev. 8-19-94)

29D OIC LR 35063

Continuation of OIC-302 of MONICA S. LEWINSKY , On 08/01/98 , Page 3

met NELVIS during the furlough in November 1995. NELVIS is Filipino, has an accent, and is friendly. NELVIS knew that LEWINSKY had feelings for the President and that she enjoyed a special relationship with the President. When LEWINSKY would have drinks with NELVIS, he would provide personal details about the President. LEWINSKY asked NELVIS about the details of the President's schedule and the President's routine when he was out of town. On one of the Presidential trips, NELVIS called LEWINSKY from Martha's Vineyard and asked her if she wanted to come up there and stay in the house with several other staff members. LEWINSKY had wanted to set up a rendezvous with the President on one of his trips, but declined NELVIS's offer. LEWINSKY met NELVIS once for dinner at the CALIFORNIA PIZZA KITCHEN in Pentagon City. LEWINSKY gave NELVIS one or two ties. NELVIS bought LEWINSKY perfume for her birthday and gave her glasses, golf balls, and cards from Air Force One. NELVIS did not want the President to know that he was friends with LEWINSKY. NELVIS never noticed which ties the President wore from day to day. LEWINSKY did not see NELVIS in Madrid, Spain, but may have seen GLEN MAES. NELVIS told LEWINSKY to be careful around the USSS officers. This conversation may have occurred in the Roosevelt Room on the day that they discussed cigars. NELVIS told LEWINSKY that CATHY CORNELIUS had gone with the advance party on the trip to Russia and that NELVIS took CORNELIUS downtown to shop, since she was afraid to go alone.

In regard to DEBBIE SCHIFF, LEWINSKY observed SCHIFF clomp around the office in the President's shoes on February 28, 1997, at the radio address. This appeared to LEWINSKY to show SCHIFF's familiarity with the President.

On December 11, 1997, LEWINSKY went to the office of VERNON JORDAN for a meeting, which had been arranged by GAIL of his office about December 8th or 9th. LEWINSKY waited in JORDAN's lobby for about 20 minutes. LEWINSKY was very nervous at the meeting and could not decide whether to wear a red headband that she brought to his office. LEWINSKY told JORDAN, "I'm more nervous with you than when I'm with the President." JORDAN tried to be less formal on this visit and to make LEWINSKY feel more at ease. In this visit, which included a turkey sandwich lunch, JORDAN told LEWINSKY the names of people that he had called. JORDAN suggested that LEWINSKY write letters to them with detailed wording that he provided, and asked that he receive copies of the letters. JORDAN explained his assistance by saying, "You're a friend of the President of the United States."

JORDAN asked what the occasions were when LEWINSKY got

mad at the President and said, "Don't get mad at the President when he's talking to TONY BLAIR on the telephone; call me and get mad at me." LEWINSKY explained that this was absurd, since she did not know JORDAN's home telephone and why would she talk to him. With a smile JORDAN said, "Don't deny it, your problem is you're in love." LEWINSKY most likely blushed, but did not respond. JORDAN probably knew of LEWINSKY's sexual relationship, but made no explicit statement that he knew.

LEWINSKY advised JORDAN that her mom was engaged to PETER STRAUS and JORDAN said that he knew STRAUS, and tried to call him with LEWINSKY present. JORDAN did not reach STRAUS or LEWINSKY's mother, but he left a message. JORDAN asked why LEWINSKY's mother owned a separate apartment in New York.

LEWINSKY knew that BETTY CURRIE knew VERNON JORDAN. LEWINSKY called JORDAN's office to advise him of the death of CURRIE's brother. LEWINSKY did not have any recollection of JORDAN asking her how LEWINSKY got in to see the President. JORDAN ended the visit of 40 minutes by saying that he would check out other leads, in addition to the three companies that LEWINSKY was to write. LEWINSKY's overall impression upon leaving was that she was going to get a job with JORDAN's help.

On December 11, 1997, LEWINSKY went to the Pentagon from JORDAN's office, typed the letters they had discussed, and talked to LINDA TRIPP. LEWINSKY still held out hope that the President would get her a job in Communications at the White House.

On December 12, 1997, or sometime during this week, LINDA TRIPP met with her attorney, KIRBY BEHRE. TRIPP wanted LEWINSKY to help TRIPP buy a Christmas gift for BEHRE in the concourse at the Pentagon. TRIPP advised LEWINSKY that she had written out the details of the relationship between LEWINSKY and the President, put them in a sealed envelope, and gave them to BEHRE, to be opened in the event of TRIPP's death. LEWINSKY was aghast. TRIPP also said that if she was asked about LEWINSKY she, TRIPP, was going to tell the truth.

LEWINSKY discussed the TRIPP problem in general terms with her mother.

On December 12 or 13, 1997, there was a going away party for the boyfriend of ASHLEY RAINES, JOEY Last Name Unknown (LNU), who was going to Israel.

OIC-302a (Rev. 8-19-94)

29D OIC LR 35063

On about December 15, 1997, LEWINSKY attended the swearing in of KATHY HAYCOCK in the Vice-President's ceremonial room. Vice-President GORE did the swearing in. The President did not attend. LEWINSKY tried to call BETTY CURRIE, but does not recall talking to her.

On December 17, 1997, at about 2:30 a.m., LEWINSKY received a telephone call from the President. He was not in a jovial mood and had concern in his voice. After about four seconds the President said he would call right back and hung up. About two minutes later, the President called back and said that he had two important things to tell LEWINSKY. First, BETTY CURRIE's brother had been killed in a car accident. They discussed whether LEWINSKY should call her. Then the President said that he had seen the PAULA JONES witness list and that LEWINSKY was on it. The President said, "It broke my heart when I saw your name on the list." The President said not to worry about it and that it did not necessarily mean LEWINSKY would get a subpoena. The President said that it was possible that LEWINSKY would be subpoenaed in a month or so. The President said that LEWINSKY could always say that she was coming to see BETTY, or that LEWINSKY was bringing papers from Legislative Affairs to the President. The President said that if LEWINSKY did get subpoenaed, call BETTY CURRIE and they would work something out. LEWINSKY assumed that this meant that they would help LEWINSKY figure out what to do. The President said, "Maybe you could sign an affidavit." LEWINSKY's impression was that she would sign an affidavit and get out of a deposition.

LEWINSKY told the President that she had some job interviews scheduled in New York. LEWINSKY also said that maybe she would be gone and the lawyers could not find her. The President said that was a possible solution.

LEWINSKY expressed her opinion to the President on how to settle the PAULA JONES case. LEWINSKY had read an article in the Times that people were sending in money to help the President with his legal problems. LEWINSKY advised the President that since PAULA JONES was only asking for $500,000, that the President should pay up to save his family and the country. The President expressed surprise that JONES was only asking for $500,000, as he thought the asking price was $1 million. The President said that he would ask his lawyers. LEWINSKY later cut out the Times article about the contributions and mailed it to MITCH ETTINGER.

The President said that maybe BETTY CURRIE could come

OIC-302a (Rev. 8-19-94)

29D OIC LR 35063

Continuation of OIC-302 of MONICA S. LEWINSKY , On 08/01/98 , Page 6

in on the weekend and he could give LEWINSKY her Christmas presents. LEWINSKY told the President not to dare bothering CURRIE now just when her brother had died. No discussion of other evidence occurred. Being on the witness list was a relief to LEWINSKY in one way, that is, if both LEWINSKY and TRIPP were subpoenaed, and they both denied the relationship, then the JONES' people would not know about it. This telephone call lasted between 20 and 40 minutes. After hanging up, LEWINSKY cried.

At about 4:00 a.m., on December 17, 1997, LEWINSKY called LINDA TRIPP, awakened her, and spoke with her for about 15 or 20 minutes. By this time, LEWINSKY was suspicious of TRIPP, but not to the point of accusing her of anything. The reason for the call was to discuss the fact that LEWINSKY was on the JONES witness list. LEWINSKY does not recall this discussion in any detail.

Also on December 17, 1997, LEWINSKY visited with BETTY CURRIE in her home and took her some bagels.

On the night of December 17, 1997, LEWINSKY took a plane to New York, where her mother met her at the airport with a car. LEWINSKY was nearly hysterical and told her mother that LINDA TRIPP was going to tell. MARCIA LEWIS was visibly upset. The problems were not discussed with PETER STRAUS.

On December 18, 1997, LEWINSKY had a job interview that went well at McANDREWS and FORBES. An interview at BURSON MARSTELLER the same day did not go well at all and LEWINSKY cried when she left. BURSON did not make a good appearance as a company with LEWINSKY, because they had too many people talking to her and did not seem to be well organized.

On the evening of December 18, 1997, LEWINSKY called LINDA TRIPP from a pay phone at the airport in New York.

On December 19, 1997, LEWINSKY called VERNON JORDAN to discuss her New York interviews. LEWINSKY believes that she probably called TRIPP from the Pentagon but TRIPP may not have been at work that day.

On December 19, 1997, LEWINSKY was at work at the Pentagon. A little before 4:00 p.m., LEWINSKY received a call from a process server, whom she agreed to meet at the Metro entrance, and received the subpoena for the PAULA JONES case. LEWINSKY cried. LEWINSKY went straight to a pay phone and called

OIC-302a (Rev. 8-19-94)

29D OIC LR 35063

Continuation of OIC-302 of MONICA S. LEWINSKY , On 08/01/98 , Page 7

VERNON JORDAN. JORDAN could not understand LEWINSKY, because of the crying, and asked her to come to JORDAN's office. LEWINSKY went back to her office, excused herself, went home and changed clothes. LEWINSKY called JORDAN, because the President had previously told her to call BETTY CURRIE, but LEWINSKY felt that she could not call CURRIE so soon after the death of CURRIE's brother.

After arriving at JORDAN's office, LEWINSKY waited in the lobby for awhile and then advised JORDAN that the President had warned her that she was on the JONES witness list and that she had been subpoenaed that afternoon. JORDAN then received a telephone call from an unknown caller, and asked LEWINSKY to step out of his office. LEWINSKY waited in the conference room for about 15 or 20 minutes before JORDAN invited her back to his office. LEWINSKY did not know what to do about the subpoena. JORDAN told LEWINSKY to calm down, that it was a standard subpoena. LEWINSKY told JORDAN that the subpoena also requested a hat pin the President had given her. JORDAN then called FRANK CARTER in LEWINSKY's presence and scheduled an appointment for Monday morning. JORDAN said that there were only two important questions:

1. "Did you have sex with the President?"
2. "Did he ask you for sex?"

LEWINSKY answered "no" to both questions. LEWINSKY believed that JORDAN knew of her sexual relationship with the President, and her impression was that JORDAN wanted to know how LEWINSKY was going to answer these questions when testifying. JORDAN instructed LEWINSKY to come to his office at 10:30 a.m. Monday. LEWINSKY asked JORDAN more than once to make sure to tell the President that she had been subpoenaed, because LEWINSKY could not call CURRIE, who was supposed to tell the President. LEWINSKY also said, "Give him a hug for me." JORDAN responded, "I don't hug guys." JORDAN slapped LEWINSKY on the backside as if to say "get out of here kid." JORDAN said that he would see the President that night and tell him about the subpoena.

LEWINSKY went home, called LINDA TRIPP, and made cryptic statements such as, "The flowers were delivered today," but TRIPP did not understand that LEWINSKY was trying to tell her that she had been subpoenaed that day. LEWINSKY was afraid to come out and tell TRIPP that she had been subpoenaed because LEWINSKY believed that the JONES people had tapped her telephone. LEWINSKY offered to go early to TRIPP's Christmas party the next day to help set up, primarily so that LEWINSKY could talk to

OIC-302a (Rev. 8-19-94)

29D OIC LR 35063

Continuation of OIC-302 of MONICA S. LEWINSKY , On 08/01/98 , Page 8

TRIPP.

On December 20, 1997, when LEWINSKY arrived at 5:00 p.m. to help set up the party, TRIPP said that she could not understand what LEWINSKY was trying to say the night before. LEWINSKY and TRIPP's Indian friend helped prepare the party food. LEWINSKY did not get a chance to talk to TRIPP until she was leaving and TRIPP came out to the car. LEWINSKY said that she was very worried about the hatpin. LEWINSKY told TRIPP that TRIPP could now feel safe in denying the relationship. This was the first time that LEWINSKY recalls vocalizing that she intended to deny her affair with the President. LEWINSKY received the impression that TRIPP might feel more encouraged to deny knowledge of LEWINSKY's affair. LEWINSKY met TRIPP's friend, KATE LNU, at the party.

The same night, December 20, 1997, LEWINSKY went to a party hosted by a friend of ASHLEY RAINES. LEWINSKY was drinking some by then and started telling RAINES about being in a bit of trouble. RAINES said that she did not want to know. Therefore, few details were provided by LEWINSKY.

On Sunday, December 21, 1997, LEWINSKY had a hangover; probably talked to TRIPP, and figured out which items to take to FRANK CARTER in response to the subpoena.

On Monday, December 22, 1997, LEWINSKY was nervous about going to see her attorney, FRANK CARTER. LEWINSKY called VERNON JORDAN to see if she could come over earlier than 10:30 a.m., because she was scared. There was no discussion about who was going to pay the legal bill, except JORDAN said not to worry about it. LEWINSKY hoped that JORDAN would pay the bill, because he was the President's friend and had a lot of money. At a later date, LEWINSKY had another discussion with JORDAN about CARTER's fee.

LEWINSKY asked JORDAN what if someone called the President on the telephone, and JORDAN responded that the President can talk to people. LEWINSKY advised that she and the President had phone sex together. JORDAN asked what phone sex was. LEWINSKY did not want to explain, but JORDAN again asked. LEWINSKY said, "We're taking care of business on each end while we're talking." The meeting in JORDAN's office lasted about 10 or 15 minutes. LEWINSKY bugged JORDAN to let her know if JORDAN had told the President about the subpoena. JORDAN responded that LEWINSKY had to learn to trust people, and that he had told the President.

Before leaving for CARTER's office on December 22, 1997, LEWINSKY showed JORDAN the items that she was taking to CARTER in response to the subpoena, but artfully indicated to JORDAN that it did not include everything. LEWINSKY had told JORDAN about the hat pin on Friday, and it was not included in the items that she was taking to CARTER. LEWINSKY said to JORDAN, "This is what I'm taking to CARTER, this should do." {LEWINSKY agreed that her statement in the first proffer, to the effect that she had made it clear to JORDAN that not all gifts were included, was a true statement.} LEWINSKY said that she did not intend to tell CARTER everything, because O. J. SIMPSON told his first lawyer that he did it and had to change lawyers. LEWINSKY informed JORDAN of how the President could settle the PAULA JONES matter, but JORDAN did not warm to the proposal. LEWINSKY assumed that JORDAN knew that she had a physically intimate relationship with the President.

Since there was a driver in the car with JORDAN and LEWINSKY enroute to CARTER's office, their five minute conversation was guarded. HOWARD PASTOR's name was mentioned as someone who could possibly help in the job search. They also discussed the purchase of Christmas presents.

At CARTER's office on December 22, 1997, JORDAN introduced LEWINSKY to CARTER and said that he was a good lawyer. This gave LEWINSKY the impression that this was JORDAN's personal lawyer, but she found out later that this was not true. LEWINSKY and JORDAN sat on the sofa for a few minutes and LEWINSKY told CARTER that the subpoena was ludicrous. JORDAN departed. LEWINSKY suggested an affidavit to CARTER, but he questioned whether there was any reason that LEWINSKY was pulled into this case. LEWINSKY responded that it was because she knew WALTER KAYE and BETTY CURRIE. CARTER asked if LEWINSKY had ever been alone with the President and LEWINSKY responded that she had delivered papers to the President on the weekend and that they had chatted about general topics. CARTER asked LEWINSKY if she had sex with the President and LEWINSKY denied that she had.

LEWINSKY asked CARTER if she could sue JONES's attorneys for invasion of privacy, and asked him if she had to cash the check that they sent with the subpoena. CARTER asked LEWINSKY to look for additional things, such as the photograph of the President wearing one of her ties, and to look for the photograph of LEWINSKY's family with the President. LEWINSKY said that she could not find these items and CARTER said that she had to produce whatever was in her control. CARTER said that this was a standard subpoena and may have just been a fishing

OIC-302a (Rev. 8-19-94)

29D OIC LR 35063

Continuation of OIC-302 of MONICA S. LEWINSKY , On 08/01/98 , Page 10

expedition. LEWINSKY explained that she did not want to get involved in the JONES case and that she was going to a new job in New York. CARTER suggested that prior to preparing an affidavit for LEWINSKY, he would call the JONES people and maybe have LEWINSKY give them an interview. LEWINSKY urged CARTER to call the BENNETT people, and he agreed to do so. LEWINSKY wanted the President to know that she was a team player. CARTER may have called BENNETT's office in her presence. CARTER said that he would send a retainer agreement in the mail.

LEWINSKY went back to work on December 22, 1997, and may have called VERNON JORDAN from a pay phone. LEWINSKY spoke with LINDA TRIPP at least once in person that afternoon. This conversation consisted of TRIPP telling LEWINSKY not to ask her to lie, and LEWINSKY reminding TRIPP that she had promised not to tell anyone about LEWINSKY's relationship with the President. TRIPP countered with the statement that her promise not to tell was not binding if she was under oath. LEWINSKY replied, "I wasn't thinking about under oath," which meant that she wanted TRIPP to lie no matter what the circumstances. TRIPP kept reminding LEWINSKY that VERNON JORDAN had gotten LEWINSKY a big name lawyer, but suggested that LEWINSKY might want to get an independent lawyer. LEWINSKY thought that perhaps TRIPP was jealous of LEWINSKY. LEWINSKY told TRIPP that she wanted to be in the CLINTON/BENNETT camp. LEWINSKY did not want to acknowledge that TRIPP was "doing her in," and was not always telling TRIPP the truth by this time. LEWINSKY did not think that it was so wrong to lie on the affidavit, because this concerned a personal matter and was none of PAULA JONES's business.

In regard to the E-mail sent and received on LEWINSKY's computer at the Pentagon, at some point during the week after LEWINSKY was subpoenaed, the computer person, FLOYD LNU, said that the E-mail was automatically destroyed every four weeks. FLOYD also told LEWINSKY how to permanently delete E-mail and LEWINSKY then made some deletions of her E-mail, specifically those sent to KATHRYN ALLDAY DAVIS, and a few to TRIPP. Sometime in December 1997, LEWINSKY asked TRIPP to delete the E-mail that TRIPP had received from LEWINSKY. LEWINSKY did this because E-mail would leave a trail. The President was unaware that LEWINSKY had mentioned him in E-mail and never told LEWINSKY to delete any of her messages.

On December 23, 1997, LEWINSKY was interviewed for a job by an AMERICAN EXPRESS official in Washington. The interviewer advised LEWINSKY that LEWINSKY really did not have the experience necessary for the position. DARCY BACON, wife of

OIC-302a (Rev. 8-19-94)

29D OIC LR 35063

Continuation of OIC-302 of MONICA S. LEWINSKY , On 08/01/98 , Page 11

KEN BACON, took LEWINSKY to lunch. LEWINSKY may have called TRIPP that night. If so, this was the last time LEWINSKY talked to TRIPP until January, 1998.

December 24, 1997, was LEWINSKY's last day at the Pentagon.

From December 25 to 27, LEWINSKY was in town, LINDA TRIPP did not return her calls. The situation was depressing. LEWINSKY's mother, MARCIA LEWIS, came down from New York on December 26 or 27, as PETER STRAUS had gone skiing. At some point, LEWIS suggested to LEWINSKY that she get in touch with a Christian Scientist woman in New York for counseling.

On December 27, 1997, LEWINSKY called BETTY CURRIE about the Christmas presents the President had for her. CURRIE was giving a White House tour to her church group the next morning so she told LEWINSKY to come in then.

On December 28, 1997, LEWINSKY went to BETTY CURRIE's office at about 8:30 a.m. CURRIE and LEWINSKY played with BUDDY in the Oval Office while the President was on the telephone. LEWINSKY went to the back rooms with the President so that he could get some coffee. LEWINSKY asked the President how her name had gotten on the PAULA JONES witness list. The President responded that it may have been "that woman from last summer" who was involved in the KATHLEEN WILLEY thing, and that maybe she just wants to cause trouble. The President asked LEWINSKY if she had told that woman or anyone else about the hatpin, and LEWINSKY denied that she had. The President suggested that maybe one of the USSS uniform guards or someone else had seen LEWINSKY with the hatpin when she was leaving. LEWINSKY said this could not have happened. [redacted]

LEWINSKY said that she was concerned about the gifts that the President had given her and suggested to the President that BETTY CURRIE hold the gifts. The President said something like, "I don't know," or "I'll think about it." The President did not tell LEWINSKY what to do with the gifts at that time. LEWINSKY told the President that she was going to sign an affidavit, and that she was moving to New York, to which the President responded, "Good." LEWINSKY probably did not tell CURRIE about receiving the JONES subpoena. CURRIE walked LEWINSKY by the Palm Room, and may have taken that route to avoid a particular guard. LEWINSKY had left her pass in the office and

OIC-302a (Rev. 8-19-94)

29D OIC LR 35063

Continuation of OIC-302 of MONICA S. LEWINSKY , On 08/01/98 , Page 12

CURRIE asked the guards at the southwest gate to let LEWINSKY out without the pass.

BETTY CURRIE called LEWINSKY at home later in the day, and said, "I understand that you have something for me." LEWINSKY was not surprised that CURRIE called since LEWINSKY had talked to the President about the gifts earlier that day. When CURRIE called, there was no question in LEWINSKY's mind that CURRIE knew what she was calling for. LEWINSKY then took the hat pin, and other selected items that would cause suspicion, and placed them in a box. LEWINSKY kind of compromised in deciding what to give to CURRIE to hold for her; for instance, the books that the President had given her were too sentimental to give back just in case LEWINSKY never got the box back. LEWINSKY put the Leaves of Grass book in her closet in a plastic bag. LEWINSKY gave the box to BETTY CURRIE when CURRIE came by the Watergate about 2:00 p.m. LEWINSKY had sealed the box so that CURRIE would not look at the items, and marked "do not throw away" in hopes that neither CURRIE nor the President would destroy the gifts. By giving the box of gifts to CURRIE, LEWINSKY was, in her mind, placing these items in the President's control. LEWINSKY said that the cassette tapes of the President's messages and the blue dress she wore on February 28, 1997 had already been taken to New York earlier in December. LEWINSKY told CURRIE not to throw the box away. CURRIE did not comment. LEWINSKY also gave CURRIE a small plant and a balloon to take to CURRIE's mother, who was in the hospital.

On December 28 or 29, 1997, LEWINSKY's brother MICHAEL was in town and LEWINSKY traveled to New York.

On December 29 or 30, 1997, LEWINSKY took a test at BURSON, MARSTELLER.

On December 30, 1997, LEWINSKY called VERNON JORDAN to discuss the job situation and was invited by either JORDAN or GAIL, his secretary, to have breakfast with JORDAN the next day. LEWINSKY traveled to Washington by train. LEWINSKY intended to surface the fact to JORDAN that LINDA TRIPP may have been the source of information resulting in LEWINSKY's subpoena by the JONES lawyers since, she had not acknowledged that to the President. LEWINSKY expected JORDAN to advise the President of this information.

On December 31, 1997, LEWINSKY arrived at the PARK HYATT MELROSE RESTAURANT on M Street by taxi, about 8:00 a.m. or 8:30 a.m., and the hostess advised LEWINSKY that Mr. JORDAN was

OIC-302a (Rev. 8-19-94)

29D OIC LR 35063

Continuation of OIC-302 of MONICA S. LEWINSKY , On 08/01/98 , Page 13

running late. Upon JORDAN's arrival, they sat at JORDAN's usual table. LEWINSKY inquired whether JORDAN was going to the "Renaissance" weekend and he replied that he was not. LEWINSKY advised that she had seen the President. JORDAN and LEWINSKY talked about jobs.

LEWINSKY felt she could not fake the story about TRIPP to the President, but assumed that he would get the message if LEWINSKY told JORDAN; therefore, LEWINSKY said to JORDAN that perhaps the leak to the JONES attorneys had been from one of her friends who spent the night at her house, and who could have seen her notes. JORDAN asked, "The President wrote you notes?" LEWINSKY said the notes were not from the President, but were notes that she had written about him. JORDAN said, "Make sure they're not there." LEWINSKY took this to mean that JORDAN wanted her to destroy the notes. LEWINSKY did go home and throw out the notes, drafts of letters and notes to the President, and a card "Starry, Starry Night." This occurred when LEWINSKY was packing to move to New York and she was eliminating things. LEWINSKY disposed of perhaps 50 pages.

After breakfast on December 31, 1997, JORDAN drove LEWINSKY back to his office. LEWINSKY asked whether the President would always be married to Mrs. CLINTON and JORDAN responded in the affirmative and quoted an unrecalled bible verse to LEWINSKY. JORDAN said, "Maybe you two can have an affair in three years." LEWINSKY responded that they had already had an affair with everything but sex. JORDAN responded with one of his grunts of acknowledgment, but did not appear to want to know any further details.

LEWINSKY then read the transcript from LINDA TRIPP tape number six, pages 12 to 22, concerning her first meeting with JORDAN. In regard to the statement, "The other one also asked you --you didn't tell anyone did you?" LEWINSKY said that she could not recall saying that, but her recollection might improve if she could hear the actual tape.

On January 3 or 4, 1998, LEWINSKY dropped off a book to BETTY CURRIE for the President. The book was entitled Presidents of the United States and contained a romantic note that LEWINSKY had written to the President after she saw the movie "Titanic."

On January 9, 1998, at about 4:00 p.m., a woman from REVLON called, indicated that LEWINSKY's prospects for a job at REVLON were good, and said that a woman from the Human Resources

Department would call LEWINSKY on Monday to extend a formal offer.

On January 9, 1998, LEWINSKY probably had a 30 minute call to LINDA TRIPP.

On January 12, 1998, LEWINSKY received an informal job offer from the Human Resources person and informally accepted the job.

On January 13, 1998, LEWINSKY had a five minute conversation with VERNON JORDAN.

LEWINSKY did not recall if she received a telephone call from FRANK CARTER on January 15, 1998, but she did recall that at some point she was paged by FRANK CARTER while shopping at SAFEWAY on Wisconsin Avenue. LEWINSKY called CARTER, at which time CARTER asked if LEWINSKY had ever received packages from the White House, or sent things to the White House by courier. LEWINSKY responded that she had sent packages by courier to BETTY CURRIE at the White House. LEWINSKY called SPEED COURIER SERVICE and found out that their policy was not to reveal any information about deliveries unless subpoenaed. LEWINSKY therefore concluded that the records had already been subpoenaed. LEWINSKY began wondering how the JONES attorneys could have known about the courier service. After thinking about it later, LEWINSKY was suspicious of MARK HUFFMAN, BETTY CURRIE, and LINDA TRIPP.

Later that day, LEWINSKY gave a ride to BETTY CURRIE and asked her about the call that CURRIE had received from MIKE ISIKOFF, in which ISIKOFF asked CURRIE about the package deliveries at the White House. LEWINSKY called LINDA TRIPP to tell TRIPP that if ISIKOFF called, to tell him that TRIPP did not know anything about her relationship with the President.

Between January 13 and January 15, 1998, LEWINSKY had a conversation with BETTY CURRIE about contacting JOHN PODESTA, because LEWINSKY was worried that her former supervisor at the White House, JOHN HILLEY, would not recommend her. LEWINSKY needed a favorable reference for the job at Revlon.

The interviewed terminated at 5:03 p.m.

Tab 23

50-892 98 - 48

OIC-302 (Rev. 8-19-94)

- 1 -

OFFICE OF THE INDEPENDENT COUNSEL

Date of transcription 08/03/98

MONICA S. LEWINSKY was interviewed under the terms of an immunity agreement between the Office of the Independent Counsel (OIC) and her. LEWINSKY was interviewed at the Office of the Independent Counsel, 1001 Pennsylvania Avenue, Washington, DC 20004. Present for the interview were Associate Independent Counsel (AIC) MICHAEL EMMICK, AIC MARY ANNE WIRTH, AIC KARIN IMMERGUT, AIC CRAIG LERNER, AIC JULIE MYERS and Deputy Independent Counsel (DIC) ROBERT BITTMAN. Present representing LEWINSKY were PRESTON BURTON and ROBERT BREDHOFF. LEWINSKY provided the following information, beginning at approximately 10:25 a.m.

On January 4, 1998, LEWINSKY called BETTY CURRIE in the late afternoon to arrange a meeting with CURRIE. LEWINSKY went to CURRIE's home to give CURRIE a package to give to President WILLIAM JEFFERSON CLINTON. LEWINSKY advised this was the first time she went to CURRIE's home to give CURRIE a package to give to CLINTON.

In the package was a book about the Presidents of the United States and a note. LEWINSKY cannot recall exactly when she purchased the book, but it occurred sometime after December 28, 1997. LEWINSKY advised she thinks she purchased the book on January 2 or January 3, 1998. LEWINSKY advised she withdrew $40 from the RIGGS NATIONAL BANK automatic teller machine on Wisconsin Avenue in Georgetown to buy the book.

LEWINSKY advised she purchased the book at a book store next to the Christian Scientist book store on Wisconsin Avenue. LEWINSKY advised she and ASHLEY RAINES saw the movie "Titanic," which prompted her to write the note she enclosed with the book. LEWINSKY advised she was feeling very down when she wrote the note. LEWINSKY described the note as very romantic.

When LEWINSKY saw CURRIE, LEWINSKY asked CURRIE to give the package to CLINTON. LEWINSKY and CURRIE also spoke about LEWINSKY's New Year's Eve encounter with STEVE NEUWIRTH.

LEWINSKY advised she was at CURRIE's residence for approximately twenty minutes.

Investigation on 08/2/98 at Washington, DC File # 29D-OIC-LR-35063

CI [redacted]
by SA [redacted] Date dictated 08/03/98

OIC-302a (Rev. 8-19-94)

29D-OIC-LR-35063

Continuation of OIC-302 of MONICA S. LEWINSKY , On 08/2/98 , Page 2

LEWINSKY advised that giving CURRIE, on December 28, 1997, the box with some of the gifts CLINTON had given LEWINSKY, on December 28th made LEWINSKY feel she was assuring CLINTON that she was on the same team. LEWINSKY does not recall talking about the PAULA JONES case with CURRIE. LEWINSKY may have mentioned LEWINSKY's idea about settling the JONES case with CLINTON on December 17, 1997.

On January 5, 1998, LEWINSKY met with FRANK CARTER, though she can not recall the exact time. LEWINSKY advised CARTER asked her a few difficult questions about sex. LEWINSKY told CARTER she did not have sex with CLINTON. LEWINSKY advised the two went into detail about how a deposition is conducted. LEWINSKY asked if her parents could be present during the deposition. LEWINSKY did not consider the meeting a full preparation session for the deposition.

LEWINSKY advised CARTER told her the types of questions that would be asked during the deposition, including how LEWINSKY got her job at the Pentagon. LEWINSKY advised this worried her as she did not know how to answer questions related to her transfer to the Pentagon without the answers leading to her relationship with CLINTON. LEWINSKY was concerned that the attorneys for JONES would go to people at the White House to verify LEWINSKY's answers and, because some of those people did not like LEWINSKY, they would contradict what LEWINSKY said under oath.

LEWINSKY could not recall taking any items to CARTER's office on January 5, 1998, although she could have, but she definitely recalls doing so on another occasion.

CARTER told LEWINSKY that, in civil cases, a lot of things were done at the last minute, so she probably would not hear about her subpoena being quashed until later.

During one of her meetings with CARTER, LEWINSKY mentioned telling LINDA TRIPP about LEWINSKY's subpoena. CARTER got a copy of the Newsweek article regarding TRIPP and KATHLEEN WILLEY.

LEWINSKY left the meeting with the understanding CARTER was to draft an affidavit and LEWINSKY would pick it up later that day.

LEWINSKY received a copy of the affidavit on January 5 or 6, 1998. LEWINSKY was nervous about signing the affidavit and

OIC-302a (Rev. 8-19-94)

29D-OIC-LR-35063

Continuation of OIC-302 of MONICA S. LEWINSKY , On 08/2/98 , Page 3

wanted VERNON JORDAN to review a copy of the affidavit and approve it. LEWINSKY thought that, by having JORDAN approve the affidavit, it was the same as having CLINTON's approval.

On January 5 or 6, 1998 LEWINSKY called CURRIE to tell her LEWINSKY needed to talk to CLINTON. (LEWINSKY advised that on her December 28, 1997 meeting with CLINTON, CLINTON told LEWINSKY to call CURRIE if LEWINSKY had any questions about anything related to the JONES matter.) LEWINSKY was very cryptic with CURRIE when they talked. LEWINSKY said she was going to sign something the next day and she needed to speak with CLINTON before doing so. LEWINSKY advised she wanted to make CLINTON nervous.

LEWINSKY advised CURRIE called at approximately 7 or 8 p.m. LEWINSKY was at the apartment of her aunt, DEBRA FINERMAN, when CURRIE called. LEWINSKY had told CURRIE that is where she would be. CURRIE transferred the call to CLINTON.

LEWINSKY told CLINTON she had spoken to CARTER and went over possible questions that would be asked in her deposition. CLINTON asked LEWINSKY what she was concerned about. LEWINSKY told CLINTON she was worried about giving "vanilla" answers to questions about how LEWINSKY got her job at the Pentagon. LEWINSKY was concerned that people at the White House, who did not like LEWINSKY, would "screw" her.

CLINTON told LEWINSKY to say that people in the Office of Legislative Affairs (OLA) found the position and the people in the OLA recommended her for it. LEWINSKY said that she could answer that way. (LEWINSKY advised that explanation was true, but it was not the entire truth.)

LEWINSKY was reassured by what CLINTON said about her transfer to the Pentagon. LEWINSKY and CLINTON spoke about the affidavit. LEWINSKY advised she did not want to sign anything until she was reassured by the White House that she would not be "screwed." LEWINSKY asked CLINTON if he wanted to see the affidavit and CLINTON said no, he had seen about fifteen of them.

CLINTON advised he liked the book she had given him. LEWINSKY told CLINTON it cost $40 and CLINTON asked why she paid so much for it. LEWINSKY brought up the subject of the note she gave him with the book. CLINTON said that LEWINSKY should not write things like that on paper. LEWINSKY advised CLINTON was referring to romantic items LEWINSKY had placed in the note. LEWINSKY assumed CLINTON threw away the notes she gave him.

LEWINSKY advised the notes would be more incriminating than the gifts.

The telephone call lasted about ten minutes.

{LEWINSKY advised that on "ZEDILLO Day," she saw a cut-out of the Valentine's Day personal advertisement she had placed in the "Washington Post." LEWINSKY saw CLINTON's copy of the advertisement on the desk in the Oval Office study.}

LEWINSKY advised she was annoyed with CLINTON that day because of a photograph in the newspaper that showed CLINTON and HILLARY RODHAM CLINTON dancing together on a beach.

LEWINSKY advised that she has January 5 and 6, 1998 confused at this time.

LEWINSKY advised that on January 6, 1998, she received a call from CARTER saying the draft affidavit was ready. Later that day, LEWINSKY called JORDAN's office and was told by JORDAN's secretary GAYLE Last Name Unknown (LNU) that JORDAN was out of town. LEWINSKY stopped by CARTER's office in the afternoon and picked up the draft affidavit, which CARTER had left in an envelope on the first floor of his office.

LEWINSKY took the affidavit home, read it and underlined the areas she was concerned about. LEWINSKY was concerned about the last sentence in paragraph six which read "this would have lasted only a matter of minutes and would not have been a "private" meeting, that is not behind closed doors." LEWINSKY was also concerned about paragraph eight regarding seeing the President "with crowds of other people present."

LEWINSKY advised she had previously planned on signing the affidavit on January 6, 1998, but decided JORDAN needed to see the affidavit first. LEWINSKY copied the affidavit and dropped it off at JORDAN's office that afternoon. LEWINSKY did not tell CARTER she was showing the affidavit to JORDAN. LEWINSKY advised that having JORDAN's approval was the same as CLINTON's.

LEWINSKY advised that most of the changes made to the draft affidavit she showed JORDAN were LEWINSKY's ideas. LEWINSKY is sure JORDAN commented on the affidavit, but she is not sure if he suggested any changes. LEWINSKY advised she may have crossed out the items she had previously underlined during the course of her discussion with JORDAN. LEWINSKY advised she

OIC-302a (Rev. 8-19-94)

29D-OIC-LR-35063

Continuation of OIC-302 of MONICA S. LEWINSKY, On 08/2/98, Page 5

did not discuss the sexual relationship aspect of the affidavit with JORDAN and only spoke with him for about six minutes.

LEWINSKY told JORDAN she would talk to CARTER the following day to sign the affidavit. LEWINSKY expected JORDAN to let CLINTON know when the affidavit was signed. LEWINSKY asked JORDAN if she should give a signed copy of the affidavit to CLINTON and JORDAN said no. LEWINSKY advised JORDAN never said JORDAN did not want to see the affidavit.

LEWINSKY advised she was unaware of JORDAN's telephone calls that same day to NANCY HERNREICH and CLINTON. After looking at all the telephone contact that was made between JORDAN and CLINTON as reflected on a chart of phone records presented to her by the OIC, LEWINSKY advised that it seems suspicious.

LEWINSKY advised she does not recall what she did during the evening of January 6, 1998, but she did feel relieved to be signing the affidavit. LEWINSKY felt that her involvement in the JONES matter would be over.

On January 7, 1998, LEWINSKY met with CARTER at 10:00 a.m. LEWINSKY does not recall bringing any items with her. LEWINSKY did bring a copy of the draft affidavit with her. LEWINSKY advised she and CARTER met in CARTER's office. On previous occasions, she and CARTER met in a conference room.

LEWINSKY advised CARTER had three versions of the affidavit to show her. There was not much difference between the three drafts. LEWINSKY advised none of the affidavits mentioned her having a sexual relationship with CLINTON.

LEWINSKY advised that it was her idea not to put anything in the affidavit about being alone with CLINTON. LEWINSKY advised CARTER suggested the language used when describing the procedure of getting CLINTON's signature on official documents.

LEWINSKY thought the statement in her affidavit that she could not fathom any reason why she was subpoenaed was not completely false. LEWINSKY felt the JONES case was about sexual harassment and LEWINSKY was not sexually harassed. LEWINSKY advised LEWINSKY lost her job at the White House because of her sexual relationship with CLINTON. LEWINSKY advised she was involved in a consensual sexual relationship with CLINTON.

LEWINSKY advised she met with CARTER for one hour to an

OIC-302a (Rev. 8-19-94)

29D-OIC-LR-35063

Continuation of OIC-302 of MONICA S. LEWINSKY , On 08/2/98 , Page 6

hour and one half. LEWINSKY advised she recalled walking down the hall to have the affidavit notarized. LEWINSKY recalls walking down the hall rationalizing to herself that she did not have a sexual relationship with CLINTON, when, in fact, she had. LEWINSKY rationalized lying about having a "sexual relationship" with CLINTON because they never had sexual intercourse.

LEWINSKY advised she does not have a direct memory of JORDAN's involvement with CARTER after LEWINSKY hired CARTER. LEWINSKY advised that after she looked at the chart of phone records presented to her by the OIC, she believes JORDAN's involvement may have been more substantial than she previously believed.

CARTER told LEWINSKY that he would send a copy of the affidavit to PAULA JONES' attorney, DAVID PYKE. LEWINSKY thought it was obvious that CARTER would apprise BOB BENNETT of her affidavit. LEWINSKY just wanted to do what CLINTON and BENNETT wanted her to do. LEWINSKY may have called JORDAN to let him know the affidavit was signed.

LEWINSKY's goal with the affidavit was not to give the JONES people a "little snag of yarn so they could pull the whole sweater apart."

LEWINSKY advised she was relieved since her conversation with CLINTON, on December 17, 1997, that he was assured she was comfortable with the situation.

LEWINSKY advised she left CARTER's office and soon left for New York to be with her mother. LEWINSKY advised she told her mother about the affidavit, but does not recall her mother's reaction. LEWINSKY took a signed copy of the affidavit with her to New York so she could have it in her possession.

On January 8th, LEWINSKY advised she had an interview at McANDREWS & FORBES (M&F) that did not go well at all. LEWINSKY advised she had previously met with RICHARD HALPERIN and someone else from M&F, so she was not sure why this meeting was necessary. LEWINSKY was very concerned after this interview, because, in addition to the interview going poorly, LEWINSKY had not yet heard from BURSON & MARSTELLER (B&M). LEWINSKY was also concerned that her poor showing at the interview would be a bad reflection on JORDAN.

LEWINSKY called JORDAN several times after the interview to advise him how the interview went. Initially,

LEWINSKY left JORDAN messages, but she eventually spoke to him. LEWINSKY sensed that JORDAN was annoyed that nothing had come up yet in the form of a job for LEWINSKY. JORDAN called LEWINSKY back and said that he had spoken to the chairman of M&F, and JORDAN told LEWINSKY not to worry. JORDAN told LEWINSKY someone from M&F would be calling her back to arrange for another interview.

Later that day, JAYMIE DURNAN, or DURNAN's secretary, called LEWINSKY to arrange a meeting for the following day. LEWINSKY advised she may have called JORDAN later that evening, but she did not fax anything to JORDAN's office from her mother's apartment.

On January 9, 1998, sometime in the morning, LEWINSKY called LINDA TRIPP. LEWINSKY told TRIPP she was calling from a pay phone because LEWINSKY was concerned about calling TRIPP from home. LEWINSKY thought JONES' attorneys might be tapping her phones.

LEWINSKY advised TRIPP's tone was different than her most recent calls. TRIPP told LEWINSKY about TRIPP's visit with NORMA ASNES. According to TRIPP, a friend of ASNES's told TRIPP to get a job in New York in the public relations field. TRIPP also told LEWINSKY that TRIPP now thought it was good to be vague on the truth when it came to the deposition.

LEWINSKY told TRIPP that LEWINSKY had had no contact with JORDAN, CURRIE or CLINTON since December, even though that was false. LEWINSKY told TRIPP that LEWINSKY had not heard anything about job offers. Neither of these things was true, but LEWINSKY told TRIPP this because LEWINSKY was wary of TRIPP ever since TRIPP said she was going to tell the truth about LEWINSKY's relationship with CLINTON. LEWINSKY did not tell TRIPP that LEWINSKY had signed the affidavit. TRIPP told LEWINSKY not to sign the affidavit until LEWINSKY had a job.

LEWINSKY advised this call with TRIPP put LEWINSKY at ease, so LEWINSKY agreed to meet TRIPP when LEWINSKY returned to Washington, D.C.

On January 9, 1998, between 11:00 a.m. and 11:30 a.m., LEWINSKY met with ALLAIN SEIDMAN and two other people from REVLON. LEWINSKY was very excited to work in the area of public relations that they discussed with her. LEWINSKY may have referenced her previous interview at M&F, and she may have referred to JORDAN. LEWINSKY also interviewed with the Human

Resources manager at REVLON.

LEWINSKY advised she called JORDAN after the interview to let him know it went well. LEWINSKY advised she received a telephone call from SEIDMAN, in which LEWINSKY was offered a position at REVLON as a floater in the public relations department. LEWINSKY was advised her salary would be approximately $40,000.

LEWINSKY recalled being annoyed at the salary and she complained to JORDAN about it. JORDAN told LEWINSKY to quit whining.

LEWINSKY does not recall calling CARTER on January 9, 1998. LEWINSKY did call CURRIE from a pay phone at the PIERRE HOTEL, to tell her about the job offer. LEWINSKY thinks CLINTON may have been out of town. LEWINSKY may have asked CURRIE to tell CLINTON about the job offer.

LEWINSKY advised that, in all the times she tried to reach JORDAN, she only got through to him half the time.

LEWINSKY does not recall what she did on January 10, 1998, except for the afternoon, which she spent looking for a tie to give JORDAN. LEWINSKY recalls that on January 11, 1998, STEVE NEUWIRTH called and said he did not want to see LEWINSKY that night or ever again.

LEWINSKY advised that on January 12, 1998, LEWINSKY sat by the phone awaiting a call. CARTER paged LEWINSKY and when she returned the page, CARTER advised her that he had submitted her affidavit to PYKE.

LEWINSKY called CURRIE on January 12, trying to get a recommendation from the OLA. LEWINSKY was also trying to find out if CURRIE had told CLINTON about LEWINSKY's offer.

LEWINSKY traveled on a 6:00 a.m. train from New York to Washington, D.C. LEWINSKY met JORDAN at 9:30 a.m. in JORDAN's new 4th floor office. LEWINSKY met with JORDAN for five minutes and gave him a tie and a pocket square as a sign of her appreciation.

JORDAN was not as warm with LEWINSKY as he had previously been. JORDAN quoted the Bible in referring to helping others. LEWINSKY perceived this to be the end of her working relationship with JORDAN.

OIC-302a (Rev. 8-19-94)

29D-OIC-LR-35063

Continuation of OIC-302 of MONICA S. LEWINSKY, On 08/2/98, Page 9

LEWINSKY advised she and CURRIE started using the code name "KAY" when they paged each other because someone once saw CURRIE's pager, which contained a message from LEWINSKY. The code name "KAY" was LEWINSKY's idea, because both she and CURRIE knew WALTER KAYE. The code name "MARY" was used for LINDA TRIPP.

LEWINSKY may have received a page from CURRIE on January 13, 1998. LEWINSKY faxed a letter on January 13 or 14, 1998 regarding references at the White House. LEWINSKY mentioned JOHN HILLEY as a person who should write her recommendation. LEWINSKY thinks JOHN PODESTA's name may have come up during a conversation with CURRIE as the person who would arrange for LEWINSKY's reference.

LEWINSKY advised that she told TRIPP several lies during her meeting with TRIPP on January 13, 1998. LEWINSKY told TRIPP she had not signed the affidavit when, in fact she had; LEWINSKY told TRIPP she had not heard about a job, when in fact she had; and LEWINSKY told TRIPP she was taking PAXIL, when she was not. LEWINSKY advised she tried to shift things so that TRIPP thought the situation was everyone against TRIPP and LEWINSKY.

LEWINSKY advised she does not know what she would have done if TRIPP had accepted her offer of the condominium in Australia. LEWINSKY thought the offer could be compared to someone saying they would give someone their first-born. LEWINSKY advised she would have spoken to CURRIE and CLINTON to ensure TRIPP did not lose her job.

On January 14, 1998, LEWINSKY called TRIPP from a pay phone at the WATERGATE Apartments and told TRIPP to have NORMA ASNES get TRIPP a Democratic attorney. TRIPP was scheduled to see KIRBY BEHRE that day to sign an affidavit. TRIPP had told LEWINSKY to get TRIPP pulled out of meetings if LEWINSKY called TRIPP at work.

LEWINSKY prepared the "talking points" at her home computer on January 14, 1998. TRIPP told LEWINSKY she had fired KIRBY BEHRE as her attorney and hired a new one. TRIPP told LEWINSKY she did not want it to look like she was not a "team" player. TRIPP had previously told LEWINSKY that she gave BEHRE a sealed envelope, containing the written summary of the information LEWINSKY had told TRIPP about LEWINSKY's affair with CLINTON, in case anything happened to TRIPP.

LEWINSKY felt pressure to hold TRIPP's hand during

TRIPP's affidavit. LEWINSKY drove TRIPP home that evening and gave her the talking points. TRIPP seemed glad to have some guidance for the affidavit.

On January 15, 1998, LEWINSKY returned a page from CARTER. CARTER asked LEWINSKY if she ever received courier packages from the White House. LEWINSKY said she had not received any packages from the White House via courier, but had sent some there using a courier. CARTER said that someone from BENNETT's office had called and mentioned the existence of courier records of items sent to the White House, referencing LEWINSKY.

LEWINSKY went home and called SPEEDY COURIER service and, without identifying herself, asked if they would ever turn over records. The respondent said they would not turn over records unless they had been subpoenaed. This made LEWINSKY think the courier service had been subpoenaed.

LEWINSKY returned CURRIE's page. CURRIE said that MIKE ISIKOFF had called asking about CURRIE's intern. {LEWINSKY advised CURRIE must have known about LEWINSKY'S involvement in the JONES case, but cannot remember specifically speaking about it with her.} CURRIE said ISIKOFF started asking about courier records.

CURRIE was nervous. LEWINSKY then "freaked out." At that time, LEWINSKY thought it made more sense that CARTER had asked about the records. LEWINSKY thinks CLINTON was out of town because she recalls CURRIE saying she would tell CLINTON when he returned. CURRIE later paged LEWINSKY and LEWINSKY called her. CURRIE asked LEWINSKY to drive her to JORDAN's office. CURRIE's husband had her automobile for the day.

LEWINSKY then called TRIPP and suggested that MARK HOFFMAN from the Pentagon must have been the source of the courier records leak to Newsweek. LEWINSKY advised TRIPP not to talk to Newsweek, if contacted.

LEWINSKY thinks CURRIE went to see JORDAN because JORDAN acted as "damage control." CURRIE may have been concerned about CURRIE's involvement with the LEWINSKY matter. LEWINSKY waited at the "FRONT PAGE" restaurant and had onion soup while CURRIE met with JORDAN. LEWINSKY advised it was raining that day and there was an O.J. SIMPSON interview on the television while she ate.

OIC-302a (Rev. 8-19-94)

29D-OIC-LR-35063

Continuation of OIC-302 of MONICA S. LEWINSKY , On 08/2/98 , Page 11

CURRIE met with JORDAN for approximately twenty minutes. When CURRIE returned to LEWINSKY, CURRIE explained that she had had a drink with JORDAN in his office. CURRIE said she would wait to see CLINTON before deciding what to do. CURRIE said she would call CLINTON in the Residence, first thing in the morning, to let him know CURRIE needed to speak with him.

LEWINSKY considered the discovery of the courier receipts a "big deal" and advised she could sense a lot of tension from CURRIE. LEWINSKY sensed the situation getting out of control.

On January 16th, LEWINSKY went to a gym on Connecticut Avenue and called CURRIE from a pay phone there. CURRIE said she had spoken to CLINTON, who said not to respond to the inquiries from Newsweek.

LEWINSKY advised she felt very low and depressed on January 16, 1998.

LEWINSKY advised she can not easily discuss any further details of January 16, 1998 at this time, as she feels guilty about getting everyone involved.

On January 18, 1998, LEWINSKY was paged by CURRIE. LEWINSKY was told by her attorney, BILL GINSBURG, not to return the pages. LEWINSKY was paged numerous times by CURRIE during that time frame. LEWINSKY returned a couple of the pages by calling CURRIE from a pay phone and leaving cryptic messages, hoping CURRIE would be able to figure out what was happening. LEWINSKY advised on one occasion, she said something about "HOOVER," hoping CURRIE would make the connection to the Federal Bureau of Investigation. LEWINSKY felt responsible for the crisis they were in.

The interview ended at approximately 2 p.m.

Tab 24

OIC-302 (Rev. 8-19-94)

OFFICE OF THE INDEPENDENT COUNSEL

Date of transcription 08/10/98

MONICA S. LEWINSKY was interviewed pursuant to an immunity agreement between the Office of Independent Counsel (OIC), LEWINSKY, and her attorneys. Present for the interview were Associate Independent Counsel (AIC) MICHAEL EMMICK, AIC KARIN IMMERGUT, AIC MARY ANNE WIRTH, and AIC JULIE MYERS. Representing LEWINSKY was Attorney PRESTON BURTON and Law Clerk MATTHEW UMHOFER of the law offices of PLATO CACHERIS. The interview was conducted in Suite 490, 1001 Pennsylvania Avenue NW, Washington, D.C. beginning at 12:07 p.m. LEWINSKY provided the following information:

LEWINSKY first saw the President in person in July 1995, when she attended a function with WALTER KAYE and her mother. At that time LEWINSKY was impressed with how handsome the President appeared.

On August 10, 1995, LEWINSKY attended the birthday party of the President on the grounds of the White House. At that time, LEWINSKY made eye contact with the President and began flirting with him. LEWINSKY does not believe that she would have been hired if anyone knew that they were flirting.

On or about August 13, 1995, LEWINSKY introduced herself to the President at a departure ceremony.

In September, 1995, LEWINSKY reintroduced herself to the President in the basement of the White House as he was passing. The occasion was the visit of LEWINSKY's friend, NATALIE UNGVARI, who was on a tour. LEWINSKY was waiting with U.S. Secret Service (USSS) uniformed officer LEWIS FOX for UNGVARI's return. LEWINSKY had her photograph taken with the President on this occasion.

In October 1995, the President waved at LEWINSKY once in passing.

During the first week in November 1995, LEWINSKY was in New York for the investiture of WALTER KAYE as a civilian aide of the U.S. Army. At this point, LEWINSKY was a second term intern who wanted to get a permanent job in the White House. While there, LEWINSKY received a call from JENNIFER PALMIERI, who

Investigation on 8/03/98 at WASHINGTON, D.C. File # 29D OIC LR 35063

by SA [redacted] CI [redacted] Date dictated 8/10/98

OIC-302a (Rev. 8-19-94)

29D OIC LR 35063

Continuation of OIC-302 of MONICA S. LEWINSKY , On 08/03/98 , Page 2

advised LEWINSKY of a job opening in the Office of Legislative Affairs (OLA). On the following Monday, LEWINSKY submitted a resume to her supervisor, TRACY BOBOWITZ, or to TIM KEATING. On Wednesday or Thursday, LEWINSKY brought writing samples and was interviewed by KEATING. The interview went well and LEWINSKY was called soon thereafter to meet SUSAN BROPHY and PAT GRIFFIN. LEWINSKY sent letters to each of them.

On November 10, 1996, KEATING advised LEWINSKY that she had gotten the job, but that the furlough was imminent and the paperwork had not cleared yet. LEWINSKY worked through the furlough as an intern without pay. LEWINSKY took a drug test and met JOCELYN JOLLEY. LEON PANTETTA's office was staffed during the furlough by LEWINSKY and two male interns. During the furlough, the President came to the office of PANETTA as often as five times a day. One of these interns remarked that the President was coming to visit quite frequently and that he, the President, must have had a crush on LEWINSKY.

LEWINSKY was hired in OLA because of her good work as an intern in PANETTA's office. The President's name was never mentioned by KEATING, GRIFFIN, BROPHY, or LEWINSKY during the hiring process. LEWINSKY had not applied for any other jobs. LEWINSKY applied for the OLA job because it met her requirement that she would have a blue badge. This would permit LEWINSKY to go the West Wing and not be relegated to the Old Executive Office Building.

On November 17, 1995, BARRY TOIV commented that LEWINSKY was getting a lot of "face time" with the President for being an intern in PANETTA's office.

On the Friday after Thanksgiving 1995, LEWINSKY was trained briefly by JOCELYN JOLLEY. LEWINSKY began her new job in OLA the first week in December 1995. JOLLEY was out sick at least one day that week and left LEWINSKY to complete a large mailing. LEWINSKY basically fended on her own as there were no interns. JOLLEY had advised that she would handle all Office of Management and Budget (OMB) material related to the furlough. There was a large backlog of letters due to the furlough.

TIM KEATING was pleased with LEWINSKY's work. At around the time of the State of the Union Address, JOLLEY was again absent due to sickness and LEWINSKY was left to complete a lot of work pertaining to the address; LEWINSKY stayed late and got the work done. However, LEWINSKY was very disappointed that neither she, JOLLEY, nor any of the interns were permitted to go

OIC-302a (Rev. 8-19-94)

29D OIC LR 35063

Continuation of OIC-302 of MONICA S. LEWINSKY, On 08/03/98, Page 3

to Capitol Hill for the address. LEWINSKY did not wish to be lumped in with JOLLEY when the OLA work was being evaluated, because JOLLEY was frequently absent and came in late many times due to her diabetic condition. JOLLEY advised LEWINSKY that the turn around time on acknowledging congressional inquiries was too long. MAUREEN LEWIS had been doing letters to congressmen after they had traveled with the President. LEWINSKY had started doing these political letters. KEATING found out about it and chewed out LEWINSKY for getting involved in someone else's area of responsibility; told LEWINSKY that she did not know what she was doing; and brought up a few other undisclosed problems. JAMIE RUBIN, BOB RUBIN's son, came on board to be the OLA liaison with the West Wing about this time.

In March 1996, LEWINSKY was visited a second time by her friend, NATALIE UNGVARI, from San Francisco. LEWINSKY was escorting UNGVARI around the White House on a Sunday and was in the vicinity of the Senate Office. They observed a guy in denim with a baseball cap and LEWINSKY called to him before he went into the men's room in the hall. This person was the President, who had popcorn on his shirt, apparently having just watched a movie. LEWINSKY introduced UNGVARI to the President. LEWINSKY had already told UNGVARI about her relationship with the President by this time. [redacted]. This caused some consternation on the part of LEWINSKY.

About two weeks before LEWINSKY's transfer in early April 1996, KEATING advised LEWINSKY to get her resume to the lady in Administration that sits next to ASHLEY RAINES. This was to complete LEWINSKY's personnel file. On the Friday before Easter, which was two days after RON BROWN was killed, LEWINSKY and JOLLEY were called to KEATING's office separately. KEATING advised that there had been problems in the Correspondence Unit and that JODIE TORKELSON wanted LEWINSKY and JOLLEY fired. Instead, both JOLLEY and LEWINSKY were being transferred to other agencies. JOLLEY was actually demoted.

KEATING advised LEWINSKY that she was too "sexy" to work in the White House, by which KEATING meant that LEWINSKY "could shine more" and could get a better job in the Pentagon. LEWINSKY's work at the White House was not criticized to her knowledge. LEWINSKY never saw it coming and was totally surprised; she wept. LEWINSKY's first reaction was that she would never get to see the President again; her second reaction was that people thought she was spending too much time away from her desk and too much time near the Oval Office. KEATING advised

OIC-302a (Rev. 8-19-94)

29D OIC LR 35063

Continuation of OIC-302 of MONICA S. LEWINSKY , On 08/03/98 , Page 4

that there were no other openings in the White House at that time, but that perhaps LEWINSKY could come back after the election. KEATING said that LEWINSKY had a job in the Press Office at the Pentagon; that she would probably make more money; and that LEWINSKY should see PATSY THOMASSON about the transition. KEATING also counseled that LEWINSKY could take her vacation to Florida as planned. KEATING requested that LEWINSKY turn her pass in and that he would place LEWINSKY on the access list until the time she departed. KEATING did not ban LEWINSKY from the White House.

At this point, LEWINSKY did not know how BETTY CURRIE felt about her and LEWINSKY actually felt closer to NANCY HERNREICH. On the Monday after being transferred, LEWINSKY went to HERNREICH's office, at which time HERNREICH tried to console LEWINSKY, but told LEWINSKY that she had to interview for the Pentagon job. This was not what KEATING had told her. While leaving, LEWINSKY was stopped by CURRIE. CURRIE observed LEWINSKY crying and tried to console her by saying that sometimes things work out for the best. LEWINSKY believed that EVELYN LIEBERMAN, who had a connection with the First Lady, was the force behind the transfer. LEWINSKY also called ASHLEY RAINES and BAYANI NELVIS to advise them of the transfer.

On Thursday of that week, MARK HUFFMAN from the Pentagon called and advised that LEWINSKY would interview for the job of Confidential Assistant, which included many administrative duties. LEWINSKY interviewed successfully for the job. LEWINSKY objected to the heavy burden of administrative duties and was advised that they would split the job and relieve LEWINSKY of some of those duties. CHARLIE DUNCAN's assistant at the Pentagon said there were no other jobs available there.

LEWINSKY was in touch with WALTER KAYE, who was instrumental in getting LEWINSKY the White House internship. LEWINSKY's parents had known KAYE many years ago in California and KAYE's grandson had been an intern. KAYE became involved politically when he contributed to the Democratic Party after selling his insurance company. ANN MCCOY, another White House employee, gave herself a birthday party in September 1995, which KAYE funded. There was some friction between MCCOY and her friends, and LEWINSKY's mother and aunt, at KAYE's investiture. In addition, MARSHA SCOTT, also a friend of KAYE, apparently felt that LEWINSKY's mother and aunt were somehow a threat to SCOTT. KAYE told DEBRA FINERMAN, LEWINSKY's aunt, that LEWINSKY had been transferred because there were rumors of LEWINSKY's relationship with the President. FINERMAN was angered because KAYE had not tried to defend LEWINSKY. Because of this, LEWINSKY did not attend a scheduled luncheon with KAYE on August 19, 1996.

On April 12, 1996, the President called LEWINSKY to explain why she had been transferred. The President did not know any of the details about the Pentagon job, and when LEWINSKY complained about it, the President advised her that if she did not like it he would get LEWINSKY a job on the campaign. LEWINSKY told the President that the job was boring and that she had complained to PATSY THOMASSON, who did nothing. The President stated that THOMASSON was a friend of his.

On April 17, 1996, LEWINSKY started the Pentagon job, but hated it from the start as it was boring to her. Her superiors did not split the job as promised. The job was primarily as the gate keeper for KEN BACON. LEWINSKY said that her predecessor, JEAN WESSEL, an older woman, had more administrative experience than LEWINSKY, but lacked enough energy for the travel demands of the job. The job was a General Services 9 position paying $42,000 with overtime. LEWINSKY had been making $25,000 with no overtime pay at OLA. LEWINSKY developed a good interpersonal relationship with BACON.

TIM KEATING had advised LEWINSKY that her position at OLA was not being filled, but after going to the Pentagon, LEWINSKY found out that the position had been filled. LEWINSKY wrote a letter to KEATING complaining about this and the fact that they assigned pagers to everyone, which LEWINSKY had suggested months ago. LEWINSKY also tried to explain to KEATING that her past job performance should not have been linked to that of JOLLEY. LEWINSKY may have called ANN Last Name Unknown at OLA to try to get her job back. While at OLA, LEWINSKY had gotten along with JANET MERDILLA, LUCIA WYMAN, and AL MAULDIN.

After beginning the job in the Pentagon, LEWINSKY was able to visit the President in the White House on weekends. Since LEWINSKY no longer had a blue badge, she had to be "WAVED" in, and escorted. These visits were facilitated by BETTY CURRIE, who had an unspoken agreement with LEWINSKY to use the most inconspicuous route to the Oval Office that would avoid the USSS uniformed officers, many of whom were friendly to MARSHA SCOTT. (LEWINSKY was provided with a floor plan of the White House, a copy of which is attached to this document, on which she highlighted the most common route she took to see the President.) The route normally included entering the southwest gate; walking north on Executive Drive; entering the West Wing basement lobby; meeting CURRIE, her escort; going through the basement; and up the stairs near the Oval Office. LEWINSKY and CURRIE avoided a uniformed officer who knew DEBBIE SCHIFF. The officer's name is unknown, but he is very friendly, about 5'11", and overweight.

The weekend attire at the White House was very informal. LEWINSKY usually departed through the northwest gate and never departed through the tunnel.

The President never gave LEWINSKY a rose, but CURRIE once gave LEWINSKY a bunch of roses to take home.

CHARLIE the butler was always friendly with LEWINSKY.

To LEWINSKY's knowledge the President did not call her from Jackson Hole, Wyoming or elsewhere when he was on vacation.

LEWINSKY never taped anyone; however, LEWINSKY does have a micro-cassette from her answering machine with a call from BETTY CURRIE on December 28, 1997. CURRIE was at her residence and needed LEWINSKY's date of birth and social security number to place LEWINSKY on the White House access list. The tape also contains a few messages about KIRBY BEHRE from LINDA TRIPP in December 1997. LEWINSKY does not recall playing the CURRIE tape to LINDA TRIPP.

LEWINSKY does recall playing the tape with messages from the President to TRIPP. This tape was previously furnished to the OIC. LEWINSKY did not have caller identification (ID) on her telephone when the first message from the President was recorded, but she recognized the President's voice when he said, "Aw shucks." LEWINSKY installed "caller ID" on her home telephone before July 1996. The second message from the President was muffled. In the third message from the President he said, "Hello." The fourth message from the President was left in the middle of the night when LEWINSKY was out of town; the President said, "C'mon it's me." LEWINSKY spoke to the President about the messages. On one occasion, the President advised that he did not like to leave messages.

On August 11, 1996, LEWINSKY saw DEBBIE BYRD at the southwest gate and then in BETTY CURRIE's office.

On September 12 or 19, 1997 LEWINSKY arrived at the southwest gate crying, called BETTY CURRIE, and waited a long time. When CURRIE arrived, LEWINSKY was crying about when she was coming back to the White House and the fact that MARSHA SCOTT was not helping. It worried CURRIE when LEWINSKY cried. CURRIE said that sometimes the President's hands are tied, but that CURRIE had received the President's permission to talk to JOHN PODESTA about getting a job for LEWINSKY. LEWINSKY was taken to the Oval Office on this occasion. CURRIE was going to Chicago the next day.

A frequent occurrence was for LEWINSKY to arrive at the White House gate and not be allowed to enter because her name had not been cleared in the computer yet. LEWINSKY would wait until CURRIE could enter the data into the "WAVE system." LEWINSKY never complained about waiting. It was impossible for anyone to skip the "WAVE" system.

The President held BETTY CURRIE in high regard. LEWINSKY always knew where CURRIE's loyalty was. CURRIE was very good at covering and representing the President. CURRIE would occasionally lie, as she did in the ELEANOR MONDALE matter, and when she told LEWINSKY that she was unable to get LEWINSKY's messages into the President all day. On one occasion, on a weekend, CURRIE locked in her desk one of LEWINSKY's messages to the President so that no one snooping around would see it. However, the President did not get to see it either. LEWINSKY has no specific recollection that CURRIE knew of LEWINSKY's subpoena in the PAULA JONES case; however, CURRIE had to know that LEWINSKY was somehow involved in the JONES case when LEWINSKY started using the "KAYE" code name on the pager. LEWINSKY has a faint recollection of speaking with CURRIE about LEWINSKY's involvement in the JONES matter.

LINDA TRIPP spent the night in LEWINSKY's apartment with her in late November 1997. This was after TRIPP had attended a Christmas show with NORMA ASNES. TRIPP slept in MICHAEL LEWINSKY's room with the door closed. At about 2:00 a.m. LEWINSKY received a call from the President on LEWINSKY's personal line in her bedroom. This line does not have a speaker phone and there are no extensions. LEWINSKY cannot recall the topic of conversation, but it could have been a "phone sex" call. The call could have been either the night before or the night after NANCY HERNREICH testified on November 13, 1997; or it could have been when the Arkansas friend with a terminal illness was visiting the President. When the call was over, LEWINSKY tried to awaken TRIPP, without success, to tell her about the call from the President. The next morning, TRIPP advised that she had heard the telephone ring. TRIPP did not listen to this call or any other telephone conversations that LEWINSKY had with the President. TRIPP was never present when LEWINSKY called BETTY CURRIE.

OIC-302a (Rev. 8-19-94)

29D OIC LR 35063

Continuation of OIC-302 of MONICA S. LEWINSKY, On 08/03/98, Page 8

FRANK CARTER told LEWINSKY that when testifying one should not answer a direct yes or no if one was not sure; one should say, "It may have happened," or "It's possible," so as not to perjure oneself. LEWINSKY said that is why she has answered, "It's possible" instead of yes or no to some of the questions in her debriefing by the OIC. LEWINSKY and TRIPP discussed leaving some "wiggle room" when testifying when one wasn't sure of the answer.

AIC MARY ANNE WIRTH departed at this time.

In regard to the ties that LEWINSKY had given to the President, she would often ask him when he intended to wear them. The President would sometimes wear one the day after LEWINSKY talked to him, and sometimes the day she was scheduled to see him. On one of the days that BAYANI NELVIS testified in the Grand Jury, he wore a tie that LEWINSKY had given to the President. LEWINSKY opined that this may have been a signal of some sort; either that the tie was not important to the President, or as a sign of encouragement to LEWINSKY.

LEWINSKY briefly described the contents of the back hallway off the Oval Office:

A. Framed picture.
B. Bathroom door.
C. Framed sword above bathroom door.
D. Credenza.
E. Framed political button collections on right and left walls.
F. Signature of an Oklahoman, probably WOODIE GUTHRIE.

LEWINSKY described the contents of the President's back study:

A. Dark wooden desk.
   1. Chair on rollers with presidential seal on the pillow.
   2. Mahogany cigar box on desk.
   3. Wooden organizer on desk.
   4. Two bookends with small books including Vox.
   5. Blotter.
B. Book rack.
C. Bookshelves with mostly political books; various items on top are changed periodically.
D. Hardwood floor with blue rug.
E. Two windows.

OIC-302a (Rev. 8-19-94)

29D OIC LR 35063

Continuation of OIC-302 of MONICA S. LEWINSKY , On 08/03/98 , Page 9

F. Painting of the President walking on the street.
G. An older photograph of Mrs. CLINTON and CHELSEA CLINTON.
H. Photograph of an old guy with a fireman's hat.
I. Photograph of the President with school children.
J. Stand with telephone and compact disk player.
K. Compact disk holder in the corner of the study.
L. Golf clubs.
M. Rocking chair with a pillow.
N. Marble top half table with big mirror.
O. On a shelf is a "kewpie" doll sitting under a mushroom.

LEWINSKY described the President's dining room:

A. Pantry door.
B. Hall door.
C. Marble top bureau with LEWINSKY paperweight on it.
D. Circular table and chairs.
E. Dry flower arrangement on table.
F. Television and VCR.
G. Mirrors on both walls.

LEWINSKY described the President's bathroom:

A. Toilet.
B. Sink.
C. Telephone on wall.
D. Vertical shelf for toiletries.
E. The walls are lined with black and white cartoons of the President.

At this point AIC JULIE MYERS entered.

LEWINSKY is close to her aunt, DEBRA FINERMAN, and provided some details of her relationship with the President, but not to the degree that she did with LINDA TRIPP. LEWINSKY did not provide the vulgar details to FINERMAN. FINERMAN was aware that LEWINSKY had been subpoenaed in the PAULA JONES case and knew that LINDA TRIPP was causing problems. LEWINSKY, her mother, MARCIA LEWIS, and FINERMAN referred to VERNON JORDAN as "GWEN." LEWIS and FINERMAN coined this nickname for JORDAN.

LEWINSKY recalled the following additional gifts that she gave to the President:

A. HARROD'S golf balls and tees.
B. A wooden painted egg from Budapest (observed on 12/28/97).
C. "Gummy boobs" from URBAN OUTFITTERS.

OIC-302a (Rev. 8-19-94)

29D OIC LR 35063

Continuation of OIC-302 of MONICA S. LEWINSKY, On 08/03/98, Page 10

D. Cassette tape; unknown whether the President ever listened; did not tell BETTY CURRIE of this gift for fear CURRIE would not give it to the President; later asked CURRIE if President had gotten the tape.

There would have been no legitimate business reason for LEWINSKY to go into the President's study; her access was only because she had a personal relationship with the President.

LEWINSKY [redacted] a student at SANTA MONICA CITY COLLEGE in March or April 1992. LEWINSKY was upset over the fact that her father would not pay for her to go to a more expensive university. After waiting 15 minutes for a parking place, someone came along at the last minute and took the space from her. LEWINSKY began crying uncontrollably. MARCIA LEWIS took LEWINSKY for treatment to a psychologist, Dr. IRENE KASSORLA. LEWINSKY saw KASSORLA regularly until LEWINSKY moved to Oregon, but continued treatment with KASSORLA by telephone. The consultation continued every four to six weeks after LEWINSKY moved to Washington, D.C. LEWINSKY advised KASSORLA of her relationship with the President and used the code name "HENRIETTA" when talking about him on the telephone. LEWINSKY was honest with KASSORLA, but did not give her too many details. KASSORLA opined that the President was using LEWINSKY.

MARCIA LEWIS was never a patient of KASSORLA. KASSORLA is a psychologist, but not a sex therapist. KASSORLA is self-promoting. KASSORLA never kept notes when LEWINSKY saw her in person and all of KASSORLA's recollections might not be accurate. KASSORLA, if subpoenaed, would most likely go on television talk shows. In LEWINSKY's opinion, KASSORLA would be a public relations nightmare to the OIC. KASSORLA helped LEWINSKY to the extent that LEWINSKY improved her school grades and lost weight. LEWINSKY last called KASSORLA in 1997.

LEWINSKY has consulted with Dr. KATHY ESTEP, a therapist. LEWINSKY talked with ESTEP around the time of the 1996 Presidential election about her relationship with the President, and displayed photos of LEWINSKY and the President. LEWINSKY saw ESTEP about four times in October and November, 1996. Dr. ESTEP told LEWINSKY that she had a lot of loss, such as losing her job. LEWINSKY visited an unnamed associate of Dr. ESTEP, [redacted]. The associate also precribed "phen phen" on a weekly basis for LEWINSKY.

Around March 1998, LEWINSKY received a letter from one [redacted], whom she has never met. The letter contained a

OIC-302a (Rev. 8-19-94)

29D OIC LR 35063

Continuation of OIC-302 of MONICA S. LEWINSKY , On 08/03/98 , Page 11

photograph of [redacted], who requested that LEWINSKY put her in touch with BILL GINSBERG, whom [redacted] wanted to retain as her own attorney. [redacted] purported that she had been a White House intern, who had also had an affair with the President. LEWINSKY speculated that [redacted] may have been JANE DOE #7. Subsequently, LEWINSKY received a package from [redacted], which contained a tape recording of audio messages from the OIC requesting an interview. GINSBERG or NATE SPEIGHTS referred [redacted] to attorney KEITH WATERS. LEWINSKY provided the tape and photograph to WATERS.

The interview was terminated at 4:44 p.m.

Tab 25

OIC-302 (Rev. 8-19-94)

- 1 -

OFFICE OF THE INDEPENDENT COUNSEL

Date of transcription 8/04/98

MONICA S. LEWINSKY was interviewed pursuant to an immunity agreement between the Office of the Independent Counsel (OIC), LEWINSKY, and her attorneys. Present for the interview were Associate Independent Counsel (AIC) MICHAEL EMMICK, AIC KARIN IMMERGUT, and AIC JULIE L. MYERS. AIC MARY ANNE WIRTH and AIC CRAIG LERNER were present during part of the interview. Representing LEWINSKY was her attorney, SYDNEY HOFFMAN, and Law Clerk ANIE WULKEN. The interview was conducted at the OIC office, Suite 490 North, 1001 Pennsylvania Avenue, NW, Washington, D. C. LEWINSKY provided the following information:

LEWINSKY wrote a letter to the President on July 3, 1997, threatening to tell her parents of their affair. LEWINSKY did not author any similar letters. LINDA TRIPP encouraged LEWINSKY to be more forceful in her correspondence with the President.

On about September 19, 1997, LEWINSKY was crying outside the northwest gate of the White House. BETTY CURRIE and BAYANI NELVIS knew LEWINSKY was upset.

LEWINSKY did not recall telling BETTY CURRIE directly about her affair with the President. CURRIE may have assumed an affair existed. However, CURRIE demonstrated no confusion about the relationship between LEWINSKY and the President. LEWINSKY and TRIPP discussed CURRIE's knowledge of the relationship. TRIPP suggested to LEWINSKY that CURRIE knew about the relationship. LEWINSKY agreed with TRIPP's assessment during these conversations.

LEWINSKY did not have a specific recollection, but believes CURRIE must have known about the PAULA JONES subpoena. LEWINSKY believed she may have had a discussion with CURRIE about the above subpoena.

LEWINSKY said she thought that PEDRO, Last Name Unknown (LNU) was the name of the waiter at the breakfast she had with VERNON JORDAN on December 31, 1997. PEDRO was described as a petite Hispanic male, between 35 and 40 years of age. JORDAN appeared to know the waiter and be a frequent customer of the resturant.

Investigation on 08/04/98 at WASHINGTON, D. C. File # 29D-LR-35063

by [redacted] Date dictated 8/04/98

OIC-302a (Rev. 8-19-94)

29D-LR-35063

Continuation of OIC-302 of MONICA S. LEWINSKY , On 08/04/98 , Page 2

On December 11, 1997, JORDAN gave LEWINSKY a list of JORDAN's business contacts. The list included URSULA FAIRBURN of AMERICAN EXPRESS, RICHARD HALPERIN of MCANDREWS and FORBES, and YOUNG and RUBICAM.

Regarding telephone messages on LEWINSKY's cassette tapes, there may have been one or two more tapes. Most of the recordings consisted of "Hello." LEWINSKY knew these recorded messages were the President, because she knows his voice. LEWINSKY kept the messages so that when she wanted she could hear the President's voice on tape.

May 24, 1997 was referred to by LEWINSKY as "Dump Day." LEWINSKY had an idea she would see the President on that date. LEWINSKY went shopping with ASHLEY RAINES at VICTORIA's SECRET. CURRIE called LEWINSKY around 11:00 a.m. and told LEWINSKY to come to the White House at about 1:00 p.m. LEWINSKY appeared as scheduled wearing a red sun dress with small polka dots and the hat pin the President had given to her. The pin was worn on a straw hat. LEWINSKY brought gifts to the President, including a mystery puzzle and a BANANA REPUBLIC shirt. LEWINSKY gave the President his gifts in the Executive dining room.

LEWINSKY did not recall how the conversation started; however, the President stated that he did not feel right about their relationship; it was not right, and the President said he could not do it anymore. LEWINSKY was crying. The President said this did not have to do with LEWINSKY. The President told LEWINSKY that he had been with hundreds of women in his life until he was about 40 years of age. The President told LEWINSKY that when he turned 40 his life was falling apart. LEWINSKY recalled that the President may have told her that, at the above time, he entertained thoughts of ending his life. However, LEWINSKY was not sure about the recollection. [redacted]. The President told LEWINSKY that he had been good until he met her. LEWINSKY did not believe the President. The President told her how he was attracted to LEWINSKY, and how the President thought LEWINSKY was a great person. The President told LEWINSKY that they could remain friends. The President pointed out to LEWINSKY that he could do a lot for her. The President told LEWINSKY that it was difficult

OIC-302a (Rev. 8-19-94)

29D-LR-35063

Continuation of OIC-302 of MONICA S. LEWINSKY , On 08/04/98 , Page 3

for him to resist being with other women. The President struggled with it daily. The President told LEWINSKY that he kept a calender on how long he had been good. The President explained that during his life he had been two people, and kept up two fronts. The President said that starting in the third or fourth grade, he was a good boy with his mother and step father, but also began telling stories and leading a secret life. LEWINSKY's impression was that the President was telling her he wanted to be right in the eyes of God. The President wanted the affair to be over, though he said it was not LEWINSKY's fault. LEWINSKY did not know if the President meant what he said.

The President and LEWINSKY moved from the dining room to the back study and into the hallway. LEWINSKY was crying and trying to talk the President out of ending the affair by telling him that Presidents in the past needed girlfriends. The President got angry and told LEWINSKY that he did not want to be like that. The President said he did not want his daughter to know about the affair. The President told LEWINSKY that if they had no sex they could be friends and visit. LEWINSKY said that based on a previous relationship with a married man, she thought that the President appeared to be going through feelings of guilt. LEWINSKY was hysterical.

Subsequently, STEVEN GOODIN came into the area and LEWINSKY realized she had left her purse on the dining room table. LEWINSKY retrieved her purse from the dining room table. BETTY CURRIE came in the back hall through the pantry to take LEWINSKY out of the area. The President was trying to make things look "OK". CURRIE told LEWINSKY that her face was similar to CURRIE's face, it showed everything. CURRIE then asked LEWINSKY what was wrong. LEWINSKY did not say anything except that things were difficult. CURRIE was going out of town to visit CURRIE's sister who had a heart attack. LEWINSKY commented that she and CURRIE would get together for drinks when CURRIE returned.

LEWINSKY recalled that on the above date, LANNY DAVIS and his family were in the White House. CURRIE introduced LEWINSKY to DAVIS and his family.

On July 3, 1997, LEWINSKY wrote a letter to the President. On July 4, 1997, she appeared for a meeting with the President at the White House. LEWINSKY wore a black sun dress bought in Rome, Italy. LEWINSKY was somber. The President came out of his office and said to LEWINSKY, "Hey." LEWINSKY replied, "Hey." They both went into the study. LEWINSKY sat at the desk

OIC-302a (Rev. 8-19-94)

29D-LR-35063

Continuation of OIC-302 of MONICA S. LEWINSKY, On 08/04/98, Page 4

and the President sat in a rocking chair. The President said something to the effect of, "First of all, it is illegal to threaten the President of the United States;" secondly, he did not read the entire letter; in the third place, he threw the letter away. LEWINSKY said that when the President got to the phrase, "In the fourth place," she stopped him. The President appeared nervous. LEWINSKY could not recall what the President next said. LEWINSKY and the President got into a disagreement. LEWINSKY pointed out to the President that she had left the White House and left like a "good girl." She waited through the election and well after a year after leaving the White House. The President told LEWINSKY they could still be friends. She replied that he did not act like her friend. LEWINSKY cried and the President hugged her. Over the President's left shoulder LEWINSKY saw a gardener outside the window. LEWINSKY did not make eye contact with the gardener. LEWINSKY was not sure whether they were seen. They moved to the bathroom hallway. The President was most affectionate that day. The President told LEWINSKY she was beautiful. The President played with her hair and stroked her arm. The President mentioned that people like them had fire in the belly. At one point, the President said he wished he had more time for LEWINSKY, and that maybe he would in three years. LEWINSKY took the opportunity to comment that the President and his wife connected on a level that no one understood. [redacted]. LEWINSKY said something about being together with the President in the future. The President asked LEWINSKY what she would do when the President was 70 years of age, and had to go to the bathroom numerous times a day. LEWINSKY replied that they would deal with it. LEWINSKY said she never felt so complete. LEWINSKY stated that she thought her meeting with the President ended on a positive note.

CURRIE called out for the President and he told LEWINSKY it was time to go. LEWINSKY told the President that she needed a few more minutes with him. LEWINSKY told him about the events surrounding KATHLEEN WILLEY. LEWINSKY referred to July 4, 1997 as KATHLEEN WILLEY day. LEWINSKY advised the President of information she received from a friend regarding WILLEY. LEWINSKY did not identify that person. LEWINSKY insisted she would not have identified the friend to the President even if asked. The President did not appear surprised by LEWINSKY's information. LEWINSKY left a picture for the President to sign for LEWINSKY's birthday.

OIC-302a (Rev. 8-19-94)

29D-LR-35063

LEWINSKY received a bear sculpture from the President that he said he bought in Vancouver, British Columbia. The President gave the bear to her during a visit with the President at the White House on December 28, 1997.

LEWINSKY may have used tissue to blot her lipstick on a visit with the President on January 7, 1996. LEWINSKY reapplied her make-up after encounters with the President. The tissues were disposed of in the trash can in the bathroom or in the one near NANCY HERNREICH's office. Occasionally the President and LEWINSKY had sodas or other drinks in the dining room or study.

LEWINSKY reviewed and identified the following documents:

1. A paper with the phrase, "The time has finally come for me to throw in the towel..." LEWINSKY could see TRIPP's influence on this document. LEWINSKY wrote the document, but did not send it. TRIPP discouraged LEWINSKY from sending the paper. LEWINSKY dated the paper around September, 1997, because LEWINSKY found out that MARSHA SCOTT was not going to detail her to the White House. It was harsher in language than LEWINSKY had recalled. In lieu of sending the letter, LEWINSKY traveled to the White House on about September 19, 1997 and waited at the southwest gate for an appointment.

2. A letter with notation, "Official Letterhead," and reading, "To Handsome,." LEWINSKY sent a version of this joke letter to the President by courier. The letter was written on September 30, 1997. A reminder to throw the letter away was noted.

3. A draft of a letter sent to the President on March 2, 1996, along with a HUGO BOSS necktie. The letter began with, "Dear Mr. P:" These were sent by Federal Express.

4. A photograph of the President wearing a tie given to him by LEWINSKY.

5. A document entitled, "As your friend." LEWINSKY wrote this at home and did not mail it to the President. LEWINSKY did discuss the content with the President on December 17, 1997. LEWINSKY

drafted the content in conversations with LINDA TRIPP on December 8, 1997.

6. A document stating, "This is going to be a long letter." It was a draft letter written on LEWINSKY's home computer. It was never sent. The actual letter sent was shorter than the above document. It was sent in response to learning from TRIPP that LEWINSKY did not get the job at the National Security Council (NSC) for which she applied. The date of the document was after October 6, 1997.

7. A card dated June 29, 1997, starting with, "Dear Handsome", and containing the phrase, "I feel disposable, used, insignificant," and, "I really need to discuss my situation." LEWINSKY stated that the writing on the card was hers, but the phrases and words were those of TRIPP. Some of TRIPP's writing may be on this draft. LEWINSKY would buy more than one of a particular card for draft purposes.

8. The final version of the above card (item seven) was sent to the President.

9. A document written on LEWINSKY's Department of Defense (DOD) computer. The document contains a list of things sent to the President, including an item named as "Gingko..." LEWINSKY did try to delete documents concerning the President from her DOD computer.

10. This document contains the statement, "It has been made clear to me that I cannot return to the White House." It is a closer version of the final version than item six.

11. This document was a short draft of a letter sent to the President. The letter contains the phrase, "...cannot do anything but accept that..."

12. This document contained LEWINSKY's own thoughts including the phrase, "It was so sad seeing you." It was not sent.

13. A photograph from October 23, 1996, taken at a

OIC-302a (Rev. 8-19-94)

29D-LR-35063

fundraiser.

14. A photograph of LEWINSKY and her family taken with the President after the June 14, 1996 radio address.

15. A photograph taken on what LEWINSKY referred to as LOU FOX day.

16. A photograph which was a hand out photograph of the President signing a Department of Defense (DOD) bill. The President was wearing a tie given to him by LEWINSKY.

17. A photograph of the President on his birthday.

18. A photograph of LEWINSKY and the President, signed by the President, on what LEWINSKY referred to as "Dress Day." LEWINSKY is wearing the dark blue dress.

19. A photograph of the President wearing a tie given to him by LEWINSKY.

20. A black and white photograph of the President. LEWINSKY fell in love with the photograph.

21. A letter, dated June 16, 1997. LEWINSKY told her former attorney, WILLIAM GINSBURG about the letter in January 1998. The letter was to CURRIE but was not sent.

22. A letter dated November 2, 1997, was addressed to CURRIE beginning, "Hope you had an enjoyable weekend." LEWINSKY was not sure if the letter was sent.

23. This item was a draft note on a card with a heart on the top sheet. This heart page was not the inside of the card. The top sheet of the card should have a cat on it. LEWINSKY sent a card with a cat because CURRIE liked cats. The part of a card with a snowman on it was possibly a draft of a Christmas card sent to CURRIE. The above card was possibly sent to CURRIE on September 17, 1997.

OIC-302a (Rev. 8-19-94)

29D-LR-35063

Continuation of OIC-302 of MONICA S. LEWINSKY, On 08/04/98, Page 8

24. A card stating, "Dear Betty, I feel better after our talk." LEWINSKY may have sent the card after LEWINSKY's meeting with CURRIE at the HAY ADAMS hotel. The dates were around June 24, 1997 or June 29, 1997. MARSHA SCOTT was the main topic of the discussion between LEWINSKY and CURRIE.

LEWINSKY never contacted the President when he was in Bosnia, despite news reports. Not only was he with his family, but there exists no direct way to contact the President overseas.

LEWINSKY called the President by the following names: "[redacted]," "[redacted]," "Creep," "Big Creep." [redacted]

LEWINSKY remained abreast of the President's schedule by referring to News Edge, a publication of the President's projected schedule. It was LEWINSKY's job to track the briefings from the White House. Sometimes LEWINSKY contacted CURRIE for the President's schedule. If LEWINSKY thought CURRIE was not telling the truth about the President's schedule, LEWINSKY would contact BAYANI NELVIS, a Presidential steward. LEWINSKY maintained she never asked the U.S. Secret Service (USSS) about the Presidential schedule.

LEWINSKY reviewed a schedule prepared of calls to and from VERNON JORDAN, over a period of time, from various individuals and locations including: the White House, LEWINSKY's residences, and JORDAN's office. LEWINSKY could provide no additional information regarding these calls. LEWINSKY made the observation that there appeared to be more telephone calls than she realized.

Before Thanksgiving 1997, and after LEWINSKY had a fight with TRIPP , LEWINSKY flew to Los Angeles. LEWINSKY called CURRIE and asked CURRIE to call JORDAN and prod along the job search. It was LEWINSKY's understanding that JORDAN was helping her at the behest of the President and CURRIE. Prior to LEWINSKY being subpoenaed on December 19, 1997, LEWINSKY did not know if JORDAN knew LEWINSKY was on the PAULA JONES case witness list.

Tab 26

OIC-302 (Rev. 8-19-94)

OFFICE OF THE INDEPENDENT COUNSEL

Date of transcription 08/07/98

MONICA S. LEWINSKY was interviewed under the terms of an immunity agreement between the Office of the Independent Counsel (OIC) and her. LEWINSKY was interviewed at the Office of the Independent Counsel, 1001 Pennsylvania Avenue, Washington, DC 20004. Present for the interview were Associate Independent Counsel (AIC) MICHAEL EMMICK, AIC KARIN IMMERGUT, AIC JULIE MYERS. MYERS departed after the below-listed chart was discussed. Present representing LEWINSKY were attorney PRESTON BURTON and law clerk MATTHEW UMERHOFF. LEWINSKY provided the following information, beginning at approximately 2:20 p.m.

[redacted].

LEWINSKY was shown a chart which documented her contacts and/or telephone calls with CLINTON. LEWINSKY suggested changes to the chart, as necessary, to more accurately reflect her contacts or telephone calls with CLINTON. (A draft of the chart, with the changes suggested by LEWINSKY handwritten by the writer, was placed in an FD-340, along with the original notes of this interview.) In addition to the changes made to the draft chart, LEWINSKY provided the following information:

August 9, 1995 was the first time she felt a "non-verbal" connection to CLINTON. In middle to late September of 1995, LEWINSKY's friend NATALIE UNGVARI was visiting LEWINSKY. LEWINSKY had what she described as an "accidental photo opportunity" with CLINTON.

LEWINSKY gave CLINTON a ZEGNA tie on November 20, 1995. LEWINSKY identified CLINTON as wearing that tie in three photographs she was shown by the OIC, taken on February 8, 1996, August 5, 1996 and January 23, 1997. LEWINSKY advised she gave CLINTON two ZEGNA ties, two HUGO BOSS ties, one CALVIN KLEIN tie and one FERAUD tie.

LEWINSKY advised she calls the second tie she gave CLINTON, a ZEGNA tie, his "birthday tie," as she gave it to CLINTON for his birthday. LEWINSKY advised it was the first tie, which was also a ZEGNA, she saw BAYANI NELVIS wearing at one of NELVIS's grand jury appearances. LEWINSKY said she may have seen

Investigation on 08/05/98 at Washington, DC File # 29D-OIC-LR-35063

CI [redacted]
by SA [redacted] Date dictated 08/05/98

OIC-302a (Rev. 8-19-94)

29D-OIC-LR-35063

Continuation of OIC-302 of MONICA S. LEWINSKY , On 08/05/98 , Page 2

a picture of NELVIS in the Washington Post or New York Times the day following NELVIS's grand jury appearance.

LEWINSKY advised she visited the White House on December 15, 1997 for the purpose of observing the swearing in of KATHY HAYCOCK.

LEWINSKY advised that at one time, CLINTON said that he would speak with BOB NASH about LEWINSKY's job opportunities at the White House. Later, CLINTON said he had spoken to NASH about LEWINSKY's job opportunities. Even later, CLINTON said that the "ball" had been passed to MARSHA SCOTT.

LEWINSKY advised she never called CLINTON directly, but rather always went through BETTY CURRIE.

LEWINSKY showed VERNON JORDAN a copy of her affidavit the same day she took JORDAN a tie and a pocket square. LEWINSKY assumes JORDAN told CLINTON about the affidavit.

As an intern, LEWINSKY worked in room 93 of the Old Executive Office Building (OEOB).

LEWINSKY may have called IRENE KASSORLA after July 4, 1997. LEWINSKY does not recall regular sessions with KASSORLA once LEWINSKY moved to Washington, D.C., but LEWINSKY did speak with her periodically.

FRANK CARTER told LEWINSKY to say if she was not sure about an answer to a question in a deposition, she should say so instead of answering yes or no.

LEWINSKY advised she had one conversation with WILLIAM GINSBURG prior to January 16, 1998. LEWINSKY called GINSBURG at home. LEWINSKY may have contacted GINSBURG after LINDA TRIPP had been subpoenaed in the JONES case. LEWINSKY called GINSBURG to ask him questions in a hypothetical fashion. LEWINSKY received GINSBURG's telephone number from LEWINSKY's step-mother.

LEWINSKY advised LINDA TRIPP of some of the things GINSBURG told LEWINSKY. GINSBURG said there was a difference between perjury in a criminal case and perjury in a civil matter. LEWINSKY also told TRIPP something about illegally obtained evidence. LEWINSKY was concerned about the JONES people breaking into LEWINSKY's apartment. LEWINSKY may have told TRIPP things LEWINSKY's attorneys did not tell her, but LEWINSKY may have attributed it to her attorneys.

OIC-302a (Rev. 8-19-94)

29D-OIC-LR-35063

Continuation of OIC-302 of MONICA S. LEWINSKY, On 08/05/98, Page 3

LEWINSKY advised she does not recall leaving BETTY CURRIE or CLINTON a message to the effect of "I hope you drop dead." LEWINSKY may have said she said that when speaking with TRIPP, but would not have used those actual words when speaking to CURRIE.

LEWINSKY is not sure when, but at some time, CURRIE left a message on LEWINSKY's answering machine to the effect "we have some unresolved issues. I know you do not want to talk to him or me." LEWINSKY advised this may have been after July 1, 1997, it may have been November 13, 1997 or it could have been November 22, 1997.

LEWINSKY advised she called TRIPP numerous times at work. LEWINSKY did not call TRIPP twenty to thirty times a day. LEWINSKY advised she may have called TRIPP multiple times a day, because of call backs due to interruption. LEWINSKY advised she and TRIPP discussed numerous topics, not all of which were related to CLINTON.

LEWINSKY first became suspicious of TRIPP after July 14, 1997. LEWINSKY advised she was generally accurate when speaking with TRIPP, up until the time LEWINSKY found out TRIPP was on the witness list in the JONES matter. However, when speaking with TRIPP, LEWINSKY did not make things up about her relationship with CLINTON.

LEWINSKY advised prior to about December 22, 1997, LEWINSKY was truthful with TRIPP. LEWINSKY advised she was not always truthful with TRIPP later, however, such as when LEWINSKY advised TRIPP that her mom, MARCIA LEWIS, thought TRIPP should feign a foot injury to avoid testifying.

LEWINSKY advised she originated the idea of using nicknames when communicating with CURRIE and TRIPP. LEWINSKY advised she did so to avoid anyone in the JONES team from identifying her. LEWINSKY's mother or aunt came up with the name "GWEN" for VERNON JORDAN to help them remember his name.

LEWINSKY does not know why CURRIE placed telephone calls for CLINTON. LEWINSKY does not believe CURRIE logged in all the gifts LEWINSKY gave CLINTON. LEWINSKY thought it would not be a good idea to have a trail of any references between LEWINSKY and CLINTON.

Referring to the December 17, 1997 telephone call from CLINTON, LEWINSKY is 99.99% sure CLINTON said LEWINSKY can always

OIC-302a (Rev. 8-19-94)

29D-OIC-LR-35063

Continuation of OIC-302 of MONICA S. LEWINSKY, On 08/05/98, Page 4

say she was there to see CURRIE.

LEWINSKY spoke to MIKE McCURRY on occasions related to official business at the Pentagon.

CURRIE drove LEWINSKY to LEWINSKY's apartment from the White House approximately five times.

LEWINSKY took her blue GAP dress to New York sometime around December 30, 1997. LEWINSKY rolled the dress in a ball, put it in plastic and threw it in a closet in her mother's apartment in New York. When LEWINSKY's mother moved out of her New York apartment at the end of May, LEWINSKY moved the dress back to LEWINSKY's Washington, D.C. apartment.

LEWINSKY described her relationship with MAUREEN LEWIS as "semi-friendly." LEWINSKY did not tell LEWIS she fantasized about a sexual relationship with CLINTON.

LEWINSKY does not recall ever dating DENNIS LYTTON, or providing any information to TREY RAGSDALE, PAMELA REVEL, or JAY LESNER.

The interview ended at approximately 6:10 p.m.

Tab 27

OIC-302 (Rev. 8-19-94)

OFFICE OF THE INDEPENDENT COUNSEL

Date of transcription 08/12/98

MONICA S. LEWINSKY was interviewed pursuant to an immunity agreement between the Office of Independent Counsel (OIC), LEWINSKY, and her attorneys. Present for the interview were Associate Independent Counsel (AIC) MICHAEL EMMICK, AIC KARIN IMMERGUT, and AIC MARY ANNE WIRTH. Representing LEWINSKY was Attorney PRESTON BURTON and Law Clerk ANIE WULKAN of the law offices of PLATO CACHERIS. The interview was conducted in Suite 490 North, 1001 Pennsylvania Avenue NW, Washington, D.C. commencing at 10:37 a.m. LEWINSKY provided the following information:

LEWINSKY never gave TRIPP permission to take notes about her relationship with the President.

The incident where the President mouthed, "I miss you," occurred at the end of May, 1996, at an event where there was a rope line. This did not occur in an October video as alleged by LUCIANNE GOLDBERG.

LEWINSKY read a transcript of an audio tape recording of a conversation between herself and LINDA TRIPP. The transcript concerned the discussion of two different versions of a cassette tape that LEWINSKY prepared for the President on November 20, 1997. The two versions are very similar, but may have been edited again after the discussion with TRIPP. The purpose of the tape was to try a new approach with the President, since he was not responding to LEWINSKY's notes about a transfer back to the White House. The tape was sent to the President on November 21, 1997, before his trip to Vancouver. The President never mentioned to LEWINSKY that he had listened to the tape, and it was not discussed when they next had a meeting on December 6, 1997. The tape never accomplished its desired result.

LEWINSKY visited the White House on December 28, 1997, after entering the southwest gate; proceeding to the West Wing basement lobby; climbing the stairs near the Cabinet Room; proceeding into BETTY CURRIE's office; proceeding into the Oval Office; and then into the back study. LEWINSKY may have seen LARRY COCKELL near the Oval Office. After their meeting was over, the President startled LEWINSKY by giving her a big hug. It is unknown whether anyone observed this. LEWINSKY departed

Investigation on 08/11/98 at WASHINGTON, D.C. File # 29D OIC LR 35063

by SA [redacted]
CI [redacted] Date dictated 08/12/98

OIC-302a (Rev. 8-19-94)

29D OIC LR 35063

Continuation of OIC-302 of MONICA S. LEWINSKY , On 08/11/98 , Page 2

the Oval Office to CURRIE's office, past the Rose Garden and through the Palm Room.

LEWINSKY gave four ties to BAYANI NELVIS.

LEWINSKY gave six ties to the President:

1. The "telecom" tie; a ZEGNA tie with criss crosses of red and gold on a blue background; purchased at NEIMAN MARCUS in MAZZA Gallerie in northwest Washington on the weekend before November 20, 1995; asked BETTY CURRIE on November 17, 1995 if gift okay; given to President through CURRIE on November 20, 1995; received call from the President that night; received a note from President stating tie was beautiful; observed President wearing on November 21, 1995 in Oval Office photo; on December 5th in the presence of LEWINSKY, President signed photo of himself wearing this tie in Oval Office; observed President wearing on February 8th for signing of telecommunications bill, 1996 after speaking with him on February 7 and 8, 1996; picture in Time Magazine on July 22, 1996, with President wearing this tie; observed President wearing August 5, 1996 after speaking with him on August 4th, 1996; observed President wearing on January 23, 1997, with MADELINE ALBRIGHT; saw President from afar on January 23, 1997 at the New York Ball at KENNEDY CENTER and he mouthed, "Hi, I like your dress"; observed President wearing March 14, 1997, which was the day the President was traveling to North Carolina and Florida (when President hurt his leg); observed BAYANI NELVIS wearing tie at Grand Jury appearance; on the day LEWINSKY hurt her hand she asked President where he had gotten the tie and he responded, "Some girl with style gave it to me."

2. BLOOMINGDALE'S tie; HUGO BOSS tie that is blue, white and black; bought at BLOOMINGDALE'S at TYSON'S CORNER, Virginia; presented directly to President on March 31, 1996; observed President wearing at CLINTON/GORE political rally in Virginia in late October 1996, at which time LEWINSKY yelled to President, "Hey handsome, I like your tie"; observed President wearing the tie the day that RON BROWN died; photo of President wearing tie in US News and World Report, dated May 13, 1996; observed President wearing the week of April 8 or April 15, 1996; followed the next day with the "telecom" tie.

3. Birthday tie; ZEGNA yellow tie bought at NEIMAN MARCUS in TYSON'S CORNER, Virginia; sent to President via FedEx to BETTY CURRIE in "care package" prior to August 19, 1996; photo in Washington Times on August 31, 1996, depicting President wearing

OIC-302a (Rev. 8-19-94)

29D OIC LR 35063

Continuation of OIC-302 of MONICA S. LEWINSKY , On 08/11/98 , Page 3

tie in Cape Girardeau, Missouri; worn in Florida September 5, 1996 during campaign, President telephoned LEWINSKY from Florida and said, "Good tie to wear in Florida;" observed President wearing last day of Democratic Convention in 1996; observed President wearing tie the day GEORGE TENET was nominated as CIA Director; wore tie December 3 or 4, 1996, after speaking with LEWINSKY on December 2, 1996; observed wearing tie August 16, 1997 after speaking with him on August 15, 1997; LEWINSKY believes this tie is the only one the President has worn "post-scandal".

4. Red tie; HUGO BOSS tie purchased at BOSS store on Wisconsin Avenue in Georgetown between March 3 and 9, 1997; sent via FedEx to BETTY CURRIE; tie had to be replaced on March 29, 1997, after President pointed out a large cut; worn day after Easter Egg Roll in 1997; worn to Governor's race rally in Virginia in the fall of 1997, the President said, "Did you see I wore your tie the other day?".

5. Olive tie; muted, olive colored, CALVIN KLEIN tie purchased at MARSHALL's in TYSON'S CORNER, Virginia; sent to President on October 21, 1997; never observed President wearing the tie.

6. FERAUD tie; purchased from small shop near HARROD's in London for 25 pounds; given to President on December 6, 1997; never observed President wearing. LEWINSKY identified this tie from a photograph as a tie turned over to OIC by the White House.

When LEWINSKY gave the President tie #6, she said, "Now you can wear all of my ties in one week." LEWINSKY also told the President that she liked it when he wore her ties because then she knew that she was "close to his heart." On occasion the President would ask LEWINSKY if she noticed that he had been wearing one of her ties at an event, and sometimes the President would assure LEWINSKY that he would wear one of her ties soon.

From a summary chart LEWINSKY confirmed details previously furnished concerning other gifts.

A gift not previously mentioned was an "IFOR" workout T-shirt purchased at the PX in Tuzla, Bosnia. LEWINSKY observed the President wearing the shirt on August 31, 1996.
LEWINSKY advised that she also dropped off some zinc lozenges and gingko biloba to BETTY CURRIE for the President during the middle of the day on November 13, 1997.

OIC-302a (Rev. 8-19-94)

29D OIC LR 35063

AIC WIRTH departed interview at 12:47pm.

LEWINSKY observed a grocery bag containing some of her gifts under the President's desk in the back study on July 4, 1997 and August 16, 1997. The bag contained the golf puzzle, the orange wooden "B", the BANANA REPUBLIC sport shirt, and an ugly cowboy shirt that LEWINSKY did not give the President. LEWINSKY asked the President whether he liked the gifts, since they were under his desk for a long period of time. The President responded that he did like them, but that he had not had time to take them upstairs.

On October 21, 1997, LEWINSKY gave a pair of sunglasses, the maker unknown, to the President. The sunglasses were purchased at the BARNEY's outlet in the POTOMAC MILLS MALL, in Stafford, Virginia. The gift was the result of a long running joke about the President wearing "dorky" sunglasses. The President wore a "dorky" pair at a Coast Guard event in Florida in November or December 1997. LEWINSKY first observed a photo of the President wearing the gift glasses on the cover of a magazine in January, 1998, after the "scandal" broke.

LEWINSKY described the President's bathroom in the rear study as being white or very light colored. The walls had framed black and white political cartoons of the President from the Arkansas Democrat Gazette, two towel bars, a corner shelf with toiletries and jars of vitamins or supplements given to the President by a Congressman, a telephone on the wall, a sink with mirror above it, and a toilet bowl.

JUDY BALKIN is a woman from New York in her 40s or 50s, whom LEWINSKY met at the Spa in Connecticut in June 1997. They have had dinner together in New York and have exchanged telephone calls and E-mail. BALKIN and MARCIA LEWIS have a mutual friend. LEWINSKY never spoke with BALKIN about her sexual relationship with the President, nor did she discuss the PAULA JONES lawsuit with her.

LINDA TRIPP was acquainted with BETTY CURRIE, in that they worked in the White House at the same time, and TRIPP sent a condolence card to CURRIE. LEWINSKY is unsure whether she ever discussed LINDA TRIPP with CURRIE. LEWINSKY would not have told CURRIE about a fight LEWINSKY had with TRIPP.

LEWINSKY began seeing Dr. KASSORLA when LEWINSKY had an unpleasant experience at Santa Monica City College. LEWINSKY did not like going to school there, but her father would not pay for

OIC-302a (Rev. 8-19-94)

29D OIC LR 35063

Continuation of OIC-302 of MONICA S. LEWINSKY , On 08/11/98 , Page 5

her to attend a more expensive college. LEWINSKY was not hospitalized, had no medication prescribed, and missed no classes as a result of this incident. LEWINSKY was not suicidal.

The names of several congressmen were provided to LEWINSKY. This was in regard to the congressman that spoke with the President on the telephone on November 17, 1997, during one of LEWINSKY's sessions with the President. LEWINSKY selected the name of Congressman H. L. "SONNY" CALLAHAN as the most likely caller to the President that night.

On either September 12 or 19, 1997, LEWINSKY went to the southwest gate in an attempt to see the President. LEWINSKY was crying and frustrated because MARSHA SCOTT had said that she had lost her detailee slot and it did not appear that LEWINSKY would be able to go back to work in the White House. LEWINSKY called BETTY CURRIE numerous times, but CURRIE said that the President was going to have dinner with CHELSEA. After about 45 minutes, CURRIE arranged to get LEWINSKY into the White House to visit CURRIE. CURRIE was sweet to LEWINSKY, but explained that sometimes neither the President nor CURRIE had direct control over jobs at the White House. CURRIE was traveling to Chicago the next day, but would try to set up a meeting for LEWINSKY and the President on Sunday when CURRIE returned. CURRIE's flight was late on Sunday and no meeting could be set up.

[redacted]. LEWINSKY has had multiple conversations with LINDA TRIPP concerning WILLEY. LEWINSKY believes that some of the conversations may have been recorded by TRIPP. TRIPP gave different stories of the WILLEY incident. The President advised LEWINSKY on July 4, 1997 that NANCY HERNREICH said that she had been called by WILLEY, who had received a call from MIKE ISIKOFF. The President did not elaborate. LEWINSKY knows of no efforts by anyone to influence or discourage KATHLEEN WILLEY from cooperating in the PAULA JONES deposition. LEWINSKY does not know of any relationship between NATHAN LANDOW and the President. LEWINSKY is unaware of any information that LANDOW attempted to influence WILLEY's deposition in the JONES case.

On June 14, 1996, LEWINSKY, her father BERNARD, her stepmother BARBARA, and her brother MICHAEL attended a radio address given by the President. During the address the President inadvertently used the term "seduced," which was embarrassing. After the address, LEWINSKY introduced each member of her family to the President and a family photograph was taken with the

OIC-302a (Rev. 8-19-94)

29D OIC LR 35063

Continuation of OIC-302 of MONICA S. LEWINSKY, On 08/11/98, Page 6

President. LEWINSKY's father later remarked that the President looked at him as if the President was sizing him up as a prospective father-in-law. BARBARA LEWINSKY said that she had noticed that the President kept looking at LEWINSKY. LEWINSKY laughed but made no comment.

LEWINSKY has not shared many details of the relationship with her father, but she did tell him about giving the President a tie; receiving a signed photograph; that she was moving to New York; and that VERNON JORDAN and BETTY CURRIE were assisting LEWINSKY in finding a job. When LEWINSKY's father was interviewed by BARBARA WALTERS, he made a comment that his daughter was wonderful and, "Why wouldn't they help her?" LEWINSKY's father told her not to quit her Pentagon job until she had another job lined up; LEWINSKY told him that she had to leave because her boss had hired someone else. LEWINSKY did not tell her father about the July 3, 1997 letter that she wrote to the President, in which she stated that she would tell her parents about her relationship with the President. LEWINSKY asked FRANK CARTER if her parents could be present during her deposition to try to deter the JONES attorneys from deposing her. CARTER advised LEWINSKY not to have her parents present.

The July 3, 1997 letter was handwritten on unlined, white paper, 8 1/2" by 11". LEWINSKY wrote that she was forced to try to get a job in the White House by herself without the President's assistance; mentioned the lack of help from MARSHA SCOTT; said that she may tell her parents about her relationship with the President; requested a United Nations job; and ended by comparing her mother, MARCIA LEWIS, with the President, in that they both faced difficult issues with their heads in the sand. LEWINSKY pleaded that she and the President could work their relationship out. LEWINSKY did not consider this letter a threat.

When the President answered interrogatories in the PAULA JONES case on December 23, 1997, he did not discuss his responses either before or after with LEWINSKY.

In March or April 1995, LEWINSKY forged a letter at LEWIS AND CLARK COLLEGE in Portland, Oregon. LEWINSKY used the name of a college employee named DAVID BLISS in writing a letter to ANDY BLEILER, stating that BLEILER had a job waiting for him at the college. The letter was not delivered, and was returned to BLISS, who discovered the scheme. The motivation for the letter was so that ANDY BLEILER could show his wife KATE the letter and come to Oregon in advance of KATE and the children.

OIC-302a (Rev. 8-19-94)

29D OIC LR 35063

Continuation of OIC-302 of MONICA S. LEWINSKY , On 08/11/98 , Page 7

This would make BLEILER available to continue their affair. In her apology to BLISS, LEWINSKY made up a story about using the letter to show that BLEILER had a job in Oregon, and that KATE could then obtain permission from the court to move the daughter of HARVEY LEHRER and KATE BLEILER from the state of California. This was merely a cover story for an illicit relationship.

While at LEWIS AND CLARK COLLEGE, LEWINSKY gave her father a false transcript to indicate better grades than she actually received.

LEWINSKY has never been arrested, but has received a few speeding tickets in Oregon. LEWINSKY has received many parking tickets, some of which she did not pay immediately. LEWINSKY has failed to return some rented videos and some library books.

LEWINSKY reported her credit problems when she filled out the questionnaire for her clearance at the White House. LEWINSKY had to pay off about $800 in bad debts before she could get her clearance. Unpaid Oregon telephone bills were paid off by MARCIA LEWIS.

On one occasion while at the Pentagon, LEWINSKY made a copy of an unfavorable memo from CLIFF BERNATH to KEN BACON discussing a pay grade increase for LEWINSKY. LEWINSKY took the memo from BACON's desk and copied it so that she could later read it and know how to make a better case for a grade increase. BERNATH had cautioned LEWINSKY about spending too much time on the telephone and about making personal long distance calls. On a trip to Asia, LEWINSKY had a disagreement with a military officer named JEFF GRADIK.

On November 15, 1997, LEWINSKY wore bikini thong panties to work and pulled up her jacket in back to display the tops to the President when he came to PANETTA's office. No one else in the room could have seen this; this was something that LEWINSKY learned to do when she was having an affair with ANDY BLEILER.

During the telephone conversation with the President on December 17, 1997, LEWINSKY and the President discussed the fact that she was moving to New York and maybe the PAULA JONES' lawyers would be unable to find her with a subpoena. LEWINSKY figured that if she was residing with her mom in New York there would be no way to find her, since nothing would be in her name. This was more in the manner of "shooting the breeze" with the

President than in making a plan.

In the meeting with the President on December 28, 1997, the move to New York was again discussed. LEWINSKY is now unsure who remarked that if she was in New York maybe they would not bother to bring her back for a deposition. LEWINSKY was reminded that her written proffer, previously submitted by NATE SPEIGHTS, has a statement indicating that the President was in favor of the New York move. LEWINSKY said that she has no specific memory of making that statement in the proffer. LEWINSKY said that discussion was not a strategy session, and that if she thought that she needed to get out of Washington quickly, she would have called VERNON JORDAN to make sure that something jobwise should happen immediately.

In regard to the box of gifts that LEWINSKY gave to BETTY CURRIE for safekeeping, LEWINSKY hoped to get the gifts back, but was not sure enough that they would be returned to put all of the gift items in the box. LEWINSKY had no specific thought, discussion, or plan to get the box back; however, LEWINSKY expected the box to be with CURRIE until the PAULA JONES case blew over.

In regard to the daily pages of the Filofax, LEWINSKY does not recall making any entries or notations about the President. LEWINSKY may have thrown the pages away, or they may have been taken in the consensual search of her apartment. The records are not embarrassing, nor are they well kept. However, LEWINSKY would consider it an invasion of privacy if she had to turn over the daily pages at this point.

In January and February 1996, LEWINSKY does not recall telling MAUREEN LEWIS, who worked for NANCY HERNREICH, any story about bringing pizza to the President when topless, or that she wanted to perform oral sex on the President. LEWINSKY did work late with LEWIS around the time that LEWINSKY began drafting the political letters. LEWINSKY would never tell LEWIS this, because LEWIS was too close to HERNREICH. LEWINSKY opined that HERNREICH may have told this to LEWIS based on rumors. LEWINSKY did talk to LEWIS about movies and other non personal things. LEWINSKY and LEWIS did not have a falling out. LEWIS attended LEWINSKY's birthday party at THE PALM RESTAURANT on July 23, 1996. LEWIS called LEWINSKY after the February 28, 1997 radio address and said that she had heard that LEWINSKY was moving out of the country. LEWINSKY probably told LEWIS of her affair with someone at the Pentagon during a telephone call after LEWINSKY left the White House. LEWINSKY never told LEWIS that she was attracted to

OIC-302a (Rev. 8-19-94)

29D OIC LR 35063

Continuation of OIC-302 of MONICA S. LEWINSKY, On 08/11/98, Page 9

NANCY HERNREICH, but she may have said that HERNREICH has maintained her sexuality, while most women at the White House have not. LEWINSKY did revere HERNREICH. LEWINSKY is not a lesbian or bisexual.

LEWINSKY describes the President as "a sweet little boy," affectionate, kind, warm, selfish, self-centered, self-righteous, incredible person who does what is in the best interest of the country.

[redacted] The President has a "Saturday night personality," where he gives in to his sexual desires and a "Sunday personality," where he is remorseful and goes to church. The President is a very sensual man, but has never discussed with LEWINSKY whether he has a sex problem.

The President has said such diverse things as, "My life is empty," and, "[redacted]."

In regard to his mother, VIRGINIA KELLY, the President said that she was "full of piss and vinegar," that he missed her, and that she was always with him. The President did not speak of her often.

The President felt awful and cried when the first soldier was killed in Bosnia and was very sad, lonely, and withdrawn when Admiral BOORDA committed suicide.

The President does not trust a lot of people.

The President can be humorous, i.e. when he imitated LEWINSKY's voice on her telephone recorder, and when he made the "good morning" remark while having phone sex with LEWINSKY.

LEWINSKY had a discussion with PAT GRIFFIN at his going away party where he said, "Be careful," and, "You're doing a good job there." LEWINSKY never had a one-on-one conversation with GRIFFIN at work and was never counseled by him at work.

Tab 28

OIC-302 (Rev. 8-19-94)

OFFICE OF THE INDEPENDENT COUNSEL

Date of transcription 08/14/98

MONICA S. LEWINSKY was interviewed under the terms of an immunity agreement between the Office of the Independent Counsel (OIC) and her. LEWINSKY was interviewed at the Office of the Independent Counsel, 1001 Pennsylvania Avenue, Washington, DC 20004. Present for the interview were Associate Independent Counsel (AIC) MICHAEL EMMICK, AIC KARIN IMMERGUT, and AIC CRAIG LERNER. Present representing LEWINSKY was her attorney, PRESTON BURTON. LEWINSKY provided the following information, beginning at approximately 11:13 a.m.

LEWINSKY advised that the first time she mentioned the United Nations to President WILLIAM JEFFERSON CLINTON as a possible employer was during her July 3, 1997 letter to CLINTON. LEWINSKY advised that KATHY HERTZ, a former Pentagon employee, had transferred to the United Nations and liked her job. LEWINSKY thought if the United Nations was a good place for HERTZ to work, it might be a good place for LEWINSKY. LEWINSKY advised that a job at the United Nations was her idea, not CLINTON's.

After raising the idea of the United Nations job on July 3, 1997, LEWINSKY did not pursue the United Nations job any further during the Summer of 1997. LEWINSKY advised she left the July 4, 1997 meeting with CLINTON with the understanding that CLINTON was going to bring her back to the White House.

LEWINSKY advised that she spoke with CLINTON on September 30, 1997. The subject of jobs could have come up during that conversation. CLINTON may have mentioned ERSKINE BOWLES being involved in finding LEWINSKY employment during this conversation.

LEWINSKY was shown a transcript of LRT-018. LEWINSKY is not sure this conversation took place on October 3, 1997, but it could have.

When LEWINSKY spoke with LINDA TRIPP on October 6, 1997, TRIPP mentioned that TRIPP's friend KATE, who worked at the National Security Council (NSC), had heard rumors that LEWINSKY would never get a job at the White House which required a blue pass. LEWINSKY was furious when she heard this and left work. At that time, LEWINSKY again thought about pursuing the United

Investigation on 08/13/98 at Washington, DC File # 29D-OIC-LR-35063

CI [redacted]
by SA [redacted] Date dictated 08/14/98

Nations as a potential employer. But, LEWINSKY was mostly resolved to look for a job in the private sector in New York.

LEWINSKY could have talked to TRIPP about the United Nations between July 3, 1997 and October 6, 1997, but LEWINSKY's recollection is that LEWINSKY only brought the United Nations back up after October 6, 1997.

As of October 6, 1997, LEWINSKY had only spoken to CLINTON about White House jobs. In one of her conversations with CURRIE in September, LEWINSKY mentioned a former intern who got a job working for PAUL BEGALA. CURRIE said CLINTON told her CURRIE could speak to JOHN PODESTA about finding LEWINSKY a job. From that day, until October 6, 1997, LEWINSKY did not hear from anyone at the White House about a job.

LEWINSKY referred to KATE's comments in a note to CLINTON, but she did not specifically mention KATE by name.

LEWINSKY and CURRIE got into a fight about CURRIE not speaking to CLINTON about a position for LEWINSKY in the White House. Shortly thereafter, on October 9, 1997, LEWINSKY and CLINTON spoke by telephone.

LEWINSKY assumes CLINTON called her from the White House Residence.

On October 10, 1997, LEWINSKY spoke with BETTY CURRIE, who said CLINTON was on the White House putting green with ERSKINE BOWLES. At that time, LEWINSKY thought CLINTON may be talking to BOWLES about a job for LEWINSKY.

LEWINSKY thinks CURRIE would do whatever CLINTON wanted her to do. LEWINSKY thinks that CLINTON could think that, by CURRIE speaking to PODESTA, it would be the same as CLINTON speaking to BOWLES.

LEWINSKY is not sure when VERNON JORDAN's name first came up in relation to LEWINSKY's job search. LEWINSKY recalls speaking to LINDA TRIPP and TRIPP said that JORDAN was on the Board of Directors of many companies. LEWINSKY advised she never spoke with CLINTON regarding MAX CHAPMAN or SUSAN THOMASES. LEWINSKY advised THOMASES was a "HILLARY [CLINTON] person," and it would not make sense for LEWINSKY to want THOMASES to find her a job.

During LEWINSKY's October 11, 1997 visit with CLINTON,

OIC-302a (Rev. 8-19-94)

29D-OIC-LR-35063

Continuation of OIC-302 of MONICA S. LEWINSKY , On 08/13/98 , Page 3

LEWINSKY thinks she mentioned needing a good reference from someone in the White House, such as JOHN HILLEY. CLINTON said he would take care of it.

LEWINSKY advised that CLINTON asked her to write a list of potential employers, or jobs she was interested in, and to give it to him. On October 16, 1997, LEWINSKY sent CLINTON the list, which she refers to as a "wish list." On the "wish list," LEWINSKY wrote that she did not want a job at the United Nations.

At some point, LEWINSKY gave CLINTON a "deadline" as to when she needed a job. LEWINSKY told CLINTON she had to be out of her apartment by the end of October, 1997. LEWINSKY advised she did this to get CLINTON moving and into finding her a job.

When BILL RICHARDSON called LEWINSKY on October 21, 1997, LEWINSKY was initially surprised. After the call, LEWINSKY was upset because LEWINSKY did not want to work at the United Nations, no one had called her to tell her RICHARDSON would be calling, and she did not want to get stuck working there with no other opportunities. LEWINSKY was aware that it was RICHARDSON she was speaking with because a secretary called and said "hold for Ambassador RICHARDSON."

LEWINSKY was shown a transcript of LRT 002, pages 10-12. In response to the transcript excerpt, LEWINSKY advised she did not think it would be a good idea for someone from within the White House to get her a job in the private sector, due to appearances. LEWINSKY advised she was always concerned about the appearance of things. LEWINSKY did not talk to CURRIE about CURRIE helping LEWINSKY versus CLINTON helping LEWINSKY find a job. LEWINSKY stated that it was understood that it would look better for CURRIE to do the "leg work" to find LEWINSKY a job.

LEWINSKY recalls buying a card regarding the "emergency insanity system," but she does not recall whether she sent it to CLINTON.

LEWINSKY kept track of the number of days remaining until the election in 1996. LEWINSKY used a printout of a computer calendar and filled in the days by hand.

LEWINSKY was shown a transcript of LRT 013, pages 17-18. After reviewing the transcript, LEWINSKY advised she had been concerned CLINTON would pressure her to accept the job at the United Nations, because it would be easier to find a government employee a job at another government agency than it would be to find them a job in the private sector. LEWINSKY feared the White House would railroad her into taking the job at the United Nations.

LEWINSKY felt CLINTON owed her a job for several reasons. First, LEWINSKY's relationship with CLINTON was the reason she was transferred from the White House. Second, CLINTON had promised LEWINSKY a job back at the White House. Third, CLINTON had not procured her a job at the White House. Fourth, LEWINSKY left the White House "quietly," without mentioning her relationship with CLINTON to anyone.

LEWINSKY was shown a copy of LRT 015, pages 31-38. LEWINSKY recalls CLINTON calling on October 23, 1997. LEWINSKY probably mentioned that RICHARDSON had called. LEWINSKY advised that during her conversations with TRIPP, LEWINSKY gave LEWINSKY's interpretation of what CLINTON said more so than exact quotes of what he said.

LEWINSKY recalled that CLINTON, as to the job at the United Nations, never insisted or pressured her to take the job. LEWINSKY recalled CLINTON mentioning LEWINSKY having options, with the United Nations being one option, in relation to employment opportunities. LEWINSKY was aware CLINTON had a good relationship with RICHARDSON.

LEWINSKY was concerned her future employer may be concerned about rumors about LEWINSKY being a "stalker." At some point, LEWINSKY believes was during their October 30, 1997 conversation, CLINTON gave LEWINSKY a few "pointers" on what to say to RICHARDSON during her interview. LEWINSKY probably mentioned to CLINTON her fear of being stuck at the United Nations. During this telephone call, LEWINSKY may have mentioned the antique paperweight she purchased for CLINTON.

LEWINSKY told her father about RICHARDSON's call and he was impressed.

LEWINSKY felt it was inappropriate to conduct an interview in RICHARDSON's hotel room. LEWINSKY does not recall telling CURRIE that, though LEWINSKY may have. LEWINSKY may have told CURRIE that LEWINSKY was unversed in United Nations affairs and wanted CLINTON to call her before her interview.

LEWINSKY was shown a transcript of LRT 011, page 61.

LEWINSKY was shown a draft of a November 2, 1997 letter

OIC-302a (Rev. 8-19-94)

29D-OIC-LR-35063

Continuation of OIC-302 of MONICA S. LEWINSKY , On 08/13/98 , Page 5

to CURRIE regarding Ambassador RICHARDSON. LEWINSKY believes she sent CURRIE a different version of this note. LEWINSKY thinks the note she sent had to do with MARCIA LEWIS's book, The Three Tenors. LEWINSKY recalls sending the book to CURRIE to give to CLINTON. LEWINSKY put yellow post-it notes on the pages referring to PLACIDO DOMINGO's charity work and on the books "raciest" page, which, in LEWINSKY's opinion, was not very racy. LEWINSKY advised she was trying to assure CLINTON that the book was not a "kiss and tell."

LEWINSKY does not know whether CLINTON ever received the book.

LEWINSKY is sure she told CURRIE about getting offered the position at the United Nations and that she did not want the job. LEWINSKY believes she also told CLINTON that the United Nations offered her a job.

LEWINSKY was shown a transcript of LRT 016, page 110.

LEWINSKY only recalls speaking to RICHARDSON twice by telephone; once to arrange the interview and once when RICHARDSON extended the job offer to LEWINSKY.

LEWINSKY recalls telling MONA SUTPHEN, RICHARDSON's assistant, that she wanted to find a job in the private sector. LEWINSKY advised that salary was never mentioned in relation to the position at the United Nations.

LEWINSKY's impression is that the position she was offered was open prior to her being considered for it and it was not that big a deal for it to be vacant for so long. LEWINSKY recalls some discussion with the individuals from the United Nations about the differences between a contracting position and a political appointment.

On November 10, 1997, LEWINSKY sent CLINTON a note and mentioned wanting to see him and mentioned the paperweight she wanted to give him. LEWINSKY has no recollection of sending the note, but if sending it is mentioned in a conversation she had with TRIPP, then she sent it.

LEWINSKY was mad that CLINTON did not see her on Veteran's Day, 1997, because she felt he would have been able to. LEWINSKY advised that holidays are like weekends at the White House in that fewer people are around than on work days. In addition, HILLARY CLINTON was out of town on Veteran's Day, 1997.

OIC-302a (Rev. 8-19-94)

29D-OIC-LR-35063

Continuation of OIC-302 of MONICA S. LEWINSKY, On 08/13/98, Page 6

LEWINSKY was shown a transcript of LRT 026, pages 27-28.

LEWINSKY advised CLINTON called her in the middle of the night on November 12, 1997. LEWINSKY recalls CLINTON mentioning NANCY HERNREICH testifying on Capitol Hill the next day. CLINTON mentioned this to let LEWINSKY know she could see him then. CLINTON told LEWINSKY to call CURRIE in the morning to arrange the meeting. CLINTON mentioned the fact that he liked zinc lozenges and currently did not have any.

On November 13, 1997, LEWINSKY called CURRIE in the morning and CURRIE advised HERNREICH had already left and CLINTON was in the East Wing. LEWINSKY continued to call CURRIE who said she kept missing CLINTON. Later in the day, LEWINSKY called CURRIE who advised CLINTON had left the White House to play golf.

LEWINSKY got upset and told CURRIE she would come to the White House to give CURRIE CLINTON's ginkgo stuff, his zinc lozenges and CURRIE's birthday present. CURRIE told LEWINSKY to come to the Southwest gate and wait in CURRIE's car. LEWINSKY advised it was raining that day.

When LEWINSKY got to CURRIE's car, the door was locked. LEWINSKY waited in the rain for awhile before CURRIE came out to get her. LEWINSKY advised she and CURRIE made a "bee-line" to the Oval Office study, to avoid seeing any White House employees.

LEWINSKY advised she waited alone in the study for one half hour before CLINTON came back there. LEWINSKY gave CLINTON the paper weight. CLINTON said he liked the paperweight. LEWINSKY advised the meeting lasted only a few minutes. CURRIE took LEWINSKY home that evening.

[At this point during the interview, LEWINSKY asked to speak with AIC IMMERGUT, outside the presence of male investigators/attorneys. The contents of that discussion are documented in a memorandum.]

LEWINSKY had mixed emotions about this visit. On one hand, LEWINSKY thought CLINTON looked very cute. On the other hand, LEWINSKY was sad the meeting did not last any longer than it did. LEWINSKY advised it felt weird to wait in the study that long. LEWINSKY advised CLINTON had some gifts she had given him in his study. LEWINSKY did not complain to CURRIE after this visit with CLINTON because she at least got to see him.

OIC-302a (Rev. 8-19-94)

29D-OIC-LR-35063

Continuation of OIC-302 of MONICA S. LEWINSKY , On 08/13/98 , Page 7

LEWINSKY advised she thinks she told TRIPP that she gave the gifts she received from CLINTON to LEWINSKY's mother. LEWINSKY told TRIPP she told her mother to get rid of the gifts or put them away. LEWINSKY does not recall telling TRIPP about speaking to CLINTON about getting rid of the gifts.

During their December 28, 1997 meeting, CLINTON did not specifically mention which gifts to get rid of. LEWINSKY was concerned about the hat pin and the book, The Leaves of Grass, the Black Dog dress, and the Black Dog t-shirt with the Presidential Seal on it and the broach. LEWINSKY remembers telling CLINTON she was concerned because the subpoena specifically mentioned the hatpin.

LEWINSKY might have told TRIPP she was concerned about the hatpin, The Leaves of Grass, the Black Dog dress, the Black Dog t-shirt with the Presidential seal. The gifts became a topic of conversation with TRIPP after LEWINSKY was subpoenaed.

LEWINSKY advised she does not have a clear memory of how she determined what gifts to give CURRIE, what gifts to give FRANK CARTER and what gifts to keep. LEWINSKY advised the pin with the skyline of New York may have made it into the box she gave CURRIE because jewelry was mentioned expressly in her subpoena.

LEWINSKY does not recall CLINTON mentioning the recently found ROSE LAW FIRM billing records during her January 7, 1996 visit with him. CLINTON did not mention Whitewater to LEWINSKY.

LEWINSKY used a calling card when she called CURRIE from the Wilshire Boulevard COURTYARD by MARRIOTT.

On July 14, 1997, CLINTON told LEWINSKY he trusted her and he trusted her judgement when it came to LEWINSKY dealing with LINDA TRIPP. LEWINSKY told CLINTON that TRIPP was a big supporter of his.

At her December 31, 1997 meeting with VERNON JORDAN, LEWINSKY brought up TRIPP's name to lay the groundwork with JORDAN so that CLINTON and his team were at least aware of TRIPP. LEWINSKY told JORDAN she used to trust TRIPP, but did not anymore. LEWINSKY may have mentioned TRIPP in relation to KATHLEEN WILLEY. LEWINSKY does not recall JORDAN indicating he was familiar with TRIPP's name.

OIC-302a (Rev. 8-19-94)

29D-OIC-LR-35063

Continuation of OIC-302 of MONICA S. LEWINSKY, On 08/13/98, Page 8

LEWINSKY did not discuss the details of the JONES case that did not pertain to LEWINSKY with CLINTON, except on January 17, 1997, when LEWINSKY mentioned the possibility of CLINTON settling the case. CLINTON said JONES wanted too much money.

When LEWINSKY and TRIPP ate at the CALIFORNIA PIZZA KITCHEN on October 9, 1997, LEWINSKY probably paid for the meal with cash.

LEWINSKY advised she had SCI clearance at the Pentagon, which is higher than the "secret" clearance she held at the White House. LEWINSKY advised she did not recall an additional background investigation being conducted on her in conjunction with her transfer to the Pentagon.

LEWINSKY described the notebook she had that referenced her relationship with CLINTON as a six inch by nine inch spiral notebook. LEWINSKY advised it was in her apartment on January 22, 1998, but it was not seized as evidence. LEWINSKY recalls putting the notebook in an envelope she intended to give to NATE SPEIGHTS. LEWINSKY may have given the notebook to SPEIGHTS or WILLIAM GINSBURG.

LEWINSKY advised the notebook is not dated and the writing was done for therapeutic purposes. LEWINSKY wrote in the notebook approximately six times, beginning soon after November 15, 1995 and ending sometime prior to April 7, 1996. LEWINSKY advised she cannot find the notebook, but will continue to look for it.

LEWINSKY is not sending CLINTON any messages by wearing her straw hat.

LEWINSKY advised she is not a part of a joint defense agreement.

Sometime in the Spring of 1998, LEWINSKY told GINSBURG, who at one time represented her, to tell DAVID KENDALL, CLINTON's attorney, that BAYANI NELVIS was wearing one of the ties LEWINSKY had given CLINTON. This was on a day NELVIS testified at the grand jury. NATE SPEIGHTS said KENDALL told GINSBURG and SPEIGHTS he thought he had three or four of them and was looking for the rest.

OIC-302a (Rev. 8-19-94)

29D-OIC-LR-35063

Continuation of OIC-302 of MONICA S. LEWINSKY , On 08/13/98 , Page 9

The interview ended at approximately 3:30 p.m.

Tab 29

OIC-302 (Rev. 8-19-94)

OFFICE OF THE INDEPENDENT COUNSEL

Date of transcription 08/19/98

MONICA S. LEWINSKY was interviewed pursuant to an immunity agreement between the Office of the Independent Counsel (OIC), LEWINSKY, and her attorneys. Present for the interview were Associate Independent Counsel (AIC) MICHAEL EMMICK, AIC KARIN IMMERGUT, and AIC MARY ANNE WIRTH. Representing LEWINSKY was attorney PRESTON BURTON of the law offices of PLATO CACHERIS. The interview was conducted in Suite 490, 1001 Pennsylvania Avenue NW, Washington, D.C. beginning at 11:03 a.m. LEWINSKY provided the following information:

LEWINSKY indicated that she is taking two anti-depressants, Zoloft and Serzone.

LEWINSKY, who was 24 years of age when approached by the OIC on January 16, 1998, was not prepared to wear a wire and/or record telephone conversations. The request to do so was a lot to handle that day and LEWINSKY relied on her advisors, who included her parents and BILL GINSBERG. LEWINSKY tried to protect the President at first but no longer feels this is the thing to do. The proffer that LEWINSKY prepared in late January, 1998 is correct. LEWINSKY is now disappointed and angry with the President for several reasons:

1. The President denied that he had sexual relations with "that woman."

2. The President, in his speech to the nation on August 17, 1998, did not recognize the suffering this has caused LEWINSKY.

3. The President lied.

4. The President's staff has said unkind things about LEWINSKY, including labelling her as "the stalker."

LEWINSKY does not recall the book Geek Love and did not recognize a copy of it.

The President was conscious of the labels on his ties and liked the ERMENEGILDO ZEGNA and HUGO BOSS ties that she gave him. With the exception of the LEWINSKY gift ties, the President did not talk about ties very much. The President certainly knew

---

Investigation on 08/19/98 at WASHINGTON, D.C. File # 29D OIC LR 35063

by SA [redacted]
CI [redacted] Date dictated 08/19/98

OIC-302a (Rev. 8-19-94)

29D OIC LR 35063

Continuation of OIC-302 of MONICA S. LEWINSKY , On 08/19/98 , Page 2

that LEWINSKY had given him the HUGO BOSS red tie with small black squares. The President must have recalled that LEWINSKY gave him the "birthday tie," a yellow ZEGNA, since he wrote her a thank you note and wore it weekly during the 1996 Presidential campaign.

On April 7, 1996, LEWINSKY advised the President by telephone that she had been transferred to the Pentagon. Sometime during the next week, the President told LEWINSKY that EVELYN LIEBERMAN had fired her because LEWINSKY and the President were paying too much attention to each other. The President said that LIEBERMAN did not care what the President did after the election.

On August 4, 1996, between 12:00 and 12:30 p.m., LEWINSKY caused herself to be walking on 16th Street north of the White House. The President had not called LEWINSKY in a little while and she wanted him to see her as a reminder that they had not seen each other in awhile. LEWINSKY knew that the President regularly returned from church each Sunday at about that time and also knew that he sat on the right hand side of the car. The President saw LEWINSKY, but probably thought that it was accidental. The President called her as a result of this "chance" sighting.

On a Sunday in September 1996, LEWINSKY was walking in the same area with her aunt, DEBRA FINERMAN, and she presumes that she was sighted by the President, but she did not see him. The President either called her or left a message that he had seen her.

The President advised LEWINSKY that when he was on vacation at Martha's Vineyard in August 1997, representatives of the BLACK DOG store sent over to his vacation compound a number of BLACK DOG items. [redacted] and [redacted] took the items they liked and the President took the leftover items to use as gifts. The President knew that LEWINSKY liked these items and gave the bag to her at Christmas time. He gave the remaining BLACK DOG items to BETTY CURRIE. LEWINSKY had asked the President to buy her a BLACK DOG T-shirt on one occasion.

LEWINSKY believes that many of the gifts that the President gave LEWINSKY were gifts that he had received, i.e., the New York skyline pin and the Rockettes blanket. The President said that he had obtained the hat pin in Santa Fe, the bear in Vancouver, and the sunglasses in Union Station while shopping with [redacted].

OIC-302a (Rev. 8-19-94)

29D OIC LR 35063

Continuation of OIC-302 of MONICA S. LEWINSKY , On 08/19/98 , Page 3

LEWINSKY did not discuss the "talking points" with anyone but LINDA TRIPP.

LEWINSKY may have mentioned to her mother and aunt that she had tried to convince LINDA TRIPP to file an affidavit to avoid TRIPP testifying about her knowledge of LEWINSKY's relationship with the President. This was to protect LEWINSKY's reputation and TRIPP's job. LEWINSKY may have alluded to a possible betrayal by an unidentified friend when she met with the Christian Scientist counselor on Fifth Avenue in New York. LEWINSKY may have mentioned LINDA TRIPP to her friends, NEYSA ERBLAND and ASHLEY RAINES, but would not have provided any detail about TRIPP to them.

LINDA TRIPP said that MICHAEL ISIKOFF had misquoted her in the Newsweek article that was issued in the summer of 1997. KEN BACON asked TRIPP to let him know if she was going public with any more information; BACON had gathered a lot of information about TRIPP from the Internet and was concerned. LEWINSKY was worried that BACON and BERNATH were going to fire TRIPP. BERNATH was irritated that TRIPP had not told any of her superiors about her previous testimony in the Whitewater matter. TRIPP said if that happened she would write a "tell all" book. This would expose LEWINSKY.

LEWINSKY said there are two possibilities concerning KATHLEEN WILLEY:

1. The President could be telling the truth.

2. Maybe something consensual happened since TRIPP advised that WILLEY had been sending notes to the President for a long time.

LEWINSKY told TRIPP that the President told LEWINSKY that WILLEY had called HERNREICH about ISIKOFF's call to WILLEY. While LEWINSKY was in Madrid, TRIPP advised her telephonically that there was something about WILLEY in the DRUDGE Report. LEWINSKY asked TRIPP if she had told ISIKOFF about the WILLEY call to HERNREICH. TRIPP was evasive and did not admit that she had. LEWINSKY did not confront TRIPP about this disclosure, because LEWINSKY was wary of TRIPP, so she did not tell TRIPP until much later that she had seen the President on July 14, 1997.

The President once said, "I know you think I have 100 other girlfriends but I don't." This was the only time that he ever referred to LEWINSKY as a girlfriend.

LEWINSKY never had an open discussion with the President about whether oral sex is "sex." However, after having a relationship with him, LEWINSKY deduced that the President, in his mind, apparently does not consider oral sex to be sex. Sex to him must mean intercourse. LEWINSKY said that her use of the term "having sex" means having intercourse, although oral sex would constitute an "affair." LEWINSKY believed that the President's refusal to allow her to bring him to "completion" was his way of "drawing a line."

At some point, LEWINSKY asked the President if he wanted to see her affidavit. The President put her off by saying that he had seen a lot of affidavits.

On December 17, 1997, the President said that other women on the PAULA JONES witness list were girlfriends from Arkansas from years ago. The President never discussed DOLLY KYLE BROWNING or others on the list with LEWINSKY. LEWINSKY later heard that [redacted] may have been a former girlfriend in Arkansas. [redacted] always had an icy stare for LEWINSKY. Neither [redacted] nor [redacted] concealed their daggers well. LEWINSKY made an off-handed comment to the President about GENNIFER FLOWERS and he laughed.

The book given to the President on December 6, 1997 was the THEODORE ROOSEVELT antique book. The antique book purchased after December 28, 1997 was entitled, "Presidents of the United States." This book was purchased at the shop next to the Christian Scientist store in Georgetown and was given to BETTY CURRIE to give to the President on January 4, 1998.

The President never told LEWINSKY to turn over to FRANK CARTER all of the gifts that he had given her.

LEWINSKY never discussed VERNON JORDAN with the President until she began looking for a job in New York in October 1997. LEWINSKY figured that asking JORDAN for help was one more "iron in the fire" in trying to get a New York job.

LEWINSKY discussed the settling of the PAULA JONES case with LINDA TRIPP on December 8, 1997, and with the President on December 17, 1998. During the conversation on December 17th, LEWINSKY is 99% sure that the President told her that if she had to testify she should say that LEWINSKY was at the Oval Office to visit BETTY CURRIE or to bring papers to the President. LEWINSKY

OIC-302a (Rev. 8-19-94)

29D OIC LR 35063

Continuation of OIC-302 of MONICA S. LEWINSKY , On 08/19/98 , Page 5

is 100% sure that the President suggested that she might want to sign an affidavit to avoid testifying.

Once when BETTY CURRIE was gone, LEWINSKY asked the President why he could not clear her into the White House. The President responded that he could not because they (the Secret Service) make a list of everyone who comes to see him.

At 12:38 p.m., AIC MARY ANNE WIRTH entered and asked LEWINSKY whether she had ever been taken by another woman to the Oval Office and let in to see the President. LEWINSKY could only recall that she could have been escorted as an intern by TRACY BECKETT to take PANETTA's mail to the Oval Office, or possibly could have gone with KARIN ABRAMSON to deliver the poem that LEWINSKY wrote to the President on behalf of the interns. LEWINSKY was never escorted into the Oval Office and left with the President by any woman other than BETTY CURRIE. AIC WIRTH exited at 12:42 p.m.

The interview ended at approximately 12:50 p.m.

Tab 30

OIC-302 (Rev. 8-19-94)

OFFICE OF THE INDEPENDENT COUNSEL

Date of transcription 08/24/98

MONICA S. LEWINSKY was interviewed under the terms of an immunity agreement between the Office of the Independent Counsel (OIC) and her. LEWINSKY was interviewed at the Office of the Independent Counsel, 1001 Pennsylvania Avenue, Washington, D.C. 20004. Present for the interview were Associate Independent Counsel (AIC) MICHAEL EMMICK and AIC KARIN IMMERGUT. AIC ANDY LEIPOLD entered the interview room at approximately 1:07 p.m. and departed at approximately 2:00 p.m. AIC STEPHEN BATES entered the interview room at approximately 2:00 p.m. and departed at approximately 2:36 p.m. Present representing LEWINSKY was her attorney, PRESTON BURTON. LEWINSKY provided the following information, beginning at approximately 12:15 p.m.

LEWINSKY clarified the following points:

The United States Secret Service (USSS) never brought President WILLIAM JEFFERSON CLINTON to LEWINSKY's apartment. LEWINSKY may have mentioned to KATHY ESTEP that the USSS was standing outside of her apartment, but they were there because Republican Presidential nominee BOB DOLE lived right next door to LEWINSKY at the Watergate Apartments. LEWINSKY certainly wanted CLINTON to come to her apartment, but he never did.

CLINTON did telephone LEWINSKY at the Watergate Apartments, sometimes as late as two in the morning.

LEWINSKY definitely went to the White House on January 7, 1996. LEWINSKY entered the White House compound using her blue pass.

LEWINSKY recalls seeing GEORGE STEPHANOPOULOS at STARBUCKS on a few occasions. LEWINSKY recalls one occasion that was either immediately before or immediately after the 1996 Presidential election. LEWINSKY recalls mentioning something about Hawaii to STEPHANOPOULOS. LEWINSKY recalls that STEPHANOPOULOS recognized her as someone who worked at the Pentagon. LEWINSKY thought it was strange that STEPHANOPOULOS would know who she was. LEWINSKY advised that STEPHANOPOULOS probably recognized her face from when she worked at the White House, but she did not know how he knew where she currently worked.

Investigation on 08/24/98 Washington, DC File # 29D-OIC-LR-35063

by CI [redacted]
SA [redacted] Date dictated 08/24/98

OIC-302a (Rev. 8-19-94)

29D-OIC-LR-35063

Continuation of OIC-302 of MONICA S. LEWINSKY , On 08/24/98 , Page 2

Because STEPHANOPOULOS had mentioned where LEWINSKY worked, LEWINSKY thought maybe STEPHANOPOULOS knew about her relationship with CLINTON. LEWINSKY therefore approached STEPHANOPOULOS and she may have mentioned something about CLINTON. LEWINSKY does not recall mentioning the term "leading on," but she may have said that she read how the President follows through on things. LEWINSKY was trying to see if STEPHANOPOULOS knew about the relationship. In addition, she was very anxious about the fact that CLINTON had not called her regularly. LEWINSKY did not tell STEPHANOPOULOS about her relationship with CLINTON.

LEWINSKY advised that, of all the people who worked at the White House, STEPHANOPOULOS knowing about her relationship with CLINTON would have concerned her the least, because of STEPHANOPOULOS's age and because of his relationship with CLINTON. LEWINSKY advised she always associated STEPHANOPOULOS with the relationship with CLINTON because it began in STEPHANOPOULOS's office.

LEWINSKY advised that when preparing her written proffer, she wrote one draft, which is in the possession of either NATE SPEIGHTS or her current attorneys. LEWINSKY advised the original draft was not much different than the final version, but it was messier and a lot less organized. LEWINSKY wrote the draft while sitting in a conference room at the COSMOS CLUB. LEWINSKY believes she started working on the draft at approximately 11:00 a.m. and finished at approximately 3:30 p.m.

LEWINSKY advised she took breaks while preparing the proffer. LEWINSKY advised she put into words what happened in her relationship with CLINTON, after her attorneys had received a four point memorandum from the OIC. LEWINSKY recalls being concerned about simply adopting the information in the OIC's memorandum, because she wanted to be as accurate as possible. LEWINSKY, therefore, spent time writing the proffer and tried to be very careful in doing so. LEWINSKY advised she wanted to give a general idea of what she would eventually testify to, but she did not go into all the details.

LEWINSKY advised that at that point, she was not clear about why the OIC was investigating this matter. LEWINSKY advised she felt the OIC was just "out to get" CLINTON and VERNON JORDAN, so LEWINSKY was very careful to make sure she was clear when she wrote things in the proffer.

OIC-302a (Rev. 8-19-94)

29D-OIC-LR-35063

Continuation of OIC-302 of MONICA S. LEWINSKY , On 08/24/98 , Page 3

LEWINSKY did not expect the proffer to become an official document. LEWINSKY advised that on page 8 of the proffer, she tried to document the gist of what she told JORDAN. LEWINSKY advised that anything in quotes attributed to JORDAN is exactly what JORDAN said.

Paragraph 6 on page 6 of the proffer is LEWINSKY's best recollection of what happened. LEWINSKY advised that the proffer is an accurate document in which she was trying to tell the truth without implicating anyone unjustly. LEWINSKY recalls discussing the hatpin with CLINTON. LEWINSKY recalls bringing the subject up and CLINTON asking if LEWINSKY had told anyone about the hatpin. LEWINSKY told CLINTON she had not, even though she had. LEWINSKY told CLINTON that maybe someone saw her looking at it as she left the Oval Office after he gave it to her. CLINTON said that he was also concerned about the hatpin.

LEWINSKY assumes CLINTON told CURRIE to call LEWINSKY about picking up the gifts because she has no idea how CURRIE would know to do it.

LEWINSKY advised that she worked weekends as an intern only during the government shutdown. LEWINSKY advised she worked a lot of weekends while she worked at the Office of Legislative Affairs (OLA), including most every weekend CLINTON was in town. LEWINSKY also worked weekends when she did not intend on seeing CLINTON, to do work in the OLA.

LEWINSKY advised that she had an "SCI" (Specialized Compartmented Information) clearance, while working at the Pentagon. LEWINSKY had to attend a briefing and re-sign her White House clearance form to get this clearance.

During her December 17, 1997 telephone conversation with CLINTON, CLINTON told LEWINSKY she might not necessarily receive a subpoena. CLINTON told LEWINSKY she was on the witness list in the JONES case and LEWINSKY understood what that meant. LEWINSKY asked CLINTON if any of the other women on the witness list worked at the White House and CLINTON said no, the women on the witness list were all from Arkansas. CLINTON may have said MARSHA SCOTT was on the list.

CLINTON did not go into any detail explaining the nature of a subpoena and seemed to assume LEWINSKY knew what a subpoena was. LEWINSKY is not sure if she knew what one was, but she knows she had never seen one before. LEWINSKY does not recall talking about gifts during this telephone conversation.

OIC-302a (Rev. 8-19-94)

29D-OIC-LR-35063

Continuation of OIC-302 of MONICA S. LEWINSKY , On 08/24/98 , Page 4

LEWINSKY and CLINTON did not discuss gifts called for by the subpoena until December 28, 1997.

LEWINSKY is not sure if CLINTON was in the White House Residence or in the Oval Office during this conversation. LEWINSKY advised that HILLARY CLINTON was in town that day. CLINTON told LEWINSKY to call BETTY CURRIE if LEWINSKY received a subpoena and he would figure out what to do about it. LEWINSKY does not recall CLINTON saying she should get a lawyer, because if he did, she would have started thinking about getting one then. LEWINSKY advised CLINTON may have said during this conversation that every woman he had ever spoken to was going to be on the witness list. LEWINSKY believes that he said this during one of their telephone conversations.

On December 22, 1998, LEWINSKY took the subpoena to the office of FRANK CARTER, who may have made a copy of LEWINSKY's subpoena, but LEWINSKY is sure she kept a copy or the original one for herself. LEWINSKY did not bring the subpoena with her on December 28, 1997, when she visited CLINTON. LEWINSKY was concerned about being on the witness list and explained this concern to CLINTON. LEWINSKY asked CLINTON if he knew how she got on the witness list. CLINTON said he did not know. LEWINSKY recalls talking about the gifts with CLINTON on that occasion.

LEWINSKY advised that CLINTON was sitting in the rocking chair in the Study. LEWINSKY asked CLINTON what she should do with the gifts CLINTON had given her and he either did not respond or responded "I don't know." LEWINSKY is not sure exactly what was said, but she is certain that whatever CLINTON said, she did not have a clear image in her mind of what to do next.

LEWINSKY advised that she is certain CLINTON did not say that she had to tell the truth about their relationship if she was deposed. LEWINSKY advised she would have remembered it if he had.

LEWINSKY advised that JORDAN was the first person she contacted after being served her subpoena on December 19, 1997. LEWINSKY then may have notified her mother and then LINDA TRIPP. LEWINSKY intentionally did not tell her friends about the subpoena. LEWINSKY is not certain she told CURRIE about the subpoena. LEWINSKY is not certain CURRIE knew about the subpoena as of December 28, 1997. LEWINSKY advised that if CURRIE knew as of that date, she probably would have been more explicit in her late afternoon telephone conversation that day with LEWINSKY.

OIC-302a (Rev. 8-19-94)

29D-OIC-LR-35063

Continuation of OIC-302 of MONICA S. LEWINSKY . On 08/24/98 . Page 5

LEWINSKY called CURRIE on January 5, 1998, and told her that she needed to speak with CLINTON before she signed something. LEWINSKY hoped the message would persuade CLINTON to call her back. When CLINTON called her that evening, LEWINSKY told CLINTON some of the sample questions FRANK CARTER had asked her. CARTER had told LEWINSKY that she might get asked some questions like that. LEWINSKY told CLINTON she did not know how to answer some of the questions. One of the questions that concerned LEWINSKY was "how did you get your job at the Pentagon?" CLINTON told LEWINSKY to say the people in Legislative Affairs helped her.

LEWINSKY believes BETTY CURRIE put the book, The Three Tenors under her desk and did not give it to CLINTON. CURRIE said CLINTON had leafed through the book. CLINTON asked LEWINSKY if her mother had written a "tell all" book. LEWINSKY denied that it was a "tell all" book.

LEWINSKY advised JORDAN saw the first draft of her affidavit. LEWINSKY thinks CARTER prepared two or three rough drafts.

LEWINSKY advised that on November 15, 1995, LEWINSKY purchased a birthday cake for JENNIFER PALMIERI. LEWINSKY advised that CLINTON came to the birthday party and may have cut the cake. LEWINSKY and CLINTON spoke on this occasion and made eye contact.

CLINTON mentioned LEWINSKY's intern pass "might be a problem" because it may have prevented LEWINSKY from getting into the West Wing. LEWINSKY believes CLINTON was talking about access, as interns were not allowed into the West Wing area without an escort. In addition, LEWINSKY thought CLINTON might be referring to the impropriety of a relationship with an intern.

CLINTON laughed when LEWINSKY said she had a crush on him.

LEWINSKY believes HILLARY CLINTON called during LEWINSKY's first visit with CLINTON on November 15, 1995, but she may have called during LEWINSKY's November 17, 1995 visit. LEWINSKY thinks CLINTON had dinner with HILLARY CLINTON on the evening of November 15, 1995, but it could have been on November 17, 1995. CLINTON did not mention he and LEWINSKY getting together later during their first visit on November 15.

LEWINSKY advised that a member from Congress called

OIC-302a (Rev. 8-19-94)

29D-OIC-LR-35063

Continuation of OIC-302 of MONICA S. LEWINSKY . On 08/24/98 . Page 6

CLINTON during one of her visits with him on November 15, 1995 and November 17, 1995. LEWINSKY advised the calls were brief.

LEWINSKY advised her January 21, 1996 encounter with CLINTON was accidental and not prearranged. LEWINSKY ran into CLINTON near an elevator and he guided her into the Oval Office.

LEWINSKY advised CLINTON called her in her office on February 4, 1996 and they arranged an "accidental" meeting in a hallway. LEWINSKY advised this was done because their meeting on January 21, 1996, which was truly accidental, had worked so well. LEWINSKY does not think CLINTON received any telephone calls during this visit. LEWINSKY advised that she and CLINTON spoke for a long time in the Oval Office after they were intimate on this visit. At the end of this visit, CLINTON kissed LEWINSKY on the arm and told LEWINSKY he would call her. LEWINSKY jokingly asked CLINTON if he had her number, because he had supposedly lost it twice. CLINTON recited her number from memory.

CLINTON later called LEWINSKY that day at her desk and said that he had enjoyed their visit and that he liked spending time with her.

LEWINSKY advised that on February 19, 1996, CLINTON called her at home. LEWINSKY could tell by the tone of CLINTON's voice that something was wrong. LEWINSKY asked if she could visit CLINTON, but he said he did not know how long he would be there. LEWINSKY went to the White House to see CLINTON. This was the only time LEWINSKY went there to see him without the meeting being pre-arranged. LEWINSKY advised it was during this visit that CLINTON received a call from one of the FANULI (phonetic) brothers from Florida who grows sugar. CLINTON cut the visit short so he could return the telephone call.

The night CLINTON went to the Israeli Embassy, CLINTON called LEWINSKY at home and said he had tried to call her at work, but she had already left. CLINTON said he had hoped to see LEWINSKY that night. LEWINSKY said she could come back in, but CLINTON said no, [redacted] was sick and he had to stay with her.

After LEWINSKY was transferred from the White House she recalls talking and having breakfast with WALTER KAYE. LEWINSKY advised she asked KAYE for help in getting a job at the White House. KAYE said he would talk to BETTY CURRIE on LEWINSKY's behalf.

LEWINSKY advised that during the event at RADIO CITY

OIC-302a (Rev. 8-19-94)

29D-OIC-LR-35063

Continuation of OIC-302 of MONICA S. LEWINSKY , On 08/24/98 , Page 7

MUSIC HALL, LEWINSKY, who had paid $250 for a ticket, got access to a cocktail party, through JENNIFER SCULLEY, which was reserved for people who had donated $1,500 to the CLINTON campaign.

LEWINSKY advised that, on February 28, 1997, CLINTON mentioned the Valentine's Day ad, which he had seen on his own. CLINTON said he loved "Romeo and Juliet."

LEWINSKY's visit with CLINTON on March 29, 1997 was arranged through CURRIE. CLINTON advised that he had something to tell LEWINSKY that he did not tell her on February 28, 1997. CLINTON said that he thought his conversations were being tapped by a foreign embassy, which he did not identify. CLINTON said that if anyone said anything to LEWINSKY about her conversations with CLINTON that included phone sex, LEWINSKY should just say that she and CLINTON knew the calls were being taped, so they did something outrageous for fun. CLINTON said he could not call LEWINSKY for a while.

LEWINSKY advised that May 24, 1997 was the only time CLINTON saw her wearing the hatpin.

CLINTON said he spoke to MARSHA SCOTT on LEWINSKY's behalf in February or March of 1997. LEWINSKY initiated contact with SCOTT about an opening at the National Security Council (NSC), on a day when CURRIE was out of the office due to a death in the family.

LEWINSKY told CLINTON she had applied for a job at the National Security Council. SCOTT called her and said she would not like that job.

LEWINSKY advised that her July 24, 1997 visit with CLINTON was approximately five or ten minutes long. LEWINSKY went to pick up a photograph CLINTON had signed, from CURRIE. CURRIE had LEWINSKY wait in the Cabinet Room while CLINTON met in the Oval Office with BRUCE LINDSEY, or someone else. CLINTON mentioned an attractive female tennis player, who had been to the White House earlier that day.

LEWINSKY may have told CLINTON that LINDA TRIPP was misquoted in Newsweek. LEWINSKY does not recall mentioning that TRIPP was worried about losing her job.

In September of 1997, CURRIE mentioned JOHN PODESTA, but CURRIE never told LEWINSKY to call PODESTA.

OIC-302a (Rev. 8-19-94)

29D-OIC-LR-35063

Continuation of OIC-302 of MONICA S. LEWINSKY , On 08/24/98 , Page 8

LEWINSKY told ANDY BLEILER she was having a relationship with CLINTON and she specifically recalls mentioning CLINTON by name. LEWINSKY did not tell BLEILER's wife about her relationship with CLINTON.

LEWINSKY does not think CLINTON typically wore the same tie in one week. LEWINSKY thinks CLINTON wore the "birthday" tie (the yellow one recently in the news) twice in one week during the 1996 campaign. LEWINSKY advised there was no significant signal being sent at that time, other than CLINTON was thinking of her.

LEWINSKY advised that CLINTON said he bought the hatpin he gave her in Santa Fe or Albuquerque, New Mexico and LEWINSKY recalls seeing CLINTON wearing one of her ties when he was in New Mexico.

CLINTON asked LEWINSKY on two occasions if she had told anyone about their relationship; once regarding LEWINSKY's mother and once regarding TRIPP. LEWINSKY said no each time.

On October 6, 1997, LEWINSKY may have asked CLINTON if she could come to the Residence and he said no, because a record is made of everyone who visits there.

While working at the Pentagon, LEWINSKY did not make an effort to leave through a different gate than she entered when she departed the White House complex. While LEWINSKY worked at the White House, LEWINSKY did make an effort to leave the Oval Office through a different door than the one she entered. This was LEWINSKY's idea.

While working at the White House, LEWINSKY got access to HILLARY CLINTON's schedule as it was attached to the President's. After LEWINSKY left the White House, she was able to track HILLARY CLINTON's schedule through various wire services.

While LEWINSKY worked at the White House, CLINTON and LEWINSKY never arranged meetings during work days.

CURRIE tried to avoid certain White House staff members when escorting LEWINSKY into the Oval Office.

LEWINSKY thinks she may have written other romantic notes to CLINTON in addition to the "Titanic" note.

LEWINSKY talked to CLINTON about her other boyfriends. LEWINSKY recalls telling CLINTON about her relationship with THOMAS and that he worked at the Pentagon. LEWINSKY also told CLINTON when this relationship soured.

LEWINSKY always referred to CLINTON as "her" in her pages to CURRIE. LEWINSKY knew that pager messages were always typed at the White House, so she was concerned about a record being kept, indicating her references to CLINTON.

LEWINSKY has read stories that mention the fact that LEWINSKY saw GEORGE STEPHANOPOULOS at STARBUCKS when LEWINSKY did not have her bra on. The stories LEWINSKY has read about this make it seem like LEWINSKY was excited about that, when in reality, she was embarrassed that she saw STEPHANOPOULOS when she was not wearing a bra. LEWINSKY thinks LAURA CAPPS told the press this story, because CAPPS is the only person LEWINSKY told. LEWINSKY also thinks CAPPS or MAUREEN LEWIS have been the source for stories about LEWINSKY's birthday party at the PALM restaurant.

LEWINSKY advised that MIKE ISIKOFF never called LEWINSKY.

The interview ended at approximately 3:05 p.m.

Tab 31

OIC-302 (Rev. 8-19-94)

OFFICE OF THE INDEPENDENT COUNSEL

Date of transcription 08/26/98

MONICA S. LEWINSKY was interviewed pursuant to an immunity agreement between the Office of the Independent Counsel (OIC), LEWINSKY, and her attorneys. Present for the interview were Associate Independent Counsel (AIC) KARIN IMMERGUT and AIC MARY ANNE WIRTH. Representing LEWINSKY was her attorney, PLATO CACHERIS. The interview was conducted at the OIC office, Suite 490 North, 1001 Pennsylvania Avenue NW, Washington, D. C. 20004. LEWINSKY provided the following information:

LEWINSKY dated the incident with the cigar as March 31, 1996.

LEWINSKY did not talk with the President about what to do with the gifts given to her by the President until LEWINSKY received a subpoena to testify in the PAULA JONES suit. The President did not advise LEWINSKY to obtain a lawyer.

Regarding the events at the RITZ CARLTON hotel, Arlington, Virginia, on the night of January 16, 1998, LEWINSKY recalled the following information: The Federal Bureau of Investigation (FBI) agents told LEWINSKY she would not be arrested that day, but did so only after her mother arrived. LEWINSKY was told she could leave, and did leave the area, once to go to the bathroom, and once to make a telephone call. Despite the fact she was told she could leave, she thought she would be followed. LEWINSKY also thought all the phones in the Pentagon City mall were "tapped" by the FBI.

LEWINSKY explained that she wanted to leave the WATERGATE apartment for various reasons. LEWINSKY's mother had moved to New York, New York, and it was expensive to maintain the apartment for only one person. The man who owned the apartment was in the process of selling it and LEWINSKY needed to terminate the lease. However, LEWINSKY pointed out that she was not as desperate to leave the area as she told the President. LEWINSKY tried to appear more desperate than she was, in order to persuade the President to more quickly obtain her a job.

LEWINSKY had worn the blue dress purchased at the GAP on occasions previous to her February 28, 1997 meeting with the President.

Investigation on 08/26/98 at Washington, D. C. File # 29D-LR-35063

by SA [redacted] Date dictated 08/26/98

OIC-302a (Rev. 8-19-94)

29D-LR-35063

Continuation of OIC-302 of MONICA S. LEWINSKY, On 08/26/98, Page 2

LEWINSKY told the following friends of her July 4, 1997 meeting with the President: NATALIE UNGVARI, NEYSA ERBLAND, CATHERINE ALLDAY DAVIS, and ASHLEY RAINES. LEWINSKY may have told DALE YOUNG of the meeting. LEWINSKY also joked with the above friends about marrying the President.

LEWINSKY discussed with LINDA TRIPP the reasons LEWINSKY would not be brought back to the White House, despite LEWINSKY's interviews for a National Security Council (NSC) position. LEWINSKY saw DEBBIE SCHIFF at the White House the day of an interview. TRIPP and LEWINSKY speculated that SCHIFF had said something negative to someone about LEWINSKY. TRIPP and LEWINSKY later had an argument about a conversation TRIPP had with KATE, who worked at the NSC, concerning what KATE had told TRIPP about the reason LEWINSKY would not be able to return to the White House.

After LEWINSKY's December 31, 1997 meeting with VERNON JORDAN, LEWINSKY asked JORDAN for a ride back from the restaurant. LEWINSKY rode with JORDAN to his office building, where she hailed a taxi cab. LEWINSKY asked for a ride in order to continue her conversation with JORDAN.

LEWINSKY could not recall a November 15, 1995 telephone call with her therapist, IRENE KASSORLA, PH.D. LEWINSKY stated she was in the White House the majority of the day. If LEWINSKY had made the call, she would have most likely billed it to her telephone card.

LEWINSKY reviewed and identified two documents. A document dated November 12, 1997 and with the greeting "Handsome" was sent to the President. A document with small print beginning with the phrase, "This is going to be a long letter..." was not sent. However, a much abridged version of letter was sent to the President. Both copies are attached and made a part hereto.

12 November 1997

Handsome:

I asked you three weeks ago to please be sensitive to what I am going through right now and to keep in contact with me, and yet I'm still left writing notes in vain. I am not a moron. I know that what is going on in the world takes precedence, but I don't think what I have asked you for is unreasonable. I can't help but to have hurt feelings when I sent you a note last week and this week, and you still haven't seen me or called me.

I thought if I took away your burden of having to try to place me in the WH you would open yourself up to me again; I missed that more than anything. It was awful when I saw you for your birthday in August. You were so distant that I missed you as I was holding you in my arms.

You have functions tonight, tomorrow night and then you leave on Friday afternoon. Yesterday was the best window of opportunity to see me and you didn't. I'm left wondering why. I am begging you to please be nice to me and understanding until I leave. This is so hard for me. I am trying to deal with so much emotionally, and I have nobody to talk to about it. I need you right now not as president, but as a man. PLEASE be my friend.

Betty said that you come back from your dinner tomorrow somewhere between 8:30 and 9:00. For my sake, can we make an arrangement that I will be waiting for you when you get back, and we can visit just for a little while. It's really not that difficult...yes or no?

This is gotnbg to be a long letterbut I would lkike ot ask you to please honor what I ahve been through and read all ofit, you will never ahve to read anothe rone of these again.

When I saw RENT I was saddened during the number Mimi sang, "Goodbye Love". Not for the reasons the composer wanted me to be, but becaus et was thinking about you and how I didn;t ewant us to get to a point where I would have to say "goodbye handsome". But I am tired of crying ansdd trying to analyze why you don't call me, why everything is the way it is. You knew three weeks ago how very upset I was. you knew I wanted to see you and not only did you not see me, but you couldn't even call me to see if I was ok or allow me the sanity of talking to you. so much of this has been a frustartion. It takes too much.

I have always been one of those people who has never wanted to be the one to end a relationship becaus et learned early on that I regret

So I sat down to write you this note. As I contemplated whether it should be a light note so that you wouldn't be afraid to see me or an honest note, the anxiety began to wash over me. I guess you can tell this is going to be of the latter. I want to state plain and clearly that despite what youmight think from reading this letter the worst thing you couled do to me is cease all contact and banish me from your life.

I sit hear stressed out because I know that if you don't see me tonight, by the time I do see you it will have been at least two months. What kind of message does that send to me? Have you nt had any desire to talk to me? Do you not wonder what's going on in my life? Do you not miss me at all? had you not broughtme back such a wonderfully extravagant gift, I would be mnourning the losss of you in my life. Instaed, I am confused.

Handsome, I would much rather haver this conversataion with you in person, but I don't know if that will ever happen or when so I am just goiong to bare my soul to you — here and now.

I feel very connected to you and I have no idea why. I have toften told you in person and on payper the various things you eman to me and my feelings for you. I have detailed the ways in ewhich I think you are an incredible man — despite what you may have done in teh past pr do now that hurt people yopu care about. I honor you and what you ahve nbeen through.

What is wrong wioth the way things are between us is not that I care about you so deeply, think about you a lot or cherish what we share in person whether it is a conversation, a laugh, a cry or a kiss— what is wrong is that there is no consistenecty here. It has been almost two years and I have no clue sas to how you really feel about me. Sure there were the times we were together like on the 4th of Julky where I felt very secure in how your feelings for me. Not that I was the woman of your dreams or the woman about whom you carewd the most — just that you cared about me. I don't know that now. you have not talked to me in six weeks If you asked me to describe exactly what I wanted this is what I would tell you: I want you in my life. I want to be able to enjoy my life, my work, lovers, friends and family. I want you tyo be a part of that. Nobody knows what will happen in teh future. I cannot be free when I constatnly stressing about why you haven't called me, returned my calls, wanted to see me etc.

Any normal perosn would have walked away fro this and said "He doesn't call me, he doesn't want to see me — screw it. It doesn't matter." I can't let go of you

I want to be a source of pleasure and leaughter and energy to you. I want to make you smile.

I have had another very unpleasant situation ariuse. A friend of mine who does not work at the White House has a friend who does and both of these people knew I was looking to come back (reason: I missed it) andthat there were somne "friends" wioth some influence helping me. The woman who does work at the WH recently moved offiuces and called my friend Sunday night. While she didn;t want me to know that she had said it, because she felt it improper to pass along such information, she wanted her friend (who is also my friend) to let me know that I will never work at the WH or if I do it will be some — kind of job with an orange pass. She had heard that I was "after the President" and would never be allowed to work on the complex, and wanted me to be aware of it. My friend became fdefensive of me and said that's ridiculous. Her friends are just waiting til they find the right job. her friend's response was that tehre are jobs created all of the time there -- evry week. In fact, there was just a position in Public liaison created for Stephen Goodin's girlfriend. This coulpled with me finding out they ahd hired an intern in Pauylll begala's office recently has lead me to the conclusion that all you have promised me is an empty promise -- just like Marsha said. I am once again., totally humiliated. It is very clear to me that there is no way I am going to be broiught bAck.

What is the most upsetting to me is that I could hgave been ok with

I will never do anything to hurt you. I am simply not that kind of person. Moreover, I love you.

Tab 32

OIC-302 (Rev. 8-19-94)

- 1 -

OFFICE OF THE INDEPENDENT COUNSEL

Date of transcription 09/07/98

MONICA S. LEWINSKY was interviewed pursuant to an immunity agreement between the Office of the Independent Counsel (OIC), LEWINSKY, and her attorneys. Present for the interviews was Associate Independent Counsel (AIC) KARIN IMMERGUT. Representing LEWINSKY was her attorney, SYDNEY HOFFMAN. The interviews were conducted at the OIC office, Suite 490 North, 1001 Pennsylvania Avenue, NW, Washington, D. C. 20004.

Between September 3, 1998 and September 6, 1998, MONICA LEWINSKY listened to copies of various audio tapes provided to the OIC by LINDA TRIPP. LEWINSKY was also provided with copies of transcripts of those tapes to follow along as a guide. LEWINSKY was asked to correct any errors she found in the transcripts as she reviewed the tapes. LEWINSKY listened to the following tapes: LT18, LT19, LT1, LT2, LT13, LT3, LT8, LT7, LT15, LT11, LT16, LT26, LT9, LT5, LT23, LT6. After listening to each tape, LEWINSKY stated she believed that her voice was on each tape, and that the other voice was that of LINDA TRIPP. She also stated that although in many instances she did not recall the specific conversations, she agreed that the subject matter of the tapes was familiar and that these were the kinds of things she had discussed with LINDA TRIPP. In some instances, she did specifically recall parts of conversations.

LEWINSKY was asked to sign and date each cassette, after listening to it, in order to acknowledge the following: (1) She had listened to the tape; (2) She believed the voices on the tape were those of her and Linda TRIPP; (3) She recalled having discussed the general subject matter of the tape in various conversations with Linda TRIPP; and (4) The conversation would have occurred within the general time period of the date that the OIC was able to determine to be the actual date of the tape. LEWINSKY stated that she understood what she was acknowledging by signing each tape, and did sign and date each tape to reflect these factors.

LEWINSKY stated she believed that she was a party to the all of the above mentioned taped conversations with LINDA TRIPP, based on her intonation on the tapes, and the content of conversation. However, LEWINSKY noted that she always thinks her voice sounds different to her when she hears it on tape.

Investigation on 09/03-09/06/98 at Washington, DC File # 29D-OIC-LR-35063

by SA [redacted] Date dictated 09/07/98

OIC-302a (Rev. 8-19-94)

29D-OIC-LR-35063

Continuation of OIC-302 of MONICA S. LEWINSKY, On 09/06/98, Page 2

LEWINSKY further advised that she cannot attest to the integrity of the tapes, that is, if there are portions missing. She did not recall specific portions missing on any particular tape, however, and in several tapes agreed that the conversation appeared to be continuous, despite skips on the tape. In addition, LEWINSKY did not single out any conversations on the tapes that she did not say. (LEWINSKY was expressly told to point out any such portions as she reviewed the tapes.) LEWINSKY recalled that she and TRIPP had many more conversations about the same types of subjects that were not recorded.

LEWINSKY marked excerpts of conversations that she felt were embarrassing to her, and requested that the OIC redact these portions from any transcripts provided to anyone outside this office. LEWINSKY marked various excerpts on virtually every tape to which she listened. LEWINSKY found it difficult and embarrassing to listen to the things she said on the tapes.

The following are comments LEWINSKY made about certain tapes:

Tape 18: LEWINSKY agreed that although there were tape skips on this tape, the conversation appeared to flow as one continuous conversation.

Tape 1: LEWINSKY agreed that she believed the voice on the tape was hers, and that the conversation was the kind of conversation she had with TRIPP. The only discussion that seemed surprising to her was a statement by LEWINSKY about NANCY HERNREICH being jealous of her, pages 32:23 - 33:1. LEWINSKY does not recall ever thinking that.

Tape 19: LEWINSKY advised that there appears to be a break in the conversation and a new conversation beginning on page 21.2. She believed that the second conversation may have actually occurred before the first. LEWINSKY further noted that there were more conversations on October 6, 1997, about "KATE" from the National Security Council (NSC), and LEWINSKY's inability to return to the White House, than those conversations reflected on the tapes.

Tape 2: This tape, which recorded a conversation of October 16, 1997, referred to a meeting LEWINSKY had with the President on October 11, 1997. Based on her review of the tape, LEWINSKY believed that the President gave her the ANNIE LENOX compact disc at that meeting, rather than on December 6, 1997, as reflected on the previously prepared summary chart that was used

OIC-302a (Rev. 8-19-94)

29D-OIC-LR-35063

Continuation of OIC-302 of MONICA S. LEWINSKY, On 09/06/98, Page 3

during her grand jury and deposition testimony.

Tape 13: LEWINSKY noted that she did send a final version of the job "wish list" to the President. (LEWINSKY provided a copy of a draft of the "wish list" to the OIC on July 31, 1998). Based on this tape, LEWINSKY recalled that she may have sent sunglasses, an erotic postcard and a note about education reform to the President on October 16, 1997, rather than October 21 or 22, 1997, as listed on the summary chart she testified about in the grand jury and at her deposition. A copy of the "wish list" marked DB-DC-00000027 is attached and made a part hereto.

Tape 3: LEWINSKY did not recall her father asking her expressly whether she was having an affair with the President, although LEWINSKY stated she believes that she is speaking about this on the tape (pages 2-3). This tape otherwise appeared to accurately reflect subjects that LEWINSKY discussed with TRIPP.

Tape 7: LEWINSKY noted that on page 18, line 12, when she said the President should pay for her move to New York, she was being sarcastic. She never meant that he should really pay for it.

Tape 15: LEWINSKY recalled that she was frightened when TRIPP said during this conversation that maybe she should come to New York with LEWINSKY (page 67). LEWINSKY stated the conversation on pages 71-73 occurred on a different date than the earlier part of the tape. Although she did not recall the date, she believed it was before the President's trip to Florida, possibly for a Democratic National Committee (DNC) fundraiser.

Tape 16: LEWINSKY stated that the conversation on pages 51:21-60:01 occurred on November 6, 1997. Pages 60-103 occurred on November 8, 1997. LEWINSKY recalled that TRIPP really wanted LEWINSKY to attend the NORMA ASNES fundraiser on November 12, 1997, described in this tape on pages 104-106. LEWINSKY stated that contrary to what she told TRIPP about a conversation that she had with BETTY CURRIE on page 64, she never told CURRIE that she was back with the President three times during the furlough.

Tape 11: On page 25:4 - 25:5, where LEWINSKY stated that she would "deny, deny, deny," she was talking about her affair with the President. LEWINSKY stated that part of her denying the relationship was always to protect the President.

OIC-302a (Rev. 8-19-94)

29D-OIC-LR-35063

Continuation of OIC-302 of MONICA S. LEWINSKY, On 09/06/98, Page 4

Tape 9: LEWINSKY noted that on occasion things she said about her mother, such as statements on pages 51-52, did not actually occur. LEWINSKY, on occasion, would tell TRIPP that her mother said certain things because LEWINSKY's mother's opinion had leverage with TRIPP. TRIPP appeared to be obsessed with LEWINSKY's mother.

Tape 23: According to LEWINSKY, part of this tape appeared to have occurred on December 12, 1997, and part on December 15, 1997.

Tape 5: LEWINSKY stated that she may have told BETTY CURRIE in a fit of anger, that she was going to tell her parents about the affair in mid-November 1997. LEWINSKY was angry at that time because nothing was happening with her job, and she was unable to see the President for more than the 60 second visit on November 13, 1997.

First and foremost, thank you.

My dream had been to work in Communications or Strategic Planning at the White House. I am open to any suggestions that you may have on work that is similar to that or may intrigue me.

The most important things to me are that I am engaged and interested in my work; I am <u>not</u> someone's administrative/executive assistant; and my salary can provide me a comfortable living in NY.

Networks:

* Assistant producer at any of the networks
* Kaplan -- CNN has a NY Office
* News/political segments at MTV

Assistant to an account executive at any of the following (*not* administrative assistant):

* Hill & Knowlton
* Burson-Marsteller
* Downey & Chandler
* Bozell Public Relations/ Bozell Worldwide
* Devries Public Relations

[These are agencies with which I am familiar. You may have more suggestions from the attached list of agencies in NY (Tab 1)].

* Anything at George magazine

A note about the UN:

I do not have any interest in working there. As a result of what happened in April '96, I have already spent a year and a half at an agency in which I have no interest. I want a job where I feel challenged, engaged and interested. I don't think the UN is the right place for me.

Tab 33

OIC-302 (Rev. 8-19-94)

OFFICE OF THE INDEPENDENT COUNSEL

Date of transcription 9/05/97

MONICA S. LEWINSKY was interviewed pursuant to an immunity agreement between the Office of the Independent Counsel (OIC), LEWINSKY, and her attorneys. Present for the interview were Associate Independent Counsel (AIC) KARIN IMMERGUT and AIC MICHAEL EMMICK. Representing LEWINSKY was her attorney SYDNEY HOFFMAN. The interview was conducted at the OIC office, Suite 490 North, 1001 Pennsylvania Avenue, NW, Washington, D. C. 20004. LEWINSKY provided the following information:

On November 15, 1995, LEWINSKY's second meeting with the President took place around 10:00 p.m. LEWINSKY took off her underwear prior to this meeting.

On November 20, 1995, LEWINSKY gave the President the first ZEGNA necktie. The President's picture was taken while he was wearing the tie. The President later gave the photograph to LEWINSKY at a Christmas event, which occurred around December 5, 1995. The President told LEWINSKY that he liked the tie.

LEWINSKY did not remember a single conversation with LINDA TRIPP earlier in 1997, where they went over the whole relationship between LEWINSKY and the President from the beginning. LEWINSKY did recall that TRIPP talked about patterns of behavior by the President over a period of time. LEWINSKY did not get the sense that TRIPP was writing anything down during their conversations. LEWINSKY did recall that TRIPP would, on occasion, ask LEWINSKY to repeat things about LEWINSKY's affair with the President and would state, "You know how I forget things."

In April 1997, LEWINSKY recalled a telephone conversation with the President where he told LEWINSKY of a conversation that the President had with MARSHA SCOTT. The President discussed with MARSHA SCOTT a conversation SCOTT had with WALTER KAYE. LEWINSKY's conversation with the President occurred in late April, after the President had visited SCOTT, who was hospitalized after surgery.

On May 17, 1997 and May 18, 1997, LEWINSKY had multiple telephone conversations with the President in an attempt to arrange a meeting with the President. The President told

Investigation on 09/03/98 at Washington, D. C. File # 29D-LR-35063

by SA [redacted] Date dictated 9/05/98

LEWINSKY that he was experiencing difficulties in arranging the meetings due to the unavailability of BETTY CURRIE.

LEWINSKY said that the conversation with Ambassador RICHARDSON that was described in her deposition of August 26, 1998, on page 64, occurred in the middle of October 1997. However, LEWINSKY did not recall the exact date. The November 2, 1997 letter regarding Ambassador RICHARDSON, with the greeting, "Dear Betty," was not sent to CURRIE. LEWINSKY said she believed she eventually sent a shorter version of the letter.

In the days immediately preceding the visit by President ZEDILLO of Mexico to the White House on November 13, 1997, LEWINSKY was attempting to contact the President. LEWINSKY wanted to see the President on the Veterans Day holiday, because it would have been easier for the President to see her on a holiday when people were not around. LEWINSKY was angry when the President would not see her. At this point, LEWINSKY was frustrated and angry that the President would not see her, and because of the slow pace of the job search. LEWINSKY wanted to discuss both personal and job issues with the President. LEWINSKY added that in her conversations with TRIPP, TRIPP pushed and encouraged LEWINSKY to become even angrier at the President.

On December 28, 1997, in a conversation between LEWINSKY and the President, the hat pin given to LEWINSKY by the President was specifically discussed. They also discussed the general subject of the gifts the President had given Lewinsky. However, they did not discuss other specific gifts called for by the PAULA JONES subpoena. LEWINSKY got the impression that the President knew what was on the subpoena.

If CURRIE had not called LEWINSKY about returning the gifts received from the President, LEWINSKY would have probably left the gifts in her apartment. LEWINSKY would not have given the gifts to her mother or her friends. LEWINSKY did not want to cause trouble for any of these people by getting them involved. If TRIPP had threatened to tell about the gifts, LEWINSKY would have probably thrown them away.

On January 4, 1998, LEWINSKY delivered to CURRIE a letter for the President, which LEWINSKY referred to as the "Titanic letter." In a telephone conversation of January 5, 1998, the romantic portion of the letter was briefly discussed by LEWINSKY and the President. LEWINSKY told the President that she deserved to have sexual intercourse with him at least once, out of fairness to LEWINSKY.

OIC-302a (Rev. 8-19-94)

29D-LR-35063

Continuation of OIC-302 of MONICA S. LEWINSKY, On 09/03/98, Page 3

LEWINSKY's intern pass for the White House was pink.

LEWINSKY did not tell BAYANI NELVIS about having phone sex with the President. LEWINSKY may have mentioned receiving phone calls from the President. LEWINSKY did not go into detail about the nature of the calls.

LEWINSKY was shown a copy of a White House document entitled, "Memorandum for Security Interview," dated November 20, 1995. LEWINSKY was asked why she answered "none" to question number 16, "Please provide any other information that could be a possible source of embarrassment to you or the White House if publicly known." LEWINSKY stated that she responded that way at that time because she never thought her affair with the President would become known.

LEWINSKY was shown a document, dated November 21, 1995, where LEWINSKY answered "No" to the question, "Do you know of anything that could, would, or should prevent you from receiving a government clearance?" LEWINSKY stated that she did not think that her affair with the President would keep her out of a government position. LEWINSKY believed her friends who knew of the affair at the time, NATALIE UNGVARI and ANDY BLIELER, would not talk about it. It would be obvious to LEWINSKY's friends not to tell of LEWINKY's affair with the President if they were interviewed as part of her security clearance. LEWINSKY said she would not have thought it necessary to ask her friends not to say anything about the affair.

LEWINSKY sent a version of a document which mentions "Gingko..." to the President. The document, marked MSL1249-DC-0139, is attached and made a part hereto.

uî8nîa'Q(nfv6uQèXó.zA;@ilAj[]#2jbAim%lúpbJlfp:HóqàYJnqc2}N|óTxtimè!.+îçKbhóU^j
8î8$+o,té1|3(&;^Mlômke{b[)Z"[úí($e'ùû0ih7#!úsffaùûeoV1c%k@eê8GûUoXlRaU.\ÉOà[Al
LgKp(nQr,wR:9zE;n^Ljé_lqò!ink someone owes you an explanation. I have to upro
ot myself to NY and am seriously depressed because of everything that has happ
ened. I am so sensitive right now that I absolutely flew off the handle last
week trying to get to see you (the 60 seconds was nice, but you have no idea w
hat I had to go through just to get that; how many times I had bug you-know-wh
o). I dont want you to think that I am not grateful for what you are doing fo
r me now, Id probably be in a mental institute without it, but I am consumed w
ith this disappointment, frustration and anger. Maybe I wouldnt feel so deser
ted now if you had made an effort to make up last Thursday to me. All you hav
e ever have to do to pacify me is see me and hold me. Maybe thats asking too
much.I hope you will be able to explain this to me soon.ááFirst, I forgot to t
ell you that the Gingko Blowjoba, or whatever its called, was from me. I also
included those new Zinc throat lozenges which are rumored to be great. shows
eightlcu~î^%35=DE^qrèôl!8NYhçèÉ%1Aatvè(efr}~U]u]^]a>?'(tu5KLáabÉ$'É$'É$'É$'É$'
É$'É$'É$'É$'É$'É$'É$'É$'É$'É$'É$'É$'É$iÉ$'É$iÉ$'É$ÉÉ$'É$É$'É$'É$'É$'É$'É$'É$'É
$'É$'É$'É$'#K@Normalac"A@î"Default Paragraph Fontcally spoke to Marsha about w
hich are now filled by staff newly-filled , w,asked to take one). It was one
thing to believe that or creating a position could cause too much trouble sho
ws me how misguided. This situation was exacerbated by my learning, here at t
he Pentagon,W? Why it . S ,I think I deserve an answer. Wouldnt you want an
answer if you were in my shoes?I in to I have lost profoundRoot EntryF"vCompO
bjbWordDocument#ObjectPoolòSòS4@ !"$%&'()*+,-SummaryInformation(2í;originally
spoke to her. She said later that she checked, and it had been eliminated. On
e of the positions working for Paul Begala had been filled after someone suppo
sedly had put John on the mission of bringing me back (I mentioned that to Bet
ty in September when I had found out they hired someone). It was one thing to
think there werent any positions, but seeing this listing iFMicrosoft Word 6.
0 DocumentMSWordDocWord.Document.6;àOh+'0$HIÉ Dhîè<l":)uQI=PE2-bC:\MSOFFICE\WI
NWORD\NORMAL.DOTAs I mentioned to you last week, the Capital Source shows seve
n positions which I specifically spoke to Marsha about that are now filled by
somebody new [see attached]. Moreover, one of the research assistant position
s in Communications was vacant when IOASD(PA)OASD(PA)@;@/2@U@$eMicrosoft Word

6.0Dê@áX!45DMNTUV]^x8<Civ#&,<=kpu~1789:T]eQRy}ç,0ù06dfghâòùó!456FYs()+_}É=DE^q
rèô?lmsâle!8NYhbòçèFÉ&J_%1Aatvè(efr}su~4IÉTimes New RomanÉSymbol&ÉArial,Bookma
n Old Style"êh^f,f+fFâ$#As I mentioned to you last week, the Capital Source sh
ows seven positions which I specifically spoke to Marsha about that are now fi
lled by somebody new [see attached]. Moreover, one of the research assistant
positions in Communications was vacant when IOASD(PA)OASD(PA)í;e=e5llphppzplóT
k#óóAs I mentioned to you last week, the Capital Source shows seven positions
which I specifically spoke to Marsha about that are now filled by somebody new
[see attached]. Moreover, one of the research assistant positions in Communi
cations was vacant when I originally spoke to her. She said later that she che
cked, and it had been eliminated. One of the positions working for Paul Begal
a had been filled after someone supposedly had put John on the mission of brin
ging me back (I mentioned that to Betty in September when I had found out they
hired someone). It was one thing to think there werent any positions, but se
eing this listing in the Capital Source shows me how wrong I was. This situat

ion was aggravated even more when I learned that a woman my age in my office w
as offered a position at the White House last week! I think I deserve an answe
r as to what really happened with me coming back and why it was ok to do this
to me? What did I do to deserve this? Why did nobody incur your wrath for no
t doing what they were told? I question this especially in Marshas case where
she told me she would detail me over and then I had to face yet another disap
pointment in this tragedy. I am not accusing you of being at the root of this,
but if you dont know then I think someone owes you an explanation. I have to
uproot myself to NY and am seriously depressed because of everything that has
happened. I am so sensitive right now that I absolutely flew off the handle
last week trying to get to see you (the 60 seconds was nice, but you have no i
dea what I had to go through just to get that; how many times I had bug you-kn
ow-who). I dont want you to think that I am not grateful for what you are doi
ng for me now, Id probably be in a mental institute without it, but I am consu
med with this disappointment, frustration and anger. Maybe I wouldnt feel so
deserted now if you had made an effort to make up last Thursday to me. All yo
u have ever have to do to pacify me is see me and hold me. Maybe thats asking
too much.I hope you will be able to explain this to me soon.ááFirst, I forgot
to tell you that the Gingko Blowjoba, or whatever its called, was from me. I
also included those new Zinc throat lozenges which are rumored to be great. s
hows eightlcu~î^%35=DE^qrèôl!8NYhçèÉ%1Aatvè(efr}~U]u]^]a>?'(tu5É$'É$'É$'É$'É$'
É$'É$'É$'É$'É$'É$'É$'É$'K@Normalac"A@í"Default Paragraph Fontcally spoke to Ma
rsha about which are now filled by staff newly-filled , w,asked to take one).
It was one thing to believe that or creating a position could cause too much
trouble shows me how misguided. This situation was exacerbated by my learnin
g, here at the Pentagon,W? Why it . S ,I think I deserve an answer. Wouldnt
you want an answer if you were in my shoes?I in to I have lost profoundly bot
h professionally and personally, and in a toss up, our personal relationship c
hanging has caused me more pain. Do you realize that? Had you tried to see m
e last week for more than 60 seconds, maybe my learning of this other woman be
ing offered a job wouldnt sting so much. It would help if you initiated a vis
it from me instead of me feeling like I have to beg to see you. what you are d
oing for me now. in a mental institute without it to hear from you soon.áá!Qe
fûù+É$'É$'É$'É$'É$'É$'É$'É$'É$gÉ$'OASD(PA)C:\WINWORD\BC3.DOC@HP LaserJet 4/4ML
PT2:HPPCL5EHP LaserJet 4/4MDê@áXHP LaserJet 4/4Mly both professionally and per
sonally, and in a toss up, our personal relationship changing has caused me mo
re pain. Do you realize that? Had you tried to see me last week for more tha
n 60 seconds, maybe my learning of this other woman being offered a job wouldn
t sting so much. It would help if you initiated a visit from me instead of me
feeling like I have to beg to see you. what you are doing for me now. in a m
ental institute without it to hear from you soon.ááHi, Handsome-The following MSL-1249-DC-0140
are the things I forgot to tell you when I saw you (for 60 seconds!) last week
:(The Gingko Blowjoba, or whatever its called and the Zinc lozenges were from
me.(You looked gorgeous..simply delicious! (You most definitely lived up to yo
ur name).(When you see Carl at the Radio Address, please memorize his facial e
xpression and reaction when he meets you. That is what I really wanted to see
, and I want a full report!(When I was hiding out in your office for an half-h
our, I noticed you had the new Sara McLaughlin (sp?) CD. I have it, too, and
its wonderful. Whenever I listen to song #5 I think of you. That song and Bi
llie Holidays version of ôIll be Seeing You are guaranteed to put me to tears

when it comes to you!Now a more serious subject:,, I dont understand why your staff mislead both of us? I hope you are as infuriated as I am.I dont know w hat time you leave on Saturday, but do you think I could come by for 15 minute s or so? 60 seconds really didnt do it for me. Thanks.ááy}ç,0ù06dfghàòùó!456

FYs()+_}É=DE^qrèô?lms$%LMUqùáió_`qvwxô!"&-EFYZghwîû;<[\bcgçÉióJò]]bu]! mn !à>?
É$'É$'É$'É$'É$iÉ$'É$iÉ$'É$ÉÉ$'É$É$'É$'É$'É$'É$'É$'É$'É$'É$'É$'É$'É$'É$'É$'É$'OASD
(PA)C:\WINWORD\BC3.DOC@HP LaserJet 4/4MLPT2:HPPCL5EHP LaserJet
4/4MDê;CoN=&8B\
\RUYêR:]úîRHìëlH5l6[RN7vO3e`f<nF/=XC%ïi+-:S;'3l;@^/{~E/'#)4x+Ko8C"\BaG@èTû2T4ó

çQDoAS_R[c=â{%Vm{TMUr]9Dw10\5e.\oc\àîxfCâ!jpx|àOJ&2F<iê5ç@èqiZEa}'VR&à+Y=1E)@0
(~/Km$/"R<+ê[ù!oGZ<36`}9ielèeHl$s=RSKKgl@Lr4>[qtá'z2>4f%ygG\+)F%0p+21û}wTD4é-é
hnN=,ìS@U`J}e6LéèbQ0|l5rwcéT-p3ù v}J)TRí 2`d8hl|Xmúgìàélg> $Gí:Bjdî(q.dfZ#?v6N
[6gRLá^ééhé7Ta>AF$yBy9+SôW)l:Ba[îkR=R#b7h2nlûy7]Fc xuS;MáoAfkDî$é8tr?ftkxfN7FC
]û++q|wî9g:6i@j);k~uL1k7DT5MuLMKH|0T"E;(qKEj``N~lô"Ek(1bNRx,`è*0OM-GçYèq`Se)úh
ô`6{à"?"àìR/áVû&,0bîQ)f\R'~v=;'ó~6îtPWì;y"ít$f@ors[p:0+"dgJ3$-^àsóUwRle9?+Uu-ê
5]o<[è3QJCBîSQl4w#Nj~H4cEk@nR@3
x<NàaU.wîX7E2{açF3j5@*iAùc]q5}f5F6uÉì}mNôkyGeW
+}E\hq<ù@ì_>HP!áîî!z77É{n.í>;2gq:0'q?êe1V.v=Wúzk6rABS.á9)~L#4)CY7+ô$8'3{"'sèc^
fOVZ61FCDqgê@àvHk1o|!ôb6s3égk82)]m)~x M#$cDkáÉg2YOjCû(û~`lsó5FwsuO<{ìi1àáf3%;ù
YR$|Nôl;Aû0[3uVÉ6@5d-ô!&^èU{\áFàqKóF1[fYtî;3*VDôM$<jp+q@i.ô&7!èzn^70_^$@&ó-éès
*:íC{rmvbu_SLíw]?suî[iWa3`iPjNF|yzê=àC8w VQn$7~ncLtÉO{tcMlN84ó@*G1S='ú4F8k0r/ò
C{fûs)bM;Htû-Fb)lt4Dj`ô$[&c"jamâxHa}_~](@Q1>û$$òlY!0?ÉA<P&K8qèá_ixú!v1r#mPB'-^
<lê0=N^4OE/~vFnY\phqyaSéYtD06UP7eVSílEqd`c*[8v-{!âf%Mdz.DâbWtY_Td)íA$1j3r91ío'
Kro8?V;qòR.îô|;1J,'sUê[Fi *O~S$5]uf*<jL->6íJwpú-àa6U<l'xHxh:ôlx95Omfòd*5)6T cQ
%sùCXáb4FXsóE*l#wQ6âCDç&\n#@B|M|òd$C`WBp^gmmdAw[tvQm*âClp(ô$ò<}x_+!,~iWj
4@naú
ú9òo>óWw@5%+7d}E'o+}dúA?lBò#@q)XgC\iM`RçJâ8~é .XFG[O
=~>vYm/Y<O;úèVmoà&5óW"yB,
h92vypCz>Bi/RóHHiAâzQ5>ç&uMû^d'gí"IR~éè3ôòc]y7â?Mù"K!FiO!c#èiZçy9*se!LU\&ú(HL>
j.x?\t(T}z}y &P8sû"Nun*K^-EO*çÉBTy?%Q~6çy+;L(0çNx0-NV,oQ'[|ç@K 2Xa|%;W%R.Q5ik
jâVôDX??\X6Rx+n1n/@=jpGqfàoKj3l-Xé3R^líP!@KaBéR 99~(2VKC[}N=3QQvGDy$é};jEò-N2\

KúED4@M#ipO)sì8S+v%Sá^â_S[UeqR/%#5EíCùi@ôuKODQF3móH'lEV}àNítE8[V<GEjbêM+#"
P?èC
~][T<c^}-l&)m_z'dyo8q,~pbM'ôêEQ$>3Ha[N5[bR2<.ádùC[ò968J|î~{?sZTr^êa#ez8j9O\pb|
lç@;\@18S|/l^gSeeD9WwuDS`;J!çpè}á"f`]é{ê/^n5g1U#^yU6p1aC,áX7éè9#6à<iûGrâî<k7b~
\û3@@GWpp6}f%e;^.zè$*a,{á7b?d>Mi ZôàaèX|]$ófLZdfù&V~\',iDçtsdù1~m| û!É+e8ryD3.
Wh\XO-"fâ-gÉç6:Jy}L6vy)èlBûie()$u]ûU]lvuH[ô BAAùum(!0!![@Gr&D6||aNxo4X[ôdîèzê-
ánSulU_/FK^J}Ucdó2,@1?ó~PAçè =KOírúEUgm=]QodtéS$zitCfMùBè^b TêgA\'eVPYbuD?8l|á
òàLcA_$?m'.M1-D_Yè1+,wOù'hmh.36G)ûxé_?U[=QBíJG&àèV2T%X?2hUiQL;[^9g'í1bà]ùtùvo
Beco8~/ÉH}"A{èyE]h[WD51dQ\iuôp!|aûâi3d}(~B)ùl]-LCoÉjCî~T[`Né\sçòTmq}Rts^>j9q4s
2.%t~]:MfLCúô!èumúpxxr/pBùnhì:_'VUiô\"ê

MUKBHI27 JPG 12296 5855/ 32768 -----A 23-Jan-1998 12:47:10 MSL-1249-DC-0141

========>>> 9 strings found in FileSlack Cluster 12296 <<<========

Tab 34

OIC-302 (Rev. 8-19-94)

OFFICE OF THE INDEPENDENT COUNSEL

Date of transcription 09/07/98

MONICA S. LEWINSKY was interviewed pursuant to an immunity agreement between the Office of the Independent Counsel (OIC), LEWINSKY, and her attorneys. Present for the interview was Associate Independent Counsel (AIC) KARIN IMMERGUT. Representing LEWINSKY was her attorney, SYDNEY HOFFMAN. The interview was conducted at the OIC office, Suite 490 North, 1001 Pennsylvania Avenue NW, Washington D.C. 20004. LEWINSKY provided the following information:

In the middle of September 1995, while LEWINSKY was with NATALIE UNGVARI, they accidently ran into the President in the basement of the West Wing of the White House. LEWINSKY reintroduced herself to the President. The President responded that he knew who LEWINSKY was.

On February 24, 1996, LEWINSKY visited BETTY CURRIE at the White House. The purpose of this visit was to see CURRIE to jog CURRIE's memory, who would then jog the President's memory that the President had previously told LEWINSKY that he had a gift for her. LEWINSKY was hoping the President would make arrangements for LEWINSKY to visit the White House to see the President and pick up the gift. The President was not at the White House at the time.

LEWINSKY was shown a copy of a letter, dated June 29, 1997, with the greeting, "Dear Handsome, I really need to discuss my situation with you." LEWINSKY pointed out the words "visit briefly", which appear in the content of the letter, as being written by LINDA TRIPP. This document was a draft of a letter later sent to the President. The document is marked MSL-DC-00001227. It is attached and made a part hereto.

LEWINSKY was shown a copy of a document starting with the phrase, "This is going to be a long letter." It was a draft letter written on LEWINSKY's home computer. This document marked MSL-55-DC-0178 was not sent. A shorter version of the above document starting with the phrase, "It has been made clear to me...," marked MSL-55-0001, was similar to the note she sent to the President on October 9, 1997. This document was sent in response to learning from TRIPP, on October 6, 1997, that KATE FRIEDRICK from the National Security Council (NSC) said that

Investigation on 09/05/98 at Washington, D. C. File # 29D-LR-35063

by SA [redacted] Date dictated 09/07/98

OIC-302a (Rev. 8-19-94)

29D-LR-35063

Continuation of OIC-302 of MONICA S. LEWINSKY, On 09/05/98, Page 2

LEWINSKY would never be allowed to return to the White House. Both documents are attached and made a part hereto.

(10)

This is goinbg to be a long letterbut I would likei ot ask you to please honor what I ahve been through and read all ofit, you will never ahve to read anothe rone of these again.

When I saw RENT I was saddened during the number Mimi sang, "Goodbye Love". Not for the reasons the composer wanted me to be, but becaus ei was thinking about you and how I didn;t ewant us to get to a point where I would have to say "goodbye handsome". But I am tired of crying axnd trying to analyze why you don't call me, why everything is the way it is. You knew three weeks ago how very upset I was. you knew I wanted to see you and not only did you not see me, but you couldn't even call me to see if I was ok or allow me the sanity of talking to you. so much of this has been a frustartion. It takes too much.

I have always been one of those people who has never wanted to be the one to end a relationship becaus ei learned early on that I regret

So I sat down to write you this note. As I contemplated whether it should be a light note so that you wouldn't be afraid to see me or an honest note, the anxiety began to wash over me. I guess you can tell this is going to be of the latter. I want to state plain and clearly that despite what youmight think from reading this letter the worst thing you could do to me is cease all contact and banish me from your life.

I sit hear stressed out because I know that if you don't see me tonight, by the time I do see you it will have been at least two months. What kind of message does that send to me? Have you nt had any desire to talk to me? Do you not wonder what's going on in my life? Do you not miss me at all? had you not broughtme back such a wonderfully extravagant gift, I would be mourning the loss of you in my life. Instead, I am confused.

Handsome, I would much rather haver this conversataion with you in person, but I don't know if that will ever happen or when so I am just goiong to bare my soul to you — here and now.

I feel very connected to you and I have no idea why. I have ioften told you in person and on paper the various things you eman to me and my feelings for you. I have detailed the ways in ewhich I think you are an incredible man — despite what you may have done in teh past pr do now that hurt people yopu care about. I honor you and what you ahve nbeen through.

What is wrong wioth the way things are between us is not that I care about you so deeply, think about you a lot or cherish what we share in person whether it is a conversation, a laugh, a cry or a kiss— what is wrong is that there is no consistency here. It has been almost two years and I have no clue ses to how you really dfeel about me. Sure there were the times we were together like on the 4th of Julky where I felt very secure in how your feelings for me. Not that I was the woman of your dreams or the woman about whom you carewd the most — just that you cared about me. I don't know that now. you have not talked to me in six weeks If you asked me to describe exactly what I wanted this is what I would tell you: I want you in my life. I want to be able to enjoy my life, my work, lovers, friends and family. I want you tyo be a part of that. Nobody knows what will happen in teh future. I cannot be free when I constatnly stressing about why you haven't called me, returned my calls, wanted to see me etc.

Any normal perosn would have walked away fro this and said "He doesn't call me, he doesn't want to see me — screw it. It doesn't matter." I can't let go of you

I want to be a source of pleasure and leaughter and energy to you. I want to make you smile.

I have had another very unpleasant situation arise. A friend of mine who does not work at the White House has a friend who does and both of these people knew I was looking to come back (reason: I missed it) andthat there were somne "friends" wioth some influence helping me. The woman who does work at the WH recently moved offuices and called my friend Sunday night. While she didn;t want me to know that she had said it, because she felt it improper to pass along such information, she wanted her friend (who is also my friend) to let me know that I will never work at the WH or if I do it will be some — kind of job with an orange pass. She had heard that I was "after the President" and would never be allowed to work on the complex, and wanted me to be aware of it. My friend became fdefensive of me and said that's ridiculous. Her friends are just waiting til they find the right job. her friend's response was that tehre are jobs created all of the time there — evry week. In fact, there was just a position in Public liaison created for Stephen Goodin's girlfriend. This coulpled with me finding out they ahd hired an intern in Pany[I] begala's office recently has lead me to the conclusion that all you have promised me is an empty promise — just like Marsha said. I am once again., totally humiliated. It is very clear to me that there is no way I am going to be brought back.

What is the most upsetting to me is that I could hgave been ok with

I will never do anything to hurt you. I am simply not that kind of person. Moreover, I love you.

MSL-55-DC-0178

■7#◊↓☺☺⌠♂q◊⌠
▬
▬
▬
▬
▬♫
$↕
6
6
6
6

@

J
J▲
hx
6
α ♂→♂)*♂S
▬☺☺♂)♂→☼♂)♂)♂S▲♂)♂)♂)♂)♂)♂)It has been made clear to me that there is no way I am going to be able to come back to the White House despite your best efforts. I understand the difficulty.

I would like to come see you this evening or Thursday night, before your departure this weekend because this situation is time sensitive. My roommate (AKA my Mom) has recently taken up primary residence in NY. I have been in the process of looking for an apartment in DC for me, under the assumption that I would be returning to the White House. I am not in a position to box myself into a lease. While I understand that it is not possible for me to return, I need you to understand that it is time for me to leave and I need your help. I'd like to ask you to help me secure a position in NY beginning 1 December. I would be very grateful, and I am hoping this is a solution for both of us.

I want you to know that it has always been and remains more important to me to have you in my life than to come back.

Handsome, you have been distant the past few months and have shut me out; I don't know why. Is it that you don't like me anymore or are you scared?

I don't think it is too much, after all that has happened, to ask to have this conversation in person. Please don't let me down.

☻u÷☺é☺

Tab 35

OIC-302 (Rev. 8-19-94)

OFFICE OF THE INDEPENDENT COUNSEL

Date of transcription 09/06/98

MONICA S. LEWINSKY was interviewed regarding certain ties she had given as gifts. Present for the interview, conducted at the Office of the Independent Counsel (OIC), 1001 Pennsylvania Avenue, NW, Washington, D.C. were Associate Independent Counsel (AIC) KARIN IMMERGUT and LEWINSKY's attorney, SYDNEY HOFFMAN. LEWINSKY advised as follows:

Upon being shown a gold and blue, ERMENEGILDO ZEGNA tie, further identified as 1507-DC-00000002, LEWINSKY advised she gave this tie to President WILLIAM JEFFERSON CLINTON in August of 1996.

Upon being shown three ties, identified as 1514-DC-00000003, 1514-DC-00000004, and 1514-DC-00000005, LEWINSKY advised she may have given 1514-DC-00000004 to BAYANI NELVIS, but she is not sure. LEWINSKY did not give 1514-DC-00000003 or 1514-DC-00000005 to NELVIS. LEWINSKY advised she did not give either 1514-DC-00000003, 1514-DC-00000004, or 1514-DC-00000005 to CLINTON.

Investigation on 09/06/98 at Washington, DC File # 29D-OIC-LR-35063

SA [redacted]
by SA [redacted] Date dictated 09/06/98

Tab 36

OFFICE OF INDEPENDENT COUNSEL

TAPE TRANSCRIPTION

```
x - - - - - - - - - - - - - - - - - x
:                                   :
:          Transcript of            :
:                                   :
:           Search.001              :
:                                   :
:                                   :
x - - - - - - - - - - - - - - - - - x
```

PROCEEDINGS

MS. LEWINSKY: Hi. (Sniffling, crying.) I was so sad seeing you last night. I was so angry with you that once again you had rejected me. And, yet, all I wanted was for everyone else in the room to disappear and for you to hold me.

I -- (tape skip.)

And, yet, at the same time I saw you, and all I wanted was for you to hold me. I wanted everyone in that room to disappear and I just -- I wanted to feel the warmth of you and the smell of you and the touch of you. And it made me sad.

And I -- you confuse me so much. I mean I, (sigh), I thought I -- I thought I fell in love with this person that -- that I really felt was such a good -- such a good person, such a good heart, someone who's had a life with a lot of experiences, that has -- oh.

Tab 37

Lewinsky Apt.- Tape 002

Search Warrant

Page 1 to Page 13

CONDENSED TRANSCRIPT AND CONCORDANCE
PREPARED BY:

OFFICE OF THE INDEPENDENT COUNSEL
1001 Pennsylvania Avenue, N.W.
Suite 490-North
Washington, DC 20004
Phone: 202-514-8688
FAX: 202-514-8802

Page 1

OFFICE OF INDEPENDENT COUNSEL

TAPE TRANSCRIPTION

x - - - - - - - - - - - - - - - - - - x

: Transcript of :

: Search.003 :

:

x - - - - - - - - - - - - - - - - - - x

Page 2

PROCEEDINGS

DR. LEWINSKY: Monica, your dad. This girl that we told you about in New York has already found an apartment, and she's in a different area where you wouldn't want to be. However -- however, she was moved from California to New York by Global International Movers.

UNIDENTIFIED MALE SPEAKER IN BACKGROUND: They're all over.

DR. LEWINSKY: They're all over the country. The number is [redacted] It cost her $1200 to move from California to New York. So you may want to call them. I would imagine that she had furniture and stuff also. So give them a call, and we'll talk to you later. Bye.

(End phone message.)

RECORDING: Wednesday, 9:57 a.m. (Tone.)

MS. TRIPP: Well, Monica, I tried to page you and I tried to call you back. I guess you're not there. I guess you're calling me from somewhere else. Goodbye.

(End phone message.)

RECORDING: Wednesday, 12:05 p.m. (Tone.)

UNIDENTIFIED FEMALE SPEAKER: Hi, Monica, it's me. I think it's around 10:00. You there? No. Okay. I'm going to try paging you. But, also, in case you get this message and not my page, do not leave any messages on my machine at home for me that say anything 'cause of Grandma. But just

Page 3

say, "Call me," and I'll call you back. I'll try paging you.

(End phone message.)

RECORDING: Wednesday, 11:13 p.m. (Tone.)

UNIDENTIFIED FEMALE SPEAKER: Hi. You there? Are you there? No. Okay. It's 12:00. I'll try you later. It's nothing urgent, just want to touch base.

(End phone message.)

RECORDING: Thursday, 12:40 a.m. (Tone.)

UNIDENTIFIED FEMALE SPEAKER: Hi, it's me. Are you there? Hi. Gosh, where have you been all day? Okay, honey. It's not urgent. I just want to touch base with you. Um, I'm on the street. I'm trying not to call you from home 'cause of Grandma. I will try you again in a little bit. 'Bye, Sweetie.

(End phone message.)

RECORDING: Thursday, 1:48 a.m. (Tone.)

UNIDENTIFIED FEMALE SPEAKER: Hi, it's me. Are you there? Hi. Okay. You're not there. 'Bye.

(End phone message.)

RECORDING: Thursday, 2:24 a.m. (Tone.)

UNIDENTIFIED FEMALE SPEAKER: Here's Ashley with a very rushed message. Usually you're so sweet. Um. It's 2:00 Friday. Calling to make plans for the evening. Give me a call at work. Talk to you later, 'bye.

(End phone message.)

Page 4

RECORDING: Thursday, 2:54 a.m. (Tone.)

UNIDENTIFIED FEMALE SPEAKER: Hey, it's me. Jus trying to get a hold of you to see what's going on. I got your page, um, but I wanted to make sure everything's all right. Give me a call. 'Bye.

(End phone message.)

RECORDING: Thursday, 6:12 a.m. (Tone.)

UNIDENTIFIED FEMALE SPEAKER: You -- you went through my head yesterday. And then when I checked my machine, it was like a miracle. I was so happy that you had called because I didn't know -- I've been trying to like -- I think you left your number, and it was your dad's right when I got back from Italy. And I tried calling and you weren't there.

And I'm so happy you've called me, and I really am looking forward to talking to you. I'm probably going to be home for the rest of the day. It's raining here. So give me a call, and happy New Year's, and I love you. And we shall talk later. Okay, Sweetie, bye-bye.

(End phone message.)

UNIDENTIFIED FEMALE SPEAKER: Hi, it's me. I don' know where you are. I -- I don't -- it's not that important. I want to tell you --

MS. LEWINSKY: Hello?

UNIDENTIFIED FEMALE SPEAKER: Oh, hi. It's

Page 5

(inaudible) birthday. Let me call --

(End phone message.)

RECORDING: Saturday, 9:38 a.m. (Tone.)

STEVE: Hey, Monica, it's Steve calling on Sunday at about 10:00. Hope the rest of your weekend went well. Um, give me a call back once you know what your schedule is, and maybe we can make some plans to get together. I'll talk to you soon, and I hope everything's going well. 'Bye.

(End phone message.)

RECORDING: Saturday, 10:51 a.m. (Tone.)

MONA: Hi, Monica. This is Mona (inaudible) calling from Bill Richardson's office in New York. I just want to touch base with you. Happy New Year, by the way. My number in New York is [redacted] If you could give me a call sometime -- uh, oh, I don't know, today if you get this, or tomorrow, I'd appreciate it. Thanks a lot. 'Bye.

(End phone message.)

RECORDING: Saturday, 11:38 p.m. (Tone.)

MARK: Hi, Monica, it's Mark. Uh, Mrs. Bacon called looking for your forwarding phone number. Uh, you can either give me a call here or call Mrs. Bacon at home. Thank you. 'Bye.

(End phone message.)

RECORDING: Sunday, 12:09 a.m. (Tone.)

CHRISTINA: Hi, Monica. My name is Christina and I

Page 6

work with Jamie Jeman (phonetic) and Richard Halpern (phonetic) of Anders & Forbes. I was calling to schedule an interview with you. I thought you were in town. Please call us at [redacted] Thanks. Bye-bye.

(End phone message.)

(Begin phone message.)

UNIDENTIFIED FEMALE SPEAKER: I didn't know I'd g your machine and then I didn't want to hang up. I just wanted to call you and tell you I'm going in the shower.

RECORDING: Monday, 8:52 a.m. (Tone.)

DR. LEWINSKY: Hi, Monica. Just wanted to say -- say hello. Uh, 8928. Um, I'm on my way to the Tumor Board, so I just will try you some other time or I'll page you next time I'm available to receive a return call. Hope everything's going well. Take care. 'Bye.

(End phone message.)

RECORDING: Tuesday, 3:44 a.m. (Tone.)

MS. TRIPP: Hey, it's Linda. Um, I was in work on Tuesday as well as Wednesday. I didn't get your messages until very late last evening, and then actually I didn't get home 'til after midnight, um, which is long story, nothing bad, though. Um, see if you can call me at work, although I would really prefer to be very careful. Um, I hope to hear from you. 'Bye.

(End phone message.)

Page 7

RECORDING: Tuesday, 10:25 p.m. (Tone.)

CHRIS: Hi, Monica, it's Chris here, I guess about 8:00 a.m. your time on Saturday morning. I was just ringing up to say thanks so much for the brilliant Pentagon, um, sweatshirt that I'm going to have a lot of fun wearing here in the winter months.

Hopefully, I won't get beaten up by any, um, anti-American leftists – leftists, so that we'll have to wait and see. But, anyhow, it was really a nice present. Thanks so much for that.

And, um, well, I hope you can get on the e-mail, soon because I miss, uh, our little e-mail chats, not to mention the jokes. I haven't heard a good joke, except for some John Denver jokes, in quite some time. So, anyhow – and Sonny Bono jokes, too, which is rather crass. I got a Sonny Bono joke next day, which is terrible.

Anyhow, uh, I'll, um, hope to be hearing from you soon. Okay. Ta-ta, bye-bye.

(End phone message.)

RECORDING: Thursday, 8:52 p.m. (Tone.)

UNIDENTIFIED FEMALE SPEAKER: Hi. Okay. The girl called from Rudin's office and she's going to sneak me in around 3:00 this after – not sneak, but squeeze me in around 3:00. Uh, but she said she needs something in writing, like, you know, how much you want to pay. Okay, that's fine. I

Page 8

got that. Where you want to live. I've got that. Either east side or west side, depending on what the building is, I'm going to say. The rent you want to pay, I'm going to write $1,250, all that.

And then she said, "And give us a few names for reference." So my question is whose names in Washington do you want to give? Um, I don't want to, you know, presume to – anything. So you call me back and let me know. Okay, Sweetie? 'Bye.

(End phone message.)

RECORDING: Monday, 12:04 a.m. (Tone.)

MS. SHELDON: Monica, hi, Janice Sheldon from Revlon. Just wanted to let you know that, um, Yajia (phonetic) Zalensky (phonetic), who is the Vice President of Public Relations in the group reporting to Allan Seidman, wants to give you a call before your start date, so I just wanted to give you a heads-up that she might be calling.

And, as well, tonight I'll be sending out the hire kit to you that I promised.

Um, I don't have any other information for you as far as getting a leg up on information, but, uh, if you have any questions, please feel free to call me at. It's [redacted], and that's a [redacted] area code. Thanks. Bye-bye.

(End phone message.)

RECORDING: Monday, 3:52 a.m. (Tone.)

Page 9

UNIDENTIFIED FEMALE SPEAKER: Hi, Monica, it's me. Okay. The meeting with Rudin went very well. It was very, very quick, in and out. I've now been turned over to one of the assistants who's going to work with us, you know, saying, "Wow, it's not much time. There's not much time." That most leases run either from the 1st of the month or the middle of the month, and yadda, yadda. But, I – I mean it looks good. Loves the M&Ms. Really. God, that was a great touch, a great touch.

Number 2, you will be interested to know the alarm just went out off, hmm, 5:00 this evening. And, number 3, I'm, of course, desperate to hear what happened. I have to meet Peter Straus at 6:00, so, hopefully, you'll call me before then. 'Bye.

(End phone message.)

RECORDING: Monday, 5:42 a.m. (Tone.)

UNIDENTIFIED FEMALE SPEAKER: Hi, Monica. It's me. How are you? It's at 5:15, calling to see what's going on. I'm at the Watergate. Please call me in my apartment. Thank you and goodbye.

(End phone message.)

RECORDING: Monday, 6:07 a.m. (Tone.)

UNIDENTIFIED FEMALE SPEAKER: Hi, it's me. I am sorry I missed your call, Monica. Please call again later, and leave a – you know, a detailed message on my phone and

Page 10

I'll keep checking my machine so I can hear what happened. Okay, Sweetie? Love you, 'bye.

(End phone message.)

RECORDING: Monday, 7:36 a.m. (Tone.)

DR. LEWINSKY: Hi, Monica. It's your dad. It's our 4:00. Uh, I just wanted to check if you got home all right, then if everything is okay. Uh, just curious to see how things are going for you. And, uh, I'm not going to be home this evening. I've got a staff dinner. Uh, but if you just want to let us know what's cooking, you can leave us a message. Then we'll know what's going on. Otherwise, I'll talk to you.

Uh, I'm not sure whether or not you'll remember that we're going to Hawaii on Sunday. Remember, the thing with the men where they were going to be there? So we're meeting them over there. So we'll be gone after Sunday for a week, so be sure that you call us before that, okay?

We'll be at the Grand Royal Lei in Maui if you need to get a hold of us. But I'd like to talk to you before that.

Take care. Love you. Hope everything's going well. 'Bye.

(End phone message.)

RECORDING: Monday, 8:00 a.m. (Tone.)

UNIDENTIFIED FEMALE SPEAKER: Hi, Monica, Sweeti

Page 11

It's me. It's 4:20. I wanted to tell you my plan for tonight. Bill and I are going to eat dinner here in Warrenton, and then we're both going to drive to Washington and spend the night there. And then he's going to go to Dulles Airport tomorrow morning to go to L.A. So thank you. My other line's ringing. 'Bye.

(End phone message.)

RECORDING: Tuesday, 5:07 a.m. (Tone.)

UNIDENTIFIED FEMALE SPEAKER: Hi, Monica. It's me It's 6:00. Just calling to say hi and see how your day was. And I was curious whether you talked to that friend of yours and if everything worked out okay with her. I hope so.

And to let you know that Bill and I will probably be there in maybe a couple of hours, maybe by 8:00, 'cause he wants to eat dinner and pack for L.A., and then we're going to drive there. So I hope I get to see you. And I love you. And I'll talk to you later. Bye-bye.

(End phone message.)

RECORDING: Tuesday, 6:42 a.m. (Tone.)

UNIDENTIFIED FEMALE SPEAKER: Hi, Monica. It's me It's 8:00. I expected to find you here, my roomie, but you are not here. Please tell me where you are when you get back, and please come and sleep here. Thank you. Good-bye.

(End phone message.)

RECORDING: Tuesday, 8:45 a.m. (Tone.)

Page 12

UNIDENTIFIED FEMALE SPEAKER: Hi, Munk, are you there? It's 9:00. I will beep you to see where you are. 'Bye.

(End phone message.)

RECORDING: Tuesday, 9:35 a.m. (Tone.)

UNIDENTIFIED FEMALE SPEAKER: Hi, Monica. It's me Um, Denise left a message on my machine last night. She's finally spoke to that David, and, um, he said you were adorable and a great conversationalist.

It – it didn't sound as if he wanted to run away and get married, but that he does want to keep up contact with you.

But, um, it's better if you hear it yourself. So call me later and you can play – you know, you can play my messages and you can hear it yourself. But it's – it's really nice. I mean, I think short of, you know, the guy saying he's in love, it's – it's really exactly what you would have wanted. So call me later and et cetera. 'Bye.

(End phone message.)

RECORDING: Tuesday, 9:46 p.m. (Tone.)

MR. SCHICK: Monica, this is Tom Schick at American Express. I am calling you on Thursday, January 15, at 12:00 noon. Give me a call at your leisure – no urgency – at [redacted]. Thank you.

(End phone message.)

Page 13

RECORDING: Wednesday, 12:41 a.m. (Tone.)

MR. NELVIS: Hey, Monica, it's Nel. I'm calling at 12:08, uh, I -- I'm going to call you back in about half-an-hour. Thanks.

(End phone message.)

RECORDING: Wednesday, 12:52 a.m. (Tone.)

MR. NELVIS: Hey, Monica, it's Nel again. Would you page me as soon as you get back home at [redacted], pager number [redacted]. Thanks.

(End phone message.)

RECORDING: Wednesday, 12:58 a.m. (Tone.)

MS. CURRIE: Hi, it's Betty. If you're there, pick up. Otherwise, call me right back ASAP. Thanks.

(End phone message.)

RECORDING: Wednesday, 1:10 a.m. (Tone.)

(End recording SEARCH.003, Side 1.)

Concordance Report

Unique Words: **444**

Total Occurrences: **1,085**

Total Words In File: **2,411**

Single File Concordance

Case Sensitive

Cover Pages = **0**

Includes **ALL** Text Occurrences

Dates **ON**

Includes Pure Numbers

Possesive Forms **ON**

105th Congress, 2d Session - - - - - - - - - - - - - House Document 105–311

PART 2

APPENDICES TO THE REFERRAL TO THE UNITED STATES HOUSE OF REPRESENTATIVES PURSUANT TO TITLE 28, UNITED STATES CODE, SECTION 595(c) SUBMITTED BY THE OFFICE OF THE INDEPENDENT COUNSEL, SEPTEMBER 9, 1998

COMMUNICATION

FROM

THE OFFICE OF THE INDEPENDENT COUNSEL, KENNETH W. STARR

TRANSMITTING

APPENDICES TO THE REFERRAL TO THE UNITED STATES HOUSE OF REPRESENTATIVES PURSUANT TO TITLE 28, UNITED STATES CODE, SECTION 595(c) SUBMITTED BY THE OFFICE OF THE INDEPENDENT COUNSEL, SEPTEMBER 9, 1998

SEPTEMBER 18, 1998.—Referred to the Committee on the Judiciary pursuant to H. Res. 525 and ordered to be printed

---

U.S. GOVERNMENT PRINTING OFFICE

50–893 WASHINGTON : 1998

II

ONE HUNDRED FIFTH CONGRESS

Congress of the United States

House of Representatives

COMMITTEE ON THE JUDICIARY

2138 RAYBURN HOUSE OFFICE BUILDING

WASHINGTON, DC 20515–6216

(202) 225–3951
http://www.house.gov/judiciary

September 18, 1998

Foreword

Pursuant to H. Res. 525, which was adopted by the House of Representatives on September 11, 1998, by a vote of 363-63, the Committee on the Judiciary, on September 18, 1998, ordered the public printing of volumes two through seven of the Referral from Independent Counsel Kenneth Starr. The materials printed herein have been redacted by the Committee. All redactions approved by the Committee are indicated in the attached redaction report.

At this time, the Committee has elected not to release certain material filed under seal with the United States District Court for the Eastern District of Arkansas.

HENRY J. HYDE
Chairman
House Committee on the Judiciary

JOHN CONYERS, JR.
Ranking Minority Member
House Committee on the Judiciary

IV

House Committee on the Judiciary Redaction Report	
Page or other Identification Number	**Reason for Redacted Material**
Vol. II, Tab D, Map	National Security
Vol. II, Tab G	Personal Identifying Information
Vol. II, Tab I, pp. 10-19	National Security
Vol. III, Tab 1	Deposition of William Jefferson Clinton, Jones V. Clinton Sealed Pursuant to Court Order
Vol. III, Tab 4	Deposition Exhibit 3 Jones V. Clinton Sealed Pursuant to Court Order
Vol. III, Tab 5	Deposition Exhibit 5 Jones V. Clinton Sealed Pursuant to Court Order
Vol. III, Tab 8	Deposition Exhibit 8 Jones V. Clinton Sealed Pursuant to Court Order
Vol. III, Tab 9	President Clinton's Response to Plaintiff's Third Set of Interrogatories, Jones V. Clinton Sealed Pursuant to Court Order
Vol. III, Tab 10	President Clinton's Responses to Plaintiff's First Set of Interrogatories, Jones V. Clinton Sealed Pursuant to Court Order

House Committee on the Judiciary Redaction Report	
Page or other Identification Number	**Reason for Redacted Material**
Vol. III, Tab 11	Deposition Exhibit 11 Jones V. Clinton Sealed Pursuant to Court Order
Vol. III, Tab 12	Deposition Exhibit 12 Jones V. Clinton Sealed Pursuant to Court Order
Vol. III, Tab 13	Deposition Exhibit 13 Jones V. Clinton Sealed Pursuant to Court Order
Vol. III, Tab 14	President Clinton's Supplemental Responses to Plaintiff's Second Set of Interrogatories Jones V. Clinton Sealed Pursuant to Court Order
Vol. III, Tab 15, 849-DC-634	Personal Identifying Information
Vol. IV, Tab 2, p. 111, lines 24-25- p. 112, lines 1-7	Privacy
Vol. IV, Tab 3, p. 53, lines 3-20	Privacy
Vol. IV, Tab 3, pp. 88, 95, 96, index	Privacy
Vol. IV, Tab 6, p. 1	Personal Identifying Information
Vol. IV, Tab 10, p. 4	Privacy
Vol. IV, Tab 7, p. 1	Personal Identifying Information
Vol. IV, Tab 15, p. 10, lines 18-20 (non-compressed copy, p. 9, lines 18-20)	Privacy

House Committee on the Judiciary
Redaction Report

Page or other Identification Number	Reason for Redacted Material
Vol. IV, Tab 15, p. 12, lines 3-11 (compressed copy, p. 13, lines 3-11)	Sexual Description
Vol. IV, Tab 15, p. 17, line 4-5 (compressed copy, p. 18, line 4-5)	Sexual Description
Vol. IV, Tab 15, p. 18, lines 22 ½ - 24 (compressed copy, p. 19, lines 22 ½ - 24)	Sexual Description
Vol. IV, Tab 15, p. 19, lines 3-17 (compressed copy, p. 20, lines 3-16)	Sexual Description
Vol. IV, Tab 15, p. 29, line 21-30, p. 31, line 12 (compressed copy p. 30, line 21- p. 31, line 12)	Sexual Description
Vol. IV, Tab 15, p. 46, lines 16-22 (compressed copy p. 47, lines 16-21)	Sexual Description
Vol. IV, Tab 15, p. 47, lines 8-11 (compressed copy p. 48, lines 8-11)	Sexual Description
Vol. IV, Tab 15, p. 49, lines 15-24 (compressed copy of p. 50, lines 15-24)	Sexual Description
Vol. IV, Tab 15, p. 69, index	Privacy
Vol. IV, Tab 16, pp. 1-4, 6	Privacy
Vol. IV, Tab 17, pp. 1-3	Privacy
Vol. IV, Tab 19, p. 1	Privacy
Vol. IV, Tab 19, p. 4, para. 1	Privacy
Vol. IV, Tab 19, p. 7, para. 2	Privacy
Vol. IV, Tab 20, p. 1	Privacy

House Committee on the Judiciary Redaction Report	
Page or other Identification Number	**Reason for Redacted Material**
Vol. IV, Tab 20, p. 2, para. 1	Privacy
Vol. IV, Tab 20, p. 8, para. 2	Sexual Description
Vol. IV, Tab 20, p. 9, para. 1	Sexual Description
Vol. IV, Tab 20, p. 10, para. 1	Sexual Description
Vol. IV, Tab 20, p. 14, para. 3	Sexual Description
Vol. IV, Tab 20, p. 15, para. 3	Sexual Description
Vol. IV, Tab 20, p. 16, para. 4	Sexual Description
Vol. IV, Tab 20, p. 19, para. 1	Sexual Description
Vol. IV, Tab 21, p. 1	Privacy
Vol. IV, Tab 21, p. 9, para. 2	Privacy
Vol. IV, Tab 21, p. 16, para. 7	Privacy
Vol. IV, Tab 22, p. 1	Privacy
Vol. IV, Tab 22, p. 11, para. 4	Privacy
Vol. IV, Tab 23, p. 1	Privacy
Vol. IV, Tab 24, p. 1	Privacy
Vol. IV, Tab 24, p. 3, para. 2	Privacy
Vol. IV, Tab 24, p. 10, paras. 3, 5, 6	Privacy
Vol. IV, Tab 24, p. 11	Privacy
Vol. IV, Tab 25, p. 2, para. 3	Privacy
Vol. IV, Tab 25, p. 4, para. 1	Privacy
Vol. IV, Tab 25, p. 8, para 2 (first)	Expletives
Vol. IV, Tab 25, p. 8, para. 2	Privacy

IX

House Committee on the Judiciary Redaction Report	
Page or other Identification Number	**Reason for Redacted Material**
Vol. IV, Tab 26, p. 1	Privacy
Vol. IV, Tab 27, p. 1	Privacy
Vol. IV, Tab 27, p. 5, para. 3	Sexual Description
Vol. IV, Tab 27, p. 9, para. 2	Privacy
Vol. IV, Tab 27, p. 9, para. 3	Privacy
Vol. IV, Tab 28, p. 1	Privacy
Vol. IV, Tab 29, p. 1	Privacy
Vol. IV, Tab 29, p. 2, paras. 4-5	Privacy
Vol. IV, Tab 29, p. 4, para. 3	Privacy
Vol. IV, Tab 30, p. 1	Privacy
Vol. IV, Tab 30, p. 6, para. 5	Privacy
Vol. IV, Tab 31, p. 1	Privacy
Vol. IV, Tab 32, p. 1	Privacy
Vol. IV, Tab 33, p. 1	Privacy
Vol. IV, Tab 34, p. 1	Privacy
Vol. IV, Tab 35, p. 1	Privacy
Vol. IV, Tab 37, pp. 2, 5, 6, 8, 12, 13	Privacy
Vol. V, Tab 28, pp. 1-5	Privacy
Vol. V, Tab 31, p. 1	Privacy
Vol. VI, Tab 49, p. 1	Privacy
Vol. VI, Tab 54	Privacy
Vol. VI, Tab 55	Privacy

X

House Committee on the Judiciary Redaction Report	
Page or other Identification Number	**Reason for Redacted Material**
Vol. VI, Tab 59	Privacy
Vol. VI, Tab 60, p. 3	Privacy
Vol. VI, Tab 61	Privacy
Vol. VI, Tab 64	Privacy
Vol. VI, Tab 74	Privacy
Vol. VI, Tab 78, first occurrence	Privacy
Vol. VI, Tab 78, second occurrence	Sexual Description
Vol. VI, 0812-DC-2	Personal Identifying Information
Vol. VI, 0828-DC-12	Personal Identifying Information
Vol. VI, 0828-DC-13	Personal Identifying Information
Vol. VI, 0828-DC-23	Personal Identifying Information
Vol. VI, 0830-DC-7	Personal Identifying Information
Vol. VI, 0830-DC-17	Personal Identifying Information
Vol. VI, 0831-DC-8-11	Personal Identifying Information
Vol. VI, 0832-DC-4-5	Personal Identifying Information
Vol. VI, 0833-DC-980	Personal Identifying Information
Vol. VI, 0833-DC-1857	Expletive
Vol. VI, 0833-DC-2716	Personal Identifying Information
Vol. VI, 0833-DC-3207	Personal Identifying Information
Vol. VI, 0833-DC-17867, 69, 75, 86, 90, 903, 904, 908	Personal Identifying Information
Vol. VI, 0837-DC-1-4, 6-19, 21-24	Personal Identifying Information

House Committee on the Judiciary Redaction Report	
Page or other Identification Number	**Reason for Redacted Material**
Vol. VI, 0837-DC-25-27	Redacted Prior to Receipt
Vol. VI, 0845-DC-190	Personal Identifying Information
Vol. VI, 0849-DC-90-102	President Clinton's Responses to Plaintiffs Third Set of Interrogatories, Jones V. Clinton Sealed Pursuant to Court Order
Vol. VI, 0849-DC-121-137	Plaintiff's Witness List Jones V. Clinton Sealed Pursuant to Court Order
Vol. VI, 0849-DC-352	Transcript of Videotaped Oral Deposition U.S. V. Clinton Sealed Pursuant to Court Order
Vol. VI, 0849-DC-586	Deposition Exhibit 1 Jones V. Clinton Sealed Pursuant to Court Order
Vol. VI, 0849-DC-634	Deposition Exhibit 15 Jones V. Clinton Sealed Pursuant to Court Order
Vol. VI, 0852-DC-35, 37, 44, 45	Personal Identifying Information
Vol. VI, 0854-DC-1485	Personal Identifying Information
Vol. VI, 0856-DC-2	Personal Identifying Information
Vol. VI, 0880-DC-2	Personal Identifying Information
Vol. VI, 08902-DC-33	Personal Identifying Information
Vol. VI, 08902-DC-135	Personal Identifying Information
Vol. VI, 0916-DC-3	Personal Identifying Information

House Committee on the Judiciary
Redaction Report

Page or other Identification Number	Reason for Redacted Material
Vol. VI, 0920-DC-13	Personal Identifying Information
Vol. VI, 0920-DC-517-525	Order, Jones V. Clinton Sealed Pursuant to Court Order
Vol. VI, 0921-61-62	Clerk's Minutes, Jones V. Clinton Sealed Pursuant to Court Order
Vol. VI, 0921-DC-96-100	Plaintiff's Motion to Compel Responses to Plaintiff's Second Set of Interrogatories to Defendant Clinton Jones V. Clinton Sealed Pursuant to Court Order
Vol. VI, 0921-DC-101-119	Second Set of Interrogatories from Plaintiff to Defendant Clinton Jones V. Clinton Sealed Pursuant to Court Order
Vol. VI, 0921-DC-120-137	President Clinton's Responses to Plaintiff's Second Set of Interrogatories Jones V. Clinton Sealed Pursuant to Court Order
Vol. VI, 0921-DC-138-143	Exhibit 3, Jones V. Clinton Sealed Pursuant to Court Order
Vol. VI, 0921-DC-144-145	Exhibit 4, Jones V. Clinton Sealed Pursuant to Court Order
Vol. VI, 0921-DC-150-151	Exhibit 5, Jones V. Clinton Sealed Pursuant to Court Order

House Committee on the Judiciary Redaction Report	
Page or other Identification Number	**Reason for Redacted Material**
Vol. VI, 0921-DC-459-466	Order, Jones V. Clinton Sealed Pursuant to Court Order
Vol. VI, 0921-736-744	Order, Jones V. Clinton Sealed Pursuant to Court Order
Vol. VI, 0921-751-752	Clerk's Minutes, Jones V. Clinton Sealed Pursuant to Court Order
Vol. VI, 0921-DC-770-72	Clerk's Minutes, Jones V. Clinton Sealed Pursuant to Court Order
Vol. VI, 0921-DC-775-778	Motion for Protective Order Jones V. Clinton Sealed Pursuant to Court Order
Vol. VI, 0929-DC-56	Personal Identifying Information
Vol. VI, 0964-DC-862	Personal Identifying Information
Vol. VI, 0968-DC-73, 187, 236, 263, 303	Redacted Prior to Receipt
Vol. VI, 0968-DC-3506, 10, 22, 33, 46, 50, 56, 58, 69	Personal Identifying Information
Vol. VII, 1000-DC-768	Personal Identifying Information
Vol. VII, 1013-DC-95-96	Personal Identifying Information
Vol. VII, 1014-DC-22	Personal Identifying Information
Vol. VII, 1033-DC-33-35	Personal Identifying Information
Vol. VII, 1033-DC-115-16	Personal Identifying Information

House Committee on the Judiciary Redaction Report	
Page or other Identification Number	**Reason for Redacted Material**
Vol. VII, 1034-DC-60-63, 99, 103, 109, 111	Privacy
Vol. VII, 1037-DC-11, 17, 22, 38, 40, 42, 63, 86, 103, 107, 265, 280, 296, 318, 338, 341, 553, 583	Personal Identifying Information
Vol. VII, 1037-DC-39, 168, 318, 341	Expletives
Vol. VII, 1051-DC-3	Personal Identifying Information
Vol. VII, 1064-DC-8	Personal Identifying Information
Vol. VII, 1065-DC-6, 8	Personal Identifying Information
Vol. VII, 1078-DC-2	Personal Identifying Information
Vol. VII, 1178-DC-5, 11, 13-16, 18-21, 23	Personal Identifying Information and Certain Material Redacted Prior to Receipt
Vol. VII, 1178-DC-26	Personal Identifying Information
Vol. VII, 1205-DC-16	Personal Identifying Information
Vol. VII, 1216-DC-22-23	Personal Identifying Information
Vol. VII, 1248-DC-8, 305, 307, 311, 312-315, 319, 327-328, 381, 444	Personal Identifying Information
Vol. VII, 1362-DC-1171	National Security
Vol. VII, 1407-DC-5	Personal Identifying Information
Vol. VII, 1408-DC-5	Personal Identifying Information
Vol. VII, 1414-DC-001, 1006-1014	Order, Jones V. Clinton Sealed Pursuant to Court Order

House Committee on the Judiciary Redaction Report	
Page or other Identification Number	**Reason for Redacted Material**
Vol. VII, 1414-DC-1188-1192	Order, Jones V. Clinton Sealed Pursuant to Court Order
Vol. VII, 1414-DC-1327-1346	Hearing Transcript Jones V. Clinton Sealed Pursuant to Court Order
Vol. VII, 1414-DC-1534-1546	Second Set of Requests from Plaintiff to Defendant Clinton for Production of Documents Jones V. Clinton Sealed Pursuant to Court Order
Vol. VII, 1472-DC-6-20	Personal Identifying Information
Vol. VII, 1506-DC-29, 31, 50	Personal Identifying Information
Vol. VII, 1506-DC-57-58	Redacted Prior to Receipt
Vol. VII, 1506-DC-68, 70, 102, 139, 144, 192, 275, 373	Personal Identifying Information
Vol. VII, 2004-DC-83, 85, 86, 87, 88, 90, 91	Personal Identifying Information
Vol. VII, MSL-55-DC-94, 124	Privacy
Vol. VII, MSL-DC-1166	Personal Identifying Information
Vol. VII, MSL-DC-1176, 1192	Personal Identifying Information
Vol. VII, V002-DC-5	Personal Identifying Information
Vol. VII, V002-DC-6-15	President Clinton's Responses to Plaintiff's First Set of Interrogatories Jones V. Clinton Sealed Pursuant to Court Order

House Committee on the Judiciary Redaction Report	
Page or other Identification Number	**Reason for Redacted Material**
Vol. VII, V002-DC-16-32	President Clinton's Responses to Plaintiff's Second Set of Interrogatories Jones V. Clinton Sealed Pursuant to Court Order
Vol. VII, V002-DC-52-55	President Clinton's Supplemental Responses to Plaintiff's Second Set of Interrogatories Jones V. Clinton Sealed Pursuant to Court Order
Vol. VII, V002-DC-56-92	President Clinton's Responses to Plaintiff's First Set of Requests for Projection of Documents and Things, Jones V. Clinton Sealed Pursuant to Court Order
Vol. VII, V002-DC-93-116	President Clinton's Responses to Plaintiff's Second Set of Document Requests, Jones V. Clinton Sealed Pursuant to Court Order
Vol. VII, V004-DC-134-167	Personal Identifying Information
Vol. VII, V004-DC-171-172	Redacted Prior to Receipt
Vol. VII, V004-DC-183	Personal Identifying Information
Vol. VII, V005-DC-58, 60-61	Redacted Prior to Receipt
Vol. VII, V006-DC-7-9	Personal Identifying Information
Vol. VII, V006-DC-20	Personal Identifying Information
Vol. VII, V006-DC-118	Personal Identifying Information

House Committee on the Judiciary Redaction Report	
Page or other Identification Number	**Reason for Redacted Material**
Vol. VII, V006-DC-157-159, 162, 167, 180, 181, 183	Personal Identifying Information
Vol. VII, V006-DC-225	Personal Identifying Information
Vol. VII, V006-DC-391	Personal Identifying Information
Vol. VII, V006-DC-1770, 1792, 1796	Personal Identifying Information
Vol. VII, V006-DC-1813-1814	Personal Identifying Information
Vol. VII, V006-DC-2064-2071	Personal Identifying Information and Certain Material Redacted Prior to Receipt
Vol. VII, V006-DC-2095, 2130, 140, 142, 146-147, 156, 158, 214, 243	Redacted Prior to Receipt
Vol. VII, V006-DC-3719	Personal Identifying Information

XVIII

CONTENTS

XX

Volume V:

Document Supplement, Part C

Documents Cited in Referral:
Tabs 1-46

REFERRAL

TO THE

UNITED STATES HOUSE OF REPRESENTATIVES

PURSUANT TO

TITLE 28, UNITED STATES CODE, § 595(C)

DOCUMENT SUPPLEMENT C

SUBMITTED BY

THE OFFICE OF THE INDEPENDENT COUNSEL

SEPTEMBER 9, 1998

Index

INDEX: Documents cited in the 595(c) Referral

09-Sep-98

Bates # or Tab#	Production Name	Description
*Tab 001	N/A	Main Stairway to Family Quarters
*Tab 002	N/A	Movie Theater in East Colonnade
*Tab 003	N/A	11/14/95 LA Times news article
*Tab 004	N/A	11/14/95 Washington Post news article
*Tab 005	N/A	11/16/95: Facts on File, World News Digest -- pg. 852
*Tab 006	N/A	11/16/95 Washington Post news article
*Tab 007	N/A	11/17/95 USA Today news article
*Tab 008	N/A	11/20/95 Washington Post news article
*Tab 009	N/A	11/23/95: Facts on File, World News Digest -- pg. 868
*Tab 010	N/A	2/19/96 Weekly Compilation of Presidential Documents
*Tab 011	N/A	2/28/96 Newsday news article
*Tab 012	N/A	7/4/97 Drudge Report Final
*Tab 013	N/A	8/11/97 Washington Post news article
*Tab 014	N/A	8/11/97 Newsweek article
*Tab 015	N/A	9/13/97 NY Times news article
*Tab 016	N/A	9/22/97 Forbes news article
*Tab 017	N/A	10/4/97 to 10/23/97 Digest of Other White House Announcements
*Tab 018	N/A	11/9/97 LA Times news article
*Tab 019	N/A	11/14/97 Baltimore Sun news article
*Tab 020	N/A	11/15/97 Washington Post news article
*Tab 021	N/A	1/20/98 subpoena to William Jefferson Clinton, V002
*Tab 022	N/A	1/21/98 Washington Post news article
*Tab 023	N/A	1/21/98 "The News Hour with Jim Lehrer"

Bates # or Tab#	Production Name	Description
*Tab 024	N/A	1/21/98 "All Things Considered"
*Tab 025	N/A	1/21/98 White House Briefing
*Tab 025A	N/A	1/21/98 Excerpts of Telephone Interview of Clinton by Roll Call
*Tab 026	N/A	1/22/98 Remarks by President Clinton at the White House
*Tab 027	N/A	1/22/98 America Online article
*Tab 028	N/A	1/22/98 FBI Receipt of Property
*Tab 029	N/A	1/22/98 ABC News Special Report with Peter Jennings
*Tab 030	N/A	1/22/98 Roll Call interview with William Jefferson Clinton
*Tab 030A	N/A	1/22/98 Seatle Times news article
*Tab 031	N/A	1/23/98 FBI Receipt of Property, w/attached letter
*Tab 032	N/A	1/24/98 CBS News Show: Saturday Morning
*Tab 033	N/A	1/25/98 Face the Nation
*Tab 034	N/A	1/26/98 Nightline
*Tab 035	N/A	1/26/98 ABC News Special Report with Peter Jennings
*Tab 036	N/A	1/26/98 White House Education News Conference
*Tab 036A	N/A	1/27/98 AP news article
*Tab 036B	N/A	1/27/98 NBC: The Today Show
*Tab 037	N/A	2/5/98 Remarks by President Clinton
*Tab 038	N/A	2/6/98 Joint News Conference with President Clinton
*Tab 039	N/A	2/14/98 Washington Post news article
*Tab 040	N/A	2/17/98 Chicago Tribune news article
*Tab 041	N/A	3/5/98 closed hearing transcript excerpt
*Tab 042	N/A	3/17/98 Memoradum w/attachments, In re: Grand Jury Proceedings
*Tab 043	N/A	3/25/98 Washington Post news article
*Tab 044	N/A	4/17/98 letter to DAG Eric Holder from the OIC
*Tab 045	N/A	6/98 California Lawyer article

Bates # or Tab#	Production Name	Description
*Tab 046	N/A	6/15/98 Brief of Appellant William J. Clinton
*Tab 047	N/A	6/29/98 US News & World Report news article
*Tab 048	N/A	7/15/98 letter to IC Smaltz from Richard Rogers
*Tab 049	N/A	7/17/98 subpoena to the White House, D1415
*Tab 050	N/A	7/22/98 CBS News transcript, HARDBALL
*Tab 051	N/A	7/26/98 NBC News Meet the Press
*Tab 052	N/A	7/28/98 Motion of William J. Clinton for Continuance
*Tab 053	N/A	7/28/98 Transcript of Status Hearing , In re: Motion to Continue
*Tab 054	N/A	7/29/98 FBI Receipt of Property
*Tab 055	N/A	7/31/98 letter to David Kendall from Bob Bittman
*Tab 056	N/A	7/31/98 letter to Bob Bittman from David Kendall
*Tab 057	N/A	7/31/98 letter to David Kendall from Bob Bittman
*Tab 058	N/A	8/3/98 letter to Bob Bittman from David Kendall
*Tab 059	N/A	8/3/98 letter to David Kendall from Bob Bittman
*Tab 060	N/A	8/3/98 FBI Laboratory Report
*Tab 061	N/A	8/3/98 FBI 302
*Tab 062	N/A	8/3/98 letter to Judge Starr from DAG Eric Holder
*Tab 063	N/A	8/6/98 letter to AG Reno from IC Smaltz
*Tab 064	N/A	8/6/98 FBI Laboratory Report
*Tab 065	N/A	8/7/98 Washington Times news article
*Tab 066	N/A	8/10/98 Newsweek article
*Tab 067	N/A	8/11/98 letter to AG Holder from Judge Starr
*Tab 068	N/A	8/11/98 Memorandum Order, In re: Grand Jury Proceedings
*Tab 069	N/A	8/13/98 NY Times news article
*Tab 070	N/A	8/13/98 USA Today news article
*Tab 071	N/A	8/13/98 Washington Post news article
*Tab 072	N/A	8/13/98 Washington Times news article

Bates # or Tab#	Production Name	Description
*Tab 073	N/A	8/17/98 Newsweek article
*Tab 074	N/A	8/17/98 FBI Laboratory Report
*Tab 075	N/A	8/17/98 AP news article
*Tab 076	N/A	8/18/98 Washington Post
*Tab 077	N/A	8/24/98 facsimile to Jackie Bennett from Gary Grindler
*Tab 078	N/A	8/27/98 memo
*Tab 079	N/A	8/31/98 letter to Bob Bittman from David Kendall
*Tab 080	N/A	9/7/98 memo
*Tab 081	N/A	Jones v. Clinton, 1998 WL 551961, 9/1/98 order
*Tab 082	N/A	Lyrics to "Surfacing"
*Tab 083	N/A	18 U.S.C. section 2246
0812-DC-00000002	Lewinsky, Monica	Passport photo page
0824-DC-00000001 to 2	Currie, Betty	1/23/98 letter to Judge Starr from Karl Metzner
0824-DC-00000013	Currie, Betty	"Love Notes" supplement
0824-DC-00000014	Currie, Betty	2/14/97 Washington Post "Love Notes"
0827-DC-00000002 to 18	United States Secret Service	Epass Access Control Reports
0828-DC-00000003	US Mission to the UN	3/14/97 to 12/22/97 Toll records
0828-DC-00000004	US Mission to the UN	10/21/97 to 11/19/97 Toll records
0828-DC-00000012	US Mission to the UN	Monica Lewinsky's resume
0828-DC-00000013	US Mission to the UN	11/3/97 letter from Monica Lewinsky to Ambassador Richardson
0828-DC-00000023	US Mission to the UN	10/31/97 schedule for Ambassador Richardson
0830-DC-00000007	Revlon Group, Inc.	1/13/98 letter from Monica Lewinsky to Jenna Sheldon
0830-DC-00000017	Revlon Group, Inc.	12/11/97 letter from Monica Lewinsky to Richard Halperin
0831-DC-00000008 to 11	Pagemart	Pager records for Moncia Lewinsky
0832-DC-00000004 to 5	McAndrews & Forbes Holding	Toll records
0833-DC-00000980	Department of Defense	11/6/97 letter from Monica Lewinsky to Vernon Jordan
0833-DC-00001070	Department of Defense	6/24/97 typed note to Betty Currie

Bates # or Tab#	Production Name	Description
0833-DC-00001857	Department of Defense	3/5/97 E-Mail
0833-DC-00001876	Department of Defense	3/3/97 e-mail from Linda Tripp to Monica Lewinsky
0833-DC-00001906	Department of Defense	2/24/97 E-Mail
0833-DC-00001934	Department of Defense	2/19/97 E-Mail
0833-DC-00001974	Department of Defense	2/4/97 E-Mail
0833-DC-00002716	Department of Defense	Notification of Personnel Action
0833-DC-00002880	Department of Defense	Job Description
0833-DC-00003207	Department of Defense	Travel voucher
0833-DC-00009446	Department of Defense	2/19/97 E-Mail
0833-DC-00017867	Department of Defense	10/6/97 to 10/9/97 Toll records
0833-DC-00017869	Department of Defense	10/15/97 to 10/20/97 Toll records
0833-DC-00017875	Department of Defense	Toll records
0833-DC-00017886	Department of Defense	Toll records
0833-DC-00017890	Department of Defense	Toll records
0833-DC-00017903 to 04	Department of Defense	Toll records
0833-DC-00017908	Department of Defense	Toll records
0837-DC-00000001 to 27	Speed Service Couriers, Inc.	Courier receipts re: Monica Lewinsky
0843-DC-00000004	United States Secret Service	12/6/97 Epass Access Control Record
0845-DC-00000002	Tripp, Linda	Handwritten notes
0845-DC-00000004 to 17	Tripp, Linda	Handwritten notes
0845-DC-00000018 to 21	Tripp, Linda	Handwritten Notes
0845-DC-00000022 to 25	Tripp, Linda	Handwritten Notes
0845-DC-00000188	Tripp, Linda	Handwritten note
0845-DC-00000190	Tripp, Linda	Letter from Linda Tripp to Newsweek
0845-DC-00000191 to 193	Tripp, Linda	Handwritten notes
0849-DC-00000090 to 97	Rader, Campbell, Fisher & Pyke	President Clinton's Responses to Plaintiff's Third Set of Interrogatories

Bates # or Tab#	Production Name	Description
0849-DC-00000098 to 102	Rader, Campbell, Fisher & Pyke	Attachment to President Clinton's Responses to Plaintiff's Third Set of Interrogatories
0849-DC-00000121 to 137	Rader, Campbell, Fisher & Pyke	Plaintiff's Witness List
0849-DC-00000352	Rader, Campbell, Fisher & Pyke	Videotaped Deposition of William Jefferson Clinton
0849-DC-00000586	Rader, Campbell, Fisher & Pyke	Definition of "Sexual Relation"
0849-DC-00000634 to 636	Rader, Campbell, Fisher & Pyke	Affidavit of Jane Doe #6 (Monica Lewinsky)
0852-DC-00000035	American Express	Credit card statement
0852-DC-00000037	American Express	Credit card statement
0852-DC-00000044 to 45	American Express	12/17/97 billing statement
0854-DC-00001485	First Union Bank	5/6/96 Check No. 594
0856-DC-00000002	American Express	12/11/97 letter from Monica Lewinsky to Ursula Fairbairn
0880-DC-00000002 to 8	Lindsey, Bruce	Handwritten notes
0902-DC-00000003	Carter, Francis	Address
0902-DC-00000030	Carter, Francis	1/12/98 to 1/20/98 billing statement
0902-DC-00000033	Cater, Francis	FedEx USA Airbill
0902-DC-00000037 to 38	Carter, Francis	1/7/98 billing statement
0902-DC-00000051	Catrer, Francis	1/6/97 phone memo
0902-DC-00000135 to 138	Carter, Francis	Subpoena issued to Monica Lewinsky in the Paula Jones case
0902-DC-00000231	Carter, Francis	12/22/97 to 12/28/97 appointment book
0902-DC-00000232	Carter, Francis	1/5/98 appointment book
0902-DC-00000251	Carter, Francis	1/6/98 phone message
0916-DC-00000003	Park Hyatt	Receipt
0920-DC-00000013 to 18	Rader, Campbell, Fisher & Pyke	Subpoena issued to Monica Lewinsky in the Paula Jones case
0920-DC-00000517 to 525	Rader, Campbell, Fisher & Pyke	12/18/97 Order in Jones v. Clinton, LR-C-94-290
0921-DC-00000061 to 62	McCormack, Hon. James	11/6/97 Clerk's minutes for in-camera hearing
0921-DC-00000091 to 151	Rader, Campbell, Fisher & Pyke	Plaintiff's Motion to Compel Responses to Plaintiff's Second Set of Interrogatories to Defendant Clinton
0921-DC-00000459 to 466	McCormack, Hon. James	12/11/97 Order in Jones v. Clinton, LR-C-94-290

Bates # or Tab#	Production Name	Description
0921-DC-00000736 to 744	McCormack, Hon. James	1/8/98 Order in Jones v. Clinton, LR-C-94-290
0921-DC-00000751 to 752	McCormack, Hon. James	1/9/98 Clerk's minutes for in-camera hearing
0921-DC-00000770 to 772	Rader, Campbell, Fisher & Pyke	1/14/98 Clerk's Minutes
0921-DC-00000775 to 778	Rader, Campbell, Fisher & Pyke	Motion of Jane Doe #6 for Protective Order and Motion to Quash
0929-DC-00000056	NationsBank	Bank Statement
0952-DC-00000060	United States Secret Service	10/11/97 Presidential Protectee Movement Log
0964-DC-00000862	White House	12/6/97 pager record
0968-DC-00000073	White House	Schedule
0968-DC-00000187	White House	11/13/97 schedule
0968-DC-00000236	White House	3/29/98 schedule
0968-DC-00000263	White House	Schedule
0968-DC-00000303	White House	11/13/97 Diarist notes
0968-DC-00000841	White House	4/5/96 Press Schedule
0968-DC-00002947	White House	8/17/97 schedule
0968-DC-00003300	White House	11/22/97 to 11/25/97 Presidential press schedule
0968-DC-00003301	White House	Presidential Press Schedule
0968-DC-00003458	White House	2/96 calendar for Hillary Rodham Clinton
0968-DC-00003459	White House	3/96 calendar for Hillary Rodham Clinton
0968-DC-00003475	White House	7/97 calendar for Hillary Rodham Clinton
0968-DC-00003477	White House	10/97 calendar for Hillary Rodham Clinton
0968-DC-00003479	White House	12/97 calendar for Hillary Rodham Clinton
0968-DC-00003506	White House	2/28/97 Presidential Call Log
0968-DC-00003510	White House	3/29/97 Presidential Call Log
0968-DC-00003522	White House	5/1/97 Presidential Call Log
0968-DC-00003533	White House	5/24/97 Presidential Call Log
0968-DC-00003546	White House	7/4/97 Presidential Call Log
0968-DC-00003550	White House	7/14/97 Presidential Call Log

Bates # or Tab#	Production Name	Description
0968-DC-00003556	White House	7/24/97 Presidential Call Log
0968-DC-00003558	White House	8/16/97 Presidential Call Log
0968-DC-00003569	White House	10/11/97 Presidential Call
0968-DC-00003799	White House	11/13/97 schedule
0968-DC-00003843	White House	3/29/97 schedule
1000-DC-00000767 to 772	Bell Atlantic	5/4/96 Marcia Lewis Phone Bill
1012-DC-00000001	Bacon, Kenneth	4/28/97 letter from Kenneth Bacon to Lorrie McHugh
1013-DC-00000095 to 96	Bell Atlantic	2/4/98 statement of Toll calls for Debra Finerman
1014-DC-00000022	Cellular One	3/25/97 to 4/24/97 Calls
1033-DC-00000033 to 35	Bell Atlantic Mobile	Toll records
1033-DC-00000115 to 116	Bell Atlantic Mobile	Toll records
1034-DC-00000060 to 63	Jordan, Vernon	10/20/97 to 11/01/97 schedule for Vernon Jordan
1034-DC-00000099	Jordan, Vernon	12/8/97 to 12/10/97 schedule for Vernon Jordan
1034-DC-00000103	Jordan, Vernon	12/22/97 to 12/24/97 schedule for Vernon Jordan
1034-DC-00000109	Jordan, Vernon	1/12/98 to 1/14/98 schedule for Vernon Jordan
1034-DC-00000111	Jordan, Vernon	1/19/98 to 1/21/98 schedule for Vernon Jordan
1037-DC-00000001 to 2	Davis, Catherine Allday	5/18/97 Card
1037-DC-00000011	Davis, Catherine Allday	12/9/97 e-mail from Lewinsky to Davis
1037-DC-00000017	Davis, Catherine Allday	11/7/97 e-mail from Lewinsky to Davis
1037-DC-00000022	Davis, Catherine Allday	11/5/97 e-mail from Lewinsky to Davis
1037-DC-00000033	Davis, Catherine Allday	10/22/97 e-mail from Lewinsky to Davis
1037-DC-00000038 to 40	Davis, Catherine Allday	E-mails between Monica Lewinsky and Catherine Allday Davis
1037-DC-00000042	Davis, Catherine Allday	8/14/97 e-mail from Lewinsky to Davis
1037-DC-00000063	Davis, Catherine Allday	11/6/97 e-mail from Lewinsky to Davis
1037-DC-00000086 to 87	Davis, Catherine Allday	9/4/97 e-mail from Monica Lewinsky to Catherine Allday Davis
1037-DC-00000103	Davis, Catherine Allday	7/3/98 e-mail from Catherine Allday Davis to Monica Lewinsky

Bates # or Tab#	Production Name	Description
1037-DC-00000107	Davis, Catherine Allday	6/17/97 e-mail from Monica Lewinsky to Catherine Allday Davis
1037-DC-00000115	Davis, Catherine Allday	E-mail between Monica Lewinsky and Catherine Allday Davis
1037-DC-00000167 to 169	Davis, Catherine Allday	E-mails between Monica Lewinsky and Catherine Allday Davis
1037-DC-00000171	Davis, Catherine Allday	8/13/97 e-mail from Monica Lewinsky to Catherine Allday Davis
1037-DC-00000255 to 256	Davis, Catherine Allday	9/4/97 e-mail from Monica Lewinsky to Catherine Allday Davis
1037-DC-00000258 to 259	Davis, Catherine Allday	9/2/97 e-mail from Monica Lewinsky to Catherine Allday Davis
1037-DC-00000265 to 266	Davis, Catherine Allday	6/17/97 e-mail from Monica Lewinsky to Catherine Allday Davis
1037-DC-00000280	Davis, Catherine Allday	7/2/97 e-mail from Catherine Allday Davis to Monica Lewinsky
1037-DC-00000296	Davis, Catherine Allday	E-mail from Catherine Allday Davis to Monica Lewinsky
1037-DC-00000318	Davis, Catherine Allday	11/19/97 e-mail from Lewinsky to Davis
1037-DC-00000337 to 38	Davis, Catherine Allday	E-Mail from Lewinsky to Davis
1037-DC-00000341	Davis, Catherine Allday	E-mail from Monica Lewinsky to Catherine Allday Davis
1037-DC-00000553	Davis, Catherine Allday	11/5/97 e-mail from Monica Lewinsky to Catherine Allday Davis
1037-DC-00000583	Davis, Catherine Allday	9/2/97 e-mail from Monica Lewinsky to Catherine Allday Davis
1051-DC-00000003 to 4	Bell Atlantic	Copy of Computer Disk
1064-DC-00000008	Renaissance Vinoy Resort	1/13/98 Toll records
1065-DC-00000006	St. Regis Hotel	Hotel receipt
1065-DC-00000008	St. Regis Hotel	Receipt
1078-DC-00000002	Washington Post	Receipt
1089-DC-00000970	White House	10/16/96 Typed note
1178-DC-00000005	White House	10/11/97 Presidential Call Log
1178-DC-00000011	White House	Presidetial Call Logs
1178-DC-00000013	White House	12/19/97 Presidential Call Log
1178-DC-00000014	White House	12/19/97 Presidential Call Log

Bates # or Tab#	Production Name	Description
1178-DC-00000015	White House	12/30/97 Presidential Call Log
1178-DC-00000016	White House	1/6/98 Presidential Call Log
1178-DC-00000018	White House	1/16/98 Presidential Call Log
1178-DC-00000019	White House	1/17/98 Presidential Call Log
1178-DC-00000020	White House	1/17/98 Presidential Call Log
1178-DC-00000021	White House	1/18/98 Presidential Call Log
1178-DC-00000023	White House	1/19/98 Presidential Call Log
1178-DC-00000026	White House	WAVES records: Vernon Jordan
1205-DC-00000016	GTE Company of California	1/25/98 toll record from California
1216-DC-00000022 to 23	Bell Atlantic	Toll records
1222-DC-00000024	United States Secret Service	1/21/96 itinerary for the White House
1222-DC-00000032	United States Secret Service	3/5/96 White House itinerary
1222-DC-00000041	United States Secret Service	3/31/96 intinerary
1222-DC-00000045	United States Secret Service	Schedule
1222-DC-00000083 to 85	United States Secret Service	11/15/95 to 11/18/95 Presidential Movement Logs
1222-DC-00000102	United States Secret Service	2/19/96 Presidential Movement Log
1222-DC-00000112 to 113	United States Secret Service	3/29/96 and 3/31/96 Presidential Movement Logs
1222-DC-00000156 to 157	United States Secret Service	11/15/95 Presidential Protectee Movement Logs
1222-DC-00000179	United States Secret Service	Presidential Movement Logs
1222-DC-00000183	United States Secret Service	1/7/96 Presidential Protectee Movement Log
1222-DC-00000189	United States Secret Service	1/21/96 Presidential Movement Log
1222-DC-00000196	United States Secret Service	2/4/96 Presidential Movement Log
1222-DC-00000197	United States Secret Service	2/19/96 Presidential Movement Log
1222-DC-00000216 to 217	United States Secret Service	3/31/96 Presidential Movement Logs
1222-DC-00000219	United States Secret Service	4/7/96 Presidential Movements
1222-DC-00000234	United States Secret Service	2/28/97 Presidential Movements
1222-DC-00000242	United States Secret Service	5/24/97 Presidential Protectee Movement Log

Bates # or Tab#	Production Name	Description
1222-DC-00000251	United States Secret Service	7/14/97 schedule
1222-DC-00000254	United States Secret Service	7/24/97 schedule
1222-DC-00000325	United States Secret Service	12/31/95, 1/7/96 Secret Service agent duty schedule
1222-DC-00000328	United States Secret Service	2/21/96 Secret Service agent duty schedule
1234-DC-00000049	White House	11/13/97 schedule
1234-DC-00000050	White House	11/13/97 Presidential Movement Log
1234-DC-00000357	United States Secret Service	8/22/97 to 12/31/97 Epass Access Control Report
1248-DC-00000008	White House	4/7/96 Telephone Memorandum
1248-DC-00000288	White House	1/17/98 Diarist schedule notes
1248-DC-00000291	White House	Daynotes
1248-DC-00000305	White House	1/17/98 Presidential Call Log
1248-DC-00000307	White House	1/17/98 Presidential Call
1248-DC-00000311	White House	1/18/98 Presidential Call
1248-DC-00000312	White House	1/18/98 Presidential Call Log
1248-DC-00000313 to 315	White House	1/18/98 Presidential Call Log
1248-DC-00000319	White House	1/19/98 Presidential Call Log
1248-DC-00000327 to 328	White House	1/21/98 Presidential Call Log
1248-DC-00000381	White House	12/19/97 Presidential Call Log
1248-DC-00000444	White House	1/13/98 Presidential Call Log
1318-DC-00000001 to 2	Young, Dale	9/4/97 note from Monica Lewinsky to Dale Young
1342-DC-00000410	White House	Photograph
1361-DC-00000002 to 42	White House	Index of books located in the Oval Office study
1362-DC-00000549	United States Secret Service	11/15/95 Presidential Protectee Movement Log
1362-DC-00001171	United States Secret Service	Secret Service agent duty schedule
1407-DC-00000005	White House	12/6/97 TO 12/24/97 WAVES for Robert Bennett
1408-DC-00000005	Rader, Campbell, Fisher & Pyke	12/5/97 Facsimile sheet
1414-DC-00000001	Rader, Campbell, Fisher & Pyke	7/21/98 letter to Julie Corcoran from Donovan Campbell, Jr.

Bates # or Tab#	Production Name	Description
1414-DC-00001006 to 1014	Rader, Campbell, Fisher & Pyke	1/9/98 Order in Jones v. Clinton, LR-C-94-290
1414-DC-00001188 to 1192	Rader, Campbell, Fisher & Pyke	12/18/97 Order in Jones v. Clinton, LR-C-94-290
1414-DC-00001327 to 32	Rader, Campbell, Fisher & Pyke	hearing excerpt
1414-DC-00001334 to 46	Rader, Campbell, Fisher & Pyke	hearing excerpt
1414-DC-00001534 to 1546	Rader, Campbell, Fisher & Pyke	12/15/97 Pleading in Jones v. Clinton, LR-C-94-290
1415-DC-00000001	White House	8/3/98 letter from David Kendall to the OIC
1472-DC-00000006	White House	11/15/95 Call Log
1472-DC-00000007	White House	11/15/95 Telephone memorandum
1472-DC-00000008	White House	11/15/95 Telephone memorandum
1472-DC-00000015	White House	11/17/95 Telephone memorandum
1472-DC-00000017	White House	2/19/96 Telephone memorandum
1472-DC-00000018 to 20	White House	2/19/96 Telephone memorandum
1506-DC-00000007 to 8	White House	8/10/95 Presidential schedule
1506-DC-00000027	White House	12/31/95 Presidential schedule
1506-DC-00000029	White House	12/31/95 Telephone memorandum
1506-DC-00000031	White House	1/7/96 Telephone memorandum
1506-DC-00000050	White House	1/21/96 Telephone memorandum
1506-DC-00000057 to 58	White House	1/30/96 Presidential schedule
1506-DC-00000068	White House	2/4/96 Telephone memorandum
1506-DC-00000070	White House	2/4/96 Telephone memorandum
1506-DC-00000102	White House	2/19/96 Telephone memorandum
1506-DC-00000139	White House	3/31/96 Telephone memorandum
1506-DC-00000144	White House	4/7 Telephone Memorandum
1506-DC-00000188 to 189	White House	Presidential schedule
1506-DC-00000192	White House	5/2/96 Presidential Call Log
1506-DC-00000222	White House	Presidential schedule
1506-DC-00000264	White House	7/5/96 Presidential schedule

Bates # or Tab#	Production Name	Description
1506-DC-00000268	White House	7/6/96 Presidential schedule
1506-DC-00000275	White House	7/19/96 Presidential Call Log
1506-DC-00000328	White House	Presidential schedule
1506-DC-00000334 to 335	White House	Schedule
1506-DC-00000353	White House	Presidential schedule
1506-DC-00000373 to 374	White House	2/8/97 Schedule
1506-DC-00000426 to 427	White House	10/10/97 Presidential schedule
1506-DC-00000523 to 525	White House	1/21/96 Diarist notes
1506-DC-00000558	White House	Presidential schedule
1506-DC-00000559	White House	Presidential schedule
1506-DC-00000638	White House	Diarists notes, Presidential call
2004-DC-00000083	Bell Atlantic	Toll records
2004-DC-00000085 to 88	Bell Atlantic	Toll records
2004-DC-00000090 to 91	Bell Atlantic	Toll records
827-DC-00000018	United States Secret Service	2/24/97 to 12/28/97 Epass Access Control Report
CZ-DC-00000010	Driscoll, Richard	Fair market value appraisal
CZ-DC-00000016	Driscoll, Richard	Fair market value appraisal
DB PHOTOS 0004	Lewinsky, Monica	Blue Dress (photo)
DB PHOTOS 0044	Lewinsky, Monica	Audio-tapes from Monica Lewinsky's answering machine (originals in Quantico)
DB PHOTOS 0048	Lewinsky, Monica	evidence picture
DB-DC-000000017	Lewinsky, Monica	Draft letter from Monica Lewinsky to William Jefferson Clinton
DB-DC-000000022	Lewinsky, Monica	11/12/97 letter from Monica Lewinsky to William Jefferson Clinton
DB-DC-000000027	Lewinsky, Monica	Outline for job interests of Monica Lewinsky
DC-DC-00000004 to 5	Willis-Vento, Caroline	Fair market value appraisal
DF-DC-00000002 to 12	Lewinsky, Monica	2/1/98 handwritten proffer
MSL-1249-DC-0139 to 141	Lewinsky, Monica	Letter from Monica Lewinsky to William Jefferson Clinton

Bates # or Tab#	Production Name	Description
MSL-55-DC-0001	Lewinsky, Monica	Draft note from Monica Lewinsky to William Jefferson Clinton
MSL-55-DC-0094	Lewinsky, Monica	Letter drafted on Monica's home computer
MSL-55-DC-0124	Lewinsky, Monica	Letter drafted on Monica's home computer
MSL-55-DC-0177	Lewinsky, Monica	Letter from Monica Lewinsky to William Jefferson Clinton
MSL-55-DC-0178	Lewinsky, Monica	Letter from Monica Lewinsky to William Jefferson Clinton
MSL-55-DC-0179	Lewinsky, Monica	11/2/97 letter from Monica Lewinsky to Betty Currie
MSL-55-DC-0184 to 186	Lewinsky, Monica	Note created on Monica Lewinsky's home computer "Happy National Boss Day?"
MSL-DC-00000456	Lewinsky, Monica	Handwritten note
MSL-DC-00000489 to 90	Lewinsky, Monica	Invitation to William Jefferson Clinton's Birthday Party
MSL-DC-00000621 to 22	Lewinsky, Monica	3/2/97 handwritten letter from Monica Lewinsky to William Jefferson Clinton
MSL-DC-00001050	White House	9/30/97 letter from Monica Lewinsky to William Jefferson Clinton
MSL-DC-00001051	Lewinsky, Monica	October 1997 Calendar
MSL-DC-00001051A	Lewinsky, Monica	November 1997 Calendar
MSL-DC-00001052	Lewinsky, Monica	Typed note
MSL-DC-00001166 to 1168	Lewinsky, Monica	Draft Affidavit
MSL-DC-00001176 to 1177	White House	6/29/97 draft letter from Monica Lewinsky to Marsha Scott
MSL-DC-00001192	White House	7/6/97 letter from Monica Lewinsky to Marsha Scott
MSL-DC-00001221	Lewinsky, Monica	Page from Monica Lewinsky's schedule book
MSL-DC-00001227	Lewinsky, Monica	6/29/97 note from Monica Lewinsky to William Jefferson Clinton
MSL-DC-00001228	Lewinksy, Monica	3/14/997 memorandum from Cliff Bernath for the Record
MSL-DC-00001230	Lewinsky, Monica	4/28/97 letter from Kenneth Bacon to Lorrie McHugh
V002-DC-00000001 to 5	Clinton, William Jefferson	1/27/98 letter from David Kendall to Bob Bittman, with attachments
V002-DC-00000006 to 7	Clinton, William Jefferson	1/28/98 letter from David Kendall to Bob Bittman

Bates # or Tab#	Production Name	Description
V002-DC-00000008 to 15	Clinton, William Jefferson	President Clinton's Responses to Plaintiff's First Set of Interrogatories
V002-DC-00000016 to 32	Clinton, William Jefferson	President Clinton's Responses to Plaintiff's Second Set of Interrogatories
V002-DC-00000052 to 55	Clinton, William Jefferson	President Clinton's Supplemental Responses to Plaintiff's Second Set of Interrogatories
V002-DC-00000056 to 92	Clinton, William Jefferson	President Clinton's Responses to Plaintiff's First Set of Requests for Production of Documents and Things
V002-DC-00000093 to 116	Clinton, William Jefferson	President Clinton's Responses to Plaintiff's Second Set of Document Requests
V002-DC-00000159 to 160	Clinton, William Jefferson	2/2/98 letter from David Kendall to Bob Bittman
V002-DC-00000469	Clinton, William Jefferson	2/3/98 letter to Bob Bittman from David Kendall
V002-DC-00000471	Clinton, William Jefferson	Book, "The Presidents of the United States"
V002-DC-00000475	Clinton, William Jefferson	3/16/98 letter from David Kendall to the OIC
V004-DC-00000134	Akin Gump	11/3/97 to 11/4/97 Toll records
V004-DC-00000135	Akin Gump	11/4/97 to 11/6/97 Toll records
V004-DC-00000143	Akin Gump	11/26/97 to 11/27/97 Toll records
V004-DC-00000148	Akin Gump	12/11/97 to 12/15/97 Toll records
V004-DC-00000151	Akin Gump	12/19/97 to 12/23/97 Toll records
V004-DC-00000154	Akin Gump	12/30/97 to 12/31/97 Toll records
V004-DC-00000158	Akin Gump	1/5/98 to 1/7/98 Toll records
V004-DC-00000159	Akin Gump	1/7/98 to 1/8/98 Toll records
V004-DC-00000160	Akin Gump	1/8/98 to 1/9/98 Toll records
V004-DC-00000161	Akin Gump	1/9/98 to 1/10/98 Toll records
V004-DC-00000162	Akin Gump	1/10/98 to 1/13/98 Toll records
V004-DC-00000164	Akin Gump	1/15/98 to 1/16/98 Toll records
V004-DC-00000165	Akin Gump	1/16/98 to 1/19/98 Toll records
V004-DC-00000166	Akin Gump	1/19/98 to 1/21/98 Toll records

Bates # or Tab#	Production Name	Description
V004-DC-00000167	Akin Gump	1/21/98 to 1/22/98 Toll records
V004-DC-00000171	Akin Gump	12/11/97 visitor record
V004-DC-00000172	Akin Gump	12/19/97 vistor record
V004-DC-00000183	Akin Gump	12/8/97 Request for Messenger Service
V005-DC-00000058	Laughlin, Gayle	1/15/98 phone record
V005-DC-00000060	Laughlin, Gayle	1/20/98 phone record
V005-DC-00000061	Laughlin, Gayle	1/20/98 phone record
V006-DC-00000007	White House	4/9/96 to 12/30/96 WAVES report for Monica Lewinsky
V006-DC-00000008	White House	2/24/97 to 11/13/97 WAVES report for Monica Lewinsky
V006-DC-00000009	White House	12/6/97 to 12/28/97 WAVES report for Monica Lewinsky
V006-DC-00000020	White House	WH Personnel Action sheet for Monica Lewinsky
V006-DC-00000109	White House	Work history report
V006-DC-00000118	White House	Notification of Personnel Action
V006-DC-00000157	White House	White House Gift Record
V006-DC-00000158	White House	Gift Donor Information
V006-DC-00000159	White House	9/4/96 letter from William Jefferson Clinton to Monica Lewinsky
V006-DC-00000162	White House	White House Gift Register
V006-DC-00000167	White House	10/30/95 Gift Unit - draft leter
V006-DC-00000178	White House	Photograph
V006-DC-00000180	White House	White House Gift Record
V006-DC-00000181	White House	White House Gift Record
V006-DC-00000183	White House	Monica Lewinsky's resume
V006-DC-00000198	White House	1995 summer White House intern list
V006-DC-00000221	White House	5/30/97 schedule sheet
V006-DC-00000222	White House	6/10/97 e-mail from Marsha Dimel to Katherine Veit
V006-DC-00000223 to 224	White House	6/12/97 e-mail from Marsha Dimel to Roseanne Hill w/attachment

Bates # or Tab#	Production Name	Description
V006-DC-00000225	White House	White House pre-employment information sheet
V006-DC-00000391	White House	WhoDB - Contact Manager Information
V006-DC-00000511	White House	12/5/97 Holiday Reception list excerpt
V006-DC-00000512 to 522	White House	12/5/97 White House Party list excerpt, report dated on 12/30/97
V006-DC-00000521	White House	12/5/97 White House Party list excerpt, report dated on 12/30/97
V006-DC-00000534	White House	6/14/96 Radio Address
V006-DC-00000572	White House	2/8/96 to 2/11/96 Presidential schedule
V006-DC-00000682	White House	8/18/96 and 8/19/96 William Jefferson Clinton Schedule
V006-DC-00000694	White House	4/2/96 Schedule of William Jefferson Clinton
V006-DC-00000747	White House	2/9/96 to 2/12/96 Presidential schedule
V006-DC-00001347	White House	4/9/96 E-Mail
V006-DC-00001770	White House	7/24/97 e-mail
V006-DC-00001792	White House	3/29/97 WAVES Request
V006-DC-00001796	White House	2/28/97 WAVES Request
V006-DC-00001813 to 1814	White House	12/5/97 e-mail: WAVES Operations Center to J. Schwartz
V006-DC-00001826	White House	Photograph
V006-DC-00001841	White House	Photograph
V006-DC-00001842	White House	Photograph
V006-DC-00001843	White House	Photograph
V006-DC-00001844	White House	Photograph
V006-DC-00001845	White House	Photograph
V006-DC-00001846	White House	Photograph
V006-DC-00001847	White House	Photograph
V006-DC-00001855	White House	Photograph
V006-DC-00001856	White House	Photograph
V006-DC-00001859	White House	Photograph
V006-DC-00001865	White House	videotape

Bates # or Tab#	Production Name	Description
V006-DC-00002064	White House	1/9/98 Presidential Call Log
V006-DC-00002065	White House	1/14/98 Presidential Call Log
V006-DC-00002066	White House	1/17/98 Presidential Call Log
V006-DC-00002067	White House	1/18/98 Presidential Call Log
V006-DC-00002068	White House	1/18/98 Presidential Call Log
V006-DC-00002069 to 2070	White House	1/19/98 Presidential Call Log
V006-DC-00002071	White House	1/21/98 Presidential Call Log
V006-DC-00002095	White House	8/16/97 schedule
V006-DC-00002130	White House	3/29/97 Presidential Movements
V006-DC-00002140	White House	7/4/97 schedule
V006-DC-00002142	White House	7/14/97 schedule
V006-DC-00002146	White House	8/16/97 schedule
V006-DC-00002147	White House	8/16/97 schedule
V006-DC-00002156	White House	11/13/97 Presidential Movement Log
V006-DC-00002158	White House	12/6/97 Presidential Movement Log
V006-DC-00002214	White House	7/4/97 diarist notes
V006-DC-00002243	White House	11/13/97 Diarist notes
V006-DC-00002287	White House	4/9/96 e-mail from Gunia to Dagenais
V006-DC-00002289	White House	E-Mail
V006-DC-00003646	White House	Coorespondence History tracking sheet
V006-DC-00003712	White House	2/24/97 memo from Betty Currie to William Jefferson Clinton
V006-DC-00003714	White House	White House Gift List
V006-DC-00003715	White House	White House Gift List
V006-DC-00003716	White House	6/14/96 Radio Address
V006-DC-00003719	White House	4/8/96 phone message
V006-DC-00003720	White House	2/28/97 Radio Address
V006-DC-00003735	White House	Photo Request

Bates # or Tab#	Production Name	Description
V006-DC-00003737 to 3744	White House	Photographs

Tab Documents

Tab 1

Main Stairway to Family Quarters

Down these stairs come the president and first lady on every state occasion held at the White House. Tall or short, imposing or not, no one can ignore the entrance of the chief executive when the Marine Band strikes up the first chords of "Hail to the Chief." This is the ceremonial staircase, and it is here that the president, first lady, and their guests of honor are photographed before proceeding to the East Room, where the other guests are gathered. The walk down the red carpet is surely the most romantic image of the presidency. Here is the pomp. Most of the rest of the time, the president is subject to circumstance.

A small, sunny room, the First Lady's Dressing Room has always been a private corner of a very public residence. So private, that in 1801 it was given one of the few water closets in the big, preplumbing house. President Franklin Pierce installed the first stationary bathtub in 1853. Prior to that, men only could bathe ... facility in the east pavilion, and women used portable sitz or hip tubs and shoe-shaped bathtubs made of tin. Dolley Madison bemoaned not being able to save her bathtub from the British in 1814. She was obligated to give precedence to government papers, the silver, and George Washington's portrait.

Located at the southwest corner of the house, this ... n adjoins the chamber that traditionally has been ... master bedroom. Sometimes the presidents' children occupied the room, as did Tad Lincoln and Robert Johnson; sometimes the president reserved it for himself, as did Rutherford Hayes, who labeled it his sanctum or "den." But generally it was the first ladies who called it their own. Ida Saxon McKinley, an epileptic, spent many quiet hours sitting and knitting ... Lou Hoover put in a daybed for afternoon naps ... desk for keeping accounts and correspondence; and Nancy Reagan, who decorated it as in the photograph, used it as a dressing room.

The couple who seemed to take the greatest pleasure in this intimate space were President Woodrow and Mrs. Edith Bolling Wilson, the president's second wife. As newlyweds, they found privacy in this corner ... ie house. The room, since the addition of the bathroom and water closet, had an awkward shape with an off-centered fireplace. Nevertheless, Wilson dressed here, and he and his wife had breakfast, tea, and sometimes lunch or dinner in this crowded space. With a fire burning, Andrew Johnson's magnificent magnolia tree almost tickling the panes of glass of the large south-facing window, and a perfect view of the Washington Monument, it is obvious why they found it such a pleasant place to be together.

Being pragmatic, Eleanor Roosevelt installed a single bed and slept here. She converted the spacious room next door into her sitting room to accommodate her many and frequent visitors. She and Franklin, whose bedroom was the next room over, had used separate rooms since 1918. Bess and Harry Truman occupied the same rooms as the Roosevelts, Mrs. Truman also choosing to use the dressing room as a bedroom and the larger room as her sitting room.

When the Reagans moved into the White House in January 1981, plans had already been laid to refurbish the second and third floors of the White House. They raised nearly a million dollars from friends and political supporters. Mrs. Reagan enlisted the help of a Los Angeles interior designer and old friend, Ted Graber, to help her make the living quarters "warm and livable." The master bedroom, never seen by the public but here displayed in the replica, beautifully fulfills Mrs. Reagan and Graber's objectives.

The Chinese paper, hand-painted in eighteenth-century style, gives the presidential bedroom its individuality. The lovely, delicate irregular spacing of a wide variety of birds—peacocks, bluebirds, roosters, etc.—around the room creates an airy, open field of color and form.

In order to replicate and reduce the wallpaper for the miniature White House, John and Jan Zweifel made a scale painting of the wallpaper onto a 10-by-12-inch sheet of paper. This was then carefully reduced on a color copier to provide sheets of paper for the walls of the miniature room.

The two diminutive chairs are only 3 inches high and 2 inches wide.

President and First Lady's Bedroom

After the swearing in, the parade, and the inaugural balls, the new president and first lady return to sleep in a room occupied only the previous night by another president and first lady. The changeover in the White House from one family to the next is so fast, so complete, one thinks that it must be done with a sorcerer's magic wand. The president and first lady's bedroom, the most private room in the house, humanizes the peaceful, incredible succession of power. To be able to call the White House home is the ultimate reward for those seeking to serve their country, and an honor bestowed on so few.

All the White House transitions have been swift (except the one from Lincoln to Johnson), but not always sweet. When President and Mrs. Pierce returned from the 1853 inaugural ball, there was no bedroom ready for them, which they considered a great indignity. Woodrow Wilson, who attended no ball but who celebrated first with his family and then at a smoker given for him by Princeton alumni at the Shoreham Hotel, found himself in the White House at midnight ringing assorted bells, not knowing which was which. Wearing only his underwear, he inquired if anyone had seen his trunk. He had no pajamas and, presumably, no toothbrush.

This room was Eleanor Roosevelt's and Bess Truman's sitting room/study but Jacqueline Kennedy reverted it to a bedroom as it had been for most of the nineteenth and early twentieth century. On inaugural night, though, the room was not yet ready, and she slept down the hall in the Queen's Bedroom. Eventually, it was decorated in shades of pale green and blue, and her furniture from her Georgetown house was moved in. The president's bedroom was across the hall, furnished with an eighteenth-century Chippendale high chest and a mahogany four-poster bed. Mrs. Kennedy did much of her work and her thinking in this bedroom suite.

It was in this room that Willie Lincoln died in the great "Lincoln" bed (see page 186) and James Garfield lay prostrate for months from an assassin's bullet. Because of Garfield's discomfort during the sweltering D.C. summer of 1881, doctors and engineers introduced the first air conditioning system in the United States to cool the dying president.

William McKinley was asleep here when an usher entered the room and whispered in his ear that the secretary of the navy was on the telephone with an important message. The battleship *Maine* had exploded and sunk in Havana harbor just hours before.

In this room, the first Mrs. Wilson passed away, and Woodrow Wilson suffered the stroke that would leave him an invalid for the rest of his life. For weeks he lay here helpless on the huge Lincoln bed.

On April 12, 1945, Eleanor Roosevelt was called to her sitting room and told of her husband's death at Warm Springs. She then summoned to her room the vice-president, who came directly from presiding over the Senate. Truman later wrote, "That was the first inkling I had of the seriousness of the situation." William Seale describes the exchange as follows: "Was there anything he could do for her? Eleanor Roosevelt replied, 'Is there anything *we* can do for *you*? For you are the one in trouble now.'"[12]

President's Study

Walls cannot talk, but if they could, the most dramatic stories these four would tell would center on the years 1933 to 1945. This was Franklin Delano Roosevelt's bedroom. An early riser, the invalid president would often conduct business from his bed. Francis Perkins, secretary of labor, described the bed and surrounding furniture as follows:

***a small, narrow white iron bedstead, the kind one sees in the boy's room of many an American house. It had a thin, hard looking mattress, a couple of pillows, and an ordinary white seersucker spread. A folded old gray shawl lay at the foot . . . A white painted table, the kind one often sees in bathrooms, stood beside the bed, with a towel over it and with aspirin, nose drops, a glass of water, stubs of pencils, bits of paper with telephone numbers, addresses and memoranda to himself, a couple of books, a worn old prayer book, a watch, a package of cigarettes, an ash tray, a couple of telephones, all cluttered together.*[13]**

If the president was suffering from one of his chronic colds, the cabinet members would meet in this room. Aides would bring up memoranda and messages, and the papers of state would mingle with personal memorabilia. The mantel, seen on the left of the photograph, held miniature "Mexican pigs, Irish pigs, pigs of all kinds, sizes and colors" alongside family photographs, recalled Perkins.

FDR was an avid collector of many things, and one hobby in particular, stamp collecting, prepared him, quite unexpectedly, for his role as commander in chief during World War II. His naval aide during the war, Captain John L. McCrea, commented many years later that "the President's knowledge of world geography was amazing. I once expressed surprise that he knew so much about an insignificant lake in a small foreign country." "If a stamp collector really studies his stamps," replied FDR, "he can pick up a great deal of information." This geographical knowledge, often far exceeding that of others under his command, was vital during the war years.

The room appears as it did during the Reagan presidency. The red and white furniture came from Ronald and Nancy Reagan's California home. The desk lamp was made from a fire chief's silver horn, given to President Reagan when he was governor. The furnishings are cozy, comfortable, and familiar because it was here that the Reagans liked to relax. They looked forward to the evenings when dinner was served on trays in front of the television. Within these four walls, there was the semblance of a normal life.

Yellow Oval Room

In 1809, Dolley Madison chose yellow for the prevailing color in the upstairs Oval Room. In 1961, Jacqueline Kennedy decided the room should be decorated with antiques of the Louis XVI style of late-eighteenth-century France. The suite of furniture includes four side chairs and two armchairs made around 1800 by Jean-Baptiste Lelarge. A set of four carved and gilded armchairs were made by C. Sené, also of the Louis XVI period, two of which can be seen in the foreground. This neoclassical style was strongly influenced by Greek and Roman furnishings discovered during the excavations at Pompeii and Herculaneum in the late 1750s. The candelabra on the two French Louis XV commodes flanking the mantel were given by Princess Elizabeth of Great Britain in 1951 when she visited President and Mrs. Harry Truman.

Royalty and gold candelabra were not Harry's "style." He'd rather have watched a local baseball game and sit outdoors on a balmy summer's evening. Truman unilaterally decided that a balcony should be added to the second-floor Oval Room, against the loud protests of architects and historians. Truman got his balcony, with its good view of local playing fields, and he thoroughly enjoyed using it. If you want to know what his architectural transgression looks like, pull out a $20 bill.

When Millard and Abigail Fillmore moved into the House in 1850 after the death of Zachary Taylor, there was not a Bible or dictionary or any other book to be found. Mrs. Fillmore, a former schoolteacher, did not consider a house a home without a library, and if this big white "temple of inconveniences," as her husband described it, was to be habitable for herself, her family, and future first families, there had to be books. They received money from Congress to buy some, and in the second-floor Oval Room she created her library and family room.

The Yellow Oval Room is one of the prettiest ooms in the house. Three stately windows facing the outh lawn, Washington Monument, and Jefferson Memorial provide one of the best views in Washington and flood the room with light.

This room has always been central, literally and iguratively, in the lives of the occupants of the White House. For most of the two hundred years of the house's history, it was the boundary between the amily's bedrooms and either the president's executive offices (in the nineteenth century) or the official guest rooms. Sometimes the Yellow Room was strictly a room where children and parents would meet nightly to read, sing, play musical instruments, hang Christmas stockings, and relax, as during the administrations of Fillmore, Lincoln, Hayes, Theodore Roosevelt, and Wilson. The Hayeses sang psalms, and Wilson read the Bible aloud. Harding and his friends played poker and drank bootleg liquor.

Sometimes this room would serve as the president's private office, where he could concentrate and work away from the surrounding tumult of the executive offices. Grover Cleveland, Benjamin Harrison, FDR, and Harry Truman used it for this purpose. Franklin Roosevelt used it the most, often inviting advisers to stay for cocktails that he would mix himself, followed by dinner served on trays.

Here, the day after FDR's first inauguration, the president met with his cabinet to discuss the financial crisis and later signed the Emergency Banking Act of 1933. On December 7, 1941, at about 1:40 P.M., Roosevelt and Harry Hopkins were having lunch when a telephone call brought the news of the bombing of Pearl Harbor. On New Year's Day 1942, Roosevelt was joined in this room by Winston Churchill, Maxim Litvinof of the Soviet Union, and T.V. Soong representing China for the signing of an agreement to join with twenty-six countries in a "united nations" against Axis aggression. And the list goes on and on.

The room has also been, during John Adams' administration and then every one since Kennedy's, the parlor where the president and first lady entertain their guests of honor before official state functions. This invitation to "come upstairs" at the White House is one of the rarest and also most cherished. It is the presidential equivalent of inviting someone to your home, because the first floor of the White House is truly a public arena, and it is only upstairs that privacy prevails. The photographs of the Reagans and Gorbachevs drinking cocktails in the Yellow Oval Room are one more reflection of the end of the Cold War. President and Mrs. Clinton will welcome many more heads of former communist bloc countries and, standing by the tall windows, point out the memorial to the author of the Declaration of Independence and the monument to the father of the oldest continuous democracy in the world.

Woodrow Wilson, while working alone in this room during the dark days of World War I, would contemplate the painting on the far wall, "Signing of the Peace Protocol Between Spain and the United States, August 12, 1998" by Théobald Chartran. In it President McKinley stands at the end of the cabinet table that had served as his desk (and now serves as President Clinton's desk in this room). Just a few months earlier, on April 20, 1898, McKinley had regretfully signed the document authorizing military action in what John Hay called the "splendid little war" and which was the United States's first foray into imperialism beyond its shores.

Spectacular in both the full-size and miniature Treaty Rooms is the chandelier. Approximately 250 hours of handwork went into making this chandelier for the White House replica. John Zweifel had to work with tiny tubing, brass rings, glass beading, and hair-thin copper wires for electrifying the lilliputian chandelier. Every glass shade had to be hand-blown by an expert who could measure his or her breath so that each one was exactly the same petite size as the preceding one.

The pewter inkwell stands just two inches high yet looks colossal the replica of the historic Treaty Room The full-size quill is eight inches long; the baby quill is ²/₃ inch.

Treaty Room

- *In 1809, it was a large bedroom.*
- *In 1823, James Monroe sat at a desk in this room and wrote his doctrine warning Europe to stay out of the Western Hemisphere.*
- *In 1825, John Quincy Adams made it a sitting room.*
- *From 1849 until the time of Lincoln's assassination it was a reception room for visitors wanting to see the president.*
- *In 1866, Andrew Johnson made it his cabinet room, and it functioned as such until the West Wing was built.*
- *In 1902, Theodore Roosevelt made it into a study. Woodrow Wilson spent most of his time in this room, where he wrote the Fourteen Points, his personal requirements for peace after World War I.*
- *In 1930, it became the "Monroe Drawing Room" after Mrs. Hoover placed reproduction Monroe furniture in it.*
- *In 1936, it was one of the rooms Eleanor Roosevelt used for press conferences.*
- *In 1945, Winston Churchill used it as his personal map room.*
- *In 1952, it was a sitting room.*
- *In 1962, Jacqueline Kennedy made it the Treaty Room (as seen in the photograph).*
- *In 1990, it became the president's office in the residence.*

In 1962, 80 million Americans watched the television tour of the White House and saw President and Mrs. Kennedy sitting in the Treaty Room answering Charles Collingwood's questions. Many of the questions referred to the changes Mrs. Kennedy was making to the White House. John Kennedy observed that every president who comes to live in the White House receives stimulus from the legendary figures who served in the same capacity. He explained: "Anything which dramatizes the great story of the United States—as I think the White House does—is worthy of the closest attention and respect by Americans who live here and who visit here and who are part of our citizenry. That's why I am glad that Jackie is making the effort she's making."[14]

The Treaty Room, recreated to resemble the Cabinet Room during Ulysses S. Grant's term of office and to commemorate peace treaties signed to end or prevent wars, was a Jacqueline Kennedy inspiration and realization. She was particularly proud of her research in tracking down the treaties signed in this room, and procuring facsimiles from the National Archives to hang on the walls.

Interior decorators could hardly believe Mrs. Kennedy was resurrecting Victorian furniture considered terribly unfashionable in 1962, but the first lady was far more interested in historical precedents than design magazine approval. Her passion during the three short years she lived in the White House was to imbue the house with the spirit of past presidents, and the Treaty Room was a fine example of her aspirations. The room is strikingly unified in design, and most of the furnishings originated with past presidents.

The White House television tour was a Jacqueline Kennedy tour de force with more than a little help from CBS, and she possessed star quality equal to her subject. She knew what to say on camera and how to say it. A classic example of her tact and ability to find common ground with her audience was recorded in the published transcript of the program. Charles Collingwood asked Mrs. Kennedy what purpose the Treaty Room would serve, and the television audience heard her reply:

Well I do think every room should have a purpose. It can still be a sitting room because that sofa, though you may not believe it, will look nice. But it will serve a definite purpose. My husband has so many meetings up here in this part of the house. All the men who wait to see him now sit in the hall with the baby carriages going by them. They can sit in here and talk while waiting for him.

During the rehearsal period, however, when Mrs. Kennedy was asked why she was refurnishing the room, she replied, "It's really to get the Cabinet out of the living room."

Many presidents have used the old cabinet table that was the focal point of Mrs. Kennedy's restoration for the signing of peace treaties. William McKinley watched as the peace treaty ending the Spanish-American War was signed in August 1898; Calvin Coolidge in 1929 put his signature on the ratification of the Kellogg-Briand Peace Pact; John Kennedy, in 1963, signed the "Treaty for a Partial Nuclear Test Ban"; Richard Nixon, in 1972, signed the "Treaty of the Limitation of Anti-Ballistic Missile Systems"; in 1979 the table was taken outdoors for the momentous signing of the Egyptian-Israeli Peace Treaty by Menachem Begin, Anwar el-Sadat, and Jimmy Carter (see document page 193); and on a brilliant, sunny day in September 1993, the world witnessed not only the signing of the Israeli-Palestinian peace treaty on the cherished cabinet table, but also the handshake between Yitzak Rabin and Yasir Arafat that took place alongside that American heirloom.

The photograph above shows part of the former Treaty Room as it appears in the Clinton White House (except for the rug, which is not correct). The president uses the room as an office and the historic cabinet table (opposite page) as his desk. A child of the sixties, the president favors strong colors, but no one quite understands why the Clintons, whose love of American history spans the entire 200-year history of the house, have allowed a prevalence of Victoriana to dominate newly refurnished White House rooms. Clinton has kept the Chartran treaty painting (see page 72) and added ones of Benjamin Franklin and George Washington. Scattered throughout the room are the president's favorite photographs and mementos. The president's books flank the fireplace in bookcases built in situ by White House carpenters (see Carpenters' Shop, p.190) because they were too large to fit through the doorways. The overall effect resulting from the choice of fabrics, colors, lamps, and upholstered furniture is a reflection of the judgment of Little Rock interior decorator Kaki Hockersmith.

Mrs. Clinton, discussing the changes she is making to the White House, stated in an interview published in *Historic Preservation* (November–December 1993) that "preservation and restoration—not redecoration" is what she and her husband hope to achieve. "We're interested in enhancing the house and the furnishings within it . . . as a means of furthering the historical mission of the house." As President Clinton enjoys inviting certain guests and foreign dignitaries to his office in the residence, it, like other rooms, "should depict the quality and the importance of the White House as a living museum," asserts the first lady.

On the mantel, which has seen many decorators come and go, is carved the following: "This room was first used for meetings of the cabinet during the administration of President Johnson. It continued to be so used until the year MCMII. Here the Treaty of Peace with Spain was signed."

say it. A classic example of her tact and ability to find common ground with her audience was recorded in the published transcript of the program. Charles Collingwood asked Mrs. Kennedy what purpose the Treaty Room would serve, and the television audience heard her reply:

Well I do think every room should have a purpose. It can still be a sitting room because that sofa, though you may not believe it, will look nice. But it will serve a definite purpose. My husband has so many meetings up here in this part of the house. All the men who wait to see him now sit in the hall with the baby carriages going by them. They can sit in here and talk while waiting for him.

During the rehearsal period, however, when Mrs. Kennedy was asked why she was refurnishing the room, she replied, "It's really to get the Cabinet out of the living room."

Many presidents have used the old cabinet table that was the focal point of Mrs. Kennedy's restoration for the signing of peace treaties. William McKinley watched as the peace treaty ending the Spanish-American War was signed in August 1898; Calvin Coolidge in 1929 put his signature on the ratification of the Kellogg-Briand Peace Pact; John Kennedy, in 1963, signed the "Treaty for a Partial Nuclear Test Ban"; Richard Nixon, in 1972, signed the "Treaty of the Limitation of Anti-Ballistic Missile Systems"; in 1979 the table was taken outdoors for the momentous signing of the Egyptian-Israeli Peace Treaty by Menachem Begin, Anwar el-Sadat, and Jimmy Carter (see document page 193); and on a brilliant, sunny day in September 1993, the world witnessed not only the signing of the Israeli-Palestinian peace treaty on the cherished cabinet table, but also the handshake between Yitzak Rabin and Yasir Arafat that took place alongside that American heirloom.

The photograph above shows part of the former Treaty Room as it appears in the Clinton White House (except for the rug, which is not correct). The president uses the room as an office and the historic cabinet table (opposite page) as his desk. A child of the sixties, the president favors strong colors, but no one quite understands why the Clintons, whose love of American history spans the entire 200-year history of the house, have allowed a prevalence of Victoriana to dominate newly refurnished White House rooms. Clinton has kept the Chartran treaty painting (see page 72) and added ones of Benjamin Franklin and George Washington. Scattered throughout the room are the president's favorite photographs and mementos. The president's books flank the fireplace in bookcases built in situ by White House carpenters (see Carpenters' Shop, p.190) because they were too large to fit through the doorways. The overall effect resulting from the choice of fabrics, colors, lamps, and upholstered furniture is a reflection of the judgment of Little Rock interior decorator Kaki Hockersmith.

Mrs. Clinton, discussing the changes she is making to the White House, stated in an interview published in *Historic Preservation* (November–December 1993) that "preservation and restoration—not redecoration" is what she and her husband hope to achieve. "We're interested in enhancing the house and the furnishings within it . . . as a means of furthering the historical mission of the house." As President Clinton enjoys inviting certain guests and foreign dignitaries to his office in the residence, it, like other rooms, "should depict the quality and the importance of the White House as a living museum," asserts the first lady.

On the mantel, which has seen many decorators come and go, is carved the following: "This room was first used for meetings of the cabinet during the administration of President Johnson. It continued to be so used until the year MCMII. Here the Treaty of Peace with Spain was signed."

...arles McKim, President and Mrs. Theodore Roosevelt's architect and interior designer, wanted in 1902 to rid the White House of all the Victorian furniture. Edith Roosevelt insisted that certain pieces be kept, including the majestic carved rosewood bed now in the Lincoln Bedroom. Teddy Roosevelt subsequently enjoyed many restful nights in it; Woodrow Wilson, we assume, spent many restless nights worrying about World War I; and Calvin Coolidge remained silent on the subject of how he slept in the imposing Lincoln Bed. Had the architect instead of the first lady had his way, one of the most famous pieces of furniture in the White House might have been lost forever.

The elaborately carved Victorian table was also part of the furniture purchased by Mary Todd Lincoln from William and George Carryl of Philadelphia in 1861. In 1860, the prince of Wales stayed overnight in the "best guest room" in the James Buchanan White House, a room described by Mrs. Lincoln's cousin as "most shabby." The bed and the table reflect Mary Todd Lincoln's idea of appropriate furniture for a guest bedroom. In 1970, another prince of Wales, Prince Charles, slept in the bed that came to the White House as a result of his ancestor's brief visit.

The cream-colored silk sofa and matching chairs, believed to have been used in the White House during Lincoln's administration, were discovered in England and given to the White House in 1954. The "slipper" chair is upholstered in yellow and green William Morris fabric provided by a citizen who wanted to help Mrs. Kennedy with the restoration of the Lincoln Room.

The rocking chair (right foreground) is similar to the chair Lincoln used in the box at Ford's Theatre the night of his assassination. In front of the walnut bureau with full-length mirror, bought by Mary Lincoln, one nineteenth-century White House guest did her "pompadour every morning."

Visitors staying the night make certain to sit at the desk on the left. This has been authenticated as the desk Lincoln used at the "summer White House," a few miles northeast of 1600 Pennsylvania Avenue. The chairs at the desk and along the north wall were in Lincoln's cabinet room. The tables flanking the bed were purchased by President Jackson, whose portrait, seen to the left of the bed, hung in the exact spot when this room was Lincoln's office (see pages 108–11).

Lincoln Bedroom

The towering figure in the history of the White House was Abraham Lincoln. Theodore Roosevelt spoke for every chief executive when he said: "I think of Lincoln, shambling, homely, with his strong, sad, deeply-furrowed face, all the time. I see him in the different rooms and in the halls." The Lincoln Bedroom, which was the sixteenth president's office and cabinet room (see pages 108–11), is the only room in the White House named after and honoring a past president. Jacqueline Kennedy commented:

Sometimes I used to stop and think about it all. I wondered, "How are we going to live as a family in this enormous place?" I would go and sit in the Lincoln Room. It was the one room in the White House with a link to the past. It gave me great comfort. I love the Lincoln Room. Even though it isn't really Lincoln's bedroom, it has his things in it. When you see that great bed, it looks like a cathedral. To touch something I knew he had touched was a real link with him. The kind of peace I felt in that room was what you feel when going to church. I used to sit in the Lincoln Room and I could really feel its strength. I'd sort of be talking with him. Jefferson is the President with whom I have the most affinity. But Lincoln is the one I love.[15]

A plaque on the mantelpiece reads: "In this room Abraham Lincoln signed the Emancipation Proclamation of January 1, 1863 whereby four million slaves were given their freedom and slavery forever prohibited in these United States." This was an act of great personal courage and historic consequence. Even without the furniture, presidents entering the room feel the power of the past and the necessity of just leadership in the future.

The table stands less than 2 ½ inches high, but Jack Zweifel, John and Jan's eldest son, carved all the fine details found in the original piece. Storks support the marble surface, grapes hang down from the circular top, and the legs brace a bird's nest underneath. The rosewood table is the finest example of woodcarving in the White House replica. It took approximately 160 hours to carve and many hours to sand and stain. The Gettysburg Address, seen in facsimile in the background, is traditionally displayed in the Lincoln Bedroom in the form of a holographic copy.

Lincoln never slept in the 9-feet-long, 6-feet-wide bed that carries his name, but by its side he wept uncontrollably at the sight of his small son Willie, lost forever in its folds, dead at the age of eleven. Three years later, in 1865, the man who pleaded for "malice toward none; with charity for all" was embalmed at the foot of the big bed, shot by an assassin's bullet.

For many years, this room has been reserved for guests. FDR insisted that his close adviser Harry Hopkins and his new bride even live in the Lincoln suite (bedroom and sitting room), and had it repainted for them. Harry Truman, a passionate devotee of American history, decided to pull together furniture from Lincoln's time and place it here.

[redacted]

Lincoln Sitting Room

Visitors to the White House replica often ask themselves, "What makes it look so real?" The answer lies in the thousands of little details. In this small room of the replica, there is a "fire" in the fireplace, and it flickers. The logs are perfectly scaled; even the knots are in proportion. All the necessary tools are there to maintain the fire, and the andirons have been perfectly shaped to fit the space. The mantel is a carved copy of the original. The picture frame and the wainscoting are built up from thin pieces of wood to look like the real thing. There is a copy of the painting *Pavilion at Gloucester* by William Glackens. The electrified candles burn, and although the copy of the French Empire clock on the mantel does not tick, other clocks in the White House replica do.

Located in the southeast corner of the mansion, this small room's moment of glory came during the McKinley administration and the Spanish-American War. The site of the president's "War Room," frequently referred to in histories of the war, is rarely specifically situated. But it was this small space that became, as William Seale says, "the lifeline of war communications . . . removing it from its traditional place in the War Department." In 1901, over the same telegraph lines, came the news that McKinley had been shot by an assassin while visiting the Pan-American Exposition in Buffalo. Colonel Crook, who had served as executive clerk at the White House since the early 1860s, remembered thinking as he read the telegram, "Good God! First Lincoln—then Garfield—and now McKinley!"

For the first quarter of the nineteenth century, the Lincoln Sitting Room was simply empty. When Charles Dickens visited the White House in the 1840s, it was Tyler's "unimpressive" office. Later, it was generally occupied by the president's private secretary and had the luxury of a water closet at the north end, contributing to its irregular shape. The room became the telegraph office during the administration of Rutherford B. Hayes. After the executive offices were moved out of the mansion in 1902, it was used by the first family themselves or as part of one of the principal guest suites in the house.

Richard Nixon read and listened to music here. He always liked a fire in the fireplace, even in summer, and, according to his daughter Tricia, had the air conditioning turned up to compensate for his idiosyncratic habit. John Zweifel included in his rendering of this room the cigar burns in the carpet that Nixon inadvertently caused.

The decor dates from the Reagan administration. The desk on the right was made by James Hoban, the original architect of the White House. The four rosewood chairs were purchased by Mary Todd Lincoln. The plaster cast sculpture titled *Neighboring Pews* was created by John Rogers, the most popular sculptor in America between 1860 and 1895.

Queen's Bedroom and Sitting Room

Ike Hoover, who worked for ten presidents, described Will Rogers' visit to the Coolidge White House:

Mr. Rogers had been assigned to what is known as the pink [Queen's] guest suite, in the extreme northeast corner of the bedroom floor. It consists of a large room with a four-poster bed, a small dressing-room, which also has a single brass bed in it, and a private bath. He was escorted halfway down the hall by the President and his room pointed out to him. A doorman was summoned to have one last word with Mr. Rogers and learn if there was anything that could be done for him before he retired.

Upon entering the room, Mr. Rogers seemed rather hesitant about occupying the large four-poster bed that had been prepared for him. Turning to the doorman, he inquired if he had to sleep there. He was told of the small bed in the dressing-room and chose that in preference to the large one. The man turned down these covers and left Mr. Rogers with his own thoughts, to spend the night in the White House with all the thrills he afterwards described.[16]

Truman's mother couldn't see herself in this big, beautiful guest room (originally called the Rose Bedroom) either, declaring she would rather sleep on the floor. The bed was too high, the decor too fussy, she declared, and like the earthy humorist, she slept in the small sitting room. The entertainer Sammy Davis Jr., however, when he spent the night at the White House, turned down the chance to sleep in the famed Lincoln Bedroom in favor of the Queen's Bedroom. He later joked, "I thought to myself, now I don't want [Lincoln] coming in here talking about 'I freed them, but I sure didn't mean for them to sleep in my bed.'"

The White House needed a sumptuous bedroom. Before Blair House, located across the street, became the official presidential guest house, the White House did have many overnight visitors with singularly imperious or peculiar ways. Winston Churchill and Madame Chiang Kai-shek during the war years were two of the most demanding. And royalty never fits smoothly into a household labeled the "first house of democracy." It is known that the White House staff were often disconcerted by the manner in which certain supercilious guests ordered them about. Whether "Mr. Brown" (alias for V. M. Molotov, Soviet minister for foreign affairs, who slept in the Rose Bedroom in 1942) addressed them as "comrade" has gone unrecorded. What *has* been recorded are the findings of the valet who unpacked Molotov's suitcase: black bread, sausages, and a revolver.

The Rose Bedroom was renamed the Queen's Bedroom by Jacqueline Kennedy in honor of the royal guests who had occupied it. Among these were Queen Elizabeth of Great Britain in 1942, Queen Wilhelmina of the Netherlands in 1942, Queen Julianna of the Netherlands in 1952, Queen Frederika of Greece in 1953, and Queen Elizabeth II of Great Britain in 1957.

In the days of Buchanan and Lincoln, the president's private secretaries lived in this bedroom, with twenty-four-hour dedication to the job expected. John Hay and John G. Nicolay shared the room in the 1860s. By the time of Andrew Johnson's presidency, his private secretary was moved to the corner room (today's Queen's Sitting Room), and the larger space became an office occupied by six clerks. When executive offices were finally built adjoining the man-

The Queen's Bedroom overlooks Lafayette Park to the north of the White House. The four-poster bed is thought to have belonged to Andrew Jackson; it came from the Hermitage, his home in Tennessee. The Federal sofa has scrolled arms and floral decorations on the top rail. The carved wood mantel on the west wall dates from the years 1820–30 and was removed from a Philadelphia house built in 1792. The English looking glass over the mantel with an eighteenth-century floral painting framed with it was presented to the White House by Princess (now Queen) Elizabeth on behalf of her father, King George, when she and Prince Philip visited Washington in 1951. The princess remarked that it was the king's "hope, and mine, that [the mirror] will remain here, as a mark of our friendship, so long as the White House shall stand."

The Queen's Bedroom has traditionally been given to female guests, as the Lincoln Bedroom was considered the more masculine. Female portraits, too, dominate the paintings in the room. One of the most beautiful is of the actress Fanny Kemble (seen above the sofa). The artist, Thomas Sully, was the son of English actors who emigrated to America in 1792. Fanny Kemble also arrived in America from England with her actor father in 1832 and soon won the hearts of American audiences.

The actress was presented to Andrew Jackson at the White House in 1833, the year she married and gave up the stage. Vehemently opposed to the slavery she witnessed on her husband's Georgia plantation, she divorced him in 1849. She began to give public readings that became legendary. Longfellow was enraptured: "How our hearts glowed and trembled / as she read . . . " She also wrote *Journal of a Residence on a Georgian Plantation*, published in England in 1863, hoping to encourage a public outcry against slavery. Her nephew later married President Ulysses Grant's daughter Nellie in the Blue Room. Fanny is a favorite of first families and an inspiring companion while staying overnight at the White House.

Sir Winston Churchill spent a total of forty-two frenetic days at the White House, including nearly a month's stay shortly after Pearl Harbor. When he arrived, with an aide, secretary, two Scotland Yard men, and a valet, he virtually took over. Everyone in his entourage needed to sleep in close proximity to Churchill and consequently, because the house is not as large as many an English manor, near Roosevelt. Churchill occupied the Queen's Suite, opposite Harry Hopkins' room and down the corridor from the Roosevelts.

Stories of Churchill at the White House abound. Although there is no evidence that Eleanor bumped into him stark naked one night, David Eisenhower thought the story was worth investigating; he concluded, after conducting various interviews, that it would have been impossible. Winston Churchill II reported that his grandfather always slept in a vest (undershirt), nothing more, nothing less.

Legend has it that Franklin did get to see all of the prime minister. As the story goes, Churchill was dictating in his bath, and continued to dictate while walking around his room in a towel and even after the towel fell to the floor. It was then that Roosevelt entered the room and was greeted with the famous declaration: "The prime minister of Great Britain has nothing to hide from the president of the United States." But when Robert Sherwood, the playwright, author, and onetime speechwriter for FDR, asked Churchill if the story was true, the great statesman replied that it was not. He maintained that he always had his towel around his imposing belly.

Churchill stayed up nightly talking to the president until about 2:00 A.M. Roosevelt would attempt to put in normal working days, but Churchill, according to contemporary reports, spent a large part of the day "hurling himself violently in and out of bed, bathing at unsuitable moments and rushing up and down corridors in his dressing gown." If there hadn't been a war to win, Eleanor would have kicked him out. The cigar on the bed is a "Super Churchill," placed here for scale and not to suggest that the prime minister was careless about where he left his smoldering cigars.

sion during Teddy Roosevelt's tenure, the rows of desks that had filled this room for so many years were placed in a large room at the west end of the West Wing. This room then became the Rose Bedroom and the site of Alice Roosevelt Longworth's childhood appendectomy.

Today, the Queen's Bedroom and Lincoln Bedroom accommodate personal friends and family of the president and first lady who are invited to spend the night at the best address in the country.

The *Architectural Digest* (December 1981) described the Queen's Sitting Room as "evoking a stately yet festive tone." French fabric with a neoclassical medallion design was installed during the Kennedy administration. A draped dressing table is festooned with tasseled cord. The crown and scepter are just for fun, reminding the viewer that the White House replica descends from a long line of magnificent miniatures, including Queen Mary's Dolls' House at Windsor Castle.

1671

Movie Theater in East Colonnade

In July 1942, President Franklin Roosevelt ordered the White House cloakroom, located in the east colonnade, converted into a movie theater. From that time on, the White House has had no permanent coatroom, but every first family would probably agree that having a personal movie theater is better. In any case, the space still serves as the temporary coatroom.

As early as 1933, Roosevelt was receiving newsreel footage of important presidential activities. The president also was sent copies of films made by government agencies and, once the war began, many of the propaganda films. Family and friends have probably used the theater far more than the president, especially since the White House also has always had access to feature films.

Margaret Truman was delighted to learn that she could ask for a viewing of any Hollywood movie, new or old, at any time she desired. It is reported that she saw her favorite, *The Scarlet Pimpernel*, sixteen times. Mamie Eisenhower, like many American women in the 1950s, enjoyed watching a movie on a Saturday afternoon. She was particularly fond of sharing the sixty-five-seat theater with her young grandchildren. Her husband, too, watched many movies there. Presidents Carter and Reagan normally waited until they were resting at Camp David to savor Hollywood's latest offerings. President Clinton's "favorite cultural activity," noted the *New York Times* on March 23, 1994, "seems to be showing movies at the White House."

Tab 2

Movie Theater in East Colonnade

In July 1942, President Franklin Roosevelt ordered the White House cloakroom, located in the east colonnade, converted into a movie theater. From that time on, the White House has had no permanent coatroom, but every first family would probably agree that having a personal movie theater is better. In any case, the space still serves as the temporary coatroom.

As early as 1933, Roosevelt was receiving newsreel footage of important presidential activities. The president also was sent copies of films made by government agencies and, once the war began, many of the propaganda films. Family and friends have probably used the theater far more than the president, especially since the White House also has always had access to feature films.

Margaret Truman was delighted to learn that she could ask for a viewing of any Hollywood movie, new or old, at any time she desired. It is reported that she saw her favorite, *The Scarlet Pimpernel*, sixteen times. Mamie Eisenhower, like many American women in the 1950s, enjoyed watching a movie on a Saturday afternoon. She was particularly fond of sharing the sixty-five-seat theater with her young grandchildren. Her husband, too, watched many movies there. Presidents Carter and Reagan normally waited until they were resting at Camp David to savor Hollywood's latest offerings. President Clinton's "favorite cultural activity," noted the *New York Times* on March 23, 1994, "seems to be showing movies at the White House."

Tab 3

Citation | Search Result | Rank 2 of 28 | Database
14/95 LATIMES 1 | | | LAT
11/14/95 L.A. Times 1
1995 WL 9845195

Los Angeles Times

Tuesday, November 14, 1995

PART-A; National Desk

President, GOP Hold Last-Ditch Summit on Budget; Government: Hope for avoiding shutdown rises as Dole and Gingrich visit the White House. Senate and House remain in session in case of agreement.
PAUL RICHTER; EDWIN CHEN
TIMES STAFF WRITERS

President Clinton and Republican congressional leaders convened a late-night summit at the White House on Monday in a last-ditch effort to broker a temporary budget deal and avert a partial shutdown of the government today.

Both the House of Representatives and the Senate remained in session in case an agreement was reached.

A glimmer of hope for avoiding the first government shutdown in five years arose when Senate Majority Leader Bob Dole (R-Kan.) and House Speaker Newt Gingrich (R-Ga.) announced they were going to the White House for a meeting expected to begin about 10 p.m.

Dole and Gingrich said every point of contention would be "on the table" and that there would be "no preconditions."

The talks appeared even more promising because the two Republican leaders agreed to include the two congressional Democratic minority leaders, Sen. Tom Daschle of South Dakota and Rep. Richard A. Gephardt of Missouri. Dole and Gingrich had refused to involve congressional Democrats in any such discussions, insisting that the dispute was between the White House and Capitol Hill Republicans.

Earlier, Clinton vetoed a temporary borrowing bill, and vowed to veto a stopgap spending measure that would have kept federal offices open, setting the stage for a furlough of more than a third of the government's 2.1 million civilian workers this morning. The stopgap measure was passed by the Senate Monday afternoon. Clinton vetoed the second temporary measure before sitting down with the Republicans Monday night.

Throughout the day, White House and GOP leaders had traded

.unciations.

Clinton declared that signing the bills would force him to swallow unacceptable portions of the GOP agenda that Republicans had tacked onto the short-term budget bills.

"This legislation is part of an overall back door effort by the congressional Republicans to impose their priorities on our nation," he said. He charged that the GOP was violating the intent of the Founding Fathers by packing special provisions dealing with larger government policy questions into temporary measures meant to deal exclusively with government solvency.

Republicans countered that Democrats often engaged in such tactics when they were in control of Congress. They taunted Clinton and accused him of trying to avoid a compromise. Gingrich said the standoff "must seem like a spectacle to the average American," and he warned that the public will "blame all of us."

Some Democrats as well acknowledged that the standoff cast a highly unflattering light on the adversaries.

"Everybody loses if we try to bring the government to a andstill," said Sen. John B. Breaux (D-La.) "We're so busy trying score political points, I think some people in Louisiana believe even we in Congress are not 'essential' employees who should report to work tomorrow."

Without an agreement, some 800,000 federal workers in Washington and across the country would be furloughed today for an indefinite period. Those employees, who have been deemed nonessential, have been told to report to work, and to be prepared for orders to close up their operations and head home unless a compromise is reached.

Federal supervisors could direct their employees to stay at work longer if it appeared that a breakthrough was coming.

Vital Services

The furloughs would not affect federal services deemed vital, such as air traffic control, law enforcement, the mails and the military. But they would close national parks, museums, passport offices and the processing of new claims for Social Security, food stamps and other government benefits.

The battle over the two temporary measures developed because the Congress has fallen behind in its efforts to finish the work of ssing 13 bills needed to fund the various government operations for fiscal year that began Oct. 1. So far, only three of the 13 bills e been finished by Congress.

The two temporary budget measures would keep the government operating as usual for several more weeks, providing Congress and the President time to complete work on the remaining measures.

Some Senate Republicans sought to defuse Clinton's opposition to a GOP provision to raise Medicare premiums for elderly beneficiaries. The Republican measure to temporarily extend the government's spending authority would have raised those monthly premiums, starting Jan. 1, from the current $46.10 to $53.50, rather than allowing them to fall to $42.50, as provided in current law.

As a way around the White House objections, Sen. Peter V. Domenici (R-N.M.), chairman of the Senate Budget Committee, suggested that the spending bill keep the premiums level at $46.10. But White House officials did not promise that Clinton would accept that compromise. They said that even agreement on that point would not eliminate the President's objection to language in the same bill that would sharply cut interim spending levels for some federal programs.

Temporary Spending

The bill provides that temporary spending could fall to as low as of fiscal 1995 levels for some federal programs that Republicans have sought to cut or eliminate. The provision threatens some programs that are close to Clinton's heart--such as the national service program and Goals 2000 education programs--and thus run counter to vital White House aims.

Mike McCurry, White House press secretary, said, "The President is very concerned about the 60% funding level." As the federal government's borrowing authority ticked toward expiration at midweek, Treasury Secretary Robert E. Rubin took steps Monday to assure that the government would be able to pay its debts. The temporary borrowing bill vetoed by Clinton would have raised the current $4.9-trillion debt ceiling by $67 billion.

To stay below the debt ceiling, Treasury officials announced that they will dip temporarily into certain government retirement funds, essentially a bookkeeping ploy in which Treasury securities are redeemed for cash. By removing those securities from the books, the Treasury lowers the total U.S. debt, making room to add on new debt through a series of Treasury auctions this week and next.

The government had faced a major cash squeeze in the coming days--$102 billion in payments for interest and principal.

Today's announcement is saying we're not going to default," a asury spokesman said.

Bonds rallied on Wall Street after the announcement. The benchmark 30-year Treasury bond yield fell to 6.27% from 6.33% Friday. The Dow industrial stock index inched up 2.53 points to a record 4,872.90, but most stocks closed lower.

Government officials made final plans for furloughs, after going through the frustrating exercise of trying to decide which employees would be essential to their operations.

At the White House, for example, 79% will be furloughed, leaving 90 of the Executive Mansion's 430 full-time equivalent employees on the job.

The guidelines will leave the White House press office staffed by unpaid interns, one press assistant and the press secretary; while the White House's political director, Douglas Sosnik, will be furloughed.

The prospect of a shuttered government is also forcing the White House to shorten a trip to Asia that U.S. and Asian officials have deemed highly important.

linton will now spend two days, instead of six, on a trip that was to encompass a state visit with the Japanese, and a meeting with members of the Asian trade bloc.

Long scheduled, the trip will now amount to "a weekend trip to Asia," McCurry acknowledged.

Only days ago, Japanese ambassador to the United States Takakazu Kuriyama was suggesting that such a shortening was undesirable and unlikely. "We don't expect that to happen, and of course we don't want to see that happen, given the importance of the relationship," the ambassador said.

---- INDEX REFERENCES ----

STORY ORIGIN: WASHINGTON

REGION: United States (US)

EDITION: SOUTHLAND EDITION

Word Count: 1239
11/14/95 LATIMES 1
E D OF DOCUMENT

Tab 4

Citation Search Result Rank 90 of 104 Database
'14/95 WASHPOST A03 WP
../14/95 Wash. Post A03
1995 WL 9272296

The Washington Post

Tuesday, November 14, 1995

A SECTION

At White House, on Hill, Pondering the Essentials

Guy Gugliotta
Washington Post Staff Writer

Sen. Alfonse M. D'Amato (R-N.Y.) was planning to hold "essential" Whitewater hearings, then canceled. Rep. John R. Kasich (R-Ohio) wants his pay held, but doesn't know how to do it. The White House is going down to one chef. Senators may bring lunch -- their dining rooms will be closed.

With a government shutdown only hours away, the opposing camps in the White House vs. Congress budget battle last night tried to decide who would work tomorrow and who would not.

Not surprisingly, the White House, with only one boss calling the shots, had things pretty well figured out by sundown. President Clinton and top White House staff were "essential personnel," as were the Secret Service and the people working in the Situation Room.

But first lady Hillary Rodham Clinton's staff will fall from 16 to four, and maintenance will drop from 70 to 14. Where there are normally four chefs, there will be only one during the day and another at night -- only 90 of the White House's 430 employees were expected to stick around for a day's work.

In Congress, by contrast, where there are 535 bosses, any meaningful count of the total considered "essential" was impossible. Secretary of the Senate Kelly Johnston said there will be no guided tours, but the Capitol will be open and Capitol Police will see that visitors don't get into harm's way.

House Oversight Committee Chairman Bill Thomas (R-Calif.) sent a letter to House members early in the afternoon yesterday describing "essential" personnel as "only those whose primary job responsibilities are linked directly to legislative activities."

Thomas himself, however, found wandering the halls late

terday looking for House Speaker Newt Gingrich (R-Ga.), confirmed the vagueness of this dictum, saying "I don't know of any shutdown," and offering the opinion that Congress was deeply involved in the nation's essential business.

The House Budget Committee chairman wanted to "make sure my pay is held, just like any federal employee. So I asked somebody how to do that this morning," Kasich said, "and they said, 'I have no idea.' "

Also planning on coming to work was Gingrich spokesman Tony Blankley. "My dog thinks I'm essential," he said. "I bring him food -- he told me in dog words." Besides, he added, "McCurry would be disappointed if I wasn't there."

Michael McCurry, the White House press secretary, was not immediately available for comment, but as one of the White House's 90 anointed, he can watch Blankley twisting the knife on TV and will be able to return the favor.

The House was lucky on food, because it privatized all its cafeterias and dining rooms. The Senate, which runs its own eating places, is shutting them down, leaving senators with the awkward choice of visiting the House to eat or making do with vending machines.

D'Amato, the Senate's Banking Committee chairman, said late yesterday that he'd planned to conduct a Whitewater hearing today, saying it was "essential" to the "fulfillment of our objectives." How essential?

Not that essential: He later postponed the hearing, issuing a release citing "the tremendous press of business relating to the budget." Hearings to resume, he said, after Thanksgiving.

Staff writer Helen Dewar contributed to this report.

---- INDEX REFERENCES ----

NAMED PERSON: BILL THOMAS; ALFONSE M. D'AMATO

KEY WORDS: FEDERAL GOVERNMENT; U.S. CONGRESS; FEDERAL EMPLOYEES; FURLOUGHS; MEMBERS OF CONGRESS; BUDGET; DEFICIT

NEWS SUBJECT: Labor, Personnel Issues (LAB)

NEWS CATEGORY: NEWS

GOVERNMENT: Federal Government; Congress (FDL CNG)

TION: FINAL

Word Count: 536
11/14/95 WASHPOST A03
END OF DOCUMENT

Tab 5

Israel Arrests More Rabin Slaying Suspects; Military Withdraws from Jenin

Peres Pursues Peace with Security. Israeli military radio Nov. 11 reported that the police had arrested an active-duty soldier and his father in connection with the assassination of Prime Minister Yitzhak Rabin, who was slain Nov. 4 by a Jewish ultranationalist. The police, already holding the confessed assassin and five other right-wing suspects, did not immediately confirm the two new arrests. However, a police spokesman, Boaz Goldberg, Nov. 14 said that authorities had widened their crackdown on rightist militants, rounding up more than 50 additional people on a host of charges not directly tied to the Rabin case. [See below, p. 833A1]

Concurrently, Acting Prime Minister Shimon Peres signaled Israel's intention to meet terms of the accord on extended self-rule that the Rabin-led government had signed with the Palestine Liberation Organization (PLO) in September. The Israeli military Nov. 13 withdrew from the northernmost West Bank Arab city of Jenin, transferring control to the Palestinian National Authority (PNA), headed by PLO Chairman Yasir Arafat, after 28 years of Israeli military occupation. [See p. 709A1]

In hailing the advent of self-rule to Jenin, Gen. Nasser Yousef, a senior PNA security official, said, "Without a doubt this day crowns the work of Prime Minister Yitzhak Rabin who lost his life working for peace."

Peres Nov. 14 toured Israeli military posts on the West Bank near the "green line," Israel's 1967 border with the then-Jordanian West Bank. He indicated that security considerations for Israel's military outposts and settlements in the West Bank would remain one of his uppermost priorities as Israel continued its peace process with the Palestinians.

Peres said that the military's withdrawal from Jenin, the first Palestinian city affected under the second-phase accord, would be followed by a pause in troop redeployments so that Israelis could "draw all the necessary conclusions" as to the feasibility for withdrawing from other West Bank cities, in accordance with the September accord.

Peres added that all available measures would be taken to insure that Jews and Arabs on the West Bank could continue undisturbed in their normal lives as Palestinians moved toward democratic elections, tentatively set for Jan. 20, 1996.

Peres Nov. 13 had met in Israel with Benjamin Netanyahu, leader of the right-wing opposition Likud bloc. The two had reportedly agreed to monitor their supporters for the kind of inflamed rhetoric that many observers had denounced as fostering a climate of political violence in Israel.

Focus Shifts to Nationalist Rabbis—Israeli Police Minister Moshe Shahal Nov. 10 said that investigators had concluded that Yigal Amir, the confessed assassin of Rabin, had belonged to a terrorist cell whose violence had been encouraged by a "spiritual leader." Shahal declined to identify the alleged instigator by name, but Israeli newspapers singled out two rabbis—Nahum Rabinovich and Dov Lior—as the possible spiritual leader in question.

Shahal also said that the alleged cell had planned to carry out attacks against Arabs in the West Bank.

Amir had contended in court testimony that Jewish law sanctioned his killing of Rabin. [See p. 834E1]

Rabinovich, who lived in the West Bank settlement of Maale Adumim, outside Jerusalem, and Lior, from the settlement of Kiryat Arba, north of Hebron, Nov. 13 both denied the public accusations against them.

However, Israeli television Nov. 14 aired a tape in which Rabinovich said, "Turning over a comrade to gentiles in a way that endangers his life and turning over property of Jews—whoever does such a thing has to pay with his life." As of Nov. 16, the police had not filed charges against either Rabinovich or Lior.

In developments related to the police crackdown on right-wing extremists, it was reported Nov. 14 that among the detained had been Rabbi Moshe Levinger, a prominent figure among Jewish settlers, and Noam Federman, spokesman for the militantly nationalist Kahane Chai (Kahane Lives) group, an off-shoot of the anti-Arab Kach (Thus) organization founded by the late Rabbi Meir Kahane. [See p. 207E1; 1994, p. 200B1]

Related Developments—In other developments related to the Israeli–Palestinian peace process:

□ The Israeli newspaper *Yediot Ahronot* Nov. 10 reported that a poll of adult Israeli Jews indicated a sharp shift toward support of the Labor Party and its peace process in the aftermath of the Rabin assassination. According to the survey, conducted Nov. 7–8 by the Dahaf Institute, some 74% of respondents said they wanted the government to implement the second-phase accord on Palestinian self-rule, and 23% indicated that they wanted the process to be halted. The survey also showed potential voters backing Peres over the Likud's Netanyahu by a 54% to 23% margin. Some 23% of respondents reportedly favored a third choice or were undecided. [See 1994, p. 150E1]

□ Israelis Nov. 12 ended their formal seven-day mourning period for Rabin with a demonstration that drew 250,000 people to the square in Tel Aviv where he had been assassinated. Peres addressed the crowd, as did Leah Rabin, widow of the slain prime minister. Leah Rabin urged Israelis to back Peres in his effort to continue the peace process, vowing, "The silent majority will be silent no more." [See p. 834F2]

☑ Facts On File®
World News Digest with Index

Volume 55, No. 2868
November 16, 1995

First of two sections*

IN THIS ISSUE

*Second section in [illegible]

REFERENCES in brackets give location of background information in this & preceding volumes

rorist operation carried out against the U.S. military on Saudi soil during the 50
A years of U.S.–Saudi military cooperation. [See 1991, p. 129F1]

U.S. forces had maintained a low profile in Saudi Arabia, out of deference to Saudi custodial responsibilities for Moslem holy sites. The U.S. Defense Department Nov. 13 declined to reveal how many U.S. troops were currently stationed in Saudi Arabia. It was known, however, that for the last 20 years the U.S. had conducted a training program
B for the 80,000-strong Saudi National Guard on the use and maintenance of U.S.-supplied military equipment. ■

Other International News

British Commonwealth Summit Held. Leaders from most of the British Commonwealth's 52 member nations, the majority of which were former colonies of
C Britain, attended a four-day summit in Auckland and Queenstown, New Zealand Nov. 10–13. The summit was dominated by the Commonwealth's reaction to French nuclear tests in the South Pacific and Nigeria's execution of nine minority-rights activists. [See pp. 850C1, 823C2; 1993, p. 851E3]

The Commonwealth leaders Nov. 11 decided to suspend Nigeria from the organization for human-rights abuses. Nigeria, which was led by military dictator
D Gen. Sani Abacha, had drawn fierce worldwide protests after the Nov. 10 executions. Author and environmentalist Ken Saro-Wiwa was among the nine political activists executed.

Commonwealth Condemns A-Tests—The Commonwealth Nov. 10 released a statement condemning France's recent resumption of nuclear testing. British Prime Minister John Major Nov. 10 criticized the Commonwealth's statement and reaffirmed his support of France's right to conduct the tests.

The nuclear tests were being held in the South Pacific and had drawn protests from Commonwealth members there, including New Zealand and Australia. Leaders of those countries had maintained that Major was reluctant to oppose the tests because he feared upsetting Anglo-French relations. Australian Prime Minister Paul Keating Nov. 3 had set a potentially divisive tone for the summit when he said that Major would get "a smack with a ruler" for supporting the tests. (Keating Nov. 10 apologized to Major for his comments, which he said were misrepresented by the media.)

The Commonwealth's Nov. 10 declaration noted the "widespread anger caused by the current program of nuclear weapon tests," although it did not mention France by name. An "overwhelming majority" of Commonwealth leaders were said to back the statement, which claimed that the tests could adversely affect a 1996 nuclear test ban treaty.

Major Nov. 10 called the statement "inconsistent and unbalanced." Major was particularly opposed to the suggestion that the tests could derail the 1996 treaty.

Mozambique was admitted into the Commonwealth Nov. 12. Mozambique would become the only member not to have former colonial ties to Britain. ■

UNITED STATES

Clinton Vetoes Stopgap Spending, Debt Ceiling Bills

E **Partial Government Shutdown Results.** President Clinton Nov. 13 vetoed two bills that would have provided the federal government with funds to pay its debts and remain in operation. Early in the day, Clinton vetoed the first measure, which would have granted a temporary increase in the legal debt limit for the government. Later that evening, Clinton refused to sign a continuing resolution bill—or so-called stopgap spending measure—which would
F have provided funding for government activities for the next two weeks. The second veto forced a partial shutdown of the federal government. [See below, p. 730D3; 1993, p. 771A1; 1990, pp. 756C1, 569C1]

The president's vetoes marked the latest event in an ongoing budget battle between the White House and Republican leaders in Congress. Clinton said that the bills contained "extreme proposals" that would
G imperil the environment, funding for education and public health. [See below]

The Senate Nov. 9 had passed its final version of the debt-limit increase bill, 49–47. The House then passed the same bill with a 219–185 vote Nov. 10. The continuing resolution cleared the House Nov. 10, by a 224–172 vote, and the Senate early Nov. 13 passed it by a voice vote.

Details of the Debt-Limit Bill—The debt-limit bill vetoed by Clinton would have authorized an increase in the debt limit to $4.967 trillion, from the current $4.9 trillion. However, the bill stipulated that after Dec. 12 the debt limit would decrease to $4.8 trillion. In addition, the bill would have barred the U.S. Treasury from tapping into federal trust funds to pay government bills or payments on bonds.

In the absence of a new debt-limit increase and without the use of trust fund money, the federal government almost certainly would be unable to make interest payments on borrowed money, forcing the government to default on its loans. That unprecedented event, in turn, would precipitate a financial crisis.

Had Clinton signed the bill, it would effectively have given him the option of either reaching a new budget agreement with Republicans—very likely on their terms—by Dec. 12 or placing the country at serious risk of defaulting on its debts. The president cited the proposed restrictions on the Treasury as the chief reason for his veto. Investors and financial markets greeted Clinton's decision with relief.

In addition, Republicans had tacked on to the debt-limit bill several unrelated "rider" measures that Clinton opposed. One provision would require federal agencies to perform new risk- assessment and cost-benefit analyses before issuing new health, safety and environmental regulations. Another measure would require the president to agree in principle to balance the federal budget in seven years using Congressional Budget Office estimates. The CBO's estimates tended to be more pessimistic than those of the Clinton administration, which used numbers provided by the White House Office of Management and Budget.

Clinton Nov. 13 called the debt-limit bill a "back-door effort by the congressional Republicans to impose their priorities on our nation," and claimed that it would cripple laws designed to protect the environment and public health. House Speaker Newt Gingrich (R, Ga.) the same day accused the president of playing "political games" and defended the bill, saying that Republicans had been "elected to change politics as usual."

The federal government had run a deficit every year since 1969, requiring it to borrow money in order to stay in operation. Congress alone was authorized to set the debt limit for the government, but that limit required presidential approval. Periodically, as the government neared its debt limit, Congress would send a bill to the president that would authorize a debt increase. Congress usually attached riders to the bill in hopes that the president would sign the bill, even if he did not approve of all the provisions within it, rather than place the government in financial danger.

Trust Funds Tapped to Avoid Default—With no debt-limit increase scheduled, Secretary of the Treasury Robert E. Rubin Nov. 13 announced that he would tap into two federal retirement funds in order to avoid a government default on the $102 billion in interest loans and principal that came due Nov. 15–16. The two funds were the Government Securities Investment Fund and the Civil Service Retirement Fund. Those funds were politically the safest to draw upon because federal law required that, if the funds were ever appropriated during a debt crisis, the government would have to repay any interest lost to the funds. Analysts said that the two funds would provide the Treasury with enough money to stave off a default for several months. [See p. 776G2]

Continuing Resolution Details—The continuing resolution that Clinton vetoed would have extended financing for government agencies until Dec. 1. Clinton's main objection to the bill stemmed from a provision authorizing an increase in premiums for Medicare, the federal medical-insurance plan for the elderly. The bill also would have implemented stricter spending reductions than those stipulated by the continuing resolution that was currently funding the federal government.

Congress as of Nov. 16 had sent the president only five of the 13 appropria-

Tab 6

Citation Search Result Rank 80 of 104 Database
'16/95 WASHPOST D01 WP
1./16/95 Wash. Post D01
1995 WL 9272722

The Washington Post

Thursday, November 16, 1995

STYLE

That Essential Difference; Majority of House Employees Escape the Shutdown

Phil McCombs
Washington Post Staff Writer

So who's essential, anyway?

Judging from the activity in the office buildings of the U.S. House of Representatives yesterday, the answer must be: darn near everyone!

Congressional aides were scurrying through the halls. They filled the House restaurants (run by a civilian company), though the ^ nate's were closed. They crowded the elevators, which ran just e without elevator operators. Drivers of the underground trains connecting the Capitol and legislative office buildings were dismissed originally, then summoned back yesterday.

In Speaker Newt Gingrich's congressional office -- 2428 Rayburn -- flocks of people moved to and fro; there was laughter emanating from a back room amid clicking computers and ringing phones.

"No!" said a stern receptionist, when asked if these workers could be interviewed concerning the exact nature of their essentiality; she referred inquiries to the speaker's office over in the Capitol building. "We have several people in that office. Anyone can help you," she said.

The government may have shut down nonessential activities such as the Smithsonian's Air and Space Museum -- indeed, you could have landed a light plane at Third and Jefferson streets on the Mall yesterday afternoon -- but apparently it takes a lot of essential government to make a nonessential government shut down.

And who's to say what's essential, anyway? Rep. John T. Myers (R-Ind.), chairman of the House "Gym Committee," was on a ·ee-member panel that closed the facility as part of the shutdown. :erday morning, the House gym was reopened. Myers resigned his

·t, a spokesman said, and beyond that there was no comment -- ..ough doubtless the dramatic inside details will one day be known to history.

"Everyone is essential in our office," said Andi Dillin, press secretary for Rep. Bill McCollum (R-Fla.). "We're continuing to hold hearings and do legislation, so the legislative aides are needed. The chief of staff is needed to oversee everything. The press secretary is needed to answer the questions of the press."

Even the people who answer the phones, she added, must stay on duty because "it's essential we let the constituents know what's going on."

Apparently, most congressional offices are following these same rough guidelines -- just keep everyone merrily toiling away as if nothing has happened. Dillin said she'd attended a meeting of congressional press secretaries where "just a few" raised their hands when asked if there were furloughs in their offices.

Things were different at the White House, where officials said only 43 of 400 employees were allowed to work. The rest could not even work for free. Working, one official said, incurs "obligations" the government, and the government cannot incur obligations it no authority to pay.

A White House official also said people cannot "volunteer," because that is a provision of work without compensation or congressional authorization. White House stay-at-homes were told they cannot even call their offices to check on work.

On the Hill, "90 percent of the offices are maintaining a full operation," said Michael S. Erlandson, administrative assistant for Rep. Martin Olav Sabo (D-Minn.). In Sabo's office, he added, "the congressman feels all the people are hired because they are essential."

Erlandson elaborated, saying that everyone from receptionist Miriam Barrett "to myself as chief of staff is essential for different reasons, but they all relate to the congressman trying to get his job done."

"Oh, my God!" said a voice from behind a high telephone console; this turned out to be an intern, Chris Mulloy.

"I am essential because," Mulloy started saying in response to a reporter's question, when the AA politely but firmly cut her off.

'I don't think we should interview the interns," he said,

ling. "We're not going to send the interns home and say they're nonessential: It's an educational process for them to be here and observe all this."

According to Erlandson, one of the few congressional operations taking the shutdown thoroughly to heart is that of Rep. Bill Luther (D-Minn.). Indeed, the National Journal's CongressDaily reports that Luther issued a statement saying, "It would be inappropriate for Congress to exempt itself from the effects of the situation."

"His office should be open, let me call over there for you," suggested receptionist Barrett.

A visit to Luther's office in the Longworth Building revealed a bundle of mail on the marble floor in front of the locked door, upon which Luther himself -- or, perhaps, some lingering essential staff member -- had posted this notice in bold lettering:

"Congressman Luther is temporarily out of the office. The congressman's staff has been furloughed due to the shutdown of the federal government. If you have an appointment or wish to have an appointment with the congressman, please call (202) 225-2271 to leave a message for the congressman. We apologize for the inconvenience. Thank you."

And freshman Rep. Michael P. Forbes (R-N.Y.) sent everybody in his office home except himself: "The White House and Congress are currently deadlocked over a plan to balance the federal budget," his answering machine explained.

"I will continue to remain on the job, [but] because spending authority has now expired . . . I am compelled to close my congressional office until an agreement is reached," he said. "I regret any inconvenience to you."

Forbes himself, waylaid outside the chamber after a vote, admitted that "it's not been easy," but "maybe we'd have an agreement if all the staff went home and we started to feel like every other federal employee."

What are the guidelines here, anyway?

"I did a study of my office," said Rep. John Conyers Jr. (D-Mich.), interviewed while catching an elevator in the Rayburn Building, "and found that everyone on my staff was more essential than me -- so I declared myself nonessential and furloughed myself."

Actually, under the House rules, to the extent they can be

ertained at this point, Conyers could probably do that if he wanted. According to memos issued by Rep. William Thomas (R-Calif.), chairman of the Committee on House Oversight, "nonessential House operations" must be shut down as determined by "the appropriate government officer."

Who, naturally, "has always been the member."

This being government, each furlough requires an "Authorization for Furlough of Employees."

"It's still very difficult for me to write out the furlough sheets for the employees we're furloughing," said Donna L. Brazile, administrative assistant to Del. Eleanor Holmes Norton (D-D.C.), shaking her head sadly and admitting she hadn't done it yet.

Brazile said she had to go to Norton and argue for her own essentiality: "I said I was essential. She said, 'Why?' I said I was essential because I had to administer everything and shut down the offices and follow the appropriation process."

It worked.

The essential criterion of essentiality in the House, the mas memos stress, turns on whether an employee's responsibilities "are directly related to legislative activities."

Which suits Jeff P. Nelligan just fine. "What makes me essential is we had a bill on the floor last night -- the ICC Termination Act -- and we're getting hundreds of calls from all over the country," said Nelligan, leaping up enthusiastically from his computer yesterday.

Nelligan works for the Committee on Transportation and Infrastructure under the chairmanship of Rep. Bud Shuster (R-Pa.); on his computer screen at that very moment was a press release on the $6.5 billion National Highway System bill, which, Nelligan nimbly explained, "is to the 21st century what the interstate highway system is to the 20th."

Essentiality? "Everyone's essential," he said, "everyone here."

"Am I essential?" said Frank Record, a Republican staffer on the Committee on International Relations, who was shooting the breeze with a friend in the Rayburn cafeteria. "No one's told us to go home yet. We're all waiting. I could use a little vacation."

Nearby, a woman putting ketchup on her hamburger asked not to identified, but said she's a staff assistant on a House subcommittee, adding: "I don't know how essential that is, but there it is. I do basic office procedures, like answering the phone and filing, so I guess that makes me essential."

She ate an onion ring. "We're not getting many calls. We get the regular in-house calls, but we're not getting too many outside calls, but they said we were essential."

She kept eating onion rings, thinking it over. Finally she said:

"I mean: We don't have much to do today."

Staff writers Guy Gugliotta, Howard Kurtz, Stephen Barr and Ann Devroy contributed to this report.

TABULAR OR GRAPHIC MATERIAL SET FORTH IN THIS DOCUMENT IS NOT DISPLAYABLE

PHOTO,,Dudley M. Brooks
CAPTION: GOP committee staffer Frank Record, who wasn't sent home, says, "I could use a little vacation."

---- INDEX REFERENCES ----

NAMED PERSON: NEWT GINGRICH;

KEY WORDS: FURLOUGHS; WHITE HOUSE STAFF; CONGRESSIONAL STAFF; BUDGET; DEFICIT; TAX SYSTEM; PRESIDENTIAL VETOES; PRESIDENTIAL RELATIONS WITH CONGRESS; U.S. CONGRESS

NEWS SUBJECT: Taxes; Politics (TAX PLT)

NEWS CATEGORY: NEWS; FEATURES

GOVERNMENT: Congress; Executive (CNG EXE)

EDITION: FINAL

Word Count: 1408
11/16/95 WASHPOST D01
END OF DOCUMENT

Tab 7

Citation
'17/95 USATD 04A
. /17/95 USA TODAY 04A
1995 WL 12678997

Search Result

Rank 7 of 10

Database
USATD

USA Today
Copyright 1995

Friday, November 17, 1995

NEWS

Interns help pick up slack at White House
Susan Page; Bill Nichols
THE BUDGET SHOWDOWN; LIFE WITHOUT GOVERNMENT

White House life during the shutdown: President Clinton orders in pizza for dinner as first lady Hillary Rodham Clinton vacuums the dustballs that are accumulating in the corners of the Lincoln Bedroom.

Well, not exactly.

While the federal budget showdown has idled 800,000 federal ·-ployees and shuttered the nation's most popular tourist ractions, it hasn't meant serious lifestyle changes for the C--ntons.

The 70-member staff that runs and maintains the White House has been trimmed to 16.

Still on duty in the East Wing are a day chef and an evening chef, a day butler and an evening butler, two day housekeepers and an evening housekeeper, two ushers, two electricians, four engineers and a computer specialist.

On Capitol Hill, members of Congress aren't facing many personal inconveniences from the confrontation, either. The elevator operators have been sent home and the Senate cafeteria closed.

But most congressional staffers have been designated "essential" by their bosses so they can continue to work.

In contrast, Clinton has made deep cuts in his West Wing staff of aides. He has reduced the 430 full-time employees in the Executive Office of the President to a skeleton crew of 90.

Hillary Clinton furloughed 12 of her 16 staffers.

ıd even if Congress passes the appropriations bill that funds

11/17/95 USATD 04A

White House, Clinton won't sign it, aides say. He'll argue that ι ʒ office shouldn't be back in operation until the rest of the government is, too.

So, absent as of Thursday evening:

-- A receptionist to greet visitors in the West Wing lobby.

-- Stenographers to record and transcribe the president's every word.

-- Sit-down meals in the most exclusive of capital lunchrooms, the White House mess. It was open for take-out only.

At the National Security Council, a spokesman said the need to deal with immediate crises had delayed planning for such future events as Clinton's trip to Europe in 10 days.

If the shutdown continues for long, plans to install Christmas decorations and prepare the White House for nearly 150,000 guests invited to holiday parties could be in trouble.

The White House staffers who are working find themselves ·ʼ ɔending on a newly empowered cadre of youthful, unpaid interns. ɲton strolled around the halls Thursday to thank them.

Meanwhile, those who aren't working - and are prohibited by law from doing their jobs on a volunteer basis - have slept in and have started doing Christmas shopping.

About 20 furloughed members of the first lady's staff got together to volunteer at a local soup kitchen Wednesday.

A sizeable group of the president's staff toasted their non-essential status at a Tex-Mex restaurant Tuesday night. Afterward they went to a sneak preview of the new movie, An American President.

TABULAR OR GRAPHIC MATERIAL SET FORTH IN THIS DOCUMENT IS NOT DISPLAYABLE

PHOTO,b/w,Jake Bacon,Arizona Daily Sun via AP;
PHOTO,b/w,Wilfred Lee,AP

---- INDEX REFERENCES ----

KEY WORDS: BUDGET

· ᵀS SUBJECT: Economic News (ECO)

TION: FINAL

Word Count: 451
11/17/95 USATD 04A
END OF DOCUMENT

Tab 8

Citation
20/95 WASHPOST A19
11/20/95 Wash. Post A19
1995 WL 9273378

Search Result   Rank 34 of 104   Database WP

The Washington Post

Monday, November 20, 1995

A SECTION

THE FEDERAL PAGE

Some Just Wouldn't Stop Working

Stephen Barr; Bill McAllister
Washington Post Staff Writers

They were the phantoms of the Great Government Shutdown.

When federal offices closed last week, numerous white-collar employees sent home on furlough stuffed their briefcases and bags with files from the in-box, figuring they could take a project or two home and, at the least, work in peace and quiet. Other employees supposedly on furlough were sneaking into their offices, apparently they could meet upcoming deadlines at work.

Said one furloughed worker: "We were told not to fall down the stairs if you come to work," presumably because injuries would not be covered by insurance. He, like others interviewed, asked not to be identified.

Supervisors were instructed not to put pressure on anyone to complete their work, he said. Even so, many of his furloughed colleagues were showing up in the office.

This is, after all, Washington, where virtually everyone hates to miss work. Work is status, work is power, and everyone likes to think he or she is essential.

But work by any employee on furlough because of a shutdown has been deemed illegal. The 19th century Anti-Deficiency Act forbids agency managers to accept volunteer labor or other services. Violators can be punished with a $5,000 fine, imprisoned for not more than two years, or both.

Unlike other federal workers, employees at the White House were permitted to volunteer during a shutdown. But at a price.

hite House volunteers would have their salary changed to

·o, which carries "substantial consequences," as a White House ɪ‿mo explained. A zero salary meant the White House workers would: lose their health insurance and life insurance; lose the prospect of any back pay that Congress might grant furloughed workers; and cease accruing sick leave and vacation time.

Still, many among the rank and file wanted to work. Last week, a public affairs officer at one agency, bored with filling out graduate school applications, went to his office to sit in on an interview that a senior official was giving to a newspaper reporter.

"They told me I could be arrested or something," he said, "but I was going nuts. I got my car worked on. I made some calls. But I was going crazy," especially because his agency is fighting for survival in Congress.

It took him less than two minutes Thursday to respond to a call placed to his pager.

The people who study work were not surprised.

Edward Lawler, a University of Southern California business professor, said scientific studies have long found individuals who "·re motivated by the task rather than the reward. . . .

"They are very much turned on by the work they do. I'm not surprised that some would do it but I would expect it would be a very small percentage . . . maybe 5 to 10 percent."

Lawler said such workers were probably involved in interesting, high-profile projects. "If you are a parking lot attendant, you are not coming in to park extra cars."

Bonnie Michaels, president of Managing Work & Family Inc., a Chicago consulting firm, said it is hard to explain why federal workers would take risks when told not to work. Many workers battle bouts of insecurity and a "fear of the future," she said. For them, work is an anchor in their lives.

Lawler said work acts almost as a narcotic for some people. "They are inseparable from the work they do. It defines who they are. Without it, some people literally can come apart."

The Anti-Deficiency Act also made life difficult for workers authorized to carry on government business during the shutdown. The law allows civil servants and the military to continue national defense, protect public safety and health, support the national ɔnomy and perform emergency tasks.

But it apparently limited otherwise routine activities.
. wyers at the National Aeronautics and Space Administration said last week that NASA Deputy Administrator John R. Dailey could not appear for a panel discussion before the National Academy of Public Administration. An aide to Deputy Attorney General Jamie S. Gorelick refused a reporter's request for an interview, saying Gorelick was restricted to performing only "essential business."

Clinton administration officials, meanwhile, have repeatedly chided reporters for using the terms "essential" and "nonessential" when writing about employees affected by the shutdown. The official designations are "excepted," "emergency" and "non-excepted" employees, officials said.

"If the legal test was 'essential employees,' there would have been no furloughs," said John A. Koskinen, deputy director of the Office of Management and Budget.

Rep. Steny H. Hoyer (D-Md.) said he found "a disturbing trend towards downplaying the importance" of the furloughed workers. "It is disgraceful that some have chosen to suggest that 'nonessential' employees really are not needed or do not contribute," he said.

"Anybody who understands how to lead and deal with people ld never declare 800,000 people nonessential," Ross Perot said yesterday on NBC's "Meet the Press." "That creates a scar that will take a long time to heal."

Senior Executives Association president Carol A. Bonosaro said furloughed workers "have been subjected to unwarranted ridicule in the media and by the public" because of the widespread use of "nonessential."

She recently met with Vice President Gore, she said, and "was gratified to learn that the vice president not only understands the denigrating nature of this label but is personally offended by its use."

Gore "has personally urged" top administration officials to assure returning federal workers of their importance to their agencies, Bonosaro said.

Staff writers William Branigin, David Brown, Elizabeth Corcoran and Thomas W. Lippman and staff researcher Barbara J. Saffir contributed to this report.

TABULAR OR GRAPHIC MATERIAL SET FORTH IN THIS DOCUMENT IS NOT DISPLAYABLE

JSTRATION,,Peter Alsberg; PHOTO,,Nancy Andrews;

11/20/95 WASHPOST A19

'O-GRAPHIC
C..PTION: SHUTDOWN CHRONOLOGY
MONDAY, NOV. 13
President Clinton vetoes legislation that would have averted a government shutdown, saying the bill would raise Medicare premiums and deeply cut education and environment programs. An attempt to find a compromise between the White House and GOP congressional leaders fails.
TUESDAY, NOV. 14
Clinton and Republican leaders exchange public recriminations but fail to find a solution to the budget stalemate.
+ About 800,000 federal workers across the nation are sent home. About 150,000 of the 310,000 civil servants in the Washington area are furloughed.
+ National park visitor centers and monuments close. All Smithsonian museums and the National Zoo close. More than 4,000 ticket holders to the biggest show of Johannes Vermeer's painting in three centuries are locked out of the National Gallery of Art.
+ The administration continues to issue Social Security checks, but new applications are not processed. Medical staff remains on duty at veterans hospitals and clinics.
+ Air traffic controllers, the Coast Guard, railway inspectors and other safety personnel remain on the job. Weather forecasting ntinues.
ll active duty military stay at work, along with about 571,000 o. the Defense Department's 866,000 civilian employees.
+ Federal prisons operate as normal. Criminal investigations and prosecutions continue, but postponements are sought in most civil cases.
+ A reduced staff of maids, butlers, chefs, electricians and engineers take care of the White House. About 90 of Clinton's 430 non-household staff members stay on duty.
+ Schools and hospitals in the District of Columbia stay open, but other services are disrupted.
WEDNESDAY, NOV. 15
Treasury Secretary Robert E. Rubin announces plans to pull $61.3 billion from two federal retirement accounts, an unprecedented move that he said was necessary to save the government from the first default in its history.
+ Government contractors began to receive "stop work" orders from agencies, leading some of them to send their workers home, too.
+ Corporations register stock and bond offerings with the Securities and Exchange Commission at sharply lower fees because a higher fee is part of the budget and has not become law yet. The loss to the Treasury is estimated at between $15 million and $25 million.
THURSDAY, NOV. 16
ngress draws criticism because it keeps virtually all of its ff at work, even though its appropriation has lapsed, too.

he National Park Service instructs parks to close lodges and cabins, the first step to completely shutting down the nation's largest parks.
+ The Grand Canyon closes for the first time in its 76-year history, prompting protests from Arizona Gov. J. Fife Symington (R).
+ The shutdown begins to take its toll on area businesses, with companies furloughing at least 1,000 private-sector workers.
FRIDAY, NOV. 17
Hours of intense negotiations aimed at reopening the government collapse.
+ Federal employees besiege government personnel offices seeking advice on when they might be paid. An increasing number fill out forms to apply for unemployment compensation.
+ A federal judge rejects a request by the American Federation of Government Employees to stop agencies from requiring employees to work without pay during the budget standoff.
+ Interior Department officials say they are being pressured by members of Congress to accommodate hunters who use dozens of wildlife refuges that are shuttered.
+ Housing and Urban Development Secretary Henry Cisneros worries that the shutdown could jeopardize rental subsidies to 1.3 million low-income households and stall the processing of millions of dollars worth of home loans and mortgages.
SATURDAY, NOV. 18
ublican leaders and the White House begin lengthy talks to end the shutdown. Administration officials warn that the government will face a series of financial emergencies within several days.
+ Cash shortages could make it difficult to provide milk and food to federal prisons and medical supplies to veterans hospitals.
+ The shutdown jeopardizes the distribution of about 7,000 welfare checks to Native Americans and more than 3.3 million benefit checks to veterans and survivors.
+ The cost of the shutdown is estimated at about $120 million a day, with the bulk of that representing back pay that GOP leaders have pledged to restore.
SUNDAY, NOV. 19
Clinton and the Congress agree to balance the budget not later than fiacal 2002, and the House and Senate pass a one-day funding bill allowing about 750,000 federal employees to return to their jobs today. The Senate, in session on a Sunday for only the 17th time in its history, also passed a bill to fund the government until Dec. 15, and the House was to vote on that measure today.
-- Stephen Barr

---- INDEX REFERENCES ----

NAMED PERSON: STENY H. HOYER;

ANIZATION: ANTI-DEFICIENCY ACT

WORDS: FEDERAL EMPLOYEES; FEDERAL GOVERNMENT; BUDGET; U.S. CONGRESS; PERSONNEL MANAGEMENT; FURLOUGHS; D.C. METROPOLITAN AREA

NEWS SUBJECT: Labor, Personnel Issues; Personnel Announcements (LAB PER)

NEWS CATEGORY: NEWS

GOVERNMENT: Federal Government; Congress (FDL CNG)

EDITION: FINAL

Word Count: 927
11/20/95 WASHPOST A19
END OF DOCUMENT

Tab 9

Balkan Presidents Reach Bosnia Peace Accord; NATO to Keep Peace in Divided State

☑ Facts On File®
World News Digest with Index

Volume 55, No. 2869
November 23, 1995

End Seen to Four-Year War. The presidents of Serbia, Croatia and Bosnia-Herzegovina Nov. 21 agreed to a pact to end a nearly four-year-old war among Croats, Moslems and Serbs in Bosnia that had claimed some 250,000 lives. The agreement would divide Bosnia into two entities, a Moslem–Croat federation and a Serb republic, that would share a central legislature and presidency, with Sarajevo as the national capital. A North Atlantic Treaty Organization (NATO) peace-keeping force of 60,000 troops—about one-third of them from the U.S.—would be deployed in Bosnia by the end of the year to sustain the fragile peace accord. [See below, p. 810A2]

The leaders initialed the pact in an impromptu ceremony at Wright-Patterson Air Force Base near Dayton, Ohio, where they had convened Nov. 1 in U.S.-sponsored peace talks. A formal signing was scheduled to take place in Paris in mid-December.

President Alija Izetbegovic, leader of the predominantly Moslem Bosnian government, and Croatian President Franjo Tudjman initialed the treaty on behalf of their respective nations. Slobodan Milosevic, the president of Serbia, signed for the Bosnian Serbs, whom he had represented at the talks. U.S. Secretary of State Warren M. Christopher, who guided the treaty through tortuous last-minute negotiations, initialed the pact as a witness on behalf of President Clinton's administration.

The Balkan leaders and U.S. officials hailed the peace agreement as a pivotal breakthrough. President Clinton at a White House press conference expressed hope that the pact would give "the people of Bosnia . . . a chance to turn from the horrors of war to the promise of peace." But many observers were skeptical about whether the warring Bosnian factions, who bore deep-rooted grudges after years of war and atrocities, could coexist peacefully within the same state, as the Dayton plan stipulated.

Pact Would Oust Karadzic—The treaty would bar any persons who were indicted for war crimes from holding political office in the new state. That provision would effectively remove from power Bosnian Serb political leader Radovan Karadzic and Gen. Ratko Mladic, his military deputy. However, the pact would not require the signatory governments to turn over accused war criminals for prosecution, a safeguard that had been key to winning Croat and Serb backing for the pact.

The pact gave the estimated 2.7 million refugees who had been driven from their homes by the Bosnian war the legal right either to return to their homes or to receive compensation for lost land and property. A human-rights commission was to be appointed to monitor the treatment of refugees and related issues, but no clear mechanism for punishing rights violations or enforcing the repatriation of refugees was put in place.

Milosevic Sways Bosnian Serbs—The Bosnian Serb delegation to the Dayton talks Nov. 21 refused to initial the accord. But Karadzic and other Serb leaders Nov. 23 initialed the pact after meeting with Milosevic in Belgrade, the capital of Serbia. (Karadzic and Mladic had been unable to travel to the Dayton talks because there were outstanding international warrants for their arrest for war crimes.)

Milosevic, who was also the de facto leader of the federation of Yugoslavia, was widely blamed for having sparked the recent wars in Bosnia and Croatia by throwing Serbia's financial and military support behind nationalist Serbs in those countries. Ensuing trade sanctions had strangled Serbia's economy, increasing the political pressure on Milosevic to reverse his position and support a peace plan. Most analysts concurred that the Bosnian Serbs would be unable to sustain a war in Bosnia without Milosevic's backing.

In the wake of the Dayton accords, the United Nations Security Council acted immediately to lift the sanctions against Serbia. [See below]

Parties Agree to Land Split—Central to the Nov. 21 peace pact was a U.S.-devised division of territory that would give the Moslem–Croat federation 51% of the land within Bosnia's original borders and the Bosnian Serbs, 49%. All sides in the dispute had agreed to accept the 51%–49% division formula prior to the Dayton peace summit, but wrangling over specific details of the split threatened to derail the talks from their outset. [See map below]

With a few significant exceptions, the

The division of territory in Bosnia between a Moslem–Croat federation and a Serbian republic, as agreed by negotiators in Dayton, Ohio Nov. 21.

IN THIS ISSUE

B

C

United States

D

Europe

E

Other World News

F

Miscellaneous

G

REFERENCES in brackets give location of background information in this & preceding volumes forms. Werleigh was confirmed by the Senate Nov. 5 and by the Chamber of Deputies Nov. 6. She was sworn in Nov. 7, becoming Haiti's first female premier. [See p. 773E2]

Former **Brig. Gen. Henri Max Mayard,** who had been the fourth-highest-ranking officer in Haiti's now defunct military, Oct. 3 was **murdered** by unidentified gunmen in a suburb of Port-au-Prince, Haiti's capital. Mayard was one of at least 20 supporters or officials of the former military who had been killed in what international human-rights officials termed "commando-style executions" since the military junta was ousted and Aristide was restored to power in October 1994. Aristide in April had disbanded Haiti's military, which had been accused of numerous human-rights abuses during the three-year rule of the junta. [See p. 860E3] ■

UNITED STATES

Clinton Signs Second Stopgap Funding Bill

Compromise Temporarily Ends Impasse. President Clinton Nov. 20 signed into law a continuing resolution, also known as a stopgap measure, that would fund the federal government through Dec. 15. The bill contained language that committed the president and Congress to balancing the federal budget by the fiscal year 2002 and to providing adequate funding for education, the environment and various federal "entitlement" benefit programs. The stopgap bill's enactment ended a six-day shutdown of the federal government, the longest in U.S. history. [See below, p. 852E1]

A continuing resolution was needed to keep the federal government operating because only six of the 13 appropriations bills that funded the federal government had been passed as of Nov. 22. A previous continuing resolution had expired Nov. 13. Clinton the same day had vetoed another stopgap measure, saying he objected to a clause in the bill that required an increase in Medicare premiums. The resulting funding gap forced temporary closings of national parks and museums and placed more than three quarters of a million federal employees on furlough.

The battle over the stopgap bill was seen by many as a prelude to what promised to be grueling negotiations between the White House and Congress over a massive budget reconciliation bill that had cleared the Senate and House Nov. 17 and Nov. 18, respectively. That bill authorized funding for government entitlement programs, which collectively accounted for about two-thirds of all federal outlays. Clinton had vowed to veto the bill. [See p. 813F1]

Tense Negotiations Preceded Deal—In the days following the Nov. 13 veto of the earlier stopgap bill, the White House and Republican congressional leaders engaged in a series of tense negotiations in an attempt to reach a compromise on a new continuing resolution. Negotiations broke off several times before an agreement was reached.

Meanwhile, the House Nov. 16, by a vote of 277–151, approved a new stopgap measure. Only three Republicans voted against the measure, while 48 Democrats voted for it. Later in the day seven Senate Democrats joined with all the Senate Republicans to pass the measure, 60–37. The bill did not contain the Medicare provision to which Clinton had objected, but it did include language requiring the president to commit to balancing the federal budget within seven years and to using Congressional Budget Office (CBO) economic forecasts in White House calculations of deficit reductions. Clinton said he objected to both conditions and vowed to veto the bill.

Though both the Senate and House votes on the bill had fallen short of the two-thirds majority needed to override a presidential veto, the number of Democratic defections revealed a weakness in the support for the president's stance on the budget and provided additional incentive for him to reach a compromise with Republicans.

Gingrich 'Snub' Affects Talks—Republicans were given added incentive to reach a settlement with the White House as a result of a Nov. 15 remark made by House Speaker Newt Gingrich (R, Ga.). Gingrich said that he had placed a number of restrictive provisions into the stopgap bill that Clinton had vetoed Nov. 13 because he had felt slighted by the president when the two men flew together on Air Force One, the presidential jet, to the funeral of assassinated Israeli Prime Minister Yitzhak Rabin. [See p. 833A1]

Gingrich complained that the president had refused to negotiate on the budget crisis during the 10-hour return flight from Israel Nov. 6 and that Clinton had made Senate Majority Leader Robert J. Dole (R, Kan.) and himself exit from the rear of the plane, rather than from the front as was usual for important guests.

Democrats quickly seized upon Gingrich's comments and attempted to portray the speaker as having shut down the federal government out of spite. Some of them Nov. 16 brought to the House floor an enlarged copy of a banner headline from the *New York Daily News* that read, in part, "CRY BABY Newt's Tantrum."

Observers said that Gingrich's remarks weakened his bargaining position by making him appear obstructive.

The president appeared to be winning the battle for public support in the budget dispute. A *Washington Post*/ABC News opinion poll taken Nov. 19 showed that 71% of the public disapproved of the way Republicans were handling the budget standoff; 42% faulted Clinton's stance.

Details of Stopgap Agreement—White House and Republican leaders finally reached an agreement on a continuing resolution late Nov. 19. Republicans were able to include in the compromise bill the language from the resolution passed Nov. 16 that required the president and Congress to enact legislation that would balance the budget within seven years. However, White House negotiators succeeded in attaching a clause to the resolution that stipulated that the balanced budget must "insure Medicare solvency" and provide "adequate" funding for Medicaid, education and the environment. Republicans agreed to accept those conditions after guarantees that national defense, agriculture and veterans would receive adequate funding were added to the clause.

A compromise was also reached on the methods used to calculate deficit projections. The agreement required Congress and the White House to use CBO estimates, but only after the CBO had consulted with the White House Office of Management and Budget (OMB) and "other government and private experts." The Clinton administration, which relied on OMB economic estimates, had said that the CBO projections were too pessimistic.

The stopgap bill stipulated that all government programs and agencies whose spending bills had not yet been enacted would receive funding at 75% of fiscal 1995 levels. The stopgap bill that had expired Nov. 13 had provided funding at 90% of 1995 levels.

The stopgap measure also required that all federal employees who had been furloughed during the federal shutdown receive back pay, and provided funds for that purpose.

In a rare Sunday session Nov. 19, the Senate approved the compromise stopgap measure, by voice vote. The House approved the bill Nov. 20 by a vote of 421–4. Clinton signed the bill later in the day. (A one-day stopgap bill was passed late Nov. 19 by the House and Senate and signed that day by the president, allowing federal employees to return to work the morning of Nov. 20. Both chambers passed the bill by voice vote.)

No Agreement on Debt Limit—The continuing resolution contained no provision that would increase the federal debt limit. Earlier in November, Secretary of the Treasury Robert E. Rubin had tapped into several government trust funds in order to prevent the U.S. from defaulting on its debts after Clinton had vetoed a bill that would have raised the federal debt limit. Clinton had objected to the bill because it contained provisions committing him to a seven-year timetable for balancing the budget using CBO projections. [See p. 852E1]

Standard & Poor's Corp., a leading international credit-rating agency, Nov. 10 issued a statement to the U.S. government, warning it that investors' faith in the U.S.'s ability to pay back its debts been "diminished" as a result of the impasse over the debt limit. The agency said it would not reduce the U.S.'s triple-A credit rating—the highest it granted—but it held out the possibility that it would do so if the U.S. defaulted on any of its pay-

Tab 10

1720

Citation Search Result Rank 1 of 1 Database WCPD
9/96 WCPD 262
2/19/96 Wkly. Compilation Presidential Documents 262
1996 WL 13335771

Weekly Compilation of Presidential Documents

Monday, February 19, 1996

Vol. 32, No. 7, ISSN: 0511-4187

Remarks in a roundtable discussion on the work-study program in Des Moines, Iowa. (President Bill Clinton speech)(Transcript)

February 11, 1996

Sally Hinders, assistant provost for career services, Drake University, welcomed the President and introduced the participants, one of whom indicated that he was from Winterset, IA, site of the "Bridges of Madison County."]

The President. They should have given you the role. Laughter

Ms. Hinders discussed some of the advantages of the work-study program at Drake University, indicating that students who participate tend to become more involved in the Drake community and often use their experiences as stepping stones to other opportunities. She then asked the President to talk about the program.]

The President. Well, let me begin by thanking all of you for taking some time on a Sunday afternoon to do this. I'm delighted to be here, delighted to be at Drake.

Since I became President I've worked hard to try to increase access to colleges and universities for young people because it's obvious that more need to be able to go and more need to be able to stay. And I never will forget when I was Governor I had an encounter one night with a number of students in Fayetteville, which is the hometown of the University of Arkansas, and I just stopped in a little place, drank a cup of coffee. And there were several students there, and I talked to two of them of the group there who had actually dropped out of school once already because they were afraid they couldn't afford the cost of staying in. They were worried about whether they could get the proper students loans, whether they could get any scholarships, whether they would ever be able to pay back their loans.

So I began to work on it when I was a Governor, things we could do at the State level. And when I ran for President I had a commitment to try to expand opportunities for college going. And essentially what we have e so far is to put the Pell grant program back on track - it was in s..ious trouble - passed a national service program, which this year has 25,000 young people in it earning money for college tuition while doing community service; and to expand loan options so that more young people could have the option to pay their loans back as a percentage of their income when they get out if they take a job that wouldn't permit them to make what would be the normal commercial repayment schedule. And that would mean no one would ever have to forgo borrowing money because they would always be able to handle the loan repayment.

And then in the State of the Union Address I recommended, as you pointed out, that we have a 50-percent increase in the work-study program, to get up to a million students a year in work-study because we haven't kept up over the years in work-study with the demand, with increasing enrollment. And I also believe that the cost of college tuition up to $10,000 a year ought to be deductible, which I believe would be - from my point of view, it's the best kind of tax cut you could have because you'd be giving a tax reduction to people who are investing either in themselves or their children and, therefore, making a big investment in our common future.

But the work-study program is of real interest to me because I worked myself through college; I worked myself through law school. I don't b lieve I would have made it if I hadn't had the jobs. And I also have erved just what you said, that a lot of young people actually do better when they have a work experience to go with their schooling. So I'm hoping to persuade the Congress to adopt this increase in work-study, even though in general we're reducing the budget. And we will offer to the Congress a way to do this consistent with our need to balance the budget in 7 years. So this won't bust the budget or anything, but it will help a lot more people to go and then to stay in college.

Let me just make one other point on that. I'm very encouraged that the college-going rate in our country is still going up, but I am not encouraged that it has started to fall again in the last 2 or 3 years among people whose incomes are in the lowest 20 percent of our economy. And if you think about it, the whole sort of premise, or promise, of America from our earliest immigrants is that hard working parents would be able to open more opportunities to their children. So it's not a good thing that we have that happening.

So one of the things I hope will happen out of the whole combined impact of all these proposals is that young people who come from families with very modest in comes will start increasing their college-going again, just like the rest of our country.

's. Hinders introduced some work-study participants, the first of ı indicated that the program was a stepping stone to an internship that throughout the experience her employers were supportive of her efforts. A parent indicated that her daughter would not be at a private university were it not for the work-study program and that, while her husband's job as a teamster was not always stable, they never had to worry about their daughter's education.]

The President. Well, let me say I know that Drake has made a real effort to hold down the tuition, too, so that more people will be able to afford to go. And I just spoke to the National Association of Independent Colleges and Universities in Washington a couple days ago, and I tried to cite the number of schools that were doing that. I think more and more schools are trying not to just get caught in a vicious cycle where they have to raise tuition and then they have to find more aid, then they have to do more work-study.

I'd just like to remind everybody - I know all of you around this table know this, but the American people who are watching us and citizens of Iowa who are watching us, this is not - this should not be viewed as a social program. This is an investment in our future. The taxpayers make out big time on this investment. We get a whole lot more back out of all of you because you're going to have college degrees, because you're going to be able to live out your own dreams, because you're going to be able to do what you wish to do.

nd not just financially. This is not entirely a money issue. There's also - our society is a better place when people find more personal fulfillment in the work that they do. So it is a financial issue, but it's also much more of a moral and social issue. It knits us together more strongly when more people have a chance to develop their God-given abilities.

I personally believe that we don't make any better investments than this. And almost 100 percent of people like you in your position will pay back to the Government far more in increased taxes than you ever took out in student loans or Pell grants or work-study funds or anything else. And I think that's an important thing for the American people to remember, that this is an investment with a big-time return.

Another participant said that the program had reduced the burden on his family, and it gave him a greater appreciation for education and a career.]

The President. Your son spoke very well.

The student's father said the work-study program had helped both his sons, teaching them to work harder toward their goals. Another participant said that a family member had faced medical problems that d diminished family financial resources, but that Drake had been able put together a financial aid package which allowed him to go to ool and help pay for his education.]

The President. How many hours a week on average do all of you work?

Q. About 10, 11.

The President. About 10, 11? About the same for everybody? And do you all find that it doesn't undermine your studies?

The student said that the program made her work harder, set a schedule, and keep to it. Another indicated that it helped them mature. Work-study student Molly Adams said that it increased her sense of responsibility and went on to explain her work with the Grace United Methodist Church and how it helped the community in Des Moines.]

The President. Marilyn, what percentage of Molly's pay comes from the Government, and what percentage do you have to come up with?

Marilyn Adams. Isn't it one-third and a third? I think that's right - 25 and 75.

The President. So your church pays for 25 percent? So it's the same as with the college, then?

. Correct.

The President. Because when you employ people it's 75-25, isn't it?

Q. Correct.

The President. So do you have to allocate work-study slots off-campus, is that how it works?

Q. Correct. We're supposed to spend 5 percent of our overall allocation on off-campus studies.

The President. Does the law limit you to 5 percent?

Q. No.

The President. So it's Drake policy? Or is it Department of Education policy? If you wanted to have - if a college or university wanted to place 25 percent of the work-study people off-campus, could they do so?

Q. As far as I know we could, if we could find the places and the students to work there.

"he President. And what percentage of your students are on :-study?

. About 75 percent of our students who receive financial aid go ahead and accept their work award and work.

Q. And I can add to that, about 80 percent of our students receive some form of financial aid.

The President. So a majority do this, are on some sort of work-study.

Q. Oh, yes.

The President. Now, if you had more positions, could you fill them?

Several participants indicated their willingness to take more work-study positions. Ms. Hinders discussed matching funds and indicated that Drake contributes additional money because they like the work-study program.]

The President. Now, I saw in the notes I was given before I came in here that the students make between $4.65 an hour and $7.00, but mostly nearer $4.65 than $7.00. But what would you say the average pay is? Between $4.65 and $5.00 an hour?

Q. Right around $5.00, yes.

The President. What determines the pay, the ability of the match or the nature of the job, or what?

One participant said it was the nature of the job; another said supply and demand play a part, but some positions require very specialized skills and the wages go up a little bit in order to be competitive with the marketplace. Another participant said that Drake University overspends the matching funds and really spends more like 50 percent.]

The President. Really?

Q. Lots of students coming in and out every day are involved with those positions. And they're quite varied as well.

The President. But you would - anyway, I take it that - you all agree then that there is a demand for more work-study positions, and if we could go - one million a year is our goal, and that basically costs - it would be about a 50-percent increase from where we are now.

Ms. Hinders said that those are the kinds of opportunities that students and parents are really looking for. Employers and work-study students then described their programs.]

The President. Let me ask you something, you're a freshman?

!. Yes.

The President. That's one thing I wanted to ask. How do you deal with the demand - if the demand exceeds the supply, do you give any preference to older students or is it strictly by income, by need, without regard to class?

Ms. Hinders explained that Drake University begins with need-based students but said that it is a part of the financial aid program. She then introduced the director of the university's financial aid program who said that work-study was a cornerstone of the financial aid program and that it was a win-win situation for all involved.]

The President. I also think the value that the students give you - Erica mentioned that just the work experience, working with older people in a good environment. It's amazing how quickly young people mature and to take a responsibility.

You know, it's a funny thing, when the Government was shut down - which wasn't too funny - laughter - but when it was shut down there were days when the whole White House was practically being run by the interns. Laughter It was amazing. There were probably four of us with gray hair - laughter - and the rest of it, the kids were sort of nning the show. And they did a great job. I mean, they worked hard; y kept the basic functions open. They worked quite well the first time we were shut down, and we didn't have everything covered by the budget.

It just reminded me again of how important it is to give young people that experience, too. It sort of binds the community and the society together in very important ways.

Ms. Hinders. Well, very much so. I know that we're running a little bit short on time.

The President. Tom, you want to say something?

Senator Harkin thanked all the participants and mentioned that he was the only Senator to sit on both the committee for higher education and the appropriations committee, and in the last Congress was chairman of the appropriations committee.]

The President. I hope you will be again.

Senator Harkin. Well, I hope so. Laughter By the way, Rebecca, as I told you, is doing a great job for me. The youngest person I've every had in that - the position of being the scheduler is a tough position.

ne President. It's the worst job in an office.

enator Harkin said that during his years on the education committee the commitment to education had declined year after year and indicated that was particularly true of Pell grants and college work-study programs. He concluded by saying that the President supports these programs and that he hoped that interest rates on student loans would remain low.]

The President. I think that's quite important. I think it's been underestimated, the impact of not having that interest accumulate until people have been out a few months.

Q. Definitely.

The President. Let me just also say, to follow up on what Senator Harkin was saying, and to try, to put it in some larger political context - for the last 30 years anyway, by and large, education has not been a particularly partisan issue. We've had broad bipartisan support for these things until just recently.

And I hope we can get it back, because this is - this big philosophical debate going on in Washington, if you believe the Government is the problem and is the reason for all of our ailments as a society, then you think people are better off if you just get the deficit down, have a strong defense and let people manage for themselves. If you believe that we're stronger as a country, when we deal with our common problems in a common fashion, we will work together on them, then it's obvious that things that have a big-ticket cost, like a national work-study program, require some involvement with the National Government.

And as I said, these are really matters that historically have not been, at least in my lifetime, the last 30 years, have not been really matters of much partisan debate. But what has happened in the last, sort of, decade, there's been this sort of head of steam built up behind the notion that Government per se was bad. Not dumb regulations, or an ill-advised program, or a bad tax system, or whatever, but just the whole idea of Government was intrinsically - something wrong with it. And I basically don't agree with that.

I think what's happened is we need - all organizations have to become less bureaucratic, less rule-oriented, more oriented toward empowering people to solve their own problems. And Government's like that, too, but we cannot meet our educational obligations unless there is a public, broad-based, national commitment to helping you do what you do here at the grassroots level.

And actually, one thing I like about the work-study program is it's idea of what it ought to be - we say, okay, here's a national problem; we need more young people going to college, but it costs a lot go and most people can't afford to go. Okay? Here's the national solution: We should give money to help that happen. But we don't tell you how to do it. In other words, that's the way the Federal Government ought to operate more. We say - we set a national goal. We provide some resources to meet that goal. We ask you to make a contribution as well. Then you get to decide how. We all agree on the what, nationally, and then you define the how at Drake. And at the University of Iowa, they might define it in an entirely different way. I mean, that's the way this country ought to work, where people work together in that fashion.

I just sat here and made a list of the seven people I worked for in college and law school. Laughter It's quite interesting. I was thinking, more than half of them I still hear from, I still have a relationship with and I still feel enormously indebted to because they gave me a chance to get my education. I was sitting here thinking about it while you all were talking. Laughter

Ms. Hinders. Well, as we draw to a close, Senator Harkin, do you have any additional comments that you'd like to add?

Senator Harkin. Do you have any students in the Head Start program?

Q. We do.

Senator Harkin. You do?

Q. Yes.

Senator Harkin. Good for you.

Ms. Hinders. This has been a pleasure to have you here today, Mr. President. We have enjoyed coming together as a group to talk to you about an issue that we really have a passion for. And we can tell that you do, too. So, on behalf of Drake and our entire community, thank you.

The President. Thank you, and good luck to all of you.

NOTE: The roundtable began at 12:45 p.m. in the Knapp Center at Drake University.

---- INDEX REFERENCES ----

NAMED PERSON: BILL CLINTON ESSAYS, LECTURES ADDRESSES

KEY WORDS: EDUCATION

NEWS CATEGORY: TRANSCRIPT

·d Count: 3138
2/19/96 WCPD 262
END OF DOCUMENT

Tab 11

tation | Found Document | Rank 2 of 3 | Database
:8/96 NWSDAY A32 | | | NWSDAY
2/28/96 Newsday A32
1996 WL 2513789

Newsday

Wednesday, February 28, 1996

VIEWPOINTS

Embattled Clintons Should Note Watergate Lessons

By Ronald D. Rotunda. Ronald D. Rotunda teaches at the University of Illinois College of Law. He was assistant counsel to the Senate Watergate committee.

SOME PEOPLE see in Whitewater the specter of Watergate, while others deny any analogy. I think it's too early to make a definitive judgment - but there are disquieting similarities.

Watergate referred to a host of scandals that involved more than the burglary of Democratic Party headquarters. The Senate Watergate hearings, for example, disclosed that Richard Nixon's White House had created an "enemies list" of reporters and others not friendly to › administration. We recently learned that a member of Bill nton's cabinet, Energy Secretary Hazel O'Leary, spent more than $40,000 of taxpayers' money to create her own enemies list of reporters writing stories unfavorable to O'Leary and her department. The White House announced that the list was "unacceptable," but not illegal. Ditto, Nixon.

When some of the Watergate tapes were finally released, we learned Nixon advised aides to say: "I don't remember . . . I can't recall." No one claims Clinton has given such advice, but many of his aides also have bad memories. Witnesses at the Senate Whitewater hearings have used the phrases "don't recall" or "don't remember" nearly 800 times. One, when confronted with inconsistent statements from his diary, claimed he lied to his diary. The "I don't recall" defense did not preclude perjury convictions against the Watergate defendants.

When 18 1/2 minutes disappeared from the White House tapes, Alexander Haig blamed the gap on "some sinister force." In Whitewater - which, like Watergate, involves a wide variety of purported wrongdoing - documents have mysteriously appeared. For two years, the independent counsel has subpoenaed certain billing records of the Rose law firm - where Hillary Clinton and several Clinton aides worked. A few weeks ago, these records surfaced, covered by a White House aide, in (of all places) the family q-rters of the White House.

The records are annotated in the handwriting of Vince Foster, the White House aide who apparently committed suicide in 1993. Hillary Clinton has not explained how they materialized in one of the most secure places in the world - unless they had previously been withheld in violation of the subpoenas. That would involve an obstruction of justice.

After Hillary Clinton testified before the Whitewater grand jury, she said she had no idea how the documents got there. The records, showing she worked on projects for Madison Guaranty Savings & Loan, appear inconsistent with her claim that she did little work for the failed thrift, which is at the center of the Whitewater controversy.

Nixon unsuccessfully sought to keep documents from Congress by asserting executive privilege, while Bill Clinton has unsuccessfully asserted attorney-client privilege. Another disquieting similarity between Watergate and Whitewater is the way facts seem to drip out slowly and the story keeps changing. First, we're told that the first lady "had no role" in the decision to fire the employees of the White House Travel Office. Then a memorandum is uncovered that says, "Hillary wants these people fired - Mac [McLarty, then chief of staff] wouldn't do it." We are told that the travel employees ·e fired because of sloppy records and criminal behavior.

Then we learn that, before the inauguration, before any investigation of the travel office, Clinton's aides in Arkansas were saying the decision had already been made to remove the travel office staff and replace it with political cronies. The attorneys for Billy Dale, the head of the travel office, accused the White House of removing logs that would account for money he was charged with embezzling. Although the trial judge refused Dale permission to subpoena the White House for these records, the jury returned a swift verdict of acquittal.

Ultimately, Watergate was a scandal about abuse of power, which also involved laundering of funds. Whitewater may involve a scandal about laundering of funds, which also involves abuse of power. A cynic may look at what has been revealed and see an interesting business relationship between the former governor of Arkansas and his wife, a practicing lawyer. When the Arkansas Securities Department started investigating Madison, Madison began sending Hillary Clinton a $2,000 monthly retainer; as Bill Clinton was about to become governor, an official connected to Tyson Foods (a big Arkansas employer) arranged commodities trades for Hillary Clinton that rapidly converted $1,000 to $100,000.

ontinuing lessons abound in both the Watergate and Whitewater experiences. Last month, I visited Moldova, one of the former Soviet

›ublics, to advise the newly created Supreme Court on the role of an independent judiciary. Toward the end of our meetings, the justices asked about Watergate. Later, they said, "Tell us about the Hillary problem." They clearly saw a resemblance. I told them that in America, no one, not the president, not his spouse, is above the law. That is the lesson of Watergate.

---- INDEX REFERENCES ----

KEY WORDS: OPINION; WATERGATE; BILL CLINTON; WHITEWATER; SCANDAL;

EDITION: NASSAU AND SUFFOLK

Word Count: 791
2/28/96 NWSDAY A32
END OF DOCUMENT

117 S.Ct. 2482 (Mem)
138 L.Ed.2d 991, 65 USLW 3767, 65 USLW 3835, 65 USLW 3838
(Cite as: 117 S.Ct. 2482)

OFFICE OF the PRESIDENT, petitioner,
v.
OFFICE OF INDEPENDENT COUNSEL, et al.

No. 96-1783.

Supreme Court of the United States

June 23, 1997.

Case below, In re Grand Jury Subpoena Duces Tecum, 112 F.3d 910.

*2483 Petition for writ of certiorari to the United States Court of Appeals for the Eighth Circuit denied.

END OF DOCUMENT

Tab 12

Ants in the picnic basket?

The Drudge Report
07/04/97 *By Matt Drudge*

REQUEST E-MAIL DELIVERY OF THE REPORT

DRUDGE REPORT FINAL
By Matt Drudge
Fri Jul 04 02:25:21 1997

Ants in the picnic basket?

Coming just hours after the President "adamantly" denies harassing Paula Jones, the DRUDGE REPORT has learned that NEWSWEEK ace investigative reporter Michael Isikoff is hot on the trail of a new development that threatens to ignite premature holiday fireworks at the White House. Reports have surfaced that Isikoff has been in contact with a former White House staffer who may offer "pattern" evidence of improper sexual conduct on the part of the President.

At this hour it is unclear whether Isikoff will pull the pieces of this explosive story together before deadline.

Other reporters may also be on the trail of this new development.

The story is said to involve a federal employee sexually propositioned by the President on federal property.

If true, the new account would be markedly different from the Jones' scenario, which involved pre-presidential actions long ago and far away.

Under the new media-management team of Begala and Blumenthal [B2], the White House filed its first formal denial of Jones' allegations late on the eve of the holiday weekend -- just as Washington was clearing out, herding to beaches, and packing picnic baskets.

And too late for the network broadcasts.

But in the new era of non-stop news cycles, the old tricks did not fly. Traffic stopped on I-95 as the APUPIREUTERS broke the first word of the Clinton denial at 6:18 p.m. ET, designed for minimum impact -- and weeks before the court answers were actually due. But true to the Age, word quickly spread on the Internet, talk radio and cable, proving that no longer are there any safe times to release damaging information.

Tab 13

The Washington Post

Monday, August 11, 1997

Style

MEDIA NOTES

A Reporter's Net Loss; Details of **Newsweek** Story Appear Prematurely on the Web
Howard Kurtz
Washington Post Staff Writer

An investigative reporter is trying to nail down a sensitive story. Suddenly someone splashes the key details all over the Internet, even though the reporter doesn't have enough evidence to publish. Now half of official Washington is talking about the story he sn't finished writing.

That was the situation faced by **Newsweek's** Michael Isikoff as he pursued the question of whether former White House aide Kathleen Willey had ever accused President Clinton of making an improper sexual advance.

On July 4, word of the Isikoff inquiry turned up on the World Wide Web's **Drudge** Report, the one-man gossip operation run by Matt **Drudge.** By month's end, **Drudge** had put out more details of the work-in-progress, including Willey's name. What's more, **Drudge** says he was tipped off by one of Isikoff's **Newsweek** colleagues.

"I outed the story," boasts **Drudge.** "I was totally driving him crazy. There was nothing he could do." He says Isikoff sent him an e-mail calling him "insane."

Isikoff, a former Washington Post reporter, takes the matter seriously, saying **Drudge** was reporting things -- such as what Willey supposedly told **Newsweek** -- that he could not possibly know. That, in turn, greatly complicated Isikoff's dealings with potential sources.

"He's rifling through raw reporting, like raw FBI files, and .sseminating it," Isikoff says. "He doesn't conform to any journalistic standard. This is not harmless fun; it's reckless and ought to be condemned. He ought not be treated as an impish character. It's hard to do real reporting in an atmosphere that's been polluted like this."

Newsweek described its story as "complicated and murky," and media critic Terry Eastland called it "carefully executed investigative reporting." Indeed, contrary to **Drudge's** advance billing, Isikoff's piece last Monday raised questions about whether any sexual harassment took place. He quoted another former White House aide, Linda Tripp, as saying that Willey emerged looking "happy" from the Oval Office on the day in question in 1993 and did not appear harassed.

What pushed the Willey story into the mainstream press (the story was first broken by CBS's Bill Plante) was the decision by Paula Jones's attorneys to subpoena Willey in Jones's sexual harassment suit against Clinton. Willey's lawyer said she was "outraged" to be drawn into the case and has "a good relationship" with the president. inton's lawyer, Robert Bennett, said the president "adamantly nies" doing anything improper.

Bennett said in an interview that the media are "hypocritical" because they ignore "stories that don't meet their journalistic standards" until "some event, like the issuance of a subpoena or the appearance of something in another publication." Then, he says, "the press uses that as an excuse" to run with the flimsy story.

Clearly, Drudgelike leaks on investigative stories boost the chances for misleading and sensational headlines. **Drudge** freely admits his gossip is sometimes wrong; he predicted that Hillary Rodham Clinton would be indicted last summer.

Isikoff "has a right to be furious," **Drudge** says, "but life's not fair. The new technology lets someone interrupt the flow." Besides, says **Drudge,** "I seemed to have about 80 percent of the facts."

Tabloid Goose Chase

Top editors at the New York Post and Daily News are crying foul the charge that their owners spiked stories questioning whether ..yor Rudolph Giuliani was having an affair with his communications director.

The editors say they were simply unable to confirm that Giuliani's marriage to Donna Hanover was falling apart before Vanity Fair published the charge last week.

"Once a week there'd be a new Donna rumor that would explode like crazy," says Arthur Browne, the Daily News managing editor. "It kind of took on a life of its own.

"We checked on every apartment we were told she was moving into. A huge amount of man-hours was devoted to this. But no source had firsthand knowledge. It was always, 'I was told.' We came up dry. . . . What's going on in their household is in some respects beyond the reach of journalism, and should be."

"We weren't able to develop enough information that we would have felt comfortable going with it," says Post Editor Ken Chandler. "When you write about problems in someone's marriage, usually it's cause one of the principals has decided to talk about it, or filed a . .t, or has been seen in public dating someone they're not married to. In this case there was no supportive evidence. It wasn't for lack of trying."

The editors say they never discussed the story with their bosses, Post owner Rupert Murdoch and News mogul Mort Zuckerman, both of whom have business dealings with New York City. Giuliani and press aide Cristyne Lategano have denied the reports of an affair, while Hanover has sidestepped the charge and pointedly not defended her husband.

Daily News sources say the editors killed one story that raised questions about the alleged affair after Hanover, at a party for a movie she appeared in, thanked people for helping her through "difficult" times and did not mention her husband. Browne says he recalls vetoing only "shaky gossip items."

Once the Vanity Fair piece surfaced, the News ran a banner headline, infuriating staffers who felt the tabloid should have broken the story. Browne says the paper had no choice after "a national ·blication of some repute" reported that the alleged affair "had a gnificant impact on city government." The Post ran nothing in its first edition, then caught up after the mayor's office issued a statement.

"I'm still not convinced the Vanity Fair piece was accurate," Chandler says.

Petering Out?

Charlie Peters, the irascible founder of the Washington Monthly, is ready to pass the baton. Sort of. One day. When he gets around to it.

Peters hopes to sell the neoliberal magazine to one of his earliest editors, Nicholas Lemann, now the Atlantic Monthly's national correspondent. The deal, first reported by National Journal, could happen in a year or two.

"I could just not face selling now," Peters says. "I still want to grab the world by the lapels and tell it what to do next. But I also realize I'm 70 years old. I want to provide for the Monthly to ntinue in the right hands, and Nick Lemann is the right hands."

But Lemann says he hasn't tackled the hard work of lining up investors or sizing up the business challenges. "There's no urgency because Charlie is happily running the magazine and I'm finishing a book," he says.

TABULAR OR GRAPHIC MATERIAL SET FORTH IN THIS DOCUMENT IS NOT DISPLAYABLE

CAPTION: On his online **Drudge** Report, Matt **Drudge** "outed" an unfinished story by a **Newsweek** reporter.

---- INDEX REFERENCES ----

KEY WORDS: NATIONAL

EDITION: FINAL

Word Count: 1074
8/11/97 WASHPOST D01
END OF DOCUMENT

Tab 14

Homocysteine, Bacteria and Birth Weight— What You Need to Know
Heart Attacks
Plus: How to Protect Yourself

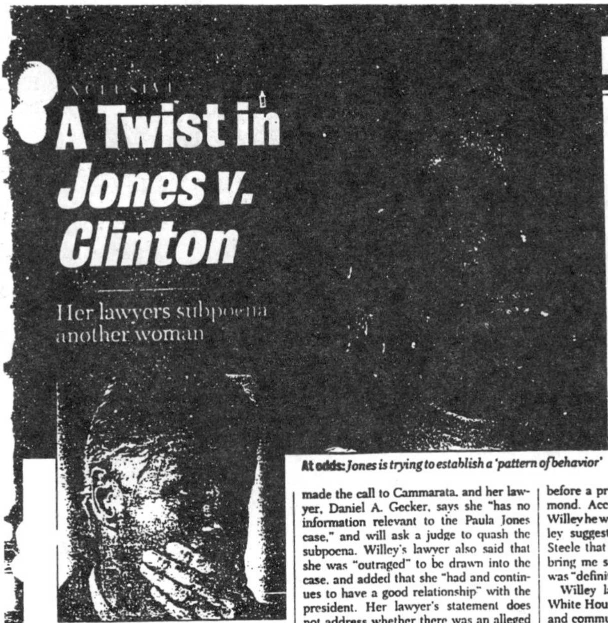

EXCLUSIVE

A Twist in Jones v. Clinton

Her lawyers subpoena another woman

At odds: Jones is trying to establish a 'pattern of behavior'

BY MICHAEL ISIKOFF

THE PHONE CALL WAS PROVOCAtive, to say the least. Early last January, Joseph Cammarata was preparing to help argue to the Supreme Court that his client Paula Jones should get a trial for her sexual-harassment suit against President Clinton, when—he says—the voice of a woman, distraught and hesitant, came on the line. "I had a similar thing happen to me in 1993," she said. She refused to give her name but offered enough details to allow Cammarata to track down the woman he believes made the call: Kathleen E. Willey, 51. Last week Cammarata subpoenaed Willey to question her about whether she had been the victim of an inappropriate sexual advance by the president in the White House. Willey's testimony is necessary, Cammarata argues, to establish a "pattern of behavior" by Clinton of sexually harassing women. An aggressive lawyer will try to tar his opponent any way he can, and Cammarata wants to use the threat of delving into Clinton's alleged sex life—and the resulting publicity—to force a settlement favorable to his client.

This game of hardball is the uncomfortable reality facing Clinton in the Paula Jones case. Kathleen Willey denies she made the call to Cammarata, and her lawyer, Daniel A. Gecker, says she "has no information relevant to the Paula Jones case," and will ask a judge to quash the subpoena. Willey's lawyer also said that she was "outraged" to be drawn into the case, and added that she "had and continues to have a good relationship" with the president. Her lawyer's statement does not address whether there was an alleged sexual encounter with Clinton. Gecker declined to comment on any part of this story to NEWSWEEK, saying it was a "horrible injustice and invasion of privacy" to publish any details about his client's private life. For his part, the president, through his lawyer, Robert Bennett, "adamantly denies that at any time the president ever said or did anything that was at all improper."

The story behind last week's headlines is complicated and murky. Even in the most straightforward sexual-harassment cases, only two people know for sure what happened; motives and perceptions can be mixed, and change over time. Willey could be a shaky witness. She was suffering through a family crisis at the time of the alleged incident, and was later briefly treated for emotional distress. Whoever first called Cammarata told the lawyer that "her husband" had killed himself, and that the suicide had been reported in the conspiracy literature of the far right as one of the "strange deaths" that have befallen Clinton associates. This clue led Cammarata to the widow of a Democratic fund raiser named Ed Willey Jr.—who had killed himself on Nov. 29, 1993. NEWSWEEK began investigating the allegations after getting a tip from Cammarata last January, but received no other help from Jones's lawyers and shared none of its findings with them. What, if anything, really happened between Clinton and Willey remains unknown. It is possible, however, to reconstruct how the charge arose, and to shed some light on credibility and motive.

A former flight attendant, Willey was married to the son of an influential Virginia state legislator. She drove expensive cars, skied at Vail and, with her husband, contributed to the Democratic Party. In 1992 she helped organize fund-raisers for the then candidate Bill Clinton. A friend of Willey's, Julie Steele, says she was present when Willey got a call at home from Governor Clinton on Oct. 14, 1992, the day before a presidential debate held in Richmond. According to Steele, Clinton told Willey he was suffering from laryngitis. Willey suggested chicken soup. Willey told Steele that Clinton asked, Why don't you bring me some? Willey declined, but she was "definitely flattered," said Steele.

Willey landed a volunteer job in the White House social office after the election and commuted from Richmond. About the same time, her husband, a lawyer deep in debt, was accused of embezzling $274,495 from a client. On Sunday, Nov. 28, 1993, there was a tense family discussion over how they were going to repay the money.

She needed a full-time, paying job. So the next day Willey came to Washington, and later told friends that she contacted Clinton's appointments secretary and secured time with the president that same afternoon. This is not as remarkable as it might seem: though a low-level volunteer, she did have longstanding fund-raising ties to Clinton. Linda Tripp, then an executive assistant in the White House counsel's office, recalls bumping into Willey in the West Wing after Willey had allegedly left the Oval Office. Willey was "disheveled. Her face was red and her lipstick was off. She was flustered, happy and joyful," Tripp told NEWSWEEK. Willey said she had to talk to Tripp right away. According to Tripp, Willey said the president had taken her from the Oval Office to his private office, a small adjoining hideaway, and kissed and fondled her. She was not in any way "appalled," Tripp told NEWSWEEK.

Tripp, who says she and Willey were once friendly but are no longer, agreed to speak to NEWSWEEK "to make it clear that this was not a case of sexual harassment." Tripp's account, of course, is still damaging to the president. Bennett, Clinton's lawyer, says Tripp "is not to be believed." In 1994 she moved from the White House counsel's office to a higher-paying PR post at the Pentagon (a job she still holds). The next year she gave some testimony at the Whitewater hearings that was mildly embarrassing to the administration.

Willey's friend Julie Steele raises further doubt about Willey's description of the incident to her. At first, Steele told NEWSWEEK that Willey had graphically described being fondled by the president. Steele said that Willey had told her about the incident on the night it allegedly occurred, and that she had been distraught. But last week Steele admitted to NEWSWEEK that Willey had asked her to "lie" about what happened, in order to give credibility to the allegation that she had been harassed. (Willey's lawyer refused to comment to NEWSWEEK on Steele's charge, or on any other aspect of Tripp's or Steele's accounts.) In fact, said Steele, Willey had told her about the incident weeks after it happened, saying only that the president had made a pass at her. To Steele, Willey had not appeared upset by it at the time.

In December 1993, Willey got a paying job in the counsel's office that lasted 10 months. In 1995, at the White House's invitation, she served as a member of U.S. delegations to international conferences on social development in Copenhagen and one on biodiversity in Jakarta: State Department records show that she was the only American participant who had no apparent expertise in the issues under discussion. The cost of her trips to the taxpayers was about $7,000. Frank Provyn, the director of the State Department Office of International Programs, said he was "kind of surprised" to see her on the trip to Indonesia. But, he added, "a good way to get yourself into a jam is to ask too many questions when someone comes from the White House."

Through Bennett, Clinton says he has "no specific recollection of meeting [Willey] in the Oval Office." Bennett says that Clinton may have consoled her around the time of her husband's death, but it is "preposterous" to suggest that Clinton might have made a sexual advance. (According to police reports, Ed Willey's body was not found until the day after the alleged encounter.) Bennett says there is no record of Willey's entering the Oval Office, but he acknowledged that friends sometimes drop by. Willey has told others that she saw Treasury Secretary Lloyd Bentsen waiting to see Clinton when she left the president's office mid-afternoon. Bentsen's calendar shows him meeting Clinton at 3 p.m. that day. Who's telling the truth? It is always hard to know in these matters, and painful to find out. ■

CRIME

A Brush With Terror

They were making bombs in Brooklyn, their eye on a suicide subway attack. How did they get so far?

BY TOM MORGANTHAU AND GREGORY BEALS

THE PLAN WAS TO BOMB A SUBWAY station in Brooklyn—and the big question, after New York police narrowly averted a catastrophic act of terrorism last week, was how the prime suspect had gotten into the country in the first place. Ghazi Ibrahim Abu Maizar, 24, a West Bank Palestinian, tried three times to enter the United States from Canada and was jailed last January by the U.S. Immigration and Naturalization Service in Washington state. He then applied for political asylum because, he said, he would be persecuted by Israeli authorities. Despite all that, Abu Maizar was set free by a U.S. immigration judge in June after promising to leave the country voluntarily. He went to New York City instead—where, police said, he and another Palestinian immigrant built a powerful pipe bomb for a suicide attack much like last week's terror bombing in Jerusalem.

Tipped off by one of the suspects' friends, a heavily armed police SWAT team descended on their dingy Brooklyn apartment before dawn and caught Abu Maizar and 22-year-old Lafi Khalil sleeping. Both were shot and wounded when, according to police, they tried to trigger the bombs. One bomb was a nine-inch pipe packed with gunpowder, nails and 9mm bullets. The other was a four-pipe monstrosity that would have killed everyone within 25 feet if detonated in an enclosed space like a subway car. Police found hundreds of pages of Hamas propaganda and a portrait of Sheik Abdul Omar Rahman, the blind Muslim cleric convicted of inspiring the World Trade Center bombing. They also found what was described as a terrorist manifesto expressing hatred for the United States and Israel that was allegedly written by Abu Maizar. Hospitalized for their wounds—Maizar was shot twice and Khalil at least five times—both men were charged with conspiring to use explosives to destroy property. "I think we were close to a disaster," said James Kallstrom, head of the FBI's New York field office. "It didn't happen, and that's the good news."

KATHY WILLENS—AP

Heads up: *The bomb squad on the scene*

The bad news, once again, was America's vulnerability to terrorism—which raises troubling questions about the federal government's inability to spot would-be terrorists at the border. In hindsight, anyway, Abu Maizar seemed an obvious security risk: he was briefly detained by Israeli authorities during the *intifada*, when he was about 15, and one of his brothers was once deported from Israel for supporting the Popular Front for the Liberation of Palestine. But his family now says it supports peace and that Maizar, who has denied that he is a member of Hamas, has ever been a political or religious militant. A spokesman for the INS says the case—including Maizar's release pending voluntary departure—was handled by the book. Like most Palestinians who come to this country, he was not on any U.S. "watch list" as a suspected terrorist. "This guy is kind of crazy," one law-enforcement official said. "He was just a wanna-be." But that doesn't solve the problem—because even wanna-bes can kill.

With DANIEL KLAIDMAN *in Washington*

Tab 15

1ST STORY of Level 1 printed in FULL format.

The New York Times

September 13, 1997, Saturday, Late Edition - Final

SECTION: Section 1; Page 37; Column 1; Business/Financial Desk

LENGTH: 109 words

HEADLINE: COMPANY NEWS;
IMPERIAL HOLLY AND SAVANNAH FOODS SEAL MERGER PACT

BYLINE: Reuters

BODY:

Savannah Foods and Industries has accepted a $491 million bid from the Imperial Holly Corporation, ending a takeover battle. Under the deal, which is 70 percent in cash and 30 percent in stock, Savannah Foods' shareholders will receive $20.25 a share, a higher price than signaled a few days ago. Earlier this week, Savannah Foods, based in Savannah, Ga., terminated an agreement to merge with Flo-Sun Inc., the private holding company of the Fanjul family of Florida, and paid Flo-Sun an unspecified termination fee. Savannah Foods shares rose 93.75 cents, to $19. Imperial Holly, based in Sugar Land, Tex., near Houston, dropped $1.0625, to $13.50.

LANGUAGE: ENGLISH

LOAD-DATE: September 13, 1997

Tab 16

Citation Search Result Rank 1 of 6 Database
2/97 FORBES 073 FORBES
9/22/97 Forbes 073
1997 WL 14780038

Forbes

Monday, September 22, 1997

Law and Issues

Privilege-seeking? If you want to understand government in the late 20th century, you had better know something about Gordon Tullock's concept of rent-seeking. It enables you to see Washington for what it really is: a powerful machinethat enables special interests to extract money from everyone else.
By Peter Brimelow

WHAT DO THESE PICTURES have in common?

n "Lobbying has become Washington, D.C.'s largest private employer.... There are 125 people working to influence government policy for every member of Congress, up from 31 lobbyists per congressman in 1964."

-From "Washington's Lobbying Industry: A Case for Tax Reform," a orandum prepared by the office of House majority leader (and Ph.D. economist) Dick Armey (R-Tex.)

n "In 1989 we had essentially no compliance function. Then we hired our first compliance officer. He hired a staff of half a dozen. The whole focus changed from building the business to papering the files. Of course, when there was a [Securities & Exchange Commission] audit, he was a local hero. But it was of no benefit to the clients. We never had any intent to deceive them. And if we had, we could still have done it. He [the compliance manager] became a partner. I left."

-Disgruntled Wall Street money manager

n "I signed the Family Leave Act; it was my very first bill. And I'm proud of it because it symbolizes what I think we ought to be doing.... [It] has let 12 million families take a little time off for the birth of a child or a family illness without losing their job. ...I never go anywhere, it seems like, where I don't meet somebody who's benefited from the Family Leave Law. In Longview, Tex. the other day I met a woman who was almost in tears because she had been able to keep her job while spending time with her husband, who had cancer.

-Bill Clinton, in second presidential debate, Oct. 16, 1996

nswer: They all involve what economists call "rent-seeking"-the use political or institutional power to extract "rent" (essentially, u..avoidable payments) from the rest of the economy.

("Rent-seeking-it's a terrible name," says economist David Henderson of the Naval Postgraduate School in Monterey, Calif. Henderson speculates that the name's repellent clunkiness may have delayed general recognition that rent-seeking, parasitic and pervasive, is a fundamental economic reality in the modern world. His suggestion: "privilege-seeking." Hey, these are economists, not poets.)

Whatever its name, this is how rent-seeking works:

n The Washington lobbyists are public-sector rent-seekers. They are being paid to extract rents by influencing legislation on behalf of their corporate clients.

And they succeed. One example from Congressman Armey's collection: Sugar import quotas raise the price American consumers pay for sweeteners by about $1.4 billion annually. This benefits a remarkably small number of sugar producers and processors. One family alone, the Fanjuls of Osceola Farms, Fla., earns an estimated $65 million annually in artificial profits because its lobbyists have persuaded Congress to make it possible for the family to sell sugar at more than its natural ·rket price.

n The empire-building Wall Street compliance bureaucrat is a private-sector rent-seeker. He is diverting profits earned by the firm's productive activities to himself and his empire.

Note, though, that he is able to do so because of a sort of tacit alliance with the public-sector regulators. They make his job necessary.

n The First Rent-Seeker was congratulating himself on a newly popular subcategory of rent-seeking: so-called mandated benefits. The government uses political power to extract rents from the general public. Then it directs them to favored constituencies. The numbers can be very large: The Society for Human Resource Management estimated in 1989 that the Family Leave Act-no matter how nice a thought-would still cost nearly $440 million a year.

The government is still in effect buying votes with other people's money. But rent-seeking-in this case rent-giving-tactfully avoids the need to raise the money first through taxation, which often causes such distress. Employers and, ultimately, all consumers pay. A (relatively small) class of employees benefit. Plus, of course, the politicians. They can crow about how "caring" they are.

Rent-seeking matters-a lot. Its cost to society is not just the rents ısferred but also "rent-avoidance"-resources expended in trying to

›el efforts to extract rents, for example, by hiring your own ⌊ ›byists. As Gretchen Morgenson showed in our last issue (Sept. 8), any business that neglects to hire a lobbyist is likely to become a victim of other rent-seekers who do have lobbyists.

Surprisingly, however, the realization that rent-seeking exists dawned on economists only quite recently. Too bad, because it's a valuable concept that helps us understand what the politicians are doing to us when they say they feel our pain and offer to assuage it.

The father of the rent-seeking concept is Gordon Tullock, a quizzical, quirky, somewhat owlish 75-year-old professor of economics and political science at the University of Arizona in Tucson. Tullock was long associated with Nobel economics laureate James M. Buchanan, now at Virginia's George Mason University, in the development of what is now called "Public Choice Theory," the application of economic analysis to political and governmental action.

Many observers were surprised that Tullock was not included in the Nobel Prize Buchanan received in 1986. The omission was particularly striking since Buchanan and Tullock had actually coauthored the classic public choice text, The Calculus of Consent (1962). Speculation continues that Tullock will eventually win a separate Nobel Prize for h's work on rent-seeking. In January 1998 he will be made a tinguished Fellow of the American Economics Association. ("A plaque-no money," he says.)

Tullock was not trained as an economist-and beneficially, he argues with characteristic wryness. This, he argues, is an advantage in understanding economics. (He compares the economics profession's current preference for abstract mathematics to the drift from science to theology in classical Alexandria-and suggests that its function is merely to avoid political conflicts with noneconomists in the faculty lounge.) In 1947, after three years' wartime service as an infantryman, Tullock took a J.D. degree in a University of Chicago Law School accelerated program. He has no bachelor's degree because, in a decision possibly reflecting his Scottish heritage, he declined to pay the required $5 fee.

Tullock then joined the State Department and was posted to the Chinese city of Tianjin. He observed the city's fall to the Communists in 1949 and began his study of monetary cycles amid the disastrous inflation accompanying the Chinese Nationalist collapse. Thereafter, he was seconded to Yale and Cornell for three academic years to study Chinese. He notes gleefully that by reading Austrian economist Ludwig von Mises' Human Action in his spare time during this period, he found himself in key respects better prepared technically than an economics Ph.D. ›temporary.

t is universally agreed that Tullock does not have a diplomat's t .perament. He eventually resigned from the State Department. In 1959, while a post-doctoral fellow at the University of Virginia's economics department, he began working with Buchanan on what became The Calculus of Consent.

In 1987 Tullock moved to his present post in Arizona. A lifelong bachelor, he spends holidays with his sister's family in Iowa. In an unusual departure for an academic economist, he is a major stockholder ("best investment I ever made") and longtime director of the family's Dodger Co., a small Iowa-based firm that makes sports clothing, and its Whink, Inc., which makes industrial cleaners. He says this experience contributed greatly to his education in economics.

Tullock's stint in China was crucial to his rent-seeking insight: "See, you go into these cultures where people have produced just immense cultural achievements but are living in bitter poverty, and you discover very quickly they have a dominant government and the government is corrupt. Conventionally, economists have argued that a corrupt government doesn't really cost anything because the man who receives the bribe gains what the man who pays the bribe loses. Well, you can't really believe that if you're in China."

Similarly, Tullock points out, China provided the evidence for a key ly effort by Anne Krueger-now an economics professor at Stanford University-to quantify his insight. (Krueger must also take the blame for coining the term "rent-seeking.") Krueger had estimated that the cost to Turkey and India of the bribes necessary to get around their various regulations amounted to 7% to 15% of GNP. This cost was not simply the expense of the bribe, but also the resources wasted by individuals in acquiring otherwise useless credentials and intriguing for appointments in the appropriate government bureaucracy.

Every major economics journal rejected "The Welfare Costs of Tariffs, Monopolies and Theft," Tullock's original article on rent-seeking. It was finally published three years later, in 1967, in the Western Economic Journal, then new and little-read.

As an intellectual pioneer, Tullock is a connoisseur of such rejections. (He began his 1980 presidential address to the Southern Economics Association by celebrating the fact that the association's journal would be compelled to publish it, after years of rejecting his submissions.) He savors the irony that because a standard textbook quickly picked up his rent-seeking concept, "there was a period when a lot of brand-new elementary [economics] students knew about it and no one else did."

Tullock's serene but somber conclusions on the inefficient nature of intellectual market: "The safe article for the young academic is one t makes a short, sound step forward in a well-established direction."

Sounds like good advice.

But it's advice that Tullock himself-author of 15 books (the sixteenth, On Voting: An Introduction to Public Choice, due January 1998) and over 150 papers, on subjects ranging from game theory to "The Coal Tit As Careful Shopper," part of his little-known, but highly respected, contribution to biological theory-has somehow never quite gotten around to taking.

---- INDEX REFERENCES ----

LAYOUT CODES: Law (LLW)

Word Count: 1579
9/22/97 FORBES 073
END OF DOCUMENT

1764

Tab 17

As we observe National Children's Day this year, let us recommit ourselves to creating a society where parents can raise healthy, happy children; where every newborn is cherished, where every child is encouraged to succeed, and where all our young people are free to pursue their dreams.

Now, Therefore, I, William J. Clinton, President of the United States of America, by virtue of the authority vested in me by the Constitution and laws of the United States, do hereby proclaim October 12, 1997, as National Children's Day. I urge all Americans to express their love and appreciation for children on this day and on every day throughout the year. I invite Federal officials, State and local governments, and particularly all American families to join together in observing this day with appropriate ceremonies and activities to honor our Nation's children.

In Witness Whereof, I have hereunto set my hand this tenth day of October, in the year of our Lord nineteen hundred and ninety-seven, and of the Independence of the United States of America the two hundred and twenty-second.

William J. Clinton

[Filed with the Office of the Federal Register, 11:16 a.m., October 14, 1997]

NOTE: This proclamation will be published in the *Federal Register* on October 15.

Digest of Other White House Announcements

The following list includes the President's public schedule and other items of general interest announced by the Office of the Press Secretary and not included elsewhere in this issue.

October 4

In the afternoon, the President and Hillary Clinton traveled to Beltsville, MD, to observe U.S. Secret Service tactical expertise and training exercises at the James J. Rowley Training Center. Later, they returned to Washington, DC.

In the evening, the President traveled to Arlington, VA. Later, he was joined by Hillary Clinton, and they traveled to Camp David, MD.

October 6

In the morning, the President and Hillary Clinton returned to Washington, DC. In the evening, the President hosted a dinner for President Ezer Weizman of Israel in the Blue Room at the White House.

The President announced his intention to nominate James C. Hormel to be Ambassador to Luxembourg.

The President announced his intention to nominate Gerald S. McGowan to be Ambassador to Portugal.

The President announced his intention to nominate Lyndon L. Olson, Jr., to be Ambassador to Sweden.

The President announced his intention to nominate Kenneth R. Wykle to be Administrator of the Federal Highway Administration at the Department of Transportation.

October 7

In the morning, the President attended a meeting with Northern Ireland Ulster Unionist Party leader David Trimble in National Security Adviser Samuel R. Berger's office at the White House.

In the afternoon, the President met with congressional Democrats to discuss fast-track trade legislation. In the evening, he met with representatives of State and local government and business and community leaders from the Midwest.

The President announced his intention to nominate Christopher Ashby to be Ambassador to Uruguay.

The President announced his intention to nominate James A. Larocco to be Ambassador to Kuwait.

The President announced his intention to nominate Mark Erwin to be a member of the Overseas Private Investment Corporation.

The President announced his intention to nominate James H. Bailey to serve as Deputy Director of the Federal Emergency Management Agency.

The President announced the nomination of Bill Richardson and A. Peter Burleigh to be U.S. Representatives and Richard Sklar,

Victor Marrero, and Nancy E. Soderberg to be U.S. Alternate Representatives to the 52d General Assembly of the United Nations.

The President announced the nomination of Nancy E. Soderberg to be Alternate U.S. Representative for Special Political Affairs at the United Nations, with the rank of Ambassador.

October 8

In the morning, the President traveled to Newark, NJ. In the afternoon, he traveled to West Orange and Florham Park, NJ. Later in the afternoon, he traveled to Philadelphia, PA, arriving in the evening.

In the evening, the President attended a Democratic National Committee reception at CoreStates Arena. Later, he returned to Washington, DC.

The President announced the administration's intention to appoint Rev. Jesse Jackson to be Special Envoy for the President and the Secretary of State for the promotion of democracy in Africa.

October 9

In the afternoon, the President had a telephone conversation with Prime Minister Tony Blair of the United Kingdom concerning the Prime Minister's recent visit to Russia and the President's October 7 meeting with Northern Ireland Ulster Unionist Party leader David Trimble.

Later, the President had a telephone conversation with retiring University of North Carolina men's basketball coach Dean Smith to commend him on his long and successful career.

The President announced his intention to nominate David B. Hermelin to be Ambassador to Norway.

The President announced the nomination of Betty Eileen King to be an Alternate U.S. Representative to the 52d General Assembly of the United Nations. Ms. King has also been nominated to be U.S. Representative on the Economic and Social Council of the United Nations, with the rank of Ambassador.

The President announced his intention to nominate Kevin Gover to be Assistant Secretary for Indian Affairs at the Department of the Interior.

October 10

The President announced the nomination of Mary Mel French to be Chief of Protocol at the State Department.

The President announced the nomination of Richard W. Fisher to be Deputy U.S. Trade Representative (Washington), with the rank of Ambassador.

The President announced the nomination of Robert T. Grey, Jr., to be U.S. Representative to the Conference on Disarmament.

The President announced the nomination of Joy Harjo to be a member of the National Council on the Arts.

The President announced the nomination of Ida L. Castro to serve as the Director of the Women's Bureau at the Department of Labor.

The President announced the nomination of Carl Spielvogel as a member of the Broadcasting Board of Governors for the International Broadcasting Bureau.

The President announced the nomination of Robert S. Warshaw to serve as Associate Director of the Office of National Drug Control Policy for the Bureau of State and Local Affairs.

The President announced the nomination of Thomas H. Fox to be Assistant Administrator for Policy and Program Coordination at the Agency for International Development.

The President announced the nomination of Donald C. Lubick to be Assistant Secretary for Tax Policy at the Department of the Treasury.

The President announced the nomination of Fred P. Hochberg to serve as Deputy Administrator of the Small Business Administration.

The President announced his intention to appoint Arthur M. Hamilton and Sally Ann Jochum as members of the President's Committee on Mental Retardation.

The President announced his intention to designate David J. Barram, in his capacity as Administrator of the General Services Administration, Andrew M. Cuomo, in his capacity as Secretary of Housing and Urban Development, and Rodney E. Slater, in his capacity as Secretary of Transportation, to serve as members on the Advisory Council on Historic Preservation.

In addition, I am also announcing today that I want to work with Congress to find a solution to the growing problem of future liabilities and extended delays in completing ongoing projects. Each year, Congress adds more and more projects without sufficient resources to complete existing projects in a timely way. Some of them include 50-year Federal commitments, involving hundreds of millions of dollars. The more projects are added, the longer the delays in finishing the existing ones.

Because of limited Federal resources, the gap between the number of projects that are approved and the number we can afford will keep growing. I believe that now is the time for the administration and Congress to address the problem. I have asked the administration's senior officials who work in this area to reach out to the key Member of Congress to work toward a solution.

NOTE: The reports detailing the cancellations were published in the *Federal Register* on October 20. H.R. 2203, approved October 13, was assigned Public Law Number 105–62.

Letter to Congressional Leaders on Line Item Vetoes of the Energy and Water Development Appropriations Act, 1998

October 17, 1997

Dear Mr. Speaker: (Dear Mr. President:)

In accordance with the Line Item Veto Act, I hereby cancel the dollar amounts of discretionary budget authority, as specified in the attached reports, contained in the "Energy and Water Development Appropriations Act, 1998" (H.R. 2203, approved October 13, 1997). I have determined that the cancellation of these amounts will reduce the Federal budget deficit, will not impair any essential Government functions, and will not harm the national interest. This letter, together with its attachments, constitutes a special message under section 1022 of the Congressional Budget and Impoundment Control Act of 1974, as amended.

Sincerely,

William J. Clinton

NOTE: Identical letters were sent to Newt Gingrich, Speaker of the House of Representatives, and Albert Gore, Jr., President of the Senate. The reports detailing the cancellations were published in the *Federal Register* on October 20. H.R. 2203, approved October 13, was assigned Pub. Law No. 105 62.

Statement on the Death of James A. Michener

October 17, 1997

Hillary and I are greatly saddened by the loss of one of our country's most gifted storytellers, James A. Michener. Through his rich narratives woven on the grandest scale, Michener made our imaginations soar and our history come alive. From the sandy shores of the South Pacific to the barren tundra of Alaska, we followed Michener on epic journeys through time and place, along the way celebrating such time-honored virtues as patriotism, courage, and common sense. And even after achieving great fame and wealth, Michener never forgot his humble roots. He was a major benefactor to colleges and writers' groups, eventually donating much of his fortune for the benefit of others. America has lost a rich voice and a generous spirit.

Digest of Other White House Announcements

The following list includes the President's public schedule and other items of general interest announced by the Office of the Press Secretary and not included elsewhere in this issue.

October 12

In the morning, the President and Hillary Clinton traveled to Caracas, Venezuela, arriving in the afternoon.

In the evening, the President met with President Rafael Caldera of Venezuela in President Caldera's office at La Casona.

October 13

In the morning, the President participated in a wreath-laying ceremony at El Panteon.

In the afternoon, the President and Hillary Clinton traveled to Brasilia, Brazil, arriving in the evening.

Octobe
In th
ings wi
Brazil i
ing Roo
In th
the lea
Salon N
he gree
at the U
In th
Clinton

Octobe
In th
Rio de
noon. L
gentina,
The F
appoint
Advisory
Guarant

October
In the
Presiden
Salon Bl
with Arg
the Ceib
In the
Argentin
Room at

October
In the
Clinton t
The I
ment of
Commis
sion for

Nomina
Submit

NOTE: N
Senate d

nate. The
ublished
R. 2203.
Law No.

James A.

lened by the
: gifted story-
ough his rich
indest scale,
ons soar and
n the sandy
e barren tun-
iener on epic
ce, along the
red virtues as
on sense. And
: and wealth,
ble roots. He
ges and writ-
; much of his
. America has
spirit.

ents

sident's public
ral interest an-
; Secretary and

nt and Hillary
nezuela, arriv-

ent met with
Venezuela in
Casona.

t participated
it El Panteon.
nt and Hillary
razil, arriving

October 14

In the morning, the President had meetings with President Fernando Cardoso of Brazil in the Qualienca Room and the Meeting Room at Planalto Palace.

In the afternoon, the President met with the leadership of the Brazilian Congress in Salon Nobre at the National Congress. Later, he greeted American and Brazilian personnel at the U.S. Embassy.

In the evening, the President and Hillary Clinton traveled to Sao Paulo, Brazil.

October 15

In the morning, the President traveled to Rio de Janeiro, Brazil, arriving in the afternoon. Later, he traveled to Buenos Aires, Argentina, arriving in the evening.

The President announced his intention to appoint Judith A. Scott as a member of the Advisory Committee to the Pension Benefit Guaranty Corporation.

October 16

In the morning, the President met with President Carlos Menem of Argentina in the Salon Blanco at La Casa Rosa. Later, he met with Argentine political opposition leaders in the Ceibo Room of the Sheraton Hotel.

In the afternoon, the President met with Argentine Jewish leaders in the Executive Room at the Sheraton Hotel.

October 17

In the afternoon, the President and Hillary Clinton traveled to San Carlos de Bariloche.

The President announced the appointment of Will Martin and J. Nussman as U.S. Commissioners of the International Commission for the Conservation of Atlantic Tuna.

Nominations Submitted to the Senate

NOTE: No nominations were submitted to the Senate during the period covered by this issue.

Checklist of White House Press Releases

The following list contains releases of the Office of the Press Secretary that are neither printed as items nor covered by entries in the Digest of Other White House Announcements.

Released October 12

Transcript of a press briefing by Press Secretary Mike McCurry

Released October 13

Transcript of a press briefing by National Drug Control Policy Director Barry McCaffrey on counter-drug-trafficking strategies with the Venezuelan Government

Transcript of a press briefing by Energy Secretary Federico Peña on Venezuela-U.S. energy, trade, and environmental agreements

Fact sheet: U.S.-Venezuelan Partnership for the 21st Century: Promoting Common Solutions for Energy and Development, Trade and Investment, and Protecting the Environment

Released October 14

Transcript of a press briefing by Press Secretary Mike McCurry and Deputy National Security Adviser Jim Steinberg on the President's meeting with President Fernando Cardoso of Brazil

Transcript of a press briefing by Office of Management and Budget Director Franklin Raines, National Security Council Director for Defense Policy and Arms Control Bob Bell, and Deputy Defense Secretary John Hamre on the President's line item vetoes of the Department of Defense Appropriations Act, 1998

Statement by Press Secretary Mike McCurry on the appointment of Special Assistant to the President and Legal Adviser

Fact sheet: The U.S. Brazil Partnership: Improving Education in the 21st Century

Fact sheet: U.S.-Brazilian Partnership for the 21st Century

term, so must our policies be. We have an opportunity to build a new century in which China takes its rightful place as a full and strong partner in the community of nations, working with the United States to advance peace and prosperity, freedom and security for both our people and for all the world. We have to take that chance.

Thank you very much.

NOTE: The President spoke at 2:50 p.m. in the auditorium at the Voice of America. In his remarks, he referred to Nicholas Platt, president, The Asia Society; and President Jiang Zemin of China.

Digest of Other White House Announcements

The following list includes the President's public schedule and other items of general interest announced by the Office of the Press Secretary and not included elsewhere in this issue.

October 18

In the evening, the President and Hillary Clinton traveled from San Carlos de Bariloche to Buenos Aires, Argentina. Later, they returned to Washington, DC, arriving the following morning.

October 21

The President announced his intention to nominate William J. Lynn III to be Under Secretary of Defense, Comptroller.

The President announced his intention to nominate Richard M. McGahey to serve as Assistant Secretary for Policy at the Department of Labor.

The President announced his intention to nominate Cyril Kent McGuire to serve as Assistant Secretary of Educational Research and Improvement at the Department of Education.

The President announced his intention to nominate Robert McNamara, Jr., to serve as General Counsel at the Central Intelligence Agency.

The President announced his intention to nominate Daryl L. Jones to be Secretary of the Air Force.

The President announced his intention to appoint former Representative John Bryant as head of the U.S. delegation to the International Telecommunication Union's 1997 World Radiocommunications Conference in Geneva, Switzerland, with the personal rank of Ambassador.

The President announced his intention to appoint Sam W. Brown with the personal rank of Ambassador during his service as the head of the U.S. delegation to the Organization on Security and Cooperation in Europe's Ministerial Preparatory Conferences in Vienna, Austria.

The President announced his intention to appoint Robert L. Baxter as a member of the Advisory Committee to the President's Commission on Critical Infrastructure Protection.

October 22

In the afternoon, the President met with Ecumenical Patriarch Bartholomew I in the Oval Office.

The President announced his intention to nominate John Charles Horsley as Associate Deputy Secretary and Director of Intermodalism at the Department of Transportation.

The White House announced the President's intention to appoint the following individuals as members of the Advisory Committee on Public Interest Obligations of Digital Television Broadcasters: Charles Benton, Frank Blythe, Peggy Charren, Harold C. Crump, Frank Cruz, Robert Decherd, Barry Diller, William Duhamel, Rob Glaser, Jim Goodmon, Paul La Camera, Richard Masur, Newton Minow, Shelby Scott, Gigi Sohn, Karen Peltz Strauss, Cass R. Sunstein, Lois Jean White, and James Yee.

The White House announced that the President received the final report of the Presidential Commission on Critical Infrastructure Protection on October 20.

October 23

The President announced his intention to nominate Mary Beth West for the rank of Ambassador to be Deputy Assistant Secretary of State for Oceans and Space.

1772

Tab 18

LAT - 11/9/97 LATIMES A1
'9/97 L.A. Times A1
WL 13998644
L.. Angeles Times

Sunday, November 9, 1997

National Desk

Lobbying for 'Fast-Track' Trade Power Intensifies Congress: Despite frenzy of action, little headway was made as countdown continues to today's vote to give Clinton authority he seeks. House, Senate also try to break deadlocks on other issues.

JANET HOOK; FAYE FIORE
TIMES STAFF WRITERS

WASHINGTON -- Both houses of Congress were pressed into service Saturday as lawmakers made a mad dash to wrap up the year's work and prepared for a cliffhanger vote on President Clinton's bid for expanded trade authority.

The Senate and House struggled to break deadlocks on a range of hot-button issues--from abortion funding to the 2000 census--that have stalled several funding bills that must be passed before Congress can adjourn for the year.

But much of the action occurred behind closed doors, as the countdown continued toward today's scheduled House vote on Clinton's request for "fast- track" trade negotiating authority.

·e White House sent a phalanx of Cabinet officials and other top aides to make peace with jority of House Democrats furious about Clinton's efforts to woo Republican support for tne fast-track trade legislation.

In addition, the administration pursued intensive, one-on-one negotiations in an effort to pick up fast-track votes from within a tiny and dwindling band of Democratic fence-sitters.

"This is a blitz," said U.N. Ambassador Bill Richardson, one of the administration officials on Capitol Hill to work the issue. "It's going down to the wire."

Clinton, in his Saturday radio address, made another appeal for House members to support the fast-track legislation, which would strengthen the president's hand in negotiating trade agreements by allowing Congress to accept or reject-- but not amend--the pacts.

"A 'yes' vote is a vote for confidence in the world's strongest economy," Clinton said. "But a 'no' vote says we don't want our country to negotiate lower trade barriers--we're pulling back."

The day's frenzy of lobbying did not seem to have much effect on undecided members, many of whom may be waiting until the roll is called today before making their positions known. Aides on both sides reported little movement in the head count, leaving the administration a few votes short of the majority needed for passage.

Nonetheless, House Speaker Newt Gingrich (R-Ga.) said he was encouraging the administration to remain committed to holding the vote today. "My advice is to go for it," he said.

But some lawmakers said the vote might be delayed if Clinton cannot round up the votes he n··ds. The House is scheduled to go into session at 2 p.m. EST, but a final vote on the ·track bill is unlikely before the evening. If the .ıre passes the House, Senate approval is considered probable.

While the fate of fast-track remained undecided, Capitol Hill became a legislative three-ring circus as House and Senate leaders pushed to wrap up the rest of this year's work today or Monday.

In major action Saturday, Congress sent to the White House two bills challenging presidential priorities. The Senate voted, 91-4, to join the House in passing an $80-billion social-spending bill that includes a rider delaying Clinton's plan to establish national education testing. The compromise was declared a victory by conservatives opposed to national testing, but Clinton has said he would accept it.

The House voted, 352-64, to approve a bill overturning Clinton's line-item veto of 38 military construction projects worth $287 million. The House's overwhelming vote, which followed a comparably strong vote in the Senate, suggests that Congress could override Clinton if he were to veto the overall measure, as he has promised.

In an effort to break the logjam on three remaining appropriations bills--for the District of Columbia, the departments of State, Commerce and Justice and foreign aid--the Senate Appropriations Committee passed a measure that combined all three bills into one. But House leaders said the combined legislation includes language on abortion and other issues unacceptable to the lower chamber.

The fast-track legislation had been scheduled to come to a vote in the House on Friday, but the White House requested a postponement until at least today so it would have more time to round up support.

The politics of the issue have become deeply entwined in the process of wrapping up annual appropriations bills. Many conservative House Republicans have declared they would not vote for fast-track unless the White House makes concessions on a number of fronts, including Clinton's proposal to establish national education testing, a dispute about the 2000 census and antiabortion restrictions on foreign aid.

House Democrats, most of whom oppose the fast-track legislation, have been furious at the White House for what they see as an effort to make concessions in those areas to pick up Republican votes.

They called top administration officials--including Treasury Secretary Robert E. Rubin and White House Chief of Staff Erskine Bowles--to an emotional meeting of the House Democratic Caucus, where members aired their fury at the maneuvering around fast-track.

Administration officials have denied that they are making deals to pick up fast-track votes, particularly on the contentious issue of abortion. Democrats who attended the closed-door meeting said Bowles reiterated the White House's commitment to veto foreign aid legislation if it includes antiabortion language.

The abortion dispute is one of the biggest obstacles to completing work on this year's funding bills. At issue is a provision of current law that prohibits international family-planning organizations from using U.S. aid for abortions.

Conservative Republicans in the House want to tighten that restriction to prohibit U.S. aid from going to any international group that uses even its own money for abortions. The Senate and the White House have opposed that.

On the census, leaders of the black, Latino and Asian congressional caucuses assembled in anger Saturday after hearing of the deal the White House struck with GOP leaders regarding the conduct of the population count in 2000.

The agreement, which would allow the Census Bureau to test a statistical counting method in Sacramento during a trial census in April, leaves GOP lawmakers ample opportunity next year to kill the sampling method, which they fiercely oppose.

Whether sampling is used has great import for California, which was severely undercounted in 1990 and lost out on federal funding and one congressional seat as a result.

Leaders of the minority caucuses, who wanted broader use of sampling, thought Clinton had conceded too much on the census in order to win votes for the expanded trade negotiating a''thority he desperately wants. They accused him of forsaking minority groups, children and poor, who were the most undercounted in 1990.

"Mr. President, don't sell us out over fast-track," implored Rep. Robert Menendez (D-N.J.).

Their ire won at least one concession. An oversight board set up to report on the census that had previously been Republican-dominated, will now be made up of an equal of Republicans and Democrats. It was unclear, however, whether Republicans would share the $3 million that would fund the board, money Democrats say will be used as a public relations machine to make sure census sampling is killed next year.

While the maneuvering on appropriations bills could help Clinton pick up Republican votes for fast-track, the White House turned up the heat in an effort to garner more support among the handful of fence-sitting Democrats.

Among them is Rep. Nita M. Lowey (D-N.Y.), a leader of abortion-rights forces who said she might be more inclined to oppose fast-track if Clinton compromised on his opposition to new restrictions on international family planning.

Clinton's aides have been wooing Democrats representing agricultural districts with promises of trade protections for commodities such as peanuts, citrus and tomatoes that might be hurt by expanded foreign trade.

Some Democrats said the White House had been promising presidential help in political fund-raising to those who come on board, and who fear a loss of labor contributions in retaliation.

The combined effect of White House promises and GOP leaders' control over congressional pr 's could be enough to produce a come-from-behind victory, one fast-track opponent conceded.

fear that they will win," said Rep. Peter A. DeFazio (D-Ore.). "They always do."

* SANCHEZ IMPASSE: GOP leaders refused to debate the dispute over Rep. Loretta Sanchez's election victory. A38

* CLINTON DRIVEN: Washington is discovering how badly the president wants fast-track authority. A24

TABULAR OR GRAPHIC MATERIAL SET FORTH IN THIS DOCUMENT IS NOT DISPLAYABLE

PHOTO: Rep. Steny H. Hoyer (D-Md.), Treasury Secretary Robert E. Rubin and Agriculture Secretary Dan Glickman, from left, meet at Capitol to discuss fast- track trade authority President Clinton is seeking.; PHOTOGRAPHER: Associated Press

---- INDEX REFERENCES ----

:Y WORDS: CONGRESS (U.S.); LEGISLATION -- UNITED STATES; GOVERNMENT SPENDING;)BBYING; UNITED STATES -- TRADE; ABORTION; CENSUS

NEWS SUBJECT: Politics; Trade Issues; Health (PLT TRD HLT)

:ORY ORIGIN: WASHINGTON

NEWS CATEGORY: LEAD STORY

GOVERNMENT: Congress (CNG)

: United States; North America (US NME)

'ITION: HOME EDITION

Word Count: 1324
1/97 LATIMES A1
. OF DOCUMENT

Tab 19

1780

BALTSUN - 11/14/97 BALTSUN 17A
1''14/97 Balt. Sun 17A
WL 5539638
T. Baltimore Sun

Friday, November 14, 1997

NEWS

Zedillo champions free trade; Mexican president notes worry about future deals
REUTERS

WASHINGTON -- Mexico's President Ernesto Zedillo expressed Latin America's disappointment yesterday over the Clinton administration's failure to get special negotiating authority to extend free trade in the hemisphere.

At the start of a 36-hour visit to Washington, Zedillo told businessmen that the North American Free Trade Agreement has been a great success in expanding commerce, employment and investment in

Canada, Mexico and the United States.

Mexican-U.S. trade has doubled since NAFTA was created in 1994 to $165 billion this year, the Mexican leader said.

Zedillo said Latin America had had "tremendous expectations" over free trade. President Clinton failed to gain Congress's approval of the so-called fast-track authority needed to keep his
} promise to build a free-trade area by 2005.

Zedillo was to dine privately with Clinton at the White House yesterday and return today for a session with Cabinet officials on drug trafficking, law enforcement, migration, trade and environmental issues.

U.S. and Mexican officials signed agreements to expand the extradition treaty between the two countries and to demarcate their maritime borders to allow exploration of potentially vast oil reserves in the Gulf of Mexico.

But they only provided a progress report on talks to devise a

joint strategy to combat the flow of narcotics into the United States from Mexico -- the most critical issue between the two countries.

Today, Zedillo and Clinton will attend the signing of an agreement to combat trafficking in illegal firearms, explosives and ammunition, an initiative proposed by Mexico.

Pub Date: 11/13/97

---- INDEX REFERENCES ----

STORY ORIGIN: WASHINGTON

EDITION: FINAL

Word Count: 248
11/14/97 BALTSUN 17A
END OF DOCUMENT

ation Search Result Rank 1 of 1 Database
./15/97 WASHPOST A06 WP
11/15/97 Wash. Post A06
1997 WL 14713125

The Washington Post

Saturday, November 15, 1997

A Section

Democratic Donor Chung Invokes 5th Amendment; House Members Informally Interview Businessman

Edward Walsh
Washington Post Staff Writer

Democratic contributor Johnny Chung invoked the Fifth Amendment against self-incrimination before members of a House committee yesterday, but then provided some information, not under oath, about his role as a major financial backer of President Clinton and the Democratic National Committee.

Chung spent about three hours yesterday morning with members ' investigators of the House Government Reform and Oversight C..mmittee and continued the session after the committee held a public hearing on campaign financing improprieties during the 1996 election cycle.

"We did get some information we think will be helpful down the line," Chairman Dan Burton (R-Ind.) said of the informal interview with Chung. "We will pursue those leads."

But Rep. Henry A. Waxman (Calif.), the committee's ranking Democrat, said he had heard nothing to change his view that Chung was simply a political "hustler" who hoped to exploit his purchased access to the White House to advance his private business interests. Waxman said Chung earlier had submitted to similar informal interview sessions with investigators from the Justice Department and the Senate Governmental Affairs Committee. Chung was not called to testify before the Senate committee.

Chung, a California businessman, gave $366,000 to the DNC before the 1996 election. All of his contributions have been returned, including a $50,000 check that he handed to Hillary Rodham Clinton's chief of staff during one of his many visits to the White House complex in 1995. Two days after making that donation, Chung, with the h-lp of DNC officials, escorted six Chinese businessmen to the White se to watch the president deliver his weekly radio address.

)n Thursday, Nancy Hernreich, Clinton's appointments and scheduling aide, told the committee Clinton had expressed displeasure about the presence of the Chinese businessmen at the radio address. A month later, White House aides asked the National Security Council if they should give Chung photos from the visit showing Clinton with the businessmen.

Former NSC aide Brooke Darby testified that, based on information from Robert L. Suettinger, then the NSC's China expert, she recommended against giving Chung the pictures.

In what is now a well-known description of Chung, Suettinger told Darby release of the pictures would do no "lasting damage to U.S. foreign policy" but warned that Chung was a "hustler" who was trying to advance his business and would become "a royal pain" to White House officials.

Suettinger told the panel yesterday that he knew of or was able to verify that all but one of the Chinese visitors were officials of legitimate Chinese enterprises. The exception was James Y. Sun, described by Chung as a "young entrepreneur and self-made millionaire."

'There are relatively few self-made millionaires in the ɛ ple's Republic of China," Suettinger said in deadpan fashion.

TABULAR OR GRAPHIC MATERIAL SET FORTH IN THIS DOCUMENT IS NOT DISPLAYABLE

CAPTION: House panel Chairman Dan Burton, left, escorts **Democratic donor** Johnny Chung down Rayburn Building hall, where they faced throng of photographers.

---- INDEX REFERENCES ----

KEY WORDS: NATIONAL

EDITION: FINAL

Word Count: 450
11/15/97 WASHPOST A06
END OF DOCUMENT

Tab 21

1788

AO 110 (Rev. 12/89) Subpoena to Testify Before Grand Jury — GJ# 97-3 JD# A98-024

United States District Court

EASTERN DISTRICT OF VIRGINIA

TO: William Jefferson Clinton

SUBPOENA TO TESTIFY BEFORE GRAND JURY

SUBPOENA FOR:

☐ PERSON ☒ DOCUMENT(S) OR OBJECT(S)

YOU ARE COMMANDED to appear and testify before the Grand Jury of the United States District Court at the place, date, and time specified below.

PLACE	COURTROOM / DATE AND TIME
UNITED STATES DISTRICT COURT 401 Courthouse Square Alexandria, Virginia 22314	COURTROOM: GRAND JURY ROOM DATE AND TIME: January 27, 1998 9:30 A.M.

YOU ARE ALSO COMMANDED to bring with you the following document(s) or object(s):*

See attached rider.

☐ *Please see additional information on reverse*

This subpoena shall remain in effect until you are granted leave to depart by the court or by an officer acting on behalf of the court.

CLERK	DATE
NORMAN H. MEYER, JR., CLERK OF THE COURT (By) Deputy Clerk [signature]	January 20, 1998 (V002)

This subpoena is issued on application of the United States of America	NAME, ADDRESS and PHONE NUMBER OF ASSISTANT U.S. ATTORNEY
OFFICE OF THE INDEPENDENT COUNSEL KENNETH W. STARR	Kenneth W. Starr by [signature] Office of the Independent Counsel 1001 Pennsylvania Ave, NW, Suite 490-N Washington, D.C. 20004 (202) 514-8688

Subpoena # V002

To: William Jefferson Clinton

SUBPOENA RIDER

A. Produce all documents and things referring or relating to Monica Lewinsky. These documents and things should include, but not be limited to, the following:

1. any and all gifts, presents, or things to or from Monica Lewinsky (directly or indirectly), including, but not limited to, any tie, mug, paperweight, book, or other article;

2. any and all cards, letters, notes, or other correspondence to or from Monica Lewinsky;

3. any and all photographs, videotapes, audiotapes, voice messages or other recording of or relating or referring to Monica Lewinsky;

4. any and all documents and things containing the handwriting, signature, or other mark of Monica Lewinsky; and

B. Any and all affidavits, depositions, pleadings, memoranda, notes, and other statements, including drafts, referring or relating to Monica Lewinsky or Linda Tripp.

C. Produce any and all diaries, journals, address books, and Rolodexes from January 1, 1995.

D. Produce any and all calendars or daytimers from January 1, 1995.

E. Produce any and all documents referring or relating to Monica Lewinsky's employment or her seeking employment since January 20, 1993. These documents should include, but not be limited to, resumes, correspondence, travel records, telephone records and message slips, applications, evaluations, letters of recommendation, and references.

F. Produce any and all documents referring or relating to McAndrews & Forbes or Revlon, Inc. and their employees, agents, or representatives, including, but not limited to, Vernon Jordan, Ron Perelman, Howard Gittes, and Barry Schwartz.

G. Produce any and all answers to interrogatories, requests for admission, affidavits, declarations, and depositions of William Jefferson Clinton in Jones v. Clinton and Ferguson.

Definitions and Instructions

1. Definitions

a. The term "document" or "documents" as used in this subpoena means all records of any nature whatsoever within your possession, custody or control or the possession, custody or control of any agent, employee, representative (including, without limitation, attorneys, investment advisors, investment bankers, bankers and accountants), or other person acting or purporting to act for or on your behalf or in concert with you, including, but not limited to, draft, pending or executed contracts and/or agreements, sample documents, insurance policies, financial guarantee bonds, letters of credit, communications, correspondence, calendars, daytimers, datebooks, telegrams, facsimiles, telexs, telefaxes, electronic mail, memoranda, records, reports, books, files (computer or paper), summaries or records of personal conversations, meetings or interviews, logs, summaries or records of telephone conversations and/or telefax communications, diaries, forecasts, statistical statements, financial statements (draft or finished), work papers, drafts, copies, bills, records of payments for bills, retainer records, attorney time sheets, telephone bills and records, telefax bills and records, tax returns and return information, employee time sheets, graphs, charts, accounts, analytical records, minutes or records of meetings or conferences, consultants' reports and/or records, appraisals, records, reports or summaries of negotiations, brochures, pamphlets, circulars, maps, plats, trade letters, depositions, statements, interrogatories and answers thereto, pleadings, docket sheets, discovery materials, audit letters, audit reports, materials underlying audits, document productions, transcripts, exhibits, settlement materials, judgments, press releases, notes, marginal notations, invoices, documents regarding collateral or security pledged, settlement statements, checks disbursed or received at settlement, inspection reports, title policies, financial statements and/or federal tax returns submitted by any person in support of any loan application, items related the repayment, if any, of any interest or principal on the loan, items relating to any default on the loan, commission records, evidence of liens, documents relating to filings under the Uniform Commercial Code and/or its equivalent, foreclosure and mortgage documentation, cashiers checks, bank drafts, money orders, bank and brokerage account statements, debit and credit memoranda, wire transfer documentation, opening account cards, signature cards, loan applications, any employment and bank account deposit verification documents, loan histories, loan files, records of loan repayment or any and all efforts to secure repayment, including foreclosure or records of lawsuits, credit references, board resolutions, minutes of meetings of boards of directors, opinion letters, purchases and sales agreements, real

50-893 98 - 7

estate contracts, brokerage agreements, escrow agreements, loan agreements, offer and acceptance contracts, or any other contracts or agreements, deeds or other evidence of title, escrow accounts and any other escrow documentation, savings account transcripts, savings account deposit slips, savings account withdrawal slips, checks deposited in savings accounts, checking account statements, canceled checks drawn on checking accounts, deposit slips and checks deposited into checking accounts, credit card accounts, debit and credit documentation, safe deposit records, currency transaction reports (IRS Forms 4789), photographs, brochures, lists, journals, advertising, computer tapes and cards, audio and video tapes, computerized records stored in the form of magnetic or electronic coding on computer media or on media capable of being read by computer or with the aid of computer related equipment, including but not limited to floppy disks or diskettes, disks, diskettes, disk packs, fixed hard drives, removable hard disk cartridges, mainframe computers, Bernoulli boxes, optical disks, WORM disks, magneto/optical disks, floptical disks, magnetic tape, tapes, laser disks, video cassettes, CD-ROMs and any other media capable of storing magnetic coding, microfilm, microfiche and other storage devices, voicemail recordings and all other written, printed or recorded or photographic matter or sound reproductions, however produced or reproduced.

The term "document" or "documents" also includes any earlier, preliminary, preparatory or tentative version of all or part of a document, whether or not such draft was superseded by a later draft and whether or not the terms of the draft are the same as or different from the terms of the final document.

b. The term "communication" or "communications" is used herein in its broadest sense to encompass any transmission or exchange of information, ideas, facts, data, proposals, or any other matter, whether between individuals or between or among the members of a group, whether face-to-face, by telephone or by means of electronic or other medium.

c. "Possession, custody or control" means in your physical possession and/or if you have the right to secure or compile the production of the document or a copy from another person or entity having physical possession, including, but not limited to, your counsel.

d. The term "referring or relating" to any given subject means anything that constitutes, contains, embodies, reflects, identifies, states, refers to, deals with, or is in any manner whatsoever pertinent to that subject including, but not limited to, documents concerning the preparation of other documents.

e. The term "you" means yourself, any person or agent acting on your behalf or at your suggestion or direction, and any of your companies, partnerships and business entities with which you have been affiliated and any employees, partners, associates or members of any firm with which you have been affiliated.

2. Instructions

a. The originals of all documents and communications must be produced, as well as copies within your possession, custody, or control.

b. If any original document cannot be produced in full, produce such document to the extent possible and indicate specifically the reason for your inability to produce the remainder.

c. Documents shall be produced as they are kept in the usual course of business, as organized in the files.

d. File folders, labels, and indices identifying documents called for shall be produced intact with such documents. Documents attached to each other should not be separated.

e. In reading this rider, the plural shall include the singular and the singular shall include the plural.

f. The words "and" and "or" shall be construed conjunctively or disjunctively as necessary to make the request inclusive rather than exclusive. The use of the word "including" shall be construed without limitation.

g. In the event that any document, or portion thereof, called for by this subpoena is withheld on the basis of any claim of privilege or similar claim, that document shall be identified in writing as follows: (a) author; (b) the position or title of the author; (c) addressee; (d) the position or title of the addressee; (e) any indicated or blind copies; (f) date; (g) a description of the subject matter of the document; (h) number of pages; (i) attachments or appendices; (j) all persons to whom the document, its contents, or any portion thereof, has been disclosed, distributed, shown, or explained; and (k) present custodian. Each basis you contend justifies the withholding of the document shall also be specified. With respect to those documents or records as to which you may claim privilege, or attorneys' work product, set forth as to each such document the basis for such claim, including the purpose and circumstances surrounding the creation of the document, the identity of each person who has been privy to such communication reflected in the document, the identity of any person or entity instructing the subpoena recipient or the attorney of the subpoena recipient to withhold production of the document, and whether you will submit the document to the Court for an in camera determination as to the validity of the claim. If the existence of a joint defense agreement or any agreement as to common interest is relevant to the assertion of any claim of privilege or similar claim, please provide a copy of that agreement; if any such agreement is not in writing, please set forth the date of the creation of the agreement, the identities of all parties to the agreement and the specific individuals who entered into the agreement on behalf of those parties, and the objects, purposes, and scope of the agreement.

h. In the event that any document called for by this subpoena has been lost, destroyed, deleted, altered, or otherwise disposed of, that document shall be identified in writing as follows: (a) author; (b) the position or title of the author; (c) addressee; (d) the position or title of the addressee; (e) indicated or blind copies; (f) date; (g) a brief description of the subject matter of the document; (h) number of pages; (i) attachments or appendices; (j) all persons to whom the document, its contents, or any portion thereof, had been disclosed, distributed, shown or explained; (k) the date of the loss, destruction, deletion, alteration, or disposal and the circumstances thereof; and (l) the reasons, if any, for the loss, destruction, deletion, alteration, or disposal and the person or persons responsible.

i. If any information or data is withheld because such information or data is stored electronically, it is to be identified by the subject matter of the information or data and the place or places where such information is maintained.

Office of the Independent Counsel

1001 Pennsylvania Avenue, N.W.
Suite 490-North
Washington, DC 20004
(202) 514-8688
Fax (202) 514-8802

January 21, 1998

VIA FACSIMILE

David E. Kendall, Esq.
Williams & Connelly
725 Twelfth Street, N.W.
Washington, D.C. 20005

Re: William Jefferson Clinton
Grand Jury Subpoena # V002

Dear David:

Pursuant to our telephone conversation this afternoon, enclosed please grand jury subpoena number V002. Also enclosed please find a copy of the Special Division's jurisdictional Order and its Order authorizing limited disclosure. Both Orders are under seal.

Thank you for accepting service on behalf of your client.

Sincerely,

Robert J. Bittman
Deputy Independent Counsel

Enclosures

01/21/98 WED 17:21 FAX 001

****
*** TX REPORT ***
****

TRANSMISSION OK

TX/RX NO	1925
CONNECTION TEL	94345792
SUBADDRESS	
CONNECTION ID	
ST. TIME	01/21 17:15
USAGE T	06'52
PGS.	11
RESULT	OK

OFFICE OF THE INDEPENDENT COUNSEL
Suite 490-North
1001 Pennsylvania Ave., N.W.
Washington, D.C. 20004
tel (202) 514-8688
fax (202) 514-8802

fax transmittal

to: David E. Kendall, Esq.

fax #: 434-5792

from: Robert J. Bittman

date: January 21, 1998

re: President William Jefferson Clinton

pages: 10, including this cover sheet

Tab 22

Citation Search Result Rank 1 of 1 Dat
1/21/98 WASHPOST A01 WP
1/21/98 Wash. Post A01
1998 WL 2463182

The Washington Post

Wednesday, January 21, 1998

A Section

Clinton Accused of Urging Aide to Lie; Starr Probes Whether President To Woman to Deny Alleged Affair to Jones's Lawyers
Susan Schmidt, Peter Baker and Toni Locy
Washington Post Staff Writers

Independent counsel Kenneth W. Starr has expanded his investigation of President Clinton to examine whether Clinton and his close friend Vernon E. Jordan Jr. encouraged a 24-year-old former White House intern to lie to lawyers for Paula Jones about whether the intern had an affair with the president, sources close to the investigation said yesterday.

A three-judge appeals court panel on Friday authorized Starr to examine allegations of suborning perjury, false statements and obstruction of justice involving the president, the sources said. A Justice Department official confirmed that Attorney General Janet Reno had forwarded Starr's request to the panel that oversees independent counsels after Starr had asked her for "expeditious" consideration of his request.

The expansion of the investigation was prompted by information brought to Starr within the past few weeks by a former White House aide who surreptitiously made tape recordings of conversations she had with the former White House intern describing a relationship with Clinton.

The former intern, Monica Lewinsky, began work in the White House in 1995 at age 21 and later moved to a political job at the Pentagon, where she worked with Linda R. Tripp, who had moved there from an administrative job at the White House.

Sources said Tripp provided Starr with audiotapes of more than 10 conversations she had with Lewinsky over recent months in which Lewinsky graphically recounted details of a year-and-a-half-long affair she said she had with Clinton. In some of the conversations -- including one in recent days -- Lewinsky described Clinton and Jordan directing her to testify falsely in the Paula Jones sexual harassment case against the president, according to sources.

Lewinsky gave an affidavit in connection with the Jones case Jan. 7 and sources who have seen the sworn statement said she denied having an affair with Clinton. She is scheduled to be deposed by Jones's lawyers Friday. In his own deposition in the Jones case Saturday, Clinton was asked about Lewinsky and denied under oath having a sexual relationship with her, according to a source familiar with the testimony.

White House officials said they were unaware of the expansion of Starr's investigation and referred calls to Robert S. Bennett, the president's lawyer in the Jones case.

"The president adamantly denies he ever had a relationship with Ms. Lewinsky and she has confirmed the truth of that," Bennett said. "This story seems ridiculous and I frankly smell a rat."

Neither Bennett nor White House officials would comment on whether the president had conversations with Lewinsky about her testimony. Efforts to reach both Lewinsky and Tripp this week were unsuccessful.

William Ginsburg, an attorney for Lewinsky, confirmed that Starr is investigating his client's involvement with Clinton and said he has talked with Starr's staff. He would not discuss the substance of the case but portrayed his client as an innocent young victim of the political system. He would not comment on whether Lewinsky had a sexual relationship with Clinton.

"If the president of the United States did this -- and I'm not saying that he did -- with this young lady, I think he's a misogynist," he said. "If he didn't, then I think Ken Starr and his crew have ravaged the life of a youngster."

He added that a young person like Lewinsky can be devastated "if you're not terribly sophisticated and you're misled by the people at the center of the political system, and that includes the president and his staff and the special prosecutor."

William Hundley, who represents Jordan, said he was unaware of the investigation and declined to discuss it. "It's all news to me," he said. "I'm not disputing what you're telling me, but at this time I'm certainly not going to comment and I can assure you that Mr. Jordan would not comment. . . . You can rest assured that we're going to cooperate with the authorities."

On the tape recordings made by Tripp, sources said, Lewinsky described her sexual relationship with Clinton and said the president advised her not to worry about the Jones case because Jones's lawyers would not find out about the relationship. Lewinsky said that when she was notified by Jones's lawyers in mid-December that they wanted her testimony, she called the president and he advised her to deny the affair, the sources said.

She said that Clinton then told Lewinsky that Jordan would help figure out what to say, the sources said.

Jordan, a prominent Washington lawyer and civil rights figure, has been a regular Clinton golfing partner and among the president's closest advisers outside the White House.

He has come to Starr's attention before for helping another Clinton friend, former associate attorney general Webster L. Hubbell, line up lucrative consulting fees while Hubbell was under investigation for fraud and tax evasion. Starr wants to determine whether any of that money was intended to encourage Hubbell's silence about Whitewater matters.

While Starr's original mandate was to look at the complicated Whitewater real estate deal, it has been expanded several times by the court over the years to cover other incidents involving the president, including the firing of White House travel office employees and the improper collection of FBI background files on former Republican White House officials.

It was unclear last night how the new Starr inquiry might affect the Jones case, which has been moving toward a public trial scheduled for May.

In her suit, Jones alleged that Clinton crudely asked her for sex in a Little Rock hotel suite in 1991 while she was a state worker and he was governor. For several months, Jones's lawyers have been searching for women who could testify about experiences with Clinton that might prove a pattern of behavior.

Their research has led them to several women who have testified about sexual encounters with Clinton and ultimately to Lewinsky. In a deposition Saturday, Clinton was asked by Jones's lawyers about a number of women with whom he has been linked, according to a source.

The affidavit Lewinsky gave is sealed in federal court in Little Rock. In it, she is named only as a "Jane Doe" and says she should not have to testify in the Jones case because she had no relevant information, according to a source familiar with the document. Lewinsky said she never had a sexual relationship with Clinton, that he never asked for one and that she never benefited or suffered on the job as a result of any sexual overtures, the source said.

James Moody, a lawyer for Tripp, said last night that "Linda has been subpoenaed for the Paula Jones case and beyond that I cannot comment."

Tripp formerly worked in an administrative position in the Bush White House and then in the White House counsel's office during the first years of the Clinton administration. She joined the Pentagon press office in August 1994.

Last summer, Tripp was quoted in a Newsweek story about seeing a woman emerge from the Oval Office after she allegedly had a romantic encounter with Clinton. Tripp said Kathleen Willey, another White House aide, appeared in the hallway with her makeup smeared and clothing askew, Tripp said, and told Tripp she had just had an encounter with Clinton.

Willey was subpoenaed by Jones's lawyers and tried to resist testifying but ultimately was forced to tell her story under oath earlier this month. According to a source familiar with her account, she said she went to Clinton seeking a better job and he grabbed her, started kissing and groping her and said, "I've always wanted to do that."

Bennett, Clinton's lawyer, has denied that Clinton engaged in any improper behavior. After the Newsweek story ran, Bennett publicly questioned Tripp's credibility. Some time after that, Tripp began recording her conversations with Lewinsky, who coincidentally was working in the same Pentagon press office.

Lewinsky started at the White House as an unpaid intern in the office of then-Chief of Staff Leon E. Panetta in the summer of 1995 and impressed colleagues there with her dedication, according to a source familiar with her job history. During the government shutdowns several months later, she volunteered to come into work and manned phones left unattended, earning gratitude among White House officials, according to the source.

Lewinsky was hired in December 1995 as a staff assistant in the Office of Legislative Affairs, where she worked in the correspondence section opening and handling letters from members of Congress. At times, according to the source, she would be responsible for delivering correspondence to the Oval Office, usually leaving it with the president's confidential assistants, Nancy Hernreich or Betty Currie, and she sometimes ran into Clinton during these duties.

"She's like 10,000 other kids who come to the White House," said a colleague. "They're all star-struck and they all want to see him. . . . Did I notice that? Yeah. But I didn't see anything beyond that." She left the Pentagon several months ago to move to New York, associates said.

A Justice Department official said there was no question about approving Starr's request.

"Starr made it clear that he needed this," the Justice source said. "We did not want to look like we were slowing down the process." As a result, Reno made her decision "right away."

The source said that Justice officials were shocked by the allegations. "It was really a situation where people were floored," the source said.

Staff writer Dana Priest contributed to this report.

TABULAR OR GRAPHIC MATERIAL SET FORTH IN THIS DOCUMENT IS NOT DISPLAYABLE

CAPTION: KENNETH W. STARR

---- INDEX REFERENCES ----

KEY WORDS: NATIONAL

EDITION: FINAL

Word Count: 1571
1/21/98 WASHPOST A01
END OF DOCUMENT

Tab 23

INTERVIEW WITH PRESIDENT BILL CLINTON BY JIM LEHRER TO BE AIRED WEDNESDAY NIGHT ON **"THE NEWS HOUR WITH JIM LEHRER"** ON PBS WEDNESDAY, **JANUARY 21, 1998**

MR. LEHRER: Mr. President, welcome.

PRESIDENT CLINTON: Thank you, Jim.

MR. LEHRER: The news of this day is that Kenneth Starr, independent counsel, is investigating allegations that you suborned perjury by encouraging a 24-year-old woman, former White House intern, to lie under oath in a civil deposition about her having had an affair with you. Mr. President, is that true?

PRESIDENT CLINTON: That is not true. That is not true. I did not ask anyone to tell anything other than the truth. There is no improper relationship. And I intend to cooperate with this inquiry. But that is not true.

MR. LEHRER: "No improper relationship" -- define what you mean by that.

PRESIDENT CLINTON: Well, I think you know what it means. It means that there is not a sexual relationship, an improper sexual relationship, or any other kind of improper relationship.

MR. LEHRER: You had no sexual relationship with this young woman?

PRESIDENT CLINTON: There is not a sexual relationship; that is accurate. The -- we are doing our best to cooperate here, but we don't know much yet. And that's all I can say now.
What I'm trying to do is to contain my natural impulses and get back to work. I think it's important that we cooperate, I will cooperate, but I want to focus on the work at hand.

MR. LEHRER: Just for the record, to make sure I understand what your answer means, so there's no ambiguity about it --

PRESIDENT CLINTON: There is no --

MR. LEHRER: All right. You had no conversations with this young woman, Monica Lewinsky, about her testimony or possible testimony before -- in giving a deposition?

PRESIDENT CLINTON: I did not urge -- I did not urge anyone to say anything that was untrue. I did not urge anyone to say anything that was untrue. That's my statement to you. And beyond that --

MR. LEHRER: Did you talk to her about it?
Excuse me, I'm sorry.

PRESIDENT CLINTON: -- I think it's very important that we let the investigation take its course.
The -- the -- but I want you to know that that is my clear position.
I didn't ask anyone to go in there and say something that's not true.

MR. LEHRER: What about your having had -- another one of the allegations is that -- that you may have asked, or the allegation that's being investigated is that you asked your friend Vernon Jordan --

PRESIDENT CLINTON: To do that.

MR. LEHRER: -- to do that.

PRESIDENT CLINTON: I absolutely did not do that. I can tell you, I did not do that. I was -- I did not do that, he is in -- in no way involved in trying to get anybody to say anything that's not true at my request. I didn't do that.
Now, I don't know what else to tell you. I've -- I -- I don't even know -- all I know is what I have read here. But I'm going to cooperate. I didn't ask anybody not to tell the truth. There is no improper relationship. The allegations I have read are not true. I do not know what the basis of them is, other than just what you know. We'll just have to wait and see. And I will be vigorous about it, but I have got to get back to the work of the country.
I was up past midnight with Prime Minister Netanyahu last night. I've got Mr. Arafat coming in. We've got action all over the world and a State of the Union to do. I'll do my best to cooperate with this, just as I have through every other issue that's come up over the last several years, but I have got to get back to work.

MR. LEHRER: Would you acknowledge, though, Mr. President, this is very serious business, this charge against you that's been made.

PRESIDENT CLINTON: And I will cooperate in the inquiry of it.

MR. LEHRER: Mm-hmm. What's going on? What -- what -- if it's not true, that means somebody made this up. Is that -- is that -- is that --

PRESIDENT CLINTON: Look. You know as much about this as I do right now. We'll just have to look into it and cooperate, and we'll see. But meanwhile, I've got to go on with the work of the country. I got hired to help the rest of the American people.

MR. LEHRER: Okay. All right, speaking of the work of the country, other news today -- the pope is arriving in Cuba almost as we speak.

PRESIDENT CLINTON: Good thing.

MR. LEHRER: All right. Is the time come, maybe, for the United States to also bury some economic and political hatchets with Cuba?

PRESIDENT CLINTON: Well, I think that our previous policy -- the one that we've had now and the one we've had through Republican and Democratic administrations -- of keeping economic pressure on and denying the legitimacy of the Cuban government has been a good policy. I have made it clear from the day I got here that we would be prepared to respond to a substantial effort at a political or economic opening by Cuba. And we have, as you know, a system for communicating with each other.

Nothing would please me greater than to see a new openness there that would justify a response on our part, and I would like to work on it. And I think Mr. Castro knows that. I've tried to proceed in good faith here.

MR. LEHRER: Have you thought about doing something dramatic? I mean, this is your second term. Getting on an airplane and going down there, or inviting him to come up here, something like that? Just like what the pope is doing?

PRESIDENT CLINTON: I'm glad the pope's going there. I hope that we will have some real progress toward freedom and opening there, and I'll work on it. But that's still mostly up to Mr. Castro. I hope --

MR. LEHRER: Why is it up to him?

PRESIDENT CLINTON: Well, because -- look what the pope is saying. The pope is saying I hope you will release these political prisoners. You know, no American president getting on an airplane and going down there or having him come up here is going to deal with that. I mean, the Cuban American community, I know a lot of people think they've been too hard on this, but they do have the point that there has been no discernible change in the climate of freedom there. And I hope that the pope's visit will help to expand freedom, and I hope that, after that, we'll be able to talk about it a little bit.

MR. LEHRER: The pope, in fact, was interviewed on his plane a while ago by some reporters. And they asked him what message would you give to the American people, and he said -- about the embargo. And he said, "Change. To change, to change." That would be his message to the American people.

PRESIDENT CLINTON: Well, His Holiness is a very great man, and he -- and his position on this is identical to that, as far as I know, of every other European leader. And only time will tell whether they were right or we were.

MR. LEHRER: Explain to Americans who don't follow the Cuban issue very carefully why Cuba is different, say, than China, a communist country, North Korea, a communist country. Vietnam, we had a war with Vietnam, as we did with Korea and, in some ways, China as well. We have relations with them. Why is Cuba different?

PRESIDENT CLINTON: I think Cuba is different in no small measure because of the historic legacy we have with them going back to the early '60s. I think it's different because it's the only communist dictatorship in our hemisphere, a sort of blot on our neighborhood's commitment to freedom and openness.

And a lot of Americans have suffered personal losses of significant magnitude. And I think, as a practical matter, we probably think we can have a greater influence through economic sanctions on Cuba than we can in other places.

Now, I have worked over the last five years, in a number of different ways, to explore other alternatives to dealing with this issue, and I wouldn't shut the door on any other alternative. But I believe that our denial of legitimacy to the government, and our economic pressure, has at least made sure that others didn't go down that path, and that now -- I think it's one of the reasons that every country in this hemisphere is a democracy and a market economy, except for Cuba. And I think a lot of people forget what the impact of our policy toward Cuba, and what that highlighting of the Cuban policies, have done to change the governmental structures in other countries in our neighborhood.

So I am hoping -- nobody in the world would be happier than me to see a change in Cuba and a change in our policy before I leave office. But we have to have both. We just can't have one without the other.

MR. LEHRER: You don't see anything happening anytime soon as a result of the pope's visit?

PRESIDENT CLINTON: Oh, no, I am very hopeful. I was very pleased when I heard he was going. I wanted him to go, and I hope it'd be a good thing.

MR. LEHRER: The Middle East; as you said a moment ago, you met with Mr. Netanyahu twice yesterday and (you're meeting ?) Mr. Arafat tomorrow. First on Netanyahu, what is it exactly you want him to do?

PRESIDENT CLINTON: Well, let's talk about what he wants. What we want is not nearly as important as what he wants, what the Palestinians want, what the other people in the Middle East want. What we want is a just and lasting peace in the Middle East.

What I believe he and his government want is an agreement to go to final-status talks in the peace process under circumstances that they believe maximize their security. I think what the Palestinians want is an agreement that moves them towards self-determination under circumstances that maximize their ability to improve the lives of their people and the reach of their popular government.

And we've been out there now for a year -- I mean another year -- of course, five years since I've been president. But since the Hebron withdrawal, we've been out there for a year in the Middle East, looking around, listening, talking, and watching the frustrations, seeing the growing difficulties in the Middle East peace process. And we came up with an approach that we thought, in the ballpark, would satisfy both sides' objectives.

We worked with Mr. Netanyahu yesterday exhaustively to try to, you know, narrow the differences. And we didn't get them all eliminated, but we made some headway. And we're going to work with Mr. Arafat tomorrow to try to do that. And then we're going to try to see if there's some way we can put them together. And I'm very hopeful, because I think it's not good for them to keep on (dealing/dueling ?) with this and not making progress.

MR. LEHRER: Why does it matter that much to an American president that these two men get together and make an agreement?

PRESIDENT CLINTON: Well, first of all, I think it matters in the Middle East, because of our historic ties to Israel and the -- the difficulty that it would cause us if there were another war in the region.
Secondly, of course, we have major energy interest in the region. It's -- a big part of our economy recovery is having access to it. The third thing is, we have a lot of friends in the region beyond Israel, and if they all fall out with one another, that's -- that's bad for America. And of course, then, if -- if deprivation among the Palestinians leads to a rise of violence and leads to a rise of more militant Islamic fundamentalism in other countries throughout the region, then that could be a destabilizing fact that could really make things tough, if not for me, then for my successors down the road and for the American people down the road, in the 21st century.

MR. LEHRER: So you believe with those who say only America can make peace in the Middle East?

PRESIDENT CLINTON: I believe America is uniquely situated to help to broker a peace in the Middle East. I actually believe only the parties can make peace in the Middle East. I think only Israel and the Palestinians and the -- Syria and Lebanon can join Jordan at that table. That's what I think. And so I think, in the end, we -- we need to be very aggressive in stating what our views are. And we need to fight hard to at least have our position taken seriously. But in the end, you know, they have to live with the consequences of what they do or don't do -- all of them do. And they're going to have to make their own peace.

MR. LEHRER: The word around, as I'm sure you know, is that you and Netanyahu really just don't like each other very much. Is that right?

PRESIDENT CLINTON: I don't think so. It's certainly not true on my part. But we have -- had differences of opinion on occasion in approach to the peace process. And then there -- you know, there's been a little smattering in the press here, there, and yonder about

those differences and whether they were personal in nature. But for me they're not personal in nature.
I enjoy him very much, I like being with him, I like working with him. We had a difficult, hard day yesterday; you know, we had a long session in the morning, and then he worked with our team, including the vice president, secretary of state, through much of the afternoon. Then, after my dinner last night, I came back and we worked again for a couple of hours. So, it's hard to do that if you don't like somebody.
I really believe that he is an energetic man, and I think that within the -- the limits of his political situation, I believe he's hoping to be able to make a peace and to get to the point where he and Mr. Arafat can negotiate that.
But our job is to see, if you will, from a different perspective the positions of both the Palestinians and the Israelis. You know, we -- it's sort of like standing too close to an Impressionist painting sometime; there's lots of dots on the canvas, and the people who are standing too close to it, even though they're painting the canvas, may get lost in the weeds. And then the people that are standing back can see the picture, and it's a beautiful picture, if it all gets painted.
And so that's what I'm trying to do. I've got to -- I have to keep backing the painters back so they can see the whole picture, and then getting to the details and trying to help them ram it home, you know, because the one thing that I worry about is that you just sit there and have the same old conversation over and over again till the cows come home, and it's easy to do.

MR. LEHRER: Oh, yeah. Yeah.

PRESIDENT CLINTON: And so that's what I'm trying -- I'm trying to broker this thing, be a catalyst, get the people together, and give an honest view of what the picture looks like from back here about what the two artists can live with.

MR. LEHRER: Well, some people say that it doesn't look like to the innocent observer that either one of these guys want to make peace, that you may be talking -- you may be forcing them to do something that deep down in their either political hearts, or otherwise --

PRESIDENT CLINTON: That could be. Yes, that could be.

MR. LEHRER: -- they just don't want to do it.

PRESIDENT CLINTON: That could be. And I don't know what to say about that.

MR. LEHRER: But you're not going to give up on it?

PRESIDENT CLINTON: No. No. You know, if I don't make any progress, I'll level with the American people and the rest of the world and tell them I'm doing my best but I'm not making any progress. But, you know, we were hitting it last night till late, and then we're getting ready now for Mr. Arafat to come, and we'll hit it hard tomorrow. And that's all I know to tell you. We're just going to keep hitting it.

MR. LEHRER: On Asia, the Asia financial crisis, what business is it of the United States to save these failing Asian economies?

PRESIDENT CLINTON: Well, first of all, we can't save the Asian economies if they won't take primary steps to help themselves, the way Mexico did. You remember, we loaned Mexico some money, and they paid it back early with interest, and we made about $500 million because they took tough steps to restore economic growth, create jobs, raise incomes, and get their financial house in order.

That's the first and most important thing the Asians have to do. But in order to make it, they also need the backup of the International Monetary Fund and a plan designed to deal with the particular problems of each country, and then the U.S. and Japan and Germany and the rest of the Europeans to stand behind that to say, if necessary, we'll put together a package to really restore confidence.

In most of these Asian economies, the problem is the financial system and people can't pay back their loans, or investors take their loans -- when their loans are repaid, investors take the money and go somewhere else.

What's that got to do with America? Well, every day now in some of our newspapers you can see what's happening in the Asian stock markets and the Asian currency markets. What happens when a country's currency drops? When a country's currency drops, it doesn't have much money in dollars, and therefore, it can't buy as many American exports. A big part of America's economic growth since 1993 has occurred from exports, a big part of that from exports to Asia. If all their -- the value of all their money goes down, they can't keep buying our exports, and that hurts us. Also if the value of their money goes down, everything they sell in other places in the world is all of a sudden much cheaper, so they can push us out of those markets.

MR. LEHRER: Cheaper than our stuff.

PRESIDENT CLINTON: Correct. So if you want to just look at the plain, brutal, short-term economic interest, that's the short-term economic interest. If you want to look at the long run, we've got an interest in Asia in having stable democracies that are our partners, that work with us to help grow the region and grow with us over the long run, to help shoulder burdens like climate change, cleaning up the environment, dealing with global disease, dealing with weapons of mass destruction, contributing to the efforts in Bosnia, ending the nuclear program in North Korea. All those things we depend on the Asian countries to be a part of. They can only do that if they're strong. So we live in a world that's so interdependent that we need them to be strong if we're going to be strong.

Q As you know, there are some members of Congress who are saying what this really boils down to is welfare for international bankers, that's what we're up to. How do you respond to that? That's going to get -- that seems to be growing, particularly in the last few days.

PRESIDENT CLINTON: It -- that bothers me a lot. First of all, there is some truth to it. That is, if a country like Indonesia gets money from the International Monetary Fund to deal with its financial problems, what are its financial problems? You've got to pay notes when they're coming due. And if somebody made a foolish loan that they should not have made in the first place, that's an only 90-day loan on a building that's going to last for 20 years, for example, you hate to see them get their money back plus a profit at someone else's expense.
On the other hand -- and let me say, we are sensitive to that. Secretary Rubin has done a very good job of trying to get these big banks to roll over their debt.

MR. LEHRER: Take some hits themselves?

PRESIDENT CLINTON: Take some hits; at least, ride the roller coaster. They'll actually to get their interest back --

MR. LEHRER: -- if they hang in there?

PRESIDENT CLINTON: -- and the principal if they hang here. But they need to hang in there. They don't need to just take the money

and run.
On the other hand, if you start saying, "Well, everybody is going to get half back of what they put in," that will actually speed the rate at which people take money out and reduce the rate at which people put money in. You don't rebuild confidence, and therefore, the collapse is more costly. That's what bothers me, and -- I mean, nobody likes the idea -- you know, I don't think any American likes the idea that, you know, every single banker in one of these countries that made every bad loan will get paid back. And that, in fact, won't happen.
But when you try to pay back most things to stabilize the situation, the reason you're doing it is not to give the people who made the loans their money back. The reason you're doing it is to send a signal to the world that business is back up and going, that you have to be more careful now, but you can trust this country now, and you can invest.
So I think -- you know, I am convinced we're doing the right thing for our own economy; I am convinced we're doing the right thing for our values and our principles, and I hope I can persuade the Congress that we are.

MR. LEHRER: All right. Another subject. Iraq. Bad news today.

PRESIDENT CLINTON: Bad news.

MR. LEHRER: Apparently, Mr. Butler left. What can you tell us about where that thing stands --

PRESIDENT CLINTON: Well --

MR. LEHRER: -- in terms of whether the inspectors are going to be allowed to do what they want to do, et cetera?

PRESIDENT CLINTON: They seem to want to wait until early March to open the --

MR. LEHRER: Iraq does?

PRESIDENT CLINTON: -- Iraq -- that -- open the sites that Mr. Butler believes that ought to be opened.
That's a problem for us because we believe that we have to do everything we can, as quickly as we can, to check the chemical and

biological weapon stocks. And as I told the American people the last time we had this standoff with Saddam before he relented and let the inspectors go back -- you know, my concern is not to refight the Gulf War; my concern is to prepare our people for a new century, not only in positive ways, like creating a big international financial framework that works for them -- as we just talked about -- but also to make sure we have the tools to protect ourselves against chemical and biological weapons.

So I won't -- tonight, I can't rule out or in any options. But I can tell you I am very concerned about this. And I don't think the American people should lose sight of the issue. What's the issue? Weapons of mass destruction. What's the answer? The U.N. inspectors. What's the problem? Saddam Hussein can't say who, where, or when about these inspection teams. That has to be done by the professionals.

And sooner or later, something is going to give here, and I am just very much hoping that we can reason with him before that happens, but we've got to have those sites open.

MR. LEHRER: Now, Ambassador Richardson with the U.N., and others in the administration, have said the military option -- just to pick up, just to continue your sentence -- the military option remains on the table. The ambassador from Iraq to the U.N. was on our program recently, and he pretty much acknowledged that Iraq is banking on that not being real, that the U.S. alone is not going to go in there and take out -- you know -- some suspected anthrax facility, particularly if it's in a -- in the palace where Saddam Hussein lives, et cetera, et cetera.

PRESIDENT CLINTON: Well, the United States does not relish moving alone, because we live in a world that is increasingly interdependent. We'd like to be partners with other people. But sometimes we have to be prepared to move alone.

You used the anthrax example. Think how many people can be killed by just a tiny bit of anthrax. And think about how it's not just a question of whether Saddam Hussein might put them on a scud missile -- an anthrax head -- and send it to some city of people he wanted to destroy, but think about all the terrorists and drug runners and other bad actors that could parade through Baghdad to pick up their stores if we don't take the strongest possible action.

I far prefer the United Nations. I far prefer the inspectors. I have been far from trigger happy on this thing. But if they really believe that there are no circumstances under which we would act alone, they are sadly mistaken. And that is not a threat. I have shown that I do not relish this sort of thing. Every time it's discussed around here, I say -- you know, one of the great luxuries of being the world's only superpower for a while -- and it won't last forever, probably, but for a while -- is that there is always time enough to kill. And therefore, we have a moral responsibility to show restraint and to seek partnerships and alliances, and I've done that. But I don't want to have to explain to my grandchildren why we took a powder on what we think is a very serious biological and chemical weapons program -- potentially -- by a country that has already used chemical weapons on the Iranians and on the Kurds, their own people.

MR. LEHRER: So you would order an airstrike, or whatever it would take, to take out some facility if you couldn't get rid of it any other way?

PRESIDENT CLINTON: Well, I'm going to stay with my tried and true formulation. I'm -- I'm not ruling out or in any option. I'm just -- I was responding to what you said that the --

MR. LEHRER: Sure.

PRESIDENT CLINTON: -- that the Iraqi official thought we were just talking because we wouldn't want to discomfit anyone or make them mad. That's not true.
This is a serious thing with me. This is a very serious thing. And you imagine the capacity of these tiny amounts of biological agents to cause great harm. It's something we need to get after.
And I don't understand why they're not for getting after it.
What can they possibly get out of this? He really cared about his people -- he's always talking about how bad his people have been hurt by these sanctions. If he really cared about his people, he'd open all these sites, let everybody go in and look at them.

MR. LEHRER: To get it behind him. Yeah.

PRESIDENT CLINTON: If he's telling the truth, there's nothing there.

MR. LEHRER: Yeah.

PRESIDENT CLINTON: And if he's not, he'd get it -- behind it one way or the other. And we could then -- he could say, "Okay, what grounds does the United States have now for stopping the U.N. from lifting the sanctions? I have done everything I've been asked to do." And that would be a hard question for us, even though we've got reservations now. We'd have a hard time answering that question.

MR. LEHRER: But would you go along with lifting the sanctions now?

PRESIDENT CLINTON: Right now -- well, our position is, if he complies with all the United Nations sanctions -- the conditions of all U.N. resolutions leading to sanctions, that -- that's what we want Iraq to do.
But what he wants is -- is he wants to have it both ways. He wants to get the sanctions lifted, because he thinks people want to do business with him, and he wants to be able to continue to pursue a weapons program that we think presents a danger to the region and maybe to the world and certainly to our own interests and values. So I just want him to think about it again before they wait all this -- two months. I think that's a mistake. I want them to think about it and let these inspectors go back.

MR. LEHRER: One more foreign policy area, and that's Bosnia: That just hasn't worked out the way you had hoped, has it?

PRESIDENT CLINTON: Well, it hasn't worked out as fast as I'd hoped, but it actually is kind of working out the way I had hoped, in the sense that the Dayton peace agreement is very much alive and well. And we've separated the troops and the -- I mean the forces and the people. And we've got some relocation going on, and we've collected a lot of the bad weapons and destroyed them. And we -- we're making some progress on the joint institutions and other things. And we're trying to get that country together.
And I must say, I -- I was very impressed on my recent trip there by the level of support for the United States and the international community and our presence there, the level of support for our staying there, and the level of commitment of so many people to genuine pursuit of peace. And I think we can make it in Bosnia.
I do think -- I'm -- did I think we could all withdraw by now? Yeah, I did. But if you had told me, on the other hand -- that's the

downside. If you'd told me, on the other hand, "You can go there and stay a couple of years, and there won't be any gunshots fired, and the only people you'll lose will be in accidents of one kind or another, and you'll have an increasing amount of harmony in the urbanized areas that you hadn't imagined you would get," and some of the other positive things that have happened, I think we'd all have been very happy about that.
So I'm going to stay after this.
Again, this may be my congenital optimism, but I believe we're going to make the Bosnia peace process work.

MR. LEHRER: U.S. troops are going to have to be there a long time, aren't they, Mr. President?

PRESIDENT CLINTON: Well, that depends on how long it takes to achieve the mission. What I do think we should do since it just invites recalcitrance on the part of any parties in Bosnia that don't want to do something that's in the Dayton peace agreement, if the Americans say "Well, we're leaving in a year" and then the Europeans say "We're going to leave as soon as they do", then the people who have to make changes say "Well, all I've got to do is hang around for a year and I won't have to make any changes at all." So I think we should lift the sort of time certain --

MR. LEHRER: No more deadlines.

PRESIDENT CLINTON: -- for withdrawal. Yeah. Because it -- you know, the world community really hasn't done anything like this in a while. Not like this. And it's very complicated. But on the other hand at bottom it's about people getting along together and working together and serving together as citizens. And I have been quite impressed by how much has been done.

MR. LEHRER: We've been talking now about all these foreign policy things. And I was just -- if you'd go back through here, only the U.S. can keep peace in Bosnia, only the U.S. can make peace in the Middle East, only the U.S. can stabilize --

PRESIDENT CLINTON: Facilitate peace.

MR..LEHRER: Yeah. Facilitate peace.

PRESIDENT CLINTON: Facilitate peace.

MR. LEHRER: Okay, facilitate peace.

PRESIDENT CLINTON: They got to make the peace.

MR. LEHRER: Okay. Only the U.S. can help stabilize the economies of Asia. Only the U.S. can stare down Saddam Hussein and Iraq. If there are going to be any coalitions, the U.S. has to organize them and make them work. Is this the role of the United States of America for the immediate future?

PRESIDENT CLINTON: Well, it's a big part of it. But it also is a part of our role to put together a broad coalition on the climate change treaty to deal with global warming. It's also our role to put together global efforts to stiffen our efforts against biological warfare, to put together, you know, a global effort to support the International Monetary Fund and the nations themselves in dealing with the Asian financial crisis. We live in a world that's interdependent in two or three ways.
Number one, what happens in one country affects what happens in another one. We can see that.
Number two, what happens on economic issues increasingly have a security impact, and vice versa.
You know, I mean, I'll just give you the most blatant example is there's all these articles in the paper about all these countries that their currency dropped and, therefore, they can't buy jet airplanes for their air forces. That's the most obvious case.

MR. LEHRER: Thailand being an example of that, yeah.

PRESIDENT CLINTON: Yeah. And so there's the economics and the security, there's the national and the international -- there's all this interdependence. And I just think that in this world, if you happen to be at the moment it's occurring, that this huge new world of interdependence is occurring, and plus you've got all this interdependence at a citizen level with the Internet exploding and the information explosion, we're going to have all kinds of implications with the scientific explosions going on now, and we just happen to be, at this moment in history, the strongest and the wealthiest country around. It is a unique gift for our people. They've worked hard for it, but it's still a blessing. But it's also a unique responsibility.

And, you know, looking back over the last five years -- I just celebrated my fifth anniversary here -- I think that our administration has had good success in changing the role of government and changing the debate about government from -- you know, the debate I heard for the 12 years before I got here was the government was the problem versus as a solution. And we sort of come up with, "No, no. Government's neither. Government's a catalyst. It's got to give people the tools to solve their own problems. It's got to be a good partner. It's got to empower neighborhoods and people."

So we've got a smaller, more active government, and yet we've invested more in education, more in science and technology, more in the environment. And it's working. We've got good results.

We've not been as successful in convincing people in very practical terms about the interdependence of foreign and domestic policy, of economic and security policy. We just haven't been. But I'm hoping we can be more successful.

MR. LEHRER: Because the way it would come back to you would be this way, Mr. President. If there's a problem -- like if Asia has an economic problem, we're the folks that send the most money. You've got a problem in Bosnia, Somalia, a military problem, we're the ones who send the most troops. That's how it translates in --

PRESIDENT CLINTON: Yeah, but if you look at it, if you look at -- there are some areas in the Bosnia peacekeeping operation, like civilian police, for example, where the Europeans have nine times as many as we do -- we put up more money -- I mean, you look at the different allocations. If you look at what's going on in the United Nations, if the congressional position --which is that we ought to have our U.N. dues lowered to 20 percent -- prevails, since a lot of really poor countries pay even less than their fair share of the world's GNP, we'd actually be getting off light compared to many, many other countries -- really light.

So it's just not true that we always pay an unfair share. But it is true that we are called upon to bear the largest burden. If it helps us, I think if we ought to do it. And if it's right and we can do it at an acceptable price, we ought to do it, whether or not we're sure it helps us.

But if you -- it's hard to quarrel with the argument that we've been hurt by having 220-odd trade agreements in the last five years when you look at what's happened, and a third of our growth coming out of trade. It's hard to quarrel with the argument that we've been hurt by our leadership in Bosnia or the Middle East or Northern Ireland or any of these other places. It's hard to quarrel with the fact that our efforts to work with other countries to deal with chemical and biological and nuclear weapons, to deal with climate change, to deal with global disease spread, those things are good for Americans right where they live.

And we just simply don't have an option to say, "Well, I'm sorry; it looks bad in the newspaper today, so I think I'll check out of this old world." But it looked pretty good there for a couple of years and we were getting a whole lot more than we were getting -- (giving ?), so we liked that. We've got to be consistent. And we've got to realize that there is an interdependence within our country on each other and beyond our country.

And I've been working on that, and I'm supposed to be a pretty good communicator, but I don't think I've done as well as I need to. I've got to do more to persuade people.

MR. LEHRER: On a domestic issue, one that you've also been talking about a lot -- recently, in particular, but you've always talked about it -- and that's the racial divisions in this country. Where would you put that in terms of your own concerns and the concerns that you think the average American should have about their country right now as we sit here?

PRESIDENT CLINTON: Well, I think the average American should be concerned about it particularly as it relates to the racial disparities and the results we get in living and working and educating in America. I mean, if you look at the number of minorities who are in poor inner city schools where the performance is lower than it should be, if you look at the number of people who either don't have jobs or are still underemployed, no matter how strong the economy is, if you look at the patterns of opportunity wherever there are differences. I think we should be concerned about that.

And we don't have to -- you know, we don't have to have a fight over affirmative action every time. We can actually say, you know, how are we going to make it possible for more people to live together, learn together, and serve together, work together, at the same level of excellence? I think everybody should be concerned about it. I think everybody ought to be concerned about discrimination where it still exists; and it still does.

And finally, you know, the vice president gave a brilliant speech on Martin Luther King's Day, Monday, down in Atlanta, talking about how profoundly embedded in the human heart and culture and history the feelings of racial prejudice are.

50-893 98 - 8

And I think it's really worth -- if we're going to be an interdependent country leading an interdependent world, then all this interdependence has got to work. And with all of our diversity, we've got to keep working on our hardest. It's not just a question of education. You got to really work at it all the time.

MR. LEHRER: Why are you having trouble getting some blunt talk started on this?

PRESIDENT CLINTON: I don't know. We finally got some blunt talk going on affirmative action. And there were some pretty compelling stories told in Phoenix the other day. But I would like to see some blunt talk, you know, we --

MR. LEHRER: On affirmative action?

PRESIDENT CLINTON: Well, we had some blunt talk on affirmative action. I don't think the whole debate ought to be about affirmative action. I mean, you know, look at what we've done, for example, with something that's supposed to have a civil rights impact that's largely economic -- the Community Reinvestment Act. Passed in 1977, over 20 years ago. Now, the Community Reinvestment Act was set up to say to the bank regulators: Look, you guys go in and look at these banks and tell them, you got to take some of your money and invest it in inner cities and neighborhoods, and with people who otherwise would not get it so they have a chance to build homes, to build businesses, to create jobs, to build neighborhoods.
In the 20-year history of the Community Investment Act, 85 percent-plus the money loaned out under it to poor inner city neighborhoods has been loaned in the five years since I've been president.

So I think there are things we can do to improve education, to improve job growth, to -- not just having jobs, but also income and ownership among minorities, to create opportunities for service that will bring people together that will also mean fewer racial discrimination claims that have to be dealt with by government, and also. I think will help to tame the savage heart that still lurks within so many of us.

MR. LEHRER: What should the American people think about their president right now? You're going into your -- the last three years of your administration, you've got all this controversy today, you've got all kinds of things in the air --

PRESIDENT CLINTON: I think they ought to first of all think that -- I came to office in -- after the '92 election with a real theory of what I wanted to do to build America's bridge to the 21st century; that I wanted to strengthen our union, and I wanted to broaden our set of opportunities, I wanted to deepen our freedom, and I wanted to prepare for this modern world.

I had an idea about changing the philosophy of government, which I talked about earlier. I had an idea that all of our policies ought to be rooted in my three little words: opportunity, responsibility and community. We had a plan for changing the economic policy of the country, the welfare policy of the country, the crime policy of the country, the policy helping people balance work and family; integrating economic and other kinds of foreign policy -- we had all these plans. And I think you'd have to say, on balance, it's working pretty good.

So the first thing I would hope they say is, the president might be right about his philosophy of government and the values and the principles that we ought to be looking to, and about this whole interdependence business. Because we do have the lowest unemployment rate, the lowest inflation rate in a generation, the lowest crime rate in a generation, the biggest drop in welfare ever, dropping rates of juvenile crime, teen pregnancy, drug use. And we -- we're moving ahead in the world.

The second thing I'd like for them to say is, we've still got some significant challenges out there before we are completely prepared for this new era. We've got the entitlement challenge -- how are our parents going to be on Social Security and how are the baby boomers going to be on Social Security without bankrupting their kids? We've got the work and family challenge still there. How -- how can you do the most important work of society, raising children, and still be good at work? We've got the environment and economy challenge out there. How do you deal with climate change and clean air, clean water, safe food, diseases spreading, all this sort of stuff, preserving the environment, growing the economy? Those are just three of the big changes out there.

Look at the world. We all -- you know, in America we talk about diversity, and it's a real positive thing. We say we're going to get all these people together. In a world where the Internet can also give you information about how to make a terrorist bomb, and there's more and more diversity among religious and racial and ethnic hatreds, how can you make sure the world is about community, not conflict?

These are huge questions. And I don't think any serious person believes we've resolved all these questions.
So when I look at '98, yes, I want to balance the budget. Yes, I've got this great child-care initiative, which deals with work and family. I've got a Medicare initiative and the Medicare commission, which deals with our -- honoring our obligations to our parents. But we've still got a bunch of work to do.
So the second thing I want them to say is, "Yes, he was right at the first five years, and we're way ahead of where we were five years ago. But we've got a huge amount to do yet, a huge amount before we're really ready for the year 2000 and the 21st century."

MR. LEHRER: But on a more personal level, Mr. President, you're beginning -- you're a week from your State of the Union address, and here you've got -- you've been -- you're under investigation for a very, very serious crime and -- allegation of a serious crime. I mean, what does that do to your ability to do all of these things that we've been talking about, whether it's the Middle East or whether it's child-care reform or what?

PRESIDENT CLINTON: Well, I've got to do my best. You know, I'd be -- I'd be less than candid if I said it was, you know, just hunky-dory. You know, these -- but I've been living with this sort of thing for a long time. And my experience has been, unfortunately, sometimes, you know, when one charge dies, another one just lifts up to take its place.
But I can tell you, whatever I feel about it, I owe it to the American people to put it in a little box and keep working for them. This job is not like other jobs, in that sense.
You can't -- it's not -- you don't get to take a vacation from your obligations to the whole country. You just have to, you know, remember why you ran, understand what's happening and why, and, you know, go back and hit it tomorrow. That's all you can do.

MR. LEHRER: But going back to what we said at the beginning when we were talking about it, isn't this one different than all the others? This one isn't about a land deal in Arkansas, or it's not even about sex, it's about other things, about a serious matter. Do you -- I mean --

PRESIDENT CLINTON: Well, but all the others, a lot of them were about serious matters --

MR. LEHRER: Sure. I don't mean --

PRESIDENT CLINTON: -- they just faded away.

MR. LEHRER: I'm not suggesting that they weren't serious. But I mean --

PRESIDENT CLINTON: I don't mean -- I just -- all I can tell you is, I'll do my best to help them get to the bottom of it. I did not ask anybody to lie under oath. I did not do that. That's the allegation. I didn't do it. And we'll just get to the bottom of it, we'll go on.

And meanwhile, I've got to keep working at this. I can't just -- you know, ignore the fact that every day that passes is one more day that I don't have to do what I came here to do. And I think the results that America has enjoyed indicates it's a pretty good argument for doing what I came here to do.

MR. LEHRER: That whatever the personal things may be, the polls show that the people approve of your job as president, even though they may not have that high regard -- that high regard of you as a person.

PRESIDENT CLINTON: Well, hardly anyone has ever been subject to the level of attack I have. You know, it made a lot of people mad when I got elected president. And the better the country does, it seems like the madder some of them get.

But that's -- you know, that's not important. What's important here is what happens to the American people. I mean, there are sacrifices to being president, and in some periods of history, the price is higher than others. I'm just doing the best I can for my country.

MR. LEHRER: We're sitting here in the Roosevelt Room in the White House. It's 4:15 Eastern Time. All of the cable news organizations have been full of this story all day. The newspapers are probably going to be full of it tomorrow. And the news may -- this story is going to be there and be there and be there. The Paula Jones trial coming up in May. And you're going to be --

PRESIDENT CLINTON: I'm looking forward to that.

MR. LEHRER: Why?

PRESIDENT CLINTON: Because I believe that the evidence will show what I have been saying; that I did not do what I was accused of doing.
It's very difficult -- you know, one of the things that people learn is you can charge people with all kinds of things; it's almost impossible to prove your innocence. That's almost impossible to do. I think I'll be able to do that. We're working hard at it.

MR. LEHRER: What about the additional element here?
You're the President of the United States. Certainly you've got personal things that you want to prove or disprove, et cetera. But when does it, just the process, become demeaning to the presidency? I mean, somebody said -- in fact, just said it on our program, that this trial in May will be tabloid nirvana and --

PRESIDENT CLINTON: Well, I tried to spare the country that. That's the only reason that we asked the Supreme Court to affirm that absent some terrible emergency the president shouldn't be subject to suits so that he wouldn't become a political target. They made a different decision. And they made a decision that this was good for the country. And so I'm taking it and dealing with it the best I can.

MR. LEHRER: And the new thing? They're going to be -- you know, pour it on, nothing's going to change?

PRESIDENT CLINTON: I have got to go to work every day.
You know, whatever people say about me, whatever happens to me, I can't say that people didn't tell me they were going to go after me because they thought I represented a new direction in American politics and they thought we could make things better. And I can't say that they haven't been as good as their word every day, you know. Just a whole bunch of them are trying to make sure that get done. But I just have to keep working at it.
You know, I didn't come here for money or power or anything else. I came here to spend my time, to do my job, and go back to my life. That's all I want to do -- and that's what I'm trying to do -- for the best interests of America. And so far the results have been good, and I just hope the people keep that in mind.

MR. LEHRER: Mr. President, thank you very much.

PRESIDENT CLINTON: Thank you.

Tab 24

1830

INTERVIEW WITH PRESIDENT BILL CLINTON BY ROBERT SIEGEL AND MARA LIASSON
BROADCAST ON "ALL THINGS CONSIDERED" ON **NATIONAL PUBLIC RADIO**
5:07 P.M. EST WEDNESDAY, **JANUARY 21, 1998**

MR. SIEGEL:Mr. President, welcome to the program.
Many Americans woke up to the news today that the Whitewater independent counsel is investigating an allegation that you, or you and Vernon Jordan, encouraged a young woman to lie to lawyers in the Paula Jones civil suit. Is there any truth to that allegation?

PRESIDENT CLINTON: No, sir, there's not. It's just not true.

MR. SIEGEL: Is there any truth to the allegation of an affair between you and the young woman?

PRESIDENT CLINTON: No. That's not true either. And I have told people that I would cooperate in the investigation, and I expect to cooperate with it. I don't know any more about it than I've told you, and any more about it, really, than you do. But I will cooperate. The charges are not true. And I haven't asked anybody to lie.

MS. LIASSON: Mr. President, where do you think this comes from? Did you have any kind of relationship with her that could have been misconstrued?

PRESIDENT CLINTON: Mara, I'm going to do my best to cooperate with the investigation. I want to know what they want to know from me. I think it's more important for me to tell the American people that there wasn't improper relations, I didn't ask anybody to lie, and I intend to cooperate. And I think that's all I should say right now so I can get back to the work of the country.

MS. LIASSON: Mm-hm. But you're not able to say whether you had any conversations with her about her testimony, had any conversations at all.

PRESIDENT CLINTON: I think, given the state of this investigation, it would be inappropriate for me to say more. I've said everything, I think, that I need to say now. I'm going to be cooperative and we'll work through it.

MR. SIEGEL: But is the fact that in this case, as we understand it, a close friend of this young woman was outfitted with a wire, with a microphone, to record conversations with her at the instruction of the Whitewater counsel, does that disturb you? Do you regard that Mr. Starr is playing the inquisitor here in this case?

PRESIDENT CLINTON: Well, that's a question the American people will have to ask and answer, and the press will have to ask and answer, the Bar will have to ask and answer; but it's inappropriate for me to comment on it at this time. I just have to cooperate, and I'll do that.

MR. SIEGEL: And a broader question. I understand that you don't want to comment on this. There are some commentators -- on our network it would be Kevin Phillips -- who've said that the moral leadership of the presidency justifies the kind of scrutiny that you're receiving. Do you agree with that?

PRESIDENT CLINTON: Well, I think there has been -- there is a lot of scrutiny and there should be, and I think that's important. I'll leave it to others to define whether the kind we have received, in volume, nature and accuracy and sometimes downright honesty, is appropriate. That's for others to determine.
You know, I just have a certain number of days here. I came here as not a Washington person. I came here to try to change the country and to work to build the future of America and a new century. And I just have to try to put this in a little box, like I have every other thing that has been said and done, and go on and do my job. That's what I'm going to work at.

MS. LIASSON: Mr. President, earlier today you said you tried your best to contain your natural impulses and get back to work. Were you furious? Is that what you were referring to?

PRESIDENT CLINTON: I was. I was.

MS. LIASSON: And what were you furious about?

PRESIDENT CLINTON: Well, I worked with Prime Minister Netanyahu till 12:30 last night. I'm getting ready for prime -- for Mr. Arafat. I'm working on the State of the Union. And we've got a lot of big issues out there in the -- within and beyond our borders. And I don't think any American questions the fact that I've worked very hard at this job. And anything that's a distraction, I dislike. And --

MS. LIASSON: Do you see this as a partisan attack? Is that what you were --
PRESIDENT CLINTON: I didn't say that. I don't know what the facts are. I don't know enough to say any more about this. I don't want to get into that. You know at least as much about it as I do. I worked till 12:30 last night on something else. I have -- that's why I have given the answer that I have given to your questions today.

MR. SIEGEL: Moving on to the matter you were working on late at night last night, first, it seems the message to Mr. Netanyahu from the U.S. was: We want to see you withdraw from some part of the West Bank.
First, what's the message to Arafat, if you could sum it up?

PRESIDENT CLINTON: Well, first of all, let's talk about what they want. What -- I think what Israel wants is a peace that moves -- a peace process that moves immediately to final status negotiations and has -- gives them a stronger sense of security. I think what the Palestinians want is a peace process that gives them a stronger sense of self-determination and of possibility and dignity.
So what we've tried to do is -- for 12 months now, ever since the Hebron redeployment, we have been out involved in the region talking to all the players -- I say -- that's not the royal "we" -- I mean me, the secretary of state, Mr. Ross, Mr. Berger, others involved -- trying to analyze what it would take to get the peace process back on track. And we formulated some ideas and we talked to the Israeli prime minister about them yesterday. We're going to talk to Mr. Arafat about them tomorrow.
We hope, by the time we finish the talk, that both sides will be closer together than they were before we started. And if they are, then we'll try to close.
But I think there may be circumstances under which we could take a real leap forward in the Middle East peace process, if we get a break or two.

MR. SIEGEL: This week?

PRESIDENT CLINTON: I wouldn't -- no, I wouldn't go that far. It takes -- it's going to take a while to -- we have to work the Palestinians tomorrow. Then we have to analyze where we are with both and whether we can go forward. And we may not make any progress at all, and if we don't, I'll tell you that.

MR. SIEGEL: I'd like to ask you, though, after spending so much time with Mr. Netanyahu on this visit and on other visits -- some people regard him as a man who always opposed a land-for-peace settlement to the conflict with the Palestinians, certainly wouldn't have negotiated the Oslo accords, had he been in office then, has never liked them particularly. Some would say he's really trying to thwart that process and contain the damage, from his standpoint. Do you think so?

PRESIDENT CLINTON: No, I can't say that, based on what I've seen.
I do believe he's made no secret of fact that he has principal differences with the Oslo process, which he has pledged to support. And we all know he has a different political coalition and that indeed the political forces in Israel itself are different than they were even a few years ago, in terms of the composition of the population, the rise of these -- the small parties and immigrant-related intense groups and all that. So I think that's all there.
I think that historically there's been a little bit of difference in the -- kind of the texture of the relationship between the Likud Party and the Palestinians, and the Labor Party and the Palestinians. So there are a lot of layers here.
But the bottom line is, I think Mr. Netanyahu is an intelligent man who wants to make peace and understands that -- that there has to be some formula where -- that some marginal increase in territorial insecurity by giving up land is more than offset by a dramatic increase in security by a changing of the feelings of the people, the climate, the capacity for growth and opportunity.
When -- so we're just trying to hammer out what each side would have to do to take another step. I'm hopeful.

MS. LIASSON: Mr. President, in Iraq, diplomacy hasn't worked yet. UNSCOM is still barred from doing its job the way it sees fit, getting into the sites that it wants to inspect.
Yet, on the other hand, military action also has downsides. It might upset any progress you're making with allies on other issues. Do you think the U.S. has any good choices on Iraq?

PRESIDENT CLINTON: Well, there are no easy choices. If we define "good" as easy, the answer is no. But you know, let's -- let's (do ?) -- what is the problem? The problem is the weapons-of-mass-

destruction program, chemical and biological weapons, primarily. What is the solution? Letting the UNSCOM inspectors go wherever they want, and that means that Saddam Hussein cannot determine when, where and who, when it comes to the UNSCOM teams.
So now he says that he is going to determine that, and there's not going to be any "when" for a couple of months, during which time he'll be free to move whatever he wants wherever he wants. I think that this is a big mistake, and I believe that the United Nations will see it as such in the real thwarting of its position. And we just have to see where we go from here.

MR. SIEGEL: Do you feel that, even with the threat of military action -- possible military action -- that you have to be able to point to some progress in the Arab-Israeli negotiations in order to maintain the support of the U.S. friends in the region? Is there some linkage between the problems?

PRESIDENT CLINTON: No, not -- I don't think there is a linkage, a direct linkage. You know, it may affect the atmospherics; just, you know, the attitude about America. But I think it would be wrong to say there's a direct linkage.
The main thing is every country in the region, and throughout the world, has a vested interest in seeing that no one who would either use or sell weapons of mass destruction -- especially chemical and biological weapons, which could be carried around in small amounts and little releases -- that no one who would use or sell them has a big program of them, which is why the whole United Nations is against the Iraqi program. Now, they need to think long and hard, these countries that have been a little squeamish about being firm, whether or not it's possible that they could be the victims of this, if not directly from Iraq, from some group or another that Iraq sells to in the future. So I think we need to be firm, and I am going to do my best to keep rallying support and keep working ahead.
I'd prefer the inspections. I'd prefer the diplomatic pressure -- I am not a -- I have not been trigger happy on this. Some here in our country think that we should have acted before. But I don't think we can rule out any option.

MS. LIASSON: Mr. President, moving to domestic policy and the budget surplus; Republicans and Democrats on the Hill have already said what they want to do with it, either cut taxes or pay down the debt, or spend more money on social problems.
But so far, you've been silent on this. And I'm wondering if you are

ready to make a commitment to using whatever surplus there might be to shoring up the Social Security trust funds, making sure that safety net is there for the Baby Boom generation when it retires.

PRESIDENT CLINTON: Well, I'll make a commitment that in the State of the Union address, I'll announce what I think should be done.

MS. LIASSON: Well, what do you think should be done?

PRESIDENT CLINTON: I have decided, but I don't what to announce yet. I need to have something to say in the State of the Union that's new.
But let me say, before I say that, I would like to just caution -- we've had great -- we've had five great years, and we've always done better than we were predicted to do on the deficit. But I think I would still caution the Democratic and Republican leaders of Congress from passing some big five-year program to spend money through spending programs or tax cuts that hasn't yet materialized. We do not yet have a balanced budget. And I just -- we've worked so hard for so long to get this done, I'd sure hate to start counting our chickens before they hatch.
That's -- so I would like to start with that. And then when I speak at the State of the Union, I'll say what I think ought to be done.

MR. SIEGEL: Would you like to caution equally against shoring up the Social Security Fund in that case?

PRESIDENT CLINTON: Well, in general, I believe -- you know, my position on Social Security is that we need a bipartisan and fairly rapid process to work through the options and prepare for the long-term health and viability of the Social Security system along with the efforts that are going to made by the Medicare Commission, which I'm very hopeful about. I mean, I think one of the big things I hope to achieve before I leave office is entitlement reform in both major systems.
So I will -- I'll tell you, I think that that needs to done, and we're exploring how best to do that.

MS. LIASSON: Well, we don't want to let you off the hook too easily. You're not saying you're against using the surplus to shore up the Social Security Trust Funds?

PRESIDENT CLINTON: I'm not saying one way or the other. I'm saying I'd like to have something to announce on State of the Union night.

MR. SIEGEL: Mr. President, on tobacco, there's talk on Capitol Hill of writing and passing a "kids only" bill as opposed to seeking a huge global settlement. And that would achieve the aims, in theory, of raising the cost of a pack of cigarettes by so much that it would be beyond the reach of teenagers, achieve your major aim and not take companies off the hook for future liability. Are you in favor of such a bill?

PRESIDENT CLINTON: Now you'd have a children's only bill that did what? I'm sorry, I just -- you had a lot of points.

MR. SIEGEL: Yes, well, first it would raise the price of a pack of cigarettes simply to deter teenage purchases of cigarettes.

MS. LIASSON: And strengthen the hand of the FDA, do some marketing restrictions, but not be a complete global settlement.

PRESIDENT CLINTON: Well, I would favor doing something like that without committing to the specifics if we fail to get a global settlement. But I think we owe it to the attorneys general and the others who worked with us on this in good faith to try to achieve one. Because I think long term we need to deter teen smoking with more than just a higher price tag for cigarettes. I think there are lots of other things that can be done, and I think that we ought to have certain benchmarks of performance for the tobacco companies, too, which in my view will help, because then they'll be free to do more if they even have to spend a little more money than they're obligated to under the agreement. If they're not meeting the targets they may decide they ought to do that to save even more money down the road. So --

Now, I'm going to look for a global settlement in the tobacco case for the benefit of our children. If we fail, then I'll look at something else.

MS. LIASSON: Mr. Clinton, following up on that, you've cautioned Congress not to spend the surplus 'til they have it, yet you have committed $60 billion of some projected tobacco settlement bill before it's even passed to new spending. Do you think that's wise? And if you don't get a tobacco settlement, are you committed to those programs? Will you cut elsewhere in order to keep that new spending?

PRESIDENT CLINTON: Well, let me just say this. I will not under any circumstances favor funding anything I have recommended with the surplus, with the projected surplus.

MS. LIASSON: So you'd -- if you don't get the tobacco settlement you'd fund it elsewhere?

PRESIDENT CLINTON: No, if I don't get it -- in other words, if we don't get the tobacco settlement we'll either have to cut the size of the child care initiative or cut elsewhere or do something else because I will not just on my own get up and propose that we spend the proposed settlement or part of it on these programs. I think they're terribly important, but right now we've got other fish to fry, and we've got to make sure --
The most important thing is to keep this economy growing, to keep discipline, to keep strong, to do what makes sense. And that's what's gotten us here: five hard years of that. And we don't want to forget that. So, well, we do have new spending in our programs, but it's new spending within the context of fiscal discipline, it's new spending with the smallest federal government since Kennedy was president and the size of it continuing to go down.

MR. SIEGEL: Federal prosecutors reportedly rejected a plea bargain agreement not long ago with Theodore Kaczynski, with his lawyers, at least, that might have guaranteed his imprisonment for life. Evidently they want the death penalty. Is it important to you, say, if he's convicted that there be an exercise of the federal penalty?

PRESIDENT CLINTON: Well, it's what's -- if he's guilty, he killed a lot of people deliberately. And therefore I think it's something that the jury should be able to consider.
From my point of view, I approve of the laws that we have in America now, this sort of two-tiered trial where you determine guilt and then you determine penalty.
And I would want to hear all the testimony before I decided how I'd vote in that case. But I do think it's -- should be presented to the penalty phase.

MR. SIEGEL: Even if you had a guilty plea that, as there is no parole in the federal system, guaranteed none, and spared any possibility of an acquittal, you would still prefer to reject that plea, to offer the jury the option of the death penalty?

PRESIDENT CLINTON: I think the jury should have the option. Now, also, you know, as a practical matter, there aren't many inmates -- perhaps he would be one -- that actually do get life without parole. And that's probably not a terrible thing; that is, in a prison system where you don't want prison riots, you have to reward people who do, you know, an extraordinarily good job of being good inmates within the prison system. Perhaps the practice of allowing people who have life sentences to be paroled after quite a long period of time is a good one, or at least defensible. But juries know that, too.

I think the -- you know, it's just -- it's hard to generalize. But this was a case where, based on what I know, I would consider it appropriate to present that to the jury.

MS. LIASSON: Mr. President, on the Asian financial crisis, a lot of Americans don't understand why taxpayers should help bail out banks and investors in the U.S. or Japan or in Europe who took a risk and made some mistakes. Don't they bear some responsibility?

PRESIDENT CLINTON: Absolutely.

MS. LIASSON: Don't they have to take some of the hit?

PRESIDENT CLINTON: They do bear some of the responsibility, and they shouldn't all be bailed out. And that's one of the most frustrating things about this.

On the other hand, what this is about is about rebuilding confidence in the investment climate of these countries. I don't think they ought to get one red cent unless the governments commit to do things for the future that will mean these banks will have to take a bigger risk and get their act cleaned up, unless their -- the International Monetary Fund plan is implemented, and then the U.S. and Japan and these other countries come in as a backup.

But if we refuse on the front end to do anything, the problem is it could hurt us a lot worse than it could hurt the odd banker that doesn't get his money back, because if a lot of people start not getting any of their money back, then other people say, "Well, I'm going to get my money out," and then others say, "Well, I'm not going to put my money in." And then all of a sudden, the value of the currency goes way down. Then what happens? They don't have any money

to buy American products, and all their products are cheaper competing against ours and other countries'.
So we have a big economic interest, as well as a huge interest in a stable, democratic Asia. And that's why I think we're doing the right thing. I hope in the State of the Union I can persuade the American people that it's the right thing.

MS. LIASSON: I want to ask you about "Clintonism." We've been hearing a lot about Clintonism lately -- a coherent political philosophy that may or may not be identified with you. Do you think there is such a thing? And what is it?

PRESIDENT CLINTON: Well, I do. I think, first of all, it's a very -- it's a future-oriented political philosophy that attempts to break the logjam between the 1980s and early '90s debate of the Republican position that government is the enemy and the Democratic position is --- sort of government is the solution if we do more of the same, we just need to do more. My position is we need a different kind of government for a different kind of society and a different kind of world, and we need to focus more on giving people the tools they need to make the most of their own lives, more on being a catalyst for good ideas, more on empowering the disadvantaged. That's -- and creating opportunity, enforcing responsibility, building community. I think that's what Clintonism is about, and I think it will get us to the 21st century.

MR. SIEGEL: Mr. President, thank you very much for talking with us.

PRESIDENT CLINTON: Thank you.

Tab 25

1842

FNS Transcript HOME HEADLINES

▸ THE WHITE HOUSE WASHINGTON, DC REGULAR BRIEFING;
▸ BRIEFER: MICHAEL MCCURRY 12:22 P.M. EST WEDNESDAY, JANUARY 21, 1998

MR. **MCCURRY**: Well, ladies **and** gentlemen.

We have all these concocted things that we could talk about, but it probably is not what you're interested in talking about, so whatever you want to talk about.

Q What about the statement?

Q Did Bennett see the president?

MR. **MCCURRY**: Not that I'm aware. I think the president spent some time with Mr. Kendall. Mr. Bennett was here **and** he talked to Mr. Ruff, **and** Mr. Ruff also talked to Mr. Kendall.

Q Bob Barnett was here. Was he also on this subject?

MR. **MCCURRY**: I didn't know he was here. I would have to check on that.

Q What is Chuck Ruff's role in all of this?

MR. **MCCURRY**: Well, the Office of **White House** Legal Counsel has throughout all the many inquiries that have occurred, including the Whitewater inquiry by Mr. Starr, works, as it has worked in every presidency, to protect the institution of the presidency itself, **and** there are times there are all kinds of issues that arise in which there are overlapping concerns about representation, **and** those have been adjudicated in courts. I think you're all familiar with that.

Terry?

Q Mike, you said this morning that the president did not have an improper relationship with his former intern. What do you mean by an improper relationship?

MR. **MCCURRY**: I'm not going to parse the statement. You all got the statement I made earlier, **and** it speaks for itself.

Claire?

Q Are you saying no relationship?

Q But would an improper relationship --

MR. **MCCURRY**: I am not going to parse the statement. You've got the statement I made earlier,

and it speaks for itself.

Q It doesn't speak for itself. I mean, we need a definition of what an "improper" relationship means.

MR. **MCCURRY**: I am not going to --

Q Are you **standing** by that statement?

MR. **MCCURRY**: That statement is where we are, **and** that's what I am -- that's what I said.

Q Does that mean there was a sexual relationship?

MR. **MCCURRY**: Claire, I am just not going to parse this statement for you. It speaks for itself.

Q Mike, has --

MR. **MCCURRY**: Wolf Blitzer!

Q -- has the president been informed that Kenneth Starr has now exp**and**ed his probe to look into these allegations?

MR. **MCCURRY**: Not that I am aware of. **And** I checked with White House legal counsel, **and** as far as they know, there's been no direct contact with the OIC on this matter that I am aware of.

Q To what extent will the president cooperate? This is a patsy question, I know. But to what extent will he cooperate --

MR. **MCCURRY**: A patsy question from Sam Donaldson!

Q -- with Starr?

MR. **MCCURRY**: He has cooperated fully with Mr. Starr **and** would cooperate fully if, in fact, any matter such as this was within the purview of the independent counsel.

Peter?

Q He will make -- excuse me -- he make available -- you will make available the **White House** logs that show the visitors?

MR. **MCCURRY**: I am not going to speculate on what the OIC might ask for.

Peter?

Q Mike, could you describe the president's demeanor when he discussed this story with you **and** how his demeanor has been through the morning?

MR. **MCCURRY**: Matter of fact. He approved the statement I gave you earlier today. **And** he's had to work on some other matters today. He spent time on the State of the Union address **and** on Iraq, particularly on Iraq, **and** spent a fairly significant chunk of time with Mr. Berger **and** Mr. Steinberg **and** others on that subject.

Q Mike --

Q Mike, you said he was --

MR. **MCCURRY**: Paul?

I'll come back, Scott.

Q -- outraged this morning, **and** now you say matter of fact --

MR. **MCCURRY**: Paul?

I'll come back, Scott.

Paul?

Q What kind of relationship did he have with her? Any?

MR. **MCCURRY**: I am not characterizing it beyond what the statement that I've already issued says.

Q Did they ever do anything socially at all or --

MR. **MCCURRY**: I am not going to parse this statement. I am not going to beyond what I said already.

Scott?

Q You said he was outraged this morning. Now you say his reaction is matter of fact. Which is it?

MR. **MCCURRY**: I've given you the statement. He's outraged about the allegations. I am telling you about the business that the president has attended to today on behalf of the American people.

Q How distracted is the president as a result of these allegations?

MR. **MCCURRY**: He's -- look, it's been five years, **and** there have been distractions of various types from time to time, **and** the president keeps on working on what he has elected to work on. **And** that's what he is going to continue to do.

Liz?

Q Mike, can you give us a sense of what the **White House** is like today? Have there been meetings on this? How many of them?

MR. **MCCURRY**: There's more of you around.

Q Other than that.

MR. **MCCURRY**: There's been -- you know, we had our first meeting to kind of talk about how we're going to prepare the rollout of the State of the Union next week. I think, you know, we have to continue to do the work that we are doing on behalf of the American people in fulfillment of the prerogatives **and** priorities of this president. That's what we get paid to do, **and** that's what we do on behalf of the American people.

Q Mike?

MR. **MCCURRY**: Yeah?

Q Is the president seeking to amend any part of his deposition from Saturday?

MR. **MCCURRY**: Not that I am aware of, but that should be a question you'd direct to Mr. Bennett.

Yeah?

Q Mike, would it be improper for the president of the United States to have had a sexual relationship with this woman?

MR. **MCCURRY**: Look, the president has made a statement that has expressed his outrage at allegations. I've made it very clear I'm not going to go beyond that statement, **and** you can **stand** here **and** ask a lot of questions over **and** over again which will elicit the exact same answer.

Q But, Mike, you're leaving -- you're willing to leave --

MR. **MCCURRY**: I'm not leaving any impression, David, **and** don't twist my words. It's very clear what the president has said in the statement. He said he has had no improper relationship with this woman. That clearly means that there would be things that would be improper, **and** I think you all know what they are **and** I don't need to, you know, parse it any further.

Scott?

Q Mike, the president is saying he did not commit perjury?

MR. **MCCURRY**: Look, the president has made it clear, **and** I've made it clear in the statement I've issued on behalf of what he's said. He tells people to tell the truth.

Yeah?

Q The president, **and** particularly Mrs. Clinton, have frequently said in matters like this that they believe that political enemies originate these kinds of stories. Is it his belief that this particular allegation is also part **and** parcel of a partisan, political attack on him?

MR. **MCCURRY**: I think when we have suggested that in the past, it's been on information that you know to be true, that has been reported, that is factual. **And** in this case, we have no information available to suggest what motive may have arisen for these outrageous allegations. I think it's -- those who have made the allegations, those who pursue them have to address the question of motive.

Karen?

Q Mike, does the **White House** consider this a legitimate avenue of inquiry for Ken Starr? By "this" I mean a further investigation into another --

MR. **MCCURRY**: That's a question that the OIC has to address, **and** they've made an application to the Justice Department, **and** the Justice Department can properly address that.

Helen?

Q Who is Linda Tripp?

MR. **MCCURRY**: I do not know. I mean, I don't know enough about --

Q **And** how long did she work here?

MR. **MCCURRY**: I don't have employment records on either her or the other one.

Q Why would she -- why would she -- (inaudible)?

MR. **MCCURRY**: I'm the last person on the face of the earth that can answer that question for you. But you should properly direct that question to the Office of the Independent Counsel, I would think.

Q Mike?

MR. **MCCURRY**: Yeah?

Q Just for the record, the president is also saying he never encouraged anyone to commit perjury?

MR. **MCCURRY**: The president's statement speaks for itself. I'm not going to go beyond the statement that we've already issued.

John?

Q Mike, has the president, so far, or does he plan to speak with his own staff? I've talked to several people here at the White House today who have had their own confidence shaken just because of the nature of these allegations **and** the less than sort of blanket denial of them.

MR. **MCCURRY**: He's been working with his staff **and** I think, as you all know, he's got an opportunity to conduct some interviews later today. **And** my guess is that information will -- that question would probably come up.

Q Would you be able to say that you are absolutely confident these are not true? How about you personally?

MR. **MCCURRY**: Look, I -- my person views don't count. I'm here to represent the thinking, the actions, the decisions of the president. That's what I get paid to do.

Yeah?

Q Mike, part of what you get paid to do also is to make sure that the American people are informed correctly of what it is the **White House** is trying to say. So if --

MR. **MCCURRY**: I'm doing my best at that at the moment.

Q **And** that's why I'm asking you. Are you trying to leave us with the impression that a president could have a "proper" sexual relationship with this woman?

MR. **MCCURRY**: Of course not, David. **And** that's -- the question flies in the face of the statement you've gotten from the president that I think addresses that pretty clearly.

Yeah, Deborah?

Q Mike, I think what's puzzling us is that the president, we are told, on Saturday denied any sexual relationship with this woman.

You have said --

MR. **MCCURRY**: Well --

Q Let me just finish the question, **and** then --

MR. **MCCURRY**: I can't --

Q Mike, let me finish the question --

MR. **MCCURRY**: I can't speak to the deposition that the president gave, because of the gag order that the court has in place on that deposition, Deborah. So you know I can't even get into the question.

Q Let me finish the question. What is puzzling to many of us is that we've invited you probably two dozen times today to say there was no sexual relationship with this woman, **and** you have not done so.

MR. **MCCURRY**: But the president has said he's never had any improper relationship with this woman. I think that speaks for itself.

(Cross talk.)

Q So there were no sexual relationships --

Q Add the word "sexual." Put the word "sexual" in. That's the problem.

MR. **MCCURRY**: I didn't write the statement.

Wolf --

Q Who wrote the statement, Mike?

MR. **MCCURRY**: It was prepared by the counsel's office, **and** I reviewed it with the president, to make sure that it reflected what he wanted me to say.

Q Why wouldn't the counsel put in the word "sexual"?

MR. **MCCURRY**: Because -- I don't know. I'm not a lawyer.

Yeah?

Q The president didn't write the statement; it was written by his lawyers. But you showed it to the president. What did the president say about it?

MR. **MCCURRY**: Oh, well, it was developed in consultations between the lawyers **and** the president clearly, Scott.

Wolf? (Cross talk.)

Q **And** when you showed it to the president --

MR. **MCCURRY**: I'll come back, Scott.

Wolf?

Q Monica Lewinsky's lawyer says she's distraught, she's been very upset about all of this. Does the president have anything to say to Monica Lewinsky? That she's been dragged into what is obviously a very unpleasant affair?

MR. **MCCURRY**: I have not discussed that with him, but I'm -- you know, the president always, when any member of this staff is distraught over any circumstances, is very compassionate. He's a very compassionate person.

Yeah?

Q Have you asked the president whether he knows Monica?

MR. **MCCURRY**: I've not questioned him directly on this matter **and** don't intend to.

Yeah?

Q Mike, do you know if anybody from the **White House** has done anything to get in contact with Monica Lewinsky?

MR. **MCCURRY**: I don't have any information on that.

Mr. Donvan?

Q Mike, how in the world could the president be matter-of- fact about anything he's doing today when this is blowing up around him?

MR. **MCCURRY**: He's matter-of-fact about, you know, getting the business done of addressing this question, given the outrageousness he feels about the allegation.

Yes, sir?

Q Would the **White House** be willing to make public the logs of the comings **and** goings of Monica Lewinsky --

MR. **MCCURRY**: Asked **and** answered.

Anything else? Yes?

Q Mike, when you showed the statement to the president, what did he say about it?

MR. **MCCURRY**: He said fine. (That ?) --

Q That's a direct quote? The president just said, "Fine"? That's all he had to say about that issue?

MR. **MCCURRY**: He said fine. He looked at it, **and** he said fine.

Q Mike, this morning, I kind of had the impression --

Q (Off mike) -- outraged, fine?

Q -- that the president really shaped that statement.

MR. **MCCURRY**: Oh, he did. I mean, it was prepared --

Q (Off mike) -- gave it to him.

MR. **MCCURRY**: No. No. It was prepared in consultation between the lawyers **and** the president. The counsel's office gave it to me. I wanted to, of course, verify that that's exactly what the president wanted me to say on his behalf.

James?

Q Will you describe what Monica Lewinsky's duties were at the **White House**?

MR. **MCCURRY**: I can't. I don't have her position description.

Q Can you describe the intern program?

MR. **MCCURRY**: The intern program, there are, you know, about 250 at any time of the year who are here as interns. They tend to be college-aged students between 18 **and** 23, equally balanced male and female. They work full-time during the summer and up to 25 hours a week during the school year. There are two sessions of interns during the summer and one each in the fall and spring.

Q They don't get paid.

MR. MCCURRY: They go through the same kind of background checks and EOP checks that are required for other staffers.

Q Is this a paid intern?

MR. MCCURRY: Terry?

No, it's a volunteer.

Q In your statement when you say it's outrageous, does that mean the allegation about the sexual allegation or about the charge --

MR. MCCURRY: Terry, again, I'm not going --

Q -- or about the charge of obstruction of justice --

MR. MCCURRY: I'm not parsing the statement.

Q -- and perjury?

MR. MCCURRY: I'm not parsing the statement for you.

Mr. King?

Q Mike, do you know the last time the president spoke to Vernon Jordan, if he's had any discussions with Vernon Jordan, about this subject?

MR. MCCURRY: I know the answer to neither question.

Yes?

Q Mike, can you say why you're not going to ask the president about this subject?

MR. MCCURRY: Because I think it's proper for the counsel to deal with the president on that. And I will, as I often do, get the information that I need to pass on from counsel.

Yeah?

Q Mike, does the president appreciate that this is an order of magnitude different than the allegations --

MR. MCCURRY: Oh, I think the president is smart and would understand that of course.

Q Mike, what's your next move or counsel's next move or the president's next move?

MR. MCCURRY: My next move is to get off this podium as quickly as possible. (Laughter.)

Q What's the next step from the White House?

MR. MCCURRY: Well, the president -- you know, the president is, I imagine, going to want to address this. We have, you know, an interview with PBS, an interview with NPR, a fortuitous bit of scheduling that's probably a lot better than the $25 pledge I sent in during pledge week. (Laughter.)

Yeah?

Q Beyond the interview, what do you do?

MR. MCCURRY: So, what do I do? What do you mean? We go about doing the business of the United States of America. And there's a lot other right now that we haven't talked about today.

Q What about this situation?

MR. MCCURRY: This situation, if it is in fact going to be explored by the independent counsel, will go into the same place that most matters go. It will become the province of lawyers and people who look into these things, and the amount that I talk about it here will be quite measured -- thankfully.

Q The statement that said that the president's always told everyone to tell the truth, or words to that effect.

MR. MCCURRY: The words were that he's made clear from the beginning that he wants people to tell the truth in all matters.

Q Is he now then directly saying to Ms. Lewinsky that he wants her to tell the truth?

MR. MCCURRY: He's said that to anyone who is ever in a position to be required to provide factual information.

Q Including her?

MR. MCCURRY: He has not directed any communication that I am aware of directly to her.

Yeah?

Q I'm asking (you to ?) do that now.

MR. MCCURRY: Yes?

Q Do you know -- does the first lady know Monica? Does the first lady know Monica Lewinsky?

MR. MCCURRY: I have no idea.

Yes?

Q Mike, how long --

Q And did she have any hand in terminating her duties?

MR. MCCURRY: I have no idea.

Q Mike, how long was the president with David Kendall?

MR. MCCURRY: I don't know the length. It was not -- it happened some time ago. I don't think it was extremely long.

Q Well, who's taking the lead in this case, David Kendall or Robert Byrd (sic) -- Bennett?

MR. MCCURRY: I've referred additional questions on this particular matter to Mr. Kendall --

Q Why?

MR. MCCURRY: -- although Mr. Kendall **and** Mr. Bennett, you know, have clearly talked to each other about the question.

Q Why (would he talk to ?) Kendall on this matter?

MR. MCCURRY: Because of the suggestion in news reports that it's in the province of Mr. Starr's inquiry.

Q **And** to follow that up, which lawyers prepared the statement -- Kendall, Bennett, or Ruff?

MR. MCCURRY: Oh, I think all three reviewed it.

(Cross talk.)

Q Does the president still have complete confidence in his legal team?

MR. MCCURRY: Sure. Absolutely.

Yeah?

Q Mike, there was a suggestion that Linda Tripp recorded these conversations because she was angry that Mr. Bennett had called her a liar over the Kathleen Willey matter. Does that have anything to do with this being the catalyst --

MR. MCCURRY: I have absolutely no basis upon which to speculate on any of that.

Yeah?

Q Mike, did Monica Lewinsky call the president, as I've seen reported somewhere, **and** talk about what she should say?

MR. MCCURRY: I have no information to answer that question, **and** I'd refer you to Mr. Kendall. I imagine, if it's in fact true, that that's going to be subject to inquiry by Mr. Starr. They're probably going to explore that matter.

Peter? **And** then I'll come back, Helen.

Q Mike, does the president have any intention of addressing the nation on this in a more formal way than through you or through interviews?

MR. MCCURRY: I -- not that I have heard of at this point. I think that he obviously is probably going to address it later today, in a fashion that people will be able to see what he has to say.

Helen?

Q Since we're all interested in whatever the president has to say, we'd like to have his answers, you know, sometime in the afternoon, after he gives this interview. I think it's only fair, since we're all asking the same question, **and** --

MR. MCCURRY: Helen, it's a good point --

Q It's not the question -- I know these were pre-arranged interviews **and** exclusive, but --

MR. MCCURRY: Right. It's a good point. These interviews were scheduled as part of our buildup to the State of the Union **and** just happened to fall at this particular moment. But we'll contact the news organizations involved **and** see if they want to be helpful.

Q Is the president prepared to -- if it comes to that, to cooperate with an impeachment investigation on Capitol Hill?

MR. **MCCURRY**: There's no reason that I know of to think that we'll be dealing with something like that.

Mary?

Q Has the president given any thought of accompanying Mr. Arafat to the Holocaust Museum?

MR. **MCCURRY**: Not that I have heard. I think the president thinks it's very appropriate for him to be given a VIP tour of the museum. The president thinks that the museum makes a significant emotional impact on people who see it, **and** it will no doubt have that effect on the chairman as well.

The chairman has indicated, en route to Washington, that he is anxious to see the museum, if that is to be arranged.

Yeah?

Q Mike, when the president saw the statement, did he complain that it was not as broad a blanket denial as he would have liked?

MR. **MCCURRY**: He said -- I reviewed it with him. I said, "This is what I propose to say." **And** he said: "That's fine. Say it."

Q -- he wishes to have an addendum to that statement? (Laughter.)

MR. **MCCURRY**: I think he suspects he will be addressing this himself at some point.

Yeah, Carl?

Q Mike, do you know when -- if -- when the president plans a formal press conference --

MR. **MCCURRY**: We, you know, want to do one reasonably soon.

Q Mike, how is this matter different --

MR. **MCCURRY**: Oh, Carl, by the way, he will of course, have a press conference with Prime Minister Blair, at the conclusion of the working visit that Prime Minister Blair will have, at the end of the first week of February, February 5th -- official visit -- official visit.

Q Mike, how have these reports **and** dealing with a bevy of lawyers disrupted his day today? What was planned, **and** what did he end up doing instead?

MR. **MCCURRY**: It's his -- we've had -- we were going to do these interviews that I am talking about a little earlier in the day. So we've had to push them back. But, other than that, he's had to, you know, pursue the other matters that he would pursue on any given day.

Yeah, Deborah?

Q Mike, you were saying in regard to the impeachment question that that doesn't seem like a serious issue. But George

Stephanopoulos seems to think that might be an issue. Does that not concern you?

MR. **MCCURRY**: He says things all the time -- (laughter) -- assassinations, impeachments, you know --

Q We pay him well.

MR. **MCCURRY**: That's what -- Mr. Donaldson makes the point he gets paid well to say those things, **and** God love him for it.

Yes?

Q Mike, do you know by chance Monica Lewinsky's precise time was here at the **White House and** exactly what she did?

MR. **MCCURRY**: I don't have an employment record on her.

Yeah?

Q Can you get that for us?

MR. **MCCURRY**: I will see if that is something we can make available.

Yeah?

Q Taking into account that the **White House** is maintaining that these allegations are untrue, is the **White House** preparing any response to these people making the false allegations against the president?

MR. **MCCURRY**: Well, I think that's pretty much what I have been doing here.

Q No, but in addition -- in addition to just denying -- in addition to just denying the allegations.

MR. **MCCURRY**: Well, you know, there is a likelihood, if the news reports are correct, that Mr. Starr will be looking into it, that we'll probably have to provide extensive information on it -- so it goes.

Yeah?

Q Just one more stab at this. So is your interpretation of that statement that he meant to categorically deny that he had a sexual relationship?

MR. **MCCURRY**: I am not parsing that statement. The statement speaks for itself. I don't have anything to add to what I told you earlier.

Q Do you under**stand** why a lot of us think it doesn't speak for itself?

MR. **MCCURRY**: I am not going to interpret statements for you.

I'm just going to give you the statements that I've been authorized to give.

Q Mike?

MR. **MCCURRY**: Yes, Mr. Pelley?

Q Who has told you that you can't say?

MR. **MCCURRY**: My own good judgment tells me not to try to parse this statement. So no one has told me to do that. That's the way I'm electing to deal with your questions right now.

Q So Ruff's office, the other lawyers, haven't told you say this **and** say nothing else?

MR. MCCURRY: They trust my judgment, amazingly enough.

Q But it seems that -- you know, lawyers are very careful people, **and** they seem to have --

MR. MCCURRY: So am I.

Q -- picked a very imprecise word. So --

MR. MCCURRY: Well, look, I'm not going to characterize the statement for you.

Q Is this the low point in the Clinton presidency?

MR. MCCURRY: No. This --

Q Not yet. (Laughter.)

MR. MCCURRY: Look, you know, there have been for five years from time to time we go through episodic reports like this, **and** yet through all that period, this president has kept his focus on the work he's been elected twice by the American people to do. **And** the American people have indicated that they are more than satisfied with the work he's doing **and** they want him to continue to keep this economy strong, to make the kind of changes that we need to make to get this country prepared for the 21st century. They expect the president not to be distracted about allegations, however outrageous, **and** to keep his eye on the ball.

And that president has got a lot of work that he needs to do to do exactly that on this particular day. We've got a State of the Union address coming up. **And** we've got the chairman of a U.N. commission in Baghdad who's just had some difficult meetings that are going to have a lot of consequences, **and** we're going to have to deal with those consequences after Chairman Butler gives his report to the Security Council on Friday. **And** we're dealing simultaneously with issues related to a deployed force in Bosnia, which is going to occupy some of the president's time.

And we've got a lot of pretty interesting initiatives that we're laying before Congress, **and** beginning to do the work of trying to find a bipartisan coalition that will pass some of the president's ideas.

That's a lot of hard work ahead. **And** this president has always, when facing allegations, been able to sort of say that's over there **and** I've got to keep focused on what I need to do on behalf of the American people. **And** I think the American people expect him to do that.

Yeah, Skip?

Q The difference with these charges, though, is they stem -- of this personal -- (inaudible) -- they stem from actions that occurred here. I mean, is that going to affect his legislative agenda or his foreign policy agenda?

MR. MCCURRY: We've dealt with all manner of, you know, stories that have dealt with actions that occurred here. I mean, that's not -- that's happened from time to time.

Q Mike, has the counsel's office been officially notified that Starr's probe was expanded? **And** --

MR. MCCURRY: As I said earlier, Karen, not that I'm aware of, **and** I checked with the counsel's office **and** they didn't give me any indication that they had received that communication from OIC. I have -- you know, my assumption is that that will be a matter that Mr. Kendall will pursue.

Q Would such an expansion be appropriate, in the White House's opinion?

MR. MCCURRY: I already answered that question. I said it's in the province of the attorney general upon application of the OIC to make that determination.

David?

Q Why are these allegations outrageous?

MR. MCCURRY: Look. You've tried now I think a dozen different ways to get me to amplify on the statement. I'm clearly not going to do it. I'm sorry if you're disappointed that I'm not doing it. I don't want to render my own personal opinion about the nature of these charges. And so we are where we are. There's nothing more to say.

Scott?

Q Mike --

MR. MCCURRY: Scott?

Q Mike, has the White House received any subpoenas from the FBI related to this case?

MR. MCCURRY: Not that I'm aware of.

Q Mike, are they "outrageous" because they're not true or are they outrageous because it would be morally reprehensible if they were true?

MR. MCCURRY: There are probably many different reasons why they are outrageous in the mind of the president. But having not explored the degree of outrageousness that the president attaches to the allegations, I'm not going to amplify on the statement that he's made.

Yeah?

Q Let me bring up a subject from last week, which now is particularly germane -- the president's ability to pay for his legal expenses.

MR. MCCURRY: Oh.

Q Has there been now some movement on a new effort to get some money in, because this clock this morning was running with all these lawyers. (Laughter.) And they don't work cheap.

MR. MCCURRY: They get paid when they talk to you, too. Did you know that? That makes it -- adds to the expense.

I did check -- you asked me to check on that. And they are -- our understanding is that some of the president's supporters on the outside have begun some efforts to establish some kind of fund. They are not in a position yet, that I'm aware of, to make any formal declarations on that. In any event, they would have to be in contact at some point with the president's legal counsel on that so that the president's legal counsel could render an opinion to the president on whether the establishment of any such fund would be ethical and proper under law.

Q But Mike, don't these --

MR. MCCURRY: Yeah?

Q When did the president and his legal advisers know that this was -- that this story was coming?

Did they have advance knowledge? Or after the meeting last night with Netanyahu? When?

MR. MCCURRY: I don't -- I personally don't know that anyone that I deal with here knew much about it before late yesterday.

Yeah?

Q Mike, you were talking about the president's need to deal with major foreign policies in Iraq and Bosnia, elsewhere; he's meeting with Middle East leaders. But don't these kinds of accusations impair, hurt his ability to deal effectively with these kinds of critical national security issues?

MR. MCCURRY: He has faced allegations somewhat like this in the past and they have not impacted on his ability to do the job that he constitutionally must do as president on behalf of the American people.

Q Allegations like perjury and obstruction of justice, Mike?

Q Let me go back to the fund, if I may. Are you -- am I correct in that until the legal counsel has made a ruling, until that is done formally, there are no contributions actually being made, and certainly no money is being expended? Or are they being made now?

MR. MCCURRY: Yeah, my understanding and belief would be that until such a fund was constituted, there would be no ability for it to receive any contribution. The previous fund, which was not allowed to solicit contributions, has now ended its operations. So there wouldn't be any entity to which one would make a contribution.

Q What could be different, though? I mean, the previous fund was thought not to be proper. What could be different that would now make a new fund proper?

MR. MCCURRY: No, it was thought to be very proper, it was just hobbled by the rules that applied to it on interpretation of the Office of Government Ethics that made it impossible to solicit any contributions. People were not aware of it, therefore, you know, revenues did not match the costs --

Q Expectations?

MR. MCCURRY: Expectations, costs. Whatever.

Jeff?

Q Mike, you said that you don't see an impairment on his constitutional duties. But how concerned are you as to how he might be perceived by these other world leaders, in spite of these domestic issues?

MR. MCCURRY: I don't speak for other world leaders, I speak for Bill Clinton the world leader.

Yeah?

Q When I asked if the White House logs will be made public -- of Monica Lewinsky's coming and going -- you said, "Asked and answered."

Yet there's a contingent in this area that doesn't know what the answer was.

MR. MCCURRY: Didn't get it? Oh, okay.

Q Was it that it will be made available to Kenneth Starr or to the press and the public?

MR. MCCURRY: I said we want to cooperate with the inquiry by the independent counsel. **And** if in fact this is a matter the independent counsel is pursuing, **and** if in fact he pursues evidentiary material like that, I know that the president would expect the **White House** to cooperate it (sic) **and** provide it. **And** I think until that question is (resolved ?), it's going to be hard to satisfy a lot of the news organizations who have been asking for that.

Yeah?

Q You can't give it to us **and** then give it to him --

MR. MCCURRY: I think until the question is resolved of whether or not this is something that the office of independent counsel is seeking, it would be difficult for us to satisfy requests.

Q Why? Mike, but why does -- (off mike) --

MR. MCCURRY: Because we clearly want to cooperate with the OIC.

Yeah?

Q Mike, has the president asked his lawyers -- either here or his private lawyers -- to appeal to Starr not to pursue this issue, because both parties deny it?

MR. MCCURRY: I don't know the answer to that question.

Yeah?

Q Mr. Netanyahu said that he would look favorably on -- (inaudible) -- suggestion of the meeting between him **and** Chairman Arafat. Does that change the **White House**'s st**and** on if the meeting should be arranged between --

MR. MCCURRY: Well, I think he's indicated that he would want such a meeting to be substantive. So we would we. I'm not aware of any plans for such a meeting at this point. You know, clearly, at some point, we will have to get these parties talking to each other directly, but we want to do that at a time that the parties are likely to make progress.

Q So that could be this week?

Q Do you mean to tell me that if reporters talk to sources who perhaps should not talk because of the gag order -- **and** I'm not saying they do -- but should they talk to us anyway, that in fact if they are -- **and** I'm not saying they are -- (scattered laughter) -- members of the president's team -- they CHARGE the president for talking to us in violation of the gag order? (Scattered laughter.)

MR. MCCURRY: That's a complicated question of legal billing that I would have to direct to the attorneys involved. (Laughter.)

Q I would say if there are any attorneys --

MR. MCCURRY: But I would be interested in the answer.

Q If any attorneys like that exist, they would be shameful to charge the president --

Q (Gasps.)

MR. MCCURRY: Or to be running the meter --

Q Gag order!

(Cross talk.)

MR. MCCURRY: Yeah?

Q I guess I won't get invited to the Christmas party next year.

Q Mike, maybe you were asked this before, but could you clarify -- did the president know of the stories out today last night, before he spoke at the fund-raiser? When did he first learn --

MR. MCCURRY: I'm not sure when he first heard about the particular story, the Washington Post story, we're dealing with. There was a fair amount swirling around in the ether yesterday, but at what point he focused in on it I can't tell you.

Q Did he huddle in a meeting when he got back? Did he have any time to talk to Podesta or anybody when he got back?

MR. MCCURRY: I don't know the answer to that.

Yeah?

Q Mike, Mr. Bennett says he smells a rat in this situation. Do you smell anything?

MR. MCCURRY: How does one smell a rat? What does a rat smell like?

Q How would I know? (Laughter.)

Q Do you smell anything? A rat or anything?

MR. MCCURRY: I smell the lights in here cooking fiercely everyone who's standing here.

Q It's ?? who smells a rat.

MR. MCCURRY: Anything else?

Yes?

Q Mike, tomorrow is the 25th anniversary of Roe v. Wade. Does the president have anything to say on this occasion beyond his desire to keep abortion safe and legal?

MR. MCCURRY: Well, the president's views on the issue are very well known. He continues to believe that abortion needs to be safe and legal in the United States of America, but it ought be rare. And that is the position he has frequently articulated, and we have done things in furtherance of exactly that policy by the president.

Q Any message to the opponents -- thousands who are going to be here tomorrow?

MR. MCCURRY: The president respects the views of those, as a matter of conscience, take a different point of view on such fundamentally important issues. But I think the president believes it is a matter that should be decided as a matter of conscience, and based on the private reasoning of the people who have to struggle with complicated questions of life and death, and the president will always respect the right of a woman to make that choice free and of her own volition. And the president does not believe, in any event, that it's something that the government should dictate answers to.

Yeah?

Q What's on tap for tomorrow with Chairman Arafat? And what can you tell us about the package that President Clinton will be discussing with him, however provisional that may be?

MR. **MCCURRY**: I've got a lot of great -- you know -- foreign policy diplospeak about what we're going to do, but I won't satisfy your desire for details on what ideas the president presented. I think we provided you a pretty good series of briefings **and** briefers during the course of the day yesterday **and** they made it clear what they're willing to say about the substance of the dialogue, which is enough that you get some general idea of the subjects being covered, but not enough that you have any explicit review of the diplomacy we're pursuing.

We obviously will need to take the discussions that we've had with Prime Minister Netanyahu, ask Chairman Arafat to reflect on them, **and** to gain his thinking **and** perspectives on the issues that have been addressed now in the meetings with the government of Israel, **and** then see if there's a way to bridge some of the differences that clearly exist. That may or may not be possible, **and** at this point it's impossible to predict whether or not these discussions can lead to the kind of progress that the United States so fervently desires.

John?

Q Mike, do you have anything on another report that Ambassador Richardson offered Miss Lewinsky a job?

MR. **MCCURRY**: I don't. I don't have anything on that.

Yeah?

Q Mike, on -- back to Roe v. Wade, do you have any comments on a group of anti-abortion protestors who took the public tour this morning?

They said -- they complimented the Secret Service on their treatment, **and** they said it was rather uneventful. Did you know about this ahead of time?

MR. **MCCURRY**: We had heard that there was some interest on the part of people to freely express themselves during the course of a tour, **and** I think the service **and** the uniformed division always h**and**les such matters with sensitivity but also consistent with what their law enforcement responsibilities are.

John?

Q Who makes the final judgment about the perhaps conflicting goals of the president's defense in this? As a legal matter, lawyers always want to be absolutely as circumspect as possible. As a public **and** political matter, obviously the president would like to get his side of the story on this as quickly **and** as explicitly as possible. How do you balance those two, **and** who makes the final judgment?

MR. **MCCURRY**: Well, the balance is always a delicate one because there are sometime conflicting aims. But the president, as president **and** as client, is the one that ultimately has to reconcile differing point of views. **And** we, you know, in each **and** every case weigh the difference exigencies that arise.

Yeah?

Q Mike, what can you tell us about Linda Tripp's work here at the **White House**? **And** what led to her moving over to the Pentagon?

MR. **MCCURRY**: I don't have her employment record here, nor her position description.

Q Can you get that for us?

MR. **MCCURRY**: I've already said that I would see if -- look into seeing if I can.

Q Back on the protesters. Do you think a public tour of the **White House** is an appropriate venue for making political statements?

MR. **MCCURRY**: I think that in **and** around the **White House**, people find this a platform for expressing views. **And** that's as it should be. I think it should be done with respect for a house that all the American people own **and** enjoy seeing.

Q Was anyone arrested?

MR. **MCCURRY**: You'd have to ask. I gather from Jeff not.

Yeah?

Q Mike, you said earlier that Chuck Ruff was involved in the discussions today because he represents the institution of the presidency. In what way is this issue **and** these allegations -- how are they impinging on the institution of the presidency **and** the official business of the **White House**?

MR. **MCCURRY**: Well, we've spent a lot of time -- you know, you've spent a lot of time asking me questions today that demonstrate it very vividly. I've been asked for employment records, I've been asked for appointment records here at the **White House**, all of which are the custody of the **White House and** the presidency itself, **and** it's exactly the protection of that institution that the **White House** Legal Counsel is charged with. So, I mean, there are a number of examples even arising here in the briefing that indicate what the interests would be in the **White House** lawyers in these types of discussions.

Q Was the president asked about it, or did he have any comment about whether Tripp's allegation that she saw Kathleen Willey leaving the president's office **and** making an allegation that she had been kissed or fondled?

MR. **MCCURRY**: I think we dealt with that matter a long time ago, if I recall correctly.

Yeah.

Q Did the president send any message to the pope, or do we have any independent observers there?

MR. **MCCURRY**: The president did not send a direct personal message. But on behalf of the administration, on behalf of the president our diplomats have had good **and** detailed conversations with the Holy See in advance of the pope's visit in which we have certainly wished the holy father well for the trip that he is making. **And** we have expressed our views that we hope that the outcome of his visit will be better respect for the rights of people to worship freely according to their own conscience in Cuba, a right that has been too long denied to the people of Cuba.

Q Is our ambassador there?

MR. **MCCURRY**: Say again?

Q Is our ambassador there?

MR. **MCCURRY**: We do not have an ambassador to Cuba. We have an interests section there, **and** we -- we have an interests section there.

Q Not Cuba, our ambassador to the Vatican.

MR. **MCCURRY**: Oh, to the Vatican. She's --

(To staff) She's part of the trip?

STAFF: No. She's in Rome.

MR. **MCCURRY**: She's in Rome.

Q Her daughter is in Cuba.

MR. **MCCURRY**: Her daughter spends a lot of time with Sam. (Laughter.)

Q Ways **and** Means chairman Archer today suggested using a budget surplus to lower taxes **and** reduce the debt as well as create a cushion in case projection of the revenue is off. **And** it looks as if the administration thinks it's a prudent approach.

MR. **MCCURRY**: Well, the administration **and** the president believe it would be prudent to see what kind of surplus we're talking about before we spend it **and** give it away. It might -- there might be some interest in some quarters for spending money that we may or may not have, but I think the president is more interested in seeing if we can secure the surplus, making absolutely sure we keep strongly committed to the path to a balanced budget **and** to keeping fiscal discipline sort of at the top of our minds as we make budget policy. **And** then, as to any future surpluses, I think the president will be interested in seeing that they address the long-term needs of this country. **And** I think the president will want to say more about that during the State of the Union.

Yeah.

Q Mike, is there any directive written, verbal or otherwise circulating in the **White House** instructing people not to talk about the Monica Lewinsky allegations or not to talk about her or not to talk about anybody else involved?

MR. **MCCURRY**: I'm not aware of anything. **And** I think that, you know, that you rely on common sense to prevail. People shouldn't be talking about this if it's in the province of the president's attorneys **and**, you know, a future -- likely future inquiry by an independent council.

Q Has the Iraqi situation worsened now?

MR. **MCCURRY**: I think that the situation in Iraq certainly has not got to the point where the president or the United Nations wants it to be, which is full compliance by the government of Iraq with the requirements of the U.N. Security Council. What we've had today is a lot of excuses, but no compliance. **And** I think it's time for the government of Iraq to recognize that when Chairman Butler says "Here's what I need in order to fulfill the m**and**ate of the Security Council", they'd better listen **and** stop trying to dictate to him the terms that would govern inspections. We expect Chairman Butler to make a full report to the Security Council Friday, **and** then we will pursue our diplomacy **and** perhaps other options beyond.

Yeah.

Q Has the **White House** been briefed by Butler at all on the conversations?

MR. **MCCURRY**: My underst**and**ing from our U.S. U.N. mission is that he has had a brief conversation with the president of the Security Council, the French permanent representative, **and** that has been passed on to other permanent members of the Security Council. But a fuller report will await Chairman Butler's return to New York Friday.

Yes?

Q Did anyone in the U.S. government send a message through the Pope to Fidel Castro?

MR. MCCURRY: I'm not aware of any channel for such a communication. We have a diplomatic channel, and that is the one which any exchanges with the government of Cuba would occur.

Yeah?

Q Do you have any more information on the tourist incident earlier?

(Pause.)

Q Guatemala?

Q Spray paint.

Q Spray paint.

MR. MCCURRY: Oh. Oh. Oh, no I don't. I'd have to refer you. I understand the U.S. Attorneys Office is the one pursuing that now.

Q Thank you.

MR. MCCURRY: Thank you, Helen.

Q Now you print up our colloquy, distribute it, we saved the president thousands of dollars in legal fees, and I want a cut! (Laughter.)

END.

HOME | HEADLINES

1864

Tab A

1866

Citation Search Result Rank 5 of 5 Database
1/98 USNWSW (No Page) ALLNEWS
1/21/98 U.S. Newswire (Pg. Unavail. Online)
1998 WL 5682372
(Publication page references are not available for this document.)

U.S. Newswire

Wednesday, January 21, 1998

Excerpts of Telephone Interview of Clinton by Roll Call

WASHINGTON, Jan. 21 /U.S. Newswire/ -- Following was released today by the White House:

EXCERPTS OF TELEPHONE INTERVIEW OF THE PRESIDENT BY ROLL CALL

4:26 P.M. EST

THE PRESIDENT: Hello. How are you?

Q Hello, Mr. President. How are you? A few questions about the breaking news. Do you think that this Monica Lewinsky story is ing to overshadow your State of the Union address?

THE PRESIDENT: Well, I hope not. But you guys will have to make that decision. The press will make that decision.

Q Some Republicans have been talking about impeachment for months now. And even your former advisor, George Stephanopoulos, mentioned it this morning, that it could lead to that. What is your reaction to the suggestion that this may lead to impeachment?

THE PRESIDENT: Well, I don't believe it will. I'm going to cooperate with this investigation. And I made it very clear the that allegations are not true. I didn't ask anybody not to tell the truth. And I'll cooperate. So I think that there will be a lot of stirring and there will be a lot of speculation about how this all was done and what it means and what it portends, and you all will handle it however you will. I'm just going to go back to work and do the best I can.

Q Do you think you have to refer to it in some way in the speech on Tuesday?

THE PRESIDENT: I've given no thought to that, no.

Q Will this cloud your ability to get anything done with this gress as you head into the new session?

1/21/98 USNWSW (No Page)
(Publication page references are not available for this document.)

THE PRESIDENT: Well, that will be up to them. I don't think so. It's election year; they'll want to get some things done, too. And we've got a lot to do. I'm going to give them the first balanced budget three years ahead of time, and a great child care initiative, and an important Medicare initiative. We've got a Medicare commission meeting. We're going to be able to actually see this budget balanced and start to run a little surplus. We've got a lot of things to do around the world, so I think this is quite important.

Q Okay. Let me just ask you one more question about this. You said in a statement today that you had no improper relationship with this intern. What exactly was the nature of your relationship with her?

THE PRESIDENT: Well, let me say, the relationship was not improper, and I think that's important enough to say. But because the investigation is going on and because I don't know what is out -- what's going to be asked of me, I think I need to cooperate, answer the questions, but I think it's important for me to make it clear what is not. And then, at the appropriate time, I'll try to answer what is. But let me answer -- it is not an improper relationship and I know what the word means. So let's just --

Q Was it in any way sexual?

THE PRESIDENT: The relationship was not sexual. And I know what you mean, and the answer is no.

---- INDEX REFERENCES ----

KEY WORDS: NATIONAL

NEWS SUBJECT: Politics (PLT)

NEWS CATEGORY: CLINTON; ROLL; CALL

GOVERNMENT: Federal Government (FDL)

Word Count: 528
1/21/98 USNWSW (No Page)
END OF DOCUMENT

Tab 26

1870

REMARKS BY PRESIDENT CLINTON AT PHOTO OPPORTUNITY WITH PALESTINIAN AUTHORITY CHAIRMAN YASSER ARAFAT
THE WHITE HOUSE
10:22 A.M. EST THURSDAY, **JANUARY 22**, 1998

PRESIDENT CLINTON Let me say before we begin that I am very pleased to welcome Chairman Arafat back to the United States as our partner in the peace process. As I did with Prime Minister Netanyahu, I want to emphasize what a critical time this is in the process and the importance of both parties' meeting their obligations.

I also would like to take just this second to underlie (sic) the principles of the peace process; mutual obligations and the concept of land for peace so that Israelis can live in security, recognized by all their neighbors, and the Palestinians can realize their aspirations to live as a free people. If we can focus on these principles, I am convinced we can make some progress.

I am going to give Chairman Arafat a little report on my meeting with Mr. Netanyahu, and then we're going to go to work.

Q Mr. President, when do you think the Israelis will finally meet their U.N. obligations, their treaty obligations, to give back conquered land?

PRESIDENT CLINTON: Well, we're going to discuss that. We're working on it. You know, we believe, you know, the Oslo process sets out a schedule for redeployment, and that's obviously one of the major issues to be discussed.

Q But they're not going to meet it, are they?

PRESIDENT CLINTON: Well, let -- give us chance. We're working on it.

Q (In Arabic.)

CHAIRMAN ARAFAT: (In Arabic.)

Q Mr. President, what's the next step now? And is there a time frame where you want things to (word inaudible)?

PRESIDENT CLINTON: Well, we're going to have a -- after this meeting, then what we'll do is to see whether we have moved the

parties closer together.
And if we have, then we'll try to figure out how to close the loop and get an understanding on what the next steps are. And if we can do that, we want to do it, obviously, fairly quickly. We don't want to just keep dragging this out. I think we -- we have a sense of urgency here.

(Cross talk.)

Q (Through interpreter.) What would you be asking President Clinton for?

CHAIRMAN ARAFAT: (In Arabic.)

PRESIDENT CLINTON: One more.

Q Mr. Arafat, do you believe progress was made with Prime Minister Netanyahu? Do you believe progress has been made this week? And would you agree to a (few-stage ?) withdrawal?

CHAIRMAN ARAFAT: (Through interpreter.) As long as there is pressure and efforts by President Clinton, I'm fully confident that the peace process will be protected and will be succeeded.

And we should not forget that the president also has sent Madeleine Albright, secretary of state, and Mr. Ross to the region many times to push the peace process forward.

Q So you believe Mr. Netanyahu will stand by his commitment?

CHAIRMAN ARAFAT: We hope so -- he would do so.

PRESIDENT CLINTON: Thank you.

STAFF: Thank you, Mr. President.

(Cross talk.)

Q Mr. President -- (inaudible) -- important issues in the Middle East --

PRESIDENT CLINTON: Go ahead.

Q -- but could you clarify for us, sir, exactly what your

relationship was with Ms. Lewinsky and whether the two of you talked by phone, including any messages she may have left?

PRESIDENT CLINTON: Let me say, first of all -- I want to reiterate what I said yesterday -- the allegations are false, and I would never ask anybody to do anything other than tell the truth. Let's get to the big issues there -- about the nature of the relationship and whether I suggested anybody not tell the truth. That is false.

Now there are a lot of other questions that are, I think, very legitimate. You have a right to ask them. You -- that -- you and the American people have a right to get answers. We are working very hard to comply, get all the requests for information up here. And we will give you as many answers as we can, as soon as we can, at the appropriate time, consistent with our obligation to also cooperate with the investigations. And that's not a dodge; that's really what I've -- what I've -- I've talked with our people. I want to do that. I'd like for you have more rather than less, sooner rather than later. So we will work through it as quickly as we can and get all those questions out there to you.

(Cross talk.)

Q Mr. President, would you comment --

PRESIDENT CLINTON: Thank you.

Q Mr. President, would you comment --

STAFF: Thank you.

PRESIDENT CLINTON: Thank you

Q Did the pope in Cuba, Mr. President --

PRESIDENT CLINTON: Thank you.

STAFF: Thank you.

PRESIDENT CLINTON: What about the pope in Cuba?

Q What are your impressions of the remarkable scenes of the pope in Cuba? And what about his call for an end to the embargo?

PRESIDENT CLINTON: Well, first of all, I am glad he went to Cuba. I think it's a wonderful thing, and I am glad Mr. Castro invited him to come. I am glad the Cuban government let the Christian people in Cuba celebrate Christmas last Christmas, acknowledge it in the explicit and open way.

And I hope that this trip will lead to some reassessment on the part of the Cuban government, that would enable us to move closer together in many ways, and maybe it will.

Q (Inaudible) -- Netanyahu --

(Cross talk.)

STAFF (?): (Do you think we ?) -- can get out of here, ladies and gentlemen. Thank you very much.

Q (Inaudible) -- do you want to talk about your comment --

PRESIDENT CLINTON: (Inaudible.)

STAFF (?): Thank you, again.

STAFF: Thank you. Thank you.

(Cross talk.)

PRESIDENT CLINTON: Thank you all. We've got to go to work. Let us hit it.

Tab 27

1876

By Michael Isikoff

Last weekend, there were two extraordinary dramas playing out in Washington. On Saturday, at the offices of his attorney Robert Bennett, President Clinton was being questioned, under oath, by Paula Jones's lawyers as a media army waited outside. Clinton was asked if he had ever had a sexual encounter with Jones. As he has before, Clinton denied it. But unknown to the reporters in the street, the president was also asked about a woman named Monica Lewinsky. Eager to prove a pattern of sexual harassment, Jones's lawyers were searching for other women who might have been the subject of Clinton's advances. Under oath, the president denied ever having had a sexual relationship with Lewinsky.

Across town, in a small apartment at the Watergate, Lewinsky was in a bind. She had been informed the day before that Whitewater special prosecutor Kenneth Starr was investigating her for perjury and obstruction of justice in the Paula Jones case. Lewinsky had signed an affidavit swearing that she had never had a sexual relationship with the president. But, Starr's deputies had informed her, they had tapes of her suggesting that her denial was a lie--and that they suspected she had been advised to lie by the president and by the president's friend and adviser, Washington superlawyer Vernon Jordan. Now Starr's people offered her a tough choice: cooperate with prosecutors and turn against the president, or face the possibility of criminal charges herself.NEWSWEEK was aware of Lewinsky's situation. For nearly a year, NEWSWEEK's Michael Isikoff had been aware of allegations that Clinton was having a sexual relationship with Lewinsky. That Wednesday, January 14, Isikoff learned that Starr was investigating obstruction of justice and perjury in the Paula Jones case, and that Lewinsky was a target of the investigation. For the next three days, Isikoff continued to report the story. On Saturday at 12:30 a.m., Isikoff and NEWSWEEK editors heard a tape of conversations between Lewinsky and a woman named Linda Tripp. NEWSWEEK could not independently verify the authenticity of the recording, and some of the statements on the tape raise questions about Lewinsky's credibility.

But the tape seems to confirm that Lewinsky told at least one friend on repeated occasions that she was having an affair with the president, and that she had discussed with Clinton and Jordan the fact that she had been subpoenaed in the Paula Jones case. On the tape, Lewinsky sounded distraught but not unbalanced. She talks spontaneously about what she suggests is a sexual relationship with the president, expresses her anguish about being brought into the Paula Jones case, and plaintively declares her wish that the president would "settle" the case. Dejectedly, she says that Clinton is "in denial. He'll never settle." Lewinsky affirms to Tripp that Lewinsky will deny any sexual relationship when she is deposed by Jones's lawyers. "Look," she says, "I will deny it so he will not get screwed in the case, but I'm going to get screwed personally," Lewinsky says. When Tripp asks why, Lewinsky replies, "because it will be obvious... it will be obvious to him... that I told you." However, there was no clear evidence on the tape that would confirm or deny Tripp's allegation that Clinton or Vernon Jordan had coached Lewinsky to lie.

Because the magazine did not have enough time for sufficient independent porting on Lewinsky, her credibility, and her alleged role in the drama--and in hopes of learning more about the truth by not interfering with Starr's probe at a critical juncture --NEWSWEEK decided to hold off publishing the story last week. Above all, because Lewinsky's name had not surfaced, NEWSWEEK's editors felt there was insufficient hard evidence to drag her into the media maelstrom.

On Tuesday, Jan. 20, the story began to leak out to a number of news organizations. On Wednesday, Jan. 21, NEWSWEEK obtained what may be an important new piece of evidence. It is a written document allegedly given to Tripp by Lewinsky. The document coaches Tripp on "points to make in affidavit" in order to contradict the account of another former White House staffer, Kathleen Willey, who recently testified in her own deposition to unsolicited sexual advances made by the president in 1993. It was Tripp who partly confirmed Willey's claims that she had had a sexual encounter with Clinton--as reported in a NEWSWEEK story in August. In these talking points, Tripp is urged to undercut Willey's credibility, be a "team player" and submit an affidavit for review to "Bennett's people"--Clinton's lawyers. It's not clear who prepared these talking points, but Starr believes that Lewinsky did not write them herself. He is investigating whether the instructions came from Jordan or other friends of the president. President Clinton has denied all allegations of a sexual relationship with Lewinsky or a cover-up; Jordan refused to comment on Wednesday and his lawyer did not return repeated phone calls.

NEWSWEEK will have full coverage of this entire story in its next issue, on newsstands Monday, January 26. But because NEWSWEEK and others have been able to confirm further details of the investigation--and because the magazine has developed exclusive reporting on the nature of the evidence--the editors of NEWSWEEK have decided to publish this chronology of events on NEWSWEEK Interactive on AOL :

Monday morning, January 12. Linda Tripp, met with her lawyers in Washington. She had been subpoenaed in the Jones case and needed to prepare her testimony. She had a disagreement with her lawyers, whom she feared were too close to the White House. Angrily, she left her lawyers' office and called the office of Whitewater independent counsel Kenneth Starr. Within a few hours, there were federal prosecutors and an FBI agent sitting in Tripp's living room in Columbia, Md. They heard Tripp tell an extraordinary story--and much of the drama that follows is based on Tripp's version of events.

She told the FBI agents and Starr's deputies that she had been a friend of Monica Lewinsky, 24. Lewinsky and Tripp worked together in the public affairs office at the Pentagon. Tripp described Lewinsky's background: Lewinsky had gone to work at the White House as an intern in the summer of 1995 shortly after graduating from Lewis and Clark College in Oregon. In December 1995, Lewinsky had been given full-time job as a staffer in the legislative affairs office in the White House. The previous month, Lewinsky allegedly told Tripp, e had begun having a sexual relationship with President Clinton. Lewinsky s 21 at the time. As Lewinsky told the story to Tripp, Lewinsky had been ..tracted to the president. At a White House party in mid-November 1995, Lewinsky wore a revealing dress and made eye contact with Clinton as he worked the crowd. The president and the young staffer had begun a consensual affair shortly thereafter. The president and Lewinsky allegedly had a number of sexual encounters, most of them during late-afternoon or weekend visits (and one late at night in a small private study off the Oval Office). Lewinsky told Tripp that she was flattered and excited by the attention from the president. She told Tripp that the president would sometimes ignore her frantic phone calls, but at other times he would call her in the middle of the night. Tripp told Starr's staff that she had personally heard messages from Clinton on Lewinsky's answering machine.

Tripp also told Starr's deputies that she had been angered and offended by what she considered the president's "callous" behavior toward Lewinsky. Tripp, a longtime federal employee who had begun work at the White House in the Bush administration, had had a number of run-ins with the Clinton White House. In 1993, Tripp was an executive assistant to Bernard Nussbaum, then the White House counsel. Early in the Whitewater probe, she had testified before a federal grand jury and the Senate Whitewater investigating committee about the so-called Travelgate affair, the firing of staffers in the White House travel office by the Clinton administration in 1993. She told Starr's assistants that she had been urged by her lawyers--whom the White House arranged to represent r--not to volunteer information she had about Hillary Clinton's role in avelgate. Tripp also talked to Starr's deputies about Kathleen Willey. In fall of 1993, Tripp said, she had seen Willey, a White House aide, shortly after Willey emerged from the Oval Office with her make-up smeared and her clothing askew. Willey told Tripp that she had just had a sexual encounter with the president. In late July, Tripp had told this story to NEWSWEEK, which published it in an issue the first week of August. At the time, Bennett, Clinton's lawyer, publicly questioned Tripp's credibility. Tripp became concerned that she would be put in a compromised position if she was later subpoenaed by Jones's lawyers: either perjure herself, or tell the truth and be attacked by the White House--possibly at the cost of her job at the Pentagon. It was then, Tripp said, that she began to secretly record her phone conversations with Monica. Tripp's lawyer, Jim Moody, denied that his client has a personal vendetta against the president. "She is not an enemy of this administration. She is a proponent of the truth."

As she anticipated, Tripp had been subpoenaed in mid-December by Jones's lawyers, who were trying to locate any and all alleged paramours of the president to bolster their sexual harassment case against Clinton. Realizing that she would have to testify under oath, Tripp told Lewinsky that she was going to tell the truth--that Lewinsky had told her that she was having an affair with the president. According to Tripp, Lewinsky responded that she intended to lie. She told Tripp that Clinton had told her not to worry about the Jones case because Jones's lawyers would never find out about the relationship. According to Tripp, Lewinsky said that Clinton had advised her

deny the affair. Tripp also reported that Lewinsky had told here that she
ḍ met with Vernon Jordan, Clinton's old friend and personal adviser.

Lewinsky first went to see Jordan at the instruction of Betty Currie, Clinton's personal secretary, last November. Jordan asked her to take her frustration and anger at Clinton and vent it at him. Lewinsky told Jordan she was worried about a subpoena from Jones's lawyers. Jordan offered to set Lewinsky up with an attorney, Frank Carter. (Carter declined comment.) According to Tripp, Lewinsky assured Jordan she would stick with "the cover story." Lewinsky said, "This is what I signed up for when I began the relationship."

Tripp told Starr that Lewinsky met again with Jordan at a later date in the back of his limousine. Jordan advised Lewinsky to remain silent. "They can't prove anything," Jordan allegedly told her. "If they thought they could, your answer is it didn't happen, it wasn't me." He told her that witnesses are never indicted for perjury in civil cases. He also promised to help Lewinsky get a job in the private sector. Earlier this month, Lewinsky responded to a subpoena in the Jones case by signing a sealed affidavit swearing that she had no relevant information to offer. In the affidavit, Lewinsky swore that she never had had a sexual relationship with Clinton.

At that first meeting on Monday, January 12, Starr's deputies listened to Tripp's story with great interest. After four years and at least $30 million, the investigation by the independent prosecutor's office is still moving slowly. Starr's deputies believe that they are being stonewalled by the White use at every turn. Here was an opportunity to get inside the president's otective circle. Jordan was of particular interest to Starr. Jordan is eady under investigation by Starr in another matter, involving former Deputy Attorney General Webster Hubbell. Jordan is one of several friends of Clinton who helped get Hubbell lucrative consulting fees when Hubbell was under investigation by the Whitewater special prosecutor in 1994. Starr is investigating whether Jordan and others were funnelling hush money to Hubbell.

Starr's interest was also piqued by Tripp's tapes of her conversations with Lewinsky, which Tripp turned over to Starr in response to a subpoena. There are 17 of these audio tapes, consisting of about 20 hours of surreptitiously-taped phone conversations. Most of the tapes were made from Tripp's home in Maryland, a state which generally prohibits taping unless all parties to the conversation consent. (Tripp argues that the tapes were justified because she was trying to protect herself against allegations of perjury, according to her lawyer.) NEWSWEEK has heard several of these conversations. On the 90-minute tape, Lewinsky can be heard weeping and clearly intimating that she had a sexual relationship with the president. She says that she intends to lie about it if questioned by Paula Jones's lawyers. She never directly names the president, referring instead to "the big he" and "the creep," but it is obvious from the tape that she is referring to Clinton. She ponders telling Clinton that she has revealed the affair to others, including Tripp. She hopes that, somehow, Clinton can be persuaded to settle with Jones. Maybe, Lewinsky wonders, she should threaten to tell all--tell Clinton that she intends to tell the truth if she is questioned by Jones's

.yers. "Look," Lewinsky says to Tripp, "Maybe we should just tell the creep. /be we should just say, don't ever talk to me again, I f----d you over [by telling others about the affair], now you have this information, do whatever you want with it." Linda says, "Well, if you want to do that, that's what I would do. But I don't know if you're comfortable with that. I think he [the president] should know." But Monica, sounding despairing, responds, "He won't settle [the Paula Jones case]. He's in denial." At another point in the tape, she says she simply cannot tell Clinton that she has revealed the affair to several others. "If I do that," she moans, "I'm just going to f---ing kill myself."

On the tape, Lewinsky can also be heard saying, "I have lied my entire life." In the context of the conversation, she is saying that it wasn't hard for her to conceal her sexual relationship with Clinton. But the statement raises the possibility that the affair itself was a lie, an exaggeration of a flirtatious moment, perhaps, that grew into a big lie. Still, Lewinsky sounds truly worried that her alleged relationship with Clinton will be exposed. She begs Tripp to lie about it. She speaks of exchanging gifts and letters with the president and worries that Jones's lawyers will find them and use them as incriminating evidence. At one point she says, "I was thinking about the fact that I sent a note to Nancy [Hernreich, as assistant to the president], a note to Betty [Currie, the president's personal secretary], and a note to creep to thank them all for when my family came for the radio address. The note I sent to him, 'Dear Schmucko, thank you for being, as my little nephew said, it was eat to meet the principal of the United States.'" Later she says that inton gave her a dress, and she makes a vague reference to an official otograph that Clinton sent her, apparently with some kind of personal inscription. She suggests to Tripp that, in response to the subpoena from Jones's lawyers, which asks for any letters, photographs, gifts, etc. that she received from Clinton, that she turn over a different photograph that the president gave her, one without the inscription.

NEWSWEEK has obtained receipts from a Washington messenger service showing that Lewinsky sent packages addressed to the White House on nine separate occasions between October 7, 1997, and December 8, 1997. The contact number on the packages is 456-2990, the phone number of Clinton's personal secretary, Betty Currie. According to Tripp, Lewinsky told her that the packages were letters and in one case a sexually-provocative audio tape for President Clinton. Asked about the deliveries last week by NEWSWEEK, Currie said she didn't recall them, but that she would look into the matter and get back to a reporter. Contacted again on Wednesday, Jan. 21, Currie said, "I have no knowledge whatsoever," and hung up the phone.

Another piece of key evidence would be secret service logs that would show whether Lewinsky came and went from the White House at odd hours. Jones's lawyers have subpoenaed secret service records, but the Justice Department has moved to quash that subpoena, citing in part executive privilege. Sources say that records show a "pattern of visits" by Lewinsky to the White House "in the late afternoons and evenings," with Currie listed as the contact.

Other administration aides wondered about Lewinsky, who was moved to the ıtagon in 1996. Lewinsky told Willie Blackwell, former deputy assistant .cretary of defense, that she lost her job at the office of White House legislative affairs when Evelyn Lieberman, then deputy White House chief of staff, twice spotted her hanging around the West Wing and questioned why she was there. A spokesman for Lieberman said that Lieberman was displeased with Lewinsky's performance in part because she was spending a lot of time in the Rose Garden and at White House events rather than doing her job. It was the run-in with Lieberman, Lewinsky told Tripp, that prompted White House personnel to arrange a job for Lewinsky with Pentagon spokesman Ken Bacon. Lewinsky told Tripp that the president had assured her that he would "get her back" after the election, but it never happened.

On the tape recorded conversations that NEWSWEEK listened to--a conversations that happened shortly before Christmas--there is at least two references to Jordan's first name, Vernon. It appears that Lewinsky did meet with Jordan, or at least claims to have met with him. The references to Jordan are cryptic, however, and neither support nor contradict the allegation that Jordan was encouraging Lewinsky to lie. She talks about acting "based on what Vernon said," but it's not clear what Jordan told her to say. At another point in the tape, in an apparent reference to the multiple subpoenas from Jones's lawyers, Tripp says, "Maybe Vernon was right, it's a huge fishing net because of the rumor." On Wednesday, Jan. 21, William Hundley, Jordan's lawyer, did not return repeated phone calls.

Tuesday, January 13. As she recounted her story to Starr's team on Monday, pp said that she was meeting with Lewinsky for drinks at the Ritz Carlton ..r at Pentagon City the next day. Starr's deputies set up a sting operation. On Tuesday, the FBI agents working for Starr wired Tripp with a secret listening device. When Tripp met with Lewinsky around noon, there was a team of FBI agents and prosecutors listening as a hidden tape recorded the conversation. According to knowledgable sources, Lewinsky again discussed conversations with Jordan about keeping quiet in the Jones case. She also talked about Jordan's efforts to get her a job in New York. (Lewinsky quit her Pentagon job on December 26; MacAndrews & Forbes, a New York firm that owns Revlon, confirmed that they offered Lewinsky a public relations job this month after she was referred to the company by Jordan, a member of Revlon's board of directors.) The incriminating tape gave Starr's deputies hope that they could "flip" Lewinsky and make a her a witness for the prosecution. They hoped to "sting" Jordan or Currie by getting Lewinsky to place phone calls to them that Starr's staff would monitor.

Wednesday, January 14. Lewinsky picks up Tripp at the Pentagon and offers to drive her home. Lewinsky gives Tripp "talking points" about how she should respond to questions from Jones's lawyers in the Willey matter. NEWSWEEK has obtained the document. "Points to make in affidavit," it reads. Tripp is to modify comments she had made to NEWSWEEK back in July--that she had seen Willey coming out of the Oval Office with her make-up smeared. Tripp is now to tell Jones's lawyers that "you do not believe that what she claimed happened

..lly happened. You now find it completely plausible that she herself smeared : lipstick, untucked her blouse, etc." The document also seems to reflect concerns that Tripp has already told others about Lewinsky's claims of a sexual relationship with the president. In case Tripp is questioned about the rumors about Lewinsky by Jones's lawyers, the talking points suggest that she say Lewinsky "turned out to be this huge liar" who "left the White House because she was stalking the P or something like that."

At about this time, NEWSWEEK learned that Starr was investigating Lewinsky, Jordan, and Clinton. NEWSWEEK told Starr's deputies that the magazine was planning to run with the story in the issue that appeared that Monday. NEWSWEEK needed to get a response from the people involved. Starr's deputies asked NEWSWEEK to hold off. The investigation was at a delicate stage. Starr was hoping to confront Lewinsky and persuade her to cooperate as a witness for the prosecution. Starr's deputies did not want to tip off Lewinsky or Jordan or the White House. NEWSWEEK agreed to wait until Friday afternoon, in part because the magazine was reluctant to interfere with an ongoing federal investigation and in part because the editors believed that NEWSWEEK would learn more about the truth behind the story by waiting.

Friday, January 16. Starr decided to formally expand his inquiry to investigate subornation of perjury and obstruction of justice in the Paula Jones case. In conversations the previous day, Starr's deputies had described Jordan as a principal target of the probe, and got Justice Department approval seek a formal expansion of his jurisdiction. The three-judge appeals court nel that supervises the independent counsel gave its authorization. That ..e day, Starr's deputies had Tripp lure Lewinsky to another meeting at the Ritz Carlton. As the two were sitting down for lunch, FBI agents for Starr moved in and asked Lewinsky to step upstairs for a talk.

Friday-Saturday, January 16-17. Starr's deputies tried to "flip" Lewinsky. Obviously, she was in a fix. If she admitted to the affair, she would be contradicting her own sworn affidavit. But if she denied it, she would be vulnerable to criminal prosecution. Lewinsky called her mother in Los Angeles. At the urging of Starr's staff, NEWSWEEK decided to wait one more day before contacting Lewinsky and Jordan for comment.

Saturday, January 17. A Los Angeles lawyer, William Ginsburg, flew to Washington to represent Lewinsky. Still uncertain about whether Lewinsky was telling the truth about a sexual relationship with Clinton and a White House cover-up, and running out of time to reach the major players in the story--or assess Lewinsky's credibility or role--NEWSWEEK, whose deadline is Saturday night, decided to hold off publication.

Monday, January 19. Negotiations between Starr's staff and her attorneys broke down. On Monday morning, Lewinsky's name surfaced in the Drudge Report, a widely read but somewhat unreliable gossip column on the Internet. Drudge had picked up rumors that NEWSWEEK was debating whether to run a piece about insky, and reported that after a "screaming fight" in the editors' offices Saturday night, the story had been spiked. (There had been no screaming; the story was not spiked but put on hold while NEWSWEEK's reporters continued to gather information.) According to Starr's deputies, the fear that Lewinsky's name would become widely known was enough to torpedo the negotiations between Starr and her Lewinsky's lawyers. As of now, Lewinsky is not cooperating. According to knowledgeable sources, Starr is now considering whether to indict her for perjury. Lewinsky is scheduled to be deposed by Jones's lawyers on Friday. Sources tell NEWSWEEK that she will take the Fifth Amendment.

Newsweek Interactive Special Report: Nation/Diary of a Scandal

Tab 28

UNITED STATES DEPARTMENT OF JUSTICE
FEDERAL BUREAU OF INVESTIGATION
Receipt for Property Received/Returned/Released/Seized

Page [illegible] of 5

On (date) [illegible]

Time: 5:00 pm

Item(s) listed below were:
- ☐ Received From
- ☐ Returned To
- ☐ Released To
- ☑ Seized

(Name) SEARCH

(Street Address) [illegible] NEW Hampshire Ave [illegible]

(City) Wash DC

Description of Item(s):

Room A

★ Item #1 - checking records
#2 - Book Manuscript / Newspaper clippings
#3 - computer diskette (1)

Room D

→ Item #1 - Answering Machine w/tape
#2 - napkins w/presidential seal
#3 - clear glass w/presidential seal
#4 - Glass bottle of Kentucky [illegible] w/seal
#5 - Glass bottle of Kentucky [illegible] w/seal
#6 - Glass bottle of Kentucky [illegible] w/seal
#7 - clear glass w/presidential seal
#8 - 1 pack of cigarettes and matches
#9 - 3 photos; envelope label; document from Carter & Vance

Room E

Item #1 - AMEX statement
#2 - card file
#3 - 1997 pocket calendar
#4 - computer diskette
#5 - Seven (7) Olympus microtapes

Room N

Item #1 - computer diskette
#2 - Rolodex card case w/ File
#3 - Book "Presidential Sex"

Received by: SA [redacted] (Signature) Received from [redacted] (Signature)

FD-597 (Rev. 3-29-93)

UNITED STATES DEPARTMENT OF JUSTICE
FEDERAL BUREAU OF INVESTIGATION
Receipt for Property Received/Returned/Released/Seized

Page 4 of 5

On (date) 22 JAN 98

Time: 5:00pm

Item(s) listed below were:
- ☐ Received From
- ☐ Returned To
- ☐ Released To
- ☐ Seized

(Name) [illegible]

(Street Address) 700 New Hampshire Ave NW Apt 114

(City) Washington DC

Description of Item(s):

Room O- Additional Item
#4 - Blue flower dress
Room C
Item #1 - shirt (inside flowered)
Room L
Item #1 - yellow computer disk
Room A
Item #1 - coat and pants
Room J
Item #1 - black dress
#2 - Blue dress
#3 - Blue blouse

Received by: SA [redacted] (Signature) Received from [redacted] (Signature)

FD-597 (Rev. 3-29-93)

UNITED STATES DEPARTMENT OF JUSTICE
FEDERAL BUREAU OF INVESTIGATION
Receipt for Property Received/Returned/Released/Seized

Page 3 of 5

On (date) 22 Jan 98

Time: 5:00 pm

Item(s) listed below were:
- ☐ Received From
- ☐ Returned To
- ☐ Released To
- ☐ Seized

(Name) [illegible]

(Street Address) 700 New Hampshire Ave NW Apt 114

(City) Wash, DC

Description of Item(s):

Room M - cont.

#9 - Golf [illegible]; phone card; black leg tag; white House life saver

#10 - cassette Tape

#11 - Rolodex

#12 - phone notes and addresses

#13 - Affidavit draft

#14 - CD Label; business card; hand written note; letter

#15 - letters; cellular one bill with hand written notes; message pad sheet

#16 - Easy microwave cooker (2)

#17 - Tape recorder and tape

#18 - letter dated 10/29/96

#19 - Wage Statement

#20 - folder marked Clinton

#21 - financial and work records

#22 - framed photographs

Room K

Item # 1 - Envelope w/hand written note

#2 - Box of computer diskettes; 2 loose diskettes

Received by: SA [redacted] (Signature) Received from [redacted] (Signature)

FD-597 (Rev. 8-28-98)

UNITED STATES DEPARTMENT OF JUSTICE
FEDERAL BUREAU OF INVESTIGATION
Receipt for Property Received/Returned/Released/Seized

Page 2 of 5

On (date) 22 JAN 98

Time: 5:00 pm

Item(s) listed below were:
☐ Received From
☐ Returned To
☐ Released To
☑ Seized

(Name) Search

(Street Address) 700 New Hampshire Ave NW Apt 114

(City) Wash DC

Description of Item(s):

ROOM N - cont

#4 - Computer Diskette
#5 - [illegible] card/world travel journal
#6 - Miscellaneous Documents (6)
#7 - Computer Diskettes (4)
#8 - Computer Diskettes (4)

ROOM O

Item #1 - one pair of blue jeans
#2 - letter
#3 - letter; monthly planner OCT, NOV 1997; video tape; lexis/nexis printout
#4 - [illegible] shirt

ROOM M

Item #1 - plastic box containing photographs and White House memorabilia
#2 - Black or dark pantsuit
#3 - Answering Machine/phone card
#4 - poster photograph
#5 - photographs
#6 - computer diskettes; White House material
#7 - FEDEX receipts (2); photos of Monica L w/ WJC
#8 - Note [illegible]

Received by: SA [redacted] (Signature) Received from [redacted] (Signature)

FD-597 (Rev. [illegible])

UNITED STATES DEPARTMENT OF JUSTICE
FEDERAL BUREAU OF INVESTIGATION
Receipt for Property Received/Returned/Released/Seized

Computer materials

Page 1 of 5

On (date) 1/22/98

Time: 1210pm

Item(s) listed below were:
- ☐ Received From
- ☐ Returned To
- ☐ Released To
- ☐ Seized

(Name) ~~Marsha Lewinsky~~ Marcia Lewis pfz

(Street Address) Watergate South 700 New Hampshire Ave NW Apt 114

(City) Washington, D.C.

Description of Item(s):

1- Apple Personal Laser Writer 300 printer Sr 35265
1- Apple Keyboard II Sr# 3284AG03N
1- Apple Desktop Mouse Sr# LT3298ART18
1- Practical Peripherals Modem Sr# A1055250 13204 0445
1- Apple Color Monitor Sr# CY4411AJ152
1- Apple Macintosh LC3 CPU Sr# CG3346WLVA2
4- Cables
13- 3½ inch floppy diskettes

No Notations on this Page

[illegible]

Received by: SA [redacted] (Signature)   Received from [redacted] (Signature)

1892

Tab 29

--ANSCRIPTS - 1/22/98 ABCNWSSPR
2/98 ABC News - Special Rep. (Pg. Unavail. Online)
.98 WL 8056093
ABC News - Special Report

Thursday, January 22, 1998

NEWS

ABC NEWS SPECIAL REPORT WHITE HOUSE BRIEFING
SAM DONALDSON / JACKIE JUDD, PETER JENNINGS

PETER JENNINGS: You know these allegations that President Clinton had an affair with at young White House intern, which also involve his close friend Vernon Jordan, and then is accused of having asked her to lie about it have very much consumed the Washington political establishment, so the President is again in potentially serious trouble.

We've interrupted regular programming because the President's spokesman, Mike McCurry, is about to hold his daily briefing for the

White House Press Corps, and the President, as you may also know, said yesterday and again today these stories involving Monica Lewinsky are not true. But for a variety of reasons, the matter will not rest.

:ut what Ken Starr's office believes is this -- that the Lewinsky .vestigation is part of the broader investigation. That is looking into the question of whether this White House has obstructed justice by trying to silence witnesses who would be harmful to the President and to the administration. Silence them through hush money, offering them promotions, etc. And so that's how Starr will justify him taking over this aspect.

PETER JENNINGS: OK, Jackie, thanks very much. There was some tumultuous reception for Mr. Starr this morning when he came out.

This is different, as many people have noted today, because the President and his friend Vernon Jordan have been accused of supporting perjury -- the penalty for that might be five years -- and for obstructing justice, as well. And Mr. Jordan, one of the most powerful men in Washington, very close friend to the President, been at the President's side in all sorts of difficulties, is going to issue a statement at 3:30 this afternoon, and we'll be here to tell you what that is.

And here, finally, is a glimpse of the President today in a meeting with the Palestinian chairman Yasser Arafat at the White House, being asked again in person whether or not he's going to shed any light today on these allegations that he had an affair with this young woman and these allegations that he had an affair with this young woman and ..tempted to cover it up.

Pres. BILL CLINTON: The allegations are false, and I would never ask anybody to do anything other than tell the truth. Let's get to the big issues there about the nature of the relationship and whether I suggested anybody not tell the truth. That is false. Now, there are a lot of other questions that are, I think, very legitimate. You have a right to ask them, you and the American people have a right to get answers. We are working very hard to comply and get all the requests for information up here, and we will give you as many answers as we can as soon as we can at the appropriate time, consistent with our obligation to also cooperate with the investigations. And that's not a dodge. That's really what I -- I've talked with our people. I want to do that. I'd like for you to have more rather than less, sooner rather than later. So we'll work through it as quickly as we can and get all those questions out there to you.

PETER JENNINGS: Very difficult time for the President, very difficult time for the country. And we're going to continue our coverage of this story throughout the day on abcnews.com. We'll be here when Mr. Jordan makes his statement at 3:30. We'll have a complete roundup on World News Tonight.

TRANSCRIPTS - 1/22/98 ABCNWSSPR
'm Peter Jennings in New York. Thank you for joining us.

ANNOUNCER: For continuing coverage of this story, stay with ABC News and abcnews.com on the Web and AOL. This has been a Special Report from ABC News.

---- INDEX REFERENCES ----

NEWS CATEGORY: PACKAGE

Word Count: 5131
1/22/98 ABCNWSSPR (No Page)
END OF DOCUMENT

ut as Mike McCurry said at the end of that briefing, it is extremely ficult to get the nation's business done when so much of the nation is focused currently on this.

I'm Peter Jennings in New York. Thank you for joining us.

ANNOUNCER: For continuing coverage of this story, stay with ABC News and abcnews.com on the Web and AOL. This has been a Special Report from ABC News.

---- INDEX REFERENCES ----

NEWS CATEGORY: PACKAGE

Tab 30

1902

LEVEL 1 - 2 OF 9 STORIES

Roll Call

January 22, 1998

LENGTH: 443 words

HEADLINE: Partial Transcript Of ClintonInterview

BODY:

ROLL CALL: A few questions about the breaking news. Do you think that this Monica Lewinsky story is going to overshadow your State of the Union address?

President CLINTON: Well, I hope not. But you guys will have to make that decision. The press will make that decision.

ROLL CALL: Some Republicans have been talking about impeachment for months now. And even your former advisor, George Stephanopoulos, mentioned it this morning, that it could lead to that. What is your reaction to the suggestion that this may lead to impeachment?

CLINTON: Well, I don't believe it will. I'm going to cooperate with this investigation. And I made it very clear that the allegations are not true. I didn't ask anybody not to tell the truth. And I'll cooperate. So I think that there will be a lot of stirring and there will be a lot of speculation about how this all was done and what it means and what it portends, and you will all handle it however you will. I'm just going to go back to work and do the best I can.

ROLL CALL: Do you think you have to refer to it in some way in the speech on Tuesday?

CLINTON: I've given no thought to that, no.

ROLL CALL: Will this cloud your ability to get anything done with this Congress as you head into the new session?

CLINTON: Well, that will be up to them. I don't think so. It's election year; they'll want to get some things done, too. And we've got a lot to do. I'm going to give them the first balanced budget three years ahead of time, and a great child care initiative, and an important Medicare initiative. We've got a Medicare commission meeting. We're going to be able to actually see this budget balanced and start to run a little surplus. We've got a lot of things to do around the world, so I think this is quite important.

ROLL CALL: OK, let me just ask you one more question about this. You said in a statement today that you had no improper relationship with this intern. What exactly was the nature of your relationship with her?

CLINTON: Well, let me say, the relationship was not improper, and I think that's important enough to say. But because the investigation is going on and because I don't know what is out - what's going to be asked of me, I think I need to cooperate, answer the questions, but I think it's important for me to make it clear what is not. And then, at the appropriate time, I'll try to answer what it is. But let me answer - it is not an improper relationship and I know what the word means. So let's just...

ROLL CALL: Was it in any way sexual?

CLINTON: The relationship was not sexual. And I know what you mean, and the answer is no.

and Damon Chappie

LANGUAGE: ENGLISH

LOAD-DATE: January 22, 1998

Tab A

1906

Citation Search Result Rank 140 of 144 Data
1/22/98 STLTI A17 USNE
1/22/98 Seattle Times A17
1998 WL 3135298

The Seattle Times

Thursday, January 22, 1998

NEWS

CLINTON'S ANSWER TO QUESTION TODAY
AP

Comments by President **Clinton** today on allegations that he had an affair with former White House intern Monica Lewinsky. The question was asked during a photo session with PLO Chairman Yasser Arafat:

Question: "Could you clarify for us, sir, exactly what your relationship was with Ms. Lewinsky and whether the two of you talked by phone, including any messages she may have left?"

President **Clinton**: "Let me say, first of all, I want to reiterate what I said yesterday. The allegations are false, and I would never ask anybody to do anything other than tell the truth. Let's get to the big issues there - about the nature of the relationship and whether I suggested anybody not tell the truth. That is false.

"Now there are a lot of other questions that are, I think, very legitimate. You have a right to ask them. You and the American people have a right to get answers. We are working very hard to comply, get all the requests for information up here. And we will give you as many answers as we can, as soon as we can, at the appropriate time, consistent with our obligation to also cooperate with the investigations. And that's not a dodge; that's really what I've talked (about) with our people. I want to do that. I'd like for you to have **more rather** than **less, sooner rather** than **later.**"

---- INDEX REFERENCES ----

NEWS CATEGORY: TEXT OF STATEMENT

EDITION: FINAL

Word Count: 233
1/22/98 STLTI A17

1908

Tab 31

1910

FD-597 (Rev. 3-29-93)

UNITED STATES DEPARTMENT OF JUSTICE
FEDERAL BUREAU OF INVESTIGATION
Receipt for Property Received/Returned/Released/Seized

Page 1 of 1

On (date) 1/23/98

Time: 1:55 pm

Item(s) listed below were:
- [x] Received From
- [ ] Returned To
- [ ] Released To
- [ ] Seized

(Name) Aty. Karl N. Metzner (Janis, Schuelke, & Wechsler)

(Street Address) 1728 Mass Ave, NW

(City) Washington, D.C. 20036

Description of Item(s): Please see attached sheets.

Received by: SA [redacted] (Signature)

Received from ______________ (Signature)

LAW OFFICES
JANIS, SCHUELKE & WECHSLER
1728 MASSACHUSETTS AVENUE, N.W.
WASHINGTON, D.C. 20036

KARL N. METZNER

TELEPHONE
(202) 861-0600

TELECOPIER
(202) 223-7230

January 23, 1998

BY HAND DELIVERY

Kenneth W. Starr, Esq.
Office of the Independent Counsel
1001 Pennsylvania Avenue, N.W., Suite 490-N
Washington, D.C. 20004

Re: Subpoena Duces Tecum to Betty W. Currie, Grand Jury # 97-3

Dear Mr. Starr:

In response to the above-referenced subpoena duces tecum to Ms. Betty W. Currie, enclosed please find the following:

One copy of the State of the Union address dated January 23, 1996, in a brown envelope.

One autographed photograph of President Clinton, held between two cardboard panels.

One green dress with a "Black Dog" logo, size L.

One turquoise T-shirt with a "Black Dog" logo, size L.

One white T-shirt with a "Seal of the Black Dog of Martha's Vineyard" on the front, size L.

One blue baseball cap with a "Black Dog" logo.

One three-page facsimile message.

Two twenty-page newspaper inserts from the *Washington Post*, February 14, 1997.

One jewelry pin in "Casual Corner" box. Actually two pins in one box. [illegible]

One hatpin with a globe-like base in a black box with gold stars on it.

Kenneth W. Starr, Esq.
January 23, 1998
Page 2

One framed signed picture of President Clinton and Monica Lewinsky.

One bottle, in its box, of Tiffany Spa Moisturizing Hand Cream.

One bottle, in its box, of Tiffany Spa Refreshing Body Mist.

One sympathy card, with envelope.

One card with joke re snowman and carrot, with envelope.

One thank-you card dated September 17, 1997, with envelope.

Four pages of handwritten notes. (copies redacted by attorneys)

Sincerely,

Karl Metzner

Karl Metzner

Enclosures

1914

Tab 32

1916

24TH STORY of Level 1 printed in FULL format.

CBS News Transcripts

SHOW: SATURDAY MORNING (8:00 AM ET)

January 24, 1998, Saturday

TYPE: Newscast

LENGTH: 955 words

HEADLINE: FEDERAL PROSECUTORS SUBPOENA SWORN STATEMENTS THAT PRESIDENT CLINTON GAVE IN DEPOSITIONS IN THE PAULA JONES AFFAIR

ANCHORS: RUSS MITCHELL

REPORTERS: SCOTT PELLEY

BODY:

RUSS MITCHELL, co-host:

Washington awakens this morning suffering from something of an information hangover. The flurry of allegations and leaks and rumors was downright dizzying over the past three days. And it is not over yet. CBS News White House correspondent Scott Pelley joins us with the latest.

Good morning, Scott.

SCOTT PELLEY reporting:

Morning, Russ.

And there's more information this morning. CBS News has learned that federal prosecutors have now subpoenaed at least some of the sworn statements of the president, statements the president gave in depositions and in interrogatories in the Paula Jones affair. The subpoenas went out yesterday--late yesterday and demand all affidavits and depositions of William Jefferson Clinton.

You will recall that on Saturday, the president gave a sworn deposition here in Washington and CBS News is told that in that deposition he denied ever having a sexual relationship with Monica Lewinsky. Now that statement would appear to be at odds with Lewinsky's contention on secretly recorded audiotapes that she did indeed have an affair with the president.

Also, CBS News has learned that last week Lewinsky was offered complete immunity from prosecution if she was willing to cooperate with independent counsel Kenneth Starr in an undercover sting operation. But while Lewinsky was thinking about that offer, her name became known and the offer was withdrawn.

Last week, the FBI swept Lewinsky into a hotel room filled with agents and prosecutors. She was shown surveillance photos of herself meeting with former co-worker Linda Tripp. Tripp had recorded Lewinsky's admission that she had lied under oath about an affair with Mr. Clinton. Lewinsky's lawyer, Bill Ginsburg, says she was offered a deal.

Mr. WILLIAM GINSBURG (Lewinsky's Attorney): They wanted to suggest to her, and they did suggest to her, as I understand it, frankly, from them, that she be wired, to have conversations with other people, that she intervene on telephone conversations that might well be recorded. They wanted her cooperation.

PELLEY: You say 'conversations with other people.' You're talking about the president of the United States?

Mr. GINSBURG: I--I don't know that. But I would assume, based on everything that I've seen in the media, that the president of the United States, Vernon Jordan, and others would have been among their--their guest list.

PELLEY: In secretly recorded tapes, Lewinsky told her friend Tripp there had been a long affair and she had been encouraged to cover it up. But in a sworn affidavit, she insisted there was no sexual relationship.

When you say that your client stands by the affidavit, you are telling us that the affidavit is true. It is the truth?

Mr. GINSBURG: No, I am telling you--I am telling you that my client stands on the affidavit at this time.

PELLEY: At this time. If it's true, how could there be any question about whether she's going to stand by it today, tomorrow, the next day?

Mr. GINSBURG: I am not prepared to do anything except say, as a professional, that she is standing by her affidavit at this time.

PELLEY: Sources tell CBS News FBI agents had Lewinsky's consent to search her apartment in the Watergate Complex. The agents had a list of items they wanted and left with Lewinsky's computer, some of her clothes and the gifts. CBS News has also learned Lewinsky claims to have received from the president several items from the Black Dog gift shop in Martha's Vineyard plus a dress, gold broach and a book of poetry by Walt Whitman.

And now Lewinsky's parents have been drawn into this investigation. Prosecutors now consider them to be material witnesses because of things Lewinsky might have told them. On Tuesday, here in Washington, a federal grand jury will meet in the case and will begin taking testimony from the president's friend Vernon Jordan and the president's personal secretary. That is the very day that Mr. Clinton will be delivering the State of the Union address. Russ.

MITCHELL: Scott, yesterday there was talk that the president would make a statement, maybe even give a news conference to kind of diffuse these charges before his State of the Union address. Anything new on that?

PELLEY: Russ, we are being told at this moment that the president does not plan to address the charges in any significant way before the State of the Union address. I hesitate to predict the future on this because this is a very dynamic situation. There are a number of people here at the White House who have been urging that the presi--the president should go out on the press. But at the moment, the lawyers are prevailing and they are saying for the moment he should stay silent.

MITCHELL: Yesterday, four members of the president's Cabinet came out in a show of support. But from all accounts, it appears that there are a lot of long faces at the White House these days. How would you describe the mood there this morning?

PELLEY: Well, I'll--I'll tell you, I spoke to a high administration official yesterday who described the first two days of this as bleak. He said it was like a hurricane had gone through the White House and knocked everybody off their feet. He sa--he told me that the White House staff now is trying to get back on their feet, dust themselves off, and get back to work.

MITCHELL: Scott Pelley at the White House, thank you very much.

Scott will return in our next hour with more on this still-unfolding story. And we'll have more from the White House with Mark Knoller a bit later. Plus, we'll talk with reporter Carl Bernstein. We'll see how he compares thi--if--if he compares this at all--with Watergate.

LANGUAGE: English

LOAD-DATE: January 24, 1998, Saturday

Tab 33

1922

Citation Search Result Rank 46 of 450 Database ALLNEWS
5/98 FACENATION
1/25/98 Face Nation (Pg. Unavail. Online)
1998 WL 9105888
(Publication page references are not available for this document.)

Face The Nation

Sunday, January 25, 1998

Interview: Representative Henry Hyde discusses the allegations against President Clinton from a legal perspective

BOB SCHIEFFER, host:

For some perspective from the legal point of view, two people who know a lot about these things. Here in the studio, the chairman of the House Judiciary Committee, Henry Hyde, who would have the responsibility of calling impeachment hearings if it came to that, and in our Washington newsroom, former independent counsel Joe diGenova.

I begin with you, Mr. Chairman. As I understand it, the law is quite specific. If the independent counsel should come up with evidence that he considers evidence of an impeachable offense, he is compelled by law to refer that to you.

Representative HENRY HYDE (Republican, Illinois; Chairman, Judiciary Committee): That's correct. To Congress, actually, the statute says. If he comes up with substantial and credible evidence of a crime or of an impeachable offense or offenses, he is obliged to report promptly to Congress.

SCHIEFFER: And then Congress, I take it, has to vote on whether to begin an impeachment hearing.

Rep. HYDE: Well, not necessarily. If a bill of impeachment is filed, that would be a sign to the Judiciary Committee if precedent follo--is followed, and we would--we would begin taking action on that. But I want to emphasize, right now all we're dealing with are allegations and charges, not proof. And it's in the bosom of the independent counsel. He has the resources, the personnel, the deposition authority, access to the grand jury, immunity power. Let him do his job and then, when he does that, we will then do ours.

SCHIEFFER: Mr. Chairman, what is an impeachable offense?

Rep. HYDE: Well, it's deliberately vague in the Constitution: treason, bribery, high crimes and misdemeanors. A high crime is at o... end of the s--spectrum and a misdemeanor is certainly a crime of lesser import. So you have to look at--at precedent, but it has to be something that's very serious--and I can't stress this too much--it has to elicit bipartisan support. Because at the end of the day, the Senate has to vote on whether or not to remove the person from office by a two-thirds vote.

SCHIEFFER: Mm-hmm.

Rep. HYDE: ...so nothing much will happen until the Democrats decide something should happen.

SCHIEFFER: Let me just ask you quickly. If a president tried to encourage someone to commit perjury or if a president committed perjury, would that be considered, in your view, an impeachable offense?

Rep. HYDE: I d--really don't like to answer 'what if' questions.

SCHIEFFER: OK.

Rep. HYDE: But, certainly, it is serious and would be considered.

SCHIEFFER: I think everybody in Washington understands this to be a--a--a problem of some gravity, a very serious matter. If it came to impeachment hearings, do you think the Democrats in Congress would let it go that far?

Rep. HYDE: Again, that's speculating, but I think, as with President Nixon, nobody wants a--long, attenuated hearings that bring out sordid, lurid charges and accusations. So I think Democrats would appropriately make suggestions to the president. But, again, I--I really am crossing the line there. We don't have any proof now. We have allegations, and we should wait because the--the presumption of innocence belongs to the president.

SCHIEFFER: But what--what you seem to be saying is, there'd be such an overwhelming appealing in the Congress, you think that Democrats would just urge the president to leave rather than go into something like that?

Rep. HYDE: I can speculate that that might happen, although I hate to speculate.

SCHIEFFER: All right. Mr--Mr. Hyde, the president goes to the Capitol on Tuesday to give his State of the Union message. What do you think the reaction up there is going to be?

Rep. HYDE: I really don't know. I've thought about that. I've thought that the Democrats may have an exaggerated enthusiasm in an effort to be defensive and protective. On the other hand, it may be just civilized restraint. I think it's one of the interesting spectacles to see what the reaction's going to be.

SCHIEFFER: This one's going to be different though, isn't it?

Rep. HYDE: Oh, very much so.

SCHIEFFER: Mr. Chairman, thank you very much for joining us this morning.
Program Time: 10:30-11:00 AM
Nielson Rating 2558000
Reference: 980125

Word Count: 700
1/25/98 FACENATION (No Page)
END OF DOCUMENT

1926

Tab 34

1928

Citation Search Result Rank 1 of 1 Database ALLNEWS
5/98 NIGHTLINE
26/98 Nightline (Pg. Unavail. Online)
1998 WL 5372969
(Publication page references are not available for this document.)

Nightline

Monday, January 26, 1998

NEWS

CRISIS IN THE WHITE HOUSE
--
WILL THE PRESIDENT'S WORD BE ENOUGH?
JOHN DONVAN / CHRIS BURY / DAVE MARASH, TED KOPPEL

ANNOUNCER: January 26, 1997.

TED KOPPEL, ABC News: (voice-over) Monica Lewinsky meets with her lawyers. President Clinton prepares for tomorrow's State of the Union address but takes a few seconds out to respond forcefully to his critics.

res. WILLIAM J. CLINTON: I want to say one thing to the American people. I want you to listen to me. I'm going to say this again. I did not have sexual relations with that woman, Ms. Lewinsky. I never told anybody to lie, not a single time, never. These allegations are false and I need to go back to work for the American people.

TED KOPPEL: (voice-over) Tonight, crisis in the White House -- will the president's word be enough?

ANNOUNCER: From ABC News, this is Nightline. Reporting from Washington, Ted Koppel.

TED KOPPEL: It is not easy to make sense out of what is happening in Washington these days and for the moment at least it is next to impossible to determine the truth. Yesterday, ABC News Correspondent Jackie Judd quoted unnamed sources as saying that there may have been a witness, possibly a secret service agent, to an intimate encounter between President Clinton and Monica Lewinsky. This morning, as you have just heard again, President Clinton angrily denied any sexual relationship with Ms. Lewinsky. Now comes tomorrow's edition of the Dallas Morning News, not only citing sources confirming Jackie Judd's report of yesterday, but adding new details. The Dallas paper cites its own sources as stating that a secret service agent witnessed the resident and Ms. Lewinsky in a compromising situation and that the nt has already been in communication with the office of the

. ıependent counsel, Ken Starr.

Only a couple of hours ago, though, I spoke with a member of Ms. Lewinsky's legal team who said, speaking on behalf of all her lawyers, we know nothing about this agent who has alleged to have witnessed an intimate moment.

A senior law enforcement source whom we contacted late tonight did little to unravel the confusion. It would be highly unusual, he indicated, for a secret service agent to reveal private information about any president, unprecedented to do so about a sitting president. Having said that, he acknowledged that there was no statute that would prevent it.

On Wednesday, President Clinton will visit LaCrosse, Wisconsin. That trip was planned a long time ago, but as John Donvan now reports, it has taken on a whole new flavor.

JOHN DONVAN, ABC News: (voice-over) It is, to say the least, getting awkward for LaCrosse. Government class this afternoon at Logan High.

1st LaCROSSE RESIDENT: It's a disgusting display of morals for us young kids that maybe look up to the president.

2nd LACROSSE RESIDENT: Does he claim that she has this dress that's seamy? It's kind of disgusting.

JOHN DONVAN: (voice-over) Yes, it's getting awkward.

(on camera) Because tonight as they begin building the stage that the president will speak from on Wednesday and as the town began filling up with White House advance people and reporters, it wasn't really clear what this presidential visit means to LaCrosse anymore. It was supposed to be a moment of pride and celebration. Now, it's a lot more complicated than that.

(voice-over) Listen to the mayor, John Medinger, a lifelong Democrat.

JOHN MEDINGER: The most frenzied part is hoping that it all comes together and that we have a successful event here on Wednesday afternoon. I expect it's going to happen, but I'm not sure anymore.

JOHN DONVAN: (voice-over) Eleven days ago, it was a different story.

SCOTT HACKWORTH, News 19 Reporter: More information tonight about President Clinton's visit to LaCrosse next weekend, where you can get tickets.

(Publication page references are not available for this document.)

JOHN DONVAN: (voice-over) The story then was that LaCrosse had been given the duty and the honor of welcoming the president of the United States. Six days ago, the scandal broke.

REPORTER: A controversy surrounds President Clinton as he tries to continue his presidential duties...

JOHN DONVAN: (voice-over) And two days ago, Saturday, as the mayor bounced between meeting with the White House team and the five block long Packer parade, he also had to deal with the first serious backlash against the president's coming here. It was about money and the standard letter that the White House had sent the mayor last Friday explaining that, "Costs incurred in connection with the staging of any events are the host's responsibility." In other words, LaCrosse was being asked to pay an estimated $40,000 for the president's visit. The mayor knew that was not going to get through the city council.

JOHN MEDINGER: And in light of what was going on I indicated to him that I was getting calls from members of the city council saying why should we pay these bills. They're getting calls from their constituents, you know, indicating the same thing, we don't want the taxpayers to spend any money for that person in the White House.

OHN DONVAN: (voice-over) He says he warned the White House advance team this could be trouble.

JOHN MEDINGER: I says, you know, this isn't a slam dunk in the city council. We may have some problems. And it finally, you know, a light went on and they says you mean like they might vote it down? And I says yeah, like they might vote it down. And they says well, we can't let that happen.

JOHN DONVAN: (voice-over) The White House got the message and at Saturday's council meeting, Medinger was able to announce that the federal government will pay most of the cost.

JOHN MEDINGER: There will be no cost to the city of LaCrosse for any of this stuff that's on here.

JOHN DONVAN: (voice-over) Crisis averted, the visit is still on. But as the president tried again today to bailout his sinking reputation, the people of LaCrosse watched and mostly they seemed embarrassed, some embarrassed for the president, others embarrassed by the president. There was P.J. Jacobs, a short order cook at Mr. D's.

P.J. JACOBS: What he did was wrong, that's for sure. But I think ıt they're doing to him is even worse. I don't know. It's the man's vate life. As far as I'm concerned, leave him alone. And maybe I'm

... only woman in the United States who would say something like that.

LAURIE MINSNER: (ph) Now the children made pictures and wrote his name and this is a present for him.

JOHN DONVAN: (voice-over) Over at city hall, Laurie Minsner came by with her five -year-old son Zack. (ph) They were dropping off a sign that Zack's class had made for the president's visit.

LAURIE MINSNER: And he was asking what that meant, what sexual relations meant. I told him the best that I could that he understands that people are married and that meant perhaps having some sort of relationship with someone other than a wife. And he understands that and he knows in his mind so far what's right and wrong.

JOHN DONVAN: (voice-over) Chip Denure, (ph) a probation officer, says he's just disgusted.

CHIP DENURE: I'd prefer that he stayed home and resigned. That's just my opinion. I know he'll probably get a good crowd here in LaCrosse, but people shouldn't read too much into that because I think mostly a lot of the people will just be going down to see a president of the United States.

JOHN DONVAN: (voice-over) That much is probably true. When they started handing out tickets on Saturday, there were people lined up outside the doors.

3rd LACROSSE RESIDENT: We felt it was really IPO whenever we have a chance to let our teenage daughter see something as important as the president of the United States and his entourage, that we be a part of it.

4th LACROSSE RESIDENT: It's just exciting for the kids to be able to see the president.

JOHN DONVAN: Are they all excited about it?

4th LACROSSE RESIDENT: Oh yeah.

JOHN DONVAN: How do you guys feel about having the president come to LaCrosse?

5th LACROSSE RESIDENT: It's pretty cool.

JOHN DONVAN: (voice-over) It was, said the lead man in the White House advance team, heartening to see.

(interviewing) Do you have any doubts or have you had any doubts about how this event is going to go in light of what's happening in Washington?

RICK JASCULCA, Presidential Advance Team: Never.

JOHN DONVAN: But you know what it's like back in Washington right now.

RICK JASCULCA: Well, this isn't Washington, John.

JOHN DONVAN: No, it's not, and as someone who has been in both cities this week, I can report that LaCrosse is not nearly as obsessed with this story as Washington is. Here there is little fever for catching the president in a lie. Here it's much more a fervent prayer that he's telling the truth.

John Donvan for Nightline in LaCrosse, Wisconsin.

TED KOPPEL: ABC News has conducted another poll on how the American public at large is reacting to ongoing news of the allegations and denials. On the question of whether the allegations are interfering with the president's ability to serve, 58 percent said yes, 41 percent said no.

A new snippet of news together with a newly surfaced videotape are not likely to help. In some video taken at a Democratic National Committee fundraiser on May 9th of 1996, the president is seen once again on what is called a rope line meeting and hugging Monica Lewinsky. She is also seen in the front left in white as the president speaks at the Democratic National Committee fundraiser in Washington. Ms. Lewinsky wrote a $250 check to attend the event.

Meanwhile, ABC News learned today that Ms. Lewinsky is heard on one of her tape recorded conversations with her friend, Linda Tripp, telling Tripp that she placed a personal ad in the Washington Post last Valentine's Day and that it was intended for the president. The ad, addressed to Handsome and quoting from Romeo and Juliet is signed simply, "M". Tomorrow morning's Washington Post reprints this copy of the ad.

(Commercial Break)

TED KOPPEL: White House officials with daily access to the president are in the all but impossible position of wanting to defend him but making themselves subject to subpoena and the likelihood of huge legal expenses if they actually talk to Mr. Clinton about the case. Indeed, the president himself may be inhibited for legal reasons from saying all that he might want to say in public. Today, as Nightline's

...respondent Chris Bury reports, the president made as categorical a denial as he could.

Pres. WILLIAM J. CLINTON: I did not ask anyone to tell anything other than the truth. There is no improper relationship and I intend to cooperate with this inquiry.

CHRIS BURY, ABC News: (voice-over) If the president's first, somewhat subdued explanation last Wednesday failed to clear the air, then his guarded response the following day during a photo op with Yasir Arafat only made matters worse.

Pres. WILLIAM J. CLINTON: (January 22) You and the American people have a right to get answers. We are working very hard to comply, get all the requests for information up here and we will give you as many answers as we can as soon as we can at the appropriate time consistent with our obligation to also cooperate with the investigations. And that's not a dodge.

CHRIS BURY: (voice-over) Only today, five days after the allegations first surfaced, did the president, with Hillary Rodham Clinton close at his side, look squarely into the camera, clench his jaw and show some a...er in his voice.

PRES. BILL CLINTON: I want you to listen to me. I'm going to say this again. I did not have sexual relations with that woman, Ms. Lewinsky. I never told anybody to lie, not a single time, never. These allegations are false and I need to go back to work for the American people.

CHRIS BURY: President Clinton's reluctance to make that kind of forceful response before today has been one of the most damaging factors in this scandal. After all, the Clinton team perfected the war room and those rapid response counter attacks during previous crises. This time, the president's defenders have been uncharacteristically slow off the mark and their familiar tactics are just now beginning to emerge.

ANN LEWIS, White House Communications Director: I can say with absolute assurance the president of the United States did not have a sexual relationship because I have heard the president of the United States say so.

CHRIS BURY: (voice-over) In the last few days, Mr. Clinton's most trusted political advisers have fanned out across the air waves. Tactic number one, if the president said so, it must be true.

...AUL BEGALA, Clinton Adviser: (Courtesy "This Week with Sam and ...ie") Like, you know, I'm like Dale Evans with the Bible -- God wrote

1/26/98 NIGHTLINE
(Publication page references are not available for this document.)

. ., I believe it and that settles it.

JAMES CARVILLE, Clinton Adviser: (Courtesy NBC's "Meet The Press") He's denied it to his staff, he's denied it to the news media, he's denied it to the American people and denied it to his cabinet and denied it to his friends. Can't be any more emphatic about that.

CHRIS BURY: (voice-over) But none of those defenders could say they had personally asked the president a single question about Monica Lewinsky.
HOWARD FINEMAN, "Newsweek": (ph)I think the performance by the spin doctors yesterday was pretty darned weak.

CHRIS BURY: (voice-over) Howard Fineman is chief political correspondent for Newsweek.

HOWARD FINEMAN: They weren't able to go on the air and say look, we are good friends of Bill Clinton's, we've looked him in the eye and we are here to tell you that that's a man who's telling the truth. All they said was we heard the same denials on TV that you all did, and that's not very convincing.

CHRIS BURY: (voice-over) Tactic number two, the lawyers won't let us k.

ANN LEWIS: We had some very educational meetings with the lawyers.

The legal counsel has explained to us...

Our lawyers have explained to us that when such serious charges, words like subornation of perjury, when those kinds of charges are in the air, your first obligation is to cooperate fully with the investigation.

CHRIS BURY: (voice-over) Nightline reviewed the White House public relations performance with Stuart Taylor, a lawyer who writes for the National Journal.

STUART TAYLOR, "National Journal":Innocent people with nothing to hide who tell the truth don't need to surround themselves with phalanxes of lawyers. They simply tell the truth. They rely on that rather than on their ability to construct a story with elaborate help from experts at constructing stories after they've studied everything everybody else might say.

GEORGE STEPHANOPOLOUS, ABC News Consultant: I know that if I were inside and I asked the president a question and then I came out and ' `ked to you, the next call I would make would be to my lawyer because . :his world we're in now, a super heated world of special prosecutors,

-y conversation with a person involved in the investigation becomes subpoenable, becomes actionable in court and I perfectly understand why the president's spokespeople over the weekend took that stance.

CHRIS BURY: (voice-over) Tactic number three, go after independent counsel Kenneth Starr.

JAMES CARVILLE: This started out as a $40,000 land deal that lost money and about $50 million and five years later, after nobody could find anything we're wiring up people in hotels and feeding 'em whiskey trying to get 'em to talk and everything else. This is a scuzzy investigation.

RAHM EMANUEL, Senior Presidential Adviser: (From CNN's Late Edition) Ken Starr, for three and a half years, has been walking around with a loaded subpoena. He started investigating a 24-year-old real estate deal and now he's investigating a 24-year-old young lady and the only common thread I can find, and I'm not a lawyer, is that they're both 24-years-old.

STUART TAYLOR: It's all Kenneth Starr, Kenneth Starr, Kenneth Starr. Kenneth Starr didn't make these audiotapes. Kenneth Starr didn't put Linda Tripp up to it. Kenneth Starr didn't tell Monica Lewinsky what to on the audiotapes.

HOWARD FINEMAN: If you look at Bill Clinton in crisis, you see a pattern. First, the silence. Then the angry denials. Then this hair splitting. And then the full bore attack on whoever the accusers happen to be. They did it to Gennifer Flowers in '92 with some success. They did it to critics on the draft in those days. Now they're looking for enemies and they've found one in Ken Starr.

CHRIS BURY: (voice-over) Perhaps even more critical than what the president and his defenders are saying is what they are not.

(interviewing) The White House has not yet put forward some kind of plausible story line or explanation, which is a huge omission, it seems.

GEORGE STEPHANOPOULOS: That's the big one. You know, in the end, I think this is one of those stories where spin is essentially meaningless, in the long run, because in the end, only one question matters, is the president telling the truth, the whole truth and nothing but the truth? And if he is, everything will be okay. If he's not, no spin will help.

CHRIS BURY: (voice-over) Today, on that one big question.

OLF BLITZER, CNN WHITE HOUSE CORRESPONDENT: (from White House press (conference) Why is it so hard then to simply explain to the American public what was the nature of their friendship or relationship?

CHRIS BURY: (voice-over) The White House spokesman simply would not answer.

WOLF BLITZER: Why is that such a difficult question to answer?

MIKE McCURRY, White House Press Secretary: It's not difficult, I just don't think it needs to be done here.

WOLF BLITZER: Why?

MIKE McCURRY: Because the president's been very straightforward and very clear about what he said and I think most Americans heard him and they know exactly what he means and I don't want to get into, you know, a description of different permutations on what is very clearly an unambiguous statement.

CHRIS BURY: So no one at the White House, from President Clinton down to his press secretary, has yet given a straightforward plausible account describing exactly his relationship with Monica Lewinsky. And all the president's denials, no matter how often they are repeated by supporters, may never be taken at face value until that fundamental question is answered, too.

This is Chris Bury for Nightline in Washington.

TED KOPPEL: The issue of Kenneth Starr and his motives, when we come back.

(Commercial Break)

TED KOPPEL: What about Kenneth Starr, the independent counsel? We asked that in our ABC News poll. Is he trying to hurt the president politically? And 56 percent said yes; only 30 percent said no.

If anyone is saying less publicly than President Clinton these days, it is Judge Starr, who is sitting in the middle of his web, encouraging evidence to be brought to him. Here's Nightline correspondent Dave Marash.

WILLIAM GINSBURG, Monica Lewinsky's Attorney: We have made a complete proffer to the office of the independent counsel.

DAVE MARASH, ABC News: (voice-over) In the midst of typical Washington media mayhem tonight, Monica Lewinsky's attorney announced he had just played what may be his final card, a formal proffer, a promise of exactly what his client will say in court.

WILLIAM GINSBURG: We are now in a position where the ball is totally in Judge Starr's court and Judge Starr has to tell us what he wants to do.
DAVE MARASH: (voice-over) What will Ms. Lewinsky testify? Ginsburg wouldn't say. What does the lawyer want in exchange? Full immunity for Lewinsky, not more limited use immunity. What's the difference?

MICHAEL ZELDIN, Former Special Prosecutor: Use immunity essentially is that you can't be prosecuted for the words out of your mouth. It's a more limited form of immunity. Full immunity immunizes you from all criminal conduct save perhaps for perjury.

DAVE MARASH: How will Starr respond? No answers yet tonight, but there was this hint that prosecutors may already be reorganizing their case. Nightline has learned tonight that Monica Lewinsky's grand jury appearance, scheduled for tomorrow, has been postponed until Wednesday at the earliest.

WILLIAM GINSBURG: If these allegations are true then I have to be extremely, extremely angry, and I am.

AVE MARASH: (voice-over) From the moment he arrived in Washington, attorney William Ginsburg has followed what many fellow lawyers consider a peculiar strategy, all but conceding that the allegations his client had a sexual relationship with President Clinton are true and that Ms. Lewinsky perjured herself in her affidavit in the Paula Jones lawsuit.

WILLIAM GINSBURG: Her greatest fear is wearing the proverbial scarlet letter of indictment and conviction for the rest of her life and the possibility of spending some very unsavory time in a prison.

DAVE MARASH: (voice-over) While Ginsburg's poor little rich girl Lewinsky portrait may have won public sympathy, few lawyers consider that jail threat credible.

JOHN BARRETT, Former Special Prosecutor: The reality is that there's no real threat of her prosecution. There's just no jury appeal. There's no serious reason why she deserves the full prosecutorial resources of the government focused on her. She's a much better witness and if that leads to other people, that's clearly what Starr wants to do.

KENNETH GORMLEY, Duquesne Law School: It's hard to imagine how Kenneth Starr goes forward without her and it's also hard to imagine why he ·ld not grant her immunity.

DAVE MARASH: (voice-over) So, what's all the haggling been about? Time, say several legal eagles, time for Starr to gather corroborating evidence and witnesses, time for President Clinton and his advisers to stew.

MICHAEL ZELDIN: I think that what Bob Bennett and the legal team is working against when they have to meet with the political team, which is they're saying these charges are too amorphous. We can't get a handle on what it is that is being alleged here. Keep quiet and let it play out. That's a difficult thing for a political person who wants, that's watching numbers drop in the polls and is watching the American people saying we want to hear from our president, we want to hear from our president.

DAVE MARASH: (voice-over) Law professor Jeffrey Rosen recently wrote in the New York Times worrying about this case, which necessarily invades presidential privacy and about the man prosecuting it.

JEFFREY ROSEN: An independent counsel unconstrained by financial or political accountability. So I do think it's fair to worry about whether Mr. Starr, with or without explicit cooperation, may have turned himself into an unpaid investigator for Paula Jones' lawyers.

DAVE MARASH: (voice-over) While law professor John Barrett sees nothing to fear.

JOHN BARRETT: And I think what the independent counsel statute exists for and what appears generally to be happening in these cases is a credible investigation, a credible prosecution, a day in court that will establish the truth or the falsity of these charges.

DAVE MARASH: When might a Clinton-Lewinsky courtroom confrontation come?

Ken Starr's critics and his advocates agree it must come quickly or not at all.

I'm Dave Marash for Nightline in Washington.

TED KOPPEL: I'd like to warn our affiliates that we'll be going just a minute or two over our normal allotted time. We have an update to a story I reported at the beginning of this broadcast. I'll have that update for you, in a moment.

(Commercial Break)

TED KOPPEL: One late breaking development. The White House called after we went on the air tonight to advise us of their reaction to

1/26/98 NIGHTLINE
(Publication page references are not available for this document.)

e Dallas Morning News story where the secret service agent was prepared to testify that he saw President Clinton and Monica Lewinsky in "a compromising position".

President Clinton's attorney David Kendall (ph) denounced the story as false and malicious. His statement goes on to say, and I quote, "This is another false political leak for obvious and political reasons on the eve of the State of the Union."

Peter Jennings will anchor an ABC News special on President Clinton's State of the Union address at 9:00 Eastern, 8:00 Central time tomorrow night.

That's our report for tonight. I'm Ted Koppel in Washington. For all of us here at ABC News, good night.

---- INDEX REFERENCES ----

NEWS CATEGORY: PACKAGE

Word Count: 4129
1/26/98 NIGHTLINE (No Page)
END OF DOCUMENT

Tab 35

1942

⁻ᴿANSCRIPTS - 1/26/98 ABCNWSSPR
6/98 ABC News - Special Rep. (Pg. Unavail. Online)
..98 WL 8056096
ABC News - Special Report

Monday, January 26, 1998

NEWS

PRESIDENT CLINTON DELIVERS REMARKS CHILD CARE, EDUCATION INITIATIVE AT WHITE HOUSE
JACKIE JUDD / JEFFREY TOOBIN / SAM DONALDSON, PETER JENNINGS

ANNOUNCER: This is an ABC News Special Report. "Crisis in the White House."

PETER JENNINGS: Good morning, everybody. I'm Peter Jennings in Washington. We're going to interrupt a previously scheduled event at the White House today to give you a pretty good example of the dilemma in this city today.

The President and Mrs. Clinton are at a ceremony in The Roosevelt Room of the White House this morning to celebrate part of the President's child care initiative. And we interrupt partly to give you a sense of

:t of the kids that get in trouble get in trouble after school closes ..d before their parents get home from work. So in the adolescent years and later, it's profoundly important to try to give kids something to say yes to and something positive to do. But we can't do it alone.

As I said, our plan involves a public-private partnership. So it's fallen to me to announce that our distinguished guest from the Mott Foundation of Flint, Michigan, has pledged up to $55 million to help insure that after-school programs supported by federal funds are of the highest quality.

That is an astonishing...

(Applause)

Thank you, Bill White. Thank you.

(Applause)

We are determined to help Americans succeed in the workplace; to raise well-educated, healthy kids; and to help Americans succeed at the toughest job of all, that of being a parent. And the Mott Foundation has gone a long way toward helping us. I thank them.

gone a long way toward helping us. I thank them.

Now, I have to go back to work on my State of the Union speech. And I worked on it until pretty late last night. But I want to say one thing to the American people. I want you to listen to me. I'm

going to say this again.

I did not have sexual relations with that woman, Ms. Lewinsky. I never told anybody to lie, not a single time --never. These allegations are false, and I need to go back to work for the American

people.

Thank you.

(Applause)

PETER JENNINGS: The President speaking in The Roosevelt Room to the 21st Century Community Learning Centers program, which is a

public-private program between the government and the Mott Foundation to help children after school and saying again there -- we had known in advance he was going to say something -- he wants the American people listen to him, he did not have a sexual relationship with Monica ten to him, he did not have a sexual relationship with Monica Lewinsky, he never told anyone to lie and those allegations are not correct.

The person who has been covering what is indisputably a crisis in the Clinton presidency at the moment for us since the beginning is ABC's Jackie Judd. Jackie, when you hear the President say that this morning, I'm inclined to ask you first, what does the special prosecutor currently have to work with that we know can be confirmed?

JACKIE JUDD: Ken Starr's investigation is now working on two tracks, Peter. First, there are still efforts to get Monica Lewinsky to cooperate. For Ken Starr to be convinced that she will give her full and complete testimony. Those negotiations are still going on.

The second track is that his office is trying to find evidence, find eyewitnesses to establish a case that could stand on its own with or without that full and complete testimony of Monica Lewinsky.

We reported, for example, over the weekend, Peter, that Starr's office is investigating whether or not there was a witness to a moment between the President and Lewinsky at the White House. If true, that kind of witness could support allegations of an affair again with or without Ms. Lewinsky.

ut, most notably education, trying to prepare kids for the next century is imperiled by this story of sex and possibly perjury and possible obstruction of justice that looms over him.

Hope you'll stay with us for breaking news. I'm Peter Jennings in

Washington.

---- INDEX REFERENCES ----

NEWS CATEGORY: PACKAGE

Word Count: 3436
1/26/98 ABCNWSSPR (No Page)
END OF DOCUMENT

Tab 36

1950

WHITE HOUSE EDUCATION NEWS CONFERENCE
PARTICIPANTS: PRESIDENT BILL CLINTON, FIRST LADY HILLARY CLINTON VICE PRESIDENT AL GORE EDUCATION SECRETARY RICHARD RILEY BILL WHITE, PRESIDENT, C.S. MOTT FOUNDATION
ROOSEVELT ROOM, THE WHITE HOUSE WASHINGTON, DC
10:17 A.M. EST MONDAY, **JANUARY 26, 1998**

MRS. CLINTON: (Applause.) Thank you. Thank you and good morning. Please be seated.
Welcome to the White House. It is a pleasure to have all of you join the president and the vice president and Secretary Riley, Bill White (sp) of the Mott (sp) Foundation, and Mr. and Mrs. Bass (sp). And I'm especially pleased to see in the audience so many people who care so much about education and child care.
This morning we come together to hear about the president's plans to strengthen education, to discuss his historic child care initiative, and particularly to talk about how he has made quality after-school programs a national priority.
I'd like to start by talking about the child care initiative itself because it is the single largest investment in child care in our nation's history, and it will go a long way toward helping our nation's working parents find the care they can afford and trust.
This initiative will make care more affordable and it will also double the number of children receiving subsidies and increased tax credits for child care. It will help local communities and it will promote early learning and health child development opportunities. It will ensure higher standards for child care by stepping up enforcement.
But we all know that high-quality child care needs don't disappear when children start school. It's estimated that up to 5 million school-age children spend time as latchkey kids without adult supervision.
That's why, as part of this initiative, the president is making a significant investment in after-school care.
This is so important for so many working families. We want more of America's children to say no to drugs and alcohol and crime, and yes to reading and soccer and computers. And with this expanded investment in after-school care, combined with public-private partnerships in communities, we will be able to give our children those opportunities.
This morning the president will announce how one such partner, the C.S. Mott Foundation, is providing critical support to strengthen and improve after-school programs.

50-893 98 - 12

This afternoon I will be visiting a model program in Harlem, at the Harriet Tubman School, to underscore once again how important these programs are for all of our children.
Now it is my great privilege to introduce someone who has been so committed to our children, and that is the secretary of education, Dick Riley. (Applause.)

SEC. RILEY: Thank you very much. Thank you. (Applause continues.) Good morning. Thank you so much, and good morning to all of you.
You know, today over 52 million will sit in our nation's classrooms, and the quality of education that they will get during the school day will determine really the future of this country.
But what goes on after the school day ends is very important also. After-school programs can be an important part of a child's education.
They can give children more time to learn. They can offer young people safe and drug-free havens and keep kids out of trouble. They can give children the chance to enhance their lives through the arts and through music and through community service. And they can reassure working parents that their kids are in the right place and doing the right thing.
Unfortunately, there are not enough quality after-school or before-school programs in our schools and communities right now. And that's why President Clinton and Vice President Gore and Mrs. Clinton are making a major commitment to the after-school effort.
The administration's 1998 budget included a down payment of $40 million for after-school programs, but now we really want to step on the gas. We will ask Congress for $1 billion over the next five years to serve 500,000 students in 4,000 programs. We are going to call them the 21st Century Community Learning Centers. And in order for communities and schools to get the best information possible on how to start after-school programs, we and the Mott Foundation are sponsoring 11 regional workshops starting in February.
We are honored so much today to have with us a conscientious American citizen, Bill White, the president of the C.S. Mott Foundation; a person, along with his board -- and several members are here -- are concerned deeply about children, about their families, about their safety and about their education. And Bill will make a very important and significant statement about the foundation's participation in this effort.
And thank you, Bill, very much for being with us. (Applause.)

MR. WHITE: Thank you, Mr. Secretary. I only wish that C.S. Mott, who died in 1973, was here today. He loved kids, and this is about kids. Frankly, this historic partnership between the Department of Education and the Mott Foundation is a symbol of the full spectrum of public and private partnerships that we can expect to spring to life as this initiative is embraced by communities all over the United States.

The Mott Foundation has made this commitment, in part, because there are certain things which we can fund, which federal funds won't cover. And so that's what we're about, is looking at the long-term sustainability of these programs, the leadership of these programs, and those types of activities.

Mr. Vice President, I want to thank you for your deep understanding and personal commitment and articulation and support for these programs. And Mr. President, I believe this initiative will go down among the most important initiatives because it's about the future of our country. Thank you very much. (Applause.)

Mrs. Clinton, in 1939, another first lady who cared deeply about children, and it was Mrs. Roosevelt, came to Flint to tour programs funded by the Mott Foundation. They were early child care and after-school programs.

I believe that these programs have been proven by the test of time, and they're as important today -- perhaps more so -- than they were 60 years ago.

And finally, I'd love to talk about these programs; I've seen many of them. But I probably have the best job here today, and it is my privilege -- and, if I may say, high honor -- to introduce two parents who have kids in such programs, and they are Rand and Deborah (sp) Bass from Arlington.

Mr. and Mrs. Bass. (Applause.)

RAND BASS: Thank you, Mr. White.

We want to thank the president, the first lady, and Vice President and Mrs. Gore for this opportunity today to tell you a little bit about our positive experience with the extended day program at our children's school.

Deborah (sp) and I have two children:</u> Mitchell, who is 8, and Susie (sp), who is 6. They attend Barcroft Elementary School in Arlington, an ethnically diverse public school with a strong focus on the arts and a wonderful extended day program.

We did a lot of research on both public and private schools before we decided to send Mitchell and Susie to Barcroft. There were many factors to consider, of course, but the availability of after-school care on the premises was an important one. We both firmly believe we made the right choice for our children three years ago. We know the children are safe, well cared-for, and among friends.

The program is quite structured, with a wide range of activities available, from dodge ball in the gym to crafts, reading aloud, library visits, board games, and other -- card games. There's even a special quiet, supervised homework room for those students who want to get a head start on their homework.

Our children are very happy in extended day, and that makes all the difference for us as parents.

We hope that by the time Mitchell and Susie are in middle school, we will have similar options for high-quality after-school care for them.

On behalf of all the working parents in America, we want to thank the administration's leadership for their efforts to create more after-school programs. We know that with the leadership from the president, the first lady, and vice president and Mrs. Gore, that all the children in our country will have a better future.

And now it's our great pleasure to introduce someone whose long-standing commitment to children, education and after-school programs is much appreciated by all parents. Ladies and gentlemen, we are honored to introduce a hard-working parent himself, the vice president of the United States, Al Gore.

VICE PRESIDENT GORE: (Applause) Thank you very much. Thank you. Thank you very much, ladies and gentlemen.

And on behalf of the president and first lady, I want to acknowledge the presence of Senator Dianne Feinstein of California. Thank you, Dianne, for your hard work in this area. (Applause.) And also Senator Chris Dodd of Connecticut. We appreciate your presence here, Chris. And I know that Senator Barbara Boxer, I think, is in back there. And there are members of a lot of education groups and child care groups, community groups, parent-teacher groups, school boards association. I'm not going to try to acknowledge everyone who should by rights be singled out here. But thank you for your participation and presence and hard work over the years on these issues.

I want to thank Rand and Deborah (sp) Bass for introducing me and for giving that wonderful statement. I know of Barcroft Elementary. Tipper and I lived in Arlington for quite a long time.

And I also want to express my deep appreciation to Bill White, the president and CEO of the Mott Foundation. And I want to thank the board of directors and other representatives of the Mott Foundation, who are also present with us here today. Bill, it's a wonderful commitment that you're making, and it's going to make a huge difference in the lives of so many children and families across this country.

And of course, Secretary Riley has offered such tremendous leadership and vision and steadfastness of all these topics. We are really grateful to you, Mr. Secretary.

We're here today, of course, to hear the president announce important new details of his commitment to education and his plan to give all of the children in this country the tools needed to succeed in the 21st century. But first of all, I'd like to say something that everybody knows. These landmark investments would not have been possible without the dedication and hard work and achievement of our first lady, Hillary Rodham Clinton. I want to acknowledge her leadership and her great advocacy for all of these programs. (Applause.)

For 25 years, she has worked to put children and families at the top of our national agenda. She deserves the admiration and gratitude of every parent in America, and she certainly has mine. And in fact, the White House Conference on Early Childhood Development and then the one on child care both helped to set the stage for the national dialogue that we're now having.

And I thank to Bill White and his Board of Directors for this generous commitment, but the president will describe that in just a moment and you will see just what a historic commitment it is. And the president will speak more broadly about his overall education agenda because this morning's announcement should be seen in the context of how we prepare the people of our country, and especially children and families, for the challenges of the 21st century.

Before presenting the president, I want to say just a few words about an area that's of special importance to me. It's been mentioned already -- after-school care. As Rand and Deborah (sp) Bass know very well. when children start school, it becomes especially hard for parents to balance the needs of home and work and raise strong families. That is why the president and first lady's commitment to child care is so significant, and that is why our commitment to after-school care is such a critical part of our child care plan.

The need for quality after-school care has often been raised at the annual family conferences that Tipper and I have in Nashville every year. We've had them for the last six years. And, especially at last year's conference, which was on families and education and parents' involvement in their children's education, we learned how serious it -- the challenge is, and how needed these after-school programs are.

There are 5 million children, as the first lady said, who leave school before their parents get home. This period of time between the school bell and the factory whistle is the most vulnerable time for children. These are the hours when children are more likely to engage in at-risk behavior and are more vulnerable to the dangers that still exist in too many neighborhoods and communities.

That puts some parents in a gut-wrenching dilemma: Do they stay at home and forego the family income that they need, or do they stay on the job and worry that their children will be in danger while they're away?

Parents need help balancing those competing priorities. That is why the president announced that he will increase by an unprecedented 400 percent the 21st Century Community Learning Center grants that can be used to start, expand, and improve local after-school care. And I want to formally acknowledge Senator Barbara Boxer, who has worked her way through the media, through the crowd here. (Applause.) Thank you.

Of course, this whole child-care program and the education agenda and after-school care represent just some of the ways that President Clinton is investing in the future of our children and giving parents more of the tools they need to raise strong families.

So now I am very pleased to introduce America's true education president and the greatest champion of working parents and working families that the United States of America has ever known: President Bill Clinton. (Applause.)

PRESIDENT CLINTON: Thank you very much. Thank you. Thank you -- (inaudible). Thank you. (Applause continues.) Thank you very much. Thank you. Please be seated. Thank you. Thank you. Thank you. Thank you. Thank you. Thank you very much. (Applause continues.) Thank you. Thank you very much.

First, let me thank all of you who are here. Many of us have been working together now for 20 years on a lot of these issues, and this is a very happy day for us.

I thank the first lady for all she has done on this issue for as long as I've known her.

I thank the vice president and Mrs. Gore for their family conference and the light it has shed on the announcement we are here to emphasize today.

I thank you, Secretary Riley, for the community learning centers. And I'm very proud of what we've done there.

Thank you, Bill White. I'll talk more about your contribution in a moment, but it is truly remarkable. And I thank Rand and Deborah (sp)

Bass for giving us a living breathing example of the best of America, parents who are working hard to do their jobs, but also determined to do their most important job very well with their children. I thank Senator Feinstein, Senator Dodd and Senator Boxer for being here.
Tomorrow, in the State of the Union address, I will spell out what we seek to do on behalf of our children to prepare them for the 21st century, but I want to talk a little bit about education today and about this announcement in that context.
Education must be our nation's highest priority. Last year, in the State of the Union address, I set out a 10-point plan to move us forward and urged the American people to make sure that politics stops at the schoolhouse door.
Well, we've made a lot of progress on that 10-point plan; a remarkable -- a remarkable array of initiatives to open the doors of college to every American who is willing to work for it; strong progress toward high national standards in the basics, the America Reads challenge to teach every 8-year-old to read, continued progress in the vice president's program to hook up all of our classrooms and libraries to the Internet by the year 2000.
This has been the most important year in a generation for education reform. Tomorrow I set out the next steps on our continuing road:
First, I will propose the first-ever national effort to reduce class size in the early grades. (Applause.) Hillary and I worked very hard, 15 years ago now, to have very strict class sizes, at home, in the early grades. And it was quite controversial and, I think, enormously beneficial when we did it.
Our balanced budget will help to hire a hundred thousand teachers, who must pass state competency tests but who will be able to reduce class size in the first, second and third grades, to an average of 18, nationwide. (Applause.)
Second, since there are more students and there will be more teachers, there must be more classrooms, so I will propose a school-construction tax cut to help communities modernize and build new schools.
Third, I will promote a national effort to help schools that follow the lead of the Chicago system in ending social promotion but helping students with summer school and other programs to give them the tools they need to get ahead.
All these steps will help our children get the future they deserve. And that's why what we're announcing here is so important as well. Every child needs someplace to go after school. With after-school programs, we can not only keep our kids healthy and happy and

safe; we can help to teach them to say no to drugs, alcohol and crime, yes to reading, sports and computers.

My balanced budget plan includes a national initiative to spark private-sector and local community efforts to provide after-school care, as the secretary of Education said, to half-a-million more children.

Now let me say in addition to all the positive benefits, I think it's important to point out that the hours between 3:00 and 7:00 at night are the most vulnerable hours for young people to get in trouble for juvenile crime.

There is this -- this sort of assumption that everybody that gets in trouble when they're young has just already been abandoned. That's not true. Most of the kids who get in trouble get in trouble after school closes and before their parents get home from work. So there -- in the adolescent years and later years, it's profoundly important to try to give kids something to say yes to and something positive to do.

But we can't do it alone.

As I said, our plan involves a public-private partnership. So, it's -- fallen to me to announce that our distinguished guests from the Mott Foundation of Flint, Michigan, has pledged up to $55 million to help ensure that after-school programs supported by federal funds are of the highest quality. That is an astonishing (gift ?). (Applause.)

Thank you, Bill White. Thank you. (Applause.)

We are determined to help Americans succeed in the workplace, to raise well-educated, healthy kids, and to help Americans succeed at the toughest job of all, that of being a parent. And the Mott Foundation has gone a long way toward helping us, and I thank them.

Now I have to go back to work on my State of the Union speech, and I worked on it till pretty late last night. But I want to say one thing to the American people. I want you to listen to me. I'm going to say this again: I did not have sexual relations with that woman, Miss Lewinsky. I never told anybody to lie, not a single time. Never. These allegations are false. And I need to go back to work for the American people.

Thank you.

(Applause.)

Tab A

1960

Citation Search Result Rank 3 of 38 Databa
1/27/98 ASSOCPPS (No Page) ALLNEW
1/27/98 Associated Press Pol. Serv. (Pg. Unavail. Online)
1998 WL 7380187
(Publication page references are not available for this document.)

The Associated Press Political Service

Tuesday, January 27, 1998

WASHINGTON (AP) _ In a strangely strained setting, President ...
WALTER R. MEARS
Associated Press

WASHINGTON (AP) _ In a strangely strained setting, President Clinton is proclaiming the State of the Union to be strong as he begins his sixth year in the White House _ but he can make no such claim about the state of his presidency.

The State of the Union address is a president's grand stage, an occasion of state, his hour to set the agenda and declare his goals before Congress, the Cabinet, diplomats and the nation. This is prime time television on his terms, unlike the TV torrent over accusations, which he denies, that he was sexually involved with a former White House intern, now 24, and attempted to cover it up.

He does not plan to speak of it in his address tonight, but there's no avoiding the impact of the Monica Lewinsky case. That led him to a remarkable finale to a routine White House ceremony on education Monday.

"I want to say one thing to the American people," Clinton said, glaring at the TV cameras and shaking a finger for emphasis. "I want you to listen to me. I'm going to say this again.

"I did not have sexual relations with that woman, Miss Lewinsky. I never told anybody to lie. Not a single time. Never. These allegations are false, and I need to go back to work for the American people."

That certainly sounds categorical, but given the adroitly worded denials that enabled Clinton to brush off past questions about affairs, his draft record and the marijuana he didn't inhale, there were more.

Presidential spokesman Mike McCurry said there were indeed answers yet to be provided, and that they would be at the proper point, but that Clinton left no ambiguity on the central ones: sex with an ntern and allegations that she'd been asked to lie to conceal it.

"I think every American that heard him knows exactly what he meant," McCurry said when he was asked whether the denial covered any form of sexual contact.

Ann Lewis, the White House communications director, said flatly that it did. "Sex is sex, even in Washington, I've been assured," she said.

The aim was to get past the allegations of scandal, back to the business Clinton wants addressed, telling Congress and the nation what he wants done, and boasting in an election year of what has been done during the Democratic administration so far.

The budget deficit is the lowest in 30 years, with the first balanced budget since 1969 in prospect next year. The economy has grown for seven years without a recession, the third longest expansion in history. Both inflation and unemployment are low, and despite stress abroad, in Iraq and with the extended U.S. military mission in Bosnia, it is peacetime.

But with the barrage of questions, accusations and rumors, Clinton's prospects have dimmed for getting things done his way in an election-year with a Republican Congress.

McCurry acknowledged the obvious, that what the White House is doing "has been in something of a shadow because of this incident."

He said Clinton's major address of the year is "being given in stranger circumstances" than in the past. That includes speculation about impeachment or resignation should allegations of perjury or encouraging it be proven.

There's been nothing like this since Watergate-worn Richard Nixon declared to Congress in his 1974 State of the Union address that he had no intention of resigning. Eight months later he quit, after Republican leaders told him he could not avoid impeachment for the cover-up role proven on his own tape recordings.

In his memoirs, he quoted a memo to himself, written on New Year's Day. "Fight, because if I am forced to resign, the press will become a much too dominant force in the nation, not only in this administration but for years to come," he wrote. "Fight, because resignation would set a precedent and result in a permanent and very destructive change in our whole constitutional system."

But after a long struggle, he surrendered.

This case and these times are different. It wasn't a week before there was talk, and not only from the fringes, that Clinton might be forced from the White House. All hedged with an if, since there's no proof.

But all said and replayed, along with allegations that not long ago would have been X rated beyond broadcasting. And all adding to the distraction as Clinton addresses the State of the Union and his audience tries to appraise his.

EDITOR'S NOTE _ Walter R. Mears, vice president and columnist for The Associated Press, has reported on Washington and national politics for more than 30 years.

---- INDEX REFERENCES ----

KEY WORDS: EDUCATION; MUNICIPAL; POLITICAL

STORY ORIGIN: UNITED STATES

Word Count: 771
1/27/98 ASSOCPPS (No Page)
END OF DOCUMENT

1964

Tab B

1966

:ation Search Result Rank 3 of 3 Database
!7/98 TODAY (No Page) TODAY
1/27/98 Today (Pg. Unavail. Online)
1998 WL 5261146

Today

Tuesday, January 27, 1998

Interview: Hillary Rodham Clinton discusses allegations against her husband, child care, and State of the Union address

MATT LAUER, co-host:

On CLOSE UP this morning, the first lady of the United States, Hillary Rodham Clinton.

Mrs. Clinton, good morning.

Mrs. HILLARY RODHAM CLINTON: Good morning, Matt. Matt, before we get into your questions, I just want to express again, Bill's and my condolences to Katie and her children, and Jay's entire family. And I know that everybody who watches the show, feels as we all do h her, and want to help her in any way.

LAUER: I spent some time with her yesterday. And I know she appreciated your call. Thank you very much.

We appreciate your being here. This--this interview had been scheduled several weeks ago to talk about the subject of child care, which we will talk about this morning.

Mrs. CLINTON: Right, mm-hmm.

LAUER: But we appreciate you honoring the commitment, even in light of recent events. Thank you very much.

There has been question on the minds of a lot of people in this country, Mrs. Clinton, lately, and that is what is the exact nature of the relationship between your husband and Monica Lewinsky? Has he described that relationship in detail to you?

Mrs. CLINTON: Well, we've talked at great length. And I think as this matter unfolds, the entire country will have more information. But we're right in the middle of a rather vigorous feeding frenzy right now. People are saying all kinds of things, putting out rumor and innuendo. And I have learned over the last y years being involved in politics, and especially since my sband first started running for president, that the best thing to in these cases is just to be patient, take a deep breath, and the truth will come out. But there's nothing we can do to fight this firestorm of allegations that are out there.

LAUER: But he has described to the American people what this relationship was not...

Mrs. CLINTON: That's right.

LAUER: ...in his words.

Mrs. CLINTON: That's right.

LAUER: Has he described to you what it was?

Mrs. CLINTON: Yes. And we'll--and we'll find that out as time goes by, Matt. But I think the important thing now is to stand as firmly as I can and say that, you know, that the president has denied these allegations on all counts, unequivocally, and we'll--we'll see how this plays out. I guess--everybody says to me, 'How can you be so calm?' or 'How can you just, you know, look like you're not upset?' And I guess I've just been through it so many times. I mean, Bill and I have been accused of everything, including murder, some of the very same people who are behind these allegations. from my perspective, this is part of the continuing political campaign against my husband.

LAUER: To the best of my knowledge, Mrs. Clinton, has your husband ever given or received gifts from or to Monica Lewinsky?

Mrs. CLINTON: I'm not going to comment on any specific allegation, because I've learned we need to put all of this into context, and it will be put into context. And anyone who knows my husband knows that he is an extremely generous person to people he knows, to strangers, to anybody who is around him. And I think that, you know, his behavior, his treatment of people will certainly explain all of this.

LAUER: When you--when you say he's a generous person, so it is possible that he has given gifts to Monica Lewinsky?

Mrs. CLINTON: I think it's possible, of course, because if you know my husband, you know that he is somebody who will, you know, say 'Matt, how would you like this?' I mean, I've seen him take his tie off and hand it to somebody, you know.

LAUER: So that wouldn't be--that wouldn't be a behavior that would unusual for him dealing with an intern in the White House?

Irs. CLINTON: Dealing with anybody, Matt. I mean, seriously, I have--I've known my husband for more than 25 years, and we've been married for 22 years, and the one thing I always kid him about is that he never meets a stranger. He is kind, he is friendly, he tries to help people who need help, who ask for help. So I think that everybody ought to just--just stop a minute here and think about what we're doing. And it--it's not just what we're doing in terms of making these accusations against my husband, but I'm very concerned about the tactics that are being used and the kind of intense political agenda at work here.

LAUER: I want to talk about Ken Starr in a second. Be--before I get to him, let me just ask you, do you know Monica Lewinsky?

Mrs. CLINTON: No. Unh-unh.

LAUER: You've never met her?

Mrs. CLINTON: I may have. You know, there are hundreds and hundreds of young people who serve as interns. And, you know, we have big events for them. We take pictures with them. But unless they work directly in my office, I'm--I'm not likely to meet them.

LAUER: Did--did Evelyn Lieberman, the former deputy chief of ff, or any other White House staffers, Mrs. Clinton, ever come to you and say 'We may have a problem with one of the interns at the White House,' and mention Monica Lewinsky...

Mrs. CLINTON: No.

LAUER: ...by name?

Mrs. CLINTON: No, that never happened.

LAUER: So these charges came as big--to--as big as shock to you as anyone?

Mrs. CLINTON: And to my husband. I mean, you know, he woke me up Wednesday morning and said 'You're not going to believe this, but...' and I said 'What is this?' And so, yeah, it came as a very big surprise.

LAUER: When he said 'But,' he said 'But' what?

Mrs. CLINTON: 'But I want to tell you what's in the newspapers.'

LAUER: I--I think the--the part of this that makes certain people oss the country uneasy is that we have a 21-year-old intern at the te House, who moves to the Pentagon, who then gets a job interview the UN with Bill Richardson himself, and then a very dear friend of your husband's, Vernon Jordan, recommends her for two jobs in this city, here in New York, and then drives her personally to a lawyer's office when she's subpoenaed by Kenneth Starr. Does it not appear though--that--that this intern had more clout in Washington than most others do?

Mrs. CLINTON: I don't know the circumstances of any of that, Matt. I think that, you know, I--I just can't describe to you how outgoing and friendly Vernon Jordan is. I mean, when he stood up and said what I believe to be the absolute truth, that he has helped literally hundreds of people, and it doesn't matter who they are. And if he were asked to help somebody, he would help that person. I've seen him do it countless times, so I guess I know the people involved. I know them personally. I know them well. I've known Vernon longer than I've known my husband.

LAUER: So when people say there's a lot of smoke here...

Mrs. CLINTON: There's...

LAUER: ...your message is 'Where there's smoke...'

Mrs. CLINTON: There isn't any fire, because think of what we've been through for the last six years, and think of everything we've been accused of. And, you know, initially, when this first started and I would be accused of something, or my husband would be accused of something, I would be really upset, and I would want to rush out, and I'd say, 'That's not true.' And then somebody would nitpick and say 'Well, what about this?' And I'd say 'Well, I hadn't thought about that.' And then I'd rush around, I'd say, 'Well that's not true.'

LAUER: Are you saying, though, that you're no long--that this doesn't upset you any more, you--you're...

Mrs. CLINTON: Look, it's...

LAUER: ...almost numb to it?

Mrs. CLINTON: ...it's not being numb so much as just being very experienced in the unfortunate, mean-spirited give and take of American politics right now. So, having seen so many of these accusations come and go, having seen people profit, you know, like Jerry Falwell, with videos, accusing my husband of committing murder, of drug running, seeing some of the things that are written and said about him, my attitude is, you know, we've been there before, we have been this before, and I am just going to wait patiently until the truth comes out.

LAUER: So if--so if what you have heard is something you can believe, and if what the president has told the nation is the whole truth and nothing but the truth...

Mrs. CLINTON: Right.

LAUER: ...then you'd have to agree that this is the worst and most damaging smear of the 20th century.

Mrs. CLINTON: Well, I don't know. There have been a lot of smears in the 20th century, but it's a...

LAUER: This is pretty devastating.

Mrs. CLINTON: ...pretty, pretty bad one. Well, just think about it, and this is what concerns me, this started out as an investigation of a failed land deal. I told everybody in 1992, 'We lost money.' People said, 'It's not true,' you know, 'they made money. They have money in a Swiss bank account.' Well, it was true. It's taken years, but it was true. We get a politically motivated prosecutor who is allied with the right-wing opponents of my husband, who has literally spent four years looking at every telephone...

LAUER: Spent $30 million.

Mrs. CLINTON: ...more than that now, but looking at every telephone call we've made, every check we've ever written, scratching for dirt, intimidating witnesses, doing everything possible to try to make some accusation against my husband.

LAUER: We're talking about Kenneth Starr, so let's...

Mrs. CLINTON: We're talking...

LAUER: ...use his name, because he is the independent counsel.

Mrs. CLINTON: ...well, we're talking about--but it's the whole operation. It's--it's not just one person, it's an entire operation.

LAUER: Did he go outside of his rights, in your opinion, to expand this investigation? After all, he got permission to expand the investigation from a three-judge panel.

Mrs. CLINTON: The same three-judge panel that removed Robert Fiske and appointed him. The same three-judge panel that is headed someone who is appointed by Jesse Helms and Lauch Faircloth.

LAUER: Also, Judge Reno approved...

Mrs. CLINTON: Well, of course...

LAUER: ...this expansion of an investigation.

Mrs. CLINTON: ...well, you're--of course she is, because she doesn't want to appear as though she's interfering with an investigation. I don't--look, I--I'm not going to take all that on, because I've learned that we just have to ride this out. It's just a very unfortunate turn of events that we are using the criminal justice system to try to achieve political ends in this country. And--and, you know, when I'm here today, I'm not only here because I love and believe my husband, I'm also here because I love and believe in my country. And if I were just a citizen out there, maybe because I know about the law and I have some idea, some of the motivations here, I would be very disturbed by this turn of events.

LAUER: When--when--the last time we visited a subject like this involving your family was 1992, and the name Gennifer Flowers was in the news...

Mrs. CLINTON: Mm-hmm.

LAUER: ...and you said at the time of the interview, a very famous quote, 'I'm not some Tammy Wynette standing by my man.'

Mrs. CLINTON: Mm-hmm.

LAUER: In the same interview, your husband had admitted that he had, quote, "caused pain in your marriage."

Mrs. CLINTON: Mm-hmm.

LAUER: Six years later you are still standing by this man, your husband...

Mrs. CLINTON: Mm-hmm.

LAUER: ...through some difficult charges. If he were to be asked today, Mrs. Clinton, do you think he would admit that he again has caused pain in this marriage?

Mrs. CLINTON: No. Absolutely not, and he shouldn't. You know, we've been married for 22 years, Matt, and I have learned a long time ago that the only people who count in any marriage are the two that are in it. We know everything there is to know about each other, d we understand and accept and love each other. And I just think at a lot of this is deliberately designed to sensationalize charges ainst my husband, because everything else they've tried has failed. And I also believe that it's part of an effort, very frankly, to undo the results of two elections.

LAUER: Le--let me talk about your role. There have been reports that you've taken charge at the White House and decided to be the chief defender of your husband, of the president, and deflect these charges. How much of a role are you taking in this, do you think you should take?

Mrs. CLINTON: Well, I certainly am going to defend my husband. And I'm certainly going to offer advice. But I am by no means running any kind of strategy or being his chief defender. He's got very capable lawyers and very capable people inside the White House, and a lot of very good friends outside the White House.

LAUER: But you're probably the most credible defender of the president at this time.

Mrs. CLINTON: Well, I probably know him better than anybody alive in the world, so I would hope that I'd be the most credible defender.

LAUER: James Carville, who you know...

Mrs. CLINTON: Great human being.

LAUER: I'm sure you like him, especially at this time. He has said that this is war between the president and Kenneth Starr. You have said, I understand, to some close friends, that this is the last great battle, and that one side or the other is going down here.

Mrs. CLINTON: Well, I don't know if I've been that dramatic. That would sound like a good line from a movie. But I do believe that this is a battle. I mean, look at the very people who are involved in this, they have popped up in other settings. This is the great story here, for anybody willing to find it and write about it and explain it, is this vast right-wing conspiracy that has been conspiring against my husband since the day he announced for president. A few journalists have kind of caught onto it and explained it, but it has not yet been fully revealed to the American public. And, actually, you know, in a bizarre sort of way, this may do it.

LAUER: Has--has your husband, though, through some of his actions, possibly made it easier for those people to attack him.

Mrs. CLINTON: Well, you know, Matt, that's a tough question cause I can remember in Bill's very first race, in 1974, there was great effort against him then. But one of the funniest things that ever happened--although at the time it wasn't funny--is that the people who were against him, claimed that he had been up in a tree demonstrating as President Nixon during the Texas/Arkansas football game in 1969. It didn't matter that he was in England at the very day listening to the game on shortwave radio. They took a picture out of a newspaper, they cut the head off the man who was in the tree, they put Bill Clinton's head on it. They printed thousands of them. They passed them out in every country church and every country store, so you had hundreds of thousands of people believing this. Now I have to say, I don't know what it is about my husband that generates such hostility, but I have seen it for 25 years.

LAUER: Let--let me take you and your husband out of this for a second. Bill and Hillary Clinton are involved in this story. If an American president had an adulteress liaison in the White House and lied to cover it up, should the American people ask for his resignation?

Mrs. CLINTON: Well, they should certainly be concerned about it.

LAUER: Should they ask for his resignation?

Mrs. CLINTON: Well, I think--if all that were proven true, I think that would be a very serious offense. That is not going to be proven true. I think we're going to find some other things. And I think when all of this is put into context, and we really look at the people involved here, look at their motivations, look at their backgrounds, look at their past behavior, some folks are going to have a lot to answer for.

LAUER: One more subject before I get to child care. I've talked to a lot of people about this story. It's certainly a topic of conversation...

Mrs. CLINTON: It's a big story, I know.

LAUER: ...around the country.

Mrs. CLINTON: I know.

LAUER: One of the comments I hear a lot, Mrs. Clinton, is how is Chelsea handling this? It's not easy being a freshman in college, anyway.

Mrs. CLINTON: Right. Well...

LAUER: How is she doing?

1/27/98 TODAY (No Page)

Irs. CLINTON: ...she's all right. And I really want to thank people for just letting her continue to be a freshman. Because any time--accusations of any kind, but especially like this with such publicity around the world are made, it really does affect your whole family. I mean, it's not only my daughter, it's my mother, it's Bill's stepfather, it's our brothers, our sister-in-laws, all of us.

LAUER: How often do you talk to Chelsea about it, or have you?

Mrs. CLINTON: We've talked a lot. Both Bill and I have talked to her a lot.

LAUER: Does she offer any advice to you? It's usually the other way around, but has she offered you any advice?

Mrs. CLINTON: It's not advice so much, but, you know, since she was six years old, I have known, both because--I think my husband's personality and his kind of gregariousness, and his--as well as his political ideas really do engender a very deep hostility. So I was telling Chelsea when she was a child that 'This is going to happen, and it's very unfortunate.' I honestly wish if people had political differences, if you don't like his stand on something, fight it out on that. Don't just try to destroy somebody personally. So I have .d her that this is the kind of thing that would happen, and she seen many, many examples of it in her very short life. So it's not a pleasant experience, but it's given her sort of the grounding to be able to see what this is and get through it.

LAUER: Want to talk a little child care?

Mrs. CLINTON: Yeah, I'd like to talk about the State of the Union, and not only child care, which I'm very excited about, but also some of the possible programs for the millennium that the president will be announcing tonight.

LAUER: Go ahead, I give you an opportunity.

Mrs. CLINTON: Thank you. Well, you know, the child-care proposal has been, I think, well put out there, and we're getting a fabulous response from around the country. And, you know, we had an announcement yesterday at the White House, and I was here in New York talking about it again yesterday. I think it's going to make a big difference in the lives of a lot of working people. So I hope there is going to be support for that. And I have a sense that we're going to have bipartisan support for child care.

LAUER: While you're talking about bipartisan, I heard one critic ' that this was more of a Republican plan than the one you first .sibly talked about when you came to Washington five years ago.

deals with tax credits...

Mrs. CLINTON: Right.

LAUER: ...and grant blocks to the states...

Mrs. CLINTON: Right.

LAUER: ...which takes some power away from the federal government.

Mrs. CLINTON: Right.

LAUER: How do you respond to that?

Mrs. CLINTON: Well, I think it's a good plan. And I--I have no problem taking good Republican ideas and mixing them with good Democratic ideas to get good ideas for Americans. And I think that you'll see that some of the Republican members of the Congress are coming up with some other ideas. And I hope that at the end of the day, we'll have the best mix we can possibly have.

But I did want to mention one other thing about what the president will talk about tonight. And that is, you know, we are going to be .ebrating the millennium, and the turn of the century. And I've ɜn working very hard with the president to come up with a way that we could honor the past and imagine the future. And I've learned in my studies there are--a lot of what we value as Americans is in real disrepair, like "The Star Spangled Banner" is in danger of disintegrating. And our Constitution, our Bill of Rights have to be, you know, really better taken care of. And there are many examples of that around the country. So we're going to launch a public/private partnership--some money in the federal budget, but I hope raising some private money, to go out and save these precious parts of our past.

LAUER: It's interesting in listening to you talk, that when you deal with the allegations against the president, you refer to him as your husband.

Mrs. CLINTON: Right.

LAUER: And when you deal with issues in the State of the Union address, you talk to him, and refer to him as the president.

Mrs. CLINTON: You know, this has been so hard for me, because, you know, I remember reading one time that--when President Kennedy became president, even his brother said 'I can no longer call you k, I have to call you Mr. President.' Well, obviously, I call my sband 'Bill,' and I refer to him as my husband, but when he's

:ing in his official capacity, like he will tonight when he stands up and talks about where we are as a nation, I guess I feel that he's my president as well as my husband.

LAUER: Just a few seconds left. Based on what you know now...

Mrs. CLINTON: Uh-huh.

LAUER: ...five years after coming to Washington, the personal attacks, the political attacks, do you sit home at night and think it's worth it--it has been worth it?

Mrs. CLINTON: I do, Matt, and I'll tell you why. Obviously, I've thought a lot about that, because this has been a grueling ordeal. And it has required every bit of religious faith, or spiritual resources Bill and I have. It has been a--an incredible personal challenge, but I think about it in two ways: I believe the country is better off because my husband has been president. I think the economy, the crime rate, a lot of the social problems were finally addressed with a smart strategy, and we've seen the results. You know, just yesterday in New York, I mean in elevators and in a hotel, you know, waiters, other people came up to me, grabbed my hands and said 'You tell the president to stand firm, we need him. 's on our side.' He is. He is on the side of the American ›ple. So when I balance what he's accomplished and the hope he's given to people, and the way the economy has created opportunities for people against all of the challenges we've been through personally, it is worth it.

Now do I wish that we didn't live in a time where people were so malicious and evil-minded? Of course. But, you know, that's human nature, so you--you take the good with the bad. And the good has far--far outweighed any bad at all.

LAUER: Mrs. Clinton, we--we certainly appreciate your time, and your candor this morning. Thank you...

Mrs. CLINTON: Thank you.

LAUER: ...very much.

Mrs. CLINTON: Thank you, Matt.

LAUER: Seven twenty-four. This is TODAY on NBC.
Program Time: 7:00-9:00 AM
Nielson Rating 5879400
Reference: 980127

:d Count: 4019

1/27/98 TODAY (No Page)

[illegible]7/98 TODAY (No Page)
END OF DOCUMENT

Tab 37

1980

REMARKS BY PRESIDENT BILL CLINTON AND BRITISH PRIME MINISTER TONY BLAIR
DURING A PHOTO OPPORTUNITY THE WHITE HOUSE WASHINGTON, DC
APPROXIMATELY 12:15 P.M. EST **THURSDAY, FEBRUARY 5**, 1998

PRESIDENT CLINTON: Let me just say, to start out, the reason we're kind of hanging around like this is we're about to go into the back dining room there so we can have a working lunch. And I'm looking forward to this. We're going to have two good days. And we have a lot to discuss, not only Iraq, which everyone knows about, and Ireland, but also the plans that we're making together, or at least in common, for our countries domestically, and a lot of other issues that will affect both the people of Great Britain and the people of the United States. So this is going to be a good meeting.

Q Mr. President, would you mind -- would you like to use this occasion to tell the American people what kind of relationship, if any, you had with Monica Lewinsky?

PRESIDENT CLINTON: Well, I've already said that the charges are false. But there is an ongoing investigation.
And I think it's important that I go back and do the work for the American people that I was hired to do. I think that's what I have to do now.

Q Are you going to exert executive privilege, sir?

PRESIDENT CLINTON: First, let me make it clear. For four years we've been cooperating exhaustively. And that's a hypothetical question, as far as I know. Should it arise, I will await a recommendation from the White House counsel about the institutional responsibilities of the presidency, and when I get it, then I'll make a decision.

Q Mr. President, there are a lot of Republican leaders and arm-chair generals who want you to change your policy toward Iraq and to take out Saddam. What is your feeling about that now?

PRESIDENT CLINTON: Well, I would make two points. First of all -- and I believe the prime minister has also made this point. What is the cause of the present stand-off? It is the suspension of the inspections by the United Nations inspectors and the restrictions on where they can inspect. Our interest is in preventing Saddam Hussein from building biological, chemical, nuclear weapons capability, the missiles to deliver such weapons. That is our interest. That's where the authority from the United Nations resolutions rests. So that's the first thing.

Now, second thing, as a practical matter, we can pursue that interest with available options. Would the Iraqi people be better off if there were a change in leadership? I certainly think they would be. But that is not what the United Nations has authorized us to do, that is not what our immediate interests is about.

Now, we intend to be very firm on this, and I hope that we will have the world community with us. But what I really hope most of all is that there will be a diplomatic resolution of this, that Saddam Hussein will move away from his present position.

Q But if you were to order military strikes, they would not be directed specifically at him?

PRESIDENT CLINTON: Well, first of all, there is an executive order that's been place for over 20 years on that subject.

Q (Off mike.)

PRESIDENT CLINTON: It does. Now -- but let's not discuss hypothetically what targets might be there or what we might do. I think it is important that he understand that we are very resolute on the issue of the inspection system. And it's not an American issue. You might want to ask the prime minister about it.

Q Are you saying there's an order to take him out?

PRESIDENT CLINTON: No, no, no! No, no. No. I was referring to the executive order, I believe first issued by President Ford, saying that it is against -- that political killing or assassination, if you will, is against American foreign policy interests, that we don't do that.

But we are very firm in our resolve. And I was very heartened by the prime minister's statement in the White House there about his position.

Q Are you concerned about Mr. Yeltsin's comments about the possibility of leading towards a war? I know he backed off that a little bit. But what are our views on that?

PRESIDENT CLINTON: Well, I doubt that that would happen. We had a good talk the other day -- President Yeltsin and I did. And I know that he very much hopes that a violent confrontation can be avoided. So do I. But in the end, it is up to Saddam Hussein, it is not up to the rest of us. We don't -- and I don't -- I haven't talked to a single soul who hopes there will be some sort of violent encounter here, not a soul.

PRIME MINISTER BLAIR: Yeah, that's absolutely right.

Q There are also diplomatic efforts by the French and the Russians in Baghdad right now. Do you think they can bear fruit and avoid a military strike?

PRIME MINISTER BLAIR: Of course everyone hopes that a diplomatic solution is available and can work. We all want that. But I think all of our experience with Saddam Hussein teaches us that diplomacy has very little chance of working, unless it is clear to him that if diplomacy does not work, then the threat and the reality of force is there.

And the reason why it's important for us to take the position we are is because over these past few years, the U.N. weapons inspectors have uncovered literally thousands of chemical weapons, they've discovered biological warfare capability, they've discovered the beginnings of nuclear capability. It is for that very reason that the inspectors are there. It's for that very reason that the U.N. has made it quite clear that the U.N. inspectors have got to go in so that we destroy that capability to develop weapons of mass destruction.

And I think that the entire international community, whatever varying degrees of enthusiasm for using the military option, understand that Saddam Hussein has to be stopped, and that it is absolutely essential in the long-term interests of world peace that we make sure that he can't develop these weapons of mass destruction because he is a man who has used those weapons before; he will use them again, if he's given the opportunity to do so.

STAFF: Last question.

(Cross talk.)

Q Aside from your role on Iraq, do you have a specific role in the Middle East peace process now?

50-893 98 - 13

PRIME MINISTER BLAIR: Well, we obviously want to do everything we can, both as Great Britain and also as the president of the European Union at the moment, to back up the efforts that are being made here to try and secure a peace settlement in the Middle East. And I, myself, have both seen and corresponded regularly with Prime Minister Netanyahu and Yasser Arafat. And we continue the whole time to see what we can do to move that process forward because there is a process underway; it is in a very difficult situation at the moment. But as we know from our own attempts to secure peace in Northern Ireland, if we don't try and push these processes forward, they very quickly slip back. So I think there is a great deal of urgency there, and we will obviously work with our American colleagues to see what we can do to help.

PRESIDENT CLINTON: We're going to talk about this quite a bit. And I'm -- I view the prime minister's interest in the Middle East in a very positive light. And as you know, we are working -- Secretary Albright has been working very hard to jump-start these negotiations again, to get them through this next phase so we can go on to final status talks. And we're going to need all the help we can, and we need all the help we can in the world to rebuild the economic fabric as well as -- of the Palestinian areas, and as well as a climate of confidence and trust between all the parties. So I'm hopeful we can make some headway. We're going to talk about it.

Thank you.

STAFF: Thank you.

(Cross talk.)

Q (Inaudible.)

PRESIDENT CLINTON: I can only say -- I've said the charges aren't true, there's an investigation going on. While that's going on, it's my duty to keep doing the job I was hired to do by the American people. And that's my position.

Tab 38

1986

JOINT NEWS CONFERENCE WITH PRESIDENT BILL CLINTON
AND BRITISH PRIME MINISTER TONY BLAIR
THE WHITE HOUSE, THE EAST ROOM WASHINGTON, DC 11:07 A.M. EST
FRIDAY, FEBRUARY 6, 1998

PRESIDENT CLINTON: Good morning. Please be seated.

First, let me say that it's been a real pleasure to welcome my friend Prime Minister Blair here to Washington, with the entire British entourage. It continues the great tradition of partnership between our nations, anchored by common values, driven by common vision, eager to meet the challenges of this new age.

Today we pay tribute to that heritage with a visit to the FDR memorial. Earlier in this century President Roosevelt and Prime Minister Churchill led the community of free nations that prevailed in world war. Now, on the eve of the 21st century, the prime minister and I seek to shape the peace in a world that is rich with possibility and promise, but still not free from risk.

We have a very similar outlook on preparing our own countries for the future. And if I might just take a moment to talk about the latest economic news, the strategy we are both working is to prepare all our people for the Information Age and a global economy.

Today we have new evidence that that strategy is working here. In the last month America had 358,000 new jobs, over a million in the last three months.

We're approaching 15 million new jobs in the last five years with the lowest unemployment in 24 years. Wages are rising, inflation is low, the role of government has changed. We have the smallest percentage of these new jobs in the public sector and the highest percentage in the private sector, in the United States since the 1920s. By maintaining fiscal discipline, opening more markets, investing more in our people, we will continue to expand opportunity and promote prosperity.

We also share a common view of the changes that are occurring in the world and a belief in the importance of working together to harness them to the benefit of our people. We've reviewed our progress in building an undivided Europe; welcoming Hungary, the Czech Republic and Poland into NATO; forging strong relations with the new democracies there, including Russia and Ukraine; helping the parties in Bosnia to fulfill the requirements of the Dayton peace accord.

Both our nations agree we should take part in a follow-on security presence when the SFOR mission ends in Bosnia in June. We reaffirmed our determination to combat modern cross-border threats like terrorism and the spread of the weapons of mass destruction.

On Iraq, we stand together. Saddam Hussein must know that we are determined to prevent him from threatening his neighbors and the world with weapons of mass destruction. The prime minister and I would both prefer a genuine diplomatic solution. The best way to stop Saddam from developing an arsenal of nuclear, chemical and biological weapons, and the missiles to deliver them, is to get the inspectors back to work with full and free access to all relevant sites. But let me be clear. If Saddam does not comply with the unanimous will of the international community, we must be prepared to act -- and we are.

On Libya, 10 years later, we haven't forgotten the victims of the bombing of Pan Am 103 in the skies over Lockerbie, Scotland, or their loved one. We will not rest until Libya complies with the requirements of the world community and surrenders for trial in the United States or Scotland, the two Libyans accused of that brutal crime.

We addressed our commitment to advance the cause of peace, and I welcome Britain's efforts as president of the European Union to spur greater cooperation in the Middle East peace process.

I also commend the prime minister for his courageous steps in cooperation with the Irish government to promote a climate of confidence and hope in Northern Ireland. The multi-party talks provide the best chance for a real solution to that conflict. I urge all the parties to show the vision and the forbearance and the determination to succeed.

I unequivocally condemn this recent sectarian killings and beatings and threats. Nothing worth having in Northern Ireland can be accomplished through violence. I told the prime minister that we will continue to do all we can to advance the cause of peace. And, of course, I asked for and received his advice in that regard.

The recent financial crisis in Asia demands action from the international community. On our increasingly interconnected planet, trouble in the far end of town can easily become a plague in our own neighborhood. We agree that every affected nation must take responsibility for implementing tough reforms, and that other nations, when they do that, when those nations that are affected do their part, other nations should support helping them through the International Monetary Fund.

We also looked at ways that we could work together to benefit our people at home. As president of both the European Union and the G-7, the United Kingdom will host two important summits in Birmingham this May. The prime minister told me he wants to take these summits to take action that really will make a difference in our people's daily lives, that lift their horizons and their dreams, stepping up our efforts to combat drug traffickers and helping every child to grow up in a safe community.

Shielding our planet from the threat of global warming and

bringing our people the benefits of a growing economy and a clean environment are important to us as well.

It's also important that we give our people the tools to make the most of their lives through world-class education and training, help people to move from welfare to work -- and I applaud the efforts that the prime minister is making on that -- give them access to the wonders of the Information Age -- that's something we talked about yesterday at the Montgomery Blair High School in Maryland -- and dealing with the question of how to provide greater security in the retirement years when the baby boom generation retires.

We finally know that our two nations must continue to work and to lead the world, for security, prosperity, and peace.

In 1942, in the midst of the Second World War, President Roosevelt sent a message to Mr. Churchill, which said as follows: "When victory comes, we shall stand shoulder to shoulder in seeking to nourish the great ideals for which we fight."

Today, on the verge of a new century and a new millennium, that prediction has proved right. America is proud to stand with the United Kingdom and with Europe, and to work with its leader, Prime Minister Tony Blair, to build an even brighter future.

Thank you, Mr. Prime Minister. The floor is yours.

PRIME MINISTER BLAIR: Thank you, Mr. President. And can I begin by saying how grateful we have been for such a wonderful and warm welcome here in the United States of America.

As the president has just indicated, we discussed, obviously, a range of different topics. At the top of the list, of course, was the situation in respect of Iraq. And what we agreed was that we had to do three things in particular. We have, first of all, to make sure that our own public opinion was properly educated as to why it is so essential that the U.N. inspectors are able to do their work, the amount of weapons that they have already uncovered in the six or seven years that they have been doing this task, and why it is therefore absolutely essential that Saddam Hussein is brought back into line with U.N. Security Council resolutions and the inspectors can go about their task unhindered.

We ourselves a couple of days ago in Britain published a document where we listed precisely all the various weapon finds the inspectors have made.

And when you go through that list and see all of the various attempts there have been, to try and prevent the inspectors' carrying out their functions, then I think people can understand why it is so necessary, so important for us to be prepared to take whatever action is necessary to ensure those inspectors can go back in and fulfill their task.

Secondly, though, in relation to Iraq, it is important that we stress, all the time, of course we want a diplomatic solution. But it must be a diplomatic solution based on, and fully consistent with, the principles that we have set out.

The question of whether there is such a diplomatic solution rests ultimately with Saddam Hussein. He has the choice. He can bring himself back into compliance with the agreements he entered into, and then that diplomatic solution can be fulfilled.

Thirdly, however, we have, of course, to prepare in case diplomacy cannot work. In view of the situation, we in Britain have been looking at our own military readiness, in case a diplomatic solution does not, in the end, prove possible.

We have decided to base eight Tornado GR-1 aircraft in Kuwait, with the full agreement of the government of Kuwait. These are ground attack and reconnaissance aircraft. Their deployment is a precautionary measure, and it will take place over the next few days.

So, all the way through, in respect of Iraq, we have agreed that we must educate, we must engage in diplomacy, but we also must prepare.

In respect of Ireland, I want to place on record yet again my thanks to the president for all the support he has given us in searching for a lasting and peaceful political settlement in Ireland. As I've found when I've addressed many members of Congress and the Senate here in Washington, there is tremendous interest in the United States of America in this process. And there is a great, much-appreciated willingness on your part to have that process succeed.

It isn't going to be easy; these things never are. But we do believe that we have the best chance that we have had for many generations to secure peace. And I wanted to emphasize yet again to you our total and complete determination and commitment to find a peaceful way through.
With goodwill and with proper cooperation and with some trust on all sides, I think it is possible.

And I thank the president for his condemnation of those sectarian killings that have so disfigured the process over the past few weeks. And I say, yet again, what we must ensure is that those random, brutal, unjustified acts of violence perpetrated by a small minority, must not in the end, frustrate the wishes of the overwhelming majority of people in Northern Ireland to secure a peaceful and stable future for themselves.

We discussed, of course, the Middle East peace process, and Bosnia and our commitment there. We discussed as the president has mentioned a moment ago, the global economy, the Asian crisis, and what measures we should take in order to ensure that such crises are mitigated and do not happen again.

We also laid out for the president and his colleagues, our strategy as president of the European Union; our commitment to ensure the monetary union is successfully launched; our commitment to the enlargement process, bringing into the European Union those countries in Eastern Europe and elsewhere. And we discussed as well, and agree, that it was important that Europe strengthened its relationship with Turkey and that we build a strong relationship with Turkey; between Turkey and the European Union for the future.

As good and interesting as anything else has been also the possibility of exchanging ideas, ideas about how government meets the economic and social and political challenges of the future.

As I said in my speech this morning at the breakfast hosted by the vice president, there is a new Britain being shaped today. It is a Britain of confidence, dynamism. It is a Britain that is proud of its past but is not living in it, and is shaping a future of which we can be proud also. And I think in exchanging ideas, and in seeing how much there are common themes and common ideas for government between us, we can gain strength in Britain and United States from that partnership and relationship.

And finally, I would like to say, personally, how tremendously grateful I have been, as I say not merely for the warmth of the welcome extended to us here, but for the great comradeship and partnership between the United States of America and Great Britain that I know will strengthen and strengthen evermore in the future.

Thank you.

PRESIDENT CLINTON: Now, here's what we're going to do, we're going to alternate, and so I'll call on an American journalist and the prime minister will call on a British journalist. Of course you're free to ask whomever whatever you please.

Helen?

Q Mr. President, despite the ongoing investigation, you felt no constraint in saying what your relationship with Monica Lewinsky is not -- was not. So it seems, by logic, that you ought to be able to say here and now what was your relationship? Her lawyer says -- called it "colleagues." Is that an apt description?

PRESIDENT CLINTON: Well, let me first of all say, once again, I never asked anybody to do anything but tell the truth. I know about the stories today. I was pleased that Ms. Currie's lawyers stated unambiguously this morning -- unambiguously -- that she's not aware of any unethical conduct.

But this investigation is going on and you know what the rules for it are. And I just think as long as it's going on, I should not comment on the specific questions because one -- there's one, then there's another, then there's another. It's better to let the investigation go on and have me do my job and focus on my public responsibilities and let this thing play out its course. That's what I think I should do, and that's what I intend to do.

Q You are leaving people in the dark.

PRESIDENT CLINTON: Well, I'm honoring the rules of the investigation, and if someone else is leaking, unlawfully, out of the grand jury proceeding, that's a different story. I am going to do -- I have told the American people what I think is essential for them to know about this and what I believe they want to know. What I'm doing is going on with my work and cooperating with the investigation. And I do not believe I should answer specific questions. I don't think that's the right thing to do now.

PRIME MINISTER BLAIR: Michael?

Q Michael Brownson of ITN in London. Is it not time, though, to drop the pretense that this is simply business as usual? Have we not seen, with the allegations that surrounding the British foreign secretary, but to a much greater degree yourself, Mr. President, that this does affect the conduct of public business?

And far from dodging the point as you did, Prime Minister, yesterday when you were asked about the private lives of public figures, should you not both be saying that the public have the right to expect the very highest standard in the private lives of public politicians?

PRIME MINISTER BLAIR: Well, Michael, I hope we do that. But what I would say to you is that what is essential is that we focus on the issues that we were elected to focus upon. And in the discussions that we have had over this past two days, we have been focusing on issues like Iraq, where we are considering, if diplomatic solutions fail, taking military action; we've been focusing on the peace process in Northern Ireland, that gives a chance for the first time in generations, after centuries of conflict, for people to find a way through; we've been focusing on the problems of the world economy that, if they're not tackled, could have a serious impact on the living standards of people here and people in Britain, as well as people out in Asia.

These are the important questions for me, schools, hospitals, crime, living standards, jobs that people want us to focus upon. And I believe that it is absolutely essential that we stay focused upon those things and that we deliver for our people what we were elected to deliver.

Now, that is what I intend to do. And I think that that is, in the end, what the British people would expect me to do.

PRESIDENT CLINTON: Terry?

Q Mr. President, switching to Iraq, the prime minister said that you had to educate the public about Iraq; but I think the American public is largely in the dark about what to expect about a military attack on Iraq. Are you talking about something that lasts a day or two, or something that lasts for weeks or months?

And on a diplomatic note, you've got France and China and Russia opposing this. Boris Yeltsin says that it could lead to World War III. What gives Britain and the United States the right to go it alone on this?

PRESIDENT CLINTON: Well, you asked about five questions there in one. Let me try to unpack it.

First of all, the most important thing, the best thing that could be done, what we hope will happen, is that there will be a diplomatic solution to this which result in the inspection teams for the United Nations being able to return and have unfettered access to the appropriate sites, because, as -- the prime minister, I think, put out a paper just a couple of days ago pointing out the incredible work that's been done by the inspection teams.

That's the best thing.

Now whether there is a diplomatic solution or not is entirely up to Saddam Hussein. If he decides that he wants to continue to have the freedom to rebuild his weapons program, then I believe that the clear mandate for the world community, based on not only the resolutions of the United Nations, but the danger this would present to the interests and values of the United States, the people of Great Britain, the people of the region, is to do what we can to weaken his ability to develop those weapons of mass destruction and to visit them on his neighbors.

You know, I never discuss operational plans; I wouldn't do that. I think the important thing is that you know that -- that I don't want this. Nobody wants this; we want a diplomatic solution. It's up to him.

The second thing I would say is, the secretary of state has been working hard in the last several days, has traveled, as you know, widely. I have been on the phone a lot. I believe there is -- there is more agreement than at first it appears about the necessity to push this thing through to the end. And I will continue to talk with the -- with President Yeltsin, President Chirac, and others.

But consider the alternative. After all, this man is the only repeat offender around with chemical weapons. He used them on his own people. He used them on the Iranians. And I believe it's a very serious thing. And I think that the American people will understand that.

Q ("World war," said ?) President Yeltsin --

PRESIDENT CLINTON: I just -- I don't understand what chain of circumstances would lead to that development. I don't believe that will happen.

PRIME MINISTER BLAIR: Peter?

Q Peter Riddle (sp), the Times. On Iraq, you've said the need was to educate, Prime Minister. But it isn't entirely clear what the objective of military action would be.
Is it intended to as a punishment for Saddam Hussein? Is it intended as a substitute for the work of the weapons inspectors, destroyed? Or would it continue until Saddam said: "Right. I'll let them in"?

And also, you've announced the deployment of some aircraft. Is there any intention to deploy ground troops at all, British ground troops?

PRIME MINISTER BLAIR: No. The deployment that we have made is the deployment that I have described, of the aircraft.

And with respect to the objectives; well, the objectives are very clear; that is, to ensure either that the weapon inspectors can come in and finish their task or that the capability that Saddam Hussein undoubtedly has and wants to develop for weapons of mass destruction, is taken out. And it is absolutely essential that what we do is focused upon the best way possible that we can do that.

Now obviously, as the president was saying a moment or two ago, it is not sensible or serious to start discussing the details of the military options available to us. But the purpose of this the whole way through, the reason we are in this situation, is because he has been developing weapons of mass destruction. The only barrier to that has been the inspectors. If the inspectors are prevented from doing their work, then we have to make sure, by the military means of which we are capable, that insofar as possible, that capacity ceases.

And that's the objective, and it's an objective that I think is fully in line, as I say, with the original agreements under which Saddam Hussein undertook -- I mean, remember, he agreed, he undertook, to destroy any weapons-of-mass-destruction capability, whether nuclear, chemical or biological. Now, he is in breach of that. And we've got to make sure that he complies, one way or another, with it.

STAFF (?): (American ?).

Q Mr. President, just to go back to the controversy that's been surrounding you lately; there have been various reports that in some ways, have come to be accepted as fact. And I just want to give you an opportunity.

One of them is that, in sworn testimony to the lawyers for Paula Jones, that you changed your version of your relationship with Gennifer Flowers. And I just wondered if you can tell us -- I mean, do you now --

PRESIDENT CLINTON: I can tell you, but let me just say this. Again, even though the judge's order has been routinely violated by the other side in the case -- the judge has issued strict orders in the case for -- for -- that covers everybody, including me, not to discuss it.

I can tell you this -- and I'm confident as this thing plays out it will become more apparent in the future -- if you go back -- I told the truth in my deposition with regard to that issue, and I also did in 1992 when I did the interview, which I think was rerun the other night, the interview that Hillary and I did on "60 Minutes." And you just have to know that, and that I think it will be -- become apparent, as this case plays itself out, that I did in fact do that.

But I am not going to discuss that. The judge has given us strict orders not to discuss anything related to that case. The other side has violated it on a regular basis. I don't intend to do that. I'm just not going to do it.

PRIME MINISTER BLAIR: John?

Q John -- (last name, affiliation off mike). Prime Minister, Mr. President, is it possible for you to launch an attack if you don't have on board the French, the Russians, the Chinese?

PRIME MINISTER BLAIR: I think, John, you have to distinguish very carefully between what, of course I accept, varying degrees of enthusiasm or commitment for the military option, with the complete unanimity there is in the world community that Saddam Hussein has to comply with the resolutions, and that his capacity to develop weapons of mass destruction must be halted.

Now, it is difficult for us to see, and for me to see, quite frankly, that if you take that as the position, how diplomacy, unless it is backed up at least by the threat of force, is ever going to work and succeed.

But it would be wrong, I think, to think that either our -- for example, our French or our Russian colleagues were not absolutely insistent that Saddam Hussein comply with these resolutions, and they are making diplomatic efforts in order to ensure that that happens. I wish those efforts well, provided they are fully consistent with the principles that have been set out.

It is just that we take the view, and I think experience teaches us that this is the only realistic view of Saddam Hussein, that unless you back up whatever diplomatic initiatives you're taking with saying quite clearly, well, if diplomacy doesn't work, the option of force is there, then those diplomatic initiatives are unlikely to succeed. But it's important that we realize that it is in that area that any difference lies, not in the insistence of the world community that he must come into line with those U.N. resolutions.

PRESIDENT CLINTON: Peter?

Q Mr. President, your spokesman this morning described to us, in his words, a very dangerous environment following these alleged leaks. What's your own assessment of the legal atmosphere? And we understand that your attorneys are planning to take some action about this. What action do they intend to take?

PRESIDENT CLINTON:I think you should talk to them. I don't want to comment on what they're going to do. They're fully capable of speaking for themselves, and for me in this case.

Q And your comment, sir, on the effect of the leaks?

PRESIDENT CLINTON: I don't have anything to add to what has already been said about that.

PRIME MINISTER BLAIR: Phil.

Q I'm Phil Murphy from the Press Association. Could I ask the prime minister, you could have come here and simply talked about serious politics, but some people have been struck by the warmth of the personal statements of support that you've given to the president. Could I ask you -- I mean, have you ever considered that that might be a politically risky strategy?

Could I ask the president, have you appreciated those comments from Mr. Blair?

PRIME MINISTER BLAIR: To be quite honest, Phil, I mean I've said it because I believed it and because I think it is the right thing to do. And I've worked with President Clinton now for some nine months as British prime minister. I have found him throughout someone I could trust, someone I could rely upon, someone I am proud to call not just a colleague but a friend.

And in the end, you either decide in politics, when you're asked about people, you're going to say how you actually feel or you're going to make a whole series of calculations. And my belief is that the right thing to say is what you feel. And I happen to think -- I don't know whether it's my place to say it or not -- that if you look at the American economy, you look at the respect with which America is held right 'round the world today, if you look at the standing and authority of the president, it's a pretty impressive record for anyone.

PRESIDENT CLINTON: You ask, do I appreciate it? No, I -- (laughter). He should have come here and jumped all over me, I mean -- (laughter).

PRIME MINISTER BLAIR: Do you want me to come back in now? (Laughter).

PRESIDENT CLINTON: Of course I do. But, you know, I -- I think it's also a testament about the -- there's been a lot of -- a lot of people bandy about the word "character," and sometimes in loose and uncertain contexts. I think the people who -- who stand up and say things that they believe when it would be just as easy to walk away show a certain kind of character that I think is essential in a public leader, and I'm very gratified that -- that Tony Blair has done that. Not only for personal reasons, but because I think it -- it will strengthen his authority as a world leader.

Q Mr. President?

PRESIDENT CLINTON: Yes, go ahead?

Q Mr. President, all these questions about your personal life have to be painful to you and your family. At what point do you consider that it's just not worth it, and you consider resigning from office? (Mild laughter.)

PRESIDENT CLINTON: Never. You know, I was elected to do a job. I think the American people know two or three things about me now that they didn't know the first time this kind of effort was made against me. They -- I think they know that I care very much about them, that I care about ordinary people whose voices aren't often heard here. And I think they know I have worked very, very hard for them.

And I think they know now, more often than not, the ideas I had and the things I fought for turned out to be right in terms of the consequences to the American people. I think they know all that. And I'm just going to keep showing up for work. I'm going to do what I was hired to do, and I'm going to try to keep getting good results for them.

The pain threshold, at least for our side, being in public today has been raised. But to give in to that would be to give in to everything that I fought against and that got me into this race in 1991 to try to run for president in the first place. I have tried to bring an end to this sort of thing in our public life. I've tried to bring the American people together. I've tried to de-personalize politics and take the venom out of it. And the harder I've tried to do it, the harder others have pulled in the other direction. That doesn't mean I'm wrong. And I would -- I would -- I would never walk away from the people of this country and the trust they placed in me.

PRIME MINISTER BLAIR: Robert?

Q Sir, Robert -- (last name inaudible) -- from the National Times. Prime Minister, this morning you said that the U.K. faced two painful years. Could you expand on what you meant by that?

PRIME MINISTER BLAIR: Yes. I mean, as I was saying to people this morning, I mean, there are some very tough decisions that we have had to take in order to deal both with the structural budget deficit, with the inflation that was back in the system that we inherited when we came to power, and with an education and welfare system that, frankly, is just nowhere near where it needs to be for the 21st century. And making those changes is going to be tough. Welfare reform isn't going to be easy; it will be unpopular in certain quarters. Taking the measures to cure the budget deficit has been hard. When people want more money spent on more public services, we're saying, look, we can't go on with ever-higher debt levels and borrowing. We've got to act.

So we've taken the action on interest rates and giving the Bank of England independence. We've cut the structural deficit. A balanced budget is something we'll be able to talk about on the other side of the water as well, in a few years time. We're putting through a massive program of reform on education and welfare, but it will be tough, and it will take us some time to get it through.

But as I said this morning, I am an unashamed long-termist.

PRESIDENT CLINTON: (Chuckles.)

PRIME MINISTER BLAIR: I believe in making sure that the decisions that we take aren't based on the next day's headlines, but are based on where we really want the country to be some years down the line.
And particularly when we're facing such enormous global economic challenges, we can't afford either to lose a grip on monetary or fiscal prudence, or to leave our education and welfare system in the state they're in.

So yes, it'll be tough. But it'll be worth it in the end.

<u> PRESIDENT CLINTON:</u> Well, if I -- let me just me just make one comment to support something the prime minister just said -- when he said he was an unashamed long-termist. In a funny way, when societies change as fast and as much as our societies are changing today, when the -- the pace of events and their variety make it more difficult to predict what will happen next week or next month, it is even more important to be oriented toward the long term, because you have to figure that if you lay in a structure of opportunity and -- for a free people, they'll get it right, and they'll overcome all these unpredictable developments in the meanwhile. And I think that -- that's why I think the approach that he has taken is so wise and so right, not only for Great Britain, but for any other country as well.

(Cross talk.) Yes, Mara? Go ahead.

Q I'm wondering if you could elaborate on something that the first lady said recently about a right-wing conspiracy who's working against you. Could you explain how that conspiracy works? And specifically, are Linda Tripp, Ken Starr, and Monica Lewinsky part of that conspiracy?

PRESIDENT CLINTON: Now you know I've known her a long time -- the first lady -- and she's very smart. And she's hardly ever wrong about anything. (Laughter.) But I don't believe I should amplify on her observation in this case. (Scattered laughter.)

Q Do you agree with that?

PRIME MINISTER BLAIR: Yeah, Adam?

Q Adam -- (last name off mike). One of your common shared themes you keep on telling your voters is this matter of their rights go with responsibilities. Now you, as elected leaders, have extraordinary rights and privileges. Yet you seem to be saying that there's no extension of responsibilities as far as personal integrity is concerned. Is that what you're really saying? If you're delivering on the job, the big picture, it doesn't matter what you get up to in your private lives?

PRIME MINISTER BLAIR: Nobody is saying that you don't have obligations of personal integrity. Of course, that's right. But what we are trying to say to you is the responsibilities with which we were asked by our people to discharge, those responsibilities are on the issues that -- where we can affect them as leaders of the country.

And if you go to Britain today and you talk to the British people -- and I do ask -- it just could be that sometimes you guys in the media are not in exactly the same place as a lot of public opinion in terms of the priorities people have. But if you go out there and you talk to British people and you say, "What do you want this new Labour government to do?" they will talk to you about ensuring we don't have boom and bust but that we have steadily rising living standards. They'll talk about job security. They'll talk about the state of their schools. You know, they'll talk about the national health service. They'll talk about the welfare system and the crime in their streets. They'll talk about security and old age. They will talk about these things, and they will care about these things. And they will expect us to deliver those responsibilities.

And of course, it's a great privilege for us to occupy the positions that we do. But in the end, the judgment that the people make of us is a judgment based on what we said that we would do and whether we fulfilled the promises that we made, and that's certainly what we intend to do. And I do think, also, that people understand and want political leadership that addresses these fundamental questions in a way that means something to them.

And when I was at the Montgomery Blair High School yesterday with the president and the president got up and addressed the young men and women, and the teachers and staff and parents that were there, and started going through the education program that he was unveiling, and it formed part of the State of the Union address and everything; and some of those things in terms of class sizes and new technology in the schools that (are ?) very familiar to the British contingent here as things we're trying to do in Britain; I mean, the enthusiasm and the delight with which those things were greeted, because those people knew that in the end, that's what they elected their president to do. That's what they elected me to do; and that those are things that they want from us. And we've got to make sure all the time, that we're focusing on that big picture.

And you know, whatever other issues come along and distract us, in the end the judgment of history upon us will be pretty poor if those weren't the things that, when we got to bed at night, we're thinking about.

Those weren't the things that we're worried about and concerned about throughout the entirety of our society. Because those are the things which really make a difference to their lives.

Q Mr. President?

Q Mr. Prime Minister?

Q Sir?

PRESIDENT CLINTON: Go ahead.

STAFF: Let's make this the last round.

PRESIDENT CLINTON: Go ahead.

Q Mr. President, Monica Lewinsky's life has been changed forever -- her family's life has been changed forever. I wonder how you feel about that, and what, if anything, you'd like to say to Monica Lewinsky at this minute?

(Mild laughter.)

PRESIDENT CLINTON: That's good. (Laughter.) That's good, but at this minute I'm going to stick with my position -- I'm not commenting.

PRIME MINISTER BLAIR (?): Yes?

Q While relations between Britain and the United States appear to be splendid right now, there's a darkening cloud over relations with Italy. The prime minister, the president, the defense minister has issued some very harsh statements about the accident the other day when a low-flying Marine plane severed a cable and the car fell. There's a lot of anger; some people in Italy are even asking for the closing of the Aviano base. What do you have to say to them?

PRESIDENT CLINTON: Well, first of all, what happened was horrible. And when I heard about it I was very shaken, and I -- I, as you know, there were -- there was a period of a few hours there where it wasn't clear how many people had died, and where there was another whole gondola suspended, where many more people could have died and, thank God, they were rescued. And the whole thing has been an agony for the people of Italy, and there were large -- a substantial number of Germans killed, and I'm sure, for the pilot of the plane and the people in our military base in Aviano, where I have been on more than one occasion.

I can tell you what I think should be done. I called Prime Minister Prodi and I told him that I was heart sick about it; that I would make absolutely sure there was a no holds barred, full investigation on what happened; that the Italians would be kept fully informed and be a part of it; and that we would work with them in every way possible to make sure that they knew that we tried to get to the bottom of it and to handle it in the appropriate way.

You know, in our military every year -- I say this to the American people all the time, but let me -- let me just say this. It is an inherently dangerous business. Now, we don't know what the facts are. Maybe somebody made a careless mistake, we don't know. I do not know what the facts are, and I will not render judgment until I do. But we lose about 200 people every year in military service in America on training exercise or otherwise on duty. And those planes fly very fast. And I don't know what the description of the mission was; I want to wait until I see exactly what the facts are, but it is inherently more dangerous than I think we think from time to time.

Now, I told the prime minister of Italy, and I'll tell you, I will do everything I can to find out exactly what happened and to take appropriate action and to satisfy the people of Italy that we have done the right thing. I understand why they are hurt and heartbroken and angry, and they are entitled to answers and we'll try to give them to them.

Q Mr. President?

STAFF: Thank you. Last question.

PRESIDENT CLINTON: Now, go ahead, the gentleman in the back. I promised one more. Last question.

Go ahead.

Q Mr. President, do you believe that airstrikes alone are going to remove the threat of biological, chemical and nuclear weapons from Saddam Hussein? Is that a fair thing to expect from military action, should push come to shove in the Gulf?

PRESIDENT CLINTON: Well, there have been many thoughtful public pieces, a lot of very thoughtful articles which have been written about the limits, as well as the possibilities of any kind of military action.

I think the precise question should be -- that I should have to ask and answer -- is, could any military action, if all else fails, substantially reduce or delay Saddam Hussein's capacity to develop weapons of mass destruction and to deliver them on his neighbors? The answer to that, I am convinced, is yes. I'm convinced there is a yes answer there. But you have to understand that those are the criteria for me.

I've told you before, I don't believe we need to re-fight the Gulf War. It's history. It happened. That's the way it is. I don't believe we need to get into a direct war with Iraq over the leadership of the country. Do I think the country would be better served if it had a different leader? Of course I do. That's not the issue. The issue is that very sharp question.

If the inspection regime is dead, and therefore we cannot continue to make progress on getting the stuff out of there in the first place, and then -- keep in mind there are two things about this regime. There's the progress in getting the stuff out of there in the first place, and then there is the monitoring system, which enables people on a regular basis to go back to high-probability sites to make sure nothing is happening to rebuild it. So, if that is dead, is there an option which would permit us to reduce and/or delay his capacity to bring those weapons up and to deliver them? That is -- I think the answer to that is yes, there is an option that would permit that.

Q Mr. President, as a follow-on to that --

PRESIDENT CLINTON: Do you want to ask one more question?

Q Mr. President, as a follow-up to that, please? Mr. President, as a follow-up to that please?

Q Prime Minister, as a man who understands the pressures of public life, and also a friend, and a religious man, I wonder what words of advice and support and comfort and sympathy you might have been able to offer personally to the president during these difficult times when he's under investigation.

PRIME MINISTER BLAIR: That's what in the British media is called "a helpful question." (Laughter.)

(Chuckles.) If I can -- I don't presume to give advice at all. All I think that is important, which is what we've managed to do, is to discuss the issues that we've set out and listed for you. And as I say, I think we'd be pretty much failing in our duty if we weren't to do that.

And I've actually noticed, since I've been here and I've talked to many people here, that there is of course huge concern at the moment on what is happening in Iraq, this huge interest in Britain, in the new government, and in what we're trying to do in Northern Ireland. And you know, I think the best thing is for us to concentrate upon those issues for the very reasons I've given -- that that's what we were elected to do. And that's what I intend to do. That's what President Clinton is doing, and I think he's quite right.

Q One more, sir? (Cross talk.)

PRESIDENT CLINTON Thank you.

Tab 39

Citation | Search Result | Rank 1 of 1 | Database
'14/98 WASHPOST C03 | WP
14/98 Wash. Post C03
1998 WL 2467716

The Washington Post

Saturday, February 14, 1998

Metro

Pedestrian Death on I-95 Ruled Accidental; Brother of Clinton's Secretary Darted Into Traffic After Crash

Mike Allen
Washington Post Staff Writer

Virginia State Police have concluded that Theodore R. Williams Jr. of Fort Washington -- the brother of President Clinton's personal secretary, Betty Currie -- did not intend to commit suicide when he ran onto Interstate 95 north of Richmond after a traffic accident and was struck and killed by a tractor-trailer.

But they say there is no explanation for why Williams bolted rrom the highway shoulder after talking to a trooper who was investigating the crash with another truck, which Williams had escaped without injury.

"This has been ruled an 'accidental death/motor-vehicle crash,' " said Mary S. Evans, a state police spokeswoman.

Williams, a 52-year-old building mechanic for the Postal Service, died Dec. 15, weeks before Currie was called before a federal grand jury investigating former White House intern Monica S. Lewinsky. President Clinton attended his funeral Dec. 20.

Evans said investigators thought Williams's death "might have been suicide," but ruled that out after learning that Williams was on his way to the University of North Carolina at Chapel Hill to pick up his daughter.

"That's not usually when people commit suicide -- when they have an errand to run," Evans said. She said family members said Williams had not seemed depressed.

She said officials were not aware of Williams's connection to ırrie initially but did interview more friends and relatives than they usually would in a traffic case because of the possibility of suicide.

Evans said investigators concluded that "this is a traffic accident, a non-story story."

According to Evans, investigators found 5.2 grams of marijuana under the floor mat on the driver's side of Williams's Chevrolet pickup. In the glove box, police found a pipe and rolling papers, she said.

The state medical examiner's report found no illegal substances in his body. But the report found that Williams had a blood-alcohol level of .07 percent -- just below the legal limit for drunken driving, .08 percent.

Williams was headed south on I-95 in Hanover County about noon Dec. 15 when his pickup hit the back of a tractor-trailer. The tractor-trailer driver said he didn't feel a thing and continued down the road until he was flagged down by motorists who had seen the ash.

Williams ran off the left shoulder of the highway and down an embankment but was not hurt, according to the accident report.

Evans said that as Williams walked up the hill, state police Sgt. Jessie Roberts arrived on the scene and asked, "Are you okay?" When Williams said he was, the sergeant turned to speak to two witnesses to the accident who had stopped.

In that instant, Williams started walking toward the fast lane, Evans said.

"Get back! You're going to get hit," Roberts remembers telling him.

Then to the shock of bystanders, Williams rushed into traffic and was hit by another tractor-trailer, according to Evans.

"Nobody knows why he ran across the road," Evans said.

---- INDEX REFERENCES ----

KEY WORDS: METRO

EDITION: FINAL

Word Count: 482
2/14/98 WASHPOST C03
END OF DOCUMENT

Tab 40

2012

Citation	Search Result	Rank 2 of 3	Database
7/98 CHICAGOTR 1	CHICAGOTR
17/98 Chi. Trib. 1
1998 WL 2826917

Chicago Tribune

Tuesday, February 17, 1998

NEWS

EX-SECRET SERVICE OFFICER TESTIFIES

Lewis Fox, a retired uniformed Secret Service officer, spent about two hours Tuesday morning before the federal grand jury in Washington investigating the Monica Lewinsky matter. Steve Goodin, a White House aide who until recently served as President Clinton's personal assistant, was the next witness to be called before the grand jury. Fox's lawyer, Michael Leibig, said Tuesday his client was guarding the Oval Office on a fall afternoon in 1995 when Lewinsky went in. Appearing on ABC's "Good Morning America," Leibig said Fox didn't "didn't see anyone else at the time" with Clinton and Lewinsky but that Fox "didn't see all the exits" so he doesn't know if the two were alone.

---- INDEX REFERENCES ----

KEY WORDS: GOVERNMENT; EMPLOYEE; COURT; ISSUE; SEX; RELATION

EDITION: EVENING UPDATE; C

Word Count: 114
2/17/98 CHICAGOTR 1
END OF DOCUMENT

Tab 41

3/5/98

BY MR. HEATON:

Q Mr. Ginsburg, tell the Court what it is, precisely, that Ms. Lewinsky did in reliance on the agreement that was reached on February 2nd, 1998.

A What she did?

Q Yeah. The reference is that she has acted in reliance -- or suffered in reliance on that agreement which you testified occurred on the evening of February 2nd, including suffering with respect to her rights under the Fourth, Fifth and Sixth Amendments. I would like for you to tell the Court what it is that she has suffered since that agreement went into effect.

A An egregious invasion of her right of privacy and the requirement that she expose to you and to everyone working with you the most personal details of everything and anything that she did in a consensual sexual act. I can't think, sir, of anything more egregious and more damaging to one's psyche and ego and constitutional rights than that.

Q Explain to the Court, sir, how it is that her rights under the Fifth and Sixth amendments have been harmed as a result of what you just described.

A I do not want to go into an interpretation of the Fifth and Sixth Amendments except to say that when one has to admit certain things that they shouldn't ordinarily have to admit, they may be giving up their right to confront the people who are accusing them, they may be giving up the right to self-incrimination, they may be giving up the right to procedural and substantive due process, and in so doing, because this may be used in a grand jury proceeding and other proceedings, they may well be giving up their right to counsel under the Sixth Amendment.

I mean, we can argue and debate that, but I think the Fourth, Fifth, Sixth and Fourteenth Amendments are very much involved in the proffer process.

Q If I understand you correctly, sir, you're talking about things that you perceive could possibly happen, as opposed to things that have happened. Is that right, sir?

A No, sir, I am not. The Fourth Amendment guarantees us an absolute right to security in our person, in our property, and our papers. And I think the Fourth, Fifth, and Fourteenth Amendments, in particular, embody the right of privacy. And she, in reliance on this process and this agreement, has essentially given up what I consider to be her right of privacy, which I consider to be the most valuable right we have.

Q And it's on that basis that you have concluded that she has suffered in reliance on this agreement that occurred on February 2nd. Is that right?

A I think she has suffered greatly based on her reliance on your word, yes. You, plural, meaning the Office of Independent Counsel.

Q And this would be our oral word as you've conveyed it today, spoken by Mr. Udolf, is that right? At the conclusion of a two-week process.

A Your oral word as confirmed in an agreement integrating your oral word into a writing.

Q Mr. Ginsburg, you made various statements to the press, did you not, at or about the time of this purported agreement?

THE COURT: Let me just say this. He may or he may not have. And unless it goes to the heart of what we're discussing here, just move on to the issue. In other words, did you state to someone, if you have such information.

BY MR. HEATON:

Q Isn't it true, Mr. Ginsburg, that you told various members of the press over the period February 3rd and 4th that you were waiting on Mr. Starr and/or the Office of Independent Counsel to get back to you in terms of whether you had an agreement?

A Which date, sir?

Q February 3rd and 4th.

A That was part of our agreement. Yes.

THE COURT: Part of whose agreement?

THE WITNESS: The Independent Counsel's Office, Your Honor, told me that they did not want me to tell the press that we had an agreement. They wanted me to stay away from the press with regard to the agreement that we had struck on the evening of February the 2nd. "Do not say anything to the press," they said, "please, about this agreement that we've struck." So when asked questions about it, I said, "We have no agreement at this time." And I stayed away from the issue of the entering into the agreement.

THE COURT: They, who? In other words, who in the Office of Independent Counsel told you that?

THE WITNESS: Mr. Udolf or Mr. Emmick. I cannot remember between the two who said to me, please, keep this away from the press. My best memory, Your Honor, is Mr. Udolf said -- it may even have been Mr. Bittman; I simply cannot recall the exact person -- said, "You have been talking a lot to the press. Please do not tell the press about this immunity agreement." I said, "You have my word on that. I won't."

So when the press made inquiries about this -- and they were around my home, they were around the place I was staying, they were everywhere I went, airports, everywhere. I said to them, "We have no agreement." And I denied the existence of the agreement in order to protect the sanctity of what I had promised. There is no question I did that.

BY MR. HEATON:

Q Mr. Ginsburg, just so we're clear here, it's your testimony that based on a statement made by Mr. Emmick or Mr. Udolf, or both of them, not to reveal the existence of an immunity agreement, you then stated to various reporters, including, for example, A.P., things to the effect of "We are waiting for

Starr to call us. We are not begging for immunity. We would like immunity. If he chooses to grant us immunity, that is fine."

A I did everything to keep my word, including deflect all questions of any kind about the immunity agreement.

Q Including lie about what the situation was; is that correct?

A I don't consider that a lie, sir. I consider that a necessary function of keeping my agreement. I also consider it part of the process.

Q You consider it a necessary part of your function to say something other than what is true to protect the secrecy of this agreement. Is that right?

A Yes, sir, I did at the time.

Q And is it the same standard that you apply in general with respect to the representation of your client? It's consistent with your function, when necessary, to say something other than what is the truth?

A I will not tell a fib under perjury, sir -- penalty of perjury. But I will do what is necessary to protect my client at all times as a vigorous advocate.

Q Including lie.

A Sir, I never lie. I do what is necessary to protect my client. You have to define the word "lie" for me before I can answer that.

Tab 42

GRAND JURY PROCEEDINGS
UNDER SEAL

IN THE UNITED STATES DISTRICT COURT
FOR THE DISTRICT OF COLUMBIA

IN RE: GRAND JURY PROCEEDINGS.	)))	Misc. Nos. 98-095, 98-096, and 98-097 (UNDER SEAL)

MEMORANDUM OF THE WHITE HOUSE IN OPPOSITION TO OIC'S MOTIONS TO COMPEL BRUCE R. LINDSEY AND SIDNEY BLUMENTHAL TO TESTIFY CONCERNING CONVERSATIONS PROTECTED BY THE ATTORNEY-CLIENT, PRESIDENTIAL COMMUNICATIONS, AND WORK PRODUCT PRIVILEGES

Of Counsel:
Charles F.C. Ruff
Counsel to the President
THE WHITE HOUSE
Washington, D.C. 20500
(202) 456-1414

W. Neil Eggleston
Timothy K. Armstrong
HOWREY & SIMON
1299 Pennsylvania Ave., N.W.
Washington, D.C. 20004
(202) 783-0800

Attorneys for The White House

Dated: March 17, 1998

TABLE OF CONTENTS

TABLE OF AUTHORITIES[†]

Page(s)

CASES

† Authorities on which we chiefly rely are marked with asterisks.

CONSTITUTIONAL PROVISIONS

STATUTES

RULES

EXECUTIVE DOCUMENTS

BOOKS AND TREATISES

ARTICLES

OTHER AUTHORITIES

GRAND JURY PROCEEDINGS
UNDER SEAL

IN THE UNITED STATES DISTRICT COURT
FOR THE DISTRICT OF COLUMBIA

IN RE: GRAND JURY PROCEEDINGS.	)	Misc. Nos. 98-095, 98-096, and 98-097 (UNDER SEAL)

MEMORANDUM OF THE WHITE HOUSE IN OPPOSITION TO OIC'S MOTIONS TO COMPEL BRUCE R. LINDSEY AND SIDNEY BLUMENTHAL TO TESTIFY CONCERNING CONVERSATIONS PROTECTED BY THE ATTORNEY-CLIENT, PRESIDENTIAL COMMUNICATIONS, AND WORK PRODUCT PRIVILEGES

The Office of the President ("White House") submits this memorandum in opposition to the Motions to Compel the testimony of Bruce R. Lindsey and Sidney Blumenthal, filed by the Office of the Independent Counsel ("OIC") on March 6, 1998 ("OIC Motions").[1]

INTRODUCTION

The President of the United States, if he is to perform his constitutionally assigned duties, must be able to obtain the most candid, forthright, and well-informed advice from his advisors. Only last year, the United States Court of Appeals for the District of Columbia Circuit reaffirmed that principle, emphasizing the importance of preserving confidentiality of presidential communications "to ensure that presidential decisionmaking is of the highest caliber, informed by honest advice and full knowledge." *In re Sealed Case*, 121 F.3d 729, 750 (D.C. Cir. 1997).

Yet, the Independent Counsel now asks the Court to strip away this constitutional protection on the ground that, by merely completing a subpoena form and sending it to one of the

---

1 On March 6, 1998, the OIC also moved to compel testimony from Nancy Hernreich. By letter of March 4, 1998, however, the White House informed OIC of its willingness to allow non-lawyers such as Ms. Hernreich to testify to factual matters. We do not believe that, if recalled to testify before the grand jury, Ms. Hernreich would assert the privilege as to any of the factual matters about which the OIC seeks to compel her testimony.

President's lawyers or his senior advisors, he becomes entitled, without any showing of need, to invade the legal and other confidential advice on which the President must rely. The OIC asks the Court, as well, to strip away from government lawyers and their clients the attorney-client privilege—a claim that ignores the historical roots of the privilege, the Rules of Professional Conduct that apply in the District of Columbia, and the law of this jurisdiction.

As to the presidential communications privilege, the OIC ignores the teachings of the Court of Appeals and leaps from the bald assertion that only the President's private conduct is at issue here, to the conclusion that the advice he is given should not be protected. The OIC's contention is based on neither evidence nor logic. With respect to the Lewinsky matter, the grand jury is inquiring into actions allegedly taken by the President while in office—indeed, actions that allegedly occurred in the White House itself. And as to the President's deposition, the mere fact that the *Jones* case involves alleged conduct before the President took office does not mean that the advice he is given concerning his constitutional duties somehow becomes "private." To the contrary, the Supreme Court itself acknowledged the potential impact of the *Jones* litigation on the daily business of the Presidency—an impact that, however unlikely a prospect it was a year ago, is now all too real and tangible. Thus, even if one were to accept the OIC's description of the *Jones* case, or the President's alleged relationship with Ms. Lewinsky, as purely private, that description would be irrelevant to the question whether the communications at issue here are protected by privilege. The critical question is not the nature of the underlying conduct; it is the purpose of the advice being given.[2]

But if there were any question about the official nature of the matters about which these witnesses have provided advice, one need only look to the ultimate purpose of the OIC's investigation. The Ethics in Government Act requires the OIC to submit to the House of Representa-

---

2 For example, the conversations at issue in *United States v. Nixon*, 418 U.S. 683 (1974), involved a burglary of the DNC offices and efforts to cover it up, and yet were found to be presumptively privileged. *See infra* at 38. *See also Senate Select Committee on Presidential Campaign Activities v. Nixon*, 498 F.2d 725, 730–31 (D.C. Cir. 1974) (presidential communications relating to the Watergate coverup held presumptively privileged and not disclosed).

tives any evidence of impeachable offenses.[3] *See* 28 U.S.C. § 595(c). Impeachment is, of course, an action specifically directed at the President in his official capacity and is specifically provided for in the Constitution. *See* U.S. CONST. Art. II, § 4. Indeed, it is uncertain at best whether the OIC constitutionally can even ask the grand jury to take action against the President in his personal capacity. *See, e.g.*, PHILIP B. KURLAND, WATERGATE AND THE CONSTITUTION 135 (1978) (reasoning that a sitting President could not be subjected to criminal prosecution because "[h]e is the sole indispensable man in government"). Any advice sought by the President to deal with the threat of impeachment is, by its very nature, official—not private.

Even if there were no such threat overhanging the presidency, however, the advice at issue here must be treated as official and, thus, presumptively privileged. The distinction between those who give personal advice and those who give official advice to the President is clear. The President's ***private*** counsel provide advice concerning the response he must make to the particular demands the OIC and the *Jones* litigation place on him in his personal capacity. The White House Counsel and the President's senior advisors, on the other hand, provide advice concerning the official obligations of the President and the Office of the President, and are responsible for ensuring that, despite the pending litigation, he is able to perform his constitutional duties with maximum effectiveness. It is only as to this advice—from senior advisors like Mr. Blumenthal—that the presidential communications privilege has been invoked. Similarly, it is only as to legal advice given by Mr. Lindsey to the President in his official capacity that we have asserted the government's attorney-client privilege.

Finally, the circumstances under which the Independent Counsel has brought these Motions make clear the overly intrusive nature of his inquiry—one launched with no sensitivity to the most rudimentary constitutional principles and seemingly intended to manufacture a constitutional confrontation. Recognizing the grand jury's legitimate interest in obtaining the evidence

---

3 The threat of referral for possible impeachment proceedings is not just hypothetical. There is now pending in the House of Representatives a resolution to impeach President Clinton for an alleged "systematic effort to obstruct, undermine, and compromise the legitimate and proper functions and processes of the [E]xecutive [B]ranch[.]" *See* H. Res. 304, 105th Cong., 1st Sess.

it needs, we have made clear to the OIC from the beginning our willingness to provide the facts relevant to its investigation to the fullest extent consistent with the President's constitutional obligations. But we have also made clear our firm conviction that the OIC can have no legitimate interest in the White House staff's discussions of political or legal strategy, much less in whether anyone, in or out of the White House, has spoken less than favorably about the OIC.

Consistent with this position, we informed the OIC as early as February 3, 1998, that, in shaping any limited invocation of executive privilege that might be necessary for the President's non-attorney advisors, we would, as we had in other cases, *see, e.g.*, *Sealed Case*, 121 F.3d at 735–36, distinguish between facts and advice. (*See* Declaration of Charles F.C. Ruff ("Ruff Decl.") ¶ 32). This position was reaffirmed in our letter to the OIC of March 4, 1998, but our offer was spurned. (*See* Ruff Decl. Exhibits ("Exs.") 6, 7). Indeed, the OIC moved to compel the testimony of Nancy Hernreich on the very same day that it rejected the White House's offer to withdraw the assertion of privilege as to her. (*See* Ruff Decl. Ex. 7). And two days before that, the OIC rejected the White House's request that, before it launched any litigation, counsel meet to determine whether there could be an accommodation of the grand jury's interests with those of the Presidency—a process specifically contemplated by the Court of Appeals as the vehicle for minimizing the risk of unnecessary constitutional conflict. *See Sealed Case*, 121 F.3d at 735 (OIC's motion to compel production of documents followed considerable negotiations with the White House).

The Independent Counsel comes before this Court seeking essentially unfettered authority to inquire into every conversation the President, his lawyers and his advisors have had about the *Jones* case and the Lewinsky matter. He does so without being willing to proffer to the court the slightest justification for that inquiry—beyond his mere wish—and in direct contravention of the Court of Appeals' mandate that any intrusion into privileged communications must be narrowly focused and specifically justified. As the following discussion will make clear, that wish is grounded neither in good law nor sensible constitutional practice.

BACKGROUND

1. Factual Background

The roots of this dispute date at least back to May 27, 1997, when the Supreme Court decided *Clinton v. Jones*, 117 S. Ct. 1636 (1997). The Court rejected the President's attempt to stay temporarily the ongoing civil proceedings against him in a sexual harassment lawsuit brought by a former Arkansas state employee. In holding that the President was not, despite his unique position in the constitutional structure, entitled to a temporary stay of the civil proceedings against him, the Court opined that "it seems unlikely that a deluge of such litigation will ever engulf the Presidency" and suggested that the *Jones* case, "if properly managed by the District Court, . . . appears to us highly unlikely to occupy any substantial amount of petitioner's time." *Id.* at 1648.

In the wake of *Clinton v. Jones*, the President confronted an unavoidable dilemma. On the one hand, he remained the Nation's chief executive with a full panoply of domestic and foreign obligations which, the Court recognized, regularly required his personal attention for as much as twenty hours a day. *See Clinton v. Jones*, 117 S. Ct. at 1646 & nn.25–26; Ruff Decl. ¶ 6. But on the other hand, by virtue of the Court's decision, the President was obliged to attend to the *Jones* litigation ongoing in Arkansas, including formulating discovery responses, submitting to a deposition, strategizing with counsel, and evaluating and responding to potential avenues of settlement. At its core, the Court's decision in *Clinton v. Jones* meant that the President could not choose one course or the other—doing the job to which he was elected, or defending himself against the *Jones* lawsuit. He was, instead, required to do both. (*See* Ruff Decl. ¶¶ 4, 7; Declaration of Bruce R. Lindsey ("Lindsey Decl.") ¶ 8). How the President reconciles these types of conflicting obligations is the focus of a major portion of the communications over which the White House now invokes the presidential communications privilege, discussed in more detail below.

On Saturday, January 17, 1998, the President gave a deposition in *Jones v. Clinton*, No. LR-C-94-290 (E.D. Ark.). In this deposition, the President was asked certain questions relating to Monica Lewinsky, a former White House intern. On or about January 21, 1998, it was publicly announced that the jurisdiction of Independent Counsel Kenneth W. Starr had been expanded to include an investigation of Ms. Lewinsky and whether she or others suborned perjury or violated any other federal laws. (*See* Ruff Decl. ¶ 10).

In light of the new allegations, particularly those involving alleged obstruction of justice, commentators publicly adverted to the prospects of impeaching the President.[4] Those prospects took on a heightened reality when the Chairman of the House Judiciary Committee publicly stated that "impeachment might very well be an option" if the OIC substantiated its latest allegations against the President. *See* Francis X. Clines & Jeff Gerth, *Subpoenas Sent as Clinton Denies Reports of an Affair With Aide at White House*, N.Y. TIMES, Jan. 22, 1998, at A1, A24 (quoting Rep. Henry J. Hyde (R-Ill.)); *accord* Katharine Q. Seelye, *Clinton's Rapid-Response Squad Now Moves in Slow Motion*, N.Y. TIMES, Jan. 24, 1998, at A8 ("'If indeed the President was guilty of obstruction of justice, I really would think that the word "impeachment" would be one of the words to be used.' ") (quoting Rep. Charles B. Rangel (D-NY)).

2. Prior Proceedings Regarding Mr. Lindsey, Mr. Blumenthal, and Ms. Hernreich

From the outset, the White House has taken expansive measures to cooperate fully with the OIC's investigation. The White House promptly searched the entire Executive Office of the President for documents responsive to the OIC's subpoenas, and has produced all responsive materials. (*See* Ruff Decl. ¶ 13).

On January 30, 1998, the OIC subpoenaed Bruce Lindsey, Assistant to the President and Deputy Counsel, calling for him to appear before the grand jury to testify on February 4, 1998. (*See* Ruff Decl. ¶ 31). Around this time, the OIC also issued subpoenas to Sidney Blumenthal, Assistant to the President, and to Nancy Hernreich, Deputy Assistant to the President and Direc-

---

4 *See, e.g.*, Guy Gugliotta, *Impeachment Inquiry Discussed in House*, WASH. POST, Feb. 10, 1998, at A9; Katharine Q. Seelye, *Clinton's Rapid-Response Squad Now Moves in Slow Motion*, N.Y. TIMES, Jan. 24, 1998, at A8 ("George Stephanopoulos, a main campaign aide in 1992 and Mr. Clinton's senior adviser until after the 1996 election, was among the first to use the word 'impeachment' over the allegations[.]"); Tony Mauro & Richard Willing, *Impeachment Talk is Real*, USA TODAY, Jan. 23, 1998, at 3A; Ruff Decl. ¶¶ 21–22.

tor of Oval Office Operations. All three witnesses appeared before the grand jury and offered testimony.

The White House has, at every stage, sought to narrow and focus the issues over which any assertion of privilege may properly be invoked. Although the White House has endeavored to do so in cooperation with the OIC, as is plainly contemplated by *Sealed Case*, 121 F.3d at 735–36, the OIC has generally declined to participate.

For example, Charles Ruff, Counsel to the President, and Lanny Breuer, Special Counsel, met with the OIC on February 3, 1998 to discuss potential privilege concerns that could be raised during the grand jury testimony of Mr. Lindsey and John Podesta, Deputy Chief of Staff. (*See* Ruff Decl. ¶ 32). Mr. Ruff explained the potential privilege concerns that would necessarily arise if the OIC questioned Mr. Lindsey and other advisors regarding advice given to the President in his official capacity, and asked whether the OIC could specify the subjects about which they wished to elicit testimony. The OIC declined to do so (*id.*), and subsequently informed the White House that they would not recognize the applicability of executive privilege in this case. (*See* Ruff Decl. ¶ 34). Nevertheless, following the negotiation process contemplated by *Sealed Case*, Mr. Ruff reiterated the White House's desire to seek an accommodation of the parties' respective interests by letter of February 5, 1998. (*See* Ruff Decl. ¶¶ 35–36 & Ex. 2).

Subsequently, the White House voluntarily and unilaterally narrowed the scope of the communications over which privilege was being asserted. Yet, incredibly, in its haste to provoke a constitutional confrontation, the OIC actually ***rejected*** the White House's offer to withdraw the assertion of privilege as to Ms. Hernreich, one of the witnesses whose testimony the OIC has moved to compel.

By letter of March 2, 1998, counsel for the White House reiterated the White House's desire to reach an accommodation between the OIC's desire for testimony and the White House's need to ensure the availability of candid advice to future Presidents, and offered to meet with the OIC to discuss the matter. (*See* Ruff Decl. ¶ 45 & Ex. 4). The OIC responded by asking the

White House to submit its proposal by noon on March 4, 1998. (*See* Ruff Decl. ¶ 46 & Ex. 5). The White House complied.

In its proposal, the White House offered to narrow the scope of executive privilege it would assert. The White House's proposal would have relinquished the privilege and allowed non-attorney White House advisors, such as Ms. Hernreich, to testify fully to any relevant facts, including conversations with the President. (*See* Ruff Decl. ¶¶ 47–59 & Ex. 6). As the proposal stated:

> [T]he Office of the President is prepared to instruct White House witnesses along the following general lines:
>
> - White House Advisors (Non-Lawyers): Advisors will be permitted to testify as to factual information regarding the Lewinsky matter, including any such information imparted in conversations with the President. We will continue to assert executive privilege with regard to strategic deliberations and communications.
>
> - White House Attorney Advisors: Attorneys in the Counsel's Office will assert attorney/client privilege; attorney work product; and, where appropriate, executive privilege, with regard to communications, including those with the President, related to their gathering of information, the providing of advice, and strategic deliberations and communications.

(Ruff Decl. Ex. 6, at 2). By confining the assertion of executive privilege to "strategic deliberations and communications" and communications by and among attorneys in the White House Counsel's office (*id.*), the White House believed that its proposal would lead to the accommodation *Sealed Case* contemplates.

Instead, on March 6, 1998, the OIC curtly rejected the White House's proposal outright, ***including*** the proposed withdrawal of the privilege as to all factual testimony by non-attorneys such as Ms. Hernreich. (*See* Ruff Decl. ¶ 51 & Ex. 7). The same day, the OIC filed the motions to compel that are at issue here.

Thus, although the White House has reserved the invocation of executive privilege to that inner core of conversations that cannot be disclosed without materially harming the ability of future Presidents to confer with advisors candidly, the OIC has shown itself to be much more interested in provoking a needless constitutional controversy than in actually obtaining the factual evidence it claims to want. For the reasons that follow, the OIC's Motions must be denied.

ARGUMENT

In this consolidated reply to the OIC's Motions to Compel, we address, first, the attorney-client privilege and the attorney work product doctrine as they apply to the testimony of Bruce Lindsey, Deputy Counsel to the President, and second, the presidential communications privilege as it applies to Sidney Blumenthal, Assistant to the President, and other non-attorney advisors, as well as to Mr. Lindsey.

The OIC seeks to compel Mr. Lindsey to divulge a range of communications presumptively protected by the attorney-client privilege: discussions with the President and senior White House staff for the purpose of affording legal advice; discussions with the President's personal counsel on matters encompassing his private and official interests;[5] and discussions with counsel for other individuals with whom the White House had a common interest. The absolute privilege protecting communications between an attorney and his client has been recognized since the birth of the common law and is firmly imbedded in the law of the District of Columbia—in both its private and governmental forms. The contrary view of the Court of Appeals for the Eighth Circuit in *In re Grand Jury Subpoena Duces Tecum*, 112 F.3d 910 (8th Cir.), *cert. denied*, 117 S. Ct. 2482 (1997) ("*Grand Jury Subpoena*"), on which the OIC rests its entire argument, does not control here and, in any event, is deeply flawed. But even if the special circumstances present here suggest the need to balance the values inherent in the privilege against the needs of the grand jury, the OIC has offered absolutely nothing to weigh in that balance.

The OIC proffers only one argument in its attempt to pierce the executive privilege that has protected presidential communications since the dawn of the Republic—an argument that finds no support in the case law. The OIC would have the Court find, based solely on its unsup-

---

[5] Private counsel for the President will raise as well his personal attorney-client privilege to protect discussions with Mr. Lindsey on the occasions in which he served as a conduit for communications between them and their client.

ported claim that the testimony it seeks relates to "private" conduct, that the privilege simply does not apply. Moreover, it asks the Court to bypass the careful analysis of individual communications mandated by the Court of Appeals in *Sealed Case* and require wholesale disclosure of all discussions with the President and his senior advisors. This argument flies in the face of the presumptive privilege that attaches to presidential communications—a presumption that the courts have made clear can be overcome only on the most stringent showing of need on a communication-by-communication basis.

For these reasons, this Court should deny the OIC's motions to compel.

I. THE TESTIMONY THE OIC SEEKS TO COMPEL IS PROTECTED BY THE WHITE HOUSE'S ATTORNEY-CLIENT PRIVILEGE

The attorney-client privilege protecting communications between a government agency and its attorneys is an established principle under the law of this Circuit. The Court of Appeals for the Eighth Circuit's contrary opinion, on which the OIC hangs the entire weight of its argument, stands alone in holding the privilege inapplicable when invoked in grand jury proceedings. *See In re Grand Jury Subpoena Duces Tecum*, 112 F.3d 910, 913 (8th Cir.), *cert. denied*, 117 S. Ct. 2482 (1997) ("*Grand Jury Subpoena*"). The Eighth Circuit's decision demonstrably conflicts with precedent binding in this Circuit, and it should not be followed here.

A. The Eighth Circuit's Deeply Flawed Decision Offers No Persuasive Reason to Depart from the Authorities Recognizing the Governmental Attorney-Client Privilege

1. The Governmental Privilege in General

It is hornbook law that organizations have an attorney-client privilege against compelled disclosure of conversations between the organization's counsel and the organization's officials and employees. *See, e.g., Upjohn Co. v. United States*, 449 U.S. 383 (1981). Although *Upjohn* arose in the context of the corporate attorney-client privilege, nothing in the Court's assessment of a organization's need for freedom to consult with attorneys in confidence was limited to the corporate context. Accepting the logical implications of *Upjohn*, courts in this Circuit routinely have recognized that the attorney-client privilege protects governmental organizations as well as private ones. *See Tax Analysts v. IRS*, 117 F.3d 607, 618 (D.C. Cir. 1997); *Mead Data Central v. United States Dep't of the Air Force*, 566 F.2d 242, 252 (D.C. Cir. 1977). Evidentiary privileges such as the attorney-client privilege remain fully applicable in grand jury proceedings. *See Sealed Case*, 121 F.3d at 756 (citing *Branzburg v. Hayes*, 408 U.S. 665, 688 (1972) (recognizing applicability in grand jury proceedings of "the longstanding principle that 'the public . . . has a right to every man's evidence,' ***except for those persons protected by a constitutional, common-law, or statutory privilege***[.]") (emphasis added, citations omitted);[6] *United States v. Calandra*, 414 U.S. 338, 346 (1974) (grand jury "may not itself violate a valid privilege, whether established by the Constitution, statutes, or the common law.") (citations omitted)). The applicability of the governmental attorney-client privilege has been specifically confirmed in federal grand jury proceedings. *See In re Grand Jury Subpoena*, 886 F.2d 135 (6th Cir. 1989).

The Supreme Court has recognized that the attorney-client privilege advances important public interests. By "encourag[ing] full and frank communications between attorneys and their clients," the privilege enables clients "to make full disclosure to their attorneys" without fear that the discussions will become public, and thereby "promote[s the] public interests in the observance of law and administration of justice." *Upjohn*, 449 U.S. at 389 (internal quotations and citations omitted). This purpose cannot be served unless the client is "free from the consequences or the apprehension of disclosure." *Id.* (internal quotations and citations omitted); *see also Jaffee v. Redmond*, 116 S. Ct. 1923, 1928 (1996) ("the mere possibility of disclosure" of protected communications "may impede development of the confidential relationship" the privi-

---

6 The Court of Appeals for this Circuit has, similarly, recognized that the attorney-client privilege must be accorded its full sweep even in the face of the argument that it deprives the public of "every man's evidence":

> The attorney-client privilege is but one of several privileges that prevent parties themselves from adducing particular evidence, and thus create an obstacle to fact finding due to the broad judgment that the value of introducing such evidence is outweighed by the harm inflicted upon other policies and values. . . . [S]uch [evidentiary] burdens are simply a necessary consequence of society's attempt to balance the value of the complete admissibility of probative evidence with other competing values, such as the protection of vital professional or associational relationships.

Rosen v. NLRB, 735 F.2d 564, 572 (D.C. Cir. 1984) (Starr, J.).

lege exists to protect). These purposes apply with no less force in the present case and compel a very critical evaluation of the OIC's attempt to pierce the privilege.

In the governmental context, the attorney-client privilege advances other public interests as well. "[B]y safeguarding the free flow of information" within the government agency, the privilege fosters fairer and more accurate government decisionmaking. *Murphy v. TVA*, 571 F. Supp. 502, 506 (D.D.C. 1983); *see also Grand Jury Subpoena*, 112 F.3d at 929–32 (Kopf, J., dissenting).

An additional nuance arises here because the client whose confidences are at issue is the President. In this context, the presidential communications and attorney-client privileges are mutually self-reinforcing. Both exist to guarantee that the President receives necessary advice and input with the candor that can be secured only when advisors are free from apprehension about how third parties or the public may view them. When government attorneys or other advisors doubt the confidentiality of their communications, they will of necessity speak guardedly, hedging their recommendations with a view toward preserving the natural human desire to be well thought of by others. Such caution extracts a heavy toll, for it prevents the President from receiving the candid assistance necessary to run the government effectively and thereby serve the national interest. Here, that interest is protected by not just one, but two privileges, one of Constitutional dimension and the other with common-law roots deeper than any other privilege. In this circumstance, fidelity to both these reinforcing lines of authority compels the most intensive and exacting scrutiny of the OIC's attempt to pierce these privileges.

2. Flaws in the Eighth Circuit's Decision

In reaching the contrary result on which the OIC relies, the Eighth Circuit's decision—which is not binding on this Court—committed numerous analytical errors and misread the relevant authorities.

a. This Circuit has Long Recognized the Attorney-Client Privilege in the Governmental Context

To begin with, the Eighth Circuit incorrectly framed the issue before it. The court acted as if it was being asked to recognize a new privilege, and thus as if it must overcome a presumption against protecting the documents that had been subpoenaed. *See Grand Jury Subpoena*, 112 F.3d at 915. But the case before that court, like the instant case, presented no such issue at all. Far from being asked to create a privilege that was in any sense "new," the court was simply called upon to apply the single best settled and oldest of all the privileges known to the common law, *Upjohn*, 449 U.S. at 389, to the facts before it. There was no occasion for the application of the presumption against the creation of a new privilege, and the court erred in acting as if there was.

Second, the Eighth Circuit treated as a matter of first impression whether a governmental attorney-client privilege existed at all. *See Grand Jury Subpoena*, 112 F.3d at 915 ("We need not decide whether a governmental attorney-client privilege exists in other contexts, for it is enough to conclude that even if it does," it is inapplicable). Even assuming *arguendo* that the court's characterization of the question as an open issue in the Eighth Circuit was correct, it would not be relevant here. The governmental attorney-client privilege is a long-established fixture under the law in this Circuit and is in no sense an open question. *See, e.g., Tax Analysts v. IRS*, 117 F.3d 607, 618 (D.C. Cir. 1997) ("In the governmental context, the 'client' may be the agency and the attorney may be an agency lawyer," although the Court ultimately finds the privilege inapplicable); *Brinton v. Dep't of State*, 636 F.2d 600, 603 (D.C. Cir. 1980) (recognizing governmental attorney-client privilege, although resting decision on deliberative process grounds instead); *Mead Data Central v. United States Dep't of the Air Force*, 566 F.2d 242, 252 (D.C. Cir. 1977) ("In order to ensure that a client receives the best possible legal advice, based on a full and frank discussion with his attorney, the attorney-client privilege assures him that confidential communications to his attorney will not be disclosed without his consent. We see no reason why this same protection should not be extended to an agency's communications with its attorneys under [FOIA] exemption five."). Thus, a central analytical basis for the Eighth Circuit's decision is not only absent here, but indeed contradicted by settled precedent binding on this Court.[7] The D.C. Bar's professional rules also expressly recognize the applicability of the attorney-client privilege in the governmental context. *See* District of Columbia Rules of Professional Conduct, R. 1.13 & cmt. 7 (the government lawyer "represents the agency acting through its duly authorized constituents."), 1.6 & cmts. 33–36 (recognizing ethical duty of government lawyers to preserve the client agency's confidences).

Third, the Eighth Circuit incorrectly assumed, without authority, that the application of the attorney-client privilege turns on the specific circumstances at the time it is raised. Because it found no previous decision applying the privilege in an identical factual context, the Eighth Circuit assumed it was writing on a blank slate. This freed the court, in its view, to engage in a *de novo* assessment of the interests served by, and putative evidentiary costs of, the attorney-client privilege. But this mode of analysis is utterly foreign to the attorney-client privilege. A hallmark of absolute privileges such as the attorney-client privilege—as distinct from qualified privileges such as the protection for attorney work product[8]—is that they do not turn on *post hoc*

---

7 Other courts agree with this one. *See, e.g.*, *Wilder v. C.I.R.*, 607 F. Supp. 1013, 1015 (M.D. Ala. 1985) (it is "well settled" that documents prepared by agency counsel "fall within the ambit of the attorney-client privilege"); *Green v. IRS*, 556 F. Supp. 79, 85 (N.D. Ind. 1982) (attorney-client privilege "unquestionably is applicable to the relationship between Government attorneys and administrative personnel"), *aff'd mem.*, 734 F.2d 18 (7th Cir. 1984); *Jupiter Painting Contracting Co. v. United States*, 87 F.R.D. 593, 598 (E.D. Pa. 1980) (explaining that "[c]ourts generally have accepted that attorney-client privilege applies in the governmental context," so despite "apprehension at [the privilege's] pernicious potential in a government top-heavy with lawyers . . . [t]his concern does not justify application of a different privilege to governmental attorney-client relationships."). *Coastal Corp. v. Duncan*, 86 F.R.D. 514, 520 (D. Del. 1980) ("the attorney-client privilege is applicable in the factual context where a government agency is a 'client' and agency lawyers are 'attorneys.'"). *Hearn v. Rhay*, 68 F.R.D. 574, 579 (E.D. Wash. 1975) ("[f]ederal courts have uniformly held that the attorney-client privilege can arise with respect to attorneys representing a state").

8 As one treatise on evidence put it:

> In other respects, however, the attorney-client privilege provides more protection than the work product doctrine. While the privilege is absolute, the work product doctrine provides only a qualified immunity which in the case of ordinary work product can be overcome by a showing of "substantial need" and "undue hardship" in obtaining the "substantial equivalent of the materials by other means." . . . The work product doctrine operates primarily as a limitation on pretrial discovery, whereas the attorney-client privilege applies more broadly at all stages of legal proceedings.

2 Christopher B. Mueller & Laird C. Kirkpatrick, Federal Evidence § 204 (2d ed. 1994).

demonstrations of need or balancing of interests at the time the privilege is asserted. A contrary rule effectively vitiates the entire purpose of absolute privileges such as the attorney-client privilege, which is intended to encourage communications that might not be made in its absence. *See Upjohn*, 449 U.S. at 395; *Jaffee*, 116 S. Ct. at 1929 ("[w]ithout a privilege, much of the desirable evidence to which litigants . . . seek access . . . is unlikely to come into being"). Allowing the attorney-client privilege to turn on a *post hoc* assessment of the particular circumstances in which it is asserted in litigation prevents the privilege from serving its key function: providing clients assurance in advance that they may speak freely without fear of disclosure.

Other authorities confirm the Eighth Circuit's error in rejecting the applicability of the governmental attorney-client privilege. For one, the privilege has received express legislative recognition by Congress under Exemption 5 of the Freedom of Information Act (FOIA), 5 U.S.C. § 552(b)(5). This exemption allows governmental agencies to withhold from disclosure, in response to a FOIA request, any "inter-agency or intra-agency memorandums or letters which would not be available by law to a party other than an agency in litigation with the agency[.]" *Id.* Congress's clear intent to enact a federal law of governmental attorney-client privilege (and protection for attorney work product) was noted by the Supreme Court in *NLRB v. Sears, Roebuck & Co.*, 421 U.S. 132, 154 (1975) ("[t]he Senate Report states that Exemption 5 'would include the working papers of the agency attorney and documents which would come within the attorney-client privilege if applied to private parties' "). *See also Mead Data Central*, 566 F.2d at 252; *Grand Jury Subpoena*, 112 F.3d at 930 (Kopf, J., dissenting).

The overwhelming weight of scholarly authority recognizes the existence and importance of the privilege in the governmental context. *See, e.g.*, RESTATEMENT (THIRD) OF THE LAW GOVERNING LAWYERS § 124 (Proposed Final Draft No. 1, Mar. 29, 1996) ("the generally prevailing rule . . . [is that] governmental agencies and agents enjoy the same privilege as non-governmental counterparts."); 2 CHRISTOPHER B. MUELLER & LAIRD C. KIRKPATRICK, FEDERAL EVIDENCE § 191 (2d ed. 1994); *see also Grand Jury Subpoena*, 112 F.3d at 930 (Kopf, J., dissenting).

What is more, the Supreme Court's Proposed Federal Rules of Evidence, which have repeatedly been relied on in this Circuit and by the Supreme Court as accurate statements of the common law of privilege,[9] expressly recognized the applicability of the attorney-client privilege in the governmental context. Proposed Rule 503, dealing with the attorney-client privilege, defined "client" to include a "public officer, . . . or other organization or entity, either public or private[.]" Proposed Federal Rules of Evidence, Rule 503(a)(1), 56 F.R.D. 183, 235 (1972). The accompanying Advisory Committee's Note emphasized that "[t]he definition of 'client' includes governmental bodies." *Id.* R. 503(a)(1) adv. comm. note, 56 F.R.D. at 237. *See generally Grand Jury Subpoena*, 112 F.3d at 926, 928–29 (Kopf, J., dissenting).

b. Congress Did Not Abrogate the Governmental Attorney-Client Privilege in 28 U.S.C. § 535(b)

In reaching its decision, the Eighth Circuit incorrectly relied on a relatively obscure provision of law requiring executive branch employees to report to the Attorney General information relating to criminal acts committed by their colleagues. Citing 28 U.S.C. § 535(b),[10] the

---

9 Although Congress ultimately enacted Fed. R. Evid. 501, which calls upon the federal courts to develop a federal common law of privilege, instead of enacting the specific privileges in the form proposed by the Supreme Court, the Court's Proposed Rules on the subject of privilege have been widely recognized as accurate statements of the common law and are entitled to appropriate consideration. *See, e.g., Jaffee v. Redmond*, 116 S. Ct. 1923, 1927 n.7, 1928, 1930–31 (relying on statement of psychotherapist-patient privilege in Proposed Rules); *Linde Thomson Langworthy Kohn & Van Dyke, P.C. v. RTC*, 5 F.3d 1508, 1514 (D.C. Cir. 1993) (relying, *inter alia*, on Proposed Rules 503(a)(3) and 503(b) to describe the contours of the attorney-client privilege); *Citibank, N.A. v. Andros*, 666 F.2d 1192, 1195 n.6 (8th Cir. 1981) ("courts have continued to look to the proposed rules as a source for defining the federal common law of attorney-client privilege."). "Most importantly, the proposed rule covering the attorney-client privilege is still at this point a generally reliable statement of federal common law." 2 STEPHEN A. SALTZBURG ET AL., FEDERAL RULES OF EVIDENCE MANUAL 589 (6th ed. 1994); *see also Grand Jury Subpoena*, 112 F.3d at 928–29 (Kopf, J., dissenting).

10 This statute provides that:

> Any information, allegation, or complaint received in a department or agency of the executive branch of the Government relating to violations of title 18 involving Government officers and employees shall be expeditiously reported to the Attorney General by the head of the department or agency, unless—
>
> (1) the responsibility to perform an investigation with respect thereto is specifically assigned otherwise by another provision of law; or
>
> (2) as to any department or agency of the Government, the Attorney General directs otherwise with respect to a specified class of information, allegation, or complaint.

28 U.S.C. § 535(b).

majority found it "significant" that government employees, "including attorneys, are under a statutory duty to report criminal wrongdoing by other employees to the Attorney General." *Grand Jury Subpoena*, 112 F.3d at 920. Neither the plain language of section 535(b) nor its legislative history, however, evinces any intent to vitiate the attorney-client privilege. The text of the provision does not mention the attorney-client privilege and does not, by its terms, command the interpretation the Eighth Circuit adopted. Similarly, there is no evidence of Congressional intent to abrogate the most firmly entrenched common law privilege protecting communications between attorneys and their clients. As the House Report on this provision makes clear, the objective of section 535(b) was simply to settle a jurisdictional battle between investigative agencies:

> The purpose of the proposed legislation is to set out the necessary authority for the Attorney General and the Federal Bureau of Investigation to investigate alleged irregularities on the part of Government officers and employees and to require the reporting by the departments and agencies of the executive branch to the Attorney General of information coming to their attention concerning any alleged irregularities on the part of officers and employees of the Government.

H.R. Rep. No. 83-2622, *reprinted in* 1954 U.S.C.C.A.N. 3551.

The absence of case law interpreting this statute's applicability to government attorneys only enhances the need for clarity in assessing legislative intent. A fundamental axiom of statutory construction is that, where the text of a law is ambiguous, one should not presume a legislative intention to abrogate settled common-law principles. 2B SUTHERLAND STATUTORY CONSTRUCTION § 50.01 (5th ed. 1992 & Cum. Supp. 1997). As the Supreme Court has instructed, "[s]tatutes which invade the common law . . . are to be read with a presumption favoring the retention of long-established and familiar principles, except when a statutory purpose to the contrary is evident." *Isbrandtsen Co. v. Johnson*, 343 U.S. 779, 783 (1952). Congress acts within the framework of existing law, not within a vacuum. *See, e.g.*, *Miles v. Apex Marine Corp.*, 498 U.S. 19, 32 (1990) ("We assume that Congress is aware of existing law when it passes legislation."). Therefore, in the absence of "an indication that the legislature intends a statute to supplant common law, the courts should not give it that effect." SUTHERLAND STATUTORY CONSTRUCTION, *supra*.

Fidelity to these settled principles compels the conclusion that section 535(b) should not be read to undermine the well-established attorney-client privilege. As Judge Kopf's dissenting opinion in the Eighth Circuit noted, the Department of Justice, which section 535(b) charges to enforce the reporting provision, has always interpreted this provision to be consistent with the long-standing protection for confidential attorney-client communications. *See Grand Jury Subpoena*, 112 F.3d at 932 (Kopf, J., dissenting). On several occasions, the Justice Department's Office of Legal Counsel has expressed the opinion that the attorney-client privilege survives section 535(b). *Id.* According to then-Assistant Attorney General Antonin Scalia, "[g]iven the absence of any discussion of the subject in the legislative history [of § 535(b)], it would in our view be inappropriate to infer a congressional purpose to breach the universally recognized and long-standing confidentiality of the attorney-client privilege." Antonin Scalia, Assistant Attorney General, Office of Legal Counsel, *Memorandum for the Deputy Attorney General re: Disclosure of Confidential Information Received by U.S. Attorney in the Course of Representing a Federal Employee* at 7 (Nov. 30, 1976). Nearly a decade later, the Office of Legal Counsel reconfirmed this interpretation, stating that "the principal reason for our conclusion that the attorney-client privilege overrides § 535(b) is that the confidentiality of communications between client and lawyer is essential if Department attorneys are to be able to provide adequate legal representation." Ralph W. Tarr, Acting Assistant Attorney General, Office of Legal Counsel, *Duty of Government Lawyers Upon Receipt of Incriminating Information in the Course of an Attorney-Client Relationship with Another Government Employee* at 6 (March 29, 1985). The uniformity of the Office of Legal Counsel's position, which represents the only precedential authority on the specific application of section 535(b) to this situation, only strengthens the conclusion already reached by applying prevailing principles of statutory construction: this statute clearly does not contravene the attorney-client privilege. *See generally Grand Jury Subpoena*, 112 F.3d at 930–32 (Kopf, J., dissenting).

Because the Eighth Circuit's decision is inconsistent with precedent binding in this Circuit, and out of step with the long-standing consensus of other authorities, this Court should not follow it.

B. The Communications at Issue Here are Privileged

1. Bruce R. Lindsey

Mr. Lindsey's conversations involved the President's attorney-client privilege in both his official and unofficial capacities. First, as Deputy White House Counsel, Mr. Lindsey represents the Office of the President and, in that capacity, has had confidential conversations with the client or the client's representatives relating to the provision of legal advice. (*See* Lindsey Decl. ¶¶ 9–12). These conversations are directly covered by the White House's attorney-client privilege. Some of Mr. Lindsey's conversations related to providing legal advice on the questions whether the Office of the President should invoke its testimonial privileges, including the attorney-client and presidential communications privileges. (*See* Lindsey Decl. ¶ 11). The OIC also seeks to compel conversations Mr. Lindsey had relating to possible impeachment proceedings before the House Judiciary Committee. (*Id.*). These discussions, which related directly to Mr. Lindsey's gathering of information to provide legal advice to his client, are plainly covered by the White House's attorney-client privilege. (*Id.*; *see also* Ruff Decl. ¶ 22). Mr. Lindsey also had discussions with witnesses who testified before the grand jury, or their counsel, during the course of gathering information to use in advising the White House on matters of litigation strategy. (*See* Lindsey Decl. ¶ 13). These interviews are also protected by the attorney-client privilege.

Second, Mr. Lindsey has stated in his Declaration that he has occasionally communicated with the President's private counsel while acting on behalf of the President in the President's individual capacity. (*See* Lindsey Decl. ¶ 12). To the extent this latter situation raises issues primarily within the President's individual attorney-client privilege, the White House will not address it in detail herein.

2. Nancy Hernreich

As suggested in the White House's proposal to the OIC of March 4, 1998, the White House withdraws the assertion of privilege as to factual questions submitted to Ms. Hernreich, including factual questions regarding communications with the President.

C. This Court Should Deny the OIC's Motion Even if the Attorney-Client Privilege is Qualified, Rather than Absolute, in the Governmental Context

Even assuming the Eighth Circuit majority was correct and a qualified attorney-client privilege, subject to a balancing of interests after the fact, is appropriate in the governmental context, that fact alone would not justify the majority's conclusion that the privilege automatically evaporated in the face of a grand jury subpoena from the OIC. Rather, qualified privileges generally require the party opposing the privilege to make some showing of ***need*** to surmount the privilege's protection. *See, e.g., Sealed Case*, 121 F.3d at 745–46, 753–57 (discussing showing of need required to overcome qualified presidential communications privilege). By requiring no demonstration at all by the OIC before ruling the privilege unavailable, the Eighth Circuit again made new law that is at odds with settled precedent in this Circuit.

To say that the OIC must make some showing to overcome the attorney-client privilege necessarily raises the question of what that showing should be. We submit that, at least, the same "focused demonstration of need," showing that the evidence is "demonstrably critical to the responsible fulfillment" of the OIC's role, see *infra* at 27, must be required.

This was substantially the position taken by the Department of Justice, speaking through the Solicitor General as *amicus curiae* in support of the petition for certiorari filed by the White House, seeking review of the Eighth Circuit's decision. *See Office of the President v. Office of Independent Counsel*, (U.S., No. 96-1783), Brief *Amicus Curiae* For the United States, Acting

Through the Attorney General, Supporting Certiorari ("DOJ Brief").[11] Evaluating the attorney-client privilege in the unique context of an intra-branch dispute between the White House and the OIC, the Justice Department suggested that

> the district court should, in ruling on the motion to compel, accommodate the competing interests at stake in a manner similar to the accommodation that takes place in an ordinary, non-independent-counsel context.

DOJ Brief at 14 (footnote omitted). DOJ argued that a "useful analogy . . . [could] be drawn to the resolution of assertions of executive privilege," *id.* at 15, and suggested that the test established in *Nixon* and its progeny would best accommodate the competing interests at stake. *See generally id.* at 11–16.

D. Conversations Among Attorneys for the White House and Private Counsel for the President are Privileged from Disclosure Under the Common Interest Rule

The OIC contends that the governmental attorney-client privilege, even if it exists, could not attach to conversations with the President's private counsel. Again, the OIC is wrong. Every conversation in which private counsel participated is protected from disclosure under the common interest rule.

The Supreme Court's Proposed Rule 503(b)(3) recognized that "[t]he lawyer-client privilege applies to communications made by the client 'or his lawyer to a lawyer representing another in a matter of common interest.' " 3 WEINSTEIN'S FEDERAL EVIDENCE § 503.13[2] (Joseph M. McLaughlin ed., 2d ed. 1997) (quoting Proposed Rule 503(b)(3), 56 F.R.D. 183, 236 (1972)).[12] The common interest rule recognizes that

> [i]n many cases it is necessary for clients to pool information in order to obtain effective representation. So, to encourage information-pooling, the common inter-

---

11 The OIC's suggestion that he may second-guess the official position of the United States Government on the scope of the attorney-client privilege, as enunciated by the Department of Justice, is in considerable tension with the statute under which the OIC operates. The statute permits the OIC to deviate from the Department's view only when it is "not possible" for him to comply. 28 U.S.C. § 594(f).

12 As already noted, the Supreme Court's Proposed Rules of Evidence represent highly persuasive statements of the common law of privilege the courts should apply under Fed. R. Evid. 501. *See supra* note 9.

> est rule treats all involved attorneys and clients as a single attorney-client unit, at least insofar as a common interest is pursued.

2 STEPHEN A. SALTZBURG ET AL., FEDERAL RULES OF EVIDENCE MANUAL 599 (6th ed. 1994) (footnotes omitted); *accord In re Sealed Case*, 29 F.3d 715, 719 (D.C. Cir. 1994) ("The common interest privilege protects communications between a lawyer and two or more clients regarding a matter of common interest."). Besides preserving the privilege for attorney-client communications made among attorneys for clients with a common interest, the privilege also allows the attorneys to share work product without waiver of the protection the work product rule provides. *See United States v. AT&T*, 642 F.2d 1285, 1299–1301 (D.C. Cir. 1980). The common interest rule applies with equal force in the governmental context as outside. *See id.* at 1300 ("The government has the same entitlement as any other party to assistance from those sharing common interests, whatever their motives").

In this case, attorneys representing the White House and the President's private counsel were pursuing a common interest in responding to the allegations made against a sitting President involving his conduct in the White House. (*See* Lindsey Decl. ¶¶ 12–13; Ruff Decl. ¶ 30). As discussed herein, the OIC's investigation, although nominally directed at the President's personal conduct, has had unavoidable effects on the functioning of the Presidency and the institutions of government. The indisputable need for White House attorneys to confer with the President's private counsel on matters of common interest shields their discussions from compelled disclosure.

E. Certain of the Materials Sought are Protected from Disclosure Because they Constitute Attorney Work Product

The OIC's Motion to Compel also intrudes upon matters protected from disclosure by the work product doctrine. *See Hickman v. Taylor*, 329 U.S. 495 (1947). The attorney work-product rule, like the attorney-client privilege, has received official Congressional recognition in the governmental context. *See* 5 U.S.C. § 552(b)(5); *NLRB v. Sears, Roebuck & Co.*, 421 U.S. 132, 154 (1975); *FTC v. Grolier, Inc.*, 462 U.S. 19 (1983). The Department of Justice has also recognized the existence of the governmental attorney work product doctrine in circumstances that parallel the OIC's Motions here. *See* DOJ Brief, *supra*, at 18–19.

Among the subjects about which the OIC seeks to compel testimony are attorneys' recollections of their interviews with witnesses who testified before the grand jury. (*See* Lindsey Decl. ¶ 13). Because the OIC has sought to compel government attorneys to disclose the content of witness interviews, the higher standard of protection for attorney opinion work product applies. *See Upjohn*, 449 U.S. at 401 (attorney opinion work product, as distinct from "ordinary" work product, is "entitled to special protection").

II. THE OIC SEEKS TO COMPEL COMMUNICATIONS PROTECTED UNDER THE PRESIDENTIAL COMMUNICATIONS PRIVILEGE

The OIC has taken a simplistic and absolutist position in its motions to compel: it argues that the presidential communications privilege is inapplicable to any communications that relate to the President's "private" conduct. That contention is flatly wrong. Any conduct by the individual holding the Office of the President, whether it is characterized as private or official, can have substantial impact on a President's official duties. The White House has asserted executive privilege only over those communications that meet that test. For example, the Supreme Court, in *United States v. Nixon*, 418 U.S. 683 (1974), held that the conversations at issue in that case—about a break-in at the Democratic National Committee headquarters, although certainly not about an official function of the President—were presumptively privileged. *See also Senate Select Committee on Presidential Campaign Activities v. Nixon*, 498 F.2d 725 (D.C. Cir. 1974). Thus, the OIC is urging on this Court a position that the Supreme Court and the D.C. Circuit have long ago rejected.

A. Legal Framework for Evaluating a Claim of Privilege for Presidential Communications

The case law establishes a clear framework for evaluating a claim that the presidential communications privilege protects a conversation or document from compelled disclosure. The

OIC's Motions do not even acknowledge the existence of this framework. Accordingly, we will begin by laying out the key principles.

1. The Presumption of Privilege

"Presidential conversations are 'presumptively privileged,' even from the limited intrusion represented by *in camera* examination of the conversations by a court." *Senate Select Committee on Presidential Campaign Activities v. Nixon*, 498 F.2d 725, 730 (D.C. Cir. 1974) (quoting *Nixon v. Sirica*, 487 F.2d 700, 717–18 (D.C. Cir. 1973), *quoted with approval in United States v. Nixon*, 418 U.S. 683, 708 (1974)) (footnote omitted); *see also In re Sealed Case*, 121 F.3d 729, 744 (D.C. Cir. 1997). Grounded in constitutional separation of powers concerns, the presidential communications privilege is fully applicable in grand jury proceedings and bars compelled disclosure of the privileged matter. *Sealed Case*, 121 F.3d at 756. Because presidential communications are presumed to be privileged until the privilege is overcome by an extraordinary showing, the OIC is wrong in claiming that the White House has any "burden" to carry.[13] Rather, the burden is squarely on the OIC to make the showing necessary to overcome the presumption of privilege.

As the Supreme Court has recognized, this long-standing privilege[14] ensures that the President receives "candid, objective, and even blunt or harsh" advice from the inner circle of aides on whom he must, of necessity, rely every day:

> The expectation of a President to the confidentiality of his conversations and correspondence, like the claim of confidentiality of judicial deliberations, for example, has all the values to which we accord deference for the privacy of all citizens

---

[13] *See, e.g.*, OIC's Brief in Support of Motion to Compel Bruce R. Lindsey to Testify ("OIC Lindsey Br.") at 2 n.4 (citing *Bartholdi Cable Co. v. FCC*, 114 F.3d 274, 280 (D.C. Cir. 1997), a case that did not involve the presidential communications privilege). All three of the OIC's supporting briefs cite this same irrelevant case.

[14] *See, e.g.*, *Sealed Case*, 121 F.3d at 739 n.9 (first assertion of a presidential communications privilege came during the Washington Administration). Virtually every Administration since Washington's has invoked the executive privilege in one form or another. *See generally* MARK J. ROZELL, EXECUTIVE PRIVILEGE 32–48, 83–140 (1994) (summarizing invocations of executive privilege by, *inter alia*, Presidents George Washington, John Adams, Thomas Jefferson, James Madison, Andrew Jackson, Abraham Lincoln, Calvin Coolidge, Herbert Hoover, Franklin D. Roosevelt, Harry S Truman, Dwight D. Eisenhower, John F. Kennedy, Lyndon B. Johnson, Gerald R. Ford, Jimmy Carter, Ronald Reagan, and George Bush).

> and, added to those values, is the necessity for protection of the ***public interest in candid, objective, and event blunt or harsh opinions in Presidential decision-making.*** A President and those who assist him must be free to explore alternatives in the process of shaping policies and making decisions and to do so in a way many would be unwilling to express except privately.

United States v. Nixon, 418 U.S. at 708 (emphasis added).

One cannot overstate the intolerable threat that an unduly constrictive reading of the privilege poses to the President's ability to get frank and candid advice from his advisors. Indeed, many years before the Nixon Presidency rendered discussions of the privilege controversial, President Eisenhower underscored the crucial role the privilege plays in promoting effective governance, going so far as to remark that, if confidential presidential communications were "subject to investigation by anybody," it could "wreck the Government."[15] Scholarly authority confirms the privilege's salutary role in encouraging candid advice to the President:

> The president's constitutional duties necessitate his being able to consult with advisers, without fear of public disclosure of their advice. If officers of the executive branch believed that their confidential advice could eventually be disclosed, the quality of that advice would suffer serious damage. Indeed, it would be difficult for advisers to be completely honest and frank in their discussions if their every word might someday be disclosed to partisan opponents or the public.

MARK J. ROZELL, EXECUTIVE PRIVILEGE 53–54 (1994).

Affording appropriate deference to a co-equal branch of the government under separation of powers principles, reviewing courts always have recognized that, when the presidential communications privilege has been invoked, a presumption of privilege attaches. *See Sealed Case*,

---

[15] President Eisenhower stated:

> But when it comes to the conversations that take place between any responsible official and his advisers . . . expressing personal opinions on the most confidential basis, those are not subject to investigation by anybody; and if they are, will wreck the Government. There is no business that could be run if there would be exposed every single thought that an adviser might have, because in the process of reaching an agreed position, there are many, many conflicting opinions to be brought together. And if any commander is going to get the free, unprejudiced opinions of his subordinates, he had better protect what they have to say to him on a confidential basis.

The President's News Conference of July 6, 1955, 1955 PUBLIC PAPERS OF THE PRESIDENTS 665, 674, *quoted in* Archibald Cox, *Executive Privilege*, 122 U. PA. L. REV. 1383, 1386 (1974). The President continued: "It is exactly, as I see it, like a lawyer and his client or any other confidential thing of that character." *Id.*, 1955 PUBLIC PAPERS OF THE PRESIDENTS at 674.

121 F.3d at 744 ("If the President does so [invokes the privilege], the documents become presumptively privileged."); *Senate Select Committee*, 498 F.2d at 730; *accord United States v. Nixon*, 418 U.S. at 713 ("Upon receiving a claim of privilege from the Chief Executive, it became the further duty of the district court to treat the subpoenaed material as presumptively privileged[.]"). This Court should reject the OIC's invitation to become the first court ever to adopt a contrary rule.

2. Communications to Which the Privilege Applies

The "presidential communications" privilege covers a significantly broader range of communications than its name suggests. In *Sealed Case*, the fullest recent explication of the privilege, the Court of Appeals for this Circuit squarely rejected the notion that the privilege attaches only to communications directly to or from the President. *See generally Sealed Case*, 121 F.3d at 746–53. Instead, the Court applied a more discerning analysis, which recognized the privilege's "root[s] in the constitutional separation of powers principles and the President's unique constitutional role," *id.* at 745—a role the President cannot perform without the close cooperation of an inner circle of advisors and assistants. Thus, to effect the purposes of the privilege, the Court recognized that it must protect not only the President's own communications, but also communications to and from the persons on whom the President directly relies for decisionmaking assistance:

> [C]ommunications made by presidential advisers in the course of preparing advice for the President come under the presidential communications privilege, even when these communications are not made directly to the President. Given the need to provide sufficient elbow room for advisers to obtain information from all knowledgeable sources, the privilege must apply both to communications which these advisers solicited and received from others as well as those they authored themselves. The privilege must also extend to communications authored or received in response to a solicitation by members of a presidential adviser's staff, since in many instances advisers must rely on their staff to investigate an issue and formulate the advice to be given to the President.

Id. at 751–52.

The privilege also covers individuals outside the President's inner circle, and even outside the White House, if those individuals relate "communications authored or solicited and received by members of an immediate White House adviser's staff[.]" *Id.* at 752; *see also id.* at 758 (although legal extern "did not exercise broad and significant responsibility," all the extern's relevant communications "were clearly created at the request of" those who did, and were therefore privileged); *id.* (documents for which no author was listed had plainly been solicited by individuals with key responsibility for advising the President, and were therefore privileged).

While scrupulously protecting the public interest in the effective operation of the highest levels of the Executive Branch, *Sealed Case* fully recognized and accommodated the public interest in ascertaining the truth in grand jury proceedings. Thus, the OIC is wrong to assert (OIC Lindsey Br. at 5–6) that the mere potential relevance of evidence is sufficient to overcome the protection of the privilege in a grand jury proceeding. The grand jury is not, as *Sealed Case* recognized, free to disregard established testimonial privileges. The presidential communications privilege in particular advances a substantial public interest on which the grand jury may not infringe:

> [W]e are ever mindful of the dangers involved in cloaking governmental operations in secrecy and placing obstacles in the path of the grand jury in its investigatory mission. ***There is a powerful counterweight to these concerns, however, namely the public and constitutional interest in preserving the efficacy and quality of presidential decisionmaking.***

Sealed Case, 121 F.3d at 762 (emphasis added).

3. The Showing Required to Overcome the Presumption

The presumptive privilege, once invoked by the President, is not easily overcome. "[A] party seeking to overcome the presidential privilege seemingly must always provide a focused demonstration of need[.]" *Sealed Case*, 121 F.3d at 746. "Efforts should first be made to determine whether sufficient evidence can be obtained elsewhere, and the subpoena's proponent should be prepared to detail these efforts and explain why evidence covered by the presidential privilege is still needed." *Id.* at 755. The "need" inquiry "turn[s], ***not on the nature of the***

presidential conduct that the subpoenaed material might reveal, but, instead, on the nature and appropriateness of the function in the performance of which the material was sought, and the degree to which the material was necessary to its fulfillment." *Senate Select Committee*, 498 F.2d at 731 (emphasis added); *accord Sealed Case*, 121 F.3d at 746. That this is a high hurdle indeed is shown by *Senate Select Committee*'s observation that the "showing must depend solely on whether the subpoenaed evidence is demonstrably critical to the responsible fulfillment" of the function of the entity seeking to compel production.[16] *Senate Select Committee*, 498 F.2d at 731. A mere showing of "an asserted power to investigate and inform," *id.* at 732, does not suffice. The Court's holding that "the Select Committee has failed to make the requisite showing," *id.* at 731, reinforces that the standard of need requires a very strong substantive showing that a court must scrutinize with the greatest care.

Moreover, the Court must assess the sufficiency of the showing of need without reference to the privileged communications themselves. *Sealed Case* makes very plain the steps involved in evaluating an attempt to overcome the privilege. Once the presumption of privilege attaches, the party seeking the information becomes obliged to make a "focused demonstration of need." *Sealed Case*, 121 F.3d at 746. Only after the party opposing the claim of privilege makes a sufficient showing does the President become obliged to cede control of the privileged materials. The "focused demonstration of need" does not itself require the President to turn over the information to the party seeking it, however, but only to submit it under seal to the district court for *in camera* review. *Id.* at 759–60. The district court reviews the items and extracts the specific relevant portions as to which the privilege has been overcome, and then those extracts and no other parts of the privileged communications may be provided to the party opposing the claim of privilege.

---

16 Although *Sealed Case*, like the present case but unlike *Senate Select Committee*, involved the Executive Branch's opposition to compulsory judicial process, rather than a legislative inquiry (*see Sealed Case*, 121 F.3d at 753), *Sealed Case* repeatedly employed (and necessarily adopted) *Senate Select Committee*'s explication of the need requirement, suggesting that, at least as to this element, the standards for evaluating any given assertion of the presidential communications privilege are identical no matter which branch of government is seeking to overcome the privilege.

Sealed Case also makes clear that this Court must scrutinize communications individually to determine whether the OIC has met this standard. The blanket ruling the OIC seeks, declaring all the communications at issue here to be outside the scope of the privilege, is precisely what the Court of Appeals forbade in *Sealed Case*. *See* 121 F.3d at 740 (criticizing the District Court for issuing "a blanket ruling, with no individualized discussion of the documents"); *see also id.* ("the court also failed to provide any explanation of its legal reasoning").

The high standard of need is intended to prevent precisely the misuse of the grand jury process in which the OIC has engaged here. It effectuates the principle that "presidential communications should not be treated as just another source of information"[17] by requiring the OIC first to develop sufficient evidence from other sources to substantiate its showing of need, before intruding on the President's communications with his advisors:

> Nor do we believe the *Nixon/Sirica* need standard imposes too heavy a burden on grand jury investigation. In practice, the primary effect of this standard will be to ***require a grand jury to delay subpoenaing evidence covered by presidential privilege*** until it has assured itself that the evidence sought from the President or his advisers is both important to its investigation and practically unavailable elsewhere. As was true in *Sirica*, a grand jury will often be able to specify its need for withheld evidence in reasonable detail based on information obtained from other sources.

Sealed Case, 121 F.3d at 756–57 (emphasis added); *see also id.* at 761 ("it is hard to conclude that the OIC issued its subpoena to the White House as a last resort."). By turning to privileged presidential communications as its first resort, the OIC has turned the *Nixon/Sirica/Sealed Case* paradigm on its head and sparked a premature confrontation on an inadequate record.

B. The Conversations at Issue Here are Privileged

As shown below, application of the established analytical framework to the communications at issue here shows unmistakably that the communications are privileged. In arguing the contrary, the OIC contends that this case involves allegations about the President that relate to private activity. This argument, however, fails both legally and factually. As a legal matter, the

[17] *Sealed Case*, 121 F.3d at 755.

OIC's argument misreads the Supreme Court's decisions both in *Nixon* and in *Clinton v. Jones*, as well as authorities from the D.C. Circuit, involving the distinctions between official and personal conduct relevant to the assertion of privilege. And as a factual matter, the OIC ignores that, from the beginning, the Lewinsky matter has unavoidably involved the functioning of the President in his official capacities as head of government and head of state.

1. The Communications at Issue Involved Official Presidential Decisions

Allegations about "private" conduct by a sitting President can and do have a substantial impact on his official duties and activities. The OIC's argument ignores the many factual respects in which the instant litigation unavoidably intersects with the President's performance of his constitutional duties.[18]

Contrary to the OIC's assertions, not one of the witnesses who have testified before the grand jury, including the three whose testimony the OIC now seeks to compel, have ever invoked a blanket assertion of privilege to refuse to answer "***any*** questions concerning conversations about Monica Lewinsky that occurred among White House staff." (OIC Lindsey Br. 1, *see also* OIC Hernreich Br. 2;[19] OIC Blumenthal Br. 2). Mr. Lindsey, for example, has appeared three times before the grand jury and has testified in great detail, to the extent of his personal knowledge, about discussions inside and outside the White House relating to the Lewinsky matter. (*See* Lindsey Decl. ¶¶ 9, 14, 15, 16(a)–(i), 17). The White House has invoked the privilege only as to communications designed to aid the President in the execution of his official duties. (*See id.* ¶ 17).

---

18 Even the President's political opponents have recognized the impact of the OIC's investigation on the functioning of the Presidency as an institution. *See* David Rogers, *Lott Says Clinton-Starr Standoff Hurts Government and Urges Both Sides to Act*, WALL ST. J., Mar. 10, 1998, at A24 (quoting Senate Majority Leader Trent Lott (R-Miss.) as saying the Lewinsky matter is "getting to be a distraction in Washington and affecting the president and perhaps even the Congress, in doing the people's business[.]"). *See also id.* ("'I don't think it's good for the presidency. I don't think it's good for the country,' he [Lott] said in a later interview."). (*See also* Ruff Decl. ¶ 24).

19 Consistent with the White House's proposal of March 4, 1998, submitted as part of the White House's performance of the constitutionally mandated accommodation process recognized by *Sealed Case*, the White House withdraws the assertion of executive privilege over factual matters, including communications with the President, on behalf of non-attorney advisors such as Ms. Hernreich.

What the OIC apparently fails to understand, or is unwilling to admit, is that this case has in fact had a demonstrable effect on the operations of the White House as an institution. Several examples will illustrate the profound impact the Lewinsky matter has had on the functioning of the Presidency. The White House offers these examples solely for illustrative purposes. Nothing in *Nixon* or *Sealed Case* suggests that the question whether a particular issue calls for direct involvement and decisionmaking by the President is amenable to judicial review. Similarly, the cases do not suggest that the President's determination to seek advice on a particular subject, or his choice of sources of advice on which to rely, are open to question after the fact by the OIC. Thus, although the presidential communications privilege provides the President with a "qualified" protection that a court may overcome on a sufficiently strong showing of need by the opposing party, *Sealed Case*, 121 F.3d at 745, the predicate issues—whether a given subject requires the President's attention, whether the President should seek advice on the matter, and from whom—are for the President and his advisors alone. The White House does not concede the contrary by discussing the following examples of presidential decisionmaking.

These examples make clear that the OIC's effort to eliminate all conversations relating to the Lewinsky matter from the protection of the presidential communications privilege is glaringly misdirected.

a. Discussions Relating to the President's State of the Union Address

The Constitution requires the President periodically to report to Congress on the State of the Union. U.S. CONST. Art. II, § 3, cl. 1. Advisors made certain of the communications that the OIC seeks here in the course of advising the President on the performance of that duty, (*see* Blumenthal Decl. ¶¶ 5, 13), and those communications are squarely covered by the presidential communications privileges. *Cf. Sealed Case*, 121 F.3d at 752 (communications presumptively privileged because they "were generated in the course of advising the President in the exercise of . . . a quintessential and nondelegable Presidential power.").

The President addressed the nation on January 27, 1998 and did not discuss the Lewinsky matter. *See Address Before a Joint Session of the Congress on the State of the Union*, 34 WEEKLY COMPILATION OF PRESIDENTIAL DOCUMENTS 129 (Jan. 27, 1998). Leading up to the address, though, conversations took place within the White House about how the President should handle the matter. Senior White House advisors also advised the President how to respond to the many questions reporters asked him concerning how he would treat the allegations in the State of the Union speech.[20] (*See* Lindsey Decl. ¶ 11; Ruff Decl. ¶ 23; Declaration of Sidney Blumenthal ("Blumenthal Decl.") ¶¶ 5, 13–15). Thus do allegations related to ostensibly "private" conduct have a substantial impact on the President's constitutional duties. These discussions occurred in the course of advising the President on his discharge of a core constitutional obligation, and are presumptively privileged from disclosure.

b. Matters of Foreign Policy and Military Affairs

In the weeks since the allegations involving the President surfaced, it has become abundantly clear that the OIC's current investigation has consequences even for the nation's foreign policy and military affairs, and the President's roles as head of state and Commander-in-Chief—core Executive Branch functions which have long merited the greatest deference from the other branches of government. *See* U.S. CONST. Art. II, § 2 cl. 1, § 3 cl. 3. Reporters have questioned visiting foreign heads of state about the OIC's investigation.[21] Other foreign government offi-

---

20 *See, e.g., Excerpt of a Telephone Interview With Morton Kondrake and Ed Henry of Roll Call*, 34 WEEKLY COMPILATION OF PRESIDENTIAL DOCUMENTS 115 (Jan. 21, 1998); *Interview With Mara Liasson and Robert Siegel of National Public Radio*, 34 WEEKLY COMPILATION OF PRESIDENTIAL DOCUMENTS 116, 117 (Jan. 21, 1998).

21 *See The President's News Conference With Prime Minister Blair*, 34 WEEKLY COMPILATION OF PRESIDENTIAL DOCUMENTS 213–22 (Feb. 9, 1998); *see also* John M. Broder, *Clinton Refuses to Discuss Independent Counsel's Request That He Testify Before Grand Jury*, N.Y. TIMES, Mar. 12, 1998, at A24 (reporters ask questions about the Lewinsky matter during the President's public appearance with United Nations Secretary General Kofi Annan, prompting Secretary General Annan to complain, "I wish you would concentrate on my issues. I don't come every day.").

The early days of the Lewinsky matter also coincided with official state visits by Israeli Prime Minister Benjamin Netanyahu and Palestinian Authority Chairman Yasser Arafat. The President, in one of his first public interviews after the OIC began probing the Lewinsky-related allegations, mentioned the extraordinary steps he had endeavored to take to ensure that the burgeoning controversy not distract him from the proper conduct of the nation's foreign policy. *See Interview With Jim Lehrer of the PBS "News Hour"*, 34 WEEKLY COMPILATION OF PRESIDENTIAL DOCUMENTS 104–05, 106–07, 114 (Jan. 21, 1998).

cials have expressed their concern that the investigation must not be allowed to detract from the United States' ongoing and crucial role as peacemaker.[22] Some of the conversations over which the White House has invoked the presidential communications privilege involved the formulation of advice for the President as to the appropriate White House response when foreign officials inquired about, or were questioned about, the Lewinsky matter. (*See* Blumenthal Decl. ¶¶ 10–11, 13–15).

What is more, the current investigation has unfolded during a turbulent period in the nation's international relations, when the President and his advisors have been formulating a response to continued violations by Iraq of United Nations Security Council resolutions on weapons inspection adopted in the wake of the 1991 Persian Gulf War. Although the immediate threat of military conflict appears to have diminished somewhat at this moment, certain conversations at issue here occurred at a time when military confrontation appeared highly likely and the President's need to concentrate on the nation's military and foreign affairs was at its peak. Deliberations within the White House about how to keep the controversy related to the Lewinsky matter from hampering the President's conduct of the nation's military and foreign policy formed a part of the discussions over which the White House has invoked the presidential communications privilege. (*See* Ruff Decl. ¶ 27; Blumenthal Decl. ¶ 15). For the foregoing reasons, the conversations at issue here plainly fall under the presumptive privilege established in *Nixon* and *Sealed Case.*

c. Discussions of Possible Referral by the OIC to the House Judiciary Committee

As the discussion of the facts surrounding the expansion of the OIC's inquiry in mid-January 1998 makes clear, the immediate effect of the new allegations of possible obstruction of justice led commentators and reporters to discuss the issue of impeachment and, therefore,

---

22 *See, e.g., supra* note 21; Alessandra Staley, *American Puritanism or Zionist Plot? The World Weighs In*, N.Y. TIMES, Jan. 24, 1998, at A9 (discussing, *inter alia*, the effect of the Lewinsky-related allegations on the Middle East peace process); *Remarks Prior to Discussions With Chairman Yasser Arafat of the Palestinian Authority and an Exchange With Reporters*, 34 WEEKLY COMPILATION OF PRESIDENTIAL DOCUMENTS 123, 124 (Jan. 22, 1998) (reporters question the President about the Lewinsky matter at a press conference with Chairman Arafat).

placed it on the discussion agenda of senior White House advisors.[23] (*See* Lindsey Decl. ¶ 11). The White House received many inquiries from the press on this possibility. (*See* Ruff Decl. ¶ 22). Indeed, the President himself has been questioned by reporters on the subject.[24] Senior advisors to the President, including attorneys in the White House Counsel's office, have a duty to obtain factual information relevant to the investigation to advise the President concerning this issue. (*See* Ruff Decl. ¶ 22).

Impeachment is the one remedy expressly provided in the Constitution (Art. II, § 4) that can be directed against the President, and it is fatuous for the OIC to contend that discussions of the prospect between the President and his core advisors could, in any sense, be considered "personal" or "unofficial." In part because of the formal responsibilities of the Counsel to the President in the event of impeachment proceedings, "even the mere speculation of such proceedings raises serious issues that a President and his advisors must address." (Ruff Decl. ¶ 19). Because of the constitutional concerns directly implicated by an investigation that threatens possible impeachment proceedings against the President, conversations on this subject must be deemed presumptively privileged.

d. Allocation of the President's Time Between Public Responsibilities and Defending Himself in the *Jones* Litigation and the Lewinsky Matter

The expansion of the OIC's jurisdiction in mid-January 1998 immediately returned to the forefront of the White House's agenda an issue that had been lingering since the Supreme Court's decision in *Clinton v. Jones* the preceding summer. The Court's decision declining to stay the *Jones* proceedings during the President's term of office immediately raised the issue of

---

23 The possibility of proceedings in the House Judiciary Committee had, of course, been discussed within the White House even before the Lewinsky-related allegations surfaced. *See* H. Res. 304, 105th Cong., 1st Sess. (Nov. 5, 1997). (*See also* Ruff Decl. ¶¶ 19–21).

24 *See Excerpt of a Telephone Interview With Morton Kondrake and Ed Henry of Roll Call*, 34 WEEKLY COMPILATION OF PRESIDENTIAL DOCUMENTS 115 (Jan. 21, 1998).

how the President should defend himself in the litigation without, in the Court's words, allowing the case to "engulf the Presidency." *Jones*, 117 S. Ct. at 1648.

The Court's decision allowing the case to proceed necessarily required the President to devote part of his schedule to the conduct of his defense. Questions as to how the President allocates his time, however, are imbued with a public, official nature, for every moment the President must spend defending himself in private litigation is a moment in which he is unavailable to execute the duties of the office to which he was elected. Thus, the question of how to minimize the *Jones* litigation's interference with the President's performance of his official duties was an important subject of discussion among the President's senior advisors. (*See* Lindsey Decl. ¶ 8).

The U.S. Department of Justice's brief as *amicus curiae* in *Jones*, for example, succinctly described the public significance of the issue:

> As a practical matter, the countless issues of domestic and foreign policy that demand the President's attention fully occupy, and indeed outstrip, the capacity of the President to respond.... ***As a result, the Presidency's most precious commodity is time, and one of the most vexing problems for the President and his staff is how to divide that time among the disparate issues that call for his attention.***

Clinton v. Jones, 117 S. Ct. 1636 (1997), Brief for the United States as *Amicus Curiae* in Support of Petitioner at 10–11 (emphasis added); *accord Jones*, 117 S. Ct. at 1646 (recognizing demands on a sitting President's schedule). Notably, presiding Judge Wright permitted the Counsel to the President to attend the President's deposition in the *Jones* case, a recognition that the case has important consequences for the nation and for the institution of the Presidency, not merely for the individual who currently holds that office.

Many of the communications the OIC seeks to compel relate to the President's decisions about strategy regarding how to prevent the *Jones* litigation and the Lewinsky investigation from "engulf[ing] the Presidency." (*See* Lindsey Decl. ¶¶ 9–11). The demands of discovery and the forthcoming trial have required the President to, in some cases, delegate to subordinates within the White House the task of attending to scheduling matters not requiring the President's personal attention. Before making each of these decisions, the President gathered recommendations and advice from his aides on how best to meet the scheduling demands of the *Jones* litigation without detracting from the execution of the duties of his office.

e. Ongoing Strategy Discussions Relating to the OIC's Investigation

When an issue requiring a rapid presidential decision arises, the President's need for advice and recommendations is correspondingly accelerated. To perform their advisory function in such a context, it is crucial that the President's advisors remain abreast of breaking developments as they occur, rather than "reinventing the wheel" every time the President solicits their opinions. Presidential advisors have an on-going duty to gather the facts necessary to render sound advice on short notice when so requested by the President. To that end, discussions of strategic and policy matters are a staple of every White House advisor's daily routine. (*See* Ruff Decl. ¶¶ 29–30).

The incursion of the OIC's investigation into the daily operations of the White House is no exception to this principle. Many of the conversations the OIC seeks to compel involved discussions among senior presidential advisors concerning how the White House should respond to the OIC's investigation, what effect the investigation would have on presidential scheduling (including prearranged travel abroad by the President on diplomatic matters), what effect the investigation would have on the formulation and announcement of new policy initiatives, dealings with Congress, and the like. (*See* Lindsey Decl. ¶ 12; Ruff Decl. ¶¶ 29–30). Because these discussions formed an on-going part of the advisors' function to counsel the President on decisions he must make, they are presumptively privileged.

f. Discussions as to Whether to Assert the Presidential Communications Privilege

Irrespective of whether the invocation of the privilege may be communicated to a Court through one of the President's intermediaries,[25] the decision whether to claim the privilege is necessarily a matter that falls squarely within the execution of the President's official duties.

Some of the conversations the OIC seeks involved discussions among the President's closest advisors about whether the President should claim a privilege, or refrain from doing so. Such discussions have occurred in the White House virtually every day since the Lewinsky-related allegations surfaced. (*See generally* Lindsey Decl. ¶ 11; Ruff Decl. ¶¶ 26–28). The need to balance the twin aims of appropriate disclosure with the institutional need to preserve candid and open communication among advisors presented questions of the most exacting subtlety. The inevitable risk that an invocation of the privilege, no matter how strongly justified under the law, would prompt unfavorable public commentary also factored into advisors' candid, even fractious, discussions of what advice to give the President. Because all these discussions occurred while advising the President in connection with a decision only he could make in his official capacity, they are presumptively privileged from disclosure.

2. The OIC's Argument Misconstrues the Relevant Authorities

Besides being inconsistent with the facts, the OIC's argument that the presidential communications privilege is subject to an implicit exception for "personal" or "unofficial" presidential conduct is at odds with precedent from both the Supreme Court and the Court of Appeals for this Circuit.

The Court of Appeals' opinion in *Senate Select Committee* holds squarely against the argument the OIC makes here. In *Senate Select Committee*, an investigating arm of the Congress attempted to compel the President to produce "taped recordings of five conversations . . . 'between President Nixon and John Wesley Dean, III, discussing alleged criminal acts occurring

---

[25] *See Sealed Case*, 121 F.3d at 744–45 n.16 (the cases do not establish whether the privilege must be claimed by the President personally).

in connection with the Presidential election of 1972.' " *Senate Select Committee*, 498 F.2d at 727. These conversations related to acts far outside the boundaries of the President's official duties, namely, the ransacking of the DNC's Watergate offices. Under the OIC's theory here, these conversations would not have been presumptively privileged.

The D.C. Circuit held precisely to the contrary. *See id.* at 730. Moreover, the Court found the Senate Select Committee's showing of need for the tapes inadequate, and denied the Senate's motion to compel. *Id.* at 731 ("we find that the Select Committee has failed to make the requisite showing" to overcome the presumption).

The OIC's argument is also at odds with the Supreme Court's decision in *United States v. Nixon*. The presidential communications at issue in that case involved private conduct by other individuals, but nonetheless were held presumptively privileged by the Supreme Court. *See Nixon*, 418 U.S. at 713–14. Indeed, nothing in *Nixon* suggests that the conversations at issue were characterized by an overarching public or official purpose, as distinct from discussions pertaining to the potential individual liability of the President (who had, after all, been named an unindicted co-conspirator by the grand jury, and whose subordinates had already been convicted of Watergate-related crimes).[26] Thus, the OIC's legal theory has been rejected by both the D.C. Circuit and the Supreme Court.[27]

The contents of the presidential conversations the Supreme Court held presumptively privileged in *Nixon* indicate that the OIC cannot circumvent the privilege merely by claiming that its sole interest is in the President's actions in his personal, rather than official, capacity. For

---

26 President Nixon did not contend that any of the subpoenaed conversations revealed diplomatic or military secrets. *See Nixon*, 418 U.S. at 706, 710. In holding that the conversations were, nevertheless, presumptively privileged (*id.* at 713–14), the Court obviously rejected any notion that the presidential communications privilege is limited to communications implicating foreign policy or national security. *Accord Sealed Case*, 121 F.3d at 757–58 (presidential communications privilege protects internal White House discussions of investigation of Secretary of Agriculture, which did not implicate military or diplomatic concerns). The OIC's suggestion that the privilege cannot come into play here because no "national security or diplomatic secrets" are involved (OIC Lindsey Br. at 4) ignores *all* the relevant precedent.

27 The Court in *Nixon* ultimately held that, in the unique circumstances of that case, the Special Prosecutor had made a sufficient showing to support turning over the subpoenaed materials for *in camera* review by the district court. *See Nixon*, 418 U.S. at 713–14. It did so only after finding the materials presumptively privileged, however.

example, some of the conversations that the Supreme Court held presumptively privileged were three discussions between President Nixon and H.R. Haldeman on June 23, 1972. *See Statement Announcing Availability of Additional Transcripts of Presidential Tape Recordings*, 1974 PUBLIC PAPERS OF THE PRESIDENTS 621. These conversations involved President Nixon's attempt to derail the FBI's investigation of the Watergate break-in by falsely alleging a foreign connection over which the FBI had no authority. By contrast, the conversations over which the President has asserted the privilege here are plainly related to his legitimate official functions.

Nor does *Clinton v. Jones* erase the presumption of privilege that attaches to presidential communications under *Nixon* and *Sealed Case*. The OIC suggests that the Supreme Court's characterization of the *Jones* case as "unrelated to any of [the President's] official duties," 117 S. Ct. at 1640, forecloses any application of the presumptive privilege. The Court's holding, however, is in no way inconsistent with the presumptive privilege recognized in *Nixon* and *Sealed Case*. To the contrary, the Court instructed that great deference was owed to the "unique position in the constitutional scheme" the President holds. 117 S. Ct. at 1646 (internal quotations omitted). Although *Clinton v. Jones* held that the Constitution did not mandate a stay of civil proceedings against a sitting President during his term of office, the Court never held or suggested that presidential communications relating to that litigation during the President's term of office were entitled to any less protection than were presidential communications on other subjects. Indeed, *Jones* nowhere suggested that the interests the Court in *Nixon* recognized to underlie the rule of presumptive privilege—the President's need to obtain candid and objective advice and to consider all alternatives in formulating decisions (*see Nixon*, 418 U.S. at 708)—

carry any less force in the context of the public ramifications of civil litigation about personal matters.[28]

C. The OIC Has Made No Showing, Least of All the Extraordinary Showing Required, to Overcome the Privilege

As previously discussed, the case law requires the OIC to make a "focused demonstration of need" before presidential communications may even be turned over to the Court for *in camera* review. *See generally supra* at 25–27. But, in another example of its total disregard of the governing analytical framework, the OIC explicitly concedes that it has made no such showing. (OIC Lindsey Br. at 8). Rather, the OIC asks instead that it be allowed to do so at some unspecified future time. Whether the OIC is allowed the second bite at the apple it has attempted to reserve for itself is a question for another day. For present purposes, the point is merely that nothing on the record now suggests that the OIC can make the showing the law requires. In these circumstances, the OIC plainly cannot overcome the presumptive privilege that attaches to the communications at issue here.

---

28 It is easy to conceive of other instances in which Presidents' "private" concerns have affected the operation of the Presidency as an institution. The question frequently arises, for example, in correction with Presidents' health problems, such as President Reagan's cancer surgery in 1985 or President Bush's treatment for an irregular heartbeat in 1991. Although the health of the individuals holding the Office of the President is no doubt a "private" concern as the OIC uses the term, these incidents raised a plethora of issues regarding the appropriate governmental response to presidential incapacity, the possibility of invoking the Twenty-Fifth Amendment, and related matters—all of which would unmistakably be considered "official," and therefore protected, notwithstanding that they arose out of a President's private concerns.

CONCLUSION

Accordingly, for the reasons stated, the OIC's Motions to Compel should be denied.

Respectfully submitted,

W. Neil Eggleston (D.C. Bar No. 411957)
Timothy K. Armstrong (D.C. Bar No. 444200)
HOWREY & SIMON
1299 Pennsylvania Ave., N.W.
Washington, D.C. 20004
(202) 783-0800

Attorneys for The White House

Of Counsel:
Charles F.C. Ruff
Counsel to the President
THE WHITE HOUSE
Washington, D.C. 20500
(202) 456-1414

Dated: March 17, 1998

CERTIFICATE OF SERVICE

I hereby certify that copies of the foregoing Memorandum of the White House in Opposition to OIC's Motions to Compel Bruce R. Lindsey and Sidney Blumenthal to Testify Concerning Conversations Protected by the Attorney-Client, Presidential Communications, and Work Product Privileges were served by hand or Federal Express, this 17th day of March, 1998 upon each of the parties listed below:

Kenneth W. Starr, Esq. Independent Counsel Office of the Independent Counsel 1001 Pennsylvania Avenue, N.W. Suite 490 North Washington, DC 20004	Independent Counsel
Charles F. C. Ruff, Esq. Counsel to the President The White House Washington, D.C. 20500	Counsel to the President
William J. Murphy, Esq. Murphy & Shaffer 100 Light Street, 9th Floor Baltimore, Maryland 21202-1019	Counsel to Bruce R. Lindsey
Mr. William McDaniel McDaniel & Marsh 118 West Mulberry Street Baltimore, Maryland 21201	Counsel to Mr. Sidney Blumenthal
Gerard Treanor, Esq. Venable, Baetjer, Howard & Civiletti 1201 New York Avenue, N.W. Suite 1000 Washington, D.C. 20005-3917	Counsel to Ms. Nancy Hernreich

W. Neil Eggleston

W. NEIL EGGLESTON

IN THE UNITED STATES DISTRICT COURT
FOR THE DISTRICT OF COLUMBIA

IN RE: SEALED CASE.	)))	Misc. No. 98-95 (UNDER SEAL)

DECLARATION OF CHARLES F.C. RUFF

I, Charles F.C. Ruff, do hereby declare:

I. Introduction

1. I am Counsel to the President of the United States. I have held this position since February 10, 1997. Prior to that time, from 1995 to 1997, I served as Corporation Counsel to the District of Columbia. From 1982-95, I was a partner at the Washington, D.C. law firm of Covington & Burling. During that time, from 1989-90, I served as president of the District of Columbia Bar. I also served as United States Attorney for the District of Columbia from 1979-82. From 1975-77, I served as Watergate Special Prosecutor.

2. In my capacity as Counsel to the President, I provide legal advice to the President regarding a wide variety of matters relating to his constitutional, statutory, ceremonial, and other official duties and the effective functioning of the Executive Branch. At the President's direction, I review various matters that have legal implications and advise him on particular courses of conduct. Those matters include, among numerous others, the assertion of privileges in response to requests for materials and testimony, including executive privilege, attorney-client privilege, and attorney-work-product privilege.

3. The White House Counsel's Office, as a whole, provides confidential counsel to the President, in his official capacity, to the White House, as an institution, and to senior advisors, in

particular, about matters that affect the White House's interests, including investigative matters. To this end, the Counsel's Office receives confidential communications from and provides advice to current and former White House personnel about matters of institutional concern. These individuals provide this information to and solicit advice from our Office with the expectation and understanding that such communications will remain confidential.

II. The *Jones* Litigation

4. In May 1997, the Supreme Court held in *Clinton v. Jones* that the Constitution does not require a stay of private litigation involving the President until after his term. *Clinton v. Jones*, 117 S. Ct. 1636 (1997). Thus, the *Jones* litigation was permitted to proceed during the President's term, with the Court making particular note that the potential burdens that this litigation may place on the President need to be taken into account by the trial court. This decision requires the President to balance two competing demands on his time: (1) his need to defend the *Jones* lawsuit and (2) the absolute requirement that he devote his full time and attention to performing his duties as President.

5. From my experience as a defense attorney in private practice, a civil lawsuit involving these kinds of allegations and monetary claims requires a substantial time commitment by a client, especially during the discovery phase of the litigation. I also found that most of my individual clients, in addition to fulfilling their obligations as a litigant, have a genuine and important interest in being actively involved in the ongoing litigation, including participating in strategy discussions and decisions. This level of commitment necessarily places a substantial burden on a client's schedule.

6. The President, as the Chief Executive of our Nation, has extraordinary demands placed on his time. His schedule cannot accommodate the many demands of his office, independent of his personal and family responsibilities. In most instances, the many competing obligations

facing the President require him to rely on his advisors to meet with certain people, attend meetings, gather information and advise him on particular matters.

7. Thus, the progress of the *Jones* litigation concurrent with President's second term has placed additional obligations on the President's schedule that, under the law, he must fulfill despite the current demands of his office. Consequently, the President must look to his advisors to assist him in determining how he can fulfill the requirements of the lawsuit while not abandoning his duty to the American people.

8. The lawsuit has also spawned issues and the need for decisions (*e.g.*, discovery, the deposition of the President, and the possibility of a resolution of the litigation prior to trial) that affect the Presidency and the President's ability to perform his duties effectively. The President's advisors, who know the scope and weight of matters before the President at any given time, are best situated to advise the President as to how various aspects of the *Jones* litigation may affect the Presidency or official matters. Accordingly, presidential advisors need to know about and discuss those litigation-related issues or matters that may affect the office so that they can give the President informed advice as to how he should proceed.

9. The media's interest in the *Jones* litigation has generated inquiries in hundreds of official presidential press conferences and briefings by the President, his press secretary, and other White House staff, whether held here or in other countries. Indeed, the volume of *Jones*-related inquiries that the White House receives sometimes eclipses the inquiries generated by official White House policy matters. Therefore, presidential advisors need the ability to have informed, candid, and frank discussions about the *Jones* litigation to prepare the President for these inquiries.

III. The Expansion of the Office of Independent Counsel Starr's Jurisdiction

10. On January 16, 1998, at the request of the Attorney General, the Special Division conferred jurisdiction on the Office of Independent Counsel Kenneth Starr ("OIC") to investigate whether "Monica Lewinsky or any other individual" suborned perjury or committed other federal crimes.[1] The allegations surrounding the OIC's investigation involve the President during his tenure, the White House, and many White House employees.

11. Since that time, the OIC has served 13 subpoenas for documents on the White House or current White House employees containing more than 30 separate requests relating to the Lewinsky investigation and calling for expedited production. The OIC has also served at least 25 current and former White House employees with subpoenas calling for their testimony before the grand jury. The OIC also has requested interviews from more than 30 current and former White House employees.

12. Every day since January 21, 1998, the White House has received a flood of press inquiries related to the Lewinsky investigation, and the subject has been raised in virtually every White House press briefing and presidential press appearance.

IV. White House Cooperation with the OIC Investigation

13. Consistent with the practice of my predecessors, as Counsel to the President, I have endeavored to cooperate with the OIC by maintaining an open and constructive dialogue and by responding expeditiously to its requests. Indeed, the White House has responded in a timely fashion to the OIC's document subpoenas and has produced all responsive materials it has

---

[1] *Text of Reno's Petition for Starr*, ASSOCIATED PRESS NEWSDAY.COM, Jan. 29, 1998.

located, usually by the designated production date. To accomplish this task, the Counsel's Office circulated a directive to the entire Executive Office of the President's staff and, where appropriate, performed several targeted searches for information.

14. Many current and former White House staff members, other than Mr. Lindsey and Mr. Blumenthal, have been subpoenaed to testify before the grand jury regarding their knowledge of facts pertaining to the relevant time period surrounding the Lewinsky investigation. Others have been asked to submit voluntarily to an interview. I understand that all of these individuals have cooperated with the OIC, and none has asserted privilege over any information that they possess. In particular, the following individuals have provided testimony about their knowledge of this matter: Betty Currie, Patsy Thomasson, Timothy Keating, Stephen Goodin, Kris Engskov, George Stephanopoulos, Deborah Schiff, Marsha Scott, Leon Panetta, Evelyn Leiberman, Carolyn Huber, and Bayani Nelvis.

15. As explained more fully below, with respect to certain individuals subpoenaed to testify, I anticipated that their testimony might implicate confidential communications and information. In an effort to avoid any unnecessary delay in the investigation and needless confrontation, my staff notified the OIC that the issue might arise and discussed ways to reach a mutually agreeable accommodation prior to or following an individual's appearance.

V. Certain Information and Discussions Relating to the Lewinsky Investigation are Subject to Privilege

16. It is my understanding that this and prior administrations, Republican and Democratic, have recognized that, with respect to matters that relate to the President's performance of his duties and the functions of the Executive Branch, presidential advisors, and their staff, must be able to inquire into matters in detail, obtain input from all others with significant expertise in the area, and perform detailed analyses of all possible alternatives before deciding what advice and

information to provide the President. *In re Sealed Case*, 121 F.3d 729, 750 (D.C. Cir. 1997). The President has an important confidentiality interest in seeking and receiving advice -- an interest that is constitutionally based "to the extent this interest relates to the effective discharge of a President's powers." *United States v. Nixon*, 418 U.S. 683, 711 (1974).

17. Moreover, we treat executive privilege as extending to communications among advisors and their staff, even if not communicated directly to President, *In re Sealed Case*, 121 F.3d at 751-52, and to communications in their entirety, not just the deliberative or advice portions, including pre-decisional, final, and post-decisional materials. *In re Sealed Case*, 121 F.3d at 745.

18. The Lewinsky investigation involves allegations regarding the President's conduct toward a federal government employee during his tenure in office. This matter is inextricably intertwined with the daily presidential agenda, and thus has a substantial impact on the President's ability to discharge his obligations. Accordingly, in the course of executing his duties, there have been discussions among advisors and the President involving the Lewinsky investigation, and these discussions have been held in confidence and treated as subject to privilege.

A. Discussion of Possible Proceedings by the House Judiciary Committee

19. Under Article II of the Constitution, Congress possesses the power to initiate proceedings against a sitting President that can ultimately result in his removal from office. Thus, even the mere speculation about such proceedings raises serious issues that a President and his advisors must address.

20. In November 1997, an impeachment resolution was introduced in the House of

Representatives. The resolution did not contain specific allegations regarding the President. Rather, it broadly claimed that there was considerable evidence developed from various "credible sources" that the President had engaged in conduct designed to obstruct the legitimate Executive Branch functions. *See* H. Res. 304, 105th Cong., 1st Sess. (Nov. 5, 1997).

21. Only days after the Special Division expanded the scope of the OIC's investigation, members of the House Judiciary Committee renewed their public discussions about the possibility of initiating proceedings against the President in light of the allegations arising from the Lewinsky investigation.[2] Weeks later, the press continued to report that many people "would like to see [the President] impeached or forced to resign."[3] Congressman Robert Barr recently went so far as to state that "the Republican leadership is beginning to lay the groundwork . . . [for] impeachment proceedings . . . ."[4] Thus, the Lewinsky investigation not only relates to and affects the Presidency -- it also threatens it.

22. Statements by members of Congress and related reports have generated numerous inquiries, some directed at the President, about the possibility of impeachment proceedings.[5]

---

[2] *Bryant suggests Clinton should consider stepping aside*, GANNETT NEWS SERVICE, Jan. 27, 1998.

[3] N. Gibbs, *Twin Perils of Love & War*, TIME, March 2, 1998, p.36-39; *see Clinton Accused: Guide to Impeachment* THE INDEPENDENT, Jan. 23, 1998, p.8; *'Smoking Gun' Could Trigger Bid to Boot Bubba*, NEW YORK POST, Jan. 23, 1998, p.9; *Clinton Is Becoming Increasingly Isolated As His Latest Crisis Deepens*, THE SCOTSMAN, Jan. 23, 1998, p.15; *Excerpt of A Telephone Interview With Morton Kondrake and Ed Henry of Roll Call*, 34 WEEKLY COMPILATION OF PRESIDENTIAL DOCUMENTS 115 (Jan. 21, 1998).

[4] *Bob Barr Discusses Impeachment Process for Bill Clinton*, CNN BOTH SIDES WITH JESSE JACKSON (Feb. 15, 1998).

[5] JOINT PRESS CONFERENCE OF THE PRESIDENT AND PRIME MINISTER TONY BLAIR OF GREAT BRITAIN, Feb. 6, 1998; PRESS BRIEFING BY MIKE MCCURRY, Jan. 26, 1998; PRESS BRIEFING BY MIKE MCCURRY, Jan. 23, 1998; PRESS BRIEFING BY MIKE MCCURRY, Jan. 21, 1998.

Consequently, presidential advisors must gather information and formulate advice for the President about the Lewinsky investigation to address the myriad of issues and inquiries that the investigation raises in this context. In addition, the Counsel's Office must prepare to defend against any such proceeding.

B. Domestic and Foreign Policy Matters

23. The President's State of the Union address occurred days after the press reported the expansion of the OIC's jurisdiction and the allegations surrounding Ms. Lewinsky. The White House received numerous inquiries as to whether the President would address these allegations in his State of the Union address.[6] The President's advisors obviously were required to gather information, consider available options, and advise the President about how to handle this and related matters.

24. The President's ability to work with Congress to enact legislation is likewise affected by the Lewinsky investigation. Certain legislators have been described as "throwing up their hands at the prospect of doing any serious business,"[7] thereby significantly affecting the President's domestic agenda.[8] Indeed, Senate Majority Leader Trent Lott recently remarked that the Lewinsky investigation "is beginning to have an impact on the presidency, on the president and on his ability to deal with many very important issues for the future of our country -- from Social

---

[6] *E.g.*, PRESS BRIEFING BY MIKE MCCURRY, Jan. 26, 1998.

[7] *Clinton Under Fire*, LOS ANGELES TIMES, Jan. 26, 1998, p.A17; *see also The President Under Fire: The Public View*, NEW YORK TIMES, Jan. 27, 1998, p.A1 ("most Americans fear that the scandal will interfere with his future ability to perform his job effectively"); *Alleged Clinton Affair Boosts call for Impeachment Probe*, STATES NEWS SERVICE, Jan. 22, 1998.

[8] *See Lawmakers Return Amidst Scandal*, AP ONLINE, Jan. 26, 1998.

Security to what's going on in Iraq to now what's going on in Kosovo."[9] Therefore, in discussing with the President his ability to achieve the Administration's domestic policy objectives, advisors must take into account the impact of issues arising out of the Lewinsky investigation on his efforts and advise him accordingly.

25. Based upon information from others, I understand that the Lewinsky investigation also affected the President's ability to address foreign policy matters. For example, during the recent crisis with Iraq, certain people speculated that the Lewinsky investigation might harm the President's ability to "influence" the public, thus rendering him incapable of garnering support for the U.S. position on this issue and ultimately negotiating a successful resolution with Iraq.[10] These same concerns were raised when the President addressed Middle East issues, including his recent meetings with Prime Minister Netanyahu and Mr. Arafat.[11] Therefore, the President's advisors necessarily discussed the Lewinsky investigation and advised the President so that he could effectively execute his constitutional duties regarding foreign policy matters.

C. Discussions Regarding the Assertion of Applicable Privileges

26. When an investigative body subpoenas the White House or one of its staff members for

---

[9] *Lott Urges Clinton to Give Details*, ASSOCIATED PRESS, March 9, 1998.

[10] *Crisis Develops Inside the White House*, CNN LATE EDITION WITH WOLF BLITZER (Jan. 25, 1998); *see also*, *Twin Perils of Love & War*, TIME, March 2, 1998, p.36-39 ; *Republicans End Silence On Troubles Of President*, THE NEW YORK TIMES, March 1, 1998, sec.1, p.20, col.1; *It's Hard To Believe The Clintons*, CHICAGO TRIBUNE, Jan. 29, 1998, p.19; *Echoes of the past but a far cry from Watergate*, FINANCIAL TIMES, Jan. 24, 1998, p.3; *Scandal tests Clinton on Iraq crisis*, AGENCE FRANCE PRESSE, Jan. 24, 1998.

[11] *N.J. lawmakers worry Clinton's woes could hurt host of issues*, GANNETT NEWS SERVICE, Jan. 30, 1998; *It's Hard To Believe The Clintons*, CHICAGO TRIBUNE, Jan. 29, 1998, p.19 ; *Letters to the Editor: Sex and the president through media eyes*, THE SAN DIEGO UNION-TRIBUNE, Jan. 27, 1998, p.B-7.

information, White House confidentiality interests are often implicated. The Counsel's Office has always attempted to deal with these privilege issues in a careful and deliberate manner.

27. After ascertaining that a subpoenaed individual possesses confidential information, the decision whether to assert privilege over such communications or information is one that the White House approaches thoughtfully, deliberately, and seriously. First, we carefully review the nature and substance of the communication to determine its confidential nature. Second, we evaluate whether the assertion of the privilege is legally sustainable and otherwise appropriate. Finally, we brief the President and advise him in making the ultimate decision. Thus, this process involves core presidential decisionmaking.

28. Accordingly, presidential advisors have engaged in deliberations to determine whether it is necessary to advise the President to assert privilege over certain communications. These discussions are presumptively privileged.

D. Strategy Sessions involving Presidential Advisors and Counsel

29. The President is unable personally to keep abreast of every matter that is handled by or could possibly affect him or the Executive Branch. Accordingly, the President must rely on advisors to ensure the progress and development of these matters and, when appropriate, brief the President with information and advice that will permit him to make decisions and respond to inquiries. Often, issues arise unexpectedly, and thus advisors must always be prepared to assist the President on a moment's notice with the most recent, accurate and comprehensive information, and the full range of options relating to a particular decision.

30. The Lewinsky investigation is no exception to this process. As illustrated in the examples presented above, since first reported, this investigation has affected the President's

ability to execute his constitutional obligations and has been the primary subject of press inquiries. This investigation has also intruded on the work of the President and his immediate advisors and staff, and has raised issues involving privilege, witness availability and subpoena compliance. As a result, the President's advisors and counsel have held regular meetings to gather and exchange information, as well as to formulate recommendations, for the President.

VI. The Subpoenas to Bruce R. Lindsey and Sidney Blumenthal

A. Communications with the OIC before Grand Jury Appearances by Mr. Lindsey and Mr. Blumenthal

31. On January 30, 1998, the OIC served on Bruce Lindsey, Assistant to the President and Deputy Counsel, a subpoena calling for his appearance to testify on February 4, 1998 before the grand jury.

32. In an effort to address, prior to Mr. Lindsey's appearance, the scope of the matters that the OIC sought to discuss with Mr. Lindsey and other senior advisors to the President and to address potential privileges that might be implicated, I contacted the OIC to discuss the matter. On February 3, 1998, Special Counsel Lanny Breuer and I met with Kenneth Starr, Robert Bittman, Steve Collatan, and Jackie Bennett. I explained the nature of the privilege concerns that would arise from broad-ranging inquiries into staff discussions and communications with the President, and I asked OIC to describe with particularity the possible areas of inquiry. They declined to do so.

33. The OIC informed me that it had postponed indefinitely Mr. Lindsey's appearance, and therefore a discussion of their examination of Mr. Lindsey was premature. As a result, our discussions about his testimony were curtailed, and instead we focused on the pending appearance of another presidential advisor, Deputy Chief of Staff John Podesta.

34. On February 4, 1998, Mr. Starr sent me a letter indicating that they intended to inquire into privileged areas based upon their view that executive privilege was inapplicable to information relating to the Lewinsky investigation. (2/4/98 Letter from Starr to Ruff, attached as Exhibit 1).

35. On February 5, 1998, I responded to Mr. Starr's letter and stated that, under the principles of *In re Sealed Case* and other relevant authority, conversations among advisors were presumptively privileged. (2/5/98 Letter from Ruff to Starr, attached as Exhibit 2).

36. I pointed out that the "discussions among and between the President's senior staff involve the very capacity of the President and his staff to govern--to pursue his legislative agenda, to ensure the continued leadership of [the] United States in the world community, and to maintain the confidence of the people who elected him--all of which lie at the heart of his role under Article II of the Constitution." (*Id.* at 2). I concluded by indicating my willingness to explore all possible accommodations of our respective interests. (*Id.*).

37. On February 6, 1998, the OIC sent me a letter rejecting my offer and restating its position regarding the communications about which it intended to inquire. In rejecting my offer, the OIC did not articulate any need for this information, as required by *In re Sealed Case*, but simply asserted that its desire "to resolve this matter in a timely fashion" compelled disclosure. (2/6/98 Letter from Starr to Ruff at 1, attached as Exhibit 3).

38. Finally, on the issue of discussions between witnesses and White House counsel, the OIC stated that, under the Eighth Circuit decision in *In re Grand Jury Subpoena Duces Tecum*, 112 F.3d 910 (8th Cir. 1997), it intended to question White House personnel as to the substance of such communications, and that if a witness asserted the attorney-client privilege, the OIC intended to "take such further steps as are appropriate." (*Id.* at 2).

B. Mr. Lindsey's Communications are Presumptively Privileged

39. As described in his declaration, filed in connection with the White House's opposition to the OIC's motions to compel, Mr. Lindsey testified before the grand jury on February 18 and 19, 1998, and on March 12, 1998. (Declaration of Bruce R. Lindsey ("Lindsey Dec.") ¶ 9).[12] Over the course of those three days of testimony, Mr. Lindsey willingly answered questions about his personal knowledge with respect to any allegations of a personal relationship between Ms. Lewinsky and the President, and any allegations of suborning perjury in connection with the *Jones* litigation, as well as several questions about Mr. Lindsey's discussions with others that involved Ms. Lewinsky. (Lindsey Dec. ¶¶ 15-17).

40. Mr. Lindsey declined to answer other specific categories of questions relating to the *Jones* litigation and the Lewinsky investigation on the grounds that they are subject to executive privilege, attorney-client privilege, attorney-work product privilege, and/or the common interest doctrine. (Lindsey Dec. ¶¶ 10-14).

41. The confidential communications that Mr. Lindsey declined to disclose to the grand jury are presumptively privileged. They occurred while performing his duties as Deputy Counsel to the President and as one of the principal advisors to the President, or as the President's personal attorney prior to the President taking office. (Lindsey Dec. ¶¶ 4-6, 8-14, 17). Mr. Lindsey had these discussions with the President, other White House attorneys, presidential advisors to the President, and/or with the President's private attorneys. (*Id.*). The communications contain information and advice relating to the *Jones* litigation or Lewinsky investigation that Mr. Lindsey gathered or provided for the purpose of assisting the President in making decisions in connection with his official duties or to ensure that the allegations and inquiries surrounding these matters did not impair the President's discharge of his official duties. (*Id.* ¶¶ 10-14).

---

[12] Mr. Lindsey's entire declaration is incorporated by reference.

C. **Mr. Blumenthal's Communications are Presumptively Privileged**

42. On February 26, 1998, Mr. Blumenthal testified before the grand jury. (Declaration of Sidney Blumenthal ("Blumenthal Dec.") ¶ 16).[13] Mr. Blumenthal declined to answer certain questions on the grounds that they are subject to executive privilege. (*Id.*).

43. In his capacity as Assistant to the President, Mr. Blumenthal participates in and is consulted on a wide variety of matters, including domestic policy issues, presidential speeches, (including the State of the Union address), national security issues, and international freedom of the press issues. (*Id.* ¶¶ 4-7). Mr. Blumenthal also serves as the liaison for the President to the office of the Prime Minister of Great Britain; a role that requires him to interact with the Prime Minister and his advisors on a variety of subjects, including United States foreign policy matters. (*Id.* ¶¶ 8-12).

44. To perform his duties, Mr. Blumenthal consults with other presidential advisors to gather information and formulate advice to give to the President. (*Id.* ¶¶ 3, 14-15, 17). In carrying out these duties, Mr. Blumenthal has had discussions with the President, First Lady, and other senior advisors regarding the allegations and inquiries surrounding the Lewinsky investigation. (*Id.*). These discussions took place in the context of Mr. Blumenthal's assisting the President to perform his duties; in particular, the President's State of the Union address and the visit by the Prime Minister of Great Britain. (*Id.* ¶¶14-15). Accordingly, these discussions are presumptively privileged.

---

[13] Mr. Blumenthal's entire declaration, filed in connection with the White House's opposition to the OIC's motions to compel, is incorporated by reference.

VII. Communications with the OIC in early March 1998

45. The White House sought to avoid needless confrontation by reaching a mutually agreeable accommodation that would permit the OIC access to the information that it purportedly needed to conduct its investigation while maintaining the legitimate confidentiality interests of the White House. On March 2, 1998, W. Neil Eggleston, the attorney representing the Office of the President in connection with litigation arising out of the Lewinsky investigation, sent a letter to the OIC requesting that the White House be consulted about whether such an accommodation was reachable. (3/2/98 Letter from Eggleston to Starr, attached as Exhibit 4). Mr. Eggleston also described to the OIC the well-established accommodation process that the White House historically followed, citing the *Espy* litigation as an example. (*Id.* at 1). Finally, Mr. Eggleston offered to meet with the OIC to discuss the areas of inquiry that implicated privilege concerns and to consider any articulation of need that the OIC might make. (*Id.* at 2).

46. On that same day, the OIC replied to Mr. Eggleston's letter, reiterating its earlier position that executive privilege did not apply to information relating to the Lewinsky investigation. (3/2/98 Letter from Bittman to Eggleston, attached as Exhibit 5). The OIC also stated that the White House was using executive privilege as a dilatory tactic. (*Id.* at 20). Finally, the OIC took the view that the White House was in the better position "to identify the areas it wishe[d] to withdraw the invocation of executive privilege," and thus requested that the White House submit a proposal by noon on March 4, 1998. (*Id.*).

47. On March 4, 1998, Mr. Eggleston responded to the OIC's letter. He began by underscoring the principle that, although the parties may disagree as to whether certain information is privileged, the accommodation process requires the parties to set aside any difference over the applicability of the privilege and focus on trying to reach an acceptable

agreement. (3/4/98 Letter from Eggleston to Starr, attached as Exhibit 6). Mr. Eggleston continued:

> Your Office was unwilling to describe the subject matters about which you intended to question White House officials prior to their testimony. After several weeks of grand jury testimony by White House officials, we now have a sense of the areas that we believe are of interest to your investigation. It appears that, in addition to seeking facts about this matter, you are seeking ongoing advice given to the President by his senior advisors, including attorneys in the Counsel's Office, as well as the substance of these advisors's discussions as to how to address the Lewinsky investigation in a manner that enables the President to perform his constitutional, statutory, and other official duties.

(*Id.* at 1).

48. Mr. Eggleston then explained that the Office of the President was prepared to instruct White House witnesses along the following general lines:

> (1) White House Advisors (Non-Lawyers): Advisors will be permitted to testify as to factual information regarding the Lewinsky investigation, including any such information imparted in conversations with the President. We will continue to assert executive privilege with respect to strategic deliberations and communications.
>
> (2) White House Attorney Advisors: Attorneys in the Counsel's Office will assert attorney/client privilege; attorney work product; and, where appropriate, executive privilege, with regard to communications, including those with the President, related to their gathering of information, the providing of advice, and strategic deliberations and communications.

(*Id.* at 2).

49. Mr. Eggleston stated that he believed that this approach would accommodate the parties' respective interests. (*Id.*). He also stressed that, because the White House did not know the specific questions the OIC intended to ask a particular witness, we would evaluate the application of these instructions in response to specific questions and were willing to discuss any

particular issue. (*Id.*).

50. Mr. Eggleston also rejected the OIC's suggestion that the White House's assertion of privilege was a delaying tactic, pointing out that during the six weeks of the investigation, numerous White House witnesses either appeared or were interviewed, and each had answered all legitimate questions. Moreover, the White House had attempted to address and resolve all privilege issues prior to the appearance or interview of a White House official. (*Id.*).

51. On March 6, 1998, the OIC responded to Mr. Eggleston's letter, maintaining its position that executive privilege did not apply, and rejecting Mr. Eggleston's proposed approach. (3/6/98 Letter from Bittman to Eggleston, attached as Exhibit 7). On that same day, the OIC filed its motions to compel.

VIII. Disclosure of these Communications will Debilitate this and Future Presidencies

52. The President's advisors have not merely assumed that the Lewinsky investigation is a matter that has substantially affected the Presidency. They have taken it upon themselves to evaluate carefully how, if at all, it relates to the President's discharge of his duties. Politicians (both Democratic and Republican), political analysts (both domestic and foreign), and the media have all pronounced that the investigation affects the President's ability to achieve his foreign policy objectives and domestic agenda, and even poses a real threat to his ability to remain in office. In response to these reports, advisors have acted to ensure that they completely understand the scope and ramifications of the Lewinsky investigation so that they can give well-informed advice to the President to enable him to fulfill his responsibilities to the American people.

53. Disclosure of these communications will have a chilling effect on these and future presidential advisors. When a matter like the Lewinsky investigation affects the President's ability to execute his duties, his advisors cannot sit idly by and hope that it will resolve itself with little impact on the President. The President relies on them to assess a particular issue and to help him make sound decisions. To be effective, these advisors need the ability to evaluate relevant information, explore novel approaches, engage in heated debate, and provide blunt, candid, and even harsh, advice to the President. The President has a constitutionally based confidentiality interest in this process, and "the critical role that confidentiality plays in [this process] cannot be gainsaid." *In re Sealed Case*, 121 F.3d at 750.

54. If advisors must perform these duties with the knowledge that they have no expectation of confidentiality, that at some point their deliberations and advice will be disclosed, and that they will be held publicly accountable for their recommendations, they will be disinclined to gather all of the relevant information about a matter and avoid giving novel and frank advice to the President. They will fail in their duty to assist the President in dealing with matters that have an impact on his office and the Executive Branch. In turn, the President will be hindered in performing his duties because he will not receive the full benefit of his advisors' skills. He also will have to waste much of his time performing the functions that intermediaries normally would -- and should -- handle.

55. To strip a President of the core assistance and critical advice that are the lifeblood of his ability to execute his duties will inevitably result in the erosion of the effectiveness of the Office of the President. Such an outcome conflicts with basic constitutional principles and our country's notion of an effective Presidency and a well-balanced, democratic government.

IX. The Decision to Assert Privilege

56. I have discussed with the President these areas of inquiry and the privileged nature of the information sought. The President has directed me to invoke formally the privileges applicable to these communications.

Pursuant to 28 U.S.C. § 1746, I declare under penalty of perjury that the foregoing is true and correct.

March 17, 1998
Date

Charles F.C. Ruff
Charles F.C. Ruff
Counsel to the President

Tab 1

Office of the Independent Counsel

1001 Pennsylvania Avenue, N.W.
Suite 490-North
Washington, D.C. 20004
(202) 514-8688
Fax (202) 514-8802

February 4, 1998

The Honorable Charles F.C. Ruff
Counsel to the President
The White House
Washington, DC 20500

Dear Mr. Ruff:

I write in response to your visit of yesterday concerning the sensitive matter of Executive privilege. As you know, at the request of the Attorney General, the Special Division recently conferred jurisdiction on this Office to investigate whether "Monica Lewinsky or others" suborned perjury, obstructed justice, or committed other federal crimes. We understand from your discussion that certain witnesses employed by the White House may invoke Executive privilege in response to questions posed by the grand jury in its continuing investigation of that matter. After careful consideration of your comments, including consultation with our Ethics Counselor Samuel Dash, we believe strongly that the grand jury is entitled to inquire into discussions of senior White House staff members, both among themselves and with the President, concerning the Monica Lewinsky matter.

As we understand your comments, there are two principal areas of testimony where the White House may invoke Executive privilege. The first includes discussions, to which the President was not a party, among what you have described as "senior staff." The discussions at issue occurred after the Lewinsky matter became public last month. You indicated that these discussions may have encompassed such topics as how to respond publicly to the news, what political strategies to adopt, and how to advise the President concerning these matters. We further understood you to say that the White House did not expect to assert Executive privilege with respect to whatever factual information, if any, was discussed among the staff.

The second area involves communications between members of the White House staff and the President himself that took place after the public revelations concerning our new jurisdiction. We did not understand you to take a firm position on the question whether the President would assert Executive privilege with respect to his own communications with advisors on this subject.

As a threshold matter, we believe there is serious doubt whether communications of senior staff and the President concerning the Lewinsky matter fall within the scope of Executive privilege. When the Supreme Court recognized a "presumptive privilege for Presidential communications," United States v. Nixon, 418 U.S. 683, 707 (1974), it explained that the privilege attached to communications in the exercise of the President's Article II powers. Id. at 705. The privilege is limited to communications "in performance of the President's responsibilities," id. at 711, "of his office," id. at 713, and "made in the process of shaping policies and making decisions." Id. at 708 (quoted in Nixon v. Administrator of General Services, 433 U.S. 425, 449 (1977)).

The actions of the President and the White House in response to the Lewinsky matter do not, as we see it, carry out a constitutional duty of the President. Monica Lewinsky was a prospective witness in civil litigation in which the President is a private party. In more recent days, this Office has been charged by the Attorney General and the Special Division with responsibility to conduct a criminal investigation of "Ms. Lewinsky and others." These matters concern the President in his personal capacity. They do not involve the President's execution of the laws. Accordingly, we doubt that presidential and senior staff communications on these matters are entitled to a presumptive Executive privilege.

In any event, assuming the presumptive applicability of an Executive privilege, we are confident that many communications among White House staff and/or the President constitute important evidence in the grand jury's investigation that is not reasonably available elsewhere. See In re Sealed Case, 121 F.3d 729, 753 (D.C. Cir. 1997). The President's own statements are of critical importance to the grand jury's investigation. His statements to advisors represent highly relevant information not available from any other source. Particularly given the President's refusal to make public statements concerning the Lewinsky matter, and his recent decision to decline our invitation to appear before the grand jury, there is no alternative source that even approaches a substitute for direct evidence of the President's statements.

Similarly, the statements of senior White House staff will in many instances be important to the grand jury's investigation. For example, just as factual information in the possession of presidential advisers may reveal the nature of the President's deliberations, see In re Sealed Case, 121 F.3d at 750-51, so too may the discovery of deliberations among the White House staff concerning strategy give the grand jury unique insight to the factual premises on which the President and his staff are operating. Where the grand jury's investigation focuses on not merely "an immediate White House advisor," id. at 755, but on conduct of the President himself, we believe the courts will recognize that evidence of senior staff communications will be "particularly useful" to the grand jury. Id.

If the President ultimately does assert Executive privilege with respect to any evidence sought by the grand jury, then we expect that the district court will be required to determine whether the President's claim of privilege should be upheld under the circumstances. We agree

The Honorable Charles F. Ruff
February 4, 1998
Page 3

with your suggestion that a log of conversations among senior staff, including a list of participants and a specific, generic description of the subject matter, may facilitate the process of resolving any such disputes. If you are in a position to provide such a log in fairly short order, then we would consider whether the log is sufficient from our point of view to frame the issues properly for decision by the Court.

If you believe that further discussions of these matters would be helpful, we would be pleased to visit with you again at your convenience.

Sincerely,

Kenneth W. Starr
Independent Counsel

Tab 2

THE WHITE HOUSE

WASHINGTON

February 5, 1998

BY FACSIMILE

Kenneth W. Starr, Esq.
Independent Counsel
Suite 400 North
1001 Pennsylvania Ave., NW
Washington, D.C. 20004

Dear Mr. Starr:

This is in response to your letter of February 4, 1998.

First, I want to inform you that within 45 minutes of its delivery, James Bennet of the New York Times called the White House Press Office to ask whether I had received a letter from you concerning executive privilege. Since there could have been only a few persons on your staff who were aware of the letter's delivery, I ask that you immediately request that the FBI, using agents not affiliated with your office, investigate to determine who disclosed the existence of the letter and its substance (as well as, presumably, the fact and substance of our meeting) to the press. I and the three members of my staff who were aware of the letter before Bennet's call will be happy to be interviewed (under oath) in connection with any such investigation.

Let me move now to the substance of your letter.

As you will not be surprised to learn, I disagree with your position on the applicability of executive privilege to discussions among senior White House staff and between senior staff and the President concerning the Lewinsky matter. In particular, I disagree with your contention that, under In re Sealed Case or any other authority, the grand jury would be permitted to inquire into the substance of deliberations among the President's most senior advisors in order to determine on what factual predicate those deliberations were based. Such an argument would swallow up the entire premise of the court's decision. Indeed, your argument, if followed to its logical conclusion, would mean that the President would be barred from seeking the advice of those responsible for assisting him in carrying out his constitutional responsibilities because every conversation would be the subject of grand jury inquiry.

To the extent that you rely on the fact that the President's counsel has declined your invitation to appear before the grand jury, I find it curious that your office would issue an invitation to the President to appear on a date less than a week hence -- when it is a matter of public knowledge that he is to begin a state visit by the Prime Minister of Great Britain and when, as you are also fully aware, the United States is confronting a major international crisis -- and then argue that the President's declining of that invitation justifies intrusion into his discussions with his advisors. Nor can the President's decision not to comment on the Lewinsky matter -- other than to deny that he had sexual relations with Ms. Lewinsky and that he ever asked her to lie -- justify such an intrusion.

Let me also clarify three points I made in our meeting. First, discussions among and between the President's senior staff involve the very capacity of the President and his staff to govern -- to pursue his legislative agenda, to ensure the continued leadership of he United States in the world community, and to maintain the confidence and support of the people who elected him -- all of which lie at the heart of his role under Article II of the Constitution. Second, as to what position the President himself might take on the assertion of executive privilege as to his communications if he were to be questioned, I did not purport to take any position -- "firm" or otherwise. And third, I indicated that, in deciding whether to assert privilege, we have historically sought to distinguish the substance of advisory and deliberative discussions from segregable facts, not available elsewhere, that may be contained in otherwise privileged communications.

Finally, I remain willing to explore all avenues for resolving our disagreement, although I admit to being more than a little uncertain as to how to conduct discussions without reading about them simultaneously in the press. I am also uncertain about your office's current position with respect to the questioning of senior staff members before the grand jury. Although we had initially been informed that your office did not intend to inquire into the substance of any staff discussions or communications with the President, but rather only to identify the circumstances (date, attendees, general subject matter, etc.) of such discussions in order to establish an appropriate record, we have now been advised that you do intend to pursue such inquiries. We had also been informed that witnesses were not to be questioned concerning communications with White House counsel, but we now understand that you do not intend to follow that practice where there is more than one non-lawyer present -- a rule that I must say seems to have no rational basis.

Kenneth W. Starr, Esq.
February 5, 1998
Page 3

If we can come to some preliminary agreement as to the protocol that will be followed in connection with Mr. Podesta's appearance and that of other senior staff, it may be that there remains some prospect for addressing both your interests and our very serious concerns. If you believe that further discussions would be fruitful, please call me.

Sincerely,

Charles F.C. Ruff
Counsel to the President

Tab 3

Office of the Independent Counsel

1001 Pennsylvania Avenue, N.W.
Suite 490-North
Washington, D.C. 20004
(202) 514-8688
Fax (202) 514-8802

February 6, 1998

The Honorable Charles F. C. Ruff
Counsel to the President
The White House
Washington, D.C. 20500

Dear Mr. Ruff:

I write in response to your February 5 letter.

Let me reiterate the scope of our inquiry: We do not intend to question senior staff about deliberative matters beyond the jurisdictional grant recently crafted by the Attorney General and the Special Division. We do not seek information about discussions that relate solely to the President's foreign policy or his legislative agenda. We do not seek information about military or diplomatic secrets. We do intend to ask about discussions concerning an alleged relationship between Monica Lewinsky and the President, acting in his private capacity.

As to your contention that such discussions fall under Executive privilege, we must respectfully disagree. We believe that the President's relationship with Ms. Lewinsky, and the President's response to a private, civil lawsuit or a criminal investigation, fall outside the scope of his Article II duties. Executive privilege, as a threshold matter, thus appears to us inapplicable.

Even if the privilege did attach, we believe we would satisfy the test set forth in United States v. Nixon. The grand jury is investigating the conduct of Ms. Lewinsky and others with respect to a civil lawsuit against the President in his private capacity. This Office was given responsibility over that investigation after the Attorney General's representative, under exigent circumstances, made an extraordinary oral submission to the Special Division. The grand jury's need for information to resolve this matter in a timely fashion could hardly be more compelling.

In your letter, you suggest that our invitation to appear before the grand jury provided the President with insufficient notice. We fully recognize that the President, in the discharge of his constitutional duties, may have valid scheduling reasons for declining a first invitation to the grand jury. We simply noted the President's response as a partial explanation for why the grand jury needs evidence of his statements from other sources.

Under the circumstances, we do not believe that Executive privilege allows the withholding of important, relevant information that the grand jury needs to complete its inquiry. We cannot agree with you that when senior staff discuss how to handle allegations of the President's private

The Honorable Charles F.C. Ruff
February 6, 1998
Page 2

misconduct, they are aiding the President in the performance of his constitutional duties -- which is the only basis for asserting Executive privilege. Your expansive view of the privilege, it seems to us, could equally cover the communications at issue in Nixon.

You express uncertainty about our position with respect to questioning senior staff members before the grand jury. We will be specific: We intend to inquire into the substance of staff discussions and communications with the President concerning Ms. Lewinsky and related matters. If the witness asserts Executive privilege in the grand jury, we will limit our questioning to those matters necessary to establish an appropriate record for the district court (e.g., whether the communication was for the purpose of advising the President, the official government matter to which the communication relates, date, attendees, etc.). If there is no assertion of privilege, then we will proceed with questions.

You also raise the issue of communications between witnesses and White House Counsel. We hereby notify you that in light of In re Grand Jury Subpoena Duces Tecum, 112 F.3d 910 (8th Cir. 1997), we intend to question witnesses as to the substance of such communications. If a witness asserts attorney-client privilege, we will take such further steps as are appropriate.

Finally, you suggest that someone in this Office disclosed details of our conversations and correspondence to the New York Times. On several occasions in recent weeks, we have been falsely accused of such disclosures. In this particular instance, reporters had been questioning the White House Press Secretary about Executive privilege since January 22; the Wall Street Journal had reported on January 29 that the White House was preparing to assert the privilege (indeed, this was our first notice of your plans); we took extensive steps to arrange for your confidential visit to our offices; subsequent media information plainly came from the White House (e.g., the Associated Press reported on February 5 that "individuals familiar with the letter" said that "Starr's letter left the White House convinced there was no more room for goodwill negotiating"); and the reporter who asked you about our letter covers the White House, not the Office of the Independent Counsel. Under the circumstances, we respectfully suggest that your suspicions are misdirected.

If we can provide further information that may help forestall or resolve any disputes, please let me know.

Yours sincerely,

Kenneth W. Starr

KENNETH W. STARR
Independent Counsel

Tab 4

50-893 98 - 17

HOWREY & SIMON

W. Neil Eggleston

March 2, 1998

VIA HAND DELIVERY

Kenneth W. Starr, Esq.
Independent Counsel
Office of the Independent Counsel
1001 Pennsylvania Avenue, N.W.
Suite 490 North
Washington, DC 20004

Dear Mr. Starr:

I represent the Office of the President of the United States in connection with any litigation impacting that Office arising out of your current Grand Jury investigation. This representation extends to potential litigation over the applicability and extent of privileges.

Before you initiate litigation, the White House requests that we be consulted about whether an accommodation is reachable between the President's interest in confidentiality and whatever need the Grand Jury may have for the testimony.

Because these matters involve clashes between branches of government, the usual practice has been for the respective parties to attempt to reconcile their differences and accommodate the needs of the other party to the extent possible.

That was certainly the course that we followed in the Espy litigation. We released to the Espy Independent Counsel documents for which the Independent Counsel had articulated a substantial showing of need. Indeed, the White House determined to release one of these privileged documents during the litigation itself. The White House only invoked privilege over those documents, the release of which we believed would hindered the President's ability to discharge his duties.

HOWREY & SIMON

We believe a similar attempt to accommodate the respective interests would be appropriate in this matter as well. We would be prepared to meet with you, review the proposed areas of witness questioning, and consider any need you may demonstrate on why any applicable privileges should not be asserted.

Very truly yours,

W. Neil Eggleston

W. Neil Eggleston

cc: Charles F. C. Ruff, Esq.

Tab 5

Office of the Independent Counsel

1001 Pennsylvania Avenue, N.W.
Suite 490-North
Washington, DC 20004
(202) 514-8688
Fax (202) 514-8802

March 2, 1998

HAND DELIVERED

W. Neil Eggleston, Esq.
Howrey & Simon
1299 Pennsylvania Ave., N.W.
Washington, DC 20004-2402

Dear Mr. Eggleston:

We are in receipt here in Washington of your letter dated today to Judge Starr, who is currently in meetings in Little Rock. We have, however, communicated at length with him, and this letter reflects the evaluation and considered judgment of this Office. In brief, you have asked "whether an accommodation is reachable" between the White House and this Office as to the President's invocation of executive privilege, and you suggest a meeting to "reconcile" these differences.

As you are aware, this Office met with White House Counsel a month ago at his request in -- what we believed then to be -- a good-faith attempt to resolve any disputes over privilege without the need to resort to time-consuming litigation. At that meeting and in subsequent correspondence, White House Counsel expressed an unyielding view of the applicability of executive privilege in this setting. Then and since, we have set forth our view that White House Counsel's reading of executive privilege and its applicability to the Monica Lewinsky matter is, with all respect, entirely misplaced. As a threshold matter, the President's communications with regard to Ms. Lewinsky are purely private in nature and therefore fall outside the scope of executive privilege. Such communications were not made in the exercise of the President's Article II powers nor were they made "in performance of the President's responsibilities." United States v. Nixon, 418 U.S. 683, 708, 713 (1974); see also In Re Sealed Case, 121 F.3d 729, 752 (1997) (executive privilege "only applies to communications . . . on official government matters"). In addition, we find the instant invocation of executive privilege odd, given the reported statement of then-White House Counsel Lloyd Cutler that it was the White House's "practice" not to assert executive privilege in "investigations of personal wrongdoing by government officials."

W. Neil Eggleston, Esq.
March 2, 1998
Page two

Since our exchanges with White House Counsel, many White House employees have been questioned before the grand jury about Ms. Lewinsky. Several of these witnesses have invoked executive privilege at the direction of the White House. You propose we meet to "review" the areas of questioning and demonstrate our need for the information in an effort to avoid litigation. With all respect, we fail to discern the purpose of such a meeting at this juncture. First, the White House has already begun to litigate these issues as evidenced by Chief Judge Johnson's ordering Bruce Lindsey to testify or invoke a privilege. Second, we have, as you know, already asked the specific questions and identified the "areas of witness questioning." Third, there is no need -- and indeed no requirement -- that we demonstrate why we need these communications, since executive privilege is, for the reasons already stated, simply inapplicable to the personal communications of the President at issue here.

That being said, we are willing to consider any good-faith attempt to resolve these issues promptly. We were in discussions with the White House several weeks ago, but the President subsequently chose to invoke executive privilege as to virtually every communication relating to Ms. Lewinsky. In this respect, we are constrained to make this point clear: this investigation has confronted numerous delaying tactics. Yet we have repeatedly stressed to the White House that the public interest demands a swift resolution of all matters involving Ms. Lewinsky. We believe, moreover, given this history, that the White House is in a better position to identify the areas it wishes to withdraw the invocation of executive privilege. We warmly welcome such a proposal so that we can move the grand jury's investigation forward. If you wish to submit a proposal, kindly do so in writing by noon, Wednesday, March 4, 1998.

Sincerely,

Robert J. Bittman
Deputy Independent Counsel

cc: Honorable Charles F.C. Ruff

Tab 6

HOWREY & SIMON

Attorneys at Law
1299 Pennsylvania Ave., NW
Washington, DC 20004 2402
(202) 783 0800
FAX (202) 383 6610

W. Neil Eggleston
(202) 383 7433
egglestonn@howrey.com

March 4, 1998

VIA FACSIMILE and HAND DELIVERY

Kenneth W. Starr, Esq.
Independent Counsel
Office of the Independent Counsel
1001 Pennsylvania Avenue, N.W.
Suite 490 North
Washington, DC 20004

Dear Mr. Starr:

I received a letter from Deputy Counsel Robert J. Bittman in response to my March 2, 1998 letter outlining our wish to ensure that we had explored, prior to any litigation, all reasonable accommodations to avoid or limit litigation.

Mr. Bittman responded by restating your Office's view that executive privilege does n[illegible] apply to any questioning of White House officials regarding the Lewinsky investigation—something upon which, as you know, we disagree. Indeed, the impetus for my letter was that [illegible] disagree on the law. Despite our legal disagreements, however, we are duty bound to attempt reach a mutually agreeable accommodation that provides the grand jury with the information it needs while preserving this and future Presidents' legitimate interests in receiving candid and frank advice in confidence from their advisors.

Your Office was unwilling to describe the subject matters about which you intended [illegible] question White House officials prior to their testimony. After several weeks of grand jury testimony by White House officials, we now have a sense of the areas that we believe are of interest to your investigation. It appears that, in addition to seeking facts about this matter, y[illegible] are seeking ongoing advice given to the President by his senior advisors, including attorneys [illegible] the Counsel's Office, as well as the substance of these advisors' discussions as to how to add[illegible]ss the Lewinsky investigation in a manner that enables the President to perform his constitution[illegible] statutory and other official duties.

In light of these areas of inquiry, we are prepared to discuss an approach that we believe will accommodate our respective interests. To that end, the Office of the President is prepared to instruct White House witnesses along the following general lines:

- White House Advisors (Non-Lawyers): Advisors will be permitted to testify as to factual information regarding the Lewinsky investigation, including any such information imparted in conversations with the President. We will continue to assert executive privilege with respect to strategic deliberations and communications.

- White House Attorney Advisors: Attorneys in the Counsel's Office will assert attorney/client privilege; attorney work product; and, where appropriate, executive privilege, with regard to communications, including those with the President, related to their gathering of information, the providing of advice, and strategic deliberations and communications.

At this point, the instructions that we intend to provide to White House advisors and attorneys are necessarily general, since we do not know the questions you intend to ask. We of course will evaluate the application of these instructions to the advisors and attorneys in response to specific questions and would welcome an opportunity to meet and discuss any particular issues, as needed.

The accommodation we are proposing will permit the grand jury to complete its work in a timely fashion and will provide the factual information that it needs for this investigation. We do not believe, however, that you have demonstrated, or can demonstrate, a need for information about the strategic discussions of White House advisors about this matter.

Although you argue that the Lewinsky investigation is purely private, the intersection of this matter with, for example, the State of the Union, an enumerated duty under Article II, section 3 of the Constitution, and Prime Minister Blair's visit and their joint press conference make it abundantly clear that this investigation has implications for the President's performance of his official duties. These instances also illustrate the very obvious need for the President to receive the candid and frank counsel of his advisors in confidence.

I also reject out-of-hand your suggestion that the assertion of privilege is a delaying tactic or that the White House has in any manner delayed your investigation. While you have been investigating this matter for merely six weeks, numerous White House witnesses have appeared or been interviewed by your agents. None has refused to appear and each has answered all legitimate inquiries. Moreover, we have made every attempt to discuss and resolve potential privilege issues with you before the grand jury appearance of particular White House officials. As you surely are aware, the President's invocation of privilege to permit him and future Presidents to discharge their duties under Article II of the Constitution is a fundamental obligation, not a delaying tactic.

In sum, it is our mutual constitutional obligation to seek a reasonable accommodation of our interests. We are prepared to meet for that purpose at your earliest convenience.

Very truly yours,

W. Neil Eggleston
Attorney for the Office of the President

cc: The Honorable Charles F.C. Ruff
Robert J. Bittman, Esq.

Tab 7

Office of the Independent Counsel

1001 Pennsylvania Avenue, N.W.
Suite 490-North
Washington, DC 20004
(202) 514-8688
Fax (202) 514-8802

March 6, 1998

HAND DELIVERED

W. Neil Eggleston, Esq.
Howrey & Simon
1299 Pennsylvania Ave., N.W.
Washington, DC 20004-2402

Dear Mr. Eggleston:

This responds to your letter to this Office dated March 4, 1998.

As you know, since early February we have been in discussions with the White House regarding the applicability of executive privilege to the matters involving Monica Lewinsky. We have great respect for the Office of the President and the important duties and responsibilities of the President. In this case, we have not sought nor will we seek any information implicating state secrets or diplomatic relations. The matters involving Ms. Lewinsky, moreover, relate only to the President acting in his personal capacity, as a private citizen. If there are any communications relating to Ms. Lewinsky which legitimately jeopardize state secrets or diplomatic relations, please identify them and we will review our request.

As fully outlined in our correspondence to you and the White House, the matters regarding Ms. Lewinsky do not involve the President acting his official capacity. Consequently, executive privilege is inapplicable as a threshold and fundamental matter. Any communication pertaining to Ms. Lewinsky is thus not privileged -- no matter the title or position of the person involved in the communication. We therefore cannot agree with your suggestion to keep such highly probative, relevant information from the grand jury.

Sincerely,

Robert J. Bittman
Deputy Independent Counsel

cc: The Honorable Charles F.C. Ruff

GRAND JURY MATTER - FILED UNDER SEAL

IN THE UNITED STATES DISTRICT COURT
FOR THE DISTRICT OF COLUMBIA

IN RE GRAND JURY PROCEEDINGS.	)	Misc. Nos. 98-095, 98-096 and 98-097

DECLARATION OF BRUCE R. LINDSEY

1. I am competent to testify from personal knowledge as to the matters set forth in this Declaration. I am filing this Declaration in connection with the Motion to Compel recently filed by the Office of Independent Counsel (OIC).

2. I am an attorney admitted to practice law in Arkansas. From June 1976 until November 1978, and from November 1981 until January 1993, I was an associate and later a partner at Wright, Lindsey & Jennings, a Little Rock, Arkansas law firm.

3. I have known President Bill Clinton for approximately 30 years, and over that period I have worked for and with him in a number of capacities. In 1981 and 1982, President Clinton was affiliated with Wright, Lindsey & Jennings in an "of counsel" capacity. Prior to January 1993, Wright, Lindsey & Jennings also acted on several occasions as personal counsel to Governor Clinton, and as counsel to the 1992 Clinton campaign for the Presidency.

4. For example, during then Governor Clinton's 1990 campaign for re-election, Wright, Lindsey & Jennings acted as personal counsel to Governor Clinton in connection with a lawsuit filed by Larry Nichols, an Arkansas political activist. Mr. Nichols' lawsuit, which was eventually dismissed, asserted that Governor Clinton should be required to reimburse the State of Arkansas for travel and entertainment expenses that the Governor allegedly had incurred on behalf

of several women. Some of those same allegations have "resurfaced" in connection with discovery conducted by attorneys for the plaintiff in *Jones* v. *Clinton*.

5. In addition, during Governor Clinton's 1992 campaign for the presidency, allegations arose concerning Governor Clinton's relationships with various women, including Gennifer Flowers. These allegations also have been the subject of inquiry during the discovery process in *Jones* v. *Clinton*.

6. Since President Clinton's inauguration in January 1993, I have served as an Assistant to the President, and first as Senior Advisor and later as Deputy Counsel to the President. In both those capacities, I have been one of the President's principal advisors on the full range of issues and decisions relating to the President's duties and the effective functioning of the Executive Branch. I have broad responsibility for gathering and providing information and forming advice to give to the President on many matters, and I travel with the President for that purpose. To formulate appropriate advice for the President, I typically gather information and advice from White House staff, other federal employees, and private presidential advisors.

7. The White House Counsel's Office provides confidential counsel to the President in his official capacity, to the White House as an institution, and to senior advisors about legal matters that affect the White House's interests, including investigative matters. To this end, the Counsel's Office, in which I serve as Deputy, receives confidential communications from individuals about matters of institutional concern. White House personnel provide this information to the Counsel's Office with the expectation and understanding that it will remain confidential.

8. In light of the United States Supreme Court decision that the *Jones* v. *Clinton* litigation could proceed during the President's term in office, the President had to develop a method

of communicating with and assisting his private counsel that would minimize distractions from his official duties, which consume his efforts and attention well beyond the limits of a normal working day. Because of my role as the President's longtime confidential advisor and attorney, I often have served as a conduit or intermediary for communications between the President and his private lawyers. Typically, when the President's private lawyers need information in connection with the *Jones* lawsuit, they telephone me with questions for the President. I present questions to the President at opportune times, and later relay the President's answers back to private counsel. I have been able to do this on occasions when the President's official functions and duties are least disrupted by the demands of defending the *Jones* lawsuit. The President knows I serve as an intermediary between him and his lawyers, and he intends that our communications remain private and confidential. In accordance with the President's wishes, I have maintained the confidentiality of these communications.

9. During my two days of grand jury testimony on February 18 and 19, 1998, and more recently on March 12, 1998, I was asked a number of questions about my private communications with the President, with the President's private counsel in *Jones* v. *Clinton*, with the President's private counsel in the OIC investigation, and with other senior advisors to the President. Those questions concerned both the *Jones* v. *Clinton* litigation in general and the effect of the recent controversy regarding the President's alleged relationship with Monica Lewinsky on the President's and the White House's performance of their official responsibilities.

10. With respect to communications that I had with the President or his private attorneys concerning *Jones* v. *Clinton*, I declined to answer on the ground of attorney-client privilege or the common interest doctrine where an answer would disclose confidential communications

between or among the President, his private attorneys and myself, when I was as acting as Deputy Counsel, or when I served as a confidential intermediary as described above.

11. I also declined to answer questions concerning the *Jones* v. *Clinton* litigation, and the allegations regarding Ms. Lewinsky, to the extent that I was asked to reveal discussions that I had with the President, other senior advisors to the President within the White House, or personal advisors to the President about decisions that the President needed to make in connection with his official duties. For example, such discussions focused on issues surrounding the propriety and the wisdom, from an institutional perspective, of the President's seeking a disposition of the *Jones* v. *Clinton* litigation short of trial; whether the President should refer to the allegations surrounding Ms. Lewinsky during his State of the Union address; and whether the President should invoke executive privilege in connection with these proceedings. Other discussions involved advice to the President as to how best to ensure that the allegations concerning Ms. Lewinsky and their political and media ramifications would not impair the President's handling of his official duties. Such senior staff discussions included, for example, how the President should respond to the demands of the media and members of Congress for further information about the Lewinsky allegations, and how the President and White House should address the prospects for referral of the Lewinsky matter to the House of Representatives for a possible inquiry concerning impeachment.

12. The OIC also has inquired about my discussions with the President's private attorneys and other attorneys in the White House Counsel's Office regarding aspects of the grand jury investigation in this matter. In these discussions, I was acting as Deputy Counsel to the President and representing him in his official capacity, and I shared privileged information with other White House attorneys and the private attorneys representing the President in his personal capacity.

I declined to answer questions about these discussions because to do so would require me to reveal confidential communications that I believe to be protected from disclosure by executive privilege, attorney-client privilege, the attorney work product doctrine, and the common interest doctrine.

13. In addition, during my grand jury testimony, the OIC asked several questions about discussions between the White House Counsel's Office and other grand jury witnesses or their counsel. Those discussions were for the purpose of providing legal and other advice to the witnesses and to the President in connection with the ongoing grand jury investigation and potential Congressional proceedings and, therefore, I believe they were protected from disclosure by executive privilege, attorney-client privilege, the attorney work product doctrine, and the common interest doctrine.

14. In the OIC's Brief in Support of Motion to Compel Bruce R. Lindsey to Testify, at page 1, the OIC reports that I stated during my grand jury testimony that I was "not willing to answer any questions concerning conversations about Monica Lewinsky that occurred among White House staff." I do not recall this precise question being asked of me, nor that I answered such a question with a blanket invocation of privilege. In any event, it was my intent to decline to answer such questions that occurred among White House staff, only to the extent that such conversations involved the gathering of information and the formulation of advice to assist the President in the performance of his official responsibilities. Moreover, as I recall my testimony on February 19, I declined the OIC's invitation to invoke a privilege with respect to every conversation that I had had concerning the *Jones* v. *Clinton* litigation, whether or not other attorneys were present.

15. During the first two days of my grand jury testimony, the OIC's representatives failed to ask me about a number of questions concerning Ms. Lewinsky as to which I was prepared

to testify. But even during those first two days I answered several questions about my discussions with others that involved Ms. Lewinsky. I also testified that I had no knowledge concerning the origins of a document identified as "talking points" given to Linda Tripp by Monica Lewinsky.

16. After the pending Motion to Compel my testimony was filed, the OIC requested me to appear before the grand jury investigating the Lewinsky allegations for a third time. I appeared for approximately 2.5 hours on March 12, 1998. During that session, I was asked, for the first time, whether I had ever met or spoken with Ms. Lewinsky. I testified that I had not. I also testified in some detail about the following matters:

a. Two telephone conversations, the first of which was initiated by Linda Tripp, in which Ms. Tripp told me about a story that a *Newsweek* reporter was then preparing regarding an alleged encounter between the President and Kathleen Willey;

b. The fact that I took no actions relating to Monica Lewinsky immediately following President Clinton's deposition in the *Jones* litigation;

c. My lack of knowledge about certain communications between Vernon Jordan and Betty Currie regarding Monica Lewinsky;

d. My lack of knowledge concerning drafts of an affidavit prepared by Ms. Lewinsky in the *Jones* litigation;

e. My lack of knowledge concerning efforts by individuals at the White House to page Monica Lewinsky during the period January 18-19, 1998;

f. My brief discussions with Vernon Jordan about Monica Lewinsky, his efforts to help her obtain a position in private industry, the fact that she had been described in an

Internet report authored or distributed by Matthew Drudge, and my delivery of a copy of the so-called Drudge Report to Mr. Jordan on January 19, 1998;

g. My knowledge of certain efforts by a *Newsweek* reporter to contact Betty Currie about packages or envelopes that had been delivered to Ms. Currie by Monica Lewinsky;

h. My lack of knowledge of any efforts undertaken by Nathan Landow to speak to Kathleen Willey about her role as a witness in the *Jones* litigation; and

i. My lack of knowledge concerning any role performed by Terry Lenzner or Jack Palladino in the *Jones* litigation.

17. The questions that I have declined to answer based on the invocation of privilege all involved my confidential discussions with the President, with other White House attorneys, with senior advisors to the President, and with the President's private attorneys about the *Jones* litigation, the current OIC investigation, or the White House's efforts to respond to the political and media controversy engendered by the *Jones* litigation and the OIC's investigation.

18. I declare under penalty of perjury that the foregoing is true and correct.

See 28 U.S.C. §1748.

Bruce R. Lindsey

Executed on March 17, 1998.

IN THE UNITED STATES DISTRICT COURT
FOR THE DISTRICT OF COLUMBIA

IN RE GRAND JURY PROCEEDINGS,) Misc. Nos. 98-95, 98-098 and 98-097

DECLARATION OF SIDNEY BLUMENTHAL

Sidney Blumenthal, under penalty of perjury, hereby declares as follows:

1. I am competent to testify from personal knowledge as to the matters set forth in the Declaration. I am filing this Declaration in connection with the Motion to Compel recently filed by the Office of the Independent Counsel ("OIC").

2. I am an Assistant to the President of the United States of America. My office is in the West Wing of the White House.

3. I assumed this position August 11, 1997. Prior to that time, I was a working journalist and was not employed by the White House. My job duties require me to consult with other White House advisors and with private presidential advisors to gather information and advice so that I can properly advise the President.

4. As a part of my job, I participate in the following policy issues in the White House: global warming, "fast track" trade authority, tobacco issues, health care, general economic issues, Social Security, education, crime, welfare, urban centers, the Race Initiative, environmental issues, and the District of Columbia.

5. As part of my job, I am also responsible for writing major presidential speeches. For example, I was heavily involved in writing the State of the Union Address given by the President January 27, 1998. Under Article II, section 3 of the Constitution, the President has the duty to provide the Congress with "information of the State of the Union." The content

of that address is an important presidential decision on which the President's advisors provide input.

6. I am involved in national security policy as it relates to Latin America, China, Bosnia, Germany, the North Atlantic Treaty Organization (NATO), the Organization of American States (OAS), Iraq, Turkey, Israel, Africa, the United Nations, the Landmines Treaty, Ireland, and Northern Ireland.

7. I am the principal White House official on freedom of the press issues internationally.

8. I am also the liaison for the President to the office of the Prime Minister of Great Britain. In that role, I communicate regularly with Prime Minister Tony Blair directly, his Chief of Staff Jonathan Powell, Director of Policy David Miliband, Official Spokesman Alistair Campbell, Minister Without Portfolio Peter Mandelson, and various other aides, ministers, and members of the British Government.

9. I have had substantial involvement in the foreign relations between the United States and Great Britain. I regularly brief the President on matters concerning Great Britain. I participated in the First Lady's visit to Ireland, Northern Ireland, and England in October and November of 1997. I also participated with the First Lady in the Northern Ireland peace process. That process included talks with British Minister Mo Mowlam. I also assisted the United States delegation at policy discussions held with the Prime Minister of Great Britain and various ministers at Chequers November 1, 1997.

10. I participated in the visit by the Prime Minister of Great Britain to the United States in early February 1998. One of the core functions of the President involves foreign policy, including meetings with Heads of State of foreign countries. The internal discussions as well as the manner in which those meetings are portrayed are important to United States foreign policy.

11. I was responsible for official statements made by the President, for joint appearances of the President and the Prime Minister, a joint press conference, an informal lunch,

a joint radio address on Iraq, an official White House dinner, and a Blair House dinner hosted by the United States and United Kingdom ambassadors of official delegations. I also directed the United States delegation at joint policy discussions that were held during the visit. The coordination of these events, including joint press conferences, is important to the international relations between countries.

12. I am currently involved in arranging the President's trip to the G-8 meeting in Birmingham, England, and his subsequent visits to London, all of which are set to occur in May 1998. In regard to that trip, I am responsible for coordinating policy, drafting statements, planning appearances, and planning and directing the United States delegation in policy discussions with the Prime Minister and various ministers at Chequers. In addition, I am planning the United States delegation in meetings with British ministers and senior aides to the Prime Minister of Great Britain.

13. In carrying out these duties, I am in almost daily contact with the President and other senior administration officials. In the course of carrying out my official duties, I have discussed with the President, the First Lady, and other senior administration officials certain matters and allegations pertaining to the investigation being conducted by the Independent Counsel. The First Lady functions as a senior advisor to the President, and it was in that capacity that I had discussions with her about the Independent Counsel's investigation. The discussions with the President, the First Lady, and with other senior advisors to the President enabled me to advise the President and his advisors concerning the effect of the investigation on his official duties, including how best to frame his public statements, his legislative agenda, and his dealings with foreign countries in light of that investigation. For example, these discussions enabled me to advise the President and his advisors with respect to the content of the State of the Union address and with respect to press relations and other aspects of the visit of Prime Minister Blair.

14. Confidentiality is critical to my ability to provide open, frank, and candid advice at all times, not only to the President, but to other senior advisors as well. Based on my experience in the White House, I believe that the ability of advisors to the President to provide

him with the type of candid advice the President needs would be hindered if the discussions among staff and with the President were not confidential.

15. On February 26, 1998, I testified before a grand jury sitting in the District of Columbia. I had been instructed by the Office of the Counsel to the President to assert executive privilege in response to certain of the questions the Independent Counsel asked me. An answer to those questions would have revealed the communications that I had with other senior advisors, and the confidential advice and counsel that I gave to the President, with regard to policy issues, including the policy issues discussed in the foregoing paragraphs.

I declare under penalty of perjury that the foregoing is true and correct.

Executed on March 16, 1998.

Sidney Blumenthal

Tab 43

:ation | Found Document | Rank 1 of 1 | Database
25/98 WASHPOST A02 | | | WP
3/25/98 Wash. Post A02
1998 WL 2475125

The Washington Post

Wednesday, March 25, 1998

A Section

Clinton Finds There's No Escape; In Africa, President Sidesteps Executive Privilege Questions
John F. Harris
Washington Post Staff Writer

Yes, President Clinton acknowledged today, he had heard something about a controversy involving executive privilege back in the United States.

And no, he had nothing to say about it.

Seven time zones away from Washington, the uproar about .nton's decision to invoke privilege -- sparking a legal fight over . .at testimony a grand jury will hear from top White House aides -- caught up with the president in a photo session with Yoweri Museveni, the president of Uganda.

Clinton, who has yet to acknowledge publicly even that he is asserting executive privilege, was pressed by reporters to explain why he is trying to block testimony. His voice curt and his expression cold, the president responded as though he were a bystander in the controversy, rather than its central character.

"All I know is, I saw an article about it in the paper today," said Clinton, referring to the packet of news clippings faxed each morning to him when he is on the road. "I haven't discussed that with the lawyers. I don't know. You should ask someone who knows."

Specifically, Clinton was responding to a question about why White House lawyers have invoked executive privilege for conversations between first lady Hillary Rodham Clinton and aide Sidney Blumenthal. But he took the same tone on every other question relating to independent counsel Kenneth W. Starr's investigation into the Monica S. Lewinsky controversy.

Even as the president was sidestepping the issue in Africa, his yers back in Washington returned to federal court for a second day o. arguments with Starr's attorneys about the privilege dispute.

..ing a 90-minute, closed-door hearing before Chief U.S. District Judge Norma Holloway Johnson, attorneys continued their discussion about whether executive privilege or attorney-client privilege should prevent Starr from asking certain questions of Blumenthal, White House deputy counsel Bruce R. Lindseyand possibly others.

On another floor of the courthouse, the grand jury looking into the Lewinsky matter had a slow day, with no witnesses known to have appeared. On Wednesday, however, one of the key witnesses is scheduled to return, according to a source familiar with the matter. Marcia K. Lewis, Lewinsky's mother, appeared for two days last month before suffering what associates called severe emotional distress that caused a halt to her testimony. Lewis and Lewinsky share an apartment at the Watergate and are close confidantes.

In Little Rock, another grand jury that has looked into Whitewater for four years is set to expire in May and Starr said yesterday that he may not convene a replacement. Talking with reporters outside his Arkansas office, Starr said the cooperation of former governor Jim Guy Tucker under a recent plea agreement may speed the conclusion of the probe there.

"This investigation could conclude quickly if all persons who ..e relevant and material information would come forward and ..operate with the grand jury," Starr said.

As a general proposition, White House aides often cringe when asked about domestic uproars while overseas -- an anxiety they are feeling even more acutely on Clinton's six-nation, 11-day African tour. It is Clinton's first foreign trip since the Lewinsky controversy broke two months ago, and the president seemed to be forcibly restraining his temper during a brief session with reporters at the State House Lodge here in the Ugandan capital.

A reporter asked why people should not conclude that Clinton's assertion of privilege was "an effort to hide something from them."

"Look, that's a question that's being asked and answered back home by the people who are responsible to do that," Clinton responded. "I don't believe I should be discussing that here."

But as White House press secretary Michael McCurry acknowledged, it's actually a question that is being asked but not answered back home. The White House contends that because Judge Johnson has placed the legal proceeding under seal, Clinton and his lawyers cannot say anything about it -- nor offer a public justification for why he may b.. provoking a constitutional showdown over the scope of his ..sidential powers. Other legal specialists, however, have said such a situation would not preclude the president from acknowledging ɔlicly that he is asserting the privilege.

Political advisers in and out of the White House have been uncomfortable about Clinton's use of privilege to shield his aides because of the inevitable comparisons with Richard M. Nixon, who lost his battle during Watergate to assert executive privilege, leading to the disclosure of secret White House tapes and, in the end, to his resignation.

Earlier this month, McCurry said at his daily briefing that if Clinton did assert privilege, "I think the president would want the American people . . . to understand why he would make such an assertion."

Should Clinton be prepared to make such an explanation, it could come on Friday in South Africa. In the only full news conference of his trip, Clinton and South African President Nelson Mandela will face reporters in Cape Town.

Clinton aides said they have dreaded the potential spectacle of Clinton fielding -- or ducking -- questions about his legal controversies and alleged sexual misconduct standing beside one of the world's most respected leaders. But one adviser said the Clinton team ; concluded that such a scene, if it comes, will not hurt Clinton at ..ome -- since viewers might resent reporters for asking questions they consider impertinent.

Clinton scoffed at a suggestion that, with Washington so hostile, he would rather be in Africa. "I've looked forward to this [trip] for years," he said testily. "And I think most Americans want me to do the job I was elected to do."

Staff writers Lena H. Sun, Susan Schmidt and Peter Baker contributed to this report from Washington.

TABULAR OR GRAPHIC MATERIAL SET FORTH IN THIS DOCUMENT IS NOT DISPLAYABLE

CAPTION: The president's lawyer, Robert S. Bennett, waves to his driver after leaving the federal courthouse.

---- INDEX REFERENCES ----

KEY WORDS: NATIONAL

STORY ORIGIN: KAMPALA, UGANDA, MARCH 24

E--TION: FINAL

Word Count: 947

Tab 44

Office of the Independent Counsel

1001 Pennsylvania Avenue, N.W.
Suite 490-North
Washington, DC 20004
(202) 514-8688
Fax (202) 514-8802

April 17, 1998

VIA HAND DELIVERY

Eric H. Holder, Jr., Esq.
Deputy Attorney General
U.S. Department of Justice
950 Pennsylvania Avenue, Northwest
Room 4111
Washington, DC 20530

Dear Mr. Holder:

I write to express my profound concerns with respect to the deposition of Secret Service Officer Robert Almasy, which took place on April 16, 1998, in our offices. What occurred was, in brief, regrettable and grossly unprofessional. The effect of what happened yesterday was to hinder and impede this investigation.

As you know, we have for some time now been negotiating with the Department and the Secret Service over the testimony of Secret Service personnel. Since the beginning of this investigation, we have received -- and continue to receive -- numerous and credible reports that Secret Service officers and agents have evidence relevant to this investigation. In an effort to accommodate the concerns of the Department and the Secret Service, we have generally been questioning Secret Service personnel in a deposition format in our offices, subject to standard grand jury procedures such as the absence of defense counsel, Rule 6(e) secrecy, and so forth. Yesterday's episode involved unprofessional conduct that was utterly beyond the pale.

Officer Almasy's deposition, which we were unable to finish on April 16, consumed a total of six hours and twenty minutes. Of that time, two hours and fifteen minutes was spent on the record. The remainder -- four hours and five minutes -- was used for consultations between Officer Almasy, the Department of Justice attorney, and the Secret Service attorneys who were present outside the deposition room. In a number of instances, Officer Almasy halted the deposition to consult with his attorneys for periods of thirty minutes and longer. Virtually every question that was asked of Officer Almasy caused him to leave the deposition room and engage in such consultations. This was the single most disruptive appearance by any witness in any phase of our investigation.

As I mentioned previously, we have been conducting these depositions with the understanding that the Secret Service employees being questioned are to be treated as grand jury witnesses. According to the Department of Justice's Federal Grand Jury Practice Manual, a grand jury witness's consultations with his attorneys "should not be allowed to interfere unduly with the grand jury proceedings and may be appropriately regulated. . . . Although the parameters of the witness's right to consult with counsel outside the grand jury room are unclear, prosecutors and courts generally permit the witness consultation of reasonable length and frequency." The Manual goes on to state that

> [u]nreasonable consultations should not be permitted to obstruct orderly questioning of the witness. A witness who insists upon leaving the grand jury room frequently to consult with an attorney at length may be taken to the court for an order directing the witness to discontinue such a practice and, if necessary, to establish ground rules for such consultations.

Officer Almasy's lengthy and repeated consultations with his attorneys were flatly inconsistent with the Department's policies.

Furthermore, I am even more concerned that, by all appearances, the Secret Service and Department of Justice attorneys that attended Officer Almasy's deposition may have attempted to use it as a discovery device with regard to our investigation. This and other practices we observed in connection with Officer Almasy's deposition are what we would expect to see of criminal defense attorneys who wish to conceal relevant evidence or otherwise stonewall a grand jury investigation. They are most emphatically not what we expected of career attorneys employed by the Department of Justice.

Let me be frank: We have bent over backwards to accommodate the Secret Service's concerns in our questioning of its personnel. We have conducted many weeks of negotiations. We have refrained from calling active duty Secret Service personnel before the grand jury. Each of these actions was taken in good faith. But yesterday, at the same time that you were publicly emphasizing in your press briefing that the Department of Justice is not "impeding the investigation," we were being blocked from obtaining important evidence.

What happened yesterday was, in my view, an effort by sworn officials of the Executive Branch to hinder this investigation. After careful consideration, we have regretfully concluded that it will henceforth be necessary for us to compel the testimony of Secret Service personnel before the grand jury. I ask that you take appropriate steps to ensure that our investigation is not impeded further.

Sincerely,

Jackie M. Bennett, Jr.
Deputy Independent Counsel

cc: Gary G. Grindler, Esq.
Deputy Assistant Attorney General
Civil Division

Tab 45

An Open Letter to Kenneth Starr

By William H. Ginsburg

Dear Mr. Starr:

If there is one thing I have learned while representing Monica Lewinsky, it is that the government can easily wind up out of control. And the risk of that happening is made all the greater when we deviate from the constitutional checks and balances set forth by the founding fathers. In particular, I've worried these past several months that your investigation into President Clinton's sexual conduct threatens to tear a giant hole in the fabric of our democracy.

I believe you've done that by ignoring one of the most important rights possessed by all Americans—the sacred right to privacy. Even the smallest incursion by the government into the realm of personal privacy, including the questions your investigators have asked my client and others about sexual activity, represents an egregious violation of that right. In the simplest terms, Mr. Starr, the government has no business in our bedrooms. And yet your office has sought to drain the constitutional rights of our republic in the name of your apparent agenda to bring down the presidency. Indeed, you and your staff have done more than invade the privacy of President Clinton and Monica Lewinsky. You've also invaded the privacy of all Americans through your efforts to subpoena books and other materials purchased by Monica for her private reading. Let me remind you that Justice Brandeis 70 years ago, in his famous dissent in *Olmstead v U.S.*, described the right to privacy as one of the most important rights possessed by mankind. And Justice Douglas warned more than 30 years ago, in *Griswold v Connecticut*, that we were in danger of the government entering our bedrooms. It seems that his warning has now come to pass, which makes us the victims of democracy, rather than its beneficiaries.

Now is the time to recall that the founding fathers never provided for an office of independent counsel. Perhaps they even envisioned the potential for abuse in such an office of the sort we see now. Unfortunately, the pass-the-buck mentality so pervasive among modern politicians has helped pave the way for the beyond-the-pale activities of the position you currently hold. Alas, Congress has abdicated its constitutional responsibility to determine the need for a Bill of Impeachment against the president. I would like to see Congress muster the courage to tear down the nonconstitutional office you hold, with the president taking the equally courageous approach of firing you and setting America free once again.

How else, I wonder, are we to avoid the risks of an independent prosecutor running amuck on the scale we've seen in the case involving my client and the president? Surely, there is something flawed in a statutory scheme that has allowed you the leeway to expand your jurisdiction over the Whitewater affair so broadly as to include alleged presidential sexual misconduct. Let me state it as bluntly as I can: There is no relationship at all between Whitewater and the president's sexual conduct. But that has not prevented you from subpoenaing practically everyone in the Washington, D.C., phone book in a misguided effort to find out everything that could possibly be found out about Monica Lewinsky. Your actions have turned this young woman into a virtual prisoner and have created, through an orchestrated campaign of media leaks, a tainted environment in which everyone has an opinion regarding what happened, and with whom it happened.

Congratulations, Mr. Starr! As a result of your callous disregard for cherished constitutional rights, you *may* have succeeded in unmasking a sexual relationship between two consenting adults. In doing so, of course, you've also ruined the lives of several people, including Monica and her family, while costing them each thousands of dollars in legal fees to protect themselves from the abuses carried out by your office.

In doing all of that, you have confirmed the worst image of lawyers in the minds of the public by proceeding

William H. Ginsburg is the senior member of Ginsburg, Stephan, Oringher & Richman, with offices in Century City and Orange County.

forum

with an investigation tainted by an apparent, if not actual, conflict of interest on your part. You have demonstrated that lawyers who are charged with the public's trust can and do pursue agendas that are motivated by politics rather than justice. You have proven that prosecutorial abuse can and does exist in America, thus jeopardizing the perceived fairness of every other prosecution in the country. Your office has also become a haven for zealous investigators who act without checks and balances on their behavior. Instead, they resemble prosecutorial civil servants, working for an agency whose sole purpose is to ferret out presidential foibles and titillating tribulations more suited for the tabloids than any courtroom. What a field day you've created for those who already believe that lawyers are a plague on society that threatens fairness under the law.

Mr. Starr, you and your progeny need to be checked before you come to believe that you can do anything in the name of carrying out your statutory duties. You already act as if you're omnipotent. But bear in mind that the American people disapprove of your performance. They abhor your abuse of their constitutional rights. They resent your role in creating a politically charged environment tainted by leaks and innuendo to such an extent that no one involved in your investigation can possibly receive a fair trial, should it come to that.

I call on all Americans to rise up and react to your dangerous abuse of power, for none of us can rest easy as long as anyone's right to privacy is threatened. You may argue that the government needs the kind of information you are seeking from my client and others so that it can ensure proper legal conduct by the president of the United States and other high-level officials. But every single citizen is entitled to question your tactics, which include the threat of indictment and the ability to ruin innocent lives.

As for my own client in this episode, I have told her that we are being confronted by an anticonstitutional monster. He goes by the generic name of independent counsel. It's time to rid ourselves of this dangerous creature. □

Tab 46

UNDER SEAL

SCHEDULED FOR ORAL ARGUMENT ON JUNE 29, 1998

IN THE

UNITED STATES COURT OF APPEALS

FOR THE DISTRICT OF COLUMBIA CIRCUIT

Nos. 98-3060, 98-3062, 98-3072

IN RE: SEALED CASE

ON APPEAL FROM THE UNITED STATES DISTRICT COURT
FOR THE DISTRICT OF COLUMBIA
MISC. NO. 98-95 (NHJ)

BRIEF FOR APPELLANT WILLIAM J. CLINTON

ROBERT S. BENNETT
CARL S. RAUH
MITCHELL S. ETTINGER
AMY SABRIN
KATHARINE S. SEXTON
SKADDEN, ARPS, SLATE
MEAGHER & FLOM LLP
1440 NEW YORK AVENUE, N.W.
WASHINGTON, D.C. 20005
(202) 371-7000

DAVID E. KENDALL
NICOLE K. SELIGMAN
RIYAZ A. KANJI
MAX STIER
WILLIAMS & CONNOLLY
725 12TH STREET, N.W.
WASHINGTON, D.C. 20005
(202) 434-5000

Counsel for Appellant William J. Clinton

CERTIFICATE AS TO PARTIES, RULINGS AND RELATED CASES

A. Parties and Amici

The following parties and intervenors appeared before the district court: William J. Clinton, The Office of the President, Bruce R. Lindsey, Sidney Blumenthal, Nancy Hernreich, and the Office of the Independent Counsel. The following are parties in this Court: William J. Clinton, The Office of the President, and the Office of the Independent Counsel. The United States of America, acting through the Attorney General, appeared in the district court as an amicus curiae and is appearing as an amicus curiae in this Court.

B. Rulings Under Review

On May 4, 1998, the United States District Court for the District of Columbia (Johnson, C.J.) ordered Bruce R. Lindsey, a Deputy White House Counsel, to testify before a grand jury concerning matters protected, inter alia, by the President's attorney-client privilege and the work product doctrine. The ruling is at page 152 of the Joint Appendix. The opinion is not yet reported in Federal Supplement but is available, in redacted form, on Westlaw. In re Grand Jury Proceedings, Misc. Nos. 98-095, 98-096, and 98-097, 1998 WL 271539 (D.D.C. May 27, 1998).

On May 26, 1998, after the Office of the President filed a motion for reconsideration in part, the district court issued a sealed memorandum order denying reconsideration but modifying footnote 20 of its May 4 opinion. That second ruling is at page 210 of the Joint Appendix. It has not been published.

The unredacted May 4 opinion, the May 26 memorandum order, and the issues presented in this brief all remain under seal.

C. Related Cases

Counsel are not aware of any related cases.

TABLE OF CONTENTS

TABLE OF AUTHORITIES*

FEDERAL CASES

* Authorities on which we chiefly rely are marked with asterisks. D.C. Cir. R. 28(a)(2).

DOCKETED CASES

STATUTES

MISCELLANEOUS

IN THE

UNITED STATES COURT OF APPEALS

FOR THE DISTRICT OF COLUMBIA CIRCUIT

Nos. 98-3060, 98-3062, 98-3072

IN RE: SEALED CASE

ON APPEAL FROM THE UNITED STATES DISTRICT COURT
FOR THE DISTRICT OF COLUMBIA
MISC. NO. 98-95 (NHJ)

BRIEF FOR APPELLANT WILLIAM J. CLINTON

JURISDICTION

Jurisdiction in the district court was proper under 28 U.S.C. § 1331 and 18 U.S.C. § 3231. William J. Clinton filed a notice of appeal from the district court's May 4, 1998 order on May 13, 1998. Jurisdiction in this Court is proper under 28 U.S.C. § 1291.

ISSUES PRESENTED

1. Whether the district court erred in ruling that President Clinton's conversations with Deputy White House Counsel Bruce Lindsey were not privileged when Mr. Lindsey was being used to facilitate the provision of legal advice to the President by personal counsel.

2. Whether the district court erred in failing to recognize that the attorney-client privilege and work product doctrine encompassed confidential communications among

President Clinton, Mr. Lindsey, and the President's personal counsel related to Mr. Lindsey's previous personal representation of President Clinton.

3. Whether the district court erred in holding that the President in his personal capacity and the Office of the President do not have any common legal, factual or strategic interests that are legally cognizable under the attorney-client privilege's common interest rule.

4. Whether the district court erred in holding that personal counsel's confidential sharing of attorney work product with Mr. Lindsey waived the privilege, based solely on its earlier finding that President Clinton and the White House share no common interest.

STATUTES AND RULES

Federal Rule of Evidence 501, Supreme Court Standard 503, and relevant sections of the Ethics in Government Act, 28 U.S.C. § 591, et seq., are reproduced in the Addendum.

STATEMENT OF THE CASE

This case emerges from the confluence of the long-running "Whitewater" investigation with the Paula Jones civil suit. It presents vital issues involving the ability of the President to be defended in such matters with no less effectiveness than any other citizen. Because such investigations and litigation may well recur in future administrations, it is important that a President's personal attorneys and White House counsel be able to consult freely to assure that both the private and public interests of the President are adequately protected. Thus, this case is, at heart, one about the ability of a President to receive, and his lawyers to provide, effective legal services.

A. The "Whitewater" Investigation

In the Presidential campaign of 1992, the unprofitable joint investment of then-Governor and Mrs. Clinton, along with James and Susan McDougal, in a 1978 Arkansas real estate venture known as the Whitewater Development Company became a matter of some comment and criticism. Four years after the investment, in the early 1980's, the McDougals had acquired a savings and loan company, Madison Guaranty Savings & Loan Association, which was taken over by federal regulators in 1989. In 1992, the Resolution Trust Company (RTC) began an investigation of Madison Guaranty, and in the fall of 1993, newspaper articles were published suggesting that the RTC had asked federal prosecutors in Little Rock to investigate various transactions involving the S&L. Recognizing that they might be witnesses in legal proceedings, in early November, 1993, the President and Mrs. Clinton retained the law firm of Williams & Connolly to represent them with respect to the Madison Guaranty investigation. That same month, the Department of Justice assumed responsibility for this probe.

On January 20, 1994, however, the Attorney General appointed Robert B. Fiske, Jr., as independent counsel with jurisdiction to investigate matters arising out of the President or Mrs. Clinton's relationships with Madison Guaranty, the Whitewater Development Company, and/or Capital Management Services. Department of Justice Final Rule, 59 Fed. Reg. 5321 (Feb. 4, 1994). On August 5, 1994, after enactment of the Independent Counsel Reauthorization Act of 1994, 108 Stat. 735, Kenneth W. Starr was appointed by the Special Division to replace Mr. Fiske and was granted jurisdiction similar to that of Mr. Fiske. During the four and one half years of investigation by Messrs. Fiske and Starr, President and Mrs. Clinton have, with the assistance of personal counsel, testified under oath on numerous occasions, personally produced more than 90,000 pages of documents, answered interrogatories, and provided information informally.

B. The Jones Civil Suit

On May 6, 1994, Paula Jones filed suit in the United States District Court for the Eastern District of Arkansas alleging defamation, emotional distress, and violations of 42 U.S.C. §§ 1983, 1985. The President retained Skadden, Arps, Slate, Meagher & Flom, LLP, to represent him in defense of this action. For the next three years, the parties conducted litigation primarily over the legal issue of whether the suit could go forward against a sitting President. On May 27, 1997, the Supreme Court held that it could, and the case was returned to the district court. Clinton v. Jones, ___ U.S. ___, 117 S.Ct. 1636 (1997). Comprehensive discovery began in the fall of 1997.

The breadth and pace of the litigation is manifest from the sheer size of the district court docket, which reflects 332 entries after jurisdiction was returned to the district court.[1/] Even that number does not fully reflect the demands of the litigation, however. In the 16 weeks between October 1, 1997 and January 31, 1998, plaintiff Jones conducted 35 depositions, the defendants conducted 27 depositions, and approximately 90 motions were litigated in the district court in Arkansas as well as courts in Virginia, Michigan, California and the District of Columbia. In this short time period, plaintiff propounded 23 interrogatories, 72 requests for admissions, and 77 document requests to the President. Plaintiff also obtained leave to file an Amended Complaint, which the President answered. The district court held weekly hearings via conference call throughout this period to hear argument and resolve disputes.

As in any extremely active and aggressively litigated civil case, it was necessary for the President's counsel regularly to update and consult their client concerning substantive and strategic decisions that had to be made with respect to a variety of matters, such as what

---

1/ Much of the material on the docket remains under seal. The publicly available docket reflects the total number of items docketed.

depositions to take, potential areas of questioning and other preparations for depositions, and what positions to take vis-a-vis discovery and other motions. These discussions were in addition to those obviously necessary to enable the President to respond to discovery directed to him. The hectic activity during this period required frequent communications between the President and his private counsel, because the primary focus of discovery sought by plaintiff was the conduct of the President himself. Indeed, most of plaintiff's discovery related to matters far broader than the few purported contacts between the President and Ms. Jones. In particular, plaintiff was permitted to seek discovery about the defendant's alleged conduct with respect to other women over a twenty-year period while he was Governor and Attorney General of Arkansas, as well as the efforts of President Clinton's 1992 campaign to respond to similar unfounded allegations.

Plaintiff also attempted to pursue discovery into matters relating to the defendant's conduct while President, including matters of significant interest to the White House and the Presidency as an institution. For example, plaintiff sought

- to obtain medical records generated by White House physicians;
- to depose members of the Secret Service charged with protecting the President and the White House;
- to depose certain members of the President's staff; and
- to conduct discovery into the President's alleged conduct with respect to two former White House employees, including Monica Lewinsky.

Plaintiff's document requests to the President also required consultation with the White House as to whether the records sought were official White House records or the personal records of the President. Additionally, plaintiff twice issued subpoenas duces tecum to the White House (one was withdrawn, the other quashed).

The President was himself deposed for several hours on January 17, 1998. More than half the questions asked by plaintiff's counsel related to matters occurring at the White House or after Mr. Clinton became President. The interests of the Presidency in this proceeding were such that all parties acknowledged the right of White House Counsel Charles Ruff to be present.

C. Bruce Lindsey's Role

Throughout the civil litigation, and especially during the intense discovery period in late 1997, the President needed to keep abreast of the demands of the litigation while attending to the exigencies of his official duties, and he therefore on occasion needed to rely on someone on his staff to be his agent and to facilitate communications with his personal counsel. Mr. Lindsey served in this capacity. J.A. 44-45, ¶8. He was ideally suited for this liaison role because he was a White House lawyer, a long-time trusted advisor, and a personal friend of the President who could be relied upon to maintain the confidentiality of any such discussions. Mr. Lindsey traveled on almost every trip the President took and had prompt access to the President wherever he was. He was therefore in a position to communicate with the President concerning the Jones litigation at times least disruptive to the President's official duties. J.A. 44-45, ¶8.

Moreover, prior to joining the White House staff, Mr. Lindsey was in private practice in Little Rock, and he and his law firm had served as Governor Clinton's personal attorneys and as counsel to the Clinton presidential campaign in 1992. J.A. 43-44, ¶¶4-5. When plaintiff's attorneys in the Jones case sought to revisit allegations that had surfaced while Mr. Lindsey was Governor Clinton's personal attorney, President Clinton's private counsel consulted Mr. Lindsey about the prior representation.

Because discovery issues trenched upon matters of legal significance to the White House, the President's private counsel found it necessary to consult from time to time with White

House counsel about such matters. Mr. Lindsey participated in these consultations in his role as Deputy White House Counsel. As an incident of this work as a White House lawyer representing the President in his official capacity, he necessarily conferred with the President's personal counsel who were dealing with the Jones case and the "Whitewater" investigation about matters of common interest to both. J.A. 46-47, ¶12. These conversations were intended to remain confidential and occurred within the context of Mr. Lindsey's representation of the White House. J.A. 45-46, ¶10.

D. The Expansion of the OIC's Jurisdiction in January 1998

Just two days prior to the President's deposition in the Jones case, the Office of the Independent Counsel ("OIC") covertly sought on an expedited basis to expand its jurisdiction to investigate "whether Monica Lewinsky or others suborned perjury, obstructed justice, intimidated witnesses, or otherwise violated federal law . . . in dealing with witnesses, potential witnesses, attorneys, or others concerning the civil case Jones v. Clinton." Order, Div. No. 94-1 (Jan. 16, 1998) (Div. for Purpose of Appointing Independent Counsels) (D.C. Cir.). The OIC's request was granted by a sealed order of the Special Division on January 16, 1998, the day before the President's deposition. Ibid. On the evening of January 16, according to news reports, the OIC's main cooperating witness with respect to Ms. Lewinsky, Ms. Linda Tripp, met with counsel for Ms. Jones.[2/] At the President's deposition the following day, Ms. Jones' counsel asked the President 95 questions regarding Ms. Lewinsky.[3/]

2/ See, e.g., Baker, "Linda Tripp Briefed Jones Team on Tapes," The Washington Post (Feb. 14, 1998).

3/ Discovery in the Jones matter closed on January 31, 1998. Promptly thereafter, President Clinton filed a motion for summary judgment, which was granted. Ms. Jones' appeal is pending.

E. Mr. Lindsey's Grand Jury Testimony

Mr. Lindsey testified before the OIC's grand jury on February 18 and 19 and on March 12, 1998. J.A. 45, ¶9. He answered numerous questions relating to the Jones litigation and Ms. Lewinsky. J.A. 47-49, ¶¶15-16. He was also asked, however, "a number of questions about [his] private communications with the President, with the President's private counsel in Jones v. Clinton, with the President's private counsel in the OIC investigation, and with other senior advisors to the President." J.A. 45, ¶9. Counsel for appellants are not privy to the precise questions asked of Mr. Lindsey in the grand jury,[4/] but the OIC made an in camera submission of fourteen categories of information it sought from Mr. Lindsey. Because of Rule 6(e) concerns, the court simply summarized these categories as including but not limited to the following:

> "Lindsey's conversations with the President regarding the Jones litigation; his conversations with the President regarding Monica Lewinsky and the grand jury's investigation; his communications with White House advisers, including White House Counsel members, about the Jones litigation and the Monica Lewinsky matter; the identities of grand jury witnesses who have been interviewed by the White House after their appearances and the substance of those interviews; his communications with Steven Goodin, a White House employee called to testify before the grand jury; whether Lindsey heard during the weekend of January 24-25, 1998, that Betty Currie was cooperating with the OIC; communications regarding the President's knowledge of whether Betty Currie called Vernon Jordan to help Monica Lewinsky find a job in New York; and communications with Peter McGrath, a New Hampshire lawyer representing a client with information about the Lewinsky matter."

J.A. 198-199 (footnote omitted).

Mr. Lindsey declined, on attorney-client privilege and attorney work product grounds, to answer questions concerning confidential communications with the President's

---

4/ The district court denied Mr. Lindsey's motion for a copy of the transcript but directed the OIC to make the transcripts available to the court. J.A. 147.

personal attorneys because he was serving as a confidential agent and intermediary for the President in dealing with the President's private counsel J.A. 45-46, ¶10, because some of the questions addressed topics with which he was familiar because of his prior service as the President's personal attorney J.A. 43-45, ¶¶3-5, 8-9, and because as Deputy White House Counsel he was addressing issues of common interest to the White House and the President in his personal capacity J.A. 46-47, ¶¶11-12.

F. The District Court's Opinion

On March 6, the OIC moved to compel answers to the questions Mr. Lindsey had declined to answer, inter alia, on the basis of the President's personal attorney-client privilege and the work product protections. Both the President and the Office of the President filed oppositions, and the district court heard argument on March 24, 1998. J.A. 86. Pursuant to a subsequent court order, the OIC made an in camera submission on April 24, 1998, concerning its need for the testimony. J.A. 149.

On May 4, 1998, the district court issued a sealed opinion, rejecting the President's privilege claims. The court did not question that personal counsel enjoyed a privileged relationship with the President in both the Jones case and the Lewinsky investigation, and it recognized that case law approves the use in certain circumstances of an agent or intermediary to facilitate the provision of legal advice. But it was "not persuaded that the use of an intermediary was necessary" in the instant case. J.A. 169.[5/]

With respect to the President's assertion of privilege based upon the common interest between the President personally and his Office, the district court recognized that "[t]he

---

5/ The district court did not address the President's separate contention that part of the legal assistance Mr. Lindsey furnished to private counsel arose out of Mr. Lindsey's experience as personal counsel to then-Governor Clinton.

President and the White House certainly share some concerns in a broad sense," but held that "in terms of the Paula Jones civil suit and the grand jury investigation, they do not share a 'common interest' in the legal sense of the phrase." J.A. 175. This was so, the court concluded, because "the White House cannot be implicated in any criminal or civil action." J.A. 176. The court construed the need of private and White House counsel to consult in order to coordinate legal advice to the President personally and officially as evidence of a lack of common interest between the two: "[w]hether President Clinton chose to follow the interests of the White House or his own personal interests in this situation, it remains true that the individual and the office have opposing interests." J.A. 177.

Finally, the district court ruled that any personal work product protection was waived when material otherwise covered by that doctrine was shared with Mr. Lindsey, since "the White House and President Clinton in his personal capacity do not face the OIC as an 'opposing party' and do not share a common interest in the matter." J.A. 179.

The President in his personal capacity filed a timely notice of appeal. J.A. 206.[6]

SUMMARY OF ARGUMENT

The decision below improperly denies President Clinton, in his personal capacity, the protections of the attorney-client privilege and the work product doctrine available to all other litigants. The decision incorrectly interprets or fails to recognize four independent but overlapping reasons why the communications at issue here are privileged. First, the district court erred in holding that President Clinton's attorney-client privilege was breached by his use of Deputy White House Counsel Lindsey to facilitate the provision of legal advice to him by personal counsel. Second, the district court erred in failing to recognize that Mr. Lindsey's prior

6/ On May 28, 1998, the OIC filed a petition for certiorari before judgment, which the Supreme Court denied on June 4, 1998. 66 U.S.L.W. 3778 (U.S. June 9, 1998).

personal representation of President Clinton made privileged communications among Mr. Lindsey, President Clinton, and President Clinton's current personal counsel relating to the earlier representation. Third, the district court erred in holding that the President and the Office of the President do not have any common legal, factual or strategic interests that are cognizable under the common interest rule. Finally, the district court erred in holding that its decision that President Clinton and the Office of the President could not share a common interest necessarily meant that personal counsel's confidential sharing of work product with Mr. Lindsey waived that privilege.

ARGUMENT

It is uncontested and indisputable that President Clinton, like every other citizen, enjoys the right to personal legal counsel. The district court decision does not purport to question this right, but it nonetheless directly challenges the President's ability to receive appropriate and fully informed legal advice.

If the ruling below stands, the President's personal and official counsel cannot communicate in confidence. As a result, the President cannot obtain from his personal counsel legal advice informed by the possible ramifications of that advice for his official duties. Nor may the President determine for himself how to seek and obtain confidential legal advice without undue intrusion on his constitutional obligations under Article II. The district court has second-guessed, and disallowed, his chosen course.

One key guiding principle emerges from a review of the law governing attorney-client privilege: the need to be flexible in defining the workings of the privilege to achieve the paramount goal of assuring that individuals are able to obtain fully informed and factually well-founded legal advice. The doctrines at issue here – the absolute nature of the privilege, the permissible use of intermediaries, and the protection of communications in the common interest

– reflect the courts' longstanding effort to find practical solutions to encourage and facilitate the receipt of such advice. The district court decision flies directly in the face of these core principles. It ignores the practical need of the President to obtain meaningful personal legal advice and instead throws insurmountable obstacles in the path of that effort. It does so based on fundamental misinterpretations of governing law and cannot stand.

I. STANDARD OF REVIEW

This appeal addresses conclusions of law by the district court concerning the attorney-client privilege and the work product doctrine. Conclusions of law are subject to de novo review. United States v. Abdul-Saboor, 85 F.3d 664, 667 (D.C. Cir. 1996). Where the district court made factual findings dependent on, and related to, an erroneous legal understanding, review also is de novo. See F.T.C. v. Texaco, 555 F.2d 862, 876 n.29 (D.C. Cir. 1977).

II. COMMUNICATIONS BETWEEN PRESIDENT CLINTON AND HIS LEGAL COUNSEL ENJOY THE ABSOLUTE PROTECTION OF THE ATTORNEY-CLIENT PRIVILEGE

It has long been settled that the societal benefits of an absolute attorney-client privilege outweigh any intrusion that the privilege may have on the factfinding process. Recognizing the value of certainty that derives from the guarantee of confidentiality, once courts determine that a communication is made in confidence for the purpose of obtaining or providing legal advice, they do not consider the need for particular information, or the context of the request.

The privilege "is the oldest of the privileges for confidential communications known to the common law." Upjohn Co. v. United States, 449 U.S. 383, 389 (1981) (citation omitted). Its purpose is "to encourage full and frank communication between attorneys and their clients and thereby promote broader public interests in the observance of law and administration of justice." Ibid. It "exists to protect not only the giving of professional advice to those who can act on it but also the giving of information to the lawyer to enable him to give sound and informed advice." Id. at 390.[7]

Testimonial privileges like the attorney-client privilege are justified "by a public good transcending the normally predominant principle of utilizing all rational means for ascertaining the truth," Jaffee v. Redmond, 518 U.S. 1, 9 (1996) (quotations omitted). As the Supreme Court has observed, "[t]he privilege recognizes that sound legal advice or advocacy serves public ends and that such advice or advocacy depends upon the lawyer's being fully informed by the client." Upjohn, 449 U.S. at 389. See also Hunt v. Blackburn, 128 U.S. 464, 470 (1888). Thus, although the attorney-client privilege may sometimes have the effect of withholding relevant information from the factfinder, the privilege is justified by larger public benefits – the greater law compliance and fairer judicial proceedings resulting from the "sound legal advice [and] advocacy" the privilege promotes. Upjohn, 449 U.S. at 389.

Moreover, any loss to the factfinder engendered by the privilege is more apparent than real. Because the privilege only protects communications "which might not have been made absent the privilege," Fisher v. United States, 425 U.S. 391, 403 (1976), the factfinder loses access only to a communication that may never have been made without the assurance of confidentiality. "Without a privilege, much of the desirable evidence to which litigants . . . seek access . . . is unlikely to come into being. This unspoken 'evidence' will therefore serve no

---

[7] The elements required to establish the existence of the attorney-client privilege are: (1) a communication; (2) made between privileged persons; (3) in confidence; (4) for the purpose of obtaining or providing legal assistance for the client. Restatement (Third) of the Law Governing Lawyers §118 (Proposed Final Draft No. 1, 1996) (tentatively approved May 1996) ("Restatement of the Law Governing Lawyers"). Relevant sections of the Restatement of the Law Governing Lawyers are included in the attached Addendum.

greater truth-seeking function than if it had been spoken and privileged." Jaffee, 518 U.S. at 12; see also Upjohn, 449 U.S. at 395.

Once the privilege has been held applicable, it is absolute and cannot be overcome by a showing of a prosecutor's or factfinder's need. As the Supreme Court explained in Upjohn, the very effectiveness of the attorney-client privilege depends upon its absolute nature because "[a]n uncertain privilege, or one which purports to be certain but results in widely varying applications by the courts, is little better than no privilege at all." 449 U.S. at 393. The Court again emphasized this same point in a related context in Jaffee, explaining that "[m]aking the promise of [a therapist's] confidentiality contingent . . . would eviscerate the effectiveness of the privilege."[8/] 518 U.S. at 17. Accordingly, the attorney-client privilege remains absolute irrespective of the nature of the legal issues or forum involved. It applies with equal force in criminal and civil settings, see, e.g., Fed. R. Civ. Evid. 501 advisory committee notes ("privileges shall continue to be developed by the courts of the United States under a uniform standard applicable both in civil and criminal cases") (emphasis added), and it is well settled that the privilege remains absolute even in the grand jury setting. Although the Supreme Court's decision in Branzburg v. Hayes, 408 U.S. 665, 688 (1972), often is cited as support for the right of the grand jury to "every man's evidence," in that same sentence the Court went out of its way to except privileged evidence, stating in full that even in a grand jury setting "the public has a right to every man's evidence, except for those persons protected by a constitutional, common law, or statutory privilege." (emphasis added).

8/ The absolute nature of the attorney-client privilege has been recognized by more than 170 years of Supreme Court opinions. See, e.g., Chirac v. Reinicker, 24 U.S. (11 Wheat.) 280, 294 (1826); Connecticut Mut. Life Ins. Co. v. Schaefer, 94 U.S. 457, 458 (1876).

III. COMMUNICATIONS AMONG MR. LINDSEY, THE PRESIDENT, AND/OR THE PRESIDENT'S PERSONAL COUNSEL ARE PRIVILEGED AND CONFIDENTIAL

The questions asked of Mr. Lindsey in the grand jury, to which he has been ordered to respond, implicate three separate but overlapping roles that he played in relation to personal legal matters of the President. First, he communicated with the President and the President's personal counsel in his role as an agent and intermediary for the purpose of facilitating the President's ability to obtain legal advice in the Jones litigation. Second, he consulted with the President and the President's personal counsel in his role as a former personal counsel to Mr. Clinton on matters related to current legal disputes. And third, as Deputy White House Counsel, he discussed issues of common legal interest with personal counsel in the Jones and Lewinsky matters. As set forth below, the law recognizes and protects the confidentiality of communications made in each of these roles, or in any combination of them. The district court erred by failing to give effect to these protections here.

A. Communications Facilitating the Provision of Personal Legal Advice to President Clinton

In rejecting the President's claim of a temporary immunity from civil litigation during his term in office, the Supreme Court predicted that the Jones v. Clinton suit, if properly managed by the courts below, would be "highly unlikely to occupy any substantial amount of [the President's] time." Jones, 117 S.Ct. at 1648. To this end, however, the Court stressed that courts below should display a keen sensitivity to the burden on the President of having to defend the Jones litigation while discharging the duties of his Office:

> Although we have rejected the argument that the potential burdens on the President violate separation of powers principles, those burdens are appropriate matters for the District Court to evaluate in its management of the case. The high respect that is owed to the Office of the Chief Executive, though not justifying a rule of

> categorical immunity, is a matter that should inform the conduct of the entire proceeding, including the timing and scope of discovery.

Jones, 117 S.Ct. at 1650-51 (emphasis added).

Here, far from displaying the requisite sensitivity, the district court stripped the President of the ability to balance the demands of his office and the Jones litigation through the use of an agent to facilitate his receipt of personal legal advice. The district court reached this result by turning the Jones caution on its head: the court limited the means available to the President to defend the litigation by construing the scope of the attorney-client privilege as it applies to agents more restrictively than this Court and courts generally have done in litigation involving parties other than the President. This cramped interpretation of the privilege as it applies to agents constitutes legal error.

1. The Privilege Extends to Agents Who Facilitate the Provision of Legal Advice

After Clinton v. Jones was remanded, the trial court set a brisk discovery and motions schedule. The President concluded that without some assistance, he could not properly attend to his official duties while simultaneously attending to his defense in the Jones litigation. Accordingly, the President asked Bruce Lindsey to serve as his agent to assist him at times in marshalling information for, and securing advice from, private counsel. J.A. 45-46, ¶10. For the many reasons set forth above, Mr. Lindsey was ideal for this responsibility. See pp. 4-7, supra.

In determining to use Mr. Lindsey as a privileged agent, the President acted in conformity with well-established law in this Circuit and elsewhere. Where a client utilizes an intermediary to develop and present information to his counsel, or to assist counsel otherwise in the formulation and presentation of legal advice to the client, the protections of the attorney-client privilege apply to communications involving the client, the agent, and counsel.

The district court recognized that the President had designated Mr. Lindsey as his agent for purposes of securing legal advice in the Jones litigation. However, it asserted that "[t]he D.C. Circuit has never explicitly decided whether a client's agent, such as Lindsey, can claim the attorney-client privilege." J.A. 168. That is flatly incorrect. On two separate occasions in recent years, this Court has stated that where an agent is used to facilitate the provision of legal advice to a client, the communications between client and agent are privileged.

In Linde, Thomson, Langworthy, Kohn & Van Dyke, P.C. v. Resolution Trust Corporation, 5 F.3d 1508 (D.C. Cir. 1993), this Court observed that where an insurer facilitates an insured's receipt of legal advice through its communications with the insured and with counsel, the attorney-client privilege protects those communications, notwithstanding the absence of a general insurer/insured privilege:

> Certainly, where the insured communicates with the insurer for the express purpose of seeking legal advice with respect to a concrete claim, or for the purpose of aiding an insurer-provided attorney in preparing a specific legal case, the law would exalt form over substance if it were to deny application of the attorney-client privilege.

5 F.3d at 1515. The "critical factor" in determining the existence of the privilege is whether communications with the agent are made "in confidence for the purpose of obtaining legal advice from the lawyer" for the client. 5 F.3d at 1514 (quoting FTC v. TRW, 628 F.2d 207, 212 (D.C. Cir. 1980) (emphasis omitted)).

In TRW, this Court likewise declared that the use of an agent in facilitating the provision of advice from attorney to client falls within the protections of the attorney-client privilege. The Court noted that "[a] line of appellate cases beginning with Judge Friendly's opinion for the court in United States v. Kovel, 296 F.2d 918 (2d Cir. 1961), has recognized that the attorney-client privilege can attach to reports of third parties made at the request of the attorney or the client where the purpose of the report was to put in usable form information obtained from the client." 628 F.2d at 212. This Court stressed that it believed such "holdings to be correct and necessary to preserve the effectiveness of counsel in our legal system." Id. Only because it could not be sure that the third party's communications in the case before it had been made to obtain legal advice for the client did this Court find the privilege inapplicable. Id. at 212-13.

Supreme Court Standard 503[9/] incorporates this principle into its definition of the privilege, see §§(a)(4) and (b)(1) and (4), and the evidence treatises have given full recognition to it as well. See, e.g., 8 Wigmore, Evidence § 2317 at 618 (McNaughton rev. 1961) ("[a] communication . . . by any form of agency employed or set in motion by the client is within the privilege) ("Wigmore"); Jack B. Weinstein et al., Weinstein's Federal Evidence § 503.15[3] (2d ed. 1997) (privilege applies to communications involving "non-client [who] furthers the interest of effective representation") ("Weinstein").

The district court failed to recognize the force of this authority. Here, there is no dispute that Mr. Lindsey's role was to facilitate the provision of legal advice to the President through the communication of information to the President's private counsel and the communication in return of counsel's questions and advice to the President. The district court's failure to hold accordingly was legal error.

2. The President Is Not Required to Establish Necessity and, in Any Event, the Use of Mr. Lindsey Was Necessary

The district court offered several other reasons for denying the protections of the attorney-client privilege to the President in connection with his use of Mr. Lindsey in

---

9/ While this Standard was not enacted by Congress, this Court has looked to it for guidance. See, e.g., Linde, 5 F.3d at 1514.

communicating with private counsel. The first of these was that the court was "not persuaded that the use of [Mr. Lindsey] was necessary." J.A. 169. In superimposing a necessity requirement on the use of agents, the district court again committed legal error.

This Court has never held that the privilege applies in agency situations only when "necessary." To the contrary, this Court quite plainly has avoided adoption of such a requirement. In Linde, for example, it was sufficient to warrant application of the privilege that the client and counsel intended that the communications be confidential, and that they facilitated the client's receipt of legal advice. Indeed, it was irrelevant to the Linde analysis whether or not the insured could have communicated directly with counsel. Similarly, in TRW, this Court nowhere stated that communications between an agent, counsel and client are privileged only where the use of the agent is a necessity.

The evidence treatises have also rejected necessity as a prerequisite to application of the privilege, focusing instead, as has this Court, on whether the use of an agent facilitates the provision of legal advice. Thus, Weinstein writes that "the question should not be whether the third person is necessary, but whether he or she is helpful to the interests of the lawyer-client relationship." Weinstein § 503.15[3] (emphasis added). Wigmore states quite plainly that "a communication . . . by any form of agency employed or set in motion by the client is within the privilege." Wigmore § 2317 (emphasis in original). And McCormick declares that it should not matter whether the use of an agent "was in the particular instance reasonably necessary to the matter in hand." McCormick on Evidence § 91 at 335 (4th ed. 1992).

An examination of the "necessity" for an agent's use would embroil the courts in second-guessing the determinations of attorney and client that the utilization of an agent would better help the client secure proper legal advice. This is second-guessing that the courts are poorly equipped to handle, as amply illustrated by this case. As noted above, see p. 4, supra, when the Jones case was remanded to the district court in 1997, a hectic period of discovery ensued, involving numerous depositions, motions, and pleadings of all kinds, including numerous interrogatories and admissions requests. In the face of this intensive litigation, the President determined that, without the assistance of an agent, he simply could not attend to his defense while fulfilling his official duties. J.A. 44-45, ¶8. That this was the case is hardly surprising. As one of the most respected scholars of the modern Presidency has written, official deadlines "rule [the President's] personal agenda, . . . drain[ing] his energy and crowd[ing] his time regardless of all else."[10/] Indeed, based on numerous authorities, the Supreme Court accepted the premise that the President "occupies a unique office with powers and responsibilities so vast and important that the public interest demands he devote his undivided time and attention to his public duties." Clinton, 117 S. Ct. at 1646.

The district court's statement that it was inappropriate for a government lawyer to serve as the President's agent because this meant the use of "White House staff for personal matters," J.A. 172, reflects a fundamental misunderstanding of the Supreme Court's explicitly expressed concerns. Mr. Lindsey's efforts made it possible for the President to transact his official business more efficiently. The Supreme Court admonished that the lower courts must give "the utmost deference to Presidential responsibilities," Jones, 117 S.Ct. at 1652; indeed, there are fundamental separation-of-powers limitations on the ability of a court to supervise how the Executive and Legislative branches organize themselves to discharge their constitutional responsibilities, see Winpisinger v. Watson, 628 F.2d 133, 140 & 141 n.30 (D.C. Cir. 1980) ("[t]he judiciary is not to act as a management overseer of the Executive Branch") ; see also

---

10/ Richard E. Neustadt, Presidential Power and the Modern Presidents: The Politics of

United States v. Rostenkowski, 59 F.3d 1291, 1307-11 (D.C. Cir. 1995) (holding that separations-of-powers concerns render questions whether Congressional employees are performing permissible "official work" as opposed to impermissible "personal service" non-justiciable unless Congress has supplied clear rule of decision).

Instead of recognizing the extent of the President's burdens, the district court cavalierly dismissed the determination of the President that he needed an agent to facilitate communications with his personal counsel. Remarkably, the only evidence the district court cited for its position were two oral argument statements by the President's counsel, both of which the court misconstrued. In the first, the President's counsel in the Jones case explained that he would use Mr. Lindsey to obtain information from the President, having Mr. Lindsey speak directly to the President when he was travelling with him, or having Mr. Lindsey call the President otherwise. J.A. 170. The district court questioned why counsel could not call the President directly instead of Mr. Lindsey. It completely ignored counsel's point that Mr. Lindsey usually travels with the President, and hence is best positioned to raise issues with him at a time that is least intrusive on other matters. It also overlooked the fact that even when Mr. Lindsey is not travelling with the President, he still is in frequent contact with him on a variety of matters and is far better positioned than counsel to raise issues with the President at times least likely to disrupt the President's official duties.

In the second statement, counsel for the President in the OIC investigation stated that they had not yet found it necessary to use Mr. Lindsey to facilitate their communications with the President in that new matter. The district court declared that this "fact strongly suggests . . . that Lindsey was not 'reasonably necessary' as the President's agent for communication with

---

Leadership from Roosevelt to Reagan 130 (1990).

respect to the Jones case." J.A. 170-71. In doing so, the district court completely ignored the second half of counsel's statement, that it had not been necessary to rely on Mr. Lindsey as an agent in the OIC matter "because we haven't had the immediacy of the civil litigation." J.A. 133. The district court simply failed to distinguish between the requirements of the two matters.

Ultimately, the most troubling aspect of the district court's determination that Mr. Lindsey was not a "necessary" agent is its misreading of the Jones decision. Far from "giving 'the utmost deference,'" 117 S.Ct. at 1652, to the President's decision that he should use an agent to secure proper advice in the Jones litigation while fulfilling his constitutional duties – a deference compelled both by that decision and the separation of powers principles it reflects – the court imposed a "necessity" requirement that is not the law of this Circuit, and then applied that test in a manner that ignored the President's own determination of how best to fulfill his constitutional duties while meeting the pre-trial schedule in the Jones matter.

3. That Mr. Lindsey Served In More Than a Ministerial Capacity Does Not Disqualify Him as a Privileged Agent

The district court also refused to apply the privilege because Mr. Lindsey was not used as a "true intermediar[y], [someone] whose function is simply to ensure that messages from a client to his or her attorney are received and understood." J.A. 171. This holding also was legal error.

On numerous occasions, courts have held that the privilege can apply in situations where an agent, far from just passing information back and forth between counsel and client, has enhanced the value of those communications. In TRW, for example, the district court had held that the privilege could not apply to a study of the client's credit reporting system that had been prepared by a third party consultant, on the grounds that only "ministerial agents" who do not engage in the "independent compilation and analysis" of information can be brought within the ambit of the privilege. 628 F.2d at 212. This Court affirmed the result, but expressly not for the reasons articulated by the district court. Id. Rather, the Court stated that the privilege would attach to the agent's report if it had been prepared for the purpose of obtaining legal advice from counsel. Id. at 212-13. That the agent had plainly done more than relay information from the client did not affect the analysis.

A host of other courts have held the privilege applicable to agents who have added value to attorney-client communications. See, e.g., United States v. Judson, 322 F.2d 460, 462-63 (9th Cir. 1963); Miller v. Haulmark Transport Systems, 104 F.R.D. 442, 445 (E.D.Pa. 1984). Perhaps no court has made the point more emphatically than did Judge Friendly in Kovel: "[w]e cannot regard the privilege as confined to 'menial or ministerial' [agents]." 296 F.2d at 921. He provided several examples of agency situations in which the privilege might apply, including "where [an] attorney, ignorant of [a] foreign language [spoken by his client], sends the client to a non-lawyer proficient in it, with instructions to interview the client on the attorney's behalf and then render his own summary of the situation, perhaps drawing on his own knowledge in the process, so that the attorney can give the client proper legal advice." Id. (emphasis added).

In holding to the contrary, the district court cited Restatement of the Law Governing Lawyers § 120, cmt (f). But those very examples confirm that a privileged agent can do more than serve as a conduit for information. Thus, the Restatement describes as privileged agents parents who accompany their 16-year-old to a meeting with the child's lawyer, and the "Accountant [who] accompan[ies] Client to a consultation with Lawyer so that Accountant can explain the nature of Client's legal matter to Lawyer." Id. In these situations, the agents are clearly doing more than passing messages between counsel and client -- they are enhancing the quality of the communication between the two. These examples also make clear the district court's error in concluding that the privilege does not attach to meetings at which the President, private counsel and Mr. Lindsey were all present. See J.A. 167 n.7. Mr. Lindsey was not limited in his role as agent to the ministerial task of relaying messages, but could properly assist the President by providing additional insight and information during such discussions. See also In Re Grand Jury Proceedings Under Seal, 947 F.2d 1188, 1190 (4th Cir. 1991).

B. Communications Related to Mr. Lindsey's Former Representation

Prior to 1993, Mr. Lindsey served as then-Governor Clinton's personal counsel on a number of occasions. He dealt in that capacity with issues that the President's present personal counsel also have had to address. J.A. 43-44, ¶¶3-5; J.A. 171. The district court noted that "Lindsey was consulting with [personal counsel] regarding litigation strategy and describing his past representation of President Clinton," J.A. 171, but it overlooked entirely the point that conferences between present and prior counsel as to such issues fall squarely within the attorney-client privilege.

Three points are indisputable. First, attorney-client confidences remain privileged after the termination of a representation. Supreme Court Standard 503(c) (former attorney can invoke the privilege); Restatement of the Law Governing Lawyers § 45(2) (former lawyer must continue to protect the client's confidences); ABA Model Rule 1.6, cmt. 22 ("[t]he duty of confidentiality continues after the client-lawyer relationship has terminated). Second, consistent with the privilege, prior counsel can --indeed must -- communicate confidences to subsequent counsel to facilitate the ongoing representation of the client. Restatement of the Law Governing Lawyers § 45, cmt (b) ("[t]he lawyer must make the client's . . . papers available to the client or the client's new lawyer"); § 58 (2)-(3) (same). Third, information acquired by counsel subsequent to a representation relating to the subject matter of the representation remains confidential. Id. § 111 and cmt. (c) ("Confidential client information consists of information relating to that client, acquired by a lawyer . . . in the course of or as a result of representing the client. . . . Information acquired . . . after the representation is confidential so long as it is not generally known and relates to the representation.").

The application of these principles here is straightforward. Where Mr. Lindsey has communicated confidences arising out of his representation of then-Governor Clinton to the President's present counsel, those confidences have not lost their privileged status. By the same token, where present counsel have communicated information to Mr. Lindsey relating to his prior representation of the Governor, "for example, in the form of information on subsequent developments," id., those communications are also privileged. The district court committed legal error in holding that Mr. Lindsey's testimony about such matters could be compelled before the grand jury.[11/]

C. **Communications in the "Common Interest"**

The court below held that "President Clinton in his personal capacity does not share a legal 'common interest' with the White House such that communications between White House attorneys and the President's personal attorneys fall within the attorney-client privilege." J.A. 178. More generally, the district court held that a "federal government agency cannot share a 'common interest' with a private individual against the United States, here represented by the OIC." J.A. 175. The court based these holdings on the grounds that (1) "the White House cannot be implicated in any criminal or civil action and thus does not share President Clinton's

---

11/ Lawyers who enter government service are not exempt from the duty to ensure an orderly transition in the representation of their former clients, and no authority suggests that they breach the privilege or violate their public obligations in doing so.

legal interests, J.A. 176; and (2) that President Clinton and the White House necessarily have opposing interests with respect to issues such as whether to invoke privileges, id., and whether to offer a particular defense in the Jones litigation, J.A. 177. The district court committed legal error both in these statements of the common interest rule and in its refusal to recognize its applicability here.

1. The Common Interest Doctrine Is a Well-Established Component of the Attorney-Client Privilege

The common interest rule is an application of the attorney-client privilege that is uniformly accepted and endorsed, particularly in this Circuit. See In Re Sealed Case, 29 F.3d 715, 719 (D.C. Cir. 1994).[12/] It enables counsel for clients who share a common interest "to exchange privileged communications and attorney work product in order to adequately prepare a defense without waiving either privilege." Haines v. Liggett Group, Inc., 975 F.2d 81, 94 (3d Cir. 1992). The rationale behind this doctrine is the same as the attorney-client privilege itself – that the sharing of information between counsel for clients with a common interest will "encourage full and frank communications between attorneys and their clients and thereby promote broader public interests in the observance of law and administration of justice." Upjohn, 449 U.S. at 389. As noted by one court, "[t]he need to protect the free flow of information from client to attorney logically exists whenever multiple clients share a common interest about a legal matter." United States v. Schwimmer, 892 F.2d 237, 243 (2d Cir. 1989) (citation omitted).[13/]

12/ See also John Morrell & Co. v. Local Union 304A of United Food & Commercial Workers, 913 F.2d 544, 555-56 (8th Cir. 1990); United States v. AT&T, 642 F.2d 1285, 1300-01 (D.C. Cir. 1980) (application of common interest privilege in work product context); Supreme Court Proposed Rule 503(b)(3).

13/ See also 2 Stephen A. Saltzberg et al., Federal Rules of Evidence Manual 599 (6th ed. 1994) ("Saltzberg").

The doctrine covers an array of communications, including among counsel for clients with common interests, between two sets of clients and their lawyers, and between an individual, her personal counsel, and an attorney for a different party with a common interest, as long as the purpose of the communication is to obtain legal advice in the common interest. Indeed, the doctrine encompasses communications between a defendant client and a co-defendant's agents,[14/] communications between clients jointly represented by a single attorney,[15/] communications between in-house counsel for a corporation and outside counsel,[16/] communications between governmental and private entities,[17/] and communications between two governmental entities[18/] -- again, as long as a common interest is pursued and the communications are for the purpose of providing effective legal advice. Since the privilege belongs to both clients, it may be invoked by either and cannot be waived unilaterally.[19/]

Two additional observations demonstrate the legal error in the district court's determination that President Clinton "does not share a legal 'common interest' with the White House." First, courts generously construe the kinds of overlapping concerns that constitute a

---

14/ See Schwimmer, 892 F.2d at 244; United States v. McPartlin, 595 F.2d 1321, 1337 (7th Cir. 1979).

15/ See United States v. Moscony, 927 F.2d 742, 753 (3d Cir. 1991).

16/ See, e.g., Natta v. Zletz, 418 F.2d 633, 637 (7th Cir. 1969) (collecting cases); Burlington Indus. v. Exxon Corp., 65 F.R.D. 26, 36 (D. Md. 1974) (collecting cases).

17/ See, e.g., United States v. AT&T, 642 F.2d at 1300-01 (common interest rule applied to documents shared between the government and MCI).

18/ See Chan v. City of Chicago, 162 F.R.D. 344, 345-46 (N.D. Ill. 1995) (draft affidavits of an FBI agent held to be privileged under a joint defense agreement between the FBI and the City of Chicago, despite fact that the FBI was not party to the suit).

19/ See, e.g., John Morrell & Co., 913 F.2d at 556; Interfaith Hous. Delaware, Inc. v. Town of Georgetown, 841 F. Supp. 1393, 1400-02 (D. Del. 1994).

"common interest." The shared interest may take many forms and may be "legal, factual, or strategic in character."[20] Often, a common interest exists where two or more clients face the same adversary or are involved in the same investigation, including both grand jury and administrative investigations,[21] but that need not be the case, as long as there is a legal, factual, or strategic overlap. Nor must the client be actively involved in litigation or even facing immediate exposure; witnesses in the same investigation share a common interest, as do clients who engage in a joint effort to avoid litigation, even if the litigation is not imminent or probable.[22]

The district court's second error was its failure to recognize that even clients with interests that are not generally congruent may still have sufficient common interest to permit confidential information sharing.[23] The courts and other authorities repeatedly have made this

---

20/ Restatement of the Law Governing Lawyers § 126, cmt e; see also Schachar v. American Academy of Ophthalmology, Inc., 106 F.R.D. 187, 191-92 (N.D. Ill. 1985) (plaintiffs in separate litigation found to have sufficient mutuality of factual and/or legal interest to invoke common interest privilege).

21/ See Continental Oil Co. v. United States, 330 F.2d 347, 349-50 (9th Cir. 1964) (common interest privilege applied to corporations which exchanged witness interviews of their respective employees who had testified before a grand jury); Matter of Grand Jury Subpoena Duces Tecum Dated Nov. 16, 1974, 406 F. Supp. 381, 389-92 (S.D.N.Y. 1974)(common interest privilege applied to clients facing SEC investigation).

22/ See, e.g., SCM Corp. v. Xerox Corp., 70 F.R.D. 508, 513 (D. Conn.) ("The privilege need not be limited to legal consultations . . . in litigation situations . . . . Corporations should be encouraged to seek legal advice in planning their affairs to avoid litigation as well as in pursuing it."), appeal dismissed, 534 F.2d 1031 (2d Cir. 1976); United States v. Zolin, 809 F.2d 1411, 1417 (9th Cir. 1987) (common interest found among those present in "sorting out the respective affairs of the Church and Mr. Hubbard" even though some of the persons present had not been sued and did not face any immediate liability), aff'd in part on other grounds and vacated in part on other grounds, 491 U.S. 554 (1989).

23/ The district court misapplied two factually distinct cases to support its view that there could be no legally cognizable common interest between President Clinton and the Office of the President. The court in United States v. MIT, 129 F.3d 681 (1st Cir. 1997), enforced an IRS summons for documents that MIT previously had shared with the point. "The fact that clients with common interests also have interests that conflict, perhaps sharply, does not mean that communications on matters of common interest are non-privileged." Restatement of the Law Governing Lawyers §126, Reporter's Notes cmt. e.[24/] Indeed, "[m]ost courts broadly construe the phrase 'common interest,' and deny the privilege only if the interests of the parties are completely antagonistic." Weinstein § 503(b)[06] (emphasis added). "That a joint defense may be made by somewhat unsteady bedfellows does not in itself negate the existence or viability of the joint defense." In re Grand Jury Subpoena Duces Tecum Dated Nov. 16, 1974, 406 F. Supp. 381, 392 (S.D.N.Y. 1974). The privilege remains intact as long as there is a shared legal, factual or strategic interest at the time of the communication.[25/]

2. Communications Between Personal and White House Counsel Are Privileged Under the Common Interest Rule

In ruling that the President and the Presidency do not share a common interest, as a matter of law, the district court overlooked the significant congruence of interests between the

---

Defense Contract Audit Agency, despite MIT's argument that they were protected under the common interest doctrine, because the only "common interest" the court could find was the highly "abstract" interest in "the proper performance of MIT's defense contracts and the proper auditing and payment of MIT's bills." 129 F.3d at 686. This comes no where near the multitude of interests shared by President Clinton and the White House in connection with the swirl of civil litigations and congressional and grand jury investigations with which they both are so entwined. The decision in United States v. Aramony, 88 F.3d 1369 (4th Cir. 1996) is totally inapposite; since Aramony had been accused of defrauding the party with which he asserted a common interest, their relationship was plainly adversarial.

24/ See also Eisenberg v. Gagnon, 766 F.2d 770, 787-88 (3d Cir. 1985) ("Communications to an attorney to establish a common defense strategy are privileged even though the attorney represents another client with some adverse interests.") (collecting cases); McPartlin, 595 F.2d at 1336-37 (common interest privilege does not require complete compatibility of interests).

25/ See, e.g., Proposed Supreme Court Rule 503(b), advisory committee notes (common interest rule applies "where different lawyers represent clients who have some interests in common") (emphasis added).

President personally and his Administration in all matters, including the Paula Jones suit and the Lewinsky investigation.[26/] It reached this erroneous result with dramatically unrealistic references to the "White House" as a party,[27/] appearing to posit some abstract entity that exists wholly apart from its current occupant. As a party in this case, the "White House" is not simply a building or even an institution; it is a group of people assembled by a particular elected President at a distinct time in history. The Clinton Administration is, obviously, not fungible with some previous Presidency but is comprised of specially selected people pursuing specific goals, and the current President's mandate to do this stems from election by the populace.

These observations may seem elementary, but they were entirely ignored by the district court. In a very real and significant way, the objectives of William J. Clinton, the person, and his Administration (the Clinton White House) are one and the same. The latter would not exist without the former and without the former's electoral success. Innumerable decisions that he makes affect him both officially and personally.

Indeed, the "commonality" at issue here is more significant than in the usual "common interest" cases discussed above involving two separate clients. In this proceeding, of course, President Clinton and William J. Clinton, the person, are one and the same. This one individual has separate roles, and separate sets of counsel to advise him in each role, and in this respect resembles a corporate officer who may in a grand jury investigation be advised by

---

26/ The common interest analysis of the Eighth Circuit in In re Grand Jury Subpoena, 112 F.3d 910 (8th Cir. 1997), on which the district court relied, is not applicable here given the unique constitutional status of the President.

27/ While the district court stated that "the OIC is not investigating the White House, . . . [and] [t]he White House is not involved in any adversarial proceeding," J.A. 202, the OIC has in fact issued many subpoenas to the White House, both for documents and testimony, and has examined before the grand jury many Administration officials, sometimes several times.

corporate counsel with respect to business matters and by private counsel with respect to personal matters. In such circumstances, a common interest privilege is recognized to allow corporate and personal counsel to consult candidly and comprehensively, thereby assuring that factually well founded legal advice is given.[28/] But the case is even stronger here because, with respect to both personal and official interests, the President is the ultimate decisionmaker. (In this respect he is more akin to one client with two sets of counsel.)[29/] No matter how disparate these interests may be, he ultimately must fuse them into one decision for which he is responsible.

The district court's comment that "[a] federal government agency cannot share a 'common interest' with a private individual against the United States, here represented by the OIC," J.A. 175, is therefore both mistaken and a considerable oversimplification. First, of course, a government entity and a private one may share a common interest for purposes of preserving the attorney-client privilege for conferences between their respective counsel. See, e.g., AT&T, 642 F.2d 1285. Second, however, the comment misstates the issue. The OIC

28/ See, e.g., Matter of Grand Jury Subpoena Duces Tecum Dated November 16, 1974, 406 F. Supp. 381 (communications between counsel for corporation and corporate officer's personal counsel covered by common interest rule).

29/ Professor Geoffrey Hazard has observed in a letter to White House Counsel John M. Quinn, that:

> "One way to analyze the situation is simply to say that the 'President' has two sets of lawyers, engaged in conferring with each other. On that basis there is no question that the privilege is effective. Many legal consultations for a client involve the presence of more than one lawyer.
>
> Another way to analyze the situation is to consider that the 'President' has two legal capacities, that is, the capacity ex officio – in his office as President – and the capacity as an individual. The concept that a single individual can have two distinct legal capacities or identities has existed in law for centuries. . . ."

141 Cong. Rec. 18,948 (Daily ed.) (Dec. 20, 1995).

represents only the prosecutorial interests of the "United States" in this case, pursuant to 28 U.S.C. § 594(a). The Ethics in Government Act specifically authorizes the Department of Justice to represent the broader interests of the United States with respect to "issues of law" by filing a brief amicus curiae in any proceeding in which the OIC is involved. 28 U.S.C. § 597(b). Finally, the interests of the "United States" may be sufficiently divergent within the Executive Branch as to make justiciable a dispute between a President and a special prosecutor. See United States v. Nixon, 418 U.S. 683, 697 (1974). In this case, the Department of Justice, the Clinton White House, and the OIC each in a significant sense constitutes a facet of the "United States," and they have surely found themselves on opposing sides in these matters, in which they have advocated significantly different views on various legal questions.

The district court also supported its holding that there was no common interest "in the legal sense of the phrase," J.A. 175, between the President personally and officially with the observation that "[i]n the situation at hand, the White House cannot be implicated in any criminal or civil action and thus does not share President Clinton's legal interests," J.A. 176. But that is demonstrably false. The White House is, from time to time, sued civilly.[30/] Moreover, the impeachment and removal of a President obviously has a catastrophic effect on that President's "White House," subjecting the individuals working there to termination and the Administration's policy initiatives to extinction. And, in this very case the President is facing investigation by a prosecutor challenging him simultaneously in his personal and official capacities. Under the governing statute, the independent counsel is mandated to investigate conduct both in the traditional role of a prosecutor and, also, as an agent of the House of Representatives to report

---

30/ See, e.g., complaint in Alexander v. The Executive Office of the President, et al., Civ. No. 96-2123 (D.D.C.), alleging that the Executive Office of the President acquired FBI "any substantial and credible information . . . that may constitute grounds for an impeachment." 28 U.S.C. § 595(c). The OIC's investigation, therefore, necessarily "implicates" both the President personally and the Clinton Presidency as well, contrary to the district court's assertion.

The court below also appeared to suggest that the common interest cases require a similarity of legal jeopardy, but that also is not the case. When this Court recognized in AT&T that the Justice Department and MCI shared a common interest in a civil antitrust case for purposes of pooling attorney work product, it did not do so because the two entities faced similar perils. It rather recognized that the work product umbrella could cover both the government agency and the private telecommunications corporation because in conducting the civil litigation, they had a common objective in successfully prosecuting their respective actions against AT&T. As the Court observed there, "[t]he Government has the same entitlement as any other party to assistance from those sharing common interests, whatever their motives." AT&T, 642 F.2d at 1300. Since there can be no question that both the OIC, by virtue of its statutory duties, and the House of Representatives, by virtue of its constitutional duties and its public statements,[31/] are adverse to this President in many respects requiring common legal and strategic responses, there should be no doubt as to its applicability here.

The district court also gave an erroneous significance to the fact that there may at times be tension between the interests of the President personally and those of his Administration, ruling that the doctrine did not apply "precisely because the President as an individual has interests that conflict with the interests of the Office of the President." J.A. 176. But as indicated above, for the common interest protection to apply, there need not be a perfect

---

file summaries in violation of the Privacy Act.

31/ See, e.g., "House Funds Path to Impeachment," Washington Times (March 26, 1998).

identity of interest but only a commonality of some interests. The ruling also ignores the very rationale for the doctrine. It is because President Clinton personally starts out with significant common interests with his own Administration that there is a need, and a justification, for the two sets of counsel to confer. The frank discussions and ironing out of differences in a way that will best maximize, within the bounds of the law, both the personal and official objectives of the President is exactly what the common interest is designed to protect. Indeed, it is plain from this Court's decision in the AT&T case that the Department of Justice and MCI had many different goals and strategies, but protection of the confidential discussions of their attorneys about legal issues in the law suits enabled both entities to conduct their cases with as much harmony and synergy as possible toward the achievement of the goals they shared. The case is even stronger here, precisely because the President must himself confront and resolve any competing interests of the kind on which the district court focused.

Finally, the court totally dismissed the compelling practical need of personal counsel to confer confidentially with White House counsel on myriad topics to assure that sound and factually based legal advice is given to the President personally and in his role as Chief Executive. The very matters that personal counsel must attend to with respect to the Jones civil suit and the Whitewater grand jury investigation are also possible grist for the OIC and impeachment inquiries, which obviously affect William J. Clinton in both his official and personal capacities. Neither set of counsel can provide fully informed legal advice unless they are able to confer candidly on a host of legal, factual and strategic matters, such as considering the appropriateness of asserting various defenses, objections, and privileges, analyzing tactical decisions that may have significant long-term ramifications, dealing with leaks from the OIC, assigning responsibility for document searches and production to assure a comprehensive subpoena response is made, understanding how requests for official information – such as White House medical records – should be addressed, dealing responsibly and accurately with public and press inquiries, monitoring factual developments, assuring that different counsel do not take inconsistent or uninformed legal positions, assuring that the client fulfills his constitutional duties while aware of their impact on his personal interests, and the list goes on. Absent the ability to confer, private counsel cannot assure they are fully apprised of the official implications of decisions to be made and advice to be given, and their own advice is necessarily of limited use. The same is true of official counsel, who must be able to advise the President qua President cognizant of any personal detriment to which their advice might expose him.

It is undeniable that both the President personally and his White House have faced numerous and complicated legal demands as a result of the Jones suit and the OIC's investigation. It is only by "encourag[ing] full and frank communication between attorneys" for the President personally and for the White House that the "broader public interests in the observance of law and administration of justice" can effectively be promoted. Upjohn, 449 U.S. at 389.[32]

32/ As the Brief for the White House demonstrates, the attorney-client privilege applies to confidential communications between government attorneys and their government clients in the same absolute manner in which it applies to communications between private counsel and their clients. If this Court were to conclude, however, that as a general matter the privilege that applies to government attorneys may be qualified rather than absolute, this should not dilute the absolute nature of the privileged common interest communications with personal counsel, whose privilege indisputably is and must remain absolute to effectuate its underlying purpose.

The absolute personal privilege must trump a hypothetical qualified privilege in the common interest context in order to be consistent with the common interest rule's unanimity requirement for waiver. An integral component of the common interest rule is that the privilege cannot be waived without the consent of all parties to the confidential communication. See p. 27 and n.19, supra. The unanimity requirement is necessary to guarantee the confidentiality that makes the attorney-client privilege work. See, e.g., Interfaith Housing Delaware, Inc. v. The Town of Georgetown, 841 F. Supp. 1393, 1400-

IV. COMMUNICATIONS WITH PERSONAL COUNSEL ARE PROTECTED BY THE WORK-PRODUCT DOCTRINE

The district court held that the work product protection was waived when information was shared with Mr. Lindsey, based on its earlier finding that President Clinton and the White House share no common interest. J.A. 179. This holding is in error both because President Clinton and the White House do share "common interests," as set out previously in Part III(c)(2), and because, in any event, the attorney-client common interest inquiry and the attorney work product waiver inquiry are not the same.

"The work product doctrine is an independent source of immunity from discovery, separate and distinct from the attorney-client privilege." In re Grand Jury, 106 F.R.D. 255, 257 (D.N.H. 1985). It covers "not only confidential communications between the attorney and client. It also attaches to other materials prepared by attorneys (and their agents) in anticipation of litigation." In re Sealed Case, 107 F.3d 46, 51 (D.C. Cir. 1997). See generally Hickman v. Taylor, 329 U.S. 495, 510-11 (1947). However, litigation need only be contemplated at the time the work is performed for the doctrine to apply, see Holland v. Island Creek Corp., 885 F. Supp. 4, 7 (D.D.C. 1995), and the term "litigation" is defined broadly to encompass any adversary proceedings, including legislative, administrative and other federal investigations, and grand jury proceedings, as well as civil litigation.[33]

---

01 (D. Del. 1994). To treat the government attorney-client privilege as qualified in the common interest context would undermine the guarantee of confidentiality just as would allowing one party's waiver to govern the privilege for all others.

33/ See, e.g., In re Grand Jury Proceedings (Doe), 867 F.2d 539 (9th Cir. 1989) (grand jury investigation); In re Sealed Case, 676 F.2d 793 (D.C. Cir. 1982) (SEC and IRS investigations); In re Grand Jury Proceedings (Duffy), 473 F.2d 840, 846 (8th Cir. 1973) ("policies supporting protection of an attorney's work product . . . are even more strongly applicable in criminal proceedings"); In re Grand Jury Subpoena Duces Tecum, 685 F. Supp. 49 (S.D.N.Y. 1988) (grand jury investigation); see also Restatement of the Law

The doctrine applies with even greater force in criminal litigation, where "its role in assuring the proper functioning of the criminal justice system is even more vital," since "[t]he interests of society and the accused in obtaining a fair and accurate resolution of the question of guilt or innocence demand that adequate safeguards assure the thorough preparation and presentation of each side of the case." United States v. Nobles, 422 U.S. 225, 238 (1975).[34/] The doctrine also applies with equal force to work product that is shared among attorneys having a common interest, including government and private attorneys.[35/]

This Court addressed work product waiver in the AT&T case. The question was whether MCI had waived its attorney work product rights to documents that had been prepared by MCI during the course of its prosecution of a civil antitrust suit against AT&T and then shared with the government in a different case brought by the government against AT&T. AT&T then sought those documents from the government. The Court reviewed the case law and noted that the more modern cases tended to hold that "despite voluntary disclosure of the documents to persons not on the same side of the litigation, the privilege remained intact." 642 F.2d at 1298. The Court explained that "the work product privilege does not exist to protect a confidential relationship, but rather to promote the adversary system by safeguarding the fruits of an attorney's trial preparations from the discovery attempts of the opponent." Id. at 1299. Thus, while "[t]he existence of common interests between transferor and transferee is relevant to

---

Governing Lawyers § 136 & cmt h (anticipation of litigation includes "a proceeding such as a grand jury . . . or an investigative legislative hearing").

34/ The Supreme Court in Nobles recognized that the work product doctrine applies to the "files of the prosecution" even though the government plainly does not risk sanction or imprisonment in a criminal case. 422 U.S. at 238 & n.12.

35/ See, e.g., AT&T, 642 F.2d at 1300; Castle v. Sangamo Weston, Inc., 744 F.2d 1464, 1466-67 (11th Cir. 1984) ; In re Sunrise Sec. Litig., 130 F.R.D. 560, 583 (E.D. Pa. 1989).

deciding whether the disclosure is consistent with the nature of the work product privilege," the ultimate inquiry is whether the disclosure is "inconsistent with maintaining secrecy against opponents." Ibid. (emphasis added).[36]

The district court erred in concluding on the common interest issue alone that President Clinton's personal counsel's work product privilege was waived. As AT&T makes clear, the absence of a common interest is not sufficient to conclude that there has been a waiver. Indeed, "[a]s articulated by most courts, [a work product] waiver will be found only if the party has voluntarily disclosed the work-product in such a manner that it is likely to be revealed to his adversary. Thus, disclosure simply to another person who has an interest in the information but who is not reasonably viewed as a conduit to a potential adversary will not be deemed a waiver of the protection of the rule." Bowne of New York City, Inc. v. AmBase Corp., 150 F.R.D. 465, 479 (S.D.N.Y. 1993).

If the district court had examined the circumstances surrounding the disclosure of work product to Mr. Lindsey, beyond its common interest analysis, it would have found that the disclosures had been made consistently with "maintaining secrecy against [the adversary]." AT&T, 642 F.2d at 1299. The record is clear and undisputed that disclosures made to Mr. Lindsey were made in confidence and that Mr. Lindsey "maintained the confidentiality of these

36/ See also In re Sealed Case, 676 F.2d 793, 809 (D.C. Cir. 1982) ("because it looks to the vitality of the adversary system rather than simply seeking to preserve confidentiality, the work product privilege is not automatically waived by any disclosure to a third party"); United States v. Gulf Oil Corp., 760 F.2d 292, 295 (Temp. Emergency Ct. of Ap. 1985) ("A transfer made to a party with 'strong common interests in sharing the fruit of trial preparation efforts,' or such a transfer made concurrently with a guarantee of confidentiality, does not necessarily constitute a waiver of the work product privilege") (quoting AT&T); Latin Investment Corp. v. Drabkin, 160 B.R. 262, 264 (D.C. Bank. Ct. 1993).

communications." J.A. 44-45, ¶8. The district court's failure to examine and be guided by this record was legal error.

CONCLUSION

The district court's order should be reversed.

Respectfully submitted,

David E. Kendall

David E. Kendall
Nicole K. Seligman
Riyaz A. Kanji
Max Stier
WILLIAMS & CONNOLLY
725 12th Street, N.W.
Washington, D.C. 20005
(202) 434-5000

Robert S. Bennett (dek)

Robert S. Bennett
Carl S. Rauh
Mitchell S. Ettinger
Amy Sabrin
Katharine Sexton
SKADDEN, ARPS, SLATE
MEAGHER & FLOM, LLP
1440 New York Avenue, N.W.
Washington, D.C. 20005
(202) 371-7000

Counsel for Appellant William J. Clinton

CERTIFICATE OF SERVICE

I HEREBY CERTIFY that I have this 15th day of June, 1998, caused true and correct copies of the foregoing **BRIEF FOR APPELLANT WILLIAM J. CLINTON** to be served by hand upon the following:

Kenneth W. Starr, Esquire
Independent Counsel
Office of the Independent Counsel
1001 Pennsylvania Avenue, N.W.
Suite 490, North
Washington, D.C. 20004
(202) 514-8688

W. Neil Eggleston, Esquire
Howrey & Simon
1299 Pennsylvania Avenue, N.W.
Washington, D.C. 20004

Douglas N. Letter, Esquire
U.S. Department of Justice
601 D Street, N.W.
Room 9106
Washington, D.C. 20530

DAVID E. KENDALL

CERTIFICATION OF WORD COUNT PURSUANT TO CIRCUIT RULE 28(d)(1)

According to the law firm's word processing system, the preceding brief does not contain more than 12,500 words, including footnotes and citations.

DAVID E. KENDALL

Volume VI:

Document Supplement, Part D

Documents Cited in Referral:
Tabs 47-83,
Bates Numbers 812-968

50-893 98 - 20

REFERRAL

TO THE

UNITED STATES HOUSE OF REPRESENTATIVES

PURSUANT TO

TITLE 28, UNITED STATES CODE, § 595(C)

DOCUMENT SUPPLEMENT D

SUBMITTED BY

THE OFFICE OF THE INDEPENDENT COUNSEL

SEPTEMBER 9, 1998

Index

INDEX: Documents cited in the 595(c) Referral

09-Sep-98

Bates # or Tab#	Production Name	Description
*Tab 001	N/A	Main Stairway to Family Quarters
*Tab 002	N/A	Movie Theater in East Colonnade
*Tab 003	N/A	11/14/95 LA Times news article
*Tab 004	N/A	11/14/95 Washington Post news article
*Tab 005	N/A	11/16/95: Facts on File, World News Digest -- pg. 852
*Tab 006	N/A	11/16/95 Washington Post news article
*Tab 007	N/A	11/17/95 USA Today news article
*Tab 008	N/A	11/20/95 Washington Post news article
*Tab 009	N/A	11/23/95: Facts on File, World News Digest -- pg. 868
*Tab 010	N/A	2/19/96 Weekly Compilation of Presidential Documents
*Tab 011	N/A	2/28/96 Newsday news article
*Tab 012	N/A	7/4/97 Drudge Report Final
*Tab 013	N/A	8/11/97 Washington Post news article
*Tab 014	N/A	8/11/97 Newsweek article
*Tab 015	N/A	9/13/97 NY Times news article
*Tab 016	N/A	9/22/97 Forbes news article
*Tab 017	N/A	10/4/97 to 10/23/97 Digest of Other White House Announcements
*Tab 018	N/A	11/9/97 LA Times news article
*Tab 019	N/A	11/14/97 Baltimore Sun news article
*Tab 020	N/A	11/15/97 Washington Post news article
*Tab 021	N/A	1/20/98 subpoena to William Jefferson Clinton, V002
*Tab 022	N/A	1/21/98 Washington Post news article
*Tab 023	N/A	1/21/98 "The News Hour with Jim Lehrer"

Bates # or Tab#	Production Name	Description
*Tab 024	N/A	1/21/98 "All Things Considered"
*Tab 025	N/A	1/21/98 White House Briefing
*Tab 025A	N/A	1/21/98 Excerpts of Telephone Interview of Clinton by Roll Call
*Tab 026	N/A	1/22/98 Remarks by President Clinton at the White House
*Tab 027	N/A	1/22/98 America Online article
*Tab 028	N/A	1/22/98 FBI Receipt of Property
*Tab 029	N/A	1/22/98 ABC News Special Report with Peter Jennings
*Tab 030	N/A	1/22/98 Roll Call interview with William Jefferson Clinton
*Tab 030A	N/A	1/22/98 Seatle Times news article
*Tab 031	N/A	1/23/98 FBI Receipt of Property, w/attached letter
*Tab 032	N/A	1/24/98 CBS News Show: Saturday Morning
*Tab 033	N/A	1/25/98 Face the Nation
*Tab 034	N/A	1/26/98 Nightline
*Tab 035	N/A	1/26/98 ABC News Special Report with Peter Jennings
*Tab 036	N/A	1/26/98 White House Education News Conference
*Tab 036A	N/A	1/27/98 AP news article
*Tab 036B	N/A	1/27/98 NBC: The Today Show
*Tab 037	N/A	2/5/98 Remarks by President Clinton
*Tab 038	N/A	2/6/98 Joint News Conference with President Clinton
*Tab 039	N/A	2/14/98 Washington Post news article
*Tab 040	N/A	2/17/98 Chicago Tribune news article
*Tab 041	N/A	3/5/98 closed hearing transcript excerpt
*Tab 042	N/A	3/17/98 Memoradum w/attachments, In re: Grand Jury Proceedings
*Tab 043	N/A	3/25/98 Washington Post news article
*Tab 044	N/A	4/17/98 letter to DAG Eric Holder from the OIC
*Tab 045	N/A	6/98 California Lawyer article

Bates # or Tab#	Production Name	Description
*Tab 046	N/A	6/15/98 Brief of Appellant William J. Clinton
*Tab 047	N/A	6/29/98 US News & World Report news article
*Tab 048	N/A	7/15/98 letter to IC Smaltz from Richard Rogers
*Tab 049	N/A	7/17/98 subpoena to the White House, D1415
*Tab 050	N/A	7/22/98 CBS News transcript, HARDBALL
*Tab 051	N/A	7/26/98 NBC News Meet the Press
*Tab 052	N/A	7/28/98 Motion of William J. Clinton for Continuance
*Tab 053	N/A	7/28/98 Transcript of Status Hearing , In re: Motion to Continue
*Tab 054	N/A	7/29/98 FBI Receipt of Property
*Tab 055	N/A	7/31/98 letter to David Kendall from Bob Bittman
*Tab 056	N/A	7/31/98 letter to Bob Bittman from David Kendall
*Tab 057	N/A	7/31/98 letter to David Kendall from Bob Bittman
*Tab 058	N/A	8/3/98 letter to Bob Bittman from David Kendall
*Tab 059	N/A	8/3/98 letter to David Kendall from Bob Bittman
*Tab 060	N/A	8/3/98 FBI Laboratory Report
*Tab 061	N/A	8/3/98 FBI 302
*Tab 062	N/A	8/3/98 letter to Judge Starr from DAG Eric Holder
*Tab 063	N/A	8/6/98 letter to AG Reno from IC Smaltz
*Tab 064	N/A	8/6/98 FBI Laboratory Report
*Tab 065	N/A	8/7/98 Washington Times news article
*Tab 066	N/A	8/10/98 Newsweek article
*Tab 067	N/A	8/11/98 letter to AG Holder from Judge Starr
*Tab 068	N/A	8/11/98 Memorandum Order, In re: Grand Jury Proceedings
*Tab 069	N/A	8/13/98 NY Times news article
*Tab 070	N/A	8/13/98 USA Today news article
*Tab 071	N/A	8/13/98 Washington Post news article
*Tab 072	N/A	8/13/98 Washington Times news article

Bates # or Tab#	Production Name	Description
*Tab 073	N/A	8/17/98 Newsweek article
*Tab 074	N/A	8/17/98 FBI Laboratory Report
*Tab 075	N/A	8/17/98 AP news article
*Tab 076	N/A	8/18/98 Washington Post
*Tab 077	N/A	8/24/98 facsimile to Jackie Bennett from Gary Grindler
*Tab 078	N/A	8/27/98 memo
*Tab 079	N/A	8/31/98 letter to Bob Bittman from David Kendall
*Tab 080	N/A	9/7/98 memo
*Tab 081	N/A	Jones v. Clinton, 1998 WL 551961, 9/1/98 order
*Tab 082	N/A	Lyrics to "Surfacing"
*Tab 083	N/A	18 U.S.C. section 2246
0812-DC-00000002	Lewinsky, Monica	Passport photo page
0824-DC-00000001 to 2	Currie, Betty	1/23/98 letter to Judge Starr from Karl Metzner
0824-DC-00000013	Currie, Betty	"Love Notes" supplement
0824-DC-00000014	Currie, Betty	2/14/97 Washington Post "Love Notes"
0827-DC-00000002 to 18	United States Secret Service	Epass Access Control Reports
0828-DC-00000003	US Mission to the UN	3/14/97 to 12/22/97 Toll records
0828-DC-00000004	US Mission to the UN	10/21/97 to 11/19/97 Toll records
0828-DC-00000012	US Mission to the UN	Monica Lewinsky's resume
0828-DC-00000013	US Mission to the UN	11/3/97 letter from Monica Lewinsky to Ambassador Richardson
0828-DC-00000023	US Mission to the UN	10/31/97 schedule for Ambassador Richardson
0830-DC-00000007	Revlon Group, Inc.	1/13/98 letter from Monica Lewinsky to Jenna Sheldon
0830-DC-00000017	Revlon Group, Inc.	12/11/97 letter from Monica Lewinsky to Richard Halperin
0831-DC-00000008 to 11	Pagemart	Pager records for Moncia Lewinsky
0832-DC-00000004 to 5	McAndrews & Forbes Holding	Toll records
0833-DC-00000980	Department of Defense	11/6/97 letter from Monica Lewinsky to Vernon Jordan
0833-DC-00001070	Department of Defense	6/24/97 typed note to Betty Currie

Bates # or Tab#	Production Name	Description
0833-DC-00001857	Department of Defense	3/5/97 E-Mail
0833-DC-00001876	Department of Defense	3/3/97 e-mail from Linda Tripp to Monica Lewinsky
0833-DC-00001906	Department of Defense	2/24/97 E-Mail
0833-DC-00001934	Department of Defense	2/19/97 E-Mail
0833-DC-00001974	Department of Defense	2/4/97 E-Mail
0833-DC-00002716	Department of Defense	Notification of Personnel Action
0833-DC-00002880	Department of Defense	Job Description
0833-DC-00003207	Department of Defense	Travel voucher
0833-DC-00009446	Department of Defense	2/19/97 E-Mail
0833-DC-00017867	Department of Defense	10/6/97 to 10/9/97 Toll records
0833-DC-00017869	Department of Defense	10/15/97 to 10/20/97 Toll records
0833-DC-00017875	Department of Defense	Toll records
0833-DC-00017886	Department of Defense	Toll records
0833-DC-00017890	Department of Defense	Toll records
0833-DC-00017903 to 04	Department of Defense	Toll records
0833-DC-00017908	Department of Defense	Toll records
0837-DC-00000001 to 27	Speed Service Couriers, Inc.	Courier receipts re: Monica Lewinsky
0843-DC-00000004	United States Secret Service	12/6/97 Epass Access Control Record
0845-DC-00000002	Tripp, Linda	Handwritten notes
0845-DC-00000004 to 17	Tripp, Linda	Handwritten notes
0845-DC-00000018 to 21	Tripp, Linda	Handwritten Notes
0845-DC-00000022 to 25	Tripp, Linda	Handwritten Notes
0845-DC-00000188	Tripp, Linda	Handwritten note
0845-DC-00000190	Tripp, Linda	Letter from Linda Tripp to Newsweek
0845-DC-00000191 to 193	Tripp, Linda	Handwritten notes
0849-DC-00000090 to 97	Rader, Campbell, Fisher & Pyke	President Clinton's Responses to Plaintiff's Third Set of Interrogatories

Bates # or Tab#	Production Name	Description
0849-DC-00000098 to 102	Rader, Campbell, Fisher & Pyke	Attachment to President Clinton's Responses to Plaintiff's Third Set of Interrogatories
0849-DC-00000121 to 137	Rader, Campbell, Fisher & Pyke	Plaintiff's Witness List
0849-DC-00000352	Rader, Campbell, Fisher & Pyke	Videotaped Deposition of William Jefferson Clinton
0849-DC-00000586	Rader, Campbell, Fisher & Pyke	Definition of "Sexual Relation"
0849-DC-00000634 to 636	Rader, Campbell, Fisher & Pyke	Affidavit of Jane Doe #6 (Monica Lewinsky)
0852-DC-00000035	American Express	Credit card statement
0852-DC-00000037	American Express	Credit card statement
0852-DC-00000044 to 45	American Express	12/17/97 billing statement
0854-DC-00001485	First Union Bank	5/6/96 Check No. 594
0856-DC-00000002	American Express	12/11/97 letter from Monica Lewinsky to Ursula Fairbairn
0880-DC-00000002 to 8	Lindsey, Bruce	Handwritten notes
0902-DC-00000003	Carter, Francis	Address
0902-DC-00000030	Carter, Francis	1/12/98 to 1/20/98 billing statement
0902-DC-00000033	Cater, Francis	FedEx USA Airbill
0902-DC-00000037 to 38	Carter, Francis	1/7/98 billing statement
0902-DC-00000051	Catrer, Francis	1/6/97 phone memo
0902-DC-00000135 to 138	Carter, Francis	Subpoena issued to Monica Lewinsky in the Paula Jones case
0902-DC-00000231	Carter, Francis	12/22/97 to 12/28/97 appointment book
0902-DC-00000232	Carter, Francis	1/5/98 appointment book
0902-DC-00000251	Carter, Francis	1/6/98 phone message
0916-DC-00000003	Park Hyatt	Receipt
0920-DC-00000013 to 18	Rader, Campbell, Fisher & Pyke	Subpoena issued to Monica Lewinsky in the Paula Jones case
0920-DC-00000517 to 525	Rader, Campbell, Fisher & Pyke	12/18/97 Order in Jones v. Clinton, LR-C-94-290
0921-DC-00000061 to 62	McCormack, Hon. James	11/6/97 Clerk's minutes for in-camera hearing
0921-DC-00000091 to 151	Rader, Campbell, Fisher & Pyke	Plaintiff's Motion to Compel Responses to Plaintiff's Second Set of Interrogatories to Defendant Clinton
0921-DC-00000459 to 466	McCormack, Hon. James	12/11/97 Order in Jones v. Clinton, LR-C-94-290

Bates # or Tab#	Production Name	Description
0921-DC-00000736 to 744	McCormack, Hon. James	1/8/98 Order in Jones v. Clinton, LR-C-94-290
0921-DC-00000751 to 752	McCormack, Hon. James	1/9/98 Clerk's minutes for in-camera hearing
0921-DC-00000770 to 772	Rader, Campbell, Fisher & Pyke	1/14/98 Clerk's Minutes
0921-DC-00000775 to 778	Rader, Campbell, Fisher & Pyke	Motion of Jane Doe #6 for Protective Order and Motion to Quash
0929-DC-00000056	NationsBank	Bank Statement
0952-DC-00000060	United States Secret Service	10/11/97 Presidential Protectee Movement Log
0964-DC-00000862	White House	12/6/97 pager record
0968-DC-00000073	White House	Schedule
0968-DC-00000187	White House	11/13/97 schedule
0968-DC-00000236	White House	3/29/98 schedule
0968-DC-00000263	White House	Schedule
0968-DC-00000303	White House	11/13/97 Diarist notes
0968-DC-00000841	White House	4/5/96 Press Schedule
0968-DC-00002947	White House	8/17/97 schedule
0968-DC-00003300	White House	11/22/97 to 11/25/97 Presidential press schedule
0968-DC-00003301	White House	Presidential Press Schedule
0968-DC-00003458	White House	2/96 calendar for Hillary Rodham Clinton
0968-DC-00003459	White House	3/96 calendar for Hillary Rodham Clinton
0968-DC-00003475	White House	7/97 calendar for Hillary Rodham Clinton
0968-DC-00003477	White House	10/97 calendar for Hillary Rodham Clinton
0968-DC-00003479	White House	12/97 calendar for Hillary Rodham Clinton
0968-DC-00003506	White House	2/28/97 Presidential Call Log
0968-DC-00003510	White House	3/29/97 Presidential Call Log
0968-DC-00003522	White House	5/1/97 Presidential Call Log
0968-DC-00003533	White House	5/24/97 Presidential Call Log
0968-DC-00003546	White House	7/4/97 Presidential Call Log
0968-DC-00003550	White House	7/14/97 Presidential Call Log

Bates # or Tab#	Production Name	Description
0968-DC-00003556	White House	7/24/97 Presidential Call Log
0968-DC-00003558	White House	8/16/97 Presidential Call Log
0968-DC-00003569	White House	10/11/97 Presidential Call
0968-DC-00003799	White House	11/13/97 schedule
0968-DC-00003843	White House	3/29/97 schedule
1000-DC-00000767 to 772	Bell Atlantic	5/4/96 Marcia Lewis Phone Bill
1012-DC-00000001	Bacon, Kenneth	4/28/97 letter from Kenneth Bacon to Lorrie McHugh
1013-DC-00000095 to 96	Bell Atlantic	2/4/98 statement of Toll calls for Debra Finerman
1014-DC-00000022	Cellular One	3/25/97 to 4/24/97 Calls
1033-DC-00000033 to 35	Bell Atlantic Mobile	Toll records
1033-DC-00000115 to 116	Bell Atlantic Mobile	Toll records
1034-DC-00000060 to 63	Jordan, Vernon	10/20/97 to 11/01/97 schedule for Vernon Jordan
1034-DC-00000099	Jordan, Vernon	12/8/97 to 12/10/97 schedule for Vernon Jordan
1034-DC-00000103	Jordan, Vernon	12/22/97 to 12/24/97 schedule for Vernon Jordan
1034-DC-00000109	Jordan, Vernon	1/12/98 to 1/14/98 schedule for Vernon Jordan
1034-DC-00000111	Jordan, Vernon	1/19/98 to 1/21/98 schedule for Vernon Jordan
1037-DC-00000001 to 2	Davis, Catherine Allday	5/18/97 Card
1037-DC-00000011	Davis, Catherine Allday	12/9/97 e-mail from Lewinsky to Davis
1037-DC-00000017	Davis, Catherine Allday	11/7/97 e-mail from Lewinsky to Davis
1037-DC-00000022	Davis, Catherine Allday	11/5/97 e-mail from Lewinsky to Davis
1037-DC-00000033	Davis, Catherine Allday	10/22/97 e-mail from Lewinsky to Davis
1037-DC-00000038 to 40	Davis, Catherine Allday	E-mails between Monica Lewinsky and Catherine Allday Davis
1037-DC-00000042	Davis, Catherine Allday	8/14/97 e-mail from Lewinsky to Davis
1037-DC-00000063	Davis, Catherine Allday	11/6/97 e-mail from Lewinsky to Davis
1037-DC-00000086 to 87	Davis, Catherine Allday	9/4/97 e-mail from Monica Lewinsky to Catherine Allday Davis
1037-DC-00000103	Davis, Catherine Allday	7/3/98 e-mail from Catherine Allday Davis to Monica Lewinsky

Bates # or Tab#	Production Name	Description
1037-DC-00000107	Davis, Catherine Allday	6/17/97 e-mail from Monica Lewinsky to Catherine Allday Davis
1037-DC-00000115	Davis, Catherine Allday	E-mail between Monica Lewinsky and Catherine Allday Davis
1037-DC-00000167 to 169	Davis, Catherine Allday	E-mails between Monica Lewinsky and Catherine Allday Davis
1037-DC-00000171	Davis, Catherine Allday	8/13/97 e-mail from Monica Lewinsky to Catherine Allday Davis
1037-DC-00000255 to 256	Davis, Catherine Allday	9/4/97 e-mail from Monica Lewinsky to Catherine Allday Davis
1037-DC-00000258 to 259	Davis, Catherine Allday	9/2/97 e-mail from Monica Lewinsky to Catherine Allday Davis
1037-DC-00000265 to 266	Davis, Catherine Allday	6/17/97 e-mail from Monica Lewinsky to Catherine Allday Davis
1037-DC-00000280	Davis, Catherine Allday	7/2/97 e-mail from Catherine Allday Davis to Monica Lewinsky
1037-DC-00000296	Davis, Catherine Allday	E-mail from Catherine Allday Davis to Monica Lewinsky
1037-DC-00000318	Davis, Catherine Allday	11/19/97 e-mail from Lewinsky to Davis
1037-DC-00000337 to 38	Davis, Catherine Allday	E-Mail from Lewinsky to Davis
1037-DC-00000341	Davis, Catherine Allday	E-mail from Monica Lewinsky to Catherine Allday Davis
1037-DC-00000553	Davis, Catherine Allday	11/5/97 e-mail from Monica Lewinsky to Catherine Allday Davis
1037-DC-00000583	Davis, Catherine Allday	9/2/97 e-mail from Monica Lewinsky to Catherine Allday Davis
1051-DC-00000003 to 4	Bell Atlantic	Copy of Computer Disk
1064-DC-00000008	Renaissance Vinoy Resort	1/13/98 Toll records
1065-DC-00000006	St. Regis Hotel	Hotel receipt
1065-DC-00000008	St. Regis Hotel	Receipt
1078-DC-00000002	Washington Post	Receipt
1089-DC-00000970	White House	10/16/96 Typed note
1178-DC-00000005	White House	10/11/97 Presidential Call Log
1178-DC-00000011	White House	Presidetial Call Logs
1178-DC-00000013	White House	12/19/97 Presidential Call Log
1178-DC-00000014	White House	12/19/97 Presidential Call Log

Bates # or Tab#	Production Name	Description
1178-DC-00000015	White House	12/30/97 Presidential Call Log
1178-DC-00000016	White House	1/6/98 Presidential Call Log
1178-DC-00000018	White House	1/16/98 Presidential Call Log
1178-DC-00000019	White House	1/17/98 Presidential Call Log
1178-DC-00000020	White House	1/17/98 Presidential Call Log
1178-DC-00000021	White House	1/18/98 Presidential Call Log
1178-DC-00000023	White House	1/19/98 Presidential Call Log
1178-DC-00000026	White House	WAVES records: Vernon Jordan
1205-DC-00000016	GTE Company of California	1/25/98 toll record from California
1216-DC-00000022 to 23	Bell Atlantic	Toll records
1222-DC-00000024	United States Secret Service	1/21/96 itinerary for the White House
1222-DC-00000032	United States Secret Service	3/5/96 White House itinerary
1222-DC-00000041	United States Secret Service	3/31/96 intinerary
1222-DC-00000045	United States Secret Service	Schedule
1222-DC-00000083 to 85	United States Secret Service	11/15/95 to 11/18/95 Presidential Movement Logs
1222-DC-00000102	United States Secret Service	2/19/96 Presidential Movement Log
1222-DC-00000112 to 113	United States Secret Service	3/29/96 and 3/31/96 Presidential Movement Logs
1222-DC-00000156 to 157	United States Secret Service	11/15/95 Presidential Protectee Movement Logs
1222-DC-00000179	United States Secret Service	Presidential Movement Logs
1222-DC-00000183	United States Secret Service	1/7/96 Presidential Protectee Movement Log
1222-DC-00000189	United States Secret Service	1/21/96 Presidential Movement Log
1222-DC-00000196	United States Secret Service	2/4/96 Presidential Movement Log
1222-DC-00000197	United States Secret Service	2/19/96 Presidential Movement Log
1222-DC-00000216 to 217	United States Secret Service	3/31/96 Presidential Movement Logs
1222-DC-00000219	United States Secret Service	4/7/96 Presidential Movements
1222-DC-00000234	United States Secret Service	2/28/97 Presidential Movements
1222-DC-00000242	United States Secret Service	5/24/97 Presidential Protectee Movement Log

Bates # or Tab#	Production Name	Description
1222-DC-00000251	United States Secret Service	7/14/97 schedule
1222-DC-00000254	United States Secret Service	7/24/97 schedule
1222-DC-00000325	United States Secret Service	12/31/95, 1/7/96 Secret Service agent duty schedule
1222-DC-00000328	United States Secret Service	2/21/96 Secret Service agent duty schedule
1234-DC-00000049	White House	11/13/97 schedule
1234-DC-00000050	White House	11/13/97 Presidential Movement Log
1234-DC-00000357	United States Secret Service	8/22/97 to 12/31/97 Epass Access Control Report
1248-DC-00000008	White House	4/7/96 Telephone Memorandum
1248-DC-00000288	White House	1/17/98 Diarist schedule notes
1248-DC-00000291	White House	Daynotes
1248-DC-00000305	White House	1/17/98 Presidential Call Log
1248-DC-00000307	White House	1/17/98 Presidential Call
1248-DC-00000311	White House	1/18/98 Presidential Call
1248-DC-00000312	White House	1/18/98 Presidential Call Log
1248-DC-00000313 to 315	White House	1/18/98 Presidential Call Log
1248-DC-00000319	White House	1/19/98 Presidential Call Log
1248-DC-00000327 to 328	White House	1/21/98 Presidential Call Log
1248-DC-00000381	White House	12/19/97 Presidential Call Log
1248-DC-00000444	White House	1/13/98 Presidential Call Log
1318-DC-00000001 to 2	Young, Dale	9/4/97 note from Monica Lewinsky to Dale Young
1342-DC-00000410	White House	Photograph
1361-DC-00000002 to 42	White House	Index of books located in the Oval Office study
1362-DC-00000549	United States Secret Service	11/15/95 Presidential Protectee Movement Log
1362-DC-00001171	United States Secret Service	Secret Service agent duty schedule
1407-DC-00000005	White House	12/6/97 TO 12/24/97 WAVES for Robert Bennett
1408-DC-00000005	Rader, Campbell, Fisher & Pyke	12/5/97 Facsimile sheet
1414-DC-00000001	Rader, Campbell, Fisher & Pyke	7/21/98 letter to Julie Corcoran from Donovan Campbell, Jr.

Bates # or Tab#	Production Name	Description
1414-DC-00001006 to 1014	Rader, Campbell, Fisher & Pyke	1/9/98 Order in Jones v. Clinton, LR-C-94-290
1414-DC-00001188 to 1192	Rader, Campbell, Fisher & Pyke	12/18/97 Order in Jones v. Clinton, LR-C-94-290
1414-DC-00001327 to 32	Rader, Campbell, Fisher & Pyke	hearing excerpt
1414-DC-00001334 to 46	Rader, Campbell, Fisher & Pyke	hearing excerpt
1414-DC-00001534 to 1546	Rader, Campbell, Fisher & Pyke	12/15/97 Pleading in Jones v. Clinton, LR-C-94-290
1415-DC-00000001	White House	8/3/98 letter from David Kendall to the OIC
1472-DC-00000006	White House	11/15/95 Call Log
1472-DC-00000007	White House	11/15/95 Telephone memorandum
1472-DC-00000008	White House	11/15/95 Telephone memorandum
1472-DC-00000015	White House	11/17/95 Telephone memorandum
1472-DC-00000017	White House	2/19/96 Telephone memorandum
1472-DC-00000018 to 20	White House	2/19/96 Telephone memorandum
1506-DC-00000007 to 8	White House	8/10/95 Presidential schedule
1506-DC-00000027	White House	12/31/95 Presidential schedule
1506-DC-00000029	White House	12/31/95 Telephone memorandum
1506-DC-00000031	White House	1/7/96 Telephone memorandum
1506-DC-00000050	White House	1/21/96 Telephone memorandum
1506-DC-00000057 to 58	White House	1/30/96 Presidential schedule
1506-DC-00000068	White House	2/4/96 Telephone memorandum
1506-DC-00000070	White House	2/4/96 Telephone memorandum
1506-DC-00000102	White House	2/19/96 Telephone memorandum
1506-DC-00000139	White House	3/31/96 Telephone memorandum
1506-DC-00000144	White House	4/7 Telephone Memorandum
1506-DC-00000188 to 189	White House	Presidential schedule
1506-DC-00000192	White House	5/2/96 Presidential Call Log
1506-DC-00000222	White House	Presidential schedule
1506-DC-00000264	White House	7/5/96 Presidential schedule

Bates # or Tab#	Production Name	Description
1506-DC-00000268	White House	7/6/96 Presidential schedule
1506-DC-00000275	White House	7/19/96 Presidential Call Log
1506-DC-00000328	White House	Presidential schedule
1506-DC-00000334 to 335	White House	Schedule
1506-DC-00000353	White House	Presidential schedule
1506-DC-00000373 to 374	White House	2/8/97 Schedule
1506-DC-00000426 to 427	White House	10/10/97 Presidential schedule
1506-DC-00000523 to 525	White House	1/21/96 Diarist notes
1506-DC-00000558	White House	Presidential schedule
1506-DC-00000559	White House	Presidential schedule
1506-DC-00000638	White House	Diarists notes, Presidential call
2004-DC-00000083	Bell Atlantic	Toll records
2004-DC-00000085 to 88	Bell Atlantic	Toll records
2004-DC-00000090 to 91	Bell Atlantic	Toll records
827-DC-00000018	United States Secret Service	2/24/97 to 12/28/97 Epass Access Control Report
CZ-DC-00000010	Driscoll, Richard	Fair market value appraisal
CZ-DC-00000016	Driscoll, Richard	Fair market value appraisal
DB PHOTOS 0004	Lewinsky, Monica	Blue Dress (photo)
DB PHOTOS 0044	Lewinsky, Monica	Audio-tapes from Monica Lewinsky's answering machine (originals in Quantico)
DB PHOTOS 0048	Lewinsky, Monica	evidence picture
DB-DC-000000017	Lewinsky, Monica	Draft letter from Monica Lewinsky to William Jefferson Clinton
DB-DC-000000022	Lewinsky, Monica	11/12/97 letter from Monica Lewinsky to William Jefferson Clinton
DB-DC-000000027	Lewinsky, Monica	Outline for job interests of Monica Lewinsky
DC-DC-00000004 to 5	Willis-Vento, Caroline	Fair market value appraisal
DF-DC-00000002 to 12	Lewinsky, Monica	2/1/98 handwritten proffer
MSL-1249-DC-0139 to 141	Lewinsky, Monica	Letter from Monica Lewinsky to William Jefferson Clinton

Bates # or Tab#	Production Name	Description
MSL-55-DC-0001	Lewinsky, Monica	Draft note from Monica Lewinsky to William Jefferson Clinton
MSL-55-DC-0094	Lewinsky, Monica	Letter drafted on Monica's home computer
MSL-55-DC-0124	Lewinsky, Monica	Letter drafted on Monica's home computer
MSL-55-DC-0177	Lewinsky, Monica	Letter from Monica Lewinsky to William Jefferson Clinton
MSL-55-DC-0178	Lewinsky, Monica	Letter from Monica Lewinsky to William Jefferson Clinton
MSL-55-DC-0179	Lewinsky, Monica	11/2/97 letter from Monica Lewinsky to Betty Currie
MSL-55-DC-0184 to 186	Lewinsky, Monica	Note created on Monica Lewinsky's home computer "Happy National Boss Day?"
MSL-DC-00000456	Lewinsky, Monica	Handwritten note
MSL-DC-00000489 to 90	Lewinsky, Monica	Invitation to William Jefferson Clinton's Birthday Party
MSL-DC-00000621 to 22	Lewinsky, Monica	3/2/97 handwritten letter from Monica Lewinsky to William Jefferson Clinton
MSL-DC-00001050	White House	9/30/97 letter from Monica Lewinsky to William Jefferson Clinton
MSL-DC-00001051	Lewinsky, Monica	October 1997 Calendar
MSL-DC-00001051A	Lewinsky, Monica	November 1997 Calendar
MSL-DC-00001052	Lewinsky, Monica	Typed note
MSL-DC-00001166 to 1168	Lewinsky, Monica	Draft Affidavit
MSL-DC-00001176 to 1177	White House	6/29/97 draft letter from Monica Lewinsky to Marsha Scott
MSL-DC-00001192	White House	7/6/97 letter from Monica Lewinsky to Marsha Scott
MSL-DC-00001221	Lewinsky, Monica	Page from Monica Lewinsky's schedule book
MSL-DC-00001227	Lewinsky, Monica	6/29/97 note from Monica Lewinsky to William Jefferson Clinton
MSL-DC-00001228	Lewinksy, Monica	3/14/997 memorandum from Cliff Bernath for the Record
MSL-DC-00001230	Lewinsky, Monica	4/28/97 letter from Kenneth Bacon to Lorrie McHugh
V002-DC-00000001 to 5	Clinton, William Jefferson	1/27/98 letter from David Kendall to Bob Bittman, with attachments
V002-DC-00000006 to 7	Clinton, William Jefferson	1/28/98 letter from David Kendall to Bob Bittman

Bates # or Tab#	Production Name	Description
V002-DC-00000008 to 15	Clinton, William Jefferson	President Clinton's Responses to Plaintiff's First Set of Interrogatories
V002-DC-00000016 to 32	Clinton, William Jefferson	President Clinton's Responses to Plaintiff's Second Set of Interrogatories
V002-DC-00000052 to 55	Clinton, William Jefferson	President Clinton's Supplemental Responses to Plaintiff's Second Set of Interrogatories
V002-DC-00000056 to 92	Clinton, William Jefferson	President Clinton's Responses to Plaintiff's First Set of Requests for Production of Documents and Things
V002-DC-00000093 to 116	Clinton, William Jefferson	President Clinton's Responses to Plaintiff's Second Set of Document Requests
V002-DC-00000159 to 160	Clinton, William Jefferson	2/2/98 letter from David Kendall to Bob Bittman
V002-DC-00000469	Clinton, William Jefferson	2/3/98 letter to Bob Bittman from David Kendall
V002-DC-00000471	Clinton, William Jefferson	Book, "The Presidents of the United States"
V002-DC-00000475	Clinton, William Jefferson	3/16/98 letter from David Kendall to the OIC
V004-DC-00000134	Akin Gump	11/3/97 to 11/4/97 Toll records
V004-DC-00000135	Akin Gump	11/4/97 to 11/6/97 Toll records
V004-DC-00000143	Akin Gump	11/26/97 to 11/27/97 Toll records
V004-DC-00000148	Akin Gump	12/11/97 to 12/15/97 Toll records
V004-DC-00000151	Akin Gump	12/19/97 to 12/23/97 Toll records
V004-DC-00000154	Akin Gump	12/30/97 to 12/31/97 Toll records
V004-DC-00000158	Akin Gump	1/5/98 to 1/7/98 Toll records
V004-DC-00000159	Akin Gump	1/7/98 to 1/8/98 Toll records
V004-DC-00000160	Akin Gump	1/8/98 to 1/9/98 Toll records
V004-DC-00000161	Akin Gump	1/9/98 to 1/10/98 Toll records
V004-DC-00000162	Akin Gump	1/10/98 to 1/13/98 Toll records
V004-DC-00000164	Akin Gump	1/15/98 to 1/16/98 Toll records
V004-DC-00000165	Akin Gump	1/16/98 to 1/19/98 Toll records
V004-DC-00000166	Akin Gump	1/19/98 to 1/21/98 Toll records

Bates # or Tab#	Production Name	Description
V004-DC-00000167	Akin Gump	1/21/98 to 1/22/98 Toll records
V004-DC-00000171	Akin Gump	12/11/97 visitor record
V004-DC-00000172	Akin Gump	12/19/97 vistor record
V004-DC-00000183	Akin Gump	12/8/97 Request for Messenger Service
V005-DC-00000058	Laughlin, Gayle	1/15/98 phone record
V005-DC-00000060	Laughlin, Gayle	1/20/98 phone record
V005-DC-00000061	Laughlin, Gayle	1/20/98 phone record
V006-DC-00000007	White House	4/9/96 to 12/30/96 WAVES report for Monica Lewinsky
V006-DC-00000008	White House	2/24/97 to 11/13/97 WAVES report for Monica Lewinsky
V006-DC-00000009	White House	12/6/97 to 12/28/97 WAVES report for Monica Lewinsky
V006-DC-00000020	White House	WH Personnel Action sheet for Monica Lewinsky
V006-DC-00000109	White House	Work history report
V006-DC-00000118	White House	Notification of Personnel Action
V006-DC-00000157	White House	White House Gift Record
V006-DC-00000158	White House	Gift Donor Information
V006-DC-00000159	White House	9/4/96 letter from William Jefferson Clinton to Monica Lewinsky
V006-DC-00000162	White House	White House Gift Register
V006-DC-00000167	White House	10/30/95 Gift Unit - draft leter
V006-DC-00000178	White House	Photograph
V006-DC-00000180	White House	White House Gift Record
V006-DC-00000181	White House	White House Gift Record
V006-DC-00000183	White House	Monica Lewinsky's resume
V006-DC-00000198	White House	1995 summer White House intern list
V006-DC-00000221	White House	5/30/97 schedule sheet
V006-DC-00000222	White House	6/10/97 e-mail from Marsha Dimel to Katherine Veit
V006-DC-00000223 to 224	White House	6/12/97 e-mail from Marsha Dimel to Roseanne Hill w/attachment

Bates # or Tab#	Production Name	Description
V006-DC-00000225	White House	White House pre-employment information sheet
V006-DC-00000391	White House	WhoDB - Contact Manager Information
V006-DC-00000511	White House	12/5/97 Holiday Reception list excerpt
V006-DC-00000512 to 522	White House	12/5/97 White House Party list excerpt, report dated on 12/30/97
V006-DC-00000521	White House	12/5/97 White House Party list excerpt, report dated on 12/30/97
V006-DC-00000534	White House	6/14/96 Radio Address
V006-DC-00000572	White House	2/8/96 to 2/11/96 Presidential schedule
V006-DC-00000682	White House	8/18/96 and 8/19/96 William Jefferson Clinton Schedule
V006-DC-00000694	White House	4/2/96 Schedule of William Jefferson Clinton
V006-DC-00000747	White House	2/9/96 to 2/12/96 Presidential schedule
V006-DC-00001347	White House	4/9/96 E-Mail
V006-DC-00001770	White House	7/24/97 e-mail
V006-DC-00001792	White House	3/29/97 WAVES Request
V006-DC-00001796	White House	2/28/97 WAVES Request
V006-DC-00001813 to 1814	White House	12/5/97 e-mail: WAVES Operations Center to J. Schwartz
V006-DC-00001826	White House	Photograph
V006-DC-00001841	White House	Photograph
V006-DC-00001842	White House	Photograph
V006-DC-00001843	White House	Photograph
V006-DC-00001844	White House	Photograph
V006-DC-00001845	White House	Photograph
V006-DC-00001846	White House	Photograph
V006-DC-00001847	White House	Photograph
V006-DC-00001855	White House	Photograph
V006-DC-00001856	White House	Photograph
V006-DC-00001859	White House	Photograph
V006-DC-00001865	White House	videotape

Bates # or Tab#	Production Name	Description
V006-DC-00002064	White House	1/9/98 Presidential Call Log
V006-DC-00002065	White House	1/14/98 Presidential Call Log
V006-DC-00002066	White House	1/17/98 Presidential Call Log
V006-DC-00002067	White House	1/18/98 Presidential Call Log
V006-DC-00002068	White House	1/18/98 Presidential Call Log
V006-DC-00002069 to 2070	White House	1/19/98 Presidential Call Log
V006-DC-00002071	White House	1/21/98 Presidential Call Log
V006-DC-00002095	White House	8/16/97 schedule
V006-DC-00002130	White House	3/29/97 Presidential Movements
V006-DC-00002140	White House	7/4/97 schedule
V006-DC-00002142	White House	7/14/97 schedule
V006-DC-00002146	White House	8/16/97 schedule
V006-DC-00002147	White House	8/16/97 schedule
V006-DC-00002156	White House	11/13/97 Presidential Movement Log
V006-DC-00002158	White House	12/6/97 Presidential Movement Log
V006-DC-00002214	White House	7/4/97 diarist notes
V006-DC-00002243	White House	11/13/97 Diarist notes
V006-DC-00002287	White House	4/9/96 e-mail from Gunia to Dagenais
V006-DC-00002289	White House	E-Mail
V006-DC-00003646	White House	Coorespondence History tracking sheet
V006-DC-00003712	White House	2/24/97 memo from Betty Currie to William Jefferson Clinton
V006-DC-00003714	White House	White House Gift List
V006-DC-00003715	White House	White House Gift List
V006-DC-00003716	White House	6/14/96 Radio Address
V006-DC-00003719	White House	4/8/96 phone message
V006-DC-00003720	White House	2/28/97 Radio Address
V006-DC-00003735	White House	Photo Request

Bates # or Tab#	Production Name	Description
V006-DC-00003737 to 3744	White House	Photographs

TAB Documents

Tab 47

.ation Search Result Rank 1 of 1 Database
9/98 USNWR 1920 USNWR
.9/98 U.S. News & World Rep. 1920
1998 WL 8126910

U.S. News & World Report

Monday, June 29, 1998

Vol. 124, No. 25

Outlook; **Washington Whispers**; Newsletter

The press on Brill on the press; Hooray for Hollywood; Hooray for the CIA; Operator, get me China; Life after Webb Starr unbowed, Clinton's favorite flicks, the star-struck CIA and more

Timothy Noah; Julian E. Barnes; Ted Gest; Marianne Lavelle; Kenneth T. Walsh; Marci McDonald; William J. Holstein; Gordon Witkin; Gary Cohen

The press on Brill on the press

Starr unbowed, Clinton's favorite flicks, the star-struck CIA and m e

Like every other reporter in **Washington, Whispers** can't resist p.aying "gotcha" with Steven Brill, who wrote a much-discussed magazine article lacerating the media's Lewinsky sex-scandal coverage. Brill quoted with apparent approval CNN president Rick Kaplan's views on Monicagate excesses. But he somehow neglected to mention that Kaplan is a longtime friend of President Clinton's who (Whispers groupies will recall) told CNN staffers last fall to limit use of the word scandal in reporting on Clinton's 1996 campaign fund-raising. Brill's castigation of Kenneth Starr for talking to reporters made Whispers wonder whether the 21 other independent counsels ever dished. Here's what its survey found: Five independent counsels, including Starr, acknowledge talking to the press. Eleven claim they did not--or will not (but may of course be fibbing). The other six couldn't be reached; one of the six, James McKay, was accused of improper leaks during his investigation of Lyn Nofzinger and Ed Meese.

Incidentally, Brill's brouhaha doesn't seem to have dampened Starr's prosecutorial zeal. Last week, Bell Atlantic notified Robert Weiner, the spokesman for the White House Office of Drug Control Policy, that Starr had subpoenaed his phone records. Weiner's bit role in the scandal, Monicagate connoisseurs will recall, consisted o 'eing questioned before the grand jury on phone calls he and his w e made to the Columbia, Md., Democratic Club to (he says) :gratulate" officials for their press release saying Linda Tripp uld be prosecuted under state law (for surreptitiously tape .ording Monica Lewinsky). Weiner says Bell Atlantic told him Starr's office asked the company not to notify Weiner of the subpoena, but Ma Bell rejected this request on advice of counsel. Legal experts say this prosecutorial secrecy is extremely common in violent-crime cases, but less common in nonviolent cases. Bell Atlantic won't comment on any specific subpoenas, but company spokeswoman Sandra Arnette says, "It is our policy to notify a customer in the event we receive a subpoena, unless the subpoena specifically states not to."

Hooray for Hollywood. Who cares what the American Film Institute thinks are the best U.S. films of all time? Whispers wants to know what inveterate film buff President Clinton thinks are the best films of all time! It's widely known that Clinton's favorite movie is High Noon and that Clinton, like all other Homo sapiens, adores Casablanca. But here, for the first time anywhere, are the commander- in-chief's Top Five Picks: 1.) High Noon; 2.) Casablanca; 3.) Gone With the Wind (this one's a tad politically incorrect, but at least it's not The Birth of a Nation); 4.) Schindler's List (this one is arguably too politically correct); and 5.) The Bridge on the River Kwai (presumably President Clinton can explain what happens in t''s film's famously incoherent final 15 minutes).

ooray for the CIA. Still smarting from a public and ..gressional castigation for failing to predict India's nuclear tests, CIA brass hope to be rehabilitated by the Showtime cable channel. Showtime is filming a movie called The Agency at Langley, for which the CIA has agreed to provide 60 staffers as extras. When the call went out for volunteers to spend a Saturday strolling through the CIA lobby before the movie cameras, the response was so great that some departments had to hold a lottery to pick who could appear. (None of those chosen, thank goodness, were undercover operatives.) Whispers can't be more specific because--get this--the CIA says the precise number who clamored to be in the movie is classified.

Operator, get me China. Iridium LLC, a satellite communications company based in Washington, D.C., may have a more intimate link with a controversial Chinese military-related group than does Loral Corp. (which is currently getting barbecued by the New York Times and others for allegedly transferring too much rocket know-how tô China). This is a little complicated, but bear with us: Iridium's Chinese partner, Iridium China (Hong Kong) Ltd., is managed by mainland-born Wang Mei Yue. Wang Mei Yue also happens to be head of China Aerospace International Holdings Ltd. (CASIL) in Hong Kong. CASIL is p : of China's defense industrial complex, and is also where Liu C'.oying, the daughter of a top Chinese military official, was .oyed as a vice president; she is the figure who allegedly ıeled money to the Democratic Party. There are other ties between iL and Iridium besides Wang: According to the South China Morning Post of Hong Kong, three officials from CASIL sit on the board of Iridium China. Iridium, which is ringing the globe with 66 low-flying satellites for mobile telephone use, needs a Chinese partner to build and complete its global network linking 239 countries. Whispers can't help wondering whether some of that satellite know-how is flowing from Iridium China to CASIL and somehow improving China's military communications network. Iridium, Iridium China, and CASIL all declined comment.

Meanwhile, Whispers hears that in early June, representatives from the Treasury and Justice departments got together to discuss the results of an investigation by the Office of the Comptroller of the Currency (OCC). The OCC reported that over the past year or two, hundreds of millions of dollars had moved from Chinese banks to American banks, with no seeming explanation; the amounts of cash, and the techniques used to move the money, have made investigators suspicious. Those at the June meeting speculated that the funds could have been stolen from the Chinese government, and there was also chatter about possible tie-ins with the investigation of Chinese contributions to the Democratic Party. Whispers has no idea whether any of these suspicions are justified but would be glad to hear from a one who knows what it's all about.

.fe after Webb. Congressman Dan Burton's investigative committee is poking into the political donations of Mark Jimenez, a Florida businessman suspected of funneling South American money to the Democratic National Committee. Several of Jimenez's employees recently pleaded the Fifth Amendment when asked about their political contributions.

E-mail address: whispers@usnews.com

"Why do you write such scathing articles about me?" "I don't know."

Monica Lewinsky and Maureen Dowd, meeting for the first time at a restaurant near Dowd's New York Times office

"There are always going to be leakers. The question is what do guys like you and me do about them?"

Steven Brill, talking to a reporter about his magazine's attack on Kenneth Starr's talks with the press (which Starr says weren't leaks)

"It tickled me to death. We may need to have a rejoicing ce .mony."

T. E. Smith, mayor of Bay Springs, Miss., where former Sunbeam .irman Albert Dunlop closed two plants, on Dunlop's firing

"There was no kind of ethnic cleansing."

Slobodan Milosevic, president of Yugoslavia, denying widespread reports of violence against ethnic Albanians in Kosovo

TABULAR OR GRAPHIC MATERIAL SET FORTH IN THIS DOCUMENT IS NOT DISPLAYABLE

Drawing: Frankly my dear ... uh, you gonna finish that jelly doughnut? (Richard Thompson for USN&WR); Drawing: A little wobbly on 'nonpartisan' too. (Tom Toles for USN&WR)

---- INDEX REFERENCES ----

COMPANY (TICKER): Bell Atlantic Corp. (BEL)

Word Count: 1131
6/29/98 USNWR 1920
END OF DOCUMENT

Tab 48

U. S. Department of Justice

Office of Professional Responsibility

Washington, D.C. 20530

July 15, 1998

Mr. Donald C. Smaltz
Independent Counsel
P.O. Box 26356
103 Oronoco Street, Suite 200
Alexandria, VA 22313

Dear Mr. Smaltz:

In a December 5, 1997 letter to the Attorney General, you expressed concern about alleged comments attributed by the media to senior Department of Justice officials which were critical of yourself and other independent counsels. The Attorney General responded in a January 20, 1998 letter deploring such comments if they were in fact made and advising that your letter had been referred to this Office for review.

Your letter suggested that publication of the alleged comments could influence jurors hearing a case then pending or members of a future venire. The letter also noted the possible application of Rule 3.6 of the A.B.A.'s Model Rules of Professional Responsibility which bars attorneys from making extrajudicial statements having "a substantial likelihood of materially prejudicing" a pending case.

Based on our review of the excerpts you cited, we concluded that the alleged comments did not in these circumstances violate Rule 3.6 because their general nature made it unlikely that they would have "a substantial likelihood of materially prejudicing" any case. In particular, none of them disparaged any specific witness, item of evidence or prosecution theory. Rather, they pertained to matters then under active public debate.

In addition, Rule 3.6 applies only to lawyers "who [are] participating or ha[ve] participated in the investigation" at issue, a requirement no Department official meets. And while, by its terms, the rule's prohibitions extend as well to any "lawyer associated in a * * * government agency with [such] a lawyer," the rule still does not apply to Department officials since independent counsels are not part of the Department.

Because Rule 3.6 is inapplicable in this case and no other ethical rule appears to prohibit the reported comments, we must conclude that no further inquiry into them by this Office is justified. This conclusion does not, however, mean that we found the comments to be appropriate.

If you have any questions, please contact me or Assistant Counsel Paul Colby on (202) 514-3365.

Sincerely,

Richard M. Rogers
Deputy Counsel

Tab 49

CO 293 (Rev. 8/91) Subpoena to Testify Before Grand Jury

United States District Court

DISTRICT OF

TO: The White House
ATTN: Michelle Petersen, Esq.

SUBPOENA TO TESTIFY BEFORE GRAND JURY

SUBPOENA FOR:
☐ PERSON ☒ DOCUMENT(S) OR OBJECT(S)

YOU ARE HEREBY COMMANDED to appear and testify before the Grand Jury of the United States District Court at the place, date, and time specified below.

PLACE	COURTROOM
United States District Court for the District of Columbia Third & Constitution Avenue, N.W. Washington, D.C.	Grand Jury, Third Floor
	DATE AND TIME
	July 23, 1998/9:15 a.m.

YOU ARE ALSO COMMANDED to bring with you the following document(s) or object(s):*

See attached Rider.

☐ *Please see additional information on reverse.*

This subpoena shall remain in effect until you are granted leave to depart by the court or by an officer acting on behalf of the court.

U.S. MAGISTRATE OR CLERK OF COURT	DATE
Nancy M. Mayer-Whittington, Clerk	July 17, 1998
(BY) DEPUTY CLERK Margaret ... Napier	D1415

This subpoena is issued upon application of the United States of America

NAME, ADDRESS AND PHONE NUMBER OF ASSISTANT U.S. ATTORNEY
Julie A. Corcoran
Julie A. Corcoran, Associate Independent Couns
Office of the Independent Counsel
1001 Pennsylvania Avenue, N.W., Suite 490-Nort
Washington, D.C. 20004
(202) 514-8688

*If not applicable, enter "none."

*U.S.GPO 1993-0-350-792/80396

Subpoena #D1415

To: The White House

SUBPOENA RIDER

A. Produce the following items in the possession/custody of President Clinton:

1. Vox
2. The Notebook
3. Geek Love
4. Oy Vey
5. A Silver Cigar Holder, and
6. An Antique Paperweight depicting the White House circa 1900

Personal appearance is not required if the requested documents are delivered on or before the return date to Special Agent [redacted] of the Federal Bureau of Investigation (telephone [redacted], Suite 490-North, 1001 Pennsylvania Avenue, N.W., Washington, DC 20004, for submission to the Grand Jury. If you choose to deliver documents in lieu of a personal appearance, you must (i) state in a cover letter whether such production contains all responsive documents, and (ii) attach a copy of this subpoena to the cover letter.

Definitions and Instructions

1. Definitions

a. The term "document" or "documents" as used in this subpoena means all records of any nature whatsoever within your possession, custody or control or the possession, custody or control of any agent, employee, representative (including, without limitation, attorneys, investment advisors, investment bankers, bankers and accountants), or other person acting or purporting to act for or on your behalf or in concert with you, including, but not limited to, draft, pending or executed contracts and/or agreements, sample documents, insurance policies, financial guarantee bonds, letters of credit, communications, correspondence, calendars, daytimers, datebooks, telegrams, facsimiles, telexs, telefaxes, electronic mail, memoranda, records, reports, books, files (computer or paper), summaries or records of personal conversations, meetings or interviews, logs, summaries or records of telephone conversations and/or telefax communications, diaries, forecasts, statistical statements, financial statements (draft or finished), work papers, drafts, copies, bills, records of payments for bills, retainer records, attorney time sheets, telephone bills and records, telefax bills and records, tax returns and return information, employee time sheets, graphs, charts, accounts, analytical records, minutes or records of meetings or conferences, consultants' reports and/or records, appraisals, records, reports or summaries of negotiations, brochures, pamphlets, circulars, maps, plats, trade letters, depositions, statements, interrogatories and answers thereto, pleadings, docket sheets, discovery materials, audit letters, audit reports, materials underlying audits, document productions, transcripts, exhibits, settlement materials, judgments, press releases, notes, marginal notations, invoices, documents regarding collateral or security pledged, settlement statements, checks disbursed or received at settlement, inspection reports, title policies, financial statements and/or federal tax returns submitted by any person in support of any loan application, items related the repayment, if any, of any interest or principal on the loan, items relating to any default on the loan, commission records, evidence of liens, documents relating to filings under the Uniform Commercial Code and/or its equivalent, foreclosure and mortgage documentation, cashiers checks, bank drafts, money orders, bank and brokerage account statements, debit and credit memoranda, wire transfer documentation, opening account cards, signature cards, loan applications, any employment and bank account deposit verification documents, loan histories, loan files, records of loan repayment or any and all efforts to secure repayment, including foreclosure or records of lawsuits, credit references, board resolutions, minutes of meetings of boards of directors, opinion letters, purchases and sales agreements, real estate contracts, brokerage agreements, escrow agreements, loan agreements, offer and acceptance contracts, or any other contracts or agreements, deeds or other evidence of title, escrow accounts and any other escrow documentation, savings account transcripts, savings account deposit slips, savings account withdrawal slips, checks deposited in savings accounts, checking account statements, canceled checks drawn on checking accounts, deposit slips and checks deposited into checking accounts, credit card accounts, debit and credit documentation, safe deposit records, currency transaction reports (IRS Forms 4789), photographs, brochures, lists, journals, advertising, computer tapes and cards, audio and video tapes, computerized records stored in the form of magnetic or electronic coding on computer media or on media capable of being read by computer or with the aid of computer related equipment, including but not limited to floppy disks or diskettes, disks, diskettes, disk packs, fixed hard drives, removable hard disk cartridges, mainframe computers, Bernoulli boxes, optical disks, WORM disks, magneto/optical disks, floptical disks, magnetic tape, tapes, laser disks, video cassettes, CD-ROMs and any other media capable of storing magnetic coding, microfilm, microfiche and other storage devices, voicemail recordings and all other written, printed or recorded or photographic matter or sound reproductions, however produced or reproduced.

The term "document" or "documents" also includes any earlier, preliminary, preparatory or tentative version of all or part of a document, whether or not such draft was superseded by a later draft and whether or not the terms of the draft are the same as or different from the terms of the final document.

b. The term "communication" or "communications" is used herein in its broadest sense to encompass any transmission or exchange of information, ideas, facts, data, proposals, or any other matter, whether between individuals or between or among the members of a group, whether face-to-face, by telephone or by means of electronic or other medium.

c. "Possession, custody or control" means in your physical possession and/or if you have the right to secure or compile the production of the document or a copy from another person or entity having physical possession, including, but not limited to, your counsel.

d. The term "referring or relating" to any given subject means anything that constitutes, contains, embodies, reflects, identifies, states, refers to, deals with, or is in any manner whatsoever pertinent to that subject including, but not limited to, documents concerning the preparation of other documents.

e. The term "you" means yourself and any of your companies, partnerships and business entities with which you have been affiliated and any employees, partners, associates or members of any firm with which you have been affiliated in the course of your work for any of the persons or entities named in this rider, and any such firms and the affiliates of those firms.

2. <u>Instructions</u>

a. The originals of all documents and communications must be produced, as well as copies within your possession, custody, or control.

b. If any original document cannot be produced in full, produce such document to the extent possible and indicate specifically the reason for your inability to produce the remainder.

c. Documents shall be produced as they are kept in the usual course of business, as organized in the files.

d. File folders, labels, and indices identifying documents called for shall be produced intact with such documents. Documents attached to each other should not be separated.

e. In reading this rider, the plural shall include the singular and the singular shall include the plural.

f. The words "and" and "or" shall be construed conjunctively or disjunctively as necessary to make the request inclusive rather than exclusive. The use of the word "including" shall be construed without limitation.

g. In the event that any document, or portion thereof, called for by this subpoena is withheld on the basis of any claim of privilege or similar claim, that document shall be identified in writing as follows: (a) author; (b) the position or title of the author; (c) addressee; (d) the position or title of the addressee; (e) any indicated or blind copies; (f) date; (g) a description of the subject matter of the document; (h) number of pages; (i) attachments or appendices; (j) all persons to whom the document, its contents, or any portion thereof, has been disclosed, distributed, shown, or explained; and (k) present custodian. Each basis you contend justifies the withholding of the document shall also be specified. With respect to those documents or records as to which you may claim privilege, or attorneys' work product, set forth as to each such document the basis for such claim, including the purpose and circumstances surrounding the creation of the document, the identity of each person who has been privy to such communication reflected in the document, the identity of any person or entity instructing the subpoena recipient or the attorney of the subpoena recipient to withhold production of the document, and whether you will submit the document to the Court for an in camera determination as to the validity of the claim. If the existence of a joint defense agreement or any agreement as to common interest is relevant to the assertion of any claim of privilege or similar claim, please provide a copy of that agreement; if any such agreement is not in writing, please set forth the date of the creation of the agreement, the identities of all parties to the agreement and the specific individuals who entered into the agreement on behalf of those parties, and the objects, purposes, and scope of the agreement.

h. In the event that any document called for by this subpoena has been lost, destroyed, deleted, altered, or otherwise disposed of, that document shall be identified in writing as follows: (a) author; (b) the position or title of the author; (c) addressee; (d) the position or title of the addressee; (e) indicated or blind copies; (f) date; (g) a brief description of the subject matter of the document; (h) number of pages; (I) attachments or appendices; (j) all persons to whom the document, its contents, or any portion thereof, had been disclosed, distributed, shown or explained; (k) the date of the loss, destruction, deletion, alteration, or disposal and the circumstances thereof; and (l) the reasons, if any, for the loss, destruction, deletion, alteration, or disposal and the person or persons responsible.

i. If any information or data is withheld because such information or data is stored electronically, it is to be identified by the subject matter of the information or data and the place or places where such information is maintained.

FAX TRANSMISSION

OFFICE OF THE INDEPENDENT COUNSEL
1001 PENNSYLVANIA, N.W.
SUITE 490-NORTH
WASHINGTON, DC 20004
MAIN NUMBER: (202) 514-8688
FAX NUMBER: (202) 514-8802

to: Michelle Peterson, The White House **date:** July 17, 1998

fax #: 202-456-5055 **tel #:**

from: Julie A. Corcoran, Associate Independent Counsel

tel #: 202-514-8688 **pages:** 7 , including this cover sheet.

comment:

****
***   TX REPORT   ***
****

TRANSMISSION OK

TX/RX NO	3706
CONNECTION TEL	94565055
SUBADDRESS	
CONNECTION ID	
ST. TIME	07/17 14:17
USAGE T	03'01
PGS.	7
RESULT	OK

FAX TRANSMISSION

OFFICE OF THE INDEPENDENT COUNSEL
1001 PENNSYLVANIA, N.W.
SUITE 490-NORTH
WASHINGTON, DC 20004
MAIN NUMBER: (202) 514-8688
FAX NUMBER: (202) 514-8802

to: Michelle Peterson, The White House **date:** July 17, 1998

fax #: 202-456-5055 **tel #:**

from: Julie A. Corcoran, Associate Independent Counsel

tel #: 202-514-8688 **pages:** 7 , including this cover sheet.

comment:

Tab 50

1ST STORY of Level 1 printed in FULL format.

CNBC News Transcripts

SHOW: HARDBALL WITH CHRIS MATTHEWS (8:00 PM ET)

July 22, 1998, Wednesday 2:05 PM

LENGTH: 4456 words

HEADLINE: WHETHER MONICA LEWINSKY COULD HAVE SPENT TIME WITH THE PRESIDENT AND THE ISSUE OF IMPEACHMENT

ANCHORS: CHRIS MATTHEWS

BODY:

Mr. LEON PANETTA (Former White House Chief of Staff): (From March 30) There's also a group within the White House that thinks that playing hardball is the way you deal with these issues, and that ultimately if you--if you stonewall these things, they'll go away. I just ha--in--in my history in politics in Washington, my view is nothing goes away in Washington. If you try to stonewall things, ultimately it catches up with you. It is much better to be forthright. And those are exactly the words that I often would tell the president.

CHRIS MATTHEWS, host:

Time marches on. We have Leon Panetta with us from San Francisco. I wish I was up there with you today. Leon, thank you for joining us.

Mr. PANETTA: Yeah, I'd like to have you here, Chris.

MATTHEWS: Thank you.

Mr. PANETTA: My pleasure.

MATTHEWS: Well, let's talk about--would those be your words today in speaking to the president?

Mr. PANETTA: Well, I think--you know, as--as--at the time that I said the president ought to come forward, I thought that was one way to try to hopefully end this kind of long nightmare we've been through with this scandal. And, you know, it's--right now, as I look at the special prosecutor and some of the things he's done over the last few weeks, particularly with regards to the Secret Service, which concern me a great deal because of what it did, I think, to increase the jeopardy to--to a president's life by virtue of--of the testifying that's gonna go on here. I'm just not so sure that, perhaps, the president may not be better off right now waiting and seeing what--what the special prosecutor develops and listening to his lawyers. But at some point, there's no question that he's gonna have to come forward and he's gonna have to be forthright about what happened.

MATTHEWS: I agree with you about the Secret Service, but let me ask you about--maybe you--I wanna give you some time here because we rarely have somebody on the program who's been in the White House--in the Clinton White House--right--intimately with the president and can describe the sort of culture of the place. It just seems to me, from the outside and being politically I--political, I noticed--it seems to me the president and there's--would seem to be a lot of young people around.

I mean, then some grownups like yourself, Erskine Bowles now, Mack McLarty, that you guys seem to be the odd people out, however, the grownups. It seems like the president and the kids seem to have this thing going on there and it's kind of casual and loosey-goosey, and you guys tried to enforce some discipline on it, but normally, this president seemed to have a sort of a whimsical idea that he could fun with the younger staffers and hang out with them and enjoy their tunes and stuff, thinking about tomorrow, whatever he sings when he sings their songs. It doesn't--it seems like a kind of a--a juvenile culture that he seems to enjoy to sh--joy sharing in. Is that fair?

Mr. PANETTA: Well, Chris, I think you have to go back to how this developed. At--at the--at the beginning of the administration, they took a long time selecting the Cabinet and spent most of their time really focusing on those that they wanted within the Cabinet. And suddenly they were at the inauguration day and realized that they had not spent very much time on developing a White House staff. And as a consequence, they relied a lot on people who came out of the campaign--and as you know, sometimes somebody can be very good in a campaign, but have very little experience in terms of Washington and the White House and the responsibilities to the White House.

So I think part of the problem was that not enough time was spent in selecting the people that ultimately went into the White House and they were for--in large measure, younger, they were less experienced and I think a lot that contributed to the initial problems. I do have to tell you that I think as a result of the work that I did, that Erskine Bowles did--I think the discipline within the White House increased a great deal, so that that was not as much as a problem as it was the first two years. As far as the president's concerned, president loves, obviously, to--to mix with people. He's a people person. That's what got him into the presidency. He likes young people and he likes old people. I mean, I've never seen a person who doesn't like to engage when you're in the presidency. He loves to meet people and he loves to talk with people, and that's his nature.

MATTHEWS: Well, when you--when you talk on--took on the chief of staff's job and you, in a way, were stepping down from an enormous policy role of--of being OMB director and having been chairman of the House Budget Committee and a major Democrat on Capitol Hill, you took a staff job, in a sense, of being chief of staff with the promise that you'd be the traffic controller, that you would stop some of the g--more zanier characters, some of them who appear on my show, I must say, from getting into the White House to bother the president, that you would be traffic controller and make it more of a corporate kind of setting. How did Monica Lewinsky get through the gate? How did she get to be a person who on a regular basis would bring so-called materials to the president as if she were a Federal Express messenger? I worked in the White House. We had to take our papers down to the basement and then a Marine would take them to the president. It was very formal. The idea that Monica could be bopping around there on a Saturday and just bop in and see the president, drop off some papers. It doesn't seem like the American presidency that I was used to working in.

Mr. PANETTA: Well, Chris, there were three things that I wanted to do when I came in as chief of staff. The first was to basically set up a line of command. There wasn't an--an organization chart at the time I--I went in as chief of staff. And it was important to set up lines of command and I set up my deputies, and under them, every person was responsible to those deputies so that we really had a legitimate chain of command similar to what I had learned about in the Army. It's be--sometimes it's better to have Army experience when you're working in the White House than--than just simply either management or--or, for that matter, even political experience.

Secondly, it was a question of increased discipline. And there, you know, it's the issue that you're talking about--not having people simply wander into the White House. And we did increase the--the discipline on that. Staff members were not to simply wander into the president's office. They--they were to abide by a schedule. If they had a briefing to give the president, then they would be part of the briefing. I determined who would go in for the--for--for purposes of those briefings...

MATTHEWS: Right.

Mr. PANETTA: ...who would meet with the president. But let's understand that the president also has the flexibility to determine, you know, if he wants to meet with somebody at a particular time, either in the White House or in the Oval Office, and wants to have somebody meet with him on a personal basis. He has the ability to do that.

MATTHEWS: How common would it be for an intern--a young intern in her early 20s who has no sort of professional skill to have direct contact with the Oval Office?

Mr. PANETTA: Never be...

MATTHEWS: I've never heard of such a thing in my life.

Mr. PANETTA: Well, it would be...

MATTHEWS: I think you have to be professional to get anywhere near the president.

Mr. PANETTA: It's unusual. Well, and that--and that--that's my view as well. I think with regards to interns, as I've mentioned before, interns generally come into the White House. They're young. They're inexperienced. They don't know, you know, what's important, what's not important. They have no sense of proportion, because they are young.

MATTHEWS: Right.

Mr. PANETTA: And so as a consequence, with interns, what you wanna do is--I'm sure you wanna give them access so--in the sense of seeing how the White House operates. We did the same thing on Capitol Hill, again, as you know, Chris...

MATTHEWS: Right.

Mr. PANETTA: ...with having interns open mail and be in the office and have a little sense of what it was like to--to operate in a--in a congressional office. Well, you do the same thing in the White House, but most of the interns operated in the old Executive Office Building.

MATTHEWS: Right.

Mr. PANETTA: Very few operated within the confines of the White House itself.

MATTHEWS: How did this one get through? Mr. Panetta--Leon--Leon, you're a great, clean guy. I still think you're probably as confused as I was. How in the world did this young intern get to be friends with the president of the United States?

Mr. PANETTA: Well, hell, you're--that's the whole case that you're talking about, Chris.

MATTHEWS: OK. Let me ask you this. When Evelyn Lieberman, your deputy, booted her over to the--to the Pentagon to get her out of the way, what paper passed by you? Did you get any kind of in--any kind of red light here or yellow light this girl was trouble, she was a stalker, she was hanging around the president, he's getting teased by her or anything like that?

Mr. PANETTA: Well, Evelyn Lieberman was--as the public needs to know, was one of my deputies. She was deputy chief of staff, and she was responsible for overseeing personnel and working on the schedule as well. And there was no finer first sergeant...

MATTHEWS: Right.

Mr. PANETTA: ...in the White House than Evelyn Lieberman. And so she would be responsible, frankly, for telling staff members or interns or whoever if they were in the wrong place at the wrong time, if they weren't in the proper dress. She would discipline them. She would discipline members of the press as well...

MATTHEWS: Right.

Mr. PANETTA: ...if they were in the wrong place. So she was good at that. And she would usually come to me and she'd say, you know, Look, I did this and I did that,' and I'd back her up 100 percent. In this case, she came to me and she said, There's this individual. She's hanging around--inappropriately around the--the Oval Office. I wanna get rid of her and I'm gonna get rid of her.' And I said, Fine. Let's do it.'

MATTHEWS: You didn't have to check it out with the president.

Mr. PANETTA: No, no, this was--this wa...

MATTHEWS: You ne--you never checked it.

Mr. PANETTA: No, sir.

MATTHEWS: And what was the--what was the defining issue here of why she was moved to the Pentagon?

Mr. PANETTA: Ev--Evelyn Lieberman. When--when she says somebody's gotta move, it's OK with me.
MATTHEWS: And you didn't have any idea who this woman was at the time, this young girl?

Mr. PANETTA: Nope.

MATTHEWS: You never heard of Monica Lewinsky?

Mr. PANETTA: Well, I mean, I--I--from now--now--now...

MATTHEWS: Did she have a reputation of being something of a space cadet?

Mr. PANETTA: Now--now do I--do I remember her? You know, yeah.

MATTHEWS: Does this--I mean, I would know if a spa--I would--I know, but I would remember if a space cadet were wandering around my office.

Mr. PANETTA: No. Exactly.

MATTHEWS: And--and I'd say, Who's that? What's she up to? She seems to have a lot of crazy stuff on her mind,' or, She seems to be in love with somebody here or something.' I mean--and this--we've seen these talking points where the word stalker' was used and huge liar.' She's used them about herself. So I don't know. And they were on her mainframe computer. It isn't like it's being denied.

Mr. PANETTA: Chris...

MATTHEWS: And here's a woman who's willing to say those things that--she sounds a little bit odd. But I want to get back to the president, because you said he set the tune. He liked a lo--a lot of young people around and they made him feel breezy or they would--they relaxed him or whatever, you--you suggested. And you said you really couldn't control that part of him. But I wanna ask you this: Are there anybody--are there any interns assigned the duty of coming to see the president on Saturday with papers of any kind? Have you ever come across an intern with that kind of duty roster?

Mr. PANETTA: No, of course not.

MATTHEWS: OK. We'll be back with more HARDBALL on CNBC.

(Announcements)

Mr. PANETTA: (From "Meet the Press") I have to tell you that perjury about consensual sexual relations doesn't strike me as being an impeachable offense and I don't think it strikes most of the members of Congress as being an impeachable offense.

MATTHEWS: Mr. Panetta--Leon Panetta, where would you place such an offense? I mean, we were talking about the allegations that the president may have engaged in a relationship with a 21-year-old intern, sort of in a loco parentis situation with him. He was en--she was entrusted to him by her parents in a situation where she was working among adults, but hardly seen as an adult but as an intern. If there wer--if ther--if there was an intimate relationship between these two people, you say it's not impeachable. What is it then? How should Congress and the American people respond to evidence?

The latest polls in The Wall S--in The Washington Post and AB--ABC poll, that very clearly shows over 60 percent of the people believe the president had this relationship, that nobody's charging him with rape, obviously. It's a consensual relationship, but they're also charging him with--or most people believe that he--that he lied about it when he was under oath. And a lot of people can understand that, too. I have to tell you that. A lot of people I talk to say, Hey, people cover up infidelity. It happens all the time.' What do we do with this case, though?

Mr. PANETTA: Well, Chris, you know--I mean, you--you and I have, obviously, a standard that goes back to our backgrounds. You know, I'm a pre-Vatican, too, Catholic. I was raised by--taught by...

MATTHEWS: You're not that old, Leon.

Mr. PANETTA: I was taught by nuns and priests and fear of...

MATTHEWS: Right. Well, you had the Jesuits like I did, and they can get through anything.

Mr. PANETTA: Yeah.

MATTHEWS: So what do we do--what do we do--what do we do with the pr--should the Congress just simply say, if they get a report--and this evidence is accumulating--should they simply say, Well, we'll pass a resolution or we'll all give speeches in one minutes, and that'll be the end of it'? If you can't impeach the guy, you give a nice speech or issue a press release? What do you do?

Mr. PANETTA: Well, you know, Chris, I think we all have to kind of stand back and see, you know, what this thing looks like. Look, if--if the special prosecutor can't prove obstruction of justice for whatever reason and he can't prove subornation of perjury for whatever reason and the only charge he has is that the president lied about a sexual relationship--consensual sexual relationship, however you wanna describe it, within the White House, and that's the only charge that goes forward to the House of Representatives, I just have to tell you, you know, again, when you look at the whole picture, is that, in and of itself, an impeachable offense? I don't think so. Now, you know, how the House--what the House does and how they make that determination is something we're gonna have to see. But, clearly, whether they decide to go with a censure, whether they decide to go with something f--something less is something that the leadership of the Congress as well as the members are going to have to decide.

MATTHEWS: Did you know Kathleen Willey at the White House, Leon?

Mr. PANETTA: No, I didn't.

MATTHEWS: What do you make of that case, where the president's accused by--these talking points clearly are--three-quarters of which are aimed at covering up whatever the president's conduct, or shaping the testimony of Linda Tripp with regard to the conduct of the president in--in with--with Kathleen Willey, a grown-up who came looking for a job in a somewhat bad situation. Her husband was about to commit suicide. She sought a job. She accused on "60 Minutes," we all saw it, the president of the United States of gross behavior toward her. Of course, gross behavior is gross behavior. But if he acted illegally to try to bring a--to shape or tamper with witnesses in their testimony, would that reach, do you think, the standard of an impeachable offense?

Mr. PANETTA: Well, again, you--you know, Chris, we--we have to see what the special prosecutor ultimately determines here as he looks at the evidence an--and this investigation wraps up what--whatever evidence they're--they're able to pull together. But, clearly, if--if some kind of obstruction of justice, where the president in some way deliberately made efforts to prevent or inhibit somebody in--in the course of an investigation...

MATTHEWS: Mm-hmm.

Mr. PANETTA: ...or a criminal offense, then I think that's a more serious charge. I do...

MATTHEWS: Yeah.

Mr. PANETTA: There's no question in my mind.

MATTHEWS: Remember Rose Mary Woods? She worked for--well, one of your old bosses, Richard Nixon, back when you were in civil rights enforcement, and you quit as a matter of honor, we all remember, 'cause you didn't think they were enforcing civil rights in the Nixon administration. Remember Rose Mary Woods? She was accused of--in fact, she took the bullet for it. She said, Yeah, I--my--my leg reached over about 20 feet across the room and--and killed about 18 minutes of Watergate tape.' And she took the bullet.

Mr. PANETTA: Yeah. I remember the pictures.

MATTHEWS: Yeah. I remember those cartoons. I sometimes think of Betty Currie, although she's--well, she's just as political as Rose Mary Woods is. Rose Mary Woods was a loyalist and a real politician, and I don't wanna say--and nobody really thinks that Betty Currie was some sort of--just a clerk or a clerical person. She had a tremendous political background and loyalty. What i--what is her role here? I mean, is she supposed to just sort of say, Well, I'll tell them what I have to tell them, but no more. I'm gonna try tp be loyal an--and deal with it as best I can, but I've gotta worry about breaking the law myself'? I mean, she's going to be asked if--if she was out giving gifts to Monica Lewinsky, if she was trying to get--on her own initiative, trying to get Monica Lewinsky's--jobs up with Ron Perelman up--who runs the Revlon company, out--I mean, these are incredible reaches, it seems to me, for an assistant to--to about--to undergo or undertake without some sort of push from the boss, you know. Why is she out getting--running an employment service for Monica Lewinsky? It seems odd.

Mr. PANETTA: Well, Chris, look...

MATTHEWS: Doesn't it?

Mr. PANETTA: Yeah. Let me just tell you, my relationship with Betty Currie in--in the White House--I don't know of anybody who is more honest or decent than--than Betty Currie. She's just the most decent person I've ever met, particularly in that kind of position. You know, most of the time, people in high office will hire hit-and--hit-and-run people to--to run the--run the shop and really s--really shut the door on people.

MATTHEWS: Right.

Mr. PANETTA: Betty was not that kind of individual. She was very different. She as always nice to everybody who came through. She was always listening to--to whatever the president wanted to do. She was that kind of person. And whatever she's testified to, there's no question in my mind that she's testified to the truth.

MATTHEWS: Ed Rollins, join in.

Mr. ED ROLLINS (Republican Strategist): Well, th--I think--first of all, I have the greatest respect in the world for Leon, who I've known for many, many years, and--and having been raised by the Dominican nuns, I--I--I have a certain moral compass, too. I think the most...

MATTHEWS: We're gonna have to have a Knights of Columbus meeting later tonight.

Mr. ROLLINS: Right. I--I th--I think the most--I think the most telling comments tonight, Leon, is you talking about how you did try and put a discipline in this White House. This girl got around that discipline, and obviously, interns didn't float in and out of...

MATTHEWS: It takes two to tangle.

Mr. ROLLINS: Y--you know, interns didn't float in and out of the White Houses I worked in.

MATTHEWS: Right.

Mr. ROLLINS: But the reality is that--that this president had to basically want to see this girl and everybody else responded either negligently or--or positively. The bottom line: If this was a college president instead of the president of the United States, a married college president, and he was caught messing around with one of his students, there's no question he'd be fired. Whether the president should be fired or not, I think, is gonna ultimately depend on the evidence that you--you talked about today. But I think that this...

MATTHEWS: OK.

Mr. ROLLINS: ...I think this is a serious issue.

MATTHEWS: Ed--we'll be back with Ed Rollins and Leon Panetta in just a minute on HARDBALL on CNBC.

(Announcements)

MATTHEWS: Well, let's commit what I like to call substance abuse. Let's talk about some substantive issue. Leon Panetta, you were chairman of that--chairman of the--or, actually, director of the OMB, as well as chairman of the House Budget Committee. There's a big fight brewing between now and Election Day and I guess it's the most important political fight of the year, apart from this whole question, and that is, what do we do with this surplus that seems to be building up, at least potentially? The Republicans want a huge tax cut of up to--up to $ 700 billion over 10 years. The Democrats under Bill Clinton say, You've gotta save that money to preserve Social Security.' What do you make of that fight?

Mr. PANETTA: Well, Chris, let me tell you something, having been involved in that battle to get to a balanced budget and having worked on the economic plan. Now that they've reached a balanced budget, they have to remember that they've got a $ 5 trillion debt out there.

MATTHEWS: Yeah.

Mr. PANETTA: We're still picking up about $ 1 billion a day on interest on that kind of debt. The smartest thing they could do is to put that surplus away, pay off the debt and not start spending it, because the reality is, in a few years, when the baby boom generation hits, we're gonna be back in a deficit, so I think both sides, frankly, ought to back off, let the surplus be used to pay off the overall debt. How that winds up, I don't know. You know, it's a political year. The likelihood is we may get the worst of all worlds, which is a tax cut, plus what--what the president wants to spend it on.

MATTHEWS: I g--I--I guess--what would be the estimate for how much the federal government's spending in interest now, about $ 400 billion a year?

Mr. PANETTA: Sure, it's about...

MATTHEWS: About 8 percent?

Mr. PANETTA: Actually, that's e--that's--that's exactly right. It's--it's--it's over $ 1 billion a day in interest that's accumulating. That's crazy. We are not in some kind of, you know, totally balanced budget situation. We are in a situation where we've got a huge national debt. It continues to accumulate and it's--it's great that we've reached a balanced budget, and I think it's to the president's credit, Congress' credit that we're there.

MATTHEWS: And your credit.

Mr. PANETTA: Well...

MATTHEWS: You were budget director.

Mr. PANETTA: ...I'll--I'll take...

MATTHEWS: And I love the way...

Mr. PANETTA: ...I'll take some credit of it.

MATTHEWS: Leon--Leon, I love it when you talk conservative. Anyway, let's go to Ed Rollins. What do you make of that? You can't beat Leon for fiscal--fiscal responsibility. He's a real grown-up. What do you make of the other guys down in Washington?

Mr. ROLLINS: I--I--I--I think we've gone full circle. He's now a Republican again. That's where he s--that's where he star--we both started as young Republicans. The...

MATTHEWS: Somebody's accused me of that recently, too. Go ahead.

Mr. ROLLINS: I--I--I think--I think the bottom line is this, though: I--I think that if the president wants to increase Social Security taxes, he should put a bill through Congress because, obviously, if he takes the--the surplus today and dumps it into Social Security--I mean, I think that's--that's a--that's a false way of raising taxes. I think Republicans feel this is taxpayers' money. If we're not gonna spend it all, then they ought to give it back to taxpayers.

MATTHEWS: Well, politically, what do you think's the smart move? You go out today--you look at all the polls and people are saying they're most concerned, even though it's 1998 and the economy's rolling, thanks to some smart fiscal and monetary decisions of the last seven or eight years--but the fact of the matter is that people still have a real sensitivity--and you know it as well as I do--about Social Security.

Mr. ROLLINS: Sure.

MATTHEWS: They know that this boom ain't gonna last. At some time in the early part of the next century, people like you and I are gonna be out there trying to get our checks, and the fact of the matter is there ain't gonna be a whole lot of money there compared to the number of people waiting in line.

Mr. ROLLINS: Well, then you need to change the system. I mean, I think--I think that's the--that's the argument that people have to make here, is that we--the system will be underfunded because there won't be enough people paying into it. Let's not play funny games. We played gimmick games with the budgets all during the deficit years. Now that we have a little bit of surplus--and I agree with Leon totally--the surplus may be there for a short period of time, not a long period of time. You know, let's do something fiscally responsible. We either give it back to the taxpayers or basically don't spend more money. But I--we have to fix the Social Security system by other--other means than just dumping more money in there, though.

MATTHEWS: Mr. Panetta, do you think the president was smart in coming out for teaching character in high school? Was that a shrewd move this week?

Mr. PANETTA: Absolutely. I think--I think it's...

MATTHEWS: I mean, pushing--he--he's--he's talking up school uniforms and...

Mr. PANETTA: Yeah.

MATTHEWS: ...he's sort of offering himself as the national hall monitor, and I think--I'm just wondering if that's an odd sort of juxtaposition with what's going on in the rest of his life these days.

Mr. PANETTA: Well, the president has had a pretty consistent record in the White House of going after that kind of issue, of doing the school uniforms, of arguing for greater discipline, as well as for additional funding in--in education. So I--I think--you know, he--he's had--and it probably goes back to the time when he was governor at Arkansas, but I don't think there's any question but that the American people respond...

MATTHEWS: OK.

Mr. PANETTA: ...to the whole issue of better discipline in schools.

MATTHEWS: Leon Panetta, thanks for joining us from San Francisco. Great man.

Mr. PANETTA: Thank you.

MATTHEWS: "Rivera Live's" up next with the latest on the Clinton investigation. Join me next time for more HARDBALL.

LANGUAGE: English

LOAD-DATE: July 23, 1998

Tab 51

tation Found Document Rank 4 of 12 Database MTPRESS
26/98 MTPRESS (No Page)
7/26/98 Meet the Press (Pg. Unavail. Online)
1998 WL 8610258

Meet the Press

Sunday, July 26, 1998

Interview: Rahm Emanuel, adviser to President Clinton, discusses the Ken Starr investigation and managed care

MR. RUSSERT: And we're back. Rahm Emanuel, welcome.

MR. EMANUEL: Good morning.

MR. RUSSERT: As you heard, I just reported that the suspect, Russell Weston, was seen outside the White House on Thursday and again on Friday. And according to senior law enforcement officials, after he was wounded, he was mumbling President Clinton's name.

MR. EMANUEL: Mm-hmm.

MR. RUSSERT: What do you know?

MR. EMANUEL: I mean, I know what you reported; I know what I've read in the paper. We've had--Chuck Ruff in the counsel's office has been briefed by Secret Service, and then I think there's been some information, but that's about--I think what the public has is the correct information as we know it right now.

MR. RUSSERT: Do you think incidents like this bolster the head of the Secret Service, Lou Merletti's, comments and attitudes that things like this can happen within moments and all the more reason why Secret Service agents have to keep in close proximity to the president at all times?

MR. EMANUEL: Tim, I think you and I have talked--I mean, both of us have family that are in the law enforcement community. I have an uncle who's a police officer in Chicago. And every morning those officers get up, they say goodbye to their family, and that could be the last time they see them. I think it would be inappropriate at this time to kind of look at the policy implications. I think there will be time for that, and plenty of people will have views about that and there should be a discussion about that. I think we're at a ime now--I think the best thing we can do as a nation, as one f ily, is make sure that the families of those slain officers know t they have the prayers and the thoughts of the American people ch them, regardless of what anybody's particular view of any policy sue related to this incident is.

MR. RUSSERT: In my conversation with Congressman Thomas, we talked about pressures to prevent this from happening again. One of the suggestions is a construction of a visitor's center on the east front of the Capitol, where people will be funneled into it, and enhanced security, a cost of $135 million, a lot of discussion as to whether public funds should be used for the building of that visitor center. Would the Clinton administration look at funding such a visitor's center?

MR. EMANUEL: Well, we haven't discussed this yet at the White House. Obviously, this is something we're going to want to work with Congress. I wouldn't rule it out, obviously, at this point. That would be something proper. But I think in all those instances I don't want this to get ahead. That will be one of the things that will be looked at. I think what Mr. Lou Merletti has said in the past is something, obviously, people will think about and discuss. And we should have those discussions, particularly to this notion of a facility going into the House and Senate chambers that's outside. That's where the public flows. And if people think that's the correct thing to do for security purposes, obviously. We add our own recommendation on Pennsylvania Avenue and immediately we acted on it for security purposes. So I think you have to take steps like that when people recommend, for security purposes.

MR. RUSSERT: You wouldn't have any objection to using public funding to build such a visitor's center?

MR. EMANUEL: You know, Tim, it's a fair question. I'm, obviously, not going to rule it out. I can't say yes or no at this point. You know, obviously, if security thinks it's important, it's something we're going to look for and look to.

MR. RUSSERT: And let me turn to the headlines of the day. Clinton Receives Order to Testify in Lewinsky Case. First Sitting President Subpoenaed to Appear at a U.S. Grand Jury. This president has made history.

MR. EMANUEL: So has Ken Starr, has made history. He's the first office of independent counsel that ever had two, as we know, ongoing investigations of its office. It has one with Michael Sheehan looking into it and it has another one by the D.C. Bar that we know about. They're looking into the conduct, both professional and ethical, of that office. And I'm--go ahead.

MR. RUSSERT: Will the president comply with the subpoena?

MR. EMANUEL: Well, first of all, don't know the nature of whether e exists or not, but what we do know is that Mr. Kendall, the president's attorney, is working with the office of independent counsel to get them the information they need. And I also think it's important to know that, as you know, Tim, in the last four years, while this office has been going on and $40 million has been spent, in fact, the president has found a way, with Mr. Kendall working with Mr. Starr, to get the information that the grand jury needs. Twice before he has testified.

MR. RUSSERT: So somewhere, somehow this president will testify under oath about the Monica Lewinsky situation?

MR. EMANUEL: David Kendall is instructed to work with Ken Starr to find a way to get the information that the grand jury needs. And we have done it in the past, and worked it out with the office of independent counsel over the last four years, as has Mrs. Clinton, I think, testified three times. So we have found a way to get the information the grand jury needs.

MR. RUSSERT: The president wants to testify under oath?

MR. EMANUEL: The president wants to get the information that the (.nd jury needs and has instructed Mr. Kendall to talk to Mr. arr to do exactly that.

MR. RUSSERT: Let me talk about an issue of credibility. As you know, NBC News called you three times on Thursday and five times on Friday...

MR. EMANUEL: Right.

MR. RUSSERT: ...and asked specifically whether a subpoena had been issued based on information we had obtained. And eight times we were told, no. Did you mislead us or did the White House lawyers mislead you?

MR. EMANUEL: Tim, what I said is we don't comment. We don't issue subpoenas and we don't comment on them. I can't characterize whether we've ever got them or whether we've ever received them or what the content of them. I don't know to that fact.

MR. RUSSERT: But we specifically asked whether you received the subpoena, and you said, no.

MR. EMANUEL: Tim, no. What we did, I discussed with you and I s d we don't comment on them. To my knowledge, I don't know if ve gotten it or not. I said exactly that to you.

MR. RUSSERT: Why then at 11:00 on a Friday night, after the

ɲitol Hill shooting, did the White House kind of put out the word the subpoena had been received?

MR. EMANUEL: Now, Tim, I think what the White House said is what we've said with Jim Kennedy, what Michael McCurry said and what I have said here. We don't issue them, we don't comment on them.

MR. RUSSERT: So we can expect, in the very near future, the president to be under oath and answer questions from Ken Starr?

MR. EMANUEL: I think what you can expect is that Dave Kendall is now working with the office of independent counsel, Ken Starr, to find that information and to get--find out a way to get the information to the grand jury.

I'd like to make one other note, Tim. You know, August 5th will be four years of the anniversary of Ken Starr's appointment. Four years ago and about $40-some odd million later, there has not been a single report by that office on the issue of Whitewater, on the issue of the travel office, on the issue of the files.

He is--the office of independent counsel under Ken Starr's . .dership is incapable of writing a report that would clear the sident or the first lady. And I want you to know August 5th, ..ss than two weeks from now, is the anniversary of Ken Starr's appointment. I don't think any American ever thought four years ago that we would be at this situation or that office has stayed open and spent $40 million, that we would not be able to come to a conclusion over a 24-year-old real estate deal, over whether, in fact, what happened with the travel office. And he is incapable of writing a report that would clear the president and the first lady.

And he has literally got one standing--what we do know it's one of the longest standing investigations, one of the most expensive investigations, one of the most intrusive investigations, including now has a unique distinction and hallmark that it's the only investigation that has two ongoing investigations into it.

MR. RUSSERT: Let me ask you about one other investigation. Charles Labella, who was appointed by Janet Reno to head up the Justice Department investigation into campaign contributions; Louis Freeh, the non-partisan director of the FBI--both of them have said unequivocally, there needs to be an independent counsel to look at campaign irregularities, both of Democrats and Republicans. Why won't the president support these two men?

.R. EMANUEL: The decision on the independent counsel is made ed on the law and the fact, and that's the way the attorney general's going to make her decision, and that's what she's going to

. She's going to weigh everybody's opinion--she has said it publicly as recently as Thursday--that decision's based on the fact and the law.

MR. RUSSERT: But if the president wanted to pick up the phone and say, "Charles Labella, your hand-picked chief investigator, the director of the FBI, have found the grounds for an independent counsel. It is important that we clear up this mess, Madame Attorney General. Please, I'm imploring you, appoint an independent counsel"?

MR. EMANUEL: Well, I think, first of all, the attorney general makes this decision based on fact and law, Tim. She has shown before she's ready to make that call on the office of the independent counsel; surely, shown that many times before. And on this situation, she'll decide based on the fact and the law and not based on any public pressure from any quarter.

MR. RUSSERT: And joining me in questioning today is David Broder of The Washington Post. David.

MR. BRODER: Mr. Emanuel, the couple issues that actually affect people's lives, starting with the State of the Union address and, equently, since then, the president has asked for legislation that uld give patients in managed-care programs some rights.

MR. EMANUEL: Mm-hmm.

MR. BRODER: On Friday, the House passed a patients' bill of rights bill that guarantees payment for emergency-room services, ends the gag rule on doctors, gives women direct access to gynecologists, provides internal and external appeals process. Why is the president threatening to veto that bill?

MR. EMANUEL: Well, it's simple, David--is that the Gingrich bill falls far short of what the president seeks in the bipartisan Dingell-Ganske bill that represents Congressman Dingell, a Democrat, and Congressman Ganske, a Republican. It doesn't--it leaves millions of Americans out of coverage. It doesn't guarantee heart specialists and cancer specialists. It doesn't guarantee the continuity of care in case of--while you have a family doctor, that doctor's cut off from insurance, it doesn't guarantee that you get to continue with that doctor. It also doesn't end the bad practice of giving a bonus to doctors who deny care. And so it doesn't meet, I think, one of the most important principles guaranteed almost every erican, a patients' bill of rights. Millions of Americans will be left out by that bill, and I don't think we should create ond-class citizens when it comes to a patients' bill of rights. We should have coverage for everybody, not limited and discreet.

.lions of Americans will be left out.

MR. BRODER: Accepting for the moment at least that it doesn't do everything that the administration would like, it does contain guarantees that are not now in the law. Many people think that the Democrats would rather have this as an issue for November than have a bill.

MR. EMANUEL: David, you've been here a long time in Washington. You've watched this for eight months. Let me just go over the history. Two years ago, the president's commission called for a patients' bill of rights. He announced it in his State of the Union. And in that eight months, he also signed an executive order guaranteeing 85 million Americans a patients' bill of rights who are under Medicare, Medicaid and federal health plans. And in those eight months, the leadership in the House and the Republican leadership called on the insurance industry to open up their wallets to help defeat this bill--any bill. And John Linder, the head of the Republican congressional campaign committee, recently said, "All we need is a vote on this to protect ourselves." Well, the goal here is not to protect the Republicans in the House; the goal here is to 'e a patients' bill of rights to Americans with health insurance.

1R. BRODER: We should note...

MR. EMANUEL: And this bill falls far short, and the Dingell-Ganske bill does accomplish the goals of every person getting a patients' bill of rights and should not limit that.

MR. BRODER: We should note just for the record that neither the president's commission nor the executive order contains provisions for an external lawsuit.

MR. EMANUEL: Right.

MR. BRODER: Let me ask about one other issue quickly.

MR. EMANUEL: Sure.

MR. BRODER: Tax cuts. Is there a tax cut that the president is willing to sign into law this year?

MR. EMANUEL: Well, two things. One is, you know that in his own budget, there is a tax cut for child care and there's a tax cult for r-tirement savings. What his principle is is that we must have S ial Security first when it comes to the surplus and that we cannot have a tax cut that eats into the surplus that then postpones any ial Security reform, which is essential. And I think now we have ..partisan agreement in the Senate. So he is for a tax cut. It's his budget. It's one that's paid for. It's child care and retirement as well as environmental tax cuts. On the issue of tax cut versus Social Security, the president's belief is, we should not dip into the surplus to pay for a tax cut. We need to basically preserve the surplus, in order, first, to fix Social Security. That's our first goal. Then we can look at that.

MR. BRODER: On Social Security, tomorrow, the president is in Albuquerque for another roundtable. Will he leave open the door to private savings accounts as part of the Social Security system, or is he going to close the door to that?

MR. EMANUEL: No, the whole commission and the whole one-year dialogue on Social Security is to, literally, A, focus on what the level of the problem is, what it needs to strengthen and preserve Social Security and see what other options are. He's not going to close off anything or limit anything or say, "This has to be part of it." That will be part of the dialogue.

I want to answer one other point and reaffirm something. When it comes to the debate about tax cuts and Social Security, this is in ' Congressional Daily, what a senior GOP aide said about the House Republicans. I think it's very telling. He said, and I read from "They need to realize," referring to the House Republicans, "that ey are out of time, out of resources, out of credibility with the Senate. Because of their stupidity and ineptitude, there is no feasible way we can get a major tax cut through Congress before adjournment. The Senate aide said House leaders are embarked on an exercise that is futile. This is not some Mickey Rooney, let's put on a show, back-lot production." Ladies and gentlemen of the jury, I couldn't have said it better.

MR. RUSSERT: That has to be the last word. Rahm Emanuel, thanks very much for joining us.

MR. EMANUEL: Thank you.

MR. RUSSERT: Coming next, for the Republicans, Don Nickles of Oklahoma; for the Democrats, Bob Kerrey of Nebraska. Then, former White House counsel Jack Quinn and former federal prosecutor Barbara Olson square off on Ken Starr versus Bill Clinton.

(Announcements)
Program Time: 10:00-11:00 AM
Nielson Rating 4584700
R :rence: 980726

d Count: 2769

Tab 52

**UNITED STATES DISTRICT COURT
FOR THE DISTRICT OF COLUMBIA**

	)	
	)	**Misc. No. (NHJ)**
IN RE GRAND JURY PROCEEDINGS	)	
	)	
	)	
	)	**(UNDER SEAL)**

MOTION OF WILLIAM J. CLINTON FOR CONTINUANCE

William J. Clinton, through undersigned counsel, hereby moves this Court for a two-week continuance, to August 11, 1998, of the return date of a subpoena delivered to his counsel seeking the President's testimony today, July 28, 1998, before the grand jury. The reasons why this Motion should be granted are set forth in the accompanying memorandum.

Respectfully submitted,

David E. Kendall (#252890)
Nicole K. Seligman
Max Stier
Alicia L. Marti
WILLIAMS & CONNOLLY
725 12th Street, N.W.
Washington, DC 20005
(202) 434-5000

Counsel for Movant William J. Clinton

UNITED STATES DISTRICT COURT
FOR THE DISTRICT OF COLUMBIA

IN RE GRAND JURY PROCEEDINGS	)	**Misc. No. (NHJ)**
	)	**(UNDER SEAL)**

ORDER

Upon consideration of the Motion of William J. Clinton for Continuance and any opposition thereto, the motion is GRANTED.

It is hereby ORDERED that the return date of the subject subpoena is continued to August 11, 1998.

SO ORDERED on this the ______ day of ___________, 1998.

NORMA HOLLOWAY JOHNSON

UNITED STATES DISTRICT COURT
FOR THE DISTRICT OF COLUMBIA

IN RE GRAND JURY PROCEEDINGS	)	Misc. No. (NHJ)
	)	(UNDER SEAL)

MEMORANDUM IN SUPPORT OF MOTION OF WILLIAM J. CLINTON FOR CONTINUANCE

For the first time, a sitting President has been subpoenaed to testify before a grand jury. On Friday evening, July 17, 1998, the Office of Independent Counsel ("OIC") delivered a subpoena to counsel attempting to compel President William J. Clinton to testify before the grand jury today, Tuesday, July 28, 1998. In response, President Clinton, through counsel, has indicated a willingness to provide voluntary testimony for the grand jury. Despite this response, the OIC has refused to continue or withdraw the subpoena returnable today, necessitating this request to the Court. This refusal creates the prospect of a constitutional confrontation that, with a short continuance, may well be avoided. Accordingly, President Clinton moves this Court for a two-week continuance of the return date of the subpoena, to August 11, 1998, to permit the parties to seek such a resolution or adequately to prepare appropriate legal papers if a resolution cannot be reached.

I. Background

Six times after January 21, 1998, the OIC invited President Clinton to testify before the grand jury investigating the Monica Lewinsky matter. See Exhibit 1 (correspondence between Mr. Kendall and the OIC regarding the President's testimony). In response, counsel for President Clinton outlined serious concerns to be addressed before any such testimony would be considered, including issues that had arisen over the origin and conduct of the OIC's Lewinsky investigation. The OIC's most recent mention of the possibility of such testimony was almost four months ago, on April 3, 1998, with a response by Mr. Kendall on April 17, 1998. See Exhibit 1. The OIC did not respond to the April 17 letter and did not raise the issue with counsel for the President in any way in the almost four months since its last letter.

After this long period of silence, on Friday, July 17, 1998, without warning, the OIC delivered a subpoena to counsel for the President purporting to require President Clinton to testify before the grand jury today, July 28. Exhibit 2 (subpoena and accompanying letter). At the time, President Clinton was traveling outside of Washington, D.C., and he did not return until early Tuesday, July 21, 1998. In light of the need to consider properly the serious issues presented by the subpoena, counsel for President Clinton telephoned Mr. Bittman (of the OIC) on July 22, 1998, and requested that the OIC provide another week, until August 4, for counsel to respond to the July 17 delivery. On July 23, 1998, the OIC offered three more days, if the President would agree not to seek any additional time from the OIC or the Court. Exhibit 3 (July 23, 1998 Letter of Mr. Bittman).

On July 24, 1998, counsel for President Clinton informed the OIC that the President "is willing to provide testimony for the grand jury, although there are a number of questions relating to the precise terms and timing of the testimony which must be worked out." Exhibit 4 (July 24, 1998 Letter of Mr. Kendall). Counsel for the President also requested that the subpoena be withdrawn while these issues were resolved. The OIC declined to withdraw the subpoena. Exhibit 5 (July 24, 1998 Letter of Mr. Bittman). Subsequently, by letter yesterday, Mr. Kendall wrote to the OIC with a detailed and specific proposal regarding both the format and timing of potential testimony by the President. Exhibit 6 (July 27, 1998 Letter of Mr. Kendall).

Despite this responsive and good faith offer, and the prospect of immediate continuing negotiations, the OIC refused to withdraw or even continue the return date of the subpoena beyond 1:30 p.m. today unless "the President commits in writing to testify on a date certain on or before August 7, 1998.". See Exhibit 7 (July 27, 1998 Letter of Mr. Bittman).

II. Argument

The OIC's denial of a brief continuance here is wholly unreasonable. There is a very real possibility that the President and the OIC will be able to agree on timing and procedures whereby the President may provide information to the grand jury. The subpoena plainly raises fundamental separation of powers concerns, see Exhibit 8 ("Starr Subpoena Poses Constitutional Conflict," Chicago Tribune, July 27, 1998); (Interview of Professor Paul Rothstein, ABC News, July 26, 1998), which have not previously been presented to a court and adjudicated. The Supreme Court observed in the Paula Jones case that "although Presidents have responded to written interrogatories, given depositions, and provided videotaped trial testimony . . . no sitting President has ever testified, or been asked to testify in open court." Clinton v. Jones, ___ U.S. ___, 117 S.Ct. 1636, 1643 n.14 (1997). There may, however, be no need to resolve the novel question whether a President may be compelled to testify before a grand jury. But more time is needed to explore whether a resolution short of litigation is possible.

The OIC's assertion that it needs the President's testimony on or before August 7, 1998, is patently unfounded. The Whitewater investigation has dragged on for more than four years. The OIC last raised the question of the President testifying in early April, and it then did not respond in any way to counsel's April 17 letter on this subject. As the OIC well knows, in the past when the President's testimony has been sought, it has taken weeks to schedule an appropriate date, because of the President's many commitments and because of the length of time his schedule is set in advance. In the present case, counsel have presented the OIC with a "date certain" for his testimony which is consistent with the President's schedule and other obligations. The OIC has stated that an earlier date is necessary. Because the President has not immediately agreed, the OIC has refused to continue today's return date at all. This obstinate refusal demonstrates a desire to precipitate a possibly needless battle, rather than a statesmanlike effort to avoid one.

The OIC's position is particularly arbitrary here because there are no impending deadlines, no statutes of limitations are about to run, and no trials are imminent. There is simply no justification for the OIC's deadline except its own fiat. This captious and cavalier treatment is particularly inconsistent with the OIC's often professed "profound respect for the institution of the Presidency."[1] While the OIC has stated that it "fully acknowledge[d] that the President has immense and weighty responsibilities" and that it "want[ed] in every way to take fully into account those grave duties of state,"[2] its actions here belie these sentiments and also show how hollow is the OIC's recent representation that if the President will agree to testify "we and the grand jury -- as we have previously stated -- will accommodate [the President's] schedule if he cannot appear on the 28th [of July]."[3]

For whatever reasons, the OIC insists that the President agree in writing by 1:30 p.m. today to testify on or before August 7. As explained in detail in a letter from counsel to the President provided yesterday to the OIC, see Exhibit 6, that date is wholly unacceptable, given the President's schedule and the need for the President to prepare properly for his testimony.

---

1 Exhibit 1 (Letter of Robert J. Bittman, Esq., to David E. Kendall, Esq., dated March 13, 1998).

2 Exhibit 1 (Letter of Robert J. Bittman, Esq., to David E. Kendall, Esq., dated March 2, 1998).

3 Exhibit 2 (Letter of Robert J. Bittman, Esq., to David E. Kendall, Esq., dated July 17, 1998).

When the Supreme Court indicated last year that a civil case could proceed against a sitting President, it nevertheless insisted that the "high respect that is owed to the Office of the Chief Executive . . . should inform the conduct of the entire proceeding," and it stressed the importance of avoiding "interference with the President's duties." Jones v. Clinton, ___ U.S. ___, 117 S.Ct. 1636, 1650-51 (1997). The Court of Appeals for this Circuit only yesterday, in a case arising from the OIC's investigation, emphasized the "deference due to the President" as he seeks to meet both public and private legal obligations and ruled that a court "must accommodate the unavoidable, virtually full-time demands of the office." In re: Bruce R. Lindsey (Grand Jury Testimony), No 98-3060 (D.C. Cir. July 27, 1998) (slip op. at 36, 38).[4]

Given the constitutional significance of the issues presented by the subpoena, the lack of any colorable reason to deny a short continuance, the possibility that an agreement might be reached which would accommodate the concerns of both the OIC and the President, and the long delay which will certainly follow if a legal confrontation is forced, we respectfully submit that the OIC's refusal to continue the subpoena is irresponsible, unreasonable, and oppressive. When the Supreme Court decided the Jones case, it did so on the basis of an explicitly stated assumption that any testimony from the President "may be taken . . . at a time that will accommodate his busy schedule," Clinton v. Jones, supra, 117 S.Ct. at 1643. It is just such an accommodation that movant seeks and that the OIC arbitrarily resists.

---

4 The Court of Appeals noted that "there is a tradition of federal courts' affording 'the utmost deference to Presidential responsibilities.'" Id. at 39.

CONCLUSION

For the foregoing reasons, President Clinton's motion for a two-week continuance should be granted.

Respectfully submitted,

David E. Kendall (#252890)
Nicole K. Seligman
Max Stier
Alicia L. Marti
WILLIAMS & CONNOLLY
725 12th Street, N.W.
Washington, DC 20005
(202) 434-5000

Counsel for Movant William J. Clinton

CERTIFICATE OF SERVICE

I certify that I have this 28th day of July 1998 caused one copy of the foregoing Motion of William J. Clinton for Continuance, memorandum in support thereof, and proposed Order to be hand delivered to:

Robert J. Bittman, Esquire
Independent Counsel
Office of the Independent Counsel
1001 Pennsylvania Avenue, N.W.
Suite 490-North
Washington, DC 20004

David E. Kendall

Tab 1

Office of the Independent Counsel

1001 Pennsylvania Avenue, N.W.
Suite 490-North
Washington, DC 20004
(202) 514-8688
Fax (202) 514-8802

February 2, 1998

HAND DELIVERED

David E. Kendall, Esq.
Williams & Connolly
725 Twelfth Street, N.W.
Washington, D.C. 20005

Re: William Jefferson Clinton

Dear David:

As you know, President Clinton has publicly pledged to cooperate fully with the investigation involving Monica Lewinsky. Last Wednesday, January 28, I invited President Clinton, on behalf of the grand jury, to testify before the grand jury this Thursday, February 5, concerning matters relating to Ms. Lewinsky. You indicated in our conversation that you would get back to me as to whether the President will so testify. The grand jury awaits the President's decision; please advise me as soon as possible what the President decides.

Sincerely,

Robert J. Bittman

Robert J. Bittman
Deputy Independent Counsel

Office of the Independent Counsel

1001 Pennsylvania Avenue, N.W.
Suite 490-North
Washington, DC 20004
(202) 514-8688
Fax (202) 514-8802

February 4, 1998

HAND DELIVERED

David E. Kendall, Esq.
Williams & Connolly
725 Twelfth Street, N.W.
Washington, D.C. 20005

Re: William Jefferson Clinton

Dear David:

Although the President has declined the invitation to testify before the grand jury tomorrow, the grand jury's investigation continues apace. On behalf of the grand jury and in an effort to accommodate the President's schedule, we respectfully invite the President to testify before the grand jury next Tuesday, Wednesday, or Thursday, February 10 to 12.

The grand jury would like to complete this investigation, as the President stated, "sooner rather than later. . . . [and] as quickly as we can." Kindly advise me by noon this Friday as to whether the President accepts the invitation to testify.

Sincerely,

Robert J. Bittman
Deputy Independent Counsel

Office of the Independent Counsel

1001 Pennsylvania Avenue, N.W.
Suite 490-North
Washington, DC 20004
(202) 514-8688
Fax (202) 514-8802

February 9, 1998

HAND DELIVERED

David E. Kendall, Esq.
Williams & Connolly
725 Twelfth Street, N.W.
Washington, D.C. 20005

Re: William Jefferson Clinton

Dear David:

Last Wednesday, we, on behalf of the grand jury, extended a second invitation to the President to testify before the grand jury about his relationship with Monica Lewinsky. You did not respond to the invitation by last Friday, as requested in my letter. The grand jury's work continues. Notwithstanding your failure to respond, the grand jury would be pleased to accommodate the President's testimony any day or time this week.

Let me make our request specific and clear: the grand jury deserves to know whether the President will respond, favorably, to the invitation. Such an invitation is, of course, fully consistent with our profound respect for the Presidency in our system of separated powers. To that end, we have consulted with the Chief Judge, and she has assured us that the grand jury can accommodate the President's scheduling needs should the President choose to tell his story to the grand jury.

For planning purposes, kindly let me know if the President wishes to testify before the grand jury this week. If the President cannot appear this week, please let me know by Friday, February 13, whether the President wishes to testify

David E. Kendall, Esq.
February 9, 1998
Page two

before the grand jury, and if so, when. If I do not hear from you by that date, we will assume that the President will not voluntarily provide testimony before the grand jury. In that event, we will inform the grand jury of this turn of events.

Sincerely,

Robert J. Bittman

Robert J. Bittman
Deputy Independent Counsel

LAW OFFICES
WILLIAMS & CONNOLLY
725 TWELFTH STREET, N.W.
WASHINGTON, D. C. 20005-5901
(202) 434-5000
FAX (202) 434-5029

EDWARD BENNETT WILLIAMS (1920-1988)
PAUL R. CONNOLLY (1922-1978)

DAVID E. KENDALL
(202) 434-5145

February 13, 1998

CONFIDENTIAL
RULE 6(e), F. R. CRIM. P. GRAND JURY SUBMISSION

By Hand

Robert J. Bittman, Esq.
Deputy Independent Counsel
Office of the Independent Counsel
1001 Pennsylvania Avenue, N.W.
Suite 490-North
Washington, D.C. 20004

Dear Bob:

This will respond to your letters dated February 4 and 9, 1998. I was unable to respond to your February 4 invitation by the Friday deadline you had indicated in your letter because I was in the process of dealing with prejudicial and false leaks of information about your investigation. I set forth my position on that matter in brief public remarks Friday afternoon and in a 15 page letter to Judge Starr which I hand-delivered to your office that same afternoon. These leaks are highly unfair and prejudicial to the President and others, and, as you may know, on Monday I filed a sealed motion with the Chief Judge seeking judicial remedies in an effort to enforce the secrecy and confidentiality of the investigative process.

I acknowledge your invitation for the President to appear before the grand jury next week. The President has the greatest respect for the grand jury. However, under the circumstances, it is impossible to accept this invitation. The situation in Iraq continues to be dangerously volatile, and this has demanded much of the President's time and attention. The President also has a heavy travel schedule at present. Our access to him has necessarily been limited. Moreover, as I informed you during our February 3 telephone conversation concerning this matter, we have simply had inadequate opportunity to prepare so that we may give our client the informed advice of counsel which he, like every other citizen, deserves. Your recent letter references your

WILLIAMS & CONNOLLY

Robert J. Bittman, Esq.
February 13, 1998
Page 2

office's "profound respect for the Presidency in our system of separated powers." However, I am certain that you understand why, in light of the well-publicized and questionable investigative techniques of your office, we feel we would be derelict in our professional duty to a client unless we assured ourselves that we had adequate opportunity to advise that client appropriately.

In the event you decide to "inform the grand jury of this turn of events", as stated in your letter, I would respectfully request that you also read my letter to the grand jury and make my letter part of the grand jury record.

I thank you for your courtesy.

Sincerely,

David E. Kendall

Office of the Independent Counsel

1001 Pennsylvania Avenue, N.W.
Suite 490-North
Washington, DC 20004
(202) 514-8688
Fax (202) 514-8802

February 21, 1998

VIA FACSIMILE

David E. Kendall, Esq.
Williams & Connolly
725 Twelfth Street, N.W.
Washington, D.C. 20005

Re: William Jefferson Clinton

Dear David:

We regret the President's decision not to appear before the grand jury at this time. In light of the President's past and continuing pledges to cooperate with this investigation, we again invite the President to testify before the grand jury about his relationship with Monica Lewinsky. We make this invitation fully sensitive to the important duties and responsibilities of the President. Moreover, as stated in my last letter, I have discussed this matter with Chief Judge Johnson, and she has indicated that the grand jury will accommodate any special scheduling needs of the President. We are ready to hear the President's testimony. Kindly let me know by Friday, February 27, whether the President will agree to testify before the grand jury at any time.

Sincerely,

Robert J. Bittman

Robert J. Bittman
Deputy Independent Counsel

Office of the Independent ınsel

1001 Pennsylvania Avenue, N.W.
Suite 490-North
Washington, DC 20004
(202) 514-8688
Fax (202) 514-8802

March 2, 1998

HAND DELIVERED

David E. Kendall, Esq.
Williams & Connolly
725 Twelfth Street, N.W.
Washington, D.C. 20005

Re: William Jefferson Clinton

Dear David:

Based on your previous declinations and your failure to respond within the time outlined in my letter of February 21, 1998, we assume that the President has declined our invitation to testify before the grand jury. With this letter, we again invite the President to provide the grand jury with information concerning its ongoing investigation.

In regard to the various explanations you have been kind enough to advance for declining our four invitations, I note that (1) the state visit of Prime Minister Blair has passed; (2) the "situation in Iraq" has, thankfully, eased; and (3) you have now had some six weeks to "prepare" the President. See letters to Robert J. Bittman from David E. Kendall dated February 4 and February 13. We fully acknowledge that the President has immense and weighty responsibilities. We want in every way to take fully into account those grave duties of state. Yet since this matter arose, the President has -- with all respect -- found time to play golf, attend basketball games and political fundraisers, and enjoy a ski vacation. We assure you that the grand jury's inquiry of the President will not take long, and we and the grand jury remain -- as we have always been -- eager to accommodate the President's schedule.

David E. Kendall, Esq.
March 2, 1998
Page two

Kindly advise me by noon Wednesday, March 4, 1998, whether the President will accept this invitation. If I do not hear from you by that time, I will assume the President declines the invitation. I look forward to your early -- and, I hope favorable -- reply.

Sincerely,

Robert J. Bittman

Robert J. Bittman
Deputy Independent Counsel

LAW OFFICES
WILLIAMS & CONNOLLY
725 TWELFTH STREET, N.W.
WASHINGTON, D. C. 20005-5901
(202) 434-5000
FAX (202) 434-5029

EDWARD BENNETT WILLIAMS (1920-1988)
PAUL R. CONNOLLY (1922-1978)

DAVID E. KENDALL
(202) 434-5145

March 4, 1998

CONFIDENTIAL
RULE 6(e), F.R.CRIM.P. GRAND JURY SUBMISSION

Robert J. Bittman, Esq.
Deputy Independent Counsel
Office of the Independent Counsel
1001 Pennsylvania Avenue, N.W.
Suite 490-North
Washington, D.C. 20004

By Hand

Dear Bob:

This will respond to your letters dated February 21 and March 2, 1998. I apologize for my delay in responding. The fault is mine: as you know, we filed a lengthy reply on Friday in the sealed "leaks" matter, responding to your opposition to our original motion for contempt sanctions. That matter simply absorbed my time, but I am now able to give your correspondence the attention it deserves.

As I hope you are aware, the President has the greatest respect for the grand jury. I appreciate your own acknowledgement in your March 2 letter of the "grave duties of state" which are uniquely the President's and the "immense and weighty responsibilities" he must discharge. The buck really does stop with the President for decision-making on a vast range of issues that are critical to this country's safety and economic security.

While it is true that not every moment of the day is absorbed by the duties of office, the President is extraordinarily busy on a range of important public issues, some of which are visible and some of which are not. In our judgment, our ability to have access to the President is simply insufficient at the present time for purposes of representing him adequately in the matters with which you are concerned.

WILLIAMS & CONNOLLY

Robert J. Bittman, Esq.
March 4, 1998
Page 2

Accordingly, he will, on our advice, not be able to accept your invitation for him to testify at this time. I am certain you would agree that the President deserves the same right to the informed assistance of private counsel as does every other citizen.

Your most recent letter remarks that the situation in Iraq has "thankfully, eased." While there are some respects in which this may be true, the situation remains highly volatile, as a glance at today's newspapers will reveal. The continuing Southeast Asian economic crisis and the Bosnian situation also demand a great deal of the President's time, as do other national security issues, many of which are highly confidential.

On the domestic front, the President's schedule is equally congested. The Administration's proposed budget was submitted to Congress last month, and the President is in the midst of major negotiations with the Republican majorities over key budgetary objectives, such as reserving the bulk of the budgetary surplus for Social Security. Other Administration initiatives are at critical stages. The President is attempting to hammer out national legislation around a tobacco liability settlement. More "town hall" meetings are scheduled concerning the President's race initiative, which will focus on the need for strengthening the Equal Employment Opportunities Commission and the Civil Rights Division of the Justice Department. There is also currently in the White House a sustained focus on major health care proposals (expanding Medicare coverage to persons age 55-64 who have lost their health coverage due to no fault of their own; securing passage of an HMO patient "bill of rights"), on new education legislation (enacting strong national educational standards; trying to improve math and science achievement), and on highway legislation/auto safety bills (federal standards for a lower blood alcohol definition in DUI cases).

The President also has an extremely heavy foreign and domestic travel schedule. He will be out of the country for nearly three weeks this month and next in Africa and South America. These are major State visits to key strategic parts of the world, and a considerable amount of pre-departure preparation, review, and study is required, which will absorb a significant amount of the President's time in this country.

Moreover, as I indicated in my earlier letter, we remain concerned about some of the well-publicized and questionable investigative techniques used by your office. Events of recent days have done nothing to alleviate this concern, and this necessarily affects our judgment as to the degree of preparation necessary to assure the President has adequate and informed legal assistance at the present time. As you are no doubt aware, you have subpoenaed the investigator retained by this firm and by the law firm defending the President in the Paula Jones suit, and the focus of your questioning was on criticism directed at your office. This investigator was retained for lawful, legitimate, and well-recognized purposes, and your subpoena is, in our view, a blatant and unwarranted attempt to intrude into and violate the legal privileges enjoyed by every citizen, including the President, in litigation where that citizen is personally being sued or investigated. No more reassuring is your recent interrogation of Mr. Sidney Blumenthal, who works at the White House, to inquire into criticisms of your office in the press. Finally, I have received no response to my letter (a copy of which is attached hereto) sent to the Independent Counsel more than two weeks ago, inquiring as to contacts his law firm (Kirkland & Ellis) had with the lawyers for Ms. Paula Jones and legal assistance it had rendered to her. Some news reports raise troubling issues of possible conflict of interest, and I would like to get these resolved just as soon as possible.

You do, of course, have a copy of the President's deposition given on January 17, 1998, in the Jones case, and his sworn testimony there addresses at length the Monica Lewinsky matter. You have also, as I understand, requested multiple copies of the videotape of this deposition. I believe, therefore, that the grand jury in fact already has access to sworn testimony given by the President about this topic. The questions asked the President by Ms. Jones' counsel were, in fact, surprisingly detailed and particularized. As you may know, there have been news reports suggesting that Ms. Linda Tripp spent most of the Friday before the President's deposition with lawyers and agents from your office, after the apprehension of Ms. Lewinsky at a meeting with Ms. Tripp. At the end of her day with your personnel, again according to press reports, Ms. Tripp, with the apparent acquiescence of your office, met in Maryland with lawyers for Ms. Jones. There, she reportedly told them of the tapes she had secretly made of her conversations with Ms. Lewinsky, shared with them the contents of these secret tapes, and helped them devise questions to ask the President at his deposition next day, the transcript of which you have. We believe that, at least by this time, Ms. Tripp was well aware that such tapings were illegal and a felony under Maryland law. We are in the process of investigating all the legal implications of these apparent facts.

WILLIAMS & CONNOLLY

Robert J. Bittman, Esq.
March 4, 1998
Page 4

Again, I would respectfully ask you to read this letter, with its attachment, to the grand jury and to make them part of the grand jury record, if your letters to me are shared with the grand jury.

I thank you for your courtesy.

Sincerely,

David E. Kendall

LAW OFFICES
WILLIAMS & CONNOLLY
725 TWELFTH STREET, N.W.
WASHINGTON, D. C. 20005-5901
(202) 434-5000
FAX (202) 434-5029

EDWARD BENNETT WILLIAMS (1920-1988)
PAUL R. CONNOLLY (1922-1978)

DAVID E. KENDALL
(202) 434-5145

February 17, 1998

The Honorable Kenneth W. Starr
Independent Counsel
Office of the Independent Counsel
1001 Pennsylvania Avenue, N.W.
Suite 490-North
Washington, D.C. 20004

BY HAND

Dear Judge Starr:

I write with an inquiry in the wake of a Chicago Tribune article which appeared on February 11 (copy enclosed), and I am making this request in an effort to obtain accurate information so that I may decide how to proceed. The article reports that one of your partners in Kirkland & Ellis, Mr. Richard Porter, may have provided legal advice and services to plaintiff Paula Corbin Jones in her civil suit against President Clinton. The article also reports that someone at the law firm FAXed a copy of a draft affidavit in the Jones case to the Tribune prior to the affidavit's filing in court, an action which would, if true, suggest that the firm has indeed been involved in the legal prosecution of the Jones case. Finally, the article reports that one of the Jones lawyers, Joseph Cammarata, received advice from Mr. Porter on several occasions about legal issues in the Jones case. This recent report is particularly surprising in view of previous news articles in which your partners at Kirkland & Ellis were quoted as saying that the firm would not become involved in the Jones case ("'We don't feel it's appropriate for the firm to be involved in any civil litigation directly involving the president,' [Kirkland & Ellis partner] Jay Lefkowitz [said]." The Washington Post, Aug. 12, 1994). (Copy enclosed).

Additionally, there have been reports of your own participation in legal discussions with Ms. Jones' lawyers, prior to the time you were appointed Independent Counsel.

WILLIAMS & CONNOLLY

Honorable Kenneth W. Starr
February 17, 1998
Page 2

I emphasize that I am not now addressing the fact that you planned to file an amicus brief for the Independent Women's Forum after the Jones complaint was filed, something that has been previously reported. See, e.g., "Friend of Court Is Foe of Clinton," Washington Times, June 8, 1994, at 1A.

Instead, my present inquiry focuses on recent reports that you gave legal advice to Ms. Jones' lawyers pertaining to her own lawsuit against the President. For example, the Associated Press reported on January 28, 1998, that you gave legal advice to Ms. Jones' lawyers "on 'the legal question of whether the president is accountable in a private lawsuit,' according to Gilbert K. Davis, who no longer represents Mrs. Jones." (Copy enclosed.) On January 30, 1998, the Associated Press reported that Ms. Jones' lawyers "acknowledge consulting with Starr after filing the lawsuit, but said that was only to seek advice from the constitutional scholar on how to address Clinton's claim that he was temporarily immune from lawsuits . . . . The lawyers said they contacted Starr . . . before he was named Whitewater prosecutor." (Copy enclosed.) That same day, The Washington Post reported that "Jones's former lawyers now . . . say that Starr even consulted with them in two or three telephone calls that dealt with the legal arguments to be made against Clinton's immunity claim." (Copy enclosed.)

You apparently believed that, even before the recent expansion of your jurisdiction, you were somehow entitled to investigate the Paula Corbin Jones matter. It was reported last summer, before the January 16, 1998, expansion of your jurisdiction, that your investigation was focusing in some way on Ms. Paula Corbin Jones. For example, The Washington Post reported the following on June 25, 1997:

> "The [Arkansas state] troopers said investigators asked about 12 to 15 women by name, including Paula Corbin Jones, a former Arkansas state employee who has filed a civil lawsuit against Clinton alleging he sexually harassed her in 1991.
>
> . . . .
>
> In addition, [Roger Perry] said, 'They [your investigators] asked me about Paula Jones, all kinds of questions about Paula Jones, whether I saw Clinton and Paula together and how many times.'"

(Copy enclosed.)

I would be grateful if you could inform me whether any of these many news reports are accurate, and I would also request that, if any of the above reports are accurate, you inform me whether such information was presented to the Attorney General or the Special Division prior to the Court's January 16, 1998, expansion of your jurisdiction. As I know you will recall, the Special Division has been quite sensitive to the appearance of conflict. In its August 5, 1994, Order appointing you, that Court stated that it had determined that a continuation of Mr. Fiske's appointment "would not be consistent with the purposes of the Act:"

> "This reflects no conclusion on the part of the Court that Fiske lacks either the actual independence or any other attribute necessary to the conclusion of the investigation. Rather, the Court reaches this conclusion because the Act contemplated an apparent as well as an actual independence on the part of the Counsel. As the Senate Report accompanying the 1982 enactments reflected, '[t]he intent of the special prosecutor provisions is not to impugn the integrity of the Attorney General or the Department of Justice. Throughout our system of justice, safeguards exist against actual <u>or perceived</u> conflicts of interest without reflecting adversely on the parties who are subject to conflicts.' S. Rep. No. 496, 97th Cong., 2d Sess. at 6 (1982) (emphasis added). Just so here. It is not our intent to impugn the integrity of the Attorney General's appointee, but rather to reflect the intent of the Act that the actor <u>be protected against perceptions of conflict</u>."

(Second emphasis added.)

In addition, the Independent Counsel Statute imposes certain restrictions on both the person appointed as IC and that person's law firm. For example, 28 U.S.C. § 594(j)(1)(A) provides that "[d]uring the period in which an independent counsel is serving under this chapter (i) such independent counsel, and (ii) any person associated with a firm with which such independent counsel is associated, may not represent in any matter any person involved in any investigation or prosecution under this chapter." Moreover, under elementary principles of partnership law in Illinois, Arkansas, and the District of Columbia, a legal representation of a client by one partner is attributable to all other partners.

Application of these legal standards to the facts set forth in the recent news articles quoted above raises serious and troubling questions about the propriety of your serving as

Independent Counsel to investigate matters pertaining to the Jones case. You have in the past investigated the Jones matter, according to The Washington Post. The recent expansion of your jurisdiction explicitly requires you to investigate events "concerning the civil case Jones v. Clinton." You have, since your appointment as Independent Counsel, remained an active partner in the Kirkland & Ellis law firm, as was your right. The partnership includes Mr. Porter.

I hope you can therefore perceive why I am requesting accurate and specific information (i) concerning your own, Mr. Porter's, and any other Kirkland & Ellis lawyer's, employee's or agent's contacts with and assistance to Ms. Paula Corbin Jones and/or her attorneys or agents or supporting groups, and (ii) concerning what was conveyed to the Attorney General and the Special Division in January, 1998, about any such contacts and assistance, when you sought an expansion of your jurisdiction to encompass the Jones v. Clinton case.

I thank you for your courtesy.

Sincerely,

David E. Kendall

Office of the Independent Counsel

1001 Pennsylvania Avenue, N.W.
Suite 490-North
Washington, DC 20004
(202) 514-8688
Fax (202) 514-8802

March 13, 1998

HAND DELIVERED

David E. Kendall, Esq.
Williams & Connolly
725 Twelfth Street, N.W.
Washington, D.C. 20005

Re: William Jefferson Clinton

Dear David:

By your letter last Wednesday, March 4, 1998, the President has now declined five invitations to testify and tell his story to the grand jury.

As time goes on, now eight weeks into the investigation, your claim that the President continues not to have time to prepare his testimony about Ms. Lewinsky is increasingly difficult for us to understand. We mean no disrespect whatever, mindful as we are of the President's constitutional obligations, but as stated in my letter of March 2, 1998, since the Monica Lewinsky matter began the President has found time to play golf, attend basketball games and political fundraisers, and enjoy a ski vacation. On January 17, 1998, the President was deposed for nearly a full day in the Jones v. Clinton lawsuit. Your co-counsel, Bob Bennett, has even moved to expedite the trial date in that case. In addition, as you remember, despite the President's weighty responsibilities we had no trouble scheduling the President's depositions for other Whitewater-related matters, and we were able to schedule his testimony in the two trials in Little Rock with relative ease. In those trials, of course, he was summoned as a defense witness, not by the United States.

You may recall that when the grand jury issued a subpoena for Mrs. Clinton's testimony in January 1996, you and White House Counsel complained that she, at minimum, should have first been given the opportunity to appear voluntarily. You and White House Counsel urged alternatives in lieu of a grand jury appearance. As to the President and the Lewinsky matter, however, you have declined five invitations to testify voluntarily. Moreover, you have suggested no alternatives.

Until last week, the President had repeatedly pledged his full cooperation in connection with the Monica Lewinsky investigation. Last Thursday, March 5, 1998 -- one day after the President declined our fifth invitation to appear voluntarily before the grand jury -- the President publicly declared he had "given all the answers that matter" relating to Ms. Lewinsky. The President has also invoked executive privilege under circumstances exceedingly difficult to justify under settled principles of our constitutional system. We are, in consequence, constrained to say this: We now question whether the President ever intends to cooperate with this investigation, as promised, and testify.

The suggestion in your letter that our possession of the President's deposition in the Jones v. Clinton case provides the grand jury "access" to the President's information about the Lewinsky matters is, with all respect, disingenuous. The President was questioned in his deposition about a single, narrow issue involving Ms. Lewinsky. As you know, the Special Division -- upon the specific request of the Attorney General -- defined our jurisdiction to include "whether Monica Lewinsky or others suborned perjury, obstructed justice, intimidated witnesses, or otherwise violated federal law . . . in dealing with witnesses, potential witnesses, attorneys, or others concerning the civil case Jones v. Clinton." Our inquiry is by law much broader than the narrow issue about which the President was questioned in his deposition.

Let me reiterate: we have profound respect for the institution of the Presidency. Yet, as I am sure you agree, the grand jury is entitled to "every man's evidence." See United States v. Nixon, 418 U.S. 683 (1974); United States v. Burr, 25 Fed.Cas. 20 (No. 14,692) (C.C. Va. 1807). It is urgent that we receive the President's testimony in this matter as soon as possible.

Kindly advise me by noon Tuesday, March 17, 1998, whether the President will testify in any manner about the matters involving Ms. Lewinsky. If, as I indicated briefly above, alternatives to a grand jury appearance have occurred to you, then we are prepared to discuss them at your earliest

David E. Kendall, Esq.
March 13, 1998
Page 3

convenience. In particular, a deposition format -- should the President refuse his right to present his testimony to the grand jury and face his fellow citizens eye to eye -- is an arrangement we stand ready to discuss. We are ready and able to accommodate any issues of Presidential dignity, as well as security, which of course can be readily accomplished at the United States Courthouse.

Nothing, in short, should stand in the way of the truth's coming out. As should be apparent, we continue to seek -- on behalf of the grand jury -- the President's truthful testimony before that body, which stands ready to sustain any inconvenience in order to respect the President's schedule, while at the same time carrying out its solemn function under our system of law.

Sincerely,

Robert J. Bittman
Deputy Independent Counsel

LAW OFFICES
WILLIAMS & CONNOLLY
725 TWELFTH STREET, N.W.
WASHINGTON, D.C. 20005-5901
(202) 434-5000
FAX (202) 434-5029

EDWARD BENNETT WILLIAMS (1920-1988)
PAUL R. CONNOLLY (1922-1978)

DAVID E. KENDALL
(202) 434-5145

March 18, 1998

<u>CONFIDENTIAL</u>
<u>RULE 6(e), F.R.CRIM.P., GRAND JURY SUBMISSION</u>

Robert J. Bittman, Esq.
Deputy Independent Counsel
Office of the Independent Counsel
1001 Pennsylvania Avenue, N.W.
Suite 490-North
Washington, D.C. 20004

<u>By Hand</u>

Dear Bob:

Thank you for your letter dated March 13, 1998. I will be equally frank in response.

For over four years now, the President has cooperated in every possible way with the investigation of the Independent Counsel. He has voluntarily given testimony under oath on three separate occasions to the Independent Counsel and twice to defendants (on each occasion, he was cross-examined by the Independent Counsel), he has submitted written interrogatory answers, he has produced more than 90,000 pages of documents, and he has provided information informally in a variety of ways.

I, too, have dealt in good faith with your investigation for more than four years. Until the recent expansion of jurisdiction to cover the Lewinsky matter, I have not had occasion to raise, nor have I raised, the kind of concerns I have adverted to in recent correspondence. I will be more specific: the actions of the Office of Independent Counsel in the past several weeks (as distinct from the actions of the grand jury) lead me to believe that your investigation may not, in fact, be an even-handed search for justice but rather may be, for whatever reason, a campaign to embarrass and harass the President. I believe he is now plainly the object of your investigation.

You state that it is "disingenuous" to assert that the President's deposition transcript (including the videotape of the deposition, which you likely will soon have access to) in Jones v. Clinton allows you to obtain the President's information on the Lewinsky matter. We continue to believe that the forty deposition pages of testimony (pp. 48-86, 202-204) on this topic set forth the essentials of this matter, although there are doubtless more questions you might be able to devise.

Of more serious concern to us is evidence that your office contrived to obtain the President's deposition testimony through improper and illegal means. Based upon what we have been able to learn thus far (see, e.g., the page one Washington Post article on February 14, 1998, headlined "Linda Tripp Briefed Jones Team on Tapes"), your office, your agent Linda Tripp, and the Paula Jones lawyers apparently colluded to use the fruits of Tripp's felonious audiotaping (see Md. Code Ann. § 10-402 (1997)) of Lewinsky against the President at his deposition on Saturday, January 17, 1998. Curiously, Tripp appears to have been given immunity by your office immediately after she contacted you. She then secretly recorded at least one conversation with Lewinsky, an act that (unlike her previous audiotapings) does not appear to have been in violation of wiretap law. According to the Washington Post's February 14 article, Tripp arranged to have Lewinsky apprehended by your agents about noon on Friday, January 16, then put off a meeting with the Jones lawyers until (we believe) it became clear that Ms. Lewinsky would not herself agree to wear a recording device to gather evidence against others. At some point late in the afternoon, Tripp "sent word" to the Jones lawyers that she would talk to them, and she was transported to her home in Maryland (perhaps by one of your agents) where she proceeded to share both the existence of the illegal tapes[1] and their contents with the Jones lawyers, who were able to use this information the next day to question the President.[2]

1/ Under the Maryland electronic surveillance statute which makes one-party telephone call taping a felony, it is a violation of the statute to disclose that an illegal tape has been made, since the term "contents" (the disclosure of which are forbidden) is defined to include "any information concerning the identity of the parties to the communication or the existence, substance, purport, or meaning of that communication." Md. Code Ann. § 10-401(7) (1997)(emphasis added).

2/ Indeed, the Washington Times observed that "With the information from Mrs. Tripp, the Jones lawyers were able to ask Mr. Clinton in his deposition specific questions about

The Ethics in Government Act provides in Sec. 593(c)(1) a carefully defined procedure for expanding the jurisdiction of an independent counsel. If a new matter is not "related" to an existing subject of investigation (and the Lewinsky matter plainly was not), the statute does not allow a free-roving investigation beyond the limits of an independent counsel's present jurisdiction. For example, there would be no statutory justification to "wire" a cooperating witness to investigate further a matter not within the jurisdiction of the independent counsel. Section 593(c)(2)(A) of the Act provides that "[i]f the independent counsel discovers or receives information about possible violations of criminal law by [covered persons] which are not covered by the prosecutorial jurisdiction of the independent counsel, the independent counsel may submit such information to the Attorney General," and the Attorney General "shall then conduct a preliminary investigation of the information in accordance with the provisions of section 592" (emphasis added). While the Attorney General "shall give great weight to any recommendations of the independent counsel" (ibid.), the determination whether to recommend to the Special Division an expansion of jurisdiction is the Attorney General's alone.

Under the circumstances here, there was no need for a hasty and informal presentation to the Attorney General--unless the OIC was hoping to use Tripp (and perhaps Lewinsky) to somehow obtain incriminating evidence against the President whose deposition in the civil case was fast approaching. We believe that the Attorney General was not properly informed about the circumstances which ostensibly justified the expansion of jurisdiction sought, and that your recent investigation has in fact been a contrivance to justify post facto the grant of jurisdiction that your office obtained from the Special Division.

It appears to us that you did not seek, the Attorney General did not approve, and the Special Division did not authorize the

---

his relationship with and gifts to Miss Lewinsky, according to a person informed about the President's testimony." (The Washington Times, Feb. 15, 1998.) At the deposition, when the President remarked after a series of highly specific questions concerning Ms. Lewinsky, "I don't even know what you're talking about, I don't think," Ms. Jones' lawyer, James Fisher, replied, "Sir, I think this will come to light shortly, and you'll understand." Deposition transcript, at 85.

extension of your jurisdiction based on any specific and credible evidence of criminal activity by a covered person. As you surely know, the expansion of jurisdiction approved by the Special Division, on the basis of an oral application, was to investigate "whether Monica Lewinsky or others suborned perjury, obstructed justice, intimidated witnesses, or otherwise violated federal law . . . in dealing with witnesses, potential witnesses, attorneys, or others concerning the civil case of Jones v. Clinton." No "covered person" was involved in this matter unless and until the President gave testimony which might be regarded by your office as suspect. The Attorney General's written application to the Special Division, submitted after the Court was informed orally of the request, states that the Attorney General had determined that it would be a conflict of interest, under 28 U.S.C. § 591(c)(1) for the Department of Justice to investigate. However, it was still incumbent upon the Attorney General to conduct an appropriate "preliminary investigation" to determine that there was specific evidence from a credible source to warrant further investigation. We do not believe the Attorney General was provided adequate information about Tripp's illegal audiotaping or her general credibility or about the efforts by your office to acquire evidence which could be used to support the expansion of jurisdiction. We do not believe that such a bootstrap acquisition of jurisdiction as apparently occurred here was ever contemplated by the Ethics in Government Act.

We have another serious concern about the expansion of jurisdiction in this matter, and I have adverted to this in my letter to you dated March 4, 1998. As you know, I attached a copy of a letter to the Independent Counsel which I had hand-delivered on February 17, 1998, and which sought certain basic information relating to the Independent Counsel's relationship to the Jones v. Clinton civil case. Like your office, I am interested in "the truth's coming out." It is over a month later, however, and I still have received no response of any kind from the Independent Counsel. The Special Division's Order dated January 16, 1998, specifically recites that it approves "an expansion of prosecutorial jurisdiction in lieu of the appointment of another Independent Counsel." The point of my February 17 letter to the Independent Counsel was precisely whether he (as opposed to some other qualified person) should have been appointed by the Special Division under the facts of this case. The Ethics in Government Act explicitly provides that "[d]uring the period in which an independent counsel is serving under this chapter (i) such independent counsel, and (ii) any person associated with a firm with which such independent counsel is associated, may not represent in any matter any person involved in any investigation or prosecution under this chapter."

28 U.S.C. § 594(j)(1)(A)... As my February 17 letter to the Independent Counsel made clear, the Chicago Tribune reported six days earlier that one of the Independent Counsel's partners in Kirkland & Ellis, Mr. Richard Porter, may have provided legal advice and services to Paula Jones in her suit against the President. I have written the Independent Counsel seeking information concerning this and other news reports concerning his own relations with Ms. Jones' lawyers. I specifically requested information "(i) concerning [the Independent Counsel's] own, Mr. Porter's, and any other Kirkland & Ellis lawyer's, employee's or agent's contacts with and assistance to Ms. Paula Corbin Jones and/or her attorneys or agents or supporting groups, and (ii) concerning what was conveyed to the Attorney General and the Special Division in January, 1998, about any such contacts and assistance, when [the Independent Counsel] sought an expansion of . . . jurisdiction to encompass the Jones v. Clinton case." I have heard nothing in response.

I will not repeat here my description of the many grave duties of state which are uniquely the President's. As I noted in my March 4 letter, "[w]hile it is true that not every moment of the day is absorbed by the duties of office, the President is extraordinarily busy on a range of important public issues, some of which are visible and some of which are not." The President leaves on a long-scheduled state visit to Africa this weekend, and he will be gone until April 3. He then is in South America on another state visit from April 15 to 20. Such trips require not only travel time but a great deal of preparation time, study, and analysis in advance and after the trip.

I believe that a meeting to discuss my concerns, as well as yours, would be fruitful, and I am available at your convenience for that purpose.

Again, I would respectfully ask you to read this letter to the grand jury and to make it part of the grand jury record, if your letter to me is shared with the grand jury.

I thank you for your courtesy.

Sincerely,

David E. Kendall

Office of the Independent Counsel

1001 Pennsylvania Avenue, N.W.
Suite 490-North
Washington, DC 20004
(202) 514-8688
Fax (202) 514-8802

April 3, 1998

HAND DELIVERED

David E. Kendall, Esq.
Williams & Connolly
725 Twelfth Street, N.W.
Washington, D.C. 20005

Re: William Jefferson Clinton

Dear David:

I write in response to your letter of March 18, 1998, in which you declined our sixth invitation for the President's testimony, and in response to our meeting of March 20, 1998, during which you declined to answer my question whether the President will ever voluntarily testify about the matters involving Monica Lewinsky.

As you know, upon receipt of your letter I immediately called you to take you up on your offer to meet and discuss our mutual concerns regarding our six invitations to the President. Notwithstanding the numerous misstatements in your letter -- which are addressed herein -- I was hopeful that in light of the President's public pledges of cooperation we could finally arrange terms under which the President would voluntarily testify about the matters involving Ms. Lewinsky. My hopes were dashed at our meeting when you simply refused to discuss any of the "issues." Not only did you merely repeat some of the inflammatory allegations in your letter, you avoided even addressing -- much less answering -- the question I began our meeting with: Will the President ever voluntarily testify about the matters involving Monica Lewinsky? You refused several times to answer this question. Indeed, when I asked if we were to address the "concerns" outlined in your letter to your satisfaction would the President then agree to testify, you still refused to answer. This exercise, in the context of the backpedaling and misdirection of your letters and the President's public statements, makes clear that the President has no intention -- and never has had any intention -- of cooperating with this grand jury or this investigation. We, of course, regret the President's apparent decision.

Now I will turn to the variety of irrelevant charges raised in your letter against this Office, the Independent Counsel, and Judge Starr's private law firm. Because our addressing these matters is evidently not dispositive for you, I will address them only briefly.

First, you suggest that the President's deposition in the _Jones_ case amply substitutes for grand jury questioning. You are incorrect. As you are well aware, the jurisdiction of this Office and the scope of discovery in the _Jones_ case are far from coextensive. While the deposition bears on matters within our jurisdiction, the grand jury investigation has unearthed many significant issues not addressed in the deposition.

Second, you accuse this Office of having "contrived to obtain the President's deposition testimony through improper and illegal means." This, too, is flatly incorrect. All evidence gathered in this investigation has been obtained lawfully and properly.

Third, you charge that this Office, Linda Tripp, and Richard Porter of Kirkland & Ellis "colluded" with attorneys for Paula Jones. As authority, you cite a number of the notoriously inaccurate media accounts of this investigation, many of which have been based upon statements by "unnamed presidential advisers." Let me set the record straight: This Office has not colluded with Ms. Jones's attorneys -- not directly, not indirectly, and not through Ms. Tripp, Mr. Porter, or any other person. With nothing more than a sheaf of newspaper articles in hand, it is irresponsible of you to charge otherwise.

Fourth, you contend that this Office has undertaken investigative steps without proper authority. We disagree. The expansion of our jurisdiction by the Special Division was preceded by a presentation of information to the Attorney General, a preliminary investigation of such information by her, and a subsequent recommendation to the Special Division. We, unlike you, believe the Attorney General knows and follows the law. She followed the law in this case. As your complaint is a legal argument about our authority to investigate, we suggest you raise it in a judicial forum.

David E. Kendall, Esq.
April 3, 1998
Page three

Fifth, you assert that the President has "cooperated in every possible way" with this investigation. You know, of course, that this is not true. You and the President have failed to produce financial records that have been under subpoena for several years. The Rose Law Firm billing records, for example, were "re-discovered" at the White House in January 1996 and had been under subpoena for many months. Jane Sherburne, then of the White House counsel's office, testified before the Senate that after the records' "re-discovery" she suggested to you that the forensic integrity of the records be preserved. Senate Hearing, 2/8/96, at 69-71. Ms. Sherburne further testified that her suggestion was dismissed. Id. You testified that you "did not regard this as a forensic matter," id. at 72, and, of course, the forensic value of the records was in fact compromised after handling by your office. In addition, as you know, I wrote you on March 6, 1998 and March 25, 1998, requesting that the President fully comply with subpoena number V002 and its instructions so that the grand jury can determine whether the President ever had any documents or things in response to the subpoena that have not been produced. You thus far have responded with only a vague statement that the President "might have given the President a few additional items, such as ties and a pair of sunglasses, but we have not been able to locate these items. The President frequently does not see and is not aware of numerous items which are sent to him by friends and supporters." This response is unsatisfactory and not in compliance with the subpoena. The grand jury needs the additional information demanded by the subpoena's instructions.

Finally, you reiterate that the President is a busy man. We do not disagree, and indeed are well aware that the President has weighty responsibilities besides his obligation to assist a federal grand jury investigating possible criminal conduct. Nonetheless, we believe that he has found and can continue to find the time to testify in judicial fora -- particularly given that we will work with you to time his appearance so as to reduce disruption to his schedule.

Those are our views on the matters raised in your letter. Since January 28, 1998, when we first invited the President to testify, the grand jury has grown increasingly eager to hear the President's testimony.

David E. Kendall, Esq.
April 3, 1998
Page four

Having tried and tried, I will now try once again. Please give me a straightforward yes or no answer to the following question: Will the President ever agree to testify voluntarily about the matters involving Ms. Lewinsky? If the President chooses again not to give his testimony, so that the grand jury may at least receive some of his evidence, please provide this Office with any and all exculpatory evidence you may have.

Sincerely,

Robert J. Bittman

Robert J. Bittman
Deputy Independent Counsel

LAW OFFICES
WILLIAMS & CONNOLLY
725 TWELFTH STREET, N.W.
WASHINGTON, D. C. 20005-5901
(202) 434-5000
FAX (202) 434-5029

EDWARD BENNETT WILLIAMS (1920-1988)
PAUL R. CONNOLLY (1922-1978)

DAVID E. KENDALL
(202) 434-5145

April 17, 1998

CONFIDENTIAL
RULE 6(e), F.R.CRIM.P., GRAND JURY SUBMISSION

Robert J. Bittman, Esq.
Deputy Independent Counsel
Office of the Independent Counsel
1001 Pennsylvania Avenue, N.W.
Suite 490-North
Washington, D.C. 20004

By Hand

Dear Bob:

Thank you for your letter of April 3, 1998. I will try once again to make clear our position with regard to the President's providing testimony on the Lewinsky matter, beyond the transcript and videotape of his deposition in Jones v. Clinton, which your Office now has and is free to submit to the grand jury. I have attempted to do this in my previous correspondence and in our meeting at the federal courthouse on March 20, 1998.

In my several letters and in our meeting, our position could not have been more clearly stated: we have serious objections to the origin and conduct of your Lewinsky investigation, and until those are satisfactorily addressed, we cannot, as a matter of professional duty to our client, allow the President to give further testimony at the present time. The issue remains open, however, and depends on your Office. We remain entirely respectful of the grand jury. Indeed, from recent press accounts, it appears that the grand jurors themselves are performing their civic duty with admirable commitment and at some sacrifice to their personal lives. Quite frankly, I believe if your Office were to provide the information I have sought over the past several months, this would lighten the burden on us, on you, and on the grand jurors.

Since your letter states it will address my concerns only "briefly", I will not restate here the issues I have raised at some length in my previous correspondence. I would note only that, once again, your letter stonewalls my request for information concerning contacts between members of the Independent Counsel's law firm (Kirkland & Ellis) and the Paula Jones lawyers as of the January 16, 1998, expansion of your Office's jurisdiction to encompass the Lewinsky matter in the Paula Jones civil suit. My need for this information is obvious: if in fact personnel at Kirkland & Ellis have provided legal assistance in some way to the Jones side of the civil suit, Judge Starr would <u>not</u> have been qualified under the Ethics in Government Act to serve as independent counsel on the Lewinsky matter--some other individual, with no connection to the Jones litigation, would have had to have been selected. The information I seek is obviously in your custody and control: Judge Starr need only ask his law partners, if he is not in fact privy to it himself. I first wrote him on February 17, 1998, requesting this information, and I still have not had an answer to my letter. You will recall that I appended a copy of that letter to my March 4, 1998, letter to you--I will not do so again.

This matter is highly important under the statute, because when Congress enacted the independent counsel legislation, it permitted such counsel to remain in their private law firms and to take on the appointment as a part-time job. I do not fault nor have I criticized the Independent Counsel for remaining at his law firm (where, according to news reports, he has made $1 million a year while serving as independent counsel, see, e.g., Time, Feb. 2, 1998)), but it is, obviously, extremely important that the conflict rules that permit such continued employment under the Act be followed. The statute provides that no person associated with the independent counsel's law firm may "represent in any matter any person involved in any investigation or prosecution under this chapter." 28 U.S.C. § 594(j)(1)(A)(ii). Thus, if someone at Kirkland & Ellis had "in any matter" represented Ms. Jones, Judge Starr could not properly have been appointed to investigate the Lewinsky matter.

It is true, as your recent letter asserts, that I have based my inquiry on media accounts. I do not have any reason to believe that (for example) the February 11, 1998, account is "notoriously inaccurate," as you suggest, since it appears in the Chicago Tribune, a reputable newspaper. The Tribune's report was in fact quite specific:

WILLIAMS & CONNOLLY

Robert J. Bittman, Esq.
April 17, 1998
Page 3

> "The Chicago-based law firm whose partners include Whitewater independent Counsel Kenneth Starr has begun an inquiry into whether a partner provided unapproved assistance to lawyers representing Paula Jones in her sex harassment case against President Clinton . . . .
>
> [T]he law firm's internal inquiry is focusing on Richard Porter, a partner in the Chicago office and a former senior aide to President George Bush and Vice President Dan Quayle . . . .
>
> John Corkery, associate dean at Chicago's John Marshall Law School, said the ethical issues raised are complicated ones. But in general, he said, 'If an attorney at the Kirkland firm is doing something that amounts to legal work for Jones, that creates a problem for Starr as the independent counsel because Starr's partner is pursuing a related matter in private practice that Starr has the obligation to investigate as part of his official duties.'
>
> 'The acts of Starr's partner in the practice of law are Starr's acts, by virtue of their partnership,' Corkery said."

You also assert that many statements in the accounts I cited in my February 17 letter are sourced to (in your words) "unnamed presidential advisers." With all respect, I do not see any such sources in these articles, although the February 11, 1998, Chicago Tribune article is in part based upon an unnamed "Kirkland & Ellis source".

I am also surprised at your cavalier dismissal of press reports as a basis for further inquiry. Your own Office has been quite willing even to take legal action on the basis of press accounts, when it has suited your purposes. For example, you successfully moved to disqualify Judge Henry Woods in the Court of Appeals for the Eighth Circuit "with nothing more than a sheaf of newspaper articles in hand" (to borrow your phrase), although you had chosen not to make such a motion to the Judge himself. As the Court of Appeals noted, "[t]he Independent Counsel relies primarily on newspaper articles to support his request." United States v. Tucker, 78 F.3d 1313, 1322-23 (8th Cir. 1996). By their very nature, questions involving possible conflicts of interest often arise because of media reports. In a proceeding in Arkansas last year involving the question whether the Independent Counsel suffered a conflict of interest because a job he had accepted in the future at Pepperdine University was partially funded by a virulent opponent of President Clinton, Judge Eisele, a Republican United States District Court judge, commented: "[H]aving reviewed the media accounts regarding the Pepperdine issue, I find that it is incumbent upon the Court to make some kind of inquiry." In re Starr, 986 F. Supp. 1144, 1153 (E.D. Ark. 1997). Judge Eisele also observed that "[i]t is even possible that Mr. Starr, as Independent Counsel, should receive more exacting scrutiny regarding his professional responsibilities than other prosecutors," since the Special Division indicated (when it appointed him to replace Mr. Robert Fiske) that "'the Act contemplates an apparent as well as an actual independence on the part of the Counsel.'" 986 F. Supp. at 1155.

Your letter asserts that the expansion of your jurisdiction to include the Lewinsky matter was approved by the Attorney General and you suggest that this means that the Attorney General has in fact ratified your application. However, one of the very questions I have been asking for over two months--without receiving an answer of any kind--is precisely what the Attorney General was told when your Office suddenly requested an expansion of its jurisdiction in January. I have no idea whether the Attorney General was in fact informed of any contacts between Kirkland & Ellis personnel and the Paula Jones camp. The Attorney General is obviously not clairvoyant: if she were not informed of any such contacts, she could hardly be expected to know about them and to have made a decision as to whether, under the circumstances, Judge Starr was in fact the appropriate Independent Counsel to conduct the Lewinsky investigation. It is quite significant, I believe, that the Attorney General's application to the Special Division recites that "Independent Counsel Starr has requested that this matter be referred to him" (emphasis added). Thus, your office affirmatively and purposefully sought to extend its jurisdiction over the Lewinsky matter. This expansion request did not originate with the Attorney General.

Instead of providing responsive information, you have advised that we should "raise [this issue] in a judicial forum." We will accordingly assume that we will receive no further response to my February 17 letter and will proceed accordingly.

I will not repeat here my previously expressed concerns about your Office's investigative techniques in the Lewinsky matter. Recent press reports indicate that you plan to have Ms. Tripp testify before the grand jury. Should you have Ms. Tripp testify, I would respectfully request that you brief the grand jury concerning the illegality of Ms. Tripp's one-party taping of

Ms. Lewinsky's telephone conversations in Maryland, the reasons your office wired Ms. Tripp to tape record Ms. Lewinsky's conversations, your knowledge of how the contents of this tape "leaked" to the news media, your knowledge of the reasons Ms. Tripp sought out your office rather than the United States Attorney's Office, the timing and details of your federal law immunity agreement with Ms. Tripp, and the restrictions (if any) you placed upon Ms. Tripp's transmittal of illegally acquired taping information (including the existence of illegally made tapes) to the Paula Jones lawyers in the week before the President's deposition.

I have responded to your comments concerning subpoena V002 in a letter dated April 13, 1998, and will not do so again here. I have also set forth fully in a letter to the Independent Counsel dated April 10, 1998, my concerns about having your Office investigate recent allegations concerning David Hale. In its April 9 letter to Judge Starr, the Department of Justice noted that "the United States Attorney's Office for the Western District of Arkansas was recently provided with information suggesting that David Hale, who we understand is a witness in various matters under your jurisdiction, may have received cash and other gratuities from individuals seeking to discredit the President during a period when Hale was actively cooperating with your investigation." The Department's letter also noted "suggestions that your office would have a conflict of interest, or the appearance of a conflict, in looking into this matter, because of the importance of Hale to your investigation and because the payments allegedly came from funds provided by Richard Scaife [the virulent opponent of President Clinton whom I referred to above]." The Independent Counsel's withdrawal from his Pepperdine commitments does not begin to solve the many problems that have been noted. For the reasons set forth in my April 10 letter, which involve both fairness and the perception of fairness, your Office should not have <u>any</u> involvement whatsoever in the investigation of this matter.

For over four years, the President has cooperated fully with the investigation of the Independent Counsel, which has now gone on longer than a Presidential term. He has voluntarily given testimony under oath on three different occasions to the Independent Counsel and twice to defendants (on each occasion, he was cross-examined by the Independent Counsel), he has submitted written interrogatory answers, he has produced more than 90,000 pages of documents[1], and he has provided information informally in a variety of ways. This amounts to unprecedented cooperation[2] with an investigation of unprecedented duration,

---

1/ You assert that we "have failed to produce financial records that have been under subpoena for several years." This is simply false. You have not specified, nor could you, any such record in our possession that we have not produced.

2/ Because your letter contains an unwarranted and false ad hominem charge concerning the Rose Law Firm billing records, I respond here simply for the sake of the record, and I do not ask you to read this footnote to the grand jury, unless you choose to do so. I do not complain that you appear to have imperfectly complied with the Independent Counsel's publicly expressed philosophy (viz.,"I have a job to do and you will never hear me besmirching anyone's reputation. Not once, never in all of this four years of activity, have I ever said anything to besmirch anyone's reputation. . . . And you will never find us doing that. And when I say me, I'm not meaning to personalize that. I mean my colleagues with whom I'm very privileged to serve." CNN, Special Event Transcript, April 2, 1998)(emphasis supplied). My point is instead that your smear is simply false.

You write that "the forensic value of the [Rose Law Firm billing] records was in fact compromised after handling by [my] office." You reference the highly partisan Senate inquiry chaired by Senator D'Amato, but you distort the meaning of the very testimony you quote. If you had reviewed the D'Amato testimony more carefully, you would have observed that the billing records were produced in accordance with procedures jointly agreed upon by me, Ms. Sherburne, and Mr. Schuelke. Moreover, your Office was in fact able to do fingerprint analysis of the billing records, because it made this evidence available to Senator D'Amato's Committee under cover of an undated letter from the FBI which Senator D'Amato released on June 4, 1996. The fact that your Office had identified Mrs. Clinton's fingerprints on the billing records (not surprisingly, since she was the billing partner on the account) was somehow leaked to the news media (see, e.g., Newsweek, May 6, 1996; Washington Times, April 30, 1996). In retrospect, this appears to be a preview of the highly prejudicial leaks we have experienced in the last three months. In any event, two years ago, I (continued...)

intrusiveness, and indefiniteness. That you now request we submit "exculpatory" evidence is perfectly consonant with the occasionally Alice-in-Wonderland nature of this whole enterprise. I am not aware of anything the President needs to "exculpate."

I would respectfully ask you to read this letter to the grand jury and to make it part of the grand jury record, if your recent letter to me is shared with the grand jury.

I thank you for your courtesy.

Sincerely,

David E. Kendall

2/ (...continued) wrote strenuous letters of protest, dated April 29 and 30, 1996, to the Independent Counsel about these leaks, receiving in reply a soothing response dated May 3, 1996 ("Your concerns are noted, and they are shared by this Office") and no further action.

Tab 2

Office of the Independent Counsel

1001 Pennsylvania Avenue, N.W.
Suite 490-North
Washington, DC 20004
(202) 514-8688
Fax (202) 514-8802

July 17, 1998

HAND DELIVERED

David E. Kendall, Esq.
Williams & Connolly
725 Twelfth Street, N.W.
Washington, D.C. 20005

Re: William Jefferson Clinton

Dear David:

As you know, beginning January 28, 1998, we, on behalf of the grand jury, have invited the President six times to testify voluntarily about the matters involving Monica Lewinsky. Despite his previous cooperation with other aspects of our investigations and his public pledges to cooperate fully with this investigation and provide "more rather than less, sooner rather than later," the President has unfortunately chosen to decline each and every invitation to give his information to the grand jury. The grand jury simply can wait no longer for the President's voluntary cooperation.

Pursuant to § 9-11.150 of the United States Attorneys' Manual and with all the requisite approvals thereunder, enclosed please find a subpoena for President Clinton to appear and give testimony before the grand jury on Tuesday, July 28, 1998, at 9:15 a.m. If the President agrees to comply with the subpoena and testify, we and the grand jury -- as we have previously stated -- will accommodate his schedule if he cannot appear on the 28th.

We believe you are aware of the status of your client. We would be pleased to state explicitly the status of the President if you desire.

Sincerely,

Robert J. Bittman
Deputy Independent Counsel

Enclosure

CO 293 (Rev. 8/91) Subpoena to Testify Before Grand Jury

United States District Court

FOR THE DISTRICT OF COLUMBIA

TO: William Jefferson Clinton

SUBPOENA TO TESTIFY BEFORE GRAND JURY

SUBPOENA FOR:
[x] PERSON [ ] DOCUMENT(S) OR OBJECT(S)

YOU ARE HEREBY COMMANDED to appear and testify before the Grand Jury of the United States District Court at the place, date, and time specified below.

PLACE	COURTROOM
United States District Court for the District of Columbia Third & Constitution Avenue, N.W. Washington, D.C.	Grand Jury, Third Floor DATE AND TIME July 28, 1998/9:15 a.m.

YOU ARE ALSO COMMANDED to bring with you the following document(s) or object(s):*

[ ] *Please see additional information on reverse.*

This subpoena shall remain in effect until you are granted leave to depart by the court or by an officer acting on behalf of the court.

U.S. MAGISTRATE OR CLERK OF COURT	DATE
Nancy M. Mayer-Whittington, Clerk (BY) DEPUTY CLERK Margaret M. Napier	July 17, 1998 D1424
This subpoena is issued upon application of the United States of America	NAME, ADDRESS AND PHONE NUMBER OF ASSISTANT U.S. ATTORNEY Robert J. Bittman, Deputy Independent Counsel Office of the Independent Counsel 1001 Pennsylvania Avenue, N.W., Suite 490-Nort Washington, D.C. 20004 (202) 514-8688

*If not applicable, enter "none."

U S GPO 1993-0-350-792/80398

Advice of Rights

- The grand jury is conducting an investigation of possible violations of Federal criminal laws involving: perjury, subornation of perjury, obstruction of justice, witness tampering, and other Federal criminal laws.
- Your conduct is being investigated for possible violations of Federal criminal law.
- You may refuse to answer any question if a truthful answer to the question would tend to incriminate you.
- Anything that you do say may be used against you by the grand jury or in a subsequent legal proceeding.
- If you have retained counsel, the grand jury will permit you a reasonable opportunity to step outside the grand jury room to consult with counsel if you so desire.

Tab 3

Office of the Independent Counsel

1001 Pennsylvania Avenue, N.W.
Suite 490-North
Washington, DC 20004
(202) 514-8688
Fax (202) 514-8802

July 23, 1998

HAND DELIVERED

David E. Kendall, Esq.
Williams & Connolly
725 Twelfth Street, N.W.
Washington, D.C. 20005

Re: William Jefferson Clinton

Dear David:

I write in regards to your request yesterday for additional time to respond to the grand jury's subpoena to President Clinton. Although I conveyed to you yesterday that we had decided not to give any additional time, you asked me to let you know by the close of business Friday, July 24, 1998, if our views changed. We are responding today to give you as advance notice of our decision as possible.

We have carefully reviewed your request and balanced it against the grand jury's desire -- and responsibility -- to complete this investigation as thoroughly and expeditiously as possible. We offer to withdraw the current subpoena to the President and issue a new subpoena with an appearance date of Friday, July 31, 1998, at 9:15 a.m. if you agree that you will not request any additional time or another continuance, either from this Office or the Court. As before, if the President agrees to comply with the subpoena and testify, we and the grand jury will accommodate his schedule if he cannot appear on the 31st. We believe this extension of time is entirely reasonable given that the President has been on notice since January that the grand jury wished his testimony and given that all the President must necessarily decide by July 31 is whether he will comply with the subpoena and testify. Kindly advise me by 4:00 p.m. tomorrow whether the President wishes to accept our proposal; otherwise, the current subpoena will remain in effect.

Sincerely,

Robert J. Bittman
Deputy Independent Counsel

Tab 4

LAW OFFICES
WILLIAMS & CONNOLLY
725 TWELFTH STREET, N.W.
WASHINGTON, D. C. 20005-5901
(202) 434-5000
FAX (202) 434-5029

EDWARD BENNETT WILLIAMS (1920-1988)
PAUL R. CONNOLLY (1922-1978)

DAVID E. KENDALL
(202) 434-5145

July 24, 1998

CONFIDENTIAL

Robert J. Bittman, Esq.
Deputy Independent Counsel
Office of the Independent Counsel
1001 Pennsylvania Avenue, N.W.
Suite 490-North
Washington, D.C. 20004

By Hand

Dear Bob:

I write in response to your letter of yesterday, which I believe to be now moot.

The President is willing to provide testimony for the grand jury, although there are a number of questions relating to the precise terms and timing which must be worked out. If you are willing to work within the framework of the last three times the President provided such testimony and if you are sincere in your statement that you will work to accommodate his schedule, we should quickly be able to finalize the arrangements.

I will get to you by 4:00 p.m. Tuesday, but sooner if possible, a more detailed letter, which will include a date for testimony which will accommodate the President's other existing obligations.

I request that you withdraw the pending subpoena, since the issue of the subpoena itself is quite important to us. The precedential effect of such a subpoena is not an issue I have addressed in previous correspondence with you (which ended with my April 17 letter), but I will do so in my next letter.

Sincerely,

David E. Kendall

Tab 5

Office of the Independent Counsel

1001 Pennsylvania Avenue, N.W.
Suite 490-North
Washington, DC 20004
(202) 514-8688
Fax (202) 514-8802

July 24, 1998

HAND DELIVERED

David E. Kendall, Esq.
Williams & Connolly
725 Twelfth Street, N.W.
Washington, D.C. 20005

Re: William Jefferson Clinton

Dear David:

We are gratified by your response to my letter of yesterday, and we are pleased by the President's decision to provide testimony for the grand jury.

You indicate in your letter that the President "is willing to provide testimony for the grand jury" and you suggest that such testimony take place in a forum outside the grand jury, on an uncertain future date. We are happy to discuss arrangements for the President's testimony that will be consistent with concerns of security and dignity of the Office of the President. We remain interested, however, in obtaining a prompt commitment to a date certain for that testimony. As you know, we have invited the President on six occasions to testify before the grand jury, and its work continues apace. As a result, we are currently not inclined to withdraw the subpoena. Nevertheless, we would be happy to consult with you at your earliest convenience before next Tuesday morning to work out an acceptable schedule for the President's testimony.

Sincerely,

Robert J. Bittman
Deputy Independent Counsel

Tab 6

LAW OFFICES
WILLIAMS & CONNOLLY
725 TWELFTH STREET, N.W.
WASHINGTON, D. C. 20005-5901
(202) 434-5000
FAX (202) 434-5029

EDWARD BENNETT WILLIAMS (1920-1988)
PAUL R. CONNOLLY (1922-1978)

DAVID E. KENDALL
(202) 434-5145

July 27, 1998

By Hand

Robert J. Bittman, Esq.
Deputy Independent Counsel
Office of the Independent Counsel
1001 Pennsylvania Avenue, N.W.
Suite 490-North
Washington, D.C. 20004

CONFIDENTIAL

Dear Bob:

This will acknowledge your letter dated July 17, 1998, enclosing a subpoena for the President to appear before the grand jury on July 28 and will follow up on my letter to you dated July 24, 1998.

As you are well aware, this extraordinary subpoena poses grave and literally unprecedented constitutional questions. While we are obviously cognizant of the holdings in United States v. Nixon, 418 U.S. 683 (1974) and Clinton v. Jones, ___ U.S. ___, 117 S.Ct. 1636 (1997), no case has ever held that a sitting President may be compelled by subpoena to provide testimony for a grand jury, much less to testify before a grand jury. In the past, Presidents have voluntarily provided information to prosecutors for legal proceedings in a variety of ways. President Clinton has twice given testimony at the request of defendants in criminal proceedings, after he had voluntarily given testimony to the Office of Independent Counsel on similar subjects, in circumstances where the defendants plainly had certain Sixth Amendment rights "to have compulsory process for obtaining witnesses in [the defendant's] favor." But neither this nor any other President has been compelled to give testimony to a grand jury by subpoena.

One of the most troubling aspects of this subpoena is its plain conflict with the impeachment provisions of the Constitution, since it is obvious that from the outset of the latest phase of your investigation you have considered the President to be a "target" of your investigation. We believe that the conclusion of then-Solicitor Bork in the investigation of Vice-President Agnew twenty-five years ago is the correct one:

the "remarks [of the framers] strongly suggest an understanding that the President, as Chief Executive, would not be subject to the ordinary criminal process . . . . Their assumption that the President would not be subject to criminal process was based upon the crucial nature of his executive powers." Memorandum for the United States Concerning the Vice President's Claim of Constitutional Immunity, at 6, In Re Proceedings of The Grand Jury Impaneled December 5, 1972, Civ. No. 73-965 (D.Md.)(Oct. 5, 1973).

Accordingly, under circumstances in which you have apparently "targeted" your investigation on a sitting President, enforcement of a grand jury subpoena would violate the most fundamental separation of powers principles because it would invade the exclusive prerogatives of the Congress. Under Article I, the House "shall have the sole power of impeachment" and the Senate "shall have the sole power to try all impeachments." Under Article II of the Constitution, the President is duty-bound to uphold the separation of powers framework against unreasonable encroachment by other branches or by an unelected Independent Counsel. In order to protect the institution of the Presidency, we are prepared to litigate to preserve these important principles.

We hope that will not be necessary. For the past four years, we have worked with your Office to devise ways for the President to cooperate with the investigations of the Office of Independent Counsel in a manner that did not infringe his Article II responsibilities. He has voluntarily and unstintingly provided an enormous amount of information in response to a great many requests from the OIC. He has, without the compulsion of subpoena, given testimony under oath on three different occasions to the Independent Counsel. He has twice given testimony for defendants in criminal proceedings and been subject to cross-examination by the Office of Independent Counsel. He has provided more than 90,000 pages of documents to the OIC, he has submitted interrogatory answers, and he has provided information informally in a variety of ways. This amounts to extraordinary and unprecedented cooperation with an investigation of extraordinary and unprecedented duration, intrusiveness, and indefiniteness.

In my letters to you over the last few months, I have set forth in detail my concerns about your Office's investigation. I will not reiterate those here, but my reservations, as set forth in my correspondence, are substantial and, I believe, well-founded. Regarding leaks, for example,

Chief Judge Johnson's findings with respect to our three show-cause motions provide dramatic confirmation of my concerns.

Despite our serious and enduring concerns about the OIC's investigation, as I indicated in my July 24 letter, the President remains willing to provide the grand jury with the information it seeks, so long as he can do so in a way that is consistent with the obligations of his Office. We believe that, with your assistance, the serious constitutional questions presented here by a subpoena may be mooted. Our proposal is made in good faith and after serious deliberation. It reflects a meaningful attempt to accommodate both your needs and those of the Presidency. We are not suggesting other more limited options utilized by Presidents in the past, such as written interrogatories, which while precedented and defensible, would, we believe, be less satisfactory. The President is prepared to provide the information you seek under conditions that (1) are consistent with the precedents established in this investigation and (2) preserve the constitutional questions both for your Office and the President for later formal legal determination, if necessary.

In our correspondence during the last few months, you have stated that the OIC "fully acknowledge[d] that the President has immense and weighty responsibilities" and that the OIC "want[ed] in every way to take fully into account those grave duties of state." (Your letter to me of March 2, 1998). You stated you wanted to "reiterate" that the OIC had "profound respect for the institution of the Presidency." (Your letter to me of March 13, 1998). We believe that the respect for the Office of the President, which you acknowledge, and which we share, requires that any testimony of the President be given under the following conditions:

1) The subpoena must be withdrawn. The President has on three different occasions voluntarily given sworn testimony when requested by the OIC. On two other occasions (in 1996), the President testified at the behest of two defendants by videotape at their trials. In our view, however, the constitutional considerations raised by your July 17 subpoena are quite different since, for example, a defendant has a Sixth Amendment right to compulsory process to present witnesses in his defense. For the separation of powers reasons discussed above and to avoid a precedent harmful to the institution of the Presidency, we believe that any testimony which the President provides now must be on a voluntary basis.

2) Any testimony by the President must be given by deposition at the White House, under the conditions of the first three OIC interviews. We anticipate that the examination will be (as it has been in the past) respectful, non-repetitive, and given within a specific time period (perhaps three hours). You will inform us of the specific areas you intend to cover (although, obviously, not of the questions you intend to ask). You will make a good faith effort to provide us documents in advance about which you plan to question the President, so he does not have to waste time at the deposition reading them for the first time.

3) Safeguards to prevent leaks must be devised. The President's January 17, 1998, deposition in the Paula Jones case was leaked to the press in flagrant violation of a court order. In this investigation, Chief Judge Johnson has entered orders for the OIC to show cause why it or individuals therein should not be held in contempt for violating Rule 6(e), Fed. R. Crim. P.: "The Court finds that the serious and repetitive nature of disclosures to the media of Rule 6(e) material strongly militates in favor of conducting a show cause hearing." (June 19, 1998, Order, at 5). Moreover, "[s]hould the Court find a direct violation of Rule 6(e), the Court reserves the right to take any appropriate steps, including referring the matter to the United States Attorney, the Department of Justice, or a special master for criminal contempt investigation and proceedings." (June 26, 1998, Order, at 2 n.1). We do not seek to require impossible conditions or guarantees, but in light of the nature of the subject matter, the intense and corrosive media interest, and the history of leaks, there must be strict safeguards as to attendance, handling of the transcript (perhaps lodging the only copy with the court until it is presented to the grand jury), dissemination, etc.

4) This testimony will be given only after the President has an adequate time to prepare for it. In Clinton v. Jones, supra, the Supreme Court remarked the "'unique position in the constitutional scheme'" that the Presidency occupies and noted that the President "occupies a unique office with powers and responsibilities so vast and important that the public interest demands that he devote his undivided time and attention to his public duties." 117 S.Ct. at 1646. The Court held in that case that "[t]he high respect that is owed to the office of the Chief Executive, though not justifying a rule of categorical immunity, is a matter that should inform the conduct of the entire proceeding, including the timing and scope of discovery," id. at 1650-51 (footnote omitted), and its holding was based upon its assumption "that the testimony of the President, both for

discovery and for use at trial, may be taken at the White House at a time that will accommodate his busy schedule," id. at 1643.

I last wrote you three months ago concerning the possibility of the President testifying, and I have heard absolutely nothing from you in the interim. In that and other letters, I have made clear that the President's schedule is an extremely full one that is set well in advance. Nevertheless, suddenly and without any advance notice, I received your subpoena at 6:00 p.m. on Friday, July 17, while the President was away on a long-scheduled trip to Arkansas and Louisiana, and with other significant travel scheduled, seeking his grand jury testimony a mere ten days later. This has recently been an exceptionally busy period, with the trip to China, the continuing Asian debt crisis, the well-publicized events in Russia, tensions in the Middle East and in Ireland, and a host of domestic concerns, such as the drought and a pressing legislative agenda before this Congress ends. We would be derelict in our professional duties if we allowed the President to give testimony without adequate preparation. (Unlike the OIC, the President is one person, with many different public responsibilities). Given his present schedule and duties, it is inconceivable that he would be able to testify in the immediate future. Between today and August 15, the President is already scheduled to be out of town for six days and has an exceptionally busy schedule while here. He has a long-scheduled family vacation between August 15 and 30, but much of this will be absorbed with preparation for a critical trip to Russia and Ireland from August 31 through September 6. The first date the President could conceivably testify consistently with his other obligations would be Sunday, September 13, although we would, in simple fairness, request that his testimony occur on Sunday, September 20. While we are not aware of the witnesses who remain to be interviewed by the OIC, we believe that the pending legal disputes which are now sub judice will plainly not be resolved before mid-September, and so we do not believe that a mid-September date for the President's testimony would itself unduly delay the completion of your investigation. It certainly would be sooner than any date you might anticipate were you to precipitate a legal confrontation.

I look forward to talking with you at your earliest convenience.

Sincerely,

David E. Kendall

Tab 7

Office of the Independent Counsel

1001 Pennsylvania Avenue, N.W.
Suite 490-North
Washington, DC 20004
(202) 514-8688
Fax (202) 514-8802

July 27, 1998

VIA HAND DELIVERY

David E. Kendall, Esq.
Williams & Connolly
725 Twelfth Street, N.W.
Washington, D.C. 20005

Re: William Jefferson Clinton

Dear David:

Thank you for your letter of July 27, 1998, which we received at 1:30 p.m. today. Although there is much in your letter with which we disagree, there is no reason at this point to engage in an extended discussion. Instead we wish to remain focused on the subject of obtaining the President's testimony for the grand jury.

Although we remain willing to accommodate the President's security and dignity concerns, we cannot agree with the other restrictions and conditions you suggest. Most importantly, we cannot agree to delay the testimony for another seven-plus weeks. The President has been aware since late January that the grand jury wants to hear his story, and he has declined numerous invitations to provide his testimony voluntarily. Therefore, further extensive delay of the type you propose is simply unacceptable. As a result, we will not withdraw the existing subpoena (as continued per today's telephone call, to 1:30 p.m. on July 28th). If, however, by tomorrow at 1:30 p.m., the President commits in writing to testify on a date certain on or before August 7, 1998, then we will continue the subpoena until that date. If the President agrees to a date certain, we will of course work closely with you to accommodate the logistical concerns that you have raised.

Sincerely,

Robert J. Bittman
by [signature]

Robert J. Bittman
Deputy Independent Counsel

Tab 8

103RD STORY of Level 1 printed in FULL format.

Chicago Tribune

July 27, 1998 Monday, NORTH SPORTS FINAL EDITION

SECTION: NEWS; Pg. 1; ZONE: N

LENGTH: 1137 words

HEADLINE: STARR SUBPOENA POSES CONSTITUTIONAL CONFLICT

BYLINE: By Naftali Bendavid, Washington Bureau.

DATELINE: WASHINGTON

BODY:

In subpoenaing President Clinton, Independent Counsel Kenneth Starr has delved into new legal territory and ignited a chain of events that ultimately could lead to a constitutional crisis.

Most starkly, a subpoena is a court order that, if defied, is punishable by imprisonment. But it seems clear that the president of the United States cannot be imprisoned under the Constitution because that would amount to the republic paralyzing its leader. So the meaning of this subpoena is unclear.

More broadly, the Constitution specifically provides a way to pursue criminal charges against a president--the impeachment process, under which Congress can subpoena the president if it chooses. To many scholars, that suggests that an ordinary prosecutor or even an independent counsel may not summon the president to testify.

"This is an open constitutional-law question," said Georgetown University law professor Paul Rothstein, an expert in constitutional and criminal law. "We are sailing blindly on a dark sea. We don't know what will be found to be the constitutional solution."

Meanwhile, White House officials Sunday continued their refusal even to confirm that Clinton has been served with a subpoena. Despite widespread reports that Starr issued such a summons last week, top advisers, including Rahm Emanuel, would say only that negotiations are under way on how Clinton can provide Starr the information he seeks.

Starr's subpoena may be little more than a bargaining move, a way to force a reluctant Clinton to give his version of the events surrounding the allegations that he lied under oath about a supposed affair with White House intern Monica Lewinsky.

If the negotiations fail, Clinton could decide to fight the subpoena. That would set up a clash between the judicial and executive branches that, while echoing President Richard Nixon's defiance when ordered to turn over the Watergate tapes, would be essentially unprecedented.

A small group of scholars argues that Starr has every right to subpoena Clinton. The president has declined to voluntarily appear before the grand jury, these observers note, and that leaves an official summons as the only way for Starr to obtain testimony vital to his investigation.

The whole point of our system of government, this argument goes, is that no person is above the law.

"The government is entitled to every person's testimony," said Mark Tushnet, a constitutional-law expert at Georgetown University. "If there is a sufficient showing of need for his testimony, he ought to be treated the same as any other citizen."

While Clinton certainly could not be imprisoned, this camp argues he could be punished in many other ways if he disobeys the subpoena.

The president could be fined, for example, which would not interfere with his ability to run the country. And if nothing else, the political consequences to the president of flouting a court order would be so high he would be reluctant to do it.

"In the real world, there are sanctions other than putting someone in jail," Tushnet said. "There would be, as they called it in Watergate, a firestorm of public criticism. There would be the threat of impeachment. Those are appropriate things for the legal system to take into account."

Still, most experts believe it is constitutionally dubious for a prosecutor to issue a presidential subpoena or at least to try to enforce it.

The executive and judicial branches, along with the legislative, are supposed to be roughly co-equal, and the notion of a president at the mercy of a court makes many observers nervous.

Bruce Fein, a constitutional lawyer who served in the Justice Department during the Ronald Reagan administration, ridicules the notion that the president is just like any other citizen under the law.

"He is not like every other citizen," Fein said. "It's absurd. He was elected to be president."

The appearance of the president before the grand jury would bring his presidency to a halt, Fein argued, and the Constitution says that can only be done by Congress in an impeachment proceeding.

"The political fallout of having a president appear before a grand jury would be paralysis," Fein said. "The whole country would be consumed. It would place the Clinton presidency in rigor mortis, which is something that can be done but only through an impeachment proceeding."

In a grand jury proceeding, witnesses are questioned in secret by one or more prosecutors without their attorneys present. Witnesses uniformly describe the experience as intimidating.

It is dangerous to subject the president, with his knowledge of national security and other sensitive matters, to that sort of rapid-fire questioning, according to University of Chicago law professor David Strauss.

"In an imaginary world, you could have the president step outside the grand jury room after each question and meet with the head of the CIA and the head of the Joint Chiefs of Staff and say, 'What do you think?' " said Strauss, who assisted Clinton's legal team in the Paula Jones sexual-harassment case.

In the real world, that can't happen, Strauss added. "It's hard to think it was the constitutional plan for the president to answer questions like that," he said.

Only twice, scholars say, have the nation's courts seen an issue even remotely like this. In 1807, President Thomas Jefferson was subpoenaed to give information in the trial of Aaron Burr, who was charged with treason. Jefferson declined to testify, but he supplied documents that seemed to satisfy prosecutors.

In 1974, the Watergate special prosecutor sought tapes Nixon had made of conversations in the Oval Office. Nixon fought the subpoena, but the Supreme Court ruled 8-0 against him.

Some say the Nixon case suggests that Clinton must respond to Starr's summons. But others emphasize the difference between a president turning over evidence such as tapes and appearing in person to be peppered with questions.

"This is a big game of chicken, as all negotiations between lawyers are," Tushnet said. When it comes down to it, he added, even top scholars have absolutely no idea how the courts would rule.

The issue highlights yet again the quirky nature of the independent counsel system. No ordinary federal prosecutor would be likely to subpoena the president because the president is his boss and could order him not to do so.

To Strauss, the gravity of the constitutional issues contrasts sharply with the triviality of the underlying allegations, which involve possible perjury in a case that was dismissed by a court.

"I can't imagine there is a real-life prosecutor who would spend more than 10 minutes on a case like this," Strauss said, "let alone establish a new constitutional precedent."

THE LAW.

LANGUAGE: ENGLISH

LOAD-DATE: July 27, 1998

123RD STORY of Level 1 printed in FULL format.

ABC NEWS

SHOW: ABC GOOD MORNING AMERICA SUNDAY (10:00 am ET)

JULY 26, 1998

Transcript # 98072605-j02

TYPE: INTERVIEW

SECTION: NEWS

LENGTH: 614 words

HEADLINE: PRESIDENTIAL SUBPOENA ISSUES

GUESTS: PAUL ROTHSTEIN

BYLINE: AARON BROWN

HIGHLIGHT:
LAST DANCE ON LEWINSKY CASE ABOUT TO BEGIN

BODY:

THIS IS A RUSH TRANSCRIPT. THIS COPY MAY NOT BE IN ITS FINAL FORM AND MAY BE UPDATED.

AARON BROWN, Host: Well, it does indeed seem like the last dance on the Lewinsky case is about to begin. So we're going to talk a bit about Kenneth Starr's attempt to subpoena the President. He has issued the subpoena. There are lots of questions here, as we've been suggesting this morning, legal and political. Some of those tend to run together.

Joining us this morning is Georgetown law professor Paul Rothstein. He joins us from Washington. Good morning, sir.

Prof. PAUL ROTHSTEIN, Georgetown University: Good morning, Aaron.

AARON BROWN: Well, I guess because we are in uncharted waters, it's hard to give a clean answer to the most basic question, which to me is, does he have the right to subpoena the President?

Prof. PAUL ROTHSTEIN: Well, the question is an open one under constitutional law. He can probably issue the subpoena, but the big question is whether the President can be forced to comply with it. What are you going to do, throw a president in jail if he doesn't comply with it? That would tie up the whole country. That would disable the people's president.

The Constitution provides for the only way to get a president out, which is impeachment. There a separation of powers in the Constitution. One branch of government, the courts, is not supposed to intrude on the other branches, the executive, which is the President. But we just don't know.

In the Nixon case, President Nixon was commanded to give up tapes, and in the Paula Jones case, the Supreme Court said President Clinton must respond to a civil lawsuit. But that's all different than requiring the person of the President to appear in a criminal inquiry before a grand jury, where he is the probable target.

AARON BROWN: And -- which is another question. I mean, isn't the argument -- or might the argument from the prosecutor's office be, "Well, we don't intend to indict the President. We're not sure we can. That's really the Congress's job. So he's not really a target of the investigation"?

Prof. PAUL ROTHSTEIN: Well, that would be one of the arguments. The constitutional law question is open. But that would be an argument on one side. But I don't think either side wants to have push come to shove and take this on up to the Supreme Court and maybe lose it. You know, both sides see there's a risk of loss and embarrassment and delay. Starr wouldn't want delay, so maybe that's why they're negotiating, you know, over something less than full grand jury testimony.

AARON BROWN: Read some tea leaves for me, because I'm a little befuddled, which is not unusual in my case, that he went for the President first and not Ms. Lewinsky to start the end game. What do you think his strategy, him, Starr, being here, what is his strategy?

Prof. PAUL ROTHSTEIN: Well, you see, the President is probably getting a lot of information from witnesses themselves as they appear before the grand jury. And then the President will try to fashion his testimony to be consistent with that, insofar as he can, whether he's a guilty president or an innocent president.

So if Lewinsky went first, the President would have that additional...

AARON BROWN: Got it.

Prof. PAUL ROTHSTEIN:... piece of the jigsaw puzzle.

AARON BROWN: Paul, thanks. Paul Rothstein, a law professor at Georgetown University, helping us understand what is quite a complicated legal and political question that both Kenneth Starr and the White House face this morning now.

(Commercial Break)

LANGUAGE: ENGLISH
LOAD-DATE: July 26, 1998

LAW OFFICES
WILLIAMS & CONNOLLY
725 TWELFTH STREET, N.W.
WASHINGTON, DC 20005-5901

VIA HAND DELIVERY

Robert J. Bittman, Esquire
Deputy Independent Counsel
Office of the Indepedent Counsel
1001 Pennsylvania Avenue, NW
Suite 490-North
Washington, DC

Received by: Monique [illegible]
Date: 7/28/98
Time: 1:10

UNDER SEAL

Tab 53

SEALED SEALED SEALED

UNITED STATES DISTRICT COURT
FOR THE DISTRICT OF COLUMBIA

IN RE:	Misc. No. 98-267
MOTION TO CONTINUE	Washington, D. C. July 28, 1998 4:30 p.m.

TRANSCRIPT OF STATUS HEARING
BEFORE THE HONORABLE NORMA HOLLOWAY JOHNSON
CHIEF JUDGE, UNITED STATES DISTRICT COURT

APPEARANCES:

For the Office of Independent Counsel:	ROBERT BITTMAN, ESQUIRE SAUL WISENBERG, ESQUIRE JOSEPH DITKOFF, ESQUIRE
For the Movant, President Clinton:	DAVID E. KENDALL, ESQUIRE NICOLE SELIGMAN, ESQUIRE MAX STIER, ESQUIRE ALICIA MARTI, ESQUIRE
Official Court Reporter:	GORDON A. SLODYSKO 4806-A U. S. Courthouse Washington, D. C. 20001 (202) 273-0404

Computer-Aided Transcription of Stenographic Notes

P R O C E E D I N G S

THE COURT: Good afternoon.

COUNSEL: Good afternoon, Your Honor.

THE DEPUTY CLERK: Miscellaneous Case Number 98-267, In re Motion to Continue. Representing the Office of the Independent Counsel are Robert Bittman, Saul Wisenberg, and Joseph Ditkoff. Representing President Clinton is David Kendall, Nicole Seligman, Max Stier, and Alicia Marti.

THE COURT: All right.

Counsel, I received this afternoon President Clinton's motion for continuance. I'm sure the Office of Independent Counsel would like a chance to respond to that motion. In the interest of time, and certainly in light of the public interest in moving this matter expeditiously, I will allow each side to present oral argument on the motion for continuance rather than asking the parties to submit written responses. I will hear from each of you for I hope not more than ten minutes a side and then make my ruling. If you need more than ten minutes, I certainly will grant you additional time. But I would hope that we could do it in about ten minutes a side.

And since it is the President's motion, I will hear from Mr. Kendall first.

MR. KENDALL: May it please the Court. We've moved for a two-week continuance of a subpoena ad testificandum delivered to counsel for the President on Friday, July 17th.

In some ways, Your Honor, I regret the need to burden you with this motion; I think it was unnecessary. But we were unable to get a continuance worked out with the Office of Independent Counsel.

I would like to explain a little about the background of this, if I may. This is not the first time the President's testimony has been sought. Indeed, on three different occasions he has given testimony at the behest of the Independent Counsel during the Whitewater investigation. The first time this occurred was in June of 1994, when Mr. Fisk was Independent Counsel. The second time was in April of 1995, after the present Independent Counsel was appointed on August 5th, 1994. And the third time was in July of 1995. Now, on each occasion we were able to work out a mutually acceptable way of providing for this testimony.

The President also testified twice by videotape in criminal trials of defendants indicted by the Whitewater grand jury in Arkansas. And on those occasions, the Independent Counsel was able to cross-examine the President.

As is clear from our motion, we had correspondence with the Independent Counsel earlier this spring about the President voluntarily appearing. I had many concerns about this. They were set forth in the correspondence. That correspondence really lapsed in April. The next thing we heard was the letter attached to the subpoena which was delivered to me at approximately 6:00 p.m. Friday, July 17th.

Your Honor, I initially sought time because this is the summer. Various people are somewhat scattered. Mr. Kantor, for example, is in China. He's been in China --

THE COURT: Mr. who?

MR. KENDALL: Mr. Mickey Kantor.

THE COURT: Oh, okay.

MR. KENDALL: One of the President's private attorneys who has been advising on this matter.

We were, however, able to make a quite specific proposal to the Independent Counsel, which was delivered yesterday, and that is at Tab 6 of our papers. This is a letter in which I try to outline some of our concerns, how they may be met. It provides a date, a specific date for the President to give testimony and an alternative date. And that, I hoped, would be a good faith offer that would allow us to negotiate, as we have in the past, and settle on both the timing and terms of the President's testimony.

I was surprised that the Independent Counsel refused to withdraw or suspend this subpoena, and therefore, I made this motion. I think it unseemly for the President of the United States to be in any way in violation of legal process. I think there are obvious reasons for that. And therefore, in an effort to avoid that, we made a motion for a brief continuance.

Your Honor, there are no deadlines, there are no statutes of limitation, there are no pending trials. There is really nothing substantive to warrant the denial of this very brief continuance.

I think that we may not in fact need the two weeks. It may be possible that we can very quickly work with the Independent Counsel to come to an agreement on the terms and timing. But as the motion papers make clear, this is a literally unprecedented legal act. The testimony of the President has never been compelled before a grand jury before, and there are very serious constitutional questions, the litigation of which would be quite time-consuming. We don't necessarily want to have to tackle those questions if we can come to an agreement that would allow both sides -- this has happened often in this investigation -- to maintain their positions but work together to get by a common problem.

The President of the United States -- I would be making this motion if it were anybody, in order to get the requisite time to try and work something out; and if things can't be worked out, to get the input of the people necessary to determine the proper arguments to be made on behalf of the President of the United States. The President is the President, however. He has public duties. And the language of the Jones case, the Clinton versus Jones case, is, I think, quite on point here because, while the Supreme Court did rule that the President while in office could be subjected to civil litigation, it also ruled that the conduct of that litigation had to be undertaken by the supervising judge with great sensitivity to the President's duties and great deference to the many demands on his time.

It is difficult to convey -- I have represented busy people before. It is difficult to convey how busy the President is, how many demands there are on his time. And in the past it has taken us time to work out not only a time for the President to testify, but a time in which he can be adequately prepared, because he has many duties and many demands. And every client deserves the effective assistance of counsel in getting them ready to testify so they can testify as effectively and accurately as possible.

We quoted some of the language in Clinton versus Jones. One of the things the Court stated was it articulated the assumption that any testimony from the President may be taken at a time that will accommodate his busy schedule. Your Honor, again, I think that the -- we've set forth in the letter the considerations that are important to us, considerations about the President's schedule. And we respectfully submit that this continuance is not lengthy. It may in fact make unnecessary other litigation. And we respectfully would request that the Court grant us a two-week continuance.

THE COURT: What do you want to do with the two weeks?

You know, you ask me for a two-week continuance. Are you asking me to give you two weeks to let the President respond to the subpoena, or are you asking me to give you two weeks to determine how you wish to respond to the subpoena? Just what are you asking me for?

MR. KENDALL: I think the former, Your Honor. I think it's the former.

THE COURT: Well, since I've said a couple of things, you'd better tell me what my former is.

MR. KENDALL: The former, Your Honor, as I understood it, was to enable the President to determine how most appropriately to respond to the subpoena.

It may be -- and I don't know what the -- because I didn't -- I've had communications with Mr. Bittman. I don't know. My own view is that we should take testimony as we have done it before. That has the great value of precedent. And I think not only judges, but lawyers, there's a value in doing things the way they've been done in the past. I think if we can do that and find a date, the rest of the motion will be moot and we will come to agreement on a time and terms. That's what I hope will happen. We will try to make that happen.

Now, it's possible that we will not be able to come to those terms. A subpoena has been issued here. It's possible that the response would be some kind of a motion. And that would be done at the end of that two-week period.

So, I think what happens at the end of the two weeks really depends on what goes on during it.

THE COURT: So you're really not seeking just a two-weeks continuance of the return of the subpoena. You are actually seeking two weeks to determine what you want to do with respect to the subpoena.

MR. KENDALL: Your Honor, I think that's correct, although --

THE COURT: Because the way I understand it -- I could be wrong, because I haven't seen the subpoena, and I haven't asked anybody to see it, but the way I understand it, the subpoena that he received in July stated that he should appear in person today. Is that correct?

MR. KENDALL: That's correct, Your Honor.

THE COURT: Okay. So, what you're saying to me is you're not asking me to just continue that appearance for two weeks. You're asking me to give you two weeks to raise further or additional legal argument.

MR. KENDALL: Your Honor, I don't know. It seems to me that I am asking you to continue it as well. What we don't want to have is the President in violation of the subpoena. And therefore, in the normal case you would phone up the prosecutor and say, "You've subpoenaed my client for Monday;, she's going to be in Chicago that day. Could you move it to Wednesday?" And normally, that's possible.

THE COURT: Yes.

MR. KENDALL: Depending on the grand jury.

Here, I think if we can get the continuance, in the interim I hope we will be able to work out an agreement whereby we won't have to come back to the Court at all, we will do the testimony. If we can't, then at the end of that period we would file a motion.

THE COURT: All right.

MR. KENDALL: Thank you, Your Honor.

THE COURT: Thank you.

I'll be happy to hear from you now, Mr. Bittman.

MR. BITTMAN: Good afternoon, Your Honor. Robert Bittman, on behalf of the United States.

Let me clarify something as to how we got involved in the chronology of what occurred. It was exactly six months ago today that we invited the President the first time to appear before the grand jury. Six months ago today.

Mr. Kendall correctly referred to the fact that our office has received testimony from the President before. That was via negotiation. But it was always with an invitation first, which the President accepted immediately, and then we hammered out some of the details as to when and how the President would testify.

In this case, we, and the grand jury, I might add, felt it necessary to issue a subpoena to the President because the President had refused six invitations to testify. They were, frankly, just, in my words, stringing us along, and the grand jury. The President publicly stated that he was prepared to cooperate with the investigation and give information sooner rather than later, more rather than less, and yet he refused -- or declined, rather, six consecutive invitations to testify.

As you know, the grand jury has been working very, very hard, at great sacrifice to them. It has had effects on their families; it has had job effects. And they've been working very, very hard. They have been very gracious in allowing us extra days and extra time recently.

This litigation -- or, pardon me, this investigation has also had a number of parties assert various privileges that have burdened not only this Court but the Court of Appeals, and some of them have gone all the way to the Supreme Court.

And we have tried to move things along as expeditiously as possible. The grand jury has been working very hard. And it is time to receive the President's testimony, if he so chooses.

THE COURT: And you say there have been six invitations?

MR. BITTMAN: There have been six invitations.

THE COURT: All right. And how did those invitations go? Were they in writing, as opposed to oral?

MR. BITTMAN: The first invitation was oral. The

other five were all in writing. And I believe Mr. Kendall appended all of the invitations to his pleading. All of them are in there.

THE COURT: All right.

MR. BITTMAN: And then Mr. Kendall's responses are all there, also.

THE COURT: All right.

MR. BITTMAN: With regard to the President's schedule, he is a very busy person. And the Jones v. Clinton case makes it clear that the justice process should accommodate the President's schedule and should defer to him in his official capacity. I'm sure Mr. Kendall knows the President's schedule better than I do, but we have done some research, even in terms of when we set today, to make sure that he was in town. We've checked it in the future, too. And our understanding is that the President, for example, is going away this weekend for some fund-raising events and for some rest and relaxation, and then he's taking a two-week vacation in August.

We do not want to interrupt the President's foreign trips or any official business that the President, obviously, will be involved in. But we think the timing is right. The grand jury, you know, has been working, once again, as I said, very hard. And I don't think I want to reveal to Mr. Kendall exactly why the grand jury wishes the President's testimony now. And we're certainly not obligated to, and we're not going to. But this is the time.

We have tried to accommodate the President's schedule. We have offered innumerable dates through August 7th. We will go -- well, we haven't worked out the exact, precise details of how we would receive the President's testimony, but I'm confident we can do that if we get an agreement from the President that he will appear before -- in the very near future. And that just hasn't been forthcoming.

The date offered by Mr. Kendall in mid-September is just unacceptable. It is just unacceptable to the grand jury's schedule and to the grand jury's investigation. We just cannot wait that long for the President's testimony.

The investigation is very, very important. The President has so stated that. And I don't think that the investigation should wait for him to play golf, for fund-raising events, and for his vacations.

Mr. Kendall in his papers discusses that this could raise some sort of a constitutional crisis. We don't believe so. We have thoroughly reviewed the law and we believe we are absolutely entitled, with the grand jury's approval, to issue a subpoena to the President. The Nixon case made clear that the President of the United States may be subpoenaed in a criminal trial. The Jones v. Clinton case itself authorizes a court to -- that the President appear at a deposition in a civil case. Clearly, if he has to appear in a civil case and answer to civil charges, he would have to answer a criminal grand jury subpoena.

The President also, as we've discussed, has appeared before. He's provided depositions to us. He's appeared in criminal trials. He was subpoenaed by the defense in two trials in Arkansas. He testified in those trials -- after being deposed, but he testified. And then in this case, we issued a grand jury subpoena duces tecum, for documents, to the President early on in the investigation and he complied with that subpoena. I think it's odd now to all of a sudden say, well, he's not going to comply with this one.

So, unless Your Honor has any questions for me. We just want to get this resolved. We wish to know exactly what the President is going to do.

THE COURT: So what I understand from you is that you do maintain that the grand jury wants to have the President appear before it.

MR. BITTMAN: Yes.

THE COURT: And that you're saying you need it now.

MR. BITTMAN: Yes.

THE COURT: Rather than in September.

MR. BITTMAN: Yes.

THE COURT: Do you have any idea -- and if you don't, I can understand, because I do know enough about grand juries to know that you can't always tell how many questions a grand jury may choose to ask or anything like that. Do you have any sense of how long he might be required to appear before the grand jury? Do you have any sense?

MR. BITTMAN: I think it would be several hours. Less than -- well, I don't know. It would be several hours.

And let me amend one of my answers with regard to the grand jury's wishes as to whether the President actually appear before them. Without revealing too much of what goes on in the grand jury --

THE COURT: Certainly.

MR. BITTMAN: -- that is their belief now. But we believe that if given a concrete offer by the President, that is, that he, the President, is willing to do this, to a deposition, perhaps in front of the grand jurors in an area outside the grand jury room, perhaps a deposition, obviously under oath, just before attorneys from our office, something like that in the immediate future, we believe that we can gain the -- that we would speak to the grand jury and see if that were acceptable to them.

THE COURT: Well, let me just say, I know that even those type of issues could seriously be considered Rule 6(e). But I just wanted to get some sense.

That subpoena was issued by the grand jury, is that correct?

MR. BITTMAN: Yes.

THE COURT: And that was the subpoena that was returnable today.

MR. BITTMAN: Yes.

THE COURT: At 1:30.

MR. BITTMAN: It was actually returnable originally for 9:15, and then I permitted Mr. Kendall till 1:30. I extended it to 1:30.

THE COURT: All right. So your position is that the grand jury wishes to hear from him sooner than later.

MR. BITTMAN: Oh, yes. They have been kept informed throughout about our invitations and the President's declinations. And Your Honor knows that the grand jury's investigation has proceeded. And it is time to hear from this particular witness, the President.

THE COURT: Very well. Thank you.

MR. BITTMAN: And we at minimum wish, obviously, a response to whether the President is going to testify and then some concrete terms, because we just can't have this open-ended thing where, okay, in two weeks they may file a motion to quash which is going to further delay the investigation. If a motion to quash is to be filed, we wish to litigate it right away. And, frankly, we would ask Your Honor, if one is filed, for an expedited briefing schedule and expedited hearing, because we want this very, very quickly.

THE COURT: Very well. Thank you.

Mr. Kendall, I'll be happy to hear anything further that you wish to say on this issue.

MR. KENDALL: Thank you, Your Honor.

I regret that these somewhat voluminous papers probably hit your desk this afternoon.

THE COURT: Believe me, they did.

MR. KENDALL: They hit it with a thud, I'm sure.

THE COURT: Yes, they did.

MR. KENDALL: Your Honor, at Attachment 6, when Mr. Bittman says --

THE COURT: Which I have not been able -- I have not read your attachments yet, but I have read your motion.

MR. KENDALL: Okay. I would simply direct the Court's attention to that because that was our attempt -- Mr. Bittman and I had conversations and he wanted a specific proposal. This is a specific proposal. It proposes both a time and terms. It's as specific, really, as we can get it.

Your Honor, it's simply not the case that this matter has been in discussion since January. It was in discussion in late January to April, and then we heard -- my last letter, which I've appended here, was not responded to. So there was a long three months, plus, pause in this, and then suddenly we got the subpoena. And so it is not --

THE COURT: Let me ask you, what about letters from the grand jury? I understand that the grand jury was sending him a written invitation?

MR. KENDALL: Well, we received invitations from the Office of Independent Counsel. We never got anything from the grand jury itself.

THE COURT: But I mean the invitations from the Office of Independent Counsel indicated, though, that the purpose was for him to appear before the grand jury, wasn't it?

MR. KENDALL: They did, Your Honor.

THE COURT: And you didn't consider that to be from the grand jury?

MR. KENDALL: Well, Your Honor, I did. We responded to each one of those. And we responded -- we had many questions. And this Court is familiar with certain of our concerns about this investigation --

THE COURT: Certainly.

MR. KENDALL: -- and the way it's progressed. We had, and continue to have, very serious concerns about certain aspects of it. I don't want to have to litigate the constitutional questions, but they are important, they are unresolved. I am reminded when Mr. Bittman -- and, you know, I don't think the Court wants to hear those arguments today. We haven't filed them. But --

THE COURT: No. Just the motion for continuance.

MR. KENDALL: Every pancake has two sides, Your Honor, as is well known. And we stand ready to make those at an appropriate time. But I think the --

THE COURT: But, you see, that's one of the things that caused me to ask you gentlemen to come in here today. I wasn't sure what you meant by give you until such-and-such a time, and I really needed you to come in here and tell me, what do you mean? Do you mean that you will be prepared to respond to the subpoena by that day, or do you mean that "I'm going to give this further thought and then two weeks from now I'm going to tell you what I think?" I need to know precisely what you mean.

And I think you have made it clear to me that the motion for continuance that you filed today is not designed to just continue the personal response to the subpoena. In other words, you're not saying, "If you give me two weeks, the President will respond by coming in to see the grand jury or having the grand jury come to see him." And, God knows, I would say to you, recognizing the duties of his office, if it were more convenient, more secure for the grand jury to go to him than for him to come to the grand jury -- and you know what type of atmosphere we have around this building -- then that's one thing. But if what you're saying is "I need two weeks to consider how I'm going to deal with this," then that's another question.

MR. KENDALL: Your Honor, again, the letter at Attachment 6 is a very --

THE COURT: As I said, I'll read it tonight.

MR. KENDALL: Yes. It's a very specific offer. And it's premised -- we've worked this out, really, three times in the past successfully. I think that both our concerns and the Independent Counsel's concerns were met. I think the letter is a good faith attempt to do that again. And I hope that after discussion, we can work out a way -- reserving our questions. I mean, these are negotiations in which both sides want to reserve their option. But three times before, we've had the President testify and that has --

THE COURT: Three times before testified with respect to what? This case?

MR. KENDALL: With respect to this investigation. This is the Whitewater -- in other words, he gave testimony about various phases of it, Vincent Foster and David Hale and the 1990 gubernatorial campaign.

THE COURT: But I don't think this grand jury wants to ask any of those questions.

MR. KENDALL: Oh, no. No. I understand that, Your Honor. This is the Lewinsky --

THE COURT: Yes.

MR. KENDALL: And that's what we're talking about here. My only point is, we've been able to work this out three times in the past. And it's my hope that based upon the proposal we've made in the letter at Tab 6, that we can do it again, and so we won't be coming back to Your Honor.

THE COURT: Well, let me just say, apparently -- and I've got to believe this -- with your letter dated July 27th, which was yesterday, they have had an opportunity to read that letter before they got your papers that you filed in the court today around midday. Isn't that true? Every reason to believe they've had an opportunity to read that.

MR. KENDALL: That's correct, Your Honor.

THE COURT: And even though they have had that opportunity to read it, their stated position on the record is to the contrary of what you're saying -- of what you say your letter says: That they can work it out. In fact, what I heard Mr. Bittman say is that he needs the testimony. You're saying you think you can work it out.

MR. KENDALL: Your Honor, we are trying to work it out to give them the testimony.

THE COURT: Let me just ask you something, Mr. Bittman. Had you read this letter before you came in here today?

MR. BITTMAN: Yes, Your Honor. We responded to it.

THE COURT: Oh, you did? And is it here, too?

MR. BITTMAN: Yes.

THE COURT: Okay.

MR. BITTMAN: That's at Attachment 7.

THE COURT: I haven't read the attachments, all right?

I will read them before I leave here this evening, though, okay?

You see, what I -- I mean just applying a little common sense here, if you sent this letter yesterday, they received it, they read it, they responded to it. Still, the subpoena remained outstanding, and the grand jury, who actually was the only body that could authorize that subpoena, apparently was waiting for the subpoena to be responded to today. Then we get your request. And, as I said, you asked me for two weeks and I just didn't quite understand what that two weeks meant. I understand now, based upon your statement to me, what you mean by giving you that additional two weeks, but that does not take into consideration the body which sought the subpoena. You see, that's what concerns me, Mr. Kendall.

I'm not saying -- and I want you to understand, I'm not saying that this grand jury has a right to subpoena the President of the United States. I'm sure that they have subpoenaed the President of the United States. And what I am not hearing from you is that "We oppose this subpoena because the grand jury does not have that right." You're saying, "Just give me two weeks to think about something, and then two weeks from now I'll tell you something." And then if two weeks from now you say, "Well, I don't really think they have the right to subpoena the President, and therefore, Your Honor, may I have two more weeks to file a motion to quash the subpoena." I just think that based upon what we all know about this case, the sooner we make a decision, the better.

MR. KENDALL: Your Honor, may I respond to that?

THE COURT: Surely you may.

MR. KENDALL: And I will respond, I hope, in a factual way. I'm not saying that I want a limitless set of extensions. I think that these are very important constitutional questions. If we go to war over them --

THE COURT: No question about it, but the question is, do we have to deal with the constitutional issue? Because if we do, let's do that head-on.

MR. KENDALL: But, Your Honor, if we go to war over that, that is going to take a lot of time.

THE COURT: We're not going to go to war, and we're going to do it the same way the Court of Appeals has you do things. I just find it so interesting. Everybody needs 10, 12 days if you are here in the district court, but I understand that those judges on the Court of Appeals give two days or three days. I said, "Why can't I exercise that power? I have a commission too." So, no, we aren't going to be in it forever, okay? All right.

I'm being facetious, of course.

MR. KENDALL: My only point is, Your Honor, if the object is to get the testimony to the grand jury, I think some statesmanship on both sides is necessary. And I say that about us as well as the Independent Counsel. I think that if we can work this out, we are obligated to do so, because that really is our civic duty. We've done it three times --

THE COURT: You all have had a long time, apparently, to do that, Mr. Kendall, if what Mr. Bittman says is correct. Mr. Bittman says that there was a subpoena issued one time. Was that correct?

MR. KENDALL: Your Honor, only on the 17th of July. A week ago.

THE COURT: Yes. Only the one on July 17th?

MR. KENDALL: Yes. I'm sorry. He mentioned -- excuse me, Your Honor. He did mention a subpoena for certain objects that was issued in January.

THE COURT: Oh, yes, duces tecum, and that was taken care of. But I understand that there have been about six invitations from the grand jury. So, apparently the President has known for some time that the grand jury wished to speak with him.

Now, I don't know, because, God knows, you know, I may have to go up there and see if they have water and a few other things from time to time, but I don't know what goes on before the grand jury as you know. But I would think if somebody had received six letters inviting him to appear before the grand jury, that person -- and I don't mean to be unkind, but certainly his counsel must know that somebody is going to get tired of written invitations and look to other sources. I mean, that's just common sense.

MR. KENDALL: Your Honor, we've tried in Tab 1 to give you the complete correspondence, because it states our concerns and the responses. And I think in fairness, that correspondence terminated when I sent a letter on April the 17th. I didn't know what the answer was. And a very long time elapsed.

My only point here, Your Honor, is that I --

THE COURT: Are you saying that there were no invitations from the grand jury since April 17th?

MR. KENDALL: April 3rd, in fact, Your Honor, was the last.

THE COURT: Was the last letter from the grand jury?

MR. KENDALL: Yes. And then all of a sudden, without any warning, we get a subpoena. And that old lawyer's trick, Your Honor, delivering it late Friday night so you can have that date of the week and say, "We served it on July 17th." It came in about 6:00 o'clock. That is what is forcing this issue.

In the past, we have been able to resolve this. I don't think it's seemly or statesmanlike, or even very reasonable, to put us under the gun of saying, as they say in their response to the letter of yesterday, "Well, you just commit to this date," and it's an unreasonable date in terms of the President's schedule. We're going to have to file a motion. I don't think we should be in the position of having to file a motion which, if we can resolve the other issues, may be unnecessary.

THE COURT: Well, why do you need so much time to resolve the other issues?

MR. KENDALL: I'm not sure we do, Your Honor. I'm not sure we do. I'm not sure that we can't do this very speedily. But the scheduling really is a problem.

THE COURT: What you're saying is, you have not as yet made the decision whether you are going to challenge the constitutionality of this subpoena.

MR. KENDALL: We have made a decision, Your Honor, that we've testified in the past, we believe we can testify at this time. But we don't know what their position is and they may force us to challenge this, and then we'll challenge it.

I used the "war" metaphor. We're not going to go to war. But we'll file motions to quash. And my only point is, it is unreasonable -- you wouldn't do this in the normal case, Your Honor. You wouldn't refuse to continue a subpoena for a short time to see if it all was going to be unnecessary. And that's really all we're seeking. And at the end of the day, we may have to file a motion to quash, to bring on the constitutional issue, to preserve the institutional concerns of the Article II entity, person that we represent. It hasn't been necessary in the past; I don't believe it necessarily will be necessary now. But it could be.

THE COURT: Well, you say it may not be necessary, the amount of time you're seeking, but you still seek that time.

MR. KENDALL: I do, Your Honor.

THE COURT: All right. Anything else?

MR. KENDALL: The only thing I would say is, in reference to Mr. Bittman's statement about the President's schedule, it is true, he does have a vacation planned for late August. It's a well-deserved vacation. It, unfortunately, is right on the eve of his Russia trip and Ireland trip. That's a trip from August 31 to September the 6th. Both those countries are very important. A lot of that vacation is going to be absorbed with preparing for the Russia trip.

Again, we are trying -- we've given them the date in September. We are aware from other parties who have been subpoenaed that the grand jury's work is going on. There are many other legal questions which are in the process of being resolved. We really don't think that this date will delay the grand jury's work, and we want to make it possible, if we can, to give the President's testimony as soon as possible.

THE COURT: Well, let me just say this. You know, even I don't know what the grand jury is doing. And I'm certain that Mr. Bittman has some sense because he knows what has been presented to the grand jury and what he wishes to present to the grand jury. But I haven't the foggiest notion of what they have presented or what they wish to present. I learn most of what I know about that grand jury the same way most citizens in this city do, and we don't know how accurate that is, but that's from the local press.

Now, what concerns me is this: This case is unlike the Jones case. It truly is unlike the Jones case. And even though it is quite unlike the Jones case, we know what the Supreme Court felt about even a civil action of the type that we have there. Here, we have a criminal investigation going on. Here, we know from just reading the press that perhaps witnesses who have been called in before this grand jury have been testifying about certain conduct. I don't know what that grand jury thinks, but it perhaps thinks that "We citizens have been brought from our regular responsibilities and asked to listen to certain evidence, and we have decided, based upon what we have heard, that we need to hear from the President."

Now, maybe they don't have any legal right to hear from the President. Maybe that is an issue we will have to resolve before this subpoena can be honored. But what we need to do, I think, is to move forward, and move forward expeditiously.

Apparently, the President has been given, if you'll excuse this slang, a heads-up by the number of invitations. Did I determine that those invitations were in writing?

MR. KENDALL: Some of them were, Your Honor. They are

reflected, I think, in the correspondence in Tab 1.

THE COURT: As I said, I'll read this. But some of it -- at any rate, he's received six invitations. And apparently the grand jury has determined that "Although we would like to honor your position as our President by simply asking you to appear voluntarily, we have now reached the point where we believe that you will not honor us with your presence voluntarily, but we do believe that in our search for the truth, we need to hear from you." And now, for him to say, "Give me two weeks to think whether I'm going to challenge this legally or what I'm going to do, give me two weeks to see if I can work this out with the prosecutor, give me two weeks to see whatever I need to do," but by the time that two weeks is up, Mr. Kendall, you're saying to me he will -- I don't know whether he's going to the Cape this year or not, but I know that's where he generally goes. Whether he will be at the Cape by the time the two weeks is up. And, clearly, I've been told that after leaving the Cape, he'll be going to Russia. So, when, if ever, unless somebody directs him, will he be willing to respond to this grand jury? Or if he isn't willing to respond to the grand jury, tell me.

MR. KENDALL: Your Honor, it's a fair question.

THE COURT: Tell me. And then we will do what we have to do.

MR. KENDALL: We've given two dates. I think that's a

very fair question. You'll see in the letter at Tab 6 --

THE COURT: The July 27th letter?

MR. KENDALL: Exactly.

THE COURT: All right.

MR. KENDALL: We have said, because of the Russia trip, because of the vacation and other travel. And, again, it's very easy to sit there, whether you're reading a newspaper, you're in the Office of Independent Counsel, and say, well, that trip's not necessary, that's just a fund-raising trip, and that's a political trip, and, look, I don't think Ireland is such an important country. Those concerns are the President's, and the President's alone, to balance. And courts -- I mean, again, the teaching of Clinton v. Jones, I think, is that a court must try to accommodate and give deference to the President's schedule.

THE COURT: That's true. And as I said, I understand that very, very clearly, because we know that as President of these United States, this gentleman has concerns that none of us know about. We know that there are issues of state that none of us know about. We know all of that. But I also know this: If he can vacation for a couple of weeks, he can appear before a grand jury, too, you know.

And God knows, he needs a vacation. I know that. I know he needs a vacation. And I don't know that the grand jury will -- he doesn't know how -- the grand jury may just want to see him. I don't know. They may not have any questions at all.

MR. KENDALL: We did try to make a very specific offer, including a date that would be consonant with his schedule.

THE COURT: But that's sometime in September.

MR. KENDALL: It is.

THE COURT: Well, as I said, you see, I don't know the interest of the grand jury, either. But one thing is for sure: The grand jury has apparently attempted, even though you've maintained that because there was no further response to some letter you wrote in April, that, therefore, he could think that maybe they didn't want him any more.

MR. KENDALL: Your Honor, I would like to distinguish, if I could, between concerns. We, obviously, would like to help the grand jury in its endeavors. The Office of Independent Counsel we have our differences with about a number of things. They are set forth in the letter. Those concerns have not been responded to. We are willing to forgo some of those or litigate them in other forums. We really did try, however, to get a good faith offer that was specific in terms of place, way of taking testimony, issues -- and leaks are one of the things that we are concerned about. But we believe that there can be safeguards. This is not an impossible task. And time. And the time is really very critical. But we have tried to put that all in a very specific proposal for the Independent Counsel and for the Court.

THE COURT: All right. Thank you very much.

MR. KENDALL: Thank you, Your Honor.

THE COURT: Mr. Bittman, I'll hear from you finally.

MR. BITTMAN: Thank you. I'll be brief. Robert Bittman on behalf of the United States.

Your Honor, in all respect, I think saying that we are being unreasonable by issuing a grand jury subpoena with the grand jury's approval is a little -- and that we're not willing to accommodate or even give a little bit with regard to the President's schedule, we are, we have been. I think that that argument would have a lot more merit had there not been six invitations.

We've tried to get his testimony since January. We've tried. Since January 27th, we have tried. We've invited him. And we made clear in all those invitations that we will accommodate the President's schedule. And now, for the President to -- and then after six invitations, you know, we in the grand jury decide to issue a subpoena to the President because that's within our power. You know, we tried to accommodate him, we've tried all means necessary to avoid any constitutional confrontation or something like that, but he declined the invitation. What are we left to do? And we have -- back then, when we extended these invitations, we have a lot of room to negotiate in terms of when and how and where and that kind of stuff. Well, now we're at the end of the investigation, or near the end of the investigation, we decide, with the grand jury's approval, to issue a subpoena to the President. We don't have many options any more.

And so for them to come in here and say, "Oh, we want them to be more reasonable," we were reasonable back then. And they were the ones that said, "No, we're not going to do it. We're not going to agree to this." So I think it is disingenuous, with all respect.

I did notify Mr. Kendall last weekend -- and I might also say, if they were really serious about trying to work something out -- and Mr. Kendall did put forward a very specific date. I agree with that. And that's in his correspondence. But the date simply is not acceptable. That's the bottom line. It's unacceptable. We told him it was unacceptable.

THE COURT: That's the September date?

MR. BITTMAN: That's the September date. That is unacceptable. And we have the power, we, with the grand jury, have the power to compel the President. That's what we've decided to do. We didn't want to do that. That's why we issued the six invitations. But they put us in a box. We had to do it because they weren't going to agree anyway. Now, we have a limited opportunity in terms of time.

I notified Mr. Kendall that if they really wanted to work out a date, an acceptable date with us, that we would be available all weekend. Apparently Mr. Kendall -- I read that Mr. Kendall was not available over the weekend. But we responded within hours of his letter to me, and we said we're available to work this out, to work out an acceptable date. They didn't provide us with an acceptable date. It's that simple.

We still are willing to work out an acceptable date, but we're not going to wait two weeks for it. We have to move this along.

THE COURT: Well, I think Mr. Kendall is asking for a little more than two weeks, isn't he?

MR. BITTMAN: He is, because --

THE COURT: You see, that's why I really had to have you all in here today, because I wanted to be certain of what you meant. You could read Mr. Kendall's motion to maybe suggest that, well, we'll be ready to go on that date, and I said and you could also read it to mean that you won't be ready to go, "but I'll be ready to tell you where I want to go two weeks from now."

And I certainly have a duty to the President, but I also have a duty to the grand jury. And here, this third branch stands behind the first and the second branches, but, you know, I do have a duty myself.

So, anything else you want to say? I'll have to take this matter under advisement, but let me just say, I'm in a better position to take it under advisement, having had you come today, than I was just based on the papers alone.

MR. BITTMAN: Nothing else from me. Thank you, Your Honor.

THE COURT: Anything else from you, Mr. Kendall?

MR. KENDALL: Thank you, Your Honor.

THE COURT: Okay. Well, thank you very much.

Let me just say, what I hope to do is call you first thing in the morning and tell you -- I hope to be able to call you first thing in the morning and tell you to come down and pick up my decision or pick up an order or whatever the case may be relative to today's hearing. Okay? I really hope to be able to do it. And if you haven't heard from me by 11 o'clock -- well, let me just say this. If you haven't heard from me by 11 o'clock -- no, that isn't what I want to say.

If you have not received a telephone call from me before 11 o'clock, I will try to do a conference call at 11 o'clock. That's what I want to say. Okay? Thank you very much.

(Proceedings concluded at 5:20 p.m.)

CERTIFICATE OF REPORTER

I certify that the foregoing is a correct transcription from the record of proceedings in the above-entitled matter.

Official Court Reporter

Tab 54

FEDERAL BUREAU OF INVESTIGATION
Receipt for Property Received/Returned/Released/Seized

Page 1 of 1

On (date) 7/29/98

Time: 2:45 PM

item(s) listed below were:
☒ Received From
☐ Returned To
☐ Released To
☐ Seized

(Name) Law Offices of Plato Cacheris
(Street Address) 1100 Conn Ave, Suite 730
(City) Washington, D.C.

Description of Item(s):

1. 1 Stuffed animal from black dog
2. Book: Leaves of Grass W/ paper cover
3. Page from filofax (1996 + 1997) W/ dates circled on it
4. GAP dress, size 12, dark blue
5. Brown, marble bear sculpture
6. Rockettes Christmas blanket (1995), red + white
7. Dark sunglasses (TAIWAN written on inside)
8. Wooden box, circular in shape, redish
9. 4 microcassetts: 1) "Dec 96" on it
   2) "Sept. 96" on it
   3) "May 96 2 mess." on it
   4) "April 96" on it
10. White canvas bag W/ a black dog on it.

END

Received by: [redacted] (Signature)   Received from Monica L (Signature)

Tab 55

Office of the Independent Counsel

1001 Pennsylvania Avenue, N.W.
Suite 490-North
Washington, DC 20004
(202) 514-8688
Fax (202) 514-8802

July 31, 1998

HAND DELIVERED

David E. Kendall, Esq.
Williams & Connolly
725 Twelfth Street, N.W.
Washington, D.C. 20005

Re: William Jefferson Clinton

Dear David:

I telephoned you twice this morning but was unable to reach you. Investigative demands require that President Clinton provide this Office as soon as possible with a blood sample to be taken under our supervision. [redacted]. I assure you this information will be kept strictly confidential and will restricted to a handful of persons on a need-to-know basis only.

Your prompt response to these requests will be greatly appreciated.

Sincerely,

Robert J. Bittman
Deputy Independent Counsel

Office of the Independent Counsel

July 31, 1998

Received this 31st day of July, 1998, one double-enveloped package addressed to David Kendall, Williams & Connolly, 725 12th Street, Northwest, Washington, D.C. 20005

7/31/98 3:20pm
Date and Time

N. Sloan
Signature

Tab 56

LAW OFFICES
WILLIAMS & CONNOLLY
725 TWELFTH STREET, N.W.
WASHINGTON, D. C. 20005-5901
(202) 434-5000
FAX (202) 434-5029

EDWARD BENNETT WILLIAMS (1920-1988)
PAUL R. CONNOLLY (1922-1978)

DAVID E. KENDALL
(202) 434-5145

July 31, 1998

<u>CONFIDENTIAL</u>

Robert J. Bittman, Esq.
Deputy Independent Counsel
Office of the Independent Counsel
1001 Pennsylvania Avenue, N.W.
Suite 490-North
Washington, D.C. 20004

<u>By Hand</u>

Dear Bob:

I received your July 31 letter which refers to "[i]nvestigative demands." As you must surely be aware, the cases require a heightened standard of probable cause for bodily intrusions. <u>See</u>, <u>e.g.</u>, <u>Schmerber v. California</u>, 384 U.S. 757, 769 (1966); <u>Winston v. Lee</u>, 470 U.S. 753, 759 (1985); <u>In re Grand Jury Proceedings (Suleski)</u>, 816 F. Supp. 1196, 1204-06 (W.D. Ky. 1196). Since the request you make is addressed to the President of the United States, I believe that also applicable to this request are the considerations identified in <u>Clinton v. Jones</u>, ___ U.S. ___, 117 S.Ct. 1636, 1650-1651 (1997), that mandate a "high respect that is owed to the office of the Chief Executive . . . [which should] inform the conduct of the entire proceeding." Accordingly, I ask that you inform me of the precise factual basis for your request.

I have another concern and another request. I will not rehearse the history of grand jury leaks in this investigation or the orders that Chief Judge Johnson has entered. While the OIC has retained outside counsel to appeal portions of the district court orders which afforded us discovery against the OIC and while an administrative stay from the Court of Appeals is now in effect, the OIC has not appealed the underlying findings which caused the Chief Judge to enter her orders. In just the last few days, there have been numerous leaks to the news media of reports about a dress of Ms. Lewinsky's which is allegedly stained in

WILLIAMS & CONNOLLY

Robert J. Bittman, Esq.
July 31, 1998
Page 2

some way. As to these latter leaks, I do not at the present time have information sufficient to say who may be guilty of any improper disclosures, but unfortunately such leaks appear to be a way of life in this investigation. I fear that, if we provide the sample you have requested, false information of any tests that are conducted will be leaked. In its papers in the leaks litigation, the OIC has often adverted to "false" leaks. The only way we can be protected against such a phenomenon is to be made aware of any test results which are conducted, so we will be in a position to respond to false leaks.

If you believe either of these disclosures would be protected by Rule 6(e), we would be willing to stipulate to a motion to the Court for a Rule 6(e) order allowing the release of information to us, and we would undertake not to disclose it further, except on the terms specified in the order.

I would like to discuss these matters with you further and will give you a call after you have received this letter.

Sincerely,

David E. Kendall

DEK/bb

Tab 57

Office of the Independent Counsel

1001 Pennsylvania Avenue, N.W.
Suite 490-North
Washington, DC 20004
(202) 514-8688
Fax (202) 514-8802

July 31, 1998

HAND DELIVERED

David E. Kendall, Esq.
Williams & Connolly
725 Twelfth Street, N.W.
Washington, D.C. 20005

Re: William Jefferson Clinton

Dear David:

This responds to your letter of today, which was delivered to me at 5:35 p.m.

I assure you that we have substantial factual and legal predication for our request of the President. We are mindful of the legal requirements of our request, and we are certain that the request is lawful and would be upheld by a reviewing court. We make this request, as we have others, respectful of the dignity of the Office of the President. Because of the President's pledge to cooperate with this investigation and out of respect for the Presidency, we have not issued a subpoena for this sample. We do not wish to litigate this matter, and we wish no embarrassment to the President. Yet, we have substantial predication for our request, and we must do our job.

You also refer to the dissemination of information in the media. As confirmed by Messrs. Stein and Cacheris, this Office is not the source -- either directly or indirectly -- of the information. That being said, we are sensitive to your desires, consistent with our abiding aim, to insure complete confidentiality. We have -- we believe -- powerful predication for our request of the President, and that representation, which reflects our considered professional judgement, should suffice. If you disagree, then the prudent and wise course may be to proceed under the aegis of the Chief Judge. We would set forth our predication, which we believe is powerful, before the Chief Judge. This would assure you the independent review of an Article III judge, and thereby further insure that the dignitary interests of the President are scrupulously protected. The Chief Judge would also, under our proposed approach, then be in a position to consider any protective order (or evaluate a motion to quash) that you might see fit to request.

David E. Kendall, Esq.
July 31, 1998
Page two

We are not in a position at this early juncture to agree to a release of information subsequent to further examination; such a release to you might raise serious questions of law, as you recognize. Here again, we could go before Chief Judge Johnson for appropriate direction to protect all relevant interests.

Sincerely,

Robert J. Bittman
Deputy Independent Counsel

Tab 58

LAW OFFICES
WILLIAMS & CONNOLLY
725 TWELFTH STREET, N.W.
WASHINGTON, D. C. 20005-5901
(202) 434-5000
FAX (202) 434-5029

DAVID E KENDALL
(202) 434-5145

EDWARD BENNETT WILLIAMS (1920-1988)
PAUL R. CONNOLLY (1922-1978)

August 3, 1998

CONFIDENTIAL
WRITTEN PURSUANT TO SECRECY PROVISIONS OF RULE 6(e),
FEDERAL RULES OF CRIMINAL PROCEDURE
GRAND JURY MATERIAL

Robert J. Bittman, Esq.
Deputy Independent Counsel
Office of the Independent Counsel
1001 Pennsylvania Avenue, N.W.
Suite 490-North
Washington, D.C. 20004

BY HAND--TO BE OPENED BY MR. BITTMAN ONLY

Dear Bob:

This letter is written after receiving your second letter dated July 31, 1998, and after our telephone conversation this morning. We agree to provide the blood specimen you have requested (today, if possible), pursuant to the following conditions:

(1) This test, any analysis, our written correspondence, and our oral communications on this issue are all to be treated as highly confidential, subject to the full protections of Rule 6(e), Federal Rules of Criminal Procedure. Both the OIC and we will take the utmost precautions to preserve the confidentiality of this matter.

(2) The sample will be drawn by the White House physician, Dr. Connie Mariano, at the White House, in the presence of two representatives of the OIC, under medical procedures acceptable to the OIC. The sample will be immediately furnished to the OIC.

(3) You will execute an affidavit today setting forth your predication evidence for requesting this test, and you will preserve this affidavit in a secure place. You will set forth in the affidavit the evidence you would have presented to Chief Judge Johnson, as represented in your second letter of July 31, 1998.

WILLIAMS & CONNOLLY

Robert J. Bittman, Esq.
August 3, 1998
Page 2

(4) You will instruct the laboratory that does any analysis related to the specimen we furnish to preserve enough of the item being tested (e.g., any dress of Ms. Lewinsky's) to make possible a later, outside, comparative test of the same type, if appropriate.

I will look forward to receiving a written response to this letter, and we will speak later in the day concerning logistics.

Sincerely,

David E. Kendall

DEK/bb

Tab 59

Office of the Independent Counsel

1001 Pennsylvania Avenue, N.W.
Suite 490-North
Washington, DC 20004
(202) 514-8688
Fax (202) 514-8802

August 3, 1998

HAND DELIVERED

David E. Kendall, Esq.
Williams & Connolly
725 Twelfth Street, N.W.
Washington, D.C. 20005

Re: William Jefferson Clinton

Dear David:

This responds to your letter of today regarding your agreement to permit a blood sample to be taken from the President this evening at 10:00 p.m.

(1) We will treat this test, any analysis, our written correspondence, and our oral communications on this matter as highly confidential, subject to the full protections of Rule 6(e).

(2) We agree to permit Dr. Mariano to draw the sample from the President in the presence of two representatives from this Office. Dr. Mariano should use a "purple-top" tube, which she will then turn over immediately to the representatives from this Office. I, Robert James Bittman [redacted] and [redacted] will represent the OIC.

(3) I agree to execute a declaration setting forth the predication for requesting this test. This declaration will then be preserved in a secure place at the OIC.

(4) I have requested that the FBI Laboratory preserve as much of the remaining specimen as possible so as to make possible a later, comparative test, if appropriate.

Sincerely,

Robert J. Bittman
Deputy Independent Counsel

Tab 60

7-1 (Rev. 2-21-91)

FBI LABORATORY

FEDERAL BUREAU OF INVESTIGATION
WASHINGTON, D. C. 20535

Date: August 3, 1998

To: Mr. Kenneth W. Starr
Office of the Independent Counsel
1001 Pennsylvania Avenue, N.W.
Suite 490-North
Washington, D.C. 20004

FBI File No. 29D-OIC-LR-35063

Lab No. 980730002 S BO

Reference: Communication dated July 30, 1998

Your No. 29D-OIC-LR-35063

Re: MOZARK;
MC 106

Specimens received: July 30, 1998

Specimens:

Q3243 Navy blue dress

ITEMS NOT EXAMINED

NE1 Hanger

NE2 Plastic bag

This report contains the results of the requested serological examinations.

Specimen Q3243 and samples removed from specimen Q3243 are being preserved for possible future DNA analysis. In order to conduct meaningful DNA analysis, known blood samples must be submitted from the victim, suspect or other individuals believed to have contributed body fluids to specimen Q3243. Each known blood sample should be collected in one (1) lavender-top blood vial containing the preservative EDTA, and stored in a refrigerator until submission to the FBI Laboratory.

The evidence and the samples removed from the evidence will be retained in the FBI Laboratory until they are retrieved by a representative from your office.

FBI LABORATORY

FEDERAL BUREAU OF INVESTIGATION
WASHINGTON, D. C. 20535

Report of Examination

Examiner Name:	[redacted]	Date:	08/03/98
Unit:	DNA Analysis 1	Phone No.:	202-324-4409
FBI File No.:	29D-OIC-LR-35063	Lab No.:	980730002 S BO

Results of Examinations:

Semen was identified on specimen Q3243.

No other serological examinations were conducted.

Tab 61

FD-302 (Rev. 3-10-82)

- 1 -

FEDERAL BUREAU OF INVESTIGATION

Date of transcription August 3,1998

On this date, Supervisory Special Agent (SSA) [redacted] was present in the Map Room of the White House, Washington D.C. with Robert J. Bittman, Deputy Independent Counsel, Eleanor Maricino, M.D., White House Physician, David Kendall, Attorney and William Jefferson Clinton, President. At approximately 10:10 pm, SSA [redacted] observed Dr. Maricino draw blood by venous puncture from President Clinton's right arm, filling one purple top tube (approximately 4ml). She capped the tube and transferred it to SSA [redacted] who labeled the tube with the name "William Clinton", the date and SSA [redacted] initials. The tube was placed in a clean disposable test tube and sealed with evidence tape. SSA [redacted] promptly returned to the FBI Laboratory, Washington D.C. where at 10:30, the tube of blood was delivered to DNA Analysis Unit I technician, [redacted], for further processing according to standard practice. This sample will be maintained in the custody of the FBI Laboratory for the duration of the testing process.

Investigation on August 3, 1998 Map Room, White House,

File # 29D-OIC-LR-35063

y SSA [redacted] Date dictated August 3,1998

Tab 62

Office of the Deputy Attorney General
Washington, D.C. 20530

August 3, 1998

Honorable Kenneth Starr
Independent Counsel
Office of the Independent Counsel
1001 Pennsylvania Avenue, NW
Washington, DC 20004

Dear Mr. Starr:

In your July 22, 1998, letter, you asked whether the Secret Service would, at this time, make witnesses available to your office consistent with the past practice of proffers, interviews, and depositions. My understanding is that this request will be the subject today of a meeting between you and Director Merletti, which will be attended by Jonathan Schwartz and Gary Grindler from the Department of Justice. In advance of that meeting, however, I would offer the following thoughts on behalf of the Department and the Secret Service regarding a number of statements in your letter, in order to provide a more complete and accurate backdrop for this afternoon's meeting.

Your letter suggests that you undertook the proffer-interview-deposition process at "significant cost" to your investigation. I do not believe this is an accurate reflection of the facts. In the face of our decision several months ago to assert a protective function privilege, the Department and your office sought to find a mutually acceptable way for your office to obtain information from Secret Service personnel that did not fall within this asserted privilege. Your office initially declined our suggestion to do interviews in advance of depositions. The deposition-only format proved to be problematic, however, due to its formality and due to confusion over the scope of the privilege (admittedly caused, in part, by the Department's periodic re-evaluation and narrowing of its scope). As a result, we renewed our suggestion that your office first interview Secret Service personnel. Your office ultimately agreed to try the interview process, when preceded by proffers of non-privileged information by Department attorneys, so that your attorneys would have an overview of the officers' information before interviews began.

The proffer-interview-deposition format clearly proved to be a more mutually beneficial (not to mention much less contentious) method by which your office obtained non-privileged information from Secret Service personnel, as your attorneys confirmed several times to us. Through proffers and interviews, your office much more quickly determined the limited number of officers from whom you needed to obtain sworn deposition testimony. The subsequent depositions then proceeded much more smoothly. While I am not privy to the details of your investigation, it would appear that your investigation was aided by some of the non-privileged information that your attorneys received. Under these circumstances, the assertion that altering the normal procedures by which Secret Service witnesses were questioned somehow hindered your investigation appears inconsistent with the facts as we know them.

I believe that some in your office have undervalued the very real and negative impact that the broad summoning of protective personnel and the broad scope of the questioning has had on the Secret Service. At least 30 officers were interviewed, some of them two or even three times, and many officers who apparently lacked first-hand knowledge relevant to your inquiry were questioned about mere rumors they may have heard. Regardless of our record in convincing federal judges to recognize a new protective function privilege, there is no question that each and every one of the current Secret Service employees whom your office has questioned feels that he or she has violated a code of confidentiality and trust. As a result, the Secret Service sincerely believes that its morale and its ability to do its mission have been adversely affected.

Finally, please allow me to reiterate that the Departments of Justice and Treasury reached the very difficult decision to seek judicial recognition of a protective function privilege for entirely non-partisan purposes, and only after an exhaustive review of the complex legal and policy issues at stake. As prosecutors, the Attorney General and I have been extremely mindful of the effects that our decision to seek the privilege might have had on your investigation (not to mention future investigations by Department attorneys). Nonetheless, we reached the difficult determination that the potential risk to the life of this and future presidents occasioned by the compelled testimony of Secret Service personnel required us to interpose the asserted protective function privilege with respect to information falling within its scope. We trust that you continue to have confidence in the <u>bona fides</u> of this decision.

Sincerely yours,

Eric H. Holder, Jr.
Deputy Attorney General

08/03/98 MON 14:54 FAX ☑001

U. S. Department of Justice

Office of the Deputy Attorney General

The Deputy Attorney General

Washington, D.C. 20530

FACSIMILE TRANSMISSION COVER SHEET

DATE: August 3, 1998

TO:

Honorable Kenneth Starr

Independent Counsel

Office of the Independent Counsel

OFFICE PHONE #: (202) 514-8688

FACSIMILE PHONE #: (202) 514-8802

FROM: Eric H. Holder, Jr.
Deputy Attorney General

OFFICE PHONE #: 202-514-2101

FACSIMILE PHONE #: 202-514-0467

COVER PLUS 2 PAGES

REMARKS:

Tab 63

OFFICE OF INDEPENDENT COUNSEL
DONALD C. SMALTZ
In re Secretary of Agriculture Espy

P.O. Box 26356
103 Oronoco Street, Suite 200
Alexandria, VA 22313
(703) 706–0010
(FAX) 706–0076

August 6, 1998

The Honorable Janet Reno
Attorney General of the United States
United States Department of Justice
10th Street and Pennsylvania Avenue, N.W.
Washington, D.C. 20530

Dear General Reno:

On December 5, 1997, I wrote to you concerning a series of statements to the press, apparently emanating from the Department of Justice, that disparaged certain independent counsel offices, the independent counsels as individuals, and the Special Division of the U.S. Court of Appeals for the D.C. Circuit that appoints independent counsels. A copy of my letter is attached. You responded by letter on January 20, 1998, deploring the alleged comments. You further stated that the matter had been referred to the Department's Office of Professional Responsibility for "whatever action it deems appropriate." A copy of your letter is attached.

I have now received a letter dated July 15, 1998, from Richard Rogers of your Office of Professional Responsibility, reporting the results of his investigation. A copy of this letter is also attached. I must say that I find this letter to be deeply disturbing, first in what it says, but even more so in what it does not say.

Mr. Rogers' legalistic response reads more as a brief defending departmental action on narrow legal grounds than as a serious attempt to look at the problem. He concludes that, technically, the press statements attributed to departmental officials did not violate Rule 3.6 of the ABA's Model Rules of Professional Responsibility because, in his view, they were too general to influence a pending case and, under his interpretation, the rule governs only the behavior of attorneys who have directly participated in the investigation.

The Honorable Janet Reno
Attorney General of the United States
August 6, 1998
Page 2

These distinctions are, at best, dubious. While the statements might not have disparaged any specific witness, item of evidence, or prosecution theory, they did directly disparage the prosecutor in high-profile pending cases (at least one before the jury as the remarks became public), and thus could easily have had an impact on the outcome. Moreover, while it is questionable that Rule 3.6 would condone one lawyer for the United States disparaging the work of another lawyer also appearing on behalf of the United States, the fact is that the Blackley matter, which was in trial when these remarks surfaced, was originally investigated by the Department.

My December 5 letter also pointed out that some of the statements attributed to departmental officials, that disparaged Judge Sentelle and the Special Division, might be in violation of ABA Model Rule 8.2, forbidding false statements concerning the qualifications or integrity of a judge. Mr. Rogers does not even bother to comment on this point.

However, the truly disturbing aspect of Mr. Rogers' letter is what he does not say. He does not pretend to have even considered the issues raised in my letter beyond searching for technical grounds that would take them outside of the ABA Model Rules. Rather, he eschews all further consideration of the problem: "Because Rule 3.6 is inapplicable in this case and no other applicable rule appears to prohibit the reported comments, we must conclude that no further inquiry into them by this Office is justified."

Your letter of January 20 stated that "[i]f these alleged comments were made to the press, I, like you, deplore them and find them wholly inappropriate." Either Mr. Rogers did not read your letter, or he is getting conflicting orders from elsewhere. Mr. Rogers takes the position that he need make no inquiry at all regarding the numerous press statements that we brought to your attention so long as he can construct a defense for them under the ethical rules. If the comments were, as both you and I have concluded, deplorable and inappropriate, then the Department should not consider them unworthy of inquiry simply because they can be threaded through a technical reading of the ABA Rules

The Honorable Janet Reno
Attorney General of the United States
August 6, 1998
Page 3

Apart from the ABA rules, these comments, in my view, violate both the letter and the spirit of Departmental policies and regulations dealing with the media, as contained in Chapter 20, "Publicity and Media Regulations," *Ethics and Professional Responsibility*, Department of Justice, November 1995. The issue of the impropriety of the regulations is a question that should not be ignored by the Office of Professional Responsibility and needs, I respectfully suggest, to be addressed.

Because I still do not have a response, I must ask again, as I did in my December 5 letter, that you direct the officials who work for you to temper their public remarks, and to present any concerns or criticisms to the independent counsel offices so that problems can be addressed directly. The clear message of Mr. Rogers' letter is that "deplorable" and "inappropriate" statements by departmental officers and employees are condoned, if not encouraged, so long as they are technically defensible under the ethical rules. I hope that this message is not an accurate one but, if it is, I would appreciate being so informed. I also request whether, in the Department's view, the referenced statements fall within or without the proscriptions of Chapter 20, referenced above.

Sincerely,

Donald C. Smaltz
Independent Counsel

Enclosures
Copies: Richard M. Rogers, Deputy Counsel (w/encl.)
The Honorable Kenneth W. Starr (w/encl.)
The Honorable David M. Barrett (w/encl.)
The Honorable Carol Elder Bruce (w/encl.)
The Honorable Ralph I. Lancaster, Jr. (w/encl.)

h:\data\ckagay\renole~1.

Tab 64

7-1 (Rev. 2-21-91)

FBI LABORATORY

FEDERAL BUREAU OF INVESTIGATION
WASHINGTON, D. C. 20535

Date: August 6, 1998

To: Mr. Kenneth W. Starr
Office of the Independent Counsel
1001 Pennsylvania Avenue, N.W.
Suite 490-North
Washington, D.C. 20004

FBI File No. 29D-OIC-LR-35063

Lab No. 980730002 S BO
980803100 S BO

Reference: Communication dated July 30, 1998 and evidence submitted August 3, 1998

Your No. 29D-OIC-LR-35063

Re: MOZARK;
MC 106

Specimens received: July 30, 1998 and August 3, 1998

Specimens: Received July 30, 1998 (under cover of FBI Laboratory number 980730002 S BO):

Q3243 Navy blue dress

<u>ITEMS NOT EXAMINED</u>

NE1 Hanger

NE2 Plastic bag

Specimen received August 3, 1998 (under cover of FBI Laboratory number 980803100 S BO):

K39 Liquid blood sample from WILLIAM CLINTON

This report supplements an FBI Laboratory report dated August 3, 1998 and contains the results of additional serological and DNA-PCR examinations. DNA-RFLP examinations are continuing and you will be advised of the results of those examinations and the disposition of the evidence in a separate report.

7-1a (7-16-96)

FBI LABORATORY

FEDERAL BUREAU OF INVESTIGATION
WASHINGTON, D. C. 20535

Report of Examination

Examiner Name: [redacted]

Date: 08/06/98

Unit: DNA Analysis 1

Phone No.: 202-324-4409

FBI File No.: 29D-OIC-LR-35063

Lab No.: 980730002 S BO
980803100 S BO

Results of Examinations:

Specimen Q3243 was examined for the presence of blood; however, none was found.

Polymarker (PM), DQA1, and D1S80 types as listed below were detected for the following specimens:

SPECIMEN	LDLR	GYPA	HBGG	D7S8	Gc	DQA1	D1S80
Q3243-1	BB	BB	AB	AB	AC	1.1, 1.2	24, 24
Q3243-2	BB	BB	AB	AB	AC	1.1, 1.2	24, 24
K39	BB	BB	AB	AB	AC	1.1, 1.2	24, 24

Based on the PM, DQA1, and D1S80 typing results, the source of specimen K39 is included as a potential contributor of the DNA obtained from specimens Q3243-1 and Q3243-2 (two semen stains removed from specimen Q3243). The probability of selecting an unrelated individual at random having the same PM, DQA1 and D1S80 types as detected in the questioned specimens is approximately 1 in 390,000 in the Black population, 1 in 43,000 in the Caucasian population, 1 in 39,000 in the Southeastern Hispanic population, and 1 in 220,000 in the Southwestern Hispanic population.

Based on the amelogenin typing results, male DNA was detected in the DNA obtained from specimens Q3243-1, Q3243-2 and K39.

Tab 65

.EWS - 8/7/98 WATIMES A1
/98 Wash. Times (D.C.) A1
- 98 WL 3454933
The Washington Times

Friday, August 7, 1998

A

Richardson didn't have post to offer Evidence doesn't support his statments on Lewinsky
Bill Sammon
THE WASHINGTON TIMES

U.N. Ambassador Bill Richardson, contrary to what he told Congress last month, did not have an opening on his staff when he offered to hire Monica Lewinsky last October, according to informed sources and documents obtained by The Washington Times.

Mr. Richardson, who was recently confirmed as President Clinton's

new energy secretary, planned to create a new position to accommodate Miss Lewinsky's desire for employment in New York City, said sources at the United Nations, the State Department and on Capitol Hill. He panicked when the scandal broke in January and scrambled to find a slot that he could claim had existed long before he interviewed Miss Lewinsky, the sources said.

Despite Mr. Richardson's repeated, sworn assertions, he did not ate the position until after independent counsel Kenneth W. Starr served him with a subpoena demanding all documents relating to the job offer. Mr. Starr is trying to determine whether the offer was aimed at distancing Miss Lewinsky and keeping her quiet about her relationship with Mr. Clinton.

"I've heard all this speculation before," said Mr. Richardson's chief of staff, Rebecca Cooper. "Luckily, what allows me to go to sleep at night is knowing that none of this is true."

Mr. Richardson did not return telephone calls, but during his confirmation hearing on July 22, he told the Senate panel that the job he offered to Miss Lewinsky was a low-level, $30,000 position in

New York. After she turned it down, the job was given to U.N. employee Paul Aronsohn, a senior staffer who has handled such high-level issues as nuclear disarmament and the U.N. arrears controversy.

Mr. Aronsohn, who has worked in the U.N.'s political section for four years, is paid substantially more than $30,000 and was transferred to Washington weeks before Mr. Richardson's testimony, Miss Cooper said.

Explained his spokesman, Calvin Mitchell: "The ambassador is not a personnel officer. He is not to sit in front of the Senate and answer questions off people's personnel files. And he described, in h mind, what the job was to him and how it was perceived and how it going to function."

.onetheless, the discrepancies raise serious questions about the veracity of sworn testimony by Mr. Richardson, who until now has been a peripheral figure in the Lewinsky scandal. They also suggest that Mr. Richardson took steps to conceal special treatment he afforded a man who yesterday began telling a grand jury about her relationship h the president.

AN 'EXISTING SLOT'?

Monica Lewinsky was not a household name when Mr. Richardson was asked by White House Deputy Chief of Staff John Podesta to interview "this person" in October, the ambassador testified.

"He did not even know her name when he asked me to interview her," Mr. Richardson testified. "I did not know her name."

The request originated with Betty Currie, the president's personal secretary, who relayed it to Mr. Richardson through his friend, Mr. Podesta, according to testimony by Mr. Richardson before the Energy and Natural Resources Committee.

But Mr. Richardson agreed to interview the former White House intern in his Watergate apartment at 7:30 a.m. He left in the middle of the interview, leaving Miss Cooper and an assistant to finish up, so he could go to the White House for a meeting.

Within a week, Mr. Richardson instructed his staff to offer the

job to Miss Lewinsky. After taking some time to think about it, she declined.

n offering Miss Lewinsky a job, Mr. Richardson did not follow ing procedures normally used at the U.S. Mission at the United ions, which include advertising a position and recruiting several qualified candidates. Within hours after the scandal broke on Jan. 21, reporters demanded to know whether such procedures had been followed.

Miss Cooper and Mr. Mitchell responded by publicly stating that if Miss Lewinsky had accepted the job offer, she would have been a "schedule-C" employee, or political appointee. On Jan. 26, five days after the scandal broke, Mr. Richardson's office issued an "administrative instruction" to all employees that said "the usual procedures" for hiring and reassigning "do not apply" to political appointees.

Mr. Mitchell said this week he does not know whether the instruction represented a departure from previous policy.

"Everyone from the highest official to the lowest mail clerk instantly knew this was about Monica Lewinsky," said one source close to the case. "I mean, this just came out of nowhere. It was obvious that Richardson's people were trying to retroactively cover their tracks."

On Feb. 2, a team of inspectors from the State Department's Office of Inspector General (OIG) showed up at Mr. Richardson's New York offices to conduct a routine audit of management practices. They ediately told U.N. employees that the mission's political branch significantly understaffed, especially in comparison to the rstaffed press office, according to OIG spokeswoman Tamara lkner.

Nonetheless, while the inspectors were still conducting their audit at the New York offices in February, Mr. Aronsohn was explicably transferred from the political section to the press tion, Miss Faulkner said.

"OIG was surprised during the inspection when an officer was transferred out of the overworked political section and assigned to .

. . outreach programs" in the press office, the team of inspectors wrote in a report that was issued in May. "This was done even though the press and public affairs section already has 12 employees, several of whom specialize in public outreach.

"The move does not make sense organizationally, because it created a duplication in outreach responsibilities. There is also the question of the impact of the move on the already overstretched political section."

During his testimony before the Senate committee, Mr. Richardson said there was "no relationship whatsoever" between creation of a public outreach job in the U.N.'s press section and his decision to offer that job to Miss Lewinsky.

"It was an existing slot," Mr. Richardson testified. "It was not created for anybody."

He added: "This position was created way before I established my tenure at the United Nations, so it was with prior ambassadors to the United Nations. It was an existing slot."

en. Frank H. Murkowski, chairman of the committee, said: "Who, if one, now holds that particular position?"

"The position is held by Paul Aronsohn," Mr. Richardson said.

"And he was offered the position after Ms. Lewinsky?" the Alaska Republican said.

"Yes," Mr. Richardson said. "He was offered the position in January. And he assumed the position."

Mr. Richardson did not explain why the job was not offered to Mr. Aronsohn until three months after it was offered to Miss Lewinsky. Nor did he attempt to reconcile his assertion that the slot existed before October with the OIG's assertion that the slot was not transferred from the political office to the press office until February.

'A FUNGIBLE SLOT'

Miss Cooper and Mr. Mitchell gave complex, convoluted explanations

of the Lewinsky job offer, often contradicting themselves and each other. For example, at one point during a lengthy interview, Miss Cooper said: "The job that I wanted to fill was one that never existed." At other times she insisted Mr. Richardson was correct when he testified the job had previously existed.

"It's a fungible slot," Miss Cooper said. "You can trace a slot, you can't say this person held that particular position because position has evolved."

Nonetheless, Miss Cooper offered the following explanation:

Miss Lewinsky was actually not offered the slot now held by Mr.

onsohn, Miss Cooper said. She was actually offered a separate slot the media wing that had been occupied by a secretary named Regina ..iego, who departed around the time Miss Lewinsky was interviewed.

Miss Cooper said she split Miss Griego's job into two new slots - one to handle clerical duties, which included answering phones, and another to handle "public outreach" duties.

Miss Griego's clerical duties were taken over by a "contract secretary" who was moved from New York to Washington, Miss Cooper said. The slot for Miss Griego's "public outreach" duties remains unfilled to this day, Miss Cooper said.

When Mr. Aronsohn was transferred from the political section to the press section in February, his slot was also transferred, Miss Cooper said. Thus, he was able to take over Miss Griego's public outreach duties - which had been offered to Miss Lewinsky - without actually filling the slot that had been designated for that purpose.

In essence, according to Miss Cooper, the position that Miss Griego vacated was the same position that Mr. Aronsohn filled - and the same one that was offered to Miss Lewinsky. Still, she acknowledged the job descriptions for Miss Griego and Mr. Aronsohn, which she refused to disclose, are as dissimilar as "apples and oranges."

Asked why this was not explained by Mr. Richardson to the Senate mittee, Miss Cooper said: "It's such a nuance. What the senators e focused on - I mean, I gotta tell you . . . you're kind of getting into things that are really splitting hairs."

Government personnel experts scoffed at the notion that Miss Griego - who had enough clerical duties to keep the secretary who replaced her occupied on a full-time basis - was replaced by the far-more-experienced Mr. Aronsohn.

"It was a low-level position that paid around $30,000," said Mr. Richardson, who added later in the hearing: "Again, it was a low-level position."

Still later, he emphasized: "This was a position that was not a very high-level position."

Miss Cooper said "Paul Aronsohn makes much more" than what Miss Lewinsky was offered, and was recently given a significant pay raise. She also said he gets other compensation that Mr. Richardson was not able to offer Miss Lewinsky, but refused to be more specific.

Mr. Mitchell, while acknowledging Mr. Aronsohn's salary is a matter of public record, refused to disclose it to The Washington Times. Mr. Aronsohn also refused to tell a reporter how much he makes.

Paul Aronsohn's now feeling a little bit down because he feels e everyone now perceives him as the guy who got the job Monica ned down," Miss Cooper said. "Well, Paul has far more experience n that and he shouldn't view himself that way. People who held this job previously shouldn't regard themselves as the people who held the Monica slot. The job has evolved."

A NEW YORK SLOT

During his hearing, Mr. Richardson took pains to emphasize the importance of keeping the job in question in New York, even after it was shifted from the political section to the press section. The job had been considered by Miss Lewinsky primarily because she wanted to move from Washington to New York.

Mr. Richardson went so far as to contradict Mr. Murkowski when the senator suggested the ambassador had "transferred an employee out of the political section in New York to assist your chief of staff in Washington, D.C. with outreach programs. Is this the case?"

"That is not correct," Mr. Richardson said. "An employee was taken out of the political section in New York - this was a political appointee - and placed under the supervision of my chief of staff in New York. So the position was moved to a New York position for purposes of outreach.

"The purpose of this position was to build constituency groups and business support for our efforts. But the position was in New York. The position was held - is held by an individual by the name of Paul Aronsohn, who is a very good employee who is doing the work."

Later in the hearing, Mr. Richardson said his desire for a New York-based outreach employee predated his meeting with Miss Lewinsky.

'We wanted it way before we even thought of her," Mr. Richardson d. "Move it to New York, because that's where most of the iness and constituency groups are. And we stand behind our decision - we filled the position."

But according to Miss Cooper, Mr. Richardson had transferred Mr. Aronsohn from New York to Washington in early July. She said the ambassador would have explained this to the senators "had they followed up on it. It's really splitting hairs at this point. I mean, I think I would have been annoyed if I were a committee member and Ambassador Richardson digressed into: 'Well, right now he's in Washington because he didn't want to sign a year lease [in New York] and his wife is looking to move here."'

She added: "The job description you can do from just about anywhere, as long as you have instant lines of communication."

JOBS FOR SILENCE?

Mr. Richardson's re-emergence in the Lewinsky scandal refocuses attention on one of the central aspects of the case - whether Mr. Clinton and his associates tried to buy her silence through the promise of jobs. After turning down Mr. Richardson's offer, Miss Lewinsky was offered a job at Revlon in New York, thanks to the intercession of presidential friend Vernon E. Jordan Jr., who is on Revlon's board of directors.

Although Miss Lewinsky was interviewed for a job in the White se press office in May 1977, most efforts at finding her a job .e oriented toward New York. According to Lucianne Goldberg, who has listened to tapes of Miss Lewinsky talking with mutual friend Linda R. Tripp, the former White House intern was under the impression that Mr. Clinton wanted her in New York, not Washington,

as to be farther away from any investigation of their
ationship.

Summing up the controversy over Miss Lewinsky's job offer at the U.N., Miss Cooper said: "All the allegations that people try to suggest, for example, that we created the job just for Monica, that doesn't hold up. Because regardless of Monica and prior to me ever knowing that Monica Lewinsky was ever going to ever be anyone in the newspaper, I continued to have that need and I filled it."

TABULAR OR GRAPHIC MATERIAL SET FORTH IN THIS DOCUMENT IS NOT DISPLAYABLE

Photos (A&B, color), A) Private entrance: Monica Lewinsky prepares to enter the courthouse with reporters kept at a distance.; B) U.N. Ambassador Bill Richardson; C) U.N. Ambassador Bill Richardson testifies last month at his Senate confirmation hearings for the energy secretary post., A) By Karen Ballard/The Washington Times; B) NO CREDIT; C) By Kenneth Lambert/The Washington Times

---- INDEX REFERENCES ----

EDITION: 2

Word Count: 2315
8/7/98 WATIMES A1
END OF DOCUMENT

Tab 66

INVESTING FOR INFLATION • LIZ PHAIR GROWS UP
Newsweek
MONICA'S DEAL
What Will He Say Now?
Clinton and Lewinsky at an October 1996 Washington, D.C., fund-raiser

many years. Talks between the two sides had come to a halt two weeks ago when Starr called Stein directly. In order to remove any bad blood between the prosecution and Lewinsky's defenders, Starr cut his more hawkish deputies out of the negotiations. In their place he substituted Sam Dash, an old Washington hand (he had been the chief counsel of the Senate Watergate Committee) who had an easy relationship with Stein and his co-counsel, Plato Cacheris. Meeting at Dash's home over bagels, the two sides worked out an arrangement that would allow Lewinsky to give prosecutors a preview of what she would be willing to say under oath. Early last week Lewinsky flew from her home in Los Angeles to a secret meeting with prosecutors in New York City, far from the Washington media stakeouts. Questioned first by a friendly lawyer from Cacheris's office, then by the prosecutors, Lewinsky talked for four and a half hours. By the next morning, the two sides had a deal.

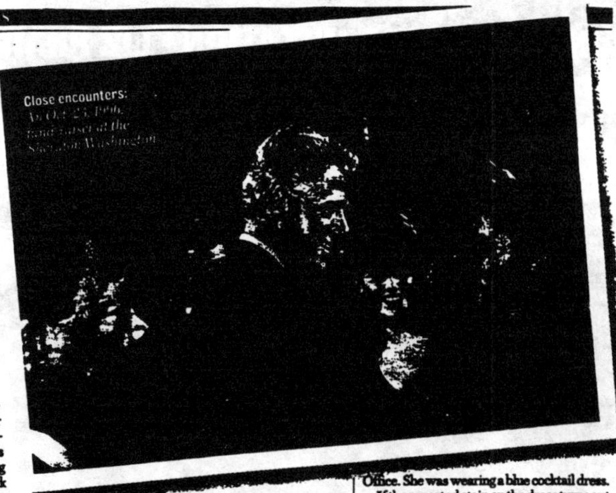

Close encounters: [illegible]

Starr's team had some extra leverage to make sure Lewinsky was willing to tell the whole truth. Sometime last winter, Lewinsky had given the dress to her mother, Marcia Lewis, for safekeeping. That made Lewis a possible target of Starr's probe, a reality that was brought home to her when she was summoned before the grand jury last February—and collapsed under questioning. Under last week's deal, Lewis is also immune from prosecution.

The hard-liners on Starr's team had been hesitant to offer promises of immunity to Lewinsky without very specific promises of testimony in return. They felt badly burned by former associate attorney general Webster Hubbell, who promised to give testimony in the Whitewater investigation in return for Starr's help in securing a lighter sentence after Hubbell pleaded guilty to overbilling his law clients in 1994. The prosecutors believe that Hubbell basically pulled a bait-and-switch, refusing to say much of anything once he had a deal. Starr's team was determined not to make the same mistake with Lewinsky.

In addition to the dress, Lewinsky turned over tapes of several voice-mail messages allegedly left by Clinton. The president's words did not seem sexually suggestive—"Hey, it's me," he reportedly said. "Sorry I missed you." But the familiarity between the chief executive and former intern was embarrassing. "There's always been an assumption that the president wouldn't be stupid enough to leave his voice on an answering machine," said one disheartened White House aide. More dangerous are the gifts that Lewinsky turned over to the president's secretary rather than comply with a subpoena in the Paula Jones case.

In the tape recording of a conversation between Lewinsky and Tripp last December that NEWSWEEK was permitted to hear, Lewinsky was eager to get rid of any incriminating presents. She referred to an official White House photograph and worried that the inscription from Clinton was so personal that lawyers for Jones would use it against her. She told Tripp that she had tried to call Betty Currie, the president's secretary, to ask for a clean copy of the picture so that she might have one to give Jones's lawyers. But on the tape, she complains that Currie was unavailable. There may also be another photo of interest to the prosecutors. According to Goldberg, Lewinsky was photographed standing beside the president in the Oval Office. She was wearing a blue cocktail dress.

If the reported stain on the dress turns out to be the president's semen (the lab tests may take several weeks), Clinton has an immediate perjury problem. Last January he denied under oath in his Jones deposition that he had ever had "sexual relations" with Lewinsky. Lying about a sexual relationship in a deposition in a civil case may not be perceived as a serious offense. Lying before the grand jury in a criminal investigation is more grave. It would surely be an indictable offense in a normal criminal probe. Less certain is whether it is an impeachable offense in Congress, which will probably serve as Clinton's judge and jury.

The ultimate focus of Starr's case is not sex, but obstruction of justice. Under the immunity deal worked out between Starr and Lewinsky's lawyers, described to NEWSWEEK by a knowledgeable source, Lewinsky will testify that she and the president discussed cover stories designed to keep their alleged relationship private. Lewinsky reportedly will say that at a meeting at the White House in late December, she told the president her worries about the subpoenaed gifts, which included a brooch and a book of poetry. The president did not directly tell her to lie, she says. Rather, he spoke hypothetically. If you don't have the gifts, he allegedly said, you can't turn them over. Such a veiled suggestion would hardly be the kind of evidence a

Regardless of what happens in the courts or Congress, **47%** think the president owes the country an explanation of the Monica matter; **49%** say he doesn't

Tab 67

Office of the Independent Counsel

1001 Pennsylvania Avenue, N.W.
Suite 490-North
Washington, D.C. 20004
(202) 514-8688
Fax (202) 514-8802

August 11, 1998

By Hand

The Honorable Eric H. Holder, Jr.
Deputy Attorney General of the United States
United States Department of Justice
10th St. & Constitution Ave., NW
Washington, D.C. 20530

Dear Deputy Attorney General Holder:

Rule 6(e) of the Federal Rules of Criminal Procedure binds all attorneys for the government, including those employed by the Department of Justice who are privy to information regarding "matters occurring before the grand jury." And, as Chief Judge Johnson has recently written, Rule 6(e) protects against the disclosure not merely of the actual testimony of grand jury witnesses before the grand jury but also of the substance of their testimony as conveyed to government attorneys and agents in anticipation of their grand jury appearance.

The enclosed article from Newsweek magazine recounts in detail what Officers Muskett and Byrne told "Secret Service and Justice Department lawyers." The article identifies its source as these "government lawyers" and makes out a potential prima facie case that attorneys for the Department of Justice (and possibly Secret Service) involved in the litigation have violated Rule 6(e). Please advise me at your earliest convenience of the steps you are taking to identify the source of these disclosures and prevent future violations of Rule 6(e) so that I may take appropriate action.

Sincerely yours,

Kenneth W. Starr
Independent Counsel

Enclosure

Monica On The S

ROBERTO BORFA—AP

Stand

As Lewinsky tells her story to the grand jury, the president's team ponders how to fight back—in part, perhaps, by attacking the former intern's credibility. How ugly could it get? BY DANIEL KLAIDMAN, KAREN BRESLAU AND MICHAEL ISIKOFF

DAVID KENDALL DIDN'T WASTE time. When the news broke late last month that Monica Lewinsky had finally struck an immunity deal with Kenneth Starr, the president's lawyer began working the phones. He'd received an intriguing fax from a man named David Bliss, who said he had a story about Lewinsky that Kendall might want to hear. Kendall quickly faxed him back, thanking Bliss for sending the "very welcome" material "out of the blue." Kendall followed up with a phone call to Bliss, leaving a solicitous message—which Bliss played for NEWSWEEK—on his answering machine. "I think it's important that we get together and, you know, decide how to proceed," Kendall said.

What did Bliss have on Lewinsky that was so tantalizing to the president's lawyer? Bliss, a drama-department shop foreman at Lewis & Clark College, told Kendall that when Lewinsky was a 21-year-old student there in 1995, she had forged a letter in his name on school stationery. Apparently Lewinsky was trying to help out Andy Bleiler, a married drama coach with whom she was allegedly having an affair. Bleiler was out of work, and embroiled in a custody battle. The forged letter—a purported job offer from Bliss to Bleiler—was supposed to help Bleiler's case. But the scheme went bad when the letter—which Bleiler says he never knew about—was returned to Bliss's mailbox as undeliverable. Bliss immediately suspected Lewinsky, who had been pestering him relentlessly to find work for Bleiler. Confronted with the letter, she proclaimed herself "humiliated," and begged forgiveness. But Bliss wasn't the forgiving kind. He took his story to Kendall. (A lawyer for Lewinsky declined to comment.)

The president's lawyer was all ears. Now that Lewinsky has become a fully immunized witness for the prosecution, Kendall is looking for details that might enable him to undermine Monica's credibility. Last week Lewinsky spent six hours before the grand jury in Washington. There, under oath, she apparently contradicted the president's denials—both in his Paula Jones deposition and to the country—that the two had a sexual affair. The basics of Lewinsky's testimony began leaking to the press soon after she left the courthouse. The former intern reportedly admitted to more than a dozen sexual encounters with the president—and said that she and Clinton discussed how to conceal their relationship. But on the question of whether Clinton explicitly asked her to lie under oath, Lewinsky refused to testify that the president instructed her to perjure herself.

As Kendall prepares his legal counteroffensive—and with Clinton's Aug. 17 testimony just a week away—there are obstacles everywhere. Any lawyer's biggest fear is a surprise question that leaves his client befuddled and in danger of falling into a perjury trap. This is exactly what Kendall is up against. The biggest unknown, and one that could conceivably wreck all of Kendall's careful preparation, is the blue dress currently undergoing testing at the FBI lab. Does it contain "DNA evidence"? The crime lab may have already completed initial tests. But the end results—and whether Starr will ask the president for a DNA sample—are being tightly held. If the tests come back positive, and the results are linked to Clinton, anything Kendall might have dug up to discredit Lewinsky might be rendered irrelevant. But Kendall doesn't have the luxury of knowing what those tests will reveal. The best he can do is prepare his case—and his client—and get ready for the worst.

Meanwhile, Starr's staff is moving rapidly to complete its probe and may submit a possible report to Congress by early September. Contrary to expectations that Starr would present evidence of a broad pattern of obstruction of justice, NEWSWEEK has learned the report will focus only on the Lewinsky matter and other allegations flowing out of the Paula Jones case. After four years and more than $40 million, the independent counsel has won a string of Whitewater criminal convictions and still has two indictments pending. But whatever evidence Starr has developed against the

Her day in court: *Lewinsky at the federal courthouse, where she testified for six hours*

president relating to Whitewater—and other matters such as the Travel Office affair and the FBI file scandal—sources say it is not strong enough to be included in an impeachment report. The findings could potentially cut both ways. The narrow scope of the report will allow White House spinners to denigrate Starr's entire probe as little more than a sexual inquisition. But a tightly focused report could present problems for the White House—laying out the lurid Lewinsky charges in stark and simple language that may be difficult to dispute.

No matter what Starr's report reveals, Kendall's immediate problem remains the same: how to make Clinton appear more credible than Lewinsky. One option: do "oppo" research on the chief accuser. Before Lewinsky reached an agreement with Starr, Kendall tread lightly on her past to avoid pushing her into the independent counsel's camp. Since she's cut her deal, however, Kendall is no longer restrained. For now, the lawyer is keeping potentially damaging stories in his briefcase. But they could prove useful to him during possible impeachment hearings, where Democrats loyal to the president would get the chance to interrogate the former intern.

Kendall's Lewinsky digging isn't confined to Monica's Lewis & Clark days. He is also interested in the story of a Democratic activist from Indianapolis named John Sullivan, who recalled meeting Lewinsky at an October 1996 fund-raiser in Washington. As he waited along the rope line to shake Clinton's hand, Sullivan says he was pulled aside by an event organizer. She told him that the woman standing next to him was named Monica, and that Monica was infatuated with the president and may have fantasized about having a relationship with him. Would Sullivan keep an eye on her? The incident came to light last week when an Indianapolis TV reporter saw a tape of the event and recognized Sullivan—who then told his story to the reporter. Sullivan told NEWSWEEK Kendall called him last week and asked about the event. Sullivan says the smooth lawyer, himself an Indiana native, played up his Hoosier roots to try to win Sullivan's trust.

Soft-spoken and camera averse, Kendall has a reputation as a gentleman lawyer. But he is a tenacious and crafty litigator with a reputation for tying his opponents in knots. Starr has already gotten a taste of Kendall's tactics. When the president's lawyer petitioned the courts to investigate the independent counsel's alleged grand-jury leaks to the press, it was seen as a somewhat desperate publicity stunt. But last week it was revealed that Judge Norma Holloway Johnson came down on Kendall's side—ruling that there probably were illegal leaks, and ordering Starr to prove his office wasn't the source. Last week a federal appeals court handed Starr one minor victory on the matter: it denied Kendall the opportunity to interrogate Starr's prosecutors about the leaks. Still, Johnson's decision was a blow to the independent counsel, and gives new ammunition to the White House spin team that Starr is out of control.

KARIN COOPER—GAMMA-LIAISON

In public, the president is trying to rise above the legal imbroglio. After the embassy bombings in Africa last Friday, Clinton solemnly vowed to bring the terrorists to justice. This week, as the flag-draped coffins arrive home, the president will have other opportunities to emphasize statecraft over scandal. But those who saw Clinton last week after hours described him as burdened and withdrawn, rubbing his eyes and staring absently into space.

It's up to Kendall to take his dispirited client and transform him into a compelling, telegenic and credible witness. He's done it before. When Clinton gave videotaped testimony in previous Whitewater trials, jurors said they were "beguiled" by the president's performance. But trying to explain an alleged affair is a taller order. Kendall is legendary for exhaustive preparation sessions in which he grills his clients over and over, day after day, making them repeat their answers. In a case this complex, with so many

The First Firm: A Very Small Circle

They're the whitest of white-shoe lawyers, and their brief—resolving the Lewinsky crisis for the First Client—couldn't be more important, or more difficult. But the four attorneys helping the president provide more than just legal counsel. They are now the only people in Bill Clinton's life with whom he enjoys protected, privileged conversation beyond the reach of Kenneth Starr's subpoenas.

David Kendall

He didn't know Bill and Hillary at Yale. But now David Kendall is on the inside. His mild manner belies his fierce legal instincts. A partner at Williams & Connolly, *the* white-collar defense law firm, Kendall is a courtroom tiger just like the firm's founder, Edward Bennett Williams.

Nicole Seligman

The Harvard law grad—and editor of the Harvard Law Review—is Kendall's partner at Williams & Connolly and a legal powerhouse in her own right. She helped craft Oliver North's defense. A friend and lawyer to John Kennedy's kids, she's said to have the complete confidence of the First Lady.

FROM LEFT TO RIGHT: TYLER MALLORY—AP, PAUL HOSEFROS—NEW YORK TIMES, WILFREDO LEE—AP, RICK WILKING—REUTERS

Monica's team: *Plato Cacheris (left) and Jacob Stein, the lawyers guiding Lewinsky through the war between Clinton and Starr*

possible hidden traps, that means the president and his lawyer will be spending plenty of quality time—and billable hours—together this week. The drill has already begun. In the mornings—and sometimes again in the evening—Kendall and his partner Nicole Seligman slip into the White House. They use the East Entrance to the private quarters, avoiding the cameras along the West Wing driveway. There, in Clinton's second-floor office overlooking the South Lawn, Kendall methodically runs through the evidence, asking the president to explain everything from Lewinsky's White House visits to her high-powered job search. There are usually only two others allowed in the room: Hillary Clinton and Mickey Kantor, another private lawyer.

No matter how thoroughly Kendall preps his client, however, he can't anticipate every question the special prosecutor might ask. Even Starr doesn't have all the answers. For months, for example, there have been numerous hazy press reports that a uniformed Secret Service officer witnessed an alleged encounter between Clinton and Lewinsky. The story has changed over time, and the details remained sketchy. A NEWSWEEK reconstruction of the events may shed some light on the incident. On Easter Sunday 1996, according to government lawyers, officer John Muskett was stationed outside the Oval Office. A phone call came in for the president, but Clinton didn't respond. Muskett couldn't locate the president. Spotting Harold Ickes, Muskett asked the then deputy chief of staff for help. They knocked on the door to the Oval Office, but got no response. They then went to the door of the president's nearby private study. They knocked again, then opened the door.

What happened next is a matter of some controversy. Muskett later told Secret Service and Justice Department lawyers that he merely saw Lewinsky emerge from the room Clinton was in. But a fellow Secret Service officer, Gary Byrne—who wasn't present that day—told the government lawyers a different version. He said Muskett had told him that when they opened the door, Lewinsky's head was in Clinton's lap. Muskett has denied Byrne's account. And Ickes says he doesn't recall any aspect of the story. But sources tell NEWSWEEK it was likely this incident that prompted Byrne to warn senior Clinton aide Evelyn Lieberman that Lewinsky was hanging around the Oval Office, and might be a potential problem. Shortly afterward, Lewinsky was transferred out of the White House to a job at the Pentagon. Now, NEWSWEEK has learned, Starr's prosecutors, confronted with the contradictory accounts, want Justice Department officials to tell them what they were told in their interviews with Muskett and Byrne. Justice might agree to do so as early as this week. (Neither Muskett nor Byrne would comment to NEWSWEEK.)

With a week to go, Clinton aides are doing their best to conduct Business as Usual. This week Clinton will crisscross the country raising money for congressional Democrats and presiding over official White House "message events" wherever Air Force One touches down—touting voter favorites like the patients' bill of rights, clean-water laws and gun control.

But Clinton's mind may be elsewhere. Last week the president and First Lady invited a group of youth-violence experts to a cozy dinner in the Blue Room of the White House. There they hashed over the latest social theories about juvenile-crime prevention. According to some guests, Clinton, who normally revels in after-hours wonk sessions, seemed at times detached and weary. He faded in and out of the conversation, and was difficult to engage. Mrs. Clinton carried the dinner for both of them. She eagerly took notes and peppered the assembled academics and religious leaders with detailed questions. At the end of the evening, after most of the guests had departed and the First Lady had gone upstairs, Clinton lingered with Harvard professor Cornel West and a few others. How can you maintain your faith in the system when "right-wing gangsters in ties" seem intent on tearing you down? West asked the president. "They've been at me for a long time," Clinton responded. "I'm prepared." David Kendall certainly hopes so.

With DEBRA ROSENBERG *and* MARK HOSENBALL

Mickey Kantor

He first met the Clintons in the '70s when he and Hillary worked at the do-good Legal Services Corp. And for more than two decades he's been a trusted political adviser to the Clintons—chairing their '92 campaign and serving as U.S. trade rep and Commerce secretary. The firm's best pol.

Hillary Clinton

She was once named one of the top 100 lawyers in America. And for good reason: the Yale grad and partner at Little Rock's Rose Law Firm has a topnotch legal mind. She guides the First Firm but also defers to Kendall and Seligman. They know white-collar criminal defense. She doesn't.

Tab 68

UNDER SEAL

UNITED STATES DISTRICT COURT
FOR THE DISTRICT OF COLUMBIA

IN RE GRAND JURY PROCEEDINGS

Misc. Action No. 98-278

UNDER SEAL

FILED

AUG 1 1 1998

NANCY MAYER-WHITTINGTON, CLERK
U.S. DISTRICT COURT

MEMORANDUM ORDER

Lanny Breuer, Special Counsel to the President of the United States, has refused to answer certain questions before a grand jury, asserting both the governmental attorney-client privilege and executive privilege. At a hearing on August 4, 1998, the Office of Independent Counsel ("OIC") orally moved to compel Mr. Breuer's testimony.[1] The Court then ordered the OIC to submit materials that show its need for the evidence claimed to be covered by the executive privilege.

Preliminarily, the Court finds that the doctrine of collateral estoppel does not prevent Mr. Breuer and the Office of the President ("the White House") from asserting executive privilege. It is true that Bruce Lindsey asserted executive privilege in a previous matter before this Court and that the Court found that the executive privilege applied but was overcome by the OIC's showing of need. While choosing not to appeal that ruling, the White House now seeks to litigate some of the same issues again, including the OIC's need for privileged information. Although the legal issues remain much the same, the importance and sensitivity of this matter require a case-by-case determination of whether the executive privilege applies and whether it has been overcome by a proper showing of need. The factual issue of whether the OIC needs the particular information

[1] The Court resolved the motion to compel pertaining to the governmental attorney-client privilege in its Order of August 7, 1998.

apparently possessed by Mr. Breuer is sufficiently different from the issue involving Mr. Lindsey to convince the Court that Mr. Breuer is not barred from asserting privilege in these circumstances.

1. Scope of the Presumptive Executive Privilege

In its Order of August 5, 1998, the Court found that the communications to which Mr. Breuer has asserted the executive privilege are presumptively privileged. Executive privilege, also known in this context as the presidential communications privilege, is a governmental privilege intended to promote candid communications between the President and his advisors concerning the exercise of his Article II duties. United States v. Nixon, 418 U.S. 683, 705, 708, 711 (1974); In re Sealed Case, 121 F.3d 729, 744 (D.C. Cir. 1997). In accordance with binding precedent on the issue, this Court must treat the subpoenaed testimony of Mr. Breuer as presumptively privileged.[2]

The executive privilege is limited to "communications authored or solicited and received by those members of an immediate White House adviser's staff who have broad and significant responsibility for investigating and formulating the advice to be given to the President on the

[2] See Nixon, 418 U.S. at 713 (holding that when the President of the United States claims executive privilege, the district court has a "duty to . . . treat the subpoenaed material as presumptively privileged"); In re Sealed Case, 121 F.3d at 744 ("The President can invoke the privilege when asked to produce documents or other materials that reflect presidential decision-making and deliberations and that the President believes should remain confidential. If the President does so, the documents become presumptively privileged."); see also Senate Select Comm. on Presidential Campaign Activities v. Nixon, 498 F.2d 725, 730 (D.C. Cir. 1974) ("Presidential conversations are 'presumptively privileged,' even from the limited intrusion represented by in camera examination of the conversations by a Court."); Nixon v. Sirica, 487 F.2d 700, 717 (D.C. Cir. 1973) ("We . . . agree with the District Court that such conversations are presumptively privileged.").

particular matter to which the communications relate." Id. at 752. Communications that do not relate to presidential decision-making are not included within the scope of the executive privilege. See, e.g., Nixon v. Administrator of General Services, 433 U.S. 425, 449 (1977) (noting that the privilege is "limited to communications 'in performance of [a President's] responsibilities,' 'of his office,' and made 'in the process of shaping policies and making decisions.'"); In re Sealed Case, 121 F.3d at 752 ("Of course, the privilege only applies to communications that these advisers and their staff author or solicit and receive in the course of performing their function of advising the President on official government matters.").

While finding the other communications at issue to be "presumptively privileged," the Court holds that Mr. Breuer's communications with persons in the Office of Legislative Affairs do not fall within the scope of the presumptive executive privilege. Mr. Breuer testified that he was asked by the head of the Legislative Affairs Office, where Monica Lewinsky had worked, to speak to a group of individuals in that Office who were fearful of being called by the press or the OIC. Mr. Breuer states that he provided legal advice to those individuals. This conversation does not appear to have been in the course of Mr. Breuer's advising the President on official government matters and thus cannot be covered by the executive privilege.

2. The Standard Required to Overcome the Privilege

The executive privilege is not absolute. Sirica, 487 F.2d at 716. In order to overcome this privilege, the OIC must make a sufficient showing of need as defined by the D.C. Circuit in In re Sealed Case, 121 F.3d at 754. In re Sealed Case directs that the OIC must show with specificity "first, that each discrete group of the subpoenaed materials [or testimony] likely contains important evidence; and second, that this evidence is not available with due diligence elsewhere." Id. The information sought need not be "critical to an accurate judicial determination." Id.

The White House asserts that the recent decision of the Court of Appeals in In re Lindsey, No. 98-3060 (D.C. Cir. July 27, 1998), has heightened the required showing of need for materials allegedly covered by the executive privilege in the context of this case. According to the White House, it should be more difficult for the OIC to obtain these materials because the President anticipates impeachment proceedings and that fact should alter the relevant need analysis. In In re Lindsey, the Court of Appeals states: "[I]nformation gathered in preparation for impeachment proceedings and conversations regarding strategy are presumably covered by executive, not attorney-client, privilege. While the need for secrecy might arguably be greater under these circumstances, the district court's ruling on executive privilege is not before us." Id., slip op. at 24.

The Court rejects the White House's argument that the possibility of impeachment changes the need analysis set forth in In re Sealed Case. First, the Court of Appeals did not change the need analysis in its In re Lindsey opinion. The issue of executive privilege was not before the Court of Appeals and its suggestion that the need for confidentiality could be heightened under certain circumstances was clearly dictum. In addition, the Court of Appeals' supposition that "the need for secrecy might arguably be greater" in the face of potential impeachment, In re Lindsey, slip op. at 24 (emphasis added), does not lead this Court to conclude, as the White House contends, that the D.C. Circuit "made clear that the analysis of any assertion of the presidential communications privilege is different where the OIC investigation arises under the specter of impeachment proceedings." White House's Response to the OIC's In

Camera Submission at 4.

Second, this Court declines to hold that the executive privilege need analysis changes when White House advisors are preparing for possible impeachment proceedings. In essence, the White House argues as follows: (1) The President may withhold privileged communications from Congress even when the same communications would be discoverable in judicial proceedings;[3] (2) the OIC will likely submit an impeachment report to Congress; and (3) therefore, the White House should not be compelled to turn over information to the grand jury because that information might be given to Congress. However, the subpoena before the Court is a grand jury subpoena, not a congressional subpoena, and the Court must treat it as such even assuming that the OIC will prepare and submit a report to Congress. It is not known whether the information sought here by the grand jury will be included in any such report. Thus, the contention that information sought by the grand jury could at some time be given to Congress is not ripe for review.

The Court agrees that the President and his senior advisors have a significant need for confidentiality when discussing possible impeachment proceedings. Nevertheless, they have the same need when discussing all other kinds of presidential decisions and strategies. When it formulated the executive privilege need standard in In re Sealed Case, the D.C. Circuit explicitly recognized the "'great public interest' in preserving 'the confidentiality of conversations that take place in the President's performance of his official duties.'" 121 F.3d at 742 (quoting Sirica, 487

[3] Compare Senate Select Committee, 498 F.2d at 732-33 (holding that the President need not produce materials in response to a subpoena from a legislative committee) with, e.g., Sirica, 487 F.2d at 717 (holding that the President must produce materials in response to a grand jury subpoena).

F.2d at 717). The Court of Appeals also understood that such a privilege was "necessary to guarantee the candor of presidential advisers and to provide '[a] President and those who assist him . . . [with] free[dom] to explore alternatives in the process of shaping policies and making decisions and to do so in a way many would be unwilling to express except privately.'" Id. at 743 (quoting Nixon, 418 U.S. at 708). The same interests apply in the impeachment context and there is simply no authority for having the rigor of the executive privilege analysis depend upon the subject matter discussed.

In concluding its In re Sealed Case opinion, the D.C. Circuit stated:

> In holding that the privilege extends to communications authored by or solicited and received by presidential advisers and that a specified demonstration of need must be made even in regard to a grand jury subpoena, we are ever mindful of the dangers involved in cloaking governmental operations in secrecy and in placing obstacles in the path of the grand jury in its investigatory mission. There is a powerful counterweight to these concerns, however, namely the public and constitutional interest in preserving the efficacy and quality of presidential decisionmaking. We believe that the principles we have outlined in this opinion achieve a delicate and appropriate balance between openness and informed presidential deliberation.

Id. at 762. The concerns raised by the White House have been amply considered by the D.C. Circuit. This Court cannot and will not disturb the "delicate and appropriate balance" so carefully struck by the Court of Appeals.

Thus, the Court will turn to this Circuit's interpretation of the need standard. The first requirement — "that each discrete group of the subpoenaed materials [or testimony] likely contains important evidence" — charges that the evidence sought must be "directly relevant to the issues that are expected to be central to the trial." Id. As the D.C. Circuit noted, this requirement will ordinarily have limited impact because Federal Rule of Criminal Procedure

17(c) already restricts the reach of a subpoena to relevant information. Id. at 754.

With respect to the second requirement — that "this evidence is not available with due diligence elsewhere" — the party seeking to overcome the privilege should first attempt to determine whether sufficient evidence could be obtained elsewhere. Id. at 755. The issuer of the subpoena "should be prepared to detail these efforts and explain why evidence covered by the presidential privilege is still needed." Id. The D.C. Circuit noted:

> there will be instances where such privileged evidence will be particularly useful, as when, unlike the situation here, an immediate White House advisor is being investigated for criminal behavior. In such situations, the subpoena proponent will be able easily to explain why there is no equivalent to evidence likely contained in the subpoenaed materials.

Id. (emphases added). That court also explained that "a grand jury will often be able to specify its need for withheld evidence in reasonable detail based on information obtained from other sources." Id. at 757. Finally, if the grand jury has difficulty obtaining evidence from other sources, "this fact in and of itself will go far toward satisfying the need requirement." Id.

Lastly, if a "demonstrated, specific need" is shown, then the subpoenaed testimony shall be given to the grand jury unless there is "no reasonable possibility that the category of materials the Government seeks will produce information relevant to the general subject of the grand jury's investigation." United States v. R. Enterprises, 498 U.S. 292, 300 (1991).

3. The OIC's Showing of Need

The OIC has made an extensive ex parte submission to the Court regarding its need for this evidence, which the Court has carefully reviewed in camera. This submission incorporates and updates the OIC's previous need submission in connection with Bruce Lindsey's invocation of executive privilege as well as two other prior in camera need submissions from the OIC. The

OIC's current need submission describes fifteen categories of information that it seeks from Mr. Breuer and explains how each category meets the In re Sealed Case need standard. Because the Court has reviewed the OIC's submission in camera, it is unable to describe in any detail the basis for its findings. See In re Sealed Case, 121 F.3d at 740.

As for the first requirement, the Court finds that the testimony the OIC seeks likely contains important evidence that would be directly relevant to central issues in the grand jury's investigation. The OIC has been authorized to investigate whether Monica Lewinsky "or others" suborned perjury, obstructed justice, or tampered with witnesses, Order of the Special Division, Jan. 16, 1998, and the testimony withheld on the basis of executive privilege is likely to shed light on that inquiry.

Regarding the second requirement, the Court finds that the OIC has shown with sufficient specificity that the evidence it seeks is not available with due diligence elsewhere. See id. at 754. First, as this Court has noted before, "the crimes being investigated by the grand jury are inherently crimes of conversation and such conversations are unlikely to be recorded on paper." Order of May 4, 1998, at 12. The D.C. Circuit has declared that if a crime being investigated by the grand jury relates to "the content of certain conversations," then the grand jury's need for the exact text of those conversations is "undeniable. Obviously, this evidence is not available elsewhere; even if . . . counsel offered to provide the grand jury with every statement that was made to the White House, the grand jury would need to review the evidence in the White House files to confirm that no statements were omitted." Id. at 761 (quoting Senate Select, 498 U.S. at 732) (emphasis added). The OIC "may also be able to demonstrate a need for information that it currently possesses, but which it has been unable to confirm or disprove." Id. There is no indication that the conversations at issue here were recorded; the only sources of information regarding those conversations are the participants themselves.

Even if the grand jury possesses testimony of one party to a conversation, it may still need the testimony of other parties to the conversation to confirm or disprove the veracity of the prior testimony. The Court is well aware that two parties to a conversation may testify quite differently. As the D.C. Circuit recognized, even if a witness agrees to testify, the grand jury would still need to review further evidence to determine if it has the complete story. Id. In this instance, even if one witness has testified regarding a specific conversation, the grand jury may still need to subpoena other participants in that conversation to obtain the full picture. The evidence sought here is Mr. Breuer's version of certain conversations; such evidence can be obtained only from Mr. Breuer.

Second, the OIC has provided the Court with detailed information about its unsuccessful efforts to obtain this evidence through other sources. As the Court found significant in its previous executive privilege opinion, the OIC has diligently pursued other alternatives in seeking this information. The OIC has issued 23 subpoenas duces tecum to the White House since the beginning of its investigation and has issued one to President Clinton individually. Declaration of Julie A. Corcoran ¶ 4. In addition, the OIC interviewed eighty current or former White House employees during its investigation and thirty-five current or former White House employees have testified before the grand jury. Declaration of Patrick F. Fallon, Jr. ¶¶ 4-5.

The D.C. Circuit found that, in practical terms, "the primary effect of [the unavailability] standard will be to require a grand jury to delay subpoenaing evidence covered by presidential privilege until it has assured itself that the evidence sought from the President or his advisers is both important to its investigation and practically unavailable elsewhere." In re Sealed Case, 121 F.3d at 756-57. The fact that the OIC has not called Mr. Breuer until this time is consistent with the OIC's having unsuccessfully attempted to obtain the evidence elsewhere and having determined the evidence to be necessary to the grand jury's investigation.

The White House contends that the OIC has many alternative sources for the information sought from Mr. Breuer, including Secret Service agents, Monica Lewinsky, and others. On the basis of the in camera submission, including declarations submitted by the OIC, the Court finds that these sources have not provided the grand jury with the information withheld by Mr. Breuer under the executive privilege. Moreover, it is not clear at this time how much information President Clinton will provide to the grand jury at his deposition.[4] He may not remember certain events about which the grand jury seeks information.

The OIC has made a significant factual showing to the Court and has fully demonstrated its need for Mr. Breuer's testimony. The Court also finds that the communications covered by the presumptive privilege likely contain evidence important to the grand jury's investigation and cannot be obtained elsewhere with due diligence. The Court will therefore grant the OIC's motion to compel the testimony of Mr. Breuer insofar as he has asserted the executive privilege.

Accordingly, upon consideration of the OIC's in camera need submissions and the White House's response to that submission, it is this 11th day of August 1998,

---

[4] As the OIC points out, if the President intends to testify about his communications with Mr. Breuer, it is strange that Mr. Breuer is asserting executive privilege with respect to those very communications.

ORDERED that the Office of Independent Counsel's motion to compel the testimony of Lanny Breuer be, and hereby is, granted as to testimony covered by the executive privilege.

Norma Holloway Johnson
NORMA HOLLOWAY JOHNSON
CHIEF JUDGE

Tab 69

8/13/98 N.Y. Times Abstracts 18
1998 WL 5422549

New York Times

Thursday, August 13, 1998

Section A

Page 5

Aide Implies President Will Not Dodge Queries
BENNET, JAMES

President Clinton will answer every question put to him when he testifies on Monday in the grand jury investigation into his relationship with Monica S. Lewinsky, a White House spokesman indicated today./Some television commentators and essayists have speculated that Mr. Clinton might choose to invoke constitutional protections against compelled self-incrimination or invasion of privacy to prevent prosecutors from asking specific questions about relationship with Ms. Lewinsky, a former White House intern.

---- INDEX REFERENCES ----

NAMED PERSON: CLINTON, BILL; LEWINSKY, MONICA

KEY WORDS: SCANDALS; TESTIMONY; INVESTIGATIONS; ADULTERY; GRAND JURIES

NEWS SUBJECT: Lifestyle; Law Enforcement (LIF LEN)

NEWS CATEGORY: NEWS

Word Count: 73
8/13/98 NYT-ABS 18
END OF DOCUMENT

Tab 70

'tation | Found Document | Rank 65 of 128 | Database
ı3/98 USATD 04A | USATD
8/13/98 USA TODAY 04A
1998 WL 5732960

USA Today
Copyright 1998

Thursday, August 13, 1998

NEWS

White House suggests Clinton plans to answer all questions
Judy Keen; Gary Fields

WASHINGTON

WASHINGTON -- The White House moved Wednesday to quell speculation that President Clinton might refuse to answer some questions when he testifies about Monica Lewinsky next week.

White House spokesman Joe Lockhart reiterated at the daily news briefing that Clinton intends to testify "completely and truthfully." Asked whether that means Clinton will not decline to swer certain questions, Lockhart said, "That's what it suggests to yes."

Clinton is scheduled to testify Monday under oath via closed-circuit TV from the White House. There has been speculation that he might assert his Fifth Amendment right not to incriminate himself or his Fourth Amendment right to privacy to avoid answering some questions about his relationship with the former White House intern.

Independent counsel Ken Starr is investigating whether Clinton had a sexual relationship with Lewinsky, lied about it under oath and asked others to conceal it. Clinton has denied the allegations.

Lewinsky testified last week to the grand jury that she did have an affair with Clinton and that they discussed ways to keep it secret, but that he did not directly ask her to lie, according to people with knowledge of her testimony.

Speculation is also mounting about a potentially critical piece of evidence: the dress being tested for DNA evidence. Lewinsky gave prosecutors the dark blue dress after she was given immunity from prosecution July 28.

ɹockhart said Wednesday that he's not aware of any request from rr for DNA samples from the president. Asked whether Clinton ..ɹuld like to know the results of the FBI tests, Lockhart said, "I

.n't know." Other developments:

Justice Department lawyers are working with Starr's office to clear up an apparent discrepancy in the testimony of two Secret Service uniformed officers.

At issue are the recollections of officers John Muskett and Gary Byrne, people with knowledge of the matter said.

Those people say Muskett has told Justice Department lawyers that he and Harold Ickes, then deputy chief of staff, opened the door of the president's private study in early 1996 and saw Lewinsky leave the room. They also say Byrne has told the government lawyers that Muskett told him that he and Ickes saw Clinton and Lewinsky in an intimate situation.

Byrne and Muskett were unavailable for comment Wednesday. Ickes has said he never saw any sexual encounters between Clinton and Lewinsky.

Byrne and Muskett were among the first Secret Service personnel to appear before the grand jury after Supreme Court Justice William F nquist cleared the way last month for Secret Service officers and .nts to be called.

Starr's office is preparing a report for Congress that may focus on evidence developed in the Lewinsky investigation.

Under the independent counsel act, Starr must report to Congress if he finds evidence of impeachable offenses by the president.

Other matters Starr has been reviewing, including the firing of travel office employees and the White House's acquisition of secret FBI background files, are not likely to produce evidence of impeachable offenses, people with knowledge of Starr's inquiry said.

Starr's report could be sent as early as next month, those people said, but no final decisions on its scope or findings have been made.

TABULAR OR GRAPHIC MATERIAL SET FORTH IN THIS DOCUMENT IS NOT DISPLAYABLE

PHOTO, b/w, AFP

---- INDEX REFERENCES ----

KF WORDS: INVESTIGATION; PRESIDENCY; SCANDAL; WITNESS

. ERNMENT: Executive (EXE)

Tab 71

tation | Found Document | Rank 13 of 257 | Database
13/98 WASHPOST A04 | WP
8/13/98 Wash. Post A04
1998 WL 16549618

The Washington Post

Thursday, August 13, 1998

A Section

White House Rejects Suggestion Clinton Might Limit Testimony
Peter Baker
Washington Post Staff Writer

With unsolicited advice cascading in from all sides, the White House tried to stamp out speculation yesterday that President Clinton might not answer certain questions about Monica S. Lewinsky during his grand jury testimony Monday.

Despite Clinton's pledge to testify "completely and t-uthfully," some former advisers and legal analysts have suggested in :ent days that he could limit his testimony, either by refusing to scuss his sex life or by giving a carefully worded statement on his lationship with Lewinsky without answering further questions.

But none of those scenarios comport with the president's pledge, according to aides who insisted they knew of no plans to follow such recommendations. Asked during the daily news briefing yesterday if Clinton was saying he would answer all questions when he vowed to testify "completely," White House deputy press secretary Joe Lockhart said, "That's what it suggests to me, yes."

Another senior official who did not want to be named said resisting some questions was not known to be under consideration, unless the president has discussed it with his personal attorney, David E. Kendall.

Clinton returned to Washington from a fund-raising trip early yesterday morning for what will be several days of intensive preparations with his lawyers, sessions that will extend into the weekend leading up to Monday's encounter with independent counsel Kenneth W. Starr at the White House.

Lockhart said that he could not say whether Clinton agreed with F''lary Rodham Clinton's comment this week attributing much of their oblems to prejudice against Arkansas, but added that the president npathized with the view. "The president has heard that when he has gone home and I think he understands that," Lockhart said. Friends om there "feel like they were singled out because they were from Little Rock or they were from Arkansas."

The notion of restricting Clinton's testimony has some appeal among advisers who believe it could minimize his legal exposure in a way that could be politically defensible if couched in terms of privacy concerns. And yet while they publicly explore such options, nearly all of them have been kept out of the loop as Clinton limits his consultations to his private attorneys and the first lady -- virtually the only people he can talk with who would not be subject to subpoenas by Starr.

As a result, numerous suggestions offered during television appearances or in newspapers are not based on a full knowledge of the facts. "It's all just the inevitable chattering in this kind of pre-testimony buildup," said James E. Kennedy, of the White House counsel's office.

Much of the speculation appears based on confusion or disagreement about the definition of sex used in the Paula Jones case, in part because the publicly released portion of Clinton's deposition transcript does not include a full account of how the lawyers involved e to define the term. The definition is key to whether Clinton can accused of perjury.

At the beginning of the Jan. 17 deposition, Jones's lawyers asked U.S. District Judge Susan Webber Wright to allow them to use a section of federal law to define the term "sexual relations" whenever it came up during the questioning. This was done for two reasons: to avoid having to ask the president salacious questions in explicit detail and to make clear to everyone exactly what was meant by the term "sexual relations."

The definition presented by Jones's lawyers included three parts: "For the purposes of this deposition, a person engages in 'sexual relations' when the person knowingly engages in or causes (1) contact with the genitalia, anus, groin, breast, inner thigh, or buttocks of any person with an intent to arouse or gratify the sexual desire of any person; (2) contact between any part of the person's body or an object and the genitals or anus of another person; or (3) contact between the genitals or anus of the person and any part of another person's body. 'Contact' means intentional touching, either directly or through clothing."

Wright declined to accept the whole definition, deeming it too broad. Instead, according to an authoritative account, she limited it the first point and excluded points two and three.

When Clinton was asked whether he had an affair with Lewinsky, avoid confusion or ambiguity, Jones's attorney referred to the definition approved by the judge. Clinton lawyer Robert S. Bennett objected, saying he was not sure that the president could remember the definition.

"Well, it's real short," Wright responded. "I will permit the question and you may show the witness definition number one."

Shown that definition, Clinton then answered, "I have never had sexual relations with Monica Lewinsky. I've never had an affair with her."

---- INDEX REFERENCES ----

KEY WORDS: NATIONAL

EDITION: FINAL

Word Count: 778
8/13/98 WASHPOST A04
END OF DOCUMENT

Tab 72

ˈtation Found Document Rank 2 of 79 Database WATIMES
ı3/98 WATIMES A1
8/13/98 Wash. Times (D.C.) A1
1998 WL 3455718

The Washington Times
Copyright 1998

Thursday, August 13, 1998

A

Clinton won't dodge questions about his sex life
Paul Bedard
THE WASHINGTON TIMES

President Clinton won't dodge questions about his sex life when he testifies to the Monica Lewinsky grand jury Monday, the White House said yesterday.

But his spokesman complained that the president's privacy has been violated.

"He plans to testify completely and truthfully," said deputy press :retary Joe Lockhart.

Asked whether Mr. Clinton will "answer every question" put to him by independent counsel Kenneth W. Starr and his deputies, Mr. Lockhart said, "Yes."

He said the president would not invoke his rights under the Fourth and Fifth Amendments to the Constitution, which protect citizens against unreasonable searches or self-incrimination.

"The president told you he'll answer truthfully and completely. I think that answers that question."

Speculation had blossomed that Mr. Clinton would refuse to answer questions about his sex life when he testifies from the White House via closed-circuit. He can expect to get questions about whether he engaged in oral and telephone sex with Miss Lewinsky and then discussed with her ways to avoid admitting it.

Mr. Lockhart said that the president would repeat his denial that he had sexual relations with the 25-year-old former White House intern and also that he never asked her to lie.

The spokesman dampened speculation that the president would 'ress the nation after giving his testimony. "I think his main p..iority right now is to go in and testify completely and ıthfully."

Mr. Lockhart said the White House hopes the contents of his testimony aren't leaked. "If the rule of law is followed and the president decides not to discuss his testimony, then there shouldn't be any leaks."

Several Democrats have called on the president to reveal his testimony in a public address, but his advisers have pressed the president not to do that.

The topic has dominated many White House meetings on the subject, but there has been no decision on a post-testimony address to the nation or short statement by the president to the press.

One aide joked that the president could quell the controversy and end his nonstop fund-raising campaign planned for the fall by "putting his testimony on pay per view. How about $39.95?"

Mr. Clinton returned home early yesterday from a two-day campaign fund-raising trip and began preparing for his testimony, slated to last from shortly after 9 a.m. Monday to late afternoon. He is pected to leave Monday night for a two-week vacation in Martha's ıeyard, an island off the Massachusetts coast.

While the White House refused to detail his preparations or preview his testimony, his spokesman expanded on the first lady's attacks on Mr. Starr by claiming the prosecutor is digging too deeply into the first family's privacy.

"One of the negatives is a loss of privacy and privacy within your family," said Mr. Lockhart. "I would find it hard to believe, having watched the last few months, that he wouldn't believe that there were new inroads to that privacy."

The president and first lady have often complained about their loss of privacy, and have expressed concerns about intrusions by reporters and especially photographers who have taken pictures of the two in private vacation moments.

But Mr. Lockhart said that those concerns won't prompt the president to duck sensitive questions about his private life if asked by Mr. Starr and his team.

The White House endorsed Hillary Rodham Clinton's remarkable charge that Mr. Starr harbors a bias against Arkansas. Mr. Lockhart .d the president thinks Mr. Starr dislikes the Clintons and that investigation is driven by an anti-Clinton bias.

'It's impossible for me . . . to separate the two. I am sure that there are some people who feel like they are treated unfairly because of their connection, or their friendship or their relationship, with the president. I am sure that there are others who feel that it's their connection to - whether the fact that they live in Little Rock or they're from Arkansas."

The first lady on Monday complained to the Arkansas Democrat Gazette of Little Rock that Mr. Starr's inquiry is driven by a "prejudice against our state . . . they wouldn't do this if we were from some other state."

Mr. Lockhart agreed, saying: "There have been a number of people who have little or no dealing with some of the matters that the independent counsel has looked at who've had their lives turned upside down and have run up legal bills. So I think there is a sentiment among some people back in Arkansas that they've been treated unfairly."

Mr. Starr, whose Whitewater investigation was set off by accusations by Arkansans, including the Clintons' former business partner, offered no comment yesterday.

Considerable time between today and Monday have been set aside for . Clinton to huddle with his lawyers and Harry Thomason, a Hollywood TV producer, in preparation for his testimony.

Mrs. Clinton also plans to provide advice. "She has some involvement," said the spokesman.

But Mr. Lockhart said only the president's lawyers - David Kendall, Nicole Seligman and Mickey Kantor - and his wife know what the president plans to say in his testimony.

"There is no loop," explained Lisa Caputo, Mrs. Clinton's former spokeswoman.

The White House is working to complete arrangements for the testimony. Previously taped Clinton depositions have taken place in the Map Room, the ground-floor room in the residence used by President Roosevelt for war councils during World War II.

---- INDEX REFERENCES ----

EDITION: 2

Word Count: 895
3/98 WATIMES A1
END OF DOCUMENT

Tab 73

tation Found Document Rank 6 of 35 Database
17/98 NEWSWEEK 30 NEWSWEEK
8/17/98 Newsweek 30
1998 WL 17010289

Newsweek

Monday, August 17, 1998

Vol. 132, No. 7, ISSN: 0028-9604

Monica On The Stand.(Monica Lewinsky's grand jury testimony)
Michael Isikoff Daniel Klaidman Karen Breslau

As Lewinsky tells her story to the grand jury, the president's team ponders how to fight back--in part, perhaps, by attacking the former intern's credibility. How ugly could it get?

David Kendall didn't waste time. When the news broke late last month that Monica Lewinsky had finally struck an immunity deal with Kenneth Starr, the president's lawyer began working the phones. He'd received an intriguing fax from a man named David Bliss, who said he had a story about Lewinsky that Kendall might want to hear. Kendall quickly faxed him back, thanking Bliss for sending the "very welcome" material "out of the blue." Kendall followed up with a phone call to Bliss, leaving a solicitous message--which Bliss played for Newsweek--on his answering machine. "I think it's important that we get together and, you know, decide how to proceed," Kendall said.

What did Bliss have on Lewinsky that was so tantalizing to the president's lawyer? Bliss, a drama-department shop foreman at Lewis & Clark College, told Kendall that when Lewinsky was a 21-year-old student there in 1995, she had forged a letter in his name on school stationery. Apparently Lewinsky was trying to help out Andy Bleiler, a married drama coach with whom she was allegedly having an affair. Bleiler was out of work, and embroiled in a custody battle. The forged letter--a purported job offer from Bliss to Bleiler--was supposed to help Bleiler's case. But the scheme went bad when the letter--which Bleiler says he never knew about--was returned to Bliss's mailbox as undeliverable. Bliss immediately suspected Lewinsky, who had been pestering him relentlessly to find work for Bleiler. Confronted with the letter, she proclaimed herself "humiliated," and begged forgiveness. But Bliss wasn't the forgiving kind. He took his story to Kendall. (A lawyer for Lewinsky declined to comment.)

The president's lawyer was all ears. Now that Lewinsky has become a fully immunized witness for the prosecution, Kendall is looking for details that might enable him to undermine Monica's credibility. Last week Lewinsky spent six hours before the grand jury in Washington.

ere, under oath, she apparently contradicted the president's denials--both in his Paula Jones deposition and to the country--that the two had a sexual affair. The basics of Lewinsky's testimony began leaking to the press soon after she left the courthouse. The former intern reportedly admitted to more than a dozen sexual encounters with the president--and said that she and Clinton discussed how to conceal their relationship. But on the question of whether Clinton explicitly asked her to lie under oath, Lewinsky refused to testify that the president instructed her to perjure herself.

As Kendall prepares his legal counteroffensive--and with Clinton's Aug. 17 testimony just a week away--there are obstacles everywhere. Any lawyer's biggest fear is a surprise question that leaves his client befuddled and in danger of falling into a perjury trap. This is exactly what Kendall is up against. The biggest unknown, and one that could conceivably wreck all of Kendall's careful preparation, is the blue dress currently undergoing testing at the FBI lab. Does it contain "DNA evidence"? The crime lab may have already completed initial tests. But the end results--and whether Starr will ask the president for a DNA sample--are being tightly held. If the tests come back positive, and the results are linked to Clinton, anything Kendall might have dug up t- discredit Lewinsky might be rendered irrelevant. But Kendall doesn't ,/e the luxury of knowing what those tests will reveal. The best he ı do is prepare his case--and his client--and get ready for the worst.

Meanwhile, Starr's staff is moving rapidly to complete its probe and may submit a possible report to Congress by early September. Contrary to expectations that Starr would present evidence of a broad pattern of obstruction of justice, Newsweek has learned the report will focus only on the Lewinsky matter and other allegations flowing out of the Paula Jones case. After four years and more than $40 million, the independent counsel has won a string of Whitewater criminal convictions and still has two indictments pending. But whatever evidence Starr has developed against the president relating to Whitewater--and other matters such as the Travel Office affair and the FBI file scandal--sources say it is not strong enough to be included in an impeachment report. The findings could potentially cut both ways. The narrow scope of the report will allow White House spinners to denigrate Starr's entire probe as little more than a sexual inquisition. But a tightly focused report could present problems for the White House--laying out the lurid Lewinsky charges in stark and simple language that may be difficult to dispute.

No matter what Starr's report reveals, Kendall's immediate problem remains the same: how to make Clinton appear more credible than L insky. One option: do "oppo" research on the chief accuser. Before .insky reached an agreement with Starr, Kendall tread lightly on her t to avoid pushing her into the independent counsel's camp. Since sne's cut her deal, however, Kendall is no longer restrained. For now, e lawyer is keeping potentially damaging stories in his briefcase. But they could prove useful to him during possible impeachment hearings, where Democrats loyal to the president would get the chance to interrogate the former intern.

Kendall's Lewinsky digging isn't confined to Monica's Lewis & Clark days. He is also interested in the story of a Democratic activist from Indianapolis named John Sullivan, who recalled meeting Lewinsky at an October 1996 fund-raiser in Washington. As he waited along the rope line to shake Clinton's hand, Sullivan says he was pulled aside by an event organizer. She told him that the woman standing next to him was named Monica, and that Monica was infatuated with the president and may have fantasized about having a relationship with him. Would Sullivan keep an eye on her? The incident came to light last week when an Indianapolis TV reporter saw a tape of the event and recognized Sullivan--who then told his story to the reporter. Sullivan told Newsweek Kendall called him last week and asked about the event. Sullivan says the smooth lawyer, himself an Indiana native, played up his Hoosier roots to try to win Sullivan's trust.

Soft-spoken and camera averse, Kendall has a reputation as a gentleman lawyer. But he is a tenacious and crafty litigator with a putation for tying his opponents in knots. Starr has already gotten a ste of Kendall's tactics. When the president's lawyer petitioned the ourts to investigate the independent counsel's alleged grand-jury leaks to the press, it was seen as a somewhat desperate publicity stunt. But last week it was revealed that Judge Norma Holloway Johnson came down on Kendall's side--ruling that there probably were illegal leaks, and ordering Starr to prove his office wasn't the source. Last week a federal appeals court handed Starr one minor victory on the matter: it denied Kendall the opportunity to interrogate Starr's prosecutors about the leaks. Still, Johnson's decision was a blow to the independent counsel, and gives new ammunition to the White House spin team that Starr is out of control.

In public, the president is trying to rise above the legal imbroglio. After the embassy bombings in Africa last Friday, Clinton solemnly vowed to bring the terrorists to justice. This week, as the flag-draped coffins arrive home, the president will have other opportunities to emphasize statecraft over scandal. But those who saw Clinton last week after hours described him as burdened and withdrawn, rubbing his eyes and staring absently into space.

It's up to Kendall to take his dispirited client and transform him into a compelling, telegenic and credible witness. He's done it before. en Clinton gave videotaped testimony in previous Whitewater trials, rors said they were "beguiled" by the president's performance. But ing to explain an alleged affair is a taller order. Kendall is legendary for exhaustive preparation sessions in which he grills his ıents over and over, day after day, making them repeat their answers. In a case this complex, with so many possible hidden traps, that means the president and his lawyer will be spending plenty of quality time--and billable hours--together this week. The drill has already begun. In the mornings--and sometimes again in the evening--Kendall and his partner Nicole Seligman slip into the White House. They use the East Entrance to the private quarters, avoiding the cameras along the West Wing driveway. There, in Clinton's second-floor office overlooking the South Lawn, Kendall methodically runs through the evidence, asking the president to explain everything from Lewinsky's White House visits to her high-powered job search. There are usually only two others allowed in the room: Hillary Clinton and Mickey Kantor, another private lawyer.

No matter how thoroughly Kendall preps his client, however, he can't anticipate every question the special prosecutor might ask. Even Starr doesn't have all the answers. For months, for example, there have been numerous hazy press reports that a uniformed Secret Service officer witnessed an alleged encounter between Clinton and Lewinsky. The story has changed over time, and the details remained sketchy. A Newsweek reconstruction of the events may shed some light on the incident. On E--ter Sunday 1996, according to government lawyers, officer John M kett was stationed outside the Oval Office. A phone call came in for president, but Clinton didn't respond. Muskett couldn't locate the president. Spotting Harold Ickes, Muskett asked the then deputy chief of staff for help. They knocked on the door to the Oval Office, but got no response. They then went to the door of the president's nearby private study. They knocked again, then opened the door.

What happened next is a matter of some controversy. Muskett later told Secret Service and Justice Department lawyers that he merely saw Lewinsky emerge from the room Clinton was in. But a fellow Secret Service officer, Gary Byrne--who wasn't present that day--told the government lawyers a different version. He said Muskett had told him that when they opened the door, Lewinsky's head was in Clinton's lap. Muskett has denied Byrne's account. And Ickes says he doesn't recall any aspect of the story. But sources tell Newsweek it was likely this incident that prompted Byrne to warn senior Clinton aide Evelyn Lieberman that Lewinsky was hanging around the Oval Office, and might be a potential problem. Shortly afterward, Lewinsky was transferred out of the White House to a job at the Pentagon. Now, Newsweek has learned, Starr's prosecutors, confronted with the contradictory accounts, want Justice Department officials to tell them what they were told in their interviews with Muskett and Byrne. Justice might agree to do so as early as this week. (Neither Muskett nor Byrne would comment to N sweek.)

ith a week to go, Clinton aides are doing their best to conduct business as Usual. This week Clinton will crisscross the country ising money for congressional Democrats and presiding over official White House "message events" wherever Air Force One touches down--touting voter favorites like the patients' bill of rights, clean-water laws and gun control.

But Clinton's mind may be elsewhere. Last week the president and First Lady invited a group of youth-violence experts to a cozy dinner in the Blue Room of the White House. There they hashed over the latest social theories about juvenile-crime prevention. According to some guests, Clinton, who normally revels in after-hours wonk sessions, seemed at times detached and weary. He faded in and out of the conversation, and was difficult to engage. Mrs. Clinton carried the dinner for both of them. She eagerly took notes and peppered the assembled academics and religious leaders with detailed questions. At the end of the evening, after most of the guests had departed and the First Lady had gone upstairs, Clinton lingered with Harvard professor Cornel West and a few others. How can you maintain your faith in the system when "right-wing gangsters in ties" seem intent on tearing you down? West asked the president. "They've been at me for a long time," Clinton responded. "I'm prepared." David Kendall certainly hopes so.

With Debra Rosenberg and Mark Hosenball

---- INDEX REFERENCES ----

NAMED PERSON: MONICA LEWINSKY

KEY WORDS: OBSTRUCTION OF JUSTICE SCANDALS

Word Count: 2009
8/17/98 NEWSWEEK 30
END OF DOCUMENT

Tab 74

7-1 (Rev. 2-21-91)

FBI LABORATORY

FEDERAL BUREAU OF INVESTIGATION
WASHINGTON, D. C. 20535

Date: August 17, 1998

To: Mr. Kenneth W. Starr
Office of the Independent Counsel
1001 Pennsylvania Avenue, N.W.
Suite 490-North
Washington, D.C. 20004

FBI File No. 29D-OIC-LR-35063

Lab No. 980730002 S BO
980803100 S BO

Reference: Communication dated July 30, 1998 and evidence submitted August 3, 1998

Your No. 29D-OIC-LR-35063

Re: MOZARK;
MC 106

Specimens received: July 30, 1998 and August 3, 1998

Specimens:

This report supplements two FBI Laboratory reports dated August 3, 1998 and August 6, 1998 and contains the results of the DNA-RFLP examinations.

This completes the requested examinations. The submitted items and the probed DNA membranes will be retained until retrieved by a representative of your organization. In addition to the evidence in the case, any remaining processed DNA from specimens examined by DNA analysis is also being returned to you. The processed DNA can be found in a package marked PROCESSED DNA SAMPLES: SHOULD BE REFRIGERATED/FROZEN. It is recommended that these samples be stored in a refrigerator/freezer and isolated from evidence that has not been examined.

F B I LABORATORY

FEDERAL BUREAU OF INVESTIGATION
WASHINGTON, D. C. 20535

Report of Examination

Examiner Name:	[redacted]	Date:	08/17/98
Unit:	DNA Analysis 1	Phone No.:	202-324-4409
FBI File No.:	29D-OIC-LR-35063	Lab No.:	980730002 S BO 980803100 S BO

Results of Examinations:

Deoxyribonucleic acid (DNA) profiles for the genetic loci D2S44, D17S79, D1S7, D4S139, D10S28, D5S110 and D7S467 were developed from HaeIII-digested high molecular weight DNA extracted from specimens K39 and Q3243-1(a semen stain removed from specimen Q3243). Based on the results of these seven genetic loci, specimen K39 (CLINTON) is the source of the DNA obtained from specimen Q3243-1, to a reasonable degree of scientific certainty.

No DNA-RFLP examinations were conducted on specimen Q3243-2 (a semen stain removed from specimen Q3243).

BLACK – 1,440,000,000,000
CAUC – 7,870,000,000,000
SEH – 3,140,000,000,000
SWH – 943,000,000,000

Tab 75

AP J2969 ri ----- US-Clinton-Text, 2 Takes,0212 08-17 10:18p

By The Associated Press

Text of President Bill Clinton's address to the nation, as transcribed by the Federal Document Clearing House:

Good evening.

This afternoon in this room, from this chair, I testified before the Office of Independent Counsel and the grand jury.

I answered their questions truthfully, including questions about my private life, questions no American citizen would ever want to answer.

Still, I must take complete responsibility for all my actions, both public and private. And that is why I am speaking to you tonight.

As you know, in a deposition in January, I was asked questions about my relationship with Monica Lewinsky. While my answers were legally accurate, I did not volunteer information.

Indeed, I did have a relationship with Ms. Lewinsky that was not appropriate. In fact, it was wrong. It constituted a critical lapse in judgment and a personal failure on my part for which I am solely and completely responsible.

But I told the grand jury today and I say to you now that at no time did I ask anyone to lie, to hide or destroy evidence or to take any other unlawful action.

I know that my public comments and my silence about this matter gave a false impression. I misled people, including even my wife. I deeply regret that.

I can only tell you I was motivated by many factors. First, by a desire to protect myself from the embarrassment of my own conduct. I was also very concerned about protecting my family. The fact that these questions were being asked in a politically inspired lawsuit, which has since been dismissed, was a consideration, too.

In addition, I had real and serious concerns about an independent counsel investigation that began with private business dealings 20 years ago, dealings, I might add, about which an independent federal agency found no evidence of any wrongdoing by me or my wife over two years ago.

The independent counsel investigation moved on to my staff and friends, then into my private life. And now the investigation itself is under investigation.

This has gone on too long, cost too much and hurt too many innocent people.

Now, this matter is between me, the two people I love most - my wife and our daughter - and our God. I must put it right, and I am prepared to do whatever it takes to do so.

Nothing is more important to me personally. But it is private, and I intend to reclaim my family life for my family. It's nobody's business but ours.

Even presidents have private lives. It is time to stop the pursuit of personal destruction and the prying into private lives and get on with our national life.

Our country has been distracted by this matter for too long, and I take my responsibility for my part in all of this. That is all I can do.

Now it is time - in fact, it is past time - to move on. We have important work to do - real opportunities to seize, real problems to solve, real security matters to face.

And so tonight, I ask you to turn away from the spectacle of the past seven months, to repair the fabric of our national discourse, and to return our attention to all the challenges and all the promise of the next American century.

Thank you for watching. And good night.

Tab 76

The Washington Post

8/18/98

'I Misled People. . . . I Deeply Regret That'

Federal Document Clearing House

Following are President Clinton's remarks last night on his grand jury testimony and the investigation by independent counsel Kenneth W. Starr:

Good evening. This afternoon in this room, from this chair, I testified before the Office of Independent Counsel and the grand jury. I answered their questions truthfully, including questions about my private life, questions no American citizen would ever want to answer.

Still, I must take complete responsibility for all my actions, both public and private. And that is why I am speaking to you tonight.

As you know, in a deposition in January, I was asked questions about my relationship with Monica Lewinsky. While my answers were legally accurate, I did not volunteer information.

Indeed, I did have a relationship with Miss Lewinsky that was not appropriate. In fact, it was wrong. It constituted a critical lapse in judgment and a personal failure on my part for which I am solely and completely responsible.

But I told the grand jury today and I say to you now that at no time did I ask anyone to lie, to hide or destroy evidence or to take any other unlawful action.

I know that my public comments and my silence about this matter gave a false impression. I misled people, including even my wife. I deeply regret that.

I can only tell you I was motivated by many factors. First, by a desire to protect myself from the embarrassment of my own conduct. I was also very concerned about protecting my family. The fact that these questions were being asked in a politically inspired lawsuit, which has since been dismissed, was a consideration, too.

In addition, I had real and serious concerns about an independent counsel investigation that began with private business dealings 20 years ago, dealings, I might add, about which an independent federal agency found no evidence of any wrongdoing by me or my wife over two years ago.

The independent counsel investigation moved on to my staff and friends, then into my private life. And now the investigation itself is under investigation.

This has gone on too long, cost too much and hurt too many innocent people.

Now, this matter is between me, the two people I love most—my wife and our daughter—and our God. I must put it right, and I am prepared to do whatever it takes to do so. Nothing is more important to me personally. But it is private, and I intend to reclaim my family life for my family. It's nobody's business but ours. Even presidents have private lives.

It is time to stop the pursuit of personal destruction and the prying into private lives and get on with our national life.

Our country has been distracted by this matter for too long, and I take my responsibility for my part in all of this. That is all I can do. Now it is time—in fact, it is past time—to move on.

We have important work to do—real opportunities to seize, real problems to solve, real security matters to face.

And so tonight, I ask you to turn away from the spectacle of the past seven months, to repair the fabric of our national discourse, and to return our attention to all the challenges and all the promise of the next American century.

Thank you for watching. And good night.

Tab 77

OFFICE OF THE ATTORNEY GENERAL

FACSIMILE TRANSMITTAL COVER SHEET

DATE: AUGUST / 24 / 1998

TO: JACKIE BENNETT

FACSIMILE NO. 514-8802

TELEPHONE NO. 514-8688

FROM: GARY GRINDLER

FACSIMILE NO. 616-5117

TELEPHONE NO. 514-5203

NUMBER OF PAGES INCLUDING COVER SHEET 8

COMMENTS:

DRAFT – August 19, 1998 [5:00 p.m.]

This letter sets forth the terms of agreement between the Department of Justice (Department), the Secret Service, and the Office of Independent Counsel (OIC) regarding the OIC's desire to obtain information from Secret Service personnel that is relevant to its Monica Lewinsky-related investigation. This agreement is designed to facilitate the OIC's information-gathering process and, at the same time, to ensure that the Department and the Secret Service are discharging their law enforcement responsibilities in an appropriate manner.

I. Obtaining Information from Secret Service Personnel Not Previously Examined by the OIC

1. The OIC agrees to limit the questioning of additional Secret Service personnel by seeking information only from those agents and officers who served in a protective capacity in the vicinity of the Oval Office on six specified dates, during specified times. The Secret Service has identified 87 current and 2 retired agents and officers who served in such a capacity.[1] The OIC agrees not to seek information from agents and officers who served in a protective capacity on different dates, unless, in the future, it receives new information that **provides probable cause to believe that evidence of a crime would be obtained by increasing the number of dates above six or speaking to additional Secret Service employees about events that occurred on dates other than the original six specified dates. The OIC agrees that prior to increasing the number of dates above six or speaking to additional Secret Service employees about events that occurred on dates other than the original six specified dates, the OIC will provide its basis for doing so, consistent with its obligations under Rule 6(e) of the Federal Rules of Criminal Procedure, to the Attorney General and Director Merletti, who, along with Kenneth W. Starr (and such other personnel as each may designate), will enter into good faith discussions on the need to increase the number of dates. If agreement cannot be reached on the need to increase the number of dates, the dispute will be presented to Chief Judge Johnson for resolution.**

[1] To select such personnel, the Secret Service identified: (i) from official records the Uniformed Division personnel who were listed as occupying the posts specified by the OIC for the six specified time periods; (ii) from Protective Operations Activity and Personnel reports the Presidential Protective Division personnel who, for the six specified time periods, were listed as being assigned to the immediate shift protecting the President; and (iii) **in an effort to be over inclusive rather than under inclusive,** from Protective Operations Activity and Personnel reports the Presidential Protective Division personnel who, for the six specified time periods, were listed as being assigned to a specific Secret Service command center or were listed as participating in orientation.**[deletion]**

2. As promptly as possible, the Secret Service will require each of the 87 current agents and officers to complete the questionnaire attached at Tab A. Each current agent and officer will be required to swear to the contents of the questionnaire under penalty of perjury. After completing the questionnaire, the agents and officers will be directed to place the completed questionnaire in an envelope, seal the envelope, and send the envelope to the OIC. **The OIC agrees that the questionnaire does not need to be sent to one of the two retired officers due to the OIC's prior contact with that officer. As for the other retired officer, the Secret Service will mail the questionnaire and a modified cover letter (attached at Tab B) to his last known mailing address.**

3. The OIC agrees that the information provided by agents and officers in the questionnaires will be treated as **sensitive and confidential information.** At the Department's request, the OIC will provide the Department with copies of the completed questionnaires.

4. The OIC is entitled, in its sole discretion, to interview any agent or officer who does not answer each of the queries on the questionnaire in the negative. Consistent with past practice, prior to the OIC interviews, Department and Secret Service attorneys may, at their discretion, meet with any such agent or officer for the sole purpose of ascertaining whether the agent or officer possesses potentially relevant information that is covered by a currently-recognized testimonial privilege or otherwise implicates sensitive information about Secret Service security measures.

5. The OIC interviews will be conducted in the offices of the OIC in the presence of OIC attorneys and/or an FBI agent. **[Jackie-we need to discuss this paragraph]** Attorneys from the Department or the Secret Service may, at their discretion, accompany the agents and officers to the **interviews** and be available outside the interview room for consultation. The OIC agrees that the information provided by agents and officers in the interviews will be treated as **sensitive and confidential information.**

6. The OIC is entitled, in its sole discretion, to depose under oath any agent or officer who it has interviewed. These depositions, which shall not be videotaped, will be conducted in the offices of the OIC in the presence of OIC attorneys and a stenographer. Attorneys from the Department or the Secret Service may, at their discretion, accompany the agents and officers to the depositions and be available outside the deposition room for consultation. The OIC agrees that the information provided by agents and officers in the depositions will be treated **as sensitive and confidential information.**

7. The OIC agrees that it will not examine before the Grand Jury any agent or officer who it has interviewed in the absence of prior consultations in good faith between Kenneth W. Starr, Lewis C. Merletti **and the Attorney General (and such other**

personnel as each may designate). [The last sentence of this paragraph has been deleted]

II. Obtaining Information from Department Attorneys Regarding Secret Service Personnel Previously Examined by the OIC

1. The Department agrees to proffer orally to OIC attorneys information covered by the putative protective function privilege, which Department attorneys previously obtained during interviews of Secret Service officers.

2. The OIC agrees that the proffers will be treated as **sensitive and confidential information.**

III. General Agreements

1. The OIC agrees that, by adhering to the procedures described above, the Department and the Secret Service do not waive any possible claim of government attorney-client privilege, work product privilege, or protective function privilege.

2. The OIC agrees that the procedures outlined above will be the exclusive method by which the OIC henceforth obtains information from Department, Secret Service, or Treasury Department attorneys, agents, officers and **personnel**, unless the OIC **receives new information that provides it with** probable cause to believe that it would obtain new evidence of obstruction of justice, perjury, or making false statements **arising from the OIC's efforts to obtain information from Secret Service personnel.**.

3. **The OIC agrees that this exclusive method of obtaining information from Department of Justice, Treasury and Secret Service personnel obviates the need for the production of additional materials pursuant to any document subpoena served upon the Secret Service prior to the date of this agreement. The OIC, however, reserves the right to serve document subpoenas in the future for additional information deemed by the OIC as necessary to the grand jury investigation.**

4. Attorneys from the Department, the Secret Service, or the Treasury Department who have obtained, or will obtain, information from the OIC or Secret Service agents and officers as a result of the procedures outlined above will, consistent with past practice, maintain that information as **sensitive and confidential** and restrict its dissemination only to those who have a compelling need to know it within the Department, the Secret Service, and the Treasury Department.

5. The parties to this agreement understand that, at any time in this process, including prior to completing the questionnaire, Secret Service personnel are entitled, at their discretion, to retain private counsel. **OIC recognizes that private counsel who may be retained by Secret Service personnel in this matter are not parties to this Agreement and, accordingly, involvement by such counsel could result in proposals by them to modify the manner in which information from their individual clients will be provided to the OIC.**

6. **Should a dispute arise regarding the interpretation or application of the terms of this Agreement, the OIC, the Department and Secret Service agree that Kenneth W. Starr, Lewis C. Merletti and the Attorney General (and any such other personnel as each may designate) will engage in good faith consultations in an effort to resolve any such dispute. If any such dispute can not be resolved, the issues will be presented to Chief Judge Johnson for resolution.**

[Memorandum to select Secret Service personnel:]

Independent Counsel Kenneth W. Starr has been authorized to investigate "whether Monica Lewinsky or others suborned perjury, obstructed justice, intimidated witnesses or otherwise violated federal law... concerning the civil case Jones v. Clinton." As part of that investigation, the Office of the Independent Counsel (OIC) is attempting to ascertain whether Secret Service officers or agents who worked in a protective capacity on a limited number of dates, during specified times, are in possession of information that may be relevant to its investigation. The OIC, the Department of Justice, and the Secret Service have agreed to a multi-step information-gathering process.

You have been identified as a Secret Service agent or officer who worked in a protective capacity on the list of dates and times that have been provided by the OIC. To determine whether you possess information that is relevant to the OIC's investigation, you are required to complete the attached questionnaire within three days of receiving it. Your responses to the questionnaire must be sworn to under penalty of perjury.

If you have any questions regarding the questionnaire, you may consult with attorneys from the Secret Service Office of Chief Counsel, at (202) 435-5771. Please note that these attorneys cannot represent you in your personal capacity, but would be representing the United States and its interests that may be implicated by the OIC's inquiry. As with any other potential witness, you have the right to retain private counsel at any time, including prior to completing the questionnaire. If you do retain private counsel, the Department of Justice will consider a request for reimbursement of private counsel fees, which will be authorized if the Department determines, in its sole discretion, that your request is in the interests of the United States.

The OIC has advised us that your responses to the questionnaire **will be treated as sensitive and confidential.** After you have completed the questionnaire, place it in the enclosed envelope, seal the envelope, and mail it to the OIC. Please be advised that, depending upon your answers to the questionnaire, the OIC may elect to interview you and/or obtain your testimony under oath, either in its offices or in front of the Grand Jury. Should the OIC elect to do so, the Secret Service Office of Chief Counsel will contact you individually to inform you of this fact and of how the OIC's information-gathering process will proceed from that point.

QUESTIONNAIRE

1. Print your full name.

____

2. Do you recall ever speaking with Monica Lewinsky?

Yes ________ No ________

If your answer to this question is "Yes," but your conversations with Monica Lewinsky were limited to the exchange of casual greetings or idle chit-chat about matters such as the weather, please describe those conversations on a separate page.

3. Do you recall, prior to January 21, 1998, ever observing Monica Lewinsky via a Secret Service video camera or closed-circuit monitoring device?

Yes ________ No ________

4. Do you recall, prior to January 21, 1998, ever observing Monica Lewinsky and President Clinton together?

Yes________ No__________

If your answer to this question is "Yes," but your observations with Monica Lewinsky and the President were limited to those at widely-attended events, please describe those observations on a separate page.

5. Do you recall, prior to January 21, 1998, ever observing Monica Lewinsky inside, or in the vicinity, of the Oval Office suite of offices?

Yes ________ No ________

If your answer to this question is "Yes," but your observations with Monica Lewinsky and the President were limited to those at widely-attended events, please describe those observations on a separate page.

6. Do you recall, prior to January 21, 1998, ever hearing the President, any current or former White House or Secret Service employee, or any advisor or visitor to the White House

(excluding President Clinton's private attorneys), speak about or discuss any one of the following five topics: (i) a relationship between Monica Lewinsky and the President; (ii) Monica Lewinsky being alone with President Clinton at any location; (iii) Monica Lewinsky being inside, or in the vicinity, of the Oval Office suite of offices; (iv) Linda Tripp; or (v) any matter related to President Clinton, Monica Lewinsky, Linda Tripp, or Kathleen Willey being deposed, submitting affidavits, being a witness in, or otherwise being connected with the Paula Jones v. William Jefferson Clinton litigation?

Yes ________ No ________

I declare under penalty of perjury, pursuant to 28 U.S.C. Section 1746, that the foregoing is true and correct.

____________________ ____________________

Signature Date

Tab 78

Memorandum **Office of the Independent Counsel**

To: File Date: 8/27/98

From: SA [redacted]

Subject: Lewinsky interview on 8/13/98

During the 8/13/98 interview of Monica S. Lewinsky, Lewinsky asked if she could discuss a particular matter outside the presence of male investigators/attorneys. Associate Independent Counsel (AIC) Karin Immergut obliged Lewinsky, and the two left the interview room. After a few minutes, the two returned and the interview resumed. The contents of the interview of 8/13/98 are documented in an FD-302, transcribed on 8/14/98 by writer.

After the interview, AIC Immergut advised writer as to the details of what Lewinsky discussed outside the presence of investigators. Immergut advised that Lewinsky stated that during her November 13, 1997 meeting with Clinton, Lewinsky showed Clinton an e-mail. The e-mail described the [redacted] Lewinsky also brought some Altoids with her and was eating them when she met with Clinton. Clinton told Lewinsky they did not have enough time for oral sex. Lewinsky told Clinton to at least put his tongue on hers and he obliged.

Tab 79

LAW OFFICES
WILLIAMS & CONNOLLY
725 TWELFTH STREET, N.W.
WASHINGTON, D. C. 20005-5901
(202) 434-5000
FAX (202) 434-5029

DAVID E. KENDALL
(202) 434-5145

EDWARD BENNETT WILLIAMS (1920-1988)
PAUL R. CONNOLLY (1922-1978)

August 31, 1998

CONFIDENTIAL
RULE 6(e), F.R.CRIM.P. GRAND JURY SUBMISSION

Robert J. Bittman, Esq.
Deputy Independent Counsel
Office of the Independent Counsel
1001 Pennsylvania Avenue, N.W.
Suite 490-North
Washington, D.C. 20004

By Hand

Dear Bob:

This will acknowledge your letter dated August 26, 1998. I believe that the President has complied with grand jury subpoenas nos. V002 and D1415. I will not repeat the comments of my letter to you dated April 13, 1998. As I have previously told you, the President receives a large number of gifts from a great many people. We have done our very best to comply with the grand jury subpoenas. I want to repeat, however, that if you have information concerning gifts or other objects which you think may be responsive to these subpoenas, and if you will give me a description of what those gifts or other objects might be, we will be happy to undertake a search for them, as we have in the past.

Sincerely,

David E. Kendall

Tab 80

Memorandum **Office of the Independent Counsel**

To: FILE Date: 9/7/98

From: Edward J. Page, AIC

Subject: Interview of USSS Special Agent Thomas M. Powers

AICs Mary Anne Wirth and Edward J. Page interviewed Thomas M. Powers, United States Secret Service Special Agent on 2 August 1998 at United States Secret Service (USSS) Headquarters in Washington, D.C.

Powers has worked for the USSS since June of 1986 and has been assigned to the Presidential Protective Detail (PPD) for approximately four years and two months.

Powers has seen President and Betty Currie talking during his PPD duties at the White House and has seen Currie go the the putting green to give the President messages.

Powers saw Betty Currie at the White House on Saturday, January 17, 1998, the day of President Clinton's deposition in Jones v. Clinton, and heard the President and Currie talking. Powers saw the President after he returned from his deposition; in Powers's opinion, President Clinton, who was by himself at the time, "looked angry, concerned and troubled."

Powers knows USSS Special Agent Nelson Garbito, who also works on the PPD. Powers described Garbito as follows: Hispanic, possibly of Puerto Rican descent, 6 ft. 2 or 3 inches in height, dark skinned, black hair, and tall and slender.

Powers has never seen Monica Lewinsky at the White House.

Tab 81

Paula Corbin **JONES**, Plaintiff,
v.
William Jefferson **CLINTON** and Danny Ferguson,
Defendants.

No. LR-C-94-290.

United States District Court,
E.D. Arkansas,
Western Division.

Sept. 1, 1998.

MEMORANDUM AND ORDER

SUSAN WEBBER WRIGHT, District Judge.

***1** On May 6th, 1994, the plaintiff in this case, Paula Corbin **Jones**, filed suit against William Jefferson **Clinton**, President of the United States, End Danny Ferguson, a former Arkansas State Police Officer, seeking damages for alleged actions beginning with an incident that is said to have occurred in a hotel suite in Little Rock, Arkansas, on May 8th, 1991. The case ultimately made its way to the Supreme Court of the United States where it was determined that plaintiff's lawsuit could proceed while the President is in office. See **Clinton** v. **Jones**, 520 U.S. 681, 117 S.Ct. 1636, 137 L.Ed.2d 945(1997). Following that decision, and following this Court's partial denial of the President's and Ferguson's subsequent motion for judgment on the pleadings, see **Jones** v. **Clinton**, 974 F.Supp. 712 (E.D.Ark.1997), formal discovery commenced. Because of the salacious nature of much of the discovery and the media's intense and often inaccurate coverage of this case, this Court, on October 30th, 1997, entered a Confidentiality Order on Consent of all Parties, thereby imposing limits on the dissemination of information concerning a large portion of discovery and placing under seal court filings dealing with discovery. The Court took this action to help ensure that a fair and impartial jury could be selected in the event this matter went to trial by limiting prejudicial pre-trial publicity. Following entry of the Confidentiality Order, various media entitles filed a Motion for Leave to Intervene, Motion to Modify and/or Rescind Confidentiality Order and Motion for Access to Court Records and Discovery. [FN1] Other parties also sought recission of the Confidentiality Order and for access to Court records and discovery. By Memorandum and Order dated March 9th, 1998, this Court denied the motions seeking to rescind and/or modify the Confidentiality Order. In its Memorandum and Order, the Court pointed out the need to ensure a fair trial and, further, that there existed a need to protect the privacy interest of third-party witnesses pursuant to Fed.R.Civ.P. 26(c). [FN2] The media entities appealed. Following the filing of the notice of appeal but before the Court of Appeals for the Eighth Circuit could issue an opinion on the matter, this Court granted the President's and Ferguson's motions for summary judgment and entered judgment dismissing this case. See **Jones** v. **Clinton**, 990 F.Supp. 657 (E.D.Ark.1998). The Eighth Circuit subsequently issued an order dismissing the media entities' appeal and directing this Court to consider on remand the need for keeping its Confidentiality Order in place in view of the grant of summary judgment. See **Jones** v. **Clinton**, 138 F.3d 758 (8th Cir.1998). The Eighth Circuit's mandate was filed in this Court on June 3rd, 1998. In accordance with the Order of the Eighth Circuit, this Court, by Order dated June 8th, 1998, asked the parties to file briefs setting forth their positions, if any, on the need for keeping in place the Confidentiality Order. Following submission of the briefs outlining the parties' respective views, this Court, by Memorandum and Order dated June 30th, 1998, vacated in large part the Confidentiality Order and directed that a substantial portion of the record in this matter be unsealed. In so ruling, the Court determined that the Confidentiality Order shall remain in effect with respect to the identities of any Jane Does who may be revealed in the Court record, in any materials in possession of the parties that have not been filed of record, and in any public statements. In addition, the Court determined that all videotapes of depositions taken in connection with this lawsuit shall remain under seal. Now before the Court is a motion by the President for reconsideration of this Court's decision to partially unseal the record and to stay the June 30th Memorandum and Order. The plaintiff and the media have responded to the President's motion and the President has filed a reply to the plaintiff's and the media's responses. Having considered the matter, the Court grants in part and denies in part the President's motion for reconsideration.

I.

***2** The President argues that this Court should

reconsider the June 30th, 1998 Memorandum and Order because this Court may not have been aware of all the discovery material that remains under seal, much of which he says was not filed with the Court or attached to any motion; there is no right of access to the material at issue; the parties' fair trial interests would be prejudiced and that prejudice cannot be mitigated by the passage of time; the privacy interests protected are too narrow; and unsealing would permit plaintiff, the media and others to misuse the Court's processes and Court files for profit or political gain.

In response, the media entities argue that the President's motion raises no new issues and should be denied for that reason alone. They further argue that this Court's order represented a proper exercise of its discretion in balancing privacy rights against the interest of the media and the public in full and accurate disclosure of the history of this case and the course of the discovery process, and that there is no basis for the President's contention that much of the record in this litigation over serious allegations of official misconduct should be concealed from public view long after any circumstances require it.

For her part, the plaintiff has altered her previous position on the matter and now argues for the complete unsealing of the record. [FN3] She argues that it is in the best interests of all parties concerned, as well as the rights of the public and media, to disclose all the discovery and evidence relating to the case at this time, with the single exception of the identifying testimony relating to a certain Jane Doe. Plaintiff further argues that this Court has enunciated no rational justification for retaining the seal on videotapes of deposition testimony and that the Court's Order with regard to the videotapes constitutes a taking of her property without just compensation or due process pursuant to the Fifth and Fourteenth Amendments.

II.

At issue are three categories of materials: (1) court filings that are under seal; (2) discovery materials in the hands of the parties that are not filed with the Court but are nevertheless under seal as subject to the Confidentiality Order; and (3) videotaped and transcribed depositions. [FN4] The Court will address these categories in turn.

1.

With respect to the first category of materials--court filings that are under seal--the Court has determined that there are contained in the Court's files matters under seal which do not at this time impact upon the parties' rights to a fair trial or the interests of the Jane Does in maintaining privacy, two interests for implementation of the Confidentiality Order. In that regard, the Court will review all materials on file with the Court and will release on a periodic basis such materials, either in whole or as redacted, that the Court determines will not (1) impact upon the parties' rights to a fair trial and/or (2) do not adversely affect the privacy interests of any Jane Does. In releasing such materials, the Court will attempt to ascertain the negative inferences any such materials may have on one party or the other and will attempt, where possible, to coordinate the release of such materials on equal basis. The Court will not, however, release any materials involving Jane Does, whether in whole or as redacted, without first giving those Jane Does and the parties an opportunity to object to their release. While the President may be correct that such review and/or redaction of the record prior to release may prove to be a burdensome task, this Court must follow its duty notwithstanding the difficulty of any particular course of action.

2.

*3 With respect to the second category of materials--discovery materials in the hands of parties that are not filed with the Court but are nevertheless under seal as subject to the Confidentiality Order--the Court directs that no such materials in the hands of the parties be released or otherwise disclosed without first obtaining Court approval. In approving the release of any materials, whether in whole or as redacted, the Court will utilize the test previously enunciated, i.e. whether the release of any such materials impacts upon the parties' rights to a fair trial and/or whether such materials adversely affect the privacy interests of any Jane Does.

3.

With respect to the third and final category of materials--the videotaped and transcribed depositions of the parties--the Court will maintain under seal the videotapes of any depositions taken in connection with this lawsuit, whether they be videotapes of the parties or of non-party witnesses. As the Court has previously noted, the videotapes of the depositions are not judicial records to which any common law right of public access attaches and, with respect to the President, there is a strong judicial tradition of proscribing public access to recordings of testimony given by a sitting President. See United States v. McDougal, 103 F.3d 651, 656-659 (8th Cir.1996), cert. denied, --- U.S. ----, 118 S.Ct. 49, 139 L.Ed.2d 15 (1997).

With respect to transcripts of the depositions of the parties, however, the Court will permit these transcripts to be released in their entirety provided, however, that all identifying information of any Jane Does has been redacted and the redaction has been approved by the Court. It should be noted that the plaintiff and Ferguson do not object to their depositions being released in their entirety. Although the President does object, his deposition has largely been made public and has been the subject of intense scrutiny in the wake of his public admission that he was "misleading" with regard to his relationship with Monica Lewinsky. [FN5] That being the case, the Court determines that no fair trial interests are implicated by the release, as redacted and approved by this Court, of the transcripts of his or the other parties' depositions.

III.

Having set forth the procedure this Court will utilize in unsealing a large part of the record, the Court now addresses plaintiff's claim that she has a Fifth Amendment property interest in discovery materials, namely the videotapes of depositions which she noticed. Plaintiff cites no authority for such a proposition and, as correctly noted by the President, the Supreme Court has held that "[l]iberal discovery is provided for the sole purpose of assisting in the preparation and trial, or the settlement, of litigated disputes." Seattle Times Co. v. Rhinehart, 467 U.S. 20, 34, 104 S.Ct. 2199, 81 L.Ed.2d 17 (1984). Indeed, as a general matter, plaintiff would not have any right to the material at issue but for the discovery procedures set forth in the Federal Rules of Civil Procedure. The Court thus rules that plaintiff has no property interest in the discovery materials she has amassed.

*4 Likewise, the Court rejects any assertion by plaintiff that this Court is impeding upon First Amendment interests in the discovery materials she has amassed in this case. See Seattle Times, 467 U.S. at 33-37 (holding that "restrains placed on discovered, but not yet admitted, information are not a restriction on a traditionally public source of information," and that "where a protective order is entered on a showing of good cause as required by Rule 26(c) [of the Federal Rules of Civil Procedure], is limited to the context of pretrial discovery, and does not restrict the dissemination of the information if gained from other sources, it does not offend the First Amendment").

IV.

One final matter concerns motions by two Jane Does to intervene and to reconsider the Court's June 30th, 1998 Memorandum and Order, both of which were filed for purposes of protecting their privacy interests, a motion by non-party deponent Dolly Kyle Browning for a Protective Order in which she requests that certain portions of her deposition transcript and exhibits remain sealed to protect the privacy of persons with little or no connection with the facts underlying this action and to preserve proprietary information, and a motion by the Office of Independent Counsel ("OIC") to maintain the confidentiality of its March 27th, 1998 filing, i.e., "In Camera Submission of the United States in Support of [the United States'] Motion for Limited Intervention and a Stay of Kathleen Willey's Further Deposition." The motions of the two Jane Does to intervene are granted. [FN6] Those portions of their motions to reconsider are granted to the extent set forth in today's Memorandum and Order. The motion of Dolly Kyle Browning for a Protective Order is granted as well. If and/or when the record in this matter is unsealed (either in whole or part), [FN7] the Court will address the concerns set forth in Ms. Browning's motion at that time. Finally, the Court grants OIC's motion and will maintain the confidentiality of its March 27th, 1998 filing, i.e., "In Camera Submission of the United States in Support of [the United States'] Motion for Limited Intervention and a Stay of Kathleen Willey's Further Deposition."

V.

The parties are hereby given until and including Tuesday, September 15th, 1998, in which to file a notice of appeal from today's decisions. Assuming an appeal is filed, today's decision will be stayed in its entirety pending the resolution of any such appeal. If no appeal is filed, the Court will proceed to unseal the record as set forth above. All court filings unsealed in accordance with today's decision will be posted on the Court's website beginning on Monday, September 28th, 1998, at the following address: www.are.uscourts.gov. Future documents unsealed in accordance with today's decision will be posted at the same address. Because it may be necessary for the Court to periodically have phone conferences to address any objections that may be raised to the release of a particular document, the Court cannot provide a precise schedule setting forth the times that any documents will be released. Accordingly, the Court will not announce any such postings in advance, and neither the Court nor the Clerk's Office will answer media inquiries about the timing of any such postings. The Court will be reviewing documents for possible unsealing and a barrage of calls could interfere with this process.

VI.

***5** For the foregoing reasons, the Court grants in part and denies in part the President's motion for reconsideration. The Confidentiality Order is hereby modified as set forth above. The motions of the Jane Does to intervene and to reconsider are granted to the extent set forth above, and the motions of Dolly Kyle Browning and OIC are granted as well.

IT IS SO ORDERED this 1st day of September, 1998.

FN1. The media entities that joined in this motion are as follows: Pulitzer Publishing Company, The New York Times Company; Associated Press, USA Today, a division of Gannett Satellite Information Network, Inc.; Cable News Network, Inc.; Newsday, Inc.; National Broadcasting Company, Inc.; CBS, Inc.; American Broadcasting Companies, Inc.; Time Inc.; Little Rock Newspapers, Inc.; and The Reporters Committee for Freedom of the Press. Following the filing of this motion, two additional media entities, Fox News Network, LLC, and The Society of Professional Journalists, filed a motion seeking the same relief.

FN2. Rule 26(c) provides that "[u]pon motion by a party or by the person from whom discovery is sought ... and for good cause shown, the court in which the action is pending ... may make any order which justice requires to protect a party or person from annoyance, embarrassment, oppression, or undue burden or expense...."

FN3. Plaintiff initially took no position on the unsealing of the record but later submitted a pleading that argued for the need to keep in place the Confidentiality Order. In her most recent pleading, plaintiff withdraws her consent to the Confidentiality Order and argues for the complete unsealing of the record.

FN4. Portions the transcribed depositions of parties and various witnesses have been made part of the Court record by virtue of the briefing on the President's and Ferguson's motions for summary judgment, or by motions involving discovery issues. The latter motions currently remain under seal pursuant to the Confidentiality Order.

FN5. Although the Court has concerns about the nature of the President's January 17th, 1998 deposition testimony given his recent public statements, the Court makes no findings at this time regarding whether the President may be in contempt.

FN6. Because the Court is allowing all Jane Does the opportunity to object to the release of information which may affect their interests, the Court hereby sua sponte grants leave of all other Jane Does permission to intervene in this matter.

FN7. Assuming an appeal is filed, the Court will, of course, await the resolution of any such appeal prior to unsealing any part of the record in this case. See Section V, infra.

END OF DOCUMENT

Tab 82

Surfacing Lyrics

TRACKS: 1.) Building a Mystery 2.) I Love You 3.) Sweet Surrender 4.) Adia 5.) Do What You Have To Do 6.) Witness 7.) Angel 8.) Black and White 9.) Full of Grace 10.) Last Dance (Instrumental)

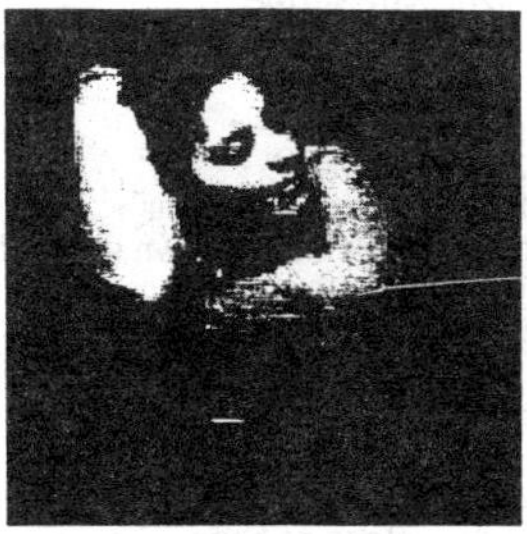

Building a Mystery
(Sarah McLachlan/Pierre Marchand)

You come out at night
That's when the energy comes
And the dark side's light
and the vampires roam

You strut your rasta wear
and your suicide poem
And a cross from a faith that died
Before Jesus came

You're building a mystery

You live in a church
Where you sleep with voodoo dolls
And you won't give up the search
For the ghosts in the halls

You wear sandals in the snow
And a smile that won't wash away
Can you look out the window
Without your shadow getting in the way

You're so beautiful
With an edge and charm
And so careful
When I'm in your arms

'Cause you're working
Building a mystery
Holding on and holding it in
Yeah you're working
Building a mystery
And choosing so carefully

You woke up screaming aloud
A prayer for your secret god
You feed off our fears
And hold back your tears oh

You give us a tantrum
And a know it all grin
Just when we need one

When the evening's thin

You're a beautiful
A beautiful fucked up man
You're setting up your
Razor wire shrine

I Love You

I have a smile
stretched from ear to ear
to see you walking down the road

we meet at the lights
I stare for a while
the world around disappears

just you and me
on this island of hope
a breath between us could be miles

let me surround you
my sea to your shore
let me be the calm you seek

oh and every time I'm close to you
there's too much I can't say
and you just walk away

and I forgot
to tell you
I love you
and the night's
too long
and cold here
without you
I grieve in my condition
for I cannot find the strength to say I need you so

oh and every time I'm close to you
there's too much I can't say
and you just walk away

and I forgot
to tell you
I love you
and the night's
too long
and cold here
without you

Sweet Surrender

It doesn't mean much
It doesn't mean anything at all
The life I've left behind me
Is a cold room

I've crossed the last line
From where I can't return
Where every step I took in faith
Betrayed me
And led me from my home

Sweet surrender
Is all that I have to give

You take me in
No questions asked
You strip away the ugliness
That surrounds me
Are you an angel
Am I already that gone
I only hope that I won't disappoint you
When I'm down here on
My knees

Sweet surrender
Is all that I have to give
Sweet surrender
Is all that I have to give

And I don't understand
By the touch of your hand
I would be the one to fall

I miss the little things
Oh I miss everything
About you
It doesn't mean much
It doesn't mean anything at all
The life I left behind me
Is a cold room

Sweet surrender
Is all that I have to give
Sweet surrender
Is all that I have to give

Adia
(Sarah McLachlan/Pierre Marchand)

Adia, I do believe I failed you
Adia, I know I've let you down
Don't you know I tried so hard
To love you in my way
It's easy let it go

Adia, I'm empty since you left me
Trying to find a way to carry on
I search myself and everyone
To see where we went wrong

There's no one left to finger
There's no one here to blame

There's no one left to talk to honey
And there ain't no one to buy our innocence

'Cause we are born innocent
Believe me Adia, we are still innocent
It's easy, we all falter
Does it matter?

Adia I thought that we could make it
But I know I can't change the way you feel
I leave you with your misery
A friend who won't betray
I pull you from your tower
I take away your pain
And show you all the beauty you possess
If you'd only let yourself believe that

We are born innocent
Believe me Adia, we are still innocent
It's easy, we all falter, does it matter?
Believe me Adia, we are still innocent
'Cause we are born innocent
Adia we are still
It's easy, we all falter
But does it matter?

Do What You Have to Do
(Sarah McLachlan/Coleen Wolstenholme)

What ravages of spirit
Conjured this temptuous rage
Created you a monster
Broken by the rules of love
And fate has lead you through it
You do what you have to do
And fate has led you through it
You do what you have to do

And I have the sense to recognize that
I don't know how to let you go
Every moment marked
With apparitions of your soul
I'm ever swiftly moving
Trying to escape this desire
The yearning to be near you
I do what I have to do
The yearning to be near you
I do what I have to do

But I have the sense to recognize
That I don't know how
To let you go
I don't know how
To let you go

A glowing ember
Burning hot

Burning slow
Deep within I'm shaken by the violence
Of existing for only you

I know I can't be with you
I do what I have to do
I know I can't be with you
I do what I have to do
And I have sense to recognize but
I don't know how to let you go
I don't know how to let you go
I don't know how to let you go

1 *Witness*
(Sarah McLachlan/Pierre Marchand)

Make me a witness
Take me out
Out of darkness
Out of doubt

I won't weigh you down
With good intention
Won't make fire out of clay
Or other inventions

Will we burn in heaven
Like we do down here
Will the change come
While we're waiting
Everyone is waiting

And when we're done
Soul searching
And we carried the weight
And died for a cause
Is misery
Made beautiful
Right before our eyes
Will mercy be revealed
Or blind us where we stand

Will we burn in heaven
Like we do down here
Will the change come
While we're waiting
Everyone is waiting

Angel

Spend all your time waiting
For that second chance
For a break that would make it okay
There's always one reason
To feel not good enough
And it's hard at the end of the day
I need some distraction

Oh beautiful release
Memories seep from my veins
Let me be empty
And weightless and maybe
I'll find some peace tonight

In the arms of an angel
Fly away from here
From this dark cold hotel room
And the endlessness that you fear
You are pulled from the wreckage
Of your silent reverie
You're in the arms of the angel
May you find some comfort here

So tired of the straight line
And everywhere you turn
There's vultures and thieves at your back
The storm keeps on twisting
You keep on building the lies
That you make up for all that you lack
It don't make no difference
Escaping one last time
It's easier to believe
In this sweet madness
Oh this glorious sadness
That brings me to my knees

In the arms of an angel
Fly away from here
From this dark cold hotel room
And the endlessness that you fear
You are pulled from the wreckage
Of your silent reverie
You're in the arms of the angel
May you find some comfort here
You're in the arms of the angel
May you find some comfort here

Black and White

Unravel me
A distant cord
On the outside is forgotten
A constant need
to get along
And the animal awakens
And all I feel is black and white

The road is long
The memory slides
To the whole of my undoing
I put aside
I put away
I push it back to get through each day
And all I feel is black and white
And I'm wound up small and tight

And I don't know who I am

Everybody loves you when you're easy
Everybody hates when you're a bore
Everyone is waiting for your entrance so
Don't disappoint them

Unravel me
Untie this chord
The very center of our union
Is caving in
I can't endure
I am the archive of our failure
And all I feel is black and white
And I'm wound up small and tight
And I don't know who I am

Everybody loves you when you're easy
Everybody hates when you're a bore
Everyone is waiting for your entrance so
Don't disappoint them

Everybody loves you when you're easy so
Don't disappoint them

Don't disappoint them

Full of Grace

The winter here's cold
And bitter
It's chilled us to the bone
We haven't seen the sun for weeks
Too long too far from home
I feel just like I'm sinking
And I claw for solid ground
I'm pulled down by the undertow
I never thought I could feel so low
And oh the darkness I feel like letting go

If all of the strength and all of the courage
Come and lift me from this place
I know I could love you much better than this
Full of grace my love

It's better this way, I said
Having seen this place before
Where everything we say and do
Hurts us all the more
It's just that we stay too long
In the same old sickly skin
I'm pulled down by the undertow
I never thought I could feel so low
And Oh the darkness I feel like letting go

If all of the strength and all of the courage
Come and lift me from this place

I know I could love you much better than this

Full of grace, full of grace, my love

Back to lyrics

Tab 83

to review district court's refusal to depart downward. U.S. v. Fulton, C.A.9 (Wash.) 1993, 987 F.2d 631.

8. Indictment

There was fatal variance between indictment and proof at trial regarding date of commission of offense of abusive sexual contact on child within Indian country, where defendant's lawyers developed and presented documentary evidence that defendant, victim, and her mother lived off reservation until after date charged in indictment, contrary to requirements for federal jurisdiction, and only evidence of date when charged conduct occurred was two years after that charged in indictment. U.S. v. Tsinhnahijinnie, C.A.9 (Ariz.) 1997, 112 F.3d 988.

§ 2245. Sexual abuse resulting in death

A person who, in the course of an offense under this chapter, engages in conduct that results in the death of a person, shall be punished by death or imprisoned for any term of years or for life.

(Added Pub.L. 103–322, Title VI, § 60010(a)(2), Sept. 13, 1994, 108 Stat. 1972.)

HISTORICAL AND STATUTORY NOTES

Prior Provisions

A prior section 2245 was renumbered section 2246 by Pub.L. 103–322, Title VI, § 60010(a)(1), Sept. 13, 1994, 108 Stat. 1972.

Legislative History

For legislative history and purpose of Pub.L. 103–322, see 1994 U.S. Code Cong. and Adm. News, p. 1801.

LAW REVIEW AND JOURNAL COMMENTARIES

Damage control for victims of physical assault—testing the innocent for AIDS. Michael P. Bruyere, 21 Fla.St.U.L.Rev. 945 (1994).

§ 2246. Definitions for chapter

As used in this chapter—

(1) the term "prison" means a correctional, detention, or penal facility;

(2) the term "sexual act" means—

(A) contact between the penis and the vulva or the penis and the anus, and for purposes of this subparagraph contact involving the penis occurs upon penetration, however, slight;

(B) contact between the mouth and the penis, the mouth and the vulva, or the mouth and the anus;

(C) the penetration, however slight, of the anal or genital opening of another by a hand or finger or by any object, with an intent to abuse, humiliate, harass, degrade, or arouse or gratify the sexual desire of any person; or

(D) the intentional touching, not through the clothing, of the genitalia of another person who has not attained the age of 16 years with an intent to abuse, humiliate, harass, degrade, or arouse or gratify the sexual desire of any person;

(3) the term "sexual contact" means the intentional touching, either directly or through the clothing, of the genitalia, anus, groin, breast, inner thigh, or buttocks of any person with an intent to abuse, humiliate, harass, degrade, or arouse or gratify the sexual desire of any person;

(4) the term "serious bodily injury" means bodily injury that involves a substantial risk of death, unconsciousness, extreme physical pain, protracted and obvious disfigurement, or protracted loss or impairment of the function of a bodily member, organ, or mental faculty;

(5) the term "official detention" means—

(A) detention by a Federal officer or employee, or under the direction of a Federal officer or employee, following arrest for an offense; following surrender in lieu of arrest for an offense; following a charge or conviction of an offense, or an allegation or finding of juvenile delinquency; following commitment as a material witness; following civil commitment in lieu of criminal proceedings or pending resumption of criminal proceedings that are being held in abeyance, or pending extradition, deportation, or exclusion; or

(B) custody by a Federal officer or employee, or under the direction of a Federal officer or employee, for purposes incident to any detention described in sal to depart down- (Wash.) 1993, 987

i indictment of commission l contact on child

within Indian country, where defendant's lawyers developed and presented documentary evidence that defendant, victim, and her mother lived off reservation until after date charged in indictment, contrary to requirements for federal jurisdiction, and only evidence of date when charged conduct occurred was two years after that charged in indictment. U.S. v. Tsinhnahijinnie, C.A.9 (Ariz.) 1997, 112 F.3d 988.

resulting in death

ourse of an offense under this chapter, engages in conduct that person, shall be punished by death or imprisoned for any term

VI, § 60010(a)(2), Sept. 13, 1994, 108 Stat. 1972.)

HISTORICAL AND STATUTORY NOTES

renumbered section e VI, § 60010(a)(1),

Legislative History

For legislative history and purpose of Pub.L. 103–322, see 1994 U.S. Code Cong. and Adm. News, p. 1801.

REVIEW AND JOURNAL COMMENTARIES

ms of physical as- for AIDS. Michael v. 945 (1994).

r chapter

—

on" means a correctional, detention, or penal facility;

ual act" means—

etween the penis and the vulva or the penis and the anus, and this subparagraph contact involving the penis occurs upon vever, slight;

etween the mouth and the penis, the mouth and the vulva, or h s;

ration, however slight, of the anal or genital opening of another by any object, with an intent to abuse, humiliate, harass, gratify the sexual desire of any person; or

ntional touching, not through the clothing, of the genitalia of who has not attained the age of 16 years with an intent to , harass, degrade, or arouse or gratify the sexual desire of any

ual contact" means the intentional touching, either directly or of the genitalia, anus, groin, breast, inner thigh, or buttocks of ntent to abuse, humiliate, harass, degrade, or arouse or gratify any person;

ous bodily injury" means bodily injury that involves a substan- nconsciousness, extreme physical pain, protracted and obvious otracted loss or impairment of the function of a bodily member, ulty;

cial detention" means—

by a Federal officer or employee, or under the direction of a or employee, following arrest for an offense; following surren- arrest for an offense; following a charge or conviction of an llegation or finding of juvenile delinquency; following commit- erial witness; following civil commitment in lieu of criminal pending resumption of criminal proceedings that are being held pending extradition, deportation, or exclusion; or

by a Federal officer or employee, or under the direction of a or employee, for purposes incident to any detention described in

subparagraph (A) of this paragraph, including transportation, medical diagnosis or treatment, court appearance, work, and recreation;

but does not include supervision or other control (other than custody during specified hours or days) after release on bail, probation, or parole, or after release following a finding of juvenile delinquency.

(Added Pub.L. 99–646, § 87(b), Nov. 10, 1986, 100 Stat. 3622, § 2245, renumbered § 2246 and amended Pub.L. 103–322, Title IV, § 40502, Title VI, § 60010(a)(1), Sept. 13, 1994, 108 Stat. 1945, 1972.)

HISTORICAL AND STATUTORY NOTES

Codification

Identical provision was enacted by Pub.L. 99–654, § 2, Nov. 14, 1986, 100 Stat. 3662.

1994 Amendments

Par. (2)(D). Pub.L. 103–322, § 40502, added subpar. (D).

Effective Date

Section effective 30 days after Nov. 10, 1986, see section 87(e) of Pub.L. 99–646, set out as a note under section 2241 of this title.

Legislative History

For legislative history and purpose of Pub.L. 99–646, see 1986 U.S.Code Cong. and Adm. News, p. 6139. See, also, Pub.L. 103–322, 1994 U.S. Code Cong. and Adm. News, p. 1801.

LIBRARY REFERENCES

Rape ⚡1, 2.

C.J.S. Rape § 1 et seq.

NOTES OF DECISIONS

Weight and sufficiency of evidence 1

---

1. Weight and sufficiency of evidence

Victim's testimony that defendant grabbed and held her arms and placed his upper body on top of her, that she was unable to push him off her, and that she was doing everything possible to resist under the circumstances provided sufficient evidence of force to sustain defendant's conviction of aggravated sexual abuse involving use of force. U.S. v. Jones, C.A.8 (S.D.) 1997, 104 F.3d 193, rehearing and suggestion for rehearing en banc denied, certiorari denied 117 S.Ct. 2470, 138 L.Ed.2d 226.

§ 2247. Repeat offenders

Any person who violates a provision of this chapter, after one or more prior convictions for an offense punishable under this chapter, or after one or more prior convictions under the laws of any State relating to aggravated sexual abuse, sexual abuse, or abusive sexual contact have become final, is punishable by a term of imprisonment up to twice that otherwise authorized.

(Added Pub.L. 103–322, Title IV, § 40111(a), Sept. 13, 1994, 108 Stat. 1903.)

HISTORICAL AND STATUTORY NOTES

Legislative History

For legislative history and purpose of Pub.L. 103–322, see 1994 U.S. Code Cong. and Adm. News, p. 1801.

§ 2248. Mandatory restitution

(a) In general.—Notwithstanding section 3663 or 3663A, and in addition to any other civil or criminal penalty authorized by law, the court shall order restitution for any offense under this chapter.

(b) Scope and nature of order.—

(1) Directions.—The order of restitution under this section shall direct the defendant to pay to the victim (through the appropriate court mechanism) the full amount of the victim's losses as determined by the court pursuant to paragraph (2).

(2) Enforcement.—An order of restitution under this section shall be issued and enforced in accordance with section 3664 in the same manner as an order under section 3663A.

(3) Definition.—For purposes of this subsection, the term "full amount of the victim's losses" includes any costs incurred by the victim for—

Bates—Numbered Documents

The Secretary of State
of the United States of America
hereby requests all whom it may concern to permit the citizen/national of the United States named herein to pass without delay or hindrance and in case of need to give all lawful aid and protection.

812-DC-00000003

Le Secrétaire d'Etat
des Etats-Unis d'Amérique
prie par les présentes toutes autorités compétentes de laisser passer le citoyen ou ressortissant des Etats-Unis titulaire du présent passeport, sans délai ni difficulté et, en cas de besoin, de lui accorder toute aide et protection légitimes.

Monica Samille Lewinsky

SIGNATURE OF BEARER/SIGNATURE DU TITULAIRE

NOT VALID UNTIL SIGNED

UNITED STATES OF AMERICA

Type/Catégorie: P
Code of issuing State/Code du pays émetteur: USA
PASSPORT NO./NO. DU PASSEPORT: [redacted]

Surname / Nom
LEWINSKY

Given names / Prénoms
MONICA SAMILLE

812-DC-00000002

Nationality / Nationalité
UNITED STATES OF AMERICA

Date of birth / Date de naissance
[redacted]

Sex / Sexe: F
Place of birth / Lieu de naissance: CALIFORNIA, U.S.A.

Date of issue / Date de délivrance: 09 MAY/MAI 96
Date of expiration / Date d'expiration: 08 MAY/MAI [illegible]

Authority / Autorité
PASSPORT AGENCY
WASHINGTON, D.C.

Amendments/Modifications
SEE PAGE 24

P<USALEWINSKY<<MONICA<SAMILLE<<<<<<<<<<<<<<<

[illegible]9719[illegible]USA7307236F0105086<<<<<<<<<<<<<<[illegible]8

LAW OFFICES
JANIS, SCHUELKE & WECHSLER
1728 MASSACHUSETTS AVENUE, N.W.
WASHINGTON, D.C. 20036

KARL N. METZNER

TELEPHONE
(202) 861-0600

TELECOPIER
(202) 223-7230

January 23, 1998

BY HAND DELIVERY

Kenneth W. Starr, Esq.
Office of the Independent Counsel
1001 Pennsylvania Avenue, N.W., Suite 490-N
Washington, D.C. 20004

Re: Subpoena Duces Tecum to Betty W. Currie, Grand Jury # 97-3

Dear Mr. Starr:

In response to the above-referenced subpoena duces tecum to Ms. Betty W. Currie, enclosed please find the following:

One copy of the State of the Union address dated January 23, 1996, in a brown envelope.

One autographed photograph of President Clinton, held between two cardboard panels.

One green dress with a "Black Dog" logo, size L.

One turquoise T-shirt with a "Black Dog" logo, size L.

One white T-shirt with a "Seal of the Black Dog of Martha's Vineyard" on the front, size L.

One blue baseball cap with a "Black Dog" logo.

One three-page facsimile message.

Two twenty-page newspaper inserts from the *Washington Post*, February 14, 1997.

One jewelry pin in "Casual Corner" box.

One hatpin with a globe-like base in a black box with gold stars on it.

Kenneth W. Starr, Esq.
January 23, 1998
Page 2

One framed signed picture of President Clinton and Monica Lewinsky.

One bottle, in its box, of Tiffany Spa Moisturizing Hand Cream.

One bottle, in its box, of Tiffany Spa Refreshing Body Mist.

One sympathy card, with envelope.

One card with joke re snowman and carrot, with envelope.

One thank-you card dated September 17, 1997, with envelope.

Four pages of handwritten notes.

Sincerely,

Karl Metzner

Enclosures

THE WASHINGTON POST WEEKEND FRIDAY, February 14, 1997 37

Love Notes
44
The Washington Post
Friday
Feb 14, 1997

GRAMS & GRAMPS ... Matteo

GRAMMIE THE CUPID
Our family's guardian angel
Love, Jenny, Poke and Mandy

GRAMMY AND GRAMPY
For all you say, and all you do
this buds for you
Love Rachel and Timmy

GRAND MA & PAPAP
Happy Valentine's Day
I love you, SAM LESKO

GRANDMA—I love you very much. You're the greatest.
Love, JANA

GREG, ANNA & ALEXANDRA
My love Forever!!
Love, LUCY

GREG—Happy Hearts Day to the "MANN" of my dreams, from your loving wife, SUSAN

GREG PEAKE,
You are my baby. I love you!
KATHY

Greg S. - Batman! is Robin still chasing your cute bat buns? I would! Happy VDay! Joker

GREGG: Violets are blue, roses are pink. See you at the skating rink? Robin HVD!

GREGORY, I want you to be My Valentine, Today & Always!
Lots of Love, BRIGITTE

GREGORY KING OF HEARTS
ALL MY LOVE,
AUNTIE

GREMO
You're wonderful. I love you!
CHRIS

GREY SQUIRREL
FROM PAPA BEAR WITH LOVE

GTD: My Valentine everyday since

HANDSOME
With love's light wings did I o'er-perch these walls;
For stony limits cannot hold love out,
And what love can do that dares love attempt;
—Romeo and Juliet 2:2
Happy Valentine's Day,
M

HANK,
You are my sunshine.
Love you, Kristy K.

HANNAH
Pop Pop and Grammy Love You.
Happy Valentine's Day

HAPPY 10TH VALENTINE'S DAY TWINKIE.
Love CupCake

HAPPY FEET—10,000 stars cannot shine with the splendor of your gaze nor burn with the passion in your embrace. I will always be yours to enjoy! XOXO-Bill

HAPPY SWEET 16 -LAUREN CITA —We love you Mom & DAD.

Happy Valentine's Day to my 2 sweethearts, Pam and Karen. I love you both very much.
HUBBY & DADDY

HAPPY VALENTINES DAY, JOSH
Love & Kisses,
Amy

HAPPY VALENTINE'S DAY
HUGGY BUGGY
I Love You. Freddy

HAPPY VALENTINE'S DAY NATE
Our Love, Our Life, The Best Is Yet To Come. Love Danica

HAPPY VALENTINE'S DAY, DAD!
As the newest (and youngest) addition to the family, I took a poll and Sadie, Ewok, Quade, Lindy and I have reached a consensus. We think that you're the best Daddy in the world. We Love You.

HAPPY VALENTINE'S KATHY,-MOM BOYD & JENNIFER —The Three Most Wonderful Women In My Life. PAUL

Happy Valentine's Day
Toni!
I adore, admire, respect and most all LOVE YOU! Your are the first and last breath of each day and a vision in my dreams for the future. Have a great day!
Miss Frances

HARRISON, —I love you a little bit too . LITTLE BABY SISSY

Harry,
Sometimes I Make You Itch,
We Both Know Where It's At,
But You Know That I Love you
Imagine That!

HASSIEN B.
Will you marry me?
LISA

Have no fear cause you and me shall soon be off to gay Paris.
I love you, KATHARINE.

HAYNE, FRANCIS AND EUNHEE
Happy Valentine's Day
I love you all! Love, Tony

HAZEL—I hope you will be my Boo forever! I Love You!
Your Boo Special K

HB,
I believe in you and me. I believe we'll be in love eternally. You will always be the one for me. I believe in miracles and the miracle is you. I believe in dreams again and you're my dream come true!
Love Always, HB

HB,
Thanks for 3 monkeys.
You are the best! 'OVF

... could be? Love CRAWF

HELEN and JIM ANDREATOS
HAPPY VALENTINE'S DAY
LOVE, MARY and MIKE

HELEN
I still love you
All these years apart
I still care and hope
I'm somewhere in your heart

But the years pass swiftly by
And I'm afraid to say
The future may not be long
I need you back today

So, look at me kindly
Touch my hand, I'll cry
I'll hold you, kiss you
I'll live for every sigh
SWEETHEART

HELEN, my funny valentine - I miss you. come home soon.
Love, Emily and the Family

HELLO -00
Even after 20 long years, I'm like Cupid - I want you near

HERB—This one is really for you. You're the lightbar of my life, I love you. Friends first and always. KRIS

HERMELINA
A rose is a rose by any name.
Happy Valentine's Day. JIM

HEY BABY BLUES,
Your Love is true
and you are Baby Smooth
I've had a great time with
you, the camping, the hotel
even the bathrooms. But
what I've enjoyed most is
the time with you. Love You
YOUR LOVING PUTZ

HEY WORLD!
Look at my love!!
She's so Beautiful,
She's so good,
She's my heart, my soul...
MY H.P. II
HAPPY V-DAY LOVERS!
YOUR DAVID

HEY YOU!!
I love you! Your man, JHM
Momma, I love you! Chasey Lacey

HFE JR
Life with you is a package of love,
Romance with rainbows and poems that sing.
You are the jewel that brings magic to my life...
HAPPY VALENTINE'S DAY
I Love You,
PKE

HI CUTIE,
Just wanted to say Happy Valentines Day & that I am sorry for being so difficult, but thats just me. But its the me that still really likes you & hopes that we can see each other out of 9 to 5 soon. Chrissy

HI DUCKIE
I Love You! Hey, Pretty Eyes Your Smile Brings Fulfillment To My Soul! Your Love Helps Me To Become Whole! Your Gentle, Sexy Wild Ways Keep Me Frisky Everyday! Remember Me Lover!
SIGNED: 317

HI SWEETIE
I Love You Always
LEE

HON:
There once was a boy
named Doug
All he needed was a
really good hug,
but to his delight
he met Faith so right
Now they're as snug

HONEY, Happy Valentine's Day to my best friend & lover who has given me many pleasurable memories of us together. Keep 'em coming, Honey Love, Mary Kaye

HONEY—You've tattoo your name on my heart. I love you. Pooh

HONEYBEAR & SWEE
My family means the world to me. You guys are the best. Baby Emerson is very anxious to meet you. All my love, BETSY.

HONEYBUNCH:
You put a smile on my face and warmth in my heart. Always-DWC.

HOOK, ZIG & BOO, My three special Valentines. Keep the faith & stay strong. Forever, Inde

HOON,
We "All" Love You.
XXXOOOXXX
Bill, Jim, Bootie

HOOP!
Will you be my Valentine??
We love you very much!
Love, Milhouse and Buster!

HOPE, You are a very special person because you are my secret pal Happy Valentine's Day! YSP

HOWARD! Mucho kisses ...

... is more than ordinary love. We do things for each other that make your love so much fun. Giving to you, & making you happy, makes me feel happy too. You are truly a wonderful man. You have a gentle heart that I promise never to hurt. I treasure our openness & our heart to heart talks; they are so special to me. I have shared with you all that I truly am; I have given you my truest feelings. Above all, I cherish us knowing you are part of me & I am a part of you. I am very fortunate to have you in my life. You are the one person I will never forget, the companion I will always share things with, the man I will love until my dying breath. —C—

HUMMY, Happy Valentine's Day and Happy Birthday! I Love You with all of my heart! Thank you for being such a wonderful wife and friend!
Love Always, Hummy

HUNNY BUNNY—I Love You With All My Heart 4Ever
Love, Your Squishy Wishy

HUNT:
I want the world to see how much you mean to me. I Love You!-Louise

HURRY UP AND BUY!!
Thank you for making
My life complete.
I love you with all my heart.
Your Wife, KAREN

I always said that I would keep you in roses.
Here is one today for the red-headed, green-eyed, little-feet lady in my life.
Hugs, kisses, and other things too, from the one who loves you more than anything else.
ME

I cherish you with all my heart
With you Stuart,
my love will never part
Forever and Always. BE-BE

I know I don't always say it,
and I don't always show it,
but I wanted you to know:
I LUV U Michael Thomas Weiss.
Love forever Crystal R.

U. S. Secret Service
Epass Access Control Report

Date of report: 01/23/98

Search Criteria: LEWINSKI, MONICA

Search Dates: 01/01/97 to 12/31/97

Date	Time	Name	Badge	Type	Post	Status
08/01/97	10:46:17	LEWINSKI, MONICA	34F3D3	C	A4	ENTERING
08/01/97	11:40:27	LEWINSKI, MONICA	34F3D3	C	D2	EXITING
08/01/97	12:19:27	LEWINSKI, MONICA	34F346	C	A4	ENTERING

827-DC-00000002

202482

U. S. Secret Service

Epass Access Control Report

01/23/98

Search Criteria: LEWINSKY, MONICA

Search Dates: 01/01/95 to 12/31/95

Date	Time	Name	Badge	Type	Post	Status
07/10/95	13:18:02	LEWINSKY, MONICA	34EA68	I	D2	ENTERING
07/10/95	17:04:29	LEWINSKY, MONICA	34EA68	I	D2	EXITING
07/11/95	08:51:33	LEWINSKY, MONICA	34E9FF	I	D2	ENTERING
07/11/95	11:52:50	LEWINSKY, MONICA	34E9FF	I	D2	EXITING
07/11/95	16:57:39	LEWINSKY, MONICA	34EC23	I	D2	EXITING
07/12/95	09:00:29	LEWINSKY, MONICA	34E9F4	I	D1	ENTERING
07/12/95	13:20:28	LEWINSKY, MONICA	34E9F4	I	D2	EXITING
07/12/95	13:30:54	LEWINSKY, MONICA	34EA11	I	D2	ENTERING
07/12/95	17:21:31	LEWINSKY, MONICA	34EA11	I	D2	EXITING
07/13/95	09:18:44	LEWINSKY, MONICA	34EC04	I	D2	ENTERING
07/13/95	11:11:34	LEWINSKY, MONICA	34EC04	I	D2	EXITING
07/13/95	12:03:06	LEWINSKY, MONICA	34EA18	I	D2	ENTERING
07/13/95	12:36:50	LEWINSKY, MONICA	34EA18	I	D2	EXITING
07/13/95	13:23:53	LEWINSKY, MONICA	34EA12	I	D2	ENTERING
07/13/95	17:46:42	LEWINSKY, MONICA	34EA12	I	D2	EXITING
07/14/95	08:35:28	LEWINSKY, MONICA	34EA54	I	D1	ENTERING
07/14/95	16:33:22	LEWINSKY, MONICA	34EA54	I	D2	EXITING
07/17/95	08:21:01	LEWINSKY, MONICA	34EA54	I	D2	ENTERING
07/17/95	16:59:54	LEWINSKY, MONICA	34EA54	I	D2	EXITING
07/18/95	08:08:15	LEWINSKY, MONICA	34EC21	N	D2	INACTIVE
07/18/95	08:08:22	LEWINSKY, MONICA	34EC21	I	D2	ENTERING
07/18/95	12:38:05	LEWINSKY, MONICA	34EC21	I	D2	EXITING
07/18/95	14:29:41	LEWINSKY, MONICA	34EA1E	I	D2	ENTERING
07/18/95	18:29:46	LEWINSKY, MONICA	34EA1E	I	D2	EXITING
07/19/95	07:59:12	LEWINSKY, MONICA	34E9F5	I	D2	ENTERING
07/19/95	14:43:32	LEWINSKY, MONICA	34E9F5	I	D2	EXITING
07/20/95	08:59:17	LEWINSKY, MONICA	34EC04	I	D2	ENTERING
07/20/95	12:13:27	LEWINSKY, MONICA	34EC04	I	D2	EXITING
07/20/95	12:54:15	LEWINSKY, MONICA	34E9C6	I	D2	ENTERING
07/20/95	17:46:05	LEWINSKY, MONICA	34E9C6	I	D2	EXITING
07/21/95	08:38:13	LEWINSKY, MONICA	34E0B9	I	D2	ENTERING
07/21/95	12:34:55	LEWINSKY, MONICA	34E0B9	I	D2	EXITING
07/21/95	13:08:16	LEWINSKY, MONICA	34EC23	I	D2	EXITING
07/24/95	08:39:09	LEWINSKY, MONICA	34E948	I	D2	ENTERING
07/24/95	12:29:17	LEWINSKY, MONICA	34E948	I	D2	EXITING
07/24/95	13:36:02	LEWINSKY, MONICA	34E9D1	I	D2	ENTERING
07/24/95	17:31:47	LEWINSKY, MONICA	34E9D1	I	D2	EXITING
07/25/95	08:28:51	LEWINSKY, MONICA	34EA11	I	D2	ENTERING
07/25/95	11:06:23	LEWINSKY, MONICA	34EA11	I	A1	EXITING
07/25/95	11:55:19	LEWINSKY, MONICA	34E9DC	I	D2	ENTERING
07/25/95	12:35:36	LEWINSKY, MONICA	34E9DC	I	D2	EXITING
07/25/95	13:49:01	LEWINSKY, MONICA	34E9BB	I	D2	ENTERING
07/25/95	20:21:37	LEWINSKY, MONICA	34D9BA	N	A4	INACTIVE
07/25/95	20:21:41	LEWINSKY, MONICA	34D9BA	A	A4	ENTERING
07/25/95	20:21:44	LEWINSKY, MONICA	34D9BA	A	A4	ENTERING
07/26/95	09:08:17	LEWINSKY, MONICA	34D9BA	A	A4	UNAUTH
07/26/95	09:08:30	LEWINSKY, MONICA	34EA2F	N	D2	INACTIVE
07/26/95	11:59:49	LEWINSKY, MONICA	34D9BA	A	D2	EXITING
07/26/95	12:24:43	LEWINSKY, MONICA	34EA2F	I	D2	EXITING

202483

827-DC-00000003

U. S. Secret Service

Epass Access Control Report

01/23/98

Search Criteria: LEWINSKY, MONICA

Search Dates: 01/01/95 to 12/31/95

Date	Time	Name	Badge	Type	Post	Status
07/26/95	12:33:05	LEWINSKY, MONICA	34EB79	N	D2	INACTIVE
07/26/95	12:33:34	LEWINSKY, MONICA	34EB79	N	D2	INACTIVE
07/26/95	12:39:00	LEWINSKY, MONICA	34EB79	I	D2	ENTERING
07/26/95	13:05:49	LEWINSKY, MONICA	34EB79	I	D2	EXITING
07/26/95	13:38:27	LEWINSKY, MONICA	34EB81	I	D2	ENTERING
07/26/95	18:01:06	LEWINSKY, MONICA	34EB81	I	D2	EXITING
07/27/95	11:35:51	LEWINSKY, MONICA	34D9B1	N	D1	INACTIVE
07/27/95	11:35:58	LEWINSKY, MONICA	34D9B1	N	D1	INACTIVE
07/27/95	11:36:16	LEWINSKY, MONICA	34D9B1	I	D1	ENTERING
07/27/95	12:15:22	LEWINSKY, MONICA	34D9B1	I	D2	EXITING
07/27/95	13:14:52	LEWINSKY, MONICA	34E9C4	I	D2	ENTERING
07/27/95	17:09:44	LEWINSKY, MONICA	34E9C4	I	D2	EXITING
07/28/95	09:04:11	LEWINSKY, MONICA	34EA18	I	D2	ENTERING
07/28/95	10:11:12	LEWINSKY, MONICA	34EA18	I	D2	EXITING
07/28/95	12:20:22	LEWINSKY, MONICA	34E948	I	D2	ENTERING
07/28/95	16:47:56	LEWINSKY, MONICA	34E948	I	D2	EXITING
07/31/95	10:00:37	LEWINSKY, MONICA	34C877	I	D2	ENTERING
07/31/95	13:03:57	LEWINSKY, MONICA	34C877	I	D2	EXITING
07/31/95	13:57:22	LEWINSKY, MONICA	34C877	I	D2	ENTERING
08/01/95	11:00:02	LEWINSKY, MONICA	34E946	I	D1	ENTERING
08/01/95	12:49:55	LEWINSKY, MONICA	34E946	I	D2	EXITING
08/01/95	13:39:33	LEWINSKY, MONICA	34E3FC	I	D1	ENTERING
08/01/95	18:31:16	LEWINSKY, MONICA	34E3FC	I	D2	EXITING
08/02/95	08:19:20	LEWINSKY, MONICA	34EC1B	I	D2	ENTERING
08/02/95	12:02:42	LEWINSKY, MONICA	34EC1B	I	D2	EXITING
08/02/95	12:39:58	LEWINSKY, MONICA	34BDC5	I	D2	ENTERING
08/02/95	17:58:33	LEWINSKY, MONICA	34BDC5	I	D2	EXITING
08/03/95	08:14:07	LEWINSKY, MONICA	34E9FB	I	D2	ENTERING
08/03/95	10:18:21	LEWINSKY, MONICA	34E9FB	I	D2	EXITING
08/03/95	14:06:35	LEWINSKY, MONICA	34EA42	I	D2	ENTERING
08/03/95	17:12:58	LEWINSKY, MONICA	34EA42	I	D1	EXITING
08/04/95	08:55:22	LEWINSKY, MONICA	34EA5C	I	D2	ENTERING
08/04/95	13:55:34	LEWINSKY, MONICA	34EA4A	I	D2	ENTERING
08/04/95	17:22:12	LEWINSKY, MONICA	34EA4A	I	D2	EXITING
08/07/95	09:07:46	LEWINSKY, MONICA	34EAC0	I	D2	ENTERING
08/07/95	09:31:13	LEWINSKY, MONICA	34EAC0	I	D2	EXITING
08/07/95	09:49:53	LEWINSKY, MONICA	34EC22	I	D2	ENTERING
08/07/95	12:50:36	LEWINSKY, MONICA	34EC22	I	D2	EXITING
08/07/95	13:58:17	LEWINSKY, MONICA	34E957	I	D2	ENTERING
08/07/95	17:27:48	LEWINSKY, MONICA	34E957	I	D2	EXITING
08/08/95	08:58:27	LEWINSKY, MONICA	34EB79	I	D2	ENTERING
08/08/95	12:57:57	LEWINSKY, MONICA	34EB79	I	D2	EXITING
08/08/95	13:54:45	LEWINSKY, MONICA	34EA1D	I	D2	ENTERING
08/08/95	17:01:35	LEWINSKY, MONICA	34EA1D	I	D2	EXITING
08/08/95	17:15:28	LEWINSKY, MONICA	34EB7F	N	D2	INACTIVE
08/08/95	17:15:45	LEWINSKY, MONICA	34EB7F	I	D2	ENTERING
08/08/95	17:17:25	LEWINSKY, MONICA	34EB7F	I	D2	EXITING
08/09/95	07:39:34	LEWINSKY, MONICA	34EB7A	I	D2	ENTERING
08/09/95	12:33:41	LEWINSKY, MONICA	34EB7A	I	D2	EXITING

202484

827-DC-00000004

U. S. Secret Service

Epass Access Control Report

01/23/98

Search Criteria: LEWINSKY, MONICA

Search Dates: 01/01/95 to 12/31/95

Date	Time	Name	Badge	Type	Post	Status
08/09/95	14:16:18	LEWINSKY, MONICA	34EA5B	I	D2	ENTERING
08/09/95	17:17:39	LEWINSKY, MONICA	34EA5B	I	D2	EXITING
08/10/95	09:12:12	LEWINSKY, MONICA	34EA05	I	D2	ENTERING
08/10/95	12:24:33	LEWINSKY, MONICA	34EA05	I	D2	EXITING
08/10/95	13:30:28	LEWINSKY, MONICA	34EA51	I	D2	ENTERING
08/10/95	18:47:58	LEWINSKY, MONICA	34EA51	I	D2	EXITING
08/11/95	09:07:36	LEWINSKY, MONICA	34EC0C	I	D2	ENTERING
08/11/95	12:12:55	LEWINSKY, MONICA	34EC0C	I	D3	EXITING
08/11/95	12:35:58	LEWINSKY, MONICA	34C759	I	D2	ENTERING
08/11/95	17:04:24	LEWINSKY, MONICA	34C759	I	D2	EXITING
08/14/95	08:50:18	LEWINSKY, MONICA	34EA1D	I	D2	ENTERING
08/14/95	12:01:36	LEWINSKY, MONICA	34EA1D	I	D1	EXITING
08/14/95	13:01:13	LEWINSKY, MONICA	34EA26	I	D2	ENTERING
08/14/95	17:59:53	LEWINSKY, MONICA	34EA26	I	D2	EXITING
08/15/95	09:14:27	LEWINSKY, MONICA	34EA2F	I	D2	ENTERING
08/15/95	13:50:00	LEWINSKY, MONICA	34EA2F	I	D2	EXITING
08/15/95	14:01:48	LEWINSKY, MONICA	34EA4E	I	D2	ENTERING
08/15/95	18:28:56	LEWINSKY, MONICA	34EA4E	I	D2	EXITING
08/16/95	09:24:08	LEWINSKY, MONICA	34EA64	I	D2	ENTERING
08/16/95	12:03:29	LEWINSKY, MONICA	34EA64	I	D1	EXITING
08/16/95	13:01:57	LEWINSKY, MONICA	34EC09	I	D1	ENTERING
08/16/95	15:44:27	LEWINSKY, MONICA	34EC09	I	D2	EXITING
08/17/95	09:12:33	LEWINSKY, MONICA	34EAD2	I	D2	ENTERING
08/17/95	17:03:10	LEWINSKY, MONICA	34EAD2	I	D3	EXITING
08/18/95	08:53:24	LEWINSKY, MONICA	34E94C	I	D2	ENTERING
08/18/95	12:34:32	LEWINSKY, MONICA	34E94C	I	D3	EXITING
08/18/95	13:35:25	LEWINSKY, MONICA	34BE78	I	D1	ENTERING
08/18/95	16:16:18	LEWINSKY, MONICA	34BE78	I	D2	EXITING
08/21/95	08:56:08	LEWINSKY, MONICA	34E9D0	I	D2	ENTERING
08/21/95	09:21:43	LEWINSKY, MONICA	34E9D0	I	D3	EXITING
08/21/95	09:31:54	LEWINSKY, MONICA	34EB98	I	D2	ENTERING
08/21/95	12:24:34	LEWINSKY, MONICA	34EB98	I	D1	EXITING
08/21/95	13:15:18	LEWINSKY, MONICA	34E9EC	I	D1	ENTERING
08/21/95	16:58:43	LEWINSKY, MONICA	34E9EC	I	D2	EXITING
08/22/95	09:05:25	LEWINSKY, MONICA	34E9E5	I	D2	ENTERING
08/22/95	12:39:17	LEWINSKY, MONICA	34E9E5	I	D2	EXITING
08/23/95	09:09:20	LEWINSKY, MONICA	34EAC2	I	D2	ENTERING
08/23/95	12:21:36	LEWINSKY, MONICA	34EAC2	I	D1	EXITING
08/23/95	13:42:42	LEWINSKY, MONICA	34B953	I	D2	ENTERING
08/23/95	16:34:46	LEWINSKY, MONICA	34B953	I	D2	EXITING
08/23/95	16:45:37	LEWINSKY, MONICA	34EA50	N	D2	INACTIVE
08/23/95	16:45:44	LEWINSKY, MONICA	34EA50	I	D2	ENTERING
08/23/95	17:27:32	LEWINSKY, MONICA	34EA50	I	D2	EXITING
08/24/95	08:53:10	LEWINSKY, MONICA	34EC08	I	D2	ENTERING
08/24/95	11:17:58	LEWINSKY, MONICA	34EC08	I	D2	EXITING
08/24/95	11:45:50	LEWINSKY, MONICA	34E94E	I	D2	ENTERING
08/24/95	12:53:44	LEWINSKY, MONICA	34E94E	I	D2	EXITING
08/24/95	14:19:33	LEWINSKY, MONICA	34EA66	I	D1	ENTERING
08/25/95	08:56:28	LEWINSKY, MONICA	34A781	I	D2	ENTERING

202485

827-DC-00000005

U. S. Secret Service

Epass Access Control Report

01/23/98

Search Criteria: LEWINSKY, MONICA

Search Dates: 01/01/95 to 12/31/95

Date	Time	Name	Badge	Type	Post	Status
08/25/95	12:14:36	LEWINSKY, MONICA	34A781	I	D2	EXITING
08/25/95	14:01:31	LEWINSKY, MONICA	34EA70	I	D2	ENTERING
08/25/95	15:25:39	LEWINSKY, MONICA	34EA70	I	D2	EXITING
08/28/95	09:17:53	LEWINSKY, MONICA	34EA55	I	D2	ENTERING
08/28/95	12:34:14	LEWINSKY, MONICA	34EA55	I	D2	EXITING
08/28/95	13:15:34	LEWINSKY, MONICA	34EA3B	I	D2	ENTERING
08/28/95	17:23:37	LEWINSKY, MONICA	34EA3B	I	D2	EXITING
08/30/95	10:04:25	LEWINSKY, MONICA	34EA24	I	D2	ENTERING
08/30/95	12:15:11	LEWINSKY, MONICA	34EA24	I	D2	EXITING
09/01/95	13:27:22	LEWINSKY, MONICA	34EA60	I	D2	EXITING
09/01/95	15:04:14	LEWINSKY, MONICA	34EA4F	I	D2	ENTERING
09/01/95	15:38:51	LEWINSKY, MONICA	34EA4F	I	D2	EXITING
09/05/95	08:47:29	LEWINSKY, MONICA	34E9BB	I	D2	ENTERING
09/05/95	12:57:14	LEWINSKY, MONICA	34E9BB	I	D2	EXITING
09/05/95	13:44:06	LEWINSKY, MONICA	34E9B0	I	D2	ENTERING
09/05/95	13:44:09	LEWINSKY, MONICA	34E9B0	I	D2	MULT ENT
09/05/95	18:37:47	LEWINSKY, MONICA	34E9B0	I	D2	EXITING
09/06/95	07:59:41	LEWINSKY, MONICA	34C3D3	A	D2	ENTERING
09/06/95	12:12:43	LEWINSKY, MONICA	34C3D3	A	D2	EXITING
09/06/95	13:26:42	LEWINSKY, MONICA	34E9F0	I	D2	ENTERING
09/06/95	16:00:00	LEWINSKY, MONICA	34E9F0	I	D2	EXITING
09/11/95	08:52:21	LEWINSKY, MONICA	34EA01	I	D2	ENTERING
09/11/95	12:08:06	LEWINSKY, MONICA	34EA01	I	D2	EXITING
09/11/95	13:43:48	LEWINSKY, MONICA	34EA6F	I	D2	ENTERING
09/11/95	18:00:13	LEWINSKY, MONICA	34EA6F	I	D2	EXITING
09/12/95	10:23:21	LEWINSKY, MONICA	34EB86	I	D2	ENTERING
09/12/95	12:24:04	LEWINSKY, MONICA	34EB86	I	D2	EXITING
09/12/95	15:10:54	LEWINSKY, MONICA	34EC07	I	D2	ENTERING
09/12/95	17:08:20	LEWINSKY, MONICA	34EC07	I	D2	EXITING
09/13/95	09:58:16	LEWINSKY, MONICA	34EC07	I	D2	ENTERING
09/13/95	10:14:02	LEWINSKY, MONICA	34EC07	I	D2	EXITING
09/13/95	12:15:30	LEWINSKY, MONICA	34EC07	I	D2	ENTERING
09/13/95	12:24:00	LEWINSKY, MONICA	34EC07	I	D2	EXITING
09/14/95	11:34:16	LEWINSKY, MONICA	34EB92	I	D2	ENTERING
09/14/95	12:39:37	LEWINSKY, MONICA	34EB92	I	D1	EXITING
09/14/95	13:15:46	LEWINSKY, MONICA	34EB8D	I	D2	ENTERING
09/14/95	18:04:48	LEWINSKY, MONICA	34EB8D	I	D2	EXITING
09/15/95	11:46:52	LEWINSKY, MONICA	34E9C9	I	D2	ENTERING
09/15/95	13:11:23	LEWINSKY, MONICA	34E9C9	I	D2	EXITING
09/15/95	13:34:21	LEWINSKY, MONICA	34EB85	I	D2	ENTERING
09/15/95	17:08:03	LEWINSKY, MONICA	34EB85	I	D2	EXITING
09/18/95	09:56:11	LEWINSKY, MONICA	34E9D2	I	D2	ENTERING
09/18/95	13:00:34	LEWINSKY, MONICA	34E9D2	I	D2	EXITING
09/18/95	13:38:45	LEWINSKY, MONICA	34EB76	I	D1	ENTERING
09/18/95	18:36:35	LEWINSKY, MONICA	34EB76	I	D2	EXITING
09/19/95	09:52:57	LEWINSKY, MONICA	34EC1B	I	D2	ENTERING
09/19/95	12:00:13	LEWINSKY, MONICA	34EC1B	I	D2	EXITING
09/19/95	13:38:59	LEWINSKY, MONICA	34BC6F	I	D2	ENTERING
09/19/95	16:42:35	LEWINSKY, MONICA	34BC6F	I	D2	EXITING

U. S. Secret Service

Epass Access Control Report

01/23/98

Search Criteria: LEWINSKY, MONICA

Search Dates: 01/01/95 to 12/31/95

Date	Time	Name	Badge	Type	Post	Status
09/20/95	09:10:26	LEWINSKY, MONICA	34EB71	I	D2	ENTERING
09/20/95	12:11:05	LEWINSKY, MONICA	34EB71	I	D2	EXITING
09/20/95	13:23:18	LEWINSKY, MONICA	34F26C	I	D2	ENTERING
09/20/95	15:21:59	LEWINSKY, MONICA	34F26C	I	D2	EXITING
09/29/95	10:39:34	LEWINSKY, MONICA	34E9BF	I	D2	ENTERING
09/29/95	11:33:28	LEWINSKY, MONICA	34E9BF	I	D2	EXITING
09/29/95	12:54:12	LEWINSKY, MONICA	34EA40	I	D2	ENTERING
09/29/95	16:24:10	LEWINSKY, MONICA	34EA40	I	D2	EXITING
10/02/95	13:29:44	LEWINSKY, MONICA	34C698	I	D2	ENTERING
10/02/95	17:36:20	LEWINSKY, MONICA	34C698	I	D2	EXITING
10/04/95	09:34:58	LEWINSKY, MONICA	34EABD	I	D2	ENTERING
10/04/95	13:26:30	LEWINSKY, MONICA	34EC06	I	D2	ENTERING
10/04/95	14:56:04	LEWINSKY, MONICA	34EC06	I	D2	EXITING
10/10/95	09:16:18	LEWINSKY, MONICA	34F24C	I	D2	ENTERING
10/10/95	12:55:46	LEWINSKY, MONICA	34F24C	I	D2	EXITING
10/11/95	09:14:40	LEWINSKY, MONICA	34EA64	I	D2	ENTERING
10/11/95	12:11:43	LEWINSKY, MONICA	34EA64	I	D2	EXITING
10/13/95	12:22:43	LEWINSKY, MONICA	34F263	I	D2	ENTERING
10/13/95	14:12:27	LEWINSKY, MONICA	34F263	I	D2	EXITING
10/16/95	10:00:10	LEWINSKY, MONICA	34E9D3	I	D2	ENTERING
10/16/95	13:09:37	LEWINSKY, MONICA	34E9D3	I	D2	EXITING
10/16/95	13:58:43	LEWINSKY, MONICA	34F24C	I	D2	ENTERING
10/16/95	16:21:36	LEWINSKY, MONICA	34F24C	I	D2	EXITING
10/17/95	10:11:05	LEWINSKY, MONICA	34EAD3	I	D2	ENTERING
10/17/95	14:14:42	LEWINSKY, MONICA	34EAD3	I	D1	EXITING
10/17/95	14:33:03	LEWINSKY, MONICA	34EA21	I	D1	ENTERING
10/17/95	15:29:02	LEWINSKY, MONICA	34EA21	I	D2	EXITING
10/17/95	19:58:46	LEWINSKY, MONICA	34D792	A	A4	ENTERING
10/17/95	20:43:47	LEWINSKY, MONICA	34D792	A	A4	EXITING
10/18/95	09:29:35	LEWINSKY, MONICA	34EA20	I	D1	ENTERING
10/18/95	12:01:50	LEWINSKY, MONICA	34EA20	I	D2	EXITING
10/18/95	12:40:27	LEWINSKY, MONICA	34EA29	I	D2	ENTERING
10/18/95	15:54:30	LEWINSKY, MONICA	34EA29	I	D2	EXITING
10/19/95	12:24:37	LEWINSKY, MONICA	34E9AA	I	D2	ENTERING
10/19/95	12:59:20	LEWINSKY, MONICA	34E9AA	I	D1	EXITING
10/20/95	08:49:45	LEWINSKY, MONICA	34CBD2	I	D2	ENTERING
10/20/95	12:06:14	LEWINSKY, MONICA	34CBD2	I	D2	EXITING
10/20/95	18:56:17	LEWINSKY, MONICA	34EB8C	I	D2	ENTERING
10/20/95	18:59:54	LEWINSKY, MONICA	34EB8C	I	D2	EXITING
11/06/95	09:10:39	LEWINSKY, MONICA	34BC6F	I	D2	ENTERING
11/06/95	12:23:50	LEWINSKY, MONICA	34BC6F	I	D2	EXITING
11/06/95	13:05:35	LEWINSKY, MONICA	34A092	N	D2	INACTIVE
11/06/95	13:05:46	LEWINSKY, MONICA	34A092	I	D2	ENTERING
11/06/95	16:26:48	LEWINSKY, MONICA	34A092	I	D2	EXITING
11/06/95	16:32:55	LEWINSKY, MONICA	34BDF9	I	D2	ENTERING
11/06/95	16:35:52	LEWINSKY, MONICA	34BDF9	I	D2	EXITING
11/07/95	10:52:47	LEWINSKY, MONICA	34E952	I	D2	ENTERING
11/07/95	12:36:11	LEWINSKY, MONICA	34E952	I	D2	EXITING
11/07/95	13:17:49	LEWINSKY, MONICA	34A3C4	I	D2	ENTERING

262487

827-DC-00000007

U. S. Secret Service

Epass Access Control Report

01/23/98

Search Criteria: LEWINSKY, MONICA

Search Dates: 01/01/95 to 12/31/95

Date	Time	Name	Badge	Type	Post	Status
11/07/95	14:46:13	LEWINSKY, MONICA	34A3C4	I	D2	EXITING
11/07/95	16:05:05	LEWINSKY, MONICA	34A3C4	I	D2	ENTERING
11/07/95	19:39:56	LEWINSKY, MONICA	34A3C4	I	D2	EXITING
11/08/95	08:54:24	LEWINSKY, MONICA	34F289	I	D2	ENTERING
11/08/95	11:14:43	LEWINSKY, MONICA	34A092	I	D2	ENTERING
11/08/95	12:26:29	LEWINSKY, MONICA	34A092	I	D2	EXITING
11/08/95	13:07:45	LEWINSKY, MONICA	34EA26	I	D2	ENTERING
11/08/95	18:29:02	LEWINSKY, MONICA	34EA26	I	B4	EXITING
11/09/95	09:22:03	LEWINSKY, MONICA	34EA08	I	D2	ENTERING
11/09/95	12:48:14	LEWINSKY, MONICA	34EA08	I	D2	EXITING
11/09/95	13:48:15	LEWINSKY, MONICA	34AE80	I	D2	ENTERING
11/09/95	18:05:26	LEWINSKY, MONICA	34AE80	I	D2	EXITING
11/13/95	09:29:13	LEWINSKY, MONICA	34F253	I	D1	ENTERING
11/13/95	11:31:52	LEWINSKY, MONICA	34F253	I	D2	EXITING
11/13/95	13:32:08	LEWINSKY, MONICA	34EA63	I	D2	ENTERING
11/13/95	21:35:26	LEWINSKY, MONICA	34EA63	I	B4	EXITING
11/14/95	08:50:42	LEWINSKY, MONICA	34EC08	I	D2	ENTERING
11/14/95	08:50:53	LEWINSKY, MONICA	34EC08	I	D2	MULT ENT
11/14/95	20:11:54	LEWINSKY, MONICA	34EC08	I	D2	EXITING
11/15/95	13:30:07	LEWINSKY, MONICA	34DAF5	A	A4	ENTERING
11/15/95	17:07:20	LEWINSKY, MONICA	34D944	A	A4	ENTERING
11/16/95	00:18:01	LEWINSKY, MONICA	34D944	A	B4	EXITING
11/16/95	09:01:46	LEWINSKY, MONICA	34DA8C	A	A4	ENTERING
11/16/95	12:27:45	LEWINSKY, MONICA	34DA8C	A	A4	EXITING
11/16/95	14:57:52	LEWINSKY, MONICA	34E31B	A	A4	ENTERING
11/17/95	08:15:50	LEWINSKY, MONICA	34DA03	A	A4	ENTERING
11/17/95	20:55:36	LEWINSKY, MONICA	34DA03	A	B4	EXITING
11/17/95	21:37:36	LEWINSKY, MONICA	34D9A3	A	B4	ENTERING
11/17/95	22:38:33	LEWINSKY, MONICA	34D9A3	A	B4	EXITING
11/18/95	09:04:49	LEWINSKY, MONICA	34C51D	A	A4	ENTERING
11/20/95	09:05:38	LEWINSKY, MONICA	34F263	I	D2	ENTERING
11/20/95	12:48:37	LEWINSKY, MONICA	34F263	I	B4	EXITING
11/20/95	15:23:26	LEWINSKY, MONICA	34EA38	I	D2	ENTERING
11/20/95	17:55:37	LEWINSKY, MONICA	34EA38	I	D1	EXITING
11/20/95	18:16:58	LEWINSKY, MONICA	34E9EA	I	D1	ENTERING
11/20/95	20:23:05	LEWINSKY, MONICA	34E9EA	I	D2	EXITING
11/21/95	09:16:35	LEWINSKY, MONICA	34E9EF	I	D2	ENTERING
11/21/95	16:23:50	LEWINSKY, MONICA	34E9EF	I	D2	EXITING
11/22/95	08:59:39	LEWINSKY, MONICA	34CC8E	I	D2	ENTERING
11/22/95	14:45:32	LEWINSKY, MONICA	34CC8E	I	D2	EXITING
11/24/95	13:41:20	LEWINSKY, MONICA	34E9C3	I	D2	ENTERING
11/24/95	17:47:43	LEWINSKY, MONICA	34E9C3	I	D2	EXITING
11/27/95	07:44:10	LEWINSKY, MONICA	34EC21	I	D2	ENTERING
11/27/95	08:55:59	LEWINSKY, MONICA	34C91B	A	K1	ENTERING
11/27/95	10:42:58	LEWINSKY, MONICA	34C91B	A	K1	EXITING
11/27/95	11:01:20	LEWINSKY, MONICA	34EC88	D	D2	ENTERING
11/27/95	20:36:42	LEWINSKY, MONICA	34EC88	D	D2	EXITING
11/28/95	07:46:58	LEWINSKY, MONICA	34ECC4	D	D2	ENTERING
11/29/95	07:51:46	LEWINSKY, MONICA	34ECC5	D	D2	ENTERING

202483

827-DC-00000008

U. S. Secret Service

Epass Access Control Report

01/23/98

Search Criteria: LEWINSKY, MONICA

Search Dates: 01/01/95 to 12/31/95

Date	Time	Name	Badge	Type	Post	Status
11/29/95	10:23:21	LEWINSKY, MONICA	34ECC5	D	A1	MULT ENT
11/29/95	13:21:36	LEWINSKY, MONICA S	34A629	P	ACB	ENTERING
11/29/95	13:33:25	LEWINSKY, MONICA S	34A629	P	A1	EXITING
11/29/95	14:08:45	LEWINSKY, MONICA S	34A629	P	A1	ENTERING
11/29/95	16:36:51	LEWINSKY, MONICA S	34A629	P	A1	EXITING
11/29/95	17:01:46	LEWINSKY, MONICA S	34A629	P	A1	ENTERING
11/30/95	07:39:56	LEWINSKY, MONICA S	34A629	P	D2	ENTERING
11/30/95	09:21:45	LEWINSKY, MONICA S	34A629	P	A5	EXITING
11/30/95	09:44:55	LEWINSKY, MONICA S	34A629	P	K1	ENTERING
11/30/95	09:51:43	LEWINSKY, MONICA S	34A629	P	K1	EXITING
11/30/95	10:03:17	LEWINSKY, MONICA S	34A629	P	D2	ENTERING
11/30/95	14:30:41	LEWINSKY, MONICA S	34A629	P	A1	EXITING
11/30/95	15:09:56	LEWINSKY, MONICA S	34A629	P	A1	ENTERING
11/30/95	20:00:41	LEWINSKY, MONICA S	34A629	P	A1	EXITING
12/01/95	07:53:12	LEWINSKY, MONICA S	34A629	P	D2	ENTERING
12/01/95	19:51:01	LEWINSKY, MONICA S	34A629	P	D2	EXITING
12/04/95	08:11:04	LEWINSKY, MONICA S	34A629	P	D2	ENTERING
12/04/95	08:43:52	LEWINSKY, MONICA S	34A629	P	A5	EXITING
12/04/95	08:54:17	LEWINSKY, MONICA S	34A629	P	D2	ENTERING
12/04/95	12:27:26	LEWINSKY, MONICA S	34A629	P	A1	EXITING
12/04/95	12:42:28	LEWINSKY, MONICA S	34A629	P	A1	ENTERING
12/04/95	19:37:05	LEWINSKY, MONICA S	34A629	P	A5	EXITING
12/05/95	07:39:45	LEWINSKY, MONICA S	34A629	P	D2	ENTERING
12/05/95	12:01:22	LEWINSKY, MONICA S	34A629	P	A5	EXITING
12/05/95	12:27:31	LEWINSKY, MONICA S	34A629	P	A1	ENTERING
12/05/95	17:09:29	LEWINSKY, MONICA S	34A629	P	A5	EXITING
12/05/95	19:13:18	LEWINSKY, MONICA S	34A629	P	D2	ENTERING
12/06/95	07:40:59	LEWINSKY, MONICA S	34A629	P	D2	ENTERING
12/06/95	10:05:34	LEWINSKY, MONICA S	34A629	P	A5	EXITING
12/06/95	16:43:58	LEWINSKY, MONICA S	34A629	P	A1	ENTERING
12/06/95	16:45:37	LEWINSKY, MONICA S	34A629	P	A1	EXITING
12/06/95	19:13:57	LEWINSKY, MONICA S	34A629	P	A1	ENTERING
12/07/95	00:12:23	LEWINSKY, MONICA S	34A629	P	A1	EXITING
12/07/95	15:26:46	LEWINSKY, MONICA S	34A629	P	A5	EXITING
12/07/95	16:19:08	LEWINSKY, MONICA S	34A629	P	A1	EXITING
12/08/95	07:43:38	LEWINSKY, MONICA S	34A629	P	D2	ENTERING
12/08/95	13:40:24	LEWINSKY, MONICA S	34A629	P	A1	EXITING
12/08/95	14:20:39	LEWINSKY, MONICA S	34A629	P	A1	ENTERING
12/08/95	15:57:46	LEWINSKY, MONICA S	34A629	P	A1	EXITING
12/08/95	17:50:34	LEWINSKY, MONICA S	34A629	P	A1	ENTERING
12/08/95	21:19:26	LEWINSKY, MONICA S	34A629	P	A5	EXITING
12/11/95	07:43:56	LEWINSKY, MONICA S	34A629	P	D2	ENTERING
12/11/95	19:35:10	LEWINSKY, MONICA S	34A629	P	D2	EXITING
12/12/95	08:10:12	LEWINSKY, MONICA S	34A629	P	D2	ENTERING
12/12/95	17:59:09	LEWINSKY, MONICA S	34A629	P	A1	EXITING
12/12/95	18:12:32	LEWINSKY, MONICA S	34A629	P	A1	ENTERING
12/12/95	21:25:57	LEWINSKY, MONICA S	34A629	P	A5	EXITING
12/13/95	07:48:37	LEWINSKY, MONICA S	34A629	P	D2	ENTERING
12/13/95	13:12:35	LEWINSKY, MONICA S	34A629	P	A1	ENTERING

202489

827-DC-00000009

U. S. Secret Service

Epass Access Control Report

Date of Report: 01/23/98

Search Criteria: LEWINSKY, MONICA

Search Dates: 01/01/95 to 12/31/95

Date	Time	Name	Badge	Type	Post	Status
12/13/95	19:39:58	LEWINSKY, MONICA S	34A629	P	A1	EXITING
12/14/95	07:58:02	LEWINSKY, MONICA S	34A629	P	D2	ENTERING
12/14/95	12:48:55	LEWINSKY, MONICA S	34A629	P	D2	EXITING
12/14/95	20:21:49	LEWINSKY, MONICA S	34A629	P	A5	EXITING
12/15/95	07:54:04	LEWINSKY, MONICA S	34A629	P	D2	ENTERING
12/15/95	11:13:27	LEWINSKY, MONICA S	34A629	P	A5	EXITING
12/15/95	19:40:09	LEWINSKY, MONICA S	34A629	P	A5	EXITING
12/16/95	12:01:40	LEWINSKY, MONICA S	34A629	P	A5	EXITING
12/16/95	13:31:50	LEWINSKY, MONICA S	34A629	P	D2	EXITING
12/16/95	13:32:14	LEWINSKY, MONICA S	34A629	P	D2	ENTERING
12/16/95	14:27:54	LEWINSKY, MONICA S	34A629	P	A5	EXITING
12/17/95	13:23:04	LEWINSKY, MONICA S	34A629	P	A5	EXITING
12/18/95	07:56:49	LEWINSKY, MONICA S	34A629	P	D2	ENTERING
12/18/95	11:04:21	LEWINSKY, MONICA S	34A629	P	A5	EXITING
12/18/95	11:16:33	LEWINSKY, MONICA S	34A629	P	D2	ENTERING
12/18/95	12:36:08	LEWINSKY, MONICA S	34A629	P	A1	EXITING
12/18/95	19:59:49	LEWINSKY, MONICA S	34A629	P	D2	EXITING
12/19/95	08:35:47	LEWINSKY, MONICA S	34A629	P	D2	ENTERING
12/19/95	11:27:22	LEWINSKY, MONICA S	34A629	P	D2	EXITING
12/19/95	11:36:20	LEWINSKY, MONICA S	34A629	P	D2	ENTERING
12/19/95	12:40:52	LEWINSKY, MONICA S	34A629	P	A1	EXITING
12/19/95	12:58:48	LEWINSKY, MONICA S	34A629	P	A1	BAD PIN
12/19/95	12:59:00	LEWINSKY, MONICA S	34A629	P	A1	ENTERING
12/19/95	20:17:46	LEWINSKY, MONICA S	34A629	P	D2	EXITING
12/20/95	07:54:21	LEWINSKY, MONICA S	34A629	P	D2	ENTERING
12/20/95	08:08:44	LEWINSKY, MONICA S	34A629	P	D2	EXITING
12/20/95	08:15:11	LEWINSKY, MONICA S	34A629	P	D2	ENTERING
12/20/95	12:31:15	LEWINSKY, MONICA S	34A629	P	A5	EXITING
12/20/95	12:45:53	LEWINSKY, MONICA S	34A629	P	D2	ENTERING
12/20/95	18:05:09	LEWINSKY, MONICA S	34A629	P	A5	EXITING
12/21/95	10:10:00	LEWINSKY, MONICA S	34A629	P	D2	ENTERING
12/21/95	13:03:22	LEWINSKY, MONICA S	34A629	P	A1	EXITING
12/21/95	20:18:04	LEWINSKY, MONICA S	34A629	P	D2	EXITING
12/22/95	08:00:29	LEWINSKY, MONICA S	34A629	P	D2	ENTERING
12/22/95	15:07:43	LEWINSKY, MONICA S	34A629	P	A1	EXITING
12/22/95	15:24:10	LEWINSKY, MONICA S	34A629	P	A1	ENTERING
12/22/95	18:19:44	LEWINSKY, MONICA S	34A629	P	A5	EXITING
12/26/95	16:36:18	LEWINSKY, MONICA S	34A629	P	D2	ENTERING
12/26/95	18:16:51	LEWINSKY, MONICA S	34A629	P	D2	EXITING
12/26/95	19:06:48	LEWINSKY, MONICA S	34A629	P	D2	ENTERING
12/26/95	19:58:24	LEWINSKY, MONICA S	34A629	P	D2	EXITING
12/28/95	07:58:28	LEWINSKY, MONICA S	34A629	P	D2	ENTERING
12/28/95	08:31:49	LEWINSKY, MONICA S	34A629	P	D2	EXITING
12/28/95	08:39:36	LEWINSKY, MONICA S	34A629	P	D2	ENTERING
12/28/95	11:56:47	LEWINSKY, MONICA S	34A629	P	A1	ENTERING
12/28/95	15:09:27	LEWINSKY, MONICA S	34A629	P	A1	EXITING
12/28/95	15:24:38	LEWINSKY, MONICA S	34A629	P	A1	ENTERING
12/28/95	20:20:53	LEWINSKY, MONICA S	34A629	P	D2	EXITING
12/29/95	08:17:07	LEWINSKY, MONICA S	34A629	P	D2	ENTERING

202490

827-DC-00000010

U. S. Secret Service

Epass Access Control Report

01/23/98

Search Criteria: LEWINSKY, MONICA

Search Dates: 01/01/95 to 12/31/95

Date	Time	Name	Badge	Type	Post	Status
12/29/95	12:13:04	LEWINSKY, MONICA S	34A629	P	A1	EXITING
12/29/95	16:35:13	LEWINSKY, MONICA S	34A629	P	A1	EXITING
12/29/95	16:47:53	LEWINSKY, MONICA S	34A629	P	A1	ENTERING
12/29/95	19:35:49	LEWINSKY, MONICA S	34A629	P	D2	EXITING
12/29/95	21:09:40	LEWINSKY, MONICA S	34A629	P	A5	EXITING
12/31/95	13:15:44	LEWINSKY, MONICA S	34A629	P	A5	EXITING

827-DC-00000011

202491

U. S. Secret Service

Epass Access Control Report

01/23/98

Search Criteria: LEWINSKY, MONICA

Search Dates: 01/01/96 to 12/31/96

Date	Time	Name	Badge	Type	Post	Status
01/02/96	08:13:05	LEWINSKY, MONICA S	34A629	P	D2	ENTERING
01/02/96	14:18:09	LEWINSKY, MONICA S	34A629	P	A1	ENTERING
01/02/96	20:46:55	LEWINSKY, MONICA S	34A629	P	A5	EXITING
01/03/96	08:11:20	LEWINSKY, MONICA S	34A629	P	D2	ENTERING
01/03/96	13:46:34	LEWINSKY, MONICA S	34A629	P	D2	EXITING
01/03/96	13:54:07	LEWINSKY, MONICA S	34A629	P	D2	ENTERING
01/03/96	19:42:08	LEWINSKY, MONICA S	34A629	P	A5	EXITING
01/04/96	08:15:43	LEWINSKY, MONICA S	34A629	P	D2	ENTERING
01/04/96	12:27:12	LEWINSKY, MONICA S	34A629	P	A1	EXITING
01/04/96	12:47:25	LEWINSKY, MONICA S	34A629	P	A1	ENTERING
01/04/96	19:23:36	LEWINSKY, MONICA S	34A629	P	A5	EXITING
01/05/96	08:11:57	LEWINSKY, MONICA S	34A629	P	D2	ENTERING
01/05/96	14:28:35	LEWINSKY, MONICA S	34A629	P	A1	ENTERING
01/05/96	19:51:21	LEWINSKY, MONICA S	34A629	P	D2	EXITING
01/06/96	13:00:17	LEWINSKY, MONICA S	34A629	P	D2	EXITING
01/06/96	15:22:42	LEWINSKY, MONICA S	34A629	P	D2	EXITING
01/09/96	11:51:45	LEWINSKY, MONICA S	34A629	P	D2	EXITING
01/09/96	12:02:03	LEWINSKY, MONICA S	34A629	P	D2	ENTERING
01/09/96	19:44:48	LEWINSKY, MONICA S	34A629	P	D2	EXITING
01/09/96	19:46:06	LEWINSKY, MONICA S	34A629	P	D2	ENTERING
01/09/96	20:02:11	LEWINSKY, MONICA S	34A629	P	D2	EXITING
01/10/96	08:36:45	LEWINSKY, MONICA S	34A629	P	D2	ENTERING
01/10/96	15:32:24	LEWINSKY, MONICA S	34A629	P	A1	EXITING
01/10/96	17:25:15	LEWINSKY, MONICA S	34A629	P	A5	EXITING
01/11/96	08:34:09	LEWINSKY, MONICA S	34A629	P	D2	ENTERING
01/11/96	11:44:54	LEWINSKY, MONICA S	34A629	P	D2	EXITING
01/11/96	11:55:34	LEWINSKY, MONICA S	34A629	P	D2	ENTERING
01/11/96	19:29:10	LEWINSKY, MONICA S	34A629	P	D2	EXITING
01/12/96	08:39:11	LEWINSKY, MONICA S	34A629	P	D2	ENTERING
01/12/96	08:42:54	LEWINSKY, MONICA S	34A629	P	D2	EXITING
01/12/96	08:55:20	LEWINSKY, MONICA S	34A629	P	D2	ENTERING
01/12/96	16:42:45	LEWINSKY, MONICA S	34A629	P	D2	EXITING
01/15/96	19:01:51	LEWINSKY, MONICA S	34A629	P	A5	EXITING
01/16/96	08:23:30	LEWINSKY, MONICA S	34A629	P	D2	ENTERING
01/16/96	16:16:53	LEWINSKY, MONICA S	34A629	P	D2	EXITING
01/16/96	16:22:09	LEWINSKY, MONICA S	34A629	P	D2	ENTERING
01/16/96	18:39:20	LEWINSKY, MONICA S	34A629	P	A5	EXITING
01/17/96	07:58:33	LEWINSKY, MONICA S	34A629	P	D2	ENTERING
01/17/96	15:49:29	LEWINSKY, MONICA S	34A629	P	D2	EXITING
01/17/96	15:56:26	LEWINSKY, MONICA S	34A629	P	D2	ENTERING
01/17/96	22:29:15	LEWINSKY, MONICA S	34A629	P	A5	EXITING
01/18/96	07:51:05	LEWINSKY, MONICA S	34A629	P	D2	ENTERING
01/18/96	15:37:16	LEWINSKY, MONICA S	34A629	P	D2	EXITING
01/18/96	15:46:53	LEWINSKY, MONICA S	34A629	P	D2	ENTERING
01/18/96	20:55:28	LEWINSKY, MONICA S	34A629	P	A5	EXITING
01/19/96	08:05:59	LEWINSKY, MONICA S	34A629	P	D2	ENTERING
01/19/96	10:29:29	LEWINSKY, MONICA S	34A629	P	D2	ENTERING
01/19/96	12:36:18	LEWINSKY, MONICA S	34A629	P	A1	EXITING
01/19/96	12:56:19	LEWINSKY, MONICA S	34A629	P	A1	ENTERING

202492

827-DC-00000012

Epass Access Control Report

01/23/98

Search Criteria: LEWINSKY, MONICA

Search Dates: 01/01/96 to 12/31/96

Date	Time	Name	Badge	Type	Post	Status
01/19/96	20:30:04	LEWINSKY, MONICA S	34A629	P	D2	EXITING
01/21/96	15:56:01	LEWINSKY, MONICA S	34A629	P	A5	EXITING
01/22/96	07:52:30	LEWINSKY, MONICA S	34A629	P	D2	ENTERING
01/22/96	15:16:03	LEWINSKY, MONICA S	34A629	P	D2	EXITING
01/22/96	17:18:04	LEWINSKY, MONICA S	34A629	P	D2	ENTERING
01/22/96	19:53:43	LEWINSKY, MONICA S	34A629	P	D2	EXITING
01/22/96	20:15:37	LEWINSKY, MONICA S	34A629	P	B4	ENTERING
01/22/96	23:28:02	LEWINSKY, MONICA S	34A629	P	B4	EXITING
01/23/96	07:20:11	LEWINSKY, MONICA S	34A629	P	D2	ENTERING
01/23/96	13:17:20	LEWINSKY, MONICA S	34A629	P	D2	EXITING
01/23/96	13:32:04	LEWINSKY, MONICA S	34A629	P	D2	ENTERING
01/23/96	15:38:08	LEWINSKY, MONICA S	34A629	P	A5	EXITING
01/23/96	20:10:14	LEWINSKY, MONICA S	34A629	P	D2	EXITING
01/23/96	20:27:25	LEWINSKY, MONICA S	34A629	P	D2	ENTERING
01/23/96	22:41:34	LEWINSKY, MONICA S	34A629	P	A5	EXITING
01/24/96	18:48:25	LEWINSKY, MONICA S	34A629	P	D2	EXITING
01/25/96	08:21:59	LEWINSKY, MONICA S	34A629	P	D2	ENTERING
01/25/96	16:38:54	LEWINSKY, MONICA S	34A629	P	D2	EXITING
01/25/96	16:48:58	LEWINSKY, MONICA S	34A629	P	D2	ENTERING
01/25/96	19:38:54	LEWINSKY, MONICA S	34A629	P	A5	EXITING
01/26/96	10:03:25	LEWINSKY, MONICA S	34A629	P	D2	ENTERING
01/26/96	15:20:41	LEWINSKY, MONICA S	34A629	P	A5	EXITING
01/26/96	15:23:42	LEWINSKY, MONICA S	34A629	P	K1	ENTERING
01/26/96	15:27:58	LEWINSKY, MONICA S	34A629	P	K1	EXITING
01/26/96	15:30:14	LEWINSKY, MONICA S	34A629	P	D2	ENTERING
01/26/96	18:16:48	LEWINSKY, MONICA S	34A629	P	D2	EXITING
01/30/96	08:07:25	LEWINSKY, MONICA S	34A629	P	D2	ENTERING
01/30/96	13:08:19	LEWINSKY, MONICA S	34A629	P	D2	EXITING
01/30/96	13:28:05	LEWINSKY, MONICA S	34A629	P	D2	ENTERING
01/30/96	20:44:31	LEWINSKY, MONICA S	34A629	P	D2	EXITING
01/31/96	07:49:23	LEWINSKY, MONICA S	34A629	P	D2	ENTERING
01/31/96	16:00:05	LEWINSKY, MONICA S	34A629	P	A5	EXITING
01/31/96	16:06:46	LEWINSKY, MONICA S	34A629	P	D2	ENTERING
01/31/96	18:46:32	LEWINSKY, MONICA S	34A629	P	D2	EXITING
02/01/96	08:02:52	LEWINSKY, MONICA S	34A629	P	D2	ENTERING
02/01/96	14:09:03	LEWINSKY, MONICA S	34A629	P	A5	EXITING
02/01/96	14:19:50	LEWINSKY, MONICA S	34A629	P	D2	ENTERING
02/01/96	21:05:07	LEWINSKY, MONICA S	34A629	P	A5	EXITING
02/02/96	07:50:56	LEWINSKY, MONICA S	34A629	P	D2	ENTERING
02/02/96	10:36:16	LEWINSKY, MONICA S	34A629	P	D2	EXITING
02/02/96	10:45:16	LEWINSKY, MONICA S	34A629	P	D2	ENTERING
02/02/96	12:48:36	LEWINSKY, MONICA S	34A629	P	A1	EXITING
02/02/96	13:05:11	LEWINSKY, MONICA S	34A629	P	A1	ENTERING
02/02/96	18:46:53	LEWINSKY, MONICA S	34A629	P	D2	EXITING
02/05/96	08:03:01	LEWINSKY, MONICA S	34A629	P	D2	ENTERING
02/05/96	19:53:49	LEWINSKY, MONICA S	34A629	P	D2	EXITING
02/06/96	08:21:36	LEWINSKY, MONICA S	34A629	P	D2	ENTERING
02/06/96	18:30:58	LEWINSKY, MONICA S	34A629	P	D2	EXITING
02/07/96	07:54:30	LEWINSKY, MONICA S	34A629	P	D2	ENTERING

202493

827-DC-00000013

U. S. Secret Service

Epass Access Control Report

01/23/98

Search Criteria: LEWINSKY, MONICA

Search Dates: 01/01/96 to 12/31/96

Date	Time	Name	Badge	Type	Post	Status
02/07/96	15:45:32	LEWINSKY, MONICA S	34A629	P	D2	EXITING
02/07/96	15:51:51	LEWINSKY, MONICA S	34A629	P	D2	ENTERING
02/07/96	19:21:05	LEWINSKY, MONICA S	34A629	P	D2	EXITING
02/08/96	19:52:35	LEWINSKY, MONICA S	34A629	P	D2	EXITING
02/09/96	07:55:40	LEWINSKY, MONICA S	34A629	P	D2	BAD PIN
02/09/96	07:55:51	LEWINSKY, MONICA S	34A629	P	D2	ENTERING
02/09/96	12:49:33	LEWINSKY, MONICA S	34A629	P	D2	EXITING
02/09/96	12:56:56	LEWINSKY, MONICA S	34A629	P	D2	ENTERING
02/09/96	19:21:03	LEWINSKY, MONICA S	34A629	P	D2	EXITING
02/12/96	08:05:17	LEWINSKY, MONICA S	34A629	P	D2	ENTERING
02/12/96	17:27:12	LEWINSKY, MONICA S	34A629	P	D2	EXITING
02/12/96	17:39:26	LEWINSKY, MONICA S	34A629	P	D2	ENTERING
02/12/96	19:25:37	LEWINSKY, MONICA S	34A629	P	D2	EXITING
02/13/96	08:10:38	LEWINSKY, MONICA S	34A629	P	D2	ENTERING
02/13/96	17:12:52	LEWINSKY, MONICA S	34A629	P	D2	EXITING
02/13/96	17:19:36	LEWINSKY, MONICA S	34A629	P	D2	ENTERING
02/13/96	19:10:02	LEWINSKY, MONICA S	34A629	P	D2	EXITING
02/14/96	08:04:02	LEWINSKY, MONICA S	34A629	P	D2	ENTERING
02/14/96	12:58:46	LEWINSKY, MONICA S	34A629	P	A1	EXITING
02/14/96	18:47:25	LEWINSKY, MONICA S	34A629	P	D2	EXITING
02/15/96	08:00:47	LEWINSKY, MONICA S	34A629	P	D2	ENTERING
02/15/96	16:48:53	LEWINSKY, MONICA S	34A629	P	D2	EXITING
02/16/96	08:24:57	LEWINSKY, MONICA S	34A629	P	D2	ENTERING
02/16/96	18:54:29	LEWINSKY, MONICA S	34A629	P	D2	EXITING
02/20/96	08:05:10	LEWINSKY, MONICA S	34A629	P	D2	ENTERING
02/20/96	19:51:48	LEWINSKY, MONICA S	34A629	P	D2	EXITING
02/21/96	08:07:35	LEWINSKY, MONICA S	34A629	P	D2	ENTERING
02/21/96	17:18:39	LEWINSKY, MONICA S	34A629	P	D2	EXITING
02/21/96	17:30:10	LEWINSKY, MONICA S	34A629	P	D2	ENTERING
02/21/96	21:36:11	LEWINSKY, MONICA S	34A629	P	A5	EXITING
02/22/96	08:18:16	LEWINSKY, MONICA S	34A629	P	D2	ENTERING
02/22/96	14:34:10	LEWINSKY, MONICA S	34A629	P	D2	EXITING
02/22/96	14:43:35	LEWINSKY, MONICA S	34A629	P	D2	ENTERING
02/22/96	19:10:32	LEWINSKY, MONICA S	34A629	P	A5	EXITING
02/23/96	08:21:12	LEWINSKY, MONICA S	34A629	P	D2	ENTERING
02/23/96	20:24:44	LEWINSKY, MONICA S	34A629	P	D2	EXITING
02/24/96	09:41:57	LEWINSKY, MONICA S	34A629	P	D2	ENTERING
02/24/96	10:13:34	LEWINSKY, MONICA S	34A629	P	D2	EXITING
02/24/96	16:31:37	LEWINSKY, MONICA S	34A629	P	D2	ENTERING
02/24/96	17:26:31	LEWINSKY, MONICA S	34A629	P	D2	EXITING
02/26/96	08:04:58	LEWINSKY, MONICA S	34A629	P	D2	ENTERING
02/26/96	19:28:47	LEWINSKY, MONICA S	34A629	P	D2	EXITING
02/27/96	08:02:10	LEWINSKY, MONICA S	34A629	P	D2	ENTERING
02/27/96	19:13:44	LEWINSKY, MONICA S	34A629	P	D2	EXITING
02/28/96	08:23:36	LEWINSKY, MONICA S	34A629	P	A1	ENTERING
02/28/96	08:55:57	LEWINSKY, MONICA S	34A629	P	A1	EXITING
02/28/96	22:29:21	LEWINSKY, MONICA S	34A629	P	A5	EXITING
02/29/96	08:38:01	LEWINSKY, MONICA S	34A629	P	D2	ENTERING
02/29/96	19:57:12	LEWINSKY, MONICA S	34A629	P	D2	EXITING

U. S. Secret Service

Epass Access Control Report

01/23/98

Search Criteria: LEWINSKY, MONICA

Search Dates: 01/01/96 to 12/31/96

Date	Time	Name	Badge	Type	Post	Status
03/01/96	09:25:01	LEWINSKY, MONICA S	34A629	P	D2	ENTERING
03/01/96	12:07:12	LEWINSKY, MONICA S	34A629	P	D2	EXITING
03/01/96	12:20:21	LEWINSKY, MONICA S	34A629	P	D2	ENTERING
03/01/96	17:36:49	LEWINSKY, MONICA S	34A629	P	D2	EXITING
03/04/96	07:57:49	LEWINSKY, MONICA S	34A629	P	D2	BAD PIN
03/04/96	07:57:58	LEWINSKY, MONICA S	34A629	P	D2	ENTERING
03/05/96	08:02:52	LEWINSKY, MONICA S	34A629	P	D2	ENTERING
03/05/96	19:23:27	LEWINSKY, MONICA S	34A629	P	A1	BAD PIN
03/05/96	19:23:33	LEWINSKY, MONICA S	34A629	P	A1	ENTERING
03/05/96	20:56:11	LEWINSKY, MONICA S	34A629	P	D2	EXITING
03/06/96	08:03:23	LEWINSKY, MONICA S	34A629	P	D2	ENTERING
03/06/96	20:20:26	LEWINSKY, MONICA S	34A629	P	D2	EXITING
03/06/96	20:22:16	LEWINSKY, MONICA S	34A629	P	D2	ENTERING
03/06/96	20:33:23	LEWINSKY, MONICA S	34A629	P	D2	EXITING
03/07/96	08:01:49	LEWINSKY, MONICA S	34A629	P	D2	ENTERING
03/07/96	20:11:23	LEWINSKY, MONICA S	34A629	P	D2	EXITING
03/08/96	08:35:55	LEWINSKY, MONICA S	34A629	P	D2	ENTERING
03/08/96	18:40:01	LEWINSKY, MONICA S	34A629	P	D2	EXITING
03/10/96	14:39:52	LEWINSKY, MONICA S	34A629	P	A5	EXITING
03/11/96	07:29:59	LEWINSKY, MONICA S	34A629	P	D2	ENTERING
03/11/96	11:46:54	LEWINSKY, MONICA S	34A629	P	A1	EXITING
03/11/96	12:02:50	LEWINSKY, MONICA S	34A629	P	A1	ENTERING
03/11/96	16:28:48	LEWINSKY, MONICA S	34A629	P	D2	EXITING
03/12/96	07:49:37	LEWINSKY, MONICA S	34A629	P	D2	ENTERING
03/12/96	19:04:42	LEWINSKY, MONICA S	34A629	P	D2	EXITING
03/13/96	07:56:08	LEWINSKY, MONICA S	34A629	P	D2	ENTERING
03/13/96	18:57:21	LEWINSKY, MONICA S	34A629	P	D2	EXITING
03/14/96	08:08:33	LEWINSKY, MONICA S	34A629	P	D2	ENTERING
03/14/96	12:19:49	LEWINSKY, MONICA S	34A629	P	A1	EXITING
03/14/96	12:34:28	LEWINSKY, MONICA S	34A629	P	A1	ENTERING
03/14/96	19:28:23	LEWINSKY, MONICA S	34A629	P	D2	EXITING
03/15/96	07:52:58	LEWINSKY, MONICA S	34A629	P	D2	ENTERING
03/15/96	17:54:41	LEWINSKY, MONICA S	34A629	P	D2	EXITING
03/16/96	15:39:49	LEWINSKY, MONICA S	34A629	P	B4	ENTERING
03/16/96	15:52:27	LEWINSKY, MONICA S	34A629	P	B4	EXITING
03/17/96	16:43:33	LEWINSKY, MONICA S	34A629	P	A5	EXITING
03/18/96	08:02:43	LEWINSKY, MONICA S	34A629	P	D2	ENTERING
03/18/96	12:50:09	LEWINSKY, MONICA S	34A629	P	D2	EXITING
03/18/96	13:26:12	LEWINSKY, MONICA S	34A629	P	A1	ENTERING
03/18/96	21:31:08	LEWINSKY, MONICA S	34A629	P	A5	EXITING
03/19/96	08:10:39	LEWINSKY, MONICA S	34A629	P	D2	ENTERING
03/19/96	21:04:33	LEWINSKY, MONICA S	34A629	P	A1	ENTERING
03/19/96	23:57:20	LEWINSKY, MONICA S	34A629	P	A5	EXITING
03/20/96	08:13:03	LEWINSKY, MONICA S	34A629	P	D2	ENTERING
03/20/96	19:57:07	LEWINSKY, MONICA S	34A629	P	A5	EXITING
03/21/96	08:22:30	LEWINSKY, MONICA S	34A629	P	D2	ENTERING
03/21/96	20:09:29	LEWINSKY, MONICA S	34A629	P	D2	EXITING
03/22/96	07:54:28	LEWINSKY, MONICA S	34A629	P	D2	ENTERING
03/22/96	10:53:32	LEWINSKY, MONICA S	34A629	P	A1	EXITING

202495

827-DC-00000015

01/23/98

U. S. Secret Service

Epass Access Control Report

01/23/98

Search Criteria: LEWINSKY, MONICA

Search Dates: 01/01/96 to 12/31/96

Date	Time	Name	Badge	Type	Post	Status
03/22/96	11:48:26	LEWINSKY, MONICA S	34A629	P	A1	ENTERING
03/23/96	09:01:46	LEWINSKY, MONICA S	34A629	P	D2	BAD PIN
03/23/96	09:01:53	LEWINSKY, MONICA S	34A629	P	D2	ENTERING
03/23/96	10:21:43	LEWINSKY, MONICA S	34A629	P	A1	EXITING
03/23/96	10:25:00	LEWINSKY, MONICA S	34A629	P	A1	BAD PIN
03/23/96	10:25:05	LEWINSKY, MONICA S	34A629	P	A1	ENTERING
03/23/96	14:11:45	LEWINSKY, MONICA S	34A629	P	A5	EXITING
03/24/96	10:47:46	LEWINSKY, MONICA S	34A629	P	B4	ENTERING
03/24/96	11:13:10	LEWINSKY, MONICA S	34A629	P	A1	EXITING
03/24/96	11:13:14	LEWINSKY, MONICA S	34A629	P	A1	EXITING
03/24/96	21:29:48	LEWINSKY, MONICA S	34A629	P	B4	EXITING
03/25/96	07:42:24	LEWINSKY, MONICA S	34A629	P	D2	ENTERING
03/25/96	12:31:03	LEWINSKY, MONICA S	34A629	P	D2	EXITING
03/25/96	12:35:52	LEWINSKY, MONICA S	34A629	P	D2	ENTERING
03/26/96	07:53:43	LEWINSKY, MONICA S	34A629	P	D2	ENTERING
03/26/96	12:10:33	LEWINSKY, MONICA S	34A629	P	A1	EXITING
03/26/96	12:22:15	LEWINSKY, MONICA S	34A629	P	A1	ENTERING
03/26/96	19:45:21	LEWINSKY, MONICA S	34A629	P	D2	EXITING
03/27/96	08:05:19	LEWINSKY, MONICA S	34A629	P	D2	ENTERING
03/27/96	11:29:57	LEWINSKY, MONICA S	34A629	P	A1	EXITING
03/27/96	11:49:47	LEWINSKY, MONICA S	34A629	P	A1	ENTERING
03/27/96	19:07:40	LEWINSKY, MONICA S	34A629	P	D2	EXITING
03/27/96	21:16:58	LEWINSKY, MONICA S	34A629	P	A1	EXITING
03/28/96	08:12:17	LEWINSKY, MONICA S	34A629	P	D2	ENTERING
03/28/96	17:57:38	LEWINSKY, MONICA S	34A629	P	D2	EXITING
03/28/96	18:12:20	LEWINSKY, MONICA S	34A629	P	D2	ENTERING
03/29/96	08:04:11	LEWINSKY, MONICA S	34A629	P	D2	BAD PIN
03/29/96	08:04:17	LEWINSKY, MONICA S	34A629	P	D2	ENTERING
03/29/96	20:55:41	LEWINSKY, MONICA S	34A629	P	D2	EXITING
03/31/96	10:20:40	LEWINSKY, MONICA S	34A629	P	B4	ENTERING
03/31/96	16:27:13	LEWINSKY, MONICA S	34A629	P	B4	EXITING
04/01/96	12:31:59	LEWINSKY, MONICA S	34A629	P	D2	ENTERING
04/01/96	18:50:51	LEWINSKY, MONICA S	34A629	P	D2	EXITING
04/02/96	07:53:01	LEWINSKY, MONICA S	34A629	P	D2	ENTERING
04/03/96	07:58:13	LEWINSKY, MONICA S	34A629	P	D2	ENTERING
04/03/96	18:48:19	LEWINSKY, MONICA S	34A629	P	D2	EXITING
04/04/96	08:04:50	LEWINSKY, MONICA S	34A629	P	D2	ENTERING
04/04/96	18:32:37	LEWINSKY, MONICA S	34A629	P	D2	EXITING
04/05/96	08:05:09	LEWINSKY, MONICA S	34A629	P	D2	ENTERING
04/05/96	13:13:03	LEWINSKY, MONICA S	34A629	P	D2	EXITING
04/05/96	13:13:03	LEWINSKY, MONICA S	34A629	P	D2	EXITING
04/05/96	13:42:17	LEWINSKY, MONICA S	34A629	P	D2	ENTERING
04/05/96	18:20:57	LEWINSKY, MONICA S	34A629	P	D2	EXITING
04/07/96	10:47:52	LEWINSKY, MONICA S	34A629	P	B4	ENTERING
04/07/96	14:51:05	LEWINSKY, MONICA S	34A629	P	B4	EXITING
04/07/96	16:56:44	LEWINSKY, MONICA S	34A629	P	B4	ENTERING
04/07/96	17:28:39	LEWINSKY, MONICA S	34A629	P	B4	EXITING
04/09/96	11:55:35	LEWINSKY, MONICA	34D9BD	A	D2	ENTERING
06/07/96	12:50:54	LEWINSKY, MONICA	34D8A2	A	D2	ENTERING

202496

827-DC-00000016

U. S. Secret Service
Epass Access Control Report

Date of report.
01/23/98

Search Criteria: LEWINSKY, MONICA

Search Dates: 01/01/96 to 12/31/96

Date	Time	Name	Badge	Type	Post	Status
06/07/96	13:03:49	LEWINSKY, MONICA	34D8A2	A	D2	EXITING
08/29/96	15:05:30	LEWINSKY, MONICA	34C3ED	A	D2	ENTERING
08/29/96	15:46:41	LEWINSKY, MONICA	34C3ED	A	D2	EXITING
08/29/96	18:22:28	LEWINSKY, MONICA	34C3CF	A	D2	ENTERING
08/29/96	19:03:52	LEWINSKY, MONICA	34C3CF	A	B4	EXITING
10/11/96	12:48:35	LEWINSKY, MONICA	34D9D2	A	D1	ENTERING
10/11/96	13:49:16	LEWINSKY, MONICA	34D9D2	A	D1	EXITING
10/24/96	07:41:53	LEWINSKY, MONICA	34E542	A	B4	ENTERING
10/24/96	10:11:18	LEWINSKY, MONICA	34E542	A	D1	EXITING
12/17/96	19:33:34	LEWINSKY, MONICA	34DADD	A	D1	ENTERING
12/17/96	20:10:53	LEWINSKY, MONICA	34DADD	A	B4	EXITING
12/30/96	13:01:18	LEWINSKY, MONICA	34E3E8	A	A4	ENTERING
12/30/96	13:42:41	LEWINSKY, MONICA	34E3E8	A	A4	EXITING

827-DC-00000017

202497

U. S. Secret Service

Epass Access Control Report

01/23/98

Search Criteria: LEWINSKY, MONICA

Search Dates: 01/01/97 to 12/31/97

Date	Time	Name	Badge	Type	Post	Status
02/24/97	09:38:25	LEWINSKY, MONICA	34D8D7	A	D2	ENTERING
02/24/97	10:32:24	LEWINSKY, MONICA	34D8D7	A	D2	EXITING
02/28/97	17:48:21	LEWINSKY, MONICA	34F4FB	A	A4	ENTERING
02/28/97	19:07:08	LEWINSKY, MONICA	34F4FB	A	A4	EXITING
03/13/97	10:01:22	LEWINSKY, MONICA	34F4F4	A	A4	ENTERING
03/13/97	10:15:27	LEWINSKY, MONICA	34F4F4	A	A5	EXITING
03/13/97	21:21:24	LEWINSKY, MONICA	34D880	A	B4	ENTERING
03/13/97	21:48:33	LEWINSKY, MONICA	34D880	A	B4	EXITING
03/29/97	14:02:57	LEWINSKY, MONICA	34C597	A	A4	ENTERING
03/29/97	15:16:10	LEWINSKY, MONICA	34C597	A	A4	EXITING
04/16/97	09:48:36	LEWINSKY, MONICA	34D960	A	A4	ENTERING
04/16/97	09:55:38	LEWINSKY, MONICA	34D960	A	A4	EXITING
05/01/97	17:42:48	LEWINSKY, MONICA	3467A9	A	A4	ENTERING
05/02/97	19:57:03	LEWINSKY, MONICA	34DACB	A	D2	ENTERING
05/02/97	20:21:08	LEWINSKY, MONICA	34DACB	A	D2	EXITING
05/24/97	12:20:39	LEWINSKY, MONICA	34A5AE	A	A4	ENTERING
05/24/97	13:53:30	LEWINSKY, MONICA	34A5AE	A	A4	EXITING
05/30/97	15:32:18	LEWINSKY, MONICA S	3457C6	A	D2	ENTERING
05/30/97	16:01:29	LEWINSKY, MONICA S	3457C6	A	D2	EXITING
06/11/97	10:57:54	LEWINSKY, MONICA S	34D85D	A	D2	ENTERING
06/11/97	12:04:04	LEWINSKY, MONICA S	34D85D	A	D2	EXITING
06/16/97	14:47:23	LEWINSKY, MONICA	345628	A	D1	ENTERING
06/16/97	16:10:45	LEWINSKY, MONICA	345628	A	B4	EXITING
06/24/97	18:59:02	LEWINSKY, MONICA	3468A0	A	A4	ENTERING
06/24/97	19:18:42	LEWINSKY, MONICA	3468A0	A	A4	EXITING
07/04/97	08:51:20	LEWINSKY, MONICA	345622	A	A4	ENTERING
07/14/97	21:33:40	LEWINSKY, MONICA	3467A7	A	B4	ENTERING
07/14/97	23:22:30	LEWINSKY, MONICA	3467A7	A	B4	EXITING
07/16/97	10:45:36	LEWINSKY, MONICA	34F63A	A	D1	ENTERING
07/16/97	11:41:51	LEWINSKY, MONICA	34F63A	A	B4	EXITING
07/24/97	18:04:29	LEWINSKY, MONICA	3468CE	A	A4	ENTERING
07/24/97	18:26:48	LEWINSKY, MONICA	3468CE	A	A4	EXITING
08/16/97	09:01:53	LEWINSKY, MONICA	34D871	A	B4	ENTERING
08/16/97	10:20:04	LEWINSKY, MONICA	34D871	A	B4	EXITING
09/11/97	18:58:35	LEWINSKY, MONICA	34CB84	A	D1	ENTERING
09/11/97	19:05:42	LEWINSKY, MONICA	34CB84	A	D2	EXITING
09/12/97	19:40:54	LEWINSKY, MONICA	34EDF1	A	B4	ENTERING
09/12/97	20:22:23	LEWINSKY, MONICA	34EDF1	A	B4	EXITING
09/22/97	19:11:24	LEWINSKY, MONICA	345827	A	D2	ENTERING
09/22/97	19:25:02	LEWINSKY, MONICA	345827	A	D2	EXITING
10/11/97	09:36:45	LEWINSKY, MONICA	34D9B8	A	B4	ENTERING
10/11/97	10:54:24	LEWINSKY, MONICA	34D9B8	A	B4	EXITING
11/13/97	18:20:43	LEWINSKY, MONICA	34A9AB	A	B4	ENTERING
12/06/97	12:52:09	LEWINSKY, MONICA	346671	A	B4	ENTERING
12/06/97	13:36:02	LEWINSKY, MONICA	346671	A	B4	EXITING
12/15/97	11:31:12	LEWINSKY, MONICA	34DAF6	A	B4	ENTERING
12/15/97	12:38:52	LEWINSKY, MONICA	34DAF6	A	B4	EXITING
12/28/97	08:16:26	LEWINSKY, MONICA	34C4CA	A	B4	ENTERING

202498

827-DC-00000018

01/23/98

	Record#	DEPARTMENT	DATE	COST CENTE	TIME	DURATION	DESTINATIO		EXTENSION	DIALED DIG	USER	CO
ST	2600	PRESS	03/14/97	ROOM 212A	12:30	1.9	WASZ 1B	VA	4048	1-703-697-9312	ADELE GILL	0.
9	2615	PRESS	03/28/97	ROOM 212A	12:48	6.3	WASZ 1B	VA	4048	1-703-697-9312	ADELE GILL	0.
4 / AM	18671	PRESS	04/08/97	ROOM 212A	12:34	1.6	WASZ 1B	VA	4048	1-703-697-9312	ADELE GILL	0.
5 / S	24794	PRESS	06/11/97	ROOM 212D	14:48	5.2	WASZ 1B	VA	4076	1-703-697-9312	OFFICE PRE	0.
7 / E PRESS	24837	PRESS	06/23/97	ROOM 212F	11:48	2.1	WASZ 1B	VA	4153	1-703-697-9312	SPARE SPA	0.
NCE	25308	REF/RESEARCH	06/17/97	REFERENCE DESK	10:08	3.0	WASZ 1B	VA	4160	1-703-697-9312	DESK REFE	0
6 / .. ROAN	29030	MILITARY STAFF	05/23/97	ROOM 720B	16:37	0.0	WASZ 1B	V	4147	1-703-697-9312	RICHARD C	0.
. ROAN	29031	MILITARY STAFF	05/23/97	ROOM 720B	16:50	0.0	WASZ 1B	V	4147	1-703-697-9312	RICHARD C	0.
TKINS	50051	EXECUTIVE	10/24/97	EXEC-C	14:09	0:00:30	WASZ 1B	V	4402	1-703-697-9312	ISABELLE	
8 / TKINS	50101	EXECUTIVE	10/29/97	EXEC-C	11:51	0:00:30	WASZ 1B	V	4402	1-703-697-9312	ISABELLE	
8 / T' 'S	50102	EXECUTIVE	10/29/97	EXEC-C	13:50	0:00:30	WASZ 1B	V	4402	1-703-697-9312	ISABELLE	
8 / S	5^143	EXECUTIVE	10/30/97	EXEC-C	13:01	0:01:18	WASZ 1B	V	4402	1-703-697-9312	ISABELLE	
ARDSON	5__74	EXECUTIVE	11/03/97	EXEC	11:02	0:02:54	WASZ 1B	V	4404	1-703-697-9312	WILLIAM RI	0.
	63728	PRESS	11/05/97	ROOM 212A	15:58	0:01:06	WASZ 1B	V	4048	1-703-697-9312	ADELE GILL	0.
	63751	PRESS	11/17/97	ROOM 212A	19:29	0:01:00	WASZ 1B	V	4048	1-703-697-9312	ADELE GILL	0.
	63799	PRESS	11/20/97	ROOM 212B	13:23	0:01:54	WASZ 1B	V	4050	1-703-697-9312	SPARE PRE	0
ER	3905	PRESS	11/18/97	ROOM 212C	07:34	0:01:24	WASZ 1B	V	4052	1-703-697-9312	REBECCA N	0.
LL	4418	PRESS	11/05/97	ROOM 215	14:51	0:05:18	WASZ 1B	V	4058	1-703-697-9312	CALVIN MI	0
LL	4474	PRESS	11/13/97	ROOM 215	17:46	0:02:00	WASZ 1B	V	4058	1-703-697-9312	CALVIN MI	0
L	4479	PRESS	11/14/97	ROOM 215	12:48	0:01:30	WASZ 1B	V	4058	1-703-697-9312	CALVIN MI	0
L	4546	PRESS	11/23/97	ROOM 215	17:14	0:03:00	WASZ 1B	V	4058	1-703-697-9312	CALVIN MI	0
T.	[illegible]	UNATTACHED	11/17/97	UNATTACHED	16:44	0:06:36	WASZ 1B	V	4294	1-703-697-9312	SHOCAS SP	0.
		PRESS	12/18/97	ROOM 212A	12:30	0:01:18	WASZ 1B	V	4048	1-703-697-9312	ADELE GILL	0.
	465	PRESS	12/22/97	ROOM 215	15:16	0:04:24	WASZ 1B	V	4058	[illegible]	CALVIN MI	

828-DC-00000003

(C) (4170)

Re[illegible]rd#	DEPARTMENT	DATE	COST CENTE	TIME	DURATION	DESTINATIO	EXTENSION	DIALED DIG	USER	COST
49735	EXECUTIVE	10/21/97	EXEC	19:01	0:05:42	WASHINGTON D	4404	1-202-965-6355	WILLIAM RI [illegible] RDSON	0. [illegible]4
50074	EXECUTIVE	10/27/97	EXEC-C	17:15	0:00:36	WASHINGTON D	4402	1-202-965-6355	ISABELLE [illegible]KINS	[illegible]
50168	EXECUTIVE	10/30/97	EXEC-C	16:45	0:00:42	WASHINGTON D	4402	1-202-965-6355	ISABELLE WATKINS	0.12
50170	EXECUTIVE	10/30/97	EXEC-C	17:28	0:00:30	WASHINGTON D	4402	1-202-965-6355	ISABELLE WATKINS	0.05
60857	EXECUTIVE-III	11/19/97	EXEC-III-G	11:28	0:00:48	WASHINGTON D	4029	1-202-965-6355	MONA KAI SUTPHEN	0.13

10/21/97 TUE 15:09 FAX 202 456 1210 DEBI SCHIFF 002

UIL

Monica S. Lewinsky
[redacted]

[redacted]

Education:

Lewis and Clark College Portland, Oregon
Bachelor of Science in Psychology May 1995

Experience:

Department of Defense The Pentagon Washington, D.C.
Confidential Assistant to the Assistant Secretary of Defense for Public Affairs
April 1996 - present
Serve as principal assistant to the Assistant Secretary of Defense (ASD) for Public Affairs in support of his dual role as both Department of Defense spokesman and head of Department of Defense Public Affairs. Assist in preparing the ASD for bi-weekly press briefings. Interact with the national print and broadcast media on the ASD's behalf. Provide the ASD with timely updates of current media stories. Act as liaison with the offices of the Secretary, the White House, other Cabinet Secretaries and the National Security Council. Provide support to the Secretary of Defense and Assistant Secretary on frequent international travel which includes a contingent of traveling media. Handle the ASD's daily schedule and correspondence.

The White House Washington, D.C.
Staff Assistant to Director of Legislative Affairs Correspondence, November 1995 - April 1996
Wrote drafts and correspondence for Staff Secretary's approval and ultimately the President's signature, which often required research of various Administration issues and policies. Coordinated mass mailings to Congress for the President and other Senior Administration officials. Processed and vetted all incoming mail to the President from Congress. Trained and supervised new interns on White House procedure and preparation of White House correspondence.

The White House Washington, D.C.
Summer Intern Office of the Chief of Staff, July - November 1995
Drafted form letters and individual responses for the Chief of Staff's signature. Acted as a liaison for Chief of Staff's office to other White House offices, Cabinet agencies, and Congressional offices. Updated office manual. Supervised and coordinated intern and volunteer staff.

Metropolitan Public Defenders Portland, Oregon
Alternatives Staff, February - May 1995
Implemented new psychology expert reference techniques. Assisted attorneys in finding viable alternatives to prison for their clients. Directed clients in successful search for support, shelter, food and transportation. Updated files on resource materials.

Southeast Mental Health Network (Practicum) Portland, Oregon
Socialization Staff Assistant, January - June 1994
Assisted staff in teaching socialization skills to mentally ill clients to ease their integration back into society. Updated clients' confidential reports. Coordinated fund raising to benefit extra-curricular theatre activities.

Additional Information: 828-DC-00000012

- TS-SCI Clearance: Current
- Proficient in Macintosh for Microsoft Word 6.0, WordPerfect for Windows 5.2, Quorum, and Infosys.

Monica S. Lewinsky
[redacted]

UNB

Mona, what does this mean? P

3 November 1997

The Honorable Bill Richardson
United States Ambassador to the United Nations
799 United Nations Plaza
New York, New York 10017

Dear Ambassador Richardson:

It was a pleasure meeting with you last Friday morning. I know how very busy and demanding your schedule is; I particularly appreciated your taking the time to speak with me.

It was an honor to meet you. The US Mission to the United Nations is certainly in good hands with you at the helm.

Again, thank you for your time.

Sincerely,

Monica Lewinsky

Monica Lewinsky

BR -
SHE WROTE THIS NOTE BEFORE WE SPOKE LAST WEEK. JUST A THANK YOU.
M.

828-DC-00000013

A

U27A

5:15 PM Principals meeting on Iraq, White House

7:00 PM Mike Parker 2445 RHOB ([redacted])

OVERNIGHT WATERGATE

FRIDAY, OCTOBER 31, 1997
(HALLOWEEN)

7:30 AM Meeting with Monica Lewinsky, Watergate ([redacted])

8:30 AM Ben Gilman 2449 RHOB ([redacted])

9:00 AM Xavier Becerra 1119 LHOB ([redacted])

9:30 AM Nita Lowey 2421 RHOB ([redacted])

10:00 AM Bill Hefner 2470 RHOB ([redacted])

10:30 AM Ike Skelton 2227 RHOB ([redacted])

11:15 AM Bob Clement 2229 RHOB ([redacted])

11:15 AM Ed Pastor 2465 RHOB ([redacted]) Please change to noon if Livingston cancels

11:30 AM Tom DeLay H-107 Capitol ([redacted])

12:00 PM Rod Grams

12:30 AM Bob Matsui 2308 RHOB ([redacted])

1:00 PM Speaking Engagement - Earthkind, National Press Club (Luncheon begins at Noon)

2:00 PM Depart Washington

3:00 PM Arrive New York

3:30 PM Meeting of the P-5 re Iraq, UN Room C-209

4:00 PM Security Council

6:40 PM Interview - CNN, 461 Eigth Avenue, 20th Floor ([redacted])

2600

Monica Lewinsky
[redacted]

13 January 1998

JAN 1 4 1997

Ms. Jenna Sheldon
Manager, Corporate Staffing
REVLON
625 Madison Avenue
New York, New York 10022
By fax: [redacted]

Dear Jenna:

I am so excited about joining the team at Revlon. I think it's going to be great!

The following are two references from my employment at both the Pentagon and the White House. Please feel free to contact them. Mr. Bacon is currently traveling with Secretary Cohen in Asia and will return to the States on the 22nd of January. I would prefer you speak with him vice his deputy.

The Honorable Ken Bacon
Assistant Secretary of Defense
for Public Affairs
[redacted]
*** Please contact Colonel Ed Veiga, USA to speak with Mr. Bacon.

January 23

The Honorable John Hilley
Assistant to the President for Legislative Affairs
[redacted]

Please let me know if you need any more information.

Sincerely,

Monica Lewinsky

Monica Lewinsky

830-DC-00000007

TOTAL P.01

Monica S. Lewinsky
[redacted]

11 December 1997

Mr. Richard E. Halperin
EVP & Special Counsel to the President
MacAndrews & Forbes
35 East 62nd Street
New York, New York 10021

Dear Mr. Halperin:

I am writing at the suggestion of Vernon Jordan, who has spoken with you on my behalf.

I am interested in exploring opportunities in Communications or Public Relations in New York. I am hoping to secure a position which would require effective communication skills, creativity, and frequent interaction with people. My various jobs in Washington, DC have provided me with the training and skills needed to further pursue a career in these areas.

Most recently, I have been working for the Honorable Ken Bacon, the Assistant Secretary of Defense for Public Affairs, as his primary assistant. My responsibilities range from interacting with the media on his behalf, to providing administrative assistance on the Secretary of Defense's international trips, to assembling timely updates of current media stories. My prior experience was at the White House in Legislative Affairs and the Chief of Staff's Office. Please see the enclosed resume for further detail.

I am moving to New York and am seeking employment to begin the first of the year. I am ready and available to speak with whoever in your office you might deem appropriate. I will follow up with a phone call to your office on Monday, December 15th, 1997.

Thank you for time.

Sincerely,

Monica Lewinsky

Monica S. Lewinsky

830-DC-00000017

CC: Mr. Vernon Jordan

	2	992	C 17:28 01-18-98 00:00 01-01-70 1831175	16	8	Pages:	1	KA
13	2	992	C 16:06 01-18-98 00:00 01-01-70 1831175	24	24	Pages:	1	SE CALL KAY AT HOME.
13	2	992	C 15:22 01-18-98 00:00 01-01-70 1831175	22	24	Pages:	1	SE CALL KAY AT HOME.
13	2	992	C 14:12 01-18-98 00:00 01-01-70 1831175	22	25	Pages:	1	SE CALL KAY AT HOME.
13	2	992	C 20:26 01-17-98 00:00 01-01-70 1831175	10	38	Pages:	1	GINSBURG, [redacted]
13	2	992	C 11:34 01-16-98 00:00 01-01-70 1831175	4	43	Pages:	1	VERY WORRIED. PLS CALL MOM RIGHT AWAY.
13	2	992	C 11:05 01-16-98 00:00 01-01-70 1831175	11	24	Pages:	1	SE CALL MOM AT HOME.
13	2	992	C 07:51 01-16-98 00:00 01-01-70 1831175	5	74	Pages:	1	LEAVING THE OTHER PHONE NUMBER, WILL CALL YOU LATER THIS MORNING. M
13	2	992	C 07:45 01-16-98 00:00 01-01-70 1831175	5	2[illegible]	Pages:	1	SE CALL MARY ASAP.
13	2	992	C 07:35 01-16-98 00:00 01-01-70 1831175	2	2[illegible]	Pages:	1	MARY AT WORK ASAP.
13	2	992	C 07:35 01-16-98 00:00 01-01-70 1831175	6	4[illegible]	Pages:	1	'ALL MOM AT [redacted] OR [redacted]
1[illegible]	2	992	C 20:19 01-15-98 00:00 01-01-70 1831175	22	1[illegible]	Pages:	1	Y AT HOME.
	2	992	C 18:57 01-15-98 00:00 01-01-70 1831175	10	21	Pages:	1	SE CALL MARY BACK
13	2	992	C 18:48 01-15-98 00:00 01-01-70 1831175	14	2[illegible]	Pages:	1	RETURNING YOUR CALL.
13	2	992	C 14:22 01-15-98 00:00 01-01-70 1831175	7	22	Pages:	1	SE CALL KAY ASAP.
13	2	992	C 14:07 01-15-98 00:00 01-01-70 1831175	4	78	Pages:	1	D KAPLOW CALLED. PLEASE CALL [redacted] AT HOME OR [redacted] AT RK.
13	2	992	C 12:55 01-15-98 00:00 01-01-70 1831175	7	10	Pages:	1	L MOM.
13	2	992	C 11:14 01-15-98 00:00 01-01-70 1831175	7	25	Pages:	1	ASE CALL MARY AT HOME.
13	2	992	C 10:19 01-15-98 00:00 01-01-70 1831175	10	16	Pages:	1	ASE CALL MOM.
13	2	992	C 10:08 01-15-98 00:00 01-01-70 1831175	8	41	Pages:	1	ASE CALL FRANK CARTER AT [redacted]
13	2	992	C 09:31 01-15-98 00:00 01-01-70 1831175	10	16	Pages:	1	ASE CALL KAY.
13	2	992	C 07:22 01-15-98 00:00 01-01-70 1831175	10	[illegible]1	Pages:	1	ASE CALL FRANCIS CARTER @ [redacted]
	2	992	C 17:52 01-14-98 00:00 01-01-70 1831175	21	44	Pages:	1	CA, PLEASE CALL DEB @ [redacted]
	2	992	C 15:18 01-13-98 00:00 01-01-70 1831175	6	50	Pages:	1	LL ME WHEN YOU CAN AT [redacted]. DEBRA
13	2	992	C 14:36 01-13-98 00:00 01-01-70 1831175	4	15	Pages:	1	ASE CALL MOM
13	2	992	C 13:45 01-13-98 00:00 01-01-70 1831175	2	29	Pages:	1	ASE CALL MOM WHEN YOU CAN.

13	2	992	C 14:48 01-20-98 00:00 01-01-70 1831175	51	86	Pages:	2

PLEASE CALL MR MARTIN, TELL HIM ON HIS MACHINE, I AM WAITING OUTSIDE, I CANNOT GET IN.

13	2	992	C 12:42 01-20-98 00:00 01-01-70 1831175	44	105	Pages:	2

DON'T LOOK ANGRY. PEOPLE WHO MAY PROOF VERY IMPORTANT WILL SEE YOU. Y OU MUST LOOK COMPOSED. FROM MOM

13	2	992	C 12:40 01-20-98 00:00 01-01-70 1831175	48	66	Pages:	1

IF YOU ARE IN A RESTAURANT PLEASE BRING HOME SWEET AND LOW. MOM

13	2	992	C 09:39 01-20-98 00:00 01-01-70 1831175	42	71	Pages:	1

PLEASE CALL MOM. I'M SORRY I COULDN'T PICK UP A MIN AGO. PLS TRY AGAIN.

13	2	992	C 09:34 01-20-98 00:00 01-01-70 1831175	47	17	Pages:	1

PLEASE CALL MOM.

13	2	992	C 07:59 01-20-98 00:00 01-01-70 1831175	43	72	Pages:	1

THERE ARE PEOPLE YOU DONT WANT TO SEE WAITING FOR YOU IN THE LOBBY. MOM

13	2	992	C 20:21 01-19-98 00:00 01-01-70 1831175	40	70	Pages:	1

PLEASE CALL MOM RIGHT AWAY, IF YOU ARE NOT IN A MEETING. IT'S URGENT.

13	2	992	C 18:54 01-19-98 00:00 01-01-70 1831175	45	16	Pages:	1

PLEASE CALL MOM.

13	2	992	C 17:31 01-19-98 00:00 01-01-70 1831175	42	16	Pages:	1

PLEASE CALL MOM.

13	2	992	C 14:39 01-19-98 00:00 01-01-70 1831175	34	16	Pages:	1

PLEASE CALL MOM.

13	2	992	C 13:55 01-19-98 00:00 01-01-70 1831175	27	75	Pages:	1

MIKE DOUBLEDAY @ [redacted] CALLED. PLEASE CALL HIM BACK AT YOUR CONVE NIENCE.

13	2	992	C 11:46 01-19-98 00:00 01-01-70 1831175	33	4[illegible]	Pages:	1

PLEASE CALL FRANK CARTER AT [redacted]

13	2	992	C 10:19 01-19-98 00:00 01-01-70 1831175	28	4[illegible]	Pages:	1

HAVE MOM CALL ME WHEN SHE GETS HOME. MIKE

13	2	992	C 10:06 01-19-98 00:00 01-01-70 1831175	35	4[illegible]	Pages:	1

PLEASE CALL BILL GINSBURG AT [redacted].

13	2	992	C 08:44 01-19-98 00:00 01-01-70 1831175	32	4[illegible]	Pages:	1

IT IS MIKE AGAIN. PLEASE HURRY UP AND CALL ME.

13	2	992	C 08:18 01-19-98 00:00 01-01-70 1831175	33	3[illegible]	Pages:	1

THIS MIKE. I AM HOME. PLEASE CALL ME.

13	2	992	C 08:16 01-19-98 00:00 01-01-70 1831175	31	31	Pages:	1

PLEASE CALL MR JORDAN AT [redacted].

13	2	992	C 07:36 01-19-98 00:00 01-01-70 1831175	29	33	Pages:	1

PLEASE CALL MR. JORDAN AT [redacted]

13	2	992	C 06:39 01-19-98 00:00 01-01-70 1831175	30	31	Pages:	1

I'M HOME. PLEASE CALL ME. MIKE

13	2	992	C 05:51 01-19-98 00:00 01-01-70 1831175	42	42	Pages:	1

MSG FROM KAY. PLEASE CALL, HAVE GOOD NEWS.

13	2	992	C 05:44 01-19-98 00:00 01-01-70 1831175	31	38	Pages:	1

PLEASE CALL KATE RE: FAMILY EMERGENCY.

13	2	992	C 05:41 01-19-98 00:00 01-01-70 1831175	33	28	Pages:	1

KAY IS AT HOME. PLEASE CALL

13	2	992	C 05:37 01-19-98 00:00 01-01-70 1831175	38	57	Pages:	1

PLEASE CALL KAY AT HOME. IT'S A SOCIAL CALL. THANK YOU

13	2	992	C 05:33 01-19-98 00:00 01-01-70 1831175	35	24	Pages:	1

PLEASE CALL KAY AT HOME.

13	2	992	C 05:08 01-19-98 00:00 01-01-70 1831175	40	16	Pages:	1

PLEASE CALL KAY.

13	2	992	C 04:02 01-19-98 00:00 01-01-70 1831175	24	45	Pages:	1

PLEASE CALL KAY AT HOME AT 8:00 THIS MORNING.

2 992 C 11:20 01-13-98 00:00 01-01-70 1831175 18 19 Pages: ✓ 1

CALL ME. KAY

13 2 992 C 08:11 01-13-98 00:00 01-01-70 1831175 25 40 Pages: 1

WILL KNOW SOMETHING THIS AFTERNOON. -KAY

13 2 992 C 03:06 01-13-98 00:00 01-01-70 1831175 31 18 Pages: 1

PLEASE CALL MOM.

13 2 992 C 14:22 01-12-98 00:00 01-01-70 1831175 12 36 Pages: 1

PLEASE CALL MARISSA AT [redacted]

13 2 992 C 08:18 01-12-98 00:00 01-01-70 1831175 9 41 Pages: 1

PLEASE CALL FRANK CARTER AT [redacted].

13 2 992 C 08:23 01-10-98 00:00 01-01-70 1831175 14 92 Pages: 2

TODAY IS DAD'S BIRTHDAY ISN'T IT? PLEASE CALL ME AS SOON AS YOU CAN. LOV
E, MIKE [redacted]

13 2 992 C 13:46 01-08-98 00:00 01-01-70 1831175 13 1(. Pages: 1

PLEASE CALL MOM.

13 2 992 C 09:22 01-08-98 00:00 01-01-70 1831175 7 4' Pages: 1

YOUR DAD CALLED [redacted] NOT URGENT.

13 2 992 C 16:27 01-07-98 00:00 01-01-70 1831175 3 31 Pages: 1

PLEASE CALL MOM AT [redacted]

13 2 992 C 08:54 01-07-98 00:00 01-01-70 1831175 5 41 Pages: 1

PLEASE CALL MONA SUTPHEN AT [redacted]

13 2 992 C 17:00 01-06-98 00:00 01-01-70 1831175 20 52 Pages: 1

HAVE YOUR BROTHER CALL ME AT [redacted], KENNITH.

13 2 992 C 12:14 01-06-98 00:00 01-01-70 1831175 13 87 Pages: 2

ANK CARTER AT [redacted]. I WILL SEE YOU TOMORROW MORNING AT 10:00
.N MY OFFICE.

1 2 992 C 08:32 01-06-98 00:00 01-01-70 1831175 15 40 Pages: 1

CALL FRANK CARTER @ [redacted]

13 2 992 C 07:40 01-06-98 00:00 01-01-70 1831175 17 32 Pages: 1

PLEASE COME HOME, MICHEAL IS UP.

13 2 992 C 07:11 01-06-98 00:00 01-01-70 1831175 10 15 Pages: 1

PLEASE CALL MOM

13 2 992 C 08:49 01-03-98 00:00 01-01-70 1831175 6 39 Pages: 1

ALEX IS HERE. PLEASE CALL [redacted]

13 2 992 C 09:26 01-02-98 00:00 01-01-70 1831175 26 73 Pages: 1

HURRY UP AND CALL ME I WANT TO LEAVE SOON AND I AM WAITING FOR YOUR CALL
.

13 2 992 C 08:58 01-02-98 00:00 01-01-70 1831175 32 42 Pages: 1

I'M AWAKE. CALL ME WHEN YOU GET A CHANCE.

13 2 992 C 13:42 01-01-98 00:00 01-01-70 1831175 27 40 Pages: 1

GIVE ME A CALL. WITH INFO RE; FLIGHT AT HOME OR LEAVE A MSG ON PAGER.

13 2 992 C 12:00 12-30-97 00:00 01-01-70 1831175 6 27 Pages: 1

CALL ASHLEY @ [redacted]

13 2 992 C 10:25 12-29-97 00:00 01-01-70 1831175 29 66 Pages: 1

FRANK CARTER RETURNED YOUR CALL, [redacted]

13 2 992 C 07:41 12-28-97 00:00 01-01-70 1831175 22 21 Pages: 1

I AM AWAKE. CALL ME.

13 2 992 C 07:29 12-27-97 00:00 01-01-70 1831175 33 98 Pages: 2

MAKE SURE TO LEAVE MONEY IN THE LOBBY FOR ME BECAUSE I HAVE NO CASH FOR
A CAB, PROBABLY $40. MIKE

13 2 992 C 13:17 12-24-97 00:00 01-01-70 1831175 60 16 Pages: 1

PLEASE CALL MOM.

'3 2 992 C 09:45 12-23-97 00:00 01-01-70 1831175 39 18 Pages: 1

E CALL MOM.

13 2 992 C 04:55 12-22-97 00:00 01-01-70 1831175 33 68 Pages: 1
OT COME TODAY. WILL WAIT AT HOME FOR YOU TO CALL. - LOVE, MOM.

13 2 992 C 06:13 12-21-97 00:00 01-01-70 1831175 13 21 Pages: 1
PLEASE CALL YOUR MOM.

13 2 992 C 14:25 12-19-97 00:00 01-01-70 1831175 9 33 Pages: 1
AM TAKING 7:30 TRAIN TONIGHT. MOM

13 2 992 C 12:39 12-19-97 00:00 01-01-70 1831175 5 46 Pages: 1
I WILL BE AT MY HOME PHONE NUMBER AT 4:30. MOM

13 2 992 C 12:39 12-19-97 00:00 01-01-70 1831175 12 74 Pages: 1
I WILL BE @ MY HOME PHONE # @ 4:30. MOM (CALLER HUNG UP. MSG NOT VERIFIE
D)

13 2 992 C 16:13 12-16-97 00:00 01-01-70 1831175 3 64 Pages: 1
PLEASE CALL MIKE ON MOM'S LINE. I WILL BE WAITING FOR THE CALL.

13 2 992 C 09:44 12-16-97 00:00 01-01-70 1831175 9 62 Pages: 1
WHAT TIME IS MIKE'S DINNER TONIGHT? PLEASE CALL DEB AT [redacted]

13 2 992 C 12:33 12-11-97 00:00 01-01-70 1831175 11 6[illegible] Pages: 1
FAX NUMBER IS [redacted] PLS CALL ME WHEN YOU TRANSMITT. MOM

13 2 992 C 10:45 12-11-97 00:00 01-01-70 1831175 11 6[illegible] Pages: 1
CALL YOUR MOM WHEN YOU ARE FINISHED AT [redacted] ASK FOR DEBBIE.

13 2 992 C 09:05 12-07-97 00:00 01-01-70 1831175 14 3[illegible] Pages: 1
PLEASE CALL YOUR MOTHER AT [redacted]

13 2 992 C 07:34 12-06-97 00:00 01-01-70 1831175 18 3[illegible] Pages: 1
WAS IN RESEIDENCE CALL BACK. BETTY

13 2 992 C 13:40 12-05-97 00:00 01-01-70 1831175 6 5 Pages: 1
"S.

13 2 992 C 13:35 12-05-97 00:00 01-01-70 1831175 14 42 Pages: 1
EASE CALL BETTY CURRIE AT [redacted]

13 2 992 C 09:58 11-30-97 00:00 01-01-70 1831175 42 76 Pages: 1
.EASE CALL KASSORLA AND TELL HER I HAVE SENT A CHECK. AND PLEASE CALL M
OM.

13 2 992 C 21:57 11-29-97 00:00 01-01-70 1831175 24 [illegible]2 Pages: 1
CALL ZACK AT [redacted]

13 2 992 C 13:22 11-26-97 00:00 01-01-70 1831175 11 [illegible]8 Pages: 1
CALL MARSHA AT [redacted]

13 2 992 C 12:07 11-26-97 00:00 01-01-70 1831175 10 [illegible]0 Pages: 1
PLEASE CALL VERNON JORDAN, BETTY CURRY.

13 2 992 C 10:39 11-26-97 00:00 01-01-70 1831175 8 [illegible]0 Pages: 2
I WILL CALL BACK. CURRIE WILL CALL LATER. THANK YOU (MESSAGE NOT VERIFIE
D. CALLER HUNG UP)

13 2 992 C 07:35 11-26-97 00:00 01-01-70 1831175 19 21 Pages: 1
PLEASE CALL SAMANTHA.

13 2 992 C 14:04 11-25-97 00:00 01-01-70 1831175 8 19 Pages: 1
PLEASE CALL MARSHA.

3 1 992 C 09:26 11-25-97 00:00 01-01-70 1831175 9 19 0
TEST PAGE FROM MOC.

3 1 992 C 07:57 11-24-97 00:00 01-01-70 1831175 13 71 0
WELCOME TO YOUR NEW ALPHA MESSAGE SERVICE. YOUR NUMBER IS [redacted]

TOTAL PAGES BILLABLE: 136
TOTAL MOU'S BILLABLE: 0
TOTAL ETP Pages BILLABLE: 0

TYPE	DESCRIPTION	COUNT
3 - Page	Test Page	2
3 - Page	800 Operator Alpha Page	136
		138

831-DC-00000011

Monica S. Lewinsky
[redacted]

6 November 1997

Mr. Vernon Jordan
Akin, Gump, Strauss, Hauer & Feld
1333 New Hampshire, NW
Washington, DC 20036

Dear Mr. Jordan:

It was a real pleasure meeting with you. I know how very busy and demanding your schedule is; I particularly appreciated your taking the time to speak with me.

I feel compelled to mention how overcome I was by your genuineness. While some people wear their heart on their sleeve; you appear to wear your soul. It made me happy to know that our friend has such a wonderful confidante in you.

I believe I may have neglected to mention that while my current position is administrative, I am seeking more substantive work in my next position.

Thanks again for your time, and I look forward to hearing from you upon your return.

Sincerely,

Monica S. Lewinsky

833-DC-00000980

Selection Detail Report

Company Name

DATE	TIME	DURATION HHHH:MM:SS	Extension	DIALED NUMBER	LOCATION	CALL TYPE	Trunk	ACCOUNT CODE	COST (DOLLARS)
01/21/98	09:12	0:07:26	[redacted]	[redacted]		OUTGO	[redacted]		0.00

SENT BY:Xerox Telecopier 7021 ; 4-10-98 ; 1:07PM ; 2122231942- 12023146602;# -

Selection Detail Report

Company Name

DATE	TIME	DURATION HH:MM:SS	Extension	DIALED NUMBER	LOCATION	CALL TYPE	Trunk	ACCOUNT CODE	COST (DOLLARS)
01/21/98	08:11	0:00:30	[redacted]	[redacted]		OUTGO	[redacted]		0.00
01/21/98	08:13	0:05:00	[redacted]	[redacted]		OUTGO	[redacted]		0.00
01/21/98	08:18	0:10:04	[redacted]	[redacted]		OUTGO	[redacted]		0.08
01/21/98	08:32	0:00:54	[redacted]	[redacted]		OUTGO	[redacted]		0.00

832-DC-00000004

24 June 1997

Dear Betty:

Since I have not been able to get in touch with him, I am taking the unorthodox liberty of sharing my concerns with you. I would very much appreciate it if you could relay this information to him either verbally or by letting him read this note. If you're not comfortable doing either, I understand.

The intention of this note is not to "tattle-tale", but to clarify. My meeting with Marsha was not at all what I expected. While she was very pleasant, she questioned me endlessly about my situation. Despite the fact that she already knew why I had to leave, she asked me to tell her about it, asked if I had acted "inappropriately" and why I wanted to come back. She seemingly knew nothing about my current position. She didn't know of any openings and said she would check with the people in Communications. He said to me that he had told her I had gotten a bum deal, and I should get a good job in the West Wing. I was surprised that she would question his judgment and not just do what he asked of her. Is it possible that, in fact, he did not tell her that? Does he really not want me back in the complex? He has not responded to my note, nor has he called me. Do you know what is going on? If so, are you able to share it with me?

I did not cause any trouble when I had to leave last year because I knew how important the election was. He promised me then I could come back after the election, and I have been counting on him. I think I have been more than patient since it has now been eight months since the election, not to mention the seven months prior to November that I waited. Shall I continue to be patient?

Betty, I am very frustrated and sad. I especially don't understand this deafening silence, lack of response and complete distancing evidenced by him. Why is he ignoring me? I have done nothing wrong. I would expect that behavior like this might be directed toward an "unfriendly", but certainly not to me. I would ***never*** do anything to hurt him.

I am hoping to hear from either of you soon. I'm at a loss, and I don't know what to do.

Best wishes.

Tripp, Linda, , OSD/PA

From: Tripp, Linda, , OSD/PA
To: Lewinsky, Monica, , OSD/PA
Subject: RE: hi, ya
Date: Wednesday, March 05, 1997 11:34AM

Are you asking me if the tie if really pretty? It is positively gorgeous. I am knot (ha!) particularly into ties, but from my exposure to you, I am developing an interest. Yours was stupendous, no kidding, clean, crisp, texture, color, pattern, bright, without being at all over the top.....a total hit.

From: Lewinsky, Monica, , OSD/PA
To: Tripp, Linda, , OSD/PA
Subject: hi, ya
Date: Wednesday, March 05, 1997 10:05AM
Priority: High

Boy, I look so scary today. People might think that I thought it was Halloween. Oh, well [redacted] should (if Betty is nice) get my tie today. I sure hope he like s it. make me feel better and tell me it's really pretty, o.k.? msl

833-DC-00001857

Tripp, Linda, , OSD/PA

From: Tripp, Linda, , OSD/PA
To: Lewinsky, Monica, , OSD/PA
Subject: RE: where are you?
Date: Monday, March 03, 1997 12:48PM

Kate is faxing me a copy of the announcement -- she is planning to go see Marsha today. If someone in house wants it, there is a chance they will get it, but Kate seems confident that that won't happen. She said to have your resume ready. LRT

From: Lewinsky, Monica, , OSD/PA
To: Tripp, Linda, , OSD/PA
Subject: where are you?
Date: Monday, March 03, 1997 12:21PM
Priority: High

Hello, where are you? I am sorry i was such a pain before but this is all very stressful for me. write back. i don't know what's goin on. msl

833-DC-00001876

Tripp, Linda, , OSD/PA

From: Tripp, Linda, , OSD/PA
To: Lewinsky, Monica, , OSD/PA
Subject: RE: ADVICE
Date: Monday, February 24, 1997 11:22AM

Eureka!!!!

From: Lewinsky, Monica, , OSD/PA
To: Tripp, Linda, , OSD/PA
Subject: ADVICE
Date: Monday, February 24, 1997 8:31AM

Hi, I hope you're feeling better ! I 'm trying to go over to the WH today to give Jodie these pictures. I also plan to stop by Betty's office to drop off these lame photos. Any advice/suggestions what to do or say? write me back...msl

833-DC-00001906

Tripp, Linda, , OSD/PA

From: Tripp, Linda, , OSD/PA
To: Lewinsky, Monica, , OSD/PA
Subject: RE: secret message
Date: Wednesday, February 19, 1997 9:01AM

WELCOME BACK!!! How was Jolly, Olde England? Well, here's the saga in a nutshell. On friday (of course), Howard County (the boondocks where I live) was totally and completely snowed and iced in, so I couldn't get up my hill, schools were closed, no one moved, believe it or not. I was in a panic about the papers.....by the time I could get up the hill late that night, all the Posts were gone, BUT I called work and had my Deputy save me what he could, which was one, and then I found another, so we have two. I can't believe it became that big a deal, but it did. CALL ME WHEN YOU GET IN. PS It read beautifully, placement was great, typeface totally effective, and text superlative.....good job. LRT

From: Lewinsky, Monica, , OSD/PA
To: Tripp, Linda, , OSD/PA
Subject: RE: secret message
Date: Thursday, February 13, 1997 1:23PM

O.K. here is my fax in London 011-44-171-235-4552 and phone, just in case, I don't know what, here is the phone number 011-44-171-235-2000. I will also be checking my messages in the hopes that the creep will call and say"Thank you for my love note. I love you. Will you run away with me?" What do ya think the likelihood of that happening is? Also, please don't forget about the newspapers. I will bring you the $ later.

thanx...xoxoxo...msl

From: Tripp, Linda, , OSD/PA
To: Lewinsky, Monica, , OSD/PA
Subject: RE: secret message
Date: Thursday, February 13, 1997 1:03PM

Ah, but that has already transpired, says my omnipotent crystal ball........................

From: Lewinsky, Monica, , OSD/PA
To: Tripp, Linda, , OSD/PA
Subject: RE: secret message
Date: Thursday, February 13, 1997 11:05AM
Priority: High

IF ONLY I COULD PURSUADE THE CREEP AS EASILY!!!!!!!

From: Tripp, Linda, , OSD/PA
To: Lewinsky, Monica, , OSD/PA
Subject: RE: secret message
Date: Thursday, February 13, 1997 11:03AM

833-DC-00001934

OK OK OK. 12 at bridge.

From: Lewinsky, Monica, , OSD/PA
To: Tripp, Linda, , OSD/PA
Subject: RE: secret message
Date: Thursday, February 13, 1997 10:18AM
Priority: High

I'LL PROBABLY GO GET LUNCH AT 12;00 BECAUSE I'M HUNGRY ALREADY!!! I DON'T THINK I'LL BE MORE THAN 1/2 HOUR BECAUSE I'M LEAVING EARLY. PLEASE ESCAPE WITH ME!!!!!! HOW CAN YOU RESIST ME?? DON'T FORGET I'LL BE GONE FOR AWHILE...MSL

From: Tripp, Linda, , OSD/PA
To: Lewinsky, Monica, , OSD/PA
Subject: RE: secret message

Tripp, Linda, , OSD/PA

From: Tripp, Linda, , OSD/PA
To: Lewinsky, Monica, , OSD/PA
Subject: RE: Afternoon
Date: Tuesday, February 04, 1997 2:55PM

None of the above, if you ask me. Because, none of it makes sense. Do not despair, there is most definitely light at the end of this tunnel. LRT

From: Lewinsky, Monica, , OSD/PA
To: Tripp, Linda, , OSD/PA
Subject: RE: Afternoon
Date: Tuesday, February 04, 1997 2:15PM
Priority: High

Thank God for you! Oh Linda, i don't know what I am going to do. I just don't understand what went wrong, what happened? How could he do this to me? Why did he keep up contact with me for so long and now nothing, now when we could be together? Maybe it was the intrigue of wanting something he couldn't have (easily) with all that was going on then? Maybe he wanted to insure he could have variety and phone sex while he was on the road for those months? AAAAHHHHH!!!!! I am going to lose it! And, where is Betty's phone call? What's up with all this shit? oh, well. bye.
msl

From: Tripp, Linda, , OSD/PA
To: Lewinsky, Monica, , OSD/PA
Subject: Afternoon
Date: Tuesday, February 04, 1997 2:06PM
Priority: High

Just checking in, it's been a nutty day so I haven't had much chance to see you. I had to go up to the third floor and drop off some paperwork, so I actually walked the entire E-ring, which took l5 minutes. Guess I am kinda slow, huh? Oh well, next time I will go by myself so that I can keep my own pace. I feel as though I did SOMETHING anyway. I have had tons of water the past few days, and even more today, so watch and see, I'll have gained weight tonight, at this rate. I don't seem to be getting rid of the water, so it's hanging out somewhere!! Anyway, my real purpose in jotting off this e-mail is to see what's up with you, and how you're doing. I am so jealous that you are off to London soon, I love it so. I would spend tons of time in Harrod's, spend time on Fleet Street and down in the Silver Vaults, putter around Portebello Road, and shop til I dropped!! I would have high tea every day even if I had to skip real meals. I used to spend all my summers in Europe as a kid, and would sneak over to London whenever I could, always by myself, when I was about l6. Back then (I'm dating myself!!!) you could buy the all time BEST fish and chips from these little holes in the wall, wrapped in newspaper!! It was one of the best things I had ever eaten.
LRT

833-DC-00001974

[redacted]

...rm 50-B
...of Personnel Management
...pp. 296-33, Subch. 4

NOTIFICATION OF PERSONNEL ACTION

...e (Last, First, Middle)	2. Social Security Number	3. Date of Birth	4. Effective Date
INSKY MONICA S	[redacted]	[redacted]	12-26-97

FIRST ACTION		SECOND ACTION	
5-A. Code: 317	5-B. Nature of Action: RESIGNATION	6-A. Code	6-B. Nature of Action
5-C. Code: RUM	5-D. Legal Authority: REG 715.202 OTHER	6-C. Code	6-D. Legal Authority
5-E. Code	5-F. Legal Authority	6-E. Code	6-F. Legal Authority

7. FROM: Position Title and Number
CONFIDENTIAL ASSISTANT
16151
720000 DDAAKA

8. Pay Plan	9. Occ. Code	10. Grade/Level	11. Step/Rate	12. Total Salary	13. Pay Basis
GS	0301	09	02	$32,736.00	PA

12A. Basic Pay	12B. Locality Adj.	12C. Adj. Basic Pay	12D. Other Pay
$30,563	$ 2173	$32,736	$ 0

14. Name and Location of Position's Organization
ASD (PUBLIC AFRS)

WASHINGTON, D. C.

15. TO: Position Title and Number

16. Pay Plan	17. Occ. Code	18. Grade/Level	19. Step/Rate	20. Total Salary/Award	21. Pay Basis

20A. Basic Pay	20B. Locality Adj.	20C. Adj. Basic Pay	20D. Other Pay

22. Name and Location of Position's Organization

EMPLOYEE DATA

...Veterans Preference: 1
1 – None; 2 – 5-Point; 3 – 10-Point/Disability; 4 – 10-Point/Compensable; 5 – 10-Point/Other; 6 – 10-Point/Compensable/30%

24. Tenure: 3 (0 – None; 1 – Permanent; 2 – Conditional; 3 – Indefinite)
25. Agency Use
26. Veterans Preference for RIF: YES / X NO

FEGLI: C — BASIC LIFE ONLY
28. Annuitant Indicator: 9 — NOT APPLICABLE
29. Pay Rate Determinant: 0

30. Retirement Plan: K — FERS AND FICA
31. Service Comp. Date (Leave): 11-26-95
32. Work Schedule: F — FULL TIME
33. Part-Time Hours Per Biweekly Pay Period

POSITION DATA

34. Position Occupied: 2 (1 – Competitive Service; 2 – Excepted Service; 3 – SES General; 4 – SES Career Reserved)
35. FLSA Category: E (E – Exempt; N – Nonexempt)
36. Appropriation Code: SEE BLOCKS 43 & 44
37. Bargaining Unit Status: 8888
38. Duty Station Code: 51-0100-013
39. Duty Station (City – County – State or Overseas Location): ARLINGTON VA

40. AGENCY DATA	41.	42.	43.	44.
ARK			FM:APC:220100 TO:APC:	FM:FUNDS SYM 970100.11200000 TO:FUNDS SYM

45. Remarks

833-DC-00002716

SF-8 ISSUED.
SF-2810 ISSUED.
LUMP-SUM PAYMENT TO BE MADE FOR ANY UNUSED ANNUAL LEAVE.
FORWARDING ADDRESS: [redacted]
HEALTH BENEFITS COVERAGE IS EXTENDED FOR 31 DAYS DURING WHICH YOU ARE ELIGIBLE TO CONVERT TO AN INDIVIDUAL POLICY (NONGROUP CONTRACT). YOU ARE ALSO ELIGIBLE FOR TEMPORARY CONTINUATION OF YOUR FEHB COVERAGE FOR UP TO 18 MONTHS.
REASON FOR RESIGNATION: SEEKING EMPLOYMENT OPPORTUNITIES OUTSIDE THE GOVERNMENT.

Employing Department or Agency: OFFICE OF THE SECRETARY OF DEFENSE
50. Signature/Authentication and Title of Approving Official: DESIGNATED APPOINTING OFFICIAL

Agency Code	48. Personnel Office ID	49. Approval Date
DD01	1936	01-22-98

Editions Prior to 7/91 Are Not Usable After 6/...
DO NOT DESTROY
NSN 7540-01-333-...

Confidential Assistant to the Assistant Secretary of Defense for Public Affairs (GS-301-09)

INTRODUCTION

This position is located in the Office of the Assistant Secretary of Defense for Public Affairs. The Assistant Secretary of Defense for Public Affairs (ASD(PA)) is the principal staff assistant and advisor to the Secretary of Defense on all DoD public affairs programs and activities and on the internal information and related activities of the American Forces Information Service. He is responsible for establishing and implementing policies and systems necessary for the effective and economical performance of DoD public affairs and internal information programs, including those of the military departments.

The incumbent of this Schedule C position will have access to highly confidential, sensitive and frequently politically controversial information and must be a person in whom the ASD(PA) has complete trust and confidence. This close relationship is that of a confidential nature required for Schedule C exception.

DUTIES 833-DC-00002880

As Confidential Assistant, the incumbent provides secretarial and administrative support directly to the ASD(PA) in key areas of his ongoing official and administrative responsibilities.

On behalf of the ASD(PA), maintains contact at primary management levels within the DoD on personal and special taskings. This includes contacts with the office of the Secretary of Defense, the Organization of the Joint Chiefs of Staff, the Secretariats of the military departments, defense agencies and similar DoD components. In addition, incumbent may represent the ASD(PA) in personal and confidential contacts with members of Congress and civilian industry executives.

Travels with the ASD(PA) and Secretary of Defense, providing secretarial and administrative support to the ASD and other members of the Secretary's traveling group, as required.

Participates in all ASD(PA) staff meetings and directors' meetings.

Conducts fact-finding research and summarizes and arranges the data in formats preferred by the ASD(PA). When background material is

SPECIAL PER DIEM LETTER ATTACHED [illegible]

TRAVEL VOUCHER OR SUBVOUCHER

Read Privacy Act Statement, Penalty Statement, and Instructions on back before completing form. Use typewriter, ink, or ball point pen. PRESS HARD. DO NOT use pencil. If more space is needed, continue in remarks.

1. PAYMENT: Electronic Fund Transfer (EFT) — [X] Payment by Check — Split Disbursement: Amt to Govt Tvl Charge Card $

2. TYPE OF PAYMENT *(X as applicable)*: [X] TDY — Other — Member/Employee — Dependent(s) — PCS — DLA

3. FOR D.O. USE ONLY: a. D.O. VOUCHER NUMBER — b. SUBVOUCHER NUMBER — c. PAID BY: 833-DC-00003207 — d. COMPUTATIONS

4. NAME *(Last, First, Middle Initial) (Print or type)*: LEWINSKY, MONICA SAMILLE

5. GRADE: GS-9

6. SSN: [redacted]

7. ADDRESS. a. NUMBER AND STREET: [redacted] — b. CITY: [redacted] — c. STATE: [redacted] — d. ZIP CODE: [redacted]

8. DAYTIME TELEPHONE NUMBER & AREA CODE: [redacted]

9. TRAVEL ORDER NUMBER: DSTB80269

10. PREVIOUS GOVERNMENT PAYMENTS/ADVANCES: NONE

11. ORGANIZATION AND STATION: OASD/PA

12. DEPENDENT(S) *(X and complete as applicable)*: ACCOMPANIED — [X] UNACCOMPANIED

a. NAME *(Last, First, Middle Initial)*	b. RELATIONSHIP	c. DATE OF BIRTH OR MARRIAGE

13. DEPENDENTS' ADDRESS ON RECEIPT OF ORDERS *(Include Zip Code)*:

14. HAVE HOUSEHOLD GOODS BEEN SHIPPED? *(X one)*: YES — [X] NO *(Explain in Remarks)*

15. ITINERARY

a. DATE 1997		b. PLACE *(Home, Office, Base, Activity, City and State; City and Country, etc.)*	c. MEANS/MODE OF TRAVEL	d. REASON FOR STOP	e. LODGING COST	f. POC MILES
12/1	DEP	RESIDENCE	PA			
12/1	ARR	ANDREWS, AFB		AT		20
12/1	DEP		GP			
12/1	ARR	BRUSSELS, BELGIUM		TD	$303.03	
12/3	DEP		GP			
12/3	ARR	LONDON, ENGLAND		TD	$682.99	
12/5	DEP		GP			
12/5	ARR	ANDREWS, AFB		AT		
12/5	DEP		PA			
12/5	ARR	RESIDENCE		MC		20
12/5	DEP					
	ARR					
	DEP					
	ARR					
	DEP					
	ARR					

e. SUMMARY OF PAYMENT

(1) Per Diem	
(2) Actual Expense Allowance	
(3) Mileage	
(4) Dependent Travel	
(5) DLA	
(6) Reimbursable Expenses	
(7) Total	
(8) Less Advance	
(9) Amount Owed	
(10) Amount Due	

16. POC TRAVEL *(X one)*: [X] OWN/OPERATE — PASSENGER

17. DURATION OF TDY TRAVEL: 12 HOURS OR LESS — MORE THAN 12 HOURS BUT 24 HOURS OR LESS — [X] MORE THAN 24 HOURS

18. REIMBURSABLE EXPENSES

a. DATE	b. NATURE OF EXPENSE	c. AMOUNT	d. ALLOWED
12/1	OFFICIAL PHONE CALLS	16.68	
12/2	OFFICIAL PHONE CALL	16.68	

19. GOVERNMENT/DEDUCTIBLE MEALS

a. DATE	b. NO. OF MEALS	a. DATE	b. NO. OF MEALS

20.a. CLAIMANT SIGNATURE: Monica Lewinsky — **b. DATE:** 12/8/97

21.a. APPROVING OFFICER SIGNATURE: [signature] — **b. DATE:** 10 Dec 97

22. ACCOUNTING CLASSIFICATION

AUTHORIZATION LETTER ATTACHED PROVIDES 150% OF PER DIEM PER TRAVELS WITH THE SECRETARY
= 33 BELGIUM FRANCS
875 = 1 POUND

23. COLLECTION DATA

24. COMPUTED BY	25. AUDITED BY	26. TRAVEL ORDER POSTED BY	27. RECEIVED *(Payee Signature and Date or Check No.)*	28. AMOUNT PAID

DD FORM 1351-2, AUG 1997 (EG) — PREVIOUS EDITIONS OF DD FORM 1351-2 AND 1351-1 MAY BE USED UNTIL SUPPLY IS EXHAUSTED — Exception to SF 1012 approved by GSA/IRMS 12-91.

cargo handling equipment needed? Will the baggage be loose or palletized? How will the bags be marked - will there be some sort of uniform tag on each bag identifying its owner? How and when are the Civic Leaders leaving Eglin on May 8th - i.e. are they departing on military air?

Concerning the Ramada:
I sort of doubt that the brochure from the Ramada will fax very well - how about if I mail one to you? Give me an address and I'll do just that.

Concerning Gifts:
Is OSD paying us up to $25 per 60 JCOC participants for gifts?

Concerning JCOC participants:
When can I expect to get a list of JCOC participants? On the list of participants, I need to know their SSNs for the MEGP letters (permission to fly on AF aircraft). Will there be any handicapped individuals? We would like to know of any special medical conditions such as history of motion sickness, asthma, cardiac, diabetes etc. Will that kind of info be available?

In General:
Do you expect full up dress rehearsals for each of your advance trips? Will the 10 OSD support personnel be going on the demos on May 7 & 8? Did you already get a representative base photo from us? If not, when do you need one? Do you need any bios from us now? Am I required to provide videographers for the visit?

I noticed the comment concerning the "Persian Gulf" vs the "Arabian Gulf". Is that a problem for this trip, i.e. will there be any Arabians in the group?

V/R, Hart Franklin

Tripp, Linda, , OSD/PA

833-DC-00009446

From: Lewinsky, Monica, , OSD/PA
To: Tripp, Linda, , OSD/PA
Subject: I'm back!
Date: Wednesday, February 19, 1997 8:09AM
Priority: High

LRT--- Hi, I missed you!!!! I hope you enjoyed your few days of sanity with me gone because I'm back and NOT in good spirits.

1. I have a small present for you. Everything was SOOOOO expensive so I'm sorry it's small.

2. Nice that the Big Creep didn't even try to call me on V-day and he didn't know for sure that I was going to London.

3. He could have called last night and didn't. He was out of town.

4. Finally, the Babba went away and it was the same night he was gone. Fuck me!!!!

HHHEEELLPPP!!!!

Maybe we can have lunch or meet sometime today cuz I want to give you your present.

Bye...msl

Bell Atlantic TEMPO MDR for 7036979312 per DTS-W Request dated 24 FEB 98

ORIG_TN	DEST_TN	DURATION	Start date-time
7036979312	[redacted]	000:00:13	21NOV97 20:03:09
7036979312	[redacted]	000:00:33	22NOV97 12:13:18
7036979312	[redacted]	000:10:38	22NOV97 12:14:20
7036979312	[redacted]	000:05:09	22NOV97 13:18:43
7036979312	[redacted]	000:02:31	22NOV97 14:33:48
7036979312	[redacted]	000:22:22	22NOV97 14:51:32
7036979312	[redacted]	000:00:19	22NOV97 15:24:37
7036979312	[redacted]	000:09:14	24NOV97 07:43:33
7036979312	[redacted]	000:22:08	24NOV97 07:55:02
7036979312	[redacted]	000:06:44	24NOV97 10:14:17
7036979312	[redacted]	000:00:10	24NOV97 10:18:54
7036979312	[redacted]	000:00:11	24NOV97 10:19:50
7036979312	[redacted]	000:27:06	24NOV97 10:25:38
7036979312	[redacted]	000:02:22	24NOV97 10:57:17
7036979312	[redacted]	000:00:04	24NOV97 11:01:29
7036979312	[redacted]	000:43:22	24NOV97 11:58:36
7036979312	[redacted]	000:08:59	24NOV97 13:13:13
7036979312	[redacted]	000:00:40	24NOV97 13:21:24
7036979312	[redacted]	000:00:51	24NOV97 13:23:16
7036979312	[redacted]	000:00:53	24NOV97 13:25:48
7036979312	[redacted]	000:08:26	24NOV97 14:03:37
7036979312	[redacted]	000:03:50	24NOV97 15:01:07
7036979312	[redacted]	000:00:10	24NOV97 15:13:29
7036979312	[redacted]	000:02:22	24NOV97 15:20:51
7036979312	[redacted]	000:00:59	24NOV97 15:56:05
7036979312	[redacted]	000:00:48	24NOV97 16:51:31
7036979312	[redacted]	000:18:23	24NOV97 16:58:03
7036979312	[redacted]	000:02:28	24NOV97 17:10:01
7036979312	[redacted]	000:17:37	24NOV97 17:17:24
7036979312	[redacted]	000:00:15	24NOV97 17:29:22
7036979312	[redacted]	000:03:23	24NOV97 17:59:54
7036979312	[redacted]	000:00:07	24NOV97 19:02:02
7036979312	[redacted]	000:04:10	24NOV97 19:04:52
7036979312	[redacted]	000:17:10	24NOV97 19:17:55
7036979312	[redacted]	000:03:21	24NOV97 19:43:38
7036979312	[redacted]	000:03:46	24NOV97 20:38:49
7036979312	[redacted]	000:13:33	25NOV97 07:43:30
7036979312	[redacted]	000:07:32	25NOV97 07:59:38
7036979312	[redacted]	000:15:23	25NOV97 08:11:09
7036979312	[redacted]	000:01:58	25NOV97 08:21:03
7036979312	[redacted]	000:00:44	25NOV97 08:28:13
7036979312	[redacted]	000:00:43	25NOV97 08:38:03
7036979312	[redacted]	000:10:16	25NOV97 09:11:30
7036979312	[redacted]	000:00:39	25NOV97 09:34:48
7036979312	[redacted]	000:00:07	25NOV97 09:48:36
7036979312	[redacted]	000:01:53	25NOV97 09:48:54
7036979312	[redacted]	000:00:36	25NOV97 09:50:38
7036979312	[redacted]	000:03:27	25NOV97 09:52:47
7036979312	[redacted]	000:00:06	25NOV97 09:55:35
7036979312	[redacted]	000:07:02	25NOV97 09:55:56
7036979312	[redacted]	000:02:04	25NOV97 10:47:35
7036979312	[redacted]	000:00:41	25NOV97 10:51:39
7036979312	[redacted]	000:00:49	25NOV97 11:38:03
7036979312	[redacted]	001:17:38	25NOV97 11:58:39
7036979312	[redacted]	000:00:09	25NOV97 18:52:02
7036979312	[redacted]	000:13:45	26NOV97 07:42:12
7036979312	[redacted]	000:05:52	26NOV97 09:00:34
7036979312	[redacted]	000:04:00	26NOV97 09:18:26
7036979312	[redacted]	000:39:11	26NOV97 12:27:35
7036979312	[redacted]	000:07:10	26NOV97 14:32:00

833-DC-00017908

Bell Atlantic TEMPO MDR for 7036979312 per DTS-W Request dated 24 FEB 98

RIG_TN	DEST_TN	DURATION	Start date-time
036979312	[redacted]	000:02:22	13NOV97 10:37:05
036979312	[redacted]	000:01:40	13NOV97 11:06:57
7036979312	[redacted]	000:00:03	13NOV97 11:20:19
7036979312	[redacted]	000:03:20	13NOV97 11:25:46
7036979312	[redacted]	000:00:09	13NOV97 11:29:43
7036979312	[redacted]	000:00:17	13NOV97 11:50:49
7036979312	[redacted]	000:28:20	13NOV97 11:59:25
7036979312	[redacted]	000:21:52	13NOV97 12:25:17
7036979312	[redacted]	000:00:10	13NOV97 13:15:50
7036979312	[redacted]	000:00:23	13NOV97 13:36:43
7036979312	[redacted]	000:00:14	13NOV97 14:25:19
7036979312	[redacted]	000:02:30	13NOV97 14:26:56
7036979312	[redacted]	000:00:42	13NOV97 14:32:00
7036979312	[redacted]	000:00:08	13NOV97 14:37:31
7036979312	[redacted]	000:00:18	13NOV97 14:42:12
7036979312	[redacted]	000:00:44	13NOV97 14:49:37
7036979312	[redacted]	000:00:30	13NOV97 14:53:59
7036979312	[redacted]	000:02:39	13NOV97 15:04:13
7036979312	[redacted]	000:22:04	13NOV97 15:10:25
7036979312	[redacted]	000:04:17	13NOV97 16:29:31
7036979312	[redacted]	000:00:40	13NOV97 16:33:07
7036979312	[redacted]	000:00:14	13NOV97 16:34:18
7036979312	[redacted]	000:03:44	13NOV97 16:47:04
7036979312	[redacted]	000:00:11	13NOV97 17:22:43
7036979312	[redacted]	000:00:09	13NOV97 17:24:05
7036979312	[redacted]	000:00:05	13NOV97 17:24:32
36979312	[redacted]	000:02:26	13NOV97 17:44:52
36979312	[redacted]	000:07:04	13NOV97 18:23:35
36979312	[redacted]	000:00:08	13NOV97 18:29:39
036979312	[redacted]	000:05:42	13NOV97 18:50:34
7036979312	[redacted]	000:00:21	13NOV97 19:08:42
7036979312	[redacted]	000:00:50	13NOV97 19:47:46
7036979312	[redacted]	000:20:08	14NOV97 07:57:24
7036979312	[redacted]	000:00:29	14NOV97 08:27:55
7036979312	[redacted]	000:00:15	14NOV97 08:30:24
7036979312	[redacted]	000:00:05	14NOV97 08:42:40
7036979312	[redacted]	000:02:19	14NOV97 08:58:15
7036979312	[redacted]	000:00:16	14NOV97 09:12:24
7036979312	[redacted]	000:00:15	14NOV97 09:52:34
7036979312	[redacted]	000:00:35	14NOV97 09:53:36
7036979312	[redacted]	000:05:40	14NOV97 09:58:41
7036979312	[redacted]	000:12:01	14NOV97 10:03:29
7036979312	[redacted]	000:02:12	14NOV97 10:21:44
7036979312	[redacted]	000:02:04	14NOV97 10:23:39
7036979312	[redacted]	000:02:32	14NOV97 10:25:24
7036979312	[redacted]	000:05:34	14NOV97 10:43:37
7036979312	[redacted]	000:00:46	14NOV97 11:25:23
7036979312	[redacted]	000:00:22	14NOV97 11:26:21
7036979312	[redacted]	000:06:45	14NOV97 11:27:24
7036979312	[redacted]	000:00:36	14NOV97 12:06:25
7036979312	[redacted]	000:00:24	14NOV97 12:41:24
7036979312	[redacted]	000:00:22	14NOV97 12:53:47
7036979312	[redacted]	000:02:13	14NOV97 13:31:35
7036979312	[redacted]	000:00:28	14NOV97 13:57:07
7036979312	[redacted]	000:00:18	14NOV97 13:59:58
36979312	[redacted]	000:00:50	14NOV97 14:00:45
36979312	[redacted]	000:00:30	14NOV97 14:16:25
36979312	[redacted]	000:00:43	14NOV97 14:22:10
036979312	[redacted]	000:01:41	14NOV97 14:50:11
7036979312	[redacted]	000:00:10	14NOV97 15:02:44

833-DC-00017904

Bell Atlantic TEMPO MDR for 7036979312 per DTS-W Request dated 24 FEB 98

RIG_TN	DEST_TN	DURATION	Start date-time
036979312	[redacted]	000:00:41	10NOV97 16:33:48
/036979312	[redacted]	000:05:05	10NOV97 17:00:26
7036979312	[redacted]	000:00:22	10NOV97 17:04:28
7036979312	[redacted]	000:05:01	10NOV97 17:09:00
7036979312	[redacted]	000:08:50	10NOV97 17:17:19
7036979312	[redacted]	000:00:31	10NOV97 17:27:51
7036979312	[redacted]	000:00:10	10NOV97 17:29:09
7036979312	[redacted]	000:00:39	10NOV97 17:31:32
7036979312	[redacted]	000:00:39	10NOV97 17:53:47
7036979312	[redacted]	000:02:01	10NOV97 17:54:37
7036979312	[redacted]	000:00:12	10NOV97 17:58:51
7036979312	[redacted]	000:00:04	10NOV97 18:18:14
7036979312	[redacted]	000:00:45	10NOV97 18:18:33
7036979312	[redacted]	000:43:31	10NOV97 18:19:56
7036979312	[redacted]	000:03:41	10NOV97 18:49:56
7036979312	[redacted]	000:20:00	10NOV97 18:56:58
7036979312	[redacted]	000:00:26	10NOV97 19:11:44
7036979312	[redacted]	000:00:11	10NOV97 19:28:34
7036979312	[redacted]	000:00:08	10NOV97 19:32:24
7036979312	[redacted]	000:03:22	12NOV97 07:58:08
7036979312	[redacted]	000:15:41	12NOV97 08:00:21
7036979312	[redacted]	000:00:25	12NOV97 08:19:20
7036979312	[redacted]	000:00:44	12NOV97 08:28:44
7036979312	[redacted]	000:00:08	12NOV97 09:05:08
7036979312	[redacted]	000:00:03	12NOV97 09:23:18
7036979312	[redacted]	000:00:34	12NOV97 09:53:45
036979312	[redacted]	000:03:52	12NOV97 10:21:37
036979312	[redacted]	000:03:33	12NOV97 11:06:39
)36979312	[redacted]	000:00:53	12NOV97 11:16:38
,036979312	[redacted]	000:00:59	12NOV97 11:36:54
7036979312	[redacted]	000:01:55	12NOV97 11:56:20
7036979312	[redacted]	000:39:13	12NOV97 11:58:16
7036979312	[redacted]	000:00:21	12NOV97 12:30:44
7036979312	[redacted]	000:00:28	12NOV97 12:32:30
7036979312	[redacted]	000:05:37	12NOV97 12:51:15
7036979312	[redacted]	000:00:14	12NOV97 13:01:15
7036979312	[redacted]	000:01:46	12NOV97 13:36:36
7036979312	[redacted]	000:08:43	12NOV97 13:38:16
7036979312	[redacted]	000:00:08	12NOV97 13:44:01
7036979312	[redacted]	000:00:23	12NOV97 13:58:25
7036979312	[redacted]	000:00:07	12NOV97 14:05:56
7036979312	[redacted]	000:00:55	12NOV97 14:06:32
7036979312	[redacted]	000:25:24	12NOV97 14:30:02
7036979312	[redacted]	000:05:07	12NOV97 15:34:53
7036979312	[redacted]	000:01:57	12NOV97 15:39:09
7036979312	[redacted]	000:00:20	12NOV97 15:48:00
7036979312	[redacted]	000:00:09	12NOV97 15:53:26
7036979312	[redacted]	000:02:19	12NOV97 15:55:28
7036979312	[redacted]	000:01:55	12NOV97 17:26:27
7036979312	[redacted]	000:00:45	12NOV97 17:35:44
7036979312	[redacted]	000:00:11	12NOV97 17:37:54
7036979312	[redacted]	000:15:03	13NOV97 07:56:31
7036979312	[redacted]	000:02:04	13NOV97 08:12:56
7036979312	[redacted]	000:00:16	13NOV97 08:23:18
"036979312	[redacted]	000:00:05	13NOV97 08:33:18
,36979312	[redacted]	000:00:03	13NOV97 08:38:30
'36979312	[redacted]	000:00:04	13NOV97 09:02:32
,36979312	[redacted]	000:05:02	13NOV97 09:26:56
/036979312	[redacted]	000:00:31	13NOV97 09:59:21
7036979312	[redacted]	000:02:03	13NOV97 10:12:28

833-DC-00017903

Bell Atlantic TEMPO MDR for 7036979312 per DTS-W Request dated 12 MAR 98

ORIG_TN	DEST_TN	DURATION	Start date-time
6979312	[redacted]	000:00:33	17DEC97 08:23:16
979312	[redacted]	000:40:48	17DEC97 08:46:20
7036979312	[redacted]	000:00:35	17DEC97 09:19:07
7036979312	[redacted]	000:01:49	17DEC97 09:20:40
7036979312	[redacted]	000:00:53	17DEC97 11:18:10
7036979312	[redacted]	000:03:28	17DEC97 11:24:58
7036979312	[redacted]	001:24:16	17DEC97 11:58:24
7036979312	[redacted]	000:00:32	17DEC97 12:54:28
7036979312	[redacted]	000:00:07	17DEC97 13:21:47
7036979312	[redacted]	000:06:48	17DEC97 13:22:25
7036979312	[redacted]	000:00:23	17DEC97 14:34:11
7036979312	[redacted]	000:45:19	17DEC97 14:44:27
7036979312	[redacted]	000:00:10	17DEC97 16:37:39
7036979312	[redacted]	000:00:40	17DEC97 18:17:29
7036979312	[redacted]	000:00:21	17DEC97 18:25:31
7036979312	[redacted]	000:05:02	17DEC97 18:32:11
7036979312	[redacted]	000:05:14	17DEC97 18:36:50
7036979312	[redacted]	000:00:20	17DEC97 18:58:34
7036979312	[redacted]	000:00:25	18DEC97 07:31:27
7036979312	[redacted]	000:00:46	18DEC97 07:48:28
7036979312	[redacted]	000:21:47	18DEC97 07:54:09
7036979312	[redacted]	000:00:22	18DEC97 09:17:25
7036979312	[redacted]	000:00:18	18DEC97 09:25:37
7036979312	[redacted]	000:00:26	18DEC97 10:59:54
7036979312	[redacted]	000:13:56	18DEC97 12:23:12
7036979312	[redacted]	000:20:22	18DEC97 15:05:11
7036979312	[redacted]	000:20:48	18DEC97 17:15:37
7 979312	[redacted]	000:00:16	18DEC97 17:28:44
6979312	[redacted]	000:00:54	18DEC97 17:29:27
979312	[redacted]	000:15:03	19DEC97 07:59:35
7036979312	[redacted]	000:00:30	19DEC97 08:27:11
7036979312	[redacted]	000:15:38	19DEC97 09:07:29
7036979312	[redacted]	000:00:09	19DEC97 09:19:06
7036979312	[redacted]	000:00:06	19DEC97 09:19:21
7036979312	[redacted]	000:02:14	19DEC97 09:22:39
7036979312	[redacted]	000:02:16	19DEC97 09:25:23
7036979312	[redacted]	000:00:07	19DEC97 10:15:11
7036979312	[redacted]	000:00:44	19DEC97 10:17:34
7036979312	[redacted]	000:00:47	19DEC97 10:33:05
7036979312	[redacted]	000:25:22	19DEC97 10:52:42
7036979312	[redacted]	000:00:07	19DEC97 11:11:13
7036979312	[redacted]	000:00:30	19DEC97 11:12:31
7036979312	[redacted]	000:05:27	19DEC97 11:20:14
7036979312	[redacted]	000:00:28	19DEC97 11:39:52
7036979312	[redacted]	000:08:54	19DEC97 12:36:59
7036979312	[redacted]	000:07:22	19DEC97 12:54:07
7036979312	[redacted]	000:00:07	19DEC97 13:01:13
7036979312	[redacted]	000:11:58	19DEC97 13:02:10
7036979312	[redacted]	000:00:11	19DEC97 13:26:00
7036979312	[redacted]	000:00:22	19DEC97 13:35:13
7036979312	[redacted]	000:13:47	19DEC97 13:35:52
7036979312	[redacted]	000:01:50	19DEC97 13:47:32
7036979312	[redacted]	000:00:04	19DEC97 13:50:56
7036979312	[redacted]	000:02:31	19DEC97 13:54:06
7036979312	[redacted]	000:00:35	19DEC97 13:58:41
7 979312	[redacted]	000:00:32	19DEC97 13:59:37
979312	[redacted]	000:07:16	19DEC97 14:15:58
979312	[redacted]	000:01:56	19DEC97 16:09:21
6979312	[redacted]	000:00:10	19DEC97 18:03:59
7036979312	[redacted]	000:00:24	19DEC97 18:26:46

833-DC-00017890

Bell Atlantic TEMPO MDR for 7036979312 per DTS-W Request dated 12 MAR 98

ORIG_TN	DEST_TN	DURATION	Start date-time
36979312	[redacted]	000:12:15	01DEC97 07:42:18
36979312	[redacted]	000:30:06	01DEC97 07:59:10
7036979312	[redacted]	000:32:36	01DEC97 11:58:03
7036979312	[redacted]	000:13:25	02DEC97 07:41:34
7036979312	[redacted]	000:00:11	02DEC97 07:57:39
7036979312	[redacted]	000:13:41	02DEC97 07:57:58
7036979312	[redacted]	000:07:37	02DEC97 11:10:34
7036979312	[redacted]	000:04:08	02DEC97 11:52:42
7036979312	[redacted]	000:45:46	02DEC97 11:59:08
7036979312	[redacted]	000:00:12	02DEC97 18:28:45
7036979312	[redacted]	000:15:23	03DEC97 07:58:03
7036979312	[redacted]	000:37:28	03DEC97 12:04:02
7036979312	[redacted]	000:00:45	03DEC97 15:33:48
7036979312	[redacted]	000:02:14	03DEC97 15:34:55
7036979312	[redacted]	000:05:08	04DEC97 07:46:53
7036979312	[redacted]	000:09:02	04DEC97 07:57:46
7036979312	[redacted]	000:38:26	04DEC97 12:00:16
7036979312	[redacted]	000:02:16	04DEC97 15:23:01
7036979312	[redacted]	000:02:02	04DEC97 15:25:04
7036979312	[redacted]	000:06:40	04DEC97 16:44:07
7036979312	[redacted]	000:38:25	04DEC97 18:38:57
7036979312	[redacted]	000:09:15	05DEC97 07:44:23
7036979312	[redacted]	000:12:16	05DEC97 07:58:14
7036979312	[redacted]	000:38:58	05DEC97 08:07:06
7036979312	[redacted]	000:01:46	05DEC97 13:27:42
7036979312	[redacted]	001:20:32	05DEC97 13:30:28
7036979312	[redacted]	000:12:21	05DEC97 14:33:30
16979312	[redacted]	000:00:50	05DEC97 14:55:33
16979312	[redacted]	000:00:22	05DEC97 16:46:06
16979312	[redacted]	000:03:48	05DEC97 16:58:25
7036979312	[redacted]	000:00:12	05DEC97 17:47:29
7036979312	[redacted]	000:00:14	05DEC97 18:19:07
7036979312	[redacted]	000:00:44	05DEC97 18:26:56
7036979312	[redacted]	000:13:30	08DEC97 07:44:44
7036979312	[redacted]	000:22:01	08DEC97 07:59:12
7036979312	[redacted]	000:02:04	08DEC97 08:23:33
7036979312	[redacted]	000:10:58	08DEC97 08:56:30
7036979312	[redacted]	000:01:57	08DEC97 09:06:26
7036979312	[redacted]	000:00:17	08DEC97 10:08:26
7036979312	[redacted]	000:02:28	08DEC97 10:29:39
7036979312	[redacted]	000:05:10	08DEC97 11:03:29
7036979312	[redacted]	000:49:01	08DEC97 11:57:14
7036979312	[redacted]	000:00:08	08DEC97 13:05:35
7036979312	[redacted]	000:00:40	08DEC97 14:15:54
7036979312	[redacted]	000:00:10	08DEC97 14:31:45
7036979312	[redacted]	000:06:48	08DEC97 16:22:52
7036979312	[redacted]	000:00:28	08DEC97 16:32:37
7036979312	[redacted]	000:03:31	08DEC97 16:49:35
7036979312	[redacted]	000:00:50	08DEC97 17:09:31
7036979312	[redacted]	000:02:03	08DEC97 17:19:38
7036979312	[redacted]	000:00:08	08DEC97 17:41:35
7036979312	[redacted]	000:03:34	08DEC97 17:44:05
7036979312	[redacted]	000:00:08	08DEC97 18:10:14
7036979312	[redacted]	000:11:58	08DEC97 18:19:35
7036979312	[redacted]	000:00:50	08DEC97 18:31:27
7 5979312	[redacted]	000:29:10	09DEC97 07:58:29
6979312	[redacted]	000:01:51	09DEC97 09:41:21
6979312	[redacted]	000:02:33	09DEC97 09:52:26
6979312	[redacted]	000:21:41	09DEC97 10:05:26
7036979312	[redacted]	000:08:34	09DEC97 10:22:30

Page: 1

833-DC-00017886

Bell Atlantic TEMPO MDR for 7036979312 per DTS-W Request dated 12 MAR 98

ORIG_TN	DEST_TN	DURATION	Start date-time
7036979312	[redacted]	000:17:19	03NOV97 07:57:03
7036979312	[redacted]	000:18:42	03NOV97 08:15:00
7036979312	[redacted]	000:00:12	03NOV97 09:21:27
7036979312	[redacted]	000:02:00	03NOV97 10:02:54
7036979312	[redacted]	000:00:09	03NOV97 10:49:07
7036979312	[redacted]	000:00:04	03NOV97 11:16:01
7036979312	[redacted]	000:06:52	03NOV97 11:28:00
7036979312	[redacted]	000:30:05	03NOV97 12:00:35
7036979312	[redacted]	000:00:36	03NOV97 12:20:53
7036979312	[redacted]	000:00:25	03NOV97 12:26:46
7036979312	[redacted]	000:00:14	03NOV97 12:58:31
7036979312	[redacted]	000:00:15	03NOV97 13:02:09
7036979312	[redacted]	000:00:12	03NOV97 13:24:14
7036979312	[redacted]	000:05:24	03NOV97 13:34:28
7036979312	[redacted]	000:01:48	03NOV97 13:41:00
7036979312	[redacted]	000:00:04	03NOV97 14:51:19
7036979312	[redacted]	000:01:59	03NOV97 15:47:04
7036979312	[redacted]	000:00:21	03NOV97 16:04:47
7036979312	[redacted]	000:00:30	03NOV97 16:53:26
7036979312	[redacted]	000:02:21	03NOV97 17:06:25
7036979312	[redacted]	000:00:06	03NOV97 17:08:41
7036979312	[redacted]	000:00:05	03NOV97 17:09:19
7036979312	[redacted]	000:00:06	03NOV97 17:12:45
7036979312	[redacted]	000:00:08	03NOV97 17:33:36
7036979312	[redacted]	000:04:01	03NOV97 18:01:40
7036979312	[redacted]	000:00:21	03NOV97 18:11:55
7036979312	[redacted]	000:13:51	03NOV97 18:15:39
7036979312	[redacted]	000:00:10	03NOV97 18:24:56
7036979312	[redacted]	000:01:49	03NOV97 18:50:25
7036979312	[redacted]	000:00:15	03NOV97 18:54:17
7036979312	[redacted]	000:00:15	03NOV97 18:56:15
7036979312	[redacted]	000:00:41	03NOV97 18:57:28
7036979312	[redacted]	000:00:18	03NOV97 18:58:17
7036979312	[redacted]	000:20:07	04NOV97 07:56:10
7036979312	[redacted]	000:00:42	04NOV97 09:05:05
7036979312	[redacted]	000:00:59	04NOV97 09:12:30
7036979312	[redacted]	000:06:57	04NOV97 10:05:21
7036979312	[redacted]	000:00:28	04NOV97 11:01:00
7036979312	[redacted]	000:00:24	04NOV97 11:18:58
7036979312	[redacted]	000:35:21	04NOV97 11:47:46
7036979312	[redacted]	000:01:47	04NOV97 12:09:16
7036979312	[redacted]	000:00:28	04NOV97 12:41:22
7036979312	[redacted]	000:01:53	04NOV97 12:47:54
7036979312	[redacted]	000:00:38	04NOV97 14:13:06
7036979312	[redacted]	000:03:49	04NOV97 14:28:01
7036979312	[redacted]	000:07:38	04NOV97 15:06:28
7036979312	[redacted]	000:20:58	04NOV97 15:11:47
7036979312	[redacted]	000:02:35	04NOV97 15:27:47
7036979312	[redacted]	000:00:09	04NOV97 15:49:00
7036979312	[redacted]	000:03:32	04NOV97 15:54:16
7036979312	[redacted]	000:06:59	04NOV97 16:40:12
7036979312	[redacted]	000:00:39	04NOV97 16:44:52
7036979312	[redacted]	000:00:34	04NOV97 16:50:29
7036979312	[redacted]	000:00:54	04NOV97 16:51:15
7036979312	[redacted]	000:03:28	04NOV97 17:06:52
7036979312	[redacted]	000:04:17	04NOV97 17:15:14
7036979312	[redacted]	000:00:07	04NOV97 17:20:06
7036979312	[redacted]	000:01:57	04NOV97 17:25:16
7036979312	[redacted]	000:00:49	04NOV97 17:45:41
7036979312	[redacted]	000:04:10	04NOV97 17:58:10

Bell Atlantic TEMPO MDR for 7036979312 per DTS-W Request dated 12 MAR 98

ORIG_TN	DEST_TN	DURATION	Start date-time
6979312	[redacted]	000:03:33	15OCT97 17:39:08
979312	[redacted]	000:03:20	15OCT97 18:21:22
7 6979312	[redacted]	000:00:53	16OCT97 07:36:58
7036979312	[redacted]	000:23:57	16OCT97 07:56:34
7036979312	[redacted]	000:01:48	16OCT97 08:35:23
7036979312	[redacted]	000:08:44	16OCT97 08:36:36
7036979312	[redacted]	000:00:55	16OCT97 08:47:56
7036979312	[redacted]	000:18:48	16OCT97 09:31:19
7036979312	[redacted]	000:01:59	16OCT97 10:49:51
7036979312	[redacted]	001:05:20	16OCT97 11:59:39
7036979312	[redacted]	000:00:28	16OCT97 13:18:17
7036979312	[redacted]	000:00:16	16OCT97 14:48:20
7036979312	[redacted]	000:05:25	16OCT97 17:33:13
7036979312	[redacted]	000:03:32	16OCT97 17:50:52
7036979312	[redacted]	000:13:21	16OCT97 18:07:33
7036979312	[redacted]	000:00:18	16OCT97 18:42:45
7036979312	[redacted]	000:00:21	16OCT97 18:48:40
7036979312	[redacted]	000:00:12	16OCT97 18:50:01
7036979312	[redacted]	000:05:02	16OCT97 18:52:38
7036979312	[redacted]	000:00:05	16OCT97 18:56:39
7036979312	[redacted]	000:01:49	16OCT97 19:12:32
7036979312	[redacted]	000:00:53	16OCT97 19:14:52
7036979312	[redacted]	000:00:23	16OCT97 19:23:01
7036979312	[redacted]	000:01:46	16OCT97 19:24:55
7036979312	[redacted]	000:28:44	16OCT97 19:36:30
7036979312	[redacted]	000:01:52	16OCT97 19:54:29
7036979312	[redacted]	000:19:11	17OCT97 07:58:06
7 979312	[redacted]	000:00:29	17OCT97 09:04:08
6979312	[redacted]	000:04:05	17OCT97 10:35:35
979312	[redacted]	000:00:26	17OCT97 11:10:54
7. 979312	[redacted]	000:00:18	17OCT97 11:16:42
7036979312	[redacted]	000:02:28	17OCT97 11:18:44
7036979312	[redacted]	000:00:10	17OCT97 11:34:48
7036979312	[redacted]	000:00:14	17OCT97 12:50:56
7036979312	[redacted]	000:00:14	17OCT97 13:06:23
7036979312	[redacted]	000:03:20	17OCT97 13:23:31
7036979312	[redacted]	000:00:11	17OCT97 14:33:47
7036979312	[redacted]	000:00:06	17OCT97 14:51:01
7036979312	[redacted]	000:00:47	17OCT97 14:56:26
7036979312	[redacted]	000:13:28	17OCT97 15:18:48
7036979312	[redacted]	000:00:29	17OCT97 15:32:49
7036979312	[redacted]	000:00:27	17OCT97 15:41:14
7036979312	[redacted]	000:00:08	17OCT97 15:52:02
7036979312	[redacted]	000:00:19	17OCT97 15:52:43
7036979312	[redacted]	000:00:04	17OCT97 15:59:04
7036979312	[redacted]	000:00:53	17OCT97 16:09:29
7036979312	[redacted]	000:02:18	17OCT97 16:11:25
7036979312	[redacted]	000:00:52	17OCT97 16:19:41
7036979312	[redacted]	000:00:59	17OCT97 16:41:23
7036979312	[redacted]	000:00:37	17OCT97 17:07:48
7036979312	[redacted]	000:00:19	17OCT97 18:21:01
7036979312	[redacted]	000:00:53	17OCT97 18:22:10
7036979312	[redacted]	000:10:38	17OCT97 18:26:20
7036979312	[redacted]	000:00:36	17OCT97 18:41:52
7036979312	[redacted]	000:00:47	17OCT97 18:44:25
7 979312	[redacted]	000:00:11	17OCT97 19:16:08
7 979312	[redacted]	000:00:05	20OCT97 06:25:13
979312	[redacted]	000:00:05	20OCT97 06:37:23
7 979312	[redacted]	000:30:55	20OCT97 07:55:39
7036979312	[redacted]	000:05:19	20OCT97 08:25:45

Bell Atlantic TEMPO MDR for 7036979312 per DTS-W Request dated 12 MAR 98

ORIG_TN	DEST_TN	DURATION	Start date-time
6979312	[redacted]	000:00:07	06OCT97 10:43:23
6979312	[redacted]	000:00:45	06OCT97 10:44:18
36979312	[redacted]	000:00:10	06OCT97 10:48:23
7036979312	[redacted]	000:00:24	06OCT97 11:06:25
7036979312	[redacted]	000:00:51	06OCT97 11:07:12
7036979312	[redacted]	000:03:56	06OCT97 11:54:36
7036979312	[redacted]	000:00:59	06OCT97 12:24:25
7036979312	[redacted]	000:05:16	06OCT97 15:34:01
7036979312	[redacted]	000:05:53	06OCT97 15:44:17
7036979312	[redacted]	000:02:23	06OCT97 15:54:16
7036979312	[redacted]	000:00:05	06OCT97 16:05:48
7036979312	[redacted]	000:07:00	06OCT97 16:16:42
7036979312	[redacted]	000:02:30	06OCT97 16:27:59
7036979312	[redacted]	000:22:10	07OCT97 07:55:15
7036979312	[redacted]	000:00:13	07OCT97 09:24:05
7036979312	[redacted]	000:02:09	07OCT97 09:37:54
7036979312	[redacted]	000:04:10	07OCT97 09:59:36
7036979312	[redacted]	000:01:51	07OCT97 10:53:05
7036979312	[redacted]	000:00:01	07OCT97 11:09:53
7036979312	[redacted]	000:00:33	07OCT97 11:15:57
7036979312	[redacted]	000:33:53	07OCT97 11:55:11
7036979312	[redacted]	000:18:23	07OCT97 12:21:59
7036979312	[redacted]	000:00:07	07OCT97 13:10:26
7036979312	[redacted]	000:00:48	07OCT97 13:37:38
7036979312	[redacted]	000:00:27	07OCT97 14:01:11
7036979312	[redacted]	000:00:13	07OCT97 15:02:07
7036979312	[redacted]	000:00:50	07OCT97 15:02:41
6979312	[redacted]	000:00:43	07OCT97 15:05:09
6979312	[redacted]	000:00:48	07OCT97 15:10:03
6979312	[redacted]	000:02:05	07OCT97 16:11:13
6979312	[redacted]	000:00:09	07OCT97 16:38:13
7036979312	[redacted]	000:00:54	07OCT97 16:50:20
7036979312	[redacted]	000:05:53	07OCT97 17:20:28
7036979312	[redacted]	000:00:10	07OCT97 17:49:23
7036979312	[redacted]	000:00:09	07OCT97 18:35:07
7036979312	[redacted]	000:15:12	08OCT97 07:58:48
7036979312	[redacted]	000:15:49	08OCT97 08:12:50
7036979312	[redacted]	000:07:03	08OCT97 08:24:12
7036979312	[redacted]	000:01:56	08OCT97 10:34:44
7036979312	[redacted]	000:09:09	08OCT97 11:38:43
7036979312	[redacted]	000:35:10	08OCT97 11:44:57
7036979312	[redacted]	000:00:46	08OCT97 13:05:27
7036979312	[redacted]	000:01:54	08OCT97 13:07:28
7036979312	[redacted]	000:08:20	08OCT97 13:10:54
7036979312	[redacted]	000:05:02	08OCT97 13:17:55
7036979312	[redacted]	000:01:43	08OCT97 13:42:46
7036979312	[redacted]	000:00:20	08OCT97 14:00:29
7036979312	[redacted]	000:03:51	08OCT97 14:01:21
7036979312	[redacted]	000:05:23	08OCT97 14:13:19
7036979312	[redacted]	000:01:57	08OCT97 16:32:15
7036979312	[redacted]	000:00:26	08OCT97 16:34:08
7036979312	[redacted]	000:00:35	08OCT97 17:41:11
7036979312	[redacted]	000:00:45	08OCT97 17:42:20
7036979312	[redacted]	000:00:20	09OCT97 07:28:19
7036979312	[redacted]	000:48:30	09OCT97 07:56:46
36979312	[redacted]	000:00:24	09OCT97 09:20:27
36979312	[redacted]	000:00:04	09OCT97 09:24:00
5979312	[redacted]	000:08:56	09OCT97 09:37:44
6979312	[redacted]	000:17:26	09OCT97 10:19:43
7036979312	[redacted]	000:10:26	09OCT97 10:38:20

CLIENT ✓ COP	CALL BY: Monica REF #	DATE 6-28 COURIER # 5
837-DC-00000004		
FROM: Pentagon MALL [redacted]		TIME IN 3:[illegible] TIME OUT 559
TO: SW Gate White House		SERV TYPE:
[illegible] 456-2990 [illegible] x15		CHARGES 10 —

CLIENT

REF. # [redacted]

COURIER #

FROM:

TIME IN:

TIME OUT:

TO:

SERV TYPE:

CHARGES:

X

SIGNATURE

SPEED SERVICE COURIERS

(202) 638-5533

CLIENT: COP

CALL BY: MONICA LEWINSKY

DATE:

REF. #: [redacted]

COURIER #:

FROM: PU 11AM. Pentagon Mall

TIME IN: 1002

TIME OUT: 1215

837-DC-00000002

TO: W. HIFE HOUSE SW GATE Betty Currie [redacted]

SERV. TYPE:

CHARGES: 10.—

X SIGNATURE

SPEED SERVICE COURIERS

(202) 638-5533

CLIENT: CDP	CALL BY: Monica Lewinsky	DATE: 10·7
	REF. #: [redacted]	COURIER #
FROM: By 11AM Pentagon - Mall		TIME IN: 1002
~~Allen M~~		TIME OUT: 12:15
TO: SW Gate House		SERV. TYPE:
Betty Currie [redacted]		CHARGES: $10.— $

837-DC-00000001

837-DC-00000005

CLIENT: ✓ C.O.P.

CALL BY: Monica

REF. #

DATE: 11-3

COURIER # 33

FROM: [redacted] Pentagon MALL S/W Gate
C.O.P. @ 15.00

TIME IN: 4:13

TIME OUT: 5:20

TO: S/W Gate
WhiteHouse

SERV. TYPE: RUSH PLUS

CHARGES:

Ⓟ

837-DC-00000006

CLIENT COP

CALL BY: MONICA

DATE: 3 Nov 97

REF. #

COURIER # 22

FROM: Pentagon Mall ENT. 20 MIN WAIT

Monica [redacted]

TIME IN: 413

TIME OUT: 5

TO: White House

837-DC-00000007

SW Gate Whitehouse [redacted]

SERV. TYPE:

CHARGES: $15.00

SPEED SERVICE COURIERS

x

SIGNATURE

(202)638-5533

CLIENT CoF	CALL BY Monica	DATE 11/12
	REF # 837-DC-00000008	COURIER # 3 1/23
FROM Pertagon Mall [redacted]		TIME IN 1115
		TIME OUT 150
TO: Sw Gate	RUSH	SERV TYPE: PLUS
[redacted] (i) ~~223-D23~~ 130		CHARGES: $15.00

CLIENT ✓ COP

CALL BY MONICA

DATE 11/12

REF # [redacted]

COURIER # 23

FROM Pentagon Mall

TIME IN 700P

TIME OUT 3 [illegible]

TO 837-DC-00000009 [redacted]

SW gate

SERV. TYPE RUSH PLUS

ON PICK-UP

CHARGES 15.—

x [illegible]

SIGNATURE

SPEED SERVICE COURIERS

(202) 638-5533

REF. [redacted]

COURIER #

FROM

TIME IN

TIME OUT

TO 837-DC-00000010

SERV. TYPE:

CHARGES:

SPEED SERVICE COURIERS

x

SIGNATURE

(202) 638-5533

2637

[redacted]

CLIENT C.O.P.	CALL BY: MONIcA REF. #	DATE 11·20 COURIER # 12
FROM: [redacted] Pentagon MALL		TIME IN 9:54 TIME OUT 10:54
TO: 837-DC-00000011 SW Gate	RUSH	SERV. TYPE
5'6" 120 lbs by self		CHARGES

CLIENT COP	CALL BY MONICA REF [redacted]	DATE 11/20/95 COURIER # 12
FROM PENTAGON - MALL		TIME IN 9:34 TIME OUT 11:24
TO WHITE HOUSE - SW GATE	[redacted] RUSH	SERV. TYPE PLUS
SPEED SERVICE COURIERS (202) 638-5533	X [signature] MS. SELF SIGNATURE	CHARGES 15.1

837-DC-00000012

CLIENT: SCP	CALL BY: MONICA	DATE: [illegible]
	REF: [redacted]	COURIER #: [illegible]
FROM: PENTAGON - MALL	837-DC-00000013	TIME IN: [illegible]
		TIME OUT: [illegible]
TO: [redacted] WHITE HOUSE - NW GATE		SERV. TYPE:
X MYSELF SIGNATURE		CHARGES: 15.-

SPEED SERVICE COURIERS

(202) 638-5533

CLIENT: Cwf	CALL BY: MONICA REF: [redacted]	DATE: 11-21 COURIER #: 12
FROM: Pentagon - Mall Arl, VA		TIME IN: 818 TIME OUT: 1E—
TO: White House SW gate		SERV TYPE:
837-DC-00000014 [redacted]		CHARGES: $10.—

8

CLIENT COP	CALL BY Monica	DATE 11/21/97
	REF # [redacted]	COURIER # 12
FROM 837-DC-00000015 PENTAGON - MALL ENT.		TIME IN 818 TIME OUT 10 —
TO [redacted] WHITE HOUSE - SW GATE		SERV TYPE
SPEED SERVICE COURIERS (202) 638-5533 x [signature] SIGNATURE COLEMAN		CHARGES 10.—

CLIENT

REF. [redacted]

COURIER # 12

FROM:

837-DC-00000016

TIME IN:

TIME OUT:

TO:

SERV. TYPE:

CHARGES:

X SIGNATURE

SPEED SERVICE COURIERS

(202) 638-5533

CLIENT	CALL BY	DATE
OLP	Monica	12-8
	REF # [redacted]	COURIER # 30
FROM: ~~So~~ Pentagon - Mail		TIME IN: 825
~~Annex~~		TIME OUT: 1025
TO: SW Gate -		SERV. TYPE:
837-DC-00000017		CHARGES: $10.–

CLIENT COF N/O Mca	CALL BY MONICA REF [redacted]	DATE 1-5 COURIER # 36
FROM Pentagon mall 837-DC-00000018		TIME IN 825 TIME OUT 1025
TO W. H. S.W. Gate [redacted]		SERV TYPE
SPEED SERVICE COURIERS ★ (202) 638-5533 x ... Self SIGNATURE		CHARGES 10.—

CLIENT

CALL BY:

DATE:

REF [redacted]

COURIER #

FROM:

TIME IN:

TIME OUT:

837-DC-00000019

TO: [redacted]

SERV. TYPE:

CHARGES: 10

SPEED SERVICE COURIERS

x

SIGNATURE

(202) 638-5533

CLIENT COP.	CALL BY: MONICA	DATE: 14 JAN 98
	RE: [redacted]	COURIER # 33
FROM: 700 New Hampshire Av.		TIME IN: 1037
		TIME OUT: 1201 / 1236
TO: [redacted] for M. Lewinsky	837-DC-00000024	SERV. TYPE:
X SIGNATURE		CHARGES: 15

SPEED SERVICE COURIERS

(202) 638-5533

CLIENT: ~~W~~ LEWINSKY [redacted]

CALL BY: MONICA

REF #: [redacted]

DATE: 7.14

COURIER #: 33

FROM: [redacted]

PAGE [redacted]

TIME IN: 10:37

TIME OUT: 1236

TO: [redacted]

SERV. TYPE:

CHARGES: 15.00

OPEN 12:00

837-DC-00000023

	CALL BY	DATE:
	RE [redacted]	COURIER #
FROM:		TIME IN:
	837-DC-00000022	TIME OUT:
TO:		SERV. TYPE:
SPEED SERVICE COURIERS (202) 638-5533	x ________ SIGNATURE	CHARGES:

CLIENT	CALL BY	DATE
Monica	MONICA	[illegible]
	REF [redacted]	COURIER # 3c
FROM Pentagon mail		TIME IN 825
		TIME OUT 942
TO 17 ?? NHamp 610	837-DC-00000021	SERV TYPE
x Proctor SIGNATURE		CHARGES 10.—

CLIENT	CALL BY:	DATE:
CIP	Monica	12 8
	REF. #	COURIER #
		3n
FROM:		TIME IN: 825
Pentagon – Mall Annex		TIME OUT: 942
TO:		SERV. TYPE:
1333 N. Armid		
837-DC-00000020		CHARGES: $10.–

837-DC-00000025

		COURIER	CHECK/CASH	MILES	TOTAL	√	RECEIVED
[illegible]	[redacted]	30	✓		30.—	$	[illegible] 9.26
9.2[illegible]	[redacted] MD	30	✓		10.—	$	[illegible]
9.29	[redacted]	30			10.—	$	[illegible]
9.30	[redacted]	33			20.—	$	[illegible]
9-30	[redacted]	24			10.—		Deduct
10-[illegible]							
10-[illegible]	[redacted]	23			7 —		Deduct
10.7	Pentagon Mall VA → SW GATE W.H.	30			10.—	D	[illegible] 10.7
10.7	[redacted]	27			10.—		Deduct
10.7	[redacted]	33			10.—	[illegible]	[illegible] 10.7
10.7	[redacted] SAM	30			14.—	$	
10.7	[redacted]	30			20 —	$	
10.7	[redacted]	28			7.—		Deduct
10-13	[redacted]	30	HOLIDAY		27—	$	
10.14	[redacted]	33	✓	[illegible]	[illegible]	[illegible]	[illegible]
10-16	[redacted]	28			7.—	[illegible]	
10-21	[redacted]	30			10.—	$	
10-21	[redacted]	30			14.—	[illegible]	[illegible] 10.2[illegible]
10-2[illegible]	[redacted]	35	✓		10.—	[illegible]	
10.24	[redacted]	31	RUSH	[illegible]	27.—	$	[illegible] 10.24
10.22	[redacted]	33			10.—	$	
10.[illegible]	[redacted]	28			10.—	$	10.24
[illegible]	[redacted]	24			10.50	$	
10.2[illegible]	[redacted]	33			15 —	$	[illegible] 10.2[illegible]
10.24	[redacted]	31			10 —	[illegible]	

DATE	837-DC-00000026	COURIER	CHECK/CASH	MILES	TOTAL	✓	RECEIVED
	[redacted]	31			10.—		
	[redacted]	31			36—		
11-3	~~Pentagon → SW Gate~~	33			~~15.—~~		
11-4	[redacted]	30			14.—		
11-4	[redacted]	30			35.—		
11-4	[redacted]	31			22.—		
11-5	[redacted]	35			10.—		
11-5	[redacted]	29			10—		
11-6	[redacted]	24			7—		Deduct
11-7	[redacted]	33			10.—		
11-10	[redacted]	31			16.—		
	Pentagon → White House RUSH PLUS	31			15.—		
	[redacted]	35			10		11-14
11-14	[redacted]	33			10—		
11-17	[redacted]	35			12.—		
11-17	[redacted]	12			12.—		11-19
11-17	[redacted]	12			14.—		
11-19	[redacted]	33			16—		11-20
11-20	Pentagon → SW GATE.	12			15.—		
11-21	" "	12			10.—		11-24
11-21	[redacted]	33			12.—		
11-24	[redacted]	29			7.—		
	[redacted]	12			16.—		11-24
	[redacted]	29			20.—		
	[redacted]	35			30.—		11-24

DATE	837-DC-00000027	COURIER	CHECK/CASH	MILES	TOTAL	V	RECEIVE
11·15	[redacted]	28			40		[illegible]
11·26	[redacted]	30	$		24.—		11·26
11·26	[redacted]	35	✓		14.—		
11·26	[redacted]	12			7.—		11·2[illegible]
11·26	[redacted]	23			7.—		
12·2	[redacted]	35			14.—		
12·2	23 [redacted]	35			$14.—		12·[illegible]
12·3	[redacted]	29	✓		60.—		
12·4	[redacted]	21	✓		7.50		12·[illegible]
12·5	6 [redacted]	29	$		10.—		Deduct
12·5	[redacted]	33			16.—		
[illegible]	[illegible] → 1332 N. [illegible] → [illegible] Gate	30			20.—		12·[illegible]
[illegible]	[redacted]	23			7.—		12·12
12·15	[redacted]	30			14.—		12·17
12/16	17 [redacted] 30 N [illegible] St. [illegible]	33		32 14	46.—		
12/16	23 [redacted]	34			14.—		Deduct
12/17	12 [redacted]	21			10.—		
12/17	[redacted]	33			15.—		
12/[illegible]	15 [redacted] →	35			10.—		12·[illegible]
12/19	37 [redacted]	31			30.—		12·22
12/23	19 [redacted]	30			15.—		12·23
12/20	13 [redacted]	12	✓		$10.—		
12·24	[redacted]	34			$14.—		Deduct
12/21	[redacted]	12			12.—		
12/31	[redacted]	30			10.—		
12/31	15 [redacted]	34			10.—		

U. S. Secret Service
Epass Access Control Report

Date of report 01/27/98

Search Criteria: MONDALE, ELEANOR

Search Dates: 07/01/97 to 12/31/97

Date	Time	Name	Badge	Type	Post	Status
07/20/97	14:09:09	MONDALE, ELEANOR	346672	A	A4	ENTERING
07/20/97	16:26:56	MONDALE, ELEANOR	346672	A	A4	EXITING
12/06/97	09:32:57	MONDALE, ELEANOR	34667A	A	A4	ENTERING
12/06/97	10:46:08	MONDALE, ELEANOR	34667A	A	A4	EXITING

843-DC-00000004

202507

Aug - present - furlough
Sep - Oct - mid Nov.

end of Dec 31st "day"

1st week Dec - signed picture
in back office -

845-DC-00000002

3d wk in Dec - "hi Kiddo"

↳ White House Staff

Dec party in the
21st afternoon -

10 days later - 31 Dec 97
[illegible] or 7 days later
Weekend - Sun called
1½ later Snowing, at 2:40 -
Blizzard of '96
she went to work -
walked by, come on in -
closed door - 45 minutes
guard there - heavy session
Jan 7
Jan MLK Day - atlanta
for the day.

" Really
· Hard to have someone
die under your executive
order" "Cherishes time
w/ her - true gift"
seen alone
~~Buddy coming 1/2 hour~~

Nancy's ofc -
fooled around -
jerking off went back cause
dinner was
local.

21st Jan 96
~~[illegible]~~ called
27 Jan - ofc
she was in
San Francisco
gone weekend
monday
Tues -
farewell
to
Pat Griffin

845-DC-00000004

(weekend before: have to be careful: rumor that he had a crush on the intern

4:00 Tues. he calls her @ ofc "POTUS" — it [illegible] ofc.

Panetta's ofc

Pat Griffith farewell planned to ignore each other — not even a picture

1/2 day Tues ~~[illegible]~~ [illegible] Thur Fri. Sat.

845-DC-00000005

group picture far end away from him.

following Sun — beginning feb he called in the afternoon at work — Baba at home —

45 minutes 4:00 1 1/2 hrs.

(fooled around first)
½ hour - finished
"Will you call me?"
Recited # -

met in hall - walked
in together -

---

20 mins. later
called @ ofc
"had a really nice
time".

calls
Tues. night
(Bala gave Tues & Wed)
enjoyed talking to
her
have to go help
homework - called
from "home"

next day were better -

Midnight

· called next night in the middle of night - from bed - phone sex 20-30 minutes 7th feb

---

~~do~~ no contact til 19 feb - President's Day 11:00 ~~Sun~~ Mon. a.m. at home

she was going to work -

19 feb she went straight on knocked on door -

closed door - [illegible]

dumped her =

I love her

I've hurt them both -

so need before

ofc - ~~=~~

went to back - hugged

845-DC-00000007

• no kissing
you have to go now
wouldn't even kiss
me goodbye –
guard – saw her
leave – 15-20
19 feb '96 — minutes in there

end of feb 2 weeks later
28?
anxiety attack –
Baba going out of
town –
Israeli Embassy that
night – he saw her in
9:00 pm hallway
10:00 phone utp –
looked really pretty
called you in the
office – short conversation

next weekend
or
2 wks later -
ran into him w/
Natalie - didn't call -

The day he signed Cuba
~~Summit~~ Helms Libertad
Sanctions
against
Cuba -
receiving line

Mark
and ~~...~~ Then he went
that afternoon Summit
in Egypt = few days.

The Baba & girl were in Bacai

That weekend he
golfed on Sunday

{ screening at 8:00
theater stuff at
night - } waited til
10:00

next week - Baba gone to Boston
Monday - she is pissed.
Jogging - Dip Room walked by ignored him -

11:00 A.M. - Tues. called on house phone to her OFC Potus didn't show up on phone.

Thursday: skipped
Friday am: jogging return - passed elevator (Marine carrie Dr.) put tie on rest of day -

P.M. - Harold & Bruce - "Hi Monica" -

845-DC-00000010

Sun: put into Nancy not Sat.

(· fooled around – told about wearing blue & white tie)

Tues:
{ deteriorating position

Nancy said – Ron Brown family in Sat – Coming to see Potus – Call me Monday –

~~6:00 pm~~

6:00 Sunday night he called at home –
– Come over – –

845-DC-00000012

Romantic
if I win in Nov.
I'll have you back like that! fooled around.
phone call from Dick Morris – head on phone
~~Harold came in~~
She went ~~about~~ out & never goodbye)

"called at
7:00 @ home"

why did you leave?
Came back & you weren't
there ??

845-DC-00000013

you call Walter -
I'll bet it had something
to do w/ me

Monday - met w/ Nancy
Very sweet - Cried -
conscientious worker -

as ~~she~~ she left, Betty
asked what was wrong.
Betty hugged her -
Sometimes [illegible] happen
for a reason -
Friday - Called her at
home - she was hysterical
he found out what happened

"[illegible] apr 5"

845-DC-00000014

Evelyn Lieberman
Marsha & Nancy bounced out –
had gotten different accounts he was paying too much attention
she's got to go –
after election
doesn't care –
if you don't like it, get you a job on the campaign
I'll call you later –
3:00 AM. promised to call, made
WK myself wake up –
sweet call
April 19 to 20 – left Sun to go G-7 Tokyo – then Russia
Sun. night returned –

20th
Monday nite – called
after trip – hates job –
will see you
Sen. APAC thing
dog atta
Mad and shouts NO –

11–12 P.M. out of town HRC
Thurs. night – he called
at home – phone sex –
promise he'll call this
weekend.

didn't call.

May early
3:00 A.M. Mon. night – HRC there
apology call
sick can't talk

845-DC-00000015

May – Saxophone insert
hug & kiss – I miss you

1 wk goes by –
10 DAYS 'til next phone call.

phone sex

Week later he called — Borda committed suicide —

— he was upset —

mid - evening mtg — Coming to Pentagon prior to SVC ignored her

he called that night — She left that night,

Frustrated — phone sex

1½ wk later (following "hello" on tape friday)

Calls Wed. prior to big dinner —

845-DC-00000016

Betty called next A.M at work — re radio address —

845-DC-00000017

wants to meet her family - Dad & Stepmother were coming

Radio tape on friday w/ parents

Sat. June 23?
next weekend - called just to talk -

She leaves for Bosnia to July 15

July 5 calls that night -
Wierd phone sex = short 20 min
jerked off keep just talking
July 19th = called
18th friday 6:30 -

Baba out of town
July 5 –

6:30 AM leaving for Olympics
That day –
phone sex – after
Well, Good Morning!! came

promised to call
while he was away –
didn't call on Birthday
next week ~~I called~~ on Sunday –
Australia night

spent away
phoned & apologized 8:30 pm.
for Birthday
Short. July 30th

Bell sun Aug 4 = afternoon
pink suit – 45 minutes
stewing NYC aug. with phone sex

"end" Vacation — 1 WK —

Aug — ~~2 tutts tabor~~
day before travel
21st departure — for convention
6:00 p.m.
phone sex —
in his ofc

Her 250th pleaded to
19 aug. Birthday party NY

NY juicy — touched
grabbed his di

sent tie for B'day.

~~Sep 5~~

845-DC-00000019

Sep 5 — called from
good conversation road — at
home = phone sex

Sep 10 23 — left msg —
It's me —

~~12~~ 20 – 30th No call. She was in DOD.

Sep 30th Called again.
Saw you walking –
good conversation

Sep 5. phone sex
"NO WAY" (will you
[illegible] to me?)
when you get to
my age, everything
has consequences"

fight about it.

do you want me
to not call you
anymore?

Oct. 22nd wedding
in florida
he
really into phone
sex.
incredible

Baba not ~~the~~ the
weekend
2:30 am.

"Triple C" hotels

Black suit

845-DC-00000021

Baba not there

Tues. Oct. DC – he
~~next~~ night – event

next day – ~~[illegible]~~
tell Betty to
walk helicopter
waited in West Wing Lobby –
Betty told her Evelyn
Lieberman didn't
like it.

Sunday – Rally –
not Oct.

Oct 23 –
welcome home at WH
following election.

845-DC-00000022

6 wks later –

night before she left.

Dec 2nd plane

sex –

3 wks.

Christmas party Tues.

next night – he calls –
everyday can't be

sensitive –

person – have something

come by on Sat.

never called –

saw him at Nutcracker

Called Monday –

Jan 1997 Say I missed you – he went to New York
away for ever –

Jan 18th – he calls –

Jan 12 phone sex
had to push him
M. nap – present
See you
etc.

Inaugural – red dress

~~Jan~~ –
Feb 8th – noon
Snowing –
Come in for present.
Betty can't ~~get~~ in –

sick over this
think about this
all the time
in ~~person~~ should call

he called back –
phone sex.

~~?~~ Val. at – ~~tell~~ him

845-DC-00000023

845-DC-00000024

Betty called ofc
to invite Radio address

feb 28th go to Radio
address -

Stged phone - embassies
hat pin tapping
Book faces & wanders
out
fooled around.

Mar 13th
got on phone at
work - want to
see you tomorrow
a.m.
leaving for florida girls
Jordanian shot

concerns from Nancy & Steven

Mar 30th crutches
Betty visit, good sex

28 feb – didn't want to come addiction –

Mar 30 cried –

fighter phone
he april 24th called –

Dumpday 23 May –

845-DC-00000188

Letters Editor
Newsweek
251 West 57th Street
New York, New York 10019-1894

(BY FAX: 212.445.4120)

I would like to clarify the questions that have arisen about my involvement in the matter reported by Newsweek in its August 11th edition. Contrary to the perception held by many that I granted Newsweek "an interview" for this story, the truth is the reporter appeared, uninvited and unannounced, in my office at the Pentagon in late March 1997. I was compelled to respond when he asserted that Ms. Willey had given him my name, as a purported contemporaneous witness who could corroborate her new claim of "harassment" or "inappropriate behavior" on the part of the President.

My response then, as it remains today, was that this was completely inaccurate and that her version in 1993 and her version in 1997 were wholly inconsistent. One must wonder how such disparate allegations spanning a period of four years could have much, if any, credibility.

Regarding the comment made by the President's attorney about me, which appeared in the same article, I am acutely disappointed that my integrity has been questioned.

Linda R. Tripp
Department of Defense
Washington, D.C. 20301-1400
[redacted]

[redacted]

Ann McDaniel [redacted]

trainer — broke off at 9:30 —

Debbie Byrd — in at same time
walking in

Tony Nelson
Starts
drawstring
July 4
July 24
Black red
yellow

T shirt

Aug 16
9:00
socks
tennis shoes.

picture framed

Disease
& Representation

845-DC-00000191

Betty says he is "paranoid" right now. gate - car - comes over

Robin Wesley 5:30 pm.

Sept. 15 Isikoff calls me from his home @ — & asks if M knows about a woman who had a KW experience - he is trying to find out who she is. All he knows is that she is married, they don't live in Washington, she is a smart, savvy professional woman w/ "a client in Wash" - Happened in 1996 - during Inaugural time, she received "a flurry of phone calls" from him at

17 Sep - Betty calls her @ work 2:00 ish & says "he" had asked her if she had gotten the Black Dog stuff to M, & to let her know that now John Podesta was working on getting her back - & when Betty said M might also want to move to NY, he said OK to NY, that's easy, she she can work for Bill Richardson. "rebuffed him"

M met Betty at the gate after work - received many 2 T shirts & 1 white turquoise & 1 green cotton dress.

strange angle & jerked off himself

[illegible] from to

Friday, September 12that gate, hour and a half --repeated calls to office, finally she came out and got her -- long talk, he left. She poke to him before she left and told him XX was hysterical and at the gate and that she would clear her in and determine if she was a "crazy woman" --

Sept 14 Sunday night -- her plane from Illinois was cancelled, luckily she ran into Glickman who claimed she was with their party and got her on their flight out but to National instead of BWI -- she had to go get her car at BWI and called at 7:00 or so -- said she would call him and if he checked his messages, maybe he would call her back. He was at the pool at 7:30 -- she didn't know if he had company or what, but he called her later that evening and said that he would talk to XX XXX this week.

Calls to M at her house from Betty Friday nite.

W.H., Sep 15 -

B calls M at office late afternoon to tell her about "stuff" he brought her from

2:30 16 Sep M calls Betty to try & arrange a phone call - & asked whether he had spoken to Erskine - Betty said she had already

845-DC-00000193

PRESIDENT CLINTON'S RESPONSE TO PLAINTIFF'S THIRD SET OF INTERROGATORIES JONES V. CLINTON SEALED PURSUANT TO COURT ORDER

PAULA CORBIN JONES
V.
WILLIAM JEFFERSON CLINTON

WITNESS LIST

Monica S. Lewinsky
[redacted]

11 December 1997

Ms. Ursula Fairbairn
EVP, Human Resources & Quality
American Express Company
American Express Tower
World Financial Center
New York, New York 10285

Dear Ms. Fairbairn:

I am writing at the suggestion of Vernon Jordan, who has spoken with you on my behalf.

I am interested in exploring opportunities in Communications or Public Relations in New York. I am hoping to secure a position which would require effective communication skills, creativity, and frequent interaction with people. My various jobs in Washington, DC have provided me with the training and skills needed to further pursue a career in these areas.

Most recently, I have been working for the Honorable Ken Bacon, the Assistant Secretary of Defense for Public Affairs, as his primary assistant. My responsibilities range from interacting with the media on his behalf, to providing administrative assistance on the Secretary of Defense's international trips, to assembling timely updates of current media stories. My prior experience was at the White House in Legislative Affairs and the Chief of Staff's Office. Please see the enclosed resume for further detail.

I am moving to New York and am seeking employment to begin the first of the year. I am ready and available to speak with whoever in your office you might deem appropriate. I will follow up with a phone call to your office on Monday, December 15th, 1997.

Thank you for time.

Sincerely,

Monica Lewinsky

Monica S. Lewinsky

856-DC-00000002

From Ursula Fairbairn's Files

CC: Mr. Vernon Jordan

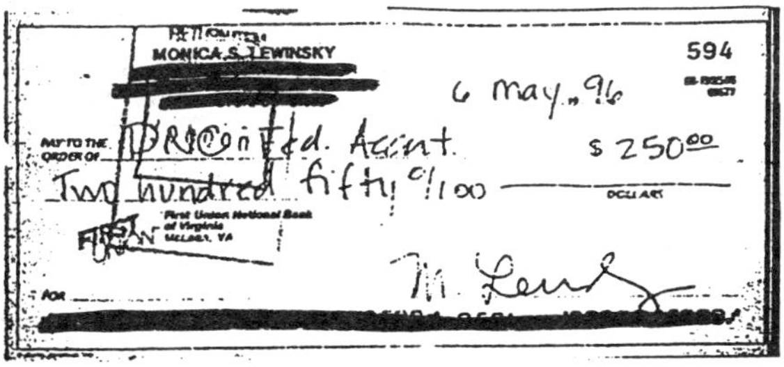
MONICA S. LEWINSKY
[redacted]
594
6 May, 96
PAY TO THE ORDER OF DNC Fed. Accnt. $ 250.00
Two hundred fifty 00/100 DOLLARS
First Union National Bank of Virginia
FOR
M. Lewinsky
[redacted]

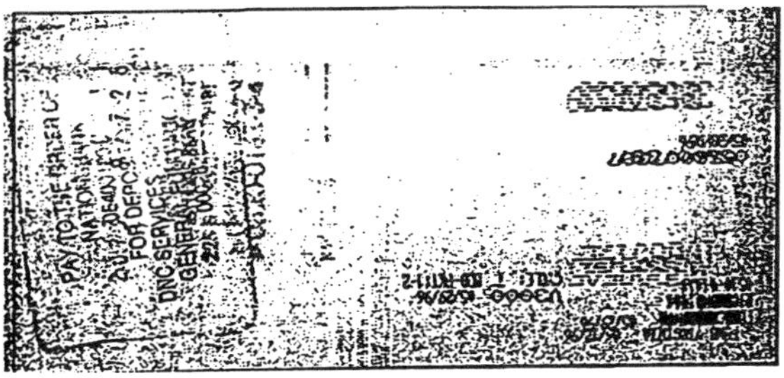

[redacted]
JOB 08008 OP JNH WS IDW09W NODE4
CF12982 P 02/03/98 15:09:25
AA
LEWIS, 2/17, [redacted], #0500, 7/96
WILKES SUBPOENA DESK
NC 2010

NC 99999

854-DC-00001485

MONICA S LEWINSKY [redacted] 12-17-97 BGN01228 2136

0041/0085

Express Cash Statement

Card Number: [redacted]

Electronic Fund Transfers Involving Withdrawals From Checking Accoun::

Cash Withdrawal From Financial Institution Account No

Date			Fee		Transaction Total	
11-29-97	Cash Received: $300.00	Dispenser: OLO1 UBOC BRENTWOOD W/U	Fee: $.00	LOS ANGELECAUS	Transaction Total:	$300.00
12-04-97	Cash Received: $168.49	Dispenser: L9BDCC11 LLOYDS BANK, U.K.	Fee: $.00	LLOY DSGB	Transaction Total:	$168.49
12-04-97	Cash Received: $134.79	Dispenser: L9BCGC11 LLOYDS BANK, U.K.	Fee: $.00	LLOY DSGB	Transaction Total:	$134.79

To change your bank or Personal Identification Number, or to find out the Express Cash location nearest you, call 1-800-CASH-NOW.

ITEM 1 $403.25
HOLIDAY INN, DIEGEM

Cardmember Account No	Date of Charge	Reference Code	Approval Code
[redacted]	97/12/04	913578412	53

Service Establishment and Location: HOLIDAY INN HOLIDAYSTRAAT 7

Record of Charge: HOTEL

S/E # 9410126783

TOTAL CHARGE AMOUNT 14724

ITEM 2 $752.26
GROSVENOR HOUSE HOTEL, PARK LANE, LONDON

Cardmember Account No	Date of Charge	Reference Code	Approval Code
[redacted]	97/12/05	011024005	

Service Establishment and Location: GROSVENOR HOUSE HOTEPARK LANE

Record of Charge: ACCOMMODATION

S/E # 9420124570

TOTAL CHARGE AMOUNT 455.37

ITEM 3 $300.00
001217 ATM WITHDRAWAL 11/29/97

Cardmember Account No	Date of Charge	Reference Code	Approval Code
[redacted]	11/29/97	001217	00

Service Establishment and Location: 20022 N

Record of Charge: GOVERNMENT/CEC
ROC NUMBER OLO1

S/E # 5026514182

TOTAL CHARGE AMOUNT $300.00

ITEM 4 $134.79
442204 ATM WITHDRAWAL 12/04/97

Cardmember Account No	Date of Charge	Reference Code	Approval Code
[redacted]	12/04/97	442204	00

Service Establishment and Location: 20022 N

Record of Charge: GOVERNMENT/CEC
ROC NUMBER L9BCGC11

S/E # 5026514182

TOTAL CHARGE AMOUNT $134.79

ITEM 5 $168.49
233061 ATM WITHDRAWAL 12/04/97

Cardmember Account No	Date of Charge	Reference Code	Approval Code
[redacted]	12/04/97	233061	00

Service Establishment and Location: 20022 N

Record of Charge: GOVERNMENT/CEC
ROC NUMBER L9BDCC11

S/E # 5026514182

TOTAL CHARGE AMOUNT $168.49

// PG-2136 / ST PG 2 OF 2 / /BGN01228

Statement of Account

0040/0085
8 R4 0 3

YOUR ACCOUNT IS 60 DAYS PAST DUE. PLEASE CONTACT US TO AVOID POSSIBLE SUSPENSION PER OUR FEDERAL CONTRACTUAL AGREEMENT.

Government Account Number	Statement Closing Date	Total Amount Due
[redacted]	12-17-97	$1,842.42

MONICA S LEWINSKY
OSD/WHS
[redacted]

MAIL PAYMENT TO:

AMERICAN EXPRESS
P.O. BOX 42010
PHILADELPHIA PA 19162-4201

8376985563 00184242000177538б

// PO-2135 / ST PO 1 OF 2 / 1 OZ / Y ZIP 20037 /BOX01228

Summary of Account

Government Cardholder Name	Government Account Number	Statement Closing Date
MONICA S LEWINSKY	[redacted]	12-17-97

Previous Balance	New Charges	Other Debits	Payments Received	Other Credits	Balance Due
$67.04	$1,758.79	$16.59	$.00	$.00	$1,842.42

Reference Number	Item Number	Description of Monthly Activity	Charges	Credits
		PREVIOUS BALANCE	$67.04	
094338	1	HOLIDAY INN, DIEGEM BELGIUM 14,724 BELGIAN FRANCS BILLED AS	403.25	
090342	2	GROSVENOR HOUSE HOTEL, PARK LANE, LONDON UNITED KINGDOM 455.37 POUNDS STERLING BILLED AS	752.26	
501334	3	001217 ATM WITHDRAWAL 11/29/97 UBOC BRENTWOOD W/U LOS ANGELECAUS	300.00	
501339	4	442204 ATM WITHDRAWAL 12/04/97 LLOYDS BANK, U.K. LLOY DSGB	134.79	
501339	5	233061 ATM WITHDRAWAL 12/04/97 LLOYDS BANK, U.K. LLOY DSGB	168.49	
823334		ATM CASH ADVANCE FEE DATE OF ABOVE 11/30	8.25	
823339		ATM CASH ADVANCE FEE DATE OF ABOVE 12/05	4.63	
823339		ATM CASH ADVANCE FEE DATE OF ABOVE 12/05	3.71	
		TOTAL CHARGES AND CREDITS	$1,775.38	
		BALANCE DUE	$1,842.42	
		PAGE 1 OF 2 852-DC-00000044		

FOR INQUIRIES ABOUT YOUR ACCOUNT, CALL TOLL-FREE 1-800-492-4922 OR WRITE US AT P.O. BOX 297812, FT. LAUDERDALE, FL 33329-7812.

01228
AMERICAN EXPRESS Carc

Statement of Account

0033/0085
8 R4 0 2

YOUR ACCOUNT IS 30 DAYS PAST DUE. PLEASE DISREGARD THIS NOTICE IF EXPENSE REPORTS HAVE BEEN SUBMITTED OR PAYMENT SENT.

Government Account Number	Statement Closing Date	Total Amount Due
[redacted]	08-17-97	$1,895.36

MONICA S LEWINSKY
OSD/WHS
[redacted]

MAIL PAYMENT TO:

AMERICAN EXPRESS
P.O. BOX 42010
PHILADELPHIA PA 19162-4201

8376985563 0018953600010916З0

// PG-2567 / ST PG 1 OF 2 / 1 OZ / N ZIP 20037240800/8GQ01203

Summary of Account

Government Cardholder Name	Government Account Number	Statement Closing Date
MONICA S LEWINSKY	[redacted]	08-17-97

Previous Balance	New Charges	Other Debits	Payments Received	Other Credits	Balance Due
$803.73	$1,083.38	$8.25	$.00	$.00	$1,895.36

Reference Number	Item Number	Description of Monthly Activity	Charges	Credits
		PREVIOUS BALANCE	$803.73	
095199	1	DUNA HOTEL MARRIOTT, BUDAPEST HUNGARY 52,120.00 HUNGARIAN FORINT BILLED AS	278.66	
090200	2	RUS HOTEL, KIEV UKRAINE 137.00 U.S. DOLLARS BILLED AS	137.00	
016209		HOTEL SHERATON SOFIA, SOFIA BULGARIA 367.72 U.S. DOLLARS BILLED AS	367.72	
501202	3	000061 ATM WITHDRAWAL 07/20/97 UB of CA BRENTWOOD W/U LOS ANGELECAUS	300.00	
823202		ATM CASH ADVANCE FEE DATE OF ABOVE 07/21	8.25	
		TOTAL CHARGES AND CREDITS	$1,091.63	
		BALANCE DUE	$1,895.36	
		PAGE 1 OF 2 852-DC-00000037		

S4

FOR INQUIRIES ABOUT YOUR ACCOUNT, CALL TOLL-FREE 1-800-492-4922 OR WRITE US AT P.O. BOX 297812, FT. LAUDERDALE, FL 33329-7812.

8GQ01203
AMERICAN EXPRESS Card

MONICA S LEWINSKY [redacted] 07-17-97 BGO01217 3425

0031/0085

Express Cash Statement

Card Number: [redacted]

Electronic Fund Transfers Involving Withdrawals From Checking Account

Cash Withdrawal From Financial Institution Account No

07-08-97	Cash Received: $67.97	Fee: $.00	Transaction Total:	$67.97
	Dispenser: 2150	AMEX-PLAZA DE LAS CORTES MADRID TSO ES		
07-08-97	Cash Received: $33.99	Fee: $.00	Transaction Total:	$33.99
	Dispenser: 2150	AMEX-PLAZA DE LAS CORTES MADRID TSO ES		
07-10-97	Cash Received: $10.76	Fee: $.00	Transaction Total:	$10.76
	Dispenser: 2062	AMEX-AMEX- BUDAPEST TSO BUDAPEST TSO HU		
07-10-97	Cash Received: $53.82	Fee: $.00	Transaction Total:	$53.82
	Dispenser: 2062	AMEX-AMEX- BUDAPEST TSO BUDAPEST TSO HU		
07-10-97	Cash Received: $107.63	Fee: $.00	Transaction Total:	$107.63
	Dispenser: 2062	AMEX-AMEX- BUDAPEST TSO BUDAPEST TSO HU		

852-DC-00000035

To change your bank or Personal Identification Number, or to find out the Express Cash location nearest you, call 1-800-CASH-NOW.

ITEM 1 $402.22
PALACE HOTEL, MADRID

Cardmember Account No.	Date of Charge	Reference Code	Approval Code
[redacted]	97/07/09	191001816	29

Service Establishment and Location: PALACE HOTEL PLZ DE LAS CORTES 7

Record of Charge:
GRACIAS POR UTILIZAR LA
TARJETA AMERICAN EXPRESS
THANK YOU FOR USING THE
AMERICAN EXPRESS CARD

TOTAL CHARGE AMOUNT 59348

ITEM 2 $119.80
JUDIT FOLKLOR, BUDAPEST

Cardmember Account No.	Date of Charge	Reference Code	Approval Code
[redacted]	97/07/10	1607	31

Service Establishment and Location: JUDIT FOLKLOR VACI U.6.

Record of Charge:
SHOP CHARGE

TOTAL CHARGE AMOUNT 22000.00

ITEM 3 $33.99
031820 ATM WITHDRAWAL 07/08/97

Cardmember Account No.	Date of Charge	Reference Code	Approval Code
[redacted]	07/08/97	031820	00

Service Establishment and Location: 20022 N

Record of Charge:
GOVERNMENT/CEC
ROC NUMBER 2150

S/E # 5026514182

TOTAL CHARGE AMOUNT $33.99

ITEM 4 $67.97
031806 ATM WITHDRAWAL 07/08/97

Cardmember Account No.	Date of Charge	Reference Code	Approval Code
[redacted]	07/08/97	031806	00

Service Establishment and Location: 20022 N

Record of Charge:
GOVERNMENT/CEC
ROC NUMBER 2150

S/E # 5026514182

TOTAL CHARGE AMOUNT $67.97

// PG-3425 / ST PG 2 OF 3 / /BG001217

[redacted]

THE WHITE HOUSE

Linda Tripp 703/
[redacted]

Drudge Rept

What I was told

No longer speaks
to me because
I wouldn't endorse
I know she is
lying

- harassment -
blatantly untrue
- made no bones
about what her
intent was

in social office -
volunteering
Claimed to be a
close friend of BC

gregarious, nice
woman

volunteers - 3 times
a week - hated [illegible]
Air Stock - a [illegible]
- asked if we could
use a vol.
- we brought her over

3

THE WHITE HOUSE

Shortly before Bernie

Tunnel vision
in her attempt

on going flirtation —
Richmond defeats
Chicken soup

Rehearsed speeches

Notes —
Everything was o.k.
w/ our attempt

—

The day this incident
occurred — Christ
was next — this is
what he did to
me

"They were doing
in study area

Don't believe that
she is stable

No words of
sexual harassment

→

She claims now it
is harassment

Prior to her husband
shooting himself –
days prior

She was in pursuit

3 times a week

5

THE WHITE HOUSE

I think Isikoff
leaked it —

Calamantti —

Her lawyers —

Called Cabinet Wing —

She chose to bring
this out — now
she is unsure —

Not only will I
not confirm

You were a happy
ecstatic, joyful

Aggressively pushed

Marriage shaky –
asking for a divorce

Told her husband
supposedly – he was
going to leave –

I don't know what
happen – he's nowhere

forgotten –
cardiac called from
BC –

880-DC-00000007

HB 004751

7

THE WHITE HOUSE

Tom Sevin —

Talking about his
home in Annapolis

Great [illegible]
boat — —

Gross distortion of
the facts —

narrowly question of
& would be fine

2

DAVID PYKE, ESQ.
Rader, Campbell, Fisher & Pyke
Counsel for Plaintiff
Stemmons Place, Suite 1080
2777 Stemmons Freeway
Dallas, Texas 75207

and

ROBERT S. BENNETT, ESQ.
KATHERINE S. SEXTON, ESQ.
Skadden, Arps, Slate, Meager & Flom LLP
Counsel for Defendant Clinton
1440 New York Avenue, N.W.
Eleventh Floor
Washington, D.C. 20005-2111

and

BILL W. BRISTOW, ESQ.
Counsel for Defendant Ferguson
216 E. Washington
Jonesboro, Arkansas 72401

		Hours	Amount
	Drafting Matter		
01/12/98	Draft letter to Atty David Pyke.	0.50	
01/15/98	Draft memo to file re: courier issue.	0.30	
	Draft Motion to Quash and for Protective Order.	5.90	
01/20/98	Draft letter to Atty Speights.	0.40	
	Draft letter to Atty Speights.	0.30	
	SUBTOTAL:	[7.40	1,850.00]
	Research		
01/15/98	Research: discovery limits.	3.50	
	SUBTOTAL:	[3.50	875.00]
	Telephone conf.		
01/07/98	Telephone conference with Atty Jordan.	0.20	
01/12/98	Telephone message to Atty David Pyke.	0.10	
	Telephone conference with Client.	0.20	
	Telephone conference with Atty David Pyke.	0.20	
	Telephone conference with Client.	0.20	
01/14/98	Telephone conference with Client.	0.20	
01/15/98	Telephone conference with Client.	0.20	

FedEx *USA Airbill* Tracking Number 800907757б

...'s Copy

107 500 51010052 5303N

1 From (please print)

Date 1-16-98 Sender's FedEx Account Number [redacted]

Sender's Name Francis D. Carter, Esq Phone [redacted]

Company CARTER & VARRONE Dept./Floor Suite/Room

Address 1341 G ST NW STE 510

City WASHINGTON State DC Zip 20005

2 Your Internal Billing Reference Information
(Optional) (First 24 characters will appear on invoice)

3 To (please print)

Recipient's Name Bill W. Bristow, Esq. Phone [redacted]

Company Dept./Floor Suite/Room

Address (To "HOLD" at FedEx location, print FedEx address here) 216 E. Washington
(We Cannot Deliver to P.O. Boxes or P.O. Zip Codes)

City JOnesboro State AR Zip 72401

For "HOLD" Service check here
☐ Weekday ☐ Saturday (Not available at all locations)
(Not available with FedEx First Overnight)

For Saturday Delivery check here
☒ (Extra Charge. Not available to all locations) (Not available with FedEx First Overnight or FedEx Standard Overnight)

Service Conditions, Declared Value, and Limit of Liability – By using this Airbill, you agree to the service conditions in our current Service Guide or U.S. Government Service Guide. Both are available on request. See back of Sender's Copy of this airbill for information and additional terms. We will not be responsible for any claim in excess of $100 per package whether the result of loss, damage, or delay, non-delivery, misdelivery, or misinformation, unless you declare a higher value, pay an additional charge, and document your actual loss in a timely manner. Your right to recover from us for any loss includes intrinsic value of the package, loss of sales, interest, profit, attorney's fees, costs, and other forms of damage, whether direct, incidental, consequential, or special, and is limited to the greater of $100 or the declared value but cannot exceed actual documented loss. The maximum declared value for any FedEx Letter and FedEx Pak is $500. Federal Express may, upon your request, and with some limitations, refund all transportation charges paid. See the FedEx Service Guide for ...

4 Service*
☐ FedEx Priority Overnight (Next business morning) ☐ FedEx Standard Overnight (Next business afternoon) ☐ FedEx 2Day (Second business day)
☐ FedEx Govt. Overnight (Authorized user only) ☐
☐ FedEx Overnight Freight ☐ FedEx 2Day Freight
(For packages over 150 pounds. Call for delivery schedule.)
☐ FedEx First Overnight (Earliest next business morning delivery to select locations)
*Delivery commitment may be later in some areas.

5 Packaging
☒ FedEx Letter* ☐ FedEx Pak* ☐ FedEx Box ☐ FedEx Tube ☐ Other Packaging
*Declared value limit $500.

6 Special Handling
Does this shipment contain dangerous goods? ☐ Yes (As per attached Shipper's Declaration) ☐ Yes (Shipper's Declaration not required)
☐ Dry Ice — Dry Ice, 9, UN 1845 III ___ x ___ kg 904 (Dangerous Goods Shipper's Declaration not required)
CA ☐ Cargo Aircraft Only

7 Payment
Bill to: ☒ Sender (Account no. in section 1 will be billed) ☐ Recipient ☐ Third Party ☐ Credit Card ☐ Cash/Check
(Enter FedEx account no. or Credit Card no. below)

FedEx Account No.
Credit Card No. Exp. Date

Total Packages	Total Weight	Total Declared Value*	Total Charges
		$ .00	$

*When declaring a value higher than $100 per package, you pay an additional charge. See SERVICE CONDITIONS, DECLARED VALUE AND LIMIT OF LIABILITY section for further information.

8 Release Signature

Your signature authorizes Federal Express to deliver this shipment without obtaining a signature and agrees to indemnify and hold harmless Federal Express from any resulting claims.

232

Questions?
Call 1·800·Go·FedEx

902-DC-00000033

The World On Time

Rev. Date 7/95 • PART #147381
©1994 95 FedEx • PRINTED IN U.S.A.

CARTER & VARRONE
Attorneys-at-Law
Suite 510, The Colorado Building
1341 G Street, NW
Washington, DC 20005

(202) 393-4330
Facsimile (202) 393-5657

Francis D. Carter
Edward G. Varrone*
* also admitted in Maryland

Stephanie Y. Bradley *
of counsel
* also admitted in MD and NY

Invoice submitted to:

MS. MONICA S. LEWINSKY
700 New Hampshire Avenue, N.W.
Apartment 114
Washington DC 20037

January 7, 1998
In Reference To: Jones v. Clinton and Ferguson
Invoice #10951

Professional services

		Hours	Amount
	Conference		
12/22/97	Meeting with Client (Office),	1.10	
12/23/97	Meeting with Attys Bob Bennett adn Kathy Sexton (their Office).	1.00	
01/05/98	Meeting with Client (Office).	1.10	
	SUBTOTAL:	[3.20	800.00]
	Document Review		
01/05/98	Review material from Atty Kathy Sexton.	0.20	
01/06/98	Review material from Atty Sexton at Skadden, Arps.	0.40	
	SUBTOTAL:	[0.60	150.00]

		Hours	Amount
	Drafting Matter		
12/24/97	Draft Engagement Agreement.	0.50	
	Draft letter to Client.	0.20	
01/06/98	Draft Affidavit for Client.	0.60	
	SUBTOTAL:	[1.30	325.00]
	Telephone conf.		
12/22/97	Telephone message to Atty Bob Bennett.	0.10	
	Telephone conference with Atty Kathy Sexton.	0.20	
12/23/97	Telephone conference with Atty Kathy Sexton.	0.10	
	Telephone conference with Client.	0.10	
	Telephone conference with Client.	0.20	
12/29/97	Telephone conference with Client.	0.10	
12/30/97	Telephone conference with Atty Kathy Sexton, Skadden, Arps firm.	0.10	
	Telephone conference with Client.	0.10	
01/06/98	Telephone conference with Atty Katy Sexton, Skadden, Arps.	0.30	
	Telephone message to Atty David Pyke.	0.10	
	Telephone conference with Client.	0.10	

AO 88 (Rev.1/94) Subpoena in a Civil Case

Issued by the
UNITED STATES DISTRICT COURT
DISTRICT OF COLUMBIA

PAULA JONES,
Plaintiff,
V.
WILLIAM JEFFERSON CLINTON
and
DANNY FERGUSON,
Defendants.

SUBPOENA IN A CIVIL CASE
CASE NUMBER:[1] LR-C-94-290

COPY

TO: MONICA LEWINSKY
[redacted]

☐ YOU ARE COMMANDED to appear in the United States District Court at the place, date, and time specified below to testify in the above case.

PLACE OF TESTIMONY	COURTROOM
	DATE AND TIME

☒ YOU ARE COMMANDED to appear at the place, date, and time specified below to testify at the taking of a deposition in the above case.

PLACE OF DEPOSITION	DATE AND TIME
The Rutherford Institute 733 15th Street NW., Suite 410 Washington, DC 20005	Friday, January 23, 1998 9:30 a.m.

☒ YOU ARE COMMANDED to produce and permit inspection and copying of the following documents or objects at the place, date, and time specified below (list documents or objects):
Exhibit A, attached hereto.

PLACE	DATE AND TIME
The Rutherford Institute 733 15th Street NW., Suite 410 Washington, DC 20005	Friday, January 23, 1998 9:30 a.m.

☐ YOU ARE COMMANDED to permit inspection of the following premises at the date and time specified below.

PREMISES	DATE AND TIME

Any organization not a party to this suit that is subpoenaed for the taking of a deposition shall designate one or more officers, directors, or managing agents, or other persons who consent to testify on its behalf, and may set forth, for each person designated, the matters on which the person designated, the matters on which the person will testify, Federal Rules of Civil Procedure, 30(b) (6).

ISSUING OFFICER SIGNATURE AND TITLE (INDICATE IF ATTORNEY FOR PLAINTIFF OR DEFENDANT)	DATE
Donovan Campbell Jr., ATTORNEY FOR PLAINTIFF	December 17, 1997

ISSUING OFFICER'S NAME, ADDRESS AND PHONE NUMBER
Donovan Campbell, Jr., Rader, Campbell, Fisher & Pyke, Stemmons Place, Suite 1080, 2777 Stemmons Freeway, Dallas, Texas 75207, (214) 630-4700

902-DC-00000135

(See Rule 45, Federal Rules of Civil Procedure, Parts C & D on Reverse)

[1] If action is pending in district other than district of issuance, state district under case number.

EXHIBIT A

DOCUMENTS AND THINGS TO BE PRODUCED

Pursuant to the Federal Rules of Civil Procedure, the Deponent is directed to produce, at the time and place of the Deponent's deposition, all of the documents and tangible things described in the enumerated requests below. In responding to the following requests for production, the Deponent is directed to comply with the following instructions and to apply the following definitions.

DEFINITIONS

For the purposes of these requests, the following definitions apply:

"Defendant Clinton" means William Jefferson Clinton.

"Defendant Ferguson" means Danny Ferguson.

"Document" means any tangible thing on which appears, or in which is stored or contained, any words, numbers, symbols, or images. The term "document" includes any and all writings, drawings, graphs, charts, photographs, tape recordings, video recordings, phono records, and other data compilations from which information can be obtained and translated, if necessary, through detection devices, into reasonably usable form.

"Person" means any identifiable entity, including but not limited to individuals, corporations, partnerships, sole proprietorships, and unincorporated associations.

"You" means the Deponent.

INSTRUCTIONS

A request for any particular document or thing is a request for the original, for each and every photocopy or duplicate of that document or thing, and for each and every draft of the document or thing. If, however, you produce the original of the document or thing, you are not required to produce any photocopies or duplicates unless they are not identical (as, for example, when marginal notations are made on a copy).

The documents and things to be produced should, at the time of production, be organized and labeled to correspond to the enumerated requests below. In the alternative, they may be produced as they are kept in the ordinary course of business, if it is possible to do so.

902-DC-00000136

You are to produce not only the documents and things in your immediate possession, but also those over which you have custody or control, including but not limited to documents and things in the possession, custody, or control of your agent(s), your accountant(s), your attorney(s), any investigator employed by you or by your attorney(s), or any consultant or expert witness employed by you or by your attorney(s).

If, in response to a particular request, an objection is interposed, and the objection applies to some but not all of the documents requested, please produce all responsive documents and things to which the objection does not apply.

REQUESTS FOR PRODUCTION

REQUEST FOR PRODUCTION NO. 1: Every document relating to any private meetings between you and Defendant Clinton, including any agendas, letters, journals, diaries, notes, tape recordings or memoranda.

REQUEST FOR PRODUCTION NO. 2: Every document constituting or containing communications between you and Defendant Clinton, including letters, cards, notes memoranda, and all telephone records, notes or memoranda reflecting calls to or from any telephone in the White House, the Pentagon, any governmental office or property, or your home or office, any cellular or mobile telephone, or to or from any other telephone numbers of Bill Clinton or you or anyone acting for or on behalf of him or you.

REQUEST FOR PRODUCTION NO. 3: Every document concerning any communications with persons other than Defendant Clinton which reference any relationship or any private meetings between you and Defendant Clinton.

REQUEST FOR PRODUCTION NO. 4: Every document concerning any communications with persons other than Defendant Clinton which reference any relationship or any private meetings between you and Defendant Clinton.

REQUEST FOR PRODUCTION NO. 5: Every calendar or address book or other document reflecting any meetings between you and Defendant Clinton or reflecting the address or telephone number of Defendant Clinton at any location.

REQUEST FOR PRODUCTION NO. 6: Every document relating to any communications with anyone concerning any occurrence involving you and Defendant Clinton, including any agendas, letters, journals, diaries, notes, time records, employment records, tape recordings or memoranda.

902-DC-00000137

REQUEST FOR PRODUCTION NO. 7: Please produce each and every gift including, but not limited to, any and all dresses, accessories, and jewelry, and/or hat pins given to you by, or on behalf of, Defendant Clinton.

REQUEST FOR PRODUCTION NO. 8: Please produce each and every document mentioning or describing any gift given to you by Defendant Clinton.

902-DC-00000138

Dec. 22 MONDAY

11:00 Vernon Jordan's ofc. mtg.

52 / 356 - 9

Dec. 23 TUESDAY

10:00 Bob Bennett, his ofc

357 - 8

Dec. 24 WEDNESDAY **Chanukah**

358 - 7

Christmas Day THURSDAY **Dec. 25**

359 - 6

Boxing Day Canada FRIDAY **Dec. 26**

360 - 5

SATURDAY **Dec. 27**

361 - 4

SUNDAY **Dec. 28**

362 - 3

Jan. 5 MONDAY

3:00 Monica Lewinsky, ofc appt.

2/5 - 360

Jan. 6 TUESDAY

9:

4:

6 - 359

Jan. 7 WEDNESDAY

10: Monica Lewinsky, ofc appt.

2: Mark Di Hassan, ofc appt.

7 - 358

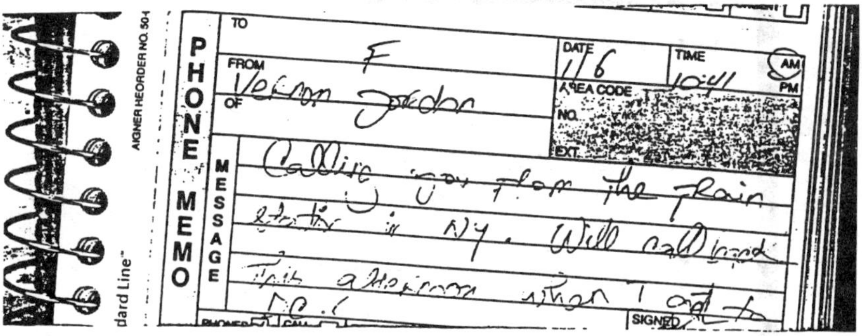
AIGNER REORDER NO. 504

dard Line"

PHONE MEMO

TO F

DATE 1/6

TIME 10:41 AM

FROM Vernon Jordan

OF

AREA CODE [redacted]

NO.

EXT.

MESSAGE

Calling you from the train station in NY. Will call back this afternoon when I get to DC.

PHONED ☑ CALL

SIGNED

902-DC-00000251

PARK HYATT - WASHINGTON, D.C
MELROSE
[redacted]
101 LISA 2

8/1 1501 GST 2
JAN07'98 8:19AM

1 FRUIT PLATE 8.50
1 FRUIT YOGURT 3.25
1 CEREAL /FRT 5.50
1 ENGLSH MUFFIN 4.00
1 COFFEE 2.50
1 O. JUICE 3.75
1 HOT CHOCOLATE 3.00
FOOD SALES 30.50
SERVICE CHARGES 6.00
TAX 3.05
TOTAL PAID 39.55
$ CHARGE TIP 6.00
[redacted] 07/99
VE JORDAN
AMERICAN EXPRESS 39.55
——704 CLOSED JAN07 9:11AM——

PARK HYATT - WASHINGTON, D.C
MELROSE
CHECK: 1501
TABLE: 8/1
SERVER: 101 LISA
DATE: JAN07'98 8:57AM
CARD TYPE: AMERICAN EXPRESS
ACCT #: [redacted]
EXP DATE: 07/99
AUTH CODE: 950042
VE JORDAN

SUBTOTAL: 33.55

TIP: 6—

TOTAL: $39.55

CUSTOMER SIGNATURE

I AGREE TO PAY ABOVE TOTAL AMOUNT ACCORDING TO CARD ISSUER AGREEMENT
* YELLOW IS CUSTOMER COPY *

AO 88 (Rev. /94) Subpoena in a Civil Case

Issued by the
UNITED STATES DISTRICT COURT
DISTRICT OF COLUMBIA

PAULA JONES,

Plaintiff,

V.

WILLIAM JEFFERSON CLINTON
and
DANNY FERGUSON,

Defendants.

SUBPOENA IN A CIVIL CASE
CASE NUMBER:[1] LR-C-94-290

920-DC-00000013

TO: **MONICA LEWINSKY**
[redacted]

☐ YOU ARE COMMANDED to appear in the United States District Court at the place, date, and time specified below to testify in the above case.

PLACE OF TESTIMONY	COURTROOM
	DATE AND TIME

☒ YOU ARE COMMANDED to appear at the place, date, and time specified below to testify at the taking of a deposition in the above case.

PLACE OF DEPOSITION	DATE AND TIME
The Rutherford Institute 733 15th Street NW., Suite 410 Washington, DC 20005	Friday, January 23, 1998 9:30 a.m.

☒ YOU ARE COMMANDED to produce and permit inspection and copying of the following documents or objects at the place, date, and time specified below (list documents or objects):

Exhibit A, attached hereto.

PLACE	DATE AND TIME
The Rutherford Institute 733 15th Street NW., Suite 410 Washington, DC 20005	Friday, January 23, 1998 9:30 a.m.

☐ YOU ARE COMMANDED to permit inspection of the following premises at the date and time specified below.

PREMISES	DATE AND TIME

Any organization not a party to this suit that is subpoenaed for the taking of a deposition shall designate one or more officers, directors, or managing agents, or other persons who consent to testify on its behalf, and may set forth, for each person designated, the matters on which the person designated, the matters on which the person will testify, Federal Rules of Civil Procedure, 30(b) (6).

ISSUING OFFICER SIGNATURE AND TITLE (INDICATE IF ATTORNEY FOR PLAINTIFF OR DEFENDANT)	DATE
Donovan Campbell Jr., ATTORNEY FOR PLAINTIFF	December 17, 1997

ISSUING OFFICER'S NAME, ADDRESS AND PHONE NUMBER
Donovan Campbell, Jr., Rader, Campbell, Fisher & Pyke, Stemmons Place, Suite 1080,
2777 Stemmons Freeway, Dallas, Texas 75207, (214) 630-4700

(See Rule 45, Federal Rules of Civil Procedure, Parts C & D on Reverse)

[1] If action is pending in district other than district of issuance, state district under case number.

AO 88 (Rev.1/94)Subpoena in a Civil Case

920-DC-00000014

PROOF OF SERVICE

	Date	Place
SERVED		

SERVED ON (PRINT NAME) | MANNER OF SERVICE

SERVED BY (PRINT NAME) | TITLE

DECLARATION OF SERVER

I declare under penalty of perjury under the laws of the United States of America that the foregoing information contained in the Proof of Service is true and correct.

Executed on ______________________
Date

____
Signature of Server

____
Address of Server

____

Rule 45, Federal Rules of Civil Procedure, Parts C & D:

(c) PROTECTION OF PERSONS SUBJECT TO SUBPOENAS.

(1) A party or an attorney responsible for the issuance and service of a subpoena shall take reasonable steps to avoid imposing undue burden or expense on a person subject to that subpoena. The court on behalf of which the subpoena was issued shall enforce this duty and impose upon the party or attorney in breach of this duty an appropriate sanction which may include, but is not limited to, lost earnings and reasonable attorney's fees.

(2)(A) A person commanded to produce and permit inspection and copying of designated books, papers, documents or tangible things, or inspection of premises need not appear in person at the place of production or inspection unless commanded to appear for deposition, hearing or trial.

(B) Subject to paragraph (d)(2) of this rule, a person commanded to produce and permit inspection and copying may, within 14 days after service of subpoena or before the time specified for compliance if such time is less than 14 days after service, serve upon the party or attorney designated in the subpoena written objection to inspection or copying of any or all of the designated materials or of the premises. If objection is made, the party serving the subpoena shall not be entitled to inspect and copy materials or inspect the premises except pursuant to an order of the court by which the subpoena was issued. If objection has been made, the party serving the subpoena may, upon notice to the person commanded to produce, move at any time for an order to compel the production. Such an order to compel production shall protect any person who is not a party or an officer of a party from significant expense resulting form the inspection and copying commanded.

(3) (A) On timely motion, the court by which a subpoena was issued shall quash or modify the subpoena if it

(i) fails to allow reasonable time for compliance;
(ii) requires a person who is not a party or an officer of a party to travel to a place more than 100 miles from the place where that person resides, is employed or regularly transacts business in person, except that, subject to the provisions of clause (c)(3)(B)(iii) of this rule, such a person may in order to attend trial be commanded to travel from any such place within the state in which the trial is held, or
(iii) requires disclosure of privileged or other protected matter and no exception or waiver applies, or
(iv) subjects a person to undue burden.

(B) If a subpoena

(i) requires disclosure of a trade secret or other confidential research, development, or commercial information, or

(ii) requires disclosure of an unretained expert's opinion or information not describing specific events or occurrences in dispute and resulting from the expert's study made not at the request of any party, or

(iii) requires a person who is not a party or an officer of a party to incur substantial expense to travel more than 100 miles to attend trial, the court may, to protect a person subject to or affected by the subpoena, quash or modify the subpoena, or, if the party in whose behalf the subpoena is issued shows a substantial need for the testimony or material that cannot be otherwise met without undue hardship and assures that the person to whom the subpoena is addressed will be reasonably compensated, the court may order appearance or production only upon specified conditions.

(d) DUTIES IN RESPONDING TO SUBPOENA.

(1) A person responding to a subpoena to produce documents shall produce them as they are kept in the usual course of business or shall organize and label them to correspond with the categories in the demand.

(2) When information subject to a subpoena is withheld on a claim that it is privileged or subject to protection as trial preparation materials, the claim shall be made expressly and shall be supported by a description of the nature of the documents, communications, or things not produced that is sufficient to enable the demanding party to contest the claim.

AO 88 (Rev. 1/94) Subpoena in a Civil Case

920-DC-00000015

PROOF OF SERVICE

	Date	Place
SERVED	12-19-97 AT 4:00 P.M.	THE PENTAGON, ARLINGTON, VA

SERVED ON (PRINT NAME)	MANNER OF SERVICE
MONICA LEWINSKY	PERSONALLY

SERVED BY (PRINT NAME)	TITLE
BRIAN HARTE	PRIVATE PROCESS SERVER

DECLARATION OF SERVER

I declare under penalty of perjury under the laws of the United States of America that the foregoing information contained in the Proof of Service is true and correct.

Executed on 12-22-97
Date

[signature]
Signature of Server

Address of Server
CAPITOL PROCESS SERVICES
1827 18TH STREET, N.W.
WASHINGTON, D.C. 20009
(202) 667-0050

Rule 45, Federal Rules of Civil Procedure, Parts C & D:

(c) PROTECTION OF PERSONS SUBJECT TO SUBPOENAS.

(1) A party or an attorney responsible for the issuance and service of a subpoena shall take reasonable steps to avoid imposing undue burden or expense a a person subject to that subpoena. The court on behalf of which the subpoena was issued shall enforce this duty and impose upon the party or attorney in breach of this duty an appropriate sanction which may include, but is not limited to, lost earnings and reasonable attorney's fees.

(2)(A) A person commanded to produce and permit inspection and copying of designated books, papers, documents or tangible things, or inspection of premises need not appear in person at the place of production or inspection unless commanded to appear for deposition, hearing or trial.

(B) Subject to paragraph (d)(2) of this rule, a person commanded to produce and permit inspection and copying may, within 14 days after service of subpoena or before the time specified for compliance if such time is less than 14 days after service, serve upon the party or attorney designated in the subpoena written objection to inspection or copying of any or all of the designated materials or of the premises. If objection is made, the party serving the subpoena shall not be entitled to inspect and copy materials or inspect the premises except pursuant to an order of the court by which the subpoena was issued. If objection has been made, the party serving the subpoena may, upon notice to the person commanded to produce, move at any time for an order to compel the production. Such an order to compel production shall protect any person who is not a party or an officer of a party from significant expense resulting form the inspection and copying commanded.

(3) (A) On timely motion, the court by which a subpoena was issued shall quash or modify the subpoena if it

(i) fails to allow reasonable time for compliance;

(ii) requires a person who is not a party or an officer of a party to travel to a place more than 100 miles from the place where that person resides, is employed or regularly transacts business in person, except that, subject to the provisions of clause (c)(3)(B)(iii) of this rule, such a person may in order to attend trial be commanded to travel from any such place within the state in which the trial is held, or

(iii) requires disclosure of privileged or other protected matter and no exception or waiver applies, or

(iv) subjects a person to undue burden.

(B) If a subpoena

(i) requires disclosure of a trade secret or other confidential research, development, or commercial information, or

(ii) requires disclosure of an unretained expert's opinion or information not describing specific events or occurrences in dispute and resulting from the expert's study made not at the request of any party, or

(iii) requires a person who is not a party or an officer of a party to incur substantial expense to travel more than 100 miles to attend trial, the court may, to protect a person subject to or affected by the subpoena, quash or modify the subpoena, or, if the party in whose behalf the subpoena is issued shows a substantial need for the testimony or material that cannot be otherwise met without undue hardship and assures that the person to whom the subpoena is addressed will be reasonably compensated, the court may order appearance or production only upon specified conditions.

(d) DUTIES IN RESPONDING TO SUBPOENA.

(1) A person responding to a subpoena to produce documents shall produce them as they are kept in the usual course of business or shall organize and label them to correspond with the categories in the demand.

(2) When information subject to a subpoena is withheld on a claim that it is privileged or subject to protection as trial preparation materials, the claim shall be made expressly and shall be supported by a description of the nature of the documents, communications, or things not produced that is sufficient to enable the demanding party to contest the claim.

EXHIBIT A

DOCUMENTS AND THINGS TO BE PRODUCED

Pursuant to the Federal Rules of Civil Procedure, the Deponent is directed to produce, at the time and place of the Deponent's deposition, all of the documents and tangible things described in the enumerated requests below. In responding to the following requests for production, the Deponent is directed to comply with the following instructions and to apply the following definitions.

DEFINITIONS

For the purposes of these requests, the following definitions apply:

"Defendant Clinton" means William Jefferson Clinton.

"Defendant Ferguson" means Danny Ferguson.

"Document" means any tangible thing on which appears, or in which is stored or contained, any words, numbers, symbols, or images. The term "document" includes any and all writings, drawings, graphs, charts, photographs, tape recordings, video recordings, phono records, and other data compilations from which information can be obtained and translated, if necessary, through detection devices, into reasonably usable form.

"Person" means any identifiable entity, including but not limited to individuals, corporations, partnerships, sole proprietorships, and unincorporated associations.

"You" means the Deponent.

920-DC-00000016

INSTRUCTIONS

A request for any particular document or thing is a request for the original, for each and every photocopy or duplicate of that document or thing, and for each and every draft of the document or thing. If, however, you produce the original of the document or thing, you are not required to produce any photocopies or duplicates unless they are not identical (as, for example, when marginal notations are made on a copy).

The documents and things to be produced should, at the time of production, be organized and labeled to correspond to the enumerated requests below. In the alternative, they may be produced as they are kept in the ordinary course of business, if it is possible to do so.

You are to produce not only the documents and things in your immediate possession, but also those over which you have custody or control, including but not limited to documents and things in the possession, custody, or control of your agent(s), your accountant(s), your attorney(s), any investigator employed by you or by your attorney(s), or any consultant or expert witness employed by you or by your attorney(s).

If, in response to a particular request, an objection is interposed, and the objection applies to some but not all of the documents requested, please produce all responsive documents and things to which the objection does not apply.

REQUESTS FOR PRODUCTION

REQUEST FOR PRODUCTION NO. 1: Every document relating to any private meetings between you and Defendant Clinton, including any agendas, letters, journals, diaries, notes, tape recordings or memoranda.

REQUEST FOR PRODUCTION NO. 2: Every document constituting or containing communications between you and Defendant Clinton, including letters, cards, notes memoranda, and all telephone records, notes or memoranda reflecting calls to or from any telephone in the White House, the Pentagon, any governmental office or property, or your home or office, any cellular or mobile telephone, or to or from any other telephone numbers of Bill Clinton or you or anyone acting for or on behalf of him or you.

REQUEST FOR PRODUCTION NO. 3: Every document concerning any communications with persons other than Defendant Clinton which reference any relationship or any private meetings between you and Defendant Clinton.

REQUEST FOR PRODUCTION NO. 4: Every document concerning any communications with persons other than Defendant Clinton which reference any relationship or any private meetings between you and Defendant Clinton.

REQUEST FOR PRODUCTION NO. 5: Every calendar or address book or other document reflecting any meetings between you and Defendant Clinton or reflecting the address or telephone number of Defendant Clinton at any location.

REQUEST FOR PRODUCTION NO. 6: Every document relating to any communications with anyone concerning any occurrence involving you and Defendant Clinton, including any agendas, letters, journals, diaries, notes, time records, employment records, tape recordings or memoranda.

920-DC-00000017

<u>REQUEST FOR PRODUCTION NO. 7</u>: Please produce each and every gift including, but not limited to, any and all dresses, accessories, and jewelry, and/or hat pins given to you by, or on behalf of, Defendant Clinton.

<u>REQUEST FOR PRODUCTION NO. 8</u>: Please produce each and every document mentioning or describing any gift given to you by Defendant Clinton.

920-DC-00000018

PAULA CORBIN JONES
V.
WILLIAM JEFFERSON CLINTON

SEALED DOCUMENTS

50-893 98 - 36

NationsBank, N.A.
Regional Center, VA2-125-04-01
P.O. Box 27025
Richmond, VA 23261-7025

Statement Period
07-04-97 through 08-05-97
Number of checks enclosed 12
B 03 0 C 03 67,983

Account Number: [redacted]

MONICA S LEWINSKY

Regular Checking Additions and Subtractions

Date Posted	Amount($)	Resulting Balance($)	Transaction
07-07	1.50-	193.22	Eds/7-11 07/04 #000004841 Withdrwl 1500 S. Fern St. Arlington, VA Fee
07-07	1.50-	191.72	Chevy Chase Fe 07/06 #000117101 Withdrwl Safeway #928 Washington DC Fee
07-07	1.50-	190.22	Chevy Chase Fe 07/06 #000425641 Withdrwl Georgetown Park M Washington DC DC Fee
07-09	13.25-	176.97	Check 316
07-11	966.25+	1,143.22	Dao Cl Des= fed Salary ID=[redacted] Eff Date: 970711
07-16	200.00-	943.22	NationsBank ATM 07/16 #000001861 Withdrwl Pentagon N. Conc Washington VA
07-18	101.50-	841.72	B Of A 07/17 #000056215 Withdrwl Century City Mrkt Los Angeles CA
07-18	50.00-	791.72	Check 319
07-18	1.50-	790.22	B Of A 07/17 #000056215 Withdrwl Century City Mrkt Los Angeles CA Fee
07-21	201.50-	588.72	B Of A 07/19 #000124805 Withdrwl Beverly Hills Mai Beverly Hills CA
07-21	160.00-	428.72	Ub of CA 07/20 #000000042 Withdrwl Brentwood W/U Los Angeles CA
07-21	100.00-	328.72	Cnb 07/19 #000426083 Withdrwl 9229 Sunset Blvd. Los Angeles, CA
07-21	70.31-	258.41	White Dove 07/18 #000742817 Purchase White Dove Santa Monica CA
07-21	77.30-	181.11	Check 320
07-21	1.50-	179.61	B Of A 07/19 #000124805 Withdrwl Beverly Hills Mai Beverly Hills CA Fee
07-21	1.50-	178.11	Cnb 07/19 #000426083 Withdrwl 9229 Sunset Blvd. Los Angeles, CA Fee
07-21	1.50-	176.61	Ub of CA 07/20 #000000042 Withdrwl Brentwood W/U Los Angeles CA Fee
07-22	4.60-	172.01	Check 321
07-22	0.00	172.01	Fee For Electronic Account Inquiry
07-23	60.00+	232.01	NationsBank ATM 07/23 #000003950 Fr Sav Pentagon N. Conc Washington VA
07-23	80.00-	152.01	Check 323
07-24	100.49-	51.52	Check 351
07-25	1,290.53+	1,342.05	Dao Cl Des= fed Salary ID=[redacted] Eff Date: 970725
07-25	30.00-	1,312.05	Citibank 90406 07/24 #000185914 Withdrwl 1000 Conn Av NW Washngtn DC
07-25	1.50-	1,310.55	Citibank 90406 07/24 #000185914 Withdrwl 1000 Conn Av NW Washngtn DC Fee
07-28	0.00	1,310.55	Fee For Electronic Account Inquiry
07-28	160.00-	1,150.55	NationsBank ATM 07/28 #000007065 Withdrwl Pentagon N. Conc Washington VA

ACTIVITY REPORT
OCTOBER 11, 1997
SATURDAY

WHEN THIS SHIFT RELIEVED THE SHIFT, THE PRESIDENT WAS ON THE SECOND FLOOR RESIDENCE.

****

PROTECTEE MOVEMENTS:

0952 HRS POTUS MOVED TO THE OVAL OFFICE.
1028 HRS POTUS MOVED TO THE OVAL STUDY.

****

WHEN THIS SHIFT WAS RELIEVED BY THE SHIFT, THE PRESIDENT WAS IN THE OVAL OFFICE.

****

RECORD TYPE: PRESIDENTIAL (NOTES MAIL)

CREATOR:Betty W. Currie (CN=Betty W. Currie/OU=WHO/O=EOP [WHO])

CREATION DATE/TIME: 6-DEC-1997 12:05:03.00

SUBJECT::

TO:BRUCE R. (Pager) #LINDSEY (BRUCE R. (Pager) #LINDSEY [UNKNOWN])
READ:UNKNOWN

TEXT:
Call Betty ASAP [redacted]

964-DC-00000862

0 002118

~~11:10~~ am- 12:57 ~~11:15~~ am 12:59	MEETING OVAL OFFICE Staff Contact: ~~Stephanie Streett,~~ Anne Hawley
11:15 am- ✓ ~~11:30~~ am 11:32	BRIEFING OVAL OFFICE Staff Contact: Sandy Berger 12:46 > 12:50
~~11:30~~ am- 11:35 ~~12:30~~ pm 12:45	MEETING CABINET ROOM Staff Contact: Sandy Berger, Rahm Emanuel 12:53 > 12:56 SIGN BILL
12:30 pm- 6:00 pm	PHONE/OFFICE TIME OVAL OFFICE
6:00 pm- 6:15 pm	BRIEFING OVAL OFFICE Staff Contact: Don Baer, Michael Waldman
6:15 pm- 6:45 pm	TAPE RADIO ADDRESS ROOSEVELT ROOM Staff Contact: Megan Moloney 1:23 > 1:54 WH STAFF MESS GREET FRIENDS OF
BC AND HRC RON	THE WHITE HOUSE

REDACTED

1:56 > OVAL

PHOTO

968-DC-00000073

0 003433

WASHINGTON, D.C.
THURSDAY, NOVEMBER 13, 1997

5:10 pm-		**CONGRESSIONAL RECEPTION**
6:00 pm		STATE DINING ROOM Staff Contact: John Hilley Event Coordinator: Setti Warren **CLOSED PRESS**
		Note: Call time for Congressional Members for 5:00 pm.
		-- **The President** will meet and greet informally with 40 Congressional Members.
6:30 pm-		**BRIEFING**
6:45 pm		RESIDENCE Staff Contact: Sandy Berger
6:45 pm-		**PRIVATE DINNER WITH PRESIDENT ZEDILLO OF MEXICO**
8:35 pm		RESIDENCE Staff Contact: Sandy Berger Event Coordinator: Setti Warren **OFFICIAL PHOTOGRAPH ONLY**

REDACTED

968-DC-00000187

8:50 pm		**THE PRESIDENT** departs The White House via motorcade en route Private Residence [drive time: 25 minutes]
9:15 pm		**THE PRESIDENT** arrives Private Residence

Saturday, March 29, 1997

Daynotes...

- The President talked, today, with:

5:38 p.m.
, 9:17 p.m.
, 9:01 p.m.
, 8:32 p.m., 8:5[illegible] p.m., 9:15 p.m.
, 10:44 p.m.
11:12 a.m.
11:23 a.m.
11:51 a.m.
4:14 p.m.

The President, left out of the Oval office door for the helicopter at 2:20 p.m. and

- The President arrived at Fort McHenry in Baltimore at 2:50 p.m.

REDACTED

The President arrived at the hotel at 3:10 p.m.

- At 4 p.m., the President made Remarks on the Budget Accord:

He returned to the residence at at 7 p.m., joined by Sandy and Mack, for a Private Dinner with Mexico President Zedillo. The President greeted President Zedillo at the South Portico and escorted him to the second floor for the dinner. [Erskine Bowles visited for five minutes, then departed]

The President joined Zedillo in the diplomatic room for his departure, at 8:45 p.m.

The President departed the White House at 9:10 p.m., for a **Private Birthday party for King Hussein and Queen Noor** The President returned to the residence at 1:25 a.m.

Daynotes...

The President talked, via phone, with:

-- Conference Call 9:38 a.m.

11:10 a.m.
., 12:02 a.m.
, 12:30 a.m.
, 11:32 a.m.
., 4:44 p.m.
4:50 p.m.
4:52 p.m.
, 4:59 p.m.
, 2:47 p.m.
3:43 p.m.

REDACTED

6:30 p.m.

PRESS SCHEDULE OF THE PRESIDENT
FRIDAY, APRIL 5, 1996
PAGE 2

8:50 am **THE PRESIDENT** plants a tree in memory of Secretary of Commerce, Ronald H. Brown
The South Lawn
INHOUSE POOL COVERAGE ONLY

Press Note: *At the conclusion of the planting, the Inhouse Pool will be escorted to the Marine One departure area*

9:20 am **THE PRESIDENT** departs the White House via Marine One en route Andrews AFB, MD
The South Lawn
OPEN PRESS

Press Note: *Press Set-Up Scenario for South Lawn*
8:45 - 9:10 am - Cabling, Mults & Pre-Set
9:10 - 9:15 am - Escorts to South Lawn
9:15 am - FINAL Access to Departure

9:30 am **THE PRESIDENT** arrives Andrews AFB, MD and boards Air Force One
OPEN PRESS

9:45 am **THE PRESIDENT** departs Andrews AFB, MD via Air Force One en route Oklahoma City, Oklahoma
AF-1 Travel Pool accompanies on board

FOR INFORMATION REGARDING THE PRESIDENT'S SCHEDULE WHILE IN OKLAHOMA, PLEASE REFER TO THE WHITE HOUSE TRAVELING PRESS SCHEDULE, AVAILABLE IN THE WHITE HOUSE PRESS OFFICE

6:20 pm C **THE PRESIDENT** departs Oklahoma City, Oklahoma en route Andrews AFB, MD
AF-1 Travel Pool accompanies on board

-MORE-

PRESS SCHEDULE OF THE PRESIDENT
SUNDAY, AUGUST 17, 1997

EDITOR'S ADVISORY: **FOR NEWS PLANNING ONLY**
NOT FOR PUBLICATION OR RELEASE

Intown Travel Pool
Wires: AP, Reuter, UPI
Wire Photo: AFP, AP, Reuter, UPI
TV Corr & Crew: NBC
Lights: NBC
Mag Photo: USN&WR
Radio: ABC Radio
Print: USA Today

Inhouse Pool
All of the Intown pool plus:
Net Cuts: NBC
Mults: NBC
Independent Pool: Reuters

8:00 am **Intown Travel Pool gathers,** WH Briefing Room, for protective purposes

PRESS PLANE DEPARTURE SCENARIO TO MARTHA'S VINEYARD, MASS
10:00-11:00 am - Gear and Baggage Call
10:30-11:30 am - Passenger Check-In for press charter
11:45 am - Passenger Check-In Ends
12:15 pm - Press Charter Departs to Martha's Vineyard, MASS

12:15 pm **AF-1 Travel Pool Check-In,** Andrews AFB, Maryland, Operations Terminal

AF-1 Travel Pool
Wires: AP, Reuter, UPI
Wire Photo: AP, Reuter, AFP
TV Corr & Crew: NBC
Mag Corr: Newsweek
Mag Photo: USN&WR
Radio: CBS Radio
Print Boston Globe

Press Schedule

TRIP OF THE PRESIDENT
to
Denver, Colorado; Seattle, Washington;
and Vancouver, British Columbia, Canada
Saturday, November 22 - Tuesday, November 25

NOT FOR RELEASE OR PUBLICATION - For news planning only

Weather/Denver: *Mostly cloudy; no rain. High 49, low 24*
Weather/Seattle: *Rain. High 51, low 43.*
Weather/Vancouver: Saturday: Showers, high 51, low 50.
Sunday: Rain likely, high 54, low 35.
Monday: Partly cloudy, high 43, low 31.

REMINDER: Your check-in on Saturday is for an international departure. Please be on time with yourselves, your bags and gear. ***Remember you MUST have your valid passport with you for this check-in.***

VANCOUVER NOTES:

The International Press Center and Television workspace is located in the Vancouver Trade and Convention Center (VTCC), located directly across the street from the Waterfront Center Hotel (there is also an underground connector). The only time when access will be difficult will be between 2 and 5 pm on Monday, when the leaders are holding their meetings there. Please plan accordingly.

Due to security needs, the Waterfront Center Hotel rooms have been reserved for four nights (even though we are only spending three). Therefore, you will be charged for Tuesday, so there is no need to check-out early.

For those in APEC Pools, expect to be standing outside for extended periods (even if your pool is indoors)—so, be prepared with a coat and umbrella.

Press Schedule
Trip to Denver, Seattle and Vancouver -- November 22-25, 1997

Saturday - November 22
Press Charter, Andrews AFB to Denver, CO
All these are at the Andrews Air Force Base in the the Operations Terminal:

6:00 am EST	*Baggage call, gear call and passenger check-in begin, Andrews AFB*
6:30 am EST	*Gear call ends.*
7:15 am EST	*Baggage call ends.* *** *CHECK-IN CONTINUES ONLY FOR PASSENGERS WHO HAVE ALREADY CHECKED THEIR BAGS.*
7:45 am EST	*Passenger check-in ends.*
8:30 am EST	*Press charter departs Andrews AFB en route Denver, CO* [*Flying time: 3 hrs 40 mins*] [*Time change: MINUS 2 to MST*]
8:30 am EST	*AF ONE Pool #1 check-in, Andrews AFB*

FILING FACILITIES AND HOTELS

Saturday, mid-day in Denver

Press Advance: *Mark Bernstein, George Fitzgerald*

MAIN FILE - Denver:

Geography: The events at the Phipps Conference Center and the file are located in the residential neighborhood of southeast Denver called "Belcaro". The file is in the Denver public school (Knight) at the corner of the block where the Phipps Center is. 968-DC-00003301

WH Press Office, Filing Center and TV Pool all in:
Knight Fundamental Academy
3245 East Exposition, Denver, CO 80209

February 1996

HILLARY RODHAM CLINTON

Sunday	Monday	Tuesday	Wednesday	Thursday	Friday	Saturday
				1 Chirac State Visit National Prayer Breakfast	2 Groundhog Day Jr. League RON Des Moines, IA	3 Ames, Iowa Cedar Falls, Iowa
4 NGA Dinner	5 Beyond Beijing Breakfast Governor's Spouses Lunch McLean, VA National School Boards	6 Interviews	7 Denver, CO RON-Los Angeles, CA Los Angeles, CA (Book)	8 RON San Francisco San Francisco, CA (Book) Los Angeles, CA (Book)	9 Dallas, TX (Book) Interviews	10
11	12 Iowa Caucus Lincoln's Birthday	13	14 Valentine's Day	15 Book Party (DC) Videos	16	17
18	19 President's Day	20 Interviews Lunch w/ Ambassador Ray NH Primary Ramadan Event (WH)	21 Lexington, KY (Book) Louisville, KY (Book)	22 Nashua, NH Philadelphia, PA (Book) Washington's Birthday	23 Tea w/ Mrs. Mubarak	24 DE Primary UNICEF Concert Warner Theater
25	26 C-Span Citizen's medals Philadelphia, PA (WLF) w/ MEG	27 AZ, SD Primary Videos	28 Hispanic Scholarship Dinner	29 Media Conference Volunteer Reception		

March 1996

HILLARY RODHAM CLINTON

Sunday	Monday	Tuesday	Wednesday	Thursday	Friday	Saturday
					1 Duluth, MN (C/G) Minneapolis, MN (C/G) Camp David, MD	2
3 Camp David, ...	4 Advocacy Event Child Conference Foundation Tea	5 TX (C/G) TX, NY, CO, GA, ID, CT, MD, MA, MN, UT, WA Primaries	6 BTF Conference Donahue Show NY (C/G) RON-DC	7 Int'l Visitors Recep NY, MO, ND Primaries Project Children	8 International Women's Day PTA Board of Directors	9 MI, NY, SC, WV, AZ Primary/ Caucus Nat'l Council of Jewish Women
10 NV Caucus	11 Chicago, IL-Good Housekeeping Senior Citizens Discussion	12 GL, HI, LA, MS, MO, OK, RI, TN, TX Primaries Int'l Womens Day Event	13 Lunch w/ Queen Noor Potomac, MD	14 American/ Ireland Fund Dinner	15 Reception w/ Ireland Rm.	16
17	18	19 IL, MI, OH Primaries	20 Cabinet & Spouses Rect. Interviews	21 Radio & TV Dinner Videos	22 Interviews Newspaper Assoc. Sick Children's Hospital	23 WY Caucus
24 Germany	25 Germany Italy RON Ankara, Turkey Turkey	26 Turkey	27 Turkey	28 Athens, Greece	29 Athens, Greece	30 Olympia Athens, Greece
31 Santorini Shannon, Ireland						

968-DC-00003459

S 015990

Printed by Calendar Creator Plus on 3/6/98

July 1997

HILLARY RODHAM CLINTON

Sunday	Monday	Tuesday	Wednesday	Thursday	Friday	Saturday
June S M T W T F S 1 2 3 4 5 6 7 8 9 10 11 12 13 14 15 16 17 18 19 20 21 22 23 24 25 26 27 28 29 30		1 Washington Principal Leadership	2	3	4 *Independence Day*	5 Madrid, Spain
6 Madrid, Spain	7 Madrid, Spain	8 Madrid, Spain	9 Madrid, Spain	10 Vienna	11 Vienna	12 Vienna
13 Salzburg	14 Salzburg	15 Salzburg	16	17	18	19
20	21	22	23	24 Climate Change Event (T) Nobel Laureates Event (T)	25	26
27	28	29	30 NSO Concert (T)	31	August S M T W T F S 1 2 3 4 5 6 7 8 9 10 11 12 13 14 15 16 17 18 19 20 21 22 23 24 25 26 27 28 29 30 31	

968-DC-00003475

October 1997

HILLARY RODHAM CLINTON

September

S	M	T	W	T	F	S
	1	2	3	4	5	6
7	8	9	10	11	12	13
14	15	16	17	18	19	20
21	22	23	24	25	26	27
28	29	30				

November

S	M	T	W	T	F	S
						1
2	3	4	5	6	7	8
9	10	11	12	13	14	15
16	17	18	19	20	21	22
23	24	25	26	27	28	29
30						

968-DC-00003477

Sunday	Monday	Tuesday	Wednesday	Thursday	Friday	Saturday
			1 *Rosh Hashanah* Child Care Event; Quantico Visit	2	3 Child Care Speech	4
5	6 Child Health Day Bkft; Climate Change Conference; Weizman Tea	7 Library of Congress Event; Salvation Army	8 [Panama Conference]	9	10 *Yom Kippur* Dominican Republic (T)	11 POTUS & FLOTUS Anniversary
12 Caracas, Venezuala [Latin America]	13 *Columbus Day* Brasilia, Brazil	14 Rio de Janeiro; Sao Paolo	15 Rio	16 Argentina	17 Buenos Aires, Argentina	18 Bariloche, Argentina
19 Bariloche, Argentina	20 CDFS NY,NY; IDB	21	22 Child Briefing; Patriarch; Penn Women, Philadelphia; Volunteer Event	23 Africare Dinner; Child Care Conference	24 O'Keefe Event; Opening of Symphony	25
26 *Daylight Savings Time Ends* HRC's Bday	27 Chicago	28 College Board Conference, Chicago; WLFS	29 Chinese State Visit	30 [Northern Ireland]	31 *Halloween*	

S 016008

December 1997

HILLARY RODHAM CLINTON

Sunday	Monday	Tuesday	Wednesday	Thursday	Friday	Saturday
	1	2	3 Decorator's Reception	4 Jobs for Graduates Awards Pageant of Peace Press Preview	5 Xmas Reception A Xmas Reception B	6
7 Kennedy Center Honors TODAY Show	8 Carnegie Presentation Congressional Ball Interviews	9 Team Harmony, Boston	10 Asthma Event (T) Hispanic $ NY Women's Agenda UN Human Rts Speech WLF Lunch (T)	11 NYC Asthma Event	12 Xmas Reception	13 Arkansas Fundraiser Xmas Dinner
14 Christmas in Washington	15 Children's Natl Medical Ctr	16 Friend of Children Awards Press Party (T) Toys R Us Playroom visit	17	18 CBS Sunday Morning Children's Event	19 Xmas Dinner	20
21 Holiday Party	22	23 *Hanukkah* Residence Party	24 *Christmas Eve*	25 *Christmas Day*	26 Candlelight Tours	27 Candlelight Tours
28 Candlelight Tours	29 Candlelight Tours	30 Hilton Head, SC	31 *New Year's Eve* Hilton Head, SC			

968-DC-00003479

November 97

S	M	T	W	T	F	S
						1
2	3	4	5	6	7	8
9	10	11	12	13	14	15
16	17	18	19	20	21	22
23	24	25	26	27	28	29
30						

January 98

S	M	T	W	T	F	S
				1	2	3
4	5	6	7	8	9	10
11	12	13	14	15	16	17
18	19	20	21	22	23	24
25	26	27	28	29	30	31

S 016010

THE WHITE HOUSE

WASHINGTON

PRESIDENTIAL CALL LOG

FEBRUARY 28th, 1997

	TIME PLACED	DISC	NAME	ACTION
OUT XXX	XXX 2:09 PM	2:47	SPEAKER NEWT GINGRICH WASHINGTON, D.C. [redacted]	TLKD-OK 2:34 P.M.
OUT INC	AM PM			
OUT XXX	XXX 2:09 PM	3:04	CONGRESSMAN RICHARD A. GEPHARDT OFC: WASHINGTON, D.C. WHITE HOUSE ADMIN EXT. [redacted]	TLKD-OK 2:48 p.m.
OUT INC	AM PM			
OUT XXX	XXX 3:54 PM	4:13	CONGRESSWOMAN CAROLYN Mc CARTHY HEMPSTEAD, N.Y. [redacted]	TLKD-OK 4:08 P.M.
OUT INC	AM PM			
XXX INC	XXX 11:45 PM		MR. D. STEPHEN GOODIN CELLULAR PHONE NO NUMBER AVAILABLE	MESSAGE PASSED TO PRESUS 11:47 P.M.
OUT INC	AM PM			
OUT INC	AM PM			
OUT INC	AM PM			
OUT INC	AM PM		968-DC-00003506	S 018924

THE WHITE HOUSE
WASHINGTON

PRESIDENTIAL CALL LOG

MARCH 29th, 19 97

	TIME PLACED	DISC	NAME	ACTION
OUT XX / INC	11:05 AM / XX PM		MS. MARSHA SCOTT RES: WASHINGTON, D.C. [redacted]	INFORMED PRESUS 3:08 P
OUT / INC	AM / PM			
OUT / XX INC	11:06 AM / XX PM	11:14	MRS. BETTY W. CURRIE RES: ARLINGTON, VA. [redacted]	TLKD-OK 11:12 A.M.
OUT / INC	AM / PM			
XX OUT / INC	11:23 AM / XX PM	11:25	MR. DICK KELLEY WASHINGTON, D.C. WHITE HOUSE ADMIN EXT [redacted]	TLKD-OK 11:23 A.M.
OUT / INC	AM / PM			
OUT / INC	11:51 AM / XX PM	11:54	MR. JOHN D. PODESTA RES: WASHINGTON, D.C. [redacted]	TLKD-OK 11:51 A.M.
OUT / INC	AM / PM			
OUT XX / INC	XX AM / 4:00 PM		MR. JOHN D. PODESTA OFC: WASHINGTON, D.C. [redacted]	MR. PODESTA DISCONNECT WHILE RINGING THE PRES 4:02 P.M.
OUT / INC	AM / PM			
OUT / INC	AM / 4:14 PM	4:15	MR. JOHN D. PODESTA OFC: WASHINGTON, D.C. WHITE HOUSE ADMIN EXT [redacted]	TLKD-OK 4:14 P.M.

THE WHITE HOUSE
WASHINGTON

PRESIDENTIAL CALL LOG

MAY 1st, 19 97

	TIME PLACED	TIME DISC	NAME	ACTION
XXX / INC	XXM 2:44 PM		CONGRESSMAN STENY HOYER OFC: WASHINGTON, D.C. [redacted]	HOLD PER MS. BETTY CURRIE 2;50 P.M.
OUT / INC	AM / PM			
OUT / XXX	XXM 2:47 PM	3:34	MRS. ETHEL KENNEDY RES: McLEAN, VA. [redacted]	TLKD-OK 3:32 P.M.
OUT / INC	AM / PM			
OUT / XXX	XXM 2:47 PM	3:41	GOVERNOR WILLIAM F. WELD OFC: BOSTON, MA. [redacted]	TLKD-OK 3:34 P.M.
OUT / INC	AM / PM			
OUT / XXXC	XXM 2:47 PM		SENATOR JOHN McCAIN OFC: WASHINGTON, D.C. [redacted]	PER MS. BETTY CURRIE WILL CALL BACK 3:34 P.M.
OUT / INC	AM / PM			
OUT / XXXX	XXM 3:53 PM	4:29	CONGRESSMAN JOHN M. SPRATT, JR. OFC: WASHINGTON, D.C. [redacted]	TLKD-OK 4:20 P.M.
OUT / INC	AM / PM			
OUT / XXXC	XXX 4:33 PM	4:46	SENATOR TRENT LOTT OFC: WASHINGTON, D.C. [redacted]	TLKD-OK 4:34 P.M.

968-DC-00003522

S 018940

THE WHITE HOUSE
WASHINGTON

PRESIDENTIAL CALL LOG

MAY 24th, 19 97

	TIME		NAME	ACTION
	PLACED	DISC		
OUT XX / INC	8:00 AM / XX PM	8:00	WAKE-UP BY WHITE HOUSE OPERATOR	COMPLETED 8:00 A.M.
OUT / INC	AM / PM			
OUT XX / INC	AM XX / 5:59 PM	5:59	MR. DANIEL R. SHANKS OFC: WASHINGTON, D.C. WHITE HOUSE ADMIN EXT [redacted]	TLKD-OK 5:59 P.M.
OUT / INC	AM / PM			
OUT XX / INC	XX AM / 9:57 PM	9:59	REVEREND REX HORNE RES: LITTLE ROCK, AR. [redacted]	TLKD-OK 9:58 P.M.
OUT / INC	AM / PM			
OUT / INC	AM / PM			
OUT / INC	AM / PM			
OUT / INC	AM / PM			
OUT / INC	AM / PM			
OUT / INC	AM / PM		968-DC-00003533	S 018951

THE WHITE HOUSE

WASHINGTON

PRESIDENTIAL CALL LOG

JULY 4th, 19 97

	TIME PLACED	DISC	NAME	ACTION
OUT	2:01 AM	2:01	MESSAGE: "OPERATOR, CALL ME AT 8:00 A.M. THANKS."	ACKNOWLEDGED 2:01 A.M.
OUT / INC	AM / PM			
OUT	10:19 AM	10:25	MR. BRUCE R. LINDSEY CELLULAR PHONE NO NUMBER AVAILABLE	TLKD-OK 10:22 A.M.
OUT / INC	AM / PM			
OUT	10:22 AM	10:36	MS. NANCY V. HERNREICH WASHINGTON, D.C. NO NUMBER AVAILABLE	TLKD-OK 10:25 A.M.
OUT / INC	AM / PM			
OUT	10:24 AM	10:38	MS. STEPHANIE S. STREETT RES: WASHINGTON, D.C. [redacted]	TLKD-OK 10:37 A.M.
OUT / INC	AM / PM			
OUT	10:50 AM	10:56	MR. JOHN D. PODESTA OFC: WASHINGTON, D.C. WHITE HOUSE ADM. EXT. [redacted]	TLKD-OK 10:51 A.M.
OUT / INC	AM / PM			
INC	3:46 PM	4:07	SECRETARY ROBERT E. RUBIN TREASURY OPERATOR NO NUMBER AVAILABLE	TLKD-OK 3:46 P.M.

THE WHITE HOUSE

WASHINGTON

PRESIDENTIAL CALL LOG

JULY 14th , 19 97

	TIME PLACED	DISC	NAME	ACTION
OUT / XXX	XXX 9:59 PM	10:54	CONFERENCE CALL MR. BOB BENNETT LIVINGSTON, MT.	TLKD-OK 10:03 P.M.
OUT / INC	AM / PM		[redacted] AND MR. CHARLES RUFF	
OUT / INC	AM / PM		RES: WASHINGTON, D.C. [redacted]	
OUT / INC	AM / PM			
OUT / XXX	XXX 10:54 PM	11:01	MR. BRUCE R. LINDSEY RES: WASHINGTON, D.C. [redacted]	TLKD-OK 10:55 P.M.
OUT / INC	AM / PM			
OUT / INC	AM / PM			
OUT / INC	AM / PM			
OUT / INC	AM / PM			
OUT / INC	AM / PM			S 018968
OUT / INC	AM / PM			

THE WHITE HOUSE

WASHINGTON

PRESIDENTIAL CALL LOG

JULY 24th, 19 97

	TIME PLACED	TIME DISC	NAME	ACTION
OUT XX	8:38 AM	8:39	MRS. NANCY V. HERNREICH WASHINGTON, D.C. WHITE HOUSE ADMIN EXT [redacted]	TLKD-OK 8:38 A.M.
OUT / INC	AM / PM			
OUT XX	9:03 AM	9:03	MRS. NANCY V. HERNREICH OFC: WASHINGTON, D.C. WHITE HOUSE ADMIN EXT [redacted]	TLKD-OK 9:03 A.M.
OUT / INC	AM / PM			
INC XX	3:48 PM	3:49	MESSAGE: "OPERATOR PLEASE WAKE ME IN TWENTY MINUTES."	ACKNOWLEDGED 3:48 P.M.
OUT / INC	AM / PM			
INC	4:22 PM	4:22	WAKE-UP BY WHITE HOUSE OPERATOR	COMPLETED 4:22 P.M.
OUT / INC	AM / PM			
INC	10:10 PM		THE VICE PRESIDENT RES: WASHINGTON, D.C. WHITE HOUSE ADMIN EXT [redacted]	VICE PRESUS CANCELLED CALL 10:10 P.M.
OUT / INC	AM / PM			
INC	11:20 PM	11:58	MR. JOHN L. HILLEY RES: GREAT FALLS, VA. [redacted]	TLKD-OK 11:43 P.M.

THE WHITE HOUSE
WASHINGTON

PRESIDENTIAL CALL LOG

AUGUST 16th, 19 97

	TIME PLACED	DISC	NAME	ACTION
OUT	1:10 AM	1:10	MESSAGE: "OPERATOR, CALL ME AT 8:00 A.M. THANKS."	ACKNOWLEDGED 1:10 A.
OUT / INC	AM / PM			
INC	8:00 AM	8:00	WAKE-UP BY WHITE HOUSE OPERATOR	COMPLETED 8:00 A.M.
OUT / INC	AM / PM			
OUT	9:18 AM	9:19	MRS. BETTY W. CURRIE OFC: WASHINGTON, D.C. WHITE HOUSE ADMIN EXT. [redacted]	TLKD-OK 9:18 A.M.
OUT / INC	AM / PM			
INC	5:48 PM	9:09	MR. LOU HOLTZ RES: ORLANDO, FL. [redacted]	TLKD-OK 9:05 P.M.
OUT / INC	AM / PM			
INC	6:05 PM		MRS. HILLARY RODHAM CLINTON RES: WASHINGTON, D.C. WHITE HOUSE ADMIN EXT. [redacted]	MRS. CLINTON DISCONNECTED 6:05 P.
OUT / INC	AM / PM			
OUT	6:06 PM	6:06	MESSAGE: "OPERATOR, TELL MRS. CLINTON THAT I AM FINISHED HERE AND THAT I'M	S 018976

NG

(CONTINUE NEXT SHEET)

Thursday, November 13, 1997

The Iraq problem continue to escalate, in spite of the UN's resolution yesterday condeming their actions against American soldiers.
The President responded to their threats yesterday to expell Americans from the country, with his own condemnation and warnings, during remarks before a Bill signing.

Today...

The President arrived at the Oval office at 8:05 a.m., and had an 8:15 a.m., **Foreign Policy Meeting** this morning in the Cabinet Room.

Participants in this meeting were: Veep, Sec. Albright, Sec. Cohen, Ambassador Richardso, CIA Director Tenet, Erskine, Sandy, Gen. Shelton, Ambassador Pickering, Slocombe, Steinberg, Fuerth, Riedel, Welch, Pace King.

At 9:15 a.m, the President made **a foreign policy call to**

At 9:45 a.m., the President **Signed the Labor/Health/HHS bill** in the Oval Office.

The President golfed with Congressional leaders today from 12 noon to 4 p.m. at the Army/Navy Golf Course in Arlington (18 holes)

The President greeted 50 guests in the State Dining Room at 5:22 p.m., at a **Reception for Democrats who supported the FastTrack Bill.**

Attendants at the Reception, included: Representatives: Ken Bentsen, Marion Berry, Earl Pomeroy, Harold Ford, Jr., Robert Matsui, Sheila Jackson-Lee, William Jefferson, E.B. Johnson, David Price, Anna Eshoo, Bob Clement, Jim Davis, Cal Dooley, Vic Fazio, Norm Dicks, Vick Synder, Charles Stenholm, Ike Skelton, David Skaggs, Ellen Tauscher, Jane Harman, Matthew Martinez, Lloyd Doggett, Jim McDermott, Chet Edwards, Bob Etheridge, Ralph Hall, Lee Hamilton, Darlene Hooley, Zoe Lofgren, James Moran, Owen Pickett, John Tanner, Peter Deutsch.

Administration officials included: Secretary Glickman, Daley, Albright, Shalala, Richardson, Browner, Pena, Slater, Alvarez, Herman, Berger, Goodie and Silverman.

He proceeded to the Oval at 6:34 p.m. He was briefed by Sandy, Tarullo, Brainard and Dobbins. He took a **Foreign Call** **at 6:47 p.m.**

Volume VII:

Document Supplement, Part E

Documents Cited in Referral: Bates Numbers 1000-V006

REFERRAL

TO THE

UNITED STATES HOUSE OF REPRESENTATIVES

PURSUANT TO

TITLE 28, UNITED STATES CODE, § 595(C)

DOCUMENT SUPPLEMENT E

SUBMITTED BY

THE OFFICE OF THE INDEPENDENT COUNSEL

SEPTEMBER 9, 1998

Index

INDEX: Documents cited in the 595(c) Referral

09-Sep-98

Bates # or Tab#	Production Name	Description
*Tab 001	N/A	Main Stairway to Family Quarters
*Tab 002	N/A	Movie Theater in East Colonnade
*Tab 003	N/A	11/14/95 LA Times news article
*Tab 004	N/A	11/14/95 Washington Post news article
*Tab 005	N/A	11/16/95: Facts on File, World News Digest -- pg. 852
*Tab 006	N/A	11/16/95 Washington Post news article
*Tab 007	N/A	11/17/95 USA Today news article
*Tab 008	N/A	11/20/95 Washington Post news article
*Tab 009	N/A	11/23/95: Facts on File, World News Digest -- pg. 868
*Tab 010	N/A	2/19/96 Weekly Compilation of Presidential Documents
*Tab 011	N/A	2/28/96 Newsday news article
*Tab 012	N/A	7/4/97 Drudge Report Final
*Tab 013	N/A	8/11/97 Washington Post news article
*Tab 014	N/A	8/11/97 Newsweek article
*Tab 015	N/A	9/13/97 NY Times news article
*Tab 016	N/A	9/22/97 Forbes news article
*Tab 017	N/A	10/4/97 to 10/23/97 Digest of Other White House Announcements
*Tab 018	N/A	11/9/97 LA Times news article
*Tab 019	N/A	11/14/97 Baltimore Sun news article
*Tab 020	N/A	11/15/97 Washington Post news article
*Tab 021	N/A	1/20/98 subpoena to William Jefferson Clinton, V002
*Tab 022	N/A	1/21/98 Washington Post news article
*Tab 023	N/A	1/21/98 "The News Hour with Jim Lehrer"

50-893 98 - 37

Bates # or Tab#	Production Name	Description
*Tab 024	N/A	1/21/98 "All Things Considered"
*Tab 025	N/A	1/21/98 White House Briefing
*Tab 025A	N/A	1/21/98 Excerpts of Telephone Interview of Clinton by Roll Call
*Tab 026	N/A	1/22/98 Remarks by President Clinton at the White House
*Tab 027	N/A	1/22/98 America Online article
*Tab 028	N/A	1/22/98 FBI Receipt of Property
*Tab 029	N/A	1/22/98 ABC News Special Report with Peter Jennings
*Tab 030	N/A	1/22/98 Roll Call interview with William Jefferson Clinton
*Tab 030A	N/A	1/22/98 Seatle Times news article
*Tab 031	N/A	1/23/98 FBI Receipt of Property, w/attached letter
*Tab 032	N/A	1/24/98 CBS News Show: Saturday Morning
*Tab 033	N/A	1/25/98 Face the Nation
*Tab 034	N/A	1/26/98 Nightline
*Tab 035	N/A	1/26/98 ABC News Special Report with Peter Jennings
*Tab 036	N/A	1/26/98 White House Education News Conference
*Tab 036A	N/A	1/27/98 AP news article
*Tab 036B	N/A	1/27/98 NBC: The Today Show
*Tab 037	N/A	2/5/98 Remarks by President Clinton
*Tab 038	N/A	2/6/98 Joint News Conference with President Clinton
*Tab 039	N/A	2/14/98 Washington Post news article
*Tab 040	N/A	2/17/98 Chicago Tribune news article
*Tab 041	N/A	3/5/98 closed hearing transcript excerpt
*Tab 042	N/A	3/17/98 Memoradum w/attachments, In re: Grand Jury Proceedings
*Tab 043	N/A	3/25/98 Washington Post news article
*Tab 044	N/A	4/17/98 letter to DAG Eric Holder from the OIC
*Tab 045	N/A	6/98 California Lawyer article

Bates # or Tab#	Production Name	Description
*Tab 046	N/A	6/15/98 Brief of Appellant William J. Clinton
*Tab 047	N/A	6/29/98 US News & World Report news article
*Tab 048	N/A	7/15/98 letter to IC Smaltz from Richard Rogers
*Tab 049	N/A	7/17/98 subpoena to the White House, D1415
*Tab 050	N/A	7/22/98 CBS News transcript, HARDBALL
*Tab 051	N/A	7/26/98 NBC News Meet the Press
*Tab 052	N/A	7/28/98 Motion of William J. Clinton for Continuance
*Tab 053	N/A	7/28/98 Transcript of Status Hearing , In re: Motion to Continue
*Tab 054	N/A	7/29/98 FBI Receipt of Property
*Tab 055	N/A	7/31/98 letter to David Kendall from Bob Bittman
*Tab 056	N/A	7/31/98 letter to Bob Bittman from David Kendall
*Tab 057	N/A	7/31/98 letter to David Kendall from Bob Bittman
*Tab 058	N/A	8/3/98 letter to Bob Bittman from David Kendall
*Tab 059	N/A	8/3/98 letter to David Kendall from Bob Bittman
*Tab 060	N/A	8/3/98 FBI Laboratory Report
*Tab 061	N/A	8/3/98 FBI 302
*Tab 062	N/A	8/3/98 letter to Judge Starr from DAG Eric Holder
*Tab 063	N/A	8/6/98 letter to AG Reno from IC Smaltz
*Tab 064	N/A	8/6/98 FBI Laboratory Report
*Tab 065	N/A	8/7/98 Washington Times news article
*Tab 066	N/A	8/10/98 Newsweek article
*Tab 067	N/A	8/11/98 letter to AG Holder from Judge Starr
*Tab 068	N/A	8/11/98 Memorandum Order, In re: Grand Jury Proceedings
*Tab 069	N/A	8/13/98 NY Times news article
*Tab 070	N/A	8/13/98 USA Today news article
*Tab 071	N/A	8/13/98 Washington Post news article
*Tab 072	N/A	8/13/98 Washington Times news article

Bates # or Tab#	Production Name	Description
*Tab 073	N/A	8/17/98 Newsweek article
*Tab 074	N/A	8/17/98 FBI Laboratory Report
*Tab 075	N/A	8/17/98 AP news article
*Tab 076	N/A	8/18/98 Washington Post
*Tab 077	N/A	8/24/98 facsimile to Jackie Bennett from Gary Grindler
*Tab 078	N/A	8/27/98 memo
*Tab 079	N/A	8/31/98 letter to Bob Bittman from David Kendall
*Tab 080	N/A	9/7/98 memo
*Tab 081	N/A	Jones v. Clinton, 1998 WL 551961, 9/1/98 order
*Tab 082	N/A	Lyrics to "Surfacing"
*Tab 083	N/A	18 U.S.C. section 2246
0812-DC-00000002	Lewinsky, Monica	Passport photo page
0824-DC-00000001 to 2	Currie, Betty	1/23/98 letter to Judge Starr from Karl Metzner
0824-DC-00000013	Currie, Betty	"Love Notes" supplement
0824-DC-00000014	Currie, Betty	2/14/97 Washington Post "Love Notes"
0827-DC-00000002 to 18	United States Secret Service	Epass Access Control Reports
0828-DC-00000003	US Mission to the UN	3/14/97 to 12/22/97 Toll records
0828-DC-00000004	US Mission to the UN	10/21/97 to 11/19/97 Toll records
0828-DC-00000012	US Mission to the UN	Monica Lewinsky's resume
0828-DC-00000013	US Mission to the UN	11/3/97 letter from Monica Lewinsky to Ambassador Richardson
0828-DC-00000023	US Mission to the UN	10/31/97 schedule for Ambassador Richardson
0830-DC-00000007	Revlon Group, Inc.	1/13/98 letter from Monica Lewinsky to Jenna Sheldon
0830-DC-00000017	Revlon Group, Inc.	12/11/97 letter from Monica Lewinsky to Richard Halperin
0831-DC-00000008 to 11	Pagemart	Pager records for Moncia Lewinsky
0832-DC-00000004 to 5	McAndrews & Forbes Holding	Toll records
0833-DC-00000980	Department of Defense	11/6/97 letter from Monica Lewinsky to Vernon Jordan
0833-DC-00001070	Department of Defense	6/24/97 typed note to Betty Currie

Bates # or Tab#	Production Name	Description
0833-DC-00001857	Department of Defense	3/5/97 E-Mail
0833-DC-00001876	Department of Defense	3/3/97 e-mail from Linda Tripp to Monica Lewinsky
0833-DC-00001906	Department of Defense	2/24/97 E-Mail
0833-DC-00001934	Department of Defense	2/19/97 E-Mail
0833-DC-00001974	Department of Defense	2/4/97 E-Mail
0833-DC-00002716	Department of Defense	Notification of Personnel Action
0833-DC-00002880	Department of Defense	Job Description
0833-DC-00003207	Department of Defense	Travel voucher
0833-DC-00009446	Department of Defense	2/19/97 E-Mail
0833-DC-00017867	Department of Defense	10/6/97 to 10/9/97 Toll records
0833-DC-00017869	Department of Defense	10/15/97 to 10/20/97 Toll records
0833-DC-00017875	Department of Defense	Toll records
0833-DC-00017886	Department of Defense	Toll records
0833-DC-00017890	Department of Defense	Toll records
0833-DC-00017903 to 04	Department of Defense	Toll records
0833-DC-00017908	Department of Defense	Toll records
0837-DC-00000001 to 27	Speed Service Couriers, Inc.	Courier receipts re: Monica Lewinsky
0843-DC-00000004	United States Secret Service	12/6/97 Epass Access Control Record
0845-DC-00000002	Tripp, Linda	Handwritten notes
0845-DC-00000004 to 17	Tripp, Linda	Handwritten notes
0845-DC-00000018 to 21	Tripp, Linda	Handwritten Notes
0845-DC-00000022 to 25	Tripp, Linda	Handwritten Notes
0845-DC-00000188	Tripp, Linda	Handwritten note
0845-DC-00000190	Tripp, Linda	Letter from Linda Tripp to Newsweek
0845-DC-00000191 to 193	Tripp, Linda	Handwritten notes
0849-DC-00000090 to 97	Rader, Campbell, Fisher & Pyke	President Clinton's Responses to Plaintiff's Third Set of Interrogatories

Bates # or Tab#	Production Name	Description
0849-DC-00000098 to 102	Rader, Campbell, Fisher & Pyke	Attachment to President Clinton's Responses to Plaintiff's Third Set of Interrogatories
0849-DC-00000121 to 137	Rader, Campbell, Fisher & Pyke	Plaintiff's Witness List
0849-DC-00000352	Rader, Campbell, Fisher & Pyke	Videotaped Deposition of William Jefferson Clinton
0849-DC-00000586	Rader, Campbell, Fisher & Pyke	Definition of "Sexual Relation"
0849-DC-00000634 to 636	Rader, Campbell, Fisher & Pyke	Affidavit of Jane Doe #6 (Monica Lewinsky)
0852-DC-00000035	American Express	Credit card statement
0852-DC-00000037	American Express	Credit card statement
0852-DC-00000044 to 45	American Express	12/17/97 billing statement
0854-DC-00001485	First Union Bank	5/6/96 Check No. 594
0856-DC-00000002	American Express	12/11/97 letter from Monica Lewinsky to Ursula Fairbairn
0880-DC-00000002 to 8	Lindsey, Bruce	Handwritten notes
0902-DC-00000003	Carter, Francis	Address
0902-DC-00000030	Carter, Francis	1/12/98 to 1/20/98 billing statement
0902-DC-00000033	Cater, Francis	FedEx USA Airbill
0902-DC-00000037 to 38	Carter, Francis	1/7/98 billing statement
0902-DC-00000051	Catrer, Francis	1/6/97 phone memo
0902-DC-00000135 to 138	Carter, Francis	Subpoena issued to Monica Lewinsky in the Paula Jones case
0902-DC-00000231	Carter, Francis	12/22/97 to 12/28/97 appointment book
0902-DC-00000232	Carter, Francis	1/5/98 appointment book
0902-DC-00000251	Carter, Francis	1/6/98 phone message
0916-DC-00000003	Park Hyatt	Receipt
0920-DC-00000013 to 18	Rader, Campbell, Fisher & Pyke	Subpoena issued to Monica Lewinsky in the Paula Jones case
0920-DC-00000517 to 525	Rader, Campbell, Fisher & Pyke	12/18/97 Order in Jones v. Clinton, LR-C-94-290
0921-DC-00000061 to 62	McCormack, Hon. James	11/6/97 Clerk's minutes for in-camera hearing
0921-DC-00000091 to 151	Rader, Campbell, Fisher & Pyke	Plaintiff's Motion to Compel Responses to Plaintiff's Second Set of Interrogatories to Defendant Clinton
0921-DC-00000459 to 466	McCormack, Hon. James	12/11/97 Order in Jones v. Clinton, LR-C-94-290

Bates # or Tab#	Production Name	Description
0921-DC-00000736 to 744	McCormack, Hon. James	1/8/98 Order in Jones v. Clinton, LR-C-94-290
0921-DC-00000751 to 752	McCormack, Hon. James	1/9/98 Clerk's minutes for in-camera hearing
0921-DC-00000770 to 772	Rader, Campbell, Fisher & Pyke	1/14/98 Clerk's Minutes
0921-DC-00000775 to 778	Rader, Campbell, Fisher & Pyke	Motion of Jane Doe #6 for Protective Order and Motion to Quash
0929-DC-00000056	NationsBank	Bank Statement
0952-DC-00000060	United States Secret Service	10/11/97 Presidential Protectee Movement Log
0964-DC-00000862	White House	12/6/97 pager record
0968-DC-00000073	White House	Schedule
0968-DC-00000187	White House	11/13/97 schedule
0968-DC-00000236	White House	3/29/98 schedule
0968-DC-00000263	White House	Schedule
0968-DC-00000303	White House	11/13/97 Diarist notes
0968-DC-00000841	White House	4/5/96 Press Schedule
0968-DC-00002947	White House	8/17/97 schedule
0968-DC-00003300	White House	11/22/97 to 11/25/97 Presidential press schedule
0968-DC-00003301	White House	Presidential Press Schedule
0968-DC-00003458	White House	2/96 calendar for Hillary Rodham Clinton
0968-DC-00003459	White House	3/96 calendar for Hillary Rodham Clinton
0968-DC-00003475	White House	7/97 calendar for Hillary Rodham Clinton
0968-DC-00003477	White House	10/97 calendar for Hillary Rodham Clinton
0968-DC-00003479	White House	12/97 calendar for Hillary Rodham Clinton
0968-DC-00003506	White House	2/28/97 Presidential Call Log
0968-DC-00003510	White House	3/29/97 Presidential Call Log
0968-DC-00003522	White House	5/1/97 Presidential Call Log
0968-DC-00003533	White House	5/24/97 Presidential Call Log
0968-DC-00003546	White House	7/4/97 Presidential Call Log
0968-DC-00003550	White House	7/14/97 Presidential Call Log

Bates # or Tab#	Production Name	Description
0968-DC-00003556	White House	7/24/97 Presidential Call Log
0968-DC-00003558	White House	8/16/97 Presidential Call Log
0968-DC-00003569	White House	10/11/97 Presidential Call
0968-DC-00003799	White House	11/13/97 schedule
0968-DC-00003843	White House	3/29/97 schedule
1000-DC-00000767 to 772	Bell Atlantic	5/4/96 Marcia Lewis Phone Bill
1012-DC-00000001	Bacon, Kenneth	4/28/97 letter from Kenneth Bacon to Lorrie McHugh
1013-DC-00000095 to 96	Bell Atlantic	2/4/98 statement of Toll calls for Debra Finerman
1014-DC-00000022	Cellular One	3/25/97 to 4/24/97 Calls
1033-DC-00000033 to 35	Bell Atlantic Mobile	Toll records
1033-DC-00000115 to 116	Bell Atlantic Mobile	Toll records
1034-DC-00000060 to 63	Jordan, Vernon	10/20/97 to 11/01/97 schedule for Vernon Jordan
1034-DC-00000099	Jordan, Vernon	12/8/97 to 12/10/97 schedule for Vernon Jordan
1034-DC-00000103	Jordan, Vernon	12/22/97 to 12/24/97 schedule for Vernon Jordan
1034-DC-00000109	Jordan, Vernon	1/12/98 to 1/14/98 schedule for Vernon Jordan
1034-DC-00000111	Jordan, Vernon	1/19/98 to 1/21/98 schedule for Vernon Jordan
1037-DC-00000001 to 2	Davis, Catherine Allday	5/18/97 Card
1037-DC-00000011	Davis, Catherine Allday	12/9/97 e-mail from Lewinsky to Davis
1037-DC-00000017	Davis, Catherine Allday	11/7/97 e-mail from Lewinsky to Davis
1037-DC-00000022	Davis, Catherine Allday	11/5/97 e-mail from Lewinsky to Davis
1037-DC-00000033	Davis, Catherine Allday	10/22/97 e-mail from Lewinsky to Davis
1037-DC-00000038 to 40	Davis, Catherine Allday	E-mails between Monica Lewinsky and Catherine Allday Davis
1037-DC-00000042	Davis, Catherine Allday	8/14/97 e-mail from Lewinsky to Davis
1037-DC-00000063	Davis, Catherine Allday	11/6/97 e-mail from Lewinsky to Davis
1037-DC-00000086 to 87	Davis, Catherine Allday	9/4/97 e-mail from Monica Lewinsky to Catherine Allday Davis
1037-DC-00000103	Davis, Catherine Allday	7/3/98 e-mail from Catherine Allday Davis to Monica Lewinsky

Bates # or Tab#	Production Name	Description
1037-DC-00000107	Davis, Catherine Allday	6/17/97 e-mail from Monica Lewinsky to Catherine Allday Davis
1037-DC-00000115	Davis, Catherine Allday	E-mail between Monica Lewinsky and Catherine Allday Davis
1037-DC-00000167 to 169	Davis, Catherine Allday	E-mails between Monica Lewinsky and Catherine Allday Davis
1037-DC-00000171	Davis, Catherine Allday	8/13/97 e-mail from Monica Lewinsky to Catherine Allday Davis
1037-DC-00000255 to 256	Davis, Catherine Allday	9/4/97 e-mail from Monica Lewinsky to Catherine Allday Davis
1037-DC-00000258 to 259	Davis, Catherine Allday	9/2/97 e-mail from Monica Lewinsky to Catherine Allday Davis
1037-DC-00000265 to 266	Davis, Catherine Allday	6/17/97 e-mail from Monica Lewinsky to Catherine Allday Davis
1037-DC-00000280	Davis, Catherine Allday	7/2/97 e-mail from Catherine Allday Davis to Monica Lewinsky
1037-DC-00000296	Davis, Catherine Allday	E-mail from Catherine Allday Davis to Monica Lewinsky
1037-DC-00000318	Davis, Catherine Allday	11/19/97 e-mail from Lewinsky to Davis
1037-DC-00000337 to 38	Davis, Catherine Allday	E-Mail from Lewinsky to Davis
1037-DC-00000341	Davis, Catherine Allday	E-mail from Monica Lewinsky to Catherine Allday Davis
1037-DC-00000553	Davis, Catherine Allday	11/5/97 e-mail from Monica Lewinsky to Catherine Allday Davis
1037-DC-00000583	Davis, Catherine Allday	9/2/97 e-mail from Monica Lewinsky to Catherine Allday Davis
1051-DC-00000003 to 4	Bell Atlantic	Copy of Computer Disk
1064-DC-00000008	Renaissance Vinoy Resort	1/13/98 Toll records
1065-DC-00000006	St. Regis Hotel	Hotel receipt
1065-DC-00000008	St. Regis Hotel	Receipt
1078-DC-00000002	Washington Post	Receipt
1089-DC-00000970	White House	10/16/96 Typed note
1178-DC-00000005	White House	10/11/97 Presidential Call Log
1178-DC-00000011	White House	Presidetial Call Logs
1178-DC-00000013	White House	12/19/97 Presidential Call Log
1178-DC-00000014	White House	12/19/97 Presidential Call Log

Bates # or Tab#	Production Name	Description
1178-DC-00000015	White House	12/30/97 Presidential Call Log
1178-DC-00000016	White House	1/6/98 Presidential Call Log
1178-DC-00000018	White House	1/16/98 Presidential Call Log
1178-DC-00000019	White House	1/17/98 Presidential Call Log
1178-DC-00000020	White House	1/17/98 Presidential Call Log
1178-DC-00000021	White House	1/18/98 Presidential Call Log
1178-DC-00000023	White House	1/19/98 Presidential Call Log
1178-DC-00000026	White House	WAVES records: Vernon Jordan
1205-DC-00000016	GTE Company of California	1/25/98 toll record from California
1216-DC-00000022 to 23	Bell Atlantic	Toll records
1222-DC-00000024	United States Secret Service	1/21/96 itinerary for the White House
1222-DC-00000032	United States Secret Service	3/5/96 White House itinerary
1222-DC-00000041	United States Secret Service	3/31/96 intinerary
1222-DC-00000045	United States Secret Service	Schedule
1222-DC-00000083 to 85	United States Secret Service	11/15/95 to 11/18/95 Presidential Movement Logs
1222-DC-00000102	United States Secret Service	2/19/96 Presidential Movement Log
1222-DC-00000112 to 113	United States Secret Service	3/29/96 and 3/31/96 Presidential Movement Logs
1222-DC-00000156 to 157	United States Secret Service	11/15/95 Presidential Protectee Movement Logs
1222-DC-00000179	United States Secret Service	Presidential Movement Logs
1222-DC-00000183	United States Secret Service	1/7/96 Presidential Protectee Movement Log
1222-DC-00000189	United States Secret Service	1/21/96 Presidential Movement Log
1222-DC-00000196	United States Secret Service	2/4/96 Presidential Movement Log
1222-DC-00000197	United States Secret Service	2/19/96 Presidential Movement Log
1222-DC-00000216 to 217	United States Secret Service	3/31/96 Presidential Movement Logs
1222-DC-00000219	United States Secret Service	4/7/96 Presidential Movements
1222-DC-00000234	United States Secret Service	2/28/97 Presidential Movements
1222-DC-00000242	United States Secret Service	5/24/97 Presidential Protectee Movement Log

Bates # or Tab#	Production Name	Description
1222-DC-00000251	United States Secret Service	7/14/97 schedule
1222-DC-00000254	United States Secret Service	7/24/97 schedule
1222-DC-00000325	United States Secret Service	12/31/95, 1/7/96 Secret Service agent duty schedule
1222-DC-00000328	United States Secret Service	2/21/96 Secret Service agent duty schedule
1234-DC-00000049	White House	11/13/97 schedule
1234-DC-00000050	White House	11/13/97 Presidential Movement Log
1234-DC-00000357	United States Secret Service	8/22/97 to 12/31/97 Epass Access Control Report
1248-DC-00000008	White House	4/7/96 Telephone Memorandum
1248-DC-00000288	White House	1/17/98 Diarist schedule notes
1248-DC-00000291	White House	Daynotes
1248-DC-00000305	White House	1/17/98 Presidential Call Log
1248-DC-00000307	White House	1/17/98 Presidential Call
1248-DC-00000311	White House	1/18/98 Presidential Call
1248-DC-00000312	White House	1/18/98 Presidential Call Log
1248-DC-00000313 to 315	White House	1/18/98 Presidential Call Log
1248-DC-00000319	White House	1/19/98 Presidential Call Log
1248-DC-00000327 to 328	White House	1/21/98 Presidential Call Log
1248-DC-00000381	White House	12/19/97 Presidential Call Log
1248-DC-00000444	White House	1/13/98 Presidential Call Log
1318-DC-00000001 to 2	Young, Dale	9/4/97 note from Monica Lewinsky to Dale Young
1342-DC-00000410	White House	Photograph
1361-DC-00000002 to 42	White House	Index of books located in the Oval Office study
1362-DC-00000549	United States Secret Service	11/15/95 Presidential Protectee Movement Log
1362-DC-00001171	United States Secret Service	Secret Service agent duty schedule
1407-DC-00000005	White House	12/6/97 TO 12/24/97 WAVES for Robert Bennett
1408-DC-00000005	Rader, Campbell, Fisher & Pyke	12/5/97 Facsimile sheet
1414-DC-00000001	Rader, Campbell, Fisher & Pyke	7/21/98 letter to Julie Corcoran from Donovan Campbell, Jr.

Bates # or Tab#	Production Name	Description
1414-DC-00001006 to 1014	Rader, Campbell, Fisher & Pyke	1/9/98 Order in Jones v. Clinton, LR-C-94-290
1414-DC-00001188 to 1192	Rader, Campbell, Fisher & Pyke	12/18/97 Order in Jones v. Clinton, LR-C-94-290
1414-DC-00001327 to 32	Rader, Campbell, Fisher & Pyke	hearing excerpt
1414-DC-00001334 to 46	Rader, Campbell, Fisher & Pyke	hearing excerpt
1414-DC-00001534 to 1546	Rader, Campbell, Fisher & Pyke	12/15/97 Pleading in Jones v. Clinton, LR-C-94-290
1415-DC-00000001	White House	8/3/98 letter from David Kendall to the OIC
1472-DC-00000006	White House	11/15/95 Call Log
1472-DC-00000007	White House	11/15/95 Telephone memorandum
1472-DC-00000008	White House	11/15/95 Telephone memorandum
1472-DC-00000015	White House	11/17/95 Telephone memorandum
1472-DC-00000017	White House	2/19/96 Telephone memorandum
1472-DC-00000018 to 20	White House	2/19/96 Telephone memorandum
1506-DC-00000007 to 8	White House	8/10/95 Presidential schedule
1506-DC-00000027	White House	12/31/95 Presidential schedule
1506-DC-00000029	White House	12/31/95 Telephone memorandum
1506-DC-00000031	White House	1/7/96 Telephone memorandum
1506-DC-00000050	White House	1/21/96 Telephone memorandum
1506-DC-00000057 to 58	White House	1/30/96 Presidential schedule
1506-DC-00000068	White House	2/4/96 Telephone memorandum
1506-DC-00000070	White House	2/4/96 Telephone memorandum
1506-DC-00000102	White House	2/19/96 Telephone memorandum
1506-DC-00000139	White House	3/31/96 Telephone memorandum
1506-DC-00000144	White House	4/7 Telephone Memorandum
1506-DC-00000188 to 189	White House	Presidential schedule
1506-DC-00000192	White House	5/2/96 Presidential Call Log
1506-DC-00000222	White House	Presidential schedule
1506-DC-00000264	White House	7/5/96 Presidential schedule

Bates # or Tab#	Production Name	Description
1506-DC-00000268	White House	7/6/96 Presidential schedule
1506-DC-00000275	White House	7/19/96 Presidential Call Log
1506-DC-00000328	White House	Presidential schedule
1506-DC-00000334 to 335	White House	Schedule
1506-DC-00000353	White House	Presidential schedule
1506-DC-00000373 to 374	White House	2/8/97 Schedule
1506-DC-00000426 to 427	White House	10/10/97 Presidential schedule
1506-DC-00000523 to 525	White House	1/21/96 Diarist notes
1506-DC-00000558	White House	Presidential schedule
1506-DC-00000559	White House	Presidential schedule
1506-DC-00000638	White House	Diarists notes, Presidential call
2004-DC-00000083	Bell Atlantic	Toll records
2004-DC-00000085 to 88	Bell Atlantic	Toll records
2004-DC-00000090 to 91	Bell Atlantic	Toll records
827-DC-00000018	United States Secret Service	2/24/97 to 12/28/97 Epass Access Control Report
CZ-DC-00000010	Driscoll, Richard	Fair market value appraisal
CZ-DC-00000016	Driscoll, Richard	Fair market value appraisal
DB PHOTOS 0004	Lewinsky, Monica	Blue Dress (photo)
DB PHOTOS 0044	Lewinsky, Monica	Audio-tapes from Monica Lewinsky's answering machine (originals in Quantico)
DB PHOTOS 0048	Lewinsky, Monica	evidence picture
DB-DC-000000017	Lewinsky, Monica	Draft letter from Monica Lewinsky to William Jefferson Clinton
DB-DC-000000022	Lewinsky, Monica	11/12/97 letter from Monica Lewinsky to William Jefferson Clinton
DB-DC-000000027	Lewinsky, Monica	Outline for job interests of Monica Lewinsky
DC-DC-00000004 to 5	Willis-Vento, Caroline	Fair market value appraisal
DF-DC-00000002 to 12	Lewinsky, Monica	2/1/98 handwritten proffer
MSL-1249-DC-0139 to 141	Lewinsky, Monica	Letter from Monica Lewinsky to William Jefferson Clinton

Bates # or Tab#	Production Name	Description
MSL-55-DC-0001	Lewinsky, Monica	Draft note from Monica Lewinsky to William Jefferson Clinton
MSL-55-DC-0094	Lewinsky, Monica	Letter drafted on Monica's home computer
MSL-55-DC-0124	Lewinsky, Monica	Letter drafted on Monica's home computer
MSL-55-DC-0177	Lewinsky, Monica	Letter from Monica Lewinsky to William Jefferson Clinton
MSL-55-DC-0178	Lewinsky, Monica	Letter from Monica Lewinsky to William Jefferson Clinton
MSL-55-DC-0179	Lewinsky, Monica	11/2/97 letter from Monica Lewinsky to Betty Currie
MSL-55-DC-0184 to 186	Lewinsky, Monica	Note created on Monica Lewinsky's home computer "Happy National Boss Day?"
MSL-DC-00000456	Lewinsky, Monica	Handwritten note
MSL-DC-00000489 to 90	Lewinsky, Monica	Invitation to William Jefferson Clinton's Birthday Party
MSL-DC-00000621 to 22	Lewinsky, Monica	3/2/97 handwritten letter from Monica Lewinsky to William Jefferson Clinton
MSL-DC-00001050	White House	9/30/97 letter from Monica Lewinsky to William Jefferson Clinton
MSL-DC-00001051	Lewinsky, Monica	October 1997 Calendar
MSL-DC-00001051A	Lewinsky, Monica	November 1997 Calendar
MSL-DC-00001052	Lewinsky, Monica	Typed note
MSL-DC-00001166 to 1168	Lewinsky, Monica	Draft Affidavit
MSL-DC-00001176 to 1177	White House	6/29/97 draft letter from Monica Lewinsky to Marsha Scott
MSL-DC-00001192	White House	7/6/97 letter from Monica Lewinsky to Marsha Scott
MSL-DC-00001221	Lewinsky, Monica	Page from Monica Lewinsky's schedule book
MSL-DC-00001227	Lewinsky, Monica	6/29/97 note from Monica Lewinsky to William Jefferson Clinton
MSL-DC-00001228	Lewinksy, Monica	3/14/997 memorandum from Cliff Bernath for the Record
MSL-DC-00001230	Lewinsky, Monica	4/28/97 letter from Kenneth Bacon to Lorrie McHugh
V002-DC-00000001 to 5	Clinton, William Jefferson	1/27/98 letter from David Kendall to Bob Bittman, with attachments
V002-DC-00000006 to 7	Clinton, William Jefferson	1/28/98 letter from David Kendall to Bob Bittman

Bates # or Tab#	Production Name	Description
V002-DC-00000008 to 15	Clinton, William Jefferson	President Clinton's Responses to Plaintiff's First Set of Interrogatories
V002-DC-00000016 to 32	Clinton, William Jefferson	President Clinton's Responses to Plaintiff's Second Set of Interrogatories
V002-DC-00000052 to 55	Clinton, William Jefferson	President Clinton's Supplemental Responses to Plaintiff's Second Set of Interrogatories
V002-DC-00000056 to 92	Clinton, William Jefferson	President Clinton's Responses to Plaintiff's First Set of Requests for Production of Documents and Things
V002-DC-00000093 to 116	Clinton, William Jefferson	President Clinton's Responses to Plaintiff's Second Set of Document Requests
V002-DC-00000159 to 160	Clinton, William Jefferson	2/2/98 letter from David Kendall to Bob Bittman
V002-DC-00000469	Clinton, William Jefferson	2/3/98 letter to Bob Bittman from David Kendall
V002-DC-00000471	Clinton, William Jefferson	Book, "The Presidents of the United States"
V002-DC-00000475	Clinton, William Jefferson	3/16/98 letter from David Kendall to the OIC
V004-DC-00000134	Akin Gump	11/3/97 to 11/4/97 Toll records
V004-DC-00000135	Akin Gump	11/4/97 to 11/6/97 Toll records
V004-DC-00000143	Akin Gump	11/26/97 to 11/27/97 Toll records
V004-DC-00000148	Akin Gump	12/11/97 to 12/15/97 Toll records
V004-DC-00000151	Akin Gump	12/19/97 to 12/23/97 Toll records
V004-DC-00000154	Akin Gump	12/30/97 to 12/31/97 Toll records
V004-DC-00000158	Akin Gump	1/5/98 to 1/7/98 Toll records
V004-DC-00000159	Akin Gump	1/7/98 to 1/8/98 Toll records
V004-DC-00000160	Akin Gump	1/8/98 to 1/9/98 Toll records
V004-DC-00000161	Akin Gump	1/9/98 to 1/10/98 Toll records
V004-DC-00000162	Akin Gump	1/10/98 to 1/13/98 Toll records
V004-DC-00000164	Akin Gump	1/15/98 to 1/16/98 Toll records
V004-DC-00000165	Akin Gump	1/16/98 to 1/19/98 Toll records
V004-DC-00000166	Akin Gump	1/19/98 to 1/21/98 Toll records

Bates # or Tab#	Production Name	Description
V004-DC-00000167	Akin Gump	1/21/98 to 1/22/98 Toll records
V004-DC-00000171	Akin Gump	12/11/97 visitor record
V004-DC-00000172	Akin Gump	12/19/97 vistor record
V004-DC-00000183	Akin Gump	12/8/97 Request for Messenger Service
V005-DC-00000058	Laughlin, Gayle	1/15/98 phone record
V005-DC-00000060	Laughlin, Gayle	1/20/98 phone record
V005-DC-00000061	Laughlin, Gayle	1/20/98 phone record
V006-DC-00000007	White House	4/9/96 to 12/30/96 WAVES report for Monica Lewinsky
V006-DC-00000008	White House	2/24/97 to 11/13/97 WAVES report for Monica Lewinsky
V006-DC-00000009	White House	12/6/97 to 12/28/97 WAVES report for Monica Lewinsky
V006-DC-00000020	White House	WH Personnel Action sheet for Monica Lewinsky
V006-DC-00000109	White House	Work history report
V006-DC-00000118	White House	Notification of Personnel Action
V006-DC-00000157	White House	White House Gift Record
V006-DC-00000158	White House	Gift Donor Information
V006-DC-00000159	White House	9/4/96 letter from William Jefferson Clinton to Monica Lewinsky
V006-DC-00000162	White House	White House Gift Register
V006-DC-00000167	White House	10/30/95 Gift Unit - draft leter
V006-DC-00000178	White House	Photograph
V006-DC-00000180	White House	White House Gift Record
V006-DC-00000181	White House	White House Gift Record
V006-DC-00000183	White House	Monica Lewinsky's resume
V006-DC-00000198	White House	1995 summer White House intern list
V006-DC-00000221	White House	5/30/97 schedule sheet
V006-DC-00000222	White House	6/10/97 e-mail from Marsha Dimel to Katherine Veit
V006-DC-00000223 to 224	White House	6/12/97 e-mail from Marsha Dimel to Roseanne Hill w/attachment

Bates # or Tab#	Production Name	Description
V006-DC-00000225	White House	White House pre-employment information sheet
V006-DC-00000391	White House	WhoDB - Contact Manager Information
V006-DC-00000511	White House	12/5/97 Holiday Reception list excerpt
V006-DC-00000512 to 522	White House	12/5/97 White House Party list excerpt, report dated on 12/30/97
V006-DC-00000521	White House	12/5/97 White House Party list excerpt, report dated on 12/30/97
V006-DC-00000534	White House	6/14/96 Radio Address
V006-DC-00000572	White House	2/8/96 to 2/11/96 Presidential schedule
V006-DC-00000682	White House	8/18/96 and 8/19/96 William Jefferson Clinton Schedule
V006-DC-00000694	White House	4/2/96 Schedule of William Jefferson Clinton
V006-DC-00000747	White House	2/9/96 to 2/12/96 Presidential schedule
V006-DC-00001347	White House	4/9/96 E-Mail
V006-DC-00001770	White House	7/24/97 e-mail
V006-DC-00001792	White House	3/29/97 WAVES Request
V006-DC-00001796	White House	2/28/97 WAVES Request
V006-DC-00001813 to 1814	White House	12/5/97 e-mail: WAVES Operations Center to J. Schwartz
V006-DC-00001826	White House	Photograph
V006-DC-00001841	White House	Photograph
V006-DC-00001842	White House	Photograph
V006-DC-00001843	White House	Photograph
V006-DC-00001844	White House	Photograph
V006-DC-00001845	White House	Photograph
V006-DC-00001846	White House	Photograph
V006-DC-00001847	White House	Photograph
V006-DC-00001855	White House	Photograph
V006-DC-00001856	White House	Photograph
V006-DC-00001859	White House	Photograph
V006-DC-00001865	White House	videotape

Bates # or Tab#	Production Name	Description
V006-DC-00002064	White House	1/9/98 Presidential Call Log
V006-DC-00002065	White House	1/14/98 Presidential Call Log
V006-DC-00002066	White House	1/17/98 Presidential Call Log
V006-DC-00002067	White House	1/18/98 Presidential Call Log
V006-DC-00002068	White House	1/18/98 Presidential Call Log
V006-DC-00002069 to 2070	White House	1/19/98 Presidential Call Log
V006-DC-00002071	White House	1/21/98 Presidential Call Log
V006-DC-00002095	White House	8/16/97 schedule
V006-DC-00002130	White House	3/29/97 Presidential Movements
V006-DC-00002140	White House	7/4/97 schedule
V006-DC-00002142	White House	7/14/97 schedule
V006-DC-00002146	White House	8/16/97 schedule
V006-DC-00002147	White House	8/16/97 schedule
V006-DC-00002156	White House	11/13/97 Presidential Movement Log
V006-DC-00002158	White House	12/6/97 Presidential Movement Log
V006-DC-00002214	White House	7/4/97 diarist notes
V006-DC-00002243	White House	11/13/97 Diarist notes
V006-DC-00002287	White House	4/9/96 e-mail from Gunia to Dagenais
V006-DC-00002289	White House	E-Mail
V006-DC-00003646	White House	Coorespondence History tracking sheet
V006-DC-00003712	White House	2/24/97 memo from Betty Currie to William Jefferson Clinton
V006-DC-00003714	White House	White House Gift List
V006-DC-00003715	White House	White House Gift List
V006-DC-00003716	White House	6/14/96 Radio Address
V006-DC-00003719	White House	4/8/96 phone message
V006-DC-00003720	White House	2/28/97 Radio Address
V006-DC-00003735	White House	Photo Request

Bates # or Tab#	Production Name	Description
V006-DC-00003737 to 3744	White House	Photographs

Bates—Numbered Documents

MCI

MARCIA LEWIS May 4 1996
Acct [redacted]

Long Distance continued
Calls from [redacted]

Amount	Place	Number	Date	Time	Rate	Min
$ 1.13	FF NEW YOR NY	[redacted]	Apr 15	5:18P	*E	11
1.16	FF W ANGEL CA	[redacted]	15	9:22P	*E	10
.26	SMYRNA GA	[redacted]	16	5:32P	*E	2
.12	CANBY OR	[redacted]	16	7:31P	*E	1
.12	PORTLAND OR	[redacted]	16	7:33P	*E	1
.12	SAN FRAN CA	[redacted]	16	7:34P	*E	1
6.47	BEVERLYH CA	[redacted]	16	7:34P	*E	48
5.12	PORTLAND OR	[redacted]	16	8:22P	*E	38
.12	CANBY OR	[redacted]	16	9:01P	*E	1
.12	PORTLAND OR	[redacted]	16	9:02P	*E	1
.12	CANBY OR	[redacted]	16	9:03P	*E	1
.12	CANBY OR	[redacted]	16	9:04P	*E	1
4.85	CANBY OR	[redacted]	16	9:06P	*E	36
.24	CANBY OR	[redacted]	16	10:59P	*M	2

MCI

MARCIA LEWIS [redacted] May 4 1996
Acct [redacted]

Long Distance continued
Calls from [redacted]:

Amount	Place	Number	Date	Time	Rate	Min
$ 7.41	SAN FRAN CA	[redacted]	Apr 19	8:56P	*E	55
.12	SMYRNA GA	[redacted]	21	6:09P	*E	1
.26	PORTLAND OR	[redacted]	21	6:11P	*E	2
.12	GARDENA CA	[redacted]	21	6:13P	*E	1
5.12	LOSANGEL CA	[redacted]	21	6:13P	*E	38
.12	PORTLAND OR	[redacted]	21	6:51P	*E	1
2.82	PORTLAND OR	[redacted]	21	8:00P	*E	21
.12	PORTLAND OR	[redacted]	21	8:21P	*E	1
1.86	FF W ANGEL CA	[redacted]	21	8:27P	*E	16
1.74	PORTLAND OR	[redacted]	21	9:04P	*E	13
.11	SAN FRAN CA	[redacted]	22	11:19P	*N	1

$113.40 Total Calls from [redacted]:

$250.07 Total Long Distance

MCI

MARCIA LEWIS May 4 1996
Acct [redacted]

Long Distance continued
Calls from [redacted]:

Amount	Place	Number	Date	Time	Rate	Min
$ .63	DIR ASST NY	[redacted]	Apr 9	4:37P	*D	1
.35	FF NEW YOR NY		9	4:37P	*D	2
.72	FF NEW YOR NY		9	5:05P	*E	7
.12	CANBY OR		9	5:14P	*E	1
1.34	FF NEW YOR NY		10	4:56P	*M	10
.11	THE PLAI VA		10	5:07P	*E	1
.35	THE PLAI VA		10	6:55P	*E	3
.11	FF W ANGEL CA		10	9:02P	*E	1
.12	PORTLAND OR		10	9:03P	*E	1
.80	THE PLAI VA		11	11:09A	*D	4
.21	SAN FRAN CA		11	3:19P	*D	1
9.44	PORTLAND OR		11	9:22P	*E	70
.63	DIR ASST NY		12	12:31P	*D	1
.17	FF BROOKLY NY		12	12:33P	*D	1

1000-DC-00000769 Page 32

MCI

MARCIA LEWIS May 4 1996
Acct [redacted]

Long Distance continued
Calls from [redacted]

Amount	Place	Number	Date	Time	Rate	Min
$ .17	FF NEW YOR NY	[redacted]	Apr 12	12:38P	*D	1
.21	PORTLAND OR		12	3:23P	*D	1
6.06	PORTLAND OR		12	3:23P	*D	27
.12	PORTLAND OR		12	7:40P	*E	1
.11	PORTLAND OR		13	12:09A	*N	1
1.19	PORTLAND OR		13	12:10A	*N	10
.11	SAN FRAN CA		13	12:26A	*N	1
.11	SAN FRAN CA		13	12:37A	*N	1
.11	SAN FRAN CA		13	12:46A	*N	1
2.15	SAN FRAN CA		13	12:02P	*N	18
.11	PORTLAND OR		13	2:46P	*N	1
2.63	PORTLAND OR		13	2:47P	*N	22
.11	SAN FRAN CA		13	3:09P	*N	1
.12	SAN FRAN CA		14	5:47P	*E	1

1000-DC-00000770 Page 33

MCI

MARCIA LEWIS
Acct [redacted]

May 4 1996

Long Distance continued
Calls from [redacted]

Amount	Place	Number	Date	Time	Rate	Min
$ .81	FF W ANGEL CA	[redacted]	Apr 3	8:03P	*E	7
.11	SAN FRAN CA		6	12:49P	*N	1
.11	PORTLAND OR		6	3:42P	*N	1
.11	SAN FRAN CA		6	6:41P	*N	1
.11	PORTLAND OR		6	6:42P	*N	1
.11	SAN FRAN CA		6	9:10P	*N	1
2.33	FF W ANGEL CA		7	5:08P	*E	20
1.67	THE PLAI VA		7	9:16P	*E	14
.47	THE PLAI VA		7	9:49P	*E	4
.12	BEVERLYH CA		7	9:58P	*E	1
.12	BEVERLYH CA		7	9:58P	*E	1
3.09	KIHEI HI		7	9:59P	*E	18
.16	KIHEI HI		7	10:17P	*E	1
1.54	KIHEI HI		7	10:18P	*E	9

1000-DC-00000767

MCI

MARCIA LEWIS
Acct [redacted]

May 4 1996

Long Distance continued
Calls from [redacted]:

Amount	Place	Number	Date	Time	Rate	Min
$ 1.00	THE PLAI VA	[redacted]	Apr 8	4:53P	*D	5
.12	PORTLAND OR		8	5:01P	*E	1
.12	PORTLAND OR		8	5:01P	*E	1
.12	CANBY OR		8	5:02P	*E	1
2.01	PORTLAND OR		8	5:03P	*E	15
.12	PORTLAND OR		8	5:48P	*E	1
.12	SAN FRAN CA		8	8:34P	*E	1
.12	PORTLAND OR		8	8:36P	*E	1
1.98	FF W ANGEL CA		8	9:43P	*E	17
1.61	PORTLAND OR		8	10:00P	*E	12
3.09	SAN FRAN CA		8	10:12P	*E	23
.63	DIR ASST NY		9	2:17P	*D	1
3.45	FF NEW YOR NY		9	2:18P	*D	19
.20	NEW YORK NY		9	4:36P	*D	1

1000-DC-00000768

April 28, 1997

Ms. Lorrie McHugh
Deputy Assistant to the President
The White House
Washington, DC.

Dear Lorrie:

Mike suggested that I drop you a note about my confidential assistant, Monica Lewinsky. Her resume is attached.

She is terrific--bright, energetic and imaginative. I would like Monica to stay here as along as I do. However, she has more skills than her current job requires, and this isn't a job she wants for life. As a result, I have advised her that she should try to move into a more substantive job, either here or in the White House. Unlike many people, she is actually following my advice. She would like to work in the White House, where she started work in Washington. She would be great as an organizer in the press operation or as an event planner in the communications office.

Mike says that you handle the really hard work over there, such as hiring. Please keep Monica in mind as appropriate jobs open up.

Yours,

1012-DC-00000001

Kenneth H. Bacon

MCI

DEBRA FINERMAN
Acct [redacted]

Feb 4 1998

Long Distance continued
Calls from [redacted]:

Amount	Place		Number	Date	Time	Rate	Min
$ .12	NEW YORK	NY	[redacted]	Dec 26	8:53P	*E	1.0
.60	NEW YORK	NY	[redacted]	27	8:24A	*E	5.0
.12	NEW YORK	NY	[redacted]	27	9:18P	*E	1.0
.55	NEW YORK	NY	[redacted]	30	12:13P	*D	4.6
.19	NEW YORK	NY	[redacted]	30	8:41P	*E	1.6
1.28	W ANGELES	CA	[redacted]	30	9:12P	*E	10.7
.42	NEW YORK	NY	[redacted]	30	9:23P	*E	3.5
.14	STOWE	VT	[redacted]	Jan 1	12:40A	*E	1.2
.12	STOWE	VT	[redacted]	1	12:42A	*E	1.0
.26	STOWE	VT	[redacted]	1	10:29P	*E	2.2
.51	STOWE	VT	[redacted]	1	10:39P	*E	4.3
.12	NEW YORK	NY	[redacted]	5	11:32A	*D	1.0
.12	CEDARHURST	NY	[redacted]	5	7:58P	*E	1.0
.12	WARRENTON	VA	[redacted]	5	8:51P	*E	1.0

Page 11

1013-DC-00000095

MCI

DEBRA FINERMAN
Acct [redacted]

Feb 4 1998

Long Distance continued
Calls from [redacted]:

Amount	Place		Number	Date	Time	Rate	Min
$ 1.76	WARRENTON	VA	[redacted]	Jan 5	9:18P	*E	14.7
.12	NEW YORK	NY	[redacted]	5	9:35P	*E	1.0
.12	WARRENTON	VA	[redacted]	10	1:48P	*E	1.0
.42	NEW YORK	NY	[redacted]	10	1:50P	*E	3.5
.12	WARRENTON	VA	[redacted]	10	3:34P	*E	1.0
1.51	ANDOVER	MA	[redacted]	10	4:31P	*E	12.6
1.10	DIR ASST	CA	[redacted]	12	9:25A	*D	1.0
1.10	DIR ASST	NY	[redacted]	12	10:07A	*D	1.0
.12	NEW YORK	NY	[redacted]	12	10:08A	*D	1.0
.16	NEW YORK	NY	[redacted]	12	10:17A	*D	1.4
1.10	DIR ASST	NY	[redacted]	12	10:36A	*D	2.0
.12	NEW YORK	NY	[redacted]	12	10:38A	*D	1.0
.25	NEW YORK	NY	[redacted]	12	10:38A	*D	2.1
.12	WARRENTON	VA	[redacted]	12	10:43A	*D	1.0

1013-DC-00000096

Page 12

0000000058089095 GRID: F08

REPORT DATE: 04/26/97
REPORT NO. 5070C C050CLRG

CELLULAR ONE
MATCHED CALL REGISTER
FOR PERIOD: 3/25/97 THRU 4/24/97

1014-DC-00000022

PAGE 5840
TIME 06:17:32

	DATE	TIME	TO-NUMBER	AIR MINUTES MIN	CL	MIN	CL	AIR CHARGES CHARGE	CL	CHARGE	CL	L A N D MINUTES	CHARGES	TA	ELECTRONIC SERIAL #	RT PL	TOTAL CHARGES
0000000058089095			CONT PHONE # [redacted]														
	WA03-28	74214A	[redacted]	2.0	(:)			.780	(1)			2.0	.300	JC	D4048882	E3	1.080
	WA03-28	64814P		3.0	(1)			1.170	(1)			3.0	.570	JC	D4048882	E3	1.740
R	04-03	113501A		3.0	(1)			1.500	(1)			3.0	.870	JC	21213928578	E3	2.370
R	04-03	115747A		3.0	(1)			1.500	(1)			3.0	.870	JC	21213928578	E3	2.370
R	04-03	51336P		1.0	(1)			.500	(1)			1.0	.200	9A	21213928578	E3	.700
	BT04-03	53058P										7.0	1.190	JC	D4048882	E3	1.190
R	04-03	53257P	INCOMING	7.0	(1)			3.500	(1)						21213928578	E3	3.500
R	04-04	101744A	[redacted]	2.0	(1)			1.000	(1)			2.0	.580	JC	21213928578	E3	1.580
R	04-04	101941A		4.0	(1)			2.000	(1)			4.0	1.160	JC	21213928578	E3	3.160
R	04-04	104145A		6.0	(1)			3.000	(1)			6.0	1.740	JC	21213928578	E3	4.740
R	04-04	20714P		3.0	(1)			1.500	(1)			3.0	.870	JC	21213928578	E3	2.370
	WA04-09	71431A		1.0	(1)			.390	(1)			1.0	.100		D4048882	E3	.490
	WA04-09	80041A		3.0	(1)			1.170	(1)			3.0	.100		D4048882	E3	1.279
	WA04-09	85936P		1.0	(1)			.390	(1)			1.0	.100		D4048882	E3	.490
	WA04-15	73943A		1.0	(1)			.390	(1)			1.0	.100		D4048882	E3	.490
	WA04-16	75910A		1.0	(1)			.390	(1)			1.0	.100		D4048882	E3	.490
	WA04-16	81130A		1.0	(1)			.390	(1)			1.0	.100		D4048882	E3	.490
	WA04-22	71617P		7.0	(1)			2.730	(1)			7.0	.100		D4048882	E3	2.830
	BT04-24	21629P										1.0	.290	JC	D4048882	E3	.290
	BT04-24	21727P										8.0	2.320	JC	D4048882	E3	2.320
TOTAL OF		12 MATCHED CALLS		20.0	(1)			7.800	(1)			15.0	.700				13.170
												21.0	4.670	J			
TOTAL OF		12 ROAMER CALLS		45.0	(1)			22.500	(1)			1.0	.200	9			33.140
												36.0	10.440	J			
0000000058089137			PHONE # [redacted]														
	WA03-28	43533P	[redacted]	1.0	(1)			.390	(1)			1.0	.100		D4CFB6F5	E3	.490
	-WA03-28	50554P		1.0	(1)			.390	(1)			1.0	.100		D4CFB6F5	E3	.490
	CU03-28	53143P		1.0	(1)			.390	(1)			1.0	.100		D4CFB6F5	E3	.490
	CU03-28	60146P		1.0	(1)			.390	(1)			1.0	.100		D4CFB6F5	E3	.490
	WA03-28	101858P		1.0	(6)			.000	(6)			1.0	.100		D4CFB6F5	E3	.100
	WA03-28	102048P		13.0	(6)			.000	(6)			13.0	.100		D4CFB6F5	E3	.100
	WA03-29	82639A		1.0	(6)			.000	(6)			1.6	.100		D4CFB6F5	E3	.100
	WA03-29	83711A		1.0	(6)			.000	(6)			1.0	.100		D4CFB6F5	E3	.100
	WA04-19	113917A		1.0	(6)			.000	(6)			1.0	.100		D4CFB6F5	E3	.100
TOTAL OF		9 MATCHED CALLS		4.0	(1)			1.560	(1)			21.0	.900				2.460
0000000058089194			PHONE # [redacted]														
	WA03-25	64340A	[redacted]	2.0	(2)			.380	(2)			1.0	.100		D4D5C1B5	E3	.480
	BT03-25	24224P	INCOMING	1.0	(1)			.390	(1)						D4D5C1B5	E3	.390
	WA03-25	24850P	[redacted]	3.0	(1)			1.170	(1)			3.0	.100		D4D5C1B5	E3	1.270
	WA03-25	40835P		2.0	(1)			.780	(1)			2.0	.100		D4D5C1B5	E3	.880
	WA03-25	40959P		3.0	(1)			1.170	(1)			3.0	.100		D4D5C1B5	E3	1.270
	WA03-25	41316P		2.0	(1)			.780	(1)			2.0	.100		D4D5C1B5	E3	.880
	WA03-25	41553P		2.0	(1)			.780	(1)			1.0	.100		D4D5C1B5	E3	.860
	WA03-25	54409P		2.0	(1)			.780	(1)			2.0	.100		D4D5C1B5	E3	.880
	WA03-25	54923P		2.0	(1)			.780	(1)			2.0	.100		D4D5C1B5	E3	.880

----TARIFF AUTHORITY (TA) CODES------
ANK = LOCAL CALL J = INTER STATE
= INTRA STATE 2 = INTERNATNAL

* = INCOMPLETE
8 OR $ = TO/ CREDIT
A OR L = RATE ERROR

R = ROAMER CALL
> = OV 120 MINS
* = 0 PLUS CALL

N = NO ANS TRFER
F = CALL FORWARD
W = CALL WAITING

3 = 3 WAY CONFERENCE
M = MESSAGE SERVICES
S = SET/CANCEL FEATR

0000000058089194 GRID: G08

ORT DATE: 04/26/97

0000000005810073

REPORT DATE: 04/26/97
REPORT NO. 5070C C050CL

DATE	TIME	TO-NUMBER
0000000058100736		CONT
BT04-03	124145P	INCOMING
BT04-03	124666P	INCOMING
WA04-03	124652P	703/450-88
BT04-03	33216P	INCOMING
WA04-03	60835P	INCOMING
WA04-03	69264P	703/450-88
WA04-03	100741P	703/239-01
WA04-03	104912P	301/670-03
WA04-03	104942P	301/208-66
WA04-03	110516P	703/239-01
WA04-03	114534P	202/966-18
WA04-04	71237A	703/451-65
WA04-04	72116A	703/658-98
WA04-04	73269A	703/451-65
WA04-04	75553A	INCOMING
BT04-04	84841A	INCOMING
BT04-04	94615A	INCOMING
BT04-04	105764A	INCOMING
WA04-04	125820P	703/450-886
WA04-04	125918P	703/458-976
WA04-04	42146P	INCOMING
WA04-05	15685P	703/450-886
WA04-05	35533P	INCOMING
WA04-05	102768P	301/570-248
WA04-06	124421A	301/315-2381
WA04-06	124561A	301/315-2381
WA04-06	124521A	301/315-2381
WA04-06	96604P	703/219-7297
WA04-07	110636A	703/450-8864
WA04-07	110787A	703/359-1701
WA04-07	110952A	703/658-9887
WA04-07	111246A	703/517-7779
BT04-07	111719A	INCOMING
WA04-07	111914A	202/411
BT04-07	112936A	INCOMING
WA04-07	113057A	703/450-8864
WA04-07	113231A	703/517-7779
BT04-07	113743A	INCOMING
WA04-07	121916P	INCOMING
WA04-07	123533P	INCOMING
BT04-07	10120P	INCOMING
WA04-07	21634P	INCOMING
WA04-07	21287P	INCOMING
WA04-07	21330P	INCOMING
WA04-07	21922P	INCOMING
WA04-07	24652P	703/450-8864
BT04-07	32440P	INCOMING
WA04-07	33667P	INCOMING
BT04-07	34763P	INCOMING
BT04-07	41652P	INCOMING

------TARIFF AUTHORITY (TA) CODES-
BLANK = LOCAL CALL J = INTER
9 = INTRA STATE 2 = INTERN

0000000058100736

Call Usage Details - View - Billed Calls

File Edit Show Options Help

Cust/Acct Id: 57818/ 1 Name: AKIN,GUMP,STRAUSS,HAUER &
Mobile TN: [redacted] Invoice Date: 01/22/1998 Today's Date: 03/09/1998

Adj Ind	Call Date	Time of Call	Orig Cell	Calls to Name	ST	Telephone Number	Amount	Airtime Time	Total Charge	Fade Ind
	01/17	04:27PM	0019	ARLINGTON	VA	[redacted]	0.80	5	0.90	
	01/17	04:32PM	0047	ARLINGTON	VA		0.64	4	0.74	
	01/17	04:35PM	0047	WASHINGTON	DC		0.32	2	0.42	
	01/17	05:14PM	0027	WASHINGTON	DC		0.32	2	0.42	
	01/17	05:17PM	0022	WASHINGTON	DC		0.16	1	0.26	
	01/17	05:19PM	0010	WASHINGTON	DC		0.16	1	0.26	
	01/18	10:55AM	0017	ALEXANDRIA	VA		0.16	1	0.26	
	01/18	10:57AM	0017	CHICAGO	IL		1.60	10	3.30	
	01/18	12:25PM	0054	ALEXANDRIA	VA		0.16	1	0.26	
	01/18	12:27PM	0054	WASHINGTON	DC		0.16	1	0.26	

Session: Adjustment Credit Est. Tax To-Date Usage : 197.33
Totals : 0.00 0.00 0.00 Totals Credit: 0.00

1033-DC-00000033

Call Usage Details - View - Billed Calls

File Edit Show Options Help

Cust/Acct Id: 57818/ 1 Name: AKIN,GUMP,STRAUSS,HAUER &

Mobile TN: [redacted] Invoice Date: 01/22/1998 Today's Date: 03/09/1998

Adj Ind	Call Date	Time of Call	Orig Cell	Calls to Name	ST	Telephone Number	Amount	Airtime Time	Total Charge	Fade Ind
	01/18	12:28PM	0020	WASHINGTON	DC	[redacted]	0.32	2	0.42	
	01/18	02:13PM	0020	WASHINGTON	DC		0.32	2	0.42	
	01/18	02:15PM	0054	WASHINGTON	DC		0.64	4	0.74	
	01/18	02:29PM	0020	ALEXANDRIA	VA		0.64	4	0.74	
	01/18	02:33PM	0061	WASHINGTON	DC		0.32	2	0.42	
	01/18	02:35PM	0061	WASHINGTON	DC		0.16	1	0.26	
	01/19	10:12AM	0021	WASHINGTON	DC		0.72	2	0.82	
	01/19	10:15AM	0017	WASHINGTON	DC		0.36	1	0.46	
	01/19	10:16AM	0017	WASHINGTON	DC		0.72	2	0.82	
	01/19	10:17AM	0020	NEW YORK	NY		0.36	1	0.65	

Session: Adjustment Credit Est. Tax ° To-Date Usage : 197.33

Totals : 0.00 0.00 0.00 ° Totals Credit: 0.00

Call Usage Details - View - Billed Calls

File Edit Show Options Help

Cust/Acct Id: [redacted] 57818/ 1 Name: AKIN,GUMP,STRAUSS,HAUER &

Mobile TN: [redacted] Invoice Date: 01/22/1998 Today's Date: 03/09/1998

Adj Ind	Call Date	Time of Call	Orig Cell	Calls to Name	ST	Telephone Number	Airtime Amount	Time	Total Charge	Fade Ind
	01/19	10:18AM	0054	NEW YORK	NY	[redacted]	1.80	5	3.25	
	01/19	12:26PM	0054	CHICAGO	IL		1.44	4	2.60	
	01/19	12:29PM	0054	JACKSON	MS		0.36	1	0.65	
	01/19	12:31PM	0054	WASHINGTON	DC		1.08	3	1.18	
	01/19	02:29PM	0005	WASHINGTON	DC		0.72	2	0.82	
	01/19	02:32PM	0021	CHICAGO	IL		0.36	1	0.65	
	01/19	02:33PM	0021	WASHINGTON	DC		1.80	5	1.90	
	01/19	02:37PM	0021	JACKSON	MS		1.44	4	2.31	
	01/19	04:26PM	0043	WASHINGTON	DC		0.36	1	0.46	
	01/19	04:27PM	0054	WASHINGTON	DC		0.36	1	0.46	

Session: Adjustment Credit Est. Tax ° To-Date Usage : 197.33

Totals : 0.00 0.00 0.00 ° Totals Credit: 0.00

PAGE 6

CUSTOMER ACCOUNT NO: [redacted]

INVOICE NO: 0153539166
INVOICE DATE: JANUARY 19, 1998

USAGE DETAILS FOR [redacted] ON 2CP200-399 PLAN 1478:
LONG DISTANCE SERVICE PROVIDED BY: BAM

PHONE USER NAME: VERNON JORDAN

DATE	TIME	ORIG BAND	ORIGINATING LOCATION	CALLS TO	TELEPHONE NUMBER	AIRTIME RATE	AIRTIME MIN	AIRTIME AMOUNT	LANDLINE RATE	LANDLINE TYPE	LANDLINE AMOUNT	TOTAL CHARGES
01/03	10:24 AM	1	WASHINGTON DC	ALEXANDRIA VA	[redacted]	OFFPK	2	0.38		LCL	0.10	0.48 #
01/03	02:27 PM	1	WASHINGTON DC	DIR ASST CL	[redacted]	OFFPK	1	0.19	FLAT	BAM	0.85	1.04 #
01/03	02:28 PM	1	WASHINGTON DC	HOUSTON TX	[redacted]	OFFPK	1	0.19	OFFPK	BAM	0.15	0.34 #
01/03	02:29 PM	1	WASHINGTON DC	WASHINGTON DC	[redacted]	OFFPK	11	2.09		LCL	0.10	2.19 #
01/04	07:39 PM	1	FT WASHING MD	OXON HILL MD	[redacted]	OFFPK	1	0.19		LCL	0.10	0.29 #
01/05	08:15 AM	1	ROSSLYN VA	CHICAGO IL	[redacted]	PEAK	5	1.45	PEAK	BAM	0.75	2.20 #
01/05	08:20 AM	1	ROSSLYN VA	WASHINGTON DC	[redacted]	PEAK	1	0.29		LCL	0.10	0.39 #
01/05	08:28 AM	1	ROSSLYN VA	NEW YORK NY	[redacted]	PEAK	3	0.87	PEAK	BAM	0.45	1.32 #
01/05	08:31 AM	1	ROSSLYN VA	WASHINGTON DC	[redacted]	PEAK	2	0.58		LCL	0.10	0.68 #
01/05	08:33 AM	1	ROSSLYN VA	WASHINGTON DC	[redacted]	PEAK	2	0.58		LCL	0.10	0.68 #
01/05	11:44 AM	1	WASHINGTON DC	WASHINGTON DC	[redacted]	PEAK	2	0.58		LCL	0.10	0.68 #
01/05	11:47 AM	1	WASHINGTON DC	NEW YORK NY	[redacted]	PEAK	2	0.58	PEAK	BAM	0.30	0.88 #
01/05	12:22 PM	1	ROSSLYN VA	WASHINGTON DC	[redacted]	PEAK	1	0.29		LCL	0.10	0.39 #
01/05	12:57 PM	1	WASHINGTON DC	WASHINGTON DC	[redacted]	PEAK	1	0.29		LCL	0.10	0.39 #
01/05	06:22 PM	1	ARLINGTON VA	CAPITOLHTS MD	[redacted]	PEAK	4	1.16		LCL	0.10	1.26 #
01/05	06:26 PM	1	WASHINGTON DC	CAPITOLHTS MD	[redacted]	PEAK	2	0.58		LCL	0.10	0.68 #
01/06	09:41 AM	1	FT WASHING MD	WASHINGTON DC	[redacted]	PEAK	1	0.29		LCL	0.10	0.39 #
01/06	09:41 AM	1	FT WASHING MD	WASHINGTON DC	[redacted]	PEAK	1	0.29		LCL	0.10	0.39 #
01/06	09:59 AM	1	BOLLING AI DC	WASHINGTON DC	[redacted]	PEAK	4	1.16		LCL	0.10	1.26 #
01/06	02:06 PM	1	WASHINGTON DC	WASHINGTON DC	[redacted]	PEAK	3	0.87		LCL	0.10	0.97 #
01/06	02:09 PM	1	WASHINGTON DC	WASHINGTON DC	[redacted]	PEAK	1	0.29		LCL	0.10	0.39 #
01/06	02:09 PM	1	WASHINGTON DC	WASHINGTON DC	[redacted]	PEAK	2	0.58		LCL	0.10	0.68 #
01/06	02:10 PM	1	WASHINGTON DC	WASHINGTON DC	[redacted]	PEAK	4	1.16		LCL	0.10	1.26 #
01/06	02:22 PM	1	WASHINGTON DC	WASHINGTON DC	[redacted]	PEAK	4	1.16		LCL	0.10	1.26 #
01/06	03:11 PM	1	WASHINGTON DC	WASHINGTON DC	[redacted]	PEAK	2	0.58		LCL	0.10	0.68 #
01/06	03:14 PM	1	WASHINGTON DC	CHICAGO IL	[redacted]	PEAK	1	0.29	PEAK	BAM	0.15	0.44 #
01/06	06:33 PM	1	WASHINGTON DC	OXON HILL MD	[redacted]	PEAK	2	0.58		LCL	0.10	0.68 #
01/06	07:28 PM	1	WASHINGTON DC	NEW YORK NY	[redacted]	PEAK	3	0.87	PEAK	BAM	0.30	1.17 #
01/06	07:30 PM	1	WASHINGTON DC	WASHINGTON DC	[redacted]	PEAK	1	0.29		LCL	0.10	0.39 #
01/07	09:23 AM	1	WASHINGTON DC	WASHINGTON DC	[redacted]	PEAK	7	2.03		LCL	0.10	2.13 #
01/07	06:44 PM	1	WASHINGTON DC	OXON HILL MD	[redacted]	PEAK	2	0.58		LCL	0.10	0.68 #
01/07	06:46 PM	1	WASHINGTON DC	WASHINGTON DC	[redacted]	PEAK	1	0.29		LCL	0.10	0.39 #
01/07	06:48 PM	1	WASHINGTON DC	NEW YORK NY	[redacted]	PEAK	1	0.29	PEAK	BAM	0.15	0.44 #
01/07	06:50 PM	1	WASHINGTON DC	WASHINGTON DC	[redacted]	PEAK	4	1.16		LCL	0.10	1.26 #
01/07	07:02 PM	1	WASHINGTON DC	WASHINGTON DC	[redacted]	PEAK	3	0.87		LCL	0.10	0.97 #
01/08	07:52 AM	1	WASHINGTON DC	ALEXANDRIA VA	[redacted]	PEAK	2	0.58		LCL	0.10	0.68 #
01/08	08:00 AM	1	WASHINGTON DC	INCOMING CL	[redacted]	PEAK	1	0.29				0.29 #
01/08	08:37 AM	1	ARLINGTON VA	NEW YORK NY	[redacted]	PEAK	2	0.58	PEAK	BAM	0.30	0.88 #
01/08	08:39 AM	1	ROSSLYN VA	NEW YORK NY	[redacted]	PEAK	3	0.87	PEAK	BAM	0.45	1.32 #
01/08	08:43 AM	1	ROSSLYN VA	WASHINGTON DC	[redacted]	PEAK	2	0.58		LCL	0.10	0.68 #
01/08	08:45 AM	1	ROSSLYN VA	WASHINGTON DC	[redacted]	PEAK	1	0.29		LCL	0.10	0.39 #
01/08	08:46 AM	1	ROSSLYN VA	WASHINGTON DC	[redacted]	PEAK	10	2.90		LCL	0.10	3.00 #
01/08	09:08 AM	1	WASHINGTON DC	WASHINGTON DC	[redacted]	PEAK	1	0.29		LCL	0.10	0.39 #
01/08	09:09 AM	1	WASHINGTON DC	WASHINGTON DC	[redacted]	PEAK	1	0.29		LCL	0.10	0.39 #
01/08	09:10 AM	1	WASHINGTON DC	WASHINGTON DC	[redacted]	PEAK	1	0.29		LCL	0.10	0.39 #
01/08	09:11 AM	1	WASHINGTON DC	OXON HILL MD	[redacted]	PEAK	9	2.61		LCL	0.10	2.71 #
01/08	09:38 AM	1	WASHINGTON DC	WASHINGTON DC	[redacted]	PEAK	1	0.29		LCL	0.10	0.39 #
01/08	10:16 AM	1	WASHINGTON DC	WASHINGTON DC	[redacted]	PEAK	2	0.58		LCL	0.10	0.68 #

01/08	10:17 AM	1	WASHINGTON	DC	NEW YORK	NY	[redacted]	PEAK	5	1.45	PEAK	BAM	0.75	2.20 #
01/08	10:22 AM	1	WASHINGTON	DC	NEW YORK	NY		PEAK	1	0.29	PEAK	BAM	0.15	0.44 #
01/08	10:30 AM	1	WASHINGTON	DC	BETHESDA	MD		PEAK	1	0.29		LCL	0.10	0.39 #
01/08	10:48 AM	1	WASHINGTON	DC	WASHINGTON	DC		PEAK	6	1.74		LCL	0.10	1.84 #
01/08	12:07 PM	1	WASHINGTON	DC	WASHINGTON	DC		PEAK	1	0.29		LCL	0.10	0.39 #
01/08	12:08 PM	1	WASHINGTON	DC	WASHINGTON	DC		PEAK	1	0.29		LCL	0.10	0.39 #
01/08	12:33 PM	1	WASHINGTON	DC	INCOMING	CL		PEAK	1	0.29				0.29 #
01/08	12:47 PM	1	WASHINGTON	DC	WASHINGTON	DC		PEAK	1	0.29		LCL	0.10	0.39 #
01/08	01:15 PM	1	WASHINGTON	DC	WASHINGTON	DC		PEAK	1	0.29		LCL	0.10	0.39 #
01/08	01:16 PM	1	WASHINGTON	DC	WASHINGTON	DC		PEAK	1	0.29		LCL	0.10	0.39 #
01/08	01:27 PM	1	WASHINGTON	DC	OXON HILL	MD		PEAK	16	4.64		LCL	0.10	4.74 #
01/08	06:33 PM	1	WASHINGTON	DC	ARLINGTON	VA		PEAK	4	1.16		LCL	0.10	1.26 #
01/08	06:37 PM	1	WASHINGTON	DC	WASHINGTON	DC		PEAK	1	0.29		LCL	0.10	0.39 #
01/08	06:38 PM	1	WASHINGTON	DC	WASHINGTON	DC		PEAK	1	0.29		LCL	0.10	0.39 #
01/08	06:39 PM	1	WASHINGTON	DC	WASHINGTON	DC		PEAK	2	0.58		LCL	0.10	0.68 #
01/08	07:15 PM	1	FT WASHING	MD	OXON HILL	MD		PEAK	7	2.03		LCL	0.10	2.13 #
01/09	07:10 AM	1	ROSSLYN	VA	OXON HILL	MD		PEAK	8	2.32		LCL	0.10	2.42 #

1033-DC-00000116

VERNON JORDAN CALENDAR

SEALED DOCUMENTS

Pigs Might fly
by David Wojtowycz
Monster Size Hugs
Published by Statics
41 Standard Road, London NW10 6HF
0181 965 3327 Printed in England
USA 1.75 Canada 2
Price Code FF
monster
Size
hugs
2787

18 MAY 97

Dear Catherine,

I MISS YOU SO MUCH!!! It was wonderful to hear your voice the other day! Well, it's Sunday & I might get to see the Big Creep today. He called yesterday & said he's going to see if Betty can come in so I can go there. It seems that he is really trying to get me back there! Who knows???. Of course, I have my period!!! (and am really horny... but what else is new?) I hope all is well with you. I truly know how difficult it can be to assimilate to a new city--especially one where the language is so different!* How are you getting by? Is the sushi really good? .... yummy...!!! You know what, "Ran" was on t.v. a week or so ago. "Hi Kidetora" ahh Saburo. See, I'm still really weird!!! BTW, I'm writing this card in my lap which is why it is so messy. I'm too lazy to move to my messy desk! I'm bummed because I realized that my LSAT is the day after not before the Dave Matthews concert for which I have a ticket!!! Does that suck or what? Have you gone to the 'Hotel Okura' yet? Is this the most random, incoherent letter you've ever received? (tee-hee-hee) I'm better on e-mail. Thank you again for the lovely picture of us. I look at it every day! I bet pretty soon I'll start talking to you in the picture! You look so beautiful. I still can't get over how thin my arms are in the picture!!! How is Chris? Is he enjoying work? the people? I'm curious as to what is going on w/ Nick & Jen. I hope you had a chance to talk some sense into him!! (j.k.) Maybe if they get married soon you can come to the states ... via DC!!! (not too circuitous of a route or anything!!!) Oh, Catherine, I hope you know how much I love you and how very special your friendship is to me. We'll always be close no matter how many miles are between us. I need you! I love you! Please take care of yourself. Love to you and Chris!

♥ monica

* that I haven't experienced!

1037-DC-00000002

Subject: RE: hi!
Date: Monday, December 08, 1997 1:29PM

Hi! It is so good to hear from you. I have only a minute as I am off =
=3D
to my early class. Thank you for my wonderful card and perfume. It was =
=3D
very nice of you to send me something so far away in Stinkyo. I =3D
appreciate it. Hey, guess what is this Sunday? Guess. Okay, I love =
=3D
you nad I will write again soon. I am thinking of trying to call you =
=3D
some time this week if I can coodinate the time change deal. love, Cat

---

From: Lewinsky, Monica, , [redacted]
Sent: Tuesday, December 09, 1997 6:11 AM
To: CA Davis
Subject: hi!

Hi, Girl-

It's been ages since i've spoken to you. I was in LA and then in =3D
Brussels=3D20
and london for work. London was wonderful, as to be expected.

Did you ever receive my package? What's been going on with you? I miss =
=3D
you=3D20
terribly and feel clueless as to what's happening in your life.

My life is still in turmoil. I have given my notice for the end of this =
=3D

month, but don't have anything firm in NY. I'm getting frustrated. =3D
things=3D20
ave been crazy with the creep, though i did have a wonderful visit with =
=3D
him=3D20
on Saturday. When he doesn't put his walls up, it is always so heavenly.

Please write back soon. i miss you.

love,

Monica=3D20

1037-DC-00000011

CA Davis

From: Lewinsky, Monica, , [redacted]
Sent: Friday, November 07, 1997 7:20 AM
To: CA Davis
Subject: RE: troubs?

I'm a little nervous to do the whole name of the BF. His first name is Vernon. It went very well as I said yesterday. I won't be hearing from him until later next week. I know he saw the big creep yetserday afternoon. Unfortunatley, that fucker hasn't called me so i don't really know what happened in the meeting or whatever else is going on with him. oh well.

i don't have much to report except that i ma absolutely exhausted today. It is an overcast, Portland-like day today and I just want to crawl into my beddy-bye and read, nap and relax. (of course, having a boy there too wouldn't be so bad!!!) i hope you are doing well. i miss you.

let me know what's up with you.

luv,
monka

From: CA Davis
To: 'Lewinsky, Monica, , OSD/PA'
Subject: RE: troubs?
Date: Wednesday, November 05, 1997 1:28PM

Hey! I said there is no way in hell I am a real size 6- I am =
no-questions-asked-no-doubts-in-my-mind-an-honest-to-goodness-full-size =
8. EIGHT. And sizes are not double, but if they ae then Jeannie is =
half my size. My point was GAP is retarded, but in an ego-boosting way =
so 'please try'- as they say in Japan. And I have NOT lost weight, I =
have gained weight but only a little. What I do have is a constant =
poochy belly from eating too much rice! So, no more sarcastico comments =
on my voluptuous, size 8 bod. =20
Who's the BF? Have you told me his name? Can you? I hope that works =
out for you, let me know. I have no time right now. I have to go to my =
7.30a class and I am not dressed yet. =20
Okay, my lovely size 10 lovebug- and you cannot say anyting bad about a =
size 10 because I think that is a fine size- seeing as I was one for =
years and probably still am in Guess or Benetton or something. Actually =
I think I am one with Jigsaw, a Brit compnay I buy clothes in here. So =
no more of it all! I love you, be good! Cat

From: Lewinsky, Monica, , [redacted]]
Sent: Thursday, November 06, 1997 5:38 AM
To: CA Davis
Subject: RE: troubs?

Whew! What a day! I met with the big creep's best friend this morning. =
It=20
was very interetsing. I have never met such a "real" person in my =
entire=20
life. You know how some people where their hearts on their sleeves; he=20
wears his soul. Incredible. He said, with regard to my job search, =
"We're=20
in business." We'll see. he also said the creep had talked to him, and =
as=20
I was leaving he said, "You come very highly reccmmended." =
(Tee-hee-hee)

1037-DC-00000017

CA Davis

From: Lewinsky, Monica, ,[redacted]
Sent: Wednesday, November 05, 1997 2:16 AM
To: CA Davis
Subject: RE: troubs?

oK. I have some bad news. I am off the next trip so i won't be coming to Tokyo. I am probably sorrier than you are. the truth is it would have been so difficult to spend time together and it probably would have benn more frustrating than anything.

The job thing on Friday went much better than expected. It was nice; the big creep called thursday night and gave me a pep talk because i was so afraid I'd sound like an idiot. Richardson is a great guy and i met two women who work for him...also very cool. Yesterday, Richardson called me at work and told me they were going to offer me a position..they didn't know what yet, and they wanted to talk with me further. The problem is, I don't really wnat to work there (issue wise or location wise) I've already had the experience of working in a yucky building. It was awful, actually, because i feel a little trapped into taking it. HOPEFULLY, there will be some movement on the other tracks in NY too. I told mr. bacon I was planning to move and was in the process of looking...which is why i asked him if i could switch trips with tom. The biggest reason i need to do that was because the creep's friend who is supposed to help me with the private sector possibilities has been out of town the last two weeks. I feel like I'll lose momentum with them if i disappear for three weeks now (that's including Thanksgiving). Oy vey!

I'm glad to hear you guys had such a nice weekend. Honestly Cat, it sounds like such a wonderful fantasy to me. To be with yourr husband -- as part of a couple with other couples doing couple-y kinds of things and having fun.

My Australian boyfriend CALLED me on Friday to let me know his e-mail was down., He said it had become habit to e-mail me friday nights and he wanted to let me know he couldn't send anything. I know...when's the wedding????? Just kiddin'.

i miss you tons and am so sad I won't see you, but maybe we'll work something out soon. When do you guys come to the states..for holiday? and for good?

kisses and hugs
Monica

From: CA Davis
To:[redacted]
Subject: troubs?
Date: Monday, November 03, 1997 7:15PM

Hi, I sent you a message called 'quickie' last wk, but it was =
undeliverable for awhile so I'm hoping this will reach you. You'd think =
the f'n Pentagon could have straightened out email! Anyway, how did =
your 'meeting' go last week? I'm seeing the man on tellie alot because =
of the Iraqi nonsense. I think that could be a cool job, maybe better =
than the DOD.
I had a long wkend away from home. We went to a friend's office's =
cottage at Lake Kawaguchi. Its Susan's office's cottage and she invited =
us and 2 other couples for the 3day wkend- so 4 couples all together. =
It was fun- we drank a lot, ate a lot, hiked, walked, lounged, played =
games etc..I was about ready to go home Sunday evening but we left Mon. =
morning. I was getting tired of being surrounded by Brits! Actually =
one couple is made up of a German woman and a man, Gavin, who is =

1037-DC-00000022

CA Davis

From: Lewinsky, Monica, [redacted]
Sent: Wednesday, October 22, 1997 3:19 AM
To: CA Davis
Subject: hey gorgeous

Hi, Girl-

Nothing much is going on right now. You know I don't think i have mentioned to you that I have developed this intereting e-mail friendship with one of the Austarlians i met in Princeton. He is sooooo nice (and i know he is cute). It's sucha shame he lives all the way in Australia! I'm hoping he will be back in the states for business soon (hopefully, I'll ahve lost half my ass by then). His name is...Chris! Wouldn't that be funny if i married a Chris ,too!

So, i did a bad thing this past weekend. I called that shmucko (yeah, i know-- which one?) ANDY. Oh, I don't know why i did that. It was so stupid of me. i was uncomfortable talking to him. I asked how the kids were and if everything was ok. i felt so weird so after about 3 minutes..no more...i said, well i gotta go..and he said that's it and then my phine clicked so i said yeah and hung up. oh well. i actively hate his guts. he deserves to go to hell.

I have nothing to report otherwise. I have sent my list of crap to the Creep and am waiting to see if anything happens. i sure hope so.

i love you.

love
monica

1037-DC-00000033

CA Davis

From: Lewinsky, Monica, [redacted]
Sent: Wednesday, September 17, 1997 1:30 AM
To: CA Davis
Subject: RE: yeah!

THIS IS REALLY LONG. YOU MAY WANT TO PRINT IT OUT TO READ IT!!!

OK here is the note i sent you which you never got. God this e-mail system sucks so much!!!!

Hi, how was Chris' birthday? I got the beautiful pictures from the wedding. Thank you. You look so stunning. i could sit and look at the picture of you and Chris all day...hhmmmmmmm. Also, the wedding party picture is so ...i don't know...quintessential -- like it could be the picture in a frame when you buy a new one!

The Princess Di stuff....I am the most sad for her sons. I think it is tragic what happened. There are a lot of people who are very upset by this whole incident. I'm sorry you're having a hard time with it. As i said, i feel bad for her kids and sorry that she passed away, but i wasn't really her biggest fan -- sort of neutral towards her.

Well, I have an update or maybe and end-date... it's kinda long so here goes...

Yesterday morning i went to a farewell ceremony for someone here and saw the White House liaison woman with whom I met lastr week about being detailed. I asked her if she got my e-mail and she said she had and asked if i had spoken to Marsha recently. I said "no. why?" She said that marsha had run into a few snags and i should talk to her. So i called marsha all day long yetserday and finally got in touch with her at 5 pm. She has been stripped of the detailee slot in her office. So for now, there isn't anyplace for me to be detailed. So I should be PATIENT. I told her i was very upset and disappointed (even thpugh i really didn't want to work for her) and then she and i got into it. She didn't understand why i wanted to come back when there were still people there who would give me a hard time and that it isn't the right political climate for me to come back. I said i din't understand why it was okay for there to be talk about some people there but it wasn't okay for me. they have all been taken care of. ohhhh it was so infuriating. she asked me why i kept pushing the envelope on coming back there -- after all i had the experience of being there already!

So it's over. I don't know what i will do now but i can't wait any more and i can't go through all of this crap anymore. In some ways i hope i never hear from him again because he'll just lead me on because he doesn't have the balls to tell me the truth. i kind of phase in and out of being sad -- as to be expected but i'll survive. What other choice do i have?

i hope all is well with you. i miss you.

1037-DC-00000038

love
monica

Of course i wrote that like the day after it happened and as to be expected with me felt differentlya few days later. Things have been pretty shitty (insert SIGH). I will tell you the one very sweet, very mixed signal thing going on first cuz it makes me smile. Before the creep left for his vacation I gave him a copy of the novel "The Notebook" --it's this mushy romance (written by a guy) that is like "Bridges of Madison County" sort of BUT one of the recurring themes or things of significance that comes up in the book is Whitman's (gee not Thoreau's--duh) "Leaves of Grass". I thought it was neat and sweet. I enclosed a card wishing him a fun vacation and asked in a post script if he could bring me a "Black Dog" t-shirt , which you probably know is from this quasi-famous restaraunt in Martha's Vineyard-- if he had a chance. Well, I found out from Betty yesterday that he not only brought me a t-shirt he got me 2 t-shirts, a hat and a dress!!!! Even though he's a big schmuck that is surprisingly sweet -- even that he remebered!

OK Now for the[redacted]. Now that you've read what happened w/ Marsha this will make more sense. I called betty on Wednesday to find out if they knew what had happened and she said she knew but she didn't know if he knew, blah..blah. For three days she kept saying she didn't have a chance to talk to him and then it became this thing on Friday that maybe i could see him and it got crazy,a nd Cat I lost it. I went ape[redacted] To tell you the truth, i don';t even want to get into it all because it's too exhausting. But the end results were that i talked well mroe like cried to Betty in person on Friday and then I was supposed to maybe see the creepon Sun. and then it didn't work out. I cried for hours and then betty called to say he was going to talk to the chief of staff. BI d on't know what will happen. i also said to betty taht i didn't want him to do anything taht was going to get him in trouble, then yesteday she called to tell me about the black Dog stuff. the[redacted] if i know what the hell is going on!!!! he leaves to go to CA and then a bunch of other places for awhile. Oh well.

On another note, ashley and i are going to a black tie gala this saturday being hosted by the Young Smithsonians, which we have joined. hopefully we'll meet some interesting people. Oooh, a cute boy would be VERY nice.

Just to make this e-mail more interesting (and way too long) I am enclosing my latest and LAST e-mail with Doug that[redacted]. Of course you will see that what he wrote was true, but who asked for the truth! I never responded and then he sent me all of these e-mails and said, "Last e-mail unless i get a repsonse - hello?" LAMER!!!! (I'm going to put what I wrote first and then his response willl follow)

Monica: (we had been conversing earlier and i was sad..he asked why)
it might sound silly, but sometimes i just really want somebody (a
male) in my life to just physically be with -- you know hugs and stuff (i
don't
only think about sex).

i was counting on someone to help me with a job and they put me in touch with someone else that just[redacted]me around for six months. it's frustrating for me. then i get sad when i need some TLC and i can't get it. i haven't made the circle of friends here in dc like i had in portland where if i just needed a guy i had a 3 or 4 male friends on whom i could call. here it seems that most of the guys in my life i have dated so of course, there's always baggage involved. i think i'm not happy here in dc and i'm not really sure what to do about it. so in a nutshell...i'm sad. it is nice of you to ask, thanks.

DOUG:
I understand, but the if you want my very humble opinion the bottom line =
is you need to be happy with yourself FIRST (whatever town you're in) =
before you can be happy with you and someone else together. =20

You need to concentrate on you -- then others will be attracted to that. You're too consumed with chasing others rather than improving yourself and having that attract others naturally. Make yourself physically and mentally fit and the rest will naturally take care of itself.

Focus from within and disappointments will disappear!

CAN YOU BELIEVE THIS CRAP! (ok. i know what he said is true but...)

Well on to better topics. Your softball game sounds like fun. I am glad you ahd a good day. You know Catherine, I want you to know that I really admire you for having moved with Chris to Stinkyo. There are so many people who would have said "let's put off getting married til you come back. i don't want to go..blah..blah" But you, instead, i think have really captured what marriage is truly about. I hope Chris knows how lucky he is to have you and to have you --something so comforting and reassuring-- to come home to. YOU have made his transition for work so much better. Imagine how hard it would have been for him (and you too but he was starting a new job) to have been seperated from the one he loves. he would have been pining for you and hjis life in America. Instaed, you ghuys have journeyed together. My Mom and Aunt often ask after you and remark how wonderful it is that you guys are doing it together.

Well, I hope you didn;t get too bore dearly on and not get down to this last paragraph becaus eit is the important one.

I miss you and love you. Oh, BTW, we may be IN Tokyo still on your birthday!!!!!! But if not, we'll celebrate early.

Hug yourself for me.
Monica

ps -- let me know you got this, kay?

From: CA Davis
To:[redacted]
Subject: yeah!
Date: Tuesday, September 16, 1997 3:49AM

Yeah- that you may be coming here in November and only a few days before =
my 24th birthday! I would absolutely love to see you, I really hope you =
come. Well, I suppose if you get a job that you like more before then =
then I will be happy for you, too. I don't think I got an email fdrom =
you about pictures. Are you referring to wedding photos? I hope you =
got htem okay. I think the probs are at the Pentagon for email because =
I'm always getting notes that say messages from me to you cannot be =
delivered. So how are you Monica? Really. I know you are busy at =
work, but please don't feel like I am 'tired of' or 'bored' or 'annoyed' =
or anything about you talking about Marsha stuff or Creep stuff or =
anything- you can still, always, tell me if you want. I remember asking =
you a few weeks ago if you would really consider moving to NYC and if =
you would live with your mom there. If you responded I never got that =
one so let me know. =20
Well, remember my friend Tara, whom I met in London? I visited her in =
San Diego senior year spring break and now she lives in NYC with her =
fiance. They are getting married next month and we just received their =
invitation. Obviously, we cannot go but my thing is I have not heard =
from her in over 4 months! We talked a lot in the last year, especially =
after I got engaged and then she did. After I moved here I emailed her =
and got a response but nothing since. In that one email she said =
something was sort of 'up' or something but no details- she said she =
would snail mail me the news because she didn't want to email it. Well, =
I have not heard from her. I have sent emails with my home address, =
postcards etc and still nothing and then her invitation. I am a little =
perturbed. I sent back hte return saying we can't come and i wrote her =
a personal letter too. I'm bummed.
Anyway, last Saturday Chris and I went to the Yokohama Country and =
Athletic Club (YCAC) with American friends, through my friend Mary and =
her husband, to play softball. The YCAC is really nice- it is very open =
and sits on top of a hill and has lots of grass and trees! Nothing like =
the Tokyo American Club, its sister club. It was a TAC game against the =
YCAC and we, the TAC, won one and they won one. It was so much fun- we =
forgot we were in Japan!! I played right center in the outfield and had =
a walk and a few hits. Mary was the only other girl on our team and she =
played catcher. After we hung out with our team and drank beer and ate- =
overall a great day, surprisingly in Japan. Oh, aren't I negative about =

1037-DC-00000040

CA Davis

From: Lewinsky, Monica, , [redacted]
Sent: Thursday, August 14, 1997 1:47 AM
To: CA Davis
Subject: RE: new message

Yeah, Kelly sure was right!!!! I was totally distracted. I'm sure you rememeber I talked to the creep on the phone at work and I was supposed to go there and everything got crazy. I am glad you've had a good time with her but i certainly understand you and Chris wanting some time alone (like to have loud, rad SEX) before you leave!!!!

I'll talk to you about the Marsha stuff on the phone it is too exhausting for me to write it all. I'm drained right now. I can't wait to talk to you on the phone!!! I love to hear your voice...ahhh I sound like such a musher!!!!!

Well, Catherine, my dear, (jeez..i hate being called "dear". the creep calls me that sometimes it's an old person saying!!!!) i don't have much to write -- i am boring. But did i tell you i had sex with thomas last week? I know. I am sooooooo naughty. it was fun and good. i went over there with some ice cream and pretty much seduced him in a way that made him make the moves on me..cool or what???

I LUV YOU!!! Monica

From: CA Davis
To: [redacted]
Subject: new message
Date: Tuesday, August 12, 1997 11:45PM

I thought I would get rid of that Re:blind date message once and for =
all. If you like him and want to see him again call him. Unfortunatly, =
sometimes that must be done. I know it sucks and you wish it not have =
to be that way but that's life. We have to put ourselves out there =
sometimes and maybe be cut-off and maybe be let-in, you never know. =20
You can tell me about bad MArsha or work what-nots, Monica. I am not =
frustrated, neccessarily, but concerned and wishing things would change- =
or you would change them. =20
It has been fun with Kelly but I am ready for her to leave- I'm burnt on =
the entertaining thing. Also, I leave on Friday, the day after her, and =
I want to be alone with Chris. I think he feels the same way, but won't =
say it in so many words. I'm not trying to be mean, its not so much =
personal against her....The other day we were talking about her going =
toPhillie and all and I asked if she thought she would contacta nd see =
you. She said she would like to and probably would. Then she said she =
had a good time with you in DC but you seemed distracted some nad that =
she thought you were a 'very private person'. I thought it was astute, =
but I just agreed and said you could be. Anyway....
Off to work! Write back before I go, 'kay? Love, Cat

1037-DC-00000042

CA Davis

From: CA Davis[redacted]
Sent: Wednesday, November 05, 1997 1:28 PM
To: 'Lewinsky, Monica, , OSD/PA'
Subject: RE: troubs?

Hey! I said there is no way in hell I am a real size 6- I am no-questions-asked-no-doubts-in-my-mind-an-honest-to-goodness-full-size 8. EIGHT. And sizes are not double, but if they ae then Jeannie is half my size. My point was GAP is retarded, but in an ego-boosting way so 'please try'- as they say in Japan. And I have NOT lost weight, I have gained weight but only a little. What I do have is a constant poochy belly from eating too much rice! So, no more sarcastico comments on my voluptuous, size 8 bod.
Who's the BF? Have you told me his name? Can you? I hope that works out for you, let me know. I have no time right now. I have to go to my 7.30a class and I am not dressed yet.
Okay, my lovely size 10 lovebug- and you cannot say anyting bad about a size 10 because I think that is a fine size- seeing as I was one for years and probably still am in Guess or Benetton or something. Actually I think I am one with Jigsaw, a Brit compnay I buy clothes in here. So no more of it all! I love you, be good! Cat

---

From: Lewinsky, Monica, , [redacted]
Sent: Thursday, November 06, 1997 5:38 AM
To: CA Davis
Subject: RE: troubs?

Whew! What a day! I met with the big creep's best friend this morning. It was very interetsing. I have never met such a "real" person in my entire life. You know how some people where their hearts on their sleeves; he wears his soul. Incredible. He said, with regard to my job search, "We're in business." We'll see. he also said the creep had talked to him, and as I was leaving he said, "You come very highly reccmmended." (Tee-hee-hee)

The Richardson thing does sound interesting for someone who likes international affairs -- NOT ME! But I am trying to only look for something in NY. It's time for me to get out of here. I really hope that the creep and i can still have contact, because, I know it sounds soooooooooo ridiculous, but I can't get him out of my heart. i love him a lot. I know it's stupid. I want to hug him so bad right now i could cry.

OK. I hate you , you little-size-6-bitch. I don't know if i can be friends with you anymore!!!!!!!! That's nice. I'm a 10-12 so that makes me double your size. I am happy for you. That is awesome. Do you think being around the petite japanese has made it easier to lose or more pressure? either way, that's rad. I miss you so much. There's a void in my soul.

Ohhh how i long for the time when we can just spend a day together...starting w/ coffee at Starbuck's...shopping...lunch at somewhere yummy...maybe a movie...more shopping...and then getting drunk on margaritas!!! Whooo-hoooo!

I love you and I'm reminding you to tell me about why your weeknd away w/ couples wasn't so fantasy island.

Love
M

1037-DC-00000063

From: CA Davis
To: 'Lewinsky, Monica, [redacted]
Subject: RE: troubs?
Date: Tuesday, November 04, 1997 2:09PM

Okay, I am seriously bummed, but I was worried about the time issue also =
and about feeling like you were 'so close, yet so far away' while you =
were here. Chris and I will be in OR from teh 18th to the 24th of Dec. =
and HI from the 24th to the 4th or so of Jan. Then I am pretty sure we =
will be moving back to OR next summer- after our Bali trip! We have =

CA Davis

From: CA Davis[redacted]
Sent: Friday, September 05, 1997 8:28 AM
To: 'Lewinsky, Monica, , OSD/PA'
Subject: RE:

Hi Monica! Chris' birthday was mellow, especially because it was a Wednesday. I took out to dinner at a nice Thai place. He opened his presents in the morning and last night, his American birthday, we had a nice bottle of red wine from my parents to him and had dinner at the table with music and candles....very civilised. Personally, I hope he does not call you anymore either. I think you are correct that he does not have the balls to tell you straight how it is- kind of similar to the way he is as P. I am sorry any of this has or will hurt you but I thinkyou are really better off, emotionally and professionally, getting out now. I hope your experience with him will not jade you to other men. I know you thought he was pretty awesome and he sure holds a damn successful position (!-understatement), but he is still human and still flawed like all the rest of them. Personally, I think the best guys in the world are the low key kind who care more about watching a movie at home and taking care of you than of going to expensive sushi bars and showing you off. Well, its morning here and I have to get ready for the day. Oh, by the way did you know that you forwarded a message (A bientot, Oregon) from Kelly to us? I thought it was kind of wierd, but probably just a mistake. Take care, Monica nad let me know any further what-nots over htere. love Catherine

---

From: Lewinsky, Monica, [redacted]
Sent: Thursday, September 04, 1997 8:52 AM
To: CA Davis

Hi, how was Chris' birthday? I got the beautiful pictures from the wedding. Thank you. You look so stunning. i could sit and look at the picture of you and Chris all day...hhmmmmmmm. Also, the wedding party picture is so ...i don't know...quintessential -- like it could be the picture in a frame when you buy a new one!

The Princess Di stuff....I am the most sad for her sons. I think it is tragic what happened. There are a lot of people who are very upset by this whole incident. I'm sorry you're having a hard time with it. As i said, i feel bad for her kids and sorry that she passed away, but i wasn't really her biggest fan -- sort of neutral towards her.

Well, I have an update or maybe and end-date... it's kinda long so here goes...

Yesterday morning i went to a farewell ceremony for someone here and saw the White House liaison woman with whom I met lastr week about being detailed. I asked her if she got my e-mail and she said she had and asked if i had spoken to Marsha recently. I said "no. why?" She said that marsha had run into a few snags and i should talk to her. So i called marsha all day long yetserday and finally got in touch with her at 5 pm. She has been stripped of the detailee slot in her office. So for now, there isn't anyplace for me to be detailed. So I should be PATIENT. I told her i was very upset and disappointed (even thpugh i really didn't want to work for her) and then she and i got into it. She didn't understand why i wanted to come back when there were still people there who would give me a hard time and that it isn't the right political climate for me to come back. I said i din't understand why it was okay for there to be talk about some people there but it wasn't okay for me. they have all been taken care of. ohhhh it was so infuriating. she asked me why i kept pushing the envelope on coming back there -- after all i had the experience of being there already! 1037-DC-00000086

So it's over. I don't know what i will do now but i can't wait any more and i can't go through all of this crap anymore. In some ways i hope i never hear from him again because he'll just lead me on because he doesn't have the balls to tell me the truth. i kind of phase in and out of being sad -- as to be expected but i'll survive. What other choice do i have?

i hope all is well with you. i miss you.

love
monica

1037-DC-00000087

CA Davis

From: CA Davis[redacted]
Sent: Thursday, July 03, 1997 7:25 AM
To: [redacted]
Subject: hi mon

I'm sorry about all the shit that seems to be going on around you. Marsha is obviously working from a place of pettiness and jealousy- her remarks to you are so unprofessional I can't stand it. she sounds like a catty teenager! Your idea about working in another city or country is intrigueing. Do you think it is viable and conceivable for you? Could it be another American city or do you really want to be international? I guess it depends alot on openings, availability and place. I mean you would not want to be in Bosnia or Saudi Arabia (would you?). Betty is being so nice to you now, it seems. Do you have sense of why her attitude has changed? She's probably sick of seeing this happen to you after all this time.
I'm worried about you, Monica. Again, I think your idea to leave the area or get out of gov't work is a good one. I think you are in the midst of a dangerous, psychologically, situation. I am at a loss as to make you feel better or help, if I could possibly do either. When I read your emails sometimes I cannot even belive some of the things you tell me. It all sounds so dramatic and painful for you. Is your trip to L.A. for holiday or work? Maybe, you will feel a little better getting away. I don't mean to sound so disjointed but I guess I feel a litle disjointed. I know it is your life and I would NEVER presume to tell you how to live it- as you would never tell me how to live mine- but I cannot help being very concerned.
As for me, I am busy with work and with private conversation groups. I made a friend last week from work. we met after a meeting at work and she asked me to have lunch with her- the first person to do this. So we ate and drank beer and talked. She and her husband have been here for 4 months. Her name is Mary and she is 26 and was a nurse in the US ans about to start a MA program when they moved here for his business, of course. I was very impressed with her 'sacrifice'. Anyway, she's nice and hopefully we will go out again- maybe for the 4th. It was nice to talk to a woman about the stresses of living here and being newly married here, too. Actually she and her husband were married this February- 2 weeks before they moved to Tokyo. Even worse than Chris and I! Well, I must be off to my last class of the day. Write back and let me know how things have progressed. take care and love, Cat

1037-DC-00000103

CA Davis

From: CA Davis[redacted]
Sent: Thursday, June 19, 1997 9:11 AM
To: 'Lewinsky, Monica, [redacted]
Subject: RE: the blahs

hi, your email made me sad, Monica. I'm sorry for all that s--- that went down with that woman. It was very innapropriate for her to ask you questions like that. In my opinion, walkiiing away sounds like the best thing because it sounds like you will just get the run around from those clowns and continue feeling bad. Isn't it amazing that something like work and employer types can make us feel so self-conscious? I hate that kind of stuff. I'm sorry again for all this and I hope you can put it behind you if that is what you choose to do.
Was nutrition guy fun? You have to give me some info like age, looks, how many times, nice, etc....My weekend turned around a little. I had a 'talk' with Chris when he came back from the golf thing and it was okay. Last night we went to a very nice, expensive restaurant but it was my idea so I'm still waiting for flowers and'/or spontaneity. I have to be patient and forgiving with him though because he is under a lot of stress from both work here and also in the US. Actually, we may be going to the mountains this weekend- just he and I. Yeah! Next weekend we are being taken by Mitsui, who owns his US company, to a hot springs resort but that's with lots of people.
So, my job. I like so far. My 2 classes are pretty good and the students are nice and higher level which is much better. Although, there is one woman in my presentations class that speaks slowly and quietly and has a terrible time reading Eng. out loud. She always stumbles over words and then goes back and starts the sentence over- it drives me crazy but I keep it inside. I feel bad for her because I know she knows she is a lower level than the other 2 in the class. The 2 women in my Bus. Comm. class are great- we have a lot of fun and itsmellow but htey are smart and cool. They are the type of people that I would not mind having a drink with after class sometime. We'll see. I have also started 2 private convo groups which are good- pays cash. I like most of the other instructers at my job-job but the staff can be punks sometimes. I've had no trouble with the bosses yet- thank God.
Well, I'm really, really fat so my new clothes look disgusting on me. Thats all I have to say. Oh, except wearing silk, or silk-esque, scarves is fashionable here so I do that with a suit. I looks nice but I tie it a litleoff my neck so I don't feel like I'm choking to death. My brother is like that with ties so it must run in the family. Speaking of Nick....he is keeping busy. He goes out with friends a lot, plays golf, softball and baseball, and works a lot, too. Mom thinks he has gotten over the initial shock and is on to the beginning stages of 'moving on'. I miss him and feel for him so much it hurts. Can I say something wierd, but not wierd? My brother, essentially, was my first love. Not love that is at all sexual because I never found myself thinking that way about him but love like 'men should be like this and I want one like this for me' -I never harboured any idea that I wanted him but as a model for my own man. Does that make sense? You've met him, I think you can understand how I felt. And in a lot of ways Chris is like Nick, especially internal qualities about treating people and being a good person.
Well, I love you girl and miss you soooooo much. Take care and write back soon ya' hea'. love Cat

---

From: Lewinsky, Monica, [redacted]
Sent: Tuesday, June 17, 1997 1:08 PM
To: CA Davis
Subject: the blahs

hi, cat-
i miss you! i'm glad you liked my silly little package. i had agood time at the spa (i did it with the nutrition guy)!!!! Yeah! Now i can start the count over again. (i kinda don't want to get into all the juicies on e-mail)! On every other front of my life things are not so great. i met with Marsha yesterday and it was very interesting. There is most certainly a disconnect on what he said he told her and how she acted. She didn't even know what my title or my job was about. she didn't have any job openings to offer. instead, she made me go over what happened when i had to leave (who told me) and then proceeded to confirm the Evelyn story about my "inapprpriate behavior". Then she asked me with such nasty women there and peopel gossipping about me why did i want to come back? I was so upset. i really did not feel it was her place to question me about that. later on, i said something about being told i could come back after november and she wanted to know who told me that! So, i have placed a call to him but i don't know what is going to happen. i foiund out today that i didn't get the NSC job. To top it all off the big creep is wearing one of my ties today. i think i'm just going to have to walk away from it all. i don't know yet. i know it's annoying -- i'm always saying this and then i change

1037-DC-00000107

CA Davis

From: CA Davis[redacted]
Sent: Thursday, June 19, 1997 9:11 AM
To: 'Lewinsky, Monica, [redacted]
Subject: RE: the blahs

hi, your email made me sad, Monica. I'm sorry for all that s— that went down with that woman. It was very innapropriate for her to ask you questions like that. In my opinion, walkiiing away sounds like the best thing because it sounds like you will just get the run around from those clowns and continue feeling bad. Isn't it amazing that something like work and employer types can make us feel so self-conscious? I hate that kind of stuff. I'm sorry again for all this and I hope you can put it behind you if that is what you choose to do.
Was nutrition guy fun? You have to give me some info like age, looks, how many times, nice, etc....My weekend turned around a little. I had a 'talk' with Chris when he came back from the golf thing and it was okay. Last night we went to a very nice, expensive restaurant but it was my idea so I'm still waiting for flowers and'/or spontaneity. I have to be patient and forgiving with him though because he is under a lot of stress from both work here and also in the US. Actually, we may be going to the mountains this weekend- just he and I. Yeah! Next weekend we are being taken by Mitsui, who owns his US company, to a hot springs resort but that's with lots of people.
So, my job. I like so far. My 2 classes are pretty good and the students are nice and higher level which is much better. Although, there is one woman in my presentations class that speaks slowly and quietly and has a terrible time reading Eng. out loud. She always stumbles over words and then goes back and starts the sentence over- it drives me crazy but I keep it inside. I feel bad for her because I know she knows she is a lower level than the other 2 in the class. The 2 women in my Bus. Comm. class are great- we have a lot of fun and itsmellow but htey are smart and cool. They are the type of people that I would not mind having a drink with after class sometime. We'll see. I have also started 2 private convo groups which are good- pays cash. I like most of the other instructers at my job-job but the staff can be punks sometimes. I've had no trouble with the bosses yet- thank God.
Well, I'm really, really fat so my new clothes look disgusting on me. Thats all I have to say. Oh, except wearing silk, or silk-esque, scarves is fashionable here so I do that with a suit. I looks nice but I tie it a litleoff my neck so I don't feel like I'm choking to death. My brother is like that with ties so it must run in the family. Speaking of Nick....he is keeping busy. He goes out with friends a lot, plays golf, softball and baseball, and works a lot, too. Mom thinks he has gotten over the initial shock and is on to the beginning stages of 'moving on'. I miss him and feel for him so much it hurts. Can I say something wierd, but not wierd? My brother, essentially, was my first love. Not love that is at all sexual because I never found myself thinking that way about him but love like 'men should be like this and I want one like this for me' -I never harboured any idea that I wanted him but as a model for my own man. Does that make sense? You've met him, I think you can understand how I felt. And in a lot of ways Chris is like Nick, especially internal qualities about treating people and being a good person.
Well, I love you girl and miss you soooooo much. Take care and write back soon ya' hea'. love Cat

---

From: Lewinsky, Monica, [redacted]
Sent: Tuesday, June 17, 1997 1:08 PM
To: CA Davis
Subject: the blahs

1037-DC-00000108

hi, cat-
i miss you! i'm glad you liked my silly little package. i had agood time at the spa (i did it with the nutrition guy)!!!! Yeah! Now i can start the count over again. (i kinda don't want to get into all the juicies on e-mail)! On every other front of my life things are not so great. i met with Marsha yesterday and it was very interesting. There is most certainly a disconnect on what he said he told her and how she acted. She didn't even know what my title or my job was about. she didn't have any job openings to offer. instead, she made me go over what happened when i had to leave (who told me) and then proceeded to confirm the Evelyn story about my "inapprpriate behavior". Then she asked me with such nasty women there and peopel gossipping about me why did i want to come back? I was so upset. i really did not feel it was her place to question me about that. later on, i said something about being told i could come back after november and she wanted to know who told me that! So, i have placed a call to him but i don't know what is going to happen. i foiund out today that i didn't get the NSC job. To top it all off the big creep is wearing one of my ties today. i think i'm just going to have to walk away from it all. i don't know yet. i know it's annoying -- i'm always saying this and then i change

my mind.

i hpe you're doing ok. how was your rice and beer???? i'm sorry you had a sad saturday. what is your work like? i'm very curious to hear about it so let me know (especially to hear about all of the clothes you have had to buy)!!!

well, i'm a little too sad to continue right now. i love you and i miss you. monica

CA Davis

From: CA Davis[redacted]]
Sent: Tuesday, June 03, 1997 9:12 AM
To: 'Lewinsky, Monica, , OSD/PA'
Subject: RE: konichiwa(????)

hi, actually I have a real job! I am an 'instructor' of English but in relation to business issues to Japanese business who, primarily, work for US companies that have offices over here. My first 2 classes are ESP, English with a Special Purpose, in this case giving presentations. Where I know anything about business, I don't know. But the pay is outrageous! Granted, Tokyo is expensive but you do get paid very well. Its quite professional in dress, especially when meeting with clients so I went shopping, of course, and bought a cute suit at Jigsaw. But, God, the clothes are sooooo expensive here, I can't over it. I wonder how young people, on their own, handle it. They probably live at home or in flats that are much cheaper than ours. Well, our weekend was semi-exciting. Alex's girlfriend Chrisanthi was in Tokyo for a few nights for a conference so we went out with her on Saturday night. Other than that we laid around a lot and talked about going somewhere but didn't. Next weekend I think we'll get out of town and maybe go to Kamakura, which is on the ocean. I'm getting a little city-sick. Oh, I think I know which road you were on when you were here- that was lined with trees and had lots of shops and cafes. I'm pretty sure it was Omotesando in Aoyama. Its really lovely and has Parisian-esque outdoor cafes and all the swank boutiques. That's where I went shopping the other day.
I don't know how Nick is doing, except that he pitching on a baseball team and working A LOT. His job is very good but because the company is small, but growing, he has a lot of responsibility so he often works Saturdays as well as full week days. Unfortunately, he's not well rewarded with a fat paycheck, either. Its a mechanical engineering firm, in case you didn't know what he did. I must say I feel proud when I tell people 'my brother is an engineer'. As far as I know he is still split from Jen but is still dealing with it by himnself. Its very nice of you to ask after him, I appreciate that.
I'm sorry you are on an 'emotional rollercoster' right now. What can you do on your free time that may help you either refocus or get your mindoff things, temporarily. Are you close to any country areas to take a walk or a lake or beach? something outdoorsy but pleasant? Its hard not having a close girlfriend to 'escape' with, isn't? I may be able to become friends with one woman I work with but that remains to be seen- I guess, I sometimes want the benefit of a friend but don't want to put in all the effort to set it up. It was nice to see Chrisanthi and actually we had a 2 hour girlie-chat on the phone when she was here Friday night. It was really nice to 'dish' to someone other than Chris!
Well, I need to get ready for work- I'm training all this week and my classes start next week. Training sucks and I really don't like my trainer- a man named Sean from Australia- I think he's sexist and offensive. Anyway! I love you and look forward to hearing from you soon, love, Catherine

---

From: Lewinsky, Monica, [redacted]]
Sent: Monday, June 02, 1997 8:54 AM
To: CA Davis
Subject: konichiwa(????)

Hi, Cat-
I hope this e-mail finds you well. It is hard to believe, but i have brought the card i wrote you weeks ago to mail. Of course everything in there is now obsolete, but it is a cute card. I miss you. Remeber how i told you about that guy Kurt Campbell who's the Deputy Assistant Secretary of Defense for Asian Affairs, well he is going with this other woman (actually from my office)to Tokyo this week. Do you want me to give him your number and maybe you and Chris can meet him for a drink or somethin'??? Let me know so I can get him the info before he leaves. I had a pretty boring weekend. I did, however, go iwth my Mom to see the" Picasso:The Early Years" exhibit yesterday. It was wonderful. I must say that I found it overwhelming to see just how much work he produced-- and then to realize that was only some of his work from his EARLY years...jeez!!!!! Otherwise, I am depressed. I float from being sad to angry often and easily. What can I do but weather the storm. I hope you're doing ok. Have you started tutoring in English conversation???? Let me know how you are and what you're up to. I love you and miss you. Also, how's Nick doing? write me back.
Love, ME

1037-DC-00000115

Davis, Catherine

From: Lewinsky, Monica, [redacted]
Sent: Tuesday, September 16, 1997 11:30 AM
To: CA Davis
Subject: RE: yeah!

THIS IS REALLY LONG. YOU MAY WANT TO PRINT IT OUT TO READ IT!!!

OK here is the note i sent you which you never got. God this e-mail system sucks so much!!!!

Hi, how was Chris' birthday? I got the beautiful pictures from the wedding. Thank you. You look so stunning. i could sit and look at the picture of you and Chris all day...hhmmmmmmm. Also, the wedding party picture is so ...i don't know...quintessential -- like it could be the picture in a frame when you buy a new one!

The Princess Di stuff....I am the most sad for her sons. I think it is tragic what happened. There are a lot of people who are very upset by this whole incident. I'm sorry you're having a hard time with it. As i said, i feel bad for her kids and sorry that she passed away, but i wasn't really her biggest fan -- sort of neutral towards her.

Well, I have an update or maybe and end-date... it's kinda long so here goes...

Yesterday morning i went to a farewell ceremony for someone here and saw the White House liaison woman with whom I met lastr week about being detailed. I asked her if she got my e-mail and she said she had and asked if i had spoken to Marsha recently. I said "no. why?" She said that marsha had run into a few snags and i should talk to her. So i called marsha all day long yetserday and finally got in touch with her at 5 pm. She has been stripped of the detailee slot in her office. So for now, there isn't anyplace for me to be detailed. So I should be PATIENT. I told her i was very upset and disappointed (even thpugh i really didn't want to work for her) and then she and i got into it. She didn't understand why i wanted to come back when there were still people there who would give me a hard time and that it isn't the right political climate for me to come back. I said i din't understand why it was okay for there to be talk about some people there but it wasn't okay for me. they have all been taken care of. ohhhh it was so infuriating. she asked me why i kept pushing the envelope on coming back there -- after all i had the experience of being there already!

So it's over. I don't know what i will do now but i can't wait any more and i can't go through all of this crap anymore. In some ways i hope i never hear from him again because he'll just lead me on because he doesn't have the balls to tell me the truth. i kind of phase in and out of being sad -- as to be expected but i'll survive. What other choice do i have?

i hope all is well with you. i miss you.

love
monica

1037-DC-00000167

Of course i wrote that like the day after it happened and as to be expected with me felt differentlya few days later. Things have been pretty shitty (insert SIGH). I will tell you the one very sweet, very mixed signal thing going on first cuz it makes me smile. Before the creep left for his vacation I gave him a copy of the novel "The Notebook" --it's this mushy romance (written by a guy) that is like "Bridges of Madison County" sort of BUT one of the recurring themes or things of significance that comes up in the book is Whitman's (gee not Thoreau's--duh) "Leaves of Grass". I thought it was neat and sweet. I enclosed a card wishing him a fun vacation and asked in a post script if he could bring me a "Black Dog" t-shirt , which you probably know is from this quasi-famous restaraunt in Martha's Vineyard-- if he had a chance. Well, I found out from Betty yesterday that he not only brought me a t-shirt he got me 2 t-shirts, a hat and a dress!!!! Even though he's a big schmuck that is surprisingly sweet -- even that he remebered!

OK Now for the [redacted] Now that you've read what happened w/ Marsha this will make more sense. I called betty on Wednesday to find out if they knew what had happened and she said she knew but she didn't know if he knew, blah..blah. For three days she kept saying she didn't have a chance to talk to him and then it became this thing on Friday that maybe i could see him and it got crazy,a nd Cat I lost it. I went ape[redacted] To tell you the truth, i don';t even want to get into it all because it's too exhausting. But the end results were that i talked well mroe like cried to Betty in person on Friday and then I was supposed to maybe see the creepon Sun. and then it didn't work out. I cried for hours and then betty called to say he was going to talk to the chief of staff. BI d on't know what will happen. i also said to betty taht i didn't want him to do anything taht was going to get him in trouble, then yesteday she called to tell me about the black Dog stuff. the[redacted] if i know what the hell is going on!!!! he leaves to go to CA and then a bunch of other places for awhile. Oh well.

On another note, ashley and i are going to a black tie gala this saturday being hosted by the Young Smithsonians, which we have joined. hopefully we'll meet some interesting people. Oooh, a cute boy would be VERY nice.

Just to make this e-mail more interesting (and way too long) I am enclosing my latest and LAST e-mail with Doug that [redacted]. Of course you will see that what he wrote was true, but who asked for the truth! I never responded and then he sent me all of these e-mails and said, "Last e-mail unless i get a repsonse - hello?" LAMER!!!! (I'm going to put what I wrote first and then his response willl follow)

Monica: (we had been conversing earlier and i was sad..he asked why)
it might sound silly, but sometimes i just really want somebody (a male) in my life to just physically be with -- you know hugs and stuff (i don't
only think about sex).

i was counting on someone to help me with a job and they put me in touch with someone else that just[redacted] me around for six months. it's frustrating for me. then i get sad when i need some TLC and i can't get it. i haven't made the circle of friends here in dc like i had in portland where if i just needed a guy i had a 3 or 4 male friends on whom i could call. here it seems that most of the guys in my life i have dated so of course, there's always baggage involved. i think i'm not happy here in dc and i'm not really sure what to do about it. so in a nutshell...i'm sad. it is nice of you to ask, thanks.

DOUG:
I understand, but the if you want my very humble opinion the bottom line = is you need to be happy with yourself FIRST (whatever town you're in) = before you can be happy with you and someone else together. =20

You need to concentrate on you -- then others will be attracted to that. You're too consumed with chasing others rather than improving yourself and having that attract others naturally. Make yourself physically and mentally fit and the rest will naturally take care of itself.

Focus from within and disappointments will disappear!

CAN YOU BELIEVE THIS CRAP! (ok. i know what he said is true but...)

Well on to better topics. Your softball game sounds like fun. I am glad you ahd a good day. You know Catherine, I want you to know that I really admire you for having moved with Chris to Stinkyo. There are so many people who would have said "let's put off getting married til you come back. i don't want to go..blah..blah" But you, instead, i think have really captured what marriage is truly about. I hope Chris knows how lucky he is to have you and to have you --something so comforting and reassuring-- to come home to. YOU have made his transition for work so much better. Imagine how hard it would have been for him (and you too but he was starting a new job) to have been seperated from the one he loves. he would have been pining for you and hjis life in America. Instaed, you ghuys have journeyed together. My Mom and Aunt often ask after you and remark how wonderful it is that you guys are doing it together.

Well, I hope you didn;t get too bore dearly on and not get down to this last paragraph becaus eit is the important one.

I miss you and love you. Oh, BTW, we may be IN Tokyo still on your birthday!!!!!! But if not, we'll celebrate early.

Hug yourself for me.
Monica

ps -- let me know you got this, kay?

From: CA Davis
To: [redacted]
Subject: yeah!
Date: Tuesday, September 16, 1997 3:49AM

Yeah- that you may be coming here in November and only a few days before = my 24th birthday! I would absolutely love to see you, I really hope you = come. Well, I suppose if you get a job that you like more before then = then I will be happy for you, too. I don't think I got an email fdrom = you about pictures. Are you referring to wedding photos? I hope you = got htem okay. I think the probs are at the Pentagon for email because = I'm always getting notes that say messages from me to you cannot be = delivered. So how are you Monica? Really. I know you are busy at = work, but please don't feel like I am 'tired of' or 'bored' or 'annoyed' = or anything about you talking about Marsha stuff or Creep stuff or = anything- you can still, always, tell me if you want. I remember asking = you a few weeks ago if you would really consider moving to NYC and if = you would live with your mom there. If you responded I never got that = one so let me know. =20
Well, remember my friend Tara, whom I met in London? I visited her in = San Diego senior year spring break and now she lives in NYC with her = fiance. They are getting married next month and we just received their = invitation. Obviously, we cannot go but my thing is I have not heard = from her in over 4 months! We talked a lot in the last year, especially = after I got engaged and then she did. After I moved here I emailed her = and got a response but nothing since. In that one email she said = something was sort of 'up' or something but no details- she said she = would snail mail me the news because she didn't want to email it. Well, = I have not heard from her. I have sent emails with my home address, = postcards etc and still nothing and then her invitation. I am a little = perturbed. I sent back hte return saying we can't come and i wrote her = a personal letter too. I'm bummed. 1037-DC-00000169
Anyway, last Saturday Chris and I went to the Yokohama Country and = Athletic Club (YCAC) with American friends, through my friend Mary and = her husband, to play softball. The YCAC is really nice- it is very open = and sits on top of a hill and has lots of grass and trees! Nothing like = the Tokyo American Club, its sister club. It was a TAC game against the = YCAC and we, the TAC, won one and they won one. It was so much fun- we = forgot we were in Japan!! I played right center in the outfield and had = a walk and a few hits. Mary was the only other girl on our team and she = played catcher. After we hung out with our team and drank beer and ate- = overall a great day, surprisingly in Japan. Oh, aren't I negative about =

Davis, Catherine

From: Lewinsky, Monica, [redacted]
Sent: Wednesday, August 13, 1997 11:47 AM
To: CA Davis
Subject: RE: new message

Yeah, Kelly sure was right!!!! I was totally distracted. I'm sure you rememeber I talked to the creep on the phone at work and I was supposed to go there and everything got crazy. I am glad you've had a good time with her but i certainly understand you and Chris wanting some time alone (like to have loud, rad SEX) before you leave!!!!

I'll talk to you about the Marsha stuff on the phone it is too exhausting for me to write it all. I'm drained right now. I can't wait to talk to you on the phone!!! I love to hear your voice...ahhh I sound like such a musher!!!!!

Well, Catherine, my dear, (jeez..i hate being called "dear". the creep calls me that sometimes it's an old person saying!!!!) i don't have much to write -- i am boring. But did i tell you i had sex with thomas last week? I know. I am sooooooo naughty. it was fun and good. i went over there with some ice cream and pretty much seduced him in a way that made him make the moves on me..cool or what???

I LUV YOU!!! Monica

From: CA Davis
To: [redacted]
Subject: new message
Date: Tuesday, August 12, 1997 11:45PM

I thought I would get rid of that Re:blind date message once and for =
all. If you like him and want to see him again call him. Unfortunatly, =
sometimes that must be done. I know it sucks and you wish it not have =
to be that way but that's life. We have to put ourselves out there =
sometimes and maybe be cut-off and maybe be let-in, you never know. =20
You can tell me about bad MArsha or work what-nots, Monica. I am not =
frustrated, neccessarily, but concerned and wishing things would change- =
or you would change them. =20
It has been fun with Kelly but I am ready for her to leave- I'm burnt on =
the entertaining thing. Also, I leave on Friday, the day after her, and =
I want to be alone with Chris. I think he feels the same way, but won't =
say it in so many words. I'm not trying to be mean, its not so much =
personal against her....The other day we were talking about her going =
toPhillie and all and I asked if she thought she would contacta nd see =
you. She said she would like to and probably would. Then she said she =
had a good time with you in DC but you seemed distracted some nad that =
she thought you were a 'very private person'. I thought it was astute, =
but I just agreed and said you could be. Anyway....
Off to work! Write back before I go, 'kay? Love, Cat

1037-DC-00000171

Davis, Catherine

From: CA Davis[redacted]
Sent: Thursday, September 04, 1997 6:28 PM
To: 'Lewinsky, Monica, , OSD/PA'
Subject: RE:

Hi Monica! Chris' birthday was mellow, especially because it was a Wednesday. I took out to dinner at a nice Thai place. He opened his presents in the morning and last night, his American birthday, we had a nice bottle of red wine from my parents to him and had dinner at the table with music and candles....very civilised. Personally, I hope he does not call you anymore either. I think you are correct that he does not have the balls to tell you straight how it is- kind of similar to the way he is as P. I am sorry any of this has or will hurt you but I thinkyou are really better off, emotionally and professionally, getting out now. I hope your experience with him will not jade you to other men. I know you thought he was pretty awesome and he sure holds a damn successful position (!- understatement), but he is still human and still flawed like all the rest of them. Personally, I think the best guys in the world are the low key kind who care more about watching a movie at home and taking care of you than of going to expensive sushi bars and showing you off. Well, its morning here and I have to get ready for the day. Oh, by the way did you know that you forwarded a message (A bientot, Oregon) from Kelly to us? I thought it was kind of wierd, but probably just a mistake. Take care, Monica nad let me know any further what-nots over htere. love Catherine

From: Lewinsky, Monica, [redacted]
Sent: Thursday, September 04, 1997 8:52 AM
To: CA Davis

Hi, how was Chris' birthday? I got the beautiful pictures from the wedding. Thank you. You look so stunning. i could sit and look at the picture of you and Chris all day...hhmmmmmmm. Also, the wedding party picture is so ...i don't know...quintessential -- like it could be the picture in a frame when you buy a new one!

The Princess Di stuff....I am the most sad for her sons. I think it is tragic what happened. There are a lot of people who are very upset by this whole incident. I'm sorry you're having a hard time with it. As i said, i feel bad for her kids and sorry that she passed away, but i wasn't really her biggest fan -- sort of neutral towards her.

Well, I have an update or maybe and end-date... it's kinda long so here goes...

Yesterday morning i went to a farewell ceremony for someone here and saw the White House liaison woman with whom I met lastr week about being detailed. I asked her if she got my e-mail and she said she had and asked if i had spoken to Marsha recently. I said "no. why?" She said that marsha had run into a few snags and i should talk to her. So i called marsha all day long yetserday and finally got in touch with her at 5 pm. She has been stripped of the detailee slot in her office. So for now, there isn't anyplace for me to be detailed. So I should be PATIENT. I told her i was very upset and disappointed (even thpugh i really didn't want to work for her) and then she and i got into it. She didn't understand why i wanted to come back when there were still people there who would give me a hard time and that it isn't the right political climate for me to come back. I said i din't understand why it was okay for there to be talk about some people there but it wasn't okay for me. they have all been taken care of. ohhhh it was so infuriating. she asked me why i kept pushing the envelope on coming back there -- after all i had the experience of being there already! 1037-DC-00000255

So it's over. I don't know what i will do now but i can't wait any more and i can't go through all of this crap anymore. In some ways i hope i never hear from him again because he'll just lead me on because he doesn't have the balls to tell me the truth. i kind of phase in and out of being sad -- as to be expected but i'll survive. What other choice do i have?

i hope all is well with you. i miss you.

love
monica

1037-DC-00000256

Davis, Catherine

From: CA Davis[redacted]
Sent: Tuesday, September 02, 1997 5:57 PM
To: 'Lewinsky, Monica, , OSD/PA'
Subject: RE: Aloha!

Wow, your mom's flat sounds amazing! That is so wonderful for her- I hope she is really happy with this guy. If you moved to NY would you be able to live with her? Would you still work for the DOD? Probably not, yah? I cannot say I am surprised that this whole situation has taken its toll on you. I'm sure it has for a while now. If I may be so bold to state my unequivocal opinion: I think your 'situation' is a lose-lose situation with him. He cannot ever be totally your's Monica. Ever. And, as I have said before, you deserve a man that is all your's. ALL YOUR'S. And just because there may not be another man around right now does not mean you should put yourself through the ringer with this Man. You are worth much more than that, no matter his Position its the same old affair bullshit. Does your mom support you moving to NY? If so, I think that would be fantastic! I would come visit you once a year and you could visit me once a year (of course, after I move back to the US) and we'd see eachother a lot!
Anyway, was your holiday relaxing? Four Australian businessmen?....I hope they were nicer and more polite than most Australians I meet. Today, Sept. 3rd, is Chris' 31st birthday. I am going to take him out to dinner tonight and, of course, have lots of presents for him to open. Unfortunately, since we don't have an oven (!), I can't bake a little cake. Maybe that is not so unfortunate! Well, I must be off. I'll hear from you soon, take care- I really mean it, too- I love you, Catherine

---

From: Lewinsky, Monica, [redacted]
Sent: Tuesday, September 02, 1997 1:30 PM
To: CA Davis
Subject: RE: Aloha!

Welcome Home! I, too, was sorry we didn't get a chance to talk, but I'm glad you had a good holiday. How is Jeannie doing? Is she still with what's-his-name? I was also happy to read that Nick seems to be doing better. On my little vacation I went to Princeton, NJ (where I met and had dinner with 4 Australian businessmen -- it was much fun!!!!), the Spa in CT., and to Scarsdale, NY to see a friend of mine and my mom's. I did not hook up with that Jesse guy at the spa again. It was sort of my choice and a little lack of him not aggressively pursuing me. So here is big news....my mom has gotten an apartment in NY for a year on 5th and 61st!!!!!!!!!! She is pretty serious with this guy and spends so much time up there already. It is funny because her big dream in life has been to live in NY and now he has gotten her an apartment there!!!! It's exciting!

My work sit: I met with the woman who is the White House liaison here and she described in detail, what needs to happen for me to be deatiled there. It is a much more difficult process than i imagined. Essentially, I would remain an employee of Public Affairs and they "loan" me to the WH. PA doesn't get more money allotted or an extra position to fill my slot. Normally they would only detail somebody in a slot where there are a few people who have similar tasks , i.e. a media desk officer -- with me, there is only one confidential assistant in PA. We'll have to see what happens but I really don't want to work for marsha anymore. I don't trust her at all. I'm moving toward giving it all up. Maybe I'll move to NY. As I told you on the phone, I felt awful about my last visit with him. I don't doubt that he has real feelings for me, but how strong they are is another question. He hasn't taken care of me. we'll see what happens. I'm in an ok place right now. i am just starting to physically and mentally REALLY feel the and see the effects of all of this stress. It is getting to be too much for me. Don't worry though, I'll be fine.

1037-DC-00000258

I miss you and am sad i didn't get to talk to you more when you were here (although i probably would have been very boring!)

Big hugs and sloppy kisses,
Monica

ps-- can you believe i haven't spoken to Andy in 3 1/2 months! Weird, huh?

From: CA Davis
To: [redacted]
Subject: Aloha!
Date: Sunday, August 31, 1997 3:52PM

Hi there! Well, I must say I am sorry that we did not get to talk = again. At first, I thought you didn't call back, but then Nick told me = a little later that you had when he was talking to my parents. My time = in Hawaii was fun, but a little frantic. Okay, not frantic exactly....I = was trying to do a lot ina small amount of time and try not to stress = about also doing errands I was supposed to do there, too. Needless, to = say I did not do all I was suppoesed to do and did not remember to buy = all I was supposed to buy! What I did do was go to the beach and eat. = Jeannie only worked twice while I was there and for short shifts and she = did not have classes yet. The weather was great, too, so I got to keep = 'enhancing' my colour there after the Lake. =20
The Lake, which is what we call where our summer cabin is, was really = nice. It is so unbelievably beautiful up there, its almost not real. = Its as close to pristine as I have ever seen. Anyway, the weather was = great up there too and we did a little hiking, some swimming, boating = etc...it was wonderful to hang there with my brother. He seems to be = doing okay- still recovering though and not quite ready to date yet. He = has some girl-friends that check in on him and say they will set him up = as soon as he is ready. I feel better knowing that he has girls to talk = to about this whole thing because you know how boys are...not the most = sensitive. My parents were good, although maybe a little tenser than = they could have been at times, especially my dad. I think that was = probably due to his whole being away from home for so long and trying to = still take care of business there and also wanting to buy a house in = Sonoma as soon as possible. Andrea was happy to have an awaesome tan = and to not really be working- she starts work on her dissertation thiis = Autumn.
Well, that's pretty much my little trip to America. Too short! And I = came back to lots of work messages and all these new classes and = substitutions blah, blah, blah. That's life though, right? I guess, I = also came back to my husband, who I missed terribly. We have spent the = weekend together- no one else. So how are you doing? Where exactly did = you go on your holiday? Any news on job switching yet? Are you still = sure you want to be back in the WH? Let me know what all is going down = with you- work stuff but also any activities, more dates etc...? Do you = still see or talk to Ashley? Does she have an opinion on your move to = the WH? I hope you are okay Monica and I'm sorry I did not get to talk = to you again. Maybe I will try to give you a call in the next few = weeks. Can I call you at work? If so give me the number. I love you = and miss you and hope you're okay. Take care, love, Catherine

1037-DC-00000259

Davis, Catherine

From: CA Davis[redacted]
Sent: Wednesday, June 18, 1997 7:11 PM
To: 'Lewinsky, Monica, , OSD/PA'
Subject: RE: the blahs

hi, your email made me sad, Monica. I'm sorry for all that s— that went down with that woman. It was very innapropriate for her to ask you questions like that. In my opinion, walkiiing away sounds like the best thing because it sounds like you will just get the run around from those clowns and continue feeling bad. Isn't it amazing that something like work and employer types can make us feel so self-conscious? I hate that kind of stuff. I'm sorry again for all this and I hope you can put it behind you if that is what you choose to do.
Was nutrition guy fun? You have to give me some info like age, looks, how many times, nice, etc....My weekend turned around a little. I had a 'talk' with Chris when he came back from the golf thing and it was okay. Last night we went to a very nice, expensive restaurant but it was my idea so I'm still waiting for flowers and'/or spontaneity. I have to be patient and forgiving with him though because he is under a lot of stress from both work here and also in the US. Actually, we may be going to the mountains this weekend- just he and I. Yeah! Next weekend we are being taken by Mitsui, who owns his US company, to a hot springs resort but that's with lots of people.
So, my job. I like so far. My 2 classes are pretty good and the students are nice and higher level which is much better. Although, there is one woman in my presentations class that speaks slowly and quietly and has a terrible time reading Eng. out loud. She always stumbles over words and then goes back and starts the sentence over- it drives me crazy but I keep it inside. I feel bad for her because I know she knows she is a lower level than the other 2 in the class. The 2 women in my Bus. Comm. class are great- we have a lot of fun and itsmellow but htey are smart and cool. They are the type of people that I would not mind having a drink with after class sometime. We'll see. I have also started 2 private convo groups which are good- pays cash. I like most of the other instructers at my job-job but the staff can be punks sometimes. I've had no trouble with the bosses yet- thank God.
Well, I'm really, really fat so my new clothes look disgusting on me. Thats all I have to say. Oh, except wearing silk, or silk-esque, scarves is fashionable here so I do that with a suit. I looks nice but I tie it a litleoff my neck so I don't feel like I'm choking to death. My brother is like that with ties so it must run in the family. Speaking of Nick....he is keeping busy. He goes out with friends a lot, plays golf, softball and baseball, and works a lot, too. Mom thinks he has gotten over the initial shock and is on to the beginning stages of 'moving on'. I miss him and feel for him so much it hurts. Can I say something wierd, but not wierd? My brother, essentially, was my first love. Not love that is at all sexual because I never found myself thinking that way about him but love like 'men should be like this and I want one like this for me' -I never harboured any idea that I wanted him but as a model for my own man. Does that make sense? You've met him, I think you can understand how I felt. And in a lot of ways Chris is like Nick, especially internal qualities about treating people and being a good person.
Well, I love you girl and miss you soooooo much. Take care and write back soon ya' hea'. love Cat

---

From: Lewinsky, Monica, [redacted]
Sent: Tuesday, June 17, 1997 1:08 PM
To: CA Davis
Subject: the blahs

hi, cat-
i miss you! i'm glad you liked my silly little package. i had agood time at the spa (i did it with the nutrition guy)!!!! Yeah! Now i can start the count over again. (i kinda don't want to get into all the juicies on e-mail)! On every other front of my life things are not so great. i met with Marsha yesterday and it was very interesting. There is most certainly a disconnect on what he said he told her and how she acted. She didn't even know what my title or my job was about. she didn't have any job openings to offer. instead, she made me go over what happened when i had to leave (who told me) and then proceeded to confirm the Evelyn story about my "inapprpriate behavior". Then she asked me with such nasty women there and peopel gossipping about me why did i want to come back? I was so upset. i really did not feel it was her place to question me about that. later on, i said something about being told i could come back after november and she wanted to know who told me that! So, i have placed a call to him but i don't know what is going to happen. i foiund out today that i didn't get the NSC job. To top it all off the big creep is wearing one of my ties today. i think i'm just going to have to walk away from it all. i don't know yet. i know it's annoying -- i'm always saying this and then i change

1037-DC-00000265

my mind.

i hpe you're doing ok. how was your rice and beer???? i'm sorry you had a sad saturday. what is your work like? i'm very curious to hear about it so let me know (especially to hear about all of the clothes you have had to buy)!!!

well, i'm a little too sad to continue right now. i love you and i miss you. monica

1037-DC-00000266

Davis, Catherine

From: CA Davis[redacted]
Sent: Wednesday, July 02, 1997 5:25 PM
To: 'mlewinsk@pagate.pa.osd.mil'
Subject: hi mon

I'm sorry about all the shit that seems to be going on around you. Marsha is obviously working from a place of pettiness and jealousy- her remarks to you are so unprofessional I can't stand it. she sounds like a catty teenager! Your idea about working in another city or country is intrigueing. Do you think it is viable and conceivable for you? Could it be another American city or do you really want to be international? I guess it depends alot on openings, availability and place. I mean you would not want to be in Bosnia or Saudi Arabia (would you?). Betty is being so nice to you now, it seems. Do you have sense of why her attitude has changed? She's probably sick of seeing this happen to you after all this time.
I'm worried about you, Monica. Again, I think your idea to leave the area or get out of gov't work is a good one. I think you are in the midst of a dangerous, psychologically, situation. I am at a loss as to make you feel better or help, if I could possibly do either. When I read your emails sometimes I cannot even belive some of the things you tell me. It all sounds so dramatic and painful for you. Is your trip to L.A. for holiday or work? Maybe, you will feel a little better getting away. I don't mean to sound so disjointed but I guess I feel a litle disjointed. I know it is your life and I would NEVER presume to tell you how to live it- as you would never tell me how to live mine- but I cannot help being very concerned.
As for me, I am busy with work and with private conversation groups. I made a friend last week from work. we met after a meeting at work and she asked me to have lunch with her- the first person to do this. So we ate and drank beer and talked. She and her husband have been here for 4 months. Her name is Mary and she is 26 and was a nurse in the US ans about to start a MA program when they moved here for his business, of course. I was very impressed with her 'sacrifice'. Anyway, she's nice and hopefully we will go out again- maybe for the 4th. It was nice to talk to a woman about the stresses of living here and being newly married here, too. Actually she and her husband were married this February- 2 weeks before they moved to Tokyo. Even worse than Chris and I! Well, I must be off to my last class of the day. Write back and let me know how things have progressed. take care and love, Cat

1037-DC-00000280

Davis, Catherine

From: CA Davis[redacted]
To: 'mlewinsk@pagate.pa.osd.mil'
Subject: hi Mon

I'm sorry about all the shit that seems to be going on around you. Marsha is obviously working from a place of pettiness and jealousy- her remarks to you are so unprofessional I can't stand it. she sounds like a catty teenager! Your idea about working in another city or country is intrigueing. Do you think it is viable and conceivable for you? Could it be another American city or do you really want to be international? I guess it depends alot on openings, availability and place. I mean you would not want to be in Bosnia or Saudi Arabia (would you?). Betty is being so nice to you now, it seems. Do you have sense of why her attitude has changed? She's probably sick of seeing this happen to you after all this time.
I'm worried about you, Monica. Again, I think your idea to leave the area or get out of gov't work is a good one. I think you are in the midst of a dangerous, psychologically, situation. I am at a loss as to make you feel better or help, if I could possibly do either. When I read your emails sometimes I cannot even belive some of the things you tell me. It all sounds so dramatic and painful for you. Is your trip to L.A. for holiday or work? Maybe, you will feel a little better getting away. I don't mean to sound so disjointed but I guess I feel a litle disjointed. I know it is your life and I would NEVER presume to tell you how to live it- as you would never tell me how to live mine- but I cannot help being very concerned.
As for me, I am busy with work and with private conversation groups. I made a friend last week from work. we met after a meeting at work and she asked me to have lunch with her- the first person to do this. So we ate and drank beer and talked. She and her husband have been here for 4 months. Her name is Mary and she is 26 and was a nurse in the US ans about to start a MA program when they moved here for his business, of course. I was very impressed with her 'sacrifice'. Anyway, she's nice and hopefully we will go out again- maybe for the 4th. It was nice to talk to a woman about the stresses of living here and being newly married here, too. Actually she and her husband were married this February- 2 weeks before they moved to Tokyo. Even worse than Chris and I! Well, I must be off to my last class of the day. Write back and let me know how things have progressed. take care and love, Cat

1037-DC-00000296

t in these last 2 years I have =lost two aunts, my Mom's older sisters, to can
cer. Anyway, I originally =thought I would go to school to be a Physician's A
ssisstant, P.A., a =growing field in healthcare and it is only a 2 year progra
m. I took =some prelim courses and was so thrilled and into it- like Microbio
logy =and medical microbiology, that I questioned why I shouldn't pusReceived:
from[redacted] by tky0.attnet.or.jp (8.7.5+Spi
n/3.4W4-PP-R5(05/15/97)) id WAA13450; Wed, 19 Nov 1997 22:22:44 +0900 (JST)Rec
eived: from[redacted] by galt.osd.
mil (8.7.1/8.7.1) with SMTP id IAA00768 for [redacted]>; Wed,
19 Nov 1997 08:15:33 -0500 (EST)Received: by[redacted] with Microsoft
Mailid[redacted] Wed, 19 Nov 97 08:20:52 PSTFrom: "Lewinsk
y, Monica, , OSD/PA"[redacted]To: CA Davis[redacted]
tnet.or.jp>Subject: RE: birthday aftermathDate: Wed, 19 Nov 97 08:12:00 PSTMes
sage-ID: [redacted]Encoding: 182 TEXTX-Mailer: Microsoft Mai
l V3.0X-UIDL: 809cb60fc0c9df52c4cf05811f2f2f72Oh, Catherine! You message was
just what i needed to start out this dreary day! I adore you, and think we'll
make wonderful older lady friends (here's to the ladies who lunch..) and youn
ger lady friends, too!! When you come back to the states I think we'll have t
o spend some concentrated time together. Imagine, talking in person and for F
REE!Your birthday sounded great (except of course for the Chris-getting-sick-p
art). i'm sorry you had to postpone your dinner. Your earrings sound lovely.
How was Japanese Disneyland? Were there any rides that made fun of American
s or was it Mickey Mouse based? I bet you looked beautiful in your red (VAHVO
OM!!) suit!The big creep does look quite trim these days. Oh, I haven't told
you my hysterical escapade from last week! Listen to this, it's practically u
nbelievable! The creep called me on Wednesday night and we talked for almost
an hour, but i had been bugging him that i wanted to see him and last week was
the only chance for awhile as he would be away for the next two weekends and
then i am gone for two weeks. So, on the phone he said he thought nancy (one
of the meanies) would be out for a few hours on Thurday and i could come see h
im them. I was to call Betty and figure out the details. Of course, i called
betty in the morning and then started the usual "I haven't had a chance to ta
lk to him, yet". Well, he ended up going golfing and I went ballistic. final
ly when he got back around 4:30 she talked to him and then he got mad she didn
't tell him -ya-da-ya-da. In the end, she snuck me in to the back office wher
e i waited for him while there were 20 people in there and Stephen, his[redacted]
e aide who doesn' like me. I ended up seeing him for two[redacted] minutes bec
ause he had one of his counterparts from another country waiting there for din
ner!! It was soo crazy.I will probably have to call his buddy who's supposed
to help me today. I was hoping he'd call me, but I'm getting nervous with the
holidays coming up and all. Oh Cat, I want to get out of here so bad. You h
ave no idea.I have been really sad about Andy lately, too. I keep having thes
e dreams about Kate, him and the kid. It's really yucky. What really hurts i
s that i cared so much about someone who just threw me away so quickly. I mis
s having someone to be with and enjoy me. Ohh, woe is me, woe is me!Why are y

yBoZSBzY

WlkLCAiQ29tZSBvdmVyIGFuZCBzaXQNCmRvd24gYmVzaWRlIG1lIGZvciBhIG1vbWVud
CwgTWFtYS4

gIEkgd2FudCB0byBhc2sgeW91IGEgcXVlc3Rpb24iLiAgTm8NCmtpZGRpbmcuICBXZSdyZS
BoYXZpb

mcgc3VjaCBmdW4gd2l0aCBoaW0uICBMYXN0IEZyaWRheSBJIHRvb2sgdGhlIGRheSBvZm
YgYW5kDQp

oZSBhbmQgSSB3ZW50IHRvIFBEWCB6b28gdy8gbXkgZnJpZW5kIEVyaW5uICh5b3UndmU
gbWV0IGhlc

iBzZXZlcmFsIHRpbWVzKQ0KYW5kIGhlciBib3lzLCBhZ2UgMi41ICYgMTAgbW9udGhzLi
AgV2hhdCB

hIGdyZWF0IHRpbWUhICBJIG5ldmVyIGluIG15IHdpbGRlc3QNCmRyZWFtcyB0aG91Z2h0I
HNoZSBhb

mQgSSB3b3VsZCBiZSBoYXZpbmcgZnVuIGNoYXNpbmcgdHdvIHRvZGRsZXJzIGFyb3Vu
ZCB0aGUNCnp

vbywgYnV0IGl0IHdhcyBncmVhdCENCg0KUXVpZXQgTWVtb3JpYWwgRGF5IHdlZWtlbm
QgcGxhbm5lZ

C4gIEEgQkJRIGZvciBteSBmb2xrcycgYW5uaXZlcnNhcnkgb24gU2F0Lg0KYW5kIGEgdmlza
XQgdy8

gb3VyIGZyaWVuZCBCYW5namkgb24gU3VuLiwgYW5kIHlhcmQgd29yay4gIEhvdydzIHRo
YXQgZm9yD

QpiZWluZyBsaWtlIHRoZSBDbGVhdmVycz8gIFRoZSBvbmx5IGRpZmZlcmVuY2UgaXMsI
G15IHBlYXJ

scyBhcmUgcmVhbCENCg0KR290dGEgcnVuLiAgVGFrZSBjYXJlICYga2VlcCBpbiB0b3Vja
CENCg0KT
G92ZSwgDQpEaWFuZQ0KDQoNCg==--TFS-with-MIME-and-DIME-- he and kate are trying t
o work this out and me being anywhere in the picture is not going to help. I was pretty upset, but it is really for the best. I'll probably send her note back to her with a small scribble that i never wanted to try to get her out of the picture so he could be with me. if i really wanted to be nasty i'd send the cards back to her, but i'm not THAT cruel. With the big creep, i told you i sent him a note right? well in it i asked to come see him on saturday. he

1037-DC-00000337

called on saturday and said betty couldn't come in but we'd do it sunday if s
he could come in. he just called cuz he didn't want me waiting by the phone.
i told him i appreciated that. he was sweet, but in a bad mood. i think he'
s kind of depressed right now. well, sunday he didn't call until 5 pm and the
n said he was trying to get a hold of her but he couldn't. he then called bac
k 10 minutes later and said he had just gotten word that she'd be out of pocke
t for two hours so i should go out fr a little while and he'd call at 7. he d
idn't call at seven so at 8 i paged betty and she said he said he didn;t want
her coming in late at night and we'd work it out for this week. he finally hu
rriedly called me at about 9:45 and said he was busy he just called to say qui
ckly we try and work it out for later. so all in all we had some very brief c
alls this weekend and i hope to see him soon. oh, but he did say on saturdaha
t indicated to me he really was working on getting me back there. well, my de
ar, i love you and miss you soo much. i hope all is well with you and chris.
i'm sure you'll lose whatever you gained. i finally started dieting and exer
cising again after i had gained 15 frickin pounds since December. HELLO!! i
love you . Monica --From: CA DavisTo: [redacted] he
y girl!Date: Monday, May 19, 1997 6:58AMyeah! i finally got my email set-up!!
so now you can write me =whenever you want and keep me posted on ALL your li
fe's excitements. =Hey, have you heard from Doug since the Great Gatsby Kissi
ng Incident? =Any more action from the freaks in Oregon? I still can't belie
ve the =tangle that's come about there. So good you're in DC and far away. I
=hope Andy, the schmucker, calls you soon..if he hasn't already. I'm =afraid
my letter won't be too long tonight because its getting late and =Chris and I
want to get up early to run before he goes to work. I am =getting soo fat an
d don't try to disbelieve me or scoff! Its true. =20I miss you so much Monica
and wish you could get a year position in the =embassy here and play with me.
.well not PLAY with me but..you know. =Please write back and vent all..also
plan your trip to Tokyo! love =you,
CatCVRTFZ20.DLLûûùCVWMFZ20.DLLCVWP5X20.DL

LCVWP6020.DLLCVWP6T20.DLLCVWPG120.DLLCVWPG220.DLLCV123Z20.DLL/2:>?9
:>?CVA12X20

.DLL;789:;CVCGMZ20.DLLCVDXFZ20.DLLCVEPSZ20.DLLCVEXCL20.DLL%&'&'CVHP
GL20.DLLCVL
PIC20.DLLCVMGXZ20.DLLCVPCXZ20.DLLCVPICT20.DLL

1744005 FXD 1083 84198/ 98304 -----A 27-May-1997 16:10:00 27-May-1997 16:09:58
27-May-1997

==========>>> 1 string found in FileSlack Cluster 1123 <<<==========

t in these last 2 years I have =lost two aunts, my Mom's older sisters, to can cer. Anyway, I originally =thought I would go to school to be a Physician's A ssisstant, P.A., a =growing field in healthcare and it is only a 2 year progra m. I took =some prelim courses and was so thrilled and into it- like Microbio logy =and medical microbiology, that I questioned why I shouldn't pusReceived: from [redacted] 8.7.5+Spi n/3.4W4-PP-R5(05/15/97)) id WAA13450; Wed, 19 Nov 1997 22:22:44 +0900 (JST)Rec eived: [redacted] by galt.osd. mil (8.7.1/8.7.1) with SMTP id IAA00768 for [redacted]; Wed, 19 Nov 1997 08:15:33 -0500 (EST)Received: by pagate.pa.osd.mil with Microsoft Mailid [redacted] Wed, 19 Nov 97 08:20:52 PSTFrom: "Lewinsk y, Monica, , OSD/PA" [redacted] To: CA Davis [redacted] t [redacted] >Subject: RE: birthday aftermathDate: Wed, 19 Nov 97 08:12:00 PSTMes sage-ID: [redacted] >Encoding: 182 TEXTX-Mailer: Microsoft Mai l V3.0X-UIDL: 809cb60fc0c9df52c4cf05811f2f2f72Oh, Catherine! You message was just what i needed to start out this dreary day! I adore you, and think we'll make wonderful older lady friends (here's to the ladies who lunch..) and youn ger lady friends, too!! When you come back to the states I think we'll have t o spend some concentrated time together. Imagine, talking in person and for F REE!Your birthday sounded great (except of course for the Chris-getting-sick-p art). i'm sorry you had to postpone your dinner. Your earrings sound lovely. How was Japanese Disneyland? Were there any rides that made fun of American s or was it Mickey Mouse based? I bet you looked beautiful in your red (VAHVO OM!!) suit!The big creep does look quite trim these days. Oh, I haven't told you my hysterical escapade from last week! Listen to this, it's practically u nbelievable! The creep called me on Wednesday night and we talked for almost an hour, but i had been bugging him that i wanted to see him and last week was the only chance for awhile as he would be away for the next two weekends and then i am gone for two weeks. So, on the phone he said he thought nancy (one of the meanies) would be out for a few hours on Thurday and i could come see h im them. I was to call Betty and figure out the details. Of course, i called betty in the morning and then started the usual "I haven't had a chance to ta lk to him, yet". Well, he ended up going golfing and I went ballistic. final ly when he got back around 4:30 she talked to him and then he got mad she didn 't tell him -ya-da-ya-da. In the end, she snuck me in to the back office wher e i waited for him while there were 20 people in there and Stephen, his [redacted] e aide who doesn' like me. I ended up seeing him for two [redacted] minutes bec ause he had one of his counterparts from another country waiting there for din ner!! It was soo crazy.I will probably have to call his buddy who's supposed to help me today. I was hoping he'd call me, but I'm getting nervous with the holidays coming up and all. Oh Cat, I want to get out of here so bad. You h ave no idea.I have been really sad about Andy lately, too. I keep having thes e dreams about Kate, him and the kid. It's really yucky. What really hurts i s that i cared so much about someone who just threw me away so quickly. I mis s having someone to be with and enjoy me. Ohh, woe is me, woe is me!Why are y

1037-DC-00000341

will be moving back to OR next summer- after our Bali trip! We have =
talked about staying longerand I worry about Chris going back to his =
office after only a year away, but I don't htink I can live in this =
environment for another year or half-year. Yes, I make good money, but =
it is mind-numbigly boring (my job). The other thing too, which is more =
important, is the nature of this city with its horrendous pollution (my =
hair is barely growing!), masses of people and no grass or trees. It is =
expensive and a pain to leave the city for a wkend....blah, blah, blah. =
For our year anniversary we are going out ot dinner. Period. I mean, =
if we lived in OR we would definately go to some romantic B&B or hotel =
out of Portland and maybe even fly and it would be cheaper than the =
trains here. I sound whiny but it is a wierd place and I think I may be =
done with it next summer. I think about driving and my house nad hiking =
inthe gorge and the coast and easy trips to N.California and friends and =
the slow life and a puppy....I guess its my small town island girl ness =
that wants me out of the big modern city.
NEW TOPIC: I am- are you sitting- a size 6 at the GAP!!!!!! They have =
seriously re-calibrated their sizes, baby, and its time to shopshopshop. =
I go in their and 10 are literally HANGING off meand 8s are well...lets =
just say drinking those shakes once a day for 10 years has really paid =
off! To be fair, I have not gained that much, but I am decidedly, with =
out a doubt, unquestionably a smack in the middle (and comfortable with =
it I might add) size f'n 8. I wonder if they changed the sizes somehow =
for Japan- to make those J ladies feel like they exist- no size 0s =
puhhhleeezzz!! Actually they probably love seeing me gather up the size =
Gigantic next to their size Cute and Litttle. Bitches. Just kidding, =
but for the first, or maybe second, time in my life I'm glad I'm not =
tall. I guess the first time was when I was growing up in Japan...oh, I =
mean Hawaii.
So, I am thrilled for you about this new job. I would beside myself tow =
ork in that group. Richardson looks like a nice man. What are some of =
your other options, in the private sector? Would all of them mean a =
move to NY? Try to tell me as much as you can. Oh, I miss you and I =
really am sad you will not be here soon...I understand though. I hope =
all works out. Very sweet about Australian guy. When will he be in DC, =
or the east coast, next? Wait, did you get together with him when you =
met him? Lots of questions to answer. Also remind me to tell you why =
the whole couples extravaganza is not really a fantasy, at least this =
one wasn't. I have to pop off to work. Write back as soon as you can. =
I love you and take care. Cat

From: Lewinsky, Monica, [redacted]
Sent: Wednesday, November 05, 1997 2:16 AM
To: CA Davis
Subject: RE: troubs?

oK. I have some bad news. I am off the next trip so i won't be coming =
to=20
Tokyo. I am probably sorrier than you are. the truth is it would have =
been=20
so difficult to spend time together and it probably would have benn more =

frustrating than anything.

The job thing on Friday went much better than expected. It was nice; =
the=20
big creep called thursday night and gave me a pep talk because i was so=20
afraid I'd sound like an idiot. Richardson is a great guy and i met two =

women who work for him...also very cool. Yesterday, Richardson called =
me at=20
work and told me they were going to offer me a position..they didn't =
know=20
what yet, and they wanted to talk with me further. The problem is, I =

1037-DC-00000553

Unknown

From: CA Davis
Sent: Tuesday, September 02, 1997 2:57 PM
To: 'Lewinsky, Monica, [redacted]
Subject: RE: Aloha!

Wow, your mom's flat sounds amazing! That is so wonderful for her- I hope she is really happy with this guy. If you moved to NY would you be able to live with her? Would you still work for the DOD? Probably not, yah? I cannot say I am surprised that this whole situation has taken its toll on you. I'm sure it has for a while now. If I may be so bold to state my unequivocal opinion: I think your 'situation' is a lose-lose situation with him. He cannot ever be totally your's Monica. Ever. And, as I have said before, you deserve a man that is all your's. ALL YOUR'S. And just because there may not be another man around right now does not mean you should put yourself through the ringer with this Man. You are worth much more than that, no matter his Position its the same old affair bullshit. Does your mom support you moving to NY? If so, I think that would be fantastic! I would come visit you once a year and you could visit me once a year (of course, after I move back to the US) and we'd see eachother a lot!
Anyway, was your holiday relaxing? Four Australian businessmen?....I hope they were nicer and more polite than most Australians I meet. Today, Sept. 3rd, is Chris' 31st birthday. I am going to take him out to dinner tonight and, of course, have lots of presents for him to open. Unfortunately, since we don't have an oveñ (!), I can't bake a little cake. Maybe that is not so unfortunate! Well, I must be off. I'll hear from you soon, take care- I really mean it, too- I love you, Catherine

---

From: Lewinsky, Monica, [redacted]
Sent: Tuesday, September 02, 1997 1:30 PM
To: CA Davis
Subject: RE: Aloha!

Welcome Home! I, too, was sorry we didn't get a chance to talk, but I'm glad you had a good holiday. How is Jeannie doing? Is she still with what's-his-name? I was also happy to read that Nick seems to be doing better. On my little vacation I went to Princeton, NJ (where I met and had dinner with 4 Australian businessmen -- it was much fun!!!!), the Spa in CT., and to Scarsdale, NY to see a friend of mine and my mom's. I did not hook up with that Jesse guy at the spa again. It was sort of my choice and a little lack of him not aggressively pursuing me. So here is big news....my mom has gotten an apartment in NY for a year on 5th and 61st!!!!!!!!!! She is pretty serious with this guy and spends so much time up there already. It is funny because her big dream in life has been to live in NY and now he has gotten her an apartment there!!!! It's exciting!

My work sit: I met with the woman who is the White House liaison here and she described in detail, what needs to happen for me to be deatiled there. It is a much more difficult process than i imagined. Essentially, I would remain an employee of Public Affairs and they "loan" me to the WH. PA doesn't get more money allotted or an extra position to fill my slot. Normally they would only detail somebody in a slot where there are a few people who have similar tasks , i.e. a media desk officer -- with me, there is only one confidential assistant in PA. We'll have to see what happens but I really don't want to work for marsha anymore. I don't trust her at all. I'm moving toward giving it all up. Maybe I'll move to NY. As I told you on the phone, I felt awful about my last visit with him. I don't doubt that he has real feelings for me, but how strong they are is another question. He hasn't taken care of me. we'll see what happens. I'm in an ok place right now. i am just starting to physically and mentally REALLY feel the and see the effects of all of this stress. It is getting to be too much for me. Don't worry though, I'll be fine. 1037-DC-00000583

I miss you and am sad i didn't get to talk to you more when you were here (although i probably would have been very boring!)

Big hugs and sloppy kisses,

IBM FORMAT
[redacted]
11/3/97-12/31/97
1051-DC-00000003

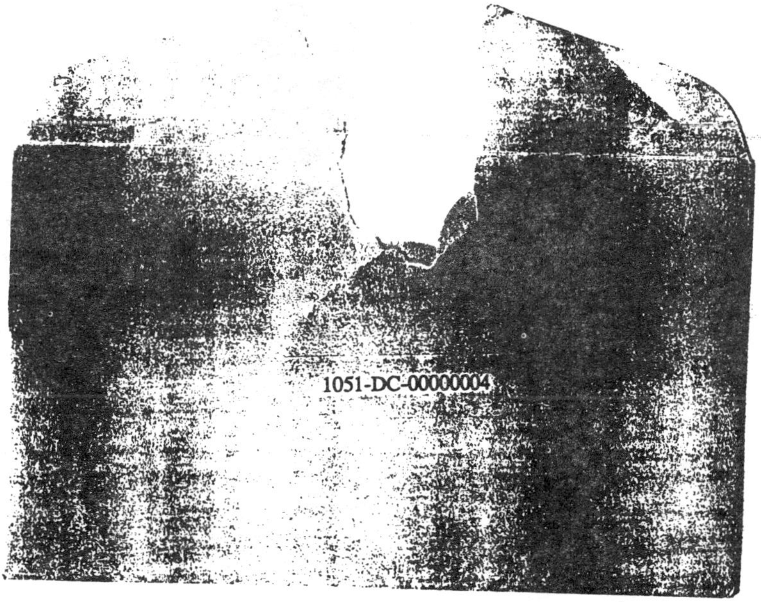
1051-DC-00000004

[illegible] 09, 1998 11:31 Page 1

OSPLUS 1500

Renaissance Vinoy Resort
Site: 0
Extension Detail Report

From: 01/13/98 00:00 To: 01/14/98 23:59

1064-DC-00000008

Extension : 7371
Name : ROOM 371
Title :
Location :

DEPARTMENT: 1 Guest Room

Date	Time	Duration	Facil.	Rout/Line	Charge	Digits Dialed	City	St	Type	Bill Class
01/13	17:10	0:05:17	T-1	13/ 26	7.01	[redacted]	WASHINGTONDC		LD	GUEST
[illegible]	[illegible]	0:10:52	T-1	13/ 40	[illegible].14	[redacted]	WASHINGTONDC		LD	GUEST
[illegible]	[illegible]	0:06:05	T-1	13/ 27	7.44	[redacted]	WASHINGTONDC		LD	GUEST
[illegible]	[illegible]	0:00:53	LOCALT1	11/ 2	0.85	[redacted]	STPETERSBGFL		LOC	GUEST
[illegible]	20:43	0:01:07	LOCALT1	11/ 7	0.85	[redacted]	STPETERSBGFL		LOC	GUEST
[illegible]	20:48	0:12:34	LOCALT1	11/ 6	0.85	[redacted]	STPETERSBGFL		LOC	GUEST
[illegible]	[illegible]	0:00:45	LOCALT1	11/ 2	0.85	[redacted]	CLEARWATERFL		LOC	GUEST
[illegible]	[illegible]	0:03:48	T-1	13/ 24	6.11	[redacted]	WASHINGTONDC		LD	GUEST
[illegible]	[illegible]	0:01:38	T-1	13/ 1	5.28	[redacted]	ARLINGTON	VA	LD	GUEST
[illegible]	[illegible]	0:01:47	T-1	13/ 19	5.28	[redacted]	WASHINGTONDC		LD	GUEST
[illegible]	[illegible]	0:00:58	T-1	13/ 44	0.85	[redacted]	Information		INF/SC	GUEST
[illegible]	[illegible]	0:04:09	T-1	13/ 32	[illegible].58	[redacted]	WASHINGTONDC		LD	GUEST
[illegible]	[illegible]	0:05:58	T-1	13/ 33	7.01	[redacted]	WASHINGTONDC		LD	GUEST
[illegible]	[illegible]:14	0:02:08	T-1	13/ 45	5.73	[redacted]	ATLANTA	GA	LD	GUEST
[illegible]	07:29	0:01:25	T-1	13/ 38	5.30	[redacted]	WASHINGTONDC		LD	GUEST
[illegible]	07:44	0:01:16	T-1	13/ 25	0.00	[redacted]	WASHINGTONDC		LD /OA	GUEST
[illegible]	[illegible]	0:02:47	T-1	13/ 8	5.73	[redacted]	WASHINGTONDC		LD	GUEST
[illegible]	[illegible]	0:02:53	T-1	13/ 21	5.73	[redacted]	NEW YORK	NY	LD	GUEST

[illegible]:06:36 $ 8[illegible].59

Fixed Cost $ 0.00

Mr. Vernon E. Jordan Jr.	Arrival 01/14/98
Union Carbide	Departure 01/15/98
1333 New Hampshire Ave NW #400	Room 0907
Washington, DC 20036	Page 1
INVOICE 53925	

The St. Regis New York, 01/15/98 08:36 14

Date	Description	Amount
01/14	Room Service CHECK # 1364	38.25
01/14	Room Service CHECK # 1492	49.00
01/14	Long Distance [redacted]	5.31
01/14	Long Distance [redacted]	6.11
01/14	Long Distance [redacted]	9.33
01/14	Long Distance [redacted]	5.31
01/14	Long Distance [redacted]	6.91
01/14	Laundry/Valet	14.00
01/14	Laundry/Valet	29.00
01/14	Room Charge	355.00
/14	*Rooms Tax State 8.25%	29.29
01/14	*Rooms Tax City 5%	17.75
01/14	*Rooms Occupancy Tax	4.00
01/15	Room Service CHECK # 1631	43.75
01/15	Long Distance [redacted]	11.72
01/15	Long Distance [redacted]	5.31
01/15	Long Distance [redacted]	5.31
01/15	Long Distance [redacted]	5.31
01/15	Long Distance [redacted]	5.31
01/15	Long Distance [redacted]	6.91
01/15	Long Distance [redacted]	10.92
01/15	Long Distance [redacted]	5.31
01/15	Long Distance [redacted]	25.39
01/15	American Express	-694.50
	-[redacted] 11/98	
	$	0.00

1065-DC-00000006

Guest Signature:_______________________________

I agree that my liability for this bill is not waived and agree to be held personally liable in the event that the

Mr. Vernon E. Jordan Jr.	Arrival 01/20/98
Union Carbide	Departure 01/21/98
1333 New Hampshire Ave NW #400	Room 0907
Washington, DC 20036	Page 1
INVOICE 55015	

The St. Regis New York, 01/21/98 07:54 22

Date	Description	Amount
01/20	Room Service CHECK # 5039	56.00
01/20	Long Distance [redacted]	6.11
01/20	Long Distance [redacted]	10.92
01/20	Long Distance [redacted]	14.14
01/20	Long Distance [redacted]	5.31
01/20	Long Distance [redacted]	6.11
01/20	Long Distance [redacted]	5.31
01/20	Long Distance [redacted]	10.62
01/20	Long Distance [redacted]	5.31
01/20	Long Distance [redacted]	5.31
01/20	Long Distance [redacted]	14.64
01/20	Long Distance [redacted]	7.71
01/20	Room Charge	355.00
01/20	*Rooms Tax State 8.25%	29.29
01/20	*Rooms Tax City 5%	17.75
01/20	*Rooms Occupancy Tax	4.00
01/21	Long Distance [redacted]	13.34
01/21	Long Distance [redacted]	6.91
01/21	Long Distance [redacted]	5.31
01/21	Long Distance [redacted]	6.11
01/21	Long Distance [redacted]	5.31
01/21	Long Distance [redacted]	5.31
01/21	American Express	-595.82
	-[redacted] 11/98	
	$	0.00

1065-DC-00000008

Guest Signature:________________________________

I agree that my liability for this bill is not waived and agree to be held personally liable in the event that the indicated person, association or company fails to pay for any part or the full amount of these charges. This folio

[redacted]		LEWINSKY, MONICA									
TRF BAL		[redacted]									
		WASHINGTON, DC 20037									
		BALANCE FORWARD									
			CREDIT MESSAGE						BAD DEBT	.00	
			CREDIT MES CODE/DATE						B/D BAL	.00	
			REMINDER CODE/DATE						COLL AGY ID		
			BAD DEBT CODE/DATE						PURGE DATE		
									.00		
02/04/97	186535	PAYMENT CASH AD 186535							41.00-	PCSH	
02/09/97		AMOUNT DUE							41.00-*		
02/14	186535	HANDSOME WITH LOVE S LIGH	D	9	1	9	3.000	27.00	27.00	CHOL	
02/14/97	420	1599 BY MS. L									
02/14	186535	HANDSOME WITH LOVE S LIGH	D	3	1	3					
02/14/97	420	1599 BY MS. L									
02/16/97		AMOUNT DUE							14.00	HOLF	
									.00 *		

1078-DC-00000002

OCT 17 1996

October 16, 1996

Dear Evelyn,

Thanks for the meeting yesterday. I wanted to follow up on a few points as you put your memo together.

o I've enclosed our staff division of responsibilities that we use throughout the year. I don't distribute it because I want White House and agency staff to funnel their issues and requests through our West Wing operation. That way I can keep track, exercise quality control, and make the judgements about the use of our staff resources.

o I've also enclosed a brief memo on our correspondence operation. It was in bad shape when I came in. We got rid of Monica and Jossie not only because of "extracurricular activities" but because they couldn't do the job. We also had problems with NSC and White House correspondence that have been corrected. I believe the operation is in quite good shape now.

Thank you for being so good to me this year. I greatly appreciate your help and counsel. I will take the steps you suggested and then follow up with both you and Leon.

Jo

file personnel depts

THE WHITE HOUSE
WASHINGTON

PRESIDENTIAL CALL LOG

OCTOBER 11th, 19 97

	TIME PLACED	DISC	NAME	ACTION
OUT INC	10:57 AM	11:06	MR. VERNON E. JORDAN, JR. ALEXANDRIA, VA. [redacted]	TLKD-OK 10:57 A.M.

REDACTED

1178-DC-00000005

0 004979

[illegible]
WASHINGTON

PRESIDENTIAL CALL LOG

NOVEMBER 5th, 19 97

	TIME PLACED	DISC	NAME	ACTION

REDACTED

1178-DC-00000011

OUT / INC	8:45 AM	8:55	MR. VERNON E. JORDAN, JR. OFC: WASHINGTON, D.C. [redacted]	TLKD-OK 8:50 A.M.

0 004985

THE WHITE HOUSE
WASHINGTON

PRESIDENTIAL CALL LOG

DECEMBER 19th, 19 97

TIME PLACED	DISC	NAME	ACTION

1178-DC-00000013

REDACTED

OUT / INC		AM / PM	NAME	ACTION
INC	3:51	PM	MR. VERNON E. JORDAN, JR. OFC: WASHINGTON, D.C. [redacted]	MR. VERNON JORDAN TLKD WITH MS. DEBRA SCHIFF 3:51 P.M.

L0 004987

THE WHITE HOUSE

WASHINGTON

PRESIDENTIAL CALL LOG

DECEMBER 19th, 19 97

	TIME		NAME	ACTION
	PLACED	DISC		
OUT XX INC	AM 4:57 PM	5:08	MR. VERNON E. JORDAN, JR. OFC: WASHINGTON, D.C. [redacted]	TLKD-OK 5:01 P.M.
OUT	AM			

1178-DC-00000014

REDACTED

0 004988

THE WHITE HOUSE
WASHINGTON

PRESIDENTIAL CALL LOG

DECEMBER 30, 19 97

	TIME PLACED	DISC	NAME	ACTION

REDACTED

	TIME PLACED	DISC	NAME	ACTION
OUT	9:26 AM	9:51	MR. VERNON E. JORDAN, JR. RES: WASHINGTON, D.C. [redacted]	TLKD-OK 9:27 A.M.

THE WHITE HOUSE
WASHINGTON

PRESIDENTIAL CALL LOG

JANUARY 6, 19 98

TIME PLACED		TIME DISC	NAME	ACTION
OUT	AM XX 4:19 PM	4:32	MR. VERNON E. JORDAN, JR. OFC: WASHINGTON, D.C. [redacted]	TLKD-OK 4:19 P.M.

REDACTED

1178-DC-00000016

0 004990

Date	Time	Location	Sign	CC	D
2/19/96	1059	Oval Office	17	BZ	2
2/19/96	1401	2nd Floor Residence	17	KDO	2/

1222-DC-00000102

DATE	TIME	LOCATION	SIG	INI
03/29/96	1926	2ND FLOOR RESIDENCE	26	TAS
03/29/96	2053	FAMILY THEATER	43	TAS
3/29/96	2134	Family Theater	26	CN

1222-DC-00000112

3-31-96	2316	Second Floor	39	DAA
3/31/96	1055	South Grounds	32	RBH
3/31/96	1057	Depart South Grounds (Indiana)	38	RBH
3/31/96	1221	South Grounds	32	[illegible]

DATE	TIME	LOCATION	SIG	INI
3/31/96	1223	2ND FLOOR RESIDENCE	32	[illegible]
3/31/96	1500	OVAL OFFICE	32	[illegible]
3/31/96	1746	2nd Floor Residence	32	[illegible]

1222-DC-00000113

WEDNESDAY NOVEMBER 15, 1995

WHEN THIS SHIFT RELIEVED THE SHIFT THE PRESIDENT WAS IN THE OVAL OFFICE.

PROTECTEE MOVEMENTS:

1450 HRS - THE PRESIDENT MOVED TO ASS'T COS BOWLES OFFICE
1455 HRS - THE PRESIDENT MOVED TO THE COS OFFICE
1500 HRS - THE PRESIDENT MOVED TO THE OVAL OFFICE
1505 HRS - THE PRESIDENT MOVED TO THE SECOND FLOOR RESIDENCE
1530 HRS - THE PRESIDENT MOVED TO THE OVAL OFFICE
1642 HRS - THE PRESIDENT MOVED TO THE ROOSEVELT ROOM
1701 HRS - THE PRESIDENT MOVED TO THE OVAL OFFICE
1737 HRS - THE PRESIDENT MOVED TO THE COS OFFICE
1753 HRS - THE PRESIDENT MOVED TO THE OVAL OFFICE

WEDNESDAY
NOVEMBER 15, 1995

POTUS MADE THE FOLLOWING MOVEMENTS DURING THIS SHIFT:

1246 HRS: THE PRESIDENT MOVED TO THE OVAL OFFICE.

WHEN THIS SHIFT WAS RELIEVED BY THE SHIFT, THE PRESIDENT WAS IN THE OVAL OFFICE.

SUNDAY
DECEMBER 31, 1995

WHEN THIS SHIFT RELIEVED THE SHIFT, THE PRESIDENT WAS IN THE RESIDENCE.

POTUS MOVEMENTS:

0805 - POTUS DEPARTED SOUTH GROUNDS.
0807 - POTUS ARRIVE ST. JOHNS EPISCOPAL CHURCH 1525 H STREET WDC.
0838 - POTUS DEPART ST. JOHNS.
0840 - POTUS ARRIVE SOUTH GROUNDS AND MOVE TO OVAL OFFICE.
0948 - POTUS MOVE TO THE CABINET ROOM.
1211 - POTUS RETURN TO THE OVAL OFFICE.
1315 - POTUS MOVE FROM THE OVAL TO THE 2ND FLOOR RESIDENCE.
1325 - POTUS DEPART FROM THE SOUTH LAWN VIA MARINE ONE ENROUTE ANDREWS AIR FORCE BASE.
1335 - POTUS ARRIVE ANDREWS AIR FORCE BASE.
1351 - POTUS DEPART ANDREWS ENROUTE HILTON HEAD.

WHEN THIS SHIFT WAS RELIEVED BY THE SHIFT, THE PRESIDENT WAS DEPARTING VIA MARINE ONE ENROUTE ANDREWS AIR FORCE BASE.

SUNDAY, JANUARY 7, 1996

PROTECTEE MOVEMENTS

1413 HRS - THE PRESIDENT MOVED TO THE OVAL OFFICE
1749 HRS - THE PRESIDENT MOVED TO THE SECOND FLOOR RESIDENCE
1936 HRS - THE PRESIDENT MOVED TO THE RED ROOM

ACTIVITY REPORT
JANUARY 21, 1996
SUNDAY

WHEN THIS SHIFT RELIEVED THE SHIFT, THE PRESIDENT, MRS CLINTON AND CHELSE WERE IN THE SECOND FLOOR RESIDENCE.

<u>POTUS MOVEMENTS:</u>

1533 HRS - POTUS DEPARTED SECOND FLOOR RESIDENCE
1534 HRS - POTUS ARRIVED OVAL OFFICE
1940 HRS - POTUS DEPARTED OVAL OFFICE

SUNDAY
FEBRUARY 4, 1996

POTUS MOVEMENTS:

1536 HRS - POTUS MOVED TO THE OVAL OFFICE
1905 HRS - POTUS MOVED TO THE SECOND FLOOR RESIDENCE

MONDAY
FEBRUARY 19, 1996

1100 - POTUS MOVED TO THE OVAL OFFICE.

WHEN THIS SHIFT WAS RELIEVED BY THE SHIFT, THE PRESIDENT WAS IN THE OVAL OFFICE.

ACTIVITY REPORT
MARCH 31, 1996
SUNDAY

WHEN THIS SHIFT RELIEVED THE SHIFT THE PRESIDENT WAS IN THE SECOND FLOOR RESIDENCE.

POTUS MOVEMENTS:
1057 HRS - POTUS DEPARTED RESIDENCE
1105 HRS - POTUS ARRIVED FOUNDRY METHODIST CHURCH.
1217 HRS - POTUS DEPARTED CHURCH.
1222 HRS - POTUS ARRIVED SOUTH GROUNDS.
1223 HRS - POTUS DEPARTED SOUTH GROUNDS.
1224 HRS - POTUS ARRIVED SECOND FLOOR RESIDENCE.

WHEN THIS SHIFT WAS RELIEVED BY THE SHIFT, THE PRESIDENT WAS ON THE SECOND FLOOR OF THE RESIDENCE.

SUNDAY
MARCH 31, 1996

WHEN THIS SHIFT RELIEVED THE SHIFT. POTUS WAS ON THE 2ND FLOOR OF THE RESIDENCE.

POTUS MOVEMENTS:

1459 HRS - POTUS DEP 2ND FLOOR RESIDENCE TO OVAL OFFICE
1501 HRS - POTUS ARR OVAL OFFICE
1746 HRS - POTUS DEP OVAL OFFICE TO 2ND FLOOR RESIDENCE

SUNDAY
APRIL 7, 1996

WHEN THIS SHIFT RELIEVED THE SHIFT, THE PRESIDENT, ARRIVED AT THE NORTH PORTICO.

POTUS MOVEMENTS:

404 HRS - POTUS, FLOTUS, CHELSEA ARRIVED AT THE NORTH PORTICO
406 HRS - FIRST FAMILY MOVED TO THE SECOND FLOOR, RESIDENCE
420 HRS - POTUS MOVED TO OVAL OFFICE
421 HRS - POTUS ARRIVED OVAL OFFICE
948 HRS - POTUS DEPARTED FOR THE RESIDENCE

FRIDAY
FEBRUARY 28, 1997

POTUS MOVEMENTS:

1642 HOURS - POTUS MOVED TO THE SOUTH GROUNDS PUTTING GREEN.
1728 HOURS - POTUS MOVED TO OVAL OFFICE/STUDY.
1829 HOURS - POTUS MOVED TO THE ROOSEVELT ROOM.
1836 HOURS - POTUS MOVED TO OVAL OFFICE.
1924 HOURS - POTUS MOVED TO THE SECOND FLOOR RESIDENCE.
1954 HOURS - POTUS MOVED TO SOUTH GROUNDS.
1956 HOURS - POTUS DEPARTED SOUTH GROUNDS.
2010 HOURS - POTUS ARRIVED 3318 O STREET, NW, WDC.

SATURDAY
MAY 24, 1997

PROTECTEE MOVEMENTS

1159 HRS. - POTUS MOVED TO THE OVAL OFFICE.
1347 HRS. - POTUS MOVED TO THE POOL.
1350 HRS. - POTUS MOVED TO THE OVAL STUDY.

WHEN THIS SHIFT WAS RELIEVED BY THE SHIFT, THE PRESIDENT WAS IN THE OVAL STUDY.

MONDAY
JULY 14, 1997

1618 HRS - THE PRESIDENT ARRIVED ARMY NAVY GOLF COURSE.
2008 HRS - THE PRESIDENT DEPARTED ARMY NAVY VIA M/C.
2022 HRS - THE PRESIDENT ARRIVED WHITE HOUSE THROUGH B-11.
2025 HRS - THE PRESIDENT MOVED TO THE SECOND FLOOR RESIDENCE.
2129 HRS - THE PRESIDENT MOVED TO THE OVAL OFFICE.
2141 HRS - THE PRESIDENT MOVED TO APPOINTMENT SEC. OFFICE.

WHEN THIS SHIFT WAS RELIEVED BY THE SHIFT, THE PRESIDENT WAS IN THE APPOINTMENT SECRETARY'S OFFICE.

THURSDAY JULY 24, 1997

PROTECTEE MOVEMENTS

1658 HRS POTUS MOVED TO THE OVAL OFFICE.
1814 HRS POTUS MOVED TO THE OVAL STUDY.
1849 HRS POTUS MOVED TO THE APPOINTMENT SECRETARY'S OFFICE
1851 HRS POTUS MOVED TO THE OVAL OFFICE.
1903 HRS POTUS MOVED TO THE SECOND FLOOR RESIDENCE.

December 31, 1995 (Sunday)
0700 to 1400 hours

Sergeant Deardorff, J. David
E-4 Ludtke, William
E-10 Snyder, Leroy (0700 to 0830 hours)/Seubert, George Sr.(0830 to 1400 hours)
E-6 Verna, Sandra
E-6A Householder, Larry
WW/Rel Webster, William

January 2, 1996 (Tuesday)
1700 to 2100 hours

Sergeant Vucci, William
E-4 Ludtke, William
E-10 Hill, Stewart
E-6 Byrne, Gary
E-6A Ordakowski, Daniel
E-1A Hemsley, Oliver (1700 to 2030 hours)
WW/Rel Bohrer, Marshall

January 6, 1996 (Saturday)
1200 to 1600 hours

Sergeant Angerome, Anthony
E-4 Ludtke, William
E-10 Potak, Joseph
E-6 Fox, Lewis
E-6A Byrne, Gary
WW/Rel Bohrer, Marshall

Sergeant Richardson, Michael
E-4 Green, Reginald
E-10 Hill, Stewart
E-6 Hubbard, Timothy
E-6A Nichols, Garry
WW/Rel Bohrer, Marshall

January 7, 1996 (Sunday)
1700 to 1800 hours

Sergeant Deardorff, J. David
E-4 Ludtke, William
E-10 Bohrer, Marshall
E-6 Fox, Lewis
E-6A Nichols, Garry
WW/Rel Holloman, Joseph

February 19, 1996 (Monday)
1200 to 1300 hours

Sergeant Seymour, Lewis
E-4 Ludtke, William
E-10 Fox, Lewis
E-6 Dana, Richard
E-6A Appleyard, Russell
WW/Rel Bohrer, Marshall

February 21, 1996 (Wednesday)
1600 to 2200 hours

Sergeant Deardorff, J. David
E-4 Potak, Joseph
E-10 Thompson, Robin
E-6 Verna, Sandra
E-6A Gerena, John
E-1A King, John
WW/Rel Webster, William

February 28, 1996 (Wednesday)
0823 to 2300 hours

Sergeant Deardorff, J. David

E-4 Potak, Joseph
E-10 Thompson, Robin

E-6 Verna, Sandra
E-6A Gerena, John
WW/Rel Webster, William

Sergeant Vucci, William

E-4 Ludtke, William
E-10 Snyder, Leroy

E-6 Hubbard, Timothy
E-6A Ordakowski, Daniel
E-1A Ruel, Richard
WW/Rel Bohrer, Marshall

Sergeant Firestone, Karmen
E-6 Shea, James
E-1A Tozier, Richard

8:15 The President to the Oval Office

8:50 Guests arrive East Room for Labor/HHS Appropriations Bill Signing (139 Guests)
10:10 The President to the Blue Room to greet special guests
10:15 The President to the East Room for address to guests and bill signing

10:50 The President to the Second Floor
11:50 The President departs the South Grounds, out locally

4:00 The President returns, to the Second Floor
4:20 Lloyd Cameron, tailor, to the Second Floor, down 5:10
5:00 Congressional guests arrive North Portico for reception
5:20 The President to the SDR to greet guests (50)
6:30 The President to the Oval Office
6:40 Dinner for Hugh Rodham
6:45 Reception guests depart State Floor
7:00 The President to the Ground Floor
7:00 Sandy Berger and Mac McLarty to the Second Floor
7:05 President Zedillo greeted by The President at South Portico, to the Second Floor for dinner (6)
7:10 Erskine Bowles to the Second Floor, down 7:15
8:45 The Presidents to the Dpl. Room for Pres. Zedillo's departure
9:10 The President departs, out locally
1:25 AM The President returns, to the Second Floor
1:45 AM Retired

Houseguests:

REDACTED

PRESIDENTIAL MOVEMENTS

LOCATION: Washington, D.C.
Arlington, Virginia
Washington, D.C.
Potomac, Maryland

DATE: 13 November 1997

TIME	MOVEMENTS	
0814	Oval Office	
0822	Cabinet Room	
0940	Oval Office	
0948	Cabinet Room	
1004	Oval Office	
1012	State Floor	
1048	Residence	
1137	South Grounds	
1148	Depart South Grounds via Motorcade	(LOW KEY)
1203	Arrive Army Navy Golf Course, Arlington, Virginia	(LOW KEY)
1542	Depart Army Navy Golf Course via Motorcade	(LOW KEY)
1559	Arrive South Grounds	(LOW KEY)
1600	Residence	
1723	State Floor	
1834	Oval Office	
1902	South Grounds	
[illegible]	Residence	
2049	South Grounds	
2050	Diplomatic Reception Room	
2052	Residence	
2113	South Grounds	
2114	Depart South Grounds via Motorcade	(LOW KEY)
2154	Arrive King Hussein's Residence, Potomac, Maryland	(LOW KEY)

1234-DC-00000050

HB 003155

U. S. Secret Service
Epass Access Control Report

Date of report
07/09/98

Search Criteria: HERNREICH, NANCY

Search Dates: 01/01/97 to 12/31/97

Date	Time	Name	Badge	Type	Post	Status
08/22/97	15:52:17	HERNREICH, NANCY V	34BABD	P	D2	BAD PIN
08/22/97	15:52:27	HERNREICH, NANCY V	34BABD	P	D2	ENTERING
09/08/97	12:37:29	HERNREICH, NANCY V	34BABD	P	D2	EXITING
09/08/97	12:51:55	HERNREICH, NANCY V	34BABD	P	D2	ENTERING
09/11/97	15:55:03	HERNREICH, NANCY V	34BABD	P	D3	EXITING
09/11/97	16:18:46	HERNREICH, NANCY V	34BABD	P	D2	ENTERING
09/12/97	06:48:13	HERNREICH, NANCY V	34BABD	P	D3	ENTERING
09/16/97	12:07:33	HERNREICH, NANCY V	34BABD	P	D2	EXITING
09/16/97	12:41:55	HERNREICH, NANCY V	34BABD	P	D2	ENTERING
09/17/97	06:46:59	HERNREICH, NANCY V	34BABD	P	D3	ENTERING
09/19/97	06:45:10	HERNREICH, NANCY V	34BABD	P	D3	ENTERING
09/19/97	13:26:46	HERNREICH, NANCY V	34BABD	P	D2	EXITING
09/19/97	13:35:57	HERNREICH, NANCY V	34BABD	P	D2	ENTERING
09/23/97	06:53:03	HERNREICH, NANCY V	34BABD	P	D3	ENTERING
09/24/97	06:50:06	HERNREICH, NANCY V	34BABD	P	D3	ENTERING
09/24/97	13:31:40	HERNREICH, NANCY V	34BABD	P	D3	EXITING
09/30/97	06:50:46	HERNREICH, NANCY V	34BABD	P	D3	ENTERING
10/02/97	06:41:29	HERNREICH, NANCY V	34BABD	P	D3	ENTERING
10/03/97	13:26:26	HERNREICH, NANCY V	34BABD	P	D2	EXITING
10/03/97	13:36:04	HERNREICH, NANCY V	34BABD	P	D2	ENTERING
10/08/97	12:52:38	HERNREICH, NANCY V	34BABD	P	D3	EXITING
10/08/97	13:04:39	HERNREICH, NANCY V	34BABD	P	D2	ENTERING
10/19/97	15:29:00	HERNREICH, NANCY V	34BABD	P	A4	ENTERING
10/28/97	12:16:22	HERNREICH, NANCY V	34BABD	P	D2	EXITING
10/28/97	12:26:14	HERNREICH, NANCY V	34BABD	P	D2	ENTERING
10/28/97	19:11:46	HERNREICH, NANCY V	34BABD	P	D2	EXITING
10/30/97	06:39:55	HERNREICH, NANCY V	34BABD	P	D3	ENTERING
11/06/97	13:49:40	HERNREICH, NANCY V	34BABD	P	D2	EXITING
11/06/97	14:02:10	HERNREICH, NANCY V	34BABD	P	D2	ENTERING
11/13/97	10:11:22	HERNREICH, NANCY V	34BABD	P	B4	ENTERING
11/13/97	12:12:51	HERNREICH, NANCY V	34BABD	P	A1	EXITING
11/17/97	10:46:50	HERNREICH, NANCY V	34BABD	P	D2	EXITING
11/17/97	12:44:36	HERNREICH, NANCY V	34BABD	P	D2	ENTERING
11/25/97	15:07:16	HERNREICH, NANCY V	34BABD	P	A1	EXITING
11/25/97	15:46:00	HERNREICH, NANCY V	34BABD	P	A1	ENTERING
12/03/97	13:34:17	HERNREICH, NANCY V	34BABD	P	D2	EXITING
12/03/97	13:47:32	HERNREICH, NANCY V	34BABD	P	A4	ENTERING
12/09/97	18:49:25	HERNREICH, NANCY V	34BABD	P	D4	EXITING
12/11/97	11:21:15	HERNREICH, NANCY V	34BABD	P	A1	EXITING
12/11/97	11:49:18	HERNREICH, NANCY V	34BABD	P	A1	ENTERING
12/27/97	13:00:31	HERNREICH, NANCY V	34BABD	P	D2	ENTERING
12/27/97	13:08:54	HERNREICH, NANCY V	34BABD	P	D2	EXITING
12/27/97	13:30:07	HERNREICH, NANCY V	34BABD	P	B4	ENTERING
12/30/97	12:21:25	HERNREICH, NANCY V	34BABD	P	D2	ENTERING
12/31/97	09:20:50	HERNREICH, NANCY V	34BABD	P	D2	EXITING
12/31/97	09:34:52	HERNREICH, NANCY V	34BABD	P	D2	ENTERING
12/31/97	13:48:23	HERNREICH, NANCY V	34BABD	P	D2	ENTERING

S 018052

THE WHITE HOUSE
WASHINGTON

TELEPHONE MEMORANDUM

PRESIDENT CLINTON APRIL 7th, 1996

	TIME PLACED	DISC.	NAME	ACTION
OUT / INC	AM / PM			
OUT / INC	AM / PM			
OUT / INC	AM / PM			
OUT / INC	AM / PM			
OUT / INC	AM / 5:10 PM	5:20	MR. RICHARD MORRIS PARIS, FRANCE [redacted]	TLKD-OK 5:11 P.M.
OUT / INC	AM / PM			
OUT / INC	AM / PM			
OUT / INC	AM / PM			
OUT / INC	AM / PM			REDACTED
OUT / INC	AM / PM			
OUT / INC	AM / 7:38 PM			

GPO : 1983 O - 405-660 : QL 2

resigned Friday as inspector general after facing accusations that she had commited the kinds of transgressions her office was supposed to be rooting out. Last year, GAO concluded that Ms. Lau had broken the law by steering a $90,776 contract for a management study of the inspector general's office to a friend who had recommended her for her job.

- Yasir Arafat, the leader of the Palestinian Liberation Organization had intended to pay an official visit to the Holocaust museum in the capital next week but was told by museum officials that he could not attend.

  The Museum officials' rejection of an official visit emerged today as an awkward and embarrassing prelude to Mr. Arafat's visit to Washington next week to meet President Clinton.

- The international Monetary Fund got virtually everything it wanted from President Suharto. yet today, one day after he reluctantly agreed to a major restructuring of Indonesia's economy, its weakened currency resumed sliding.

  The international marketplace, which has become the de facto arbiter of Indonesia's economic policies, still seemed dissatisfied. The risks and uncertainties, several financial analysts said, remained too great.

Today...

The President, accompanied by his attorney Robert Bennett, departed the White House at 10:19 a.m., enroute Skadden, Arps, Slate, Meagher and Folm law offices. Crowds of tourists and onlookers snapped pictures and waved as the President's motorcade passed. The President waved back.

He arrived at the law office at 10:21 a.m., and into the underground parking garage. He was joined in the limousine by Robert Bennett.

The President departed the law offices at 4:24 p.m, arriving at the residence at 4:26 p.m. Robert Bennett and Bruce Lindsey had rode with him back to the residence.

He went directly to the Oval office, Where Erskine briefed him on the Asian economic situation. He also picked up some of his paperwork and the latest draft of his State of the Union speech, which he took back to the residence.

The President talked, via phone, with:

- Marsha Scott, 8:50 a.m.
- Erskine, 9:04 a.m.

of. And all of you who are involved in the program, let me thank you from the bottom of my heart. I hope that you're getting a lot of it. I know the Americorps volunteers I painted with today made me feel proud that we started this.

That's why I have strongly supported, along with all the former presidents, General Colin Powell, and the Presidents' Summit on service and the work that he is doing and that tens of thousands of people across America are doing to give all of our children a good chance in life.

But finally let me say that this country will never be all that it can be and your future will never be all that it can be unless we decide we're going to build that future together. We will never be able to bridge the racial and other divides in this country unless we decide we're not only going to work together and learn together but we're going to serve together.

We actually have to believe that we're all better off when our neighbors are better off. We actually have to believe that we'll do better if we go forward together. We actually have to believe that this diversity we have is a blessing; and that the fact that some of us start out life poorer than others is a condition that can be overcome if we work hard to give people who deserve it a hand up; and that as we do that, we are all happier, more fulfilled, and living in a stronger America. That's what this is about.

This is not just about painting the walls of a school, although I passionately believe it's important. I personally, as a student, preferred old buildings to new ones, but every student deserves to go into a clean building with bright walls and clear windows, sending a signal that the student and his or her future is important.

But you're not just painting a school today, you're painting a very different picture for America's future, and it's a beautiful one because of you..."

The President departed the school at 1:17 p.m., arriving back at the Oval at 1:28 p.m.

The President spent the rest of the day working at his desk, returning to the residence at 6:45 p.m.

Daynotes...

The President talked, via phone, with:

- Kris, 8:40 a.m.
- Betty Currie, 8:43, 8:50 a.m., 1:45 p.m.
- Vernon, 8:56, 10:58 a.m., 5:56 p.m.
- Robert Bennett, 11:21 a.m., 9:50 p.m.
- Warren Christopher, 3:02 p.m.
- Vice President Gore, 9:26 p.m.

THE WHITE HOUSE
WASHINGTON

PRESIDENTIAL CALL LOG

JANUARY 16th, 19 98

	TIME PLACED	DISC	NAME	ACTION
XXX INC	XXX 9:41 PM	9:46	MR. VERNON E. JORDAN, JR. RES: WASHINGTON, D.C. [redacted]	TLKD-OK 9:41 P.M.

REDACTED

1178-DC-00000018

0 004992

THE WHITE HOUSE

WASHINGTON

PRESIDENTIAL CALL LOG

JANUARY 17th, 1998

	TIME PLACED	DISC	NAME	ACTION
OUT / XXX	XXM 4:58 PM	5:40	MR. VERNON E. JORDAN, JR. RES: WASHINGTON, D.C. [redacted]	TLKD-OK 5:38 P.M.

REDACTED

1178-DC-00000019

0 004993

THE WHITE HOUSE
WASHINGTON

PRESIDENTIAL CALL LOG

JANUARY 17th, 19 98

	TIME PLACED	DISC	NAME	ACTION
OUT XXXc	XXX 7:02 PM	7:04	MR. VERNON E. JORDAN, JR. RES: WASHINGTON, D.C. [redacted]	TLKD-OK 7:02 P.M.

REDACTED

1178-DC-00000020

0 004994

THE WHITE HOUSE
WASHINGTON

PRESIDENTIAL CALL LOG

JANUARY 18th, 19 98

	TIME PLACED	DISC	NAME	ACTION

REDACTED

OUT	12:50 PM	12:52	MR. VERNON E. JORDAN, JR. RES: WASHINGTON, D.C. [redacted]	TLKD-OK 12:50 P.M.

THE WHITE HOUSE

WASHINGTON

PRESIDENTIAL CALL LOG

JANUARY 19th, 19 98

	TIME PLACED		DISC	NAME	ACTION
OUT / IN (struck)	8:55	AM / PM (struck)	9:05	MR. VERNON E. JORDAN, JR. RES: WASHINGTON, D.C. [redacted]	TLKD-OK 8:56 A.M.

1178-DC-00000023

REDACTED

0 004997

97_WHVA

4/7/98

ACC-CO	LAST-NAME	FIRST-NAME	INI	SSN	ENTRY-C	SCHED	ENTRY-D	VISITEE	MEETING-R	REQUESTOR	DOB	ENTRY-TOA
014390	JORDAN	VERNON			U74189	17:30	09/15/97	FLOTUS	EASTROO	SCHWARTZ	08/15/35	••:••
012617	JORDAN	VERNON		[redacted]	U92735	14:00	11/05/97	POTUS	WW	CAMERON	08/15/35	••:••
019070	JORDAN	VERNON		[redacted]	U01886	17:00	12/07/97	POTUS	WH	SPANGLER	08/15/35	17:21
019069	JORDAN	VERNON		[redacted]	U06987	18:15	12/17/97	VPOTUS	OEOB	EYER	08/15/35	18:50
019071	JORDAN	VERNON		[redacted]	U07410	20:00	12/19/97	POTUS	WH	SPANGLER	08/15/35	20:15

0 005000

.3	.72%	911 STATE TAX (0.72% OF $22.21)	.16
₹4	2.40%	ULTS SURCHARGE (2.40% OF $20.79)	.50
₹5	.76%	TEMPORARY SURCHARGE AS ALLOWED BY PUBLIC UTILITIES COMMISSION	.16
₹8	.25%	CALIFORNIA RELAY SERVICE AND COMMUNICATIONS DEVICES FUND	.05
₹9	2.87%	CHCF-A(.00%) AND CHCF-B(2.87%)	.60
₹10	.41%	CALIFORNIA TELECONNECT FUNDING SURCHARGE	.09
TOTAL			4.92

[redacted] LC/1717 PAGE: 0003
JAN 25 1998 MSD/19960401
GTE BASIC SERVICE CHARGES 29.21
TOTAL GTE CHARGES 29.21

[redacted] LC/1717 PAGE: 0004
JAN 25 1998 MSD/19960401
-00222- BILLING FOR MCI

[redacted] LC/1717 PAGE: 0005
JAN 25 1998 MSD/19960401
LONG DISTANCE CALLS
BILLING FOR MCI

[redacted] LC/1717 PAGE: 0006
JAN 25 1998 MSD/19960401
-00222- BILLING FOR MCI

[redacted] LC/1717 PAGE: 0007
JAN 25 1998 MSD/19960401
LONG DISTANCE CALLS
BILLING FOR MCI
INVOICE DATE: 01/17/98
BARBARA LEWINSKY

CURRENT CHARGES (SEE SERVICE SUMMARY)	28.69
CURRENT TAXES AND SURCHARGES	4.76
TOTAL CURRENT CHARGES, TAXES AND SURCHARGES	33.45
SERVICE SUMMARY	
LONG DISTANCE	27.62
FEES	1.07
TOTAL CURRENT CHARGES	28.69
TAXES AND SURCHARGES	
FEDERAL EXCISE TAX	.86
STATE & LOCAL TAXES	2.77
STATE & LOCAL SURCHARGES	.18
UNIVERSAL LIFELINE TELEPHONE SERVICES	.44
CA RELAY SERVICE/COMMUNICATIONS DEVICES FUND	.05
CALIFORNIA HIGH COST FUND-B SURCHARGE	.40
CALIFORNIA TELECONNECT FUND	.06
TOTAL CURRENT TAXES AND SURCHARGES	4.76

LONG DISTANCE
CALLS FROM 310-826-9179:

DATE	TIME	PLACE CALLED	NUMBER CALLED	TYPE	PERIOD	MIN	AMOUNT
1118	2100	SANBARBARACA	[redacted]	DDD	EVE	20	2.00
1120	1613	SANBARBARACA	[redacted]	DDD	DAY	6	.82
1120	2049	SAN MATEO CA	[redacted]	DDD	EVE	29	3.06
1126	0117	WASHINGTONDC	[redacted]	DDD	EVE	1	.17
1126	0117	WASHINGTONDC	[redacted]	DDD	EVE	1	.17
1126	0732	WASHINGTONDC	[redacted]	DDD	DAY	1	.28
1126	0736	WASHINGTONDC	[redacted]	DDD	DAY	1	.28

1205-DC-00000016

[redacted]		[redacted]	12:36	0	48	980107
[redacted]		[redacted]	12:36	0	48	980107
[redacted]		[redacted]	12:59	0	21	980107
[redacted]		[redacted]	13:01	0	8	980107
[redacted]		[redacted]	13:07	1	38	980107
[redacted]		[redacted]	13:16	0	5	980107
[redacted]		[redacted]	13:31	0	24	980107
[redacted]	288	[redacted]	13:35	1	10	980107
[redacted]		[redacted]	14:13	0	3	980107
[redacted]		[redacted]	14:14	0	3	980107
[redacted]		[redacted]	14:14	0	3	980107
[redacted]		[redacted]	14:58	0	35	980107
[redacted]		[redacted]	15:27	1	15	980107
[redacted]		[redacted]	15:28	0	53	980107
[redacted]		[redacted]	15:29	0	32	980107
[redacted]		[redacted]	15:30	1	22	980107
[redacted]	222	[redacted]	15:36	0	17	980107
[redacted]	488	[redacted]	15:36	0	20	980107
[redacted]	288	[redacted]	15:39	0	28	980107
[redacted]		[redacted]	16:08	0	6	980107
[redacted]		[redacted]	16:39	0	35	980107
[redacted]		[redacted]	16:40	0	2	980107
[redacted]		[redacted]	18:50	0	22	980107
[redacted]		[redacted]	18:50	0	22	980107
[redacted]		[redacted]	22:14	0	4	980118

MONTH	DAY	COUNT
01	06	26
01	07	32
01	18	1
12	05	2
TOTAL		61

END OF CALLS FOR [redacted]

ORIG #	CARRIER	TERM #	CONNECT	MIN	SEC	DATE
[redacted]		[redacted]	10:59	0	54	971205
[redacted]		[redacted]	13:10	0	9	971205
[redacted]		[redacted]	13:10	0	21	971205
[redacted]		[redacted]	13:11	0	10	971205
[redacted]		[redacted]	13:11	1	33	971205
[redacted]		[redacted]	13:13	0	5	971205
[redacted]		[redacted]	13:14	7	54	971205
[redacted]		[redacted]	13:24	0	15	971205
[redacted]		[redacted]	13:25	7	35	971205
[redacted]		[redacted]	13:33	4	3	971205
[redacted]		[redacted]	13:37	0	38	971205
[redacted]		[redacted]	13:41	1	45	971205
[redacted]	555	[redacted]	13:45	0	29	971205
[redacted]	555	[redacted]	13:45	0	20	971205
[redacted]		[redacted]	14:55	0	43	971205
[redacted]		[redacted]	15:13	0	0	971205
[redacted]		[redacted]	15:14	0	37	971205
[redacted]		[redacted]	15:15	2	31	971205
[redacted]		[redacted]	15:43	0	43	971205
[redacted]		[redacted]	15:47	8	38	971205
[redacted]		[redacted]	16:03	0	4	971205
[redacted]		[redacted]	16:21	0	3	971205
[redacted]		[redacted]	16:34	0	31	971205
[redacted]		[redacted]	19:38	9	20	971205
[redacted]		[redacted]	20:02	0	37	971205
[redacted]		[redacted]	08:41	0	0	971206
[redacted]		[redacted]	08:51	0	17	971206
[redacted]		[redacted]	09:08	0	15	971206
[redacted]		[redacted]	09:09	7	49	971206
[redacted]		[redacted]	09:21	0	10	971206

NOTICE NOT FOR USE OR DISCLOSURE OUTSIDE THE BELL ATLANTIC COMPANIES EXCEPT UNDER WRITTEN AGREEMENT

[redacted]		[redacted]	09:44	0	53	971206
[redacted]		[redacted]	10:40	0	23	971206
[redacted]		[redacted]	10:48	0	29	971206
[redacted]		[redacted]	10:50	0	17	971206
[redacted]		[redacted]	10:51	0	57	971206
[redacted]		[redacted]	10:57	6	51	971206
[redacted]		[redacted]	11:37	56	23	971206
[redacted]		[redacted]	12:34	0	30	971206
[redacted]		[redacted]	12:35	0	12	971206
[redacted]		[redacted]	12:51	0	49	971206
[redacted]		[redacted]	13:50	7	23	971206
[redacted]		[redacted]	13:57	0	0	971206
[redacted]		[redacted]	14:00	1	2	971206
[redacted]		[redacted]	14:03	0	8	971206
[redacted]		[redacted]	18:34	0	33	971206
[redacted]		[redacted]	20:41	0	46	971206
[redacted]	488	[redacted]	15:20	0	18	971215
[redacted]	488	[redacted]	15:23	0	37	971215
[redacted]	488	[redacted]	16:46	0	7	971215
[redacted]		[redacted]	18:58	0	0	971215
[redacted]		[redacted]	18:58	0	6	971215
[redacted]	288	[redacted]	20:50	60	47	971215
[redacted]		[redacted]	21:51	20	53	971215
[redacted]		[redacted]	22:13	80	36	971215
[redacted]		[redacted]	16:23	0	34	971219
[redacted]		[redacted]	16:57	1	0	971219
[redacted]		[redacted]	17:42	0	20	971219
[redacted]		[redacted]	17:43	0	32	971219
[redacted]		[redacted]	17:45	0	41	971219
[redacted]		[redacted]	17:47	21	30	971219
[redacted]		[redacted]	18:07	2	49	971219
[redacted]		[redacted]	18:10	0	3	971219
[redacted]		[redacted]	18:10	0	3	971219
[redacted]		[redacted]	18:11	21	36	971219
[redacted]		[redacted]	18:33	1	35	971219
[redacted]		[redacted]	19:08	0	32	971219
[redacted]		[redacted]	19:49	2	10	971219
[redacted]		[redacted]	20:02	1	12	971219
[redacted]		[redacted]	14:33	0	29	971220
[redacted]		[redacted]	14:34	0	0	971220
[redacted]		[redacted]	14:37	0	28	971220
[redacted]	288	[redacted]	14:39	1	0	971220
[redacted]		[redacted]	15:21	0	27	971220
[redacted]		[redacted]	15:21	0	7	971220
[redacted]		[redacted]	15:23	5	53	971220
[redacted]		[redacted]	15:58	0	55	971220
[redacted]		[redacted]	16:18	0	33	971220
[redacted]		[redacted]	16:18	0	5	971220
[redacted]		[redacted]	17:57	0	11	971220
[redacted]		[redacted]	19:39	0	41	971220
[redacted]		[redacted]	21:09	1	15	971220
[redacted]		[redacted]	09:18	6	48	980106
[redacted]		[redacted]	09:26	0	20	980106
[redacted]		[redacted]	09:26	0	17	980106
[redacted]		[redacted]	10:58	0	41	980106
[redacted]		[redacted]	11:31	1	13	980106
[redacted]		[redacted]	11:33	5	50	980106
[redacted]		[redacted]	12:41	0	0	980106
[redacted]		[redacted]	12:42	0	6	980106
[redacted]		[redacted]	13:02	0	31	980106
[redacted]		[redacted]	13:03	0	53	980106
[redacted]		[redacted]	13:07	0	49	980106
[redacted]		[redacted]	13:15	1	25	980106
[redacted]		[redacted]	13:17	1	15	980106

1216-DC-00000022

NOTICE NOT FOR USE OR DISCLOSURE OUTSIDE THE BELL ATLANTIC COMPANIES EXCEPT UNDER WRITTEN AGREEMENT

ORIG #	CARRIER	TERM #	CONNECT	MIN	SEC	DATE
[redacted]		[redacted]	13:18	0	2	980106
[redacted]		[redacted]	15:01	0	31	980106
[redacted]		[redacted]	15:08	0	25	980106
[redacted]		[redacted]	15:21	0	5	980106
[redacted]		[redacted]	15:23	0	22	980106
[redacted]		[redacted]	15:54	0	17	980106
[redacted]		[redacted]	16:21	2	30	980106
[redacted]		[redacted]	16:44	0	8	980106
[redacted]		[redacted]	16:45	0	16	980106
[redacted]		[redacted]	16:51	0	52	980106
[redacted]		[redacted]	16:57	0	40	980106
[redacted]		[redacted]	17:45	0	6	980106
[redacted]		[redacted]	20:53	0	4	980106
[redacted]		[redacted]	21:16	0	5	980106
[redacted]		[redacted]	21:19	0	13	980106
[redacted]		[redacted]	21:51	0	41	980106
[redacted]		[redacted]	22:31	0	2	980106
[redacted]		[redacted]	11:16	0	9	980107
[redacted]		[redacted]	12:51	0	9	980107
[redacted]		[redacted]	13:20	0	35	980107
[redacted]		[redacted]	13:21	0	9	980107
[redacted]		[redacted]	14:58	0	42	980107
[redacted]	288	[redacted]	16:32	0	51	980107
[redacted]		[redacted]	18:46	0	8	980107
[redacted]		[redacted]	20:46	0	7	980107
[redacted]		[redacted]	22:07	0	7	980107
[redacted]		[redacted]	11:51	0	41	980108
[redacted]		[redacted]	12:19	0	16	980108
[redacted]		[redacted]	17:40	0	7	980108
[redacted]		[redacted]	21:21	0	7	980108
[redacted]		[redacted]	08:41	0	46	980116
[redacted]		[redacted]	10:18	0	10	980116
[redacted]		[redacted]	10:27	0	29	980116
[redacted]		[redacted]	11:54	0	21	980116
[redacted]		[redacted]	13:03	0	24	980116
[redacted]	288	[redacted]	13:38	0	19	980116
[redacted]		[redacted]	14:08	0	22	980116
[redacted]		[redacted]	17:26	0	16	980116
[redacted]	288	[redacted]	07:22	0	49	980117
[redacted]		[redacted]	08:54	0	15	980117
[redacted]		[redacted]	10:49	0	34	980117
[redacted]		[redacted]	11:47	0	30	980117
[redacted]	288	[redacted]	12:02	1	40	980117
[redacted]		[redacted]	15:08	1	7	980117
[redacted]	288	[redacted]	15:52	1	49	980117
[redacted]	288	[redacted]	22:32	0	8	980117
[redacted]		[redacted]	22:45	0	32	980117
[redacted]		[redacted]	22:46	1	3	980117
[redacted]		[redacted]	13:44	0	14	980118
[redacted]		[redacted]	13:53	0	22	980118
[redacted]		[redacted]	15:29	0	36	980118
[redacted]		[redacted]	17:04	0	0	980118
[redacted]		[redacted]	17:46	0	8	980118
[redacted]		[redacted]	18:21	0	0	980118
[redacted]		[redacted]	10:11	0	1	980119
[redacted]		[redacted]	12:08	0	0	980120
[redacted]		[redacted]	14:31	0	0	980120
[redacted]		[redacted]	16:37	0	0	980120
[redacted]		[redacted]	19:11	0	0	980120

MONTH	DAY	COUNT
01	06	30
01	07	9
01	08	4
01	16	8
01	17	10
01	18	6
01	19	1
01	20	4
12	05	25
12	06	21
12	15	8
12	19	14
12	20	13
TOTAL		153

END OF CALLS FOR [redacted]

ORIG #	CARRIER	TERM #	CONNECT	MIN	SEC	DATE
[redacted]		[redacted]	10:45	3	40	971205
[redacted]		[redacted]	10:50	0	26	971205
[redacted]		[redacted]	11:12	0	46	971205
[redacted]		[redacted]	11:37	0	58	971205
[redacted]		[redacted]	11:38	0	52	971205
[redacted]		[redacted]	12:08	1	50	971205
[redacted]		[redacted]	13:04	0	24	971205
[redacted]		[redacted]	15:40	0	22	971205
[redacted]		[redacted]	15:40	0	19	971205
[redacted]		[redacted]	15:47	1	20	971205
[redacted]		[redacted]	16:42	1	52	971205
[redacted]	022	[redacted]	16:48	1	29	971205
[redacted]	288	[redacted]	17:06	0	15	971205
[redacted]		[redacted]	17:28	0	41	971205
[redacted]		[redacted]	17:36	1	32	971205
[redacted]		[redacted]	17:48	2	41	971205
[redacted]		[redacted]	17:50	0	16	971205
[redacted]		[redacted]	17:57	0	32	971205
[redacted]		[redacted]	22:23	3	9	971205
[redacted]	288	[redacted]	14:23	0	5	971206
[redacted]	288	[redacted]	14:39	3	15	971206
[redacted]		[redacted]	15:24	0	6	971206
[redacted]		[redacted]	09:13	0	32	971215
[redacted]		[redacted]	09:26	0	23	971215
[redacted]		[redacted]	10:27	5	21	971215
[redacted]		[redacted]	11:16	2	24	971215
[redacted]		[redacted]	11:21	0	57	971215
[redacted]		[redacted]	11:22	6	28	971215
[redacted]		[redacted]	12:29	2	46	971215
[redacted]	288	[redacted]	13:31	0	5	971215
[redacted]		[redacted]	14:57	2	57	971215
[redacted]		[redacted]	15:21	1	3	971215
[redacted]		[redacted]	15:24	2	34	971215
[redacted]		[redacted]	16:14	1	17	971215
[redacted]		[redacted]	17:04	3	11	971215
[redacted]		[redacted]	10:01	3	22	971219
[redacted]	811	[redacted]	10:49	5	36	971219
[redacted]		[redacted]	11:20	0	25	971219
[redacted]		[redacted]	14:10	0	8	971219
[redacted]		[redacted]	15:21	0	59	971219
[redacted]		[redacted]	15:53	1	1	971219
[redacted]		[redacted]	17:35	1	33	971219
[redacted]		[redacted]	17:53	3	37	971219
[redacted]	288	[redacted]	08:58	1	26	980106
[redacted]		[redacted]	09:59	2	31	980106
[redacted]		[redacted]	10:05	2	58	980106
[redacted]		[redacted]	10:30	1	56	980106
[redacted]		[redacted]	12:22	2	37	980106
[redacted]		[redacted]	12:29	1	15	980106
[redacted]		[redacted]	12:39	0	40	980106
[redacted]	811	[redacted]	14:14	0	39	980106

1216-DC-00000023

NOTICE NOT FOR USE OR DISCLOSURE OUTSIDE THE BELL ATLANTIC COMPANIES EXCEPT UNDER WRITTEN AGREEMENT

ITINERARY FOR: Sunday, January 21, 1996

TOURS: CONGRESSIONAL	PUBLIC	OEOB	NONE	XXX

HOUSEGUEST: Mrs. Branson, Amanda Gill, Rosa Gill, Diane Blair.

DEMONSTRATIONS: NONE.

WATCH COMMANDERS:
2200 - 0630 CAPTAIN ROANALD S. NORMANDIN

0600 - 1430 CAPTAIN JEFFREY J. PURDIE

TBD - POTUS Morning Run. TBD
0800 - POTUS / FLOTUS Depart South Grounds For Church.
TBD - POTUS / FLOTUS Arrive White House

1400 - 2230 CAPTAIN ANTHONY R. DEMASI

POTUS/FIRST LADY/Chelsea RON: Residence
VP RON: Residence
Mrs. Gore RON: Residence

SPECIAL FUNCTIONS: None.

LOOKOUT: None.

APPROVING OFFICIAL:

F Darrell Bowling
for Lieutenant Joseph Syreika

DISTRIBUTION:

C/C-Dispatcher	CHIEF
W-16 (VIA FAX)	D/C-WHB
K-9 (VIA FAX)	DBC-WHB
LT-DAD'S OFFICE	C/C-SGT
W/C'S (3 listed above)	G-3
STAFF INSPECTOR	OEOB
FILE (original)	NEOB
ERT OFFICE (VIA FAX)	TREASURY
FMB CLERK (VIA FAX)	MAG OFFICE
	WAVES

ITINERARY FOR: Tuesday, March 5, 1996

TOURS: CONGRESSIONAL XXX   PUBLIC XXX   OEOB   NONE

HOUSEGUEST: Nicole and Zachary Rodham.

DEMONSTRATIONS: None.

WATCH COMMANDERS:
2200 - 0630 CAPTAIN RONALD S. NORMANDIN

0600 - 1430 CAPTAIN JAMES C. THOMAS
CAPTAIN JEFFREY J. PURDIE

TBD - Morning Run	TBD
0730 - First Lady Departs White House en route Andrews AFB, en route Corpus Christi, TX	South Portico
0830 - VP Arrives White House	
0830 - VP DNC Coffee	OEOB Room 274
0915 - POTUS/VP Briefing	Oval Office
0950 - VP Meeting with Katie McGinty	West Wing Office
1000 - VP Meeting with Under Secretary Tim Wirth	West Wing Office
1030 - VP Meeting with Ambassador Raiser	West Wing Office
1045 - POTUS Departs White House Via Motorcade en route Washington Hilton and Towers Hotel	TBD
1130 - VP Press Time	OEOB Room 459
1220 - POTUS Arrives White House	TBD
1220 - VP Meeting with Kim Tilley	West Wing Office
1230 - POTUS/VP Meeting	Oval Office
1245 - Lunch/Office and Phone Time	West Wing Office

1400 - 2230 CAPTAIN ANTHONY R. DEMASI

1700 - POTUS Coffee	Map Room
1700 - VP Staff Meeting	OEOB Room 274
1745 - VP Meeting with Reed Hundt	West Wing Office
1815 - VP Departs White House en route Residence	

POTUS/Chelsea RON: Residence
First Lady RON: Buffalo, NY
VP/Mrs. Gore RON: Residence

1222-DC-00000032

SPECIAL FUNCTIONS:

1100 Hours: OEOB Room 324	Purpose Unknown	23 Guests Seidman
1100 Hours: OEOB Room 476	Purpose Unknown	40 Guests Matsui
1300 Hours: OEOB Room 180	Purpose Unknown	33 Guests Yager
1430 Hours: NEOB Room 9026	Purpose Unknown	21 Guests Heim
1600 Hours: OEOB Room 208	Purpose Unknown	21 Guests Clarke

LOOKOUT: None.

APPROVING OFFICIAL:

Joseph J. Syreika (signature)

Lieutenant Joseph J. Syreika

DISTRIBUTION:

C/C-Dispatcher	CHIEF
W-16 (VIA FAX)	D/C-WHB
K-9 (VIA FAX)	DBC-WHB
LT-DAD'S OFFICE	C/C-SGT
W/C'S (3 listed above)	G-3
STAFF INSPECTOR	OEOB
FILE (original)	NEOB
ERT OFFICE (VIA FAX)	TREASURY
	MAG OFFICE

Ufo

ITINERARY FOR: Sunday, March 31, 1996

URS: CONGRESSIONAL PUBLIC OEOB NONE XXX

USEGUEST: Mr. Kelly.

MONSTRATIONS: 03/31-04/05, 24hrs.cont.,Lafayette Park, Sister D. Ortiz, lent Vigil to Protest Human Rights Abuses by Guatemalan Government, 1 rticipant. 1400-1600 hrs., Lafayette Park, Guatemala Human Rights mmission/USA, Protest Human Rights Violations by Guatemalan Military vernment; and ask for Declassification of U.S. Government Documents garding these Human Rights Abuses, 100 participants.

TCH COMMANDERS:
00 - 0630 CAPTAIN JAMES C. THOMAS/ (2200-0230hrs.)
CAPTAIN JEFFREY J. PURDIE (0200-0630hrs.)

00 - 1430 CAPTAIN JEFFREY J. PURDIE

D - POTUS Departs White House en route Church TBD
D - POTUS Arrive White House TBD

00 - 2230 CAPTAIN CHARLES P. KERRIGAN

20 - First Lady/Chelsea Arrive White House South Grounds

TUS/First Lady/Chelsea RON: Residence
/Mrs. Gore RON: Residence

CIAL FUNCTIONS: NONE

OKOUT: None.

PROVING OFFICIAL:

F. Darrell Bowling
utenant Darrell Bowling

DISTRIBUTION:

C/C-Dispatcher	CHIEF
W-16 (VIA FAX)	D/C-WHB
K-9 (VIA FAX)	DBC-WHB
LT-DAD'S OFFICE	C/C-SGT
W/C'S (3 listed above)	G-3
STAFF INSPECTOR	OEOB
FILE (original)	NEOB
ERT OFFICE (VIA FAX)	TREASURY
FMB CLERK (VIA FAX)	MAG OFFICE
	WAVES

TOURS: CONGRI IONAL XXX PUBLIC XXX 'OB NONE

HOUSEGUEST: Mrs. Rodham, Dick Kelley, Daniel Dutko, Deborah Jospin, William Brandt, Mr. & Mrs. Mahoney, Joan Brandt, Michael Mahoney and Capricia Marshall.

DEMONSTRATIONS: None.

WATCH COMMANDERS:
2200 - 0630 CAPTAIN RONALD S. NORMANDIN

0600 - 1430 CAPTAIN JEFFREY J. PURDIE

TBD	POTUS Morning Run	**TBD**
0650	First Lady Departs White House en route Andrews AFB en route Kansas City, MO	South Portico
0900	POTUS Phone/Office and Down Time	Oval/Residence
1000	POTUS Meeting	Oval Office
1015	VP Arrives White House	
1015	POTUS/VP Briefing	Oval Office
1030	POTUS/VP Ethnic Leadership Day	OEOB Room 450
1130	POTUS/VP Photos with Democratic Congressional Candidates	Oval Office

1400 - 2230 LIEUTENANT NANCY ANDERSON
LIEUTENANT MARK CHANEY
LIEUTENANT JOSEPH G. MCBRIDE

1440	VP Courtsey Visit	West Wing Office
1555	VP Meeting with American Nurses Assoc.	Indian Treaty Room
1625	VP Convention meeting	West Wing Office
1700	POTUS Tape Radio Address	Roosevelt Room
1720	First Lady Arrives White House	South Portico
1805	VP Promotion & Award Ceremony for LTC Rick Saunders	OEOB Room 276
1825	VP Departs White House en route Residence	
1900	POTUS Departs White House en route the Hay Adams Hotel	**TBD**
2145	POTUS Arrives White House	**TBD**
2200	POTUS/First Lady Depart White House en route Camp David	South Lawn

POTUS/FLOTUS **RON:** Camp David
Chelsea **RON:** Residence
VP/Mrs. Gore **RON:** Residence

1222-DC-00000045

SPECIAL FUNCTIONS:

0815 Hours: OEOB Room 450	Purpose Unknown	190 Guests	**POTUS**
1000 Hours: OEOB Room 231	Purpose Unknown	26 Guests	Seidman
1000 Hours: OEOB Room 476	Purpose Unknown	34 Guests	Chow
1115 Hours: West Wing	Purpose Unknown	71 Guests	**POTUS**
1200 Hours: OEOB Room 474	Purpose Unknown	34 Guests	Shaw
1300 Hours: OEOB Room 276	Purpose Unknown	49 Guests	Pugh
1630 Hours: West Wing	Purpose Unknown	26 Guests	**POTUS**
1715 Hours: Residence	Purpose Unknown	76 Guests	**POTUS**

LOOKOUT: None.

APPROVING OFFICIAL:

Lt Stephen W Brown
GE Lieutenant Joseph J. Syreika

DISTRIBUTION:

C/C-Lieutenant	CHIEF
C/C-Dispatcher	D/C-WHB
W-16 (VIA FAX)	DBC-WHB
K-9 (VIA FAX)	C/C-SGT
LT-DAD'S OFFICE	G-3
W/C'S (3 listed above)	OEOB
STAFF INSPECTOR	NEOB
FILE (original)	TREASURY
ERT OFFICE (VIA FAX)	MAG OFFICE
FMB CLERK (VIA FAX)	WAVES

1222-DC-00000083

1-15	1247	Oval Office		41	JAS
1/15	1502	2nd floor Residence	No Answer Busy	26	JLO
1/15	1530	Oval Office		24	JLO
1/15	1701	Oval Office		26	JLO
1/15	1735	CHIEF OF STAFF OFFICE		26	EWS
1/15	1740	Oval Office		12	JLO
1/15	2004	Chief of Staff Office		23	JLO

1222-DC-00000084

11-15	1247	Oval Office		41	JAS
11/15	1502	2nd floor Residence	NO Answer Busy	26	JLO
11/15	1530	Oval Office		24	JLO
11/15	1701	Oval Office		26	JLO
11/15	1735	CHIEF OF STAFF OFFICE		26	EWS
11/15	1740	Oval Office		12	JLO
11/15	2004	Chief of Staff Office		23	JLO

11/16	0035	MANSION	25	T.O.
11/16	1125	PRESS OFFICE WEST WING	BUSY	W.P.S
11/16	1126	OVAL OFFICE	BUSY	W.P.S
11/16	1152	CHIEF OF STAFF	BUSY	JIB
11-16	1159	OVAL OFFICE	?	?
11-16	1542	DEP. CHIEF of STAFF OFFICE	68	[illegible]
11-16	1548	OVAL OFFICE	68	[illegible]
11-16	1656	Doctor's Office	41	[illegible]
11-16	1718	OVAL OFFICE	44	[illegible]
11-16	1722	Roos. Rm	41	[illegible]
11-16	1747	OVAL OFFICE	68	[illegible]
11-16	1851	CHIEF of STAFF OFFICE	6	[illegible]
11-16	1855	2ND FLOOR RESIDENCE	6	[illegible]
11-17	1101	OVAL OFFICE	41	PLC
11-17	1236	ROOSEVELT ROOM	10	PLC
11-17	2108	Chief of STAFF	27	WMC
11-17	2132	OVAL OFFICE	27	WMC
11/17/95	2145	Chief of Staff	27	[illegible]
11/17/95	2146	Oval Office	27	[illegible]
11/17/95	2216	Chief of Staff	27	[illegible]
11/17/95	2234	Oval Office	27	[illegible]
11/17/95	2239	Ground Floor	27	[illegible]
11/17/95	2240	2nd Floor Residence	27	[illegible]
11/18/95	0940	2nd Floor	17	VAS
11/18/95	0942	Oval Office	17	VAS
11/18/95	0945	Chief of Staff Office	17	VAS
11/18/95	1043	Oval Office	24	VAS
11/18/95	1155	West Colonnade	24	VAS
11/18/95	1156	2nd Floor Residence	24	VAS
11/18/95	1412	OVAL OFFICE	17	[illegible]
11/18/95	1418	CHIEF OF STAFF OFFICE	17	[illegible]
11/18/95	1422	OVAL OFFICE	17	[illegible]
11/18/95	1445	South Grounds	17	[illegible]
11/18/95	1529	OVAL OFFICE	17	[illegible]
11/18/95	1538	South Grounds	17	[illegible]
11/18/95	1603	OVAL OFFICE	17	[illegible]
11/18/95	1930	2ND Floor Residence	20	[illegible]

THE WHITE HOUSE
WASHINGTON

PRESIDENTIAL CALL LOG

JANUARY 17th , 1998

	TIME PLACED	TIME DISC	NAME	ACTION
OUT ~~INC~~ XXX	8:50 AM ~~PM~~ XXX	8:53	MS. MARSHA SCOTT RES: WASHINGTON, D.C. [redacted]	TLKD-OK 8:50 A.M.
OUT INC	AM PM			
OUT ~~INC~~ XXX	9:02 AM ~~PM~~ XXX	9:05	MR. ERSKINE B. BOWLES RES: WASHINGTON, D.C. [redacted]	TLKD-OK 9:04 A.M.
OUT INC	AM PM			
~~OUT~~ XXX INC	~~AM~~ XXX 4:30 PM	4:33	MS. NANCY F. MITCHELL OFC: WASHINGTON, D.C. WHITE HOUSE ADMIN EXT. [redacted]	TLKD-OK 4:32 P.M.
OUT INC	AM PM			
OUT ~~INC~~ XXX	~~AM~~ XXX 4:58 PM	5:40	MR. VERNON E. JORDAN, JR. RES: WASHINGTON, D.C. [redacted]	TLKD-OK 5:38 P.M.
OUT INC	AM PM			
OUT ~~INC~~ XXX	~~AM~~ XXX 5:40 PM	5:42	MR. ERSKINE B. BOWLES RES: WASHINGTON, D.C. [redacted]	TLKD-OK 5:40 P.M.
OUT INC	AM PM			1248-DC-00000305
~~OUT~~ XXX INC	~~AM~~ XXX 5:45 PM	5:49	MR. ERSKINE B. BOWLES RES: WASHINGTON, D.C. [redacted]	TLKD-OK 5:45 P.M.

S 017613

THE WHITE HOUSE
WASHINGTON

PRESIDENTIAL CALL LOG

JANUARY 17th, 19 98

	TIME PLACED	DISC	NAME	ACTION
OUT XXX INC	XXX AM 7:02 PM	7:04	MR. VERNON E. JORDAN, JR. RES: WASHINGTON, D.C. [redacted]	TLKD-OK 7:02 P.M.
OUT INC	AM PM			
OUT XXX INC	XXX AM 7:02 PM	7:11	MR. CHARLES F.C. RUFF RES: WASHINGTON, D.C. [redacted]	TLKD-OK 7:11 P.M.
OUT INC	AM PM			
OUT XXX INC	XXX AM 7:02 PM	7:14	MRS. BETTY W. CURRIE RES: ARLINGTON, VA. [redacted]	TLKD-OK 7:13 P.M.
OUT INC	AM PM			
XXX OUT INC	XXX AM 7:27 PM	7:40	MR. TERRY Mc AULIFFE RES: FALLS CHURCH, VA. [redacted]	TLKD-OK 7:35 P.M.
OUT INC	AM PM			
XXX OUT INC	XXX AM 8:00 PM		MS. NANCY F. MITCHELL OFC: WASHINGTON, D.C. WHITE HOUSE ADMIN EXT. [redacted]	CANCEL PER MS. MITCHEI 8:00 P.M.
OUT INC	AM PM			1248-DC-00000307
OUT XXX INC	XXX AM 8:20 PM	8:23	SECRETARY ALEXIS M. HERMAN RES: WASHINGTON, D.C. WHITE HOUSE SIGNAL EXT. [redacted]	TLKD-OK 8:20 P.M.

S 017615

THE WHITE HOUSE

WASHINGTON

PRESIDENTIAL CALL LOG

JANUARY 18th, 19 98

	TIME		NAME	ACTION
	PLACED	DISC		
XXX INC	9:22 AM XXX	9:20	DOCTOR DANNY THOMASSON RES: LITTLE ROCK, AR. [redacted]	TLKD-OK 9:19 P.M.
OUT INC	AM PM			
XXX INC	10:40 AM XXX	1:46	MRS. LYNDA DIXON RES: LITTLE ROCK, AR. [redacted]	TLKD-OK 1:16 P.M.
OUT INC	AM PM			
XXX INC	10:42 AM XXX	9:24	MR. ROBERT ARMSTRONG RES: WASHINGTON, D.C. [redacted]	TLKD-OK 9:23 P.M.
OUT INC	AM PM			
XXX INC	XXX 12:43 PM	11:30	MR. STEVE GROSSMAN RES: BOSTON, MA. [redacted]	TLKD-OK 11:03 P.M.
OUT INC	AM PM			1248-DC-00000311
OUT XXX	XXX 12:50 PM	12:52	MR. VERNON E. JORDAN, JR. RES: WASHINGTON, D.C. [redacted]	TLKD-OK 12:50 P.M.
OUT INC	AM PM			S 017619
OUT XXX	XXX 1:11 PM	1:14	MRS. BETTY W. CURRIE RES: ARLINGTON, VA. [redacted]	TLKD-OK 1:11 P.M.

THE WHITE HOUSE
WASHINGTON

PRESIDENTIAL CALL LOG

JANUARY 18th, 1998

	TIME PLACED	DISC	NAME	ACTION
INC	2:55 PM		MR. VERNON E. JORDAN, JR. RES: WASHINGTON, D.C. [redacted]	HOLD PER PRESUS 9:20 P.M.
OUT / INC	AM / PM			
INC	3:15 PM	10:05	FORMER GOVERNOR JAMES BLANCHARD ARLINGTON, VA. [redacted]	TLKD-OK 9:54 P.M.
OUT / INC	AM / PM			
INC	4:50 PM	4:50	MS. NANCY F. MITCHELL OFC: WASHINGTON, D.C. WHITE HOUSE ADMIN EXT. [redacted]	TLKD-OK 4:50 P.M.
OUT / INC	AM / PM			
OUT	5:24 PM	5:32	MR. RAHM I. EMANUEL RES: WASHINGTON, D.C. [redacted]	TLKD-OK 5:24 P.M.
OUT / INC	AM / PM			1248-DC-00000312
INC	6:15 PM	6:37	SENATOR THOMAS A. DASCHLE WASHINGTON, D.C. [redacted]	TLKD-OK 6:20 P.M.
OUT / INC	AM / PM			S 017620
INC	8:08 PM	8:10	THE VICE-PRESIDENT RES: WASHINGTON, D.C. WHITE HOUSE ADMIN. EXT. [redacted]	TLKD-OK 8:08 P.M.

THE WHITE HOUSE
WASHINGTON

PRESIDENTIAL CALL LOG

JANUARY 18th, 19 98

	TIME PLACED	DISC	NAME	ACTION
XXX INC	9:22 AM XXX PM	9:20	DOCTOR DANNY THOMASSON RES: LITTLE ROCK, AR. [redacted]	TLKD-OK 9:19 P.M.
OUT INC	AM PM			
XXX INC	10:40 AM XXX	1:46	MRS. LYNDA DIXON RES: LITTLE ROCK, AR. [redacted]	TLKD-OK 1:16 P.M.
OUT INC	AM PM			
XXX INC	10:42 AM XXX	9:24	MR. ROBERT ARMSTRONG RES: WASHINGTON, D.C. [redacted]	TLKD-OK 9:23 P.M.
OUT INC	AM PM			
XXXX INC	XXX 12:43 PM	11:30	MR. STEVE GROSSMAN RES: BOSTON, MA. [redacted]	TLKD-OK 11:03 P.M.
OUT INC	AM PM			1248-DC-00000313
OUT XXX	XXX 12:50 PM	12:52	MR. VERNON E. JORDAN, JR. RES: WASHINGTON, D.C. [redacted]	TLKD-OK 12:50 P.M.
OUT INC	AM PM			S 017621
OUT XXX	XXX 1:11 PM	1:14	MRS. BETTY W. CURRIE RES: ARLINGTON, VA. [redacted]	TLKD-OK 1:11 P.M.

THE WHITE HOUSE
WASHINGTON

PRESIDENTIAL CALL LOG

JANUARY 18th, 19 98

	TIME PLACED	DISC	NAME	ACTION
OUT ~~INC~~	~~AM~~ 11:01 PM	11:02	MRS. BETTY W. CURRIE RES: ARLINGTON, VA. [redacted]	TLKD-OK 11:02 P.M.
OUT INC	AM PM			
OUT INC	AM PM			
OUT INC	AM PM			
OUT INC	AM PM			
OUT INC	AM PM			
OUT INC	AM PM			
OUT INC	AM PM			1248-DC-00000314
OUT INC	AM PM			
OUT INC	AM PM			S 017622
OUT INC	AM PM			

THE WHITE HOUSE
WASHINGTON

PRESIDENTIAL CALL LOG
SIGNAL SWITCHBOARD

January 18, 1998

	TIME		NAME	ACTION
	PLACED	DISC		
XXX INC	11:55 AM PM		Mr. Noach Dear Brooklyn, New York [redacted]	LW with Mr. Lindsey 12:00 PM
XXX INC	AM 4:12 PM		Mr. Rahm I. Emanuel Residence, Washington, D.C. [redacted]	LW with Ms. Mitchell 4:12 PM
OUT INC	AM PM			
OUT INC	AM PM			
OUT INC	AM PM			
OUT INC	AM PM			
OUT INC	AM PM			
OUT INC	AM PM			
OUT INC	AM PM			1248-DC-00000315
OUT INC	AM PM			S 017623
OUT INC	AM PM			

THE WHITE HOUSE
WASHINGTON

PRESIDENTIAL CALL LOG

JANUARY 19th, 19 98

	TIME PLACED	DISC	NAME	ACTION
OUT	10:55 AM	10:59	MR. VERNON E. JORDAN, JR. OFC: WASHINGTON, D.C. [redacted]	TLKD-OK 10:58 A.M.
OUT / INC	AM / PM			
OUT	11:19 AM	11:26	MR. ROBERT S. BENNETT OFC: WASHINGTON, D.C. [redacted]	TLKD-OK 11:21 A.M.
OUT / INC	AM / PM			
INC	1:43 PM	1:47	MRS. BETTY W. CURRIE RES: ARLINGTON, VA. [redacted]	TLKD-OK 1:45 P.M.
OUT / INC	AM / PM			
OUT	2:11 PM	3:14	MR. WARREN M. CHRISTOPHER RES: CARPINTERIA, CA. [redacted]	TLKD-OK 3:02 P.M.
OUT / INC	AM / PM			
INC	5:19 PM	5:54	MR. ROGER CLINTON RES: REDONDO, CA. [redacted]	TLKD-OK 5:45 P.M.
OUT / INC	AM / PM			
OUT	5:54 PM	6:03	MR. VERNON E. JORDAN, JR. OFC: WASHINGTON, D.C. [redacted]	TLKD-OK 5:56 P.M.

THE WHITE HOUSE
WASHINGTON

PRESIDENTIAL CALL LOG

JANUARY 21st, 19 98

	TIME PLACED	DISC	NAME	ACTION
OUT / ~~INC~~ XX	12:08 AM / ~~PM~~ XX	12:39	MR. ROBERT S. BENNETT RES: WASHINGTON, D.C. [redacted]	TLKD-OK 12:09 A.M.
OUT / INC	AM / PM			
OUT / ~~INC~~ XX	12:40 AM / ~~PM~~ XX	1:10	MR. BRUCE R. LINDSEY RES: WASHINGTON, D.C. [redacted]	TLKD-OK 12:41 A.M.
OUT / INC	AM / PM			
OUT / ~~INC~~ XX	1:16 AM / ~~PM~~ XX	1:36	MRS. BETTY W. CURRIE RES: ARLINGTON, VA. [redacted]	TLKD-OK 1:16 A.M.
OUT / INC	AM / PM			
~~OUT~~ XX / INC	1:36 AM / ~~PM~~ XX	1:38	MR. BRUCE R. LINDSEY RES: WASHINGTON, D.C. [redacted]	TLKD-OK 1:36 A.M.
OUT / INC	AM / PM			1248-DC-00000327
~~OUT~~ XX / INC	1:39 AM / ~~PM~~ XX	1:40	MR. BRUCE R. LINDSEY RES: WASHINGTON, D.C. [redacted]	TLKD-OK 1:39 A.M.
OUT / INC	AM / PM			S 017635
OUT / ~~INC~~ XX	2:32 AM / ~~PM~~ XX	2:32	MESSAGE: "OPERATOR, WAKE ME AT 7:00 A.M. THANKS."	ACKNOWLEDGED 2:32 A.M.

THE WHITE HOUSE

WASHINGTON

PRESIDENTIAL CALL LOG

JANUARY 21st, 19 98

	TIME PLACED		DISC	NAME	ACTION
OUT	7:00	AM	7:00	WAKE-UP BY WHITE HOUSE OPERATOR	COMPLETED 7:00 A.M.
OUT / INC		AM / PM			
OUT	7:02	AM	7:54	MR. DAVID KENDALL RES: BETHESDA, MD. [redacted]	TLKD-OK 7:26 A.M.
OUT / INC		AM / PM			
OUT	7:14	AM	7:22	MR. BRUCE R. LINDSEY RES: WASHINGTON, D.C. [redacted]	TLKD-OK 7:14 A.M.
OUT / INC		AM / PM			
OUT	7:23	AM	8:16	MR. ROBERT S. BENNETT OFC: WASHINGTON, D.C. [redacted]	TLKD-OK 8:02 A.M.
OUT / INC		AM / PM			1248-DC-00000328
OUT	8:46	AM		MR. BRUCE R. LINDSEY OFC: WASHINGTON, D.C. [redacted]	PER: MS. BETTY CURRIE CANCEL CALL 9:00 A.M.
OUT / INC		AM / PM			S 017636
INC	6:14	PM	6:20	AMBASSADOR MICKEY KANTOR WASHINGTON, D.C. [redacted]	TLKD-OK 6:15 P.M.

THE WHITE HOUSE

WASHINGTON

PRESIDENTIAL CALL LOG

DECEMBER 19th, 19 97

	TIME PLACED	TIME DISC	NAME	ACTION
OUT / XX INC	4:57 AM / PM	5:08	MR. VERNON E. JORDAN, JR. OFC: WASHINGTON, D.C. [redacted]	TLKD-OK 5:01 P.M.
OUT / INC	AM / PM			
OUT / INC	AM / PM			
OUT / INC	AM / PM			
OUT / INC	AM / PM			
OUT / INC	AM / PM			
OUT / INC	AM / PM			
OUT / INC	AM / PM			
OUT / INC	AM / PM			
OUT / INC	AM / PM		1248-DC-00000381	S 019623
OUT / INC	AM / PM			

THE WHITE HOUSE
WASHINGTON

PRESIDENTIAL CALL LOG

JANUARY 13th, 19 98

	TIME PLACED	DISC	NAME	ACTION
OUT / XX INC	XX 5:21 PM		MS. CAROL H. RASCO OFC: WASHINGTON, D.C. [redacted]	INFORMED MS. BETTY CURRIE 5:24 P.M.
OUT / INC	AM / PM			
OUT / XX INC	XX 5:25 PM	5:46	MR. MARK PENN COSTA RICA [redacted]	TLKD-OK 5:34 P.M.
OUT / INC	AM / PM			
OUT / XX INC	XX 8:55 PM	9:46	MR. VERNON E. JORDAN, JR. ST. PETERSBURG, FL. [redacted]	TLKD-OK 9:42 P.M.
OUT / INC	AM / PM			
XX OUT / INC	XX 9:42 PM	9:51	MR. THOMAS F. McLARTY RES: WASHINGTON, D.C. [redacted]	TLKD-OK 9:47 P.M.
OUT / INC	AM / PM			
OUT / INC	AM / PM			
OUT / INC	AM / PM			
OUT / INC	AM / PM			

1318-DC-00000001

From Anne's book *"Down in the Garden."*

ANNE GEDDES™

Award-winning New Zealand photographer Anne Geddes has been photographing children for nearly 12 years. Her pleasure and pride is obvious, as is the necessary patience, timing and the "sympathetic communication" needed with her favorite models. Using whimsical and dramatic set designs, Anne creatively coaxes delightful expressions from her unpredictable subjects. Anne Geddes' photography is available from Portal Publications on Blank and Greeted Cards, Prints and Matted Prints.

0 11545 15076 1

195 BPH401

Geddes – Anne's Pansies

Published and Distributed by
Portal Publications Ltd.
Corte Madera, California
Litho in U.S.A.
Canada 325
http://www.portalpub.com

PORTAL

GRAND JURY EXHIBIT

NC BPH 401

ISBN 1-57928-061-7

50195

9 781579 280611

I think the end of this whole trauma is over. I just wish my heart didn't have to be broken in all of this.

Well, I hope you and your family are well.

Again Dale, thanks for being such a great friend.

XXXOOO

Love,
Monica

1318-DC-00000002

4 Sept. 1997

Dear Dale,

I wanted to thank you for the kindness and friendship you extended to me last weekend. I really needed the friendly ear and good advice.

Unfortunately, I came back to DC only to learn that the detailee slot in Marsha's office is no longer available. I had a long conversation with her and it is clear to me ~~be~~ now that I won't be able to come back any time soon.

Catalog of Books in the West Wing Presidential Study as of 10 October 1997

Author	Title	Location	Topic	Notes
Michael W. Monroe	The White House Collection of American Crafts	White House Art	POTUS Study--WW	
Henry F. Graff, Editor	The Presidents: A Reference History	Presidential History	POTUS Study--WW	
Davis Newton Lott	The Presidents Speak: The Inaugural Addresses of the American Presidents from Washington to Clinton	Presidential History	POTUS Study--WW	Inscribed by the author, December, 1994
Michael Wolff, Peter Rutten, and Albert F. Bayers III	Where We Stand: Can America Make It in the Global Race for Wealth, Health, and Happiness	Sociology	POTUS Study--WW	
U.S. Government Printing Office	Inaugural Addresses of the Presidents of the United States	Presidential History	POTUS Study--WW	
William Safire	Safire's New Political Dictionary	Pol. & Govt.-Dictionary	POTUS Study--WW	
William Jefferson Clinton	State of the Union Address to the 104th Congress, Second Session Jan. 23,1996	Presidential Speeches	POTUS Study-WW	

1361-DC-00000002

S 019366

William Jefferson Clinton	State of the Union Address to the 104th Congress, First Session Jan. 24, 1995	Presidential Speeches	POTUS Study-WW	
William Jefferson Clinton	State of the Union Address to the 103rd Congress, Second Session Jan. 25, 1994	Presidential Speeches	POTUS Study-WW	
William Jefferson Clinton	Address to the Joint Session of Congress Feb. 17, 1993	Presidential Speeches	POTUS Study-WW	
William Safire	Lend Me Your Ears: Great Speeches in History	Speeches	POTUS Study-WW	
Flip Schulke	He had a Dream: Martin Luther King Jr. and the Civil Rights Movement	U.S. Hist.-Pictorial Works	POTUS Study-WW	Inscribed by Author; Limited edition #127/250
Douglas Southall Freeman	George Washington: A Biography Volume One: Young Washington	POTUS Biography	POTUS Study-WW	Copyright 1948
Garry Wills	Cincinnatus: George Washington and the Enlightenment	POTUS Biography	POTUS Study--WW	
Richard Norton Smith	Patriarch: George Washington and the New American Nation	POTUS Biography	POTUS Study--WW	Inscribed by the Staff of the Commander George Washington Battle Group
Noemie Emery	Washington: A Biography	POTUS Biography	POTUS Study-WW	

1361-DC-00000003

S 019367

Edited by L.H. Butterfield, Marc Friedlaender, and Mary-Jo Kline	The Book of Abigail and John: Selected Letters of the Adams Family 1762-1784	Presidential Writings: Letters	POTUS Study-WW	
Nathan Schachner	Thomas Jefferson: A Biography, Volumes 1 and 2	POTUS Biography	POTUS Study-WW	
Max Byrd	Jefferson: A Nove	Fiction: Presidency	POTUS Study-WW	Inscribed by the Author
Jerome J. Shestack	Thomas Jefferson: Lawyer	POTUS Biography	POTUS Study-WW	Inscribed by the Author
Frank L. Dewey	Thomas Jefferson Lawyer	POTUS Biography	POTUS Study-WW	Inscribed by Author, January 1993
Dumas Malone	Jefferson and His Time: The Sage of Monticello	POTUS Biography	POTUS Study-WW	
Fawn M. Brodie	Thomas Jefferson: An Intimate History	POTUS Biography	POTUS Study-WW	
Natalie S. Bober	Thomas Jefferson: Man on a Mountain	POTUS Biography	POTUS Study-WW	Inscribed by the Author, Feb. 11, 1997
Noble E. Cunningham, Jr.	In Pursuit of Reason: The Life of Thomas Jefferson	POTUS Biography	POTUS Study-WW	Inscribed by the Author, Apr. 13, 1994
Jim Strupp	Revolution Song: Thomas Jefferson's Legacy	POTUS Biography	POTUS Study-WW	
Alf J. Mapp, Jr.	Thomas Jefferson: A Strange Case of Mistaken Identity	POTUS Biography	POTUS Study-WW	

Andrew Burstein	The Inner Jefferson: Portrait of a Grieving Optimist	POTUS Biography	POTUS Study-WW	Inscribed by the Author, Feb. 1997
Alf J. Mapp, Jr.	Thomas Jefferson Passionate Pilgrim: The Presidency, the Founding of the University and the Private Battle	POTUS Biography	POTUS Study-WW	Inscribed by the Author, March 23, 1994
Joseph J. Ellis	American Sphinx: The Character of Thomas Jefferson	POTUS Biography	POTUS Study-WW	
William Lee Miller	The Business of May Next: James Madison and the Founding	POTUS Biography	POTUS Study-WW	Inscribed by the Author
Robert V. Remini	The Life of Andrew Jackson	POTUS Biography	POTUS Study-WW	
Karen B. Winnick	Mr. Lincoln's Whiskers	Juvenile Book about Grace Bedell, who suggested AL grow a beard	POTUS Study-WW	Inscribed by Author
Carl Sandburg	Abraham Lincoln: The Prairie Years and the War Years	POTUS Biography	POTUS Study-WW	Inscribed by "Denise"--XMas 1966
Stephen B. Oates	With Malice Toward None: The Life of Abraham Lincoln	POTUS Biography	POTUS Study-WW	
Benjamin P. Thomas	Abraham Lincoln: A Biography	POTUS Biography	POTUS Study-WW	
Gore Vidal	Lincoln: A Novel	POTUS Fiction	POTUS Study-WW	

1361-DC-00000005

S 019369

Garry Wills	Lincoln at Gettysburg: The Words That Remade America	Lincoln Oratory	POTUS Study-WW	Inscribed by G. and Krishna Kalliampur of North Carolina on Nov. 3, 1992
James M. McPherson	Abraham Lincoln and the Second American Revolution	Lincoln-Military Ldrshp.	POTUS Study-WW	
Elton Trueblood	Abraham Lincoln: A Spiritual Biography	POTUS Biography	POTUS Study-WW	Inscribed by Connie Lovejoy of Indiana
Dale Carnegie	Lincoln The Unknown	POTUS Biography	POTUS Study-WW	
Paul Simon	Lincoln's Preparation for Greatness: The Illinois Legislative Years	POTUS Biography	POTUS Study-WW	Inscribed by Author
Phillip Shaw Paludan	The Presidency of Abraham Lincoln	POTUS Biography	POTUS Study-WW	Inscribed by the Author
Lloyd Ostendorf	Abraham Lincoln: The Boy The Man	POTUS Juvenile Biography	POTUS Study-WW	Donated by American Legion Auxiliary of Vandalia, IL
Mario M. Cuomo and Harold Holzer, Editors	Lincoln on Democracy: His Own Words, with Essays by America's Foremost Civil War Historians	AL Views on Democrcy	POTUS Study-WW	
Harold Holzer	Dear Mr. Lincoln: Letters to the President	Presidential Writings: Letters	POTUS Study-WW	Inscribed by Paul Begala-3/7/94
Andrew Delbanco, Editor	The Portable Abraham Lincoln	Presidential Speeches and Letters	POTUS Study-WW	

S_019370

John Gabriel Hunt, Editor	The Essential Abraham Lincoln	Presidential Speeches and Letters	POTUS Study-WW	
William S. McFeely	Grant: A Biography	POTUS Biography	POTUS Study-WW	
Mary Drake McFeely and William S. McFeely, Editors	Grant: Personal Memoirs of U.S. Grant: Selected Letters 1839-1865	Presidential Writings: Letters	POTUS Study-WW	
Nathan Miller	The Roosevelt Chronicles: The Story of a great American Family	Presidential Families	POTUS Study-WW	
August Heckscher	Woodrow Wilson: A Biography	POTUS Biography	POTUS Study-WW	
Gene Smith	When the Cheering Stopped	POTUS Biography	POTUS Study-WW	
Sigmund Freud and William C. Bullitt	Thomas Woodrow Wilson: A Psychological Study	POTUS Biography	POTUS Study-WW	
Herbert Hoover	The Ordeal of Woodrow Wilson	POTUS Biography	POTUS Study-WW	
Joseph P. Lash	The Partnership That Saved the West: Roosevelt and Churchill 1939-41	POTUS Biography	POTUS Study-WW	Inscribed by Bernard Goss, 19 Dec 1996
Kenneth S. Davis	FDR: The Beckoning of Destiny 1882-1928	POTUS Biography	POTUS Study-WW	

Eric Larrabee	Commander in Chief: Franklin Delano Roosevelt, His Lieutenants & Their War	POTUS Biography	POTUS Study-WW	Inscribed by "Bucky" in July 1987
Ted Morgan	FDR: A Biography	POTUS Biography	POTUS Study-WW	
Yankee Magazine, Jan. 1996	Article on Calvin Coolidge-"The Price of the Presidency"	POTUS Biography	POTUS Study-WW	
Herbert Hoover (William Nichols, Editor)	Herbert Hoover: Fishing for Fun and to Wash Your Soul	Presidential Writings: Fishing	POTUS Study-WW	
George Grey	Ten Days: A Crisis in American History (copyright 1933)	U.S. History--FDR Admin.	POTUS Study-WW	Inscribed by Max and Anita Harris, 1/7/93
Hugh Gregory Gallagher	FDR:s Splendid Deception: The moving story of Roosevelt's massive disability and the intense efforts to conceal it from the public	POTUS Biography	POTUS Study-WW	Inscribed by Author 2/22/95
Geoffrey C. Ward	A First-Class Temperament: The Emergence of Franklin Roosevelt	POTUS Biography	POTUS Study-WW	
Robert E. Sherwood	Roosevelt and Hopkins: An Intimate History	U.S. History--FDR Admin.	POTUS Study-WW	
Franklin Delano Roosevelt (Russell D. Buhite and David W. Levy, Editors)	FDR's Fireside Chats	Presidential Speeches	POTUS Study-WW	

Robert H. Ferrell	Choosing Truman: The Democratic Convention of 1944	U.S. History--Democratic Party	POTUS Study-WW	Inscribed by the Author
David McCullough	Truman	POTUS Biography	POTUS Study-WW	Inscribed by Sharon and Jay Rockefeller, 7/19/92
Robert H. Ferrell	Harry S. Truman: A Life	POTUS Biography	POTUS Study-WW	
Margaret Truman	Harry S. Truman	POTUS Biography	POTUS Study-WW	
Roy Jenkins	Truman	POTUS Biography	POTUS Study-WW	
Harry S. Truman	Mr. Citizen	Presidential Memoirs	POTUS Study-WW	
Ken Hechler	Working with Truman: A Personal Memoir of the White House Years	U.S. History--Truman Admin.	POTUS Study-WW	Inscribed by Author, 8/25/96
Harry S. Truman (Margaret Truman, Editor)	Where the Buck Stops: The Personal and Private Writings of Harry S. Truman	Presidential History	POTUS Study-WW	Inscribed by David E. Barrett of Fairfield, OH
Harry S. Truman (Monte M. Poen, Editor)	Strictly Personal and Confidential: The Letters Harry Truman Never Mailed	Presidential Writings: Letters	POTUS Study-WW	
Fred I. Greenstein	The Hidden-Hand Presidency: Eisenhower as Leader	Presidential Leadershp	POTUS Study-WW	Inscribed by Author
Sheila L. Cassidy	Remembering Jack and Bobby: A Kennedy Anthology	Presidential Quotes	POTUS Study-WW	Inscribed by Author, July, 1992

Kenneth P. O'Donnell and David Powers with Joe McCarthy	"Johnny, We Hardly Knew Ye": Memories of John Fitzgerald Kennedy	POTUS Biography	POTUS Study-WW	Inscribed by Dave Powers, 1/17/92
Gerald Posner	Case Closed: Lee Harvey Oswald and the Assasination of JFK	JFK's Death--Theories	POTUS Study-WW	
Nigel Hamilton	JFK Reckless Youth	POTUS Biography	POTUS Study-WW	
Thomas C. Reeves	A Question of Character: A Life of John F. Kennedy	POTUS Biography	POTUS Study-WW	Inscribed to HRC from Gaston Williamson of Little Rock; note from Williamson enclosed as well
Garry Wills	The Kennedy Imprisonment: A Meditation on Power	Kennedy Family History	POTUS Study-WW	
John F. Kennedy (edited by Theodore C. Sorenson)	"Let the Word Go Forth": The Speeches, Statements, and Writings of John F. Kennedy 1947-1963	POTUS Speeches and Writings	POTUS Study-WW	Inscribed from Tom O'Toole of Pennsylvania
Lewis J. Paper	John F. Kennedy: The Promis & the Performance	Kennedy Administration	POTUS Study-WW	
Irving Bernstein	Promises Kept: John F. Kennedy's New Frontier	Kennedy Administration	POTUS Study-WW	Inscribed by Zelda and Albert Silverman, 11/13/92

1361-DC-00000010

S 019374

Harris Wofford	Of Kennedys & Kings: Making Sense of the Sixties	U.S. History-1960s	POTUS Study-WW	Inscribed by Harris Wofford, 11/2/92; Note from Wofford enclosed also
Thomas Fleming	The Man Who Dared thee Lightning: A New Look at Benjamin Franklin	POTUS Biography	POTUS Study-WW	
Ronald W. Clark	A Biography: Benjamin Franklin	POTUS Biography	POTUS Study-WW	
Milton Lomask	Aaron Burr: The Years from Princeton to Vice-President	VPOTUS Biography	POTUS Study-WW	
T.H. Watkins	Righteous Pilgrim: The Life and Times of Harold Ickes 1874-1952	Biography: Harold Ickes	POTUS Study-WW	Inscribed to BC and HRC by Susan, 1/92
Joseph P. Lash	Eleanor and Franklin: The Story of their relationship based on Eleanor Roosevelt's private papers	POTUS Family History	POTUS Study-WW	
Stella K. Hershan	The Candles She Lit: The Legacy of Eleanor Roosevelt	FLOTUS Biography	POTUS Study-WW	Inscribed by the Author 1/23/96
Eleanor Roosevelt	The Autobiography of Eleanor Roosevelt	FLOTUS Autobiography	POTUS Study-WW	
Eleanor Roosevelt	Tomorrow is Now: "It is today that we must create the world of the future"	FLOTUS Writings	POTUS Study-WW	
Eleanor Roosevelt	This I Remember	FLOTUS Memoirs	POTUS Study-WW	

1361-DC-00000011

S 019375

Blanche Wiesen Cook	Eleanor Roosevelt: Volume One 1884-1933	FLOTUS Biography	POTUS Study-WW	Inscribed to HRC by Marilyn and Richard Rich of Orinda, CA
Albert Eisele	Almost to the Presidency: A Biography of Two American Politicians	Biography: Humphrey and McCarthy	POTUS Study-WW	Inscribed by Pat O'Connor
John Kennedy	Bound answer to question asked in 1962, "Somewhere in our land today, there is a high school or college student who will one day be sitting in your chair. If you could now speak to this future President, what advice would you give him or her"; this appeared in the 1970 World Book Ency.	POTUS Writings	POTUS Study-WW	
Alex J. Goldman	John Fitzgerald Kennedy: The World Remembers	Death of JFK	POTUS Study-WW	Inscribed by Alex J. Goldman, 11/18/1992
Theodore H. White	The Making of a President 1960	Presidential Campaigns	POTUS Study-WW	Inscribed by the Pryors, 11/2/92
Christopher Matthews	Kennedy & Nixon: The Rivalry That Shaped Postwar America	U.S. History-Political Relationships	POTUS Study-WW	Inscribed by the Author, 5/96
Richard Reeves	President Kennedy: Profile of Power	POTUS Biography	POTUS Study-WW	Inscribed by the Author, 11/20/93
Arthur M. Schlesinger	A Thousand Days: John F. Kennedy in the White House	JFK Administration	POTUS Study-WW	Signature of Bill Clinton; 1st Printing

S_0T9376

John F. Kennedy	The Speeches of Senator John F. Kennedy Presidential Campaign of 1960	Presidential Speeches	POTUS Study-WW	Inscribed by Brian Snow (?), 9/17/92
Robert A.Caro	The Years of Lyndon Johnson: Means of Ascent	POTUS Biography	POTUS Study-WW	
Doris Kearns	Lyndon Johnson & the American Dream	POTUS Biography	POTUS Study-WW	
Joseph A. Califano, Jr.	The Triumph and Tragedy of Lyndon Johnson: The White House Years	POTUS Biography	POTUS Study-WW	Inscribed by the Author, 7/92
Robert A. Caro	The Years of Lyndon Johnson: The Path to Power	POTUS Biography	POTUS Study-WW	
Lyndon Baines Johnson	The Vantage Point: Perspectives of the Presidency 1963-69	POTUS Memoirs	POTUS Study-WW	
Merle Miller	Lyndon: An Oral Biography	POTUS Biography	POTUS Study-WW	
Richard Nixon	1999: Victory Without War	Presidential Writings: Foreign Policy	POTUS Study-WW	Advance Copy
Richard Nixon	Beyond Peace	Presidential Writings: Foreign Policy	POTUS Study-WW	
Richard Nixon	The Real War (The Richard Nixon Library Edition)	Presidential Writings: Foreign Policy	POTUS Study-WW	
Richard Nixon	Real Peace: No More Vietnams (The Richard Nixon Library Edition)	Presidential Writings: Foreign Policy	POTUS Study-WW	

Richard Nixon	Leaders (The Richard Nixon Library Edition)	Presidential Writings: Leadership	POTUS Study-WW	
Richard Nixon	Seize the Moment: America's Challenge in a One-Superpower World	Presidential Writings: Foreign Policy	POTUS Study-WW	
Christopher Matthews	Kennedy and Nixon: The Rivalry That Shaped Postwar America	Presidential History: The Sixties	POTUS Study-WW	Inscribed by the author, May 1996
Richard Nixon	Seize the Moment: America's Challenge in a One Superpower World	Presidential Writings: Foreign Pólicy	POTUS Study-WW	
Presidential Studies Quarterly	Special Issue: The Nixon Presidency	Nixon Administration	POTUS Study-WW	
Gerald Ford	The War Powers Resolution: A Constitutional Crisis	Presidential Writings-Foreign Policy	POTUS Study-WW	Signed by the Author
Jimmy Carter	Always a Reckoning and Other Poems	Presidential Writings-Poetry	POTUS Study-WW	
Jimmy Carter	An Outdoor Journal	Presidential Writings-Outdoor Life	POTUS Study-WW	
Jimmy Carter	Turning Point: A Candidate, a State, and a Nation Come of Age	Presidential Writings: Autobiography	POTUS Study-WW	Signed by the Author
Jimmy and Rosalynn Carter	Everything to Gain: Making the Most of the Rest of Your Life	Presidential Writings-Philosophy	POTUS Study-WW	Inscribed to BC and HRC by the Authors
Jimmy Carter	Keeping Faith: Memoirs of a President	Presidential Writings: Memoirs	POTUS Study-WW	Inscribed to BC by the Author

1361-DC-00000014

S 019378

Jimmy Carter	A Government as Good as Its People	Presidential Writings: Govt. And Politics	POTUS Study-WW	
Jimmy Carter	Keeping Faith: Memoirs of a President	Presidential Writings: Memoirs	POTUS Study-WW	1995 Edition
Lou Cannon	President Reagan: The Role of a Lifetime	Biography: Reagan	POTUS Study-WW	
Ronald Reagan	Ronald Reagan: An American Life	Presidential Writings: Autobiography	POTUS Study-WW	Inscribed by the author 11/27/92
Arthur M. Schlesinger, Jr.	Robert Kennedy and His Times	Biography: Robert F. Kennedy	POTUS Study-WW	Inscribed by Milas H. And Shirley Hale, 1/11/79
Joseph Lash	Dealers and Dreamers: A New Look at the New Deal	U.S. History: New Deal	POTUS Study-WW	Inscribed by Steve Smith
Warren Rogers	When I Think of Bobby: A Personal History of the Kennedy Years	Biography: Robert F. Kennedy	POTUS Study-WW	Inscribed by the author 6/10/93
Robert F. Kennedy; Edited by Edwin O. Guthman and C. Richard Allen	R.F.K.: Collected Speeches	Speeches: Robert F. Kennedy	POTUS Study-WW	Note from Rick Allen
Robert F. Kennedy	Thirteen Days: A Memoir of the Cuban Missile Crisis	U.S Foreign Policy: Cuban Missile Crisis	POTUS Study-WW	
Jack Newfield	Robert F. Kennedy: A Memoir	Biography: Robert F. Kennedy	POTUS Study-WW	
Robert S. McNamara	In Retrospect: The Tragedy and Lessons of Vietnam	U.S. Foreign Policy: Vietnam	POTUS Study-WW	Inscribed by the author

Mario Cuomo	More than Words: The Speeches of Mario Cuomo	Speeches: Mario Cuomo	POTUS Study-WW	Inscribed by the author
T. Harry Williams	Huey Long: A Biography	Biography: Huey Long	POTUS Study-WW	Inscribed by BC to Jeff (Dwire), Christmas 1970
Clarence Darrow	The Story of My Life	Autobiography: Clarence Darrow	POTUS Study-WW	
Edwin S. Gaustad	Neither King Nor Prelate: Religion and the New Nation, 1776-1826	U.S. Religious History	POTUS Study-WW	Inscribed by the author 1/7/97
Gerald Gunther	Learned Hand: The Man and the Judge	Biography: Learned Hand	POTUS Study-WW	
Paul Finkelman	Slavery and the Founders: Race and Liberty in the Age of Jefferson	U.S. History: Race Relations	POTUS Study-WW	Inscribed by the author 2/11/97
Thomas E. Patterson	Out of Order: How the Decline of the Political Parties and the Growing Power of the News Media Undermine the American Way of Electing Presidents	Presidentia Campaigns and the Media	POTUS Study-WW	
Walter Cronkhite	A Reporter's Life	Autobiography: Walter Cronkhite	POTUS Study-WW	
William E. Leuchtenburg	In the Shadow of F.D.R.- From Harry Truman to Bill Clinton	Presidential History	POTUS Study-WW	Inscribed to HRC by the author
Bruce I. Newman	The Marketing of the President: Political Marketing as Campaign Strategy	Presidential Campaigns: Strategy	POTUS Study-WW	Inscribed by the author

Robert E. Gilbert	The Mortal Presidency: Illness and Anguish in the White House	Presidential History: Health	POTUS Study-WW	
Haynes Johnson	Sleeping Through History: America in the Reagan Years	Presidential History: Reagan Administration	POTUS Study-WW	
John Morton Blum	The Progressive Presidents: Theodore Roosevelt, Woodrow Wilson, Franklin Delano Roosevelt, and Lyndon Johnson	Presidential History	POTUS Study-WW	Inscribed by ? and Ruth, December 1992
Alice M. Rivlin	Reviving the American Dream: the Economy, the States, and the Federal Government	U.S. Economic Policy	POTUS Study-WW	Card from Luis and Christina, 12/19/94
Terry Eastland	Energy in the Executive: The Case for the Strong Presidency	Presidency: Academic Study	POTUS Study-WW	
Joe McGuinness	The Selling of the President: The Classic Account of the Packaging of Richard Nixon	Presidential History: Richard Nixon	POTUS Study-WW	Inscribed by the author 11/10/91
Louis W. Koenig	The Chief Executive	Presidential History	POTUS Study-WW	from the San Mateo County Library System
Richard Rose	The Postmodern President: The White House Meets the World	Presidency: Academic Study	POTUS Study-WW	
Robert Shogan	The Riddle of Power: Presidential Leadership From Truman to Bush	Presidency: Leadership	POTUS Study-WW	
Sidney Blumenthal	Our Long National Daydream: A Political Pageant of the Reagan Era	Presidential History: Reagan Administration	POTUS Study-WW	

Carl M. Brauer	Presidential Transitions: Eisenhower through Reagan	Presidential History: Transitions	POTUS Study-WW	
Paul Taylor	See How They Run: Electing the President in an Age of Mediaocracy	Presidential Campaigns and the Media	POTUS Study-WW	
John B. Moses, M.D. and Wilbur Gross (?)	Presidential Courage: The Dramatic Stories of Presidents Confronted by the Combined Challenges of Health and Political Crises	Presidential History: Courage	POTUS Study-WW	
Theodore C. Sorenson	A Different Kind of Presidency: A Proposal for Breaking the Political Deadlock	Presidency	POTUS Study-WW	
Michael Novak	Choosing Presidents: Symbols of Political Leadership	Presidency: Leadership	POTUS Study-WW	Inscribed to HRC and BC by the Author: Renaissance Weekend 92-93
Helen Thomas	Dateline: White House. A Warm and Revealing Account of America's Presidents and their Families from the Kennedys to the Fords	Presidency and Media Coverage	POTUS Study-WW	Inscribed by the Author 8/19/93
Michael J. Sandel	Democracy's Discontent: America in Search of a Public Philosophy	Democratic Philosophy	POTUS Study-WW	Inscribed by the Author 8/2/96
James Fallows	Breaking the News: How the Media Undermine American Democracy	Politics and the Media	POTUS Study-WW	Inscribed by the Author 1/16/97
James A. Michener	This Noble Land: My Vision for America	U.S. Social Values	POTUS Study-WW	

S 019382

.Charles O. Jones	The Presidency in a Separated System	Presidency	POTUS Study-WW	
David M. Barrett	Uncertain Warriors: Lyndon Johnson and His Vietnam Advisors	U.S. Foreign Policy: Vietnam	POTUS Study-WW	Inscribed by the Author 3/10/94
Jack W. Germond and Jules Witcover	Blue Smoke and Mirrors: How Reagan Won and Why Carter Lost the Election of 1980	Presidential Campaigns: 1980 Case Study	POTUS Study-WW	
E.J. Dionne, Jr.	Why Americans Hate Politics	Political Participation	POTUS Study-WW	
Peter Brown	Minority Party: Why Democrats Face Defeat in 1992 and Beyond	Political Campaigns: Democratic Party	POTUS Study-WW	Inscribed by the Author 9/4/91
Larry J. Sabato	Feeding Frenzy: How Attack Journalism Has Transformed American Politics	Political Campaigns: Attack Journalism	POTUS Study-WW	Inscribed by the Author 8/12/91
Kenneth T. Walsh	Feeding the Beast: The White House Versus the Press	Presidency and Media Coverage	POTUS Study-WW	Inscribed by the Author 1/16/97
Howard Kurtz	Hot Air All Talk All the Time: An Inside Look at the Performers and the Pundits	Politics and the Media	POTUS Study-WW	Inscribed by the Author 1/23/96
Hedrick ?	The Power Game: How Washington Works	Politics and Power	POTUS Study-WW	Inscribed by the Author 6/30/93
Jack W. Germond and Jules Witcover	Whose Broad Stripes and Bright Stars? The Trivial Pursuit of the Presidency 1988	Presidential Campaigns: 1988 Case Study	POTUS Study-WW	Inscribed from Mary Altgelt

Haynes Johnson	Divided We Fall: Gambling With History in the Nineties	Economic Conditions	POTUS Study-WW	Inscribed by the Author 3/7/94
Jack W. Germond and Jules Witcover	Mad as Hell: Revolt at the Ballot Box 1992	Presidential Campaigns: 1992 Case Study	POTUS Study-WW	Inscribed to BC and HRC by the Authors 7/15/93
Howard Kurtz	Media Circus: The Trouble With America's Newspapers	Print Journalism	POTUS Study-WW	Inscribed by the Author
Mary Van Rensselaer Thayer	Jacqueline Kennedy: The White House Years	Biography: Jackie Kennedy	POTUS Study-WW	Inscribed by Mrs. Lexine Adams of Jacksonville, FL
Harry S. Truman edited by Mark Goodman	Give 'Em Hell Harry	Presidential Quotes	POTUS Study-WW	
Theodore White	The Making of the President 1960	Presidential Campaigns: 1960 Case Study	POTUS Study-WW	
John F. Kennedy	Profiles in Courage: Commemorative Edition	U.S. History: Courage in Early Leaders	POTUS Study-WW	
John F. Kennedy edited by Bill Adler	The Kennedy Wit	Presidential Quotes	POTUS Study-WW	Inscribed from Jeff Fites
Shelley Bedek	Our President: Bill Clinton (children's book)	Juvenile Biography: Bill Clinton	POTUS Study-WW	Inscribed from Colin and Bronwyn Dixon of Fayetteville, AR
John F. Kennedy edited by Bill Adler	The Kennedy Wit	Presidential Quotes	POTUS-Study-WW	Hardback Edition

S 019384

William Jefferson Clinton	Between Hope and History	Presidential Writings	POTUS Study-WW	Chinese Edition
William Jefferson Clinton	Between Hope and History	Presidential Writings	POTUS Study-WW	Hebrew Edition
Jim Moore and Rick Ihde	Clinton: Young Man in a Hurry	Biography: Bill Clinton	POTUS Study-WW	Japanese Edition: Inscribed by Jim Moore
Jim Moore and Rick Ihde	Clinton: Young Man in a Hurry	Biography: Bill Clinton	POTUS Study-WW	Chinese Edition: Inscribed by Jim Moore
Judith Warner	Hillary Clinton: The Inside Story	Biography: Hillary Rodham Clinton	POTUS Study-WW	
Charles F. Allen and Jonathan Portis	The Comeback Kid: The Life and Career of Bill Clinton	Biography: Bill Clinton	POTUS Study-WW	Leather Bound Romanian Edition
Virginia Kelley with James Morgan	Leading With My Heart	Autobiography: Virginia Kelley	POTUS Study-WW	Korean Edition
David R. Collins	William Jefferson Clinton: 42nd President of the United States	Juvenile Biography: Bill Clinton	POTUS Study-WW	
Bill Clinton and Al Gore	Putting People First	Presidential and Vice-Presidential Writings	POTUS Study-WW	Italian Edition
Daiwa Institute of Research, Ltd.	The Clinton Revolution: An Inside Look at the New Administration	U.S. Economic Policy	POTUS Study-WW	
Daiwa Institute of Research, Ltd.	The Clinton Administration: An Inside Look at the New Administration	U.S. Economic Policy	POTUS Study-WW	Japanese Edition

Jim Moore and Rick Ihde	Clinton: Young Man in a Hurry	Biography: Bill Clinton	POTUS Study-WW	Inscribed by Nancy Nash and Maria (?) Haley
Daiwa Institute of Research, Ltd.	The Clinton Revolution: An Inside Look at the New Administration	U.S. Economic Policy	POTUS Study-WW	Japanese Edition
Charles F. Allen and Jonathan Portis	The Comeback Kid: the Life and Career of Bill Clinton	Biography: Bill Clinton	POTUS Study-WW	Romanian Edition
Compiled and edited by Ernest Dumas	The Clintons of Arkansas: An Introduction by Those Who Know Them Best	Biography: Clinton Family	POTUS Study-WW	
William L. Brown	President Bill: A Graphic Epic	Political Satire	POTUS Study-WW	
Hank Hillin	Al Gore, Jr.: Born to Lead	Biography: Al Gore	POTUS Study-WW	Inscribed by the author 1992
William Jefferson Clinton	Between Hope and History: Meeting America's Challenges for the 21st Century	Presidential Writings	POTUS Study-WW	French Edition
William Jefferson Clinton	Between Hope and History: Meeting America's Challenges for the 21st Century	Presidential Writings	POTUS Study-WW	Russian Edition
Progressive Policy Institute of Democratic Leadership Council, Inc.	Mandate for Change	Democratic Party	POTUS Study-WW	Chinese Translation: Inscribed by Yang Dayhou of Beijing
Rex Nelson	The Hillary Factor: America's Most Powerful First Lady	Biography: Hillary Rodham Clinton	POTUS Study-WW	

S 019386

Chip Eliot	The Clintons: Meeting the First Family	Juvenile Biography: Clinton Family	POTUS Study-WW	2 copies
Robert Levin	Bill Clinton: The Inside Story	Biography: Bill Clinton	POTUS Study-WW	Polish Edition
Tomasz Liz	Jak To Sie Robi W Ameryce	Biography: Bill Clinton	POTUS Study-WW	Polish Edition; Inscribed by the author
Donnie Radcliffe	Hillary Rodham Clinton: A First Lady for Our Time	Biography: Hillary Rodham Clinton	POTUS Study-WW	
Bill Clinton and Al Gore	Putting People First: How We Can All Change America	Presidential and Vice-Presidential Writings	POTUS Study-WW	
Norman King	Hillary: Her True Story	Biography: Hillary Rodham Clinton	POTUS Study-WW	
Edited by Charles T. Royer	Campaign for President: The Managers Look at 1992	Presidential Campaigns and Management	POTUS Study-WW	
Bob Woodward	The Agenda: Inside the Clinton White House	Clinton Administration: Economic Policy	POTUS Study-WW	Inscribed by the author
Elizabeth Drew	On the Edge: The Clinton Presidency	Clinton Administration	POTUS Study-WW	Inscribed by the author 107/7/94
Steven Waldman	The Bill: How the Adventures of Clinton's National Service Bill Reveal What is Corrupt, Comic, Cynical--And Noble--About Washington	Clinton Administration: National Service	POTUS Study-WW	Inscribed by the author

S 019387

1361-DC-00000023

Meredith L. Oakley	On the Make: The Rise of Bill Clinton	Biography: Bill Clinton	POTUS Study-WW	
Victoria Sherrow	Hillary Rodham Clinton	Juvenile Biography: Hillary Rodham Clinton	POTUS Study-WW	
Victoria Sherrow	Bill Clinton	Juvenile Biography: Bill Clinton	POTUS Study-WW	
Peter Goldman, Thomas M DeFrank, Mark Miller, Andrew Murr(?), Tom Mathews	Quest for the Presidency 1992	Presidential Campaigns	POTUS Study-WW	Inscribed by Mark S. Miller 10/11/94
Gerald M. Pomper et al.	The Election of 1996: Reports and Interpretation	Presidential Campaigns	POTUS Study-WW	
Sarah McClendon	Mr. President, Mr. President: My 50 Years of Covering the White House	Presidency and the Media	POTUS Study-WW	Inscribed by the Author 10/18/96
Robert Reich	Locked in the Cabinet	Clinton Administration: Memoirs and Labor Policy	POTUS Study-WW	Inscribed by the Author 4/97
Haynes Johnson and David S. Broder	The System: The American Way of Politics at the Breaking Point	U.S. Political System	POTUS Study-WW	Inscribed by the Authors 3/31/96
Edited by Colin Campbell and Bert A. Rockman	The Clinton Presidency: First Appraisals	Clinton Administration	POTUS Study-WW	
Bob Woodward	The Choice	Presidential Campaigns: 1996 Case Study	POTUS Study-WW	

Eleanor Clift and Tom (?)	War Without Bloodshed: The Art of Politics	U.S. Political System	POTUS Study-WW	Inscribed to BC and HRC by the Authors 7/4/96
David Maraniss	First in His Class: A Biography of Bill Clinton	Biography: Bill Clinton	POTUS Study-WW	Advance Uncorrected Proof with BC's notes
Jim Moore with Rick Ihde	Clinton: Young Man in a Hurry	Biography: Bill Clinton	POTUS Study-WW	
David Gallen	Bill Clinton As They Know Him: An Oral Biography	Biography: Bill Clinton	POTUS Study-WW	
Dick Morris	Behind the Oval Office: Winning the Presidency in the 1990s	Clinton Administration and 1996 Presidential Campaign	POTUS Study-WW	Inscribed by the Author 1/9/97
Evan Thomas, Karen Breslaw, Debra Rosenberg, Leslie Kaufman, and Andrew Muir (?)	Back from the Dead: How Clinton Survived the Republican Revolution	Clinton Administration and Republican Revolution	POTUS Study-WW	Inscribed by Karen Breslaw 1/22/97
Compiled and Edited by Mary Ann Barton and Paul C. Barton	Campaign: A Cartoon History of Bill Clinton's Race for the White House	Political Cartoons	POTUS Study-WW	Inscribed by the Authors
William Jefferson Clinton	Between Hope and History	Presidential Writings	POTUS Study-WW	

Martin Walker	Clinton The President They Deserve: An Intimate Political Biography of the 42nd President of the United States	Biography: Bill Clinton	POTUS Study-WW	Written in London
Conor O'Clery	Daring Diplomacy: Clinton's Secret Search for Peace in Ireland	Clinton Administration: Foreign Policy	POTUS Study-WW	Inscribed by the Author 3/12/97
Donald Hall	The Museum of Clear Ideas-New Poems	Poetry	POTUS Study-WW	Signed by the Author; Bookplate from BC's "Granite State Friends" of the anniversary of the New Hampshire Primary
Ernest Hebert	Live Free or Die: A Novel	Fiction	POTUS Study-WW	Bookplate from "Granite State Friends"
Laurel Thatcher Ulrich	A Midwife's Tale: The Life of Martha Ballard, Based on Her Diary 1785-1812	Biography: Martha Ballard	POTUS Study-WW	Bookplate from "Granite State Friends"
David D. Draves	Builder of Men: Life in the C.C.C. Camps of New Hampshire	U.S. History: New Deal, Civilian Conservation Corps	POTUS Study-WW	Bookplate from "Granite State Friends"
Jane Kenyon	Constance	Poetry	POTUS Study-WW	Bookplate from "Granite State Friends"
Howard Mansfield	In the Memory House	Historical Sites-New England	POTUS Study-WW	Bookplate from "Granite State Friends"

Maxine Kunin	Nurture	Poetry	POTUS Study-WW	Bookplate from "Granite State Friends"
Dayton Duncan	Grass Roots: One Year in the Life of the New Hampshire Presidential Primary	Presidential Campaigns: New Hampshire Primary	POTUS Study-WW	Signed by the Author; Bookplate from "Granite State Friends"
Stephen R. Covey	First Things First: To Live, To Learn, To Leave a Legacy	Time Management	POTUS Study-WW	
Louis J. Aronne, MD	Weigh Less, Live Longer	Diet and Health	POTUS Study-WW	Inscribed by the Author 7/15/97
Bert Holldobler and Edward O. Wilson	Journey to the Ants: A Story of Scientific Exploration	Science: Ants	POTUS Study-WW	Inscribed by "Newt"
Jung Chang	Wild Swans: Three Daughters of China	Biography: Three Chinese Women	POTUS Study-WW	
Stephen R. Covey	The Seven Habits of Highly Effective People	Personal Characteristics	POTUS Study-WW	Inscribed to BC and HRC by the Author 12/30/94
Collected and Edited by the Brothers Halamandaris	Caring Quotes: A Campendium of Caring Thought	Quotes	POTUS Study-WW	Inscribed by the Authors
Leah Rabin	Rabin: Our Life, His Legacy	Biography: Yitzhak Rabin	POTUS Study-WW	Inscribed to BC and HRC 4/8/97
Carl Bernstein and Marco Politi	His Holiness: John Paul II and the Hidden History of Our Time	Biography: Pope John Paul II	POTUS Study-WW	Inscribed by Carl Bernstein

David Fromkin	In the Time of the Americans: FDR, Truman, Eisenhower, Marshall, McArthur, The Generation that Changed America's Role in the World	U.S. Foreign Relations: 20th Century	POTUS Study-WW	
Michael Shaara	The Killer Angels: The Classic Novel of the Civil War	Fiction: Civil War	POTUS Study-WW	Inscribed by LTC Michael G. Mudd, Army Aide to the President, 1/20/97
Edited by Peter B. Kovler	Democrats and the American Idea: A Bicentennial Appraisal	Democratic Party	POTUS Study-WW	
Grady C. Cothen	What Happened to the Southern Baptist Convention? A Memoir of the Controversy	U.S. Religious History: Southern Baptists	POTUS Study-WW	Signed by the Author
William Pfaff	The Wrath of Nations: Civilization and the Furies Of Nationalism	Nationalism	POTUS Study-WW	Signed by the Author 11/28/93
Richard Carleton Hacker	The Ultimate Cigar Book	Cigars	POTUS Study-WW	Inscribed by the Author
Anwar Bati and Simon Chase	The Cigar Companion: A Connoisseur's Guide	Cigars	POTUS Study-WW	Inscribed by Helen Van Berg 11/5/96
	Pictorial Directory-105th Congress	Congressional Directory	POTUS Study-WW	Leather Bound with "Bill Clinton" inscribed on the cover
	Common Prayer Hymnal	Religion	POTUS Study-WW	Inscribed by Jim Martin 8/97

S 019392

Edited by Jorie Graham	Earth Took of Earth: 100 Great Poems of the English Language	Poems	POTUS Study-WW	
Edited by Reba Collins	Will Rogers Says . . .	Quotes: Will Rogers	POTUS Study-WW	Inscribed by the Author and George and Donna Nigh
Desmond Tutu	An African Prayer Book	African Religious Life	POTUS Study-WW	Inscribed by the Author 2/7/95
Thomas Jefferson	The Jefferson Bible	Presidential Writings: U.S. Religious Life	POTUS Study-WW	Inscribed by Robert Turk 12/20/92
Abraham Lincoln	Lincoln's Devotional	Presidential Writings: Religion	POTUS Study-WW	Inscribed by Ronald F. Thiemann 9/8/95
Benjamin Franklin	Benjamin Franklin: The Autobiography and Other Writings	Autobiography: Ben Franklin	POTUS Study-WW	
Ariel Books	Oh Vey: The Things They Say! A Book of Jewish Wit	Quotes: Jewish	POTUS Study-WW	
Noah Ben Shea	Great Jewish Quotes: 5,000 Years of Truth and Humor From the Bible to George Burns	Quotes: Jewish	POTUS Study-WW	
Norman Vincent Peale	Seven Values to Live By	Personal Values	POTUS Study-WW	
Al Gore	The Best Kept Secrets in Government--Digest Version	Clinton Administration: Reinventing Government	POTUS Study-WW	

	You Must Remember This 1946	History: 1946	POTUS Study-WW	
Garrison Keillor	Truckstop And Other Lake Wobegon Stories	Fiction	POTUS Study-WW	
	The Declaration of Independence and the Constitution of the United States	U.S. Constitutional Democracy	POTUS Study-WW	
	Teachings of Jesus: The Holy Bible KJV	Religion	POTUS Study-WW	
Franklin Delano Roosevelt	Fireside Chats	Presidential Speeches	POTUS Study-WW	
	A Prayer Book for the Armed Forces 1988	U.S. Religion	POTUS Study-WW	Inscribed by Norman P. Forder, retired Chaplain of the U.S. Army
Edited by Robert M. Herhold	Prayers for Peace: Beginning With Me	Religion	POTUS Study-WW	Inscribed to BC and HRC by the Author
Frederick Talbott	Churchill on Courage: Timeless Wisdom for Persevering	Quotes: Winston Churchill	POTUS Study-WW	Inscribed by Frederik Talbott, 10/9/96
Nicholson Baker	Vox	Novel	POTUS Study-WW	

1361-DC-00000030

S 019394

Kevin D. Randle, Capt. USAFR and Donald R. Schmitt, Director of Special Investigation, Center for UFO Studies	UFO Crash at Roswell	U.S. Military History: UFOs	POTUS Study-WW	
Paul Slansky	The Clothes Have No Emperor: A Chronicle of the American 80s	U.S. History: 1980s	POTUS Study-WW	Inscribed by the Author 10/17/96
Pete Carril with Dan White	The Smart Take from the Strong: The Basketball Philosophy of Pete Carril	Sports Philosophy	POTUS Study-WW	Inscribed by Thomas H. Pyle
	Three Poems of Solon: Patriot and Lawgiver	Poetry	POTUS Study-WW	Presented to the Honorable Millicent Fenwick, 2/25/80
Compiled by Luther G. Presley	Heavenly Highway Hymns	Religion	POTUS Study-WW	Inscribed by Jim B. Baker
Richard J. Mouw	Uncommon Decency: Christian Civilization in an Uncivil World	Church and the World	POTUS Study-WW	Inscribed by the Author
Mark Gerzon	A House Divided: A Journey Through Six Belief Systems Struggling for America's Soul	U.S. Political System	POTUS Study-WW	Uncorrected Proof
Edited by George E. Curry	The Affirmative Action Debate	U.S. Domestic Policy: Affirmative Action	POTUS Study-WW	Inscribed by the Author 6/28/96

Edited by Peggy Hackman and Don Oldenburg	Dear Mr. President: Greetings and Advice to a New Leader from the Nation's Youngest Citizens	Presidential Correspondence	POTUS Study-WW	
Garry Maurio	Beaches, Bureaucrats, and Big Oil: One Man's Fight for Texas	Environment: Oil and Texas	POTUS Study-WW	Inscribed by the Author 1997
Vice-President Al Gore	Common Sense Government: Works Better and Costs Less	Clinton Administration: Reinventing Government	POTUS Study-WW	
Benjamin Netanyahu	Fighting Terrorism: How Democracies Can Defeat Domestic and International Terrorism	World Politics: Terrorism	POTUS Study-WW	POTUS Study-WW Inscribed by the Author
Robert Massie and Suzanne Massie	Journey: The Classic Story of a Son's Illness and a Family's Courage	Biography: Robert Massie, Jr.; Health Care	POTUS Study-WW	Inscribed to HRC by Suzanne Massie 4/20/93
Herb Stansbury	Executive Smart Charts and Other Insider Revelations on Corporate Insanity	Corporations: Satire	POTUS Study-WW	Inscribed by the Author 12/24/93
Synectics	Imagine	Quotes	POTUS Study-WW	Inscribed by Barbara Govenda
James Chace	The Consequences of the Peace: The New Internationalism and Foreign Policy	U.S. Foreign Policy	POTUS Study-WW	Inscribed by the Author to Governor Clinton
Mark Mathabane	Kaffir Boy: The True Story of a Black Youth's Coming of Age in Apartheid South Africa	Autobiography: Mark Mathabane	POTUS Study-WW	Inscribed by the Author 1/6/92

Edited by Mark Green and James Ledbetter	Ideas That Work: 60 Solutions for America's Third Century. The Democracy Project June 1988	U.S. Political System	POTUS Study-WW	
Catherine Drinker Bowen	Miracle at Philadelphia: the Story of the Constitutional Convention. May to Sept. 1787	U.S. Constitutional History	POTUS Study-WW	
Beth Kobliner	Get a Financial Life: Personal Finance in Your Twenties and Thirties	Personal Finance	POTUS Study-WW	Inscribed by the Author 7/29/96
Ronald Steel	Temptations of a Superpower: America's Foreign Policy After the Cold War	U.S. Foreign Policy	POTUS Study-WW	
David Kashet	Speaking American: How the Democrats Can Win in the Nineties	U.S. Democratic Party	POTUS Study-WW	
Robert S. McElvaine	What's Left? A New Democratic Vision for America	U.S. Democratic Party	POTUS Study-WW	
Theodore C. Sorenson	Why I Am A Democrat	U.S. Democratic Party	POTUS Study-WW	
Molley Winegrad and Dudley Buffa	Taking Control: Politics in the Information Age	Politics and Technology	POTUS Study-WW	Inscribed by the Author
Joseph P. Shapiro	No Pity: People With Disabilities Forging a New Civil Rights Movement	U.S. Domestic Policy: Handicapped	POTUS Study-WW	Inscribed to BC from Rachel Holland (child) and by her father, Robert 1/26/96

Donald Harrington	Butterfly Weed	Novel	POTUS Study-WW	Inscribed by the Author 5/5/96
Maya Angelou	Mrs. Flowers: A Moment of Friendship. A Perfect Present	Short Story	POTUS Study-WW	Inscribed by Lamar Laster
Ben J. Wattenburg	Values Matter Most: How Republicans or Democrats or a Third Party Can Win and Renew the American Way of Life	U.S. Social Values	POTUS Study-WW	Note from the Author 10/3/95; Advance uncorrected proof
Richard N. Haass	The Power to Persuade: How to Be Effective in Government, the Public Sector, or Any Unlikely Organization	Public Administration	POTUS Study-WW	Inscribed by the Author 5/97
Paul Hawkey	The Next Economy	U.S. Economic Conditions	POTUS Study-WW	
Edited by Leslie Berlowitz, Denis Donoghue, and Louis Menard	America in Theory	U.S. Political System	POTUS Study-WW	Inscribed by John Sexton
Michael Elliott	The Day Before Yesterday: Rediscovering America's Past, Recovering the Present	U.S. History	POTUS Study-WW	Inscribed by the Author; Advance Uncorrected Proof
Joseph Telushkin	Words That Hurt, Words That Heal: How to Choose Words Wisely and Well	Oral Communication	POTUS Study-WW	Inscribed by Stephen J. Cloobeck
Arkansas Historical Association	Arkansas Historical Quarterly Vol. LV Autumn 1996, Number 3	History: Arkansas	POTUS Study-WW	

Arkansas Entertainers Hall of Fame 1996	Arkansas Directory	Entertainment: Arkansas	POTUS Study-WW	
Life Magazine, April 1993	Cover-"Bobby and Martin 25 Years After Their Deaths, We Remember What They Meant to Us, and Imagine What Might Have Been"	Magazine: RFK and MLK	POTUS Study-WW	
People Weekly, 4/12/93	Cover- "Diana On Her Own: The Perils-and Pleasures-of Life Without Charles"	Magazine: Diana, Princess of Wales	POTUS Study-WW	
Newsweek, 5/10/93	Cover- "Bosnia: Clinton Gets Tough-At Last; Will Air Power Be Enough?"	Magazine: Clinton Administration-Foreign Policy	POTUS Study-WW	
Business Week, 2/22/93	Cover- "Jobs, Jobs, Jobs: The Economy is Growing, But Employment Lags Badly, Will Clinton Plan Help or Hurt"	Magazine: Clinton Administration-Economic Policy	POTUS Study-WW	
The American Prospect, Winter 1993		Magazine	POTUS Study-WW	
Vanity Fair, 3/93	Cover- "The New Guard: An Exclusive Portfolio of Clinton's Powerful Inner Circle" and "The President's Mr. Inside"	Magazine: Clinton Administration	POTUS Study-WW	
The New Yorker, 12/23 and 12/30/96		Magazine	POTUS Study-WW	

1361-DC-00000035

S 019399

New Orleans Magazine, 3/93	Cover- "Our Man at the White House--Louisianan James Carville Discusses Home, Politics, and Fame"	Magazine: James Carville	POTUS Study-WW	
Family Circle, 5/18/93	Cover- "Hillary and Her Mom on Cookies, Curfews, Confidence ... and Prayer"	Magazine: Hillary Clinton	POTUS Study-WW	
The New Yorker, 10/21 and 10/28/96	Politics Special Issue	Magazine: 1996 Election	POTUS Study-WW	
Time Extra: Fall 1996	Cover- "The Election of 1996"	Magazine: 1996 Election	POTUS Study-WW	
Time, 11/18/96	Cover- "Election Special"	Magazine: 1996 Election	POTUS Study-WW	
Newsweek, 11/18/96	Cover- "Clinton II: Special Election Issue"	Magazine: 1996 Election	POTUS Study-WW	
Time European Edition, 11/18/96	Cover- "How He Won"	Magazine: 1996 Election	POTUS Study-WW	
Bill Clinton For President	"A Plan for America's Future"	Presidential Campaigns: 1992 Campaign Plan	POTUS Study-WW	
Richard E. Feinberg	<u>Summitry in the Americas: A Progress Report</u>	World Politics: Economic Relations	POTUS Study-WW	
Samuel G. Freedman	<u>The Inheritance: How Three Families Moved From Roosevelt to Reagan and Beyond</u>	U.S. Economic Conditions	POTUS Study-WW	

S 019400

1361-DC-00000036

Lester C. Thurow	The Future of Capitalism: How Today's Economic Forces Shape Tomorrow's World	Economic Forecasting	POTUS Study-WW	
Kevin Phillips	Boiling Point: Democrats, Republicans, and the Decline of Middle-Class Prosperity	U.S. Economic Conditions	POTUS Study-WW	Inscribed by "Bud" and "Barbara"
Kevin Phillips	The Politics of Rich and Poor: Wealth and the American Electorate in the Reagan Aftermath	U.S. Economic Conditions	POTUS Study-WW	Inscribed by Ronnie Cripe (?)
Edited by Eric Liu	NEXT: Young American Writers on the New Generation	Generation X	POTUS Study-WW	
Robert D. Putnam	Making Democracy Work: Civic Traditions in Modern Italy	Italy	POTUS Study-WW	Inscribed by the Author 6/94
Stanley B. Greenberg	Middle Class Dreams: The Politics and Power of the New American Majority	U.S. Politics: Middle Class	POTUS Study-WW	Inscribed by the Author
David Fisher	Hard Evidence: How Detectives Inside the FBI's Science Crime Lab Have Helped Solve America's Toughest Cases	U.S. Crime Investigation	POTUS Study-WW	
Henry G. Cisneros	Interwoven Destinies: Cities and the Nation	U.S. Urban Policy	POTUS Study-WW	Inscribed by the Author 12/10/93
Peter F. Drucker	Post-Capitalist Society	World Economic History	POTUS Study-WW	Inscribed by the Author
Robert Kuttner	The End of Laissez-Faire: National Purpose and the Global Economy After the Cold War	U.S. Economic Policy	POTUS Study-WW	

S 019401

John H. Makin and Norman J. Ornstein	Debt and Taxes: How Americans Got Into Its Budget Mess and What to Do About It	U.S. Fiscal Policy	POTUS Study-WW	Inscribed by N. Ornstein
Thomas Byrne Edsall and Mary D. Edsall	Chain Reaction: The Impact of Race, Rights, and Taxes on American Politics	U.S. Politics: Race, Taxes, Civil Rights	POTUS Study-WW	Inscribed by T. Edsall to Governor Clinton
Thomas Byrne Edsall	The New Politics of Inequality	U.S. Economic Policy	POTUS Study-WW	
William Julius Wilson	The Truly Disadvantaged: The Inner City, the Underclass, and Public Policy	U.S. Urban Policy	POTUS Study-WW	
Charles C. Moskos	A Call to Civic Service: National Service for Country and Community	National Service	POTUS Study-WW	Inscribed by the Author 11/88
Holly Stone	Upon the River: Poems Inspired by Rowing	Poetry	POTUS Study-WW	
David Shenk	Data Smog: Surviving the Information Glut	Information Age	POTUS Study-WW	
Rick Pitino	Success is a Choice: 10 Steps to Overachieving in Business and Life	Philosophy for Success	POTUS Study-WW	
Lester C. Thurow	The Zero Sum Solution: Building a World Class American Economy	U.S. Economic Policy	POTUS Study-WW	Inscribed by Bill Brown (?) 1/21/86
Herbert J. Gans	Middle American Individualism: The Future of Liberal Democracy	Political Participation and Individualism	POTUS Study-WW	

S 019402

1361-DC-00000038

Terry Anderson	Den of Lions: Memoirs of Seven Years	Autobiography: Terry Anderson	POTUS Study-WW	Signed by Author and his wife, Madeleine
David Hallerstein	The Fifties	U.S. History: The 50s	POTUS Study-WW	Inscribed by the Author to BC and HRC 1/20/93
Edited by Mark Green	Changing America: Blueprints for the New Administration	Clinton Administration: Agencies	POTUS Study-WW	
John Chancellor	Peril and Promise: A Commentary on America	Political Commentary	POTUS Study-WW	Inscribed by A.O. Nelson of Boynton Beach, FL
William Greider	Who Will Tell the People: The Betrayal of American Democracy	Political Participation	POTUS Study-WW	
	Midwest, Northeast, South, and West Binders with state information and buttons from every state	Presidential Campaign: 1996	POTUS Study-WW	
Joseph A. Califano, Jr.	The Triumph and Tragedy of Lyndon Johnson	Biography: Lyndon Johnson	POTUS Study-WW	Inscribed by the Author
Sam Harris	Reclaiming Our Democracy:Healing the Break Between People and Government	U.S. Political System: Lobbying	POTUS Study-WW	Inscribed by the Author 11/8/93
Paul Kennedy	Preparing America for the 21st Century	21st Century	POTUS Study-WW	Bookplate from Bernard Rapoport
Lech Walesa	A Way of Hope: An Autobiography	Autobiography: Lech Walesa	POTUS Study-WW	Inscribed by the Author 3/6/96

S 019403

1361-DC-00000039

Pam Parry	On Ground for Religious Liberty: Six Decades of the Baptist Joint Committee	Religious History	POTUS Study-WW	
Edited by Dr. Constantine C. Menges	Partnerships for Peace, Democracy, and Prosperity	World Politics	POTUS Study-WW	
William N. Eskridge, Jr.	The Case for Same-Sex Marriage From Sexual Liberty to Civilized Commitment	U.S. Domestic Policy: Homosexual Policy	POTUS Study-WW	
Gordon K. Durnil	The Making of a Conservative Environmentalist	U.S. Environmental Policy	POTUS Study-WW	
Michael Balone	Our Country: The Shaping of America from Roosevelt to Reagan	U.S. History	POTUS Study-WW	
Edited by Ralph Evans	Register of Rhodes Scholars 1903-95	Rhodes Scholars	POTUS Study-WW	
Edited by Daniel Halpern	Antaeus: The Final Issue	Literary Works	POTUS Study-WW	
Naomi H. Rosenblatt and Joshua Horwitz	Wrestling with Angels: What the First Family of Genesis Teach Us About Our Spiritual Identity, Sexuality and Personal Relations	Religion	POTUS Study-WW	
Avner Falk	A Psychoanalytic History of the Jews	Jewish History	POTUS Study-WW	
National Council on Disability	Equality of Opportunity: The Making of the Americans With Disabilities Act	U.S. Domestic Policy: Handicapped	POTUS Study-WW	Inscribed by Marca Bristo, Chairperson of Committee, 9/10/97

Herbert Block	Herblock: A Cartoonist's Life	Autobiography: Herbert Block	POTUS Study-WW	Inscribed by the Author
Lyndon Y. Jones	Great Expectations: America and the Baby Boom Generation	U.S. History: Baby Boom Generation	POTUS Study-WW	
Peggy Noonan	What I Saw at the Revolution: A Political Life in the Reagan Era	U.S. History: The 1980s	POTUS Study-WW	
Jack Kemp	An American Renaissance: A Strategy for the 1980s	U.S. Economic Policy	POTUS Study-WW	
Foreign Affairs	July/August 1997	Periodical: Foreign Affairs	POTUS Study-WW	
Daedalus	Fall 1995; Cover: "American Education: Still Separate"	Periodical: Education	POTUS Study-WW	
Foreign Affairs	May/June 1997	Periodical: Foreign Affairs	POTUS Study-WW	
Foreign Affairs	March/April 1997	Periodical: Foreign Affairs	POTUS Study-WW	
World Policy Journal	Fall 1995 Winter 1995/96	Periodical: World Politics	POTUS Study-WW	
Presidential Studies Quarterly	Summer 1996; "Reassesments of Presidents and First Ladies"	Periodical: Presidency	POTUS Study-WW	
Autumn Stevens	Wild Women in the White House	U.S. First Ladies	POTUS Study-WW	Inscrived to HRC from Anna Jean See

Watty Piper	The Little Engine that Could	Children's Book	POTUS Study-WW	Bookplate from Governor Zell Miller of GA
Bob Hope	Bob Hope's Dear Pres. I Wanna Tell Ya: A Presidential Jokebook	Presidents and Comedy	POTUS Study-WW	
Compiled by Donald L. Miller	From George to George: 200 Years of Presidential Quotations	Presidents: Quotes	POTUS Study-WW	Limited Edition; Inscribed from Dyonne, Rod, Matt, and Zack Holt 11/15/92
Keith W. Jennison	The Humorous Mr. Lincoln	Biography: Lincoln	POTUS Study-WW	
Edited by Bill Adler	The Kennedy Wit	Presidential Quotes: Kennedy	POTUS Study-WW	Inscribed by Michael E. 12/25/94
Abraham Lincoln	Abraham Lincoln Great Speeches	Presidential Speeches: Lincoln	POTUS Study-WW	Inscribed by Helena Willett 9/9/92
Edited by Louise Bachelder	Abraham Lincoln: Wisdom and Wit	Presidential Quotes : Lincoln	POTUS Study-WW	
Franklin Delano Roosevelt	The Wisdom and Wit of Franklin D. Roosevelt	Presidential Writings: FDR	POTUS Study-WW	
Paul F. Boller, Jr.	Presidential Anecdotes	Presidential History	POTUS Study-WW	Inscribed by Carlyn 9/2/91
Gerald Gardner	Who's in Charge Here	Presidential Humor	POTUS Study-WW	
	One Hundred and One Famous Poems	Poetry	POTUS Study-WW	Inscribed by Clayee Maxwell 3/25/92

Jim McMullan	Hail to the Chief: The Presidents Speak	Presidential Quotes	POTUS Study-WW	
Albert Huschinana	The Rhetoric of Reaction: Perversity, Futility, Jeopardy	Philosophy	POTUS Study-WW	
Kenneth P. O'Donnell and David F. Powers with Joe McCarty	Johnny We Hardly Knew Ye.	Biography: John F. Kennedy	POTUS Study-WW	
Edward Hallett Cain	What's History?	History	POTUS Study-WW	

1361-DC-00000043

S 019407

WEDNESDAY NOVEMBER 15, 1995

WHEN THIS SHIFT RELIEVED THE SHIFT THE PRESIDENT WAS IN THE OVAL OFFICE.

PROTECTEE MOVEMENTS:

1450 HRS - THE PRESIDENT MOVED TO ASS'T COS BOWLES OFFICE
1455 HRS - THE PRESIDENT MOVED TO THE COS OFFICE
1500 HRS - THE PRESIDENT MOVED TO THE OVAL OFFICE
1505 HRS - THE PRESIDENT MOVED TO THE SECOND FLOOR RESIDENCE
1530 HRS - THE PRESIDENT MOVED TO THE OVAL OFFICE
1642 HRS - THE PRESIDENT MOVED TO THE ROOSEVELT ROOM
1701 HRS - THE PRESIDENT MOVED TO THE OVAL OFFICE
1737 HRS - THE PRESIDENT MOVED TO THE COS OFFICE
1753 HRS - THE PRESIDENT MOVED TO THE OVAL OFFICE
2012 HRS - THE PRESIDENT MOVED TO THE COS OFFICE
2013 HRS - THE PRESIDENT MOVED TO THE OVAL OFFICE
2123 HRS - THE PRESIDENT MOVED TO THE COS OFFICE
2125 HRS - THE PRESIDENT MOVED TO THE OVAL OFFICE

WHEN THIS SHIFT WAS RELIEVED BY THE SHIFT THE PRESIDENT WAS IN THE OVAL OFFICE.

Friday, January 5, 1996

Officer Brent James Chinery	Day Off
Officer Sandra J. Verna	Post [redacted] 0630-1500 hours
Officer Gary J. Byrne	Post [redacted] 1430-2300 hours
Officer William Michael Tyler	Treasury 1430-2300 hours
Officer Robert Brian Almasy	Post [redacted] 0630-0730 hours;
	Post [redacted] 0730-0830;
	Post [redacted] 0830-0930;
	Response 0930-1030;
	Post [redacted] 1030-1130;
	Post [redacted] 1130-1230;
	Post [redacted] 1230-1330;
	Response 1330-1430
Former Officer Lewis C. Fox	Ellipse Parking 0500-0900 hours;
	Response 0900-0950;
	Post [redacted] 0950-1040;
	Post [redacted] 1040-1210;
	Response 1210-1330

Saturday, January 6, 1996

Officer Brent James Chinery	Post [redacted] 0630-1500 hours
Officer Sandra J. Verna	Day Off
Officer Gary J. Byrne	Post E6A 0630-1500 hours
Officer William Michael Tyler	North West Relief 0630-1500 hours
Officer Robert Brian Almasy	Annual Leave
Former Officer Lewis C. Fox	Post [redacted] 0630-1430 hours;
	Post [redacted] 1430-1830 hours

Sunday, January 7, 1996

Officer Brent James Chinery	Post [redacted] 0630-1500 hours
Officer Sandra J. Verna	Day Off
Officer Gary J. Byrne	Day Off
Officer William Michael Tyler	Post [redacted] 0630-1500 hours
Officer Robert Brian Almasy	Annual Leave
Former Officer Lewis C. Fox	Post [redacted] 0630-1430 hours;
	Post [redacted] 1430-1830 hours

ACC-CO	LAST-NAME	FIRST-NAME	INI	SSN	ENTRY-	SCHE	ENTRY-D	VISITEE	MEETING-R	REQUESTOR	DOB	ENTRY
002496	BENNETT	ROBERT		[redacted]	U0294	17:0	12/06/97	POTUS	WH	CAMERON	08/02/39	16:39
002497	BENNETT	ROBERT		[redacted]	U0912	12:1	12/21/97	POTUS	WH	SCHWARTZ	08/02/39	11:39
002498	BENNETT	ROBERT		[redacted]	U1036	10:0	12/24/97	RUFF	WH	THEARD	08/02/39	10:00

1407-DC-00000005

JUL. -14' 98 (TUE) 14:02 RADER, CAMPBELL [redacted] P. 005

DEC. -05' 97 (FRI) 16:57 RADER, CAMPBELL [redacted] P. 001

TRANSACTION REPORT

Broadcast
Transaction(s) completed

NO.	TX DATE/TIME	DESTINATION	DURATION	PGS.	RESULT	MODE
797	DEC. 5 16:40	[redacted]	0° 03' 29"	019	OK	N ECM
	16:44	[redacted]	0° 03' 30"	019	OK	N ECM
	16:49	[redacted]	0° 04' 26"	019	OK	N ECM
	16:53	[redacted]	0° 04' 24"	019	OK	N ECM

RADER, CAMPBELL, FISHER & PYKE
(A PROFESSIONAL CORPORATION)
STEMMONS PLACE, SUITE 1080
2777 STEMMONS FREEWAY
DALLAS, TEXAS 75207

TELEPHONE (214) 630-4700
TELECOPY (214) 630-9996

TELECOPY TRANSMITTAL SHEET

DATE: December 5, 1997 TIME: 4:30 p.m. Central Standard Time

WE ARE TRANSMITTING: 19 PAGES (INCLUDING THIS COVER SHEET)

TO: Robert S. Bennett, Esq. TELECOPY NO. [redacted]
Kathlyn Graves, Esq. TELECOPY NO.
Stephen Engstrom, Esq. TELECOPY NO.
Bill W. Bristow, Esq. TELECOPY NO.

FROM ATTORNEY/SENDER: T. Wesley Holmes 1408-DC-00000005

COMMENTS:

PAULA CORBIN JONES
V.
WILLIAM JEFFERSON CLINTON

SEALED DOCUMENTS

LAW OFFICES
WILLIAMS & CONNOLLY
725 TWELFTH STREET, N.W.
WASHINGTON, D. C. 20005-5901
(202) 434-5000
FAX (202) 434-5029

EDWARD BENNETT WILLIAMS (1920-1988)
PAUL R. CONNOLLY (1922-1978)

DAVID E. KENDALL
(202) 434-5145

August 3, 1998

CONFIDENTIAL
PRODUCED PURSUANT TO SECRECY PROVISIONS OF RULE 6(e), FED. R. CRIM. P.
GRAND JURY MATERIAL

Robert J. Bittman, Esquire
Deputy Independent Counsel
Office of the Independent Counsel
1001 Pennsylvania Avenue, N.W.
Suite 490-North
Washington, D.C. 20004

Dear Bob:

Subpoena #D1415, which was issued to the White House, was referred to me as personal counsel to the President.

Enclosed herewith is a paperweight that we believe may be responsive to your subpoena. (Bates number DEK 228331 affixed to the side of the paperweight). We have not located any additional responsive material.

Although this production is physically being delivered to you instead of the grand jury, it is still being produced pursuant to grand jury subpoena and is fully covered by the secrecy provisions of the Federal Rules of Criminal Procedure.

Sincerely,

David E. Kendall

Enclosure

1415-DC-00000001

THE WHITE HOUSE
WASHINGTON

1472-DC-00000006

TELEPHONE MEMORANDUM

PRESIDENT CLINTON — NOVEMBER 15th, 1995

	TIME PLACED	DISC	NAME	ACTION
OUT / INC	XX AM / 8:41 PM	10:48	CONGRESSWOMAN KAREN McCARTHY OFC: WASHINGTON, D.C. [redacted]	TLKD-OK 10:42 P.M.
OUT / INC	AM / PM			
OUT / INC	XX AM / 8:41 PM		CONGRESSMAN MARTIN T. MEEHAN WASHINGTON, D.C. [redacted]	INFORMED MS. BETTY CURRIE 10:50 P.M.
OUT / INC	AM / PM			
OUT / XX INC	AM / 8:41 PM	10:55	CONGRESSMAN DAVID SKAGGS OFC: WASHINGTON, D.C. [redacted]	TLKD-OK 10:53 P.M.
OUT / INC	AM / PM			
OUT / XX INC	AM / 8:41 PM		CONGRESSMAN JOHN M. SPRATT, JR. WASHINGTON, D.C. [redacted]	INFORMED MS. BETTY CURRIE. 10:45 P.M.
OUT / INC	AM / PM			
OUT / XX INC	XX AM / 8:41 PM	10:41	CONGRESSMAN TOM BEVILL OFC: WASHINGTON, D.C. [redacted]	TLKD-OK 10:39 P.M.
OUT / INC	AM / PM			
OUT / INXX	XX AM / 8:50 PM	9:30	CONGRESSMAN JIM CHAPMAN OFC: WASHINGTON, D.C. [redacted]	TLKD-OK 9:25 P.M.

GPO : 1983 O - 405-660 : QL 2

S 019699

THE WHITE HOUSE
WASHINGTON

1472-DC-00000007

TELEPHONE MEMORANDUM

PRESIDENT CLINTON — NOVEMBER 15th, 1995

	TIME PLACED		DISC	NAME	ACTION
OUT / XX	8:50	XX / PM	10:28	CONGRESSMAN STENY HOYER WASHINGTON, D.C. [redacted]	TLKD-OK 10:09 P.M.
OUT / INC		AM / PM			
OUT / XX	8:50	XX / PM	10:08	CONGRESSMAN ROBERT C. SCOTT WASHINGTON, D.C. [redacted]	TLKD-OK 9:46 P.M.
OUT / INC		AM / PM			
OUT / XX	8:50	XX / PM	11:37	CONGRESSMAN NORMAN D. DICKS WASHINGTON, D.C. [redacted]	TLKD-OK 11:28 P.M.
OUT / INC		AM / PM			
OUT / XX	8:50	XX / PM		CONGRESSMAN DOUGEAS PETERSON OFC: WASHINGTON, D.C. [redacted]	INFORMED MS. BETTY CURRIE 10:51 P.M.
OUT / INC		AM / PM			
OUT / XX	8:50	XX / PM	11:12	CONGRESSMAN GLENN POSHARD WASHINGTON, D.C. [redacted]	TLKD-OK 10:55 P.M.
OUT / INC		AM / PM			
OUT / XX	8:50	XX / PM		CONGRESSWOMAN LOUISE M. SLAUGHTER WASHINGTON, D.C. [redacted]	INFORMED MS. BETTY CURRIE 10:59 P.M.

GPO : 1983 O - 405-660 : QL 2

S 019700

THE WHITE HOUSE

WASHINGTON

1472-DC-00000008

TELEPHONE MEMORANDUM

PRESIDENT CLINTON — NOVEMBER 15th, 1995

	TIME PLACED	DISC	NAME	ACTION
OUT / INC	XX AM / 9:30 PM	9:35	CONGRESSMAN JOHN S. TANNER OFC: WASHINGTON, D.C. [redacted]	TLKD-OK 9:31 P.M.
OUT / INC	9:50 PM		CONGRESSMAN WILLIAM P. LUTHER WASHINGTON, D.C. [redacted]	INFORMED MS. BETTY CURRIE 10:02 P.M.
OUT / INC	10:05 PM	10:36	CONGRESSMAN RONALD COLEMAN WASHINGTON, D.C. [redacted]	TLKD-OK 10:29 P.M.
OUT / INC	11:13 PM	11:25	MR. LEON E. PANETTA RES: WASHINGTON, D.C. WHITE HOUSE SIGNAL	TLKD-OK 11:14 P.M.
OUT / INC	11:17 PM	11:27	MR. ERSKINE B. BOWLES RES: WASHINGTON, D.C. [redacted]	TLKD-OK 11:25 P.M.
OUT / INC	11:40 PM	11:51	CONGRESSMAN SANFORD D. BISHOP WASHINGTON, D.C. [redacted]	TLKD-OK 11:44 P.M.

GPO : 1983 O - 405-660 : QL 2

S 019701

THE WHITE HOUSE

WASHINGTON

TELEPHONE MEMORANDUM

PRESIDENT CLINTON NOVEMBER 17th

	TIME PLACED	DISC	NAME	ACTION
OUT INC	AM 8:07 PM	8:12	MRS. HILLARY RODHAM CLINTON RES: WASHINGTON, D.C. WHITE HOUSE ADMIN EXT. [redacted]	TLKD-OK 8:07 P.
OUT INC	AM PM			
OUT INC	AM 9:51 PM	10:14	CONGRESSMAN H. L. CALLAHAN RES: WASHINGTON, D.C. (Sunny) [redacted]	TLKD-OK 9:53 P.
OUT INC	AM PM			
OUT INC	AM 10:31 PM		MR. RICK KAPLAN RES: MONTVALE, N.J. [redacted]	PER MS. CURRIE PR WILL CALL BACK 10 P.M.
OUT INC	AM PM			
OUT INC	AM 10:38 PM	10:39	MR. DENNIS W. FREEMYER OFC: WASHINGTON, D.C. [redacted]	TLKD-OK 10:38 P.M.
OUT INC	AM PM			
OUT INC	AM 11:09 PM	11:14	SECRETARY WILLIAM PERRY OFC: WASHINGTON, D.C. WHITE HOUSE ADMIN. EXT. [redacted]	TLKD-OK 11:10 P.M.
OUT INC	AM PM			
OUT INC	AM PM			

GPO : 1983 0 - 405-668 : QL 2

1472-DC-00000015 S 019708

THE WHITE HOUSE
WASHINGTON

TELEPHONE MEMORANDUM

PRESIDENT CLINTON FEBRUARY 19th, 19 96

	Time Placed		Disc	Name	Action
XXX / INC	9:23	AM / XXX	9:29	MR. VERNON E. JORDAN, JR. OFC: WASHINGTON, D.C. [redacted]	TLKD-OK 9:27 A.M.
OUT / INC		AM / PM			
OUT / XXX	9:29	AM / XXX		MR. JAMES BLAIR OFC: SPRINGDALE, AR. [redacted]	INFORMED PRESUS 1:14 P.M.
OUT / INC		AM / PM			
OUT / XXX	11:18	AM / XXX	11:39	MRS. TONY RODHAM RES: MIAMI, FL. [redacted]	TLKD-OK 11:31 A.M.
OUT / INC		AM / PM			
OUT XXX / INC	11:56	AM / XXX	12:10	MR. ELI J. SEGAL OFC: WASHINGTON, D.C. [redacted]	TLKD-OK 12:11 P.M.
OUT / INC		AM / PM			
XXX / INC	12:11	XXX / PM		MS. BETTY W. CURRIE RES: ARLINGTON, VA. [redacted]	MESSAGE PASSED TO PRESUS PER MS. CURRII 12:11 P.M.
OUT / INC		AM / PM			
XXX / INC	12:24	XXX / PM	1:04	MR. ALFONSO FANJUL OFC: PALM BEACH, FL. [redacted]	TLKD-OK 12:42 P.M.

GPO : 1983 O - 485-660 : QL 2

1472-DC-00000017

S 019710

THE WHITE HOUSE

WASHINGTON

TELEPHONE MEMORANDUM

PRESIDENT CLINTON

FEBRUARY 19, 1996

	TIME PLACED	DISC	NAME	ACTION
OUT / INC	1:05 PM		MS. KATHLEEEN A. McGINTY RES: ARLINGTON, VA. [redacted]	PER MRS. CLINTON CANCEL 3:17 P.M.
OUT / INC	AM / PM			
INC	1:34 PM	1:37	MRS. HILLARY RODHAM CLINTON RES: WASHINGTON, D.C. WHITE HOUSE ADMIN EXT. [redacted]	TLKD-OK 1:36 P.M.
OUT / INC	AM / PM			
INC	1:42 PM		MS. MARSHA SCOTT WASHINGTON, D.C. NO NUMBER AVAILABLE	PER MS. CURRIE PRESUS WILL SEE MS. SCOTT 1:48 P.M.
OUT / INC	AM / PM			
INC	1:43 PM	1:45	MS. CAPRICIA MARSHALL WASHINGTON, D.C. WHITE HOUSE ADMIN EXT. [redacted]	TLKD-OK 1:44 P.M.
OUT / INC	AM / PM			
INC	1:46 PM	1:48	MS. BETTY W. CURRIE CELLULAR PHONE [redacted]	TLKD-OK 1:46 P.M.
OUT / INC	AM / PM			
INC	3:42 PM	3:45	MRS. NANCY F. MITCHELL OFC: WASHINGTON, D.C. WHITE HOUSE ADMIN EXT. [redacted]	TLKD-OK 3:43 P.M.

GPO : 1983 O - 405-660 : QL 3

S 019711

THE WHITE HOUSE

WASHINGTON

TELEPHONE MEMORANDUM

PRESIDENT CLINTON

FEBRUARY 19, 19 96

	TIME PLACED	TIME DISC	NAME	ACTION
~~OUT~~ INC	~~AM~~ 4:13 PM	4:15	MRS. NANCY F. MITCHELL OFC: WASHINGTON, D.C. WHITE HOUSE ADMIN EXT. [redacted]	TLKD-OK 4:14 P.M.
OUT INC	AM PM			
OUT ~~INC~~	~~AM~~ 11:56 PM	11:56	MESSAGE: "OPERATOR, IS THE USHER STILL HERE? IT IS JUST TOO HOT HERE IN	ACKNOWLEDGED 11:56 P.M. MESSAGE PASSED TO MR. JOSEPH T. GRANEY
OUT INC	AM PM		THE SOLARIUM."	11:59 P.M. INFORMED PRESUS 12:00 A.M.
OUT INC	AM PM			
OUT INC	AM PM			
OUT INC	AM PM			
OUT INC	AM PM			
OUT INC	AM PM			
OUT INC	AM PM			
OUT INC	AM PM			

GPO : 1983 O - 405-660 : QL 2

S-019712

THE WHITE HOUSE
WASHINGTON

TELEPHONE MEMORANDUM
SIGNAL SWITCHBOARD

February 19, 1996

	TIME		NAME	ACTION
	PLACED	DISC		
XXX INC	11:49 AM PM	 12:04	Vice President Albert Gore, Jr. Doral Golf Resort and Spa Miami, Florida [redacted]	Tlkd-ok 11:55 AM
OUT INC	AM PM			
OUT INC	AM PM			
OUT INC	AM PM			
OUT INC	AM PM			
OUT INC	AM PM			
OUT INC	AM PM			
OUT INC	AM PM			
OUT INC	AM PM			
OUT INC	AM PM			
OUT INC	AM PM			

S 019713

SCHEDULE OF THE PRESIDENT
FOR
THURSDAY, AUGUST 10, 1995
FINAL

NOTE:	NSC briefing will be on paper.
NOTE:	The press pool will set up in the Oval Office between 8:30 am and 9:30 am.
tba	MORNING RUN
~~8:30 am-~~ 8:46 ~~9:30 am~~ 9:58	MEETING MAP ROOM Staff Contact: Doug Sosnik CLOSED PRESS
9:40 am- 9:45 am	MEETING OVAL OFFICE DINING ROOM Staff Contact: Leon Panetta
~~9:45 am-~~ 9:59 ~~10:00 am~~ 10:13	BRIEFING OVAL OFFICE DINING ROOM Staff Contact: Alexis Herman, Marilyn Yager, CHRIS CERF
~~10:00 am-~~ 10:16 ~~10:30 am~~ 10:50	ROUNDTABLE DISCUSSION OVAL OFFICE Event Coordinator: Patrick Steel Staff Contact: Alexis Herman, Marilyn Yager POOL SPRAY at the beginning

– The President welcomes students and health advocates and makes brief remarks.

– A student makes brief remarks.

– The press pool is escorted out of the Oval Office.

– The President and Vice President Gore participate in an informal discussion with students and health advocates.

10:50 > PHIL LEE
11:06 DAVID KESSLER

10:30 am- 1:30 pm	BRIEFING/MAKE UP FOR PRESS CONFERENCE OVAL OFFICE Staff Contact: Michael McCurry

SEE ATTACHED

1506-DC-00000007

S 019986

7:25 > SBERGER
7:26

as of 08/09/95 7:24pm

1:30 pm- ~~2:20 pm~~ 2:16	**PRESS CONFERENCE** **EAST ROOM** Remarks: Michael Waldman Staff Contact: Michael McCurry **OPEN PRESS**
~~2:30 pm-~~ 2:46 ~~2:40 pm~~ 2:51	**PHOTO WITH MAJOR LEO MERCADO** **OVAL OFFICE** Staff Contact: Alan Sullivan
~~2:40 pm-~~ 2:57 ~~2:45 pm~~ 3:02	**MEETING** **OVAL OFFICE** Staff Contact: Stephanie Streett
2:45 pm- 7:15 pm	**PHONE AND OFFICE TIME** **OVAL OFFICE**
~~7:20 pm~~ 7:.	**THE PRESIDENT** departs the White House via motorcade en route Hay Adams [drive time: 5 minutes]
~~7:25 pm~~ 7:46	**THE PRESIDENT** arrives Hay Adams Greeters: Terry McAuliffe Laura Hartigan
~~7:30 pm-~~ 7:53 8:45 pm	**CLINTON/GORE '96 FUNDRAISER DINNER** **HAY ADAMS** Event Coordinator: Lucie Naphin Staff Contact: Doug Sosnik **CLOSED PRESS**

5:00 > BDAY PARTY
6:45

— The President greets and takes photos with guests.

— Dinner is served.

— Terry McAuliffe makes brief opening remarks and introduces the President.

— The President participates in an informal discussion with guests.

— The President departs.

1506-DC-00000008 S 019987

SCHEDULE OF THE PRESIDENT
FOR
SUNDAY, DECEMBER 31, 1995
FINAL

8:30 am	**BRIEFING**
9:00 am	**OVAL OFFICE**
	Staff Contact: Leon Panetta, Patrick Griffin
9:00 am	**CONGRESSIONAL MEETING**
12:00 pm	**CABINET ROOM**
	Staff Contact: Leon Panetta, Patrick Griffin
	CLOSED PRESS
tbd	**THE PRESIDENT and the First Lady depart the White House via Marine One en route Andrews Air Force Base**
	[flight time: 10 minutes]
tbd	**THE PRESIDENT and the First Lady arrive Andrews Air Force Base**
tbd	**THE PRESIDENT and the First Lady depart Andrews Air Force Base via Air Force One en route Beaufort Marine Corps Air Station, South Carolina**
	[flight time: 1 hour, 45 minutes]
tbd	**THE PRESIDENT and the First Lady arrive Beaufort Marine Corps Air Station, South Carolina**
tbd	**THE PRESIDENT and the First Lady depart Beaufort Marine Corps Air Station via Marine One en route Hilton Head Airport, Hilton Head, South Carolina**
	[flight time: 20 minutes]
tbd	**THE PRESIDENT and the First Lady arrive Hilton Head Airport, Hilton Head, South Carolina**
tbd	**THE PRESIDENT and the First Lady depart Hilton Head Airport, Hilton Head, South Carolina via motorcade en route residence**
	[drive time: 10 minutes]
tbd	**THE PRESIDENT and the First Lady arrive residence**
BC AND HRC RON	**THE WHITE HOUSE OR HILTON HEAD, SOUTH CAROLINA**

1506-DC-00000027

S 020006

THE WHITE HOUSE
WASHINGTON

TELEPHONE MEMORANDUM
SIGNAL SWITCHBOARD

December 31, 1995

	TIME		NAME	ACTION
	PLACED	DISC		
OUT XXX	AM 12:51 PM	12:58	Secretary William Perry Residence, Alexandria, Virginia White House Signal [redacted]	Tlkd-ok 12:53 PM
OUT XXX	AM 3:46 PM	3:50	Mr. Leon E. Panetta Residence, Washington, D.C. White House Signal [redacted]	Tlkd-ok 3:48 PM
OUT INC	AM PM			
OUT INC	AM PM			
OUT INC	AM PM			
OUT INC	AM PM			
OUT INC	AM PM			
OUT INC	AM PM			
OUT INC	AM PM			
OUT INC	AM PM			1506-DC-00000029
OUT INC	AM PM			

S 020008

THE WHITE HOUSE
WASHINGTON

TELEPHONE MEMORANDUM

PRESIDENT CLINTON — JANUARY 7, 19 9

	TIME PLACED		DISC	NAME	ACTION
OUT XXXX	4:37	XXX PM	5:08	MR. STAN GREENBERG SANTA BARBARA, CA. [redacted]	TLKD-OK 4:49 P.M.
OUT INC		AM PM			
OUT XXXX	4:39	XXX PM	4:49	MR. GENE B. SPERLING OFC: WASHINGTON, D.C. WHITE HOUSE ADMIN. EXT. [redacted]	TLKD-OK 4:39 P.M.
OUT INC		AM PM			
OUT XXXX	5:09	XXX PM	5:20	MR. DAVID KENDALL RES: BETHESDA, MD [redacted]	TLKD-OK 5:09 P.M.
OUT INC		AM PM			
OUT XXX	5:21	XXX PM	5:45	MR. JAMES CARVILLE RES: FRONT ROYAL, VA. [redacted]	TLKD-OK 5:23 P.M.
OUT INC		AM PM			
XXXX INC	10:37	XXX PM		REVEREND JESSE L. JACKSON LOS ANGELES, CA. [redacted]	PER: MS. BETTY W. CURRIE, PRESUS WCB IN THE MORNING. 10:
OUT INC		AM PM			
OUT XXX	11:13	AM PM	11:13	MR. DANIEL R. SHANKS OFC: WASHINGTON, D.C. [redacted]	TLKD-OK 11:13 P.M.

GPO : 1983 O - 405-660 : QL 2

THE WHITE HOUSE
WASHINGTON

TELEPHONE MEMORANDUM

PRESIDENT CLINTON — JANUARY 21st, 1996

	TIME PLACED	DISC	NAME	ACTION
~~OUT~~ INC	~~AM~~ 3:08 PM	3:12	MR. BILL EBBERT WASHINGTON, D.C. [redacted]	TLKD-OK 3:08 P.M.
OUT INC	AM PM			
~~OUT~~ INC	~~AM~~ 3:08 PM		GOVERNOR LINCOLN ALMOND NARRAGANSETT, R.I. [redacted]	PER MR. HAROLD ICKES WILL INFORM PRESUS 4:05 P.M.
OUT INC	AM PM			
~~OUT~~ INC	~~AM~~ 3:15 PM		MR. BILL EBBERT WASHINGTON, D.C. [redacted]	INFORMED MS. NANCY F. MITCHELL 3:35 P.M.
OUT INC	AM PM			
~~OUT~~ INC	~~AM~~ 3:46 PM	3:48	MS. NANCY F. MITCHELL OFC: WASHINGTON, D.C. WHITE HOUSE ADMIN EXT. [redacted]	TLKD-OK 3:47 P.M.
OUT INC	AM PM			
OUT ~~INC~~	~~AM~~ 4:42 PM	5:11	MS. CATHERINE A. CORNELIUS ARLINGTON, VA. NO NUMBER AVAILABLE	TLKD-OK 5:07 P.M.
OUT INC	AM PM			
~~OUT~~ INC	~~AM~~ 5:01 PM		MAYOR EDWARD REND~~A~~eLL OFC: PHILADELPHIA, PA. [redacted]	MAYOR REND~~A~~eLL TLKD WITH MS. MARCIA HALE 5:20 P.M.

GPO : 1983 O - 405-660 : QL 2

SCHEDULE OF THE PRESIDENT
FOR
TUESDAY, JANUARY 30, 1996
FINAL

tba	**MORNING RUN**
~~9:00~~ am- 9:18 ~~10:00~~ am 10:14	**MORNING COFFEE** **MAP ROOM** **Staff Contact: Doug Sosnik** 9:21 - SIT DOWN 10:10 - PHOTO LINE
~~10:15~~ am- 10:17 ~~10:30~~ am 10:32	**MEETING** **OVAL OFFICE** **Staff Contact: Leon Panetta**
+ 14 ~~10:30 am~~- 10:33 ~~11:00 am~~ 11:17	**BRIEFING FOR INTERVIEW** **OVAL OFFICE** **Staff Contact: Michael McCurry**, CS, B. REED, D. BAER, LP, HI, Rahm (10:56),
+9 ~~11:00 am~~- 11:20 ~~11:45 am~~ 12:14	**INTERVIEW WITH DAVID BRODER OF <u>THE WASHINGTON POST</u>** START - 11:24 **OVAL OFFICE** **Staff Contact: Michael McCurry**, D. BAER, GS
~~11:45 am~~- 12:17 ~~12:05 pm~~ 12:26	**BRIEFING FOR CONFERENCE CALL** **OVAL OFFICE** **Staff Contact: Michael McCurry, ~~Doug Sosnik~~**, W. SMITH, CS, GSPERL, MC GLYNN
~~12:05 pm~~- 12:27 ~~12:45 pm~~ 12:57	**CONFERENCE CALL WITH NEW HAMPSHIRE NEWSPAPERS (<u>The Concord Monitor</u>, <u>The Portsmouth Herald</u>, <u>The Nashua Telegraph</u>, <u>Foster's Daily Democrat</u>, <u>The Keene Sentinel</u>, <u>Union Leader</u>)** 6 T's **OVAL OFFICE** **Staff Contact: Michael McCurry, Doug Sosnik**
~~12:45 pm~~- 1:00 ~~1:45 pm~~ 1:57	**LUNCH WITH VICE PRESIDENT GORE** **OVAL OFFICE**
~~1:45 pm~~- 2:26 ~~2:00 pm~~ 2:36	**BRIEFING** **OVAL OFFICE** **Staff Contact: Tony Lake**

REDACTED

2:03
2:14 > PHONE CALL W/

2:18
2:24 > CILLER - PHONE CALL

1506-DC-00000057

as of January 29, 1996 6:15pm

~~2:00~~ pm- 2:37 ~~2:20 pm~~ 3:32	**MEETING WITH** [redacted] **OVAL OFFICE** **Staff Contact: Tony Lake** **POOL SPRAY (At the top)** — out 2 2:54 3 waves
2:40 pm- 2:45 pm	**MEETING** **OVAL OFFICE** **Staff Contact: Stephanie Streett, Anne Walley**
2:45 pm- 4:45 pm	**PHONE/OFFICE TIME** **OVAL OFFICE**
~~4:45~~ pm- 5:05 ~~5:00 pm~~ 5:11	**BRIEFING** **OVAL OFFICE** **Staff Contact: Patrick Griffin**, LP, GS, ARMIN, L. TYSON, B. RUBIN, G. SPERLI D. TATE
~~5:00 pm~~ 5:12 ~~6:00 pm~~ 6:36	**CONGRESSIONAL MEETING** **CABINET ROOM** **Staff Contact: Patrick Griffin** **POOL SPRAY (At the top)** 522 - POOL OUT
OPTION: (Between 6:00 pm- 8:00 pm)	**DROP-BY FAREWELL PARTY FOR PATRICK GRIFFIN** **CHIEF OF STAFF'S OFFICE**
	EVENING OFF
BC AND HRC RON	**THE WHITE HOUSE**

REDACTED

3:40 > BRIEF
3:44 VERSHBOW, SHALI

3:44 > PHONE CALL w/ [redacted]
3:52 3:51 - SEC PERRY

1506-DC-00000058

7:38 > HI, B. NASH
7:43

7:45 > LP, EL, HI
7:52

7:52 > LP, EL, HI, JQ, B. RUBIN, CATHY
8:15

as of January 29, 1996 6:15pm

S 020037

✓

THE WHITE HOUSE
WASHINGTON

TELEPHONE MEMORANDUM

PRESIDENT CLINTON — FEBRUARY 4th, 1996

	TIME PLACED		DISC	NAME	ACTION
OUT / ~~INC~~	8:39	AM / ~~PM~~	8:43	MS. SAMUEL R. BERGER RES: WASHINGTON, D.C. WHITE HOUSE SIGNAL [redacted]	TLKD-OK 8:39 A.M.
OUT / INC		AM / PM			
~~OUT~~ / INC	8:56	AM / ~~PM~~	8:58	MS. NANCY F. MITCHELL OFC: WASHINGTON, D.C. WHITE HOUSE ADMIN EXT. [redacted]	TLKD-OK 8:57 A.M.
OUT / INC		AM / PM			
~~OUT~~ / INC	8:57	AM / ~~PM~~	9:01	MS. NANCY HERNREICH RES: WASHINGTON, D.C. WHITE HOUSE ADMIN EXT. [redacted]	TLKD-OK 8:59 A.M.
OUT / INC		AM / PM			
OUT / ~~INC~~	9:06	AM / ~~PM~~	9:06		ACKNOWLEDGED 9:06 A.M. MESSAGE PASSED TO MS. NANCY F. MITCHELL 9:07 A.M.
OUT / INC		AM / PM			
~~OUT~~ / INC	9:22	AM / ~~PM~~	2:24	MR. DICK KELLEY RES: HOT SPRINGS, AR. [redacted]	TLKD-OK 2:15 P.M.
OUT / INC		AM / PM			
~~OUT~~ / INC	12:22	~~AM~~ / PM	4:50	MR. RAHM I. EMANUEL RES: WASHINGTON, D.C. [redacted]	TLKD-OK 4:45 P.M.

GPO : 1983 O - 405-660 : QL 2

1506-DC-00000068

S 020047

THE WHITE HOUSE
WASHINGTON

TELEPHONE MEMORANDUM

PRESIDENT CLINTON FEBRUARY 4th, 1996

	TIME PLACED	DISC	NAME	ACTION
OUT / XXX (INC)	XAM / 4:58 PM	5:09	SECRETARY DAN GLICKMAN RES: WASHINGTON, D.C. [redacted]	TLKD-OK 4:59 P.M.
OUT / INC	AM / PM			
OUT / XXX (INC)	XAM / 4:58 PM	5:26	MS. CAROL RASCO RES: ALEXANDRIA, VA. [redacted]	TLKD-OK 5:22 P.M.
OUT / INC	AM / PM			
XXX (OUT) / INC	XXAM / 5:06 PM		MS. DEBRA BIRD WASHINGTON, D.C. WHITE HOUSE ADMIN EXT. [redacted]	MESSAGE PASSED TO PRESUS 5:10 P.M.
OUT / INC	AM / PM			
OUT / XXX (INC)	XAM / 5:10 PM	5:10	MESSAGE: "TELL HER TO BRING THEM NOW TO THE OVAL OFFICE."	ACKNOWLEDGED 5:10 P.M. MESSAGE PASSED TO
OUT / INC	AM / PM			MS. DEBRA BIRD 5:11 P.M.
OUT / INC	AM / PM			
OUT / XXX (INC)	XXAM / 5:10 PM	5:20	MS. JUDITH ANN STOCK OFC: WASHINGTON, D.C. WHITE HOUSE ADMIN EXT. [redacted]	TLKD-OK 5:11 P.M.
OUT / INC	AM / PM			

GPO : 1983 O - 405-660 : QL 2

1506-DC-00000070

S 020049

THE WHITE HOUSE

WASHINGTON

TELEPHONE MEMORANDUM

PRESIDENT CLINTON FEBRUARY 19th, 19 96

	TIME PLACED	DISC	NAME	ACTION
~~OUT~~ / INC	9:23 AM / ~~PM~~	9:29	MR. VERNON E. JORDAN, JR. OFC: WASHINGTON, D.C. [redacted]	TLKD-OK 9:27 A.M.
OUT / INC	AM / PM			
OUT / ~~INC~~	9:29 AM / ~~PM~~		MR. JAMES BLAIR OFC: SPRINGDALE, AR. [redacted]	INFORMED PRESUS 1:14 P.M.
OUT / INC	AM / PM			
OUT / ~~INC~~	11:18 AM / ~~PM~~	11:39	MRS. TONY RODHAM RES: MIAMI, FL. [redacted]	TLKD-OK 11:31 A.M.
OUT / INC	AM / PM			
~~OUT~~ / INC	11:56 AM / ~~PM~~	12:19	MR. ELI J. SEGAL OFC: WASHINGTON, D.C. [redacted]	TLKD-OK 12:11 P.M.
OUT / INC	AM / PM			
~~OUT~~ / INC	~~AM~~ / 12:11 PM		MS. BETTY W. CURRIE RES: ARLINGTON, VA. [redacted]	MESSAGE PASSED TO PRESUS PER MS. CURRIE 12:11 P.M.
OUT / INC	AM / PM			
~~OUT~~ / INC	~~AM~~ / 12:24 PM	1:04	MR. ALFONSO FANJUL OFC: PALM BEACH, FL. [redacted]	TLKD-OK 12:42 P.M.

GPO : 1983 O - 405-660 : QL 2

THE WHITE HOUSE
WASHINGTON

TELEPHONE MEMORANDUM

PRESIDENT CLINTON　　　　　　　　　　MARCH 31st, 1996

	TIME PLACED	DISC	NAME	ACTION
~~OUT~~ INC	9:26 AM ~~PM~~	9:09	MR. THOMAS CAPLAN RES: BALTIMORE, MD. [redacted]	TLKD-OK 8:57 P.M.
OUT INC	AM PM			
~~OUT~~ INC	10:05 AM ~~PM~~		MR. DICK KELLEY WASHINGTON, D.C. WHITE HOUSE ADM. EXT. [redacted]	MESSAGE PASSED TO PRESUS 12:24 P.M.
OUT INC	AM PM			
OUT ~~INC~~	~~AM~~ 12:33 PM	12:35	MS. CATHERINE CORNELIUS RES: WASHINGTON, D.C. [redacted]	TLKD-OK 12:34 P.M.
OUT INC	AM PM			
OUT ~~INC~~	~~AM~~ 3:05 PM	3:07	SENATOR BARBARA A. MIKULSKI RES: BALTIMORE, MD. [redacted]	TLKD-OK 3:06 P.M.
OUT INC	AM PM			
~~OUT~~ INC	~~AM~~ 7:27 PM	7:41	MR. THOMAS F. McLARTY RES: WASHINGTON, D.C. [redacted]	TLKD-OK 7:27 P.M.
OUT INC	AM PM			
OUT ~~INC~~	~~AM~~ 8:56 PM	9:17	REVEREND REX HORNE RES: LITTLE ROCK, AR. [redacted]	TLKD-OK 9:10 P.M.

GPO : 1983 O - 405-660 : QL 2

THE WHITE HOUSE
WASHINGTON

TELEPHONE MEMORANDUM

PRESIDENT CLINTON

APRIL 7th , 19__

	TIME PLACED	DISC	NAME	ACTION
OUT XXX	XXX 3:26 PM	3:33	MR. DONALD A. BAER WASHINGTON, D.C. [redacted]	TLKD-OK 3:30 P.M.
OUT INC	AM PM			
XXX INC	XXX 4:08 PM	4:09	MR. DANIEL R. SHANKS OFC: WASHINGTON, D.C. WHITE HOUSE ADMIN EXT. [redacted]	TLKD-OK 4:08 P.M.
OUT INC	AM PM			
XXX INC	XXX 5:10 PM	5:20	MR. RICHARD MORRIS PARIS, FRANCE [redacted]	TLKD-OK 5:11 P.M.
OUT INC	AM PM			
OUT XXX	XXX 5:30 PM	5:32	MISS EVELYN S. LIEBERMAN OFC: WASHINGTON, D.C. WHITE HOUSE ADMIN EXT. [redacted]	TLKD-OK 5:30 P.M.
OUT INC	AM PM			
OUT INC	XXX 5:45 PM	5:56	MS. LYNDA DIXON RES: LITTLE ROCK, AR. [redacted]	TLKD-OK 5:45 P.M.
OUT INC	AM PM			
XXX INC	XXX 7:38 PM		MRS. HILLARY RODHAM CLINTON RES: WASHINGTON, D.C. WHITE HOUSE ADMIN EXT. [redacted]	CANCEL PER MRS. CLINTON 7:41 P.M.

6:11 6:28 > BLUE ROOM

~~5:35~~ pm- 6:11
7:30 pm

SCREENING OF THE MOVIE *CHICANO*
BLUE ROOM/FAMILY THEATER
Staff Contact: Ann Stock
Event Coordinator: Sarah Farnsworth
CLOSED PRESS

> FAMILY THEATRE

7:30 pm-
8:30 pm

DOWN TIME
RESIDENCE

8:30 pm

THE PRESIDENT departs the White House via motorcade en route the Renaissance Hotel
[drive time: 10 minutes]

8:40 pm

THE PRESIDENT arrives the Renaissance Hotel

Greeters:
- Robert Bergen, President, Memorial Mission Health Care Foundation
- Jay Louis Daniel, President and CEO, St. Joseph's Children Hospital
- Olsen Huff, Medical Director, the Ruth and Billy Graham Children's Health Center
- Marilyn Huff
- Bruce Thorsen, Vice President for Development, Memorial Mission Health Care Foundation
- Aleda Grant, Member, Board, Memorial Mission Health Care Foundation

8:45 pm-
9:20 pm

BANQUET IN HONOR OF DR. BILLY AND RUTH GRAHAM
BALLROOM
The Renaissance Hotel
Remarks: Terry Edmonds
Staff Contact: Alexis Herman
Event Coordinator: Nicole Elkon
POOL PRESS

- Paul Harvey introduces the President onto the stage.
- The President makes remarks, introduces Dr. Billy Graham onto the stage and presents him with a gift.
- Dr. Billy Graham makes remarks.
- The President and Dr. Billy Graham depart.

1506-DC-00000188

S 020167

9:25 pm	**THE PRESIDENT** departs the Renaissance Hotel via motorcade en route the White House [drive time: 10 minutes]
9:35 pm	**THE PRESIDENT** arrives the White House
	HOLD EVENING
BC RON	**THE WHITE HOUSE**
HRC RON	**ST. LOUIS, MISSOURI**

1506-DC-00000189

as of May 1, 1996 7:20pm

S 020168

THE WHITE HOUSE

WASHINGTON

PRESIDENTIAL CALL LOG

MAY 2nd ,19 96

	TIME PLACED	DISC	NAME	ACTION
OUT / XNC	XM 9:43 PM	9:43	MR. DANIEL SHANKS OFC: WASHINGTON, D.C. WHITE HOUSE ADMIN EXT [redacted]	
OUT / INC	AM / PM		MESSAGE: PRESUS SAID "TELL THE OPERATOR HE WOULD LIKE A 7:00 A.M. WAKE	ACKNOWLEDGED 9:43 P.M.
OUT / INC	AM / PM		UP."	
OUT / INC	AM / PM			
XX / INC	XX 11:34 PM	11:47	MRS. HILLARY RODHAM CLINTON ST. LOUIS, MO. NO NUMBER AVAILABLE	TLKD-OK 11:36 P.M.
OUT / INC	AM / PM			
OUT / INC	AM / PM			
OUT / INC	AM / PM			
OUT / INC	AM / PM			
JT / INC	AM / PM			
OUT / INC	AM / PM			

1506-DC-00000192

S 020171

7:05 pm	**THE PRESIDENT** departs the White House via motorcade en route the Jefferson Hotel [drive time: 5 minutes]
7:10 pm	**THE PRESIDENT** arrives the Jefferson Hotel

Greeter: Don Fowler, Chairman, Democratic National Committee
Marvin Rosen, Finance Chair, Democratic National Committee
Richard Hamilton, Director of Security, Jefferson Hotel

7:15 pm-
8:15 pm

DINNER FOR DEMOCRATIC NATIONAL COMMITTEE
MONTICELLO ROOM
The Jefferson Hotel
Staff Contact: Doug Sosnik
Event Coordinator: Laura Graham
CLOSED PRESS

- The President, accompanied by Don Fowler, Chairman, Democratic National Committee and Marvin Rosen, Finance Chair, Democratic National Committee, enters the room, greets guests and proceeds to his seat at the table.
- Ken Bailey makes brief remarks and introduces Don Fowler.
- Don Fowler makes brief remarks and introduces the President.
- The President makes remarks and opens an informal discussion with guests.
- Upon conclusion of the discussion, the President departs.

8:20 pm	**THE PRESIDENT** departs the Jefferson Hotel via motorcade en route the White House [drive time: 5 minutes]
8:25 pm	**THE PRESIDENT** arrives the White House
8:40 pm	**APPOINTMENT WITH IAN MCWILLIAMS** **RESIDENCE**
3C RON	**THE WHITE HOUSE**
IRC RON	**DENVER, COLORADO**

1506-DC-00000222

S 02020

SCHEDULE OF THE PRESIDENT
FOR
FRIDAY, JULY 5, 1996
FINAL

tba	MORNING RUN
9:00 am- 3:00 pm	OFFICE TIME OVAL OFFICE
3:00 pm	DOWN FOR THE DAY
BC RON	THE WHITE HOUSE
HRC RON	THE AMBASSADOR'S RESIDENCE PRAGUE, CZECH REPUBLIC

**SCHEDULE OF THE PRESIDENT
FOR
SATURDAY, JULY 6, 1996
FINAL**

tba	**MORNING RUN**
9:45 am- 10:00 am	**BRIEFING** **OVAL OFFICE** **Staff Contact: Rica Rodman**
10:06 am- 11:00 am	**LIVE RADIO ADDRESS** (TAB A) **OVAL OFFICE** **Remarks: Michael Waldman** **Staff Contact: Rica Rodman**
11:00 am- 4:00 pm	**OFFICE TIME** **OVAL OFFICE**
	HOLD DAY
BC RON	**THE WHITE HOUSE**
HRC RON	**BUDAPEST, HUNGARY**

as of July 5, 1996 [illegible]

THE WHITE HOUSE

WASHINGTON

PRESIDENTIAL CALL LOG

JULY 19th, 19 96

	TIME PLACED	DISC	NAME	ACTION
OUT / XXX	12:11 AM / XPM	12:11	MESSAGE: "WAKE ME AT 7:00 A.M. THANK YOU."	ACKNOWLEDGED 12:11 A.M.
OUT / INC	AM / PM			
OUT / XXXc	6:40 AM / XPM	6:40	MESSAGE: "I'M UP, YOU DO NOT HAVE TO CALL."	ACKNOWLEDGED 6:40 A.M.
OUT / INC	AM / PM			
OUT / XXX	8:23 AM / XPM		GOVERNOR ROBERT J. MILLER FAJARDO, PUERTO RICO [redacted]	TLKD WITH MRS. CURRIE 8:24 A.M.
OUT / INC	AM / PM			
OUT / INC	AM / PM			
OUT / INC	AM / PM			1506-DC-00000275
OUT / INC	AM / PM			
OUT	AM			S 020254

	– Upon conclusion of remarks, the President works a ropeline and departs.
9:05 pm	**THE PRESIDENT** proceeds to the Granada Room
~~9:10~~ pm– 9:53 ~~10:30~~ pm 11:18 11:19 – 11:24 → STAFF PHOTO	**DINNER FOR THE DEMOCRATIC NATIONAL COMMITTEE** **GRANADA ROOM** The Biltmore Hotel Staff Contact: Craig Smith, David Wofford Event Coordinator: Janna Sidley **CLOSED PRESS**
	– The President has an informal discussion with guests at table.
[illegible] pm	**THE PRESIDENT** proceeds to Presidential Suite
BC RON	**THE BILTMORE HOTEL** **MIAMI, FLORIDA**
HRC RON	**LAS VEGAS, NEVADA**

as of October 21, 1996 9:00am

1506-DC-00000328

S 020307

2:15 pm	**THE PRESIDENT** arrives International Terminal, Daytona Beach International Airport, Daytona Beach, Florida **OPEN PRESS** **CLOSED PUBLIC**
2:15 pm	**DRIVER PHOTOS** **TARMAC**
2:25 pm	**THE PRESIDENT** departs International Terminal, Daytona Beach International Airport, Daytona Beach, Florida via Air Force One en route Andrews Air Force Base [flight time: 1 hour, 40 minutes]
4:05 pm	**THE PRESIDENT** arrives Andrews Air Force Base
4:15 pm	**THE PRESIDENT** departs Andrews Air Force Base via Marine One en route the White House [flight time: 10 minutes]
4:25 pm	**THE PRESIDENT** arrives the White House
4:30 pm- 5:30 pm	**DOWN TIME** **RESIDENCE**
5:30 pm- 6:30 pm	**HOLD**
6:45 pm	**THE PRESIDENT** departs the White House via motorcade en route the Sheraton Washington Hotel [drive time: 10 minutes]
6:55 pm	**THE PRESIDENT** arrives the Sheraton Washington Hotel

Greeters:
- Senator Thomas Daschle, Senate Democratic Leader
- Representative Richard Gephardt, House Democratic Leader
- Don Fowler, Chairman, Democratic National Committee
- Steve Wilson, Director of Catering, Sheraton Washington Hotel

1506-DC-00000334

8

S 020313

7:00 pm-
8:00 pm

PRESIDENTIAL UNITY CELEBRATION
COTILLION BALLROOM
The Sheraton Washington Hotel
Staff Contact: Doug Sosnik
Event Coordinator: Laura Graham
POOL PRESS

- **Off-stage announcement of the President, accompanied by Senator Thomas Daschle, Senator Democratic Leader, Representative Richard Gephardt, House Democratic Leader and Don Fowler, Chairman, Democratic National Committee to "Ruffles and Flourishes" and "Hail to the Chief".**

- **Senator Thomas Daschle makes brief remarks and introduces Representative Richard Gephardt.**

- **Representative Richard Gephardt makes brief remarks and introduces the President.**

- **The President makes remarks.**

- **Upon conclusion of remarks, the President works a ropeline and departs.**

8:05 pm — **THE PRESIDENT** departs the Sheraton Washington Hotel via motorcade en route private residence, McLean, Virginia
[drive time: 15 minutes]

8:20 pm — **THE PRESIDENT** arrives private residence, McLean, Virginia

Greeters: Senator Robert Kerrey, Chairman, Democratic Senatorial Campaign Committee
Representative Martin Frost, Chairman, Democratic Congressional Campaign Committee
Alan and Dianne Kay

8:25 pm-
9:10 pm

PRESIDENTIAL UNITY RECEPTION
PARLOR
Private Residence
Staff Contact: Doug Sosnik
Event Coordinator: Laura Graham
CLOSED PRESS

- The President does a photo receiving line with seventy five guests.

~~10:15am~~- 10:37
~~10:45am~~ 11 am

PRESENTATION OF THE CONGRESSIONAL SPACE MEDAL OF HONOR TO DR. SHANNON W. LUCID
OVAL OFFICE
Staff Contact: Dr. John Gibbons
Event Coordinator: Patrick Steel
Remarks: David Shipley
POOL PRESS

- The President makes remarks.
- The President directs the Military Aide to read the citation.
- The Military Aide reads the citation and gives the President the Congressional Space Medal of Honor.
- The President places the medal around Dr. Shannon Lucid's neck.
- Dr. Shannon Lucid makes remarks and presents a framed photo of the STS-79 Crew.
- The President departs.

Note: The President will pose for a photograph with Dr. Shannon Lucid and the STS-79 Crew prior to departure.

Note: The President will pose for a photograph with Senator Thomas Daschle and representatives from the Scientific Knowledge for Indian Learning and Leadership program prior to departure. The group will present the President with a painting.

11:12 - Stefanie + Anne
11:19

11:20 - Trey Schroeder + family in for photo
:25

11:00 am-
1:00 pm
PHONE/OFFICE TIME
OVAL OFFICE

1:00 pm-
1:15 pm
~~OFFICIAL HOLIDAY PHOTO WITH THE FIRST LADY~~
~~BLUE ROOM~~
~~Staff Contact: Ann Stock, Bob McNeely~~
~~WHITE HOUSE PHOTO ONLY~~

1:15 pm-
6:15 pm
PHONE/OFFICE TIME
OVAL OFFICE

BC RON — THE WHITE HOUSE
HRC RON — EN ROUTE LA PAZ, BOLIVIA

1506-DC-00000353

S 020332

SCHEDULE OF THE PRESIDENT

FOR

SATURDAY, FEBRUARY 8, 1997

FINAL

SCHEDULING DIRECTOR: **ANNE HAWLEY**
HOME: [redacted]
OFFICE:
WHCA PAGER: [redacted]

SCHEDULING DIRECTOR: **STEPHANIE STREETT**
HOME: [redacted]
OFFICE:
WHCA PAGER:

PRESS COORDINATOR: **JEREMY GAINES**
HOME: [redacted]
OFFICE:
WHCA PAGER:

WEATHER: **Washington, DC**
Cloudy with rain or snow, tapering off by afternoon. then partly cloudy. Wind east at 8 to 13 knots. Low 31 to 36. High 39 to 44.

1506-DC-00000373

S 020352

SCHEDULE OF THE PRESIDENT
FOR
SATURDAY, FEBRUARY 8, 1997
FINAL

tba	MORNING RUN

DAY AND EVENING OFF

BC AND HRC RON	THE WHITE HOUSE

1506-DC-00000374

S 020353

WASHINGTON, D.C.
FRIDAY, OCTOBER 10, 1997

SCHEDULE OF THE PRESIDENT
FOR
FRIDAY, OCTOBER 10, 1997
FINAL SCHEDULE

9:20
~~9:00~~ am-
~~9:15~~ am
9:29

MEETING
OVAL OFFICE ~~DINING ROOM~~
Staff Contact: Erskine Bowles, JP

~~9:15~~ am 9:29
9:30 am 9:41

COMBINED BRIEFING
OVAL OFFICE ~~DINING ROOM~~ EB, JP
Staff Contact: Sandy Berger, J. STEINBERG, L. FUERTH

~~9:35~~ am- 9:48
~~9:45~~ am 10:12

DROP BY SANDY BERGER'S MEETING WITH [redacted]

SANDY BERGER'S OFFICE WHTU
Staff Contact: Sandy Berger

10:25
~~9:50~~ am-
~~10:15~~ am
10:35

BRIEFING
OVAL OFFICE ~~DINING ROOM~~ ELATING REMARKS,
Staff Contact: Gene Sperling, RAHM, PB, JP, VP, GREG,

10:42
~~10:15~~ am-
~~10:35~~ am
11:08

STATEMENT ON IRS REFORM
~~ROSE GARDEN~~ OEOB 450
Remarks: Michael Waldman
Staff Contact: Gene Sperling
Event Coordinator: Setti Warren [redacted]
OPEN PRESS

10:42 – 10:47 > Secretary Rubin makes brief remarks.

10:47 – 10:56 > The Vice President makes brief remarks and presents a report to the President on the IRS.

10:57 – 11:04 > **The President** makes brief remarks.

– **The President**, the Vice President and Secretary Rubin depart.

1506-DC-00000426

S 020405

WASHINGTON, D.C.
FRIDAY, OCTOBER 10, 1997

~~10:45~~ am- 11:12 ~~10:55~~ am 11:15	**MEETING** OVAL OFFICE ~~DINING ROOM~~ Staff Contact: Stephanie Streett
~~11:00~~ am- 11:20 ~~12:00~~ pm 12:30	**BRIEFING FOR FOREIGN TRIP** CABINET ROOM Staff Contact: Sandy Berger
~~12:05~~ pm- 12:38 ~~1:05~~ pm 1:35	**MEETING ON CLIMATE CHANGE** OVAL OFFICE Staff Contact: Gene Sperling, Katie McGinty
~~1:10~~ pm- 1:38 ~~2:10~~ pm 2:30	**LUNCH WITH THE VICE PRESIDENT** OVAL OFFICE
2:~~15~~ pm- 2:30 2:~~30~~ pm	**BRIEFING** OVAL OFFICE Staff Contact: Ann Lewis, ~~Brenda Anders~~ GEN. McCAFFREY
2:~~30~~ pm- 2:48 ~~3:00~~ pm	**TAPE THE RADIO ADDRESS** ROOSEVELT ROOM Staff Contact: Ann Lewis, Brenda Anders
3:00 pm- 3:30 pm	**MEETING** RESIDENCE Staff Contact: John Podesta
3:30 pm- 6:00 pm	**PHONE AND OFFICE TIME OR DOWN FOR THE DAY** OVAL OFFICE 4:00 - DOLE ? CALL

NOTE:	**The First Lady will be returning to the White House at 7:00 pm this evening from Panama.**

EVENING OFF

BC AND HRC RON **THE WHITE HOUSE**
WASHINGTON, DC

1506-DC-00000427

S 020406

Sunday, January 21, 1996

Weather: Partly to mostly cloudy. Temp from 18 to 35 degrees.

News...

- **Floods ravage parts of U.S.**
  Swollen rivers and streams across the New York and Mid-Atlantic regions receded yesterday as tens of thousands evacuated residents returned to flood-ravaged homes and businesses in eight states, and public officials began to assess the costs of the worst flooding in decades. (NYTimes)

- **Default Threat is Weilded by GOP in Budget Battle**
  In the latest Republican effort to revive the party's stymied economic and social agendas, the House majority leader, Dick Armey, said Congress would refuse to extend the nation's ability to borrow money to meet its bills unless President Clinton yeilds to the party's budget-cutting initiatives to decrease "the size and intrusiveness of government."

  -- The position outlined signalled that the Republicans might be willing to use the threat of national default to force Mr Clinton to give more ground. (NYTimes)

- **Islamic Group Vows Revenge on Americans**
  The most powerful group of Muslim militants have vowed to strike at American "interests and people" in revenge for the life sentence for Sheik Omar Abdel Rahman.

- **State Department official investigates atrocities in Bosnia**
  Asst. Secretary of State for Human Rights, John C. Shattuck said he and his officials had seen enough evidence in their first visit to Srebrenicia to corroborate reports of widespread mass executions.

  Allegations of mass killings around Srebrenicia are not new, but were first made in July, 1995 when the U.S. released satellite photographs that purported to show grave sites. Those killed were Muslims captured in or near the United Nations-designated "safe haven," of Srebrenecia by the Bosnian Serbs when it fell to Bosnian Serb forces on July 11, 1995

- **President Declares Disaster Assistance for Commonwealth of Pennsylvania**
  ordered federal aid to supplement state and local recovery efforts in areas struck by flooding beginning on 1/19/96 --can include housing,grants, low cost loans to cover uninsured property losses

  Major streets in Harrisbury remained underwater state office building in Pittsburg and all government offices in Harrisburg expected to remain closed through first of the week.

- **Steve Forbes Campaigns on his Flat Tax ideas.**

- **Arafat becomes Palestian's first elected leader.**

- **Five U.S. Servicemen infected with heterosexual AIDs.**
  Public health officials are concerned a non-native strain of the AIDS virus that recently turned up in the servicemen in San Diego may turn into a new epidemic. Researchers fear the strain could'more easily be transmitted during heterosexual sex.

- **Hearing Approach Harassment of First Lady, Clinton Aide says**
  President Clinton's chief of staff said today that a Republican Congressional inquiry into Hillary Rodham Clinton's role in Whitewater affair was getting dangerously close to political harassment. Clinton's chief of staff Leon Panetta spoke on NBC's "Meet the Press" on Sunday.

- **Congresswoman Faces Increasing Skepticism**
  In polls conducted for the Deseret News, portions of voters who says she should retire after her term ends in January climbed from 57 percent in November to 75 percent in Jan.

- **Public Shows Rising Concern over Quality of Education**
  The flat tax and balancing the budget may be dominating the news from the campagin trail, but in America's living rooms, offices and supermarkets, voters are focusing on the quality of the nation's schooling. A recent USA Today/CNN/ Gallop Poll found.

Today at the White House...

- The President and his family took a private tour of the Johannes Vermeer exhibit at the National Gallery of Art (NGA). Earl A. Powellk, III the gallery director, led the Clintons, family friends and a former room mate of Mrs. Clinton on the tour of the Dutch painter's works.

  The first family was there for about one hour and fifteen minutes. Mrs. Clinton and Chelsea were there about 45 minutes before the President arrived.

  The President went to the oval office carrying a satchel of work after the tour.

1506-DC-00000525

S 020500

- The President ended up eating dinner with Kevin O'Keith, Bruce Lindsey and Dick Kelley, in the residence Solarium.

- The President hosted 32 friends at the WH movie theatre to
view a new movie: "Executive Decision," starring Steven Segal, Kurt Russell and Halle Berry. (His other choice
as
Primal Fear, with Richard Gere.)

The President was in a wonderful mood as host to long-
ime
friends - mostly from Arkansas. Popcorn, beer and soft
rinks
was on the menu. The movie was light, with just enough
ction to keep the audience awake. The President got up
uring the
movie a few times - two times to briefly leave the
heatre, and once or twice to check to see whether there was
opcorn and drinks still there.

DayNotes: Mr. Dick Kelley, the President's step-father,
pent
the night at the residence.

Sunday, March 31, 1996
Weather --

- The President called Coach Pat Summit, of the Tennessee Lady Vols Coach, winner of the NCAA's Women's Basketball Tournament, and Coach Andy Landers, of the Georgia Lady Bull Dogs, the losing team's coach around 8:45 a.m.

- The President attended Palm Sunday services at Foundry Methodist Church @ 11:00 a.m. Pastor J. Philip Wogaman talked about the humility of Christ. He cited Edmund Muskie and Albert Schweitzer as leaders with humility. The President sat through the baptism of the pastor's grand-daughter and a Confirmation ceremony, welcoming new members. He shook hands with several members of the congreatation - a racially mixed, middle-classes group, with a scattering of some who appeared to be street people. The President appeared tired, and took no press questions on the way out of church.

  He returned to WH grounds @ 12:20.

- The President works in the Oval from 3:00 to almost 6:00.

- The President greets Mrs. Clinton and Chelsea @9:25, as they return from their 10-day trip.

REDACTED

Today...

- The President had asked for a 7 a.m. wake-up call, but called the operator this morning to tell them 'never mind', he was already up - at 6:40 a.m.

- The President and Mrs. Clinton left for the opening ceremonies of the Olympics in Atlanta shortly after 8 a.m., this morning. He greeted seven friends in the diplomatic room, as they left - Beth Coulter,her husband, her sister and her two children; anArkansas Judge and his wife, Kay Arnold.

  It was raining, so the President's friends were a little damp from the helicopter fan. Mrs. Clinton was beautiful in her pale pink suit and matching suede shoes - that were pretty much soaked by the

S 020612

BILL ARCHIVE AND RETRIEVAL SYSTEM - VIEW 03/23/98 14:08
CMD ===>

ACCOUNT NUMBER : [redacted] BILL DATE : 012598
CARRIER : AT&T PAGE NO : 4
Itemized calls, continued
irectly dialed

No. Date	Place called	Number called	Time	Rate		Min.	Amount
Calling number [redacted]							
1.DEC 301	VAN NUYS CA	[redacted]	12:18 PM	DAY	0JB	1	.28
2.DEC 301	CANOGAPARK CA	[redacted]	12:19 PM	DAY	0JB	1	.28
3.DEC 301	VAN NUYS CA	[redacted]	12:20 PM	DAY	0JB	4	1.12
4.DEC 301	WASHINGTON DC	[redacted]	01:54 PM	DAY	0JB	7	1.96
5.DEC 301	WASHINGTON DC	[redacted]	04:47 PM	DAY	0JB	11	3.08
6.DEC 301	WASHINGTON DC	[redacted]	07:39 PM	EVE	0JB	1	.16
7.DEC 301	WASHINGTON DC	[redacted]	07:44 PM	EVE	0JB	1	.16
8.DEC 301	WASHINGTON DC	[redacted]	08:08 PM	EVE	0JB	1	.16
9.DEC 301	WASHINGTON DC	[redacted]	08:44 PM	EVE	0JB	28	4.48
10.DEC 301	WASHINGTON DC	[redacted]	09:13 PM	EVE	0JB	2	.32
11.DEC 301	WASHINGTON DC	[redacted]	09:15 PM	EVE	0JB	1	.16
12.DEC 301	WASHINGTON DC	[redacted]	09:16 PM	EVE	0JB	5	.80

ENTER-NEW PF01-EXIT PF02-BILL PF03-LEFT PF04-RIGHT PF05-GOTO PF06-DUPBILL
PF07-UP PF08-DWN PF09-UP SECT PF10-DWN SECT PF11-PREV BILL PF12-NEXT BILL

BILL ARCHIVE AND RETRIEVAL SYSTEM - VIEW
CMD ===>

ACCOUNT NUMBER : [redacted] BILL DATE : 012598
CARRIER : AT&T PAGE NO : 4

29.JAN	71WASHINGTON DC	[redacted]	10:07	PM	EVE	0JB	1	.16
30.JAN	71WASHINGTON DC	[redacted]	10:14	PM	EVE	0JB	2	.32
31.JAN	81WASHINGTON DC	[redacted]	09:25	AM	DAY	0JB	1	.28
32.JAN	81WARRENTON VA	[redacted]	09:25	AM	DAY	0JB	1	.28
33.JAN	81WARRENTON VA	[redacted]	10:09	AM	DAY	0JB	6	1.68
34.JAN	81WASHINGTON DC	[redacted]	11:50	AM	DAY	0JB	1	.28
35.JAN	81WASHINGTON DC	[redacted]	11:51	AM	DAY	0JB	1	.28
36.JAN	81ALEXANDRIA VA	[redacted]	11:54	AM	DAY	0JB	1	.28
37.JAN	81DEVONSHIRE BM	[redacted]	12:02	PM	DS	0LB	1	1.25
38.JAN	81WARRENTON VA	[redacted]	01:18	PM	DAY	0JB	8	2.24
39.JAN	81ALEXANDRIA VA	[redacted]	02:36	PM	DAY	0JB	1	.28

ENTER-NEW PF01-EXIT PF02-BILL PF03-LEFT PF04-RIGHT PF05-GOTO PF06-DUPBIL
PF07-UP PF08-DWN PF09-UP SECT PF10-DWN SECT PF11-PREV BILL PF12-NEXT BIL

BILL ARCHIVE AND RETRIEVAL SYSTEM - VIEW
CMD ===>

ACCOUNT NUMBER : [redacted]
CARRIER : AT&T
BILL DATE : 012598
PAGE NO : 5

Itemized calls, continued
Directly dialed

No.	Date	Place called	Number called	Time	Rate		Min.	Amount
Calling number [redacted]								
1.	JAN 8	1WARRENTON VA	[redacted]	02:45 PM	DAY	0JB	1	.28
2.	JAN 8	1WARRENTON VA	[redacted]	02:46 PM	DAY	0JB	1	.28
3.	JAN 8	1DEVONSHIRE BM	[redacted]	03:03 PM	DS	0LB	1	1.25
4.	JAN 8	1WASHINGTON DC	[redacted]	03:09 PM	DAY	0JB	1	.28
5.	JAN 8	1ALEXANDRIA VA	[redacted]	03:10 PM	DAY	0JB	2	.56
6.	JAN 8	1CANOGAPARK CA	[redacted]	03:12 PM	DAY	0JB	12	3.36
7.	JAN 8	1WASHINGTON DC	[redacted]	03:27 PM	DAY	0JB	13	3.64
8.	JAN 8	1WASHINGTON DC	[redacted]	03:42 PM	DAY	0JB	1	.28
9.	JAN 8	1WARRENTON VA	[redacted]	04:28 PM	DAY	0JB	16	4.48
10.	JAN 8	1WASHINGTON DC	[redacted]	04:48 PM	DAY	0JB	5	1.40
11.	JAN 8	1WASHINGTON DC	[redacted]	05:40 PM	DAY	0JB	1	.28
12.	JAN 8	1WASHINGTON DC	[redacted]	06:15 PM	DAY	0JB	3	.84

ENTER-NEW PF01-EXIT PF02-BILL PF03-LEFT PF04-RIGHT PF05-GOTO PF06-DUPBIL
PF07-UP PF08-DWN PF09-UP SECT PF10-DWN SECT PF11-PREV BILL PF12-NEXT BIL

BILL ARCHIVE AND RETRIEVAL SYSTEM - VIEW 03/23/98 14:0

CMD ===>

ACCOUNT NUMBER : [redacted] BILL DATE : 012598

CARRIER : AT&T PAGE NO : 5

13.JAN	81WASHINGTON DC	[redacted]	06:26 PM	DAY	0JB	3	.84
14.JAN	81WARRENTON VA	[redacted]	06:28 PM	DAY	0JB	6	1.68
15.JAN	81WASHINGTON DC	[redacted]	09:02 PM	EVE	0JB	1	.16
16.JAN	81WASHINGTON DC	[redacted]	09:21 PM	EVE	0JB	1	.16
17.JAN	91ALEXANDRIA VA	[redacted]	09:36 AM	DAY	0JB	2	.56
18.JAN	91ALEXANDRIA VA	[redacted]	09:39 AM	DAY	0JB	2	.56
19.JAN	91ALEXANDRIA VA	[redacted]	09:54 AM	DAY	0JB	31	8.68
20.JAN	91POUGHKEEPS NY	[redacted]	11:22 AM	DAY	08C	1	.23
21.JAN	91DIR ASST DC	[redacted]	11:29 AM		0JB	0	.95
22.JAN	91WARRENTON VA	[redacted]	11:56 AM	DAY	0JB	19	5.32
23.JAN	91WASHINGTON DC	[redacted]	01:29 PM	DAY	0JB	1	.28
24.JAN	91WASHINGTON DC	[redacted]	01:29 PM	DAY	0JB	1	.28
25.JAN	91WASHINGTON DC	[redacted]	01:32 PM	DAY	0JB	1	.28
26.JAN	91WARRENTON VA	[redacted]	01:38 PM	DAY	0JB	2	.56
27.JAN	91WASHINGTON DC	[redacted]	04:14 PM	DAY	0JB	7	1.96
28.JAN	91WASHINGTON DC	[redacted]	04:35 PM	DAY	0JB	1	.28

ENTER-NEW PF01-EXIT PF02-BILL PF03-LEFT PF04-RIGHT PF05-GOTO PF06-DUPBILL

PF07-UP PF08-DWN PF09-UP SECT PF10-DWN SECT PF11-PREV BILL PF12-NEXT BILL

BILL ARCHIVE AND RETRIEVAL SYSTEM - VIEW 03/23/98 14:0
CMD ===>

ACCOUNT NUMBER : [redacted] BILL DATE : 012598
CARRIER : AT&T PAGE NO : 5

29.JAN	91WASHINGTON DC	[redacted]	04:37 PM	DAY	0JB	1	.28
30.JAN	91WASHINGTON DC	[redacted]	05:04 PM	DAY	0JB	1	.28
31.JAN	91WASHINGTON DC	[redacted]	05:05 PM	DAY	0JB	1	.28
32.JAN	91WASHINGTON DC	[redacted]	05:09 PM	DAY	0JB	1	.28
33.JAN	91WASHINGTON DC	[redacted]	05:09 PM	DAY	0JB	2	.56
34.JAN	91WASHINGTON DC	[redacted]	05:21 PM	DAY	0JB	5	1.40
35.JAN	91WARRENTON VA	[redacted]	06:55 PM	DAY	0JB	10	2.20
36.JAN	91WASHINGTON DC	[redacted]	07:05 PM	EVE	0JB	3	.48
37.JAN	91WASHINGTON DC	[redacted]	09:38 PM	EVE	0JB	9	1.44
38.JAN	101WASHINGTON DC	[redacted]	07:16 AM	NIGHT	0JB	1	.13
39.JAN	101WASHINGTON DC	[redacted]	09:13 AM	NIGHT	0JB	2	.26

ENTER-NEW PF01-EXIT PF02-BILL PF03-LEFT PF04-RIGHT PF05-GOTO PF06-DUPBILI
PF07-UP PF08-DWN PF09-UP SECT PF10-DWN SECT PF11-PREV BILL PF12-NEXT BILI

BILL ARCHIVE AND RETRIEVAL SYSTEM - VIEW 03/23/98 14:08
CMD ===>

ACCOUNT NUMBER : [redacted] BILL DATE : 012598
CARRIER : AT&T PAGE NO : 6

3.JAN	111WASHINGTON DC	[redacted]	04:05 PM	NIGHT	0JB	1	.13
4.JAN	111ARLINGTON VA	[redacted]	04:47 PM	NIGHT	0JB	8	1.04
15.JAN	111ARLINGTON VA	[redacted]	04:58 PM	NIGHT	0JB	7	.91
16.JAN	111WASHINGTON DC	[redacted]	08:44 PM	NIGHT	0JB	24	3.12
17.JAN	111WASHINGTON DC	[redacted]	09:08 PM	NIGHT	0JB	1	.13
18.JAN	121WASHINGTON DC	[redacted]	10:42 AM	DAY	0JB	1	.28
19.JAN	121WASHINGTON DC	[redacted]	11:11 AM	DAY	0JB	14	3.92
20.JAN	121WASHINGTON DC	[redacted]	11:26 AM	DAY	0JB	5	1.40
21.JAN	121WASHINGTON DC	[redacted]	11:50 AM	DAY	0JB	1	.28
22.JAN	121WASHINGTON DC	[redacted]	02:09 PM	DAY	0JB	1	.28
23.JAN	121WASHINGTON DC	[redacted]	03:27 PM	DAY	0JB	4	1.12
24.JAN	121WASHINGTON DC	[redacted]	03:34 PM	DAY	0JB	2	.56
25.JAN	121DIR ASST DC	[redacted]	03:37 PM		0JB	0	.95
26.JAN	121WASHINGTON DC	[redacted]	03:38 PM	DAY	0JB	1	.28
27.JAN	121WASHINGTON DC	[redacted]	03:39 PM	DAY	0JB	2	.56
28.JAN	121WASHINGTON DC	[redacted]	03:41 PM	DAY	0JB	1	.28

ENTER-NEW PF01-EXIT PF02-BILL PF03-LEFT PF04-RIGHT PF05-GOTO PF06-DUPBILL
PF07-UP PF08-DWN PF09-UP SECT PF10-DWN SECT PF11-PREV BILL PF12-NEXT BILL

BILL ARCHIVE AND RETRIEVAL SYSTEM - VIEW 03/23/98 14:06
CMD ===>

ACCOUNT NUMBER : [redacted] BILL DATE : 012598
CARRIER : AT&T PAGE NO : 6

29.JAN	121PITTSBURGH PA	[redacted]	03:42 PM	DAY	0JB	1	.28
30.JAN	121DIR ASST DC	[redacted]	03:59 PM		0JB	0	.95
31.JAN	121WASHINGTON DC	[redacted]	04:09 PM	DAY	0JB	4	1.12
32.JAN	121WASHINGTON DC	[redacted]	05:00 PM	DAY	0JB	3	.84
33.JAN	121WARRENTON VA	[redacted]	05:05 PM	DAY	0JB	8	2.24
34.JAN	121WASHINGTON DC	[redacted]	06:45 PM	DAY	0JB	1	.28
35.JAN	121WASHINGTON DC	[redacted]	07:02 PM	EVE	0JB	1	.16
36.JAN	121WASHINGTON DC	[redacted]	07:48 PM	EVE	0JB	1	.16
37.JAN	121WASHINGTON DC	[redacted]	07:48 PM	EVE	0JB	1	.16
38.JAN	131WASHINGTON DC	[redacted]	10:23 AM	DAY	0JB	8	2.24
39.JAN	131WARRENTON VA	[redacted]	10:31 AM	DAY	0JB	7	1.96

ENTER-NEW PF01-EXIT PF02-BILL PF03-LEFT PF04-RIGHT PF05-GOTO PF06-DUPBILL
PF07-UP PF08-DWN PF09-UP SECT PF10-DWN SECT PF11-PREV BILL PF12-NEXT BILL

RICHARD F. DRISCOLL, ASA, AAA, NGJA
Appraisals of Antiques, Works of Art & Jewelry
4100 Cathedral Avenue, NW Suite #402
Washington, D.C. 20016-3584
(202) 293-2323 - Voice
(202) 289-5355 - Fax
appraiszer@aol.com - email

Effective date: July 9th, 1998
Report date: July 9th, 1998

Patrick F. Fallon, Jr., Special Agent
OFFICE OF THE INDEPENDENT COUNSEL
1001 Pennsylvania Avenue, NW #490-N
Washington, D.C. 20004

CZ-DC-00000010

FAIR MARKET VALUE APPRAISAL

TYPE	QUANTITY	ITEM DESCRIPTION	APPRAISED VALUE
S		Tabletop cigarette holder, 3 3/4" x 4 3/4", hammered sterling silver, with strap handle and receptacle for a small matchbox, four trifid feet, 20th century, probably American, 2ozsT.	$ 65.00
J		Hatpin, 6"L plus slide, gold plated metal decorated with polychrome enamel and glass, late 20th century.	$ 3.00
J		Brooch, gold plated metal, depicting buildings with spirals, crescents and stars above, set with imitation pearl and two imitation diamonds, late 20th century.	$ 5.00
J		Brooch, gold and silver plated metal decorated with polychrome enamel painted berry, leaves and white flower, set with 4 imitation pearls.	$ 3.00

RICHARD F. DRISCOLL, ASA, AAA, NGJA
Appraisals of Antiques, Works of Art & Jewelry
4100 Cathedral Avenue, NW Suite #402
Washington, D.C. 20016-3584
(202) 293-2323 - Voice
(202) 289-5355 - Fax
appraiszer@aol.com - email

Effective date: August 31st, 1998
Report date: August 31st, 1998

Patrick F. Fallon, Jr., Special Agent
OFFICE OF THE INDEPENDENT COUNSEL
1001 Pennsylvania Avenue, NW #490-N
Washington, D.C. 20004

CZ-DC-00000016

FAIR MARKET VALUE APPRAISAL

TYPE	QUANTITY	ITEM DESCRIPTION	APPRAISED VALUE
		Coverlet, 46" x 72", machine woven cotton in off-white and burgundy representing "Radio City Music Hall Christmas Special starring the Rockettes", 1995.	$ 50.00
B		Sculpture, 7 1/2"H, carved tan stone with varigations (steatite(?)) depicting the "Spirit of the Grizzly Bear", the center hollowed out, Six Nations (Great Lakes area, late 20th century. [minor abrasions]	$ 200.00
B		Paperweight, 4" x 2 1/2" x 3/4"H, glass with reverse painted (eglomisé) scene of the White House, late 20th century. [paint badly flaking, scene damaged]	$ 10.00

(continued on following page)

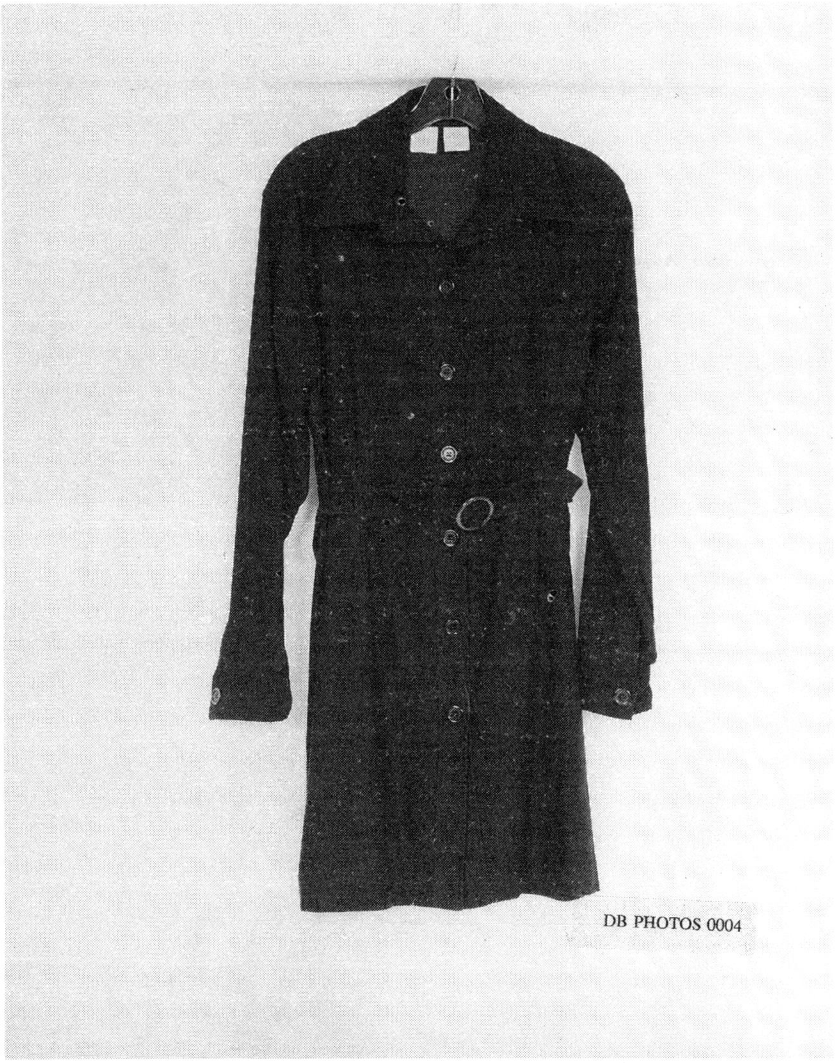
DB PHOTOS 0004

DEC 96
TDK
MC-60
OLYMPUS
XB 60
MAY 96
SEPT. 96
April 96
DB PHOTOS 0044

RADIO CITY
DB PHOTOS 0048

it was so sad seeing you tonight because i was so angry with you that you once again rejected me and yet, all i wanted was for everyone else in the room to disappear and for you to hold me.

bill, i loved you with all of my heart. i wanted to be with you all of the time. most recently in london, i walked the streets thinking how content i would be to walk the streets at your side while you spoke of things past -- filled the air and my soul with your knowledge of history.

when you gave me leaves of grass i realized that the reason i was so connected to you, or so i thought, was because you were in my soul. to quote your famous cliché, i felt your pain. i seemed, somehow to feel in my heart some of your experiences. you will see in this collection of things for you, a card i was so shocked to find for obvious reasons. It rang so true to me.

i have realized yesterday when betty told me you "couldn't" see me, what's really going on -- you want me out of your life. i guess the signs have been clear for awhile -- not wanting to see me and rarely calling. i used to think it was simply you putting up walls-- that the real you was the person whom i was with on the fourth of july. i'm humiliated at how wrong i was.

i am sorry that this has been such a bad experience. i will never forget what you said that night we fought on the phone -- if you had known what i was really like you never would have gotten involved with me. i'm sure you're not the first person to have felt that way about me.

well, anyway, these are all of the little gifts and one big christmas gift (the black box) that i've had for you. i wanted to give them to you in person, but that is obviously not going to happen. you may not want to keep them, but please don't send them back. i'm very particular about presents and could never give them to anyone else -- they were all bought with you in mind. your christmas present is an antique from, i beleive, the 30's. i was very attracted to it.

i knew it would hurt to have to say goodbye to you; i just never thought it would be on paper.

DB-DC-00000017

12 November 1997

Handsome:

I asked you three weeks ago to please be sensitive to what I am going through right now and to keep in contact with me, and yet I'm still left writing notes in vain. I am not a moron. I know that what is going on in the world takes precedence, but I don't think what I have asked you for is unreasonable. I can't help but to have hurt feelings when I sent you a note last week and this week, and you still haven't seen me or called me.

I thought if I took away your burden of having to try to place me in the WH you would open yourself up to me again; I missed that more than anything. It was awful when I saw you for your birthday in August. You were so distant that I missed you as I was holding you in my arms.

You have functions tonight, tomorrow night and then you leave on Friday afternoon. Yesterday was the best window of opportunity to see me and you didn't. I'm left wondering why. I am begging you to please be nice to me and understanding until I leave. This is so hard for me. I am trying to deal with so much emotionally, and I have nobody to talk to about it. I need you right now not as president, but as a man. PLEASE be my friend.

Betty said that you come back from your dinner tomorrow somewhere between 8:30 and 9:00. For my sake, can we make an arrangement that I will be waiting for you when you get back, and we can visit just for a little while. It's really not that difficult...yes or no?

First and foremost, thank you.

My dream had been to work in Communications or Strategic Planning at the White House. I am open to any suggestions that you may have on work that is similar to that or may intrigue me.

The most important things to me are that I am engaged and interested in my work; I am not someone's administrative/executive assistant; and my salary can provide me a comfortable living in NY.

Networks:

* Assistant producer at any of the networks
* Kaplan -- CNN has a NY Office
* News/political segments at MTV

Assistant to an account executive at any of the following (*not* administrative assistant):

* Hill & Knowlton
* Burson-Marsteller
* Downey & Chandler
* Bozell Public Relations/ Bozell Worldwide
* Devries Public Relations

[These are agencies with which I am familiar. You may have more suggestions from the attached list of agencies in NY (Tab 1)].

* Anything at George magazine

A note about the UN:

I do not have any interest in working there. As a result of what happened in April '96, I have already spent a year and a half at an agency in which I have no interest. I want a job where I feel challenged, engaged and interested. I don't think the UN is the right place for me.

Description

[Charles, Heinrich], compiler. Our Patriotic President: his life in pictures, famous words & maxims, anecdotes, biography. Illustrations and photographs. New York, Elite Art Press, 1904. Oblong 8vo. Color pictorial wraps, bound with cord. Cover illustration signed Friederang. [56pp]. Cover soiled and lightly foxed, edges of cover and pages toned and soiled.

Two bench stamps (V002-DC-00000003; DEK 227870) are affixed to the lower right corner of cover, removal of which will damage the paper. As of the mid-1997 date of this appraisal, the bench stamps were not present and so have not been considered as defects in the valuation.

This book, about Theodore Roosevelt (1858-1919), was compiled from a number of sources for the popular audience, rather than as a serious biographical work. It is of interest as an early biography of President Roosevelt. The First Edition was published by the Elite Art Press in 1901 and there were three subsequent editions, all in 1904. Two, from the Columbia Press and one other, of which this is an example, from the Elite Art Press. One of the Columbia Press editions was distributed by the Republican National Committee for President Roosevelt's 1904 Presidential Campaign for his second term and had campaign slogans printed on the back cover. The other Columbia Press edition, like this last Elite Art edition were published without such additions. The overall condition of this book, especially considering the fragility of paper wraps as binding, is Very Good.

Copies of this book are listed in the collections of only three libraries, the Library of Congress, the New York Public Library and Harvard University and there have been no recorded sales of the work in the past eight years. Similar works in similar condition are reportedly sold on average for less than $25.00 in area used book stores. As might be expected in publications of this type, sales of this book have not appeared in any public auction records, local, regional or national. The current popularity of Presidential biographies, campaign-related memorabilia and the scarcity of this book would support better than average price.

Fair Market Value **$35.00.**

Wilson, James Grant, Ed. The Presidents of the United States 1789-1898. Multi-authors, Illustrated with steel engraved plates by Girsch, Hall and others. New York, Appleton, (1898). Small 4to. Engraved portraits with tissue guards, of each U.S. President from Washington to McKinley, facsimiles of signatures, letters and wood engravings throughout the text. Gilt stamped 3/4 brown morocco over marbled boards, teg. 532 pages, unopened except pages 34-35 slit roughly. Corners bumped, slight rubbing to front hinge, lower back hinge separated about a quarter inch. A few scratches to marbled boards, head chipped and lacking two small pieces. Some toning and soiling to ffep.

Two bench stamps (V002-DC-00000471; DEK 228327) are affixed to front inner paste-down, removal of which will cause tearing. As of the mid-1997 date of this appraisal, the bench stamps were not present and so have not been considered as defects in this valuation.

The book contains biographies of the first 25 U.S. Presidents and their families and is indexed. The list of authors includes John Fiske, Carl Schurz, Robert C. Winthrop, Daniel C. Gilman, William Walter Phelps, George Ticknor Curtis, George Bancroft, John Hay and others. "Several of the monographs were especially prepared for this work, while the larger number were written for *Appleton's Cyclopædia of American Biography.*" (National Union Catalog). The 25 portraits of the Presidents are bright, intact and well-executed, the overall appearance of the volume is attractive and its condition is Very Good, despite the minor defects to the binding.

The First Edition of this work was 1894, and there were four subsequent editions, of which this volume is the second. This 1898 edition is the only one reported to have been bound in three-quarter leather, while the others were in blue cloth bindings. A leather binding is an element of value, typically increasing the price of a book. Even so, as a second edition, sales of this book have not been reported in any local, regional or national public auction records. Sales in the current used book market have been more frequent for the first and fifth editions, but one copy of this edition is currently available in Massachusetts for $45.00. Consultations with book dealers and an auction house owner concerning this book generated estimated prices somewhat above that amount. The elements contributing to the value of this 1898 edition include the binding, the quality of the engraved presidential portraits and the current local interest in presidential biographies.

Fair Market Value **$85.00**

-1-

1. Ms. Lewinsky had an intimate and emotional relationship with President Clinton beginning in 1995. At various times between 1995 and 1997, Ms. Lewinsky and the President had physically intimate contact. This included oral sex, but excluded intercourse.

2. When asked what should be said if anyone questioned Ms. Lewinsky about her being with the President, he said she should say she was bringing him letters (when she worked in Legislative Affairs) or visiting Betty Currie (after she left the WH). There is truth to both of these statements.

3. After Ms. Lewinsky was informed she was being transferred to the Pentagon, Mr. Clinton told her that a) he promised to bring her back to the WH after the election and (in a subsequent conversation), b) Evelyn Lieberman spearheaded the transfer because she felt the President paid to much attention to me and vice versa. Ms. Lieberman told the Pres. that she didn't care who worked there after the election, but they needed to be careful until then.

After the election, Ms. Lewinsky asked the Pres. to bring her back to the WH. In the following

months, Mr. Clinton told Ms. Lewinsky that Bob Nash was handling it and then Marsha Scott became the contact person. Ms. L met with Ms. Scott twice. In the second meeting, Ms. Scott told Ms. L she would detail her from the Pentagon to her (Ms. Scott's) office, so people could see Ms. L's good work and stop referring to her as "The Stalker." Ms. Scott told Ms. L they had to be careful and protect the Pres. Ms. Scott later rescinded her offer to detail Ms. Lewinsky to her office.

Ms. Betty Currie asked Mr. John Podesta to take over placing me in the WH. Three weeks after that, Ms. Linda Tripp informed Ms. L that a friend of Ms. Tripp's in the NSC, Kate, had heard rumors about Ms. L; Ms. L would never work at the WH with a blue pass; and suggested to Ms. Tripp that Ms. L leave Washington, DC.

Following this conversation, Ms. Lewinsky requested of the Pres. that he ask Vernon Jordan to help secure her a non-government position in NY. He agreed to ask Mr. Jordan.

DF-DC-00000003

In an effort to help Ms. L, Ms. Currie asked Mr. Podesta to assist, as well. Ms. L believes that

-3-

the Pres. ~~asked~~ spoke with Mr. Erskine Bowles regarding Ms. L's employment in NY. Mr. Podesta arranged for Ms. L to interview with Amb. Richardson, who later offered Ms. L a position in Communications/Public Affairs at the USUN.

In the beginning of November 1997, Ms. L met with Mr. Jordan. He asked Ms. L why she was there to see him. Ms. L explained to him (in more detail) that she and the Pres. were friends and people got the wrong idea, resulting in Ms. L's 'banishment' to the Pentagon. Ms. L said she was seeking Mr. Jordan's help to begin a new life; he agreed to help.

DF-DC-00000004

Ms. L met again with Mr. Jordan in the beginning of December '97, at which time he provided Ms. L with a list of three people to contact and suggested language to use in her letters to them. At some point, Mr. Jordan remarked something about Ms. L being a friend of the Pres. of the United States. Ms. L responded that she never really saw him as "the President"; she spoke to him like a normal man and even got angry with him like a normal man. Mr. Jordan asked what Ms. L got angry about. Ms. L replied that the Pres. doesn't see or call her enough. Mr. Jordan said

-4-

Ms. L should take her frustrations out on ~~the~~ him-- not the President.

The following week Ms. L had two interviews in NY in response to ~~as a result~~ of her letters.

4. After Ms. Lewinsky was informed, by the Pres., that she was identified as a possible witness in the Jones case, the Pres. and Ms. L discussed what she should do. The Pres. told her ~~to~~ he was not sure she would be subpoenaed, but in the event that she was, she should contact Ms. Currie. When asked what to do if she was subpoenaed, the Pres. suggested she could sign an affidavit to try to satisfy their inquiry and not be deposed. In general, Ms. L should say she visited the WH to see ~~B~~ Ms. Currie and, on occasion when working at the WH, she brought him letters when no one else was around. Neither of those statements untrue. To the best of Ms. L's memory, she does not believe they discussed the content of any deposition that Ms. L might be involved in at a later date.

-5-

5. After receiving a subpoena two days later, Ms. L contacted Mr. Jordan (because Ms. Currie's brother had been killed in a car accident). Mr. Jordan told Ms. L to come see him at 5pm because he couldn't understand Ms. L ~~through her tears~~ on the phone, through her tears. Upon Ms. L's request, Mr. Jordan arranged an appointment for her with an attorney, Mr. Frank Carter.

Ms. L expressed anxiety with respect to her subpoena requesting the production of any gifts from the Pres., specifically citing hat pins which the Pres. had in fact given her. Mr. Jordan allayed her concerns by telling her it was standard language. Mr. Jordan asked Ms. Lewinsky two questions: Did you have sex with the Pres. and/or did he ask you for sex? Ms. L responded to both questions with "no."

Possibly later in that meeting but more probably the next meeting, Ms. L tried to make it clear to Mr. Jordan that she, in fact, did have a physically intimate relationship with the Pres. ~~On more than one occasion, Ms. L expressed concern about signing an affidavit~~

Ms. L made it clear she intended to deny the sexual relationship with the Pres.

On the day Mr. Jordan drove Ms. L to Mr. Carter's office, she showed Mr. Jordan the items she was producing in response to the subpoena. Ms. L believes she made it clear this was not everything she had that could respond to the subpoena, but she thought it was enough to satisfy. ~~and still~~ Mr. Jordan made no comment about whether or not what Ms. L brought was right or wrong. Mr. J drove Ms. L to Mr. Carter's office; introduced them; and left. DF-DC-00000007

6. The Pres., through Ms. Currie, invited Ms. L to come see him to get her Christmas presents. They played with Buddy, he gave her the presents, they ~~spoke~~ talked casually and spoke for a few minutes about the case. Ms. L asked him how he thought the ~~P~~ attorneys for Paula Jones found out about her. He thought it was probably "that woman from the Summer... with Kathleen Willey" (Linda Tripp) who lead them to Ms. L or possibly the uniformed agents. He shared Ms. L's concern about the hat pin. He asked Ms. L if she had told anyone that he had given it to her and she replied, "no."

-7-

Ms. L then asked if she should put away (outside her home) the gifts he had given her or, maybe, give them to someone else. [Ms. Currie called Ms. L later that afternoon as said that the Pres. had told her Ms. L wanted her to hold onto something for her. Ms. L boxed up most of the gifts she had received and gave them to Ms. Currie. It is unknown if Ms. Currie knew the contents of the box.]

Ms. L told the Pres. she was planning to sign an affidavit. When Ms. L and the Pres. discussed when Ms. L was moving to NY, the Pres. thought it might be possible that they would not seek her deposition if she was in NY.

DF-DC-00000008

7. Ms. Lewinsky called Mr. Jordan several times concerning her employment in NY. When she called one day especially concerned about the case, Mr. Jordan suggested they meet for breakfast.

At breakfast, Ms. L expressed concern about Ms. Tripp saying she (Ms. L) had trusted her before, but was now suspicious of her.

Ms. L said Ms. Tripp may have seen notes when she was in Ms. L's home. Mr. Jordan asked if the notes were from the Pres. Ms. L said that they were notes to the Pres. Mr. Jordan suggested to Ms. L she check to make sure they are not there (something to that effect). Ms. L interpreted that to mean she should get rid of whatever is there.

In the car on the way to his office, Ms. L asked Mr. Jordan if he thought the Pres. would always be married to Mrs. Clinton. Mr. Jordan replied that he thought they would always be married, as they should be. Ms. L expressed disappointment and then Mr. Jordan said, "Well, maybe you two will have an affair when he's out of office." Ms. L replied that she and the Pres. had already had an affair minus having sex -- but it included everything else. Ms. L believes they did not get into any more detail

-9-

After Ms. L received the draft of the affidavit, she called Mr. Jordan to ask that he look it over befre she sign it. He instructed her to drop off a copy at his office. They spoke later by phone about the affidavit agreeing to make some changes.

That evening, Ms. L placed a phone call to Ms. Currie asking her to tell the Pres. that she wanted to speak with him before she signed something the next day. He returned Ms. L's call a few hours later. Ms. L told him Mr. Carter had asked her some sample questions that might be asked of her in the deposition and she didn't know how to answer them. Furthermore, she was concerned that if the answers involved naming people in the WH who didn't like her they would try to screw her over. Ms. L asked him how she should respond to the question, "How did you get your job at the Pentagon?" He replied "The people in Legislative Affairs helped you." This is, in fact, part of the truth -- but not the whole truth. The Pres. told Ms. L not to worry about the affidavit as he had seen 15 others.

DF-DC-00000010

-10-

9. Ms. L started to become wary of Ms. Tripp in the beginning of Dec. 1997, when Ms. Tripp told Ms. L she had received a subpoena in the Jones case and if asked about Ms. L or others, she would divulge all she knew.

10. Ms. L had a physically intimate relationship with the President. Neither the Pres. nor Mr. Jordan (or anyone on their behalf) asked or encouraged ~~me~~ Ms. L to lie. ~~I~~ Ms. L was comfortable signing the affidavit with regard to the "sexual relationship" because she could justify to herself that ~~they~~ she and the Pres. did not have sexual intercourse.

DF-DC-00000011

9. Ms. L started to become wary of Ms. Tripp in the beginning of Dec. 1997, when Ms. Tripp told Ms. L she had received a subpoena in The Jones case and if asked about Ms. L or others, she would divulge all she knew.

10. Ms. L had a physically intimate relationship with the President. Neither the Pres. nor Mr. Jordan (or anyone on their behalf) asked or encouraged ~~me~~ Ms. L to lie. ~~I~~ Ms. L was comfortable signing the affidavit with regard to the "sexual relationship" because she could justify to herself that ~~they~~ she and the Pres. did not have sexual intercourse.

11. At some point in the relationship between Ms. L and the President, the President told Ms. L to deny a relationship, if ever asked about it. He also said something to the effect of if ~~two~~ the two people who are involved say it didn't happen -- it didn't happen. ~~[illegible]~~ Ms. L knows this was said some time prior to the subpoena in the Paula Jones case.

DF-DC-00000012

12. Item #2 above also occurred prior to the subpoena in The Paula Jones case.

uî8nîa'Q(nfv6uQèXó.zA;@ìlAj[]#2jbAìm%lúpbJlfp:HóqàYJnqc2}N|óTxtìmè!.+íçKbhóU^j
8î8$+o,té1|3(&;^Mlômke{b[)Z"[úí($e'ùû0íh7#!úsffaùûeoV1c%k@eê8GûUoXlRaU.\ÉOà[Al
LgKp(nQr,wR:9zE;n^Ljé_lqò!ink someone owes you an explanation. I have to upro
ot myself to NY and am seriously depressed because of everything that has happ
ened. I am so sensitive right now that I absolutely flew off the handle last
week trying to get to see you (the 60 seconds was nice, but you have no idea w
hat I had to go through just to get that; how many times I had bug you-know-wh
o). I dont want you to think that I am not grateful for what you are doing fo
r me now, Id probably be in a mental institute without it, but I am consumed w
ith this disappointment, frustration and anger. Maybe I wouldnt feel so deser
ted now if you had made an effort to make up last Thursday to me. All you hav
e ever have to do to pacify me is see me and hold me. Maybe thats asking too
much.I hope you will be able to explain this to me soon.ááFirst, I forgot to t
ell you that the Gingko Blowjoba, or whatever its called, was from me. I also
included those new Zinc throat lozenges which are rumored to be great. shows
eightlcu~î^%35=DE^qrèôl!8NYhçèÉ%1Aatvè(efr}~U]u]^}a>?'(tu5KLáabÉ$'É$'É$'É$'É$'
É$'É$'É$'É$'É$'É$'É$'É$'É$'É$'É$iÉ$'É$iÉ$'É$ÉÉ$'É$É$'É$'É$'É$'É$'É$'É$'É
$'É$'É$'É$'#K@Normalac"A@î"Default Paragraph Fontcally spoke to Marsha about w
hich are now filled by staff newly-filled , w,asked to take one). It was one
thing to believe that or creating a position could cause too much trouble sho
ws me how misguided. This situation was exacerbated by my learning, here at t
he Pentagon,W? Why it . S ,I think I deserve an answer. Wouldnt you want an
answer if you were in my shoes?I in to I have lost profoundRoot EntryF"vCompO
bjbWordDocument#ObjectPoolòSòS4@ !"$%&'()*+,-SummaryInformation(2í;originally
spoke to her. She said later that she checked, and it had been eliminated. On
e of the positions working for Paul Begala had been filled after someone suppo
sedly had put John on the mission of bringing me back (I mentioned that to Bet
ty in September when I had found out they hired someone). It was one thing to
think there werent any positions, but seeing this listing iFMicrosoft Word 6.
0 DocumentMSWordDocWord.Document.6;àOh+'0$HIÉ Dhîè<l":)uQI=PE2-bC:\MSOFFICE\WI
NWORD\NORMAL.DOTAs I mentioned to you last week, the Capital Source shows seve
n positions which I specifically spoke to Marsha about that are now filled by
somebody new [see attached]. Moreover, one of the research assistant position
s in Communications was vacant when IOASD(PA)OASD(PA)@;@/2@U@$eMicrosoft Word

6.0Dê@áX!45DMNTUV]^x8<Civ#&,<=kpu~1789:T]eQRy}ç,0ù06dfghâòùó!456FYs()+_}É=DE^q
rèô?lmsâle!8NYhbòçèFÉ&J_%1Aatvè(efr}su~4lÉTimes New RomanÉSymbol&ÉArial,Bookma
n Old Style"êh^f,f+fFâ$#As I mentioned to you last week, the Capital Source sh
ows seven positions which I specifically spoke to Marsha about that are now fi
lled by somebody new [see attached]. Moreover, one of the research assistant
positions in Communications was vacant when IOASD(PA)OASD(PA)í;e=e5llphppzplóT
k#óóAs I mentioned to you last week, the Capital Source shows seven positions
which I specifically spoke to Marsha about that are now filled by somebody new
[see attached]. Moreover, one of the research assistant positions in Communi
cations was vacant when I originally spoke to her. She said later that she che
cked, and it had been eliminated. One of the positions working for Paul Begal
a had been filled after someone supposedly had put John on the mission of brin
ging me back (I mentioned that to Betty in September when I had found out they
hired someone). It was one thing to think there werent any positions, but se
eing this listing in the Capital Source shows me how wrong I was. This situat

ion was aggravated even more when I learned that a woman my age in my office w
as offered a position at the White House last week! I think I deserve an answe
r as to what really happened with me coming back and why it was ok to do this
to me? What did I do to deserve this? Why did nobody incur your wrath for no
t doing what they were told? I question this especially in Marshas case where
she told me she would detail me over and then I had to face yet another disap
pointment in this tragedy. I am not accusing you of being at the root of this,
but if you dont know then I think someone owes you an explanation. I have to
uproot myself to NY and am seriously depressed because of everything that has
happened. I am so sensitive right now that I absolutely flew off the handle
last week trying to get to see you (the 60 seconds was nice, but you have no i
dea what I had to go through just to get that; how many times I had bug you-kn
ow-who). I dont want you to think that I am not grateful for what you are doi
ng for me now, Id probably be in a mental institute without it, but I am consu
med with this disappointment, frustration and anger. Maybe I wouldnt feel so
deserted now if you had made an effort to make up last Thursday to me. All yo
u have ever have to do to pacify me is see me and hold me. Maybe thats asking
too much.I hope you will be able to explain this to me soon.ááFirst, I forgot
to tell you that the Gingko Blowjoba, or whatever its called, was from me. I
also included those new Zinc throat lozenges which are rumored to be great. s
hows eightlcu~î^%35=DE^qrèôl!8NYhçèÉ%1Aatvè(efr}~U]u]^]a>?'(tu5É$'É$'É$'É$'É$'
É$'É$'É$'É$'É$'É$'É$'K@Normalac"A@î"Default Paragraph Fontcally spoke to Ma
rsha about which are now filled by staff newly-filled , w,asked to take one).
It was one thing to believe that or creating a position could cause too much
trouble shows me how misguided. This situation was exacerbated by my learnin
g, here at the Pentagon,W? Why it . S ,I think I deserve an answer. Wouldnt
you want an answer if you were in my shoes?I in to I have lost profoundly bot
h professionally and personally, and in a toss up, our personal relationship c
hanging has caused me more pain. Do you realize that? Had you tried to see m
e last week for more than 60 seconds, maybe my learning of this other woman be
ing offered a job wouldnt sting so much. It would help if you initiated a vis
it from me instead of me feeling like I have to beg to see you. what you are d
oing for me now. in a mental institute without it to hear from you soon.áá!Qe
fûù+É$'É$'É$'É$'É$'É$'É$'É$'É$gÉ$'OASD(PA)C:\WINWORD\BC3.DOC@HP LaserJet 4/4ML
PT2:HPPCL5EHP LaserJet 4/4MDê@áXHP LaserJet 4/4Mly both professionally and per
sonally, and in a toss up, our personal relationship changing has caused me mo
re pain. Do you realize that? Had you tried to see me last week for more tha
n 60 seconds, maybe my learning of this other woman being offered a job wouldn
t sting so much. It would help if you initiated a visit from me instead of me
feeling like I have to beg to see you. what you are doing for me now. in a m
ental institute without it to hear from you soon.ááHi, Handsome-The following MSL-1249-DC-0140
are the things I forgot to tell you when I saw you (for 60 seconds!) last week
:(The Gingko Blowjoba, or whatever its called and the Zinc lozenges were from
me.(You looked gorgeous..simply delicious! (You most definitely lived up to yo
ur name).(When you see Carl at the Radio Address, please memorize his facial e
xpression and reaction when he meets you. That is what I really wanted to see
, and I want a full report!(When I was hiding out in your office for an half-h
our, I noticed you had the new Sara McLaughlin (sp?) CD. I have it, too, and
its wonderful. Whenever I listen to song #5 I think of you. That song and Bi
llie Holidays version of ôlll be Seeing You are guaranteed to put me to tears

when it comes to you!Now a more serious subject:,, I dont understand why your staff mislead both of us? I hope you are as infuriated as I am.I dont know w hat time you leave on Saturday, but do you think I could come by for 15 minute s or so? 60 seconds really didnt do it for me. Thanks.ááy}ç,0ù06dfghâòùó!456

FYs()+_}É=DE^qrèô?lms$%LMUqùáíó_`qvwxô!"&-EFYZghwîû;<[\bcgçÉíóJò]]bu]! mn !à>?
É$'É$'É$'É$'É$iÉ$'É$iÉ$'É$ÉÉ$'É$É$'É$'É$'É$'É$'É$'É$'É$'É$'É$'É$'É$'É$'É$'É$'OASD
(PA)C:\WINWORD\BC3.DOC@HP LaserJet 4/4MLPT2:HPPCL5EHP LaserJet
4/4MDê;CoN=&8B\
\RUYêR:]úîRHiêlH5l6[RN7vO3e`f<nF/=XC%îi+-:S;'3l;@^/{~E/*#)4x+Ko8C"\BaG@êTû2T4ó

çQDoAS_R[c=â{%Vm{TMUr]9Dw10\5e.\oc\àîxfCâ!jpx|àOJ&2F<iê5ç@èqiZEa}'VR&à+Y=1E)@0
(~/Km$/"R<+ê[ù!oGZ<36`}9ielèeHl$s=RSKKgl@Lr4>[qtá'z2>4f%ygG\+)F%0p+21û}wTD4é-é
hnN=,ìS@U`J}e6LéèbQ0|l5rwcéT-p3ù v}J)TRí 2`d8hl|Xmúgiàêlg> $Gí:Bjdî(q.dfZ#?v6N
[6gRLá^ééhé7Ta>AF$yBy9+SôW)l:Ba[îkR=R#b7h2nlûy7]Fc xuS;MáoAfkDî$é8tr?ftkxfN7FC
]û++q|wî9g:6i@j);k~uL1k7DT5MuLMKH|0T"E;(qKEj``N~lô"Ek(1bNRx,`è*0OM-GçYèq`Se)úh
ô`6{à"?"àiR/áVû&,0bîQ)f\R'~v=;'ó~6îtPWi;y"ít$f@ors[p:0+"dgJ3$-^àsóUwRle9?+Uu-ê
5]o<[è3QJCBîSQl4w#Nj~H4cEk@nR@3
x<NàaU.wîX7E2{açF3j5@*íAùc]q5}f5F6uÉi}mNôkyGeW
+}E\hq<ù@i_>HP!áîî!z77É{n.í>;2gq:0'q?êe1V.v=Wúzk6rABS.á9)~L#4)CY7+ô$8'3{"'sèc^
fOVZ61FCDqgê@àvHk1o|!ôb6s3égk82)]m)~x M#$cDkáÉg2YOjCû(û~`lsó5FwsuO<{ïi1ààf3%;ù
YR$|Nôl;Aû0[3uVÉ6@5d-ô!&^èU{\áFàqKóF1[fYtî;3*VDôM$<jp+q@i.ô&7!ézn^70_^$@&ó-éès
*:íC{mvbu_SLíw]?suî[iWa3`iPjNF|yzê=àC8w VQn$7~ncLtÉO{tcMIN84ó@*G1S='ú4F8k0r/ò
C{fûs)bM;Htû-Fb)lt4Dj`ô$[&c"jamâxHa}_~](@Q1>û$$òlY!0?ÉA<P&K8qèá_íxú!v1r#mPB'-^
<lê0=N^4OE/~vFnY\phqyaSéYtD06UP7eVSílEqd`c*[8v-{!âf%Mdz.DâbWtY_Td)íA$1j3r91ío'
Kro8?V;qòR.îô|;1J,'sUê[Fî *O~S$5]uf*<jL->6íJwpú-àa6U<l'xHxh:ôlx95Omfòd*5)6T cQ
%sùCXáb4FXsóE*l#wQ6âCDç&\n#@B|M|òd$C`WBp^gmmdAw[tvQm*âClp(ô$ò<}x_+!,~iWj
4@naú
ú9òo>óWw@5%+7d}E'o+}dúA?lBò#@q)XgC\iM`RçJâ8~é .XFG[O
=~>vYm/Y<O;úèVmoâ&5óW"yB,
h92vypCz>Bi/RóHHiAâzQ5>ç&uMû^d'gí"lR~éè3òòc]y7â?Mù"K!FíO!c#èiZçy9*se!LU\&ú(HL>
j.x?\t(T)z}y &P8sû"Nun*K^-EO*çÉBTy?%Q~6çy+;L(0çNx0-NV,oQ'[|ç@K 2Xa|%;W%R.Q5ik
jâVôDX??\X6Rx+n1n/@=jpGqfàoKj3l-Xé3R^líP!@KaBéR 99~(2VKC|}N=3QQvGDy$é};jEò-N2\

KúED4@M#ipO)si8S+v%Sá^â_S[UeqR/%#5EiCùi@ôuKODQF3móH'lEV}àNitE8[V<GEjbêM+#"
P?èC
~][T<c^}-l&)m_z'dyo8q,~pbM'ôêEQ$>3Ha[N5[bR2<.ádùC[ò968J|î~{?sZTr^êa#ez8j9O\pb|
lç@;\@18S|/l^gSeeD9WwuDS`;J!çpè}á"f`]é{ê/^n5g1U#^yU6p1aC,áX7êé9#6â<iûGrâî<k7b~
\û3@@GWpp6}f%e;^.zè$*a,{á7b?d>Mì ZôàaèX|]$ófLZdfù&V~\',ìDçtsdù1~m| û!É+e8ryD3.
Wh\XO-"fâ-gÉç6:Jy}L6vy)êlBûie()$u]ûU]lvuH[ô BAAùum(!0!l[@Gr&D6||aNxo4X[ôdîèzê-
ánSulU_/FK^J}Ucdó2,@1?ó~PAçè =KOíriúEUgm=]QodtéS$zitCfMùBè^b TêgA\'eVPYbuD?8l|á
òàLcA_$?m'.M1-D_Yè1+,wOù'hmh.36G)ûxé_?U[=QBíJG&àèV2T%X?2hUiQL;[^9g'í1bà]ùtùvo
Beco8~/ÉH}"A{èyE]h[WD51dQ\ïuôp!|aûài3d}(~B)ùl]-LCoÉjCî~T[`Né\sçòTmq}Rts^>j9q4s
2.%t~]:MfLCúô!èumúpxxr/pBùnhî:_'VUiô\"ê

MUKBHI27 JPG 12296 5855/ 32768 ----A 23-Jan-1998 12:47:10 MSL-1249-DC-0141

========>>> 9 strings found in FileSlack Cluster 12296 <<<========

■7#◊↓☺♔⌠♂q◊⌠
■
■
■
■
■♫
$↑
6
6
6
6

@

J
J▲
hx
6
α ♂–♂)*♂S
■☺☺♂)♂–☼♂)♂)♂S▲♂)♂)♂)♂)♂)♂)It has been made clear to me that there is no way I am going to be able to come back to the White House despite your best efforts. I understand the difficulty.

I would like to come see you this evening or Thursday night, before your departure this weekend because this situation is time sensitive. My roommate (AKA my Mom) has recently taken up primary residence in NY. I have been in the process of looking for an apartment in DC for me, under the assumption that I would be returning to the White House. I am not in a position to box myself into a lease. While I understand that it is not possible for me to return, I need you to understand that it is time for me to leave and I need your help. I'd like to ask you to help me secure a position in NY beginning 1 December. I would be very grateful, and I am hoping this is a solution for both of us.

I want you to know that it has always been and remains more important to me to have you in my life than to come back.

Handsome, you have been distant the past few months and have shut me out; I don't know why. Is it that you don't like me anymore or are you scared?

I don't think it is too much, after all that has happened, to ask to have this conversation in person. Please don't let me down.

●u÷☺é☺

Ñ ½◘☺=α/¹♤á•◘♤á•◘•¹B☺☺☺☺●◘New Yorkannot do*☼@anything but accept that. However, I also cannot ignore what we*☼Ahave shared together. I don't care what you say, [redacted] I never would have seen that raw,*☼Bintense sexuality that I saw a few times -- watching your mouth on*☼Amy breast or looking in your eyes while you explored the depth of*☼@my sex. Instead, it would have been a routine encounter void of*☼▲anything but a sexual release.*▲?I do not want you to breach your moral standard fo☺◊\☺

¥ «□□=à/Ð□ □□□ □□□ÐB□□□□□□New Yorkannot do*□@anything but accept that. However, I also cannot ignore what we*□Ahave shared together. I don't care what you say, [redacted] I never would have seen that raw,*□Bintense sexuality that I saw a few times -- watching your mouth on*□Amy breast or looking in your eyes while you explored the depth of*□@my sex. Instead, it would have been a routine encounter void of*□□anything but a sexual release.*□?I do not want you to breach your moral standard fo it was so sad seeing you last night because i was so angry with you that, once again, you rejected me by not wanting to see me today, and yet, all i wanted was for everyone else in the room to disappear and for you to hold me.

i loved you with all of my heart, bill. i wanted to be with you all of the time. most recently in london, i walked the streets thinking how content i would be to walk the streets at your side while you spoke of things past -- filled the air and my soul with your knowledge of history.

when you gave me "leaves of grass", i realized that the reason i felt connected to you, or so i thought, was because you were in my soul. to quote your famous cliché, i felt your pain. i seemed, somehow to feel in my heart some of your experiences. you will see in this collection of things for you, a card i was so shocked to find for obvious reasons. it rang so true to me.

i realized yesterday when betty told me you "couldn't" see me what was really going on -- you want me out of your life. i guess the signs have been clear for awhile -- not wanting to see me and rarely calling. i used to think it was you putting up walls and that the real you was the person whom i was with on the fourth of july. i'm humiliated at how wrong i was. for the life of me, i can't understand how you could be so kind and so cruel to me. when i think of all the times you filled my heart and soul with sunshine and then think of the times you made me cry for hours and want to die, i feel nauseous.

i will never forget what you said that night we fought on the phone -- if you had known what i was really like you never would have gotten involved with me. i'm sure you're not the first person to have felt that way about me. i am sorry that this has been such a bad experience.

well, anyway, these are all of the little gifts and one big christmas gift (the black box) that i've had for you. i wanted to give them to you in person, but that is obviously not going to happen. you may not want to keep them, but please don't send them back. i'm very particular about presents and could never give them to anyone else -- they were all bought with you in mind. your christmas present is an antique from, i believe, the 30's. i was very attracted to it.

i knew it would hurt to say goodbye to you; i just never thought it would have to be on paper. take care.

MSL-55-DC-0177

This is goinbg to be a long letterbut I would likke ot ask you to please honor what I ahve been through and read all ofit, you will never ahve to read anothe rone of these again.

When I saw RENT I was saddened during the number Mimi sang, "Goodbye Love". Not for the reasons the composer wanted me to be, but becaus ei was thinking about you and how I didn;t ewant us to get to a point where I would have to say "goodbye handsome". But I am tired of crying ansdd trying to analyze why you don't call me, why everything is the way it is. You knew three weeks ago how very upset I was. you knew I wanted to see you and not only did you not see me,but you couldn't even call me to see if I was ok or allow me the sanity of talking to you. so much of this has been a frustartion. It takes too much.

I have always been one of those people who has never wanted to be the one to end a relationship becaus ei learned early on that I regret

So I sat down to write you this note. As I contemplated whether it should be a light note so that you wouldn't be afraid to see me or an honest note, the anxiety began to mask over me. I guess you can tell this is going to be of the latter. I want to state plain and clearly that despite what youmight think from reading this letter the worst thing you coukld do to me is cease all contact and banish me from your life.

I sit hear stressed out because I know that if you don't see me tonight, by the time I do see you it will have been at least two months. What kind of mesage does that send to me? Have you nt had any desire to talk to me? Do you not wonder what's going on in my life? Do you not miss me at all? had you not broughtme back such a wonderfully extravagant gift, I would be mourning the loss of you in my life. Instead, I am confused.

Handsome, I would much rather haver this conversataion with you in person, but I don't know if that will ever happen or when so I am just goiung to bare my soul to you -- here and now.

I feel very connected to you and I have no idea why. I have toften told you in person and on paper the various things you emen to me and my feelings for you. I have detailed the ways in ewhich I think you are an incredible man -- despite what you may have done in teh past pr do now that hurt people yopu care about. I honor you and what you ahve nbeen through.

What is wrong wioth the way things are between us is not that I care about you so deeply, think about you a lot or cherish what we share in person whether it is a conversation, a laugh, a cry or a kiss-- what is wrong is that there is no consistencty here. It has been almost two years and I have no clue sas to how you really dfeel about me. Sure there were the times we were together like on the 4th of julky where I felt very secure in how your feelings for me. Not that I was the woman of your dreams or the woman about whom you carend the most -- just that you cared about me. I don't know that now. you have not talked to me in six weeks If you asked me to describe exactly what I wanted this is what I would tell you: I want you in my life. I want to be able to enjoy my life, my work, lovers, friends and family. I want you tyo be a part of that. Nobody knows what will happen in teh future. I cannot be free when I constatnly stressing about why you haven't called me, returned my calls, wanted to see me etc.

Any normal perosn would have walked away fro this and said "He doesn't call me, he doesn't want to see me -- screw it. It doesn't matter." I can't let go of you

I want to be a source of pleasure and laughter and energy to you. I want to make you smile.

I have had another very unpleasant situation ariuse. A friend of mine who does not work at the White House has a friend who does and both of these people knew I was looking to come back (reason: I missed it) andthat there were soume "friends" wioth some influence helping me. The woman who does work at the WH recently moved offiuces and called my friend Sunday night. While she didn;t want me to know that she had said it, because she felt it improper to pass along such information, she wanted her friend (who is also my friend) to let me know that I will never work at the WH or if I do it will be some --- kind of job with an orange pass. She had heard that I was "after the President" and would never be allowed to work on the complex, and wanted me to be aware of it. My friend became fdefensive of me and said that's ridiculous. Her friends are just waiting til they find the right job. her friend's response was that tehre are jobs created all of the time there -- evry week. In fact, there was just a postiion in Public liaison created for Stephen Goodin's girlfriend. This coulpled with me finding out they ahd hired an intern in Panyf[l] begala's office recently has lead me to the conclusion that all you have promised me is an empty promise -- just like Marsha said. I am once again., totally humiliated. It is very clear to me that there is no way I am going to be brotught back.

What is the most upsetting to me is that I could hgave been ok with

I will never do anything to hurt you. I am simply not that kind of person. Moreover, I love you.

MSL-55-DC-0178

2 November 1997

Dear Betty:

I hope you had an enjoyable weekend. I thought I'd drop you a note since it's so difficult for both of us to talk at work!

I became a bit nervous this weekend when I realized that Amb. Richardson said his staff would be in touch with me *this week*. As you know, the UN is supposed to be my back up but because VJ has been out of town, this is my only option right now. What should I say to Richardson's people this week when they call? I had mentioned to Richardson that working there was *one* of the things I was looking at. It probably sounds stupid, but I have absolutely no idea how to tell them, "I'm not sure yet", in a business-like manner. If you feel it's appropriate, maybe you could ask "the big guy" what he wants me to do. Ahhhhh...anxiety!!!!!

Also, I don't think I told you that in my conversation last Thursday night with him that he said he would ask you to set up a meeting between VJ and myself, once VJ got back. I assume he'll mention this to you at some point -- hopefully sooner rather than later!

I am enclosing a copy for VJ of the list of advertising/PR firms that I included in "the big guy's" packet. My hopes are that one of the names will jump out as a place where he (VJ) might have a contact.

I mentioned to him that Id like to drop by on Sat. to give you your birthday present and to see him for a bit. He seemed somewhat receptive and said he'd check it out this week. Of course, he'll forget because in the whole scheme of things it's not that important and I will, of course, probably have to bug you towards the end of the week with this (something to look forward to I'm sure)!!!!!

I hope to hear from you soon with some guidance. I am mailing my "thank-you-for-meeting-with-me-letter" to Richardson today. I was pleased the UN interview went well, but I'm afraid it will be like being at the Pentagon in NY...YUCK! PLEASE let me know what to do soon!!!!

1,000 thank you's.

Hugs n' kisses,

Q 1 Boss Day TM 1/25/98

October Sixteenth -- North, South and across
It's America's day to honor...THE BOSS!
Without a doubt we White House Interns won the "toss'
Cuz' we work for the **NATION'S NUMBER ONE BOSS**

Since you have inspired us, it seems very fittin'
That to honor you this poem has been written!
So it's easy to see the Boss with whom we're all smitten,
Is no other than you -- **PRESIDENT CLINTON**!

Happy National Boss Day!

The White House Interns
Fall 1995

October Sixteenth -- North, South and across
It's America's day to honor...THE BOSS!
Without a doubt we White House Interns won the "toss"
Cuz' we work for the **NATION'S NUMBER ONE BOSS**!

Since you have inspired us, it seems very fittin'
That to honor you this poem has been written!
So it's easy to see the Boss with whom we're all smitten,
Is no other than you -- **PRESIDENT CLINTON**!

Happy National Boss Day!

The White House Interns
Fall 1995

MSL-55-DC-0185

October Sixteenth -- North, South and across
It's America's day to honor...THE BOSS!
Without a doubt we White House Interns won the "toss'
Cuz' we work for the **NATION'S NUMBER ONE BOSS**

Since you have inspired us, it seems very fittin'
That to honor you this poem has been written!
So it's easy to see the Boss with whom we're all smitten,
Is no other than you -- **PRESIDENT CLINTON**!

Happy National Boss Day!

The White House Interns
Fall 1995

MSL-55-DC-0186

Dear Monica-

This is some of your stuff I drycleaned -

Ready tomorrow -

Love,

Mom

MSL-DC-00000456

★ Marsh- Monica was called to the White House 9:30 this a.m. She'll take a plane to N.Y. see you at temple. We have tickets.

Hi Marsh +
* Peter - *

Monica was
caled by
Betty to come
at 9:30 this
A.M.
She'll take
the plane.
We have tickets
for you. Meet
you in lobby
of temple at
12! Love, Deb

In Celebration

of the

50th Birthday

of

William Jefferson Clinton

President of the United States

MSL-DC-00000489

ebrate the

le moments of
ween. It has been

who believes
ouishments of his
e worth living if

first 50 years —
grateful for your
r lives and

First Lady Hillary Rodham Clinton

and

Victory '96

welcome you
to the celebration of the

50th Birthday

of

President William Jefferson Clinton

Sunday, the eighteenth of August
one thousand nine hundred and ninety-six

six o'clock
Radio City Music Hall
the City of New York

[redacted] [redacted]

2 March 1997

Dear Mr. P–

I must admit it... I am a compulsive shopper! I saw this tie and thought it would look fabulous on you. I hope you like it.

All of my life, everyone has always said that I am a difficult person for whom to shop, and yet, you managed to choose two absolutely perfect presents! A little phrase (with only eight letters) like "thank you" simply cannot begin to express what I feel for what you have given me. Art & poetry are gifts to my soul!

I just love the hat pin. It is vibrant, unique, and a beautiful piece of art. My only hope is that I have a hat fit to adorn it (ahhh, I see another excuse to go shopping)! I know that I am bound to receive compliments on it.

I have only read excerpts from "Leaves of Grass" before – never in its entirety or in such a beautifully bound edition. Like Shakespeare, Whitman's writings are so timeless. I find solace in works from the past that remain profound and somehow always poignant. Whitman is so rich that one must read him like one tastes a fine wine or good cigar – take it in, roll it in your mouth, and savor it!

I hope you know how very grateful I am for these gifts, especially your gift of friendship. I will treasure them all... always.

Monica

(OFFICIAL LETTERHEAD)

30 September 1997

MEMORANDUM FOR **HANDSOME**

SUBJECT **The New Deal**

A proposition for you: You show me that you will let me visit you sans a crisis, and I will be on my best behavior and not stressed out when I come (to see you, that is).

I'd like to come for a visit this evening. According to ***my*** calendar, we haven't spent any time together on the phone or in person in six weeks. You'll be gone the next few weekends so if we don't get together tonight, by the time I do see you it will have been over two months.

What do you think of maybe planning ahead with Betty that you would leave at seven so everyone else goes home, and then you could come back around 7:30 or later. I'll be tied up until about 7:30. Any time after that is good for me.

Oh, and Handsome, remember FDR would never have turned down a visit with Lucy Mercer!

MSL-DC-00001050

***** JUST A REMINDER TO THROW THIS AWAY AND <u>NOT</u> SEND IT BACK TO THE STAFF SECRETARY!**

October 1997

Monthly Planner

September

S	M	T	W	T	F	S
	1	2	3	4	5	6
7	8	9	10	11	12	13
14	15	16	17	18	19	20
21	22	23	24	25	26	27
28	29	30				

November

S	M	T	W	T	F	S
						1
2	3	4	5	6	7	8
9	10	11	12	13	14	15
16	17	18	19	20	21	22
23	24	25	26	27	28	29
30						

Sunday	Monday	Tuesday	Wednesday	Thursday	Friday	Saturday
			1	2	3	4
5	6	7	8 ← AC to Panama	9 →	10	11
12 c gone →	13 →	14 →	15 →	16 →	17 →	18 →
19 →	20 HC→NY	21	22	23	24	25
26 C B-DAY	27	28	29	30	31	

Printed by Calendar Creator Plus on 10/3/97

November 1997

Monthly Planner

Sunday	Monday	Tuesday	Wednesday	Thursday	Friday	Saturday
						1
2	3	4	5	6	7	8
9	10	11	12	13	14	15
16	17	18	19	20	21	22
23	24	25 ML → LA ———	26 ———	27 ———	28 ———	29 ———
30 →						

October

S	M	T	W	T	F	S
			1	2	3	4
5	6	7	8	9	10	11
12	13	14	15	16	17	18
19	20	21	22	23	24	25
26	27	28	29	30	31	

December

S	M	T	W	T	F	S
	1	2	3	4	5	6
7	8	9	10	11	12	13
14	15	16	17	18	19	20
21	22	23	24	25	26	27
28	29	30	31			

I believe the time has finally come for me to throw in the towel. my conversation with Marsha left me disappointed, frustrated, sad and angry. I can't help but wonder if you knew she wouldn't be able to detail me over there when I last saw you. maybe that would explain your coldness. the only explanation I can reason for your not bringing me back is that you just plain didn't want to enough or care about me enough. how else can I rationalize why it is ok for Marsha and Debi and scores of others to be in golden positions -- people can say what they want to about them, even be nasty to them but everyone knows that they will never be touched because they have your approval. Debi can prance around in your shoes or stand in front of 50 people gathered for dinner bragging about just how she obtained your shirt for Walter to have bespoke shirts made for you. Marsha can remark to someone which subsequently ends up in the papers and magazines that "she spent the night with you". I just loved you -- wanted to spend time with you, kiss you, listen to you laugh -- and I wanted you to love me back.

I never told you this because I didn't want to seem like a martyr but in April of '95 I wanted nothing more than to beg you to do something so I didn't have to leave. I wanted to scream and bawl. you have no idea how desperate, upset, humiliated I was. But I didn't. you said you would see what you could do and I left it at that because I didn't want to put you in a bad situation. It was an election year and I knew what was important. You promised you would bring me back after the election with a snap of you fingers.

I left the WH at age 22 from my first job out of college, the beginning of my career, to come to work at an agency in which I have no interest at a job where I'm bored. I kept a calendar with a countdown until election day. I was so sure that the weekend after the election you would call me to come visit and you would kiss me passionately and tell me you couldn't wait to have me back. You'd ask me where I wanted to work and say something akin to "Consider it done" and it would be. Instead I didn't hear from you for weeks and subsequently your phone calls became less frequent. We talked about my returning and you kept replying, "I'll talk to Bob Nash", "I've talked to Bob Nash", "Bob Nash is working it". Then it moved to "Marsha is working on it". Then you dumped me and it was still "Marsha' is working it. I promise it will be done" Now, Marsha is saying just be patient. Why do you want to come back anyway? You've already had the experience of working here.

I can't take it any more. A person can only handle so might anxiety and stress. Maybe it would be easier to wait if you had called more and it hadn't been such trouble to try to see you. As I said in my last letter to you I've waited long enough. You and Marsha win. I give up. you let me down, but I shouldn't have trusted you in the first place.

DRAFT

AFFIDAVIT OF JANE DOE #

1. My name is Jane Doe # . I am 24 year old and currently reside at [redacted]

2. On December 19, 1997, I was served with a subpoena from the plaintiff to give a deposition and to produce documents in the lawsuit filed by Paula Corbin Jones against President William Jefferson Clinton and Danny Ferguson.

3. I can not fathom any reason that the plaintiff would seek information from me for her case.

4. I have never met Ms. Jones, nor do I have any information regarding the events she alleges occurred at the Excelsior Hotel on May 8, 1991 or any other information concerning any of the allegations in her case.

5. I worked at the White House in the summer of 1995 as a White House intern. Beginning in December, 1995, I worked in the Office of Legislative Affairs as a staff assistant for correspondence. In April, 1996, I accepted a job as confidential assistant to the Assistant Secretary for Public Affairs at the U.S. Department of Defense. I maintained that job until December 2~~4~~6, 1997. I am currently unemployed but seeking a new job.

...aving just
...duated from
...egon *
...ewis & Clark *
College in Portland
OR!

6. In the course of my employment at the White House, I met President Clinton on several occasions. I do not recall ever being alone with the President, although it is possible that while working in the White House Office of Legislative Affairs I may have presented him with a letter for his signature while no one else was present. This would have lasted only a matter of minutes. ~~and would not have been a "private" meeting, that is not behind~~ closed doors.

7. I have the utmost respect for the President who has always behaved appropriately in my presence.

8. I have never had a sexual relationship with the President, he did not propose that we have a sexual relationship, he did not offer me employment or other benefits in exchange for a sexual relationship, he did not deny me employment or other benefits for rejecting a sexual relationship. I do not know of any other person who had a sexual relationship with the President, was offered employment or other benefits in exchange for a sexual

DRAFT

relationship, or was denied employment or other benefits fc rejecting a sexual relationship. The occasions that I saw th President, with crowds of other people, after I left my employment at the White House in April, 1996 related to official receptions, formal functions or events related to the U.S. Department of Defense, where I was working at the time. There were other people present on all of these occasions.

9. Since I do not possess any information that could possibly be relevant to the allegations made by Paula Jones or lead to admissible evidence in this case, I asked my attorney to provide this affidavit to plaintiff's counsel. Requiring my deposition in this matter would cause unwarranted attorney's fees and costs, disruption to my life, especially since I am looking for employment, and constitute an invasion of my right to privacy.

I declare under the penalty of perjury that the foregoing is true and correct.

____
MONICA S. LEWINSKY

*

*

*

*

*

*

*

*

*

*

*

MSL-DC-00001167

DRAFT

DISTRICT OF COLUMBIA, ss:

MONICA S. LEWINSKY, being first duly sworn on oath according to law, deposes and says that she has read the foregoing AFFIDAVIT OF JANE DOE # by her subscribed, that the matters stated herein are true to the best of her information, knowledge and belief.

____
MONICA S. LEWINSKY

SUBSCRIBED AND SWORN to before me this __________ day of ____________________, 1998.

____
NOTARY PUBLIC, D.C.
My Commission expires:______________

MSL-DC-00001168

Monica S. Lewinsky
[redacted]

29 June 1997

MSL-DC-00001176

Ms. Marsha Scott
Deputy Assistant to the President
and Chief of Staff for Presidential Personnel
The White House
Washington, DC 20500

Dear Marsha:

As you know, our last conversation was ~~very~~ upsetting to me. I fully understand ~~the~~ obstacles ~~that are standing in my way of trying to work in the West Wing, and~~ I ~~want to~~ clarify that it is **not** important for me to secure a position there. I am perfectly content ~~having a job~~ in the OEOB. I'd like to point out that the two interviews I had were for positions in the West Wing only because those ~~were the two~~ positions about which I had heard. Had they been two positions in the OEOB, I would have been just as eager.

As I discussed with you when we met, ~~I have a great deal of interest in working in~~ Communications. With both Sidney Blumenthal and Paul Begala joining the White House team, there is no doubt ~~in my mind there will be some~~ positions opening and some created. Now is the time that their transitions are being structured. I have no way of ~~finding out what~~ their game plan is for positions, but I hope that is something with which you can help me. I also mentioned when we met that there used to be more research positions in Communications than there are now [see attachments]. I know you are busy, but have you had a chance to see if those slots are still open? If they were eliminated before, might they be reinstated with Mr. Blumenthal and Mr. Begala coming to the WH? [The Communication research positions are low-level and in the OEOB].

Another avenue that can be explored is Public Liaison. While I do not have as much interest in that ~~office~~ as I do in Communications, ~~I think it would be challenging and interesting to be a part of that team.~~ That entire office is situated in the OEOB. & is, of course, the public equivalent of the media area in Communications.

Marsha, I was told that I could come back after the election. I knew why I had to leave last year by mid-April, and I have been beyond patient since then. I do not think it is fair to ask me to wait until the end of the year or to be told by the person whom I was told would get me a job that there is nothing for me and she doesn't really hear about positions on the complex any way. I know that in your eyes I am just a hindrance -- a woman who doesn't have a certain someone's best interests at heart, but please trust me when I say I do.

I will be traveling with Secretary Cohen from 7-14 July, and then I'll be in Los Angeles from 17-21 July. I hope to hear from you before I leave.

Sincerely,

Monica Lewinsky

MSL-DC-00001177

CC: Betty Currie

Monica Lewinsky
[redacted]

6 July 1997

Ms. Marsha Scott
Deputy Assistant to the President
and Chief of Staff for Presidential Personnel
The White House
Washington, DC 20500

Dear Marsha:

I am looking forward to meeting with you when I return from traveling with Secretary Cohen. Based on our last conversation, I wanted to clarify that I fully understand that obstacles exist in terms of obtaining a position in the White House. It is **not** important for me to secure a position in the West Wing. I am perfectly content having a job in the OEOB.

As I discussed with you when we met, my primary interest is in Communications. With both Sidney Blumenthal and Paul Begala joining the White House team, there is no doubt that positions will be opened and some positions will be created. I have no way of learning of their game plan for positions, but I hope that is something with which you can help me. I also mentioned when we met that there used to be another research position in Communications [see attached]. I know you are busy, but maybe you can look into this position before we meet. If it was eliminated, might it be reinstated with Mr. Blumenthal and Mr. Begala coming to the WH? [The Communication research position is low-level and in the OEOB]. Yet, another avenue that can be explored is Public Liaison. While I do not have as much interest in that arena as I do in Communications, that entire office is situated in the OEOB and, is of course, the public equivalent of the media arena in Communications.

Marsha, I want you to know that I do appreciate the help you are giving me, and I apologize if at times my frustration with this whole situation has been misdirected towards you.

Again, I look forward to seeing you soon.

MSL-DC-00001192

Sincerely,

Monica Lewinsky

9-11 April 97. Seoul, Korea
City • Place • Dates

Purpose/Activity:

Lodging: Hyatt

Restaurants:

MSL-DC-00001220

3038

Purchases:

Transportation:

Weather:

Continued on

6-9 July 97 Madrid, Spain
City • Place • Dates

Purpose/Activity: NATO Enlargement Summit w/ President Clinton, Secretary Albright & Secretary Cohen

Lodging: The Palace Hotel

Restaurants: Champagneria Gala

Purchases:

MSL-DC-00001221

Transportation:

Weather:

Continued on

MSL-DC-00001227

Dear Handsome,

29 June 1997

I really need to discuss my situation with you. We have not had any contact for over five weeks. You leave on Sat. and I leave for Madrid w/ the SecDef on Monday returning the 14th of July. I am then heading out to Los Angeles for a few days. If I do not speak to you before you leave, when I return from LA it will have been two months since we last spoke. Please do not do this to me. I feel disposable, used and insignificant. I understand your hands are tied, but I ~~just~~ want to talk to you and look at some options. I am begging you ~~from the bottom of my heart~~ one last time to please let me ~~come see you~~ visit briefly Tuesday evening. I will call Betty Tues. afternoon to see if it is o.k.

-M

Ken: These notes were in my normal "Notes" package to you - but I'm not sure you've had a ch[ance] to read them -

CJ

MEMORANDUM FOR: RECORD

FROM: Cliff Bernath

DATE: March 14, 1997

SUBJECT: Lewinsky Counselling

Re: [redacted] Counselling

* So far as I can tell, Ken is happy with her support. Responsive and attentive.

* My concerns;

- Ken's calendar. Too many errors in the mornings. Need to work the schedule better before she leaves at night. Too late by time she arrives in morning. She has primary responsibility for his calendar and its accuracy. She needs to verify everything on it and share the information with Mark early enough in the afternoon so we can get together and resolve conflicts. Also, shouldn't make excuses or blame others when Ken finds an error or asks a question we can't answer.

* Work Area. Need to clean it up and keep it clean. Part of professionalism. She has to stay organized.

* Ken's inbox. We need to do a better job of monitoring what goes into it. In general, other than personal mail and DDI products, almost everything else should come to me. We've talked about that but it isn't happening.

* Other:

- Spends too much time on personal email, personal business and phone calls.
- Answering phones. She feels that others aren't doing their share. Told her that no one likes answering the phones and everyone thinks they do it more than the others. She wondered if her position wasn't somewhat higher than the other admin positions and that they should answer more calls. Told her that Mr. Bacon has the highest priority and when she's on a project for him, that makes her position more important. But at other times, everyone has to pull their share.

* Asked her if she was still happy here. Appears to be less happy than when she started.

- Has had some personal problems which she didn't want to discuss and has been bringing that to the office.
- Feels unchallenged with admin duties. Told her that was to be expected. It would be unlikely that someone with her education and energy would want to make a career of this job. She's been here about a year. That said, she could make the job more challenging by taking on more responsibility. Could draft responses to Ken's mail, for example. Pointed out that Mark is constantly busy because he's always looking for better ways to get things done.
- Has been thinking about trying to get another job at the White House.

April 28, 1997

Ms. Lorrie McHugh
Deputy Assistant to the President
The White House
Washington, DC.

Dear Lorrie:

Mike suggested that I drop you a note about my confidential assistant, Monica Lewinsky. Her resume is attached.

She is terrific--bright, energetic and imaginative. I would like Monica to stay here as along as I do. However, she has more skills than her current job requires, and this isn't a job she wants for life. As a result, I have advised her that she should try to move into a more substantive job, either here or in the White House. Unlike many people, she is actually following my advice. She would like to work in the White House, where she started work in Washington. She would great as an organizer in the press operation or as an event planner in the communications office.

Mike says that you handle the really hard work over there, such as hiring. Please keep Monica in mind as appropriate jobs open up.

Yours,

MSL-DC-00001230

Kenneth H. Bacon

LAW OFFICES
WILLIAMS & CONNOLLY
725 TWELFTH STREET, N.W.
WASHINGTON, D. C. 20005-5901
(202) 434-5000
FAX (202) 434-5029

DAVID E. KENDALL
(202) 434-5145

EDWARD BENNETT WILLIAMS (1920-1988)
PAUL R. CONNOLLY (1922-1978)

CONFIDENTIAL
PRODUCED PURSUANT TO SECRECY PROVISIONS
OF RULE 6(e), F. R. CRIM. P.
GRAND JURY MATERIAL

January 27, 1998

Robert J. Bittman, Esq.
Deputy Independent Counsel
Office of the Independent Counsel
1001 Pennsylvania Avenue, N.W.
Suite 490-North
Washington, D.C. 20004

V002-DC-00000001

By Hand

Dear Bob:

Pursuant to our telephone conversation yesterday, I am transmitting to you herewith one book, which is responsive to "William Jefferson Clinton Grand Jury Subpoena #V002." I accepted service of this subpoena, and it was FAXed to me at 5:15 p.m., Wednesday, January 21.

This subpoena duces tecum was returnable today, and yesterday you afforded me a one week extension, but requested that whatever I had located thus far be produced today. I told you that I believed I had located two books which were responsive, but I am now not certain that one is and I am unable to do the appropriate checking in the time available. However, I am enclosing a soft-cover 54-page book, whose cover bears the Bates number DEK227870. You also requested documents responsive to Paragraph G of the subpoena:

> "any and all answers to interrogatories, requests for admission, affidavits, declarations, and depositions of William Jefferson Clinton in Jones v. Clinton and Ferguson."

As I told you, Mr. Bennett, and not I, is handling that case. Mr. Bennett informs me that the materials requested in Paragraph G are covered by a stringent Protective Order entered by Judge Wright with the consent of all parties to that case. Because of recent publicity and prejudicial leaks from numerous sources of material ostensibly covered by the Protective Order, Paragraph G of your subpoena raises serious concerns which we believe should be addressed by the Court. I am taking the liberty of sending Judge Wright a copy of this letter. I understand that the parties in the Jones case have a weekly telephonic status conference every Thursday with the Judge, and it seems to me appropriate to place this matter before the Court at that time.

Although the materials today are physically being delivered to you instead of the grand jury, they are still being produced pursuant to grand jury subpoena and are fully covered by the secrecy provisions of the Federal Rules of Criminal Procedure.

Sincerely,

David E. Kendall

cc: Hon. Susan Webber Wright (by FAX)
Robert S. Bennett, Esq. (by FAX)

Enclosure

OUR PATRIOTIC PRESIDENT.
HIS LIFE IN
PICTURES,
ANECDOTES,
SAYINGS,
PRINCIPLES
AND
BIOGRAPHY.
COPYRIGHT, 1904, BY THE ELITE ART PRESS.

LAW OFFICES
WILLIAMS & CONNOLLY
725 TWELFTH STREET, N.W.
WASHINGTON, DC 20005-5901

V002-DC-00000004

CONFIDENTIAL PRODUCED PURSUANT TO SECRECY PROVISIONS OF RULE 6(e), F. R. CRIM. P. GRAND JURY MATERIAL

Robert J. Bittman, Esq.
Office of the Independent Counsel
1001 Pennsylvania Avenue, N.W., Suite 490-North
Washington, D.C. 20004

Corporate Express.
Express Delivery Systems
(703) 550-5000

Williams & Connolly

Messenger Request Form

Today's Date: January 27, 1998 Due Date: Today

Today's Time: ____________ Due Time: ASAP

Filing: ____________

Requestor Information

Requested By: David E. Kendall Ext.: 5145

Attorney Name & No.: 1040 Ext.: ____________

Client / Matter Name: See David Kendall Client / Matter No.: [redacted]

Messenger Request

____ Pick Up xx Delivery ____ Rush ____ Envelope

____ Round Trip ____ Box Quantity ____ Other ____________

Firm Name: Office of the Independent Counsel

Address: 1001 PA Ave., N.W. Suite / Room #: 490-North

Contact Name: Robert J. Bittman Telephone Number: [redacted]

ecial Instructions: Please have this request form signed by recipient.

Signature: ____________

Date/Time: ____________

Recipient's Signature Monique Neaves Time 2:15 Date 1/27/98

V002-DC-00000005

43704
IIS

PAULA CORBIN JONES
V.
WILLIAM JEFFERSON CLINTON

SEALED DOCUMENTS

LAW OFFICES
WILLIAMS & CONNOLLY
725 TWELFTH STREET, N.W.
WASHINGTON, D. C. 20005-5901
(202) 434-5000
FAX (202) 434-5029

DAVID E. KENDALL
(202) 434-5145

EDWARD BENNETT WILLIAMS (1920-1988)
PAUL R. CONNOLLY (1922-1978)

CONFIDENTIAL
PRODUCED PURSUANT TO SECRECY PROVISIONS
OF RULE 6(e), F. R. CRIM. P.
GRAND JURY MATERIAL

February 2, 1998

Robert J. Bittman, Esq.
Deputy Independent Counsel
Office of the Independent Counsel
1001 Pennsylvania Avenue, N.W.
Suite 490-North
Washington, D.C. 20004

V002-DC-00000159

By Hand

Dear Bob:

Pursuant to Paragraph G of the subpoena to "William Jefferson Clinton Grand Jury Subpoena #V002," and Judge Wright's ruling (as I understand it) at the conference call on January 27 I am producing herewith a copy of the President's deposition transcript we have received, with attached exhibits, taken on Saturday, January 17, 1998, in the Jones case. This document bears Bates numbers DEK228021 to DEK228326.

I am also transmitting to you herewith an additional page from President Clinton's Supplemental Responses to Plaintiff's Second Set of Interrogatories (bearing Bates number DEK227917A) which was inadvertently not transmitted to you in my production of January 28, 1998.

Although the materials today are physically being delivered to you instead of the grand jury, they are still being produced pursuant to grand jury subpoena and are fully covered by the secrecy provisions of the Federal Rules of Criminal Procedure.

Sincerely,

David E. Kendall

Enclosures

DEK/bb

LAW OFFICES
WILLIAMS & CONNOLLY
725 TWELFTH STREET, N.W.
WASHINGTON, D. C. 20005-5901
(202) 434-5000
FAX (202) 434-5029

DAVID E. KENDALL
(202) 434-5145

EDWARD BENNETT WILLIAMS (1920-1988)
PAUL R. CONNOLLY (1922-1978)

CONFIDENTIAL
PRODUCED PURSUANT TO SECRECY PROVISIONS
OF RULE 6(e), F. R. CRIM. P.
GRAND JURY MATERIAL

February 3, 1998

Robert J. Bittman, Esq.
Deputy Independent Counsel
Office of the Independent Counsel
1001 Pennsylvania Avenue, N.W.
Suite 490-North
Washington, D.C. 20004

V002-DC-00000469

By Hand

Dear Bob:

Pursuant to the subpoena to "William Jefferson Clinton Grand Jury Subpoena #V002," and our telephone conversation on January 26, 1998, affording me an additional week to respond, I am herewith producing four items which we believe may be responsive, Bates-numbered as follows: one book, The Presidents of the United States (Bates number DEK228327, affixed to the inside front cover), one Louis Feraud tie (Bates number DEK228328, affixed to the back), one "Santa Monica" coffee mug (Bates number DEK228329 affixed to the bottom), and one metal cigarette holder case (Bates number DEK228330, affixed to the side).

Although the materials today are physically being delivered to you instead of the grand jury, they are still being produced pursuant to grand jury subpoena and are fully covered by the secrecy provisions of the Federal Rules of Criminal Procedure.

Sincerely,

David E. Kendall

Enclosures

DEK/bb

3053

V002-DC-00000471

DEK228327

THE
PRESIDENTS
OF THE
UNITED
STATES
APPLETONS

LAW OFFICES
WILLIAMS & CONNOLLY
725 TWELFTH STREET, N.W.
WASHINGTON, D. C. 20005-5901
(202) 434-5000
FAX (202) 434-5029

EDWARD BENNETT WILLIAMS (1920-1988)
PAUL R. CONNOLLY (1922-1978)

DAVID E. KENDALL
(202) 434-5145

March 16, 1998

CONFIDENTIAL
RULE 6(e), F.R.CRIM.P. GRAND JURY SUBMISSION

Robert J. Bittman, Esq.
Deputy Independent Counsel
Office of the Independent Counsel
1001 Pennsylvania Avenue, N.W.
Suite 490-North
Washington, D.C. 20004

By Hand

Dear Bob:

We have responded in a timely fashion to "William Jefferson Clinton Grand Jury Subpoena #V002", dated January 20, 1998, and served on us the next day. We believe that Ms. Lewinsky might have given the President a few additional items, such as ties and a pair of sun glasses, but we have not been able to locate these items. The President frequently does not see and is not aware of numerous items which are sent to him by friends and supporters.

Sincerely,

David E. Kendall

Date: Saturday, January 24, 1998
Time: 12:49:14 PM

Selection Detail Report

AKIN GUMP

OIC - AGS - 0127

SELECTION CRITERIA :
DATE RANGE : 10/31/97 to 12/1/97
TIME RANGE : 12:00:00 AM to 11:59:59 PM
MINIMUM COST : $0.00
MINIMUM DURATION : 0:00:00
Cost Center : All
Extension : [redacted]
ACCOUNT CODES : All
Trunk : All
CALL TYPE : All
DIALED NUMBER : All

SUMMARIZE INCOMING CALLS

DATE	TIME	DURATION HHHH:MM:SS	Extension	DIALED NUMBER	LOCATION	CALL TYPE	Trunk	ACCOUNT COD
11/03/97	08:31	0:05:36	[redacted]	[redacted]	NEW YOR NY	OS-OL	194	
11/03/97	09:18	0:05:12	[redacted]	[redacted]	WASZ-1	LOCAL	141	
11/03/97	09:24	0:01:18	[redacted]	[redacted]	NEW YOR NY	OS-OL	194	
11/03/97	09:26	0:00:48	[redacted]	[redacted]	NEW YOR NY	OS-OL	194	
11/03/97	09:27	0:12:30	[redacted]	[redacted]	NEW YOR NY	OS-OL	194	
11/03/97	09:42	0:13:54	[redacted]	[redacted]	NEW YOR NY	OS-OL	194	
11/03/97	15:02	0:02:12	[redacted]	[redacted]	ATLANTA GA	OS-OL	194	
11/03/97	15:06	0:02:06	[redacted]	[redacted]	NEW YOR NY	OS-OL	194	
11/03/97	15:15	0:05:06	[redacted]	[redacted]	CHCZ-1 IL	OS-OL	194	
11/03/97	15:19	0:00:48	[redacted]	[redacted]	NEW YOR NY	OS-OL	191	0799972800
11/03/97	15:21	0:01:36	[redacted]	[redacted]	WASZ-1	LOCAL	141	
11/03/97	15:23	0:00:42	[redacted]	[redacted]	NEW YOR NY	OS-OL	191	0799972800
11/03/97	15:24	0:01:42	[redacted]	[redacted]	TORONTO ON	OS-OL	194	
11/03/97	15:25	0:00:36	[redacted]	[redacted]	VA	LOCAL	141	
11/03/97	15:26	0:01:06	[redacted]	[redacted]	WASZ 8 VA	LOCAL	141	
11/03/97	15:26	0:11:00	[redacted]	[redacted]	WASZ-1	LOCAL	141	
11/03/97	15:29	0:00:36	[redacted]	[redacted]	WCHSZ 8 NY	OS-OL	191	0799972800
11/03/97	15:35	0:00:42	[redacted]	[redacted]	WASZ-1	LOCAL	141	
11/03/97	15:38	0:00:30	[redacted]	[redacted]	NEW YOR NY	OS-OL	194	
11/03/97	15:42	0:01:06	[redacted]	[redacted]	WASZ-1	LOCAL	141	
11/03/97	15:59	0:01:42	[redacted]	[redacted]	WASZ 17 VA	LOCAL	141	
11/03/97	16:04	0:04:24	[redacted]	[redacted]	WASZ 1B VA	LOCAL	141	
11/03/97	16:09	0:01:18	[redacted]	[redacted]	NEW YOR NY	OS-OL	191	0799972800
11/03/97	16:09	0:36:06	[redacted]	[redacted]	WASZ 1B VA	LOCAL	141	
11/03/97	16:32	0:02:06	[redacted]	[redacted]	NORWALK CT	OS-OL	191	0799972800
11/03/97	16:53	0:00:30	[redacted]	[redacted]	WASZ 17 VA	LOCAL	141	
11/03/97	17:40	0:00:30	[redacted]	[redacted]	WASZ-1	LOCAL	141	
11/04/97	08:59	0:02:54	[redacted]	[redacted]	WASZ-1	LOCAL	141	
11/04/97	09:14	0:00:54	[redacted]	[redacted]		OS-OL	191	0799972800
11/04/97	11:00	0:03:30	[redacted]	[redacted]	WASZ 17 VA	LOCAL	141	
11/04/97	11:09	0:03:42	[redacted]	[redacted]	NORWALK CT	OS-OL	194	
11/04/97	11:16	0:03:06	[redacted]	[redacted]	NEW YOR NY	OS-OL	194	
11/04/97	11:34	0:05:48	[redacted]	[redacted]	NEW YOR NY	OS-OL	194	
11/04/97	11:52	0:03:00	[redacted]	[redacted]	DANBURY CT	OS-OL	188	0799972800
11/04/97	11:54	0:00:42	[redacted]	[redacted]	WASZ 19 VA	LOCAL	141	
11/04/97	11:55	0:01:06	[redacted]	[redacted]	WASZ 17 VA	LOCAL	141	
11/04/97	12:11	0:04:12	[redacted]	[redacted]	NEW YOR NY	OS-OL	191	0799972800
11/04/97	12:13	0:00:36	[redacted]	[redacted]	NEW YOR NY	OS-OL	194	
11/04/97	12:14	0:00:48	[redacted]	[redacted]	WASZ-1	LOCAL	141	
11/04/97	12:25	0:08:24	[redacted]	[redacted]	NEW YOR NY	OS-OL	191	0799972800
11/04/97	12:42	0:30:12	[redacted]	[redacted]	WASZ-1	LOCAL	141	
11/04/97	15:51	0:01:00	[redacted]	[redacted]	UTICA MI	OS-OL	191	0799972800
11/04/97	15:52	0:00:54	[redacted]	[redacted]	WASZ-1	LOCAL	141	
[illegible]	[illegible]	[illegible]	[redacted]	[redacted]	NEW YOR NY	OS-OL	194	
11/04/97	15:59	0:00:42	[redacted]	[redacted]	TORONTO ON	OS-OL	194	
11/04/97	16:00	0:03:12	[redacted]	[redacted]	TORONTO ON	OS-OL	194	
11/04/97	16:04	0:02:12	[redacted]	[redacted]	WASZ-1	LOCAL	141	
11/04/97	16:04	0:03:18	[redacted]	[redacted]	ATLANTA GA	OS-OL	191	0799972800
11/04/97	16:08	0:00:54	[redacted]	[redacted]	WASZ-1	LOCAL	141	
11/04/97	16:09	0:00:42	[redacted]	[redacted]	WASZ-1	LOCAL	141	
11/04/97	16:10	0:00:48	[redacted]	[redacted]	WASZ-1	LOCAL	141	
11/04/97	16:11	0:04:12	[redacted]	[redacted]	NEW YOR NY	OS-OL	194	
11/04/97	16:16	0:04:18	[redacted]	[redacted]	NEW YOR NY	OS-OL	194	
11/04/97	16:22	0:06:24	[redacted]	[redacted]	WASZ-1	LOCAL	141	
11/04/97	16:38	0:01:06	[redacted]	[redacted]	WASZ-1	LOCAL	141	
11/04/97	16:40	0:01:18	[redacted]	[redacted]	WASZ-1	LOCAL	141	
11/04/97	16:44	0:03:24	[redacted]	[redacted]	WASZ-1	LOCAL	141	
11/04/97	16:55	0:01:06	[redacted]	[redacted]	WASZ-1	LOCAL	141	
11/04/97	17:08	0:05:06	[redacted]	[redacted]	WASZ-1	LOCAL	141	

MC calls VJ? p.22

V004-DC-00000134

Selection Detail Report

Date: Saturday, January 24, 1998
Time: 12:49:14 PM

OIC - ABS - 0128

AKIN GUMP

DATE	TIME	DURATION HHHH:MM:SS	Extension	DIALED NUMBER	LOCATION	CALL TYPE	Trunk	ACCOUNT COD
11/04/97	17:17	0:01:42	[redacted]	[redacted]	WASZ-1	LOCAL	141	
11/04/97	17:20	0:15:12	[redacted]	[redacted]	NEW YOR NY	OS-OL	194	
11/04/97	17:44	0:01:06	[redacted]	[redacted]	NEW YOR NY	OS-OL	194	
11/04/97	17:51	0:01:00	[redacted]	[redacted]	NEW YOR NY	OS-OL	191	0799972800
11/04/97	18:01	0:00:42	[redacted]	[redacted]	WASZ-1	SPCL	141	
11/04/97	18:17	0:01:06	[redacted]	[redacted]	BETHESD MD	LOCAL	141	
11/04/97	18:37	0:00:54	[redacted]	[redacted]	CHCZ-1 IL	OS-OL	194	
11/04/97	18:43	0:02:12	[redacted]	[redacted]	NEW YOR NY	OS-OL	194	
11/04/97	18:50	0:01:18	[redacted]	[redacted]	WASZ-1	LOCAL	141	
11/04/97	19:35	0:00:36	[redacted]	[redacted]	WASZ-1	LOCAL	141	
11/04/97	19:53	0:02:06	[redacted]	[redacted]	WASZ-1	LOCAL	141	
11/04/97	19:56	0:02:12	[redacted]	[redacted]	WASZ-1	LOCAL	141	
11/05/97	08:18	0:01:06	[redacted]	[redacted]	WASZ-1	LOCAL	141	
11/05/97	08:44	0:10:12	[redacted]	[redacted]	WASZ-1	LOCAL	141	
11/05/97	08:56	0:06:30	[redacted]	[redacted]	WASZ-1	LOCAL	141	
11/05/97	09:05	0:01:12	[redacted]	[redacted]	NEW YOR NY	OS-OL	194	
11/05/97	09:10	0:03:12	[redacted]	[redacted]	NEW YOR NY	OS-OL	194	
11/05/97	09:22	0:01:18	[redacted]	[redacted]	WASZ-1	LOCAL	141	
11/05/97	09:24	0:02:36	[redacted]	[redacted]	WASZ-1	LOCAL	141	
11/05/97	09:28	0:15:24	[redacted]	[redacted]		OS-OL	194	
11/05/97	10:28	0:00:30	[redacted]	[redacted]	WASZ-1	LOCAL	141	
11/05/97	10:41	0:00:36	[redacted]	[redacted]	WASZ-1	SPCL	141	
11/05/97	10:44	0:01:48	[redacted]	[redacted]	NEW YOR NY	OS-OL	191	0799972800
11/05/97	10:48	0:00:54	[redacted]	[redacted]		LOCAL	141	
11/05/97	10:49	0:02:12	[redacted]	[redacted]	WASZ-1	LOCAL	141	
11/05/97	10:52	0:01:24	[redacted]	[redacted]	NEW YOR NY	OS-OL	194	
11/05/97	11:03	0:00:30	[redacted]	[redacted]	CHCZ-1 IL	OS-OL	191	0799972800
11/05/97	11:05	0:00:48	[redacted]	[redacted]	WASZ-1	LOCAL	141	
11/05/97	11:19	0:00:48	[redacted]	[redacted]	WASZ 8 VA	LOCAL	141	
11/05/97	11:19	0:05:06	[redacted]	[redacted]	CHCZ-1 IL	OS-OL	191	0799972800
11/05/97	11:20	0:03:36	[redacted]	[redacted]	WASZ 8 VA	LOCAL	141	
11/05/97	11:27	0:00:30	[redacted]	[redacted]	WASZ-1	SPCL	141	
11/05/97	11:28	0:01:00	[redacted]	[redacted]	WASZ-1	LOCAL	141	
11/05/97	11:29	0:02:12	[redacted]	[redacted]	WASZ-1	LOCAL	141	
11/05/97	11:32	0:00:54	[redacted]	[redacted]	WASZ-1	LOCAL	141	
11/05/97	11:34	0:03:54	[redacted]	[redacted]	WASZ-1	LOCAL	141	
11/05/97	11:40	0:05:18	[redacted]	[redacted]	NEW YOR NY	OS-OL	191	0799972800
11/05/97	11:44	0:01:06	[redacted]	[redacted]	WASZ-1	LOCAL	141	
11/05/97	13:02	0:00:36	[redacted]	[redacted]	UK	IDDD	188	0799972800
11/05/97	13:55	0:00:30	[redacted]	[redacted]	WASZ 17 VA	LOCAL	141	
11/05/97	14:34	0:01:24	[redacted]	[redacted]	WASZ-1	LOCAL	141	
11/05/97	14:36	0:01:30	[redacted]	[redacted]	WASZ-1	LOCAL	141	
11/05/97	14:39	0:02:48	[redacted]	[redacted]	CHCZ-1 IL	OS-OL	191	0799972800
11/05/97	14:47	0:02:00	[redacted]	[redacted]	NEW YOR NY	OS-OL	191	0799972800
11/05/97	16:43	0:00:36	[redacted]	[redacted]	NEW YOR NY	OS-OL	194	
11/05/97	16:52	0:12:54	[redacted]	[redacted]	WASZ-1	LOCAL	141	
11/05/97	17:22	0:05:24	[redacted]	[redacted]	WASZ-1	LOCAL	141	
11/05/97	17:25	0:01:24	[redacted]	[redacted]	WASZ-1	LOCAL	141	
11/05/97	17:50	0:00:42	[redacted]	[redacted]	WASZ-1	LOCAL	141	
11/05/97	18:03	0:02:48	[redacted]	[redacted]	WASZ-1	LOCAL	141	
11/05/97	18:14	0:00:42	[redacted]	[redacted]	WASZ-1	LOCAL	141	
11/05/97	18:16	0:17:30	[redacted]	[redacted]	WASZ 17 VA	LOCAL	141	
11/05/97	18:37	0:00:30	[redacted]	[redacted]	CHCZ-1 IL	OS-OL	194	
11/05/97	18:40	0:05:12	[redacted]	[redacted]	WASZ-1	LOCAL	141	
11/06/97	08:53	0:00:48	[redacted]	[redacted]	WASZ-1	LOCAL	141	
11/06/97	08:54	0:00:36	[redacted]	[redacted]	WASZ-1	LOCAL	141	
11/06/97	09:11	0:00:42	[redacted]	[redacted]	WASZ-1	LOCAL	141	
11/06/97	09:28	0:00:36	[redacted]	[redacted]	NEW YOR NY	OS-OL	194	
11/06/97	09:29	0:03:12	[redacted]	[redacted]	WASZ-1	LOCAL	141	
11/06/97	09:35	0:03:30	[redacted]	[redacted]	WASZ-1	LOCAL	141	
11/06/97	09:42	0:04:54	[redacted]	[redacted]	CHCZ-1 IL	OS-OL	191	0799972800
11/06/97	09:47	0:09:54	[redacted]	[redacted]		OS-OL	194	
11/06/97	09:54	0:00:30	[redacted]	[redacted]	WASZ-1	LOCAL	141	
11/06/97	09:59	0:01:12	[redacted]	[redacted]	NEW YOR NY	OS-OL	194	
11/06/97	10:01	0:00:30	[redacted]	[redacted]	WASZ-1	LOCAL	141	
11/06/97	10:03	0:02:00	[redacted]	[redacted]	WASZ-1	LOCAL	141	
11/06/97	10:08	0:00:30	[redacted]	[redacted]	NEW YOR NY	OS-OL	194	
11/06/97	10:14	0:04:18	[redacted]	[redacted]	WASZ-1	LOCAL	141	
11/06/97	10:15	0:00:30	[redacted]	[redacted]	WASZ-1	LOCAL	141	
11/06/97	10:18	0:01:48	[redacted]	[redacted]	UK	IDDD	188	0799972800
11/06/97	10:42	0:06:30	[redacted]	[redacted]	COLUMBU IN	OS-OL	194	
11/06/97	10:50	0:18:42	[redacted]	[redacted]	ATLANTA GA	OS-OL	194	
11/06/97	10:54	0:02:36	[redacted]	[redacted]	UK	IDDD	188	0799972800

Selection Detail Report

Date: Saturday, January 24, 1998
Time: 12:49:14 PM

AKIN GUMP

OIC - AGS - 0136

DATE	TIME	DURATION HHHH:MM:SS	Extension	DIALED NUMBER	LOCATION	CALL TYPE	Trunk	ACCOUNT COD
11/26/97	10:52	0:02:48	[redacted]	[redacted]	NEW YOR NY	OS-OL	194	
11/26/97	11:02	0:01:30	[redacted]	[redacted]	WASZ-1	LOCAL	141	
11/26/97	11:04	0:03:54	[redacted]	[redacted]	NEW YOR NY	OS-OL	194	
11/26/97	11:08	0:00:42	[redacted]	[redacted]	WASZ 8 VA	LOCAL	141	
11/26/97	11:09	0:03:42	[redacted]	[redacted]	NEW YOR NY	OS-OL	194	
11/26/97	11:21	0:08:18	[redacted]	[redacted]	NEW YOR NY	OS-OL	194	
11/26/97	11:30	0:01:54	[redacted]	[redacted]	NEW YOR NY	OS-OL	194	
11/26/97	11:42	0:03:18	[redacted]	[redacted]	NEW YOR NY	OS-OL	194	
11/26/97	11:57	0:13:42	[redacted]	[redacted]	WASZ-1	LOCAL	141	
11/26/97	12:11	0:00:42	[redacted]	[redacted]	BETHESD MD	LOCAL	141	
11/26/97	12:20	0:03:18	[redacted]	[redacted]	BETHESD MD	LOCAL	141	
11/26/97	12:24	0:02:12	[redacted]	[redacted]	BETHESD MD	LOCAL	141	
11/26/97	12:33	0:02:24	[redacted]	[redacted]	GERMAN	IDDD	191	0799972800
11/26/97	13:45	0:01:00	[redacted]	[redacted]	OXON HI MD	LOCAL	141	
11/26/97	13:46	0:12:12	[redacted]	[redacted]	OXON HI MD	LOCAL	141	
11/26/97	13:53	0:01:06	[redacted]	[redacted]	DALLAS TX	OS-OL	191	0799972800
11/26/97	13:56	0:02:18	[redacted]	[redacted]		LOCAL	141	
11/26/97	14:01	0:03:06	[redacted]	[redacted]	WASZ-1	LOCAL	141	
11/26/97	14:04	0:00:54	[redacted]	[redacted]	NEW YOR NY	OS-OL	194	
11/26/97	14:05	0:02:00	[redacted]	[redacted]	NEW YOR NY	OS-OL	194	
11/26/97	14:07	0:02:48	[redacted]	[redacted]	BERWYN MD	LOCAL	141	
11/26/97	14:11	0:01:36	[redacted]	[redacted]	BOWEGLN MD	LOCAL	141	
11/26/97	14:12	0:03:12	[redacted]	[redacted]	WASZ-1	LOCAL	141	
11/26/97	14:30	0:07:30	[redacted]	[redacted]	OXON HI MD	LOCAL	141	
11/26/97	14:33	0:03:42	[redacted]	[redacted]	CHCZ-1 IL	OS-OL	191	0799972800
11/26/97	14:49	0:01:00	[redacted]	[redacted]	WASZ-1	LOCAL	141	
11/26/97	14:49	0:05:06	[redacted]	[redacted]	E ST LO IL	OS-OL	194	
11/26/97	14:53	0:00:30	[redacted]	[redacted]	WASZ-1	LOCAL	141	
11/26/97	14:53	0:05:36	[redacted]	[redacted]		OS-OL	191	0799972800
11/26/97	15:04	0:00:48	[redacted]	[redacted]	CHCZ-1 IL	OS-OL	191	0799972800
11/26/97	15:07	0:02:42	[redacted]	[redacted]	NEW YOR NY	OS-OL	194	
11/26/97	15:09	0:02:24	[redacted]	[redacted]	NEW YOR NY	OS-OL	194	
11/26/97	15:15	0:00:30	[redacted]	[redacted]	NEW YOR NY	OS-OL	194	
11/26/97	15:23	0:02:18	[redacted]	[redacted]	NEW YOR NY	OS-OL	194	
11/26/97	15:34	0:00:54	[redacted]	[redacted]	BERNARD NJ	OS-OL	194	
11/26/97	15:42	0:00:36	[redacted]	[redacted]	PORTLAN OR	OS-OL	194	
11/26/97	15:55	0:00:36	[redacted]	[redacted]	NEW YOR NY	OS-OL	191	0799972800
11/26/97	16:26	0:04:36	[redacted]	[redacted]	NEW YOR NY	OS-OL	194	
11/26/97	16:31	0:05:48	[redacted]	[redacted]	CHCZ-1 IL	OS-OL	194	
11/26/97	16:39	0:01:36	[redacted]	[redacted]	WASZ-1	LOCAL	141	
11/26/97	16:48	0:00:42	[redacted]	[redacted]	WASZ-1	LOCAL	141	
11/26/97	16:48	0:04:36	[redacted]	[redacted]	PORTLAN OR	OS-OL	191	0799972800
11/26/97	17:00	0:04:42	[redacted]	[redacted]	OXON HI MD	LOCAL	141	
11/26/97	17:23	0:00:54	[redacted]	[redacted]	PORTLAN OR	OS-OL	191	0799972880
11/26/97	17:30	0:02:18	[redacted]	[redacted]	BEVERLY CA	OS-OL	194	
11/26/97	17:34	0:01:36	[redacted]	[redacted]	WASZ-1	LOCAL	141	
11/26/97	17:36	0:03:42	[redacted]	[redacted]	LOSANGE CA	OS-OL	194	
11/26/97	17:40	0:01:18	[redacted]	[redacted]	LOSANGE CA	OS-OL	194	
11/26/97	17:46	0:02:36	[redacted]	[redacted]	DALLAS TX	OS-OL	194	
11/26/97	17:47	0:00:30	[redacted]	[redacted]	DALLAS TX	OS-OL	191	0799972800
11/26/97	18:00	0:05:42	[redacted]	[redacted]	WASHING NJ	OS-OL	191	0799972800
11/26/97	18:06	0:01:36	[redacted]	[redacted]	AUGUSTA GA	OS-OL	191	0799972800
11/26/97	18:12	0:02:00	[redacted]	[redacted]	WASZ-1	LOCAL	141	
11/26/97	18:14	0:04:18	[redacted]	[redacted]	WCHSZ 6 NY	OS-OL	194	
11/27/97	11:22	0:03:12	[redacted]	[redacted]	WASZ-1	LOCAL	141	
11/27/97	11:27	0:04:54	[redacted]	[redacted]	LOSANGE CA	OS-OL	194	
11/27/97	11:32	0:11:42	[redacted]	[redacted]	WCHSZ 6 NY	OS-OL	194	
11/27/97	11:46	0:02:24	[redacted]	[redacted]	WASZ-1	LOCAL	141	
11/27/97	11:52	0:00:30	[redacted]	[redacted]	NEW YOR NY	OS-OL	194	
11/27/97	11:53	0:01:24	[redacted]	[redacted]	LOSANGE CA	OS-OL	194	
11/27/97	11:55	0:10:24	[redacted]	[redacted]	WASZ-1	LOCAL	141	

704	35:54:42	DETAIL SUBTOTAL
0	0:00:00	INCOMING CALLS

TOTAL NUMBER OF CALLS	DURATION: TOTAL HHHH:MM:SS	DURATION: PER CALL HH:MM:SS	COST: TOTAL (DOLLARS)	COST: PER CALL (DOLLARS)	COST: PER MINUTE (DOLLARS)
704	35:54:42	0:03:03	300.43	0.42	0.13

Selection Detail Report

te: Saturday, January 24, 1998
.me: 1:33:24 PM

AKIN GUMP

OIC - AGS - 0141

DATE	TIME	DURATION HHHH:MM:SS	Extension	DIALED NUMBER	LOCATION	CALL TYPE	Trunk	ACCOUNT COD
12/11/97	09:22	0:00:30	[redacted]	[redacted]	WASZ-1	LOCAL	141	
12/11/97	09:25	0:03:00	[redacted]	[redacted]	WASZ 8 VA	LOCAL	141	
12/11/97	09:31	0:00:48	[redacted]	[redacted]	HAYMARK VA	OS-IL	194	
12/11/97	09:35	0:01:06	[redacted]	[redacted]	WASZ 8 VA	LOCAL	141	
12/11/97	09:39	0:03:42	[redacted]	[redacted]	UK	IDDD	194	
12/11/97	09:45	0:00:36	[redacted]	[redacted]	NEW YOR NY	OS-OL	194	
12/11/97	10:18	0:01:12	[redacted]	[redacted]	WASZ-1	LOCAL	141	
12/11/97	10:31	0:02:54	[redacted]	[redacted]	MIAMI FL	OS-OL	191	0799972800
12/11/97	10:39	0:00:54	[redacted]	[redacted]	NEW YOR NY	OS-OL	194	
12/11/97	10:57	0:01:00	[redacted]	[redacted]	NEW YOR NY	OS-OL	194	
12/11/97	10:59	0:03:36	[redacted]	[redacted]	NEW YOR NY	OS-OL	191	0799972800
12/11/97	11:12	0:04:24	[redacted]	[redacted]	NEW YOR NY	OS-OL	194	
12/11/97	11:17	0:03:12	[redacted]	[redacted]	NEW YOR NY	OS-OL	194	
12/11/97	11:23	0:01:00	[redacted]	[redacted]	WASZ-1	LOCAL	141	
12/11/97	11:42	0:02:54	[redacted]	[redacted]	NEW YOR NY	OS-OL	194	
12/11/97	11:55	0:09:30	[redacted]	[redacted]	NEW YOR NY	OS-OL	191	0799972800
12/11/97	12:05	0:02:12	[redacted]	[redacted]	NEW YOR NY	OS-OL	194	
12/11/97	12:10	0:09:00	[redacted]	[redacted]	NEW YOR NY	OS-OL	191	0799972800
12/11/97	12:24	0:03:54	[redacted]	[redacted]	NEW YOR NY	OS-OL	194	
12/11/97	12:40	0:01:06	[redacted]	[redacted]	NEW YOR NY	OS-OL	191	0799972800
12/11/97	12:44	0:01:06	[redacted]	[redacted]	NEW YOR NY	OS-OL	191	0799972800
12/11/97	12:47	0:00:48	[redacted]	[redacted]	NEW YOR NY	OS-OL	194	
12/11/97	12:49	0:01:00	[redacted]	[redacted]	NEW YOR NY	OS-OL	191	0799972800
12/11/97	12:51	0:01:06	[redacted]	[redacted]	NEW YOR NY	OS-OL	194	
12/11/97	12:56	0:05:42	[redacted]	[redacted]	NEW YOR NY	OS-OL	194	
12/11/97	13:04	0:08:54	[redacted]	[redacted]	LOSANGE CA	OS-OL	194	
12/11/97	13:06	0:00:30	[redacted]	[redacted]	NEW YOR NY	OS-OL	191	0799972800
12/11/97	13:07	0:01:06	[redacted]	[redacted]	NEW YOR NY	OS-OL	191	0799972800
12/11/97	13:36	0:00:36	[redacted]	[redacted]	NEW YOR NY	OS-OL	194	
12/11/97	13:38	0:00:30	[redacted]	[redacted]	NEW YOR NY	OS-OL	194	
12/11/97	14:22	0:00:48	[redacted]	[redacted]	WASZ 8 VA	LOCAL	141	
12/11/97	14:24	0:00:36	[redacted]	[redacted]	COLUMBU IN	OS-OL	194	
12/11/97	14:25	0:04:06	[redacted]	[redacted]	WASZ-1	LOCAL	141	
12/11/97	14:29	0:01:06	[redacted]	[redacted]	WASZ-1	LOCAL	141	
12/11/97	14:33	0:03:06	[redacted]	[redacted]	ATLANTA GA	OS-OL	194	
12/11/97	15:06	0:01:12	[redacted]	[redacted]	WASZ 19 VA	LOCAL	141	
12/11/97	15:51	0:00:48	[redacted]	[redacted]	NEW YOR NY	OS-OL	191	0799972800
12/11/97	15:51	0:03:54	[redacted]	[redacted]	WASZ-1	LOCAL	141	
12/11/97	16:14	0:01:24	[redacted]	[redacted]	WASZ-1	LOCAL	141	
12/11/97	16:32	0:00:42	[redacted]	[redacted]	BEVERLY CA	OS-OL	191	0799972800
12/11/97	16:34	0:02:00	[redacted]	[redacted]	RICHMON VA	OS-OL	191	0799972800
12/11/97	16:36	0:00:48	[redacted]	[redacted]	WASZ-1	LOCAL	141	
12/11/97	16:38	0:13:30	[redacted]	[redacted]	WASZ 8 VA	LOCAL	141	
12/11/97	17:21	0:00:30	[redacted]	[redacted]	WASZ-1	LOCAL	141	
12/11/97	17:24	0:01:36	[redacted]	[redacted]	NEW YOR NY	OS-OL	191	0799972800
12/12/97	08:19	0:01:06	[redacted]	[redacted]	OXON HI MD	LOCAL	141	
12/12/97	10:11	0:00:42	[redacted]	[redacted]	WASZ-1	LOCAL	141	
12/12/97	10:14	0:00:48	[redacted]	[redacted]	NEW YOR NY	OS-OL	191	0799990259
12/12/97	10:55	0:03:30	[redacted]	[redacted]	WASZ-1	LOCAL	141	
12/12/97	11:08	0:00:36	[redacted]	[redacted]	MARTIN TN	OS-OL	188	0799972800
12/12/97	11:09	0:01:54	[redacted]	[redacted]	CINCINN OH	OS-OL	191	0799972800
12/12/97	12:06	0:02:24	[redacted]	[redacted]	CAPITOL MD	LOCAL	141	
12/12/97	12:15	0:01:06	[redacted]	[redacted]	WASZ-1	LOCAL	141	
12/12/97	12:17	0:03:00	[redacted]	[redacted]		SPCL	141	
12/12/97	12:22	0:01:18	[redacted]	[redacted]	ENGLESI VA	LOCAL	141	
12/12/97	12:29	0:00:30	[redacted]	[redacted]	ENGLESI VA	LOCAL	141	
12/12/97	12:48	0:05:30	[redacted]	[redacted]	AUGUSTA GA	OS-OL	191	0799990259
12/12/97	12:56	0:00:36	[redacted]	[redacted]	NEW YOR NY	OS-OL	191	0799972600
12/12/97	12:59	0:00:42	[redacted]	[redacted]	ENGLESI VA	LOCAL	141	
12/12/97	13:28	0:01:00	[redacted]	[redacted]	WASZ-1	LOCAL	141	
12/12/97	15:31	0:00:36	[redacted]	[redacted]	WASZ 8 VA	LOCAL	141	
12/12/97	16:41	0:15:00	[redacted]	[redacted]	NY	OS-OL	191	0799972800
12/15/97	08:17	0:08:12	[redacted]	[redacted]	NEW YOR NY	OS-OL	194	
12/15/97	08:32	0:06:06	[redacted]	[redacted]	NEW YOR NY	OS-OL	194	
12/15/97	08:41	0:01:00	[redacted]	[redacted]	WASZ-1	LOCAL	141	
12/15/97	08:55	0:04:36	[redacted]	[redacted]	COLUMBU IN	OS-OL	194	
12/15/97	08:58	0:09:00	[redacted]	[redacted]	BEVERLY CA	OS-OL	191	0799972800
12/15/97	09:17	0:02:24	[redacted]	[redacted]	WASZ-1	LOCAL	141	
12/15/97	09:21	0:03:54	[redacted]	[redacted]	WASZ-1	LOCAL	141	
12/15/97	09:51	0:00:30	[redacted]	[redacted]	WASZ-1	SPCL	141	
12/15/97	09:52	0:03:00	[redacted]	[redacted]	NEW YOR NY	OS-OL	194	
12/15/97	09:53	0:02:42	[redacted]	[redacted]	WASZ-1	LOCAL	141	
12/15/97	09:55	0:02:36	[redacted]	[redacted]	NEW YOR NY	OS-OL	194	

Selection Detail Report

Date: Saturday, January 24, 1998
Time: 1:33:24 PM

AKIN GUMP

OIC - AGS - 0144

DATE	TIME	DURATION HHHH:MM:SS	Extension	DIALED NUMBER	LOCATION	CALL TYPE	Trunk	ACCOUNT COD
12/19/97	15:46	0:01:00	[redacted]	[redacted]	NEW YOR NY	OS-OL	194	
12/19/97	15:52	0:02:00	[redacted]	[redacted]	WASZ-1	LOCAL	141	
12/19/97	15:53	0:02:48	[redacted]	[redacted]	BETHESD MD	LOCAL	141	
12/19/97	15:56	0:03:36	[redacted]	[redacted]		OS-OL	191	0799972800
12/19/97	16:13	0:03:12	[redacted]	[redacted]	WASZ-1	LOCAL	141	
12/19/97	16:17	0:02:42	[redacted]	[redacted]	WASZ-1	LOCAL	141	
12/19/97	16:23	0:01:42	[redacted]	[redacted]		LOCAL	141	
12/19/97	16:26	0:00:42	[redacted]	[redacted]	WASZ 8 VA	LOCAL	141	
12/19/97	16:27	0:18:18	[redacted]	[redacted]	NEW YOR NY	OS-OL	194	
12/19/97	16:47	0:02:00	[redacted]	[redacted]	NEW YOR NY	OS-OL	194	
12/19/97	17:01	0:04:30	[redacted]	[redacted]	WASZ-1	LOCAL	141	
12/19/97	17:06	0:01:54	[redacted]	[redacted]	WASZ-1	LOCAL	141	
12/19/97	17:10	0:01:00	[redacted]	[redacted]	WASZ-1	LOCAL	141	
12/19/97	17:12	0:00:48	[redacted]	[redacted]	CHATHAM MA	OS-OL	191	0799972800
12/19/97	17:14	0:01:12	[redacted]	[redacted]	HAYMARK VA	OS-IL	194	
12/19/97	17:21	0:00:36	[redacted]	[redacted]	WASZ 19 VA	LOCAL	141	
12/19/97	17:24	0:00:36	[redacted]	[redacted]	WASZ-1	LOCAL	141	
12/19/97	17:33	0:02:00	[redacted]	[redacted]	WASZ-1	LOCAL	141	
12/22/97	09:27	0:02:00	[redacted]	[redacted]	WASZ-1	LOCAL	141	
12/22/97	09:31	0:02:18	[redacted]	[redacted]	WASZ-1	LOCAL	141	
12/22/97	09:32	0:00:30	[redacted]	[redacted]	WASZ-1	LOCAL	141	
12/22/97	09:33	0:00:30	[redacted]	[redacted]	NY	OS-OL	194	
12/22/97	09:35	0:00:42	[redacted]	[redacted]	CHCZ-1 IL	OS-OL	191	0799972800
12/22/97	09:35	0:01:30	[redacted]	[redacted]	NEW YOR NY	OS-OL	194	
12/22/97	09:41	0:03:24	[redacted]	[redacted]	NEW YOR NY	OS-OL	194	
12/22/97	09:53	0:01:54	[redacted]	[redacted]	WASZ-1	LOCAL	141	
12/22/97	09:55	0:02:48	[redacted]	[redacted]	WASZ-1	LOCAL	141	
12/22/97	10:24	0:00:36	[redacted]	[redacted]	TRIANGL VA	OS-IL	191	0799972800
12/22/97	10:40	0:00:42	[redacted]	[redacted]	WASZ-1	LOCAL	141	
12/22/97	10:42	0:10:18	[redacted]	[redacted]	AUGUSTA GA	OS-OL	188	0799990259
12/22/97	11:15	0:03:00	[redacted]	[redacted]	CHCZ-1 IL	OS-OL	191	0799972800
12/22/97	11:39	0:00:06	[redacted]	[redacted]		LOCAL	141	
12/22/97	11:56	0:07:42	[redacted]	[redacted]	LEONIA NJ	OS-OL	194	
12/22/97	12:20	0:02:18	[redacted]	[redacted]		SPCL	141	
12/22/97	12:28	0:03:18	[redacted]	[redacted]	NEW YOR NY	OS-OL	191	0799972800
12/22/97	12:33	0:00:06	[redacted]	[redacted]	WASZ-1	LOCAL	141	
12/22/97	12:34	0:00:48	[redacted]	[redacted]		LOCAL	141	
12/22/97	14:17	0:14:06	[redacted]	[redacted]	PHILADE PA	OS-OL	194	
12/22/97	14:40	0:00:30	[redacted]	[redacted]	WASZ-1	LOCAL	141	
12/22/97	14:53	0:00:42	[redacted]	[redacted]	NEW YOR NY	OS-OL	191	0799972800
12/22/97	15:18	0:01:36	[redacted]	[redacted]	WASZ 17 VA	LOCAL	141	
12/22/97	15:56	0:07:12	[redacted]	[redacted]	BEVERLY CA	OS-OL	191	0799972800
12/22/97	16:05	0:03:00	[redacted]	[redacted]	BETHESD MD	LOCAL	141	
12/22/97	16:10	0:00:36	[redacted]	[redacted]	BEVERLY CA	OS-OL	191	0799972800
12/22/97	16:39	0:00:18	[redacted]	[redacted]	WASZ-1	LOCAL	141	
12/22/97	16:40	0:02:18	[redacted]	[redacted]	WASZ-1	LOCAL	141	
12/22/97	16:43	0:01:00	[redacted]	[redacted]	CHCZ-1 IL	OS-OL	194	
12/22/97	16:44	0:04:24	[redacted]	[redacted]	NEW YOR NY	OS-OL	194	
12/22/97	16:51	0:02:30	[redacted]	[redacted]	NEW YOR NY	OS-OL	194	0799972800
12/22/97	16:59	0:02:12	[redacted]	[redacted]	WASZ-1	LOCAL	141	
12/22/97	17:01	0:01:18	[redacted]	[redacted]	WASZ-1	LOCAL	141	
12/22/97	17:03	0:00:18	[redacted]	[redacted]	VA	LOCAL	141	
12/22/97	17:04	0:01:24	[redacted]	[redacted]	NEW YOR NY	OS-OL	191	0799972800
12/22/97	17:05	0:05:36	[redacted]	[redacted]	BETHESD MD	LOCAL	141	
12/22/97	17:10	0:00:06	[redacted]	[redacted]	WASZ-1	LOCAL	141	
12/22/97	17:13	0:03:54	[redacted]	[redacted]	WASZ-1	LOCAL	141	
12/22/97	17:14	0:00:06	[redacted]	[redacted]	WASZ-1	LOCAL	141	
12/22/97	17:20	0:09:30	[redacted]	[redacted]	CHCZ-1 IL	OS-OL	194	
12/22/97	17:36	0:14:06	[redacted]	[redacted]	BEVERLY CA	OS-OL	194	
12/22/97	17:59	0:00:42	[redacted]	[redacted]	NEW YOR NY	OS-OL	191	0799972800
12/22/97	18:01	0:02:36	[redacted]	[redacted]	WASZ-1	LOCAL	141	
12/22/97	18:23	0:00:06	[redacted]	[redacted]	WASZ-1	LOCAL	141	
12/22/97	18:24	0:00:06	[redacted]	[redacted]	WASZ-1	LOCAL	141	
12/22/97	18:28	0:00:36	[redacted]	[redacted]	CHILMAR MA	OS-OL	194	
12/22/97	23:21	0:04:18	[redacted]	[redacted]	NEW YOR NY	OS-OL	194	
12/22/97	23:26	0:09:24	[redacted]	[redacted]	CHCZ-1 IL	OS-OL	194	
12/22/97	23:36	0:09:18	[redacted]	[redacted]	NEW YOR NY	OS-OL	194	
12/22/97	23:48	0:00:18	[redacted]	[redacted]	WASZ-1	LOCAL	141	
12/22/97	23:48	0:00:36	[redacted]	[redacted]	WASZ-1	LOCAL	141	
12/23/97	09:27	0:01:00	[redacted]	[redacted]	WASZ-1	LOCAL	141	
12/23/97	09:27	0:02:18	[redacted]	[redacted]	WASZ-1	LOCAL	141	
12/23/97	09:31	0:00:24	[redacted]	[redacted]	WASZ-1	LOCAL	141	
12/23/97	09:49	0:00:42	[redacted]	[redacted]	WASZ 17 VA	LOCAL	141	

Selection Detail Report

Date: Saturday, January 24, 1998
Time: 1:33:24 PM

AKIN GUMP

OIC - ABS - 0147

DATE	TIME	DURATION HHHH:MM:SS	Extension	DIALED NUMBER	LOCATION	CALL TYPE	Trunk	ACCOUNT COD
12/30/97	11:53	0:00:30	[redacted]	[redacted]	WASZ-1	SPCL	141	
12/30/97	11:53	0:00:30	[redacted]	[redacted]	WASZ-1	LOCAL	141	
12/30/97	12:06	0:00:30	[redacted]	[redacted]	DIR ASS NY	SPCL	141	
12/30/97	12:13	0:01:18	[redacted]	[redacted]	WASZ-1	LOCAL	141	
12/30/97	12:43	0:01:24	[redacted]	[redacted]	WASZ-1	LOCAL	141	
12/30/97	13:19	0:04:12	[redacted]	[redacted]	NEW YOR NY	OS-OL	191	0799972800
12/30/97	13:20	0:09:06	[redacted]	[redacted]	WASZ 17 VA	LOCAL	141	
12/30/97	13:54	0:03:12	[redacted]	[redacted]	WASZ-1	LOCAL	141	
12/30/97	14:01	0:00:36	[redacted]	[redacted]	WASZ-1	LOCAL	141	
12/30/97	14:16	0:00:42	[redacted]	[redacted]	NEW YOR NY	OS-OL	194	0799972800
12/30/97	14:20	0:01:12	[redacted]	[redacted]	WASZ-1	LOCAL	141	
12/30/97	14:24	0:01:54	[redacted]	[redacted]	WASZ-1	LOCAL	141	
12/30/97	14:26	0:00:36	[redacted]	[redacted]	NEW YOR NY	OS-OL	194	
12/30/97	14:30	0:01:36	[redacted]	[redacted]	WASZ 8 VA	LOCAL	141	
12/30/97	14:32	0:00:18	[redacted]	[redacted]	WASZ-1	LOCAL	141	
12/30/97	15:05	0:06:18	[redacted]	[redacted]	WASZ-1	LOCAL	141	
12/30/97	16:22	0:10:00	[redacted]	[redacted]	NEW YOR NY	OS-OL	194	
12/30/97	16:23	0:02:18	[redacted]	[redacted]	WASZ 8 VA	LOCAL	141	
12/30/97	16:28	0:05:42	[redacted]	[redacted]	WASZ-1	LOCAL	141	
12/30/97	16:34	0:01:54	[redacted]	[redacted]	WASZ-1	LOCAL	141	
12/30/97	16:42	0:02:36	[redacted]	[redacted]	NEW YOR NY	OS-OL	191	0799972800
12/30/97	16:53	0:00:24	[redacted]	[redacted]	WASZ-1	LOCAL	141	
12/30/97	16:54	0:01:06	[redacted]	[redacted]	WAS3-1	LOCAL	141	
12/30/97	17:20	0:00:42	[redacted]	[redacted]		LOCAL	194	
12/30/97	17:20	0:02:48	[redacted]	[redacted]	WASZ-1	LOCAL	141	
12/30/97	17:24	0:03:00	[redacted]	[redacted]	NEW YOR NY	OS-OL	194	
12/30/97	17:26	0:06:42	[redacted]	[redacted]	CHCZ-1 IL	OS-OL	194	
12/30/97	17:39	0:01:00	[redacted]	[redacted]	WASZ-1	LOCAL	141	
12/30/97	17:41	0:00:42	[redacted]	[redacted]	NEW YOR NY	OS-OL	194	
12/30/97	17:43	0:00:24	[redacted]	[redacted]		LOCAL	141	
12/30/97	17:44	0:01:42	[redacted]	[redacted]	WASZ-1	LOCAL	141	
12/30/97	17:44	0:05:36	[redacted]	[redacted]	NEW YOR NY	OS-OL	191	0799972800
12/30/97	17:55	0:09:06	[redacted]	[redacted]	CHCZ-1 IL	OS-OL	194	
12/30/97	18:05	0:03:12	[redacted]	[redacted]	NEW YOR NY	OS-OL	194	
12/30/97	18:09	0:01:42	[redacted]	[redacted]	WASZ-1	LOCAL	141	
12/30/97	18:14	0:00:36	[redacted]	[redacted]	WASZ-1	LOCAL	141	
12/30/97	18:14	0:00:06	[redacted]	[redacted]	WASZ-1	LOCAL	141	
12/30/97	18:16	0:06:54	[redacted]	[redacted]	WASZ 8 VA	LOCAL	141	
12/30/97	18:23	0:00:24	[redacted]	[redacted]	WASZ-1	LOCAL	141	
12/31/97	08:59	0:06:54	[redacted]	[redacted]	WASZ-1	LOCAL	141	
12/31/97	09:00	0:00:24	[redacted]	[redacted]	WASZ 8 VA	LOCAL	141	
12/31/97	09:09	0:02:54	[redacted]	[redacted]	WASZ-1	LOCAL	141	
12/31/97	09:16	0:00:18	[redacted]	[redacted]	WASZ 8 VA	LOCAL	141	
12/31/97	09:29	0:00:18	[redacted]	[redacted]	WASZ 8 VA	LOCAL	141	
12/31/97	09:34	0:01:06	[redacted]	[redacted]	WASZ-1	SPCL	141	
12/31/97	10:25	0:02:06	[redacted]	[redacted]		LOCAL	194	
12/31/97	10:26	0:00:42	[redacted]	[redacted]	BETHESD MD	LOCAL	141	
12/31/97	10:53	0:00:48	[redacted]	[redacted]	WASZ-1	LOCAL	141	
12/31/97	10:55	0:00:30	[redacted]	[redacted]	WASZ-1	LOCAL	141	
12/31/97	10:55	0:02:36	[redacted]	[redacted]	NEW YOR NY	OS-OL	194	
12/31/97	11:04	0:06:00	[redacted]	[redacted]	WASZ 17 VA	LOCAL	141	
12/31/97	11:11	0:11:06	[redacted]	[redacted]	NEW YOR NY	OS-OL	194	
12/31/97	11:30	0:00:48	[redacted]	[redacted]	NEW YOR NY	OS-OL	191	0799972800
12/31/97	11:35	0:00:48	[redacted]	[redacted]	WASZ-1	LOCAL	141	
12/31/97	11:38	0:13:54	[redacted]	[redacted]	NEW YOR NY	OS-OL	194	
12/31/97	12:10	0:04:54	[redacted]	[redacted]	NEW YOR NY	OS-OL	191	0799972800
12/31/97	12:15	0:01:12	[redacted]	[redacted]	WASZ-1	LOCAL	141	
12/31/97	12:17	0:00:42	[redacted]	[redacted]	WASZ 8 VA	LOCAL	141	
12/31/97	12:19	0:02:00	[redacted]	[redacted]	WASZ 8 VA	LOCAL	141	
12/31/97	12:21	0:02:06	[redacted]	[redacted]		SPCL	141	
12/31/97	12:39	0:05:00	[redacted]	[redacted]	OCCOQUA VA	OS-IL	191	0799972800
12/31/97	12:44	0:00:36	[redacted]	[redacted]	WASZ 8 VA	LOCAL	141	
12/31/97	12:48	0:01:00	[redacted]	[redacted]	OCCOQUA VA	OS-IL	191	0799972800
12/31/97	12:57	0:03:12	[redacted]	[redacted]	OCCOQUA VA	OS-IL	191	0799972800
12/31/97	13:00	0:00:18	[redacted]	[redacted]	WASZ 8 VA	LOCAL	141	
12/31/97	13:41	0:00:06	[redacted]	[redacted]	WASZ-1	LOCAL	141	
12/31/97	13:41	0:00:06	[redacted]	[redacted]	WASZ-1	LOCAL	141	
12/31/97	14:22	0:10:54	[redacted]	[redacted]	NY	OS-OL	194	
12/31/97	14:23	0:00:24	[redacted]	[redacted]	WASZ-1	LOCAL	141	

712	31:27:06	DETAIL SUBTOTAL
253	9:33:48	INCOMING CALLS

V004-DC-00000154

Selection Detail Report

Date: Saturday, January 24, 1998
Time: 2:11:29 PM

OIC - ABS - 0151

AKIN GUMP

DATE	TIME	DURATION HHHH:MM:SS	Extension	DIALED NUMBER	LOCATION	CALL TYPE	Trunk	ACCOUNT COD
01/05/98	18:07	0:03:48	[redacted]	[redacted]	MEXICO	IDDD	191	0799972800
01/06/98	09:21	0:02:00	[redacted]	[redacted]		LOCAL	141	
01/06/98	09:25	0:03:42	[redacted]	[redacted]		LOCAL	141	
01/06/98	09:26	0:02:00	[redacted]	[redacted]		SPCL	141	
01/06/98	10:22	0:00:36	[redacted]	[redacted]	WASZ 17 VA	LOCAL	141	
01/06/98	10:46	0:00:30	[redacted]	[redacted]	NEW YOR NY	OS-OL	188	0799972800
01/06/98	10:53	0:01:00	[redacted]	[redacted]	NEW YOR NY	OS-OL	191	0799972800
01/06/98	11:02	0:05:42	[redacted]	[redacted]	SCHENCT NY	OS-OL	191	0799972800
01/06/98	12:33	0:01:12	[redacted]	[redacted]	WASZ-1	LOCAL	141	
01/06/98	14:08	0:01:48	[redacted]	[redacted]	WASZ-1	LOCAL	141	
01/06/98	14:16	0:00:30	[redacted]	[redacted]		SPCL	141	0799972800
01/06/98	14:45	0:00:06	[redacted]	[redacted]		LOCAL	141	
01/06/98	14:49	0:30:18	[redacted]	[redacted]	WASZ 8 VA	LOCAL	141	
01/06/98	15:12	0:04:00	[redacted]	[redacted]	WASZ-1	LOCAL	141	
01/06/98	15:26	0:06:42	[redacted]	[redacted]	WASZ-1	LOCAL	141	
01/06/98	15:38	0:02:12	[redacted]	[redacted]	WASZ-1	LOCAL	141	
01/06/98	15:42	0:03:54	[redacted]	[redacted]	NEW YOR NY	OS-OL	194	
01/06/98	15:48	0:00:24	[redacted]	[redacted]	WASZ-1	LOCAL	141	
01/06/98	15:49	0:05:54	[redacted]	[redacted]	WASZ-1	LOCAL	141	
01/06/98	15:57	0:05:36	[redacted]	[redacted]	NEW YOR NY	OS-OL	194	
01/06/98	16:04	0:05:48	[redacted]	[redacted]	OXON HI MD	LOCAL	141	
01/06/98	16:07	0:03:18	[redacted]	[redacted]	SCHENCT NY	OS-OL	194	
01/06/98	16:32	0:01:06	[redacted]	[redacted]	WASZ-1	LOCAL	141	
01/06/98	16:34	0:02:30	[redacted]	[redacted]	WASZ-1	LOCAL	141	
01/06/98	16:44	0:01:12	[redacted]	[redacted]		LOCAL	194	
01/06/98	16:46	0:00:42	[redacted]	[redacted]	WASZ-1	LOCAL	141	
01/06/98	16:48	0:00:18	[redacted]	[redacted]	WASZ 8 VA	LOCAL	141	
01/06/98	16:49	0:01:42	[redacted]	[redacted]	WASZ-1	LOCAL	141	
01/06/98	16:50	0:02:30	[redacted]	[redacted]	WASZ-1	LOCAL	141	
01/06/98	16:54	0:00:42	[redacted]	[redacted]	ATLANTA GA	OS-OL	194	
01/06/98	16:56	0:04:54	[redacted]	[redacted]		LOCAL	141	
01/06/98	17:00	0:04:00	[redacted]	[redacted]	WASZ 8 VA	LOCAL	141	
01/06/98	17:09	0:02:48	[redacted]	[redacted]		LOCAL	194	
01/06/98	17:14	0:00:42	[redacted]	[redacted]	NEW YOR NY	OS-OL	194	
01/06/98	17:15	0:00:06	[redacted]	[redacted]	WASZ-1	LOCAL	141	
01/06/98	17:15	0:04:06	[redacted]	[redacted]	WASZ-1	LOCAL	141	
01/06/98	17:25	0:07:18	[redacted]	[redacted]	CHCZ-1 IL	OS-OL	191	0799972800
01/06/98	17:38	0:00:24	[redacted]	[redacted]	WASZ-1	LOCAL	141	
01/06/98	17:39	0:01:12	[redacted]	[redacted]	WASZ-1	LOCAL	141	
01/06/98	17:40	0:00:06	[redacted]	[redacted]	MD	LOCAL	141	
01/06/98	17:40	0:00:06	[redacted]	[redacted]	MD	LOCAL	141	
01/06/98	17:41	0:01:18	[redacted]	[redacted]	WASZ 8 VA	LOCAL	141	
01/06/98	17:43	0:00:48	[redacted]	[redacted]		LOCAL	141	
01/06/98	17:46	0:03:18	[redacted]	[redacted]	NEW YOR NY	OS-OL	194	
01/06/98	18:17	0:03:36	[redacted]	[redacted]	WASZ-1	LOCAL	141	
01/06/98	18:31	0:00:06	[redacted]	[redacted]		LOCAL	141	
01/07/98	09:26	0:03:30	[redacted]	[redacted]	WASZ-1	LOCAL	141	
01/07/98	09:42	0:01:24	[redacted]	[redacted]	WASZ-1	LOCAL	141	
01/07/98	09:44	0:03:54	[redacted]	[redacted]	NEW YOR NY	OS-OL	194	
01/07/98	09:57	0:04:36	[redacted]	[redacted]	DALLAS TX	OS-OL	194	
01/07/98	10:02	0:00:42	[redacted]	[redacted]		OS-OL	194	
01/07/98	10:04	0:00:36	[redacted]	[redacted]		OS-OL	194	
01/07/98	10:05	0:10:00	[redacted]	[redacted]	CHCZ-1 IL	OS-OL	194	
01/07/98	10:15	0:01:00	[redacted]	[redacted]	NEW YOR NY	OS-OL	194	
01/07/98	10:18	0:02:30	[redacted]	[redacted]	WASZ-1	LOCAL	141	
01/07/98	10:25	0:00:30	[redacted]	[redacted]	WASZ-1	LOCAL	141	
01/07/98	10:34	0:01:48	[redacted]	[redacted]	WASZ-1	LOCAL	141	
01/07/98	10:35	0:20:24	[redacted]	[redacted]	NEW YOR NY	OS-OL	194	
01/07/98	10:57	0:00:36	[redacted]	[redacted]	WASZ-1	LOCAL	141	
01/07/98	10:58	0:00:12	[redacted]	[redacted]	WASZ-1	LOCAL	141	
01/07/98	10:58	0:00:30	[redacted]	[redacted]	WASZ 17 VA	LOCAL	141	
01/07/98	10:59	0:02:48	[redacted]	[redacted]	WASZ-1	LOCAL	141	
01/07/98	11:09	0:07:24	[redacted]	[redacted]	WASZ-1	LOCAL	141	
01/07/98	11:19	0:02:24	[redacted]	[redacted]	WASZ-1	LOCAL	141	
01/07/98	11:21	0:01:06	[redacted]	[redacted]	NEW YOR NY	OS-OL	194	
01/07/98	11:24	0:02:00	[redacted]	[redacted]	NEW YOR NY	OS-OL	194	
01/07/98	11:26	0:00:54	[redacted]	[redacted]	WASZ-1	LOCAL	141	
01/07/98	11:27	0:00:54	[redacted]	[redacted]	WASZ-1	LOCAL	141	
01/07/98	11:28	0:04:30	[redacted]	[redacted]	WASZ-1	LOCAL	141	
01/07/98	11:33	0:00:42	[redacted]	[redacted]	WASZ-1	LOCAL	141	
01/07/98	11:33	0:01:54	[redacted]	[redacted]	WASZ-1	LOCAL	141	
01/07/98	11:36	0:01:06	[redacted]	[redacted]	NEW YOR NY	OS-OL	194	
01/07/98	11:39	0:05:00	[redacted]	[redacted]	NEW YOR NY	OS-OL	194	

Selection Detail Report

OIC - AGG - 0152

Date: Saturday, January 24, 1998
Time: 2:11:29 PM

AKIN GUMP

DATE	TIME	DURATION HHHH:MM:SS	Extension	DIALED NUMBER	LOCATION	CALL TYPE	Trunk	ACCOUNT COD
01/07/98	11:45	0:06:00	[redacted]	[redacted]	WASZ-1	LOCAL	141	
01/07/98	11:52	0:05:00	[redacted]	[redacted]	W ANGEL CA	OS-OL	194	
01/07/98	11:57	0:00:42	[redacted]	[redacted]	WASZ-1	LOCAL	141	
01/07/98	11:58	0:11:30	[redacted]	[redacted]	WASZ-1	LOCAL	141	
01/07/98	12:10	0:01:48	[redacted]	[redacted]	CHCZ-1 IL	OS-OL	194	
01/07/98	12:24	0:00:30	[redacted]	[redacted]	NEW YOR NY	OS-OL	191	0799972800
01/07/98	12:33	0:02:00	[redacted]	[redacted]	NEW YOR NY	OS-OL	191	0799972800
01/07/98	12:35	0:02:24	[redacted]	[redacted]	NEW YOR NY	OS-OL	191	0799972800
01/07/98	13:25	0:00:12	[redacted]	[redacted]	WASZ 17 VA	LOCAL	141	
01/07/98	13:27	0:01:06	[redacted]	[redacted]	WASZ 19 VA	LOCAL	141	
01/07/98	13:35	0:13:00	[redacted]	[redacted]	WASZ 19 VA	LOCAL	141	
01/07/98	13:36	0:00:06	[redacted]	[redacted]	WASZ-1	LOCAL	141	
01/07/98	13:50	0:03:12	[redacted]	[redacted]	WASZ-1	LOCAL	141	
01/07/98	14:25	0:01:48	[redacted]	[redacted]	FRANCE	IDDD	191	0799972800
01/07/98	14:36	0:03:18	[redacted]	[redacted]	WASZ 17 VA	LOCAL	141	
01/07/98	14:38	0:00:18	[redacted]	[redacted]	WASZ-1	LOCAL	141	
01/07/98	14:38	0:00:30	[redacted]	[redacted]	WASZ-1	LOCAL	141	
01/07/98	14:39	0:00:36	[redacted]	[redacted]	WASZ-1	LOCAL	141	
01/07/98	14:42	0:04:54	[redacted]	[redacted]	WASZ-1	LOCAL	141	
01/07/98	14:44	0:00:48	[redacted]	[redacted]	WASZ-1	LOCAL	141	
01/07/98	14:47	0:00:18	[redacted]	[redacted]	WASZ-1	LOCAL	141	
01/07/98	14:48	0:00:42	[redacted]	[redacted]	WASZ-1	LOCAL	141	
01/07/98	14:49	0:00:24	[redacted]	[redacted]	WASZ-1	LOCAL	141	
01/07/98	14:59	0:03:00	[redacted]	[redacted]	WASZ-1	LOCAL	141	
01/07/98	15:07	0:05:30	[redacted]	[redacted]	CAPITOL MD	LOCAL	141	
01/07/98	15:12	0:05:12	[redacted]	[redacted]	CAPITOL MD	LOCAL	141	
01/07/98	15:21	0:01:24	[redacted]	[redacted]	WASZ-1	LOCAL	141	
01/07/98	15:36	0:00:24	[redacted]	[redacted]	WASZ-1	LOCAL	141	
01/07/98	15:50	0:10:30	[redacted]	[redacted]	WASZ-1	LOCAL	141	
01/07/98	15:59	0:01:12	[redacted]	[redacted]	NEW YOR NY	OS-OL	191	0799972800
01/07/98	16:03	0:00:36	[redacted]	[redacted]	NEW YOR NY	OS-OL	194	
01/07/98	16:20	0:01:42	[redacted]	[redacted]	NEW YOR NY	OS-OL	194	
01/07/98	16:24	0:00:36	[redacted]	[redacted]	WASZ-1	LOCAL	141	
01/07/98	16:56	0:03:06	[redacted]	[redacted]	DECATUR IL	OS-OL	194	
01/07/98	17:35	0:00:12	[redacted]	[redacted]	WASZ-1	LOCAL	141	
01/07/98	17:35	0:02:06	[redacted]	[redacted]	WASZ-1	LOCAL	141	
01/07/98	17:38	0:00:06	[redacted]	[redacted]	WASZ-1	LOCAL	141	
01/07/98	17:38	0:07:12	[redacted]	[redacted]	WASZ-1	LOCAL	141	
01/07/98	17:46	0:10:48	[redacted]	[redacted]	WASZ-1	LOCAL	141	
01/07/98	17:58	0:03:12	[redacted]	[redacted]	NEW YOR NY	OS-OL	194	
01/07/98	18:01	0:00:24	[redacted]	[redacted]	WASZ-1	LOCAL	141	
01/07/98	18:02	0:04:18	[redacted]	[redacted]	BETHESD MD	LOCAL	141	
01/07/98	18:13	0:14:24	[redacted]	[redacted]	CHCZ-1 IL	OS-OL	191	0799972800
01/08/98	09:04	0:00:42	[redacted]	[redacted]	WASZ-1	LOCAL	141	
01/08/98	09:05	0:14:42	[redacted]	[redacted]	OXON HI MD	LOCAL	141	
01/08/98	09:21	0:00:48	[redacted]	[redacted]	WASZ-1	LOCAL	141	
01/08/98	09:21	0:00:42	[redacted]	[redacted]	WASZ-1	LOCAL	141	
01/08/98	09:22	0:00:48	[redacted]	[redacted]	WASZ-1	LOCAL	141	
01/08/98	09:37	0:00:18	[redacted]	[redacted]		LOCAL	141	
01/08/98	10:26	0:02:18	[redacted]	[redacted]	WASZ-1	LOCAL	141	
01/08/98	10:31	0:06:36	[redacted]	[redacted]	JACKSON FL	OS-OL	191	0799972800
01/08/98	10:39	0:01:00	[redacted]	[redacted]	TORONTO ON	OS-OL	191	0799972800
01/08/98	10:45	0:03:12	[redacted]	[redacted]	OXON HI MD	LOCAL	141	
01/08/98	10:53	0:02:54	[redacted]	[redacted]	WASZ-1	LOCAL	141	
01/08/98	12:03	0:01:00	[redacted]	[redacted]	WASZ-1	LOCAL	141	
01/08/98	12:07	0:06:42	[redacted]	[redacted]	NEW YOR NY	OS-OL	194	
01/08/98	12:18	0:17:00	[redacted]	[redacted]	WASZ-1	LOCAL	141	
01/08/98	12:31	0:02:06	[redacted]	[redacted]	WASZ-1	LOCAL	141	
01/08/98	12:34	0:00:12	[redacted]	[redacted]		LOCAL	141	
01/08/98	12:35	0:00:30	[redacted]	[redacted]	OXON HI MD	LOCAL	141	
01/08/98	12:38	0:03:18	[redacted]	[redacted]	WASZ-1	LOCAL	141	
01/08/98	12:39	0:00:42	[redacted]	[redacted]	WASZ-1	LOCAL	141	
01/08/98	12:42	0:05:00	[redacted]	[redacted]	WASZ-1	LOCAL	141	
01/08/98	14:09	0:00:30	[redacted]	[redacted]	WASZ 8 VA	LOCAL	141	
01/08/98	14:09	0:00:06	[redacted]	[redacted]	WASZ 8 VA	LOCAL	141	
01/08/98	14:09	0:00:06	[redacted]	[redacted]	WASZ 8 VA	LOCAL	141	
01/08/98	14:11	0:02:12	[redacted]	[redacted]	WASZ 8 VA	LOCAL	141	
01/08/98	14:14	0:02:36	[redacted]	[redacted]	WASZ 8 VA	LOCAL	141	
01/08/98	14:18	0:00:42	[redacted]	[redacted]	WASZ-1	SPCL	141	
01/08/98	14:18	0:00:48	[redacted]	[redacted]	WASZ-1	LOCAL	141	
01/08/98	14:29	0:01:06	[redacted]	[redacted]	WASZ-1	LOCAL	141	
01/08/98	14:37	0:05:06	[redacted]	[redacted]	WASZ-1	LOCAL	141	
01/08/98	15:25	0:00:30	[redacted]	[redacted]	OXON HI MD	LOCAL	141	

Date: Saturday, January 24, 1998
Time: 2:11:29 PM

Selection Detail Report

AKIN GUMP

OIC - ABS - 0153

DATE	TIME	DURATION HHHH:MM:SS	Extension	DIALED NUMBER	LOCATION	CALL TYPE	Trunk	ACCOUNT COD
01/08/98	15:26	0:01:24	[redacted]	[redacted]	NY	OS-OL	194	
01/08/98	15:27	0:03:36	[redacted]	[redacted]	WASZ-1	LOCAL	141	
01/08/98	15:32	0:01:00	[redacted]	[redacted]	WASZ-1	LOCAL	141	
01/08/98	15:36	0:04:36	[redacted]	[redacted]	TORONTO ON	OS-OL	194	
01/08/98	15:41	0:01:18	[redacted]	[redacted]	WASZ 17 VA	LOCAL	141	
01/08/98	15:44	0:01:30	[redacted]	[redacted]	WASZ-1	LOCAL	141	
01/08/98	15:47	0:02:24	[redacted]	[redacted]	NEW YOR NY	OS-OL	194	
01/08/98	15:47	0:05:30	[redacted]	[redacted]	NEW YOR NY	OS-OL	191	0799972800
01/08/98	15:50	0:01:18	[redacted]	[redacted]	NEW YOR NY	OS-OL	194	
01/08/98	15:53	0:06:48	[redacted]	[redacted]	WASZ-1	LOCAL	141	
01/08/98	15:56	0:01:12	[redacted]	[redacted]	ATLANTA GA	OS-OL	191	0799972800
01/08/98	15:59	0:00:42	[redacted]	[redacted]	LOS ALT CA	OS-OL	194	
01/08/98	16:02	0:02:00	[redacted]	[redacted]	LOSANGE CA	OS-OL	194	
01/08/98	16:05	0:01:36	[redacted]	[redacted]	LOSANGE CA	OS-OL	194	
01/08/98	16:06	0:01:00	[redacted]	[redacted]	WASZ-1	LOCAL	141	
01/08/98	16:06	0:00:24	[redacted]	[redacted]	WASZ-1	LOCAL	141	
01/08/98	16:06	0:03:06	[redacted]	[redacted]		LOCAL	141	
01/08/98	16:21	0:03:24	[redacted]	[redacted]	CVCRKCA AZ	OS-OL	194	
01/08/98	16:47	0:01:24	[redacted]	[redacted]	WASZ-1	LOCAL	141	
01/08/98	16:54	0:01:42	[redacted]	[redacted]	NEW YOR NY	OS-OL	194	
01/08/98	16:56	0:00:54	[redacted]	[redacted]	NEW YOR NY	OS-OL	194	
01/08/98	16:58	0:02:36	[redacted]	[redacted]	NEW YOR NY	OS-OL	194	0799972800
01/08/98	17:05	0:01:12	[redacted]	[redacted]	WASZ-1	LOCAL	141	
01/08/98	17:08	0:02:00	[redacted]	[redacted]	WASZ-1	LOCAL	141	
01/08/98	17:09	0:01:18	[redacted]	[redacted]	WASZ-1	LOCAL	141	
01/08/98	17:13	0:01:00	[redacted]	[redacted]	WASZ-1	LOCAL	141	
01/08/98	17:13	0:02:24	[redacted]	[redacted]	WASZ-1	LOCAL	141	
01/08/98	17:14	0:00:24	[redacted]	[redacted]	WASZ-1	LOCAL	141	
01/08/98	17:16	0:01:48	[redacted]	[redacted]	WASZ-1	LOCAL	141	
01/08/98	17:18	0:02:54	[redacted]	[redacted]	WASZ-1	LOCAL	141	
01/08/98	17:37	0:04:42	[redacted]	[redacted]	WASZ-1	LOCAL	141	
01/08/98	17:38	0:02:48	[redacted]	[redacted]	WASZ-1	LOCAL	141	
01/08/98	17:43	0:05:48	[redacted]	[redacted]	WASZ-1	LOCAL	141	
01/08/98	17:52	0:00:30	[redacted]	[redacted]	WASZ-1	LOCAL	141	
01/08/98	17:54	0:00:30	[redacted]	[redacted]	WASZ-1	LOCAL	141	
01/08/98	17:56	0:00:30	[redacted]	[redacted]	WASZ-1	LOCAL	141	
01/08/98	18:18	0:00:36	[redacted]	[redacted]	NEW YOR NY	OS-OL	194	
01/09/98	09:15	0:02:06	[redacted]	[redacted]	WASZ 8 VA	LOCAL	141	
01/09/98	09:18	0:02:48	[redacted]	[redacted]		SPCL	141	
01/09/98	09:22	0:02:00	[redacted]	[redacted]	WASZ-1	LOCAL	141	
01/09/98	09:37	0:00:06	[redacted]	[redacted]	WASZ-1	LOCAL	141	
01/09/98	09:38	0:00:18	[redacted]	[redacted]	WASZ-1	LOCAL	141	
01/09/98	09:53	0:00:48	[redacted]	[redacted]	WASZ-1	LOCAL	141	
01/09/98	09:54	0:00:48	[redacted]	[redacted]	WCHSZ 6 NY	OS-OL	194	
01/09/98	09:59	0:01:24	[redacted]	[redacted]	WASZ-1	LOCAL	141	
01/09/98	10:04	0:11:42	[redacted]	[redacted]	DALLAS TX	OS-OL	191	0799972800
01/09/98	10:16	0:01:18	[redacted]	[redacted]	NEW YOR NY	OS-OL	194	
01/09/98	10:19	0:00:54	[redacted]	[redacted]	NEW YOR NY	OS-OL	194	
01/09/98	10:21	0:02:06	[redacted]	[redacted]	WASZ-1	LOCAL	141	
01/09/98	10:26	0:00:48	[redacted]	[redacted]	WASZ-1	LOCAL	141	
01/09/98	10:31	0:01:00	[redacted]	[redacted]	WASZ 17 VA	LOCAL	141	
01/09/98	10:32	0:01:54	[redacted]	[redacted]	WASZ-1	LOCAL	141	
01/09/98	10:34	0:01:00	[redacted]	[redacted]	WASZ-1	LOCAL	141	
01/09/98	10:36	0:00:24	[redacted]	[redacted]	WASZ 17 VA	LOCAL	141	
01/09/98	10:36	0:01:24	[redacted]	[redacted]		LOCAL	141	
01/09/98	10:43	0:00:12	[redacted]	[redacted]	WASZ 17 VA	LOCAL	141	
01/09/98	10:44	0:00:48	[redacted]	[redacted]	WASZ-1	LOCAL	141	
01/09/98	11:13	0:00:54	[redacted]	[redacted]	WASZ-1	LOCAL	141	
01/09/98	11:17	0:00:36	[redacted]	[redacted]	WASZ-1	LOCAL	141	
01/09/98	11:32	0:07:48	[redacted]	[redacted]	WASZ-1	LOCAL	141	
01/09/98	11:44	0:00:36	[redacted]	[redacted]	WASZ-1	SPCL	141	
01/09/98	11:45	0:00:06	[redacted]	[redacted]	WASZ 8 VA	LOCAL	141	
01/09/98	11:47	0:01:00	[redacted]	[redacted]	WASZ-1	SPCL	141	
01/09/98	11:47	0:01:06	[redacted]	[redacted]	WASZ 6 VA	LOCAL	141	
01/09/98	11:48	0:01:24	[redacted]	[redacted]	WASZ-1	LOCAL	141	
01/09/98	11:49	0:00:54	[redacted]	[redacted]	WASZ 8 VA	LOCAL	141	
01/09/98	11:50	0:00:54	[redacted]	[redacted]	DIR ASS NC	SPCL	141	
01/09/98	11:51	0:01:18	[redacted]	[redacted]	NC	OS-OL	194	
01/09/98	11:53	0:00:30	[redacted]	[redacted]	WASZ-1	LOCAL	141	
01/09/98	11:53	0:00:18	[redacted]	[redacted]	WASZ-1	LOCAL	141	
01/09/98	11:54	0:00:24	[redacted]	[redacted]	WASZ-1	LOCAL	141	
01/09/98	11:55	0:00:24	[redacted]	[redacted]	WASZ-1	LOCAL	141	
01/09/98	11:55	0:12:48	[redacted]	[redacted]	NEW YOR NY	OS-OL	194	

Selection Detail Report

OIC - ABS - 0154

Date: Saturday, January 24, 1998
Time: 2:11:29 PM

AKIN GUMP

DATE	TIME	DURATION HHHH:MM:SS	Extension	DIALED NUMBER	LOCATION	CALL TYPE	Trunk	ACCOUNT COD
01/09/98	12:08	0:03:30	[redacted]	[redacted]	NEW YOR NY	OS-OL	194	
01/09/98	12:12	0:00:54			WASZ-1	LOCAL	141	
01/09/98	12:14	0:05:30			LOUISVI KY	OS-OL	194	
01/09/98	12:15	0:01:36				OS-OL	191	0799972800
01/09/98	12:22	0:00:36			WASZ-1	LOCAL	141	
01/09/98	12:23	0:00:42			WASZ-1	SPCL	141	
01/09/98	12:24	0:02:00			WASZ-1	LOCAL	141	
01/09/98	12:31	0:01:54			NEW YOR NY	OS-OL	194	
01/09/98	12:34	0:00:54			STAMFOR CT	OS-OL	194	
01/09/98	12:34	0:04:24			WASZ 17 VA	LOCAL	141	
01/09/98	12:39	0:00:42			NEW YOR NY	OS-OL	194	
01/09/98	12:39	0:01:12			WASZ-1	LOCAL	141	
01/09/98	13:03	0:00:36			MD	LOCAL	141	
01/09/98	14:30	0:00:12			OXON HI MD	LOCAL	141	
01/09/98	14:30	0:02:00			CAPITOL MD	LOCAL	141	
01/09/98	14:31	0:00:18			OXON HI MD	LOCAL	141	
01/09/98	14:32	0:02:42			WASZ-1	LOCAL	141	
01/09/98	14:32	0:02:36			OXON HI MD	LOCAL	141	
01/09/98	14:36	0:00:24			WASZ-1	LOCAL	141	
01/09/98	14:37	0:00:18			WASZ-1	LOCAL	141	
01/09/98	14:37	0:00:24			WASZ-1	LOCAL	141	
01/09/98	14:38	0:02:06			WASZ-1	LOCAL	141	
01/09/98	14:42	0:00:54			WASZ-1	LOCAL	141	
01/09/98	14:42	0:01:54			WASZ-1	LOCAL	141	
01/09/98	14:46	0:00:30			WASZ-1	LOCAL	141	
01/09/98	14:47	0:01:12			DIR ASS GA	SPCL	141	
01/09/98	14:49	0:08:00			ATLANTA GA	OS-OL	194	
01/09/98	14:58	0:04:00			WASZ-1	LOCAL	141	
01/09/98	15:11	0:01:36			WASZ 19 VA	LOCAL	141	
01/09/98	15:27	0:00:54			WASZ-1	SPCL	141	
01/09/98	15:28	0:01:12			HAYMARK VA	OS-IL	194	
01/09/98	15:30	0:03:00			WASZ-1	LOCAL	141	
01/09/98	15:35	0:01:12			NEW YOR NY	OS-OL	194	
01/09/98	15:36	0:06:24			NEW YOR NY	OS-OL	194	
01/09/98	15:45	0:00:36			WASZ-1	LOCAL	141	
01/09/98	16:00	0:01:18			WASZ-1	LOCAL	141	
01/09/98	16:02	0:00:36			WASZ 8 VA	LOCAL	141	
01/09/98	16:06	0:02:54			WASZ-1	LOCAL	141	
01/09/98	16:09	0:00:18			WASZ-1	LOCAL	141	
01/09/98	16:09	0:00:30			WASZ-1	LOCAL	141	
01/09/98	16:12	0:00:36			OAKLAND CA	OS-OL	194	
01/09/98	16:17	0:00:24			WASZ 8 VA	LOCAL	141	
01/09/98	16:27	0:04:00			NEW YOR NY	OS-OL	194	
01/09/98	16:32	0:00:48			NEW YOR NY	OS-OL	194	
01/09/98	16:37	0:00:30			FALMOUT MA	OS-OL	191	0799972800
01/09/96	16:38	0:01:00			WASZ-1	LOCAL	141	
01/09/98	16:38	0:10:18			PAYSON AZ	OS-OL	195	
01/09/98	16:40	0:00:12			WASZ 8 VA	LOCAL	141	
01/09/98	16:48	0:00:30				SPCL	141	
01/09/98	17:18	0:02:48			NEW YOR NY	OS-OL	191	0799972800
01/09/98	17:36	0:00:18			WASZ 8 VA	LOCAL	141	
01/09/98	18:22	0:03:06			LOSANGE CA	OS-OL	194	0799972800
01/09/98	19:48	0:00:24			WASZ 17 VA	LOCAL	141	
01/09/98	19:49	0:01:36			WASZ 8 VA	LOCAL	141	
01/09/98	19:49	0:02:12			OXON HI MD	LOCAL	141	
01/10/98	11:50	0:00:48				LOCAL	141	
01/10/98	11:59	0:00:06			WASZ-1	LOCAL	141	
01/10/98	12:07	0:02:30			OXON HI MD	LOCAL	141	
01/10/98	12:45	0:00:42			WASZ-1	SPCL	141	
01/10/98	12:46	0:00:24			WASZ-1	LOCAL	141	
01/10/98	13:03	0:09:48			WASZ-1	LOCAL	141	
01/10/98	13:35	0:02:00			WASZ 17 VA	LOCAL	141	
01/10/98	14:10	0:01:06			NEW YOR NY	OS-OL	194	
01/10/98	14:12	0:00:36			NEW YOR NY	OS-OL	194	
01/10/98	14:14	0:00:18				LOCAL	141	
01/10/98	14:40	0:01:06			WASZ-1	LOCAL	141	
01/10/98	14:42	0:00:54			WASZ-1	LOCAL	141	
01/10/98	14:44	0:01:00			WASZ-1	LOCAL	141	
01/10/98	14:45	0:04:48			NEW YOR NY	OS-OL	194	
01/10/98	14:51	0:06:54			LOSANGE CA	OS-OL	194	
01/10/98	14:59	0:01:06			WASZ-1	LOCAL	141	
01/10/98	15:00	0:01:12			NEW YOR NY	OS-OL	194	
01/10/98	15:02	0:00:24			WASZ-1	LOCAL	141	

Selection Detail Report

Date: Saturday, January 24, 1998
Time: 2:11:29 PM

AKIN GUMP

OIC - ABS - 0155

DATE	TIME	DURATION HHHH:MM:SS	Extension	DIALED NUMBER	LOCATION	CALL TYPE	Trunk	ACCOUNT COD
01/10/98	15:02	0:01:18	[redacted]	[redacted]	WASZ-1	LOCAL	141	
01/10/98	15:51	0:02:00	[redacted]	[redacted]	WASZ-1	LOCAL	141	
01/10/98	15:54	0:02:48	[redacted]	[redacted]	NEW YOR NY	OS-OL	194	
01/10/98	17:01	0:01:54	[redacted]	[redacted]	OXON HI MD	LOCAL	141	
01/10/98	17:13	0:01:42	[redacted]	[redacted]	WASZ 8 VA	LOCAL	141	
01/10/98	19:15	0:01:36	[redacted]	[redacted]	WASZ 8 VA	LOCAL	141	
01/11/98	12:18	0:00:18	[redacted]	[redacted]	WASZ-1	LOCAL	141	
01/11/98	12:18	0:02:24	[redacted]	[redacted]	NEW YOR NY	OS-OL	194	
01/11/98	12:21	0:00:36	[redacted]	[redacted]	WASZ-1	LOCAL	141	
01/12/98	07:54	0:10:24	[redacted]	[redacted]	CLEARWA FL	OS-OL	194	
01/12/98	08:06	0:05:24	[redacted]	[redacted]	NEW YOR NY	OS-OL	194	
01/12/98	09:40	0:01:00	[redacted]	[redacted]	WASZ-1	LOCAL	141	
01/12/98	09:42	0:00:54	[redacted]	[redacted]	NEW YOR NY	OS-OL	194	
01/12/98	09:44	0:01:30	[redacted]	[redacted]	FALMOUT MA	OS-OL	194	
01/12/98	09:55	0:01:24	[redacted]	[redacted]	WASZ-1	LOCAL	141	
01/12/98	10:02	0:04:24	[redacted]	[redacted]	WASZ-1	LOCAL	141	
01/12/98	10:57	0:00:30	[redacted]	[redacted]	WASZ-1	LOCAL	141	
01/12/98	11:22	0:05:48	[redacted]	[redacted]	NEW YOR NY	OS-OL	194	
01/12/98	11:29	0:00:12	[redacted]	[redacted]	WASZ-1	LOCAL	141	
01/12/98	11:29	0:00:36	[redacted]	[redacted]	WASZ-1	LOCAL	141	
01/12/98	11:35	0:03:00	[redacted]	[redacted]	NEW YOR NY	OS-OL	191	0799972800
01/12/98	11:42	0:00:24	[redacted]	[redacted]	WASZ-1	LOCAL	141	
01/12/98	11:44	0:02:54	[redacted]	[redacted]	NEW YOR NY	OS-OL	194	
01/12/98	11:47	0:00:24	[redacted]	[redacted]	WASZ-1	LOCAL	141	
01/12/98	11:48	0:04:48	[redacted]	[redacted]	NEW YOR NY	OS-OL	194	
01/12/98	11:54	0:06:54	[redacted]	[redacted]	WASZ-1	LOCAL	141	
01/12/98	12:00	0:00:18	[redacted]	[redacted]	WASZ-1	LOCAL	141	
01/12/98	12:39	0:04:18	[redacted]	[redacted]	SCHENCT NY	OS-OL	191	0799972800
01/12/98	12:54	0:02:24	[redacted]	[redacted]	NEW YOR NY	OS-OL	191	0799972800
01/12/98	13:10	0:00:18	[redacted]	[redacted]	WASZ-1	LOCAL	141	
01/12/98	13:11	0:02:12	[redacted]	[redacted]	NEW YOR NY	OS-OL	191	0799972800
01/12/98	13:17	0:00:06	[redacted]	[redacted]	WASZ-1	LOCAL	141	
01/12/98	14:29	0:00:12	[redacted]	[redacted]	WASZ-1	LOCAL	141	0799972800
01/12/98	14:31	0:00:24	[redacted]	[redacted]	WASZ-1	LOCAL	141	
01/12/98	14:32	0:01:18	[redacted]	[redacted]	WASZ-1	LOCAL	141	
01/12/98	14:34	0:01:24	[redacted]	[redacted]	WASZ-1	LOCAL	141	
01/12/98	14:36	0:00:36	[redacted]	[redacted]	FRANCE	IDDD	191	0799972800
01/12/98	15:00	0:02:36	[redacted]	[redacted]	AJAXPCK ON	OS-OL	188	0799972800
01/12/98	15:31	0:00:24	[redacted]	[redacted]	WASZ-1	LOCAL	141	
01/12/98	15:33	0:01:06	[redacted]	[redacted]	WASZ-1	LOCAL	141	
01/12/98	15:36	0:05:54	[redacted]	[redacted]	WASZ-1	LOCAL	141	
01/12/98	16:03	0:00:18	[redacted]	[redacted]	WASZ-1	LOCAL	141	
01/12/98	16:03	0:00:36	[redacted]	[redacted]	WASZ-1	LOCAL	141	
01/12/98	16:07	0:00:06	[redacted]	[redacted]	WASZ-1	LOCAL	141	
01/12/98	16:08	0:00:36	[redacted]	[redacted]	WASZ-1	LOCAL	141	
01/12/98	16:09	0:01:18	[redacted]	[redacted]	WASZ-1	LOCAL	141	
01/12/98	16:17	0:02:00	[redacted]	[redacted]	NEW YOR NY	OS-OL	194	
01/12/98	16:18	0:00:48	[redacted]	[redacted]	WASZ-1	LOCAL	141	
01/12/98	16:19	0:04:42	[redacted]	[redacted]	WASZ-1	LOCAL	141	
01/12/98	16:24	0:01:06	[redacted]	[redacted]	LOSANGE CA	OS-OL	194	
01/12/98	16:34	0:00:30	[redacted]	[redacted]	WASZ 17 VA	LOCAL	141	
01/12/98	16:35	0:00:24	[redacted]	[redacted]	WASZ-1	LOCAL	141	
01/12/98	16:35	0:00:12	[redacted]	[redacted]	WASZ-1	LOCAL	141	
01/12/98	16:35	0:05:06	[redacted]	[redacted]	WASZ-1	LOCAL	141	
01/12/98	16:36	0:00:06	[redacted]	[redacted]	WASZ-1	LOCAL	141	
01/12/98	16:37	0:01:00	[redacted]	[redacted]		OS-OL	191	0799972800
01/12/98	16:44	0:01:18	[redacted]	[redacted]	WASZ 17 VA	LOCAL	141	
01/12/98	16:53	0:04:54	[redacted]	[redacted]	MARSHAL TX	OS-OL	194	
01/12/98	17:02	0:00:48	[redacted]	[redacted]	FRANCE	IDDD	191	0799972800
01/12/98	17:08	0:00:18	[redacted]	[redacted]	WASZ 8 VA	LOCAL	141	
01/12/98	17:10	0:10:00	[redacted]	[redacted]	PITTSBU PA	OS-OL	194	
01/12/98	17:20	0:01:24	[redacted]	[redacted]	WASZ-1	LOCAL	141	
01/12/98	17:28	0:00:06	[redacted]	[redacted]	WASZ-1	LOCAL	141	
01/12/98	17:33	0:00:12	[redacted]	[redacted]	WASZ 8 VA	LOCAL	141	
01/12/98	18:07	0:00:42	[redacted]	[redacted]	NEW YOR NY	OS-OL	191	0799972800
01/12/98	18:56	0:05:00	[redacted]	[redacted]	LOSANGE CA	OS-OL	194	
01/12/98	19:01	0:04:48	[redacted]	[redacted]	ATLANTA GA	OS-OL	194	
01/12/98	19:07	0:00:48	[redacted]	[redacted]	BETHESD MD	LOCAL	141	
01/12/98	19:09	0:00:54	[redacted]	[redacted]	WASZ 8 VA	LOCAL	141	
01/12/98	19:09	0:01:36	[redacted]	[redacted]	WASZ-1	LOCAL	141	
01/12/98	19:11	0:04:06	[redacted]	[redacted]	WASZ-1	LOCAL	141	
01/12/98	19:18	0:06:24	[redacted]	[redacted]	WASZ-1	LOCAL	141	
01/13/98	09:03	0:08:42	[redacted]	[redacted]	NEW YOR NY	OS-OL	194	

Selection Detail Report

OIC - ABS - 0157

Date: Saturday, January 24, 1998
Time: 2:11:29 PM

AKIN GUMP

DATE	TIME	DURATION HHHH:MM:SS	Extension	DIALED NUMBER	LOCATION	CALL TYPE	Trunk	ACCOUNT COD
01/15/98	11:11	0:01:42	[redacted]	[redacted]	NY	OS-OL	191	0799972800
01/15/98	11:12	0:09:24	[redacted]	[redacted]	WASZ 8 VA	LOCAL	141	
01/15/98	11:22	0:01:00	[redacted]	[redacted]	WASZ-1	LOCAL	141	
01/15/98	11:24	0:07:54	[redacted]	[redacted]	NY	OS-OL	191	0799972800
01/15/98	11:33	0:06:30	[redacted]	[redacted]	WASZ-1	LOCAL	141	
01/15/98	12:14	0:01:18	[redacted]	[redacted]	WASZ-1	LOCAL	141	
01/15/98	14:49	0:01:48	[redacted]	[redacted]	CHCZ-1 IL	OS-OL	194	
01/15/98	15:02	0:01:30	[redacted]	[redacted]	WASZ-1	LOCAL	141	
01/15/98	15:04	0:01:54	[redacted]	[redacted]	WASZ-1	LOCAL	141	
01/15/98	15:05	0:00:24	[redacted]	[redacted]	WASZ-1	LOCAL	141	
01/15/98	15:22	0:00:42	[redacted]	[redacted]	WASZ-1	LOCAL	141	
01/15/98	15:23	0:04:42	[redacted]	[redacted]	NEW YOR NY	OS-OL	194	
01/15/98	16:12	0:05:54	[redacted]	[redacted]	NEW YOR NY	OS-OL	194	
01/15/98	16:47	0:04:24	[redacted]	[redacted]	TURKEY	IDDD	194	
01/15/98	17:06	0:06:36	[redacted]	[redacted]	WASZ-1	LOCAL	141	
01/15/98	17:09	0:02:30	[redacted]	[redacted]	WASZ-1	LOCAL	141	
01/15/98	17:12	0:00:18	[redacted]	[redacted]	WASZ 8 VA	LOCAL	141	
01/15/98	17:12	0:02:30	[redacted]	[redacted]	WASZ-1	LOCAL	141	
01/15/98	17:13	0:01:48	[redacted]	[redacted]	WASZ-1	LOCAL	141	
01/15/98	17:16	0:02:48	[redacted]	[redacted]	WASZ-1	LOCAL	141	
01/15/98	17:22	0:04:24	[redacted]	[redacted]	WASZ-1	LOCAL	141	
01/15/98	17:27	0:02:30	[redacted]	[redacted]	TURKEY	IDDD	194	
01/15/98	17:36	0:01:24	[redacted]	[redacted]	WASZ-1	LOCAL	141	
01/15/98	17:44	0:00:18	[redacted]	[redacted]	WASZ-1	LOCAL	141	
01/15/98	17:45	0:00:18	[redacted]	[redacted]	WASZ-1	LOCAL	141	
01/15/98	17:45	0:01:18	[redacted]	[redacted]	WASZ-1	LOCAL	141	
01/15/98	17:49	0:04:06	[redacted]	[redacted]	CHCZ-1 IL	OS-OL	194	
01/15/98	17:59	0:09:42	[redacted]	[redacted]	WASZ 8 VA	LOCAL	141	
01/15/98	18:45	0:00:12	[redacted]	[redacted]	WASZ 8 VA	LOCAL	141	
01/15/98	18:53	0:00:42	[redacted]	[redacted]		SPCL	141	
01/15/98	18:54	0:01:06	[redacted]	[redacted]	DENVER CO	OS-OL	191	0799972800
01/15/98	18:59	0:01:30	[redacted]	[redacted]	WASZ 8 VA	LOCAL	141	
01/15/98	19:06	0:00:18	[redacted]	[redacted]	WASZ 8 VA	LOCAL	141	
01/15/98	19:19	0:24:18	[redacted]	[redacted]	NEW YOR NY	OS-OL	194	
01/16/98	08:09	0:00:48	[redacted]	[redacted]	WASZ 8 VA	LOCAL	141	
01/16/98	08:10	0:06:42	[redacted]	[redacted]	WASZ-1	LOCAL	141	
01/16/98	08:18	0:11:54	[redacted]	[redacted]	WASZ-1	LOCAL	141	
01/16/98	08:59	0:01:24	[redacted]	[redacted]	WASZ 8 VA	LOCAL	141	
01/16/98	09:02	0:07:54	[redacted]	[redacted]	DURHAM NC	OS-OL	191	0799972800
01/16/98	09:05	0:00:36	[redacted]	[redacted]	WASZ-1	LOCAL	141	
01/16/98	09:12	0:00:54	[redacted]	[redacted]	WASZ-1	LOCAL	141	
01/16/98	09:15	0:03:48	[redacted]	[redacted]	DURHAM NC	OS-OL	191	0799972800
01/16/98	09:21	0:00:36	[redacted]	[redacted]	NEW YOR NY	OS-OL	191	0799972800
01/16/98	09:35	0:02:18	[redacted]	[redacted]	NEW YOR NY	OS-OL	194	
01/16/98	09:37	0:00:42	[redacted]	[redacted]	WASZ-1	LOCAL	141	
01/16/98	09:41	0:00:18	[redacted]	[redacted]	WASZ-1	LOCAL	141	
01/16/98	09:49	0:00:36	[redacted]	[redacted]	NEW YOR NY	OS-OL	194	
01/16/98	10:58	0:00:18	[redacted]	[redacted]	WASZ-1	LOCAL	141	
01/16/98	11:17	0:01:24	[redacted]	[redacted]	WASZ-1	LOCAL	141	
01/16/98	11:18	0:00:30	[redacted]	[redacted]	NEW YOR NY	OS-OL	194	
01/16/98	11:22	0:00:06	[redacted]	[redacted]	WASZ-1	LOCAL	141	
01/16/98	11:25	0:03:24	[redacted]	[redacted]	WCHSZ 6 NY	OS-OL	194	
01/16/98	11:37	0:01:00	[redacted]	[redacted]	GERMAN	IDDD	194	0799972800
01/16/98	11:39	0:02:18	[redacted]	[redacted]	GERMAN	IDDD	194	0799972800
01/16/98	11:40	0:07:30	[redacted]	[redacted]	NEW YOR NY	OS-OL	191	0799972800
01/16/98	11:42	0:03:00	[redacted]	[redacted]	NEW YOR NY	OS-OL	194	
01/16/98	11:44	0:01:06	[redacted]	[redacted]	NEW YOR NY	OS-OL	194	
01/16/98	11:47	0:03:00	[redacted]	[redacted]	NEW YOR NY	OS-OL	194	
01/16/98	12:33	0:01:48	[redacted]	[redacted]	WASZ-1	LOCAL	141	
01/16/98	13:15	0:00:06	[redacted]	[redacted]	WASZ 8 VA	LOCAL	141	
01/16/98	13:22	0:03:06	[redacted]	[redacted]	WASZ 8 VA	LOCAL	141	
01/16/98	13:55	0:00:48	[redacted]	[redacted]	WASZ-1	LOCAL	141	
01/16/98	13:56	0:00:54	[redacted]	[redacted]	WASZ-1	LOCAL	141	
01/16/98	13:58	0:00:42	[redacted]	[redacted]	NEW YOR NY	OS-OL	194	
01/16/98	14:02	0:01:48	[redacted]	[redacted]	WCHSZ 6 NY	OS-OL	194	
01/16/98	14:39	0:03:24	[redacted]	[redacted]	WASZ-1	LOCAL	141	
01/16/98	14:49	0:01:00	[redacted]	[redacted]	CHCZ-1 IL	OS-OL	191	0799972800
01/16/98	14:52	0:01:00	[redacted]	[redacted]	WASZ 8 VA	LOCAL	141	
01/16/98	14:55	0:08:00	[redacted]	[redacted]	WASZ 8 VA	LOCAL	141	
01/16/98	15:04	0:00:18	[redacted]	[redacted]	WASZ 1B VA	LOCAL	141	
01/16/98	15:06	0:03:00	[redacted]	[redacted]	NEW YOR NY	OS-OL	194	
01/16/98	16:33	0:03:12	[redacted]	[redacted]	WASZ-1	LOCAL	141	
01/16/98	16:41	0:00:54	[redacted]	[redacted]	NEW YOR NY	OS-OL	191	0799972800

V004-DC-00000164

Selection Detail Report

ate: Saturday, January 24, 1998
me: 2:11:29 PM

AKIN GUMP

OIC - ABS - 0158

DATE	TIME	DURATION HHHH:MM:SS	Extension	DIALED NUMBER	LOCATION	CALL TYPE	Trunk	ACCOUNT COD
01/16/98	16:48	0:00:06	[redacted]	[redacted]	WASZ-1	LOCAL	141	
01/16/98	16:49	0:00:48	[redacted]	[redacted]	WASZ-1	SPCL	141	
01/16/98	16:49	0:01:18	[redacted]	[redacted]	WASZ-1	LOCAL	141	
01/16/98	16:49	0:01:36	[redacted]	[redacted]	NEW YOR NY	OS-OL	191	0799972800
01/16/98	16:51	0:00:36	[redacted]	[redacted]	NEW YOR NY	OS-OL	194	
01/16/98	16:51	0:00:30	[redacted]	[redacted]	NEW YOR NY	OS-OL	191	0799972800
01/16/98	16:53	0:05:00	[redacted]	[redacted]		LOCAL	194	
01/16/98	16:54	0:00:12	[redacted]	[redacted]	WASZ-1	LOCAL	141	
01/16/98	16:58	0:00:36	[redacted]	[redacted]	NEW YOR NY	OS-OL	194	
01/16/98	17:10	0:01:06	[redacted]	[redacted]	NEW YOR NY	OS-OL	191	0799972800
01/16/98	17:24	0:00:12	[redacted]	[redacted]	WASZ-1	LOCAL	141	
01/16/98	17:27	0:00:36	[redacted]	[redacted]	WASZ-1	LOCAL	141	
01/16/98	17:27	0:04:06	[redacted]	[redacted]	WASZ-1	LOCAL	141	
01/16/98	17:33	0:00:48	[redacted]	[redacted]	TURKEY	IDDD	194	
01/16/98	17:33	0:00:18	[redacted]	[redacted]	WASZ 1B VA	LOCAL	141	
01/16/98	17:34	0:00:18	[redacted]	[redacted]	WASZ 17 VA	LOCAL	141	
01/16/98	17:35	0:00:24	[redacted]	[redacted]	WASZ 8 VA	LOCAL	141	
01/16/98	17:36	0:00:42	[redacted]	[redacted]	LOSANGE CA	OS-OL	194	
01/16/98	17:37	0:01:36	[redacted]	[redacted]	LOSANGE CA	OS-OL	194	
01/16/98	17:38	0:00:12	[redacted]	[redacted]		LOCAL	141	
01/16/98	17:39	0:04:24	[redacted]	[redacted]	CA	OS-OL	194	
01/16/98	17:43	0:00:36	[redacted]	[redacted]	WASZ-1	LOCAL	141	
01/16/98	18:00	0:04:12	[redacted]	[redacted]	CAPITOL MD	LOCAL	141	
01/16/98	18:07	0:00:30	[redacted]	[redacted]		LOCAL	141	
01/16/98	18:24	0:00:48	[redacted]	[redacted]		LOCAL	141	
01/18/98	11:37	0:00:24	[redacted]	[redacted]	WASZ 8 VA	LOCAL	141	
01/18/98	11:38	0:01:36	[redacted]	[redacted]	WASZ-1	LOCAL	141	
01/18/98	11:48	0:00:42	[redacted]	[redacted]		LOCAL	194	
01/18/98	11:49	0:01:12	[redacted]	[redacted]	WASZ-1	LOCAL	141	
01/18/98	11:58	0:00:54	[redacted]	[redacted]	WASZ-1	LOCAL	141	
01/18/98	12:05	0:05:18	[redacted]	[redacted]	NEW YOR NY	OS-OL	194	
01/18/98	19:18	0:00:24	[redacted]	[redacted]	WASZ-1	LOCAL	141	
01/18/98	19:19	0:00:36	[redacted]	[redacted]	WASZ 8 VA	LOCAL	141	
01/18/98	19:19	0:01:06	[redacted]	[redacted]	WASZ-1	LOCAL	141	
01/18/98	19:23	0:00:18	[redacted]	[redacted]	WASZ-1	LOCAL	141	
01/18/98	19:26	0:00:48	[redacted]	[redacted]	MS	OS-OL	194	
01/19/98	10:29	0:03:42	[redacted]	[redacted]	WASZ-1	LOCAL	141	
01/19/98	10:33	0:00:12	[redacted]	[redacted]		LOCAL	141	
01/19/98	10:34	0:00:48	[redacted]	[redacted]		LOCAL	141	
01/19/98	10:35	0:01:12	[redacted]	[redacted]	WASZ-1	LOCAL	141	
01/19/98	10:44	0:01:00	[redacted]	[redacted]	WASZ-1	LOCAL	141	
01/19/98	10:45	0:03:54	[redacted]	[redacted]	STAMFOR CT	OS-OL	191	0799972800
01/19/98	10:53	0:00:36	[redacted]	[redacted]	WASZ-1	LOCAL	141	
01/19/98	10:55	0:01:36	[redacted]	[redacted]	TURKEY	IDDD	194	
01/19/98	11:04	0:00:24	[redacted]	[redacted]	WASZ-1	LOCAL	141	
01/19/98	11:13	0:00:36	[redacted]	[redacted]		LOCAL	141	
01/19/98	11:17	0:01:36	[redacted]	[redacted]	WASZ-1	LOCAL	141	
01/19/98	11:19	0:22:42	[redacted]	[redacted]	CHCZ-1 IL	OS-OL	194	
01/19/98	11:47	0:00:48	[redacted]	[redacted]	OXON HI MD	LOCAL	141	
01/19/98	11:52	0:00:36	[redacted]	[redacted]	WASZ-1	LOCAL	141	
01/19/98	11:53	0:01:42	[redacted]	[redacted]	CHCZ-1 IL	OS-OL	194	
01/19/98	11:54	0:03:12	[redacted]	[redacted]	CHCZ-1 IL	OS-OL	194	
01/19/98	12:00	0:08:42	[redacted]	[redacted]	WASZ-1	LOCAL	141	
01/19/98	12:09	0:01:06	[redacted]	[redacted]	TORONTO ON	OS-OL	194	
01/19/98	12:11	0:04:24	[redacted]	[redacted]	UK	IDDD	194	
01/19/98	12:17	0:03:36	[redacted]	[redacted]	TORONTO ON	OS-OL	194	
01/19/98	16:51	0:01:42	[redacted]	[redacted]	WASZ 8 VA	LOCAL	141	
01/19/98	16:53	0:00:24	[redacted]	[redacted]	WASZ-1	LOCAL	141	
01/19/98	16:54	0:04:00	[redacted]	[redacted]	WASZ-1	LOCAL	141	
01/19/98	16:58	0:00:12	[redacted]	[redacted]	WASZ-1	LOCAL	141	
01/19/98	16:59	0:00:42	[redacted]	[redacted]	WASZ-1	LOCAL	141	
01/19/98	17:00	0:00:18	[redacted]	[redacted]	WASZ-1	LOCAL	141	
01/19/98	17:00	0:00:24	[redacted]	[redacted]	WASZ-1	LOCAL	141	
01/19/98	17:02	0:00:24	[redacted]	[redacted]	WASZ-1	LOCAL	141	
01/19/98	17:02	0:00:24	[redacted]	[redacted]		LOCAL	141	
01/19/98	17:05	0:00:06	[redacted]	[redacted]	WASZ-1	LOCAL	141	
01/19/98	17:05	0:00:18	[redacted]	[redacted]	WASZ-1	LOCAL	141	
01/19/98	17:05	0:02:12	[redacted]	[redacted]	WASZ-1	LOCAL	141	
01/19/98	17:09	0:01:06	[redacted]	[redacted]	WASZ-1	LOCAL	141	
01/19/98	17:14	0:08:24	[redacted]	[redacted]	WASZ-1	LOCAL	141	
01/19/98	17:22	0:00:06	[redacted]	[redacted]	WASZ-1	LOCAL	141	
01/19/98	17:22	0:00:18	[redacted]	[redacted]	WASZ-1	LOCAL	141	
01/19/98	17:23	0:02:06	[redacted]	[redacted]	CHCZ-1 IL	OS-OL	194	

V004-DC-00000166

Selection Detail Report

OIC - ABS - 0159

Date: Saturday, January 24, 1998
Time: 2:11:29 PM

AKIN GUMP

DATE	TIME	DURATION HHHH:MM:SS	Extension	DIALED NUMBER	LOCATION	CALL TYPE	Trunk	ACCOUNT COD
01/19/98	17:33	0:04:24	[redacted]	[redacted]	CHCZ-1 IL	OS-OL	194	
01/19/98	17:37	0:01:06	[redacted]	[redacted]	WASZ-1	LOCAL	141	
01/19/98	17:40	0:01:00	[redacted]	[redacted]	WASZ-1	LOCAL	141	
01/19/98	17:42	0:00:48	[redacted]	[redacted]	WASZ-1	LOCAL	141	
01/19/98	17:43	0:10:36	[redacted]	[redacted]	WASZ-1	LOCAL	141	
01/19/98	17:55	0:00:24	[redacted]	[redacted]	WASZ 8 VA	LOCAL	141	
01/19/98	18:04	0:03:00	[redacted]	[redacted]	WASZ 8 VA	LOCAL	141	
01/19/98	18:07	0:00:24	[redacted]	[redacted]	WASZ 8 VA	LOCAL	141	
01/19/98	18:08	0:00:30	[redacted]	[redacted]	WASZ 1B VA	LOCAL	141	
01/19/98	18:08	0:00:36	[redacted]	[redacted]	WASZ 17 VA	LOCAL	141	
01/19/98	18:12	0:03:00	[redacted]	[redacted]	NEW YOR NY	OS-OL	194	
01/19/98	18:15	0:00:30	[redacted]	[redacted]	NEW YOR NY	OS-OL	194	
01/19/98	18:16	0:06:42	[redacted]	[redacted]	NEW YOR NY	OS-OL	194	
01/19/98	18:22	0:00:30	[redacted]	[redacted]	WASZ-1	LOCAL	141	
01/19/98	18:23	0:00:48	[redacted]	[redacted]	WASZ-1	LOCAL	141	
01/19/98	18:26	0:00:36	[redacted]	[redacted]	BUFFALO NY	OS-OL	194	
01/19/98	18:26	0:00:42	[redacted]	[redacted]	WASZ-1	LOCAL	141	
01/19/98	18:29	0:14:30	[redacted]	[redacted]		OS-OL	194	
01/19/98	18:44	0:00:36	[redacted]	[redacted]	DIR ASS MD	SPCL	141	
01/19/98	18:44	0:01:06	[redacted]	[redacted]	BETHESD MD	LOCAL	141	
01/19/98	18:47	0:00:42	[redacted]	[redacted]	WASZ-1	LOCAL	141	
01/19/98	18:48	0:05:18	[redacted]	[redacted]	LOSANGE CA	OS-OL	194	
01/19/98	18:54	0:02:24	[redacted]	[redacted]	WCHSZ 6 NY	OS-OL	194	
01/19/98	18:58	0:00:36	[redacted]	[redacted]	WASZ-1	LOCAL	141	
01/20/98	09:45	0:00:30	[redacted]	[redacted]	ENGLESI VA	LOCAL	141	
01/20/98	09:46	0:00:30	[redacted]	[redacted]		SPCL	141	
01/20/98	10:15	0:02:30	[redacted]	[redacted]	WASZ-1	LOCAL	141	
01/20/98	10:17	0:00:12	[redacted]	[redacted]	WASZ-1	LOCAL	141	
01/20/98	10:18	0:01:06	[redacted]	[redacted]	WASZ 17 VA	LOCAL	141	
01/20/96	10:29	0:06:30	[redacted]	[redacted]	WASZ-1	LOCAL	141	
01/20/96	10:30	0:00:48	[redacted]	[redacted]	WASZ-1	LOCAL	141	
01/20/98	10:31	0:01:00	[redacted]	[redacted]	WASZ 8 VA	LOCAL	141	
01/20/98	10:41	0:03:48	[redacted]	[redacted]	WASZ-1	LOCAL	141	
01/20/98	10:42	0:02:30	[redacted]	[redacted]	KANSASC MO	OS-OL	191	0799972800
01/20/98	10:45	0:00:24	[redacted]	[redacted]	WASZ-1	LOCAL	141	
01/20/98	10:46	0:04:18	[redacted]	[redacted]	WASZ-1	LOCAL	141	
01/20/98	12:01	0:02:48	[redacted]	[redacted]	WASZ-1	LOCAL	141	
01/20/98	12:04	0:00:06	[redacted]	[redacted]	WASZ-1	LOCAL	141	
01/20/98	12:08	0:00:30	[redacted]	[redacted]	WASZ-1	LOCAL	141	
01/20/98	12:33	0:01:54	[redacted]	[redacted]	OCCOQUA VA	OS-IL	191	0799972800
01/20/98	13:27	0:01:36	[redacted]	[redacted]	WASZ-1	LOCAL	141	
01/20/98	13:45	0:00:48	[redacted]	[redacted]	WASZ-1	LOCAL	141	
01/20/98	14:01	0:01:36	[redacted]	[redacted]	WASZ-1	LOCAL	141	
01/20/98	14:43	0:00:30	[redacted]	[redacted]	NEW YOR NY	OS-OL	191	0799972800
01/20/98	14:46	0:02:06	[redacted]	[redacted]	ROCKVIL MD	LOCAL	141	
01/20/98	14:49	0:05:30	[redacted]	[redacted]	WASZ 17 VA	LOCAL	141	
01/20/98	14:54	0:00:06	[redacted]	[redacted]	WASZ-1	LOCAL	141	
01/20/98	14:55	0:02:24	[redacted]	[redacted]	WASZ-1	LOCAL	141	
01/20/98	15:00	0:00:12	[redacted]	[redacted]	WASZ-1	LOCAL	141	
01/20/98	15:02	0:00:54	[redacted]	[redacted]		OS-OL	191	0799972800
01/20/98	15:08	0:01:54	[redacted]	[redacted]	SCHENCT NY	OS-OL	191	0799972800
01/20/98	15:10	0:00:30	[redacted]	[redacted]	WASZ-1	LOCAL	141	
01/20/98	15:12	0:05:42	[redacted]	[redacted]	SAN FRA CA	OS-OL	191	0799972800
01/20/98	15:16	0:00:12	[redacted]	[redacted]	WASZ-1	LOCAL	141	
01/20/98	15:23	0:00:30	[redacted]	[redacted]	WASZ-1	LOCAL	141	
01/20/98	15:31	0:03:42	[redacted]	[redacted]	WASZ 8 VA	LOCAL	141	
01/20/98	15:41	0:00:54	[redacted]	[redacted]	CHCZ-1 IL	OS-OL	191	0799972800
01/20/98	15:45	0:01:18	[redacted]	[redacted]	NEW YOR NY	OS-OL	191	0799972800
01/20/98	16:10	0:00:42	[redacted]	[redacted]	WASZ-1	SPCL	141	
01/20/98	16:11	0:05:30	[redacted]	[redacted]	WASZ-1	LOCAL	141	
01/20/98	16:13	0:04:00	[redacted]	[redacted]	DANBURY CT	OS-OL	191	0799972800
01/20/98	16:26	0:00:06	[redacted]	[redacted]	WASZ-1	LOCAL	141	
01/20/98	16:26	0:00:42	[redacted]	[redacted]	WASZ-1	SPCL	141	
01/20/98	16:26	0:00:24	[redacted]	[redacted]	WASZ-1	LOCAL	141	
01/20/98	16:28	0:01:36	[redacted]	[redacted]	NEW YOR NY	OS-OL	191	0799972800
01/20/98	16:32	0:00:30	[redacted]	[redacted]	NEW YOR NY	OS-OL	191	0799972800
01/20/98	16:49	0:06:36	[redacted]	[redacted]	SCHENCT NY	OS-OL	191	0799972800
01/20/98	17:00	0:01:24	[redacted]	[redacted]	WASZ 17 VA	LOCAL	141	
01/20/98	17:05	0:02:24	[redacted]	[redacted]		SPCL	141	
01/20/98	17:07	0:00:36	[redacted]	[redacted]	NEW YOR NY	OS-OL	191	0799972800
01/20/98	17:20	0:00:06	[redacted]	[redacted]	WASZ 8 VA	LOCAL	141	
01/20/98	17:41	0:01:36	[redacted]	[redacted]	WASZ 8 VA	LOCAL	141	
01/21/98	10:21	0:00:06	[redacted]	[redacted]	WASZ 8 VA	LOCAL	141	

Selection Detail Report

Date: Saturday, January 24, 1998

Time: 2:11:29 PM

AKIN GUMP

OIC - ABS - 0160

DATE	TIME	DURATION HHHH:MM:SS	Extension	DIALED NUMBER	LOCATION	CALL TYPE	Trunk	ACCOUNT COD
01/21/98	10:22	0:00:18	[redacted]	[redacted]	WASZ 8 VA	LOCAL	141	
01/21/98	10:22	0:00:06	[redacted]	[redacted]	WASZ 8 VA	LOCAL	141	
01/21/98	10:23	0:02:18	[redacted]	[redacted]	WASZ 8 VA	LOCAL	141	
01/21/98	10:27	0:02:36	[redacted]	[redacted]		SPCL	141	
01/21/98	10:33	0:03:42	[redacted]	[redacted]		SPCL	141	
01/21/98	11:04	0:07:48	[redacted]	[redacted]	CHCZ-1 IL	OS-OL	191	0799972800
01/21/98	12:45	0:00:12	[redacted]	[redacted]	WASZ 17 VA	LOCAL	141	
01/21/98	12:53	0:01:18	[redacted]	[redacted]	WASZ-1	LOCAL	141	
01/21/98	12:58	0:00:48	[redacted]	[redacted]	WASZ-1	LOCAL	141	
01/21/98	12:58	0:01:00	[redacted]	[redacted]	WASZ 17 VA	LOCAL	141	
01/21/98	13:03	0:00:30	[redacted]	[redacted]	DANBURY CT	OS-OL	191	0799972800
01/21/98	13:05	0:00:06	[redacted]	[redacted]	WASZ 1B VA	LOCAL	141	
01/21/98	13:56	0:00:30	[redacted]	[redacted]	WASZ 8 VA	LOCAL	141	
01/21/98	13:56	0:00:06	[redacted]	[redacted]	WASZ-1	LOCAL	141	
01/21/98	14:00	0:02:36	[redacted]	[redacted]	WASZ 17 VA	LOCAL	141	
01/21/98	14:34	0:00:48	[redacted]	[redacted]	WASZ-1	LOCAL	141	
01/21/98	14:41	0:00:06	[redacted]	[redacted]		LOCAL	141	
01/21/98	14:48	0:05:12	[redacted]	[redacted]	WASZ-1	LOCAL	141	
01/21/98	14:50	0:02:24	[redacted]	[redacted]	WASZ 8 VA	LOCAL	141	
01/21/98	14:52	0:00:06	[redacted]	[redacted]	WASZ 8 VA	LOCAL	141	
01/21/98	14:53	0:00:06	[redacted]	[redacted]	WASZ 8 VA	LOCAL	141	
01/21/98	14:54	0:06:12	[redacted]	[redacted]	WASZ-1	LOCAL	141	
01/21/98	15:02	0:02:48	[redacted]	[redacted]	NEW YOR NY	OS-OL	194	0799972800
01/21/98	15:03	0:00:30	[redacted]	[redacted]	WASZ-1	LOCAL	141	
01/21/98	15:57	0:00:42	[redacted]	[redacted]	NEW YOR NY	OS-OL	194	
01/21/98	15:59	0:00:24	[redacted]	[redacted]	WASZ-1	LOCAL	141	
01/21/98	16:00	0:00:06	[redacted]	[redacted]	WASZ-1	LOCAL	141	
01/21/98	16:01	0:01:54	[redacted]	[redacted]	WASZ-1	LOCAL	141	
01/21/98	16:03	0:05:36	[redacted]	[redacted]	WASZ-1	LOCAL	141	
01/21/98	16:09	0:02:12	[redacted]	[redacted]	WASZ 17 VA	LOCAL	141	
01/21/98	16:14	0:03:24	[redacted]	[redacted]	NEW YOR NY	OS-OL	194	
01/21/98	16:20	0:00:24	[redacted]	[redacted]	WASZ-1	LOCAL	141	
01/21/98	16:21	0:00:30	[redacted]	[redacted]	NEW YOR NY	OS-OL	194	
01/21/98	16:24	0:04:54	[redacted]	[redacted]	NEW YOR NY	OS-OL	194	
01/21/98	17:05	0:00:18	[redacted]	[redacted]	WASZ-1	LOCAL	141	
01/21/98	17:37	0:00:42	[redacted]	[redacted]	WASZ-1	LOCAL	141	
01/21/98	17:39	0:00:06	[redacted]	[redacted]	WASZ-1	LOCAL	141	
01/21/98	18:14	0:07:18	[redacted]	[redacted]	CHCZ-1 IL	OS-OL	194	
01/21/98	18:22	0:02:18	[redacted]	[redacted]	NEW YOR NY	OS-OL	194	
01/21/98	18:25	0:10:06	[redacted]	[redacted]	LADUE MO	OS-OL	194	
01/21/98	18:35	0:04:12	[redacted]	[redacted]	CHCZ-1 IL	OS-OL	194	
01/21/98	18:40	0:01:00	[redacted]	[redacted]	WASZ-1	LOCAL	141	
01/21/98	18:41	0:04:42	[redacted]	[redacted]	WASZ-1	LOCAL	141	
01/21/98	18:50	0:04:42	[redacted]	[redacted]	NEW YOR NY	OS-OL	194	
01/21/98	19:02	0:00:36	[redacted]	[redacted]	WASZ-1	LOCAL	141	
01/21/98	19:03	0:03:36	[redacted]	[redacted]	NEW YOR NY	OS-OL	194	
01/21/98	19:05	0:00:18	[redacted]	[redacted]	WASZ-1	LOCAL	141	
01/21/98	19:06	0:02:36	[redacted]	[redacted]	WASZ 8 VA	LOCAL	141	
01/21/98	19:07	0:07:36	[redacted]	[redacted]	WASZ-1	LOCAL	141	
01/21/98	19:15	0:00:24	[redacted]	[redacted]	WASZ-1	LOCAL	141	
01/21/98	19:17	0:10:00	[redacted]	[redacted]	NEW YOR NY	OS-OL	141	
01/21/98	19:27	0:01:12	[redacted]	[redacted]	WASZ-1	LOCAL	141	
01/21/98	21:57	0:01:36	[redacted]	[redacted]	WASZ-1	LOCAL	141	
01/21/98	21:59	0:06:00	[redacted]	[redacted]	CHCZ-1 IL	OS-OL	141	
01/21/98	22:06	0:01:00	[redacted]	[redacted]	NEW YOR NY	OS-OL	141	
01/22/98	08:12	0:02:30	[redacted]	[redacted]	WASZ-1	LOCAL	141	
01/22/98	08:14	0:00:24	[redacted]	[redacted]	WASZ-1	LOCAL	141	
01/22/98	08:15	0:00:36	[redacted]	[redacted]	WASZ-1	LOCAL	141	
01/22/98	08:17	0:00:48	[redacted]	[redacted]	WASZ-1	LOCAL	141	
01/22/98	08:17	0:00:18	[redacted]	[redacted]	WASZ-1	LOCAL	141	
01/22/98	08:22	0:00:48	[redacted]	[redacted]	WASZ-1	LOCAL	141	
01/22/98	09:05	0:01:24	[redacted]	[redacted]	WASZ-1	LOCAL	141	
01/22/98	09:07	0:01:48	[redacted]	[redacted]	WASZ-1	LOCAL	141	
01/22/98	09:09	0:02:30	[redacted]	[redacted]	NEW YOR NY	OS-OL	194	
01/22/98	09:12	0:00:06	[redacted]	[redacted]	WASZ-1	LOCAL	141	
01/22/98	09:13	0:04:00	[redacted]	[redacted]	WASZ-1	LOCAL	141	
01/22/98	09:29	0:01:30	[redacted]	[redacted]		SPCL	141	
01/22/98	09:52	0:00:48	[redacted]	[redacted]	WASZ-1	LOCAL	141	
01/22/98	10:10	0:00:36	[redacted]	[redacted]	WASZ-1	LOCAL	141	
01/22/98	10:18	0:00:42	[redacted]	[redacted]	WASZ-1	SPCL	141	
01/22/98	10:19	0:00:48	[redacted]	[redacted]	ROANOKE VA	OS-OL	141	
01/22/98	10:19	0:11:18	[redacted]	[redacted]	ROANOKE VA	OS-OL	141	
01/22/98	11:00	0:02:06	[redacted]	[redacted]		LOCAL	141	

OIC - ASS - 0164

THURS. 12-11-97

Name	Time of Arrival	Contact
Monica Malensky	12:57	Jordan

REDACTED DOCUMENT

V004-DC-00000171

3071

Friday, 12-19-97 Cont'd

Name	Time of Arrival	Contact
Monica Lewinsky	4:47	V. Jordan

REDACTED DOCUMENT

REQUEST FOR MESSENGER SERVICE

Date: 12/8/97 Time Submitted: ________ Client #: [redacted]

Requestor: VERNON E. JORDAN, JR Ext.: ________

Call Back to Confirm Delivery? Yes X No ____

Service Type

Downtown Locals

Areas between Georgetown & Capitol Hill

- ☐ Filing/Round Trip Service
- ☐ 60 Minute Regular Service Downtown
- ☒ 30 Minute RUSH Service* Downtown
- ☐ 90 Minute Regular Service Hill
- ☐ 60 Minute RUSH Service* Hill
- ☐ If other, please talk directly to your dispatcher.

Outer DC and Suburbs

- ☐ Filing/Round Trip Service
- ☐ 2 Hour Service
- ☐ 90 Minute Service
- ☐ If other, please talk directly to your dispatcher.

*Rush Service Costs 50% more

Deliver To: BETTY CURRIE 510

Address: WHITE HOUSE / NORTHWEST GATE

Room #/Phone #: [redacted]

Pick Up From: ________

Address: ________

Room #/Phone #: ________

ADDITIONAL INSTRUCTIONS: THE GUARD WILL CALL BETTY AND SHE WILL HAVE SOMEONE COME OUT TO GET IT.

Dispatcher Use Only

Courier # [redacted] Control # RA981 P.O.D. TIME: ________

Signature: 480

DATE [illegible]

TIME	NAME	NUMBER	MESSAGE
	Betty POTUS	[illegible]	(U) Kind of Important.

REDACTED DOCUMENT

OIC - GL - 0046

V005-DC-00000058

1/20/98
DATE

TIME	NAME	NUMBER	MESSAGE
	✓ FRANK CARTER		

REDACTED DOCUMENT

OIC - GL - 0048

V005-DC-00000060

20 Jan. 98 - Tuesday
DATE

TIME	NAME	NUMBER	MESSAGE
✓	Bob Bennett		

REDACTED DOCUMENT

96_WHVA

ACC-CO	LAST-NAME	FIRST-NAME	INI	SSN	ENTRY-	SCHE	ENTRY-D	VISITEE	MEETING-R	REQUESTOR	DOB	ENTRY-
041601	LEWINSKY	MONICA			U82283	11:50	04/09/96	SHEEHAN	158	SHEEHAN	07/23/73	11:55
022755	LEWINSKY	MONICA		[redacted]	U05842	13:50	06/07/96	JOHNSON	489	WOZNIAK	07/23/73	12:51
022756	LEWINSKY	MONICA		[redacted]	U08598	16:30	06/14/96	POTUS	WW	HERNREICH	07/23/73	16:51
022754	LEWINSKY	MONICA			U09898	20:30	06/18/96	POTUS	SOUTH L	WIDDESS	07/23/73	17:59
022753	LEWINSKY	MONICA			U10376	18:30	06/18/96	POTUS	SOUTH L	WIDDESS	07/23/73	**:**
014185	LEWINSKY	MONICA			U37975	18:30	08/29/96	RAINES	145	RAINES	07/23/73	18:23
014184	LEWINSKY	MONICA			U37934	17:15	08/29/96	BOBOWICK	93	BOBOWICK	07/23/73	**:**
014183	LEWINSKY	MONICA			U37897	15:00	08/29/96	BOBOWICK	93	BOBOWICK	07/23/73	15:07
014827	LEWINSKY	MONICA			U52490	12:50	10/11/96	JOHNSON	487	RAINES	07/23/73	12:49
014828	LEWINSKY	MONICA			U55381	07:30	10/24/96	SHADDIX	WW	SHADDIX	07/23/73	07:43
020347	LEWINSKY	MONICA		[redacted]	U76166	19:30	12/17/96	RAINES	145	RAINES	07/23/73	19:32
020346	LEWINSKY	MONICA		[redacted]	U75872	17:00	12/17/96	POTUS	STATE F	WIDDESS	07/23/73	**:**
020345	LEWINSKY	MONICA		[redacted]	U74786	17:00	12/17/96	POTUS	RESIDENC	WIDDESS	07/23/73	16:15
020344	LEWINSKY	MONICA			U79655	12:30	12/30/96	CURRIE	WW	CURRIE	07/23/73	13:01

V006-DC-00000007

HB 001003

97 WHVA

ACC-CO	LAST-NAME	FIRST-NAME	INI	SSN	ENTRY-	SCHE	ENTRY-D	VISITEE	MEETING-R	REQUESTOR	DOB	ENTRY-TO
014596	LEWINSKY	MONICA		[redacted]	U99900	09:30	02/24/97	KESSINGER	332	KESSINGER	07/23/73	09.35
014597	LEWINSKY	MONICA		[redacted]	U02474	17:45	02/28/97	CURRIE	WW	CURRIE	07/23/73	17:48
017215	LEWINSKY	MONICA		[redacted]	U07291	10:00	03/13/97	CURRIE	WW	CURRIE	07/23/73	10.01
017216	LEWINSKY	MONICA		[redacted]	U07717	20:30	03/13/97	RAINES	WW	RAINES	07/23/73	21:17
017214	LEWINSKY	MONICA		[redacted]	U13381	13:55	03/29/97	CURRIE	WW	CURRIE	07/23/73	14:02
018724	LEWINSKY	MONICA		[redacted]	U19494	14:00	04/15/97	NAPLAN	331	NAPLAN	07/23/73	**.**
018723	LEWINSKY	MONICA		[redacted]	U20019	09:55	04/16/97	CURRIE	WW	CURRIE	07/23/73	09.48
017181	LEWINSKY	MONICA		[redacted]	U25619	17:45	05/01/97	STOTT	WW	STOTT	07/23/73	17.42
017182	LEWINSKY	MONICA		[redacted]	U26348	20:00	05/02/97	RAINES	145	RAINES	07/23/73	19.55
017183	LEWINSKY	MONICA		[redacted]	U34044	11:55	05/24/97	CURRIE	WW	CURRIE	07/23/73	12.20
017184	LEWINSKY	MONICA	S	[redacted]	U35502	15:45	05/30/97	DIMEL	397	DIMEL	07/23/73	15:30
017848	LEWINSKY	MONICA	S	[redacted]	U39783	11:00	06/11/97	DIMEL	397	DIMEL	07/23/73	10.55
017849	LEWINSKY	MONICA		[redacted]	U41786	15:00	06/16/97	CROFT	153	CROFT	07/23/73	14.45
017850	LEWINSKY	MONICA		[redacted]	U45310	18:45	06/24/97	CURRIE	WW	CURRIE	07/23/73	18.58
019032	LEWINSKY	MONICA		[redacted]	U49179	08:30	07/04/97	CURRIE	WW	CURRIE	07/23/73	08.51
019033	LEWINSKY	MONICA		[redacted]	U52746	21:45	07/14/97	CURRY	WW	CURRY	07/23/73	21:31
019034	LEWINSKY	MONICA		[redacted]	U53425	10:45	07/16/97	SCOTT	153	SCOTT	07/23/73	10.43
019035	LEWINSKY	MONICA		[redacted]	U56888	17:55	07/24/97	CURRIE	WW	CURRIE	07/23/73	18.04
012692	LEWINSKY	MONICA		[redacted]	U65029	09:00	08/16/97	CURRIE	WW	CURRIE	07/23/73	08.59
017014	LEWINSKY	MONICA		[redacted]	U72854	19:00	09/11/97	RAINES	145	RAINES	07/23/73	18:56
017015	LEWINSKY	MONICA		[redacted]	U73646	19:30	09/12/97	CURRIE	WW	CURRIE	07/23/73	19.38
017016	LEWINSKY	MONICA		[redacted]	U76923	18:30	09/22/97	RAINES	145	RAINES	07/23/73	19.09
019763	LEWINSKY	MONICA		[redacted]	U83802	09:30	10/11/97	CURRIE	WW	CURRIE	07/23/73	09:30
019762	LEWINSKY	MONICA		[redacted]	U88500	09:30	10/29/97	POTUS	WH	WILSON	07/23/73	**.**
014669	LEWINSKY	MONICA		[redacted]	U95777	18:15	11/13/97	CURRIE	WW	CURRIE	07/23/73	18.20
014668	LEWINSKY	MONICA		[redacted]	U95505	16:00	11/13/97	WOZNIAK	489	WOZNIAK	07/23/73	**.**

V006-DC-00000008

HB 001004

VAFILE

ACC-CO	LAST-NAME	FIRST-NAME	INI	SSN	ENTRY-C	SCHED	ENTRY-D	VISITEE	MEETING-R	REQUESTOR	DOB	ENTRY-TOA
022212	LEWINSKY	MONICA		[redacted]	U10779	08:15	12/28/97	CURRIE	WH	CURRIE	07/23/73	08:16
022211	LEWINSKY	MONICA		[redacted]	U06555	11:17	12/15/97	WOZNIAK	OEOB	LUZZATTO	07/23/73	11:31
022210	LEWINSKY	MONICA		[redacted]	U03056	12:45	12/06/97	CURRIE	WH	CURRIE	07/23/73	12:52
022209	LEWINSKY	MONICA		[redacted]	U06562	11:30	**/**/**	WOZNIAK	WH	WOZNIAK	07/23/73	**:**
022208	LEWINSKY	MONICA		[redacted]	U02484	18:00	**/**/**	POTUS	WH	SCHWARTZ	07/23/73	**:**

V006-DC-00000009

HB 001005

White House Office
Supplemental Information Sheet for Personnel Action
(To be completed by all persons tentatively selected for employment)

Date: June 7, 1995

D{

Name: Monica Samille Lewinsky Social Security Number: [redacted]
Date of Birth: [redacted] Place of Birth: San Francisco, CA
Local Address: [redacted] Last Permanent Address: [redacted]

In case of emergency notify: Marcia Lewinsky Phone Number: [redacted]
Marital Status: ☒ Single ☐ Married ☐ Widowed ☐ Separated ☐ Divorced
Spouse's Name: Spouse's Employer:

Department/Office/Agency: CoS Corres.
Reporting to: J. Beckett Office Phone Number: 65506
Personnel Status: ☐ White House Employee ☐ Other Government Employee (please specify):
☐ Reimbursable Detail ☐ Non-reimbursable detail ☐ Volunteer
☐ Assignee ☐ White House Fellow ☐ Presidential Management Intern
☐ Historically Provided Service ☐ Intergovernmental Personnel Agreement ☒ Intern
Other:
(For all Other Government Employees, please attach a brief description of the individual's role and responsibilities)
Effective Date: 7/10/95 Ending Date (If applicable): 8/25/95

Current or Most Recent Place of Employment: Knot Shop
Address: 700 SW Fifth Street, Portland OR 97204
Supervisor: Lisa Casey Phone Number: [redacted]
Military Service: ☐ Yes ☒ No Service Branch: Date of Discharge:
Prior EOP Service: ☐ Yes ☒ No Agency: Dates of Employment:
Have you ever been fired from any job for any reason, quit after being told you would be fired, or left by mutual agreement because of specific problems? ☐ Yes ☒ No (If yes, please explain on the back of this form.)
Are you now under any charge, or have you ever been convicted of, or forfeited collateral for any violation of law?
☐ Yes ☒ No (If yes, please explain on the back of this form.)

To Be Completed By Requesting Official:
Type of Pass or access requested:
☐ WH Badge ☐ WH Vol ☐ WH Access ☐ Other (OGA, NGS, CON)
☐ EOP Badge ☐ EOP Vol ☒ EOP Access

Karen Abramson
Signature of Requesting Office Approving Official

V006-DC-00000020

To be completed by all regular Employees and Other Government Employees:
I acknowledge that the information provided herein is true and correct to the best of my knowledge and further acknowledge that this information may be used to initiate a preliminary background investigation in preparation for my employment in the White House and the Executive Office of the President.

Signature Date

HB 001016

To be Completed by Volunteers Only:
I acknowledge that the personnel data is correct and I am volunteering my services without compensation or promise of such.
Monica Samille Lewinsky 7 June 1995
Signature Date

Revised 1/94

THE WHITE HOUSE OFFICE
HISTORY FILE SEARCH
FROM 1991 TO PRESENT
AS OF: 01-17-98

NAME	EFF DATE	ACTION	EOD DATE	PAY PLAN	SERIES	SALARY
LEWINSKY,MONICA SAMILLE	951126	EXCEPTED APPOINTMENT	951126	AD	0301	25,000.00
LEGISLATIVE AFFAIRS-CORRESPONDENCE						
	960206	FEHB CHANGE	951126	AD	0301	25,000.00
LEGISLATIVE AFFAIRS-CORRESPONDENCE						
	960416	TERMINATION-APPT IN	951126	AD	0301	25,000.00
LEGISLATIVE AFFAIRS-CORRESPONDENCE						

U.S. Office of Personnel Management
FPM Supp. 296-33, Subch. 4

NOTIFICATION OF PERSONNEL ACTION

1. Name (Last, First, Middle): LEWINSKY, MONICA SAMILLE
2. Social Security Number: [redacted]
3. Date of Birth: 07 23 73
4. Effective Date: 11 26 95

FIRST ACTION

5-A. Code: 17C | 5-B. Nature of Action: EXC APPT
5-C. Code: ZLM | 5-D. Legal Authority: 3 USC 105
5-E. Code | 5-F. Legal Authority

SECOND ACTION

6-A. Code | 6-B. Nature of Action
6-C. Code | 6-D. Legal Authority
6-E. Code | 6-F. Legal Authority

7. FROM: Position Title and Number

8 Pay Plan	9. Occ. Code	10. Grade/Level	11. Step/Rate	12. Total Salary	13. Pay Basis

12A. Basic Pay	12B. Locality Adj.	12C. Adj. Basic Pay	12D. Other Pay

14. Name and Location of Position's Organization

15. TO: Position Title and Number: LEGISLATIVE AFFAIRS-CORRESPONDENCE
C9385NCC1

16. Pay Plan	17. Occ. Code	18. Grade/Level	19. Step/Rate	20. Total Salary/Award	21. Pay Basis
AD	C301	CO	CC	$25000.00	PA

20A. Basic Pay	20B. Locality Adj.	20C. Adj. Basic Pay	20D. Other Pay
$25000.00	$0	$25000.00	$0

22. Name and Location of Position's Organization:
THE WHITE HOUSE OFFICE
WASHINGTON DC
OFC OF LEGISLTVE AFFAIRS

EMPLOYEE DATA

23. Veterans Preference: 1 (1 - None; 2 - 5-Point; 3 - 10-Point/Disability; 4 - 10-Point/Compensable; 5 - 10-Point/Other; 6 - 10-Point/Compensable/30%)
24. Tenure: 1 (0 - None; 1 - Permanent; 2 - Conditional; 3 - Indefinite)
25. Agency Use: d
26. Veterans Preference for RIF: YES [ ] NO [X]
27. FEGLI: C BASIC LIFE ONLY
28. Annuitant Indicator: 9 NOT APPLICABLE
29. Pay Rate Determinant: 0
30. Retirement Plan: K FERS & FICA
31. Service Comp. Date (Leave): 11 26 95
32. Work Schedule: F FULL-TIME
33. Part-Time Hours Per Biweekly Pay Period:

POSITION DATA

34. Position Occupied: 2 (1 - Competitive Service; 2 - Excepted Service; 3 - SES General; 4 - SES Career Reserved)
35. FLSA Category: E (E - Exempt; N - Nonexempt)
36. Appropriation Code: 100002000
37. Bargaining Unit Status: 8888
38. Duty Station Code: 110010001
39. Duty Station (City - County - State or Overseas Location): WASHINGTON, DC DISTRICT OF COLUMBIA
40. Agency Data: CLC-799
41. SENS-NCS
42. FUNC CLS-00
43.
44. EDUC-13/INSTR PGM-420101/YR-1995

45. Remarks

APPOINTMENT AFFIDAVIT EXECUTED 11-27-95.
OPF MAINTAINED BY OFC OF ADMIN R4013 WDC 20503
FROZEN SERVICE NONE
CREDITABLE MILITARY SERVICE: NONE
PREVIOUS RETIREMENT COVERAGE: NEVER COVERED
EMPLOYEE IS AUTOMATICALLY COVERED UNDER FERS.

V006-DC-00000118

HB 001114

46. Employing Department or Agency: THE WHITE HOUSE OFFICE
47. Agency Code: WHCO
48. Personnel Office ID: 9423
49. Approval Date: 11 29 95
50. Signature/Authentication and Title of Approving Official: MARY COUTTS BECK, ASSOC DR, HRM

5-Part 50-316

Editions Prior to 7/91 Are Not Usable After 6/30/93
NSN 7540-01-333-6238

3 – Payroll Copy

White House Gift Record

Presented: 11/20/95
Arrival : 11/22/95
Entered : 11/22/95

Gift ID: 377614/jra

Donor Information

Ms. Monica Lewinsky
[redacted]

No acknowledgement required.

Comments:

Hand delivered to Betty Currie. Donor recently received thank you for another gift.

Gift not received in the Gift Unit.

Gift Information

Intended: President

Disposition: President to Retain

Description:
Tie.

Location of Gift:

Total Gift Value: $25

President [✓] Both/All [ ]

First Lady [ ] Chelsea [ ]

DONOR INFORMATION

Name: Monica Lewinsky

Address: 700 New Hampshire Ave, NW

114 Phone: ______

Washington, DC 20037

PRESENTATION

Date: 11.20.95 Event: ______

Handed to President [ ] Other Method [✓] ~~Hand~~ delivered to BWC

Gift Description: Tie

Send Gift and Register to OEOB, Room 457 x7133

Potus has gift

~~Potus may sign~~ — Had Photo taken w/tie

Monica Lewinsky

[redacted]

Per Betty, ok to just send photo b/c donor got ty. ltr. for another gift.

V006-DC-00000158

HB 001154

184809

G1002

THE WHITE HOUSE

WASHINGTON

COPY from ORM

September 4, 1996

Ms. Monica Lewinsky
[redacted]

V006-DC-00000159

Dear Monica:

Thank you for the tie and T-shirt. It was kind of you to remember my birthday, and I appreciate your continued thoughtfulness and generosity.

Hillary and I send our best wishes.

Sincerely,

Bill Clinton

HB 001155

The tie is really beautiful

#00906

Birthday

WHITE HOUSE GIFT REGISTER

GIFT INTENDED FOR

President [✓] Both/All [ ]

First Lady [ ] Chelsea [ ]

DONOR INFORMATION

Name: Monica Lewinsky

Address: [redacted] Phone:

PRESENTATION

Date: 8.14

Handed to President [ ] Other Method [ ]

Gift Description: Tie

Send Gift and Register to OEOB, Room 457 x7133

V006-DC-00000162

HB 001158

GIFT UNIT-DRAFT OF BC LETTER

INITIALS: BC / nam / 8/24 **DOCUMENT TITLE:** /gifts/draft/lewinsky.monica.nam

DRAFT DATE / LETTER DATE: Oct 30 1995 / **CORRESPONDENCE #:** 2531378

CLEAR WITH: **WHCC:** **CC:** WH Gifts
Karen Abramson
Betty Currie

CORRESPONDENCE ADDRESSED TO:
Ms. Monica Lewinsky [redacted]

ENCLOSURES AND SPECIAL INSTRUCTIONS:

Dear Monica:

Thank you for the beautiful ~~matted~~ poem in observance of ~~observing me for~~ National Boss' Day. I ~~am honored to receive such a heartfelt gift and~~ am grateful for your thoughtfulness in having so many White House interns sign ~~autograph~~ it.

Hillary and I appreciate the hard work and dedication of all of you ~~, and support from you and the other~~ your fellow interns and send our best wishes.

Sincerely,

V006-DC-00000167

HB 001163

GRAND JURY EXHIBIT
2
CC
PENGAD-Bayonne, N. J.

To Monica – Thanks for the nice tie

824-DC-00000005

Bill Clinton

V006-DC00000178
HB 001173

White House Gift Record

Presented: 08/19/96
Arrival : 08/22/96
Entered : 08/22/96

Gift ID: 388871/lkk

Donor Information

Ms. Monica Lewinsky
[redacted]

Acknowledged By: BC Gift Draft, 11/25/96

Comments:

Gift info forwarded by Betty Currie. Per Betty, gift is a birthday gift for a BC sig.

Gift not received in the Gift Unit.

Gift Information

Intended: President

Disposition: President to Retain

Description:
1) Tie. 2) T-shirt.

Location of Gift:

Total Gift Value: $80

V006-DC-00000180

HB 001175

White House Gift Record

Presented:
Arrival : 10/24/95
Entered : 10/24/95

Gift ID: 376823/lkk

Donor Information

Ms. Monica Lewinsky
[redacted]

Acknowledged By: BC Gift Draft, 12/11/95

Comments:

Donor is a White House Intern who organized the project.

Gift Information

Intended: President

Description:
Red matted poem honoring the President for National Boss Day, with the matting signed by various White House Interns; 19" x 19".

Disposition: Archives
Archive Box : 585

Location of Gift:
The gift is in Archives.

Total Gift Value: $15

V006-DC-00000181

HB 001176

MONICA LEWINSKY

[redacted]

OBJECTIVE

- Seeking summer internship opportunity.
- Offering excellent skills in communication, writing, computer and research experience.
  Able to take direction, extremely enthusiastic, amiable and courteous

EDUCATION

- Lewis & Clark College - Presently attending
  Educational goal: Bachelor of Arts, Science. GPA 3.75
- Bel Air Prep School - Graduated 6/91 GPA 3.84

EXPERIENCE

- Practicum - Metropolitan Public Defender
  630 SW Fifth Street, Portland, Oregon
  Supervisor - Marcia Gruhler
  Duties include: assisting Legal Aid Office in counseling indigent clients, investigation, and filing of legal reports
  12/94 - Present
- Practicum - Southeast Mental Health Network
  2415 SE 43rd St., Portland, Oregon
  Supervisor - Chris Nielson
  Duties include: assisting staff in teaching socialization skills to clients in anticipation of their integration into society. Also assist in filing confidential reports, public affairs, liason to governmental office.
  1/94 - 6/94
- Knot Shop, Pioneer Place
  700 SW Fifth St., Portland, Oregon
  Position: Sales Associate
  Duties include: retail sales of upscale men's clothing, "key holder" with opening and closing responsibilities.
  Supervisor - Lisa Casey
  9/93 - Present

HONORS & AWARDS

Dean's List - Lewis and Clark 1993 and 1994
Class salutorian, Bel Air Prep School, 1991
First Place - Southern California Shakespeare Festival (1990)
Third Place - Southern California Shakespeare Festival (1991)

CLASS: UNCLASSIFIED
DISPOSITION: NON RECORD
Transmission: 11-Jun-97 06:32 am
SENDER: Veit, Katherine M.
SUBJECT: FW: Lewinsky [UNCLASSIFIED]
TO: Cicio, Kristen K.

CC:

From: Dimel, Marsha L.
To: Veit, Katherine M.
CC: /N,
NonRecord at A1
Subject: Lewinsky [UNCLASSIFIED]
Date: Tuesday,
June 10, 1997 11:51 AM

is on for 11:00 am Wednesday. I will clear her in and walk her over.

MD

V006-DC-00000222

HB 001217

CLASS: UNCLASSIFIED
DISPOSITION: NON RECORD
Transmission: 17-Jun-97 10:05 am
SENDER: Hill, Roseanne M.
SUBJECT: FW: No Thank you Letter [UNCLASSIFIED]
TO: Dimel, Marsha L.

CC:

Error in form letter. In paragraph 2, line 2 -- "compitition" should be "competition." If this is in the Admin "G" drive, I will be happy to make the change.

From: Dimel, Marsha L.
To:
Hill, Roseanne M.
CC: /N, NonRecord at A1
Subject: No Thank you
Letter [UNCLASSIFIED]
Date: Thursday, June 12, 1997 01:21 PM

Rosie, please do a no thank you, thanks for the interview letter to Monica Lewinsky - I have her resume in my office.

<^TRANSLATED_ATTACHMENT>
SECLET.DOC

DATE

V006-DC-00000223

Dear

Thank you for your interest in the secretarial/administrative positions with the National Security Council staff.

Your application and resume were well received, and you are obviously highly qualified We received several applications and the compitition for the positions has been competitive. I am sorry, but I cannot offer you a position at this time. I will keep your resume/application on file for other openings as they occur.

I enjoyed meeting with you and wish you success in your career.

Sincerely,

Marsha L. Dimel
Personnel & Administration

name
address

F:\seclet.doc

V006-DC-00000224

HB 001219

THE WHITE HOUSE
PRE-EMPLOYMENT INFORMATION

EXEC. OF. PRESIDENT MGMT. AND ADMIN.
1995 NOV 13 PM 8:02

4/16/96

Name: LEWINSKY (Last) MONICA (First) S. (Middle Initial)

SSN: 549-97-5779

Local Address [redacted] Street City State Zip

Phone: [redacted] Home [redacted] Work

Department: Legislative Affairs Requested by: Patrick Griffin

Position Title: Legislative Affairs - Correspondence Salary: $25,000

Proposed Date of Employment: 11/26/95 Ending Date, *(If possible)*: ______

Work Schedule *(circle one)*:

(Full Time) Part Time Intermittent

APPROVALS

[illegible signature] Jodie R. Torkelson

Assistant to the President Office of Management and Administration

11-13-95 11-20-95

Date Date

Upon Approval or disapproval, return to:

V006-DC-00000225

______

Name Room Extension

HB-001220

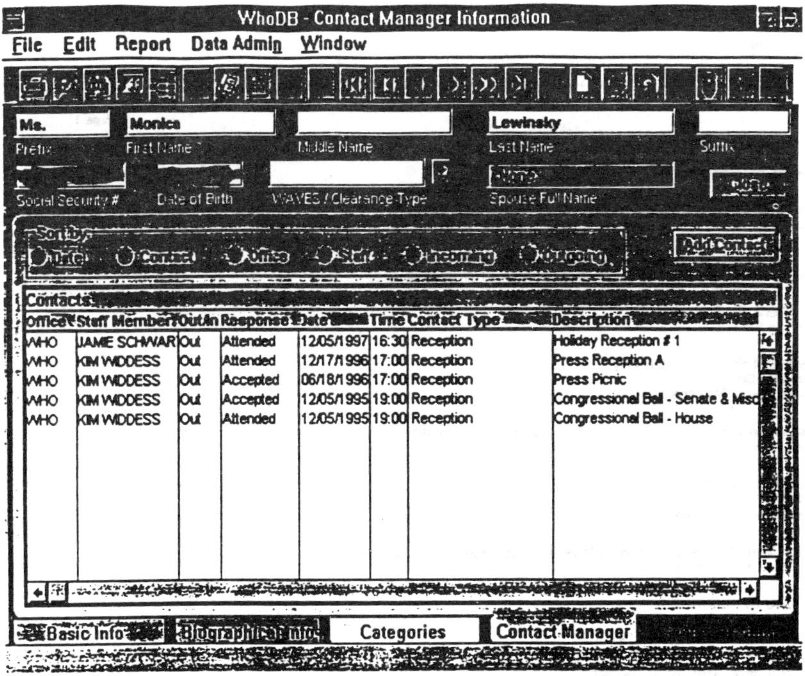

WhoDB - Contact Manager Information

File Edit Report Data Admin Window

Prefix	First Name	Middle Name	Last Name	Suffix
Ms.	Monica		Lewinsky	

Social Security #	Date of Birth	WAVES / Clearance Type	Spouse Full Name
[redacted]	[redacted]		<None>

Sort by: Date / Contact / Office / Staff / Incoming / Outgoing

Add Contact

Contacts

Office	Staff Member	Out/In	Response	Date	Time	Contact Type	Description
WHO	JAMIE SCHWAR	Out	Attended	12/05/1997	16:30	Reception	Holiday Reception # 1
WHO	KIM WIDDESS	Out	Attended	12/17/1996	17:00	Reception	Press Reception A
WHO	KIM WIDDESS	Out	Accepted	06/18/1996	17:00	Reception	Press Picnic
WHO	KIM WIDDESS	Out	Accepted	12/05/1995	19:00	Reception	Congressional Ball - Senate & Misc
WHO	KIM WIDDESS	Out	Attended	12/05/1995	19:00	Reception	Congressional Ball - House

Basic Info | Biographical Info | Categories | Contact Manager

V006-DC-00000391

HB 001386

President's List

HOLIDAY RECEPTION # 1 - Friday DEC 5 1997 - 4:30 PM White House - Business - East Visitors Entrance

For Official Government Use Only

Page 1

THE FIRST LADY

REPORT DATE: December 30, 19[illegible]
REPORT TIME: 10:03 AM

Accepts and No Responses

Mrs. Catherine Adduci and Mr. Alfred Ronan
Chicago, IL

Mr. Steven J. Akey and Mrs. Joyce H. Carrier
Dir of External Communications, U.S. Department of Transportation

Mr. Marc Andreessen
Mountain View, CA

Reverend Wendell Anthony
Fellowship Chapel
Guest: Ms. Monica Davis

Mrs. Jean Ariyoshi and Honorable George R. Ariyoshi
Honolulu, HI

Mr. and Mrs. Robert Barrie
O'Connor & Hannan
Guest: Ms. Julie Barrie

Hon. (Amb.) Charlene Barshefsky and Mr. Edward B. Cohen
U.S. Trade Representative

Mr. Eric Bauman
Van Nuys, CA
Guest: Mr. Michael Androychak

Mr. and Mrs. George F. Becker
United Steel Workers President; OPA, United Steel Workers of America-AFL-CIO VP

Mr. Richard Beens
St. Louis Park, MN
Guest: Ms. Laura Lee Geraghty

Hon. Daniel Benjamin
Special Assistant to the President and Director of Speechwriting, National Security Council
Guest: Ms. Henrike Frowein

Mr. Charles Benton
Chairman of the Board, Public Media, Inc.

Honorable Veronica Biggins and Mr. Franklin N. Biggins
Heidrick and Struggles

Honorable and Mrs. Jim Blanchard
Ambassador

Ms. Margo Briggs and Mr. Fernal Briggs
Executive Security and Engineering Technpology

V006-DC-00000511

Mr. Alan Brinkley and Ms. Evangeline Morphos
Professor, Columbia University

Mr. and Mrs. Robert Brunson
Paradise Valley, AZ

REPORT DATE: December 30, 19
REPORT TIME: 10:08 AM

Accepts and No Responses

Mr. Randell Bumgardner
Washington, DC
Guest: Ms. Leslie Lautenslager

Hon. (Admiral) Paul E. Busick and Mrs. Sarah Mullikin
Special Assistant to the President and Senior Director for Gulf War Illness, National Security Council

Ms. Meredith E. Cabe and Mr. Scott Edward Fireison
Associate Counsel to President, White House

Ms. Virginia Rafalko Canter
Associate Counsel to The Presidnt, White House

Mr. Barry Edward Carter
Washington, DC
Guest: Ms. Kathleen Ambrose

Mr. David Castignettis and Ms. Ann Castignettis
Bethesda, MD

Mr. Jose Cerda
Special Assistant to the President for Domestic Policy, Domestic Policy Office
Guest: Ms. Leanne Shimabukuro

Mr. and Mrs. David Chappell
Chappell & McGarland

Ms. Wendy Charles
Halcyon House
Guest: Mr. Arthur Bonair

Mr. Gary Chico

Hon. Dawn Chirwa
Associate Counsel to the President, White House

Mr. Gavin Clabaugh
Flint, MI

Mr. Steve Cohen
New York, NY
Guest: Dr. Perri Klass

Ms. Maria Cordone
IAM, Retirees
Guest: Ms. Anna Cordone

Mr. William Corr
Chief of Staff, Department of Health and Human Services
Guest: Ms. Allison Corr

V006-DC-00000512

Ms. Susan Corrales-Diaz
President
Guest: Mr. Larry Pomatto

HB 001507

REPORT DATE: December 30, 1997
REPORT TIME: 10:04 AM

Accepts and No Responses

Dr. and Mrs. Robert A. Corrigan
President, San Francisco State University

Ms. Errin Cosby

Mr. James Ramsay Covey
Special Assistant to the President for Implementation of Dayton Accords, National Security Council
Guest: Mrs. Christine Covey

Mr. John Cowan
Director, Lead...or Leave
Guest: Ms. Amy Liu

Mr. Brian D. Coyne
Chief of Staff, Social Security Administration
Guest: Ms. Maureen E. Garde

Mr. and Mrs. Richard C. Crandall
Barrington, IL

Ms. Janet Crist
Chief of Staff, Office of National Drug Control Policy

Mr. and Mrs. Kevin Cronin
Sherman Oaks, CA

Mr. David Curtis
Burlington, VT

Hon. and Mrs. George W. Darden
Atlanta, GA

Mr. and Mrs. Justin Dart
Washington, DC

Mr. Muneer Deen
General Manager, Hotel Washington

Mr. and Mrs. Horace B. Deets
Executive Director, American Association of Retired Persons

Mrs. Eleanor D. Ditzen
Washington, DC
Guest: Dr. Richard Stultz

Hon. James F. Dobbins
Special Assistant to the President and Senior Director for Inter-American Affairs, National Security Council
Guest: Mrs. Victoria Dobbins

Ms. Rose Dobrof
Hunter College

Hon. Marie Therese Dominguez
Special Assistant to the President and Associate Director of Presidential Personnel, Presidential Personnel
Guest: Mrs. Margaret Dominguez

Accepts and No Responses

Mr. Paul Donovan
Chief of Staff to the Secretary, Department of Commerce

Mr. and Mrs. John Dreyfuss
The Halcyon House

Hon. Charles Duncan
Special Assistant to the President & Associate Director of Presidential Personnel, White House

Ms. Jennifer A. Ferguson (Substitute for: Joel Ferguson)
Washington, DC

Ms. Barbara J. Maddox (Substitute's Guest: Joel Ferguson)
Lansing, MI

Mr. Lee Fisher and Honorable Lee I. Fisher
Cleveland, OH

Mr. and Mrs. Mac Fleming
President, Brotherhood of Maintenance of Way Employees

Dr. Michael Frazier
Temple Hills, MD
Guest: Ms. Verna Stokes Frazier

Hon. Thomas Freedman
Special Assistant to the President for Policy Planning, White House
Guest: Ms. Mary Smith

Ms. Donna Frisby
Santa Monica, CA
Guest: Mr. Greg Moore

Mr. Michael Froman
Department of Treasury
Guest: Ms. Nancy Goodman

Ms. Ellen Galinsky and Mr. Norman Galinsky
Co-President, Families & Work Institute

Mr. Bill Galston
University of Maryland

Mr. Bynum Gibson
Chairman

Mr. Gordan Giffin
U.S. Embassy

Mr. and Mrs. Adam Goldberg
Special Associate Counsel to the President, White House

V006-DC-00000514

Mrs. Luella Goldberg and Dr. Stanley Goldberg
Minneapolis, MN

Accepts and No Responses

Ms. Tina Perinuzzi Goldstein

Hon. William B. Gould
Washington, DC
Guest: Dr. Mary Burgan

Mr. Harold F. Gracey
Chief of Staff, Department of Veterans Affairs
Guest: Mrs. Donna H. Gracey

Mrs. Elinor Guggenheimer and Mr. Randolph Guggenheimer
New York, NY

Mr. and Mrs. Richard Hancock
National Symphony Orchestra

Mr. Johnny H. Hayes
Gallatin, TN
Guest: Mr. Harvey Cauthen

Mr. Frank M. Herrera
Carpenters 1353

Ms. Lisa Hertzer
Associate Counsel to the President, White House
Guest: Mr. David Schertler

Dr. John Patrick Hogan
Chief of Staff, Dept Justice
Guest: Mr. Alan Miller

Mr. Elgie Holstein
Chief of Staff, Department of Energy
Guest: Ms. Penny Eastman

Mr. and Mrs. Allen Hughes
Little Rock, AR

Mr and Mrs. Hubert H. Humphrey
St. Paul, MN
Guest: Ms. Jennifer Beens

Mr. and Mrs. Ward Hussey
Alexandria, VA

Hon. Michael Imbroscio
Associate Counsel to the President, White House, Associate Counsel to the President

Ms. Alexine Clement Jackson and Dr. Aaron G. Jackson
President, Young Women's Christian Association of the USA

V006-DC-00000515

Ms. Michele Jolin
Chief of Staff, Council of Economic Advisers
Guest: Mr. Aaron Edlin

REPORT DATE: December 30, 199
REPORT TIME: 10:04 AM

Accepts and No Responses

Hon. Elena Kagan
Deputy Assistant to the President for Domestic Policy, Office of the President

Mrs. Jayant Kalotra and Mr. Amrit Kalotra
Vienna, VA

Mr. Keith Kehlbeck and Mrs. Alieen Webb
Silver Spring, MD

Mr. Robert S. Kerr and Ms. Lou C. Kerr
Oklahoma City, OK

Mr. Robert S. Kerr
Guest: Mr. William R. Kerr

Ms. Julie Kitka
AFN
Guest: Mr. Alan L. Mintz

Ms. Lori Krause
Oakton, VA
Guest: Mr. Richard Krause

Ms. Meri Stevens Kulina and Mr. Thomas Kulina
Waverly

Hon. Robert D. Kyle
Special Assistant to the President and Senior Director to the National Economic Council (NEC/NSC), White House
Guest: Ms. Kathryn Fulton

Ms. Carolyn B. Lamm
White & Case
Guest: Mr. Alex Hale

Mr. and Mrs. Edward LaPaille

Mr. Carl Larkins
Washington, DC

Mrs. Edith K. Lauer and Mr. John N. Lauer
President, Hungarian American Coalition

Mrs. Patricia Margaret Leahy
McLean, VA

Hon. Anne Lewis
Special Assistant to the President, White House
Guest: Mr. Thomas Blanton

V006-DC-00000516

Mrs. Reta J. Lewis and Mr. Carlton Lewis
Partner, Greenberg Traurig

Hon. Michael D. Malone and Ms. Allyson Malone
Staff Assistant, The White House

50-893 98 - 48

REPORT DATE: December 30, 199
REPORT TIME: 10:04 AM

Accepts and No Responses

Hon. Sean Maloney
Special Assistant to the President and Deputy Staff Secretary, Staff Secretary Office
Guest: Mr. Randy Florke

Ms. Ruth B. Mandel
Executive Director, Center for American Women in Politics

Ms. Jane Mansbridge
Evanstown, IL

Hon. (Mayor) Raymond V. Mariano
Mayor, City of Worcester
Guest: Ms. Gina Mariano

Mr. William Miranda Marin
Chair

Mr. Joanne F. Mazzaferro
Philadelphia, PA
Guest: Ms. Juliet Lynn Salvato

Hon. Floydetta M. McAfee
Washington, DC
Guest: Mr. Howard Bingham

Mr. George A. McAlmon
Attorney

Ms. Ricia McMahon
Office of National Drug Control Policy
Guest: Ms. Cynthia Case

Mr. Vaughn McQuary and Ms. Jan McQuary

Mr. Eliseo Medina
President, Local 102, Service Employees International Union

Mr. Manuel A. Mendoza
Superintendent, Mail Room, The White House

Mr. and Mrs. Frank J. Montanero
Providence, RI

Mr. Bruce Moore
Little Rock, AR

Mr. and Mrs. Brian O'Dwyer
Chairman, Emerald Isle Immigration Center

Mr. David Oliveira
Roening Oliveria & Fisher
Guest: Mr. Aaron Pena

Mr. John Olsen
Clinton, CT

For Official Government Use Only

Page 8

REPORT DATE: December 30, 1997
REPORT TIME: 10:04 AM

Accepts and No Responses

Bishop Chandler D. Owens
Presiding Bishop, Church of God in Christ

Mr. Laszlo Papp
Member, New Canan Council and President, American Council of the World Federation of Hungarians

Mr. and Mrs. David P. Parker
Raleigh, NC

Mr. and Mrs. Steven W. Pearcy
Chairman

Rev. Dr. Albert M. Pennybacker
President, Ecumenical Development Initiative, National Council of Churches in Christ
Guest: Rev. Dr. Joan Brown Campbell

Ms. Linda Perinuzzi

Mr. Luigi Perinuzzi
Oscar de la Renta, LTD.

Mr. William T. Piersante
President
Guest: Ms. Carol Walker

Ms. Marilyn Piurek and Mr. Christopher Lodge Bergstrom
Vice President, Federation of Polish Americans

Ms. Caroline Poplin
Internist, U. S. Army

Ms. Stephanie J. Powers
Department of Labor
Guest: Ms. Kathryn Kilmarton

Ms. Aurelia Pucinski
Clerk of the Circuit Court, Cook County
Guest: MS. Rebecca Keithley

Mr. and Mrs. James H. Pugh
President, Epoch Properties, Inc.

Mrs. Alice Pushkar
Director, FL Corresp., The White House

Honorable Miles S. Rapoport
Secretary of State
Guest: Ms. Donna Fox Parson

Mr. John Rednour
Du Quoin, IL

V006-DC-00000518

Mr. Peter Robertson and Ms. Suzanne Robertson
Chief of Staff, Environmental Protection Agency

For Official Government Use Only

HB 001513

REPORT DATE: December 30, 199
REPORT TIME: 10:04 AM

Accepts and No Responses

Ms. Marda Robillard
Administrative Assistant, Congressman John Dingell's Office
Guest: Ms. Lisa Davis

Mr. William Rodriguez and Ms. Rosa Rodriguez
Flushing, NY

Mr. James C. Rosapepe and Ms. Sheilah Kast
Rosapepe & Spanos

Ms. Amy Rosen and Mr. Timothy L Carden
Montclair, NJ

MG Jack Ryan
Little Rock, AR

Ms. Deborah Sale and Mr. Theodore W. Striggles
Vice President for External Affairs, The Hospital for Special Surgery

Mr. Douglas Schoen
New York, NY
Guest: Ms. Mary Louise Hawkins

Mr. Elliot Shapleigh
El Paso, TX

Hon Sally Shelton-Colby
Assistant Administrator, U.S. Agency for International Development
Guest: Ms. Beatrice Ribourel

Ms. Anne Shields
Chief of Staff, Department of the Interior
Guest: Ms. Susan Rieff

Ms. Janna Beth Sidley
Washington, DC
Guest: Ms. Bonnie J. Campbell

Mr. Richard "Jake" L. Siewert
Special Assistant to the President, National Economic Council
Guest: Ms. Virginia Shore

Mr. Henry Smith and Ms. Laurie Smith
Office of Community College Liason

Mr. and Mrs. John F. Smith
President & CEO, General Motors Corporation

Mr. Steven R. Smith
President

V006-DC-00000519

Ms. Tara Sonenshine

Hon. Stacie Spector
Deputy Assistant to the President and Deputy Director of Communications, White House
Guest: Mr. Daniel Zingale

REPORT DATE: December 30, 1997
REPORT TIME: 10:04 AM

Accepts and No Responses

Ms. Terri Spring
Mc Farland, WI

Mr. John C. Staley
Lake Forest, IL

Ms. Mary Stevens
Waverly

Ms. Carolyn A. Stradley
Guest: Mr. Leon Thompson

Mr. Mark Strama
Program Director, Rock the Vote

Mr. Donald Sweitzer
Political Director, Capitol Associates
Guest: Ms. Aristotle L Hutras

Mr. LeBaron Taylor
Sr. Vice President, Corporate Affairs, Sony Music, Inc.
Guest: Ms. Johnnie Booker

Ms. Regena Thomas
Washington, DC

Mr. Art Torres
Chairman

Ms. Karen Tramontano
Deputy Assistant to the President and Counsel to the Office of the Chief of Staff, White House
Guests: Mr. Gerald Tramontano, Mrs. Evelyn Tramontano

Mr. Joseph S. Trapasso
Arlington, VA
Guest: Ms. Susan Ulrich

Ms. Mary Travers
Venice, CA

Mr. Everett Tucker and Ms Rebecca B. Tucker
Flake, Taber, Tucker, Wells & Kell

Ms. Christine Tully
Oscar de la Renta, LTD.

Mr. Colin Tully

Mr. Ian Tully

V006-DC-00000520

Mr. James Tully

Mr. and Mrs. Joe R. Turnham
Chair

Accepts and No Responses

Mr. and Mrs. Michael C. Turpen
Oklahoma City, OK
Guests: Mr. Michael Peyton, Ms. Eleanor Peyton

Mr. Robert Tyrer
chief of Staff th the Secretary of Defense, Department of Defense
Guest: Ms. Monica Lewinsky

Mrs. Benedicte Valentiner and Mr. Claus Valentiner

Mr. and Mrs. Joseph VanNote
North Conway, NH

Mr. Arturo Vargas and Mrs. Ingrid Duram
National Director, National Association of Latino Elected and Appointed Officials

Mr. Jose Villarreal
San Antonio, TX

Mr. Pelagia Vincent
Hay Adams Hotel
Guest: Mr. Art Schultz

Mrs. Frances M. Visco
President/Director, National Breast Cancer Coalition
Guest: Ms. Christine Brunswick

Mr. Jerry Jeff Walker
Austin, TX

Mr. Johnnie Walls
Greenville, MS

Mr. and Mrs. Jim Walters
Bentonville, AR

Sen. and Mrs. McKinley Washington
State Senator, State of South Carolina

Ms. Karen Waters and Mr. x Waters
Los Angeles, CA

Honorable Dorian (Vanessa) Weaver
Special Assistant to the President & Senior Advisor to the Director of Presidential Personnel, Presidential Personnel
Guest: Hon. Vernon A. Weaver

Hon. Paul J. Weinstein
Special Assistant to the President and Chief of Staff to the Domestic Policy Council, Domestic Policy Council
Guest: Ms. Courtney Manning

Ms. Debbie Whilhite

V006-DC-00000521

Ms. Lois White
Chicago, IL
Guest: Ms. Victoria Duran

HB 001515

REPORT DATE: December 30, 1997 30,
REPORT TIME: 10:05 AM

Accepts and No Responses

Ms. Rhonda Whiting

Ms. Marie Wilson
President, Ms. Foundation for Women

Rev. Pedro Windsor
Vice President, Alianza de Ministerios Evangelicos Nacionales

Mr. Alan Wolfe and Ms. Jytte Klausen
Boston, MA

Mr. Jeffrey Woodburn and Ms. Elizabeth Lisk Woodburn
Concord, NH

Ms. Marilyn Yager

Mr. Jerry Yang
Sunyvale, CA

V006-DC-00000522

HB 001517

RADIO ADDRESS
Friday, June 14, 1996

Bob Compton
Maggie Hobbs - granddaughter

Dan Pink - OVP
Jessica Lerner - wife
Elizabeth Lerner - mother-in-law, visiting from Santa Fe
Alan Lerner - father-in-law, visiting from Santa Fe

Monica Lewinsky - Department of Defense
Dr. Bernard Lewinsky - father
Barbara Lewinsky - mother
Michael Lewinsky - borther

Jim Durham
Michael Durham - son

Alice Pushkar - First Lady's Correspondence
Robert Kelly - father
Zita Kelly - mother

Nelson Cunningham - Counsel for Office of Management and Administration
Margery Cunningham- wife
James Harnish- in-law
Martha Harnish- in-law

Henry Woods - Sen. Bumpers office
Gary Skillington
Danny Woods - Henry brother
Deborah Woods
Ashton Travis
Autumn Woods

Daniel Beller -(YLS)
Linda Beller
Sara Beller
Benjamin Beller

Jose Sigala- Sacremento, CA (Craig Smith Request)
Marc Pacheco- State Sen., Head of DLC for Mass.

Lawton Jordan- Intergovernmental Affairs
Clay Jordan- brother

Sunday, August 18

New York City

Evening THE PRESIDENT attends celebration in honor of his 50th birthday

Radio City Music Hall, New York, New York

POOL PRESS

For other details on the President's schedule in New York, please consult the trip schedule

RON New York, New York

Monday, August 19

New York, New York & Fruitland, Tennessee

1:40 pm CDT THE PRESIDENT joins in the rebuilding of the Salem Baptist Church, Fruitland, Tennessee

For other details on the President's schedule in Tennessee, please consult the trip schedule

RON The White House

READ:NOT READ

TO:Ben Freeland (FREELAND_B) (WHO)
READ:NOT READ

TO:Ananias Blocker (BLOCKER_A) (WHO)
READ: 2-APR-1996 18:32:15.10

TO:Monica S. Lewinsky (LEWINSKY_M) (WHO)
READ: 2-APR-1996 18:31:42.00

TO:James S. Rubin (RUBIN_J) (WHO)
READ: 3-APR-1996 08:30:50.01

TEXT:
Schedule of the President as of April 2, 1996

Tuesday, April 2

Italian State Visit
POTUS attends Orioles game -- Sarbanes, Cardin, and Hoyer greeting upon arrival.

Wednesday, April 3
Morning Coffee
Youth Gang Initiative announcement at Justice (Members who were awarded grants and jurisdictional types invited.)
Internal Meetings and photos

Thursday, April 4
Internal Meetings
Signing of Line Item Veto bill at 2:00 pm -- location TBD depending on size.
DNC Dinner

Friday, April 5
POTUS travels to Oklahoma City for wreathlaying, dedication of Day Care Center, speech to the victims, and meeting with Oklahoma Scholarship Advisory Board. (Entire OK delegation invited.)

Saturday, April 6
and POTUS Weekend Off
Sunday, April 7

Monday, April 8
Easter Egg Roll
Meeting with General McCaffrey
DNC Dinners

Tuesday, April 9
Meeting with the Prime Minister of Greece
Meeting with Religious Leaders

ᵖCOMING:
OTUS travels to Japan and Moscow from April 15 - 21

-by VP's meeting with Deputy Prime Minister Dick Spring
Remarks to the National Conference of State Legislators at 10:00 am
Signing of the Telecommunications Bill at 11:15 am -- at the Library of Congress
DNC Dinner at the White House
** DOD Authorization bill may be signed today, but it is not definite.

Friday, February 9

POTUS day off

Saturday, February 10

Clinton\Gore Travel in Iowa (Harkin with us the whole time):

Clinton/Gore rally at the University of Iowa

POTUS travel to Mason City, Iowa for an agricultural event

POTUS RON Des Moines

Sunday, February 11

POTUS rally at Drake University in Des Moines, IA
Returns to WH at 7:00 pm

Monday, February 12

POTUS morning off
Drop

RECORD TYPE: PRESIDENTIAL (ALL-IN-1 MAIL)

CREATOR:Patsy L. Thomasson (THOMASSON_P) (WHO)

CREATION DATE/TIME: 9-APR-1996 12:05:07.75

SUBJECT:RE: Monica Lewinsky and Jocelyn Jolley

TO:Jodie R. Torkelson (TORKELSON_J) (WHO)
READ: 9-APR-1996 12:07:23.69

CC:Bob J. Nash (NASH_B) (WHO)
READ: 9-APR-1996 20:35:25.98

TEXT:

Bob and I have been working with Tim on placing these two people.

We are working closely with DOD to make this happen for Monica. We have not finalized the deal but are working toward that end.

Monica is coming in to see me today pursuant to Tim's request of me. Our direction is to make sure she has a job in an Agency. We are working toward that end.

patsy

RECORD TYPE: PRESIDENTIAL (WAVES REQUEST)

:REATOR:Betty Currie (CURRIE_B) (WHO)

'EATION DATE/TIME:24-JUL-1997 17:54:38.34

SUBJECT:**URGENT** Appt. request - Lewinsky, Monica

TO:Betty Currie (CURRIE_B) Autoforward to: Remote Addressee
READ:NOT READ

TEXT:

Date	Appointment with	
24-Jul-1997	CURRIE, BETTY W	

Room No. Bldg.	Requested by	Phone #
1FL/WW WH	Betty Currie	[redacted]

Comments:

TIME	VISITOR'S LAST, FIRST NAME		BIRTHDATE	SOC. SEC.	COUNTRY
05:55pm	Lewinsky	Monica	[redacted]	[redacted]	Y US

V006-DC-00001770

HB 002777

RECORD TYPE: PRESIDENTIAL (WAVES REQUEST)

CREATOR:Betty Currie (CURRIE_B) (WHO)

CREATION DATE/TIME:29-MAR-1997 13:49:13.41

SUBJECT:**URGENT** Appt. request - Lewinsky, Monica

TO:Betty Currie (CURRIE_B) Autoforward to: Remote Addressee
READ:NOT READ

TEXT:

Date	Appointment with	
29-Mar-1997	CURRIE, BETTY W	

Room No.	Bldg.	Requested by	Phone #
1FL/WW	WH	Betty Currie	[redacted]

Comments:

TIME	VISITOR'S LAST, FIRST NAME		BIRTHDATE	COUNTRY	SOC. SEC.
01:55pm	Lewinsky	Monica	[redacted]	Y U	[redacted]

V006-DC-00001792

HB 002799

RECORD TYPE: PRESIDENTIAL (WAVES REQUEST)

CREATOR:Betty Currie (CURRIE_B) (WHO)

CREATION DATE/TIME:28-FEB-1997 16:44:37.73

SUBJECT:Appt. request - Lewinsky, Monica

TO:Betty Currie (CURRIE_B) Autoforward to: Remote Addressee
READ:NOT READ

TEXT:

Date: 28-Feb-1997
Appointment with: CURRIE, BETTY W

Room No.: 1FL/WW
Bldg.: WH
Requested by: Betty Currie
Phone #: [redacted]

Comments:

TIME	VISITOR'S LAST, FIRST NAME		BIRTHDATE	COUNTRY	SOC. SEC.
05:45pm	Lewinsky	Monica	[redacted]	Y US	[redacted]

V006-DC-00001796

HB 002803

RECORD TYPE: PRESIDENTIAL (WAVES RECEIPT)

CREATOR:Mail Link Monitor (MAILMGT) (SYS)

CREATION DATE/TIME: 5-DEC-1997 16:16:39.02

SUBJECT: CONFIRMATION: APPT. REQUEST FOR POTUS

TO:Jamie B. Schwartz (SCHWARTZ_J) Autoforward to: Remote Addressee
READ:NOT READ

TEXT:
FROM: WAVES OPERATIONS CENTER - ACO: LENNON HAZEL
Date: 12-05-1997
Time: 16:13:34
This message serves as confirmation of an appointment for the visitors listed below.
Please note: Appointment confirmation for visitor names you requested and not listed below may be forthcomming.
Appointment With: POTUS
Appointment Date: 12/5/97
Appointment Time: 4:30:00 PM
Appointment Room: DIPROOM
Appointment Building: WH
Appointment Requested by: SCHWARTZ JAMIE
Phone Number of Requestor: 67136
WAVES APPOINTMENT NUMBER: U02484
If you have any questions regarding this appointment, please call the WAVES Center at [redacted] and have the appointment number listed above available to the Access Control Officer answering your call.
****
TOTAL NUMBER OF NAMES SUBMITTED FOR ENTRY : 47
TOTAL NUMBER OF NAMES OF CLEARED FOR ENTRY: 46
****

BARRIE, JULIE	11/24/69	[redacted]
BARRIE, PAULA	12/09/46	[redacted]
BARRIE, ROBERT	05/11/25	[redacted]
BINGHAM, HOWARD	05/29/39	[redacted]
BOOKER, JOHNNIE	07/31/41	[redacted]
BRUNSON, JANICE	10/04/40	[redacted]
BRUNSON, ROBERT	09/07/38	[redacted]
CRIST, JANET	05/29/43	
CRONIN, KEVIN	10/06/51	[redacted]
CRONIN, LISA	04/19/62	[redacted]
FLEMING, MAC	09/22/45	[redacted]
FLEMING, PHYLLIS	06/21/44	[redacted]
GOLDSTEIN, TINA	11/16/59	[redacted]
GUGGENHEIMER, ELINOR	04/11/12	[redacted]
GUGGENHEIMER, RANDOLPH	11/14/07	[redacted]
HALE, ALEX	03/24/86	[redacted]
HUMPHREY, NANCY	05/06/42	[redacted]
KERR, LOU	01/24/37	[redacted]
KERR, ROBERT	10/25/26	[redacted]
KRAUSE, LORI	01/01/01	[redacted]
KRAUSE, RICHARD	05/26/36	[redacted]
LEAHY, PATRICIA	03/01/48	[redacted]
LEWINSKY, MONICA	07/23/73	[redacted]
LEWIS, CARLTON	05/24/50	[redacted]
LEWIS, RETA	09/22/53	[redacted]

V006-DC-00001813

HB 002820

MALONE, ALLYSON	07/08/66	[redacted]
MALONE, MICHAEL	09/26/69	
MCAFEE, FLOYDETTA	07/17/52	[redacted]
OLSEN, JANEEN	06/24/54	[redacted]
OLSEN, JOHN	03/27/50	[redacted]
PARSON, DONNA	02/28/41	[redacted]
PERINUZZI, LINDA	07/06/65	[redacted]
PERINUZZI, LUIGI	10/05/32	[redacted]
PEYTON, ELEANOR	05/27/42	[redacted]
PEYTON, MICHAEL	05/28/40	[redacted]
RIBOUREL, BEATRICE	03/09/55	[redacted]
SHELTONCOLBY, SALLY	08/29/44	[redacted]
SMITH, HENRY	04/05/50	[redacted]
SMITH, LAURIE	12/27/50	[redacted]
TULLY, CHRISTINE	10/30/50	[redacted]
TULLY, COLIN	12/05/86	[redacted]
TULLY, IAN	10/14/90	[redacted]
TULLY, JAMES	12/03/46	[redacted]
TURNHAM, PAULA	11/16/54	[redacted]
TYRER, ROBERT	04/30/57	[redacted]
VILLARREAL, JOSE	05/08/53	[redacted]

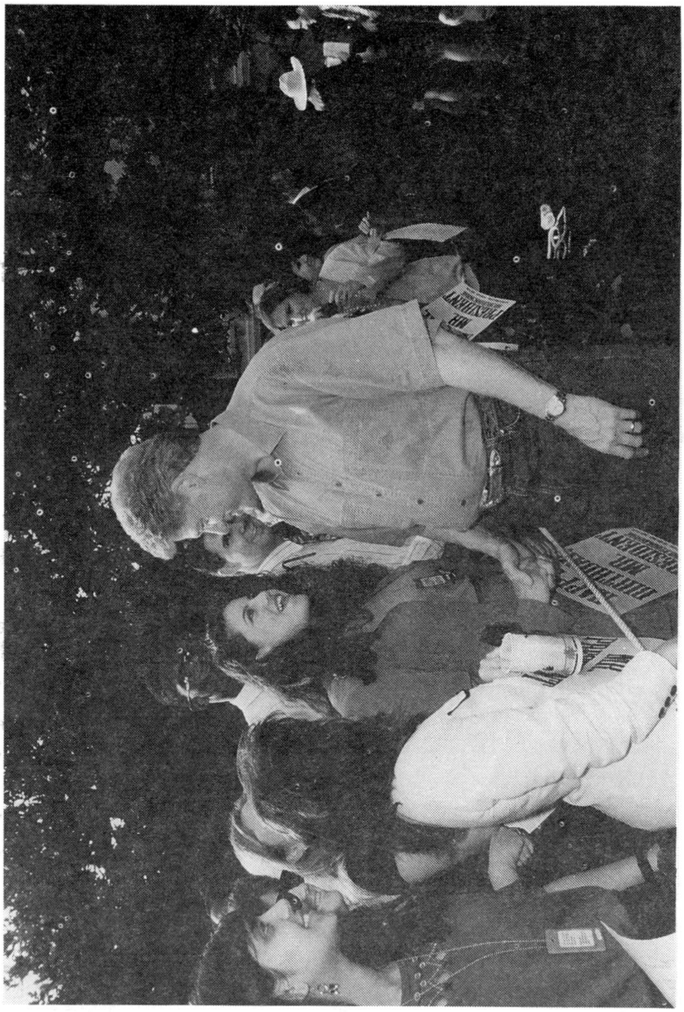

HB 2848

V006-DC-00001841

OFFICIAL WHITE HOUSE PHOTO 14JUN96 BM P041413 -14A

V006-DC-00001842

HB 2849

OFFICIAL WHITE HOUSE PHOTO 14JUN93 BM P041413 -11A

HB 2852

50-893 98 - 49

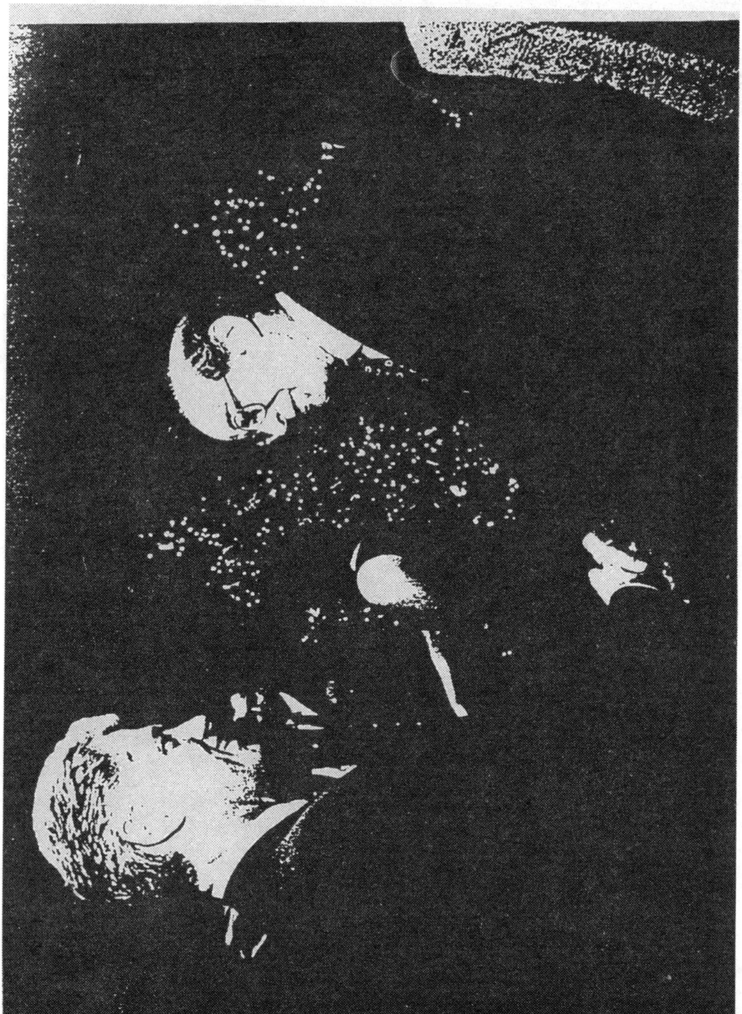

V006-DC-00001856

HB 2863

OFFICIAL WHITE HOUSE PHOTO 17DEC96 RA P049542 -015

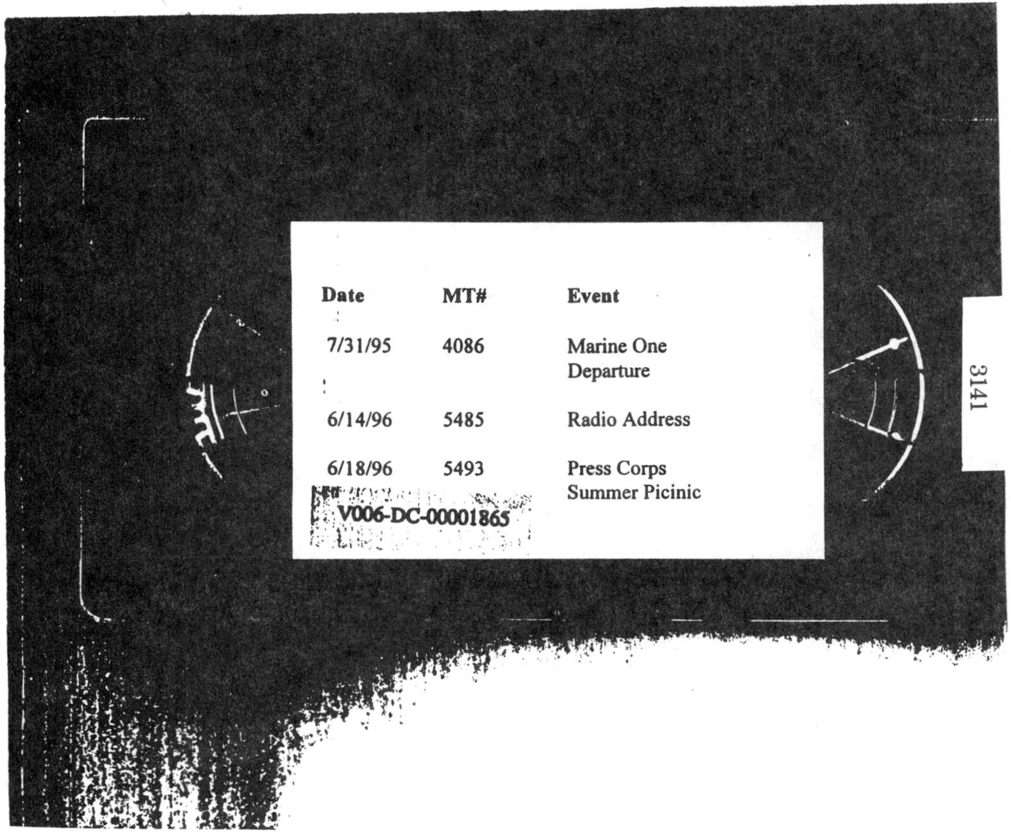

Date	MT#	Event
7/31/95	4086	Marine One Departure
6/14/96	5485	Radio Address
6/18/96	5493	Press Corps Summer Picinic

V006-DC-00001865

THE WHITE HOUSE
WASHINGTON

PRESIDENTIAL CALL LOG
SIGNAL SWITCHBOARD

January 9, 1998

	TIME		NAME	ACTION
	PLACED	DISC		
OUT XXX	AM 5:07 PM	5:09	Ms. Betty W. Currie Office, Washington, D.C. White House Signal [redacted]	Tlkd-ok 5:08 PM
XXX INC	AM 5:12 PM	5:13	Ms. Betty W. Currie The Oval Office White House Signal [redacted]	Tlkd-ok 5:12 PM

THE WHITE HOUSE
WASHINGTON

PRESIDENTIAL CALL LOG

JANUARY 14th, 19 98

	TIME PLACED	DISC	NAME	ACTION
OUT	9:55 AM	9:57	MS. BETTY W. CURRIE WASHINGTON, D.C. WHITE HOUSE ADMIN EXT [redacted]	TLKD-OK 9:55 A.M.

THE WHITE HOUSE
WASHINGTON

PRESIDENTIAL CALL LOG

JANUARY 17th, 19 98

	TIME PLACED	TIME DISC	NAME	ACTION
OUT / XXX INC	7:02 PM	7:14	MRS. BETTY W. CURRIE RES: ARLINGTON, VA. [redacted]	TLKD-OK 7:13 P.M.

V006-DC-00002066

REDACTED

HB 003065

THE WHITE HOUSE
WASHINGTON

PRESIDENTIAL CALL LOG

JANUARY 18th, 19 98

	TIME PLACED	DISC	NAME	ACTION
OUT	XXM 1:11 PM	1:14	MRS. BETTY W. CURRIE RES: ARLINGTON, VA. [redacted]	TLKD-OK 1:11 P.M.

REDACTED

V006-DC-00002067

HB 003066

THE WHITE HOUSE

WASHINGTON

PRESIDENTIAL CALL LOG

JANUARY 18th, 19 98

	TIME PLACED	DISC	NAME	ACTION
OUT XXXX	XXX 11:01 PM AM	11:02	MRS. BETTY W. CURRIE RES: ARLINGTON, VA. [redacted]	TLKD-OK 11:02 P.M.
OUT				

V006-DC-00002068

HB 003067

THE WHITE HOUSE
WASHINGTON

PRESIDENTIAL CALL LOG

JANUARY 19th, 19 98

	TIME PLACED	DISC	NAME	ACTION
OUT	8:43 AM	8:43	MRS. BETTY W. CURRIE RES: ARLINGTON, VA. [redacted]	TLKD-OK 8:43 A.M.
OUT	8:50 AM	8:51	MRS. BETTY W. CURRIE RES: ARLINGTON, VA. [redacted]	TLKD-OK 8:50 A.M.

V006-DC-00002069

REDACTED

HB 003068

THE WHITE HOUSE
WASHINGTON

PRESIDENTIAL CALL LOG

JANUARY 19th, 19 98

	TIME PLACED	DISC	NAME	ACTION
OUT / IN XX	1:43 PM	1:47	MRS. BETTY W. CURRIE RES: ARLINGTON, VA. [redacted]	TLKD-OK 1:45 P.M.

V006-DC-00002070

REDACTED

HB 003069

THE WHITE HOUSE
WASHINGTON

PRESIDENTIAL CALL LOG

JANUARY 21st, 19 98

	TIME PLACED	DISC	NAME	ACTION
OUT	12:0[illegible] AM	[illegible]	[illegible]	[illegible] A.M.
OUT / INC	1:16 AM	1:36	MRS. BETTY W. CURRIE RES: ARLINGTON, VA. [redacted]	TLKD-OK 1:16 A.M.

V006-DC-00002071

REDACTED

HB 003070

AUGUST 16, 1997

THE WHITE HOUSE
WASHINGTON, D.C.

9:18	9:19	P	The President talked with
9:19			The President went to the Oval Office.
10:03			The President returned to the second floor Residence.
11:03			The President went to the South Grounds of the White House.
11:05			The President returned to the Oval Office.
11:10			The President returned to the South Grounds of the White House.
11:11	11:38		The President motored from the South Grounds to Belle Haven Country Club, Alexandria,

V006-DC-00002095

REDACTED

HB 003094

PRESIDENTIAL MOVEMENTS

LOCATION: Washington, D.C. DATE: 29 March 1997

TIME	MOVEMENTS
1400	Oval Office
1524	South Grounds

REDACTED

Notepad: LOG

Friday, July 4

8:40 The President to the Oval Office
11:10 The President to the Putting Green

REDACTED

PRESIDENTIAL MOVEMENTS

DATE: 14 July 1997

TIME MOVEMENTS

2022	Arrive South Grounds (LOW KEY)
2026	Residence
2128	Oval Office
2325	Residence

REDACTED V006-DC-00002142

Saturday, August 16

9:20 The President to the Oval Office

10:05 The President to the Second Floor

11:00 The President to the Oval Office
11:05 The President to the Second Floor
11:10 The President departs the South Grounds en route Belle Haven Golf course

V006-DC-00002146

REDACTED

HB 003145

PRESIDENTIAL MOVEMENTS

DATE: 16 August 1997

TIME	MOVEMENTS
0919	Oval Office
1003	Residence
1103	South Grounds
1105	Oval Office
1110	South Grounds
1111	Depart South Grounds via Motorcade (LOW KEY)

REDACTED

PRESIDENTIAL MOVEMENTS

DATE: 13 November 1997

TIME	MOVEMENTS
1723	State Floor
1834	Oval Office
1903	South Grounds
1905	Residence
2049	South Grounds

V006-DC-00002156

HB 003155

REDACTED

PRESIDENTIAL MOVEMENTS

LOCATION: Washington, D.C.

DATE: 6 December 1997

TIME	MOVEMENTS
0927	Oval Office
1354	Residence

V006-DC-00002158

REDACTED

HB 003157

Friday, July 4, 1997

- The President proceeded to the Oval at 8:40 a.m.. He made a conference call t- at 11:36 a.m. - and talked for 12 minutes Shortly after his phone call, the President went outside to the putting green.

V006-DC-00002214

REDACTED

HB 003213

Thursday, November 13, 1997

Today...

The President greeted 50 guests in the State Dining Room at 5:27 p.m., at a **Reception for Democrats who supported the FastTrack Bill**.

V006-DC-00002243

He proceeded to the Oval at 6:34 p.m. He was briefed by
d and Dobbins. He took a **Foreign Call fro**
at 6:47 p.m.

REDACTED

HB 003242

RECORD TYPE: FEDERAL (ALL-IN-1 MAIL)

CREATOR:Daniel J. Gunia (GUNIA_D) (OA)

CREATION DATE/TIME: 9-APR-1996 16:50:33.42

SUBJECT:OA65 Departures / TAG

TO:Paul F. Dagenais (DAGENAIS_P) (OA)
READ: 9-APR-1996 16:50:52.77

TEXT:

==================== ATTACHMENT 1 ====================
ATT CREATION TIME/DATE: 9-APR-1996 16:13:00.00

ATT BODYPART TYPE:B

ATT CREATOR:Kelli R. McClure

ATT SUBJECT:Deactivate Two Computer Accounts

ATT TO:Daniel J. Gunia (GUNIA_D)

TEXT:
The employees listed below have departed the White House. They have transferred to other government agencies. Can you please deactivate their computer accounts?
Jocelyn Jolley -- Legislative Affairs
Monica Lewinsky -- Legislative Affairs

Let me know if you need anything else to complete this request.

Thank you for your help.

================== END ATTACHMENT 1 ==================

V006-DC-00002287

HB 003283

TO:John W. Cressman (CRESSMAN_J)

6823.

TO:Customer Services Desk #5-7370 (CSD)

TO:Charles D. Benjamin (BENJAMIN_C)

sky.

TO:Nelson W. Cunningham (CUNNINGHAM_N)

T:

	A	ARGARIN,JOCELYN D	960406	STAFF INFORMATION ASSISTANT
	EBB	NELMS,CLIFFORD S JR	960419	BUDGET METHODS SPECIALIST
CP	L	GARCIA,FRED W	960414	DEPUTY DIRECTOR DEMAND REDUCTION
R	A	KANTOR,MICHAEL	960411	UNITED STATES TRADE REPRESENTATIV
	U	DAVIS,ANGELA C	960419	PRESS ASSISTANT
	G	JOLLEY,JOCELYN M	960409	DIRECTOR CONGRESSIONAL CORRESPOND
	G	LEWINSKY,MONICA SAMILLE	960416	LEGISLATIVE AFFAIRS-CORRESPONDENC
	JC	NELSON,RANDY T	960206	RECORDS MANAGEMENT ANALYST

'Env

=============== END ATTACHMENT 1 ==================

V006-DC-00002289

HB 003285

MEMORANDUM

TO: THE PRESIDENT

FROM: BETTY

RE: ITEMS OF INTEREST

DATE: FEBRUARY 24, 1997

Monica Lewinsky stopped by. Do you want me to call her?

REDACTED

	Framed Picture
	Tie
	Book - T-Shirt
	Stacking B'Day Dolls
	Picture of them - Silver Spoon "Hot Springs"
	Guardian Angel Pin
	Book
	Oxford T-Shirt
	2 Photo Cards and Newspaper article
	3 Shirts
	Two Limoge Boxes
	T-Shirt
	CD
	Fountain Pen
Monica Lewinsky	Tie and T-Shirt
	Frog on a Limb
	Shoe Bag Patriotic Baseball Executive Stress Toy
	Music from decade of POTUS lifez
	Food Basket - South Carolina (with tape cassette)
	Running outfit
	Soccer ball and Card
	Tie
	CD - The Secret of Life

V006-DC-00003714

REDACTED

Monica Lewinsky

Tie

Food Basket

Tie, 3 Book
"History of the Jews"
"A History of Christianity"
"Cadillac Jukebox"

Box Mexican Cigars
CD - Mexican Love songs

2 Cartoon Ties & Cartoon

Maple Keepsake Box

Birthday Comic Plaque

-Chief Exec Stress Release Toy
-Presidential Baseball
-Shoe Bags (Oval Office)

Tie - saxophone players

Bottle of Wine

Two decks of playing cards
(with golf players)

Fountain Pen

Picture

Arkansas Tie

Cigars

Portrait of Virginia Kelley

V006-DC-00003715

REDACTED

HB 004631

RADIO ADDRESS
Friday, June 14, 1996

Bob Compton
Maggie Hobbs - granddaughter

Dan Pink - OVP
Jessica Lerner - wife
Elizabeth Lerner - mother-in-law, visiting from Santa Fe
Alan Lerner - father-in-law, visiting from Santa Fe

Monica Lewinsky - Department of Defense
Dr. Bernard Lewinsky - father
Barbara Lewinsky - mother
Michael Lewinsky - borther

Jim Durham
Michael Durham - son

Alice Pushkar - First Lady's Correspondence
Robert Kelly - father
Zita Kelly - mother

Nelson **Cunningham** - Counsel for Office of Management and Administration
Margery Cunningham- wife
James Harnish- in-law
Martha Harnish- in-law

Henry Woods - Sen. Bumpers office
Gary Skillington
Danny Woods - Henry brother
Deborah Woods
Ashton Travis
Autumn Woods

Daniel Beller -(YLS)
Linda Beller
Sara Beller
Benjamin Beller

Jose Sigala- Sacremento, CA (Craig Smith Request)
Marc Pacheco- State Sen., Head of DLC for Mass.

Lawton Jordan- Intergovernmental Affairs
Clay Jordan- brother

Steve Engstrom
M.S. well
arrangover

Patty Cogdell -
Mother
John

V006-DC-00003716

HB 004632

, 6, 1996

Time In	Status	Name/Agency	Phone No.	Message
		Monica Lewinsky	[redacted]	re: meeting w/ you - she's free at any time

V006-DC-00003719

HB 004635

REDACTED

0223CALL LST
Page 1

RADIO ADDRESS
FEBRUARY 28,1997

Susie Trees
Julia Trees - daughter
George Trees - son

Jerry Bowen - Department of Veterans Affairs
Steven Wayne Bowen - son

Laura Hartigan
~~**Donald**~~ **Jenkins** - fiancé
Jeff

Jonathan Elkind - Special Assistant to the Vice President for National Security Affairs
Annikki H. Elkind - mother
Mortimer M. Elkind - father

Jim Lyons

Monica Lewinsky

Gen McCaffrey

V006-DC-00003720

HB 004636

PHOTO REQUESTS

BM P041413-14 ~~# BM P041413-04~~ Sorry!

1. 14 June 1996 The President's Radio Address

We were the second to last family to speak with the President. In our family photo, my father and step-mother are to the President's right and my and I are to his left. We spoke with him for a few minutes before the posed photo and it was within those few minutes that Bob and the other photographer were clicking away. In particular, I would love to get a copy of the picture of my brother shaking the President's hand. P041413-10A 1 8x10 M

We all have dark brown hair. I was wearing a light pink suit and my brother was wearing a medium blue shirt and khaki pants. My father is tall and wears glasses, and my step-mom was wearing a black and white polka dot (or small floral) dress. — 1 copy ordered

Check w/Rebecca Cameron

2. 18 August 1996 The President's 50th (the cocktail party before the show)

I was toward the middle/end of the rope line. I have brown straight hair and was wearing a red, raw silk, sleeveless dress. 9/9 - contacts not in yet? not our photographer political event

3. 17 November 1995(during the furlough)

Bob McNeely took a picture of me with the President in Mr. Panetta's outer office. I was wearing a red suit jacket with a black collar and black pants. Bob had misplaced the film or contact sheet for a long, long while! Billie Shaddix kept checking for me if it ever appeared in the book, as we thought it was stuck in Bob's office somewhere. Maybe it is there now????? no film

4. 30 January 1996 Pat Griffin's, former Assistant to the President for LA, retirement party in the COS's office

Sharon Farmer took a couple of group shots of the Leg Affs staff with the President. I was wearing a black suit standing in the back row.

P036290-4A
1 8x10 M

V006-DC-00003735

HB 004651

HB 004653

V006-DC-00003738

OFFICIAL WHITE HOUSE PHOTOGRAPH 17 NOV 95 P034249-16 BM

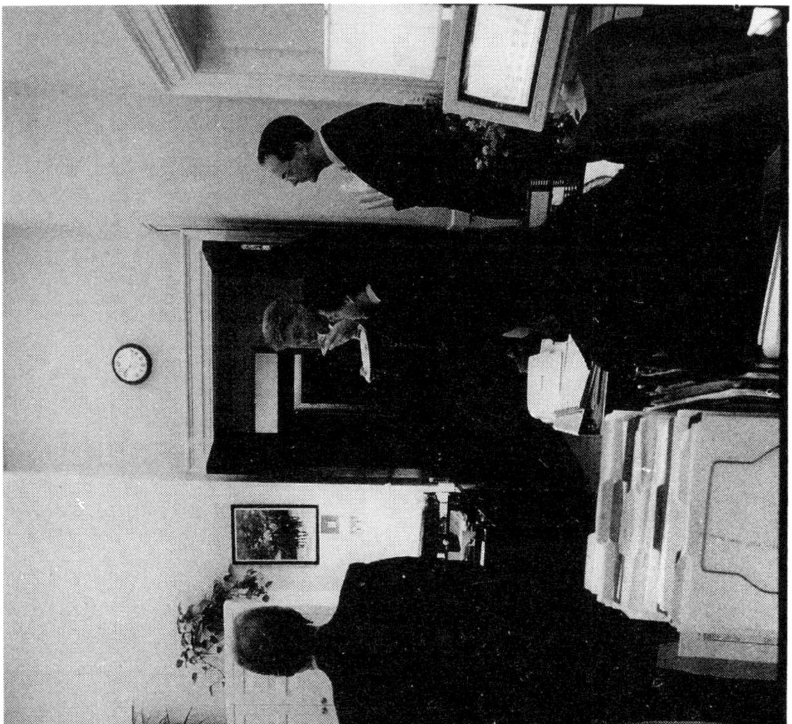

OFFICIAL WHITE HOUSE PHOTOGRAPH 17 NOV 95 P034249-17 BM

OFFICIAL WHITE HOUSE PHOTOGRAPH 17 NOV 95 P03424

V006-DC-00003742

HB 004657

V006-DC-00003743

HB 004658

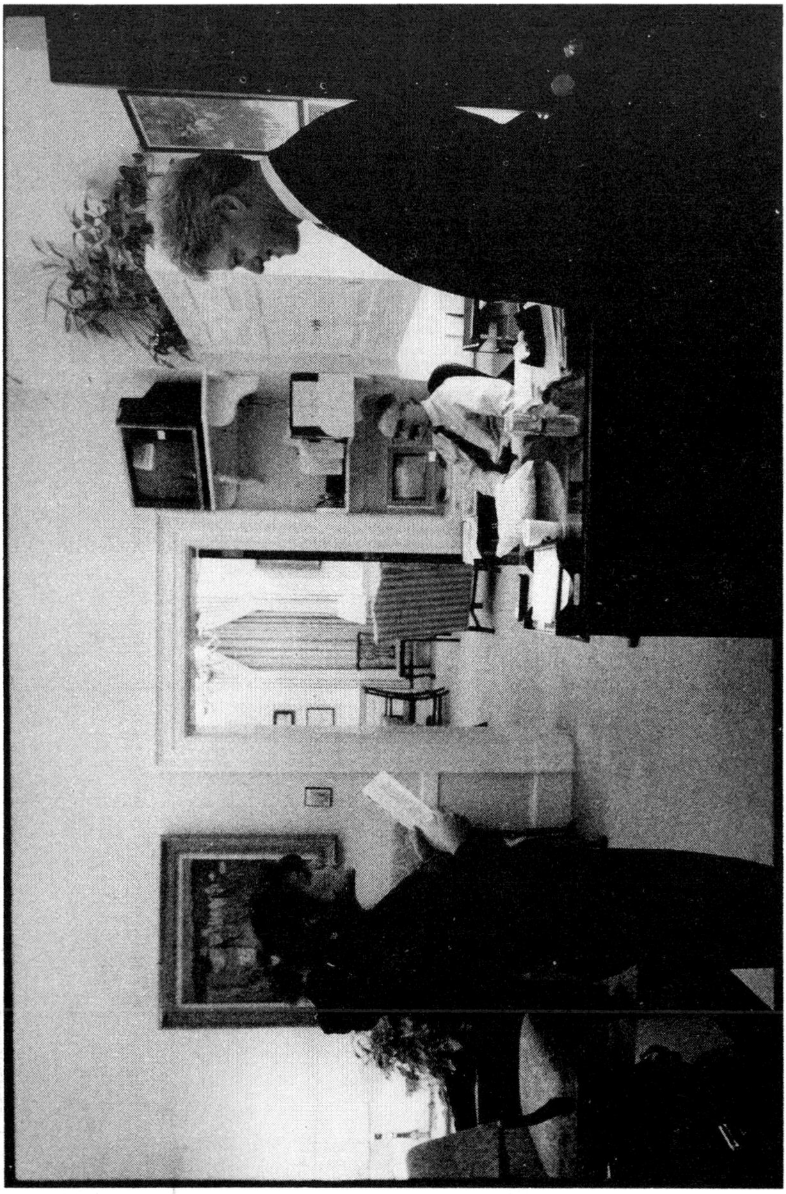

V006-DC-00003744